GALLOP

WITH CONFIDENCE

FROM RACING GUIDES **TO HARD HITTING AUTOBIOGRAPHIES**

TRAINERS JUMPS STA...

DOROTHY PAGET GRA... RACING POST

RACING POST

FIFTY SHADES OF HAY David... RACING POST

BOB CHAMPION MBE I'M CHAM... ...AL ME BOB

RACING POST

The Scudamores THREE C... RACING POST

GEORGE BAKER Taking My Time RACING POST

CHURCHILL at the GALLOP Brough Scott RACING POST

CUE CARD THE PEOPLE'S CHAMPION RACING POST LEGENDS

The Form Book® JUMPS ANNUAL 2017–2018 Raceform

THERE IS SOMETHING FOR EVERYONE AT

RACING POST SHOP

Leading the Field in Fibre Feeding

Natural Nutrients - Low Starch - Digestive Health

Discover more at **www.dengie.com**

0845 345 5115*

Dengie

*call charges apply, see website for details

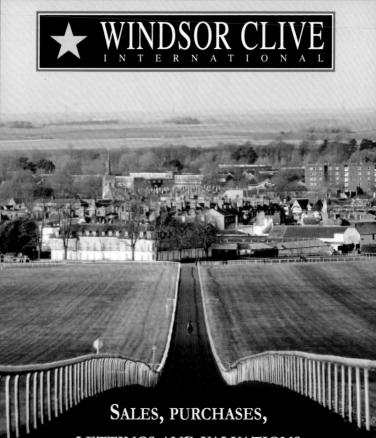

FROM TRAINING TO TRACK.

Introducing the **NEW** Traditional Training & Epsom Race Ranges.

Photo by Henry Kinchin

HORSES
IN TRAINING 2019

129th YEAR OF PUBLICATION

Raceform

INDEX TO GENERAL CONTENTS

Editor	Richard Lowther; Raceform Ltd., 27 Kingfisher Court, Hambridge Road, Newbury, RG14 5SJ E-mail: richard.lowther@racingpost.com
Production Editor	Adrian Gowling; Bloodstock Services, Weatherbys
Production Assistant	Alan Mosley; Bloodstock Services, Weatherbys
Typesetting	Maggie Elvie; Printing Services, Weatherbys, Sanders Road, Wellingborough, NN8 4BX.
Orders	Raceform Ltd., Sanders Road, Wellingborough, Northants NN8 4BX. Tel: 01933 304858 www.racingpost.com/shop E-mail: Shop@racingpost.com
Advertisements	Gary Millone, Archant Dialogue, Prospect House, Rouen Road, Norwich, NR1 1RE Tel: 01603 772463 E-mail: gary.millone@archantdialogue.co.uk
ISBN	978-1-83950-003-9

INDEX TO ADVERTISERS

2019

RACING FIXTURES

AND SALE DATES

(SUBJECT TO ALTERATION)

Flat fixtures are in **Black Type**; Jump in Light Type; Irish in *Italic*;
asterisk (☆) indicates an evening or Twilight meeting;
† indicates an All Weather meeting. Sale dates are at foot of fixtures

MARCH

Sun	Mon	Tues	Wed	Thur	Fri	Sat
31 Ascot **Doncaster** *Limerick*					**1** Doncaster *Dundalk*☆ **Lingfield Park**† Newbury **Newcastle**†☆	**2** **Chelmsford City**†☆ Doncaster Kelso **Lingfield Park**† *Navan* Newbury
3 Huntingdon *Leopardstown* Sedgefield	**4** Fakenham *Leopardstown* Southwell **Wolverhampton**†☆	**5** Exeter Newcastle **Southwell**†☆	**6** Catterick Bridge Fontwell Park **Kempton Park**†☆ **Lingfield Park**†	**7** Carlisle **Chelmsford City**†☆ **Southwell**† *Thurles* Wincanton	**8** *Dundalk*†☆ Leicester **Lingfield Park**† **Newcastle**†☆ Sandown Park	**9** Ayr *Gowran Park* Hereford **Kempton Park**†☆ Sandown Park **Wolverhampton**†
10 Musselburgh *Naas* Warwick	**11** **Kempton Park**†☆ Plumpton Stratford-On-Avon Taunton	**12** Cheltenham Sedgefield **Southwell**† **Wolverhampton**†☆	**13** Cheltenham Huntingdon **Kempton Park**†☆ **Lingfield Park**†	**14** Cheltenham Hexham **Southwell**†☆ Towcester	**15** **Chelmsford City**†☆ Cheltenham *Dundalk*†☆ Fakenham **Lingfield Park**†	**16** *Down Royal* Fontwell Park Kempton Park *Limerick* Newcastle Uttoxeter **Wolverhampton**†☆
				Cheltenham Sale		
17 Carlisle Ffos Las *Limerick* *Wexford*	**18** Exeter *Navan* Plumpton Southwell	**19** Huntingdon Taunton Wetherby	**20** Chepstow Haydock Park Market Rasen	**21** Chepstow *Cork* Ludlow Sedgefield	**22** *Dundalk*†☆ **Lingfield Park**† Musselburgh Newbury **Newcastle**†☆	**23** Bangor-On-Dee Kelso **Kempton Park**†☆ **Lingfield Park**† Newbury *Thurles*
				Ascot Sale		
24 Carlisle *Downpatrick* Exeter *Naas*	**25** **Lingfield Park**† Wincanton **Wolverhampton**†☆	**26** *Clonmel* Hereford Hexham **Wolverhampton**†☆	**27** **Kempton Park**†☆ **Lingfield Park**† Market Rasen **Southwell**†	**28** **Chelmsford City**†☆ Newcastle Warwick **Wolverhampton**†	**29** *Dundalk*†☆ Fontwell Park **Lingfield Park**† **Newcastle**†☆ Wetherby	**30** Doncaster **Kempton Park**† *Navan* **Southwell**†☆ Stratford-On-Avon Uttoxeter

APRIL

Sun	Mon	Tues	Wed	Thur	Fri	Sat
	1	**2**	**3**	**4**	**5**	**6**
	Ayr	Lingfield Park†	Kempton Park†☆	Aintree	Aintree	Aintree
	Ludlow	**Musselburgh**	*Leopardstown*	**Chelmsford City**†☆	Chepstow	Chepstow
	Newcastle†☆	Wolverhampton†☆	Market Rasen	**Southwell**†	Leicester	*Leopardstown*
			Southwell†	Taunton	Sedgefield	**Lingfield Park**†
			Wincanton		*Wexford*☆	Newcastle
					Wolverhampton†☆	**Wolverhampton**†☆
		Ascot Sale	*Ascot Sale*	*Goffs (UK) Sale at Aintree*		
7	**8**	**9**	**10**	**11**	**12**	**13**
Cork	Kelso	Exeter	Kempton Park†☆	**Chelmsford City**†	Ayr†	Ayr
Fairyhouse	**Redcar**	*Gowran Park*☆	**Lingfield Park**†	*Limerick*	*Ballinrobe*☆	Bangor-On-Dee
Ffos Las	**Windsor**	**Pontefract**	**Nottingham**	**Newcastle**†☆	Fontwell Park	*Curragh*
Plumpton		Southwell	Warwick	Towcester	**Kempton Park**†	**Newbury**
				Wetherby	**Newbury**	**Thirsk**
						Wolverhampton†☆
		Keeneland Sale		*Osarus Sale*		
14	**15**	**16**	**17**	**18**	**19**	**20**
Dundalk†	Hexham	Exeter	**Beverley**	**Chelmsford City**†☆	Bath	**Brighton**☆
Stratford-On-Avon	**Pontefract**	**Newmarket**	Cheltenham	Cheltenham	**Lingfield Park**†	Carlisle
Tramore	*Tramore*	**Wolverhampton**†☆	*Dundalk*†☆	*Clonmel*☆	**Newcastle**†	*Cork*
Wincanton	**Windsor**		**Newmarket**	**Newmarket**		Haydock Park
			Southwell†☆	**Ripon**		**Kempton Park**†
						Musselburgh
						Newton Abbot
						Nottingham☆
	Tattersalls Sale	*Tattersalls Sale*	*Tattersalls Sale*			
21	**22**	**23**	**24**	**25**	**26**	**27**
Cork	Chepstow	*Fairyhouse*☆	*Dundalk*†☆	**Beverley**	Chepstow☆	**Doncaster**☆
Fairyhouse	*Cork*	**Lingfield Park**†☆	**Epsom Downs**	**Chelmsford City**†☆	**Doncaster**	**Haydock Park**
Ffos Las	*Fairyhouse*	Ludlow	Fontwell Park	Kempton Park☆	*Kilbeggan*☆	**Leicester**
Market Rasen	Fakenham	Sedgefield	Perth	Perth	Perth	*Limerick*
Plumpton	Huntingdon	**Wolverhampton**†☆	Southwell☆	*Tipperary*☆	**Sandown Park**	**Ripon**
Southwell†	Plumpton	**Yarmouth**	Taunton☆	Warwick	Towcester☆	Sandown Park
	Redcar					*Wexford*
	Wolverhampton†					**Wolverhampton**†☆
			Goffs (UK) Sale	*Goffs (UK) Sale*	*Cheltenham Sale*	
28	**29**	**30**				
Navan	Ayr	Ayr☆				
Salisbury	*Naas*☆	**Brighton**				
Sligo	**Southwell**††	**Chelmsford City**†☆				
Wetherby	**Thirsk**☆	**Nottingham**				
	Windsor☆	*Punchestown*☆				
	Wolverhampton†	**Yarmouth**				

MAY

Sun	Mon	Tues	Wed	Thur	Fri	Sat
			1	**2**	**3**	**4**
			Ascot Bath☆ Brighton☆ Pontefract Punchestown☆ Southwell†	Chelmsford City†☆ Musselburgh Punchestown☆ Redcar Salisbury☆ Southwell† Goffs Sale Tattersalls Sale	Cheltenham☆ Chepstow Dundalk†☆ Lingfield Park† Musselburgh Newcastle†☆ Punchestown☆ Tattersalls Sale	Doncaster☆ Goodwood Hexham☆ Newmarket Punchestown Thirsk Uttoxeter
5	**6**	**7**	**8**	**9**	**10**	**11**
Gowran Park **Hamilton Park** Newmarket	**Bath** **Beverley** Curragh Down Royal Kempton Park Warwick **Windsor**	Ayr Ballinrobe☆ Exeter☆ Fakenham **Wetherby** **Wolverhampton†☆**	**Chester** Fontwell Park☆ Gowran Park☆ Kelso Newton Abbot **Southwell†☆**	Chelmsford City†☆ **Chester** Huntingdon Tipperary☆ Wincanton☆ Worcester	**Ascot** **Chester** Cork☆ Downpatrick☆ Market Rasen **Nottingham**☆ Ripon☆ **Wolverhampton†☆** Arqana Sale	**Ascot** Cork **Haydock (Mixed)** Hexham☆ **Lingfield Park** Naas **Nottingham** Thirsk☆ Warwick☆ Arqana Sale
12	**13**	**14**	**15**	**16**	**17**	**18**
Killarney Leopardstown Ludlow Plumpton	Kempton Park Killarney☆ **Musselburgh** Roscommon☆ Towcester **Windsor**☆ **Wolverhampton†**	**Beverley** **Chepstow** Killarney☆ Sedgefield Southwell☆ Wincanton☆ Tattersalls (IRE) Sale	**Bath**☆ Newton Abbot Perth☆ Punchestown☆ **Yarmouth** **York**	Clonmel☆ Fontwell Park☆ **Newmarket**☆ Perth **Salisbury** **York**	Aintree☆ **Hamilton Park**☆ Kilbeggan☆ Leopardstown☆ **Newbury** **Newmarket** **York**	Bangor-On-Dee **Doncaster**☆ Navan **Newbury** **Newmarket** **Thirsk** Uttoxeter☆ Arqana Sale
19	**20**	**21**	**22**	**23**	**24**	**25**
Market Rasen Naas **Ripon** Stratford-On-Avon	**Carlisle** **Leicester**☆ **Redcar** Towcester **Windsor**☆	**Brighton** Hexham☆ Huntingdon☆ **Nottingham** Sligo☆ **Wolverhampton†** Goffs (UK) Sale	**Ayr** Cork☆ **Kempton Park†☆** Southwell☆ Warwick Wexford☆ **Yarmouth** Goffs (UK) Sale	Chelmsford City†☆ **Chepstow** **Goodwood** **Lingfield Park** **Sandown Park**☆ Tipperary☆ Goffs (UK) Sale Tattersalls (IRE) Sale	**Bath** Curragh Downpatrick☆ **Goodwood** **Haydock Park** **Pontefract**☆ Worcester☆ Tattersalls (IRE) Sale	Cartmel **Chester** Curragh Flos Las☆ **Goodwood** **Haydock Park** Salisbury☆ **York**
26	**27**	**28**	**29**	**30**	**31**	
Curragh Fontwell Park Kelso Uttoxeter	Ballinrobe☆ Cartmel **Chelmsford City†** Huntingdon **Leicester** **Redcar** **Windsor**	**Ayr**☆ Ballinrobe☆ **Brighton** **Leicester** **Redcar** **Southwell†☆**	**Beverley** Cartmel☆ Gowran Park☆ **Hamilton Park** Newton Abbot Warwick☆	**Carlisle**☆ Fairyhouse☆ Limerick☆ **Lingfield Park** **Sandown Park**☆ **Wetherby** **Yarmouth** Cheltenham Sale	**Carlisle** Chelmsford City†☆ **Doncaster**☆ Down Royal☆ **Epsom Downs** Stratford-On-Avon☆ Tramore☆ **Wolverhampton†** Baden-Baden Sale	

JUNE

Sun	Mon	Tues	Wed	Thur	Fri	Sat
30 Cartmel Uttoxeter **Windsor**						**1** **Doncaster** **Epsom Downs** Hexham **Lingfield Park**☆ **Musselburgh** *Navan* Stratford-On-Avon☆ *Tramore* Worcester
2 Fakenham *Kilbeggan* *Listowel* **Nottingham**	**3** **Brighton** *Gowran Park* *Listowel* **Thirsk** **Windsor**☆ **Wolverhampton**†☆	**4** Bangor-On-Dee **Lingfield Park**†☆ **Newcastle**†☆ Southwell *Tipperary*☆ *Ascot Sale*	**5** Fontwell Park **Kempton Park**†☆ Newton Abbot **Nottingham** **Ripon**☆ *Wexford*	**6** **Chelmsford City**†☆ *Ffos Las*☆ **Hamilton Park** **Haydock Park** *Leopardstown*☆ **Ripon**	**7** Bath☆ **Brighton** *Clonmel*☆ *Curragh*☆ **Goodwood**☆ **Haydock Park**☆ Market Rasen Uttoxeter	**8** **Beverley** **Chelmsford City**† **Chepstow** **Haydock Park** **Lingfield Park**☆ *Navan* **Newmarket**
9 **Goodwood** Perth	**10** **Leicester** **Pontefract**☆ *Roscommon*☆ Stratford-On-Avon **Windsor**☆	**11** **Carlisle**☆ **Lingfield Park**† *Roscommon*☆ **Salisbury** **Thirsk**☆ *Goffs Sale*	**12** Fontwell Park **Hamilton Park**☆ **Haydock Park** **Kempton Park**☆ *Punchestown*☆ **Yarmouth** *Goffs Sale*	**13** **Haydock Park**☆ *Leopardstown*☆ **Newbury** **Nottingham** Uttoxeter☆ **Yarmouth**	**14** Aintree☆ **Chepstow** *Cork*☆ *Fairyhouse*☆ **Goodwood**☆ Newton Abbot☆ **Sandown Park** **York**	**15** **Bath** **Chester** *Downpatrick* Hexham **Leicester**☆ *Limerick* **Sandown Park** Worcester☆ **York**
16 **Doncaster** *Downpatrick* *Gowran Park* **Salisbury**	**17** **Carlisle** **Catterick Bridge** *Kilbeggan*☆ **Nottingham**☆ **Windsor**☆ *Goffs London Sale*	**18** **Ascot** **Beverley**☆ **Brighton**☆ *Sligo*☆ Stratford-On-Avon **Thirsk**	**19** **Ascot** **Chelmsford City**†☆ **Hamilton Park** **Ripon**☆ Uttoxeter *Wexford*☆	**20** **Ascot** **Chelmsford City**† *Ffos Las*☆ *Leopardstown*☆ **Lingfield Park**†☆ **Ripon**	**21** **Ascot** **Ayr**☆ *Down Royal*☆ **Goodwood**☆ *Limerick*☆ Market Rasen **Newmarket**☆ **Redcar**	**22** **Ascot** **Ayr** *Down Royal* **Haydock Park**☆ **Lingfield Park**☆ **Newmarket** Perth **Redcar**
23 Hexham **Pontefract** *Tipperary* Worcester	**24** *Ballinrobe*☆ **Chepstow** Southwell **Windsor**☆ **Wolverhampton**†☆	**25** **Beverley** **Carlisle** **Newbury**☆ Newton Abbot☆	**26** Bath☆ **Carlisle** **Kempton Park**†☆ *Naas*☆ **Salisbury** Worcester *Tattersalls (IRE) Sale*	**27** *Curragh*☆ **Hamilton Park**☆ **Leicester**☆ **Newcastle**† **Newmarket** **Nottingham** *Tattersalls (IRE) Sale*	**28** Cartmel **Chester**☆ *Curragh* **Doncaster** **Newcastle**†☆ **Newmarket**☆ **Yarmouth**	**29** **Chester** *Curragh* **Doncaster**☆ **Lingfield Park**☆ **Newcastle**† **Newmarket** **Windsor** **York**

JULY

Sun	Mon	Tues	Wed	Thur	Fri	Sat
	1 Catterick Bridge☆ Pontefract Windsor☆ Wolverhampton†	**2** Brighton Chepstow☆ Hamilton Park Stratford-On-Avon☆ Arqana Sale	**3** Bath☆ Bellewstown☆ Kempton Park†☆ Musselburgh Thirsk Worcester Arqana Sale	**4** *Bellewstown☆* Epsom Downs☆ Haydock Park Newbury☆ *Perth* *Tipperary☆* Yarmouth	**5** *Bellewstown☆* Beverley☆ Chelmsford City†☆ Doncaster Haydock Park☆ Newton Abbot Sandown Park *Wexford☆*	**6** *Bellewstown☆* Beverley Carlisle☆ Chelmsford City† Haydock Park Leicester *Naas* Nottingham☆ Sandown Park
7 Ayr *Limerick* Market Rasen	**8** Ayr Ripon☆ *Roscommon☆* Windsor☆ Worcester	**9** Brighton☆ Pontefract *Roscommon☆* Uttoxeter☆ Wolverhampton† Fasig-Tipton Sale Tattersalls Sale	**10** Bath☆ Catterick Bridge Kempton Park†☆ Lingfield Park Yarmouth Fasig-Tipton Sale Tattersalls Sale	**11** Carlisle Doncaster Epsom Downs☆ *Leopardstown☆* Newbury☆ Newmarket Tattersalls Sale	**12** Ascot Chepstow☆ Chester☆ *Cork☆* Ffos Las☆ Newmarket York Tattersalls Sale	**13** Ascot Chester Hamilton Park☆ *Limerick* *Navan* Newmarket Newton Abbot Salisbury☆ York
14 *Fairyhouse* *Perth* *Sligo* Stratford-On-Avon	**15** Ayr *Downpatrick* *Killarney☆* Ripon Windsor☆ Wolverhampton†☆	**16** Bath Beverley *Killarney☆* Nottingham☆ Southwell☆ Ascot Sale	**17** Catterick Bridge *Fairyhouse☆* *Killarney☆* Lingfield Park† Uttoxeter Wolverhampton†☆ Yarmouth☆	**18** Chepstow Epsom Downs☆ Hamilton Park *Killarney* Leicester *Leopardstown☆* Worcester☆	**19** Hamilton Park☆ Haydock Park *Kilbeggan☆* *Killarney* Newbury Newmarket☆ Nottingham Pontefract☆ Goresbridge Sale	**20** Cartmel *Curragh* Doncaster☆ Haydock Park☆ Market Rasen Newbury Newmarket Ripon
21 *Curragh* Newton Abbot Redcar Stratford-On-Avon *Tipperary*	**22** Ayr *Ballinrobe☆* Beverley☆ Cartmel Windsor☆	**23** *Ballinrobe☆* Chelmsford City†☆ Musselburgh Southwell☆ Wolverhampton†	**24** Bath Catterick Bridge Leicester☆ Lingfield Park *Naas☆* Sandown Park☆	**25** Doncaster☆ *Leopardstown☆* *Limerick☆* Newbury☆ Sandown Park Worcester Yarmouth	**26** Ascot Chepstow☆ *Down Royal☆* Newmarket☆ Thirsk Uttoxeter *Wexford☆* York☆	**27** Ascot Chester *Gowran Park☆* Lingfield Park☆ Newcastle† Newmarket Salisbury☆ York
28 Pontefract Uttoxeter	**29** Ayr Ffos Las☆ *Galway☆* Newton Abbot Windsor☆	**30** Beverley *Galway☆* Goodwood *Perth☆* Worcester☆ Yarmouth Goffs (UK) Sale at Goodwood	**31** *Galway☆* Goodwood Leicester☆ *Perth* Redcar Sandown Park☆			

AUGUST

Sun	Mon	Tues	Wed	Thur	Fri	Sat
				1 Epsom Downs☆ Ffos Las☆ *Galway* Goodwood Nottingham *Stratford-On-Avon*	**2** Bangor-On-Dee Bath☆ *Galway☆* Goodwood Musselburgh☆ Newmarket☆ Wolverhampton†	**3** Chelmsford City† Doncaster *Galway* Goodwood Hamilton Park☆ Lingfield Park☆ Newmarket Thirsk
4 Chester *Galway* Market Rasen	**5** Carlisle☆ *Cork* Kempton Park† *Naas* Ripon Windsor☆ Fasig-Tipton Sale	**6** Catterick Bridge Newbury Nottingham†☆ Ripon☆ *Roscommon☆* Goffs (UK) Sale Fasig-Tipton Sale	**7** Bath Brighton Kempton Park†☆ Pontefract *Sligo* Yarmouth☆ Goffs (UK) Sale	**8** Brighton Haydock Park *Leopardstown☆* Newcastle†☆ Sandown Park *Sligo☆* Yarmouth	**9** Brighton Chelmsford City†☆ *Curragh☆* Haydock Park☆ Musselburgh Newmarket☆ Thirsk	**10** Ascot Ayr☆ Chelmsford City† Haydock Park *Kilbeggan☆* Lingfield Park☆ Newmarket Redcar
11 *Downpatrick* Leicester *Tipperary* Windsor	**12** Ayr *Ballinrobe☆* Catterick Bridge Windsor☆ Wolverhampton†☆	**13** Carlisle☆ Ffos Las Lingfield Park†☆ Nottingham Tattersalls (IRE) Sale	**14** Beverley *Gowran Park☆* Kempton Park†☆ Newton Abbot Salisbury *Worcester☆* Tattersalls (IRE) Sale	**15** Beverley *Leopardstown☆* Lingfield Park† Salisbury *Tramore☆* Yarmouth☆ Tattersalls (IRE) Sale	**16** Chelmsford City†☆ *Curragh☆* Newbury Newmarket☆ Nottingham Thirsk☆ *Tramore☆* Wolverhampton†	**17** Bath☆ *Cork* Doncaster Market Rasen☆ Newbury Newmarket Perth Ripon *Tramore☆* Arqana Sale
18 Pontefract Southwell *Tramore* Arqana Sale	**19** Bangor-On-Dee☆ Catterick Bridge Lingfield Park† *Roscommon☆* Windsor☆ Arqana Sale	**20** Brighton Hamilton Park Kempton Park† Newton Abbot *Sligo☆* Yarmouth☆ Ascot Sale Arqana Sale	**21** Bath Carlisle Kempton Park†☆ *Killarney* *Worcester☆* York	**22** Chepstow Fontwell Park☆ *Killarney* Leicester☆ Stratford-On-Avon York	**23** Chelmsford City†☆ *Curragh☆* Ffos Las Goodwood☆ *Killarney☆* Newmarket Salisbury☆ York	**24** Cartmel Chelmsford City† Goodwood *Kilbeggan☆* *Killarney* Newmarket Redcar☆ Windsor☆ York
25 Beverley Goodwood Yarmouth	**26** Cartmel Chepstow *Downpatrick* Epsom Downs Ripon Southwell†	**27** *Ballinrobe☆* Bath☆ Epsom Downs Musselburgh☆ Ripon Goffs (UK) Sale	**28** *Bellewstown☆* Catterick Bridge Kempton Park†☆ Lingfield Park Musselburgh *Worcester☆* Goffs (UK) Sale	**29** *Bellewstown☆* Carlisle Chelmsford City† Ffos Las Fontwell Park☆ Sedgefield☆ *Tipperary☆* Goffs (UK) Sale	**30** Bangor-On-Dee *Curragh☆* *Down Royal* Hamilton Park☆ Newcastle†☆ Sandown Park Thirsk Wolverhampton†☆ Baden-Baden Sale	**31** Beverley Chelmsford City†☆ Chester *Down Royal* Lingfield Park†☆ Newton Abbot Sandown Park Wolverhampton†

SEPTEMBER

Sun	Mon	Tues	Wed	Thur	Fri	Sat
1 **Brighton** *Cork* Worcester	**2** **Brighton** **Chepstow** Hexham☆ *Roscommon*☆ **Windsor**☆	**3** **Catterick Bridge** **Goodwood** **Kempton Park**†☆ **Salisbury**☆ Osarus Sale	**4** **Bath** **Chelmsford City**†☆ **Hamilton Park**☆ Southwell Uttoxeter Osarus Sale	**5** **Chelmsford City**†☆ *Clonmel*☆ **Haydock Park** **Lingfield Park**†☆ **Salisbury** Sedgefield	**6** **Ascot** **Haydock Park** **Kempton Park**†☆ *Kilbeggan*☆ **Musselburgh**☆ **Newcastle**†	**7** **Ascot** **Haydock Park** **Kempton Park**† *Navan* Stratford-On-Avon **Thirsk** *Wexford* **Wolverhampton**†☆
8 Fontwell Park *Listowel* **York** Keeneland Sale	**9** **Brighton** *Listowel* Newton Abbot Perth **Wolverhampton**†☆ Keeneland Sale	**10** **Catterick Bridge** Kelso☆ **Leicester** *Listowel* Worcester Ascot Sale Keeneland Sale	**11** **Carlisle** **Doncaster** **Kempton Park**†☆ *Laytown* *Listowel* Uttoxeter Keeneland Sale	**12** **Chelmsford City**†☆ **Chepstow** **Doncaster** **Epsom Downs** *Listowel* Keeneland Sale	**13** **Chester** **Doncaster** *Listowel* **Salisbury**☆ **Sandown Park** Keeneland Sale	**14** **Bath** **Chelmsford City**† **Chester** **Doncaster** *Leopardstown* **Lingfield Park**† *Listowel* **Musselburgh**☆ Goffs Sale Keeneland Sale
15 **Bath** *Curragh* **Ffos Las** Keeneland Sale	**16** **Brighton** *Galway*☆ **Kempton Park**†☆ **Thirsk** Worcester Keeneland Sale	**17** **Chepstow** *Galway*☆ **Newcastle**†☆ Redcar Yarmouth Keeneland Sale	**18** **Beverley** Kelso☆ *Naas*☆ **Sandown Park** Yarmouth Goffs (UK) Sale Keeneland Sale	**19** **Ayr** **Chelmsford City**†☆ **Pontefract** **Southwell**†☆ Yarmouth Goffs (UK) Sale Keeneland Sale	**20** **Ayr** *Ballinrobe*☆ *Dundalk*†☆ **Newbury** **Newcastle**†☆ Newton Abbot Keeneland Sale	**21** **Ayr** **Catterick Bridge** **Chelmsford City**† *Gowran Park* **Newbury** **Newmarket** **Wolverhampton**†☆ SGA Sale Keeneland Sale
22 **Hamilton Park** Plumpton	**23** *Fairyhouse*☆ **Hamilton Park** **Kempton Park**†☆ **Leicester** Warwick	**24** **Beverley** **Chelmsford City**†☆ **Lingfield Park**† Warwick Tattersalls (IRE) Sale	**25** **Goodwood** **Kempton Park**†☆ **Newcastle**†☆ Perth **Redcar** *Sligo* Tattersalls (IRE) Sale	**26** **Chelmsford City**†☆ **Newmarket** Perth **Pontefract** **Southwell**†☆ Tattersalls (IRE) Sale	**27** *Downpatrick* *Dundalk*†☆ **Haydock Park** **Newcastle**†☆ **Newmarket** Worcester	**28** **Chelmsford City**†☆ **Chester** *Curragh* **Haydock Park** Market Rasen *Navan* **Newmarket** Ripon
29 *Curragh* **Epsom Downs** **Musselburgh**	**30** **Bath** **Hamilton Park** Newton Abbot *Roscommon*†☆ **Wolverhampton**†☆					

OCTOBER

Sun	Mon	Tues	Wed	Thur	Fri	Sat
		1 Ayr *Cork* **Kempton Park†☆** Sedgefield Southwell Goffs Sale	**2** Bangor-On-Dee Huntingdon **Kempton Park†☆** **Newcastle†☆** **Nottingham** Goffs Sale	**3** **Chelmsford City†☆** *Clonmel* **Lingfield Park†** **Salisbury** Warwick **Wolverhampton†☆** Goffs Sale	**4** **Ascot** *Dundalk†☆* Fontwell Park *Gowran Park* Hexham **Southwell†☆**	**5** **Ascot** Fontwell Park *Gowran Park* **Newmarket** **Redcar** **Wolverhampton†☆** Arqana Sale
6 Kelso *Tipperary* Uttoxeter	**7** **Newcastle†☆** Pontefract Stratford-On-Avon *Tipperary* **Windsor** Tattersalls Sale	**8** **Brighton** **Catterick Bridge** **Chelmsford City†☆** *Galway* Leicester Tattersalls Sale	**9** **Kempton Park†☆** Ludlow Navan **Newcastle†☆** **Nottingham** Towcester Tattersalls Sale	**10** Ayr Exeter **Kempton Park†☆** **Southwell†☆** *Thurles* Worcester	**11** Chepstow *Downpatrick* *Dundalk†☆* **Newcastle†☆** **Newmarket** **York**	**12** Chepstow *Fairyhouse* Hexham *Limerick* **Newmarket** **Wolverhampton†☆** **York**
13 *Curragh* **Goodwood** *Limerick* Newton Abbot	**14** *Gowran Park* **Musselburgh** **Windsor** **Wolverhampton†☆** **Yarmouth** Tattersalls Sale	**15** Hereford Huntingdon **Kempton Park†☆** Leicester *Punchestown* Tattersalls Sale	**16** **Bath** **Kempton Park†☆** **Nottingham** *Punchestown* **Southwell†☆** Wetherby Tattersalls Sale	**17** **Brighton** Carlisle **Chelmsford City†☆** *Tramore* Wincanton **Wolverhampton†☆** Tattersalls Sale	**18** *Dundalk†☆* Fakenham **Haydock Park** **Newcastle†☆** **Redcar** Uttoxeter Tattersalls Sale Baden-Baden Sale	**19** **Ascot** **Catterick Bridge** *Ffos Las* *Leopardstown* Market Rasen Stratford-On-Avon **Wolverhampton†☆** Tattersalls Sale Baden-Baden Sale
20 *Cork* Kempton Park *Naas* Sedgefield	**21** Plumpton **Pontefract** **Southwell†☆** **Windsor** Fasig-Tipton Sale	**22** Exeter **Kempton Park†☆** **Newcastle†** **Yarmouth** Fasig-Tipton Sale Arqana Sale	**23** Fontwell Park **Kempton Park†☆** Navan **Newmarket** **Wolverhampton†☆** Worcester Goffs UK Sale Fasig-Tipton Sale Arqana Sale	**24** Carlisle **Chelmsford City†☆** Ludlow Southwell *Thurles* **Wolverhampton†☆** Goffs UK Sale Fasig-Tipton Sale Arqana Sale	**25** Cheltenham **Doncaster** *Dundalk†☆* **Newbury** **Newcastle†☆** Goffs UK Sale Goresbridge Sale	**26** **Chelmsford City†☆** Cheltenham **Doncaster** *Galway* Kelso *Leopardstown* **Newbury**
27 Aintree *Galway* *Wexford* Wincanton	**28** Ayr *Galway* **Kempton Park†☆** Leicester **Redcar** *Wexford* Tattersalls Sale	**29** Bangor-On-Dee **Catterick Bridge** Chepstow **Southwell†☆** Tattersalls Sale	**30** *Dundalk†☆* Fakenham **Kempton Park†☆** **Nottingham** Taunton **Wolverhampton†☆** Tattersalls Sale	**31** **Chelmsford City†☆** *Clonmel* **Kempton Park†☆** **Lingfield Park†** Newton Abbot Stratford-On-Avon Tattersalls Sale		

NOVEMBER

Sun	Mon	Tues	Wed	Thur	Fri	Sat
					1 *Down Royal*†☆ *Dundalk*†☆ **Newcastle**†☆ **Newmarket** Uttoxeter Wetherby *Osarus Sale* Tattersalls Sale	**2** Ascot Ayr **Chelmsford City**†☆ *Down Royal* **Newmarket** Wetherby
3 Carlisle *Cork* Huntingdon *Naas* Goffs Sale Fasig-Tipton Sale Keeneland Sale	**4** Hereford **Kempton Park**† **Newcastle**†☆ Plumpton Goffs Sale Keeneland Sale	**5** Exeter *Fairyhouse* **Kempton Park**†☆ **Redcar** **Southwell**† Goffs Sale Keeneland Sale	**6** Chepstow *Dundalk*†☆ **Kempton Park**†☆ Musselburgh **Nottingham** **Wolverhampton**†☆ Goffs Sale Keeneland Sale	**7** **Chelmsford City**†☆ Market Rasen Newbury Sedgefield **Southwell**†☆ *Thurles* Ascot Sale Keeneland Sale	**8** *Dundalk*†☆ Fontwell Park Hexham **Newcastle**†☆ Warwick Keeneland Sale Tattersalls (IRE) Sale	**9** Aintree **Doncaster** Kelso *Naas* **Southwell**†☆ Wincanton SGA Sale Keeneland Sale Tattersalls (IRE) Sale
10 Ftos Las *Navan* Sandown Park Keeneland Sale Tattersalls (IRE) Sale	**11** Carlisle *Fairyhouse* Kempton Park Stratford-On-Avon Keeneland Sale Tattersalls (IRE) Sale	**12** Hereford Huntingdon Lingfield Park Keeneland Sale Tattersalls (IRE) Sale	**13** Ayr Bangor-On-Dee Exeter Keeneland Sale Tattersalls (IRE) Sale	**14** *Clonmel* Ludlow Sedgefield Taunton Keeneland Sale Tattersalls (IRE) Sale	**15** Cheltenham *Dundalk*†☆ Newcastle Southwell Cheltenham Sale Keeneland Sale Tattersalls (IRE) Sale	**16** Cheltenham **Lingfield Park**† *Punchestown* Uttoxeter Wetherby **Wolverhampton**†☆ Tattersalls (IRE) Sale
17 Cheltenham *Cork* Fontwell Park *Punchestown* Goffs Sale	**18** Leicester Plumpton **Southwell**†☆ **Wolverhampton**† Goffs Sale Arqana Sale	**19** **Chelmsford City**†☆ Fakenham **Kempton Park**†☆ Lingfield Park Goffs Sale Arqana Sale	**20** Chepstow *Dundalk*† **Kempton Park**†☆ Warwick Goffs Sale Arqana Sale	**21** **Chelmsford City**†☆ Market Rasen **Newcastle**† *Thurles* Wincanton Goffs Sale	**22** Ascot Catterick Bridge *Dundalk*†☆ Ftos Las **Newcastle**†☆ Goffs Sale	**23** Ascot *Gowran Park* Haydock Park Huntingdon **Lingfield Park**† **Wolverhampton**†☆ Goffs Sale
24 Exeter *Navan* Uttoxeter Goffs Sale	**25** Kempton Park Ludlow Musselburgh Tattersalls Sale	**26** *Punchestown* Sedgefield Southwell **Wolverhampton**†☆	**27** Hereford **Kempton Park**†☆ **Southwell**† Wetherby Tattersalls Sale	**28** **Chelmsford City**†☆ **Lingfield Park**† Taunton *Thurles* Towcester Tattersalls Sale	**29** Doncaster *Dundalk*†☆ **Kempton Park**†☆ *Limerick* Newbury **Southwell**† Tattersalls Sale	**30** Bangor-On-Dee Doncaster *Fairyhouse* Newbury Newcastle **Wolverhampton**†☆ Tattersalls Sale

DECEMBER

Sun	Mon	Tues	Wed	Thur	Fri	Sat
1	**2**	**3**	**4**	**5**	**6**	**7**
Carlisle *Fairyhouse* Leicester	Musselburgh Plumpton **Wolverhampton**†☆	Lingfield Park Southwell **Wolverhampton**†☆	Haydock Park **Kempton Park**†☆ **Lingfield Park**† Ludlow	*Clonmel* Leicester Market Rasen **Southwell**†☆ Wincanton	*Dundalk*†☆ Exeter **Newcastle**†☆ Sandown Park Sedgefield	Aintree Chepstow *Navan* Sandown Park Wetherby **Wolverhampton**†☆
	Tattersalls Sale	Tattersalls Sale	Tattersalls Sale	Tattersalls Sale	Goffs (UK) Sale	Arqana Sale
8	**9**	**10**	**11**	**12**	**13**	**14**
Cork Huntingdon Kelso *Punchestown*	**Lingfield Park**† Musselburgh **Newcastle**†☆	Fontwell Park *Tramore* Uttoxeter **Wolverhampton**†☆	Hexham **Kempton Park**†☆ Leicester **Lingfield Park**†	**Chelmsford City**†☆ Newcastle Taunton Warwick	Bangor-On-Dee **Chelmsford City**†☆ Cheltenham Doncaster *Dundalk*†☆	Cheltenham Doncaster *Fairyhouse* Hereford **Newcastle**† **Wolverhampton**†☆
	Ascot Sale					
Arqana Sale	Arqana Sale	Arqana Sale	Goffs Sale	Goffs Sale	Cheltenham Sale	
15	**16**	**17**	**18**	**19**	**20**	**21**
Carlisle *Navan* Southwell	Ffos Las *Naas* Plumpton **Wolverhampton**†☆	Catterick Bridge Fakenham Lingfield Park	*Dundalk*†☆ **Lingfield Park**† Ludlow Newbury **Newcastle**†☆	Exeter **Southwell**†† Towcester **Wolverhampton**†☆	Ascot *Dundalk*†☆ **Southwell**† Uttoxeter **Wolverhampton**†☆	Ascot Haydock Park **Lingfield Park**† Newcastle *Thurles*
22	**23**	**24**	**25**	**26**	**27**	**28**
				Down Royal Fontwell Park Huntingdon Kempton Park *Leopardstown* *Limerick* Market Rasen Sedgefield Wetherby Wincanton	Chepstow Kempton Park *Leopardstown* *Limerick* Wetherby **Wolverhampton**†	Catterick Bridge Leicester *Leopardstown* *Limerick* **Lingfield Park**† Newbury
					Wolverhampton†	
29	**30**	**31**				
Doncaster Kelso *Leopardstown* *Limerick* **Southwell**†	Haydock Park **Lingfield Park**† Taunton	**Lingfield Park**† *Punchestown* Uttoxeter Warwick				

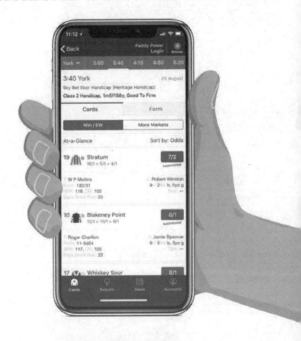

DATES OF PRINCIPAL RACES

(SUBJECT TO ALTERATION)

JANUARY

Ballymore Novices' Hurdle (Cheltenham) 1st
Betbright Dipper Novices' Steeplechase (Cheltenham) 1st
Download The Betbright App Handicap Steeplechase (Cheltenham) 1st
Dornan Engineering Relkeel Hurdle (Cheltenham) 1st
EBF Stallions & Cheltenham Pony Club Standard Open National Hunt Flat Race (Cheltenham) 1st
Betway Hogmaneigh Handicap Hurdle (Musselburgh) 1st
Betway 'Auld Reekie' Handicap Steeple Chase (Musselburgh) 1st
Savills Chase (Tramore) 1st
32Red Handicap Stakes (Kempton Park) 5th
Unibet Mares' Hurdle Race (Sandown Park) 5th
Unibet Tolworth Novices' Hurdle (Sandown Park) 5th
Unibet Veterans Handicap Steeplechase Final (Sandown Park) 5th
Sky Sports Racing Sussex National Handicap Steeple Chase (Plumpton) 6th
Lawlor's of Naas Novices' Hurdle (Naas) 6th
32Red Conditions Stakes (Kempton Park) 9th
Watt Fences North Yorkshire Grand National H'cap Steeple Chase (Catterick Bridge) 10th
Charnwood Forest Mares' Chase (Leicester) 10th
Weatherbys Chatteris Fen Juvenile Hurdle (Huntingdon) 11th
Unibet Lanzarote Handicap Hurdle (Kempton Park) 12th
32Red Casino Steeple Chase (Kempton Park) 12th
McCoy Contractors Civil Engineering Classic Handicap Steeple Chase (Warwick) 12th
Ballymore Leamington Novices' Hurdle (Warwick) 12th
McCoy Contractors 2019 Construction News Award Finalist Hampton Novices' Chase (Warwick) 12th
BetVictor Dan Moore Memorial Handicap Steeple Chase (Fairyhouse) 12th
Sky Bet Moscow Flyer Novices' Hurdle (Punchestown) 13th
Total Event Rental Novices' Steeple Chase (Punchestown) 13th
Kristoffersen Carpets & Flooring Handicap Hurdle (Kelso) 13th
William Hill Leading Racecourse Bookmaker Handicap Steeple Chase (Kelso) 13th
Alan Swinbank Mares' Standard Open NH Flat Race (Market Rasen) 17th
Weatherbys Racing Bank Handicap Steeple Chase (Market Rasen) 17th
Healthy Pets Somerset National Handicap Steeple Chase (Wincanton) 17th
Navan Handicap Hurdle (Navan) 19th
Betway Casino Handicap Stakes (Lingfield Park) 19th
Patrick Coyne Memorial Altcar Novices' Steeple Chase (Haydock Park) 19th
Sky Bet Supreme Trial Rossington Main Novices' Hurdle (Haydock Park) 19th
The New One Unibet Champion Hurdle Trial (Haydock Park) 19th
Peter Marsh Handicap Steeple Chase (Haydock Park) 19th
OLBG.com Warfield Mares' Hurdle (Ascot) 19th
Matchbook Holloway's Handicap Hurdle (Ascot) 19th
Matchbook Clarence House Steeple Chase (Ascot) 19th
Bet365 Handicap Steeple Chase (Ascot) 19th
Weatherbys Portman Cup Chase (Taunton) 19th
Coolmore EBF Mares Novices' Steeple Chase (Thurles) 20th
Kinloch Brae Steeple Chase (Thurles) 20th
Goffs Thyestes Handicap Steeple Chase (Gowran Park) 24th
Galmoy Hurdle (Gowran Park) 24th
Sky Bet Top Price Promise Fillies' Juvenile Hurdle (Doncaster) 25th
Pertemps Lady Protectress Mares' Chase (Huntingdon) 25th
Napoleons Casino & Restaurant Owlerton Sheffield Lightning Novices' Chase (Doncaster) 26th
Sky Bet Handicap Steeple Chase (Doncaster) 26th
Albert Bartlett River Don Novices' Hurdle (Doncaster) 26th
OLBG.com Yorkshire Rose Mares' Hurdle (Doncaster) 26th
Spectra Cyber Security Solutions Trophy Handicap Steeple Chase (Cheltenham) 26th
Galliardhomes.com Cleeve Hurdle (Cheltenham) 26th
JCB Triumph Trial Finesse Juvenile Hurdle (Cheltenham) 26th
Betbright Trial Cotswold Steeple Chase (Cheltenham) 26th
Ballymore Classic Novices' Hurdle (Cheltenham) 26th
Timeform Novices' Handicap Steeple Chase (Cheltenham) 26th
Steel Plate And Sections Handicap Hurdle (Cheltenham) 26th
Solerina Mares' Novices' Hurdle (Fairyhouse) 26th
Woodlands Novices' Steeple Chase (Naas) 27th
Limestone Lad Hurdle (Naas) 27th
Ladbrokes EBF Fillies' Handicap Stakes (Wolverhampton) 28th
Frome Scoffolding (For The Dick Hunt Trophy) Handicap Steeple Chase (Wincanton) 31st

FEBRUARY

Betway Winter Derby Trial Stakes (Lingfield Park) 2nd
Betway Cleves Stakes (Lingfield Park) 2nd
Bet365 Scottish County Hurdle (Musselburgh) 2nd
Bet365 Edinburgh National Handicap Steeple Chase (Musselburgh) 2nd
Heroes Handicap Hurdle (Sandown Park) 2nd
Masters Handicap Steeple Chase (Sandown Park) 2nd
Scilly Isles Novices' Steeple Chase (Sandown Park) 2nd
Contenders Hurdle (Sandown Park) 2nd
Elmbridge Handicap Steeple Chase (Sandown Park) 2nd
William Hill Towton Novices' Steeple Chase (Wetherby) 2nd
Frank Ward Solicitors Arkle Novices' Steeple Chase (Leopardstown) 2nd
BHP Insurances Irish Champion Hurdle (Leopardstown) 2nd
Nathaniel Lacy Golden Cygnet Novices' Hurdle (Leopardstown) 2nd
Coral Dublin Steeple Chase (Leopardstown) 2nd
Goffs (Colts & Geldings) Irish National Hunt Flat Race (Leopardstown) 2nd
Coral.ie Leopardstown Handicap Hurdle (Leopardstown) 2nd
Leopardstown Handicap Chase (Leopardstown) 2nd
Bet365 Scottish Triumph Hurdle Trial Juvenile Hurdle (Musselburgh) 3rd
Tattersalls Ireland Spring 4yo Hurdle (Leopardstown) 3rd
Unibet Irish Gold Cup (Leopardstown) 3rd
Flogas Novices' Steeple Chase (Leopardstown) 3rd
Deloitte Novices' Hurdle (Leopardstown) 3rd
Mares Irish National Hunt Flat Race (Leopardstown) 3rd
Chanelle Group Leopardstown Steeple Chase (Leopardstown) 3rd
Leopardstown Handicap Hurdle (Leopardstown) 3rd
EBF Mares Handicap Hurdle (Leopardstown) 3rd
Mansion Bet Sidney Banks Memorial Novices' Hurdle (Huntingdon) 7th
Mansion Bet Handicap Hurdle (Huntingdon) 7th
Warwick Castle Handicap Steeple Chase (Warwick) 9th
Kingmaker Novices' Steeple Chase (Warwick) 9th
OLBG.com Warwick Mares' Hurdle (Warwick) 9th
Betfair Hurdle (Handicap) (Newbury) 9th
Betfair Denman Steeple Chase (Newbury) 9th
Betfair Exchange Game Spirit Steeple Chase (Newbury) 9th
Betfair Each Way Edge Novices' Limited Handicap Steeple Chase (Newbury) 9th
Betfair Bet In-Play Handicap Hurdle (Newbury) 9th
Best Odds On The Betfair Exchange Bumper (Newbury) 9th
Betway Sprint Handicap Stakes (Wolverhampton) 9th
Opera Hat Mares' Steeple Chase (Naas) 9th
Exeter Novices' Hurdle (Exeter) 10th
Exeter Veterans' Handicap Steeple Chase (Exeter) 10th
Exeter Racecourse Mares Steeple Chase (Exeter) 10th
Grand National Trial Handicap Steeple Chase (Punchestown) 10th
Timeform Morebattle Hurdle (Kelso) 14th
Kelso Steeple Chase (Kelso) 14th
Powerstown Novice Hurdle (Clonmel) 14th
Castel Royal Artillery Gold Cup Steeple Chase (Sandown Park) 15th
Weatherbys GSB Jane Seymour Mares' Novices' Hurdle (Sandown Park) 15th
Albert Bartlett Prestige Novices' Hurdle (Haydock Park) 16th
William Hill Rendlesham Hurdle (Haydock Park) 16th
William Hill Grand National Trial Handicap Steeple Chase (Haydock Park) 16th
Sodexo Reynoldstown Novices' Steeple Chase (Ascot) 16th
Betfair Ascot Steeple Chase (Ascot) 16th
Keltbray Swinley Chase (Limited Handicap) (Ascot) 16th
Ascot Handicap Hurdle (Ascot) 16th
Betway Kingwell Hurdle (Wincanton) 16th
Red Mills Trial Hurdle (Gowran Park) 16th
Red Mills Steeple Chase (Gowran Park) 16th
Boyne Hurdle (Navan) 17th
Ten Up Novices' Steeple Chase (Navan) 17th
Sky Sports Racing Virgin 535 Veterans' Handicap Steeple Chase (Doncaster) 20th
sunbets.co.uk Handicap Stakes (Newcastle) 20th
32Red Casino Conditions Stakes (Newcastle) 20th
Quevega Mares' Hurdle (Punchestown) 20th
Michael Purcell Novices' Hurdle (Thurles) 21st
Budbrooke Handicap Steeple Chase (Warwick) 22nd
Devon National Handicap Steeple Chase (Exeter) 22nd
Betway Winter Derby Stakes (Lingfield Park) 23rd
Betway Hever Sprint Stakes (Lingfield Park) 23rd
Betfred Eider Handicap Steeple Chase (Newcastle) 23rd
888Sport Handicap Steeple Chase (Kempton Park) 23rd
888Sport Adonis Juvenile Hurdle (Kempton Park) 23rd

888Sport Pendil Novices' Steeple Chase (Kempton Park) 23rd
Sky Bet Dovecote Novices' Hurdle (Kempton Park) 23rd
Winning Fair Juvenile Hurdle (Fairyhouse) 23rd
At The Races Bobbyjo Steeple Chase (Fairyhouse) 23rd
Totepool National Spirit Hurdle (Fontwell Park) 24th
Paddy Power Johnstown Novices' Hurdle (Naas) 24th
Paddy Power Newlands Steeple Chase (Naas) 24th
Nas na Riogh Novices' Handicap Steeple Chase (Naas) 24th
32Red Casino Fillies' Handicap Stakes (Newcastle) 28th

MARCH

Patton Stakes (Dundalk) 1st
Ladbrokes Spring Cup Stakes (Lingfield Park) 2nd
William Hill Grimthorpe Handicap Steeple Chase (Doncaster) 2nd
William Hill Great Cheltenham Offers Handicap Steeple Chase (Doncaster) 2nd
William Hill Join Plus In Shop Mares' Novices' Hurdle (Doncaster) 2nd
Totescoop6 Premier Kelso Novices' Hurdle (Kelso) 2nd
Totepool.com Premier Steeple Chase (Kelso) 2nd
William Hill Supporting Greatwood Gold Cup Handicap Steeple Chase (Newbury) 2nd
Elite Racing Club Supporting Greatwood Veterans' Handicap Steeple Chase (Newbury) 2nd
Flyingbolt Novices' Steeple Chase (Navan) 2nd
Winteron Young Chaser Series Final Handicap Steeple Chase (Sedgefield) 3rd
Bet & Watch At 188Bet Cambridgeshire National Handicap Steeple Chase (Huntingdon) 3rd
TRI Equestrian Carrickmines Handicap Steeple Chase (Leopardstown) 3rd
Road To The Kentucky Derby' Conditions Stakes (Kempton Park) 6th
32Red Handicap Stakes (Kempton Park) 6th
Grand Military Gold Cup Amateur Riders' Classified Steeple Chase (Sandown Park) 8th
SunRacing.co.uk Lady Wulfruna Stakes (Wolverhampton) 9th
sunbets.co.uk Lincoln Trial Handicap Stakes (Wolverhampton) 9th
Betway Handicap Stakes (Wolverhampton) 9th
Matchbook Imperial Cup Handicap Hurdle (Sandown Park) 9th
EBF Matchbook VIP "National Hunt" Novices' Handicap Hurdle (Final) (Sandown Park) 9th
EBF Stallions / TBA Mares' Standard Open National Hunt Flat Race (Sandown Park) 9th
Shamrock Handicap Steeple Chase (Gowran Park) 9th
Leinster National (Naas) 10th
Directors Plate Novices' Steeple Chase (Naas) 10th
Irish Racing Writers Kingsfurze Novices' Hurdle (Naas) 10th
Unibet Champion Hurdle Challenge Trophy (Cheltenham) 12th
Racing Post Arkle Challenge Trophy Novices' Steeple Chase (Cheltenham) 12th
Sky Bet Supreme Novices' Hurdle (Cheltenham) 12th
Ultima Handicap Steeple Chase (Cheltenham) 12th
National Hunt Challenge Cup Amateur Riders' Novices' Steeple Chase (Cheltenham) 12th
Close Brothers Novices' Handicap Steeple Chase (Cheltenham) 12th
OLBG David Nicholson Mares' Hurdle (Cheltenham) 12th
Betway Queen Mother Champion Steeple Chase (Cheltenham) 13th
RSA Insurance Novices' Steeple Chase (Cheltenham) 13th
Ballymore Baring Bingham Novices' Hurdle (Cheltenham) 13th
Coral Cup Handicap Hurdle (Cheltenham) 13th
Weatherbys Champion Bumper (A Standard Open NH Flat race) (Cheltenham) 13th
Glenfarclas Steeple Chase (Cross Country) (Cheltenham) 13th
Boodles Fred Winter Juvenile Handicap Hurdle (Cheltenham) 13th
Pertemps Network Final Handicap Hurdle (Cheltenham) 14th
Fulke Walwyn Kim Muir Challenge Cup Handicap Steeple Chase (Cheltenham) 14th
Brown Advisory & Merriebelle Stable Plate Handicap Steeple Chase (Cheltenham) 14th
Sun Racing Stayers' Hurdle (Cheltenham) 14th
Ryanair Festival Trophy Steeple Chase (Cheltenham) 14th
JLT Golden Miller Novices' Steeple Chase (Cheltenham) 14th
Trull House Stud Dawn Run Mares' Novices' Hurdle (Cheltenham) 14th
Magners Cheltenham Gold Cup Steeple Chase (Cheltenham) 15th
JCB Triumph Hurdle Juvenile Hurdle (Cheltenham) 15th
Johnny Henderson Grand Annual Handicap Steeple Chase (Cheltenham) 15th
Randox Health County Handicap Hurdle (Cheltenham) 15th
St James's Place Foxhunter Challenge Cup (Cheltenham) 15th
Albert Bartlett Spa Novices' Hurdle (Cheltenham) 15th
Martin Pipe Conditional Jockeys' Handicap Hurdle (Cheltenham) 15th
Betfred Midlands Grand National Handicap Steeple Chase (Uttoxeter) 16th
Betfred Supports Jack Berry House Novices' Handicap Steeple Chase (Uttoxeter) 16th
Betfred 'Treble Odds On LUCKY15's' Handicap Hurdle (Uttoxeter) 16th
Matchbook Silver Bowl Handicap Steeple Chase (Kempton Park) 16th
Matchbook Racing Is Commission Free Silver Plate Handicap Hurdle (Kempton Park) 16th
188BET Mobile Veterans' Handicap Steeple Chase (Carlisle) 17th
Dawn Run EBF Mares' Novices' Steeple Chase (Limerick) 17th
Shannon Spray EBF Mares' Novices' Hurdle (Limerick) 17th
An Uaimh Steeple Chase (Navan) 18th

EBF Novices' Final Handicap Steeple Chase (Navan) ... 18th
Be Wiser Juvenile Handicap Hurdle (Newbury) ... 23rd
EBF & TBA Mares' National Hunt Novices' Hurdle Final Limited Handicap (Newbury) ... 23rd
Goffs UK Spring Sales Bumper (A Standard Open NH Flat Race) (Newbury) ... 23rd
Liz Adam Memorial Steeplechase (Kelso) ... 23rd
Edinburgh Gin Handicap Hurdle (Kelso) ... 23rd
totescoop6 Handicap Hurdle (Kelso) ... 23rd
Native Upmanship Novices' Steeple Chase (Thurles) ... 23rd
EBF Park Express Stakes (Naas) ... 24th
Racing UK Jump To It St Marys Lands Handicap Steeplechase (Warwick) ... 28th
Unibet Doncaster Mile Stakes (Doncaster) ... 30th
Unibet Lincoln Handicap Stakes (Doncaster) ... 30th
Unibet Cammidge Trophy Stakes (Doncaster) ... 30th
Better Odds With Matchbook Magnolia Stakes (Kempton Park) ... 30th
Matchbook Betting Podcast Rosebery Handicap Stakes (Kempton Park) ... 30th
Cork Sprint Stakes (Navan) ... 30th
Ascot Juvenile Handicap Hurdle (Ascot) ... 31st
Ascot Novices' Handicap Steeple Chase (Ascot) ... 31st
Kevin McManus Bumper (Limerick) ... 31st
Hugh McMahon Memorial Novices' Steeple Chase (Limerick) ... 31st

APRIL

Boyne Cup Handicap Steeplechase (Ludlow) ... 1st
Betway Stayers' Handicap Stakes (Newcastle) ... 1st
Heritage Stakes (Leopardstown) ... 3rd
Randox Health Fox Hunters Handicap Steeple Chase (Aintree) ... 4th
Aintree Hurdle (Aintree) ... 4th
Betway Bowl Steeple Chase (Aintree) ... 4th
Manifesto Novices' Steeple Chase (Aintree) ... 4th
Doom Bar Anniversary Juvenile Hurdle (Aintree) ... 4th
Red Rum Handicap Steeple Chase (Aintree) ... 4th
Nickel Coin Mares' Open National Hunt Flat Race (Aintree) ... 4th
Randox Health Topham Handicap Steeple Chase (Aintree) ... 5th
JLT Melling Steeple Chase (Aintree) ... 5th
Betway Mildmay Novices' Steeple Chase (Aintree) ... 5th
Doom Bar Sefton Novices' Hurdle (Aintree) ... 5th
Betway Top Novices' Hurdle (Aintree) ... 5th
Alder Hey Children's Charity Handicap Hurdle (Aintree) ... 5th
Weatherbys Racing Bank Standard Open National Hunt Flat Race (Aintree) ... 5th
Randox Health Grand National Handicap Steeple Chase (Aintree) ... 6th
Ryanair Liverpool Stayers' Hurdle (Aintree) ... 6th
Doom Bar Maghull Novices' Steeple Chase (Aintree) ... 6th
Betway Mersey Novices' Hurdle (Aintree) ... 6th
Gaskells Handicap Hurdle (Aintree) ... 6th
Betway Handicap Steeple Chase (Aintree) ... 6th
Pinsent Masons Handicap Hurdle (Aintree) ... 6th
Leopardstown 2000 Guineas Trial Stakes (Leopardstown) ... 6th
Leopardstown 1000 Guineas Trial Stakes (Leopardstown) ... 6th
Ballysax Stakes (Leopardstown) ... 6th
Rathbarry Novices' Hurdle (Fairyhouse) ... 7th
Coolmore NH Sires Festival Novices' Hurdle (Fairyhouse) ... 7th
Total Enjoyment Mares' Bumper (Fairyhouse) ... 7th
Noblesse Stakes (Cork) ... 7th
totepool Barry Hills Further Flight Stakes (Nottingham) ... 10th
Hillhouse Quarry Handicap Steeple Chase (Ayr) ... 12th
Coral.co.uk Seafield Trophy Hurdle (Ayr) ... 12th
John Porter Stakes (Newbury) ... 13th
Greenham Stakes (Newbury) ... 13th
Dubai Duty Free Fred Darling Stakes (Newbury) ... 13th
Elite Racing Club Supporting Greatwood Spring Cup Handicap (Newbury) ... 13th
Coral Scottish Grand National Handicap Chase (Ayr) ... 13th
QTS Scottish Champion Hurdle (A Limited Handicap) (Ayr) ... 13th
Dawn Homes Novices' Championship Handicap Chase (Ayr) ... 13th
Jordan Electrics Ltd Future Champion Novices' Chase (Ayr) ... 13th
Scotty Brand Handicap Chase (Ayr) ... 13th
Gladness Stakes (Curragh) ... 13th
Alleged Stakes (Curragh) ... 13th
Bet365 Feilden Stakes (Newmarket) ... 16th
Lanwades Stud Nell Gwyn Stakes (Newmarket) ... 16th
Bet365 European Free Handicap (Newmarket) ... 16th
Bet365 Craven Stakes (Newmarket) ... 17th
Connaught Access Flooring Abernant Stakes (Newmarket) ... 17th
Barchester Healthcare Silver Trophy Handicap Steeple Chase (Cheltenham) ... 17th
Bet365 Earl of Sefton Stakes (Newmarket) ... 18th

EBF Thoroughbred Breeders' Association Mares' Novices' Handicap Chase (Cheltenham) 18th
Catesby Estates PLC Mares' Handicap Hurdle (Cheltenham) 18th
Huw Stevens, Jo Whiley Afterparty Onsale Mares' Novices' Hurdle (Cheltenham) 18th
Arkells Brewery Fillies' Juvenile Handicap Hurdle (Cheltenham) 18th
Betway Handicap Stakes (Bath) 19th
Dribuild Group Handicap Stakes (Bath) 19th
Whitsbury Manor Stud / British EBF Lansdown Stakes (Bath) 19th
Burradon Stakes (Newcastle) 19th
Betway Handicap (Newcastle) 19th
Betway All-Weather Sprint Championships Conditions Stakes (Lingfield Park) 19th
Sun Racing All-Weather Mile Championships Conditions Stakes (Lingfield Park) 19th
Betway Easter Classic All-Weather Middle Distance Ch'ships Conditions Stakes (Lingfield Park) 19th
Betway All-Weather Marathon Championships Conditions Stakes (Lingfield Park) 19th
Ladbrokes 3 Year Old All-Weather Championships Conditions Stakes (Lingfield Park) 19th
Sun Racing All-Weather Championships Apprentice Handicap (Lingfield Park) 19th
32Red All-Weather Fillies' and Mares' Championships Conditions Stakes (Lingfield Park) 19th
Smarkets Challenger Two Mile Handicap Hurdle Final (Haydock Park) 20th
Smarkets Challenger Stayers Handicap Hurdle Final (Haydock Park) 20th
Smarkets Challenger Mares' Handicap Hurdle Final (Haydock Park) 20th
Smarkets Challenger Staying Handicap Chase Final (Haydock Park) 20th
Smarkets Challenger Middle Distance Handicap Chase Final (Haydock Park) 20th
Smarkets Challenger Series Mares' Handicap Chase Final (Haydock Park) 20th
Smarkets Tim Molony Handicap Chase (Haydock Park) 20th
Racing UK Snowdrop Fillies' Stakes (Kempton Park) 20th
Racing UK Queen's Prize Handicap Stakes (Kempton Park) 20th
Scottish Sprint Cup Handicap Stakes (Musselburgh) 20th
Royal Mile Handicap Stakes (Musselburgh) 20th
Queen's Cup Handicap Stakes (Musselburgh) 20th
Siddell Environmental Services West Wales National Handicap Chase (Ffos Las) 21st
Totepool Sussex Champion Hurdle (Plumpton) 21st
Ryanair Gold Cup (Fairyhouse) 21st
EBF Mares' Novices' Hurdle Final (Fairyhouse) 21st
John Fowler Memorial Mares' Steeple Chase (Fairyhouse) 21st
INHSO Final Novices' Handicap Hurdle (Fairyhouse) 21st
Imperial Call Steeple Chase (Cork) 21st
Easter Handicap Hurdle (Cork) 21st
188BET Supports The Injured Jockeys Fund Handicap Steeplechase (Chepstow) 22nd
Totesport.com Sussex Champion Chase Handicap (Plumpton) 22nd
Percy Maynard 4yo Hurdle (Fairyhouse) 22nd
Keelings Hurdle (Fairyhouse) 22nd
Boylesports Irish Grand National Steeple Chase (Fairyhouse) 22nd
Greenogue Novices' Handicap Steeple Chase (Fairyhouse) 22nd
Glasscarn Handicap Hurdle (Fairyhouse) 23rd
Fairyhouse Chase (Fairyhouse) 23rd
Investec Corporate Banking Great Metropolitan Handicap (Epsom) 24th
Investec Blue Riband Trial Stakes (Epsom) 24th
Investec City and Suburban Handicap (Epsom) 24th
EBF Stallions Gold Castle 'National Hunt' Novices' Hurdle (Perth) 24th
All New Discovery River Tay Handicap Steeplechase (Perth) 25th
Bet365 Mile Stakes (Sandown Park) 26th
Bet365 Gordon Richards Stakes (Sandown Park) 26th
Bet365 Classic Trial Stakes (Sandown Park) 26th
TBA Fair Maid Of Perth Steeplechase (Perth) 26th
Heineken UK Highland National Handicap Steeplechase (Perth) 26th
totepool EBF Stallions King Richard III Stakes (Leicester) 27th
Best Odds Guaranteed At 188Bet Handicap Stakes (Haydock Park) 27th
Bet and Watch At 188Bet Handicap Stakes (Haydock Park) 27th
Download The Award-Winning Attheraces App Handicap Stakes (Ripon) 27th
Bet365 Gold Cup Steeple Chase (Sandown Park) 27th
Bet365 Celebration Chase (Sandown Park) 27th
Bet365 Oaksey Chase (Sandown Park) 27th
Bet365 Select Hurdle (Sandown Park) 27th
Bet365 Hurdle (Sandown Park) 27th
Bet365 Championship Novices' Hurdle (Sandown Park) 27th
Bet365 Josh Gifford Novices' Handicap Steeplechase (Sandown Park) 27th
Committed Stakes (Navan) 28th
Vintage Crop Stakes (Navan) 28th
Salsabil Stakes (Navan) 28th
Prix Ganay (Parislongchamp) 28th
Woodlands Sprint Stakes (Naas) 29th
Growise Novices' Steeple Chase (Punchestown) 30th
Evening Herald Champion Novices' Hurdle (Punchestown) 30th
Boylesports Champion Steeple Chase (Punchestown) 30th
Kilashee Handicap Hurdle (Punchestown) 30th

MAY

Merriebelle Stable Pavilion Stakes (Ascot) 1st
Longines Sagaro Stakes (Ascot) 1st
Paradise Stakes (Ascot) 1st
Irish Daily Mirror War of Attrition Novices' Hurdle (Punchestown) 1st
Bibby Financial Punchestown Gold Cup (Punchestown) 1st
Champion Bumper (Punchestown) 1st
Guinness Handicap Steeple Chase (Punchestown) 1st
Liss A Paoraigh Mares' Bumper (Punchestown) 1st
Ryanair Novices' Steeple Chase (Punchestown) 2nd
Ladbrokes World Series Hurdle (Punchestown) 2nd
Three.ie Handicap Steeple Chase (Punchestown) 2nd
Ballymore Eustace Handicap Hurdle (Punchestown) 2nd
Mares' Novices' Hurdle (Punchestown) 2nd
Tattersalls Ireland Champion Novices' Hurdle (Punchestown) 3rd
Punchestown Champion Hurdle (Punchestown) 3rd
Punchestown Novices' Handicap Steeple Chase (Punchestown) 3rd
Glencarraig Lady Mares' Handicap Steeple Chase (Punchestown) 3rd
AES Champion 4yo Hurdle (Punchestown) 4th
Ballymore Handicap Hurdle (Punchestown) 4th
EBF Mares' Champion Hurdle (Punchestown) 4th
QIPCO 2000 Guineas Stakes (Newmarket) 4th
QIPCO Jockey Club Stakes (Newmarket) 4th
QIPCO Palace House Stakes (Newmarket) 4th
Daisy Warwick Stakes (Goodwood) 4th
EBF Conqueror Stakes (Goodwood) 4th
Newmarket Stakes (Newmarket) 4th
Spring Lodge Handicap Stakes (Newmarket) 4th
Commission Free Racing At Matchbook Handicap Stakes (Goodwood) 4th
Thirsk Hunt Cup (Wetherby) 4th
Bet365 Staffordshire Plate Handicap Steeplechase (Uttoxeter) 5th
QIPCO 1000 Guineas Stakes (Newmarket) 5th
QIPCO Dahlia Stakes (Newmarket) 5th
Pretty Polly Stakes (Newmarket) 5th
Longholes.com Handicap Stakes (Newmarket) 5th
Qatar Racing Handicap Stakes (Newmarket) 5th
Victor McCalmont Stakes (Gowran Park) 5th
Tetrarch Stakes (Curragh) 6th
Mooresbridge Stakes (Curragh) 6th
Athasi Stakes (Curragh) 6th
Snellings Norfolk National Handicap Steeplechase (Fakenham) 7th
Chester Vase Stakes (Chester) 8th
Boodles Diamond Handicap Stakes (Chester) 8th
Arkle Finance Cheshire Oaks Stakes (Chester) 8th
Vintage Tipple Stakes (Gowran Park) 8th
Ormonde Stakes (Chester) 9th
Homeserve Dee Stakes (Chester) 9th
Gateley PLC Handicap Stakes (Chester) 9th
Abbey Logistics Handicap Stakes (Chester) 9th
Huxley Stakes (Chester) 10th
Chester Cup Stakes (Chester) 10th
Polonia Stakes (Cork) 10th
188Bet Chester Plate Stakes (Chester) 10th
Crabbie's Earl Grosvenor Handicap Stakes (Chester) 10th
Boodles Diamond Handicap Stakes (Chester) 10th
Derby Trial Stakes (Lingfield Park) 11th
Oaks Trial Stakes (Lingfield Park) 11th
Chartwell Stakes (Lingfield Park) 11th
Swinton Handicap Hurdle (Haydock Park) 11th
Pertemps Network Long Distance Handicap Hurdle (Haydock Park) 11th
Pertemps Network Intermediate Handicap Steeplechase (Haydock Park) 11th
Spring Trophy Stakes (Haydock Park) 11th
Totescoop6 Victoria Cup Handicap Stakes (Ascot) 11th
EBF Breeders' Series Fillies' Handicap Stakes (Ascot) 11th
Buckhounds Stakes (Ascot) 11th
Weatherbys EBF Kilvington Stakes (Nottingham) 11th
Blue Wind Stakes (Naas) 11th
Sole Power Stakes (Naas) 11th
Derrinstown Derby Trial Stakes (Leopardstown) 12th
Derrinstown 1000 Guineas Trial Stakes (Leopardstown) 12th
Amethyst Stakes (Leopardstown) 12th
Killarney Handicap Hurdle (Killarney) 12th
Tourist Attraction Mares Hurdle (Killarney) 12th

JUNE

Investec Derby Stakes (Epsom)	1st
Investec Diomed Stakes (Epsom)	1st
Princess Elizabeth Stakes (Epsom)	1st
Investec Corporate Banking 'Dash' Handicap Stakes (Epsom)	1st
Western Toyota 2000GT Heritage Sprint Handicap Stakes (Musselburgh)	1st
Maggie Dickson Stakes (Musselburgh)	1st
Investec Private Banking Handicap Stakes (Epsom)	1st
Investec Out Of The Ordinary Handicap Stakes (Epsom)	1st
Investec Asset Management Handicap Stakes (Epsom)	1st
Betfred Watch Sky Sports In Our Shops Handicap Stakes (Doncaster)	1st
Qipco Prix du Jockey Club (Chantilly)	2nd
EBF Nottinghamshire Oaks Stakes (Nottingham)	2nd
Nijinsky (for King George V Cup) Stakes (Leopardstown)	6th
Glencairn Stakes (Leopardstown)	6th
Silver Stakes (Curragh)	7th
Ballyogan Stakes (Curragh)	7th
Achilles Stakes (Haydock Park)	8th
Betway Pinnacle Stakes (Haydock Park)	8th
Betway John O'Gaunt Stakes (Haydock Park)	8th
Trucking By Brian Yeardley Two Year Old Trophy Stakes (Beverley)	8th
Hilary Needler Trophy (Beverley)	8th
Animal Health Trust Handicap Stakes (Newmarket)	8th
John Sunley Memorial Handicap Stakes (Newmarket)	8th
AHT Charoty Lottery Handicap Stakes (Newmarket)	8th
Margaret Giffen Memorial Handicap Stakes (Newmarket)	8th
Essex Sprint Handicap (Chelmsford City)	8th
Moulsham Mile Handicap (Chelmsford City)	8th
Energy Check City Of Perth Gold Cup Steeplechase (Perth)	9th
Abingdon Stakes (Newbury)	13th
Ballycorus Stakes (Leopardstown)	13th
Munster Oaks Stakes (Cork)	14th
Ganton Stakes (York)	14th
Midsummer Sprint Stakes (Cork)	14th
EBF Breeders' Series Handicap Stakes (York)	14th
Scurry Stakes (Sandown Park)	15th
Grand Cup Stakes (York)	15th
Pavers Foundation Catherine Memorial Sprint Handicap Stakes (York)	15th
JCB Handicap Stakes (York)	15th
EBF Cathedral Stakes (Salisbury)	16th
Prix de Diane Longines (Chantilly)	16th
Queen Anne Stakes (Ascot)	18th
St James's Palace Stakes (Ascot)	18th
King's Stand Stakes (Ascot)	18th
Coventry Stakes (Ascot)	18th
Wolferton Handicap Stakes (Ascot)	18th
Ascot Handicap Stakes (Ascot)	18th
Prince Of Wales's Stakes (Ascot)	19th
Duke of Cambridge Stakes (Ascot)	19th
Queen Mary Stakes (Ascot)	19th
Jersey Stakes (Ascot)	19th
Royal Hunt Cup (Ascot)	19th
Queen's Vase Stakes (Ascot)	19th
Charlotte Stakes (Chelmsford City)	19th
Gold Cup Stakes (Ascot)	20th
Ribblesdale Stakes (Ascot)	20th
Norfolk Stakes (Ascot)	20th
Hampton Court Stakes (Ascot)	20th
Britannia Handicap Stakes (Ascot)	20th
King George V Handicap Stakes (Ascot)	20th
Coronation Stakes (Ascot)	21st
Commonwealth Cup Stakes (Ascot)	21st
King Edward VII Stakes (Ascot)	21st
Albany Stakes (Ascot)	21st
Duke of Edinburgh Handicap Stakes (Ascot)	21st
Sandringham Handicap Stakes (Ascot)	21st
Windsor Castle Stakes (Ascot)	22nd
Diamond Jubilee Stakes (Ascot)	22nd
Hardwicke Stakes (Ascot)	22nd
Chesham Stakes (Ascot)	22nd
Wokingham Handicap Stakes (Ascot)	22nd
Queen Alexandra Stakes (Ascot)	22nd
Sun Stud EBF Handicap Stakes (Ayr)	22nd

JULY

Aphrodite Stakes (Newmarket) 20th
Irish Oaks Stakes (Curragh) 20th
Jebel Ali Anglesey Stakes (Curragh) 20th
Minstrel Stakes (Curragh) 20th
Sapphire Stakes (Curragh) 21st
Kilboy Estate Stakes (Curragh) 21st
Sweet Mimosa Stakes (Naas) 24th
EBF Star Stakes (Sandown Park) 25th
Tyros Stakes (Leopardstown) 25th
Silver Flash Stakes (Leopardstown) 25th
Vinnie Roe Stakes (Leopardstown) 25th
EBF Valiant Stakes (Ascot) 26th
EBF Lyric Stakes (York) 26th
Her Majesty's Plate Stakes (Down Royal) 26th
King George VI & Queen Elizabeth Stakes (Ascot) 27th
Princess Margaret Stakes (Ascot) 27th
Wooldridge Group Pat Eddery Stakes (Ascot) 27th
Porsche Handicap Stakes (Ascot) 27th
Winkfield Stakes (Ascot) 27th
Gigaset International Handicap Stakes (Ascot) 27th
Sky Bet York Stakes (York) 27th
Sky Bet Pomfret Stakes (Pontefract) 28th
Prix Rothschild (Deauville) 28th
Qatar Goodwood Cup Stakes (Goodwood) 30th
Qatar Lennox Stakes (Goodwood) 30th
Qatar Vintage Stakes (Goodwood) 30th
Castlegar Novices' Hurdle (Galway) 30th
Qatar Sussex Stakes (Goodwood) 31st
Markel Insurance Molecomb Stakes (Goodwood) 31st
thetote.com Galway Plate (Handicap Steeple Chase) (Galway) 31st

AUGUST

Qatar Nassau Stakes (Goodwood) 1st
Qatar Richmond Stakes (Goodwood) 1st
Qatar Gordon Stakes (Goodwood) 1st
Guinness Galway Hurdle (Galway) 1st
Ballybrit Novices' Steeple Chase (Galway) 1st
Corrib EBF Fillies Stakes (Galway) 1st
Qatar King George Stakes (Goodwood) 2nd
Bombay Sapphire Glorious Stakes (Goodwood) 2nd
Oak Tree Stakes (Goodwood) 2nd
Bonhams Thoroughbred Stakes (Goodwood) 2nd
L'Ormarins Queens Plate Stakes (Goodwood) 2nd
Golden Mile Handicap (Goodwood) 3rd
Qatar Lillie Langtry Stakes (Goodwood) 3rd
Unibet Stewards' Cup Handicap Stakes (Goodwood) 3rd
EBF Chalice Stakes (Newmarket) 3rd
Mervue Handicap Hurdle (Galway) 4th
Queensferry Stakes (Chester) 4th
LARC Prix Maurice de Gheest (Deauville) 8th
Ballyroan Stakes (Leopardstown) 9th
Keeneland Phoenix Stakes (Curragh) 9th
QREC Phoenix Sprint Stakes (Curragh) 10th
Rose of Lancaster Stakes (Haydock Park) 10th
EBF Dick Hern Stakes (Haydock Park) 10th
German-thoroughbred.com Sweet Solera Stakes (Newmarket) 10th
El Gran Senor Stakes (Tipperary) 11th
Prix du Haras de Fresnay-Le-Buffard Jacques Le Marois (Deauville) 11th
EBF Upavon Stakes (Salisbury) 14th
Tattersalls Sovereign Stakes (Salisbury) 15th
Invesco Desmond Stakes (Leopardstown) 15th
St Hugh's Stakes (Newbury) 16th
Royal Whip Stakes (Curragh) 16th
Ballycullen Stakes (Curragh) 16th
Hungerford Stakes (Newbury) 17th
Geoffrey Freer Stakes (Newbury) 17th
Denford Stud Stakes (Newbury) 17th
Flying Fillies' Stakes (Pontefract) 18th
Darley Prix Morny (Deauville) 18th
Darley Prix Jean Romanet (Deauville) 18th
Juddmonte International Stakes (York) 21st
Betway Great Voltigeur Stakes (York) 21st
Tattersalls Acomb Stakes (York) 21st
Ruby Stakes (Killarney) 21st

Yorkshire Oaks Stakes (York) ... 22nd
Sky Bet Lowther Stakes (York) ... 22nd
EBF Galtres Stakes (York) ... 22nd
Goffs UK Premier Yearling Stakes (York) ... 22nd
EBF Stonehenge Stakes (Salisbury) ... 22nd
Coolmore Nunthorpe Stakes (York) ... 23rd
Weatherbys Hamilton Lonsdale Cup Stakes (York) ... 23rd
Al Basti Equiworld Gimcrack Stakes (York) ... 23rd
Curragh Stakes (Curragh) ... 23rd
Galileo EBF Futurity Stakes (Curragh) ... 23rd
Debutante Stakes (Curragh) ... 23rd
Mount Brandon Handicap Hurdle (Killarney) ... 23rd
Lough Leane Handicap Steeple Chase (Killarney) ... 23rd
Celebration Mile (Goodwood) ... 23rd
March Stakes (Goodwood) ... 24th
Prestige Stakes (Goodwood) ... 24th
Hopeful Stakes (Newmarket) ... 24th
Winter Hill Stakes (Windsor) ... 24th
August Stakes (Windsor) ... 24th
Strensall Stakes (York) ... 24th
Roses Stakes (York) ... 24th
Sky Bet Melrose Handicap Stakes (York) ... 24th
Sky Bet Ebor Handicap Stakes (York) ... 24th
Sky Bet City of York Stakes (York) ... 24th
Weatherbys Bank Supreme Stakes (Goodwood) ... 25th
Champion 2 Year Old Trophy Stakes (Ripon) ... 26th
Fairy Bridge Stakes (Tipperary) ... 29th
Abergwaun Stakes (Tipperary) ... 29th
Round Tower Stakes (Curragh) ... 30th
Snow Fairy Stakes (Curragh) ... 30th
Flame of Tara Stakes (Curragh) ... 30th
Solario Stakes (Sandown Park) ... 31st
Atalanta Stakes (Sandown Park) ... 31st
Beverley Bullet Stakes (Beverley) ... 31st
Chester Handicap Stakes (Chester) ... 31st

SEPTEMBER

Shadwell Dick Poole Fillies' Stakes (Salisbury) ... 5th
Sprint Cup Stakes (Haydock Park) ... 7th
Superior Mile Stakes (Haydock Park) ... 7th
Ascendant Stakes (Haydock Park) ... 7th
Sirenia Stakes (Kempton Park) ... 7th
September Stakes (Kempton Park) ... 7th
Prix du Moulin de Longchamp (Parislongchamp) ... 7th
Lavazza Handicap Stakes (Ascot) ... 7th
Garrowby Stakes (York) ... 8th
Listowel Stakes (Listowel) ... 8th
Latrigue 4yo Handicap Hurdle (Listowel) ... 9th
Scarbrough Stakes (Doncaster) ... 10th
Guinness Kerry National (Handicap Steeple Chase) (Listowel) ... 11th
DFS Park Hill Stakes (Doncaster) ... 12th
William Hill May Hill Stakes (Doncaster) ... 12th
Weatherbys Racing Bank £300,000 2yo Stakes (Doncaster) ... 12th
Ladbrokes Handicap Hurdle (Listowel) ... 12th
Doncaster Cup Stakes (Doncaster) ... 13th
Flying Childers Stakes (Doncaster) ... 13th
Japan Racing Association Sceptre Stakes (Doncaster) ... 13th
Flying Scotsman Stakes (Doncaster) ... 13th
William Hill St Leger Stakes (Doncaster) ... 14th
Park Stakes (Doncaster) ... 14th
Champagne Stakes (Doncaster) ... 14th
Stand Cup Stakes (Chester) ... 14th
QIPCO Irish Champion Stakes (Leopardstown) ... 14th
Coolmore Matron Stakes (Leopardstown) ... 14th
Clipper Logistics Solonoway Stakes (Leopardstown) ... 14th
KPMG Golden Fleece Stakes (Leopardstown) ... 14th
Kilternan Stakes (Leopardstown) ... 14th
Goffs Vincent O'Brien National Stakes (Curragh) ... 15th
Moyglare Stud Stakes (Curragh) ... 15th
Comer Group International St Leger Stakes (Curragh) ... 15th
Moyglare Stud Blandford Stakes (Curragh) ... 15th
Derrinstown Stud Flying Five Stakes (Curragh) ... 15th
Qatar Prix Vermeille (Parislongchamp) ... 15th
Fortune Stakes (Sandown Park) ... 18th

OCTOBER

Dubai Autumn Stakes (Newmarket) 12th
EBF Boadicea Stakes (Newmarket) 12th
Zetland Stakes (Newmarket) 12th
Dubai £500,000 Cesarewitch Handicap Stakes (Newmarket) 12th
Rockingham Stakes (York) 12th
Chepstow Contract Rentals Silver Trophy Hurdle (Chepstow) 12th
Smerdon Tree Services Novices' Steeple Chase (Chepstow) 12th
Join The Coral Champions Club For Free Handicap Chase (Chepstow) 12th
Legacy Stakes (Curragh) 13th
Waterford Testimonial Stakes (Curragh) 13th
Lanwades & Staffordstown Studs Silken Glider Stakes (Curragh) 13th
Ladbrokes Munster National Handicap Steeple Chase (Limerick) 13th
Greenmount Park Novices' Hurdle (Limerick) 13th
EBF Mares' Hurdle (Limerick) 13th
EBF Beckford Stakes (Bath) 16th
Carvills Hill Steeple Chase (Punchestown) 16th
Buck House Novices' Steeple Chase (Punchestown) 16th
Mercury Stakes (Dundalk) 18th
QIPCO Champion Stakes (Ascot) 19th
Queen Elizabeth II Stakes (Ascot) 19th
QIPCO British Champions Fillies & Mares Stakes (Ascot) 19th
QIPCO British Champions Sprint Stakes (Ascot) 19th
QIPCO British Champions Long Distance Cup Stakes (Ascot) 19th
Balmoral Handicap Stakes (Ascot) 19th
Killavullan Stakes (Leopardstown) 19th
Trigo Stakes (Leopardstown) 19th
Garnet Stakes (Naas) 20th
Bluebell Stakes (Naas) 20th
Kinsale Handicap Steeple Chase (Cork) 20th
Matchbook VIP Hurdle (Kempton Park) 20th
Matchbook Novices' Hurdle (Kempton Park) 20th
Silver Tankard Stakes (Pontefract) 21st
Knockaire Stakes (Leopardstown) 26th
Eyrefield Stakes (Leopardstown) 26th
Criterium de Saint-Cloud (Saint-Cloud) 26th
Vertem Futurity Trophy Stakes (Doncaster) 26th
Doncaster Stakes (Doncaster) 26th
Worthington's St Simon Stakes (Newbury) 26th
Worthington's Horris Hill Stakes (Newbury) 26th
Radley Stakes (Newbury) 26th
Bettyville Steeplechase (Wexford) 27th
Monet's Garden Old Roan Handicap Steeple Chase (Aintree) 27th
Criterium International (Parislongchamp) 27th
Prix Royal-Oak (Parislongchamp) 27th
Fleur de Lys Stakes (Lingfield Park) 31st
EBF River Eden Stakes (Lingfield Park) 31st

NOVEMBER

Bosra Sham EBF Stakes (Newmarket) 1st
Bet365 Handicap Steeple Chase (Wetherby) 1st
Weatherbys Wensleydale Juvenile Hurdle (Wetherby) 1st
WKD Hurdle (Down Royal) 1st
Hamptons EBF Mares Novices' Hurdle (Down Royal) 1st
Cooley Stakes (Dundalk) 1st
Weatherbys James Seymour Stakes (Newmarket) 2nd
Ben Marshall Stakes (Newmarket) 2nd
EBF Montrose Stakes (Newmarket) 2nd
Sodexo Gold Cup Handicap Steeple Chase (Ascot) 2nd
Byrne Group Handicap Steeple Chase (Ascot) 2nd
Ascot Handicap Hurdle (Ascot) 2nd
Bet365 Charlie Hall Steeple Chase (Wetherby) 2nd
Bet365 West Yorkshire Hurdle (Wetherby) 2nd
OLBG.com Mares' Hurdle (Wetherby) 2nd
Jnwine Champion Steeple Chase (Down Royal) 2nd
Skymas Steeple Chase (Down Royal) 2nd
Mac's Joy Handicap Hurdle (Down Royal) 2nd
Paddy Power Cork Grand National Handicap Steeple Chase (Cork) 3rd
Paddy Power EBF Novices' Steeple Chase (Cork) 3rd
Paddy Power EBF Novices' Hurdle (Cork) 3rd
Finale Stakes (Naas) 3rd
Colin Parker Steeple Chase (Carlisle) 3rd
Floodlit Stakes (Kempton Park) 4th
188Bet Haldon Gold Cup Steeple Chase (Exeter) 5th
Bud Booth Steeple Chase (Market Rasen) 7th

EBF Gillies Stakes (Doncaster)...9th
Wentworth Stakes (Doncaster)...9th
Badger Ales Handicap Steeple Chase (Wincanton)...9th
Unibet Elite Handicap Hurdle (Wincanton)..9th
Rising Stars Novices' Steeple Chase (Wincanton)...9th
Brown Lad Handicap Hurdle (Naas)..9th
Poplar Square Steeple Chase (Naas)...9th
Fishery Lane 4yo Hurdle (Naas)..9th
Future Stars Steeple Chase (Sandown Park)..10th
Lismullen Hurdle (Navan)..10th
Fortria Steeple Chase (Navan)...10th
For Auction Novices' Hurdle (Navan)..10th
Canter Novices' Steeple Chase (Bangor-on-Dee)..13th
Clonmel Oil Steeple Chase (Clonmel)...14th
EBF TA Morris Memorial Mares Steeple Chase (Clonmel)...14th
Ballymore Hyde Novices' Hurdle (Cheltenham)...15th
BetVictor Handicap Steeple Chase (Cheltenham)..16th
Churchill Stakes (Lingfield Park)..16th
Golden Rose Stakes (Lingfield Park)...16th
BetVictor Gold Cup Steeple Chase (Cheltenham)..16th
Solutions Handicap Hurdle (Cheltenham)...16th
JCB Triumph Hurdle Trial (Cheltenham)..16th
Karndean Mares' Open National Hunt Flat Race (Cheltenham)..16th
Morgiana Hurdle (Punchestown)...16th
Grabel Mares Hurdle (Punchestown)...16th
Unibet Greatwood Handicap Hurdle (Cheltenham)..17th
Shloer Cheltenham Steeple Chase (Cheltenham)..17th
Racing Post Arkle Trophy Trial Novices' Steeple Chase (Cheltenham)...17th
Sky Bet Supreme Trial Novices' Hurdle (Cheltenham)...17th
High Sheriff National Hunt Flat Race (Cheltenham)...17th
Florida Pearl Novices' Steeple Chase (Punchestown)..17th
Craddockstown Novices' Steeple Chase (Punchestown)..17th
Hyde EBF Stakes (Kempton Park)...20th
Thurles Steeple Chase (Thurles)..21st
Coral Hurdle (Ascot)..23rd
Christy 1965 Steeple Chase (Ascot)...23rd
Lancashire Steeple Chase (Haydock Park)..23rd
Betfair Exchange Handicap Hurdle (Haydock Park)...23rd
Newton Novices' Hurdle (Haydock Park)...23rd
Monksfield Novices' Hurdle (Navan)..24th
Proudstown Handicap Hurdle (Navan)...24th
Ladbrokes Troytown Handicap Steeple Chase (Navan)..24th
ITBA Mares Bumper (Navan)..24th
OLBG Mares' Hurdle (Kempton Park)..25th
Long Distance Hurdle (Newbury)..29th
Berkshire Novices' Steeple Chase (Newbury)..29th
Ballyhack Handicap Steeple Chase (Fairyhouse)...30th
Ladbrokes Trophy Handicap Steeplechase (Newbury)...30th
Ladbrokes John Francome Novices' Chase (Newbury)...30th
Gerry Feilden Hurdle (Newbury)...30th
Ladbrokes Novices' Hurdle (Newbury)..30th
Fighting Fifth Hurdle (Newcastle)...30th
Rehearsal Handicap Steeple Chase (Newcastle)...30th

DECEMBER

Houghton Mares' Steeple Chase (Carlisle)...1st
Bar One Royal Bond Novices' Hurdle (Fairyhouse)..1st
Bar One Haltons Grace Hurdle (Fairyhouse)...1st
Bar One Drinmore Novices' Steeple Chase (Fairyhouse)...1st
New Stand Handicap Hurdle (Fairyhouse)...1st
Porterstown Handicap Steeple Chase (Fairyhouse)...1st
Winter Festival Juvenile Hurdle (Fairyhouse)..1st
Wild Flower Stakes (Kempton Park)...4th
Ballymore Winter Novices' Hurdle (Sandown Park)...6th
Becher Handicap Steeple Chase (Aintree)...7th
Many Clouds Steeple Chase (Aintree)...7th
Betway Juvenile Hurdle (Aintree)...7th
Betfair Tingle Creek Steeple Chase (Sandown Park)...7th
December Handicap Hurdle (Sandown Park)..7th
Henry VIII Novices' Steeple Chase (Sandown Park)...7th
Klairon Davis EBF Novices' Steeple Chase (Navan)...7th
John Durkan Memorial Steeple Chase (Punchestown)...8th
Kerry Group Hilly Way Steeple Chase (Cork)...8th
Kerry Group Cork Stayers Novices' Hurdle (Cork)..8th

Lombardstown EBF Mares Novices' Steeple Chase (Cork) 8th
Betfred Peterborough Steeple Chase (Huntingdon) 8th
Henrietta Knight Open National Hunt Flat Race (Huntingdon) 8th
Lady Godiva Novices' Steeple Chase (Warwick) 12th
C F Roberts Handicap Steeple Chase (Cheltenham) 13th
Caspian Caviar Gold Cup Handicap Steeple Chase (Cheltenham) 14th
Unibet International Hurdle (Cheltenham) 14th
Albert Bartlett Bristol Novices' Hurdle (Cheltenham) 14th
Bet365 Summit Juvenile Hurdle (Doncaster) 14th
Bet365 December Novices' Chase (Doncaster) 14th
Navan Novices' Hurdle (Navan) 15th
Tara Handicap Hurdle (Navan) 15th
Foxrock Handicap Steeple Chase (Navan) 15th
Future Champions Bumper (Navan) 15th
TBA Mares' Novices' Steeple Chase (Newbury) 18th
Noel Novices' Steeple Chase (Ascot) 20th
Sky Bet Supreme Trial Kennel Gate Novices' Hurdle (Ascot) 20th
Championship Open National Hunt Flat Race (Ascot) 20th
Betfair Handicap Hurdle (Ascot) 21st
JLT Long Walk Hurdle (Ascot) 21st
Silver Cup Handicap Steeple Chase (Ascot) 21st
Abram Mares' Novices' Hurdle (Haydock Park) 21st
Quebec Stakes (Lingfield Park) 21st
Boreen Belle EBF Mares Novices' Hurdle (Thurles) 21st
32Red King George VI Steeple Chase (Kempton Park) 26th
32Red Christmas Hurdle (Kempton Park) 26th
32Red Kauto Star Novices' Steeple Chase (Kempton Park) 26th
188Bet Rowland Meyrick Steeple Chase (Wetherby) 26th
Racing Post Novices' Steeple Chase (Leopardstown) 26th
Knight Frank Juvenile Hurdle (Leopardstown) 26th
Greenmount Park Novices' Steeple Chase (Limerick) 26th
Coral Welsh National Handicap Steeple Chase (Chepstow) 27th
coral.co.uk Future Champions Finale Juvenile Hurdle (Chepstow) 27th
32Red Desert Orchid Steeple Chase (Kempton Park) 27th
32Red.com Wayward Lad Novices' Steeple Chase (Kempton Park) 27th
Paddy Power Future Champions Novices' Hurdle (Leopardstown) 27th
Paddy Power Dial A Bet Steeple Chase (Leopardstown) 27th
Paddy Power Handicap Steeple Chase (Leopardstown) 27th
Tim Duggan Memorial Handicap Steeple Chase (Limerick) 27th
Savills Christmas Steeple Chase (Leopardstown) 28th
Squared Financials Christmas Hurdle (Leopardstown) 28th
Sporting Limerick 4yo Hurdle (Limerick) 28th
Challow Novices' Hurdle (Newbury) 28th
Silver Vase Steeple Chase (Doncaster) 29th
Ryanair December Hurdle (Leopardstown) 29th
Fort Leney Novices' Steeple Chase (Leopardstown) 29th
Willis Towers Watson EBF Mares Hurdle (Leopardstown) 29th
Dorans Pride Novices' Hurdle (Limerick) 29th
Weatherbys Novices' Hurdle (Taunton) 30th

The list of Principal Races has been supplied by the BHA and Horse Racing Ireland and is provisional. In all cases, the dates, venues, and names of sponsors are correct at time of going to press, but also subject to possible alteration.

INDEX TO TRAINERS

†denotes Permit to train under N.H. Rules only

Name	Team No.
†BRACE, MR DAVID	059
BRADLEY, MR MILTON	060
BRADSTOCK, MR MARK	061
BRENNAN, MR BARRY	062
†BREWIS, MISS RHONA	063
BRIDGER, MR JOHN	064
BRIDGWATER, MR DAVID	065
BRISBOURNE, MR MARK	066
BRISLAND, MR ROBYN	067
BRITTAIN, MR ANTONY	068
BROOKE, MRS JULIA	069
†BROOKE, LADY SUSAN	070
BROTHERTON, MR ROY	071
BROWN, MR ALAN	072
BROWN, MR ANDI	073
†BROWN, MR DAVID	074
†BRYANT, MISS MICHELLE	075
†BUCKETT, MRS KATE	076
BUCKLER, MR BOB	077
BURCHELL, MR DAI	078
BURKE, MR K. R.	079
BURKE, MR KEIRAN	080
†BURNS, MR HUGH	081
BURROWS, MR OWEN	082
BUTLER, MR JOHN	083
BUTLER, MR PADDY	084
†BUTTERWORTH, MRS BARBARA	085

C

Name	Team No.
†CABBLE, MISS LOUISE	086
CAMACHO, MISS JULIE	087
CAMPION, MR MARK	088
CANDLISH, MS JENNIE	089
CANDY, MR HENRY	090
CANN, MR GRANT	091
CANTILLON, MR DON	092
CARR, MRS RUTH	093
CARROLL, MR DECLAN	094
CARROLL, MR TONY	095
CARSON, MR TONY	096
CARTER, MR LEE	097

Name	Team No.
CASE, MR BEN	098
CHAMINGS, MR PATRICK	099
CHANNON, MR MICK	100
CHAPMAN, MR MICHAEL	101
†CHAPMAN, MR RYAN	102
CHAPPET, MR FABRICE	103
CHAPPLE-HYAM, MS JANE	104
CHAPPLE-HYAM, MR PETER	105
CHARLTON, MR ROGER	106
CHISMAN, MR HARRY	107
CLEMENT, MR NICOLAS	108
CLOVER, MR TOM	109
COAKLEY, MR DENIS	110
COLE, MR PAUL	111
COLLINS, MR PAUL	112
COLTHERD, MR STUART	113
†CONWAY, MR SEAN	114
CORBETT, MRS SUSAN	115
†CORNWALL, MR JOHN	116
COULSON, MR JAKE	117
COWARD, MISS JACQUELINE	118
COWELL, MR ROBERT	119
COX, MR CLIVE	120
COYLE, MR TONY	121
CRAGGS, MR RAY	122
CRATE, MR PETER	123
CRISFORD, MR SIMON	124
CROMWELL, MR GAVIN	125
CROOK, MR ANDREW	126
CUNNINGHAM-BROWN, MR KEN.	127
CURRAN, MR SEAN	128
CURTIS, MISS REBECCA	129
CUTHBERT, MISS HELEN	130

D

Name	Team No.
D'ARCY, MR PAUL	131
DACE, MR LUKE	132
DALGLEISH, MR KEITH	133
DALY, MR HENRY	134
DANDO, MR PHILLIP	135
DARTNALL, MR VICTOR	136

Name	Team No.
FORSTER, MISS SANDY	215
FOSTER, MISS JOANNE	216
FOX, MR JIMMY	217
FRANCE, MISS SUZZANNE	218
†FRANKLAND, MR DEREK	219
FROST, MR JAMES	220
FROST, MR KEVIN	221
FROUD, MR HUGO	222
FRY, MR HARRY	223
FRYER, MISS CAROLINE	224
FURTADO, MR IVAN	225

G

Name	Team No.
GALLAGHER, MR JOHN	226
GALLAGHER, MR THOMAS	227
GANSERA-LÉVÊQUE, MRS ILKA	228
GARDNER, MRS SUSAN	229
†GASSON, MRS ROSEMARY	230
GEORGE, MR PAUL	231
GEORGE, MR TOM	232
GIFFORD, MR NICK	233
GILLARD, MR MARK	234
GIVEN, MR JAMES	235
GOLDIE, MR JIM	236
GOLLINGS, MR STEVE	237
GORDON, MR CHRIS	238
GOSDEN, MR JOHN	239
GRAHAM, MRS HARRIET	240
GRANT, MR CHRIS	241
GRASSICK, MR JAMES	242
GRASSICK, MR MICHAEL	243
GRAY, MR CARROLL	244
GREATREX, MR WARREN	245
GREENALL, MR OLIVER	246
GRETTON, MR TOM	247
GRIFFITHS, MR DAVID C.	248
†GRIFFITHS, MR SIRRELL	249
GRISSELL, MRS DIANA	250
GROUCOTT, MR JOHN	251
GUEST, MR RAE	252
GUEST, MR RICHARD	253
GUNDRY, MS POLLY	254

H

Name	Team No.
HAGGAS, MR WILLIAM	255
HALES, MR ALEX	256
HALFORD, MR MICHAEL	257
HAMER, MRS DEBRA	258
HAMILTON, MRS ALISON	259
†HAMILTON, MRS ANN	260
HAMMOND, MR MICKY	261
HANMER, MR GARY	262
HANNON, MR RICHARD	263
HARKER, MR GEOFFREY	264
†HARPER, MR RICHARD	265
HARRINGTON, MRS JESSICA	266
HARRIS, MISS GRACE	267
HARRIS, MR MILTON	268
HARRIS, MR RONALD	269
HARRIS, MR SHAUN	270
HARRISON, MISS LISA	271
HASLAM, MR BEN	272
HAWKE, MR NIGEL	273
†HAWKER, MR MICHAEL	274
HAWKER, MR RICHARD	275
†HAYNES, MR JONATHAN	276
HAYWOOD, MISS GAIL	277
HEDGER, MR PETER	278
HENDERSON, MR NICKY	279
HENDERSON, MR PAUL	280
HERRINGTON, MR MICHAEL	281
HIATT, MR PETER	282
HILL, MRS LAWNEY	283
HILLS, MR CHARLES	284
HOAD, MR MARK	285
HOBBS, MR PHILIP	286
HOBSON, MISS CLARE	287
HOBSON, MR RICHARD	288
HODGE, MR JOHN	289
HODGES, MR RON	290
†HOGARTH, MR HENRY	291

Name	Team No.
HOLLINSHEAD, MISS SARAH	292
HOLLINSHEAD, MRS STEPH	293
HOLT, MR JOHN	294
HONEYBALL, MR ANTHONY	295
HOWLING, MR PAUL	296
HUGHES, MRS JO	297
HUGHES, MR RICHARD	298
HUMPHREY, MRS SARAH	299
†HUNTER, MR KEVIN	300
HURLEY, MISS LAURA	301

I

Name	Team No.
INGRAM, MR ROGER	302
IVORY, MR DEAN	303

J

Name	Team No.
JACKSON, MISS TINA	304
†JAMES, MISS HANNAH	305
JAMES, MR LEE	306
JARDINE, MR IAIN	307
JARVIS, MR WILLIAM	308
JEFFERSON, MISS RUTH	309
JENKINS, MR J. R.	310
†JESSOP, MR ALAN	311
†JESTIN, MR FERGUS	312
JEWELL, MRS LINDA	313
JOHNSON, MR BRETT	314
JOHNSON HOUGHTON, MISS EVE	315
JOHNSON, MR KENNY	316
†JOHNSON, MRS SUSAN	317
JOHNSTON, MR MARK	318
JONES, MR ALAN	319

K

Name	Team No.
KEIGHLEY, MR MARTIN	320
KEIGHTLEY, MR SHAUN	321
KELLETT, MR CHRISTOPHER	322
KELLEWAY, MISS GAY	323
KENIRY, MRS STEF	324
KENT, MR NICK	325

Name	Team No.
†KERR, MR LEONARD	326
KING, MR ALAN	327
KING, MR NEIL	328
KIRBY, MR PHILIP	329
KIRK, MR SYLVESTER	330
KITTOW, MR STUART	331
KNIGHT, MR WILLIAM	332
KUBLER, MR DANIEL	333

L

Name	Team No.
LACEY, MR TOM	334
LAFFON-PARIAS, MR CARLOS	335
†LAMPARD, MR NICK	336
LANIGAN, MR DAVID	337
LAVELLE, MISS EMMA	338
LEAVY, MR BARRY	339
LEE, MISS KERRY	340
LEECH, MRS SOPHIE	341
LEESON, MISS TRACEY	342
LEWIS, MRS SHEILA	343
LITTMODEN, MR NICK	345
LLEWELLYN, MR BERNARD	346
LLOYD-BEAVIS, MISS NATALIE	347
LOCKWOOD, MR ALAN	348
LONG, MR JOHN E.	349
LONGSDON, MR CHARLIE	350
LOUGHNANE, MR DANIEL MARK	351
LOUGHNANE, MR DAVID	352
LYCETT, MR SHAUN	353

M

Name	Team No.
MACKIE, MR JOHN	354
†MADDISON, MR PETER	355
MADGWICK, MR MICHAEL	356
MAIN, MRS HEATHER	357
MALZARD, MRS ALYSON	358
MANGAN, MR JAMES JOSEPH	359
MANN, MR CHARLIE	360
MARGARSON, MR GEORGE	361
MARTIN, MR ANDREW J.	362

Name	Team No.
†MARTIN, MISS NICKY	363
MASON, MR CHRISTOPHER	364
MASON, MRS JENNIFER	365
†MATHEW, MR ROBIN	366
†MATHIAS, MISS JANE	367
MCBRIDE, MR PHILIP	368
MCCAIN, MR DONALD	369
MCCARTHY, MR TIM	370
MCENTEE, MR PHIL	371
MCGRATH, MR MURTY	372
MCGREGOR, MRS JEAN	373
MCJANNET, MR LUKE	374
MCLINTOCK, MS KAREN	375
MCPHERSON, MR GRAEME	376
MCWILLIAMS, MR TONY	377
MEADE, MR MARTYN	378
MEADE, MR NOEL	379
†MECHIE, MR NEIL	380
MEEHAN, MR BRIAN	381
MENUISIER, MR DAVID	382
MENZIES, MISS REBECCA	383
MIDDLETON, MR PHIL	384
MIDGLEY, MR PAUL	385
MILLMAN, MR ROD	386
MITCHELL, MR NICK	387
MITCHELL, MR RICHARD	388
†MITFORD-SLADE, MR RICHARD	389
MOFFATT, MR JAMES	390
MOHAMMED, MR ISMAIL	391
MONGAN, MRS LAURA	392
MOORE, MR GARY	393
MOORE, MR J. S.	394
MORGAN, MISS KELLY	395
MORGAN, MISS LAURA	396
MORRIS, MR MOUSE	397
MORRIS, MR PATRICK	398
MORRISON, MR HUGHIE	399
MOUBARAK, MR MOHAMED	400
MUIR, MR WILLIAM	401
MULHALL, MR CLIVE	402
MULHOLLAND, MR NEIL	403

Name	Team No.
MULLANEY, MR LAWRENCE	404
MULLINEAUX, MR MICHAEL	405
MULLINS, MR SEAMUS	406
MULLINS, MR WILLIE P.	407
MURPHY, MISS AMY	408
MURPHY, MR MIKE	409
MURPHY, MR OLLY	410
MURTAGH, MR BARRY	411

N

Name	Team No.
NAYLOR, DR JEREMY	412
†NEEDHAM, MR JOHN	413
NELMES, MRS HELEN	414
NEWCOMBE, MR TONY	415
NEWLAND, DR RICHARD	416
NEWTON-SMITH, MISS ANNA	417
NICHOLLS, MR ADRIAN	418
NICHOLLS, MR PAUL	419
NIVEN, MR PETER	420
NORMILE, MRS LUCY	421
NORTON, MR JOHN	422
NOSEDA, MR JEREMY	423

O

Name	Team No.
O'BRIEN, MR A. P.	424
O'BRIEN, MR DANIEL	425
O'BRIEN, MR FERGAL	426
O'KEEFFE, MR JEDD	427
O'MEARA, MR DAVID	428
†O'NEILL, MISS DANIELLE	429
O'NEILL, MR JOHN	430
O'NEILL, MR JONJO	431
O'SHEA, MR JOHN	432
OLIVER, MR HENRY	433
OSBORNE, MR JAMIE	434
OWEN, MISS EMMA	435

P

Name	Team No.
PALMER, MR HUGO	436
PATTINSON, MR MARK	437

Name	Team No.
PAULING, MR BEN	438
PEACOCK, MR RAY	439
PEARCE, MRS LYDIA	440
PEARS, MR OLLIE	441
PERRATT, MISS LINDA	442
PERRETT, MRS AMANDA	443
PHELAN, MR PAT	444
PHILLIPS, MR ALAN	445
PHILLIPS, MR RICHARD	446
PINFIELD, MR TIM	447
PIPE, MR DAVID	448
POGSON, MR CHARLES	449
PORTMAN, MR JONATHAN	450
POWELL, MR BRENDAN	451
PRESCOTT BT, SIR MARK	452
PRICE, MISS KATY	453
PRICE, MR RICHARD	454
PRITCHARD, MR PETER	455

Q

Name	Team No.
QUINN, MR DENIS	456
QUINN, MR JOHN	457
QUINN, MR MICK	458

R

Name	Team No.
RALPH, MR ALASTAIR	459
REED, MR TIM	460
REES, MR DAVID	461
REGAN, MR SEAN	462
†RETTER, MRS JACKIE	463
RICHARDS, MRS LYDIA	464
RICHARDS, MR NICKY	465
RICHES, MR JOHN DAVID	466
RIMELL, MR MARK	467
ROBERTS, MR DAVE	468
ROBERTS, MR MIKE	469
ROBINSON, MISS SARAH	470
ROBSON, MISS PAULINE	471
ROPER, MR WILLIAM M.	472
†ROSS, MR RUSSELL	473

Name	Team No.
ROTHWELL, MR BRIAN	474
ROWE, MR RICHARD	475
ROWLAND, MISS MANDY	476
ROYER-DUPRE, MR ALAIN DE	477
RUSSELL, MS LUCINDA	478
RYAN, MR JOHN	479
RYAN, MR KEVIN	480

S

Name	Team No.
SADIK, MR AYTACH	481
SALAMAN, MR MATTHEW	482
SANDERSON, MR GARY	483
SANTOS, MR JOSE	484
SAUNDERS, MR MALCOLM	485
SAYER, MRS DIANNE	486
SCARGILL, DR JON	487
†SCOTT, MR DERRICK	488
SCOTT, MR GEORGE	489
SCOTT, MR JEREMY	490
SCOTT, MISS KATIE	491
SCUDAMORE, MR MICHAEL	492
SHAW, MR DEREK	493
SHAW, MRS FIONA	494
†SHEARS, MR MARK	495
SHEPPARD, MR MATT	496
SHERWOOD, MR OLIVER	497
SIDDALL, MISS LYNN	498
SIMCOCK, MR DAVID	499
SKELTON, MR DAN	500
SLACK, MR KEN	501
SLY, MRS PAM	502
SMAGA, MR DAVID	503
SMART, MR BRYAN	504
SMITH, MR CHARLES	505
SMITH, MR JULIAN	506
SMITH, MR MARTIN	507
SMITH, MR R. MIKE	508
SMITH, MR RALPH J.	509
SMITH, MRS SUE	510
SMITH, MISS SUZY	511
SMYLY, MR GILES	512

Name	Team No.
SNOWDEN, MR JAMIE	513
SOWERSBY, MR MIKE	514
SPEARING, MR JOHN	515
SPENCER, MR RICHARD	516
SPENCER, MR SEB	517
SPILLER, MR HENRY	518
STACK, MR FOZZY	519
STANFORD, MR EUGENE	520
STEPHEN, MRS JACKIE	521
STEPHENS, MR ROBERT	522
STONE, MR WILLIAM	523
STOREY, MR WILF	524
STOUTE, SIR MICHAEL	525
STRONGE, MRS ALI	526
SUMMERS, MR ROB	527
†SWINSWOOD, MR ALEX	528
SYMONDS, MR TOM	529

T

Name	Team No.
TATE, MR JAMES	530
TATE, MR TOM	531
TEAGUE, MR COLIN	532
TEAL, MR ROGER	533
TETT, MR HENRY	534
THOMAS, MR SAM	535
†THOMASON-MURPHY, MRS JOANNE	536
THOMPSON, MR DAVID	537
THOMPSON, MR RONALD	538
†THOMPSON, MR VICTOR	539
THOMSON, MR SANDY	540
TINKLER, MR NIGEL	541
TIZZARD, MR COLIN	542
TODHUNTER, MR MARTIN	543
TOMPKINS, MR MARK	544
TREGONING, MR MARCUS	545
TUER, MR GRANT	546
TUITE, MR JOSEPH	547
TURNER, MR BILL	548
TUTTY, MRS KAREN	549
TWISTON-DAVIES, MR NIGEL	550

U

Name	Team No.
UNETT, MR JAMES	551
USHER, MR MARK	552

V

Name	Team No.
VARIAN, MR ROGER	553
VAUGHAN, MR ED	554
VAUGHAN, MR TIM	555
VON DER RECKE, MR CHRISTIAN	556

W

Name	Team No.
WADHAM, MRS LUCY	557
WAGGOTT, MISS TRACY	558
WAINWRIGHT, MR JOHN	559
WALFORD, MR MARK	560
WALFORD, MR ROBERT	561
WALKER, MR ED	562
WALL, MR CHRIS	563
WALL, MR TREVOR	564
WALLIS, MR CHARLIE	565
WALTON, MRS JANE	566
†WALTON, MR JASON	567
WALTON, MRS SHEENA	568
WARD, MR JASON	569
†WATKINS, MISS TRACEY	570
WATSON, MR ARCHIE	571
WATSON, MR FREDERICK	572
WATT, MRS SHARON	573
WAUGH, MR SIMON	574
WEBBER, MR PAUL	575
WELD, MR DERMOT K.	576
WEST, MR ADAM	577
WEST, MISS SHEENA	578
WEST, MR SIMON	579
†WESTON, MR DAVID	580
WESTON, MR TOM	581
WEYMES, MR JOHN	582
WHILLANS, MR ALISTAIR	583
WHILLANS, MR DONALD	584
WHITAKER, MR RICHARD	585

Y

PROPERTY OF HER MAJESTY

The Queen

Colours: Purple, gold braid, scarlet sleeves, black velvet cap with gold fringe

Trained by **Sir Michael Stoute**, Newmarket

1 **ELECTOR**, 4, b g Dansili—Enticement
2 **SEXTANT**, 4, b g Sea The Stars (IRE)—Hypoteneuse (IRE)

THREE-YEAR-OLDS

3 **CALCULATION**, br g Dubawi (IRE)—Estimate (IRE)
4 **CLARION**, b f Dubawi (IRE)—Caraboss
5 **INVICTUS SPIRIT**, b c Frankel—Daring Aim
6 **SOVEREIGN GRANT**, b c Kingman—Momentary
7 **WEMYSS WARE (IRE)**, b c Dubawi (IRE)—White Moonstone (USA)

TWO-YEAR-OLDS

8 **APPROXIMATE**, b f 6/2 Dubawi (IRE)—Estimate (IRE) (Monsun (GER))
9 **FIRST RECEIVER**, b c 29/1 New Approach (IRE)—Touchline (Exceed And Excel (AUS))
10 **GLITTERING GIFT**, ch c 4/2 Dubawi (IRE)—Golden Stream (IRE) (Sadler's Wells (USA))
11 **QUICK WALTZ**, b f 9/2 Australia—Momentary (Nayef (USA))
12 **VINDICATE**, ch c 20/3 Lope de Vega (IRE)—Aurore (IRE) (Fasliyev (USA))

Trained by **William Haggas**, Newmarket

13 **SENIORITY**, 5, ch g Dubawi (IRE)—Anna Palariva (IRE)

THREE-YEAR-OLDS

14 **BREAK OF DAY**, b f Shamardal (USA)—Dawn Glory
15 **DESERT CARAVAN**, b g Oasis Dream—Sequence (IRE)
16 **FLAREPATH**, b f Exceed And Excel (AUS)—Fiery Sunset
17 **MAGNETIC CHARM**, b f Exceed And Excel (AUS)—Monday Show (USA)
18 **SHREWDNESS**, br f Lawman (FR)—Shama (IRE)
19 **SPACE WALK**, b c Galileo (IRE)—Memory (IRE)

TWO-YEAR-OLDS

20 B c 1/2 Oasis Dream—Ananas (Nayef (USA))
21 **AWARD SCHEME**, b f 22/2 Siyouni (FR)—Queen's Prize (Dansili)
22 **DUSTY DREAM**, b f 14/4 Dubawi (IRE)—Memory (IRE) (Danehill Dancer (IRE))
23 **KEW PALACE**, b f 2/2 Kingman—Shama (IRE) (Danehill Dancer (IRE))
24 **PORTRAY**, b c 30/3 Dubawi (IRE)—Placidia (IRE) (Sea The Stars (IRE))
25 **SOUND MIXER**, b f 19/2 Cable Bay (IRE)—Medley (Danehill Dancer (IRE))

Trained by **Richard Hannon**, Marlborough

THREE-YEAR-OLDS

26 **EQUAL SUM**, br f Paco Boy (IRE)—Hypoteneuse (IRE)
27 **TOPICAL**, b g Toronado (IRE)—Star Value (IRE)

PROPERTY OF HER MAJESTY

The Queen

TWO-YEAR-OLDS

28 DIVINE COVEY, gr f 4/4 Dark Angel (IRE)—Pack Together (Paco Boy (IRE)))
29 ON PARADE, b g 21/3 Paco Boy (IRE)—Flash of Gold (Darshaan)

Trained by **Roger Charlton**, Beckhampton

THREE-YEAR-OLDS

30 WEST NEWTON, b c Kitten's Joy (USA)—Queen's Prize

TWO-YEAR-OLDS

31 CODE OF CONDUCT, b c 10/4 Siyouni (FR)—Sequence (IRE) (Selkirk (USA))
32 EVENING SUN, b c 24/3 Muhaarar—Fiery Sunset (Galileo (IRE))

Trained by **Michael Bell**, Newmarket

33 FABRICATE, 7, b g Makfi—Flight of Fancy

THREE-YEAR-OLDS

34 EIGHTSOME REEL, b c Iffraaj—Set To Music (IRE)
35 REGULAR, ch g Exceed And Excel (AUS)—Humdrum
36 YOUTHFUL, b g Shamardal (USA)—Good Hope

TWO-YEAR-OLDS

37 CHOSEN STAR, ch f 2/3 Dubawi (IRE)—Yodelling (USA) (Medaglia d'Oro (USA))
38 CLOUD DRIFT, b c 29/3 Toronado (IRE)—Humdrum (Dr Fong (USA))
39 FORMALITY, b c 7/3 Frankel—Silver Mirage (Oasis Dream)
40 GOOD TRY, b f 4/3 Iffraaj—Good Hope (Cape Cross (IRE))
41 HIGH SHINE, b f 27/3 Paco Boy (IRE)—Hypoteneuse (IRE) (Sadler's Wells (USA))
42 OTAGO, b c 26/1 Cable Bay (IRE)—Spinning Top (Alzao (USA))

Trained by **Andrew Balding**, Kingsclere

43 NATURAL HISTORY, 4, b g Nathaniel (IRE)—Film Script

THREE-YEAR-OLDS

44 COMPASS, b g Henrythenavigator (USA)—Medley

TWO-YEAR-OLDS

45 KING'S LYNN, b c 19/2 Cable Bay (IRE)—Kinematic (Kyllachy)
46 PUNCTUATION, b c 7/5 Dansili—Key Point (IRE) (Galileo (IRE))

PROPERTY OF HER MAJESTY

The Queen

Trained by **John Gosden**, Newmarket

THREE-YEAR-OLDS

47 GOLD STICK (IRE), b c Dubawi (IRE)—Gamilati
48 PIANISSIMO, b c Teofilo (IRE)—Perfect Note

TWO-YEAR-OLDS

49 DAUNTLESS, b c 27/3 Dubawi (IRE)—Enticement (Montjeu (IRE))
50 DESERT FLYER, b f 19/2 Shamardal (USA)—White Moonstone (USA) (Dynaformer (USA))
51 INNOVATION, b f 22/3 Dubawi (IRE)—Free Verse (Danehill Dancer (IRE))
52 LIGHTNESS (IRE), b f 23/3 Shamardal (USA)—Serene Beauty (USA) (Street Cry (IRE))

Trained by **Richard Hughes**, Upper Lambourn

THREE-YEAR-OLDS

53 PUZZLE, b g Paco Boy (IRE)—Appleton Drove (USA)

TWO-YEAR-OLDS

54 CRANBERRY, ch f 1/4 Toronado (IRE)—Raymi Coya (CAN) (Van Nistelrooy (USA))

Trained by **Christophe Clement**, U.S.A.

THREE-YEAR-OLDS

55 RAFFLE, b c Iffraaj—Raymi Coya (CAN)

To be allocated

TWO-YEAR-OLDS

56 EIGHT BELLS, b c 30/1 Henrythenavigator (USA)—Dawn Glory (Oasis Dream)
57 SPANISH DANCE, b c 5/4 Lope de Vega (IRE)—Set To Music (IRE) (Danehill Dancer (IRE))
58 UNDERLINE, b c 2/5 Zoffany (IRE)—Caraboss (Cape Cross (IRE))

Trained by **Nicky Henderson**, Lambourn

59 HAMILTON'S FANTASY, 4, b f Mount Nelson—Romantic Dream
60 ITALIAN SUMMER, 4, br f Milan—Midsummer Magic
61 KEEN ON, 5, b g Kayf Tara—Romantic Dream
62 STEAL A MARCH, 4, b g Mount Nelson—Side Step
63 SUNSHADE, 6, b m Sulamani (IRE)—Spring Flight

Trained by **Charlie Longsdon**, Chipping Norton

64 FORTH BRIDGE, 6, b g Bernardini (USA)—Sally Forth
65 HEATHER SONG, 5, b m Kayf Tara—Bella Macrae
66 NO TRUMPS, 5, b m Black Sam Bellamy (IRE)—Magic Score

SOME TRAINERS' STRINGS ARE TAKEN FROM THE BHA RACING ADMINISTRATION WEBSITE AND INCLUDE HORSES LISTED ON THERE AS IN 'PRE-TRAINING', 'AT GRASS' OR 'RESTING'

---

1 | MR N. W. ALEXANDER, Kinneston

Postal: Kinneston, Leslie, Glenrothes, Fife, KY6 3JJ
Contacts: PHONE (01592) 840774 MOBILE (07831) 488210
E-MAIL nicholasalexander@kinneston.com WEBSITE www.kinneston.com

1 **ANDHAAR**, 13, b g Bahri (USA)—Deraasaat **Bissett Racing**
2 **ANOTHER MATTIE (IRE)**, 12, b g Zagreb (USA)—Silver Tassie (FR) **Quandt & Cochrane**
3 **ARNICA**, 6, b g Champs Elysees—Cordoba **Mr N. W. Alexander**
4 **ARTIC MANN**, 5, b g Sulamani (IRE)—Line Artic (FR) **Mr T. J. Hemmings**
5 **BALLYNANTY (IRE)**, 7, gr g Years (IRE)—Reina Blanca **J Douglas Miller & Ken McGarrity**
6 **BENNY'S SECRET (IRE)**, 9, br g Beneficial—Greenhall Rambler (IRE) **Mr B. C. Castle**
7 **BERTALUS (IRE)**, 10, b g City Honours (USA)—Deep Dalus (IRE) **Quandt & Cochrane**
8 **BUFFALO BALLET**, 13, b g Kayf Tara—Minora (IRE) **Mr Hw Turcan & Sir Simon Dunning**
9 **CALIVIGNY (IRE)**, 10, b g Gold Well—Summer Holiday (IRE) **Hugh Hodge Ltd & Alexander Family**
10 **CHARM OFFENSIVE (FR)**, 5, b m Le Triton (USA)—Gio Lison (FR) **The Nags to Riches Partnership**
11 **CHRISTMAS IN USA (FR)**, 7, b g Shaanmer (IRE)—Diamond of Diana (FR) **Bowen & Nicol**
12 **CLAN LEGEND**, 9, ch g Midnight Legend—Harrietfield **Clan Gathering**
13 **CRAIGANBOY (IRE)**, 10, b g Zagreb (USA)—Barnish River (IRE) **Quandt, Cochrane, Lysaght**
14 **DANCE OF FIRE**, 7, b g Norse Dancer (IRE)—Strictly Dancing (IRE) **Team Kinneston Club**
15 **EAGLE RIDGE (IRE)**, 8, b g Oscar (IRE)—Azaban (IRE) **Ken McGarrity & Partner**
16 **ELVIS MAIL (FR)**, 5, gr g Great Pretender—Queenly Mail (FR) **The Ladies Who**
17 **ETOILE D'ECOSSE (FR)**, 5, gr m Martaline—Etoile de Mogador (FR) **Douglas Miller, Coltman, Dunning, Turcan**
18 **FIG'S PRIDE (IRE)**, 6, br m Stowaway—Roseboreen (IRE) **Mrs F. C. C. Harper Gow**
19 **FLY RORY FLY (IRE)**, 7, b g Milan—Thousand Wings (GER) **Turcan D-Miller Stewart Burnham Dunning**
20 **JET MASTER (IRE)**, 13, b g Brian Boru—Whats The Reason (IRE) **Mr HW Turcan & Sir Simon Dunning**
21 **JUST BROOKE**, 9, ch m Black Sam Bellamy (IRE)—Sports Express **Bissett Racing**
22 **KILLER CROW (IRE)**, 10, ch g Presenting—Rivervail (IRE) **Alexander Family**
23 **LAKE VIEW LAD (IRE)**, 9, gr g Oscar (IRE)—Missy O'brien (IRE) **Mr T. J. Hemmings**
24 **LANDECKER (IRE)**, 11, br g Craigsteel—Winsome Breeze (IRE) **N Hodge & I Hodge**
25 **LEFT BACK (IRE)**, 7, b g Oscar (IRE)—Baldrica (IRE) **Clan Gathering**
26 **LET THERE BE LOVE (IRE)**, 4, b g Shantou (USA)—Zolotaya **Mr B. C. Castle**
27 **MANETTI (IRE)**, 7, b g Westerner—Mrs Wallensky (IRE) **Sandy's Angels**
28 **MARLEE MASSIE (IRE)**, 10, b g Dr Massini (IRE)—Meadstown Miss (IRE) **Mr J. K. McGarrity**
29 **MCGINTY'S DREAM (IRE)**, 8, b g Flemensfirth (USA)—Laboc **Kinneston Racing**
30 **MOORES NOVELTY (IRE)**, 7, b g Sholokhov (IRE)—Moricana (GER) **Mrs S. M. Irwin**
31 **MORE MADNESS (IRE)**, 12, b g Dr Massini (IRE)—Angelic Angel (IRE) **J. F. Alexander**
32 **MY SON JOHN**, 5, ch g Bahri (USA)—Cogolie (FR) **Mr J. Threadgall**
33 **NOT THE CHABLIS (IRE)**, 5, b g Scorpion (IRE)—De Street (IRE) **Turcan, Dunning, Price, Stewart, Burnham**
34 **OFF THE HOOK (IRE)**, 7, b m Getaway (GER)—Call Her Again (IRE) **Mrs I. Hodge**
35 **PEAK OF BEAUTY (IRE)**, 6, b m Mountain High (IRE)—Minoras Return (IRE) **Mr D. Walker**
36 **RIDE THE LIGHTNING**, 6, b g Dalakhani (IRE)—Bright Halo (IRE) **Mr HW Turcan & Sir Simon Dunning**
37 **ROAD TO GOLD (IRE)**, 10, b br g Gold Well—Haut de Gamme (IRE) **Mrs J. Douglas Miller**
38 **ROSSINI'S DANCER**, 14, b g Rossini (USA)—Bint Alhabib **Mr N. W. Alexander**
39 4, B g Dylan Thomas (IRE)—Sarahall (IRE) **Mr N. W. Alexander**
40 **SILK OR SCARLET (IRE)**, 7, ch g Mahler—Spirit of Clanagh (IRE) **Ken McGarrity & Dudgeon, Cundall, Liddle**
41 **SPIRIT OF KAYF**, 8, b g Kayf Tara—Over Sixty **Mrs J. A. Morris**
42 **TED VEALE (IRE)**, 12, b g Revoque (IRE)—Rose Tanner (IRE) **Alexander Family**
43 **THE BISHOP (IRE)**, 11, b g Winged Love (IRE)—Charlie's Mary (IRE) **J. F. Alexander**
44 **THE ORANGE ROGUE (IRE)**, 12, br g Alderbrook—Classic Enough **Mrs S. M. Irwin**
45 **UP HELLY AA KING**, 8, ch g And Beyond (IRE)—Gretton **Jean Matterson & Partner**

Other Owners: Mr Nicholas Alexander, Mrs Nicholas Alexander, Mr Jamie Alexander, Alexander Family, Mr A. A. Bissett, Mrs J. Bissett, Mr A. J. Bowen, Lady Burnham, The Hon Thomas Cochrane, Mrs David Coltman, Mrs J. Douglas Miller, Dudgeon, Cundall, Liddle, Mr Andrew Duncan, Sir Simon Dunning, Miss F. M. Fletcher, Mrs I. Hodge, Mrs N. Hodge, Hugh Hodge Ltd, Mr Cornelius Lysaght, Miss Jean Matterson, Mr Ken McGarrity, Mr A. G. Nicol, Mrs D. Price, Miss S. Quandt, Mr A. D. Stewart, Mr H. W. Turcan.

Assistant Trainer: Catriona Bissett

Jockey (NH): Lucy Alexander. **Conditional:** Grant Cockburn. **Apprentice:** Lucy Alexander. **Amateur:** Mr Kit Alexander.

2 | **MISS LOUISE ALLAN, Newmarket**
Postal: **2 London Road, Newmarket, Suffolk, CB8 0TW**
Contacts: **MOBILE (07703) 355878**
E-MAIL louiseallan1@hotmail.co.uk

1 **ARTICLE OF WAR (IRE)**, 6, b g Definite Article—Form A Circle (IRE) **Mr P. W. Clifton**
2 **HARD TOFFEE (IRE)**, 8, b g Teofilo (IRE)—Speciale (USA) **Miss V. L. Allan**
3 **NOISY NEIGHBOUR**, 5, b m Malinas (GER)—Mooreheigh **A. M. Smith**
4 **NORMANDY BLUE**, 4, ch g Le Havre (IRE)—Ballerina Blue (IRE) **Providence Racing**
5 **RONNI LAYNE**, 5, b m Native Ruler—Cindy Incidentally **Mr Tim Urry & Mrs B. Urry**
6 **THEREDBALLOON**, 13, ch g Sulamani (IRE)—Sovana (FR) **Miss V. L. Allan**

Other Owners: Mr J. N. Endersby, Mrs B. Urry, Mr T. Urry.

3 | **MR CONRAD ALLEN, Newmarket**
Postal: **Trainer did not wish details of his string to appear**

4 | **MR ERIC ALSTON, Preston**
Postal: **Edges Farm Stables, Chapel Lane, Longton, Preston, Lancashire, PR4 5NA**
Contacts: **PHONE (01772) 612120 FAX (01772) 619600 MOBILE (07879) 641660**
E-MAIL eric1943@supanet.com

1 **ACCLAIM THE NATION (IRE)**, 6, b g Acclamation—Dani Ridge (IRE) **Mr C. F. Harrington**
2 **BOUDICA BAY (IRE)**, 4, b f Rip Van Winkle (IRE)—White Shift (IRE) **The Grumpy Old Geezers**
3 **CASTERBRIDGE**, 7, b g Pastoral Pursuits—Damalis (IRE) **Liam & Tony Ferguson**
4 **HARRY'S RIDGE (IRE)**, 4, b g Acclamation—Dani Ridge (IRE) **Mr C. F. Harrington**
5 **JABBAROCKIE**, 6, b g Showcasing—Canina **M Balmer, K Sheedy, P Copple, C Dingwall**
6 **LYDIATE LADY**, 7, b m Piccolo—Hiraeth **The Scotch Piper Racing**
7 **MAGHFOOR**, 5, b g Cape Cross (IRE)—Thaahira (USA) **Jo-co Partnership**
8 **MAID IN INDIA (IRE)**, 5, br m Bated Breath—Indian Maiden (IRE) **Mr C. F. Harrington**
9 **REDROSEZORRO**, 5, b g Foxwedge (AUS)—Garter Star **Red Rose Partnership**
10 **SIR WALTER (IRE)**, 4, b g Camacho—Damalis (IRE) **Liam & Tony Ferguson**
11 **SPIRIT POWER**, 4, b g Swiss Spirit—Verasina (USA) **The Selebians**
12 **STRATEGIC (IRE)**, 4, b g Kodiac—Run To Jane (IRE) **Paul Buist & John Thompson**

THREE-YEAR-OLDS

13 **FOX HILL**, b f Foxwedge (AUS)—Siryena **Whitehills Racing Syndicate**
14 **LADY KINSALE**, gr f Farhh—Night Haven **The Longton Pals**

TWO-YEAR-OLDS

15 **LUCKYFORSOME (IRE)**, b f 16/5 Henrythenavigator (USA)—
Samadilla (IRE) (Mujadil (USA)) **Edges Farm Racing Stables Ltd**

Other Owners: Miss M. C. Balmer, Mrs J. E. Buist, Mr P. G. Buist, Mrs D. L. Cooney, Mr E. Cooney, Mr P. J. Copple, Mr C. A. Ferguson, M. L. Ferguson, Mr J. A. Green, Mr T. Jones, Mr M. S. Kelly, Mr A. J. Raven, M. M. Taylor, Mr J. Thompson.

Assistant Trainer: Mrs Sue Alston

5 | **MR CHARLIE APPLEBY, Newmarket**
Postal: **Godolphin Management Co Ltd, Moulton Paddocks, Newmarket, Suffolk, CB8 7PJ**
WEBSITE www.godolphin.com

1 **AFRICAN JAZZ (IRE)**, 4, b g Cape Cross (IRE)—Monday Show (USA)
2 **AQABAH (USA)**, 4, gr ro g Exchange Rate (USA)—Fast Tip (USA)
3 **AURUM (IRE)**, 4, b c Exceed And Excel (AUS)—Rachelle (IRE)
4 **AUXERRE (IRE)**, 4, b g Iffraaj—Roscoff (IRE)
5 **BLAIR HOUSE (IRE)**, 6, ch g Pivotal—Patroness
6 **BLUE POINT (IRE)**, 5, b h Shamardal (USA)—Scarlett Rose
7 **BOYNTON (USA)**, 5, ch g More Than Ready (USA)—Baffled (USA)

MR CHARLIE APPLEBY - Continued

8 **BRUNDTLAND (IRE)**, 4, b br c Dubawi (IRE)—Future Generation (IRE)
9 **CELESTIAL SPHERES (IRE)**, 5, b g Redoute's Choice (AUS)—Copernica (IRE)
10 **CROSS COUNTER**, 4, b g Teofilo (IRE)—Waitress (USA)
11 **D'BAI (IRE)**, 5, b g Dubawi (IRE)—Savannah Belle
12 **DATHANNA (IRE)**, 4, b f Dubawi (IRE)—Colour (AUS)
13 **DUBHE**, 4, b g Dubawi (IRE)—Great Heavens
14 **EMOTIONLESS (IRE)**, 6, b g Shamardal (USA)—Unbridled Elaine (USA)
15 **EYNHALLOW**, 5, b g Nathaniel (IRE)—Ronaldsay
16 **FESTIVAL OF AGES (USA)**, 5, b g Medaglia d'oro (USA)—November (USA)
17 **FIRST CONTACT (IRE)**, 4, gr g Dark Angel (IRE)—Vanishing Grey (IRE)
18 **FIRST NATION**, 5, b g Dubawi (IRE)—Moyesii (USA)
19 **GHAIYYATH (IRE)**, 4, b c Dubawi (IRE)—Nightime (IRE)
20 **GHOSTWATCH (IRE)**, 4, b g Dubawi (IRE)—Nature Spirits (FR)
21 **GLORIOUS JOURNEY**, 4, b c Dubawi (IRE)—Fallen For You
22 **GOLD TOWN**, 4, b g Street Cry (IRE)—Pimpernel (IRE)
23 **ISPOLINI**, 4, b g Dubawi (IRE)—Giants Play (USA)
24 **KEY VICTORY (IRE)**, 4, b c Teofilo (IRE)—Patroness
25 **LOXLEY (IRE)**, 4, b c New Approach (IRE)—Lady Marian (GER)
26 **MAGIC LILY**, 4, ch f New Approach (IRE)—Dancing Rain (IRE)
27 **MASAR (IRE)**, 4, ch c New Approach (IRE)—Khawlah (IRE)
28 **MYTHICAL MAGIC (IRE)**, 4, b g Iffraaj—Mythie (FR)
29 **NORDIC LIGHTS**, 4, ch g Intello (GER)—Marika
30 **OASIS CHARM**, 5, b g Oasis Dream—Albaraka
31 **OLD PERSIAN**, 4, b c Dubawi (IRE)—Indian Petal
32 **ON THE WARPATH**, 4, ch g Declaration of War (USA)—Elusive Pearl (USA)
33 **POETIC CHARM**, 4, b f Dubawi (IRE)—Speirbhean (IRE)
34 **SALSABEEL (IRE)**, 5, b g Exceed And Excel (USA)—Tokyo Rose (UAE)
35 **SECRET ADVISOR (FR)**, 5, b g Dubawi (IRE)—Sub Rose (IRE)
36 **SETTING SAIL**, 4, b g Dansili—West Wind
37 **SILVERBOOK**, 4, b g New Approach (IRE)—Sahraah (USA)
38 **SOLILOQUY**, 4, b f Dubawi (IRE)—Dysphonia (AUS)
39 **STAGE MAGIC (IRE)**, 4, b g Dark Angel (IRE)—Witnessed
40 **SYMBOLIZATION (IRE)**, 4, b br c Cape Cross (IRE)—Yorkshire Lass (IRE)
41 **VINTAGER**, 4, ro g Mastercraftsman (IRE)—White And Red (IRE)
42 **WALTON STREET**, 5, b g Cape Cross (IRE)—Brom Felinity (AUS)
43 **WILD ILLUSION**, 4, b f Dubawi (IRE)—Rumh (GER)
44 **ZAMAN**, 4, b g Dutch Art—Wake Up Call

THREE-YEAR-OLDS

45 **ACT OF REASON (IRE)**, gr g Dark Angel (IRE)—Sur Choix
46 **AL HILALEE**, b c Dubawi (IRE)—Ambivalent (IRE)
47 **AMERICAN GRAFFITI (FR)**, ch g Pivotal—Adventure Seeker (FR)
48 **ART DU VAL**, b c No Nay Never (USA)—Aquarelle Rare
49 **ART SONG (USA)**, b c Scat Daddy (USA)—Practice (USA)
50 **BEYOND REASON (IRE)**, b f Australia—No Explaining (IRE)
51 **BORDER ZONE (IRE)**, ch g Shamardal (USA)—Long Lashes (USA)
52 **CERATONIA**, b f Oasis Dream—Rumh (GER)
53 **CIRQUE ROYAL**, b c Cape Cross (IRE)—Botanique (IRE)
54 **COURT POET**, b c Dubawi (IRE)—Belenkaya (USA)
55 **DAWN CRUSADE (IRE)**, ch f Dawn Approach (IRE)—Magical Crown (USA)
56 **DIVINE IMAGE (USA)**, ch f Scat Daddy (USA)—Sure Route
57 **DIVINE JUSTICE (IRE)**, b f Galileo (IRE)—Temida (IRE)
58 **ENCHANTING MAN**, ch g Dawn Approach (IRE)—Al Baidaa
59 **EXPRESSIONISM (IRE)**, b f Galileo (IRE)—Lady Springbank (IRE)
60 **GOOD FORTUNE**, b c New Approach (IRE)—Mazuna (IRE)
61 **GREAT ESTEEM (IRE)**, b g Dubawi (IRE)—Woven Lace
62 **JALMOUD**, ch c New Approach (IRE)—Dancing Rain (IRE)
63 **KINVER EDGE (USA)**, b br g Speightstown (USA)—Peace Preserver (USA)
64 **LA PELOSA (IRE)**, b f Dandy Man (IRE)—Lauren's Girl (IRE)
65 **LINE OF DUTY (IRE)**, ch c Galileo (IRE)—Jacqueline Quest (IRE)
66 **LOVER'S KNOT**, b f Invincible Spirit (IRE)—Patroness
67 **MARHABAN (IRE)**, b c New Approach (IRE)—Arsaadi (IRE)
68 **MOONLIGHT SPIRIT (IRE)**, b c Dubawi (IRE)—Moonsail
69 **MYSTERY LAND**, b g Sea The Stars (IRE)—Lady Rosamunde
70 **NASHIRAH**, b f Dubawi (IRE)—Perfect Light (IRE)

MR CHARLIE APPLEBY - Continued

71 **ONE VISION (IRE),** ch g Shamardal (USA)—Music Chart (USA)
72 **OPHELIA'S DREAM,** ch f Dubawi (IRE)—Hibaayeb
73 **ORCHID STAR,** b f Dubawi (IRE)—Pleione (FR)
74 **PEARL OF FREEDOM,** ch f Pivotal—La Pelegrina (USA)
75 **PERSUADING (IRE),** b g Oasis Dream—Short Skirt
76 **QUORTO (IRE),** b c Dubawi (IRE)—Volume
77 **SILENT MORNING,** b f Pivotal—Veil of Silence (IRE)
78 **SPACE BLUES (IRE),** ch c Dubawi (IRE)—Miss Lucifer (FR)
79 B c Dubawi (IRE)—Speirbhean (IRE)
80 **STAR SAFARI,** b c Sea The Stars (IRE)—Intimhir (IRE)
81 **SUMMER FLAIR (IRE),** gr f Dubawi (IRE)—Summer Fete (IRE)
82 **TOHAZIE,** b c Teofilo (IRE)—Ghanaian (FR)
83 B c Dubawi (IRE)—Vanity Rules
84 **VELORUM (IRE),** b c Sea The Stars (IRE)—Lily's Angel (IRE)
85 **WINGS OF TIME,** b g Invincible Spirit (IRE)—Marie de Medici (USA)
86 **ZAKOUSKI,** b c Shamardal (USA)—O'giselle (AUS)

TWO-YEAR-OLDS

87 Ch f 16/3 Starspangledbanner (AUS)—A Huge Dream (IRE) (Refuse To Bend (IRE)) (750000)
88 B c 9/4 Dubawi (IRE)—Abhisheka (IRE) (Sadler's Wells (USA))
89 B f 23/4 Invincible Spirit (IRE)—Albaharah (USA) (Arch (USA))
90 B c 13/3 Oasis Dream—Alessandria (Sunday Silence (USA))
91 B c 10/4 Dubawi (IRE)—Anjaz (USA) (Street Cry (IRE))
92 B c 18/3 Kodiac—Anthem Alexander (IRE) (Starspangledbanner (AUS)) (600000)
93 B br c 4/2 Dubawi (IRE)—Arethusa (USA) (A P Indy (USA))
94 Gr f 17/1 Dark Angel (IRE)—Aspen (AUS) (Exceed And Excel (AUS))
95 B f 23/2 Dubawi (IRE)—Bastet (IRE) (Giant's Causeway (USA)) (800000)
96 B c 4/2 Dark Angel (IRE)—Beautiful Ending (Exceed And Excel (AUS))
97 B f 8/3 Dubawi (IRE)—Betimes (New Approach (IRE))
98 Gr c 10/2 Fast Company (IRE)—Blanc de Chine (IRE) (Dark Angel (IRE))
99 Ch c 27/2 Dubawi (IRE)—Braided (USA) (Elusive Quality (USA))
100 B c 8/4 Dubawi (IRE)—Bright Beacon (Manduro (GER))
101 B c 15/3 Shamardal (USA)—Certify (USA) (Elusive Quality (USA))
102 B c 25/2 Sea The Stars (IRE)—Chicago Dancer (IRE) (Azamour (IRE)) (1000000)
103 Ch f 27/3 Dubawi (IRE)—Colour (AUS) (More Than Ready (USA))
104 Ch f 5/3 Dubawi (IRE)—Dancing Rain (IRE) (Danehill Dancer (IRE))
105 B f 15/1 New Approach (IRE)—Dancing Sands (IRE) (Dubawi (IRE))
106 B f 31/1 Invincible Spirit (IRE)—Desert Blossom (IRE) (Shamardal (USA))
107 B f 24/4 Dubawi (IRE)—Discourse (USA) (Street Cry (IRE))
108 Ch c 29/3 Dubawi (IRE)—Eastern Joy (Dubai Destination (USA))
109 Br c 12/3 Golden Horn—Elegant Shadow (GER) (Shamardal (USA))
110 Br c 28/3 Sea The Stars (IRE)—Elle Same (Samum (GER)) (900000)
111 Ch c 21/2 Dubawi (IRE)—Ethereal Sky (IRE) (Invincible Spirit (IRE))
112 Ch c 31/3 Dubawi (IRE)—Falls of Lora (IRE) (Street Cry (IRE))
113 B c 21/4 Dubawi (IRE)—Fintry (IRE) (Shamardal (USA))
114 B f 25/4 Camelot—Flawless Beauty (Excellent Art) (421406)
115 B c 14/4 Dubawi (IRE)—Floristry (Fasliyev (USA))
116 Ch c 9/5 City Zip (USA)—Forest Gamble (USA) (Forest Wildcat (USA)) (352733)
117 B c 22/2 Dubawi (IRE)—Galatee (FR) (Galileo (IRE))
118 Ch f 22/2 Dubawi (IRE)—Giants Play (USA) (Giant's Causeway (USA)) (1200000)
119 B f 8/5 Teofilo (IRE)—Good Friend (IRE) (Shamardal (USA))
120 Ch f 4/3 Exceed And Excel (AUS)—Good Place (USA) (Street Cry (IRE))
121 B f 27/3 Dubawi (IRE)—Great Virtues (IRE) (Teofilo (IRE))
122 Ch c 16/3 Dubawi (IRE)—Hanky Panky (IRE) (Galileo (IRE))
123 Ch c 16/3 Dubawi (IRE)—Hidden Gold (IRE) (Shamardal (USA))
124 B c 13/2 New Approach (IRE)—Hoodna (IRE) (Invincible Spirit (IRE))
125 Ch f 25/3 Pivotal—Indian Petal (Singspiel (IRE))
126 Br c 28/3 Dark Angel (IRE)—Inspiriter (Invincible Spirit (IRE))
127 B c 10/2 Into Mischief (USA)—Involved (USA) (Speightstown (USA)) (119929)
128 B c 22/2 Dubawi (IRE)—J Wonder (USA) (Footstepsinthesand) (850000)
129 B f 7/4 Sea The Stars (IRE)—Janey Muddles (IRE) (Lawman (FR)) (650000)
130 Gr ro c 11/3 American Pharoah (USA)—Joyful Victory (CAN) (Tapit (USA)) (141093)
131 B f 18/2 Dubawi (IRE)—Karenine (High Chaparral (IRE))
132 B f 28/1 Galileo (IRE)—Keenes Royale (Red Ransom (USA)) (1200000)
133 Ch c 22/2 American Pharoah (USA)—Kindle (USA) (Indian Charlie (USA)) (1552028)

MR CHARLIE APPLEBY - Continued

134 B c 1/1 New Approach (IRE)—La Arenosa (IRE) (Exceed And Excel (AUS))
135 B f 27/4 Shamardal (USA)—Lailani (Unfuwain (USA))
136 B f 2/3 Kodiac—Lake Nona (Authorized (IRE)) (150000)
137 Gr f 9/4 Galileo (IRE)—Laugh Out Loud (Clodovil (IRE)) (700000)
138 B c 11/3 Shamardal (USA)—Lava Flow (Dalakhani (IRE))
139 B f 24/3 Shamardal (USA)—Long Lashes (Rock Hard Ten (USA))
140 Ch f 25/3 Dubawi (IRE)—Look At Me (IRE) (Danehill Dancer (IRE)) (180000)
141 B c 14/4 Dubawi (IRE)—Lyric of Light (Street Cry (IRE))
142 B f 30/1 Shamardal (USA)—Majestic Queen (IRE) (Kheleyf (USA))
143 B c 23/3 Dubawi (IRE)—Marie de Medici (USA) (Medicean)
144 B f 20/2 Kodiac—Marsh Daisy (Pivotal) (435000)
145 B br f 14/3 Medaglia d'oro (USA)—Miss Empire (USA) (Empire Maker (USA)) (335097)
146 B f 5/2 Dark Angel (IRE)—Mistrusting (IRE) (Shamardal (USA))
147 B c 10/2 Medaglia d'oro (USA)—Moulin de Mougin (USA) (Curlin (USA)) (917107)
148 B f 29/1 Camelot—Musical Sands (Green Desert (USA)) (370000)
149 B f 26/2 Teofilo (IRE)—Najoum (Giant's Causeway (USA))
150 B c 24/4 Dubawi (IRE)—O'giselle (AUS) (Octagonal (NZ))
151 B br c 22/1 Dubawi (IRE)—Odeliz (IRE) (Falco (USA)) (600000)
152 Ch c 22/3 New Approach (IRE)—Patroness (Dubawi (IRE))
153 B c 24/1 Dubawi (IRE)—Perfect Light (IRE) (Galileo (IRE))
154 B c 11/2 Dubawi (IRE)—Pink Rose (Shirocco (GER))
155 B f 25/2 Shamardal (USA)—Policoro (IRE) (Pivotal)
156 B c 23/2 Galileo (IRE)—Posset (Oasis Dream) (1100000)
157 B f 19/4 Dubawi (IRE)—Qualify (IRE) (Fastnet Rock (AUS))
158 B f 20/2 Exceed And Excel (AUS)—Raphinae (Dubawi (IRE))
159 B c 11/4 Dubawi (IRE)—Rumh (GER) (Monsun (GER))
160 B f 30/1 Shamardal (USA)—Sahraah (USA) (Kingmambo (USA))
161 B c 7/2 New Approach (IRE)—Savannah Belle (Green Desert (USA)) (425000)
162 B f 17/3 War Front (USA)—Secret Gesture (Galileo (IRE))
163 B c 15/2 Dubawi (IRE)—Shirocco Star (Shirocco (GER)) (1100000)
164 B c 11/3 Dubawi (IRE)—Sperry (IRE) (Shamardal (USA))
165 B f 31/1 Invincible Spirit (IRE)—Spinning Cloud (USA) (Street Cry (IRE))
166 Ch c 7/3 Siyouni (FR)—Stirring Ballad (Compton Place) (320000)
167 B c 14/2 Curlin (USA)—Stoweshoe (USA) (Flatter (USA)) (917107)
168 B c 18/2 Quality Road (USA)—Strawberry Sense (USA) (A P Indy (USA)) (687830)
169 Ch c 16/2 Shamardal (USA)—Summer Flower (IRE) (Oasis Dream)
170 B c 22/3 Shamardal (USA)—Surprise Moment (IRE) (Authorized (IRE))
171 B f 3/3 Dubawi (IRE)—Tearless (Street Cry (IRE))
172 B c 8/1 Galileo (IRE)—Terror (IRE) (Kodiac) (900000)
173 B f 25/4 Dubawi (IRE)—Time Control (Sadler's Wells (USA)) (700000)
174 B c 20/2 Shamardal (USA)—Trieste (Dubawi (IRE))
175 B c 28/2 Shamardal (USA)—Tulips (IRE) (Pivotal)
176 B f 26/3 Sea The Stars (IRE)—Valais Girl (Holy Roman Emperor (IRE)) (632110)
177 B f 4/4 Dubawi (IRE)—Veil of Silence (IRE) (Elusive Quality (USA))
178 B f 19/1 Dubawi (IRE)—Voleuse de Coeurs (IRE) (Teofilo (IRE)) (500000)
179 B gr f 3/3 Dubawi (IRE)—Wedding March (IRE) (Dalakhani (IRE))
180 B c 21/2 Dubawi (IRE)—Wedding Toast (USA) (Street Sense (USA))
181 B f 9/4 Shamardal (USA)—Woven Lace (Hard Spun (USA))
182 B f 9/3 Dubawi (IRE)—Yellow Rosebud (IRE) (Jeremy (USA))
183 B c 31/3 Dubawi (IRE)—Yummy Mummy (Montjeu (IRE)) (1200000)
184 B f 18/4 Australia—Za'hara (IRE) (Raven's Pass (USA)) (400336)
185 B c 25/2 Shamardal (USA)—Zibelina (IRE) (Dansili)

Jockey (flat): William Buick.

6

MR MICHAEL APPLEBY, Oakham
Postal: **The Homestead, Langham, Oakham, Leicestershire, LE15 7EJ**
Contacts: **PHONE (01572) 722772 MOBILE (07884) 366421**
E-MAIL **mickappleby@icloud.com** WEBSITE www.mickappleby.com

1 ADMIRAL ANSON, 5, br h Bahri (USA)—Bromeigan **I. R. Hatton**
2 ADMIRAL ROOKE (IRE), 4, b g Rock of Gibraltar (IRE)—Qenaa **Slipstream Racing**
3 AIRSHOW, 4, ch g Showcasing—Belle des Airs (IRE) **Middleham Park Racing C**
4 AL REEF (IRE), 4, b g Shamardal (USA)—Alazeya (IRE) **Mr C. Buckingham**

MR MICHAEL APPLEBY - Continued

5 **AUTUMN LEAVES**, 4, b f Helmet (AUS)—Jadwiga **Central Racing Ltd**
6 **BARRINGTON (IRE)**, 5, b g Casamento (IRE)—Mia Divina **Mr Frank McAleavy & Mr Ian McAleavy**
7 **BEYEH (IRE)**, 11, b m King's Best (USA)—Cradle Rock (IRE) **T. R. Pryke**
8 **BIDDING WAR**, 4, ch f Champs Elysees—Locharia **Mr W. M. Brackstone**
9 **BIG COUNTRY (IRE)**, 6, b g High Chaparral (IRE)—Mount Eliza (IRE) **The Horse Watchers**
10 **BOOK OF DREAMS (IRE)**, 4, b g Dream Ahead (USA)—Moonbi Ridge (IRE) **Mr C. Buckingham**
11 **BRIGADOON**, 12, b g Compton Place—Briggsmaid **Mr Nick Hoare**
12 **BUSY STREET**, 7, b g Champs Elysees—Allegro Viva (USA) **Khdrp & Martyn Elvin**
13 **CALL OUT LOUD**, 7, b g Aqlaam—Winner's Call **Kings Head Duffield Racing Partnership**
14 **CASH N CARRIE (IRE)**, 5, b m Casamento (IRE)—Tales of Erin (IRE) **Mick Appleby Racing**
15 **CASHEL (IRE)**, 4, b g Sepoy (AUS)—Snow Dust **Laurence Bellman & David Ward**
16 **CASPIAN PRINCE (IRE)**, 10, ch g Dylan Thomas (IRE)—Crystal Gaze (IRE) **Mr S. Louch**
17 **CHANNEL PACKET**, 5, b h Champs Elysees—Etarre (IRE) **I. R. Hatton**
18 **CHESS MOVE**, 4, b g Kodiac—Azia (IRE) **Mr C. Bacon**
19 **COCKNEY BOY**, 6, ch g Cockney Rebel (IRE)—Menha **Mick Appleby Racing**
20 **CONSTITUENT**, 4, b g High Chaparral (IRE)—Arum Lily (USA) **Midest Partnership**
21 **DANCING DARCY (FR)**, 6, b m Shirocco (GER)—Polymiss (FR) **E. R. Hanbury**
22 **DANZENA**, 4, b f Denounce—Danzanora **Mr A. M. Wragg**
23 **DANZENO**, 8, b g Denounce—Danzanora **Mr A. M. Wragg**
24 **DEBATABLE (IRE)**, 4, b f Cape Cross (IRE)—Controversy **Mr C. Buckingham**
25 **DECORATION OF WAR (IRE)**, 4, b g Declaration of War (USA)—Sea Paint (IRE) **Slipstream Racing**
26 **DEINONYCHUS**, 8, b g Authorized (IRE)—Sharp Dresser (USA) **I. R. Hatton**
27 **DI'S GIFT**, 10, b g Generous (IRE)—Di's Dilemma **Mr & Mrs T. W. Readett-Bayley**
28 **DON'T DO IT (IRE)**, 4, b g Casamento (IRE)—Innclassic (IRE) **Thornley Naylor Grifiths Mulhern Johnson**
29 **DREAM SERENADE**, 6, b m Dream Eater (IRE)—Lady Santana (IRE) **Tykes & Terriers Racing Club**
30 **EPITAPH (IRE)**, 5, b g Henrythenavigator (USA)—Chartres (IRE) **Looksarnteverything Partnership**
31 **EPONINA (IRE)**, 5, b m Zoffany (IRE)—Dame Rochelle (IRE) **Mrs E. Cash**
32 **EZANAK (IRE)**, 6, b g Sea The Stars (IRE)—Ebaza (IRE) **WPL Group Holdings Limited**
33 **FANTASY KEEPER**, 5, b g Mayson—Expressive **The Fantasy Fellowship B**
34 **GIBENO (IRE)**, 5, b g Fastnet Rock (AUS)—Dance To The Top **CNC Routing Limited**
35 **GLORY OF PARIS (IRE)**, 5, b g Sir Prancealot (IRE)—Paris Glory (USA) **Mr C. Bacon**
36 **GREATEST JOURNEY**, 7, ch g Raven's Pass (USA)—Sensationally **The Hobbits**
37 **HIGH COMMAND (IRE)**, 6, b g High Chaparral (IRE)—Plaza (USA) **Equinox Racing**
38 **INDIGO PRINCESS**, 6, b m Native Ruler—Red To Violet **Mr P. A. Jarvis**
39 **IT MUST BE FAITH**, 9, b g Mount Nelson—Purple Rain **Mick Appleby Racing**
40 **KHAAN**, 4, ch c Kheleyf (USA)—Sharp Dresser (USA) **I. R. Hatton**
41 **LANDSCAPE (FR)**, 11, b g Lando (GER)—Universelle **Mr N. Hassan**
42 **LION HEARTED (IRE)**, 5, b g Lope de Vega (IRE)—Ros The Boss (IRE) **Slipstream Racing**
43 **MICHELE STROGOFF**, 6, b g Aqlaam—Maschera d'oro **Mr S. Louch**
44 **MOONRAKER**, 7, ch g Starspangledbanner (AUS)—Licence To Thrill **The Kettlelites**
45 **MRS BELLAMY**, 6, b m Black Sam Bellamy (IRE)—Jaxelle (FR) **E. R. Hanbury**
46 **MULLIONHEIR**, 7, b g Mullionmileanhour (IRE)—Peyto Princess **The Horse Watchers**
47 **NULIFE (IRE)**, 7, ch g Generous (IRE)—Kizmehoney (IRE) **Mr Mick Appleby**
48 **ONE MORE CHANCE (IRE)**, 4, b f Epaulette (AUS)—Hi Katriona (IRE) **T. R. Pryke**
49 **OYSTER CARD**, 6, b g Rail Link—Perle d'or (IRE) **The Perle d'Or Partnership**
50 **POINT ZERO (IRE)**, 4, b g Dandy Man (IRE)—Alchimie (IRE) **The Horse Watchers**
51 **PRINCELY**, 4, b c Compton Place—Royal Award **Central Racing Ltd**
52 **PRINCIPIA**, 4, b f High Chaparral (IRE)—Zero Gravity **The Slater Family**
53 **QALLAAB (IRE)**, 4, ch g Dawn Approach (IRE)—Gazebo **Mr R. Oliver**
54 **QUEENS ROYALE**, 5, b m Royal Applause (IRE)—Sofia Royale **Mr Wayne Brackstone, Mr Steve Whitear**
55 **QUILA SAEDA (GER)**, 5, b m Campanologist (USA)—Quirigua **Mr W. M. Brackstone**
56 **RAAKID (IRE)**, 7, ch g Raven's Pass (USA)—Perfect Hedge **Mr W. Sewell & Mr Michael Appleby**
57 **RED TOUCH (USA)**, 7, b br g Bluegrass Cat (USA)—Touchnow (CAN) **Mick Appleby Racing**
58 **SAAHEQ**, 5, b g Invincible Spirit (IRE)—Brevity (USA) **The Horse Watchers**
59 **SAINT MAC**, 4, b g Nathaniel (IRE)—Noahs Ark (IRE) **T. R. Pryke**
60 **SECRET LIGHTNING (FR)**, 7, ch m Sakhee's Secret—Dimelight **Mick Appleby Racing**
61 **SELLINGALLTHETIME (IRE)**, 8, ch g Tamayuz—Anthyllis (GER) **Central Racing Ltd**
62 **SHARGIAH (IRE)**, 6, ch g New Approach (IRE)—Zacheta **Mr C. Buckingham**
63 **SIDE EFFECT**, 4, br f Harbour Watch (IRE)—Fame Is The Spur **Mr R. Oliver**
64 **SOMETHING LUCKY (IRE)**, 7, gr g Clodovil (IRE)—Lucky Leigh **Dream Racing Club**
65 **SPACE BANDIT**, 4, ch g Shamardal (USA)—Hometime **Rod In Pickle Partnership**
66 **STAR OF SOUTHWOLD (FR)**, 4, bl g Le Havre (FR)—Into The Wild (FR) **Middleham Park Racing XXXIII**
67 **SUMMER ANGEL**, 4, gr f Mastercraftsman (IRE)—City Image **Mr C. Bacon**
68 **SUNBRIGHT (IRE)**, 4, b f Dawn Approach (IRE)—Crossover **M. Appleby**
69 **TAN**, 5, b g Aqlaam—Sunburnt **Mr S. Louch**

MR MICHAEL APPLEBY - Continued

70 **TAN ARABIQ**, 6, b g Arabian Gleam—Tanning **Sarnian Racing**
71 **THE GREAT WALL (USA)**, 5, b g Bernardini (USA)—Music Room (USA) **The Horse Watchers**
72 **THE LOCK MASTER (IRE)**, 12, b g Key of Luck (USA)—Pitrizza (IRE) **Kenneth George Kitchen**
73 **TOY THEATRE**, 5, b m Lonhro (AUS)—Puppet Queen (USA) **Mr L. J. M. J. Vaessen**
74 **WILLY SEWELL**, 6, b g Multiplex—Cherished Love (IRE) **Mr W. J. Sewell**
75 **YEAH BABE**, 4, b f Yeats (IRE)—Blues In Cee (IRE) **Mrs L. White**
76 **YUPPY LOVE**, 4, ch f Universal (IRE)—Wheresthewireshirl (USA) **Mr N. Skelton**
77 **ZAPPER CASS (FR)**, 6, b g Elusive City (USA)—Moonlight Cass (IRE) **Mr S. Louch**

THREE-YEAR-OLDS

78 **ABBI DAB**, b f Equiano (FR)—Megaleka **North Cheshire Trading & Storage Ltd**
79 **BEST HAAF**, b c Haafhd—Beyeh (IRE) **T. R. Pryke**
80 **BLUELION**, ch g Sleeping Indian—Shirley's Pride **Goldrush Racing**
81 **CLIPSHAM TIGER (IRE)**, b g Bungle Inthejungle—Texas Queen **Mr F. Morley**
82 **CONGRESS PLACE (IRE)**, b f Compton Place—Queen of The Tarts **Orpen Horses Ltd.**
83 **DRAGON BEAT (IRE)**, ch f Dragon Pulse (IRE)—Dreamaway (IRE) **Mr Craig Buckingham**
84 **EQUIANO PERLE**, b f Equiano (FR)—Perle d'or (IRE) **The Perle d'Or Partnership**
85 **FREE LOVE**, b f Equiano (FR)—Peace And Love (IRE) **The North South Syndicate**
86 **FREEDOM'S BREATH**, b f Bated Breath—Quest For Freedom **Mr L. J. Vaessen**
87 **GET IT READY (IRE)**, ch f Compton Place—Candy Mountain **Dream Racing Club**
88 **LADS ORDER (IRE)**, b g Lilbourne Lad (IRE)—Maid To Order (IRE) **Mr Craig Buckingham**
89 **LINCOLN PARK**, b c Kyllachy—Twilight Pearl **Craig Buckingham & Gary Dewhurst**
90 **LOCH NESS MONSTER (IRE)**, b c War Command (USA)—Celestial Dream (IRE) **Mr Matthew Taylor**
91 **LONIMOSS BARELIERE (FR)**, b c Palamoss (IRE)—Lonia Blue (IRE) **Mr Nick Skelton**
92 **MALLONS SPIRIT (IRE)**, b f Rip Van Winkle (IRE)—Que Sera Sera **Chilworth in Arms Partnership**
93 **NIGHT FURY**, b c Sir Percy—Hell Hath No Fury **Mr C. Bacon**
94 **NO SHOES NATION**, ch f Monsieur Bond (IRE)—Stunning Icon **Mr S. Tolley**
95 **QUDURAAT**, ch f Teofilo (IRE)—Ejadah (IRE) **Mrs B. A. Matthews**
96 **SESAME (IRE)**, b f Slade Power (IRE)—Tiger Spice **Mr L. A. Bellman**
97 **WALKMAN (IRE)**, b c War Command (USA)—Mooching Along (IRE) **Mr A. Altazi**
98 **WHENAPOET**, b c Poet's Voice—If Or When (IRE) **Mr L. J. M. J. Vaessen**

Trainer did not supply details of his two-year-olds.

Other Owners: Laurence Bellman, Mr A. M. Blewitt, Mr Wayne Brackstone, Mr Craig Buckingham, Mr M. Bulley, Mr A. D'Arcy, Mr Gary Dewhurst, Mr Christopher Dixon, Mr Martin R. Dixon, Mr Martyn Elvin, Mr Dominic Finn, Mr M. J. Golding, Mr Michael Gromett, Mr Mick Harris, Mr N. Hassan, Mr Richard Hoiles, J H & N J Foxon Ltd, Kings Head Duffield Racing Partnership, Mr C. Le Page, Mr A. W. Le Page, Mr Stephen J. S. Lee, Mr Anthony Linnett, Mr Ian McAleavy, Mr Frank McAleavy, Mr T. S. Palin, Mr D. Parkinson, Mr David Pick, Mr M. Prince, Mrs T. W. Readett-Bayley, Mr T. W. Readett-Bayley, Mr W. Sewell, Mr David Skelton, Mr Trevor Gordon Slater, Mr C. P. Smith, Mr Peter Sumner, Mr Stephen Sutton, Mr Matthew Taylor, Mr L. Thornley, Mr B. Totty, Mr Mark Ward, Mr D. Ward, Mr J. R. Wherritt, Mr S. J. Whitear.

Assistant Trainer: Jonathan Clayton

Jockey (flat): Sylvestre De Sousa, Luke Morris, Andrew Mullen, Alistair Rawlinson. **Jockey (NH):** Richard Johnson, Jack Quinlan. **Apprentice:** Kevin Lundie. **Amateur:** Miss Serena Brotherton.

---

7   **MR DAVID ARBUTHNOT, Dorking**
Postal: Henfold House Cottage, Henfold Lane, Beare Green, Dorking, Surrey, RH5 4RW
Contacts: PHONE (01306) 631529 FAX (01306) 631529 MOBILE (07836) 276464
E-MAIL dwparbuthnot@hotmail.com WEBSITE www.henfoldracing.co.uk

1 **ALKOPOP (GER)**, 5, gr g Jukebox Jury (IRE)—Alkeste (GER) **A. T. A. Wates**
2 **ARIA ROSE**, 4, b g Cityscape—Leelu **P. Banfield**
3 **DANGLYDONTASK**, 8, b g Lucky Story (USA)—Strat's Quest **P. Banfield**
4 **DARING DEPLOY (IRE)**, 13, b g Deploy—Daring Perk (IRE) **The Daring Partnership**
5   4, B f Shantou (USA)—Erins Stage (IRE) **A. T. A. Wates**
6 **EYE OF AN EAGLE**, 6, b g Linda's Lad—Vie des Aigles (FR) **A. T. A. Wates**
7 **EYES UP (FR)**, 5, ch g Muhtathir—High Destiny (FR) **A. T. A. Wates**
8 **GO FORRIT (FR)**, 5, b g Jeremy (USA)—Ben Roseler (IRE) **A. T. A. Wates**
9 **KAP AUTEUIL (FR)**, 4, b g Kapgarde—Turboka (FR) **A. T. A. Wates**
10 **MY FRIENDLY COUSIN**, 4, ro g Carlotamix (FR)—The Strawberry One **The Kykie Allsopp Partnership**
11 **NEVERBEEN TO PARIS (IRE)**, 4, b g Champs Elysees—Island Paradise (IRE) **Mr P. M. Claydon**
12 **NICKOBOY (FR)**, 4, b g Full of Gold (FR)—Dikanika (FR) **A. T. A. Wates**
13 **QUEENS PRESENT (IRE)**, 8, ch m Presenting—Fairy Dawn (IRE) **A. T. A. Wates**

MR DAVID ARBUTHNOT - Continued

14 **SNOWBALL (IRE)**, 12, gr g Alderbrook—Rosafi (IRE) **The Daring Partnership**
15 **SOLDIER TO FOLLOW**, 4, b c Soldier Hollow—Nota Bene (GER) **Mr A T A Wates & Mrs S Wates**
16 **STROLLAWAYNOW (IRE)**, 12, b g Oscar (IRE)—Rose of Salome (IRE) **A. T. A. Wates**
17 **WINDSPIEL (FR)**, 6, b g Sholokhov (IRE)—Wildlife (GER) **A. T. A. Wates**

Other Owners: Mr W. P. Harriman, Mrs J. E. B. Leigh-Pemberton, Mrs S. M. Wates, Mr K. Wiggert.

Jockey (NH): Tom Cannon, Daryl Jacob.

---

8 | **MR RICHARD ARMSON, Melbourne**
Postal: **Scotlands Farm, Burney Lane, Staunton-Harold, Melbourne, Derbyshire, DE73 8BH**

1 **ALBURN**, 9, b g Afflora (IRE)—Burn Brook **R. J. Armson**
2 **KEYNOTE (IRE)**, 4, b g Dragon Pulse (IRE)—Taalluf (USA) **R. J. Armson**
3 **KILCARAGH BOY (IRE)**, 10, b b King's Theatre (IRE)—Histologie (FR) **R. J. Armson**
4 **MAX O (IRE)**, 9, b g Brian Boru—Myglass (IRE) **R. J. Armson**
5 4, B g Imperial Monarch (GER)—Presenting Lazarus (IRE) **R. J. Armson**

---

9 | **MR PETER ATKINSON, Northallerton**
Postal: **Yafforth Hill Farm, Yafforth, Northallerton, North Yorkshire, DL7 0LT**
Contacts: **PHONE (01609) 772598 MOBILE (07751) 131215**

1 **IRISH ROE (IRE)**, 8, b m Vinnie Roe (IRE)—Betty's Best (IRE) **Mrs L. Atkinson**
2 **MINI DREAMS**, 7, b m Josr Algarhoud (IRE)—Mini Minster **Mr P. G. Atkinson**
3 **REVERANT CUST (IRE)**, 8, gr g Daylami (IRE)—Flame Supreme (IRE) **Mr P. G. Atkinson**

---

10 | **MR MICHAEL ATTWATER, Epsom**
Postal: **Tattenham Corner Stables, Tattenham Corner Road, Epsom Downs, Surrey, KT18 5PP**
Contacts: **PHONE (01737) 360066 MOBILE (07725) 423633**
E-MAIL Attwaterracing@hotmail.co.uk WEBSITE www.attwaterracing.com

1 **ASK THE GURU**, 9, b g Ishiguru (USA)—Tharwa (IRE) **Canisbay Bloodstock**
2 **BEAT ROUTE**, 12, ch g Beat Hollow—Steppin Out **Canisbay Bloodstock**
3 **BIG TIME MAYBE (IRE)**, 4, b g Dandy Man (IRE)—Divine Design (IRE) **Dare To Dream Racing**
4 **EMBANKMENT**, 10, b g Zamindar (USA)—Esplanade **Canisbay Bloodstock**
5 **FREE TALKIN**, 4, b f Equiano (FR)—Where's Broughton **Canisbay Bloodstock**
6 **HORNBY**, 4, b g Equiano (FR)—Kindia (IRE) **Canisbay Bloodstock**
7 **JEOPARDY JOHN**, 4, b g Delegator—Daysiwaay (IRE) **J J's Syndicate**
8 **JUST THAT LORD**, 6, ch g Avonbridge—Lady Filly **Mrs M. S. Teversham**
9 **LAWN RANGER**, 4, b g Cityscape—Baylini **Canisbay Bloodstock**
10 **LORD DEL BOY**, 4, b g Delegator—Lady Prodee **Mrs M. S. Teversham**
11 **MORE SALUTES (IRE)**, 4, b c Acclamation—Champion Place **Katy & Lol Pratt**
12 **MOUNTAIN RESCUE (IRE)**, 7, b g High Chaparral (IRE)—Amber Queen (IRE) **The Attwater Partnership**
13 **MUSIC MAJOR**, 6, br g Bertolini (USA)—Music Maid (IRE) **The Attwater Partnership**
14 **NATCH**, 4, b g Nathaniel (IRE)—Angara **Mr A. C. D. Main**
15 **NOBLE DEED**, 9, ch g Kyllachy—Noble One **Canisbay Bloodstock**
16 **OUR LORD**, 7, gr g Proclamation (IRE)—Lady Filly **Mrs M. S. Teversham**
17 **PALACE MOON**, 14, b g Fantastic Light (USA)—Palace Street (USA) **Canisbay Bloodstock**
18 **PASSING CLOUDS**, 4, b g Kheleyf (USA)—Steppin Out **Canisbay Bloodstock**
19 **REAL ESTATE (IRE)**, 4, b c Dansili—Maskunah (IRE) **Mr A. C. D. Main**
20 **SHEILA'S FANCY (IRE)**, 5, ch g Casamento (IRE)—Fancy Vivid (IRE) **Dare To Dream Racing**
21 **STORM BOY**, 4, b c Paco Boy (IRE)—Evenstorm (USA) **B. Gubby**
22 **SUKHOVEY (USA)**, 4, b f Lookin At Lucky (USA)—Allencat (USA) **The Attwater Partnership**
23 **WARRANTED**, 6, b h Authorized (IRE)—Steppin Out **Canisbay Bloodstock**

THREE-YEAR-OLDS

24 **APRON STRINGS**, b f Mayson—Royal Ivy **Canisbay Bloodstock**
25 **BEG FOR MERCY**, b c Heeraat (IRE)—Plead (FR) **Attwater Hunt Partnership**
26 **DANIEL DRAVOT**, b g Nathaniel (IRE)—Zubova **Mr J. M. Duggan & Mr S. Brown**

MR MICHAEL ATTWATER - Continued

27 **ENYAMA (GER)**, b f Camelot—Ella Ransom (GER) **The Attwater Partnership**
28 **LEE ROY**, ch c Leroidesanimaux (BRZ)—Steppin Out **Canisbay Bloodstock**
29 **SAVOY BROWN**, b c Epaulette (AUS)—Kindia (IRE) **Canisbay Bloodstock**
30 **STORM GIRL**, b f Paco Boy (IRE)—Evenstorm (USA) **B. Gubby**
31 **THE CRUISING LORD**, b g Coach House (IRE)—Lady Filly **Mrs M. S. Teversham**

Other Owners: Mr B. M. Attwater, Mr M. J. Attwater, The Attwater Partnership, Mr Scott Brown, Mr James Michael Duggan, Mrs Nicola Hunt, Mr R. A. Hunt, Mr R. F. Kilby, Mr M. G. Mackenzie, Mrs Katy Pratt, Mr Lol Pratt, Richard and Nicola Hunt, Mr I. Sharrock, Mr W. P. L. Smith, Miss Maureen Stopher, Mr Antony Waters.

Assistant Trainer: S. Sawyer

---

11 **MR JENE-RENE AUVRAY, Calne**
Postal: **West Nolands Farm, Nolands Road, Yatesbury, Calne, Wiltshire, SN11 8YD**
Contacts: **MOBILE (07798) 645796**
E-MAIL jr@jrauvrayracing.co.uk WEBSITE www.jrauvrayracing.co.uk

1 **FIRST LINK (USA)**, 4, b f First Defence (USA)—Magic Motif (USA) **Mr S. K. McPhee**
2 **IONA ISLAND**, 6, b m Dutch Art—Still Small Voice **J. R. Auvray**
3 **KNOCKMAOLE BOY (IRE)**, 7, b g Echo of Light—Kashmir Lady (FR) **N. R. Kelly**
4 **MONTMORE (FR)**, 7, b g Montmartre (FR)—One For Me **Sara Spratt, Nigel Kelly & Alison Auvray**
5 **NAFAAYES (IRE)**, 5, ch m Sea The Stars (IRE)—Shamtari (IRE) **Mr S. K. McPhee**

Other Owners: Lady Elisa May-Smith, Mrs A. L. Auvray, Mrs S. Spratt.

---

12 **MR ALAN BAILEY, Newmarket**
Postal: **Cavendish Stables, Hamilton Road, Newmarket, Suffolk, CB8 7JQ**
Contacts: **PHONE (01638) 664546 FAX (01638) 664546 MOBILE (07808) 734223**
E-MAIL baileya12@sky.com

1 **ENIGMATIC (IRE)**, 5, b g Elnadim (USA)—Meanwhile (IRE) **Mr T. Milner**
2 **ESSPEEGEE**, 6, b g Paco Boy (IRE)—Goldrenched (IRE) **The Skills People Group Ltd**
3 **FLEETING FREEDOM**, 4, b f Equiano (FR)—Fleeting Image **A. Bailey**
4 **GAMEKEEPER BILL**, 5, b g Beat All (USA)—Granny McPhee **A J McNamee & L C McNamee**
5 **GNAAD (IRE)**, 5, b g Invincible Spirit (IRE)—Areyaam (USA) **Capla Developments & A Bailey**
6 **GO FAR**, 9, b g Dutch Art—Carranita (IRE) **Mr R. J. H. West**
7 **GRASMERE (IRE)**, 4, b f Society Rock (IRE)—Silk Point (IRE) **MPR XLIV, Mr C Martin, Mrs A Shone**
8 **INTERROGATION (FR)**, 4, b g Redback—Amalea (IRE) **Mr T. Milner**
9 **PABLOW**, 4, b g Delegator—Limonia (GER) **Tregarth Racing & Partner**
10 **STRICTLY ART (IRE)**, 6, b g Excellent Art—Sadinga (IRE) **Strictly Fools and Horses Club**
11 **VIMY RIDGE**, 7, ch g American Post—Fairy Shoes **Dr S. P. Hargreaves**
12 **WIDNES**, 5, b g Showcasing—Largo (IRE) **Dr S. P. Hargreaves**

THREE-YEAR-OLDS

13 **CLEM A**, b g Helmet (AUS)—Mondovi **The Skills People Group Ltd**
14 **INTERROGATOR (IRE)**, b c Tamayuz—Arbeel **Mr T. Milner**
15 **SIRIUS SLEW**, b g Epaulette (AUS)—Slewtoo **Mr T. Milner**
16 **YOUR MOTHERS' EYES**, b c Aussie Rules (USA)—Sanctum **Capla Developments & A Bailey**

Other Owners: AB Racing Limited, Mr H. Hall, Mr C. M. Martin, A. J. McNamee, Mr L. McNamee, Middleham Park Racing XLIV, T. S. Palin, M. Prince, Mrs M. Shone, Mr P. Stubbins, Tregarth Racing, Mr R. L. Williams.

Assistant Trainer: Joseph Edwin Parr

Amateur: Miss Jessica Cooley.

13 MRS CAROLINE BAILEY, Holdenby
Postal: Holdenby Lodge, Spratton, Northants, NN6 8LG
Contacts: PHONE (01604) 883729 (Home) (01604) 770234 (Yard) FAX (01604) 770423
MOBILE (07831) 373340
E-MAIL caroline.bailey66@yahoo.com WEBSITE www.carolinebaileyracing.co.uk

1 CAPTAIN CARGO, 7, b g Sulamani (IRE)—Raffles (FR) **M. Tucker**
2 CARLI KING (IRE), 13, b g Witness Box (USA)—Abinitio Lady (IRE) **Varley, Lloyd & Bailey**
3 CARLO ROCKS (IRE), 9, b g Carlo Bank (IRE)—Rock Garden (IRE) **Mrs S. Tucker**
4 CROSSPARK, 9, b g Midnight Legend—Blue Shannon (IRE) **C. W. Booth**
5 DONT TELL THE WIFE, 5, b g Midnight Legend—Dizzy Frizzy **Varley, Lloyd & Bailey**
6 DYLIEV (FR), 6, ch m Dylan Thomas (IRE)—Coreliev (FR) **Herron, Nicholson, Proctor & Richards**
7 EARLY RETIREMENT (IRE), 7, b g Daylami (IRE)—Deep Lilly **Mr J. M. B. Strowbridge**
8 ELKSTONE, 8, b g Midnight Legend—Samandara (FR) **Tredwell, Robinson, Proctor & Nicholson**
9 GLOBAL BONUS (IRE), 10, b g Heron Island (IRE)—That's The Bonus (IRE) **Mrs S. Carsberg**
10 GLOBAL DOMINATION, 11, b g Alflora (IRE)—Lucia Forte **Mrs S. Carsberg**
11 GLOBAL DREAM, 9, ch g Lucarno (USA)—Global Girl **Mrs S. Carsberg**
12 GOLD INGOT, 12, ch g Best of The Bests (IRE)—Realms of Gold (USA) **Mr J Cowan & Mr B Jessup**
13 LADY MASTER, 6, b m Native Ruler—Elmside Katie **Mr P. Dixon Smith**
14 MALAPIE, 11, b g Westerner—Victorian Lady **Varley, Lloyd & Bailey**
15 MARINERS MOON (IRE), 8, ch g Mount Nelson—Dusty Moon **Lets Have A Go**
16 RECKLESS BEHAVIOR (IRE), 7, b g Gold Well—Wee Wallis **Bailey, Jessup, Lloyd & Varley**
17 THE CAPTAIN (IRE), 6, b g Millenary—Quilt **Mr C Flinton & Mr G Bailey**
18 TROUFION (FR), 10, gr g Smadoun (FR)—La Troussardiere (FR) **K. F. J. Loads**

Other Owners: G. T. H. Bailey, Mr R. J. Burton, Mr M. Copley, Mr James E. Cowan, C. Flinton, Mr M. S. Herron, Mr B. P. Jessup, Mr R. B. Lloyd, Mr K. M. Nicholson, Mr P. S. C. Proctor, Mr S. A. Richards, Mrs B. D. Robinson, J. Tredwell, Mr M. Varley.

Jockey (NH): Sean Bowen, Harry Skelton. Amateur: Mr Thomas McClorey.

14 MR KIM BAILEY, Cheltenham
Postal: Thorndale Farm, Withington Road, Andoversford, Cheltenham, Gloucestershire, GL54 4LL
Contacts: PHONE (01242) 890241 FAX (01242) 890193 MOBILE (07831) 416859
E-MAIL info@kimbaileyracing.com WEBSITE www.kimbaileyracing.com

1 ABBREVIATE (GER), 8, b g Authorized (IRE)—Azalee (GER) **Mr & Mrs K. R. Ellis**
2 ADJOURNED, 4, gr g Rip Van Winkle (IRE)—Bite of The Cherry **The Jury**
3 AGENT MEMPHIS (IRE), 7, b m Scorpion (IRE)—
Forces of Destiny (IRE) **Mrs I. C. Sellars & Major & Mrs P. Arkwright**
4 ALFIE CORBITT (IRE), 6, b g Arakan (USA)—Millanymare (IRE) **Highclere T'bred Racing - Alfie Corbitt**
5 ALIANDY (IRE), 8, b g Presenting—Water Rock **A & S Enterprises Ltd**
6 ANOTHER VENTURE (IRE), 8, ch g Stowaway—Hard Luck (IRE) **Racing For Maggie's Partnership**
7 ARTHUR'S SIXPENCE, 5, b g Vinnie Roe (IRE)—Loose Change (IRE) **Stillmoremoneythan**
8 BALLETICON (IRE), 5, b g Arakan (USA)—Miss Garbo (IRE) **Inn For A Penny**
9 BANDON ROC, 8, b g Shirocco (GER)—Azur (IRE) **The WOW Partnership**
10 BEN ARTHUR (IRE), 9, b g Marienbard (IRE)—Oscartrainer (IRE) **Mr & Mrs Mark Laws**
11 BLAZON, 6, b g Dansili—Zante **The Blazing Optimists**
12 CHARBEL, 8, b g Iffraaj—Eoz (IRE) **Mrs Julie Martin & David R. Martin**
13 CHAZZA (IRE), 5, b g Mahler—Presenting Proform (IRE)
14 CIRANO DE SIVOLA (FR), 7, gr g Vendangeur (IRE)—Wild Rose Bloom (FR) **Mr Gary Tardi & Mrs Lin Austin**
15 CLOONE LADY (IRE), 7, b m Milan—Cloone Leader (IRE) **Mr J. F. Perriss**
16 COMMODORE BARRY (IRE), 6, br g Presenting—Specifiedrisk (IRE) **The Commodores**
17 COTTEEMCAVENNIGOAL (IRE), 4, b g Kalanisi (IRE)—Brega Queen (IRE) **Mr S. L. Keane**
18 CRESSWELL LEGEND, 8, b g Midnight Legend—Cresswell Willow (IRE) **Mrs V. W. H. Johnson**
19 DANDY DAN (IRE), 6, b g Midnight Legend—Playing Around **Mr P. J. Andrews**
20 DIAMOND GAIT, 6, b m Passing Glance—Milliegait **Mr N. Carter**
21 DIVA RECONCE (FR), 6, b m Kap Rock (FR)—Kruscyna (FR) **Mrs I. C. Sellars & Major & Mrs P. Arkwright**
22 DOCTOR HAZE, 8, b g Dr Massini—Gypsy Haze **Partnership Terminated**
23 4, B f Flemensfirth (USA)—Dorabelle (IRE) **Mr & Mrs Paul & Clare Rooney**
24 EARLY LEARNER, 7, b m Sulamani (IRE)—Slow Starter (IRE) **Hot To Trot Jumping**
25 EL PRESENTE, 6, b g Presenting—Raitera (FR) **Davies Pilkington Yarborough Brooke**
26 ESPOIR DE ROMAY (FR), 5, b g Kap Rock (FR)—Miss du Seuil (FR) **The Midgelets**
27 FIRST FLOW (IRE), 7, b g Primary (USA)—Clonroche Wells (IRE) **A. N. Solomons**
28 FUBAR (IRE), 5, ch g Le Fou (IRE)—Petite Mielle (IRE) **Mr & Mrs Bevan**

MR KIM BAILEY - Continued

29 **FULL TILT**, 6, b g Flying Legend (USA)—Proper Posh **Mr & Mrs M Laws & Mr & Mrs P Woodhall**
30 **GALLOWS POINT**, 6, b g Black Sam Bellamy (IRE)—Jolika (FR) **Mr Dan Hall & Mrs Julie & David R Martin**
31 **GLENFORDE (IRE)**, 8, ch g Flemensfirth (USA)—Feel The Pride (IRE) **Share My Dream**
32 **HAPPYGOLUCKY (IRE)**, 5, b br g Jeremy (USA)—Mydadsabishop (IRE)
33 **HES NO TROUBLE (IRE)**, 6, b g Scorpion (IRE)—She's No Trouble (IRE) **Jockey Club Ownership (SW 2018)**
34 **ILLUMINATED BEAUTY (IRE)**, 6, b m Flemensfirth (USA)—Native Beauty (IRE) **Mr J. F. Perriss**
35 **IMPERIAL AURA (IRE)**, 6, b g Kalanisi (IRE)—Missindependence (IRE) **Imperial Racing Partnership 2016**
36 **INCA ROSE**, 4, ch g Malinas (GER)—Cinderella Rose **The Coln Valley Partnership**
37 **JOHNNY OCEAN (IRE)**, 7, b g Whitmore's Conn (USA)—Soda Bread (IRE) **Mrs Julie Martin & David R. Martin**
38 5, B g Stowaway—Kilmac Princess (IRE) **Mr K. C. Bailey**
39 **KNOCKANRAWLEY (IRE)**, 11, gr g Portrait Gallery (IRE)—Hot Lips (IRE) **Kim Bailey Racing Partnership VIII**
40 **LADY OF THE NIGHT**, 6, b m Midnight Legend—Even Flo **Mr J. F. Perriss**
41 **LORD APPARELLI**, 4, ch g Schiaparelli (GER)—La Marette **The Schiaparellis**
42 5, B g Millenary—Lovely Hand (IRE)
43 **MASTEEN (FR)**, 7, b g Astarabad (USA)—Manson Teene (FR) **This Horse Is For Sale Partnership**
44 **MERGEELA (IRE)**, 4, ch b f September Storm (GER)—Sweetbriar Rose **Have Fun Racing Partnership**
45 **MINELLA WARRIOR (IRE)**, 7, b g King's Theatre (IRE)—
　　　　　　　　　　　　　　　　　　　　　Bobbi's Venture (IRE) **Mrs Julie Martin & David R. Martin**
46 **MISS GEMSTONE**, 5, ch m Midnight Legend—Real Treasure **The Real Partnership**
47 **MON PALOIS (FR)**, 7, b g Muhaymin (USA)—Gastinaise (FR) **Mrs E. A. Kellar**
48 **MR GREY SKY (IRE)**, 5, gr g Fame And Glory—Lakil Princess (IRE) **Mr P. J. Andrews**
49 **NEWTIDE (IRE)**, 6, br g Getaway (GER)—C'est Fantastique (IRE) **Lady Dulverton**
50 **PARTY FUZZ**, 4, b g Great Pretender—Very Special One (IRE) **Mr P. J. Andrews**
51 **PEEPING TOM (IRE)**, 6, b g Morozov (USA)—Orcadian Dawn (USA) **I-Spy Syndicate**
52 **POND ROAD (IRE)**, 5, ch g No Risk At All (FR)—Califea (FR) **No Risk Syndicate**
53 **PRINCE LLYWELYN**, 5, ch g Schiaparelli (GER)—La Marette **Mr P. Bennett-Jones**
54 **RED RIVER (IRE)**, 6, ch g Beneficial—Socker Toppen (IRE) **The Red River Syndicate**
55 **ROBIN THE RAVEN (IRE)**, 7, b g Robin des Pres (FR)—Omyn Supreme (IRE) **S W Racing**
56 **ROCKY'S TREASURE (IRE)**, 8, b g Westerner—Fiddlers Bar (IRE) **Mr J. F. Perriss**
57 **ROSE TO FAME**, 5, b m Fame And Glory—Cinderella Rose **Jones Broughtons Wilson Weaver**
58 **ROSMUC RELAY (IRE)**, 7, b g Presenting—Aughrim Vic (IRE) **Mr J. F. Perriss**
59 **ROYAL SUPREMO (IRE)**, 8, b g Beneficial—Slaney Athlete (IRE) **The Supremes**
60 **SADLERMOR (IRE)**, 5, b g Morozov (USA)—Lucyjane (IRE) **Elphick, Sperling & KBR**
61 **SEA STORY**, 6, b m Black Sam Bellamy (IRE)—Charlottes Webb (IRE) **John & Susie Kottler, Emma Buchanan**
62 **SHANTOU EXPRESS (IRE)**, 4, ch g Shantou (USA)—Spanker **The Second Chancers**
63 **SILVER KAYF**, 7, gr g Kayf Tara—Silver Spinner **The Lucky Spinners**
64 **STATION MASTER**, 8, b g Scorpion (IRE)—Gastounette (IRE) **Mrs P. A. Perriss**
65 **SUBWAY SURF (IRE)**, 5, b m Milan—Dante Rouge (IRE) **Surf On The Turf**
66 **SUNBLAZER (IRE)**, 9, gr g Dark Angel—Damask Rose **Mr N. Carter**
67 **TALK OF FAME**, 4, b g Fame And Glory—Princess Oriane (IRE) **Lady Dulverton**
68 **THE EDGAR WALLACE (IRE)**, 4, b g Flemensfirth (USA)—Annalecky (IRE) **Mr P. J. Andrews**
69 **THE MILAN GIRL (IRE)**, 5, b m Milan—En Vedette (FR) **Mr & Mrs Paul & Clare Rooney**
70 **THIBAULT**, 6, b g Kayf Tara—Seemarye **Mr T. D. J. Syder**
71 **THOSE TIGER FEET (IRE)**, 5, b g Shantou (USA)—Luca Lite (IRE) **Mr P. J. Andrews**
72 **TWO FOR GOLD (IRE)**, 6, b g Gold Well—Two of Each (IRE) **May We Never Be Found Out Partnership 2**
73 **VINNDICATION (IRE)**, 6, b g Vinnie Roe (IRE)—Pawnee Trail (IRE) **Moremoneythan**
74 **WANDRIN STAR (IRE)**, 8, b g Flemensfirth (USA)—Keralba (USA) **Mrs P. A. Perriss**
75 **WHAT A BALOO (IRE)**, 4, b g Jeremy (USA)—Luca Lite (IRE) **Share My Dream**
76 **WINTER GLORY (IRE)**, 4, b g Fame And Glory—Winter Shadows (FR) **A Sheppard, J Webber, R Sheppard**
77 **YEAVERING BELLE**, 5, ch m Midnight Legend—Fruit Yoghurt **Mrs V. J. McKie**
78 **YOUNEVERCALL (IRE)**, 8, b g Yeats (IRE)—Afarka (IRE) **Youneverknow Partnership**

Other Owners: Major P. W. F. Arkwright, Mrs Sandra G. E. Arkwright, Mrs L. L. Austin, Mrs C. Bailey, Mr R. H. Beevor, Mr O. S. W. Bell, Mr Q. Bevan, Mrs C. Bevan, Sir F. Brooke, Mr S. W. Broughton, Sir M. F. Broughton, Mrs E. S. Buchanan, Mr D. J. Burke, Mr S. R. Cannon, Mr D. M. Clancy, Mr K. T. Clancy, M. E. T. Davies, Mrs E. Ellis, K. R. Ellis, Mrs L. H. Field, D. A. Hall, Lady M. P Hatch, The Hon H. M. Herbert, Highclere Thoroughbred Racing Ltd, Mr R. S. Hoskins, Mrs N. Jones, Mr M. Kay, Mr P. S. Kerr, Mr H. Kimbell, Mr J. Kottler, Mrs S. E. Kottler, Mrs J. M. Laws, Mr M. Laws, D. R. Martin, Mrs J. M. T. Martin, Mr C. W. Mather, Mr R. A. Pilkington, Mr I. Robinson, Mrs C. Rooney, Mr P. A. Rooney, Mrs N. P. Sellars, Mr R. Sheppard, Mr J. A. Stanley, Mrs S. J. Steer-Fowler, Dr J. M. Steer-Fowler, Mr G. Tardi, Miss M. L. Taylor, Mrs R. B. Weaver, Mr J. Webber, T. C. Wilson, Mr P. W. Woodhall, Mrs F. M. Woodhall, The Earl Of Yarborough.

Assistant Trainer: Mathew Nicholls

Jockey (NH): David Bass, Tom Bellamy. **Conditional:** Richard Condon, Mikey Hamill.

15 MR GEORGE BAKER, Chiddingfold
Postal: **Robins Farm, Fisher Lane, Chiddingfold, Godalming, Surrey, GU8 4TB**
Contacts: **PHONE (01428) 682059 MOBILE (07889) 514881**
E-MAIL gbakerracing@gmail.com WEBSITE www.georgebakerracing.com

1 **ATOMIC JACK**, 4, b g Nathaniel (IRE)—Indigo River (IRE) **George Baker and Partners - Super Six**
2 **BARRITUS**, 4, b g Exceed And Excel (AUS)—Flambeau **Barton Partnership**
3 **BORDERFORCE (FR)**, 6, b g American Post—Miss Vic (USA) **Mr Julian Pittam & Mr Michael Watt**
4 **CONFRERIE (IRE)**, 4, b g Society Rock (IRE)—Intellibet One **New Confidence Partnership**
5 **CRAGWOOD ROYALE (IRE)**, 4, b f Invincible Spirit (IRE)—Lady Glinka (IRE) **FTP Equine Holdings Ltd**
6 **CRAZY HORSE**, 6, b g Sleeping Indian—Mainstay **Bowden & Baker**
7 **CRISTAL SPIRIT**, 4, b g Nathaniel (IRE)—Celestial Girl **Mr G. Baker**
8 **DAZIBAO (FR)**, 6, ch g Muhaymin (USA)—Adjinne (FR) **Turf Club 2018**
9 **GEORGE BAKER (IRE)**, 12, b g Camacho—Petite Maxine **George Baker & Partners**
10 **GOODBYE LULU (IRE)**, 4, b f Exceed And Excel (AUS)—Guarantia **George Baker & Partners**
11 **HARRY HURRICANE**, 7, b g Kodiac—Eolith **Dare To Dream Racing**
12 **HIGHWAY ONE (USA)**, 5, b m Quality Road (USA)—Kinda Wonderful (USA) **On The Game Partnership**
13 **INFANTA ISABELLA**, 5, b m Lope de Vega (IRE)—Shemissa (IRE) **The Chriselliam Partnership**
14 **JUST PERFECT**, 4, ch g Mastercraftsman (IRE)—Downhill Dancer (IRE) **Thurloe Thoroughbreds XLIII**
15 **LA MAQUINA**, 4, b g Dutch Art—Miss Meltemi (IRE) **George Baker and Partners - Super Six**
16 **MAMILLIUS**, 6, b g Exceed And Excel (AUS)—Laika Lane (USA) **The Mamillius Partnership**
17 **MANTON GRANGE**, 6, b g Siyouni (FR)—Emulate **Goltz And Baker Partnership**
18 **THE GATES OF DAWN (FR)**, 4, ch g Iffraaj—Cheap Thrills **Miss Emily Asprey & Christopher Wright**
19 **THE LAMPLIGHTER (FR)**, 4, b g Elusive City (USA)—Plume Rouge **The Lamplighter Syndicate**
20 **WALTER SICKERT (IRE)**, 5, b g Galileo (IRE)—Alta Anna (FR) **Mr M. A. Sherwood**
21 **WATCH TAN**, 4, gr f Harbour Watch (IRE)—High Tan **Seaton Partnership**
22 **WILLOW GRACE**, 4, ch f Harbour Watch (IRE)—Sparkling Montjeu (IRE) **Mrs C. E. Cone**

THREE-YEAR-OLDS
23 **ADELANTE (FR)**, ch f Zoffany (IRE)—Make Up **Mr George Baker**
24 **ANOTHER APPROACH (FR)**, b f Dawn Approach (IRE)—Marmoom Flower (IRE) **The Double P Partnership**
25 **BARNADY FREDERICK (FR)**, b g Sunday Break (JPN)—Miss Alabama (FR) **George Baker & Partners**
26 **CONFAB (USA)**, gr g Exchange Rate (USA)—Callmenancy (USA) **Confidence Partnership**
27 **CONFILS (FR)**, b f Olympic Glory (IRE)—Mambo Mistress (USA) **Confidence Partnership**
28 **CULTURE**, b g Dream Ahead (USA)—Talon Bleu (FR) **Highclere Thoroughbred Racing - Dream On**
29 **GOLD BERE (FR)**, b br g Hurricane Cat (USA)—Sanisa (FR) **Mr P. Bowden**
30 **PRINCESSE BASSETT**, b f Wootton Bassett—Mariposa (USA) **Free French 2**
31 **QUEEN OFTHEJUNGLE (IRE)**, b f Bungle Inthejungle—Campbellite **Miss Emily Asprey & Christopher Wright**
32 **RENEGADE MASTER**, b g Paco Boy (IRE)—Candle **G. E. Powell**

TWO-YEAR-OLDS
33 **CAPTAIN TATMAN (FR)**, b g 29/1 Olympic Glory (IRE)—Florida (FR) (King's Best (USA)) (14327) **Paul Bowden**
34 **DYAMI (FR)**, b br g 4/2 Bated Breath—Zaltana (USA) (Cherokee Run (USA)) (46354) **Mark & Lavinia Sherwood**
35 **FEAR NAUGHT**, b gr c 25/1 Brazen Beau (AUS)—Tanda Tula (IRE) (Alhaarth (IRE)) (47619) **Seaton Partnership**
36 B f 11/3 Al Kazeem—Pennard (FR) (High Chaparral (IRE)) (33712) **FTP Equine Holdings Ltd**
37 **POWER OF LOVE**, b g 7/3 Paco Boy (IRE)—A Legacy of Love (IRE) (Sea The Stars (IRE)) **Mrs Brenda Karn Smith**
38 B g 2/3 Rajsaman (FR)—Souvigny (FR) (Silver Rainbow) **FTP Equine Holdings Ltd**
39 **VICTOCHOP (FR)**, b g 15/3 Captain Chop (FR)—Ma Victoryan (FR) (Kheleyf (USA)) (18541) **Paul Bowden**

Other Owners: Simon Ackroyd, Julian Adams, Miss E. Asprey, Mrs C. E. S. Baker, Mr George Baker, Mr P. Bowden, Angela Bray, Carbine Club Of London, Mr W. H. Carson, Mrs E. Carson, Mr A. N. Cheyne, Tom Earl, Mr Richard Evans, Mrs R. S. Evans, Sir Alex Ferguson, Mr A. Flintoff, Mr Hugh Grant, Wayne Hennessey, Highclere Thoroughbred Racing Ltd, Miss L. Hurley, E. L. James, Camilla Johnson, Edward Johnson, Col Sandy Malcolm, Mr Mike McGeever, Mr O. J. W. Pawle, Mr Peter Russell, Mr I. Sharrock, Mr W. P. L. Smith, Earl Spencer, Mr J. A. B. Stafford, Mr Anthony Waters, Mr Michael Watt, Mr Christopher Wright.

Assistant Trainers: Patrick Murphy, Valerie Murphy

Jockey (flat): Pat Cosgrave, Liam Keniry. **Jockey (NH):** Andrew Tinkler.

16 MR ANDREW BALDING, Kingsclere

Postal: **Park House Stables, Kingsclere, Newbury, Berkshire, RG20 5PZ**
Contacts: **PHONE (01635) 298210 FAX (01635) 298305**
E-MAIL admin@kingsclere.com WEBSITE www.kingsclere.com

1 **ANGEL ISLINGTON (IRE)**, 4, gr f Dark Angel (IRE)—Doregan (IRE) **Mr A. Gemmell**
2 **BACACARAT (IRE)**, 4, b g Raven's Pass (USA)—Mathuna (IRE) **King Power Racing Co Ltd**
3 **BALLYQUIN (IRE)**, 4, b c Acclamation—Something Mon (USA) **Mr J. Palmer-Brown**
4 **BEAT THE BANK (IRE)**, 5, b g Paco Boy (IRE)—Tiana **King Power Racing Co Ltd**
5 **BELLE MEADE (IRE)**, 5, ch m Roderic O'Connor (IRE)—Hazardous **Dr Bridget Drew & Mr R. A. Farmiloe**
6 **BERKSHIRE BLUE (IRE)**, 4, b g Champs Elysees—Lemon Rock **Berkshire Parts & Panels Ltd**
7 **CALIBURN (IRE)**, 4, b c Camelot—Enchanted Evening (IRE) **M M Stables**
8 **CLEONTE (IRE)**, 6, ch g Sir Percy—Key Figure **King Power Racing Co Ltd**
9 **CONSULTANT**, 4, b g Kodiac—Mary Goodnight **Highclere Thoroughbred Racing-Ennis Hill**
10 **CROSSING THE LINE**, 4, br f Cape Cross (IRE)—Terentia **Sheikh J. D. Al Maktoum**
11 **DANCING STAR**, 6, b m Aqlaam—Strictly Dancing (IRE) **J. C. Smith**
12 **DANZAN (IRE)**, 4, b g Lawman (FR)—Charanga **Mr B. Greenwood/Mr R. Homburg & Partner**
13 **DIOCLETIAN (IRE)**, 4, b c Camelot—Saturday Girl **Mr R. J. C. Wilmot-Smith**
14 **DONJUAN TRIUMPHANT (IRE)**, 6, b h Dream Ahead—Mathuna (IRE) **King Power Racing Co Ltd**
15 **DREAM CATCHING (IRE)**, 4, b g Dream Ahead (USA)—Selfara **Mr M Payton & Mr A M Balding**
16 **FAIR COP**, 5, b m Exceed And Excel (AUS)—Speed Cop **J. C. Smith**
17 **FLINTROCK (GER)**, 4, br c Sinndar (IRE)—Four Roses (IRE) **Mr G. C. B. Brook**
18 **FOX MAFIA (IRE)**, 4, b c Dawn Approach (IRE)—Zibilene **King Power Racing Co Ltd**
19 **FOXTROT LADY**, 4, ch f Foxwedge (AUS)—Strictly Dancing (IRE) **J. C. Smith**
20 **GENETICS (FR)**, 5, b g Manduro (GER)—Garmerita (FR) **DJT Racing Partnership**
21 **HAVANA JANE**, 4, b f Havana Gold (IRE)—Le Badie **Farleigh Racing**
22 **HERE COMES WHEN (IRE)**, 9, br g Danehill Dancer (IRE)—Quad's Melody (IRE) **Mrs F. H. Hay**
23 **ICONIC GIRL**, 4, b f Cape Cross (IRE)—Snoqualmie Star **J. C. Smith**
24 **INTRANSIGENT**, 10, b g Trans Island—Mara River **Kingsclere Racing Club**
25 **ISOMER (USA)**, 5, ch g Cape Blanco (IRE)—Nimue (USA) **Mr A. M. Balding**
26 **LISSITZKY (IRE)**, 4, b g Declaration of War (USA)—Tarfshi **Mr N. D. Morris**
27 **LORELINA**, 6, b m Passing Glance—Diktalina **Mr Tim Wixted & Mr Tony Anderson**
28 **MAID UP**, 4, gr f Mastercraftsman (IRE)—Complexion **Brightwalton Bloodstock Limited**
29 **MAX ZORIN (IRE)**, 5, b g Cape Cross (IRE)—My Chelsea **Thoroughbreds - Pegasus**
30 **MIZUKI (IRE)**, 4, b f Sea The Stars (IRE)—Bright Snow (USA) **Mr S. Mistry**
31 **MONTALY**, 8, b g Yeats (IRE)—Le Badie (IRE) **Farleigh Racing**
32 **MORANDO (FR)**, 6, gr g Kendargent (FR)—Moranda (FR) **King Power Racing Co Ltd**
33 **MUST BE MAGIC (IRE)**, 4, b f Camelot—Saturn Girl (IRE) **M. Tabor**
34 **NATURAL HISTORY**, 4, b g Nathaniel (IRE)—Film Script **Her Majesty The Queen**
35 **OCALA**, 4, ch f Nathaniel (IRE)—Night Carnation **G. Strawbridge**
36 **PEGGY MINTER**, 4, b f Iffraaj—Miss Lacey (IRE) **Mr N. D. Morris**
37 **PERFECT ILLUSION**, 4, b g Nathaniel (IRE)—Chicita Banana **Mr & Mrs R Gorell/N Botica & Partner**
38 **PIVOINE (IRE)**, 5, b g Redoute's Choice (AUS)—Fleur de Cactus (IRE) **King Power Racing Co Ltd**
39 **SEASEARCH**, 4, b g Passing Glance—Seaflower Reef (IRE) **Kingsclere Racing Club**
40 **SHAILENE (IRE)**, 4, ch f Rip Van Winkle (IRE)—Snow Key (USA) **G. Strawbridge**
41 **SIMOON (IRE)**, 5, b g Sixties Icon—Astragal **Lord J. Blyth**
42 **STONE OF DESTINY**, 4, b g Acclamation—Irishstone (IRE) **King Power Racing Co Ltd**
43 **STRAIGHT RIGHT (FR)**, 5, b g Siyouni (FR)—Sailor Moon (IRE) **King Power Racing Co Ltd**
44 **WHITEFOUNTAINFAIRY (IRE)**, 4, ch f Casamento (IRE)—Groupetime (USA) **King Power Racing Co Ltd**
45 **WINGINGIT (IRE)**, 5, ch m Helmet (AUS)—Chirkova (USA) **Mrs B. M. Keller**
46 **YOUNG BERNIE**, 4, b g Sixties Icon—Hot Pursuits **Mr B McGuire & Partner**
47 **ZWAYYAN**, 6, ch g Pivotal—Mail The Desert (IRE) **King Power Racing Co Ltd**

THREE-YEAR-OLDS

48 **ADMIRALS BAY (GER)**, b g Mount Nelson—Astragal **Lord J. Blyth**
49 **AGENT BASTERFIELD (IRE)**, b c Raven's Pass (USA)—Maridiyna (IRE) **Mr Philip Fox & Partner**
50 **ALDENTE**, gr f Archipenko (USA)—Albacocca **Miss E. K. E. Rausing**
51 **BANGKOK (IRE)**, b c Australia—Tanaghum **King Power Racing Co Ltd**
52 **BAROSSA RED (IRE)**, ch g Tamayuz—I Hearyou Knocking (IRE) **Another Bottle Racing 2**
53 **BE MORE**, b f Shamardal (USA)—Pearl Dance (USA) **G. Strawbridge**
54 **BELL ROCK**, b c Kingman—Liberally (IRE) **Mrs F. H. Hay**
55 **BLOOD EAGLE (IRE)**, b c Sea The Stars (IRE)—Directa Princess (GER) **Mrs F. H. Hay**
56 **BOUTONNIERE (USA)**, b g Istan (USA)—Asscher Rose (USA) **Miss A. Nesser**
57 **BYE BYE HONG KONG (USA)**, b c Street Sense (USA)—Light And Variable (USA) **King Power Racing Co Ltd**
58 **BYE BYE LADY (FR)**, b f Sea The Stars (IRE)—Peinture Rose (USA) **King Power Racing Co Ltd**

MR ANDREW BALDING - Continued

59 **CALEDONIAN BELLE (IRE),** ch f Mastercraftsman (IRE)—Impressionist Art (USA) **Mrs F. H. Hay**
60 **CHIL CHIL,** b f Exceed And Excel (AUS)—Tiana **King Power Racing Co Ltd**
61 **COMPASS,** b g Henrythenavigator (USA)—Medley **Her Majesty The Queen**
62 **CONSTRAINT,** b f Sinndar (IRE)—Inhibition **Kingsclere Racing Club**
63 **DASHING WILLOUGHBY,** b c Nathaniel (IRE)—Miss Dashwood **Mick and Janice Mariscotti**
64 **DISCO DORIS,** b f Poet's Voice—Discophilia **Mrs P. I. Veenbaas**
65 **DOUNE CASTLE,** b c Camelot—Ape Attack **Mick and Janice Mariscotti**
66 **DUDLEY'S BOY,** b g Passing Glance—Lizzie Tudor **Ms K. Gough**
67 **DUTCH TREAT,** ch f Dutch Art—Syann (IRE) **Mildmay Racing & D. H. Caslon**
68 **EAGLE QUEEN,** ch f Dubawi (IRE)—Opera Gal **J. C. Smith**
69 **EDINBURGH CASTLE (IRE),** b c Sea The Stars (IRE)—Evensong (GER) **Mrs F. H. Hay**
70 **FIRE ISLAND,** b f Iffraaj—Pink Flames (IRE) **Qatar Racing Limited**
71 **FIRELIGHT (FR),** b f Oasis Dream—Freedom's Light **G. Strawbridge**
72 **FLASHCARD (IRE),** ch g Fast Company (IRE)—Portico **Kennet Valley Thoroughbreds II**
73 **FORSETI,** b g Charm Spirit (IRE)—Ravensburg **Mick and Janice Mariscotti**
74 **FOX CHAIRMAN (IRE),** b c Kingman—Starfish (IRE) **King Power Racing Co Ltd**
75 **FOX LEICESTER (IRE),** gr c Dark Angel (IRE)—Pop Art (IRE) **King Power Racing Co Ltd**
76 **FOX MORGAN,** b g Paco Boy—Alovera (IRE) **King Power Racing Co Ltd**
77 **FOX PREMIER (IRE),** b c Frankel—Fann (USA) **King Power Racing Co Ltd**
78 **FOX SHINJI,** b c Iffraaj—Keene Dancer **King Power Racing Co Ltd**
79 **FOX TAL,** b c Sea The Stars (IRE)—Maskunah (IRE) **King Power Racing Co Ltd**
80 **FOX WIN WIN (IRE),** ch c Lope de Vega (IRE)—What A Picture (FR) **King Power Racing Co Ltd**
81 **GALLATIN,** b f Kingman—Fantasia **G. Strawbridge**
82 **GEOMATRICIAN (FR),** b c Mastercraftsman (IRE)—Madonna Dell'orto **Mr D. E. Brownlow**
83 **GOOD BIRTHDAY (IRE),** b c Dabirsim (FR)—Chica Loca (FR) **King Power Racing Co Ltd**
84 **GRACE AND DANGER (IRE),** b f Teofilo (IRE)—Opinionated (IRE) **N M Watts/D Powell/Mrs I A Balding**
85 **HAPPY POWER (IRE),** gr c Dark Angel (IRE)—Tamarisk (GER) **King Power Racing Co Ltd**
86 **HAT YAI (IRE),** b c Garswood—Takizada (IRE) **King Power Racing Co Ltd**
87 **HAVANA ROCKET (IRE),** b c Havana Gold (IRE)—Mawaakeb (USA) **Rocket Racing**
88 **HERO HERO (IRE),** b c No Nay Never (USA)—Fancy (IRE) **King Power Racing Co Ltd**
89 **I'M AVAILABLE (IRE),** b f Nathaniel (IRE)—Night Carnation **G. Strawbridge**
90 **INCLYNE,** ch f Intello (GER)—Lady Brora **Kingsclere Racing Club**
91 **INDOMITABLE (IRE),** b g Invincible Spirit (IRE)—Mousse Au Chocolat (USA) **J. C. Smith**
92 **JOHNNY KIDD,** ch g Australia—Sabreon **Chelsea Thoroughbreds-shakin' All Over 1**
93 **KING POWER,** ch f Frankel—Prowess (IRE) **King Power Racing Co Ltd**
94 **LANDA BEACH (IRE),** b c Teofilo (IRE)—Jameela's Dream **Mr Philip Fox & Partner**
95 **LARIAT,** ch c Poet's Voice—Lasso **Mick and Janice Mariscotti**
96 **LAURA'S LEGACY,** b f Passing Glance—Rebecca Romero **Kingsclere Racing Club**
97 **LE DON DE VIE,** b g Leroidesanimaux (BRZ)—Leaderene **Mick and Janice Mariscotti**
98 **LOOK AROUND,** b f Kingman—Magic America (USA) **G. Strawbridge**
99 **LUCK OF CLOVER,** b f Phoenix Reach (IRE)—Diktalina **Mr Tim Wixted & Mr Tony Anderson**
100 **MAYNE (IRE),** b c Dansili—Pink Damsel (IRE) **Mrs F. H. Hay**
101 **MISTER FAWKES,** b c Phoenix Reach (IRE)—Sister Moonshine **M. J. Caddy**
102 **MUCHO TALENTO,** b c Intello (GER)—Moiava (FR) **Transatlantic Racing**
103 **MUNSTEAD MOONSHINE,** ch f Sir Percy—Royal Patron **Lady G. A. Brunton**
104 **NEVER DO NOTHING (IRE),** b g Casamento (IRE)—Purple Tigress **Mr A Brooke-Rankin & Partner**
105 **OLOROSO (IRE),** ch g Fast Company (IRE)—Convidada (IRE) **Roger Hetherington & Jeremy Carey**
106 **PARADISE BOY (FR),** ch c Mamool (IRE)—Palace Secret (GER) **Mr G. Rafferty**
107 **PASS THE GIN,** br f Passing Glance—Oasis Spirit **Kingsclere Racing Club**
108 **PATTAYA,** b f Poet's Voice—Talampaya (USA) **King Power Racing Co Ltd**
109 **PEMPIE (IRE),** ch f Lope de Vega (IRE)—Penelope Star (GER) **Thurloe Thoroughbreds XLV**
110 **PIPER ARROW,** b g War Command (USA)—Zeyran (IRE) **Mr D. E. Brownlow**
111 **POT LUCK,** b f Phoenix Reach (IRE)—Marajuana **Kingsclere Racing Club**
112 **PURDEY'S GIFT,** b c Camelot—Saphira's Fire (IRE) **Sheikh J. D. Al Maktoum**
113 **QUEEN'S SOLDIER (GER),** b g Soldier Hollow—Queen Mum (GER) **Martin & Valerie Slade**
114 **RAISE YOU (IRE),** ch c Lope de Vega (IRE)—Hikari (IRE) **Mr J. Palmer-Brown**
115 **RANCH HAND,** b g Dunaden (FR)—Victoria Montoya **Kingsclere Racing Club**
116 **RECTORY ROAD,** b g Paco Boy—Caerlonore (IRE) **Park House Partnership**
117 **RIVERFRONT (FR),** gr c Reliable Man—Why Worry (FR) **Mr L Register & Partner**
118 **RUX POWER,** b f Kingman—Cut Short (USA) **King Power Racing Co Ltd**
119 **SAWASDEE (IRE),** br c Shamardal (USA)—Beneventa **King Power Racing Co Ltd**
120 **SEA SCULPTURE,** b g Archipenko (USA)—Seaflower Reef (IRE) **Kingsclere Racing Club**
121 **SEEUSOON (IRE),** b c Sea The Moon (GER)—Village Fete **P. H. Betts**
122 **SHINE SO BRIGHT,** gr c Oasis Dream—Alla Speranza **King Power Racing Co Ltd**
123 **SNEAKY PEEK,** b f Nayef (USA)—Casual Glance **Kingsclere Racing Club**

MR ANDREW BALDING - Continued

124 **SPIRIT OF NICOBAR,** b f Dunaden (FR)—Sweet Mandolin **J. C. & S. R. Hitchins**
125 **SPIRIT WARNING,** b g Charm Spirit (IRE)—Averami **Kingsclere Racing Club**
126 **STAY FOREVER (FR),** br f Harbour Watch (IRE)—Stybba **Kingsclere Racing Club**
127 **STRICT TEMPO,** ch f Norse Dancer (IRE)—Strictly Dancing (IRE) **J. C. Smith**
128 **TOP POWER (FR),** ch c Le Havre (IRE)—Altamira **King Power Racing Co Ltd**
129 **TRIBAL CRAFT,** ch f Mastercraftsman (IRE)—Snoqualmie Star **J. C. Smith**
130 **TUK POWER,** b f Dubawi (IRE)—Soon (IRE) **King Power Racing Co Ltd**
131 **UNPLUGGED (IRE),** b c Alhebayeb (IRE)—Crown Light **Mr & Mrs R. M. Gorell**
132 **VAKILITA (IRE),** ch f Iffraaj—Vakiyla (FR) **Mrs C. J. Wates**
133 **WATCH AND LEARN,** b f Havana Gold (IRE)—Charlecote (IRE) **C. C. Buckley**
134 **WEDDING BLUE,** b c Kingman—Wedding Morn (IRE) **G. Strawbridge**
135 **YELLOW LABEL (USA),** br g Hat Trick (JPN)—Kazam (USA) **Mr L. L. Register**

TWO-YEAR-OLDS

136 Ch c 31/1 Zoffany (IRE)—Almost Always (IRE) (Galileo (IRE)) (37926)
137 **ANGEL GREY (IRE),** gr f 23/4 Gutaifan (IRE)—Violet's Gift (IRE) (Cadeaux Genereux) (38000) **Mr J. Maldonado**
138 B c 19/3 Archipenko (USA)—Avon Lady (Avonbridge) (12000) **Mr I. A. Balding**
139 B c 15/4 Acclamation—Bahati (IRE) (Intikhab (USA)) (78000) **Biddestone Racing**
140 Ch f 26/2 Roderic O'Connor (IRE)—Berkshire Beauty (Aqlaam) (5000) **Berkshire Parts & Panels Ltd**
141 B f 10/3 Swiss Spirit—Berkshire Honey (Sakhee's Secret) (5000) **Berkshire Parts & Panels Ltd**
142 **CADEAU D'OR (FR),** ch c 3/5 Le Havre (IRE)—Hill of Grace (Desert Prince (IRE)) (42000) **John & Anne Soul**
143 B f 15/4 Phoenix Reach (IRE)—Cape Victoria (Mount Nelson) **Kingsclere Racing Club**
144 B f 22/2 Passing Glance—Chesil Beach (Phoenix Reach (IRE)) (761) **Kingsclere Racing Club**
145 Ch c 22/1 Lope de Vega (IRE)—Childa (IRE) (Duke of Marmalade (IRE)) (220000) **PDR Properties**
146 **COMPENSATE,** b c 25/3 Sixties Icon—Hala Madrid (Nayef (USA)) **Mr N Watts & Mrs I A Balding**
147 B c 28/4 No Nay Never (USA)—Dark Missile (Night Shift (USA)) **Mr J. C. Smith**
148 **DUBAI STATION,** b c 19/2 Brazen Beau (AUS)—Princess Guest (IRE) (Iffraaj) (30000) **J. C. Smith**
149 **ELHAM VALLEY (FR),** gr c 22/2 Tin Horse (IRE)—
                          Dame du Floc (IRE) (Peintre Celebre (USA)) (10113) **Martin & Valerie Slade**
150 B c 1/5 Holy Roman Emperor (IRE)—Entre Nous (IRE) (Sadler's Wells (USA)) (35000) **Michaelson/Greenwood**
151 Ch f 8/5 Gio Ponti (USA)—Escape To Victory (Salse (USA)) (40033) **Mrs B. M. Keller**
152 B c 6/4 Dansili—Fantasia (Sadler's Wells (USA)) **Mr G. Strawbridge**
153 **FOX DUTY FREE (IRE),** b c 30/3 Kingman—Bugie d'amore (Rail Link) (280000) **King Power Racing Co Ltd**
154 Ch c 10/3 Starspangledbanner (AUS)—French Flirt (Peintre Celebre (USA)) (52000) **Sheikh J. D. Al Maktoum**
155 Ch c 3/4 New Approach (IRE)—Gainful (USA) (Gone West (USA)) (95000) **Mr Al Thani**
156 **GAME AND SET,** b f 11/2 Zoffany (IRE)—Grace And Favour (Montjeu) (IRE)) **Coln Valley Stud**
157 B f 5/5 Golden Horn—Gaze (Galileo (IRE)) (75000) **Mildmay Racing**
158 **GROUP ONE POWER,** b c 4/4 Lope de Vega (IRE)—
                          Lady Aquitaine (USA) (El Prado (IRE)) (90000) **King Power Racing Co Ltd**
159 **GROVE FERRY (IRE),** b c 7/3 Excelebration (IRE)—
                          Rebelline (IRE) (Robellino (USA)) (28571) **Martin & Valerie Slade**
160 **ISAAC MURPHY (FR),** b c 17/3 Makfi—Compose (Anabaa (USA)) **Mr R. J. C. Wilmot-Smith**
161 **KHALIFA SAT (IRE),** b c 24/3 Free Eagle (IRE)—Thermopylae (Tenby) (33712) **Ahmad Al Shaikh**
162 **KING'S LYNN,** b c 19/2 Cable Bay (IRE)—Kinematic (Kyllachy) **Her Majesty The Queen**
163 B c 20/2 Muhaarar—Kiyoshi (Dubawi (IRE)) **Qatar Racing Limited**
164 B c 24/4 Manduro (GER)—La Ville Lumiere (Rahy (USA)) (18541)
165 B f 16/4 Roderic O'Connor (IRE)—Lady Brora (Dashing Blade) **Kingsclere Racing Club**
166 Gr f 28/4 Kodiac—Lixirova (FR) (Slickly (FR)) **Mr G. Strawbridge**
167 B c 23/2 Kingman—Lochridge (Indian Ridge) **Mr J. C. Smith**
168 **MACHIOS,** b c 13/5 Maxios—Astragal (Shamardal (USA)) **Lord J. Blyth**
169 Ch c 23/4 Bated Breath—Masandra (IRE) (Desert Prince (IRE)) (31000)
170 B c 31/3 Iffraaj—Merry Me (IRE) (Invincible Spirit (IRE)) **Mrs F. H. Hay**
171 B c 2/3 Mayson—Moon Goddess (Rainbow Quest (USA)) (40000) **The Pink Hat Partnership**
172 B c 6/4 Nathaniel (IRE)—Mosqueras Romance (Rock of Gibraltar (IRE)) (190000) **King Power Racing Co Ltd**
173 B f 17/2 Gleneagles (IRE)—Mythie (FR) (Octagonal (NZ)) (69110) **Thurloe Thoroughbreds XLVIII**
174 B f 22/1 Camelot—Nyanza (GER) (Dai Jin) **Hunscote Stud**
175 Ch c 1/3 Zoffany (IRE)—One So Marvellous (Nashwan (USA)) (65000) **Mick and Janice Mariscotti**
176 B c 8/4 Nathaniel (IRE)—Opera Glass (Barathea (USA)) **Mr J. C. Smith**
177 Ch c 26/4 Lope de Vega (IRE)—Party (IRE) (Cadeaux Genereux) (50000) **PDR Properties**
178 Ch c 1/3 Sea The Moon (GER)—Pax Aeterna (USA) (War Front (USA)) (35000) **Mick and Janice Mariscotti**
179 B f 8/3 Al Kazeem—Perfect Delight (Dubai Destination (USA)) **Dr B Drew & Partners**
180 B f 25/3 Footstepsinthesand—Portico (Pivotal) (50568) **Kennet Valley T'Breds**
181 B c 12/2 Pivotal—Privacy Order (Azamour (IRE)) (90000) **Mr Al Thani**
182 B c 17/1 Mastercraftsman (IRE)—Promise Me (IRE) (Montjeu (IRE)) (50000) **Mick & Janice Mariscotti**
183 **PUNCTUATION,** b c 7/5 Dansili—Key Point (IRE) (Galileo (IRE)) **Her Majesty The Queen**

MR ANDREW BALDING - Continued

184 Br c 2/2 Lawman (FR)—Quads (IRE) (Shamardal (USA)) (42140) **Mrs F. H. Hay**
185 B g 5/3 Nayef (USA)—Rebecca Romero (Exceed And Excel (AUS)) **Kingsclere Racing Club**
186 RICK BLAINE (IRE), b c 18/3 Ruler Of The World (IRE)—
                                  Saturday Girl (Peintre Celebre (USA)) (17699) **Chelsea Thoroughbreds**
187 B f 5/3 Fastnet Rock (AUS)—Rohain (IRE) (Singspiel (IRE)) **Mildmay Racing**
188 SHADN (IRE), b f 5/4 No Nay Never (USA)—Amethyst (IRE) (Sadler's Wells (USA)) (40000) **Al Rabban Racing**
189 Ch c 23/4 Tamayuz—Solandia (IRE) (Teofilo (IRE)) (55000) **Another Bottle Racing**
190 SPANISH ANGEL (IRE), br c 14/4 Gutaifan (IRE)—
                                    City Dazzler (IRE) (Elusive City (USA)) (16856) **Mr J. Maldonado**
191 STRATACASTER, b c 19/2 Oasis Dream—Deuce Again (Dubawi (IRE)) (70000) **Castle Down Racing**
192 B f 20/2 Australia—Strictly Dancing (IRE) (Danehill Dancer (IRE)) **Mr J. C. Smith**
193 B f 24/2 Charm Spirit (IRE)—Stybba (Medicean) **Qatar Racing Limited**
194 Ch c 6/2 Sir Percy—Sunny Again (Shirocco (GER)) (42140) **Berkshire Parts & Panels Ltd**
195 B f 9/2 Invincible Spirit (IRE)—Sweepstake (IRE) (Acclamation) (160000) **Sheikh J. D. Al Maktoum**
196 B f 27/4 Mount Nelson—Sweet Mandolin (Soviet Star (USA)) **Messrs J. C. & S. R. Hitchins**
197 B br c 7/4 Kitten's Joy (USA)—Sweeter Still (IRE) (Rock of Gibraltar (IRE)) (63492) **Qatar Racing Limited**
198 THAI POWER (IRE), b c 22/3 Kingman—Roscoff (IRE) (Daylami (IRE)) (425000) **King Power Racing Co Ltd**
199 B c 18/1 Zoffany (IRE)—Thought Is Free (Cadeaux Genereux) **Mrs F. H. Hay**
200 B f 8/3 Showcasing—Tiana (Diktat) (140000) **Sheikh J. D. Al Maktoum**
201 Ch c 17/3 Lope de Vega (IRE)—Via Milano (FR) (Singspiel (IRE)) **PDR Properties**
202 B f 5/3 Australia—Weeping Wind (Oratorio (IRE)) **Rifa Mustang Pty Ltd**
203 B c 29/3 Mukhadram—Zubova (Dubawi (IRE)) (18000) **Berkshire Parts & Panels Ltd**

Other Owners: Mr H. A. Al Jehani, Mr A. A. Al Shaikh, Mr A. K. M. K. Al-Rabban, Mr M. Almutairi, Mr M. Almutairi, Mr A. W. Anderson, Another Bottle Racing, Mr I. A. Balding, Mrs I. A. Balding, Mr A. M. Balding, Mr A. Black, Mrs J. E. Black, Mr N. Botica, Mr John Bridgman, Mr A. Brooke Rankin, His Honour Judge J. Carey, Mr D. H. Caslon, Chelsea Thoroughbreds - Shakin' All Over, Chelsea Thoroughbreds Ltd, Mrs G. Cullen, Mr Peter Done, Dr Bridget Drew & Partners, Mr N. R. R. Drew, Miss Pippa Drew, Dr Bridget Drew, Mr R. A. Farmiloe, Mr P. E. Felton, Sir Alex Ferguson, Mr Philip Fox, Mrs W. Gorell, Mr & Mrs R. M. Gorell, Mr R. Gorell, Mr B. Greenwood, Mr N. G. R. Harris, Mr P. G. Hazell, Mr R. R. Hetherington, Highclere Nominated Partner Limited, Highclere Thoroughbred Racing Ltd, Mr S. Hill, Mr J. C. Hitchins, Mr S. R. Hitchins, Lady Hobhouse, Sir C. J. S. Hobhouse, Mr Roy Homburg, Mr R. S. Hoskins, G. R. Ireland, Mrs E. A. Ireland, Mrs Julia Lukas, Mrs Janice Mariscotti, Mr Mick Mariscotti, Mr Ged Mason, Mr B. P McGuire, Mildmay Racing, Mrs Terry Miller, Mr O. J. W. Pawle, Mr Michael Payton, Mr David F. Powell, Mr T. J. Ramsden, Mr L. L. Register, Mrs V. J. M. Slade, Mr D. M. Slade, Mr M. Smith (Leicester), Mrs A. R. Soul, Mr J. O. Soul, Mr J. A. B. Stafford, Mr N. M. Watts, Mr T. P. Wixted.

Assistant Trainer: Nigel Walker

Jockey (flat): David Probert, Jason Watson, Rob Hornby, Oisin Murphy. **Apprentice:** Josh Bryan, William Carver, William Cox, Kayleigh Stephens.

MR JOHN BALDING, Doncaster
Postal: **Mayflower Stables, Saracens Lane, Scrooby, Doncaster, South Yorkshire, DN10 6AS**
Contacts: **HOME (01302) 710096 FAX (01302) 710096 MOBILE (07816) 612631**
E-MAIL j.balding@btconnect.com

1 FORTINBRASS (IRE), 9, b g Baltic King—Greta d'argent (IRE) **Mr W. Herring**
2 GEMBARI, 4, b g Denounce—Zagarock **Mr R. Hull**
3 NATIONAL ANTHEM, 4, ch c Intikhab (USA)—Song of Passion (IRE) **Mr M. Mckay**
4 ORIENTAL RELATION (IRE), 8, gr g Tagula (IRE)—Rofan (USA) **Neil Grantham & David Bichan**
5 RAZIN' HELL, 8, b g Byron—Loose Caboose (IRE) **Timms, Timms & McCabe**
6 SHOWBOATING (IRE), 11, b g Shamardal (USA)—Sadinga (IRE) **Mr M & Mrs L Cooke & Mr A McCabe**
7 SIEGE OF BOSTON (IRE), 6, ch g Starspangledbanner (AUS)—Milton of Campsie **Mr M. Mckay**
8 UNDERCOVER BROTHER, 4, ch g Captain Gerrard (IRE)—Socceroo **Mr J. M. Lacey**
9 YOU'RE COOL, 7, b g Exceed And Excel (AUS)—Ja One (IRE) **Mr D Bichan & Mr F Connor**

Other Owners: Mr David Bichan, Mr D. Bichan, Mr F. S. Connor, Mr M. Cooke, Mr K. N. Grantham, Mr A. J. McCabe, Mr Matthew Timms, Mr A. C. Timms.

Assistant Trainers: Claire Edmunds, Jason Edmunds

Jockey (flat): Lewis Edmunds. **Apprentice:** Izzy Clifton.

18 MR RICHARD J. BANDEY, Tadley
Postal: **Plantation House, Wolverton, Tadley, Hampshire, RG26 5RP**
Contacts: **PHONE (01635) 298963**

1 BASTANTE (FR), 8, b m Khalkevi (IRE)—Pocahontas (FR) **The Plantation Prosecco Partnership**
2 BOLLIN BANKSY, 4, b c Bollin Eric—Royal Eberspacher (IRE)
3 BUCK'S BEAUTIFUL (FR), 5, ch m Maresca Sorrento (FR)—Buck's Beauty (FR) **Mr R. J. Bandey**
4 ELSKA, 7, b m Norse Dancer (IRE)—Alska (FR) **Mr R. J. Bandey**
5 EYESOPENWIDEAWAKE (IRE), 8, b g Stowaway—Namesake **The King's Men**
6 FIRST ASSEMBLY (IRE), 5, b g Arcadio (GER)—Presenting Katie (IRE) **Mr S. R. Cross**
7 HARD STATION (IRE), 10, b g Bandari—Vinecroft (IRE) **Mr & Mrs T O'Donohoe**
8 SURYA (FR), 4, b f Mount Nelson—Salute The Sun (FR)
9 THE BOOGIEMAN, 5, b g Delegator—Great Quest (IRE) **Headdock & Bandey**

Other Owners: R. B. Denny, Mr A. Headdock, Mr T. L. O'Donohoe, Mrs E. E. O'Donohoe, E. J. Saunders.

19 MR JACK BARBER, Crewkerne
Postal: **Higher Peckmoor, Henley, Crewkerne, Somerset, TA18 8FF**
Contacts: **PHONE (01460) 76555 MOBILE (07904) 185720**
E-MAIL info@jackbarberracing.co.uk WEBSITE www.jackbarberracing.co.uk

1 AMZAC MAGIC, 7, b g Milan—Queen's Banquet **A. A. Hayward**
2 ASK THE WEATHERMAN, 10, b g Tamure (IRE)—Whatagale **Mr David Martin & Mr Paul Barber**
3 BALLYKNOCK CLOUD (IRE), 8, gr g Cloudings (IRE)—Ballyknock Present (IRE) **Ballyknock Cloud Syndicate**
4 DARCY WARD (FR), 6, b g Doctor Dino (FR)—Alzasca (FR) **Phil Fry & Charlie Walker**
5 DOYANNIE (IRE), 5, ch m Doyen (IRE)—Annie May (IRE) **R. Barber**
6 EARTH SPIRIT, 6, b g Black Sam Bellamy—Samandara (FR) **Mrs C. E. Penny**
7 GULSHANIGANS, 7, b g Sakhee (USA)—Gulshan **Barber, French, Newton & Wright**
8 JIMAL MAGIC (FR), 5, b g Irish Wells (FR)—Night Cire (FR) **T.Hayward & Osborne House Partners**
9 KING CALVIN (IRE), 7, b g King's Theatre (IRE)—Lerichi (IRE) **P. L. Hart**
10 L'CHAMISE, 6, b m Apple Tree (FR)—Colline de Fleurs **DASH Racing**
11 LAMANVER BEL AMI, 5, b g Black Sam Bellamy (IRE)—Lamanver Homerun **Dr D. Christensen**
12 LAMANVER ODYSSEY, 7, b m Lucarno (USA)—Lamanver Homerun **Dr D. Christensen**
13 4, Ch g Mahler—Letthisbetheone (IRE)
14 LINE OF BEAUTY, 5, b m Helmet (AUS)—Bisou **Mrs Rebecca Philipps & John Troy**
15 5, B m Shirocco (GER)—Mew Gull **Lady N. F. Cobham**
16 MOVIE THEATRE, 7, b g Multiplex—Tintera (IRE) **The Movie Theatre Syndicate**
17 4, B g Black Sam Bellamy (IRE)—One Wild Night **Tony Hayward & Jack Barber**
18 POSH TOTTY, 12, ch m Midnight Legend—Well Bred **Barber, Hall, James & Slocombe**
19 REBEL COMMANDER (IRE), 7, b g Flemensfirth (USA)—Pharney Fox (IRE) **Mr J. Barber**
20 REDMOND (IRE), 9, b g Tikkanen (USA)—Medal Quest (FR) **Walters, Bennett, Martin & Higgs**
21 4, B f Malinas (GER)—Samandara (FR)
22 SHINTORI (FR), 7, b g Enrique—La Masai (FR) **Mrs R. E. Vicary**
23 SMART BOY (IRE), 8, b g Mahler—Supreme Style (IRE) **Mr P. C. Barfoot**
24 THREE IN ONE (IRE), 7, b g Court Cave (IRE)—Star Bui (IRE) **Wessex Racing Club**
25 VARDS, 9, b g Tamure (IRE)—Bank On Lady **R. Barber**
26 WHAT'LLBEWILLBE (IRE), 5, b g Mahler—Letterwoman (IRE) **Mr J. Barber**

Other Owners: P. K. Barber, Mr J. J. Barber, Mr D. Bear, Mr D. Bennett, Mr J. F. Blackburn, Mr S. M. Couling, R. P. Fry, Mrs S. J. Higgs, Mr D. J. Martin, Mrs G. R. Martin, Mrs R. Philipps, Mr J. M. Troy, C. C. Walker, Mr P. E. Walters.

20 MRS STELLA BARCLAY, Garstang
Postal: **Lancashire Racing Stables, The Paddocks, Strickens Lane, Barnacre, Garstang, Lancashire, PR3 1UD**
Contacts: **PHONE (01995) 605790 MOBILE (07802) 764094**
E-MAIL paul@lancashireracingstables.co.uk

1 BERTILATETHANNEVER, 7, b g Bertolini (USA)—Monica Geller **Betty's Brigade**
2 BIGDABOG, 4, b g Sayif (IRE)—Alice's Girl **Mr P. S. McGuire**
3 BINGO CONTI (IRE), 8, b g Coastal Path—Regina Conti (FR) **The Four Aces**
4 DEOLALI, 5, b g Sleeping Indian—Dulally **The Bounty Hunters**
5 FEARAUN (IRE), 4, b g Arakan (USA)—Brosna Time (IRE) **Mr K. J. Dodd**
6 FREE RANGE (IRE), 9, b g Subtle Power (IRE)—Tullyspark Rose (IRE) **Winks Racing**

MRS STELLA BARCLAY - Continued

7 **HOW MUCH IS ENOUGH (IRE)**, 8, b m Moon Ballet (IRE)—Silankka **Network Racing**
8 **LATE FOR THE SKY**, 5, b m Shirocco (GER)—China Lily (USA) **Mr P. J. Metcalfe**
9 **LITTLE STEVIE**, 7, b g Overbury (IRE)—Candy's Room (IRE) **Mr K. J. Dodd**
10 **MANSFIELD**, 6, b g Exceed And Excel (AUS)—Jane Austen (IRE) **The Style Council**
11 **MARIETTA ROBUSTI (IRE)**, 4, b f Equiano (FR)—La Tintoretta (IRE) **Messrs Chrimes, Winn & Wilson**
12 **MELABI (IRE)**, 6, b g Oasis Dream—Briolette (IRE) **J. H. Chrimes**
13 **MELANNA (IRE)**, 8, b m Camacho—Colour's Red (IRE) **Brandsby Racing**
14 **MISSESGEEJAY**, 9, br m Beat All (USA)—Riverbank Rainbow **The Coz Syndicate**
15 **MOONBI CREEK (IRE)**, 12, b g Fasliyev (USA)—Moonbi Range (IRE) **The Cataractonium Racing Syndicate**
16 **NICKY NOOK**, 6, b m Captain Gerrard (IRE)—Rose Bounty **Leslie Buckley & Stella Barclay**
17 **ONDA DISTRICT (IRE)**, 7, b g Oasis Dream—Leocorno (IRE) **Messrs Chrimes, Winn & Wilson**
18 **PRINCE OF TIME**, 7, ch g Bahamian Bounty—Touching (IRE) **Mr B. Hartley**
19 **SEVILLA**, 6, b m Duke of Marmalade (IRE)—Glittering Prize (UAE) **The Haydock Badgeholders**
20 **STREPITANT**, 6, b g Dubawi (IRE)—Shawanda (IRE) **Mrs S. E. Barclay**
21 **TEN TREES**, 9, b m Millkom—Island Path (IRE) **The Most Wanted Partnership**
22 **WEDDING BREAKFAST (IRE)**, 5, ch m Casamento (IRE)—Fair Countenance (IRE) **J. H. Chrimes**

THREE-YEAR-OLDS

23 B f Doncaster Rover (USA)—Awaywithefairies **Mr P. J. Metcalfe**
24 **LITTLE THORNTON**, b f Swiss Spirit—Lee Miller (IRE) **CCCNLP**
25 **SHARRABANG**, b g Coach House—Dulally **The Bounty Hunters**

TWO-YEAR-OLDS

26 B gr f 21/5 Hellvelyn—Aiaam Al Wafa (IRE) (Authorized (IRE)) **Betty's Brigade**
27 **ANNIEMATION (IRE)**, b c 3/3 Acclamation—Cafetiere (Iffraaj) (15238) **Mr W. Buckley**
28 **BELLE VOCI**, gr f 9/2 Hellvelyn—Oricano (Arcano (IRE)) **Stella Barclay**
29 B f 25/4 Coach House (IRE)—Ella Rosie (Dubai Destination (USA)) **Lancashire Racing Stables Ltd**
30 Gr f 13/1 Hellvelyn—Sambarina (IRE) (Victory Note (USA)) **Paul Clarkson**

Other Owners: Mr B. Aspinall, Mrs L. Buckley, Mr J. Calderbank, Mr P. M. Clarkson, Mr M. Watkinson, J. M. Winn.

---

21 MRS TRACEY BARFOOT-SAUNT, Wotton-under-Edge
Postal: Cosy Farm, Huntingford, Charfield, Wotton-under-Edge, Gloucestershire, GL12 8EY
Contacts: **PHONE** (01453) 520312 **FAX** (01453) 520312 **MOBILE** (07976) 360626

1 **DODDINGTON DI**, 7, b g Sulamani (IRE)—Maxilla (IRE) **A Good Days Racing**
2 **GAME IN THE PARK (FR)**, 6, b g Walk In The Park (IRE)—Learning Game (USA) **P. J. Ponting**
3 **HERE COMES MOLLY (IRE)**, 8, ch m Stowaway—Grange Melody (IRE) **Mrs T. M. Barfoot-Saunt**
4 **HOLEINTHEWALL BAR (IRE)**, 11, b g Westerner—Cockpit Lady (IRE) **Mrs T. M. Barfoot-Saunt**
5 **ICONIC IMAGE (IRE)**, 10, b g Kayf Tara—Fontaine Jewel (IRE) **Mr G. C. Barfoot-Saunt**
6 **MUTASHABEK (USA)**, 9, b g Arch (USA)—Siyadah (USA) **P. J. Ponting**
7 **ZOUCH**, 4, b g Sakhee's Secret—Sabrina Brown **P. J. Ponting**

---

22 MR MAURICE BARNES, Brampton
Postal: Tarnside, Farlam, Brampton, Cumbria, CA8 1LA
Contacts: **PHONE** (01697) 746675 **MOBILE** (07760) 433191
E-MAIL anne.barnes1@btinternet.com

1 **APACHE PILOT**, 11, br g Indian Danehill (IRE)—Anniejo **Mr M. A. Barnes**
2 **BAFANA BLUE**, 8, b g Blueprint (IRE)—Anniejo **Hogarth, Morris & Percival Racing**
3 **BARNEY'S CAULKER**, 8, b g Captain Gerrard (IRE)—Little Cascade **Mr M. A. Barnes**
4 **CARRIGDHOUN (IRE)**, 14, gr g Goldmark (USA)—Pet Tomjammar (IRE) **Mr M. A. Barnes**
5 **DESERT ISLAND DUSK**, 8, b g Superior Premium—Desert Island Disc **Miss A. P. Lee**
6 **FARLAM KING**, 6, b g Crosspeace (IRE)—Second Bite **Castle Racing & Partner**
7 **FAROCCO (GER)**, 6, b g Shirocco (GER)—Fantasmatic (GER) **Miss A. P. Lee**
8 **FISHER GREEN (IRE)**, 6, b g Rip Van Winkle (IRE)—Prealpina (IRE) **D. Carr**
9 **FLYING JACK**, 9, b g Rob Roy (USA)—Milladella (FR) **The 3 Whisperers**
10 **HOPE FOR GLORY**, 10, b g Proclamation (IRE)—Aissa **Mr M. A. Barnes**
11 **ITSNOTYOUITSME**, 6, b g Milan—Brochrua (IRE) **J. Wade**
12 **KNOCKOURA (IRE)**, 7, b g Westerner—Lisselton Thatch (IRE) **The Edinburgh Woollen Mill Ltd**
13 5, B m Fair Mix (IRE)—Lady Sambury **Mr J. Wills**

MR MAURICE BARNES - Continued

14 4, B f Malinas (GER)—Lady Sambury **Mr J. Wills**
15 LOULOUMILLS, 9, b m Rob Roy (USA)—Etching (USA) **Mr G. R. S. Nixon & Mr M. Barnes**
16 NO SUCH NUMBER, 11, b g King's Best (USA)—Return (USA) **Miss Hazel Crichton**
17 OH NO, 7, b g Indian Danehill (IRE)—See My Girl **Mr J. Duckworth**
18 OISHIN, 7, b g Paco Boy (IRE)—Roshina (IRE) **Ring Of Fire & Partner**
19 PLACEDELA CONCORDE, 6, b g Champs Elysees—Kasakiya (IRE) **Hogarth, Morris & Percival Racing**
20 QUICK BREW, 11, b g Denounce—Darjeeling (IRE) **The Wizards**
21 REGARDE MOI, 11, b g King's Best (USA)—Life At Night (IRE) **Mr M. A. Barnes**
22 ROLLERRULER, 5, b g Native Ruler—Roll Over Rose (IRE) **Mr R. W. Powell**
23 SMART PACO, 5, ch g Paco Boy (IRE)—La Gifted **Mr M. A. Barnes**
24 SPINNING SCOOTER, 9, b g Sleeping Indian—Spinning Coin **Miss Hazel Crichton & Partner**
25 TOP CAT DJ (IRE), 11, ch g St Jovite (USA)—Lady Coldunell **Miss A. P. Lee**
26 TRYNWYN, 9, b m Grape Tree Road—Brass Buckle (IRE) **Miss A. P. Lee**

THREE-YEAR-OLDS

27 DAPPER DAISY, ch f Dapper—Overpriced **Mr M. A. Barnes**

TWO-YEAR-OLDS

28 DAPPER GENT, b g 26/5 Dapper—Overpriced (Chocolat de Meguro (USA)) **Mr M. A. Barnes**

Other Owners: Mr M. Barnes, Castle Racing, Mr J. G. Graham, Mr Keith Greenwell, Mr G. R. Hogarth, Mr S. J. Houliston, Mr S. G. Johnston, Mr Richard Lane, Mr A J Morris, Mr Steven Nightingale, Mr G. R. S. Nixon, Mr N. North, Mr V. A. Percival, Ring Of Fire, Mr R. Towler, The Whisperers.

Conditional: Dale Irving.

---

23   MR BRIAN BARR, Sherborne
Postal: **Tall Trees Stud, Longburton, Sherborne, Dorset, DT9 5PH**
Contacts: **PHONE (01963) 210173 MOBILE (07826) 867881**
E-MAIL **brianbarrracing@hotmail.com** WEBSITE **www.brianbarrracing.co.uk**
Twitter: **@brianbarrracing**

1 ARCHIE (IRE), 7, b g Fast Company (IRE)—Winnifred **Inspire Racing**
2 BABBLING STREAM, 8, b g Authorized (IRE)—Elasouna (IRE) **Recommended Freight Ltd & Trade Trux**
3 BLACK ANTHEM (IRE), 7, b g Royal Anthem (USA)—
                                 Rockababy (IRE) **The Highly Recommended Partnership 3**
4 BLAINE, 9, ch g Avonbridge—Lauren Louise **Mr G. Hitchins**
5 BONNE NUIT, 4, b g Arvico (FR)—Frosted Grape (IRE) **Miss T. R. Johnson**
6 CALL SIGN CHARLIE, 5, gr m Arakan (USA)—Ardea Brave (IRE) **Inspire Racing Club Ltd**
7 CHARLIE PAPA LIMA (IRE), 8, b g Winged Love (IRE)—Fairylodge Scarlet (IRE) **SMLC Racing**
8 CLONDAW WHISPER (IRE), 6, b g Court Cave (IRE)—Whispering (IRE) **Inspire Racing**
9 HOKE COLBURN (IRE), 7, b g Beneficial—Ravaleen (IRE) **Miss D. Hitchins**
10 IOWEU, 6, br m Cockney Rebel (IRE)—Doliouchka (USA) **Mr G. Hitchins**
11 JOHNI BOXIT, 4, ch g Sakhee's Secret—Pink Supreme **Brian Barr Racing Club**
12 KABOOBEE, 4, ch g Pastoral Pursuits—Crossbow **James Barnard & Daisy Hitchins**
13 KAHDIAN (IRE), 9, br g Rock of Gibraltar (IRE)—Katiykha (IRE) **Mr G. Hitchins**
14 MAJORETTE, 5, ch m Major Cadeaux—So Discreet **Chris Clark & Daisy Hitchins**
15 MIGHTY MISSILE (IRE), 8, ch g Majestic Missile (IRE)—Magdalene (FR) **Daisy Hitchins & Neil Budden**
16 NANNY MAKFI, 6, b m Makfi—Pan Galactic (USA) **Chris Clark**
17 5, Ch m Sans Frontieres (IRE)—Parkality (IRE) **Mr I. Allison**
18 PAS DE BLANC, 4, b f Major Cadeaux—Mancunian Way **Mr A. Kirkham**
19 ROBIN DE BROOME (IRE), 7, b g Robin des Pres (IRE)—Croghan Lass (IRE) **Inspire Racing Club Ltd**
20 STORM FIRE, 6, b g Fair Mix—Tara Gale **Mr I. Allison**
21 TOOLATETODELEGATE, 5, b m Delegator—Little Caroline (IRE) **Inspire Racing Club & Partner**
22 TRISTAN DE GANE (FR), 4, bl g Sinndar (IRE)—Adamise (FR) **Mr G. Hitchins**

THREE-YEAR-OLDS

23 HAATS OFF, ch f Haafet (USA)—Lahqa (IRE) **Inspire Racing Club Ltd**
24 MERITABLE, b f Nathaniel (IRE)—Dream Wild
25 UPSIDE, b f Showcasing—Milford Sound

MR BRIAN BARR - Continued

TWO-YEAR-OLDS
26 Bl f 26/3 Mukhadram—Dusting (IRE) (Acclamation) (4500)
27 B f 8/2 Black Sam Bellamy (IRE)—Frosted Grape (IRE) (Kheleyf (USA)) (1904) **Brian Barr**
28 B g 15/3 Hallowed Crown (AUS)—Peaceful Soul (USA) (Dynaformer) (4500)
29 B c 5/3 Gale Force Ten—Sabaidee (IRE) (Beat Hollow) (1000) **Inspire Racing**
30 B f 14/4 Due Diligence (USA)—Three Ducks (Diktat) (1500)

Other Owners: Mr James Barnard, Mr Neil Budden, Mr Chris J. Clark, Miss Daisy Hitchins, Mrs Katrina Hitchins, Mr Chris Keey, Recommended Freight Ltd, Mr D. J. Rogers, Tradetrux Ltd.

Assistant Trainer: Daisy Hitchins (07975) 754622

Conditional: Jonjo O'Neill. **Amateur:** Mr S Wood.

---

24 MR RON BARR, Middlesbrough
Postal: **Carr House Farm, Seamer, Stokesley, Middlesbrough, Cleveland, TS9 5LL**
Contacts: **PHONE (01642) 710687 MOBILE (07711) 895309**
E-MAIL christinebarr1@aol.com

1 DOMINANNIE (IRE), 6, b m Paco Boy (IRE)—English Rose (USA) **Mrs V. G. Davies**
2 GO BANANAS, 4, b f Bahamian Bounty—Ribbon Royale **Mrs C. Barr**
3 GRACEFUL ACT, 11, b m Royal Applause—Minnina (IRE) **Mr D. Thomson & Mrs R. E. Barr**
4 MIDNIGHT WARRIOR, 4, b g Teofilo (IRE)—Mauri Moon **Mr K. Trimble**
5 MIGHTASWELLSMILE, 5, b m Elnadim (USA)—Intishaar (IRE) **Mr K. Trimble**
6 MITCHUM, 10, b g Elnadim (USA)—Maid To Matter **R. E. Barr**
7 PEARL'S CALLING (IRE), 4, ch f Dandy Man (IRE)—Celtic Heroine (IRE) **Mrs V. G. Davies**

Other Owners: Mrs R. E. Barr, M. Bell, P Cartmell, D. Chadwick, Mr D. Thomson, K. Trimble, Z. Tuck.

Assistant Trainer: Mrs C. Barr

Amateur: Miss V. Barr.

---

25 MR DAVID BARRON, Thirsk
Postal: **Maunby House, Maunby, Thirsk, North Yorkshire, YO7 4HD**
Contacts: **PHONE (01845) 587435 FAX (01845) 587331**
E-MAIL david.barron@maunbyhouse.com

1 ABOVE THE REST (IRE), 8, b g Excellent Art—Aspasias Tizzy (USA) **L. G. O'Kane**
2 BERTIEWHITTLE, 11, ch g Bahamian Bounty—Minette **JKB Racing & Partners 2**
3 BLACK SALT, 5, b g Equiano (FR)—Marine Girl **All About York II & Partner**
4 CARPET TIME (IRE), 4, b g Intense Focus (USA)—Beal Ban (IRE) **Mr J Knotts & Partner**
5 CLON COULIS (IRE), 5, b m Vale of York (IRE)—Cloneden (IRE) **Ms Colette Twomey**
6 ESPRIT DE CORPS, 5, b g Sepoy (AUS)—Corps de Ballet (IRE) **L. G. O'Kane**
7 FAKE NEWS, 4, b g Paco Boy (IRE)—Day Creek **Dr N. J. Barron**
8 FAST TRACK, 8, b g Rail Link—Silca Boo **Mrs S. C. Barron**
9 GUNMETAL (IRE), 6, gr g Clodovil (IRE)—March Star (IRE) **Ne-chance & Mr L O' Kane**
10 KODI BEACH, 4, b g Kodiac—Annie Beach (IRE) **Mrs S. C. Barron**
11 KRIPKE (IRE), 4, b g Fast Company (IRE)—Tranquil Sky **Mrs S. C. Barron**
12 KYNREN (IRE), 5, b g Clodovil (IRE)—Art of Gold **Elliott Brothers & Peacock & Partner**
13 MAGICAL MOLLY JOE, 5, b m Arabian Gleam—Magical Music **Mr Lee Woolams & Partner**
14 MAMA AFRICA (IRE), 5, b m Big Bad Bob (IRE)—
Colourpoint (USA) **Mrm.Rozenbroek/Harrowgatebloodstockltd**
15 MR COCO BEAN (USA), 5, b g Gio Ponti (USA)—Ing Ing (FR) **Mr S. G. Raines**
16 POET'S PRIDE, 4, b g Arcano (IRE)—Amber Heights **Mrlaurenceo'Kane/Harrowgatebloodstockltd**
17 RECKLESS ENDEAVOUR (IRE), 6, b g Kodiac—Red Fanfare **Ne-chance & Mr L O' Kane**
18 SWIFT EMPEROR (IRE), 7, b g Holy Roman Emperor (IRE)—Big Swifty (IRE) **Mr David Ellis & Partner**
19 VENTUROUS (IRE), 6, ch g Raven's Pass (USA)—Bold Desire **Mrlaurenceo'Kane/Harrowgatebloodstockltd**
20 WILLYTHECONQUEROR (IRE), 6, b g Kodiac—Jazzie (FR) **Ne-chance & Mr L O' Kane**

THREE-YEAR-OLDS
21 Ch g Harbour Watch (IRE)—Annie Beach (IRE) **Mrs S. C. Barron**
22 CARAMEL CURVES, b f Mayson—Shannon Spree **Harrowgate Bloodstock Ltd**
23 B br f Bated Breath—Dee Dee Girl (IRE) **Dr N. J. Barron**

MR DAVID BARRON - Continued

24 **FORT BENTON (IRE)**, b g Big Bad Bob (IRE)—Pira Palace (IRE) **Dr N. J. Barron**
25 **FROSTED LASS**, gr f Zebedee—Jofranka **Mrs Anne Atkinson & Partner**
26 **GIFTED ZEBEDEE (IRE)**, b g Zebedee—Zakyah **Harrowgate Bloodstock Ltd**
27 **HARRIBO**, b c Farhh—Polly Adler **Mr A. C. Cook**
28 Gr g Worthadd (IRE)—Lady Georgina **Dr N. J. Barron**
29 **LOFTY**, b g Harbour Watch (IRE)—Curly Come Home **Mrh.D.Atkinson/Harrowgatebloodstockltd**
30 **MARTHA MCEWAN (IRE)**, b f Lilbourne Lad (IRE)—Ever Evolving (FR) **Mr P. Toes**
31 **OLIVIA R (IRE)**, ch f Excelebration (IRE)—Rozene (IRE) **Mr M. J. Rozenbroek**
32 **OLYMPIC SPIRIT**, ch g Olympic Glory (IRE)—Magic Florence (IRE) **Mr H. D. Atkinson**
33 **PARADISE PAPERS**, b f Lethal Force (IRE)—Day Creek **Dr N. J. Barron**
34 **PETITE MAGICIAN (IRE)**, b f Requinto (IRE)—Personal Design (IRE) **D G Pryde & D Van Der Hoeven**
35 B f Harbour Watch (IRE)—Red Shareef **Harrowgate Bloodstock Ltd**
36 B f Gregorian (IRE)—Resist **Mr J G Brown & Partner**
37 **SALTIE GIRL**, b f Intikhab (USA)—Marine Girl **T D Barron & Partner**
38 Ch g Cityscape—Sorcellerie **Harrowgate Bloodstock Ltd**
39 B g Epaulette (AUS)—Sparkle Park **Dr N. J. Barron**
40 **THREE ROSES (IRE)**, b f Holy Roman Emperor (IRE)—Khobaraa **Mr M. J. Rozenbroek**
41 **VIGORITO**, b f Arcano (IRE)—Lucy Parsons (IRE) **Harrowgate Bloodstock Ltd & Associate**

TWO-YEAR-OLDS

42 B f 10/2 Due Diligence (USA)—Amitola (IRE) (Choisir (AUS)) (12000) **Dr N. J. Barron**
43 B f 23/3 Swiss Spirit—Annie Beach (IRE) (Redback) (3809) **Mrs S. C. Barron**
44 **CARRIESMATIC**, b f 7/4 Passing Glance—Concentrate (Zamindar (USA)) (1714) **Mrs G. M. Swinglehurst**
45 B c 4/2 Morpheus—Click And Go (IRE) (Kodiac) (1010) **Harrowgate Bloodstock Ltd**
46 Ch f 18/1 Tagula (IRE)—Ever Evolving (FR) (Elusive Quality (USA)) (1263) **Mr P. Toes**
47 **GREYFIRE**, gr c 26/2 Shooting To Win (AUS)—Ancestral Way (Mtoto) (28571) **Mr D Ellis & Syps Ltd**
48 B f 14/3 Fountain of Youth (IRE)—Jofranka (Paris House) **Harrowgate Bloodstock Ltd**
49 Ch c 20/2 Intense Focus (USA)—Joli Elegant (IRE) (Dylan Thomas (IRE)) (5056) **Harrowgate Bloodstock Ltd**
50 B c 16/4 Canford Cliffs (IRE)—Khobaraa (Invincible Spirit (IRE)) (3809) **Mr M. J. Rozenbroek**
51 Gr f 24/2 Farhh—La Gessa (Largesse) (21000) **L. G. O'Kane**
52 B f 2/4 Fountain of Youth (IRE)—La Zamora (Lujain (USA)) (761) **Harrowgate Bloodstock Ltd**
53 B c 10/4 Lethal Force (IRE)—Lead A Merry Dance (Bertolini (USA)) (6666) **Harrowgate Bloodstock Ltd**
54 B c 2/4 Swiss Spirit—Lucy Parsons (IRE) (Thousand Words) (9523) **Harrowgate Bloodstock Ltd & Associate**
55 B c 15/4 Brazen Beau (AUS)—Maziona (Dansili) (30476) **Harrowgate Bloodstock Ltd**
56 **MERESIDE BLUE**, b f 12/2 Sepoy (AUS)—Moonbi Haven (IRE) (Medicean) (10000) **Mereside Racing Limited**
57 B c 20/3 Intense Focus (USA)—Moonbi Haven (IRE) (Definite Article) (4381) **Harrowgate Bloodstock Ltd**
58 B c 24/4 Poet's Voice—Pretty Majestic (IRE) (Invincible Spirit (IRE)) (2200) **Harrowgate Bloodstock Ltd**
59 B f 19/2 Casamento (IRE)—Sheezastorm (IRE) (Fast Company (IRE)) (1200) **Harrowgate Bloodstock Ltd**
60 B c 3/4 Brazen Beau (AUS)—Vespasia (Medicean) (5000) **Mr R Miquel & Partner**

Other Owners: All About York II, Mrs A. Atkinson, Mr T. D. Barron, J. G. Brown, R. J. Cornelius, J. M. Elliott, C. R. Elliott, Elliott Brothers And Peacock, Mr D. B. Ellis, Mr M. Hilton, Mrs J. Ingham, Mr N. N. Kane, Mr J. Knotts, R. C. Miquel, Ne-Chance, Mr G. R. Pooley, D. G. Pryde, SYPS (UK) Ltd, Trinity Bloodstock, D. R. Tucker, Mr J. Wells, Mr L. Woolams, Mr D. P. van der Hoeven.

Assistant Trainer: Nicola-Jo Barron

---

26 | **MR PASCAL BARY, Chantilly**
Postal: **5 Chemin des Aigles, 60500 Chantilly, France**
Contacts: **PHONE (0033) 3445 71403 FAX (0033) 3446 72015 MOBILE (0033) 6075 80241**
E-MAIL p-bary@orange.fr

1 **BOLTING (USA)**, 6, b r War Front (USA)—Beta Leo (USA) **Flaxman Stables Ireland Ltd**
2 **BUGLE MAJOR (USA)**, 4, gr ro c Mizzen Mast (USA)—Conference Call **K. Abdullah**
3 **CAPTAIN'S GIRL (FR)**, 4, b f Captain Marvelous (IRE)—New Style (GER) **Equotair**
4 **GOLD VIBE (IRE)**, 6, ch g Dream Ahead (USA)—Whisper Dance (USA) **Sutong Pan**
5 **MOUNT POPA (IRE)**, 4, b g Maxios—Mimalia (USA) **Course Investment Corporation**
6 **SPINNING MEMORIES (IRE)**, 4, b f Arcano (IRE)—Hanalei Memories (USA) **Sutong Pan**
7 **STUDY OF MAN (IRE)**, 4, b c Deep Impact (JPN)—Second Happiness (USA) **Flaxman Stables Ireland Ltd**
8 **TESTON (FR)**, 4, ch g Rio de La Plata (USA)—Tianshan (FR) **G. Sandor**

THREE-YEAR-OLDS

9 **AERONAUTICAL (USA)**, b f Medaglia d'oro (USA)—Witching Hour (FR) **Flaxman Stables Ireland Ltd**
10 **AMHARA (USA)**, ch f Union Rags (USA)—Sea of Laughter (USA) **Flaxman Stables Ireland Ltd**

MR PASCAL BARY - Continued

11 **BOARDMAN**, b c Kingman—Nimble Thimble (USA) **K. Abdullah**
12 **CABALLINE**, b f Motivator—Likelihood (USA) **K. Abdullah**
13 **FUN LEGEND**, b c Frankel—Body And Soul (IRE) **Sutong Pan**
14 **GAZELLE (FR)**, b f Siyouni (FR)—Grande Rousse (FR) **Haras du Mezeray**
15 **GLACIATE**, b f Kingman—Winter Silence **K. Abdullah**
16 **KENBAIO (FR)**, gr c Kendargent (FR)—Baia Chope (FR) **Guy Pariente Holding SPRL**
17 **KENMORE (FR)**, b g Kendargent (FR)—Moranda (FR) **Laghi France**
18 **KENWINA (FR)**, ch f Kendargent (FR)—Ponte Bawi (IRE) **Guy Pariente Holding SPRL**
19 **LE BARYTON (FR)**, ch c Australia—Bright Sky (IRE) **R. G. Ehrnrooth**
20 **LE MONT (FR)**, b c Le Havre (FR)—Miss Bio (FR) **Franklin Finance SA**
21 **LUCKY DOE (IRE)**, ch f Dawn Approach (IRE)—Blessed Luck (IRE) **Mr Alaric de Murga SAS**
22 **MANDAAR (FR)**, b c Canyon Creek (IRE)—Madeleine's Blush (USA) **G. Sandor**
23 **MEXAL (FR)**, b f Olympic Glory (IRE)—Texaloula (FR) **Laghi France**
24 **MONCEAU**, b c Dansili—Palmette **K. Abdullah**
25 **MONTABOT (FR)**, b g Le Havre (IRE)—Salamon **Franklin Finance SA**
26 **NOCTILUCENT (IRE)**, b f Olympic Glory (IRE)—Teepee (JPN) **Course Investment Corporation**
27 **OBLIGATE (FR)**, b f Frankel—Responsible **K. Abdullah**
28 **OBOE (USA)**, gr ro f Mizzen Mast (USA)—Flute (USA) **K. Abdullah**
29 **OLENDON (FR)**, ch f Le Havre (IRE)—Talema (FR) **Franklin Finance SA**
30 **PRICE RANGE (USA)**, b c First Defence (USA)—Price Tag **K. Abdullah**
31 **RETHOVILLE (FR)**, b f Anodin (IRE)—Absolute Lady (IRE) **Franklin Finance SA**
32 **SILVERY PRINCE (FR)**, b c Kendargent (FR)—Princess Liu (IRE) **Mr Alaric de Murga SAS**
33 **SISTER MIDNIGHT (IRE)**, b f Dark Angel (IRE)—Yoga (IRE) **Course Investment Corporation**
34 **SOUND OF VICTORY (IRE)**, b c Sea The Stars (IRE)—Sakarya (IRE) **Ecurie J. L. Bouchard**
35 **STANLEY BEACH**, b f Kingman—Our Little Secret (IRE) **Sutong Pan**
36 **STORMYZA (FR)**, gr f Nathaniel (IRE)—Stormyra (FR) **Guy Pariente Holding SPRL**
37 **THEMATIC (USA)**, b g Noble Mission—Gateway (USA) **K. Abdullah**
38 **THIRD OF MARCH (IRE)**, b f Camacho—Kimola (IRE) **Chen Sze Long**
39 **TIKI (IRE)**, b c Galileo (IRE)—Second Happiness (USA) **Flaxman Stables Ireland Ltd**
40 **TRAPPIST ONE (IRE)**, b g Maxios—Game of Legs (FR) **Course Investment Corporation**
41 **VADROUILLEUR (FR)**, b g Dream Ahead (USA)—Vita (FR) **Laghi France**
42 **VENT MARIN (FR)**, b c Cape Cross (IRE)—Chasse Maree (FR) **Haras du Mezeray**
43 **VICTORIA PEAK (IRE)**, gr f Dark Angel (IRE)—Ellasha **Sutong Pan**
44 **WILD RYE**, ch f Bated Breath—Imbabala **K. Abdullah**

TWO-YEAR-OLDS

45 **AQUITAINE (IRE)**, ch f 3/4 Australia—Divine Music (IRE) (Gold Away (IRE)) (46354) **Mr Alaric de Murga SAS**
46 **BACKFIELDINMOTION (FR)**, b f 12/5 Siyouni (FR)—
    Noelani (IRE) (Indian Ridge) (80067) **Team Valor International**
47 **BARAKATLE**, gr c 19/3 Poet's Voice—Baraket Fayrouz (FR) (Barathea (IRE)) **Cabkhat SRO**
48 B c 11/2 Olympic Glory (IRE)—Borgia Gold (IRE) (Cape Cross (IRE)) (54782) **Ecurie J. L. Bouchard**
49 **CALCULATING**, b c 27/2 Camelot—Sea Meets Sky (FR) (Dansili) **Course Investment Corporation**
50 **CUBIT**, b f 4/4 Bated Breath—Mirabilis (USA) (Lear Fan (USA)) **K. Abdullah**
51 B c 22/4 Le Havre (IRE)—Davantage (IRE) (Galileo (IRE)) **Ecurie des Monceaux & Laurence Bary**
52 **FURTHER MEASURE (USA)**, b c 1/1 English Channel (USA)—Price Tag (Dansili) **K. Abdullah**
53 **GREENLAND (USA)**, b br f 15/3 War Front (USA)—
    Daisy Devine (USA) (Kafwain (USA)) **Flaxman Stables Ireland Ltd**
54 **HIDDEN LAND (USA)**, ch f 9/1 Hard Spun (USA)—
    Absolute Crackers (IRE) (Giant's Causeway (USA)) **Flaxman Stables Ireland Ltd**
55 **HONDOUVILLE (FR)**, b f 30/1 Le Havre (IRE)—Hello Fuji (Dansili) **Franklin Finance SA**
56 **HURRICANE CLOUD**, b c 1/3 Frankel—Gooseley Chope (FR) (Indian Rocket) **Guy Pariente Holding SPRL**
57 **IL BRIO (JPN)**, b c 19/2 Deep Impact (JPN)—Ryzhkina (IRE) (Storm Cat (USA)) **Hidetoshi Yamamoto**
58 **JULIUSJULIUSSON (USA)**, b c 28/1 War Front (USA)—
    Hoop of Colour (USA) (Distorted Humor (USA)) **Flaxman Stables Ireland Ltd**
59 **KENLOVA (FR)**, b f 17/2 Kendargent (FR)—
    Ice Love (FR) (Three Valleys (USA)) (50568) **Gerard Laboureau & Guy Pariente**
60 **KENYX (FR)**, b c 3/2 Kendargent (FR)—Onyx (FR) (Orpen (USA)) (42140) **Gerard Laboureau & Guy Pariente**
61 **KETIL (USA)**, b c 5/2 Karakontie (JPN)—
    Matroshka (IRE) (Red Ransom (USA)) (42140) **Flaxman Stables Ireland Ltd**
62 B c 8/5 Elvstroem (AUS)—Kikinda (FR) (Daliapour (IRE)) (84281) **Ecurie J. L. Bouchard**
63 **LAND OF MAYBE (USA)**, ch f 10/4 American Pharoah (USA)—
    Pachattack (USA) (Pulpit (USA)) **Flaxman Stables Ireland Ltd**
64 **LE SOLAIRE**, b c 7/2 Siyouni (FR)—Apsara (FR) (Darshaan) **Course Investment Corporation**
65 **MUSICAL MAST (USA)**, gr ro c 18/3 Mizzen Mast (USA)—Flute (USA) (Seattle Slew (USA)) **K. Abdullah**
66 **PANNOTIA**, ch f 2/3 Le Havre (IRE)—Continental Drift (USA) (Smart Strike (CAN)) **K. Abdullah**

MR PASCAL BARY - Continued

67 **RUSKIN (IRE)**, b c 26/3 Le Havre (IRE)—Malicieuse (IRE) (Galileo (IRE)) **Course Investment Corporation**
68 **SARTILLY (FR)**, b f 10/4 Le Havre (IRE)—Salamon (Montjeu (IRE)) **Franklin Finance SA**
69 Ch c 16/3 Iffraaj—Satiriste (Shamardal (USA)) (84281) **Ecurie J. L. Bouchard**
70 **THANIELLA (FR)**, ch c 4/3 Nathaniel (IRE)—Matorio (FR) (Oratorio (IRE)) **Guy Pariente Holding SPRL**

Assistant Trainer: Baratti Mario

---

27 ## MISS REBECCA BASTIMAN, Wetherby
Postal: Goosemoor Farm, Warfield Lane, Wetherby, West Yorkshire, LS22 5EU
Contacts: PHONE (01423) 359783 (01423) 359397 MOBILE (07818) 181313
E-MAIL rebeccabastiman@hotmail.co.uk

1 **AMAZING GRAZING (IRE)**, 5, b g Intense Focus (USA)—North Light Rose (USA) **The Redhotgardogs 2**
2 **BE BOLD**, 7, ch g Assertive—Marysienka **Mr N Barber & Partner**
3 **BOING**, 4, b g Bated Breath—Lomapamar **Let's Be Lucky Racing**
4 **DARK DEFENDER**, 6, b g Pastoral Pursuits—Oh So Saucy **Partnership**
5 **DONNELLY'S RAINBOW (IRE)**, 6, b g Lilbourne Lad (IRE)—Donnelly's Hollow (IRE) **Miss R. Bastiman**
6 **EDGAR ALLAN POE (IRE)**, 5, b g Zoffany (IRE)—Swingsky (IRE) **I B Barker / P Bastiman**
7 **ELERFAAN (IRE)**, 5, b g Shamardal (USA)—Gorband (USA) **Ms M. Austerfield**
8 **FOXY BOY**, 5, ch g Foxwedge (AUS)—Suzy Wong **Grange Park Racing Club & Partner**
9 **FRENCH FLYER (IRE)**, 4, b g Pour Moi (IRE)—Leavingonajetplane (IRE) **Miss R. Bastiman**
10 **FUMBO JUMBO (IRE)**, 6, b m Zebedee—Baraloti (IRE) **Miss R. Bastiman**
11 **GHALIB (IRE)**, 7, ch g Lope de Vega (IRE)—Gorband (USA) **Ms M. Austerfield**
12 **GONE WITH THE WIND (GER)**, 8, b g Dutch Art—Gallivant **Mrs P. Bastiman**
13 **HARBOUR PATROL (IRE)**, 7, b g Acclamation—Traou Mad (IRE) **Miss R. Bastiman**
14 **HAYADH**, 6, gr g Oasis Dream—Warling (IRE) **Miss R. Bastiman**
15 **HIGHLIGHT REEL (IRE)**, 4, b g Big Bad Bob (IRE)—Dance Hall Girl (IRE) **Miss R. Bastiman**
16 **HITMAN**, 6, b g Canford Cliffs (IRE)—Ballymore Celebre (IRE) **Ms M. Austerfield**
17 **INDIAN CHIEF (IRE)**, 9, b g Montjeu (IRE)—Buck Aspen (USA) **Castle Construction (North East) Ltd**
18 **JACOB'S PILLOW**, 8, b g Oasis Dream—Enticing (IRE) **Miss R. Bastiman**
19 **JOHN CAESAR (IRE)**, 8, b g Bushranger (IRE)—Polish Belle **Mrs K. Hall & Mrs P. Bastiman**
20 **LEESHAAN (IRE)**, 4, b g Bated Breath—La Grande Elisa (IRE) **Let's Be Lucky Racing 18 & Partner**
21 **LOGI (IRE)**, 5, b g Kodiac—Feet of Flame (USA) **Let's Be Lucky Racing 12**
22 **LOW PROFILE**, 4, ch g Galileo (USA)—Dynaforce (USA) **Ms M Austerfield & the 8 Amigos**
23 **MAJESTE**, 5, b g Acclamation—Winged Valkyrie (IRE) **Let's Be Lucky Racing 17 & Partner**
24 **MILTON ROAD**, 4, b g Mazameer (IRE)—Blakeshall Girl **Mr W. L. Donaldson**
25 **MUHAJJAL**, 5, b g Cape Cross (IRE)—Muqantara (USA) **Let's Be Lucky Racing**
26 **NATAJACK**, 5, ch g Showcasing—Douro **Let's Be Lucky Racing 15**
27 **NEWSTEAD ABBEY**, 9, b g Byron—Oatcake **Lets Be Lucky Racing 20 & Partner**
28 **NINGALOO (GER)**, 5, b g Siyouni (FR)—Notre Dame (GER) **Ms M. Austerfield**
29 **ROARING FORTIES (IRE)**, 6, b g Invincible Spirit (IRE)—Growling (IRE) **Mrs K Hall & Partner**
30 **ROYAL BRAVE (IRE)**, 8, b g Acclamation—Daqtora **James Edgar & William Donaldson**
31 **TIERCEL**, 5, b g Olden Times—Sharp Mode (USA) **Lets Be Lucky Racing 19 & Partner**
32 **WENSLEY**, 4, b g Poet's Voice—Keladora (USA) **Mr John Smith & Mrs P. Bastiman**
33 **ZESHOV**, 8, b g Acclamation—Fathoming (USA) **Mrs P. Bastiman**
34 **ZUMURUD (IRE)**, 4, gr g Zebedee—Thaisy (USA) **Ms M. Austerfield**

THREE-YEAR-OLDS

35 **JOSIEBOND**, ch f Monsieur Bond (IRE)—Smiddy Hill **I. B. Barker**
36 **SINGMAN**, b c Dandy Man (IRE)—Singitta **Ms M. Austerfield**
37 **SIRIUSLY QUICK (IRE)**, gr g Footstepsinthesand—Annacurra (IRE) **Mr G. White**
38 **STAYCATION (IRE)**, b g Acclamation—Staceymac (IRE) **Miss R. Bastiman**

TWO-YEAR-OLDS

39 Ch g 14/3 Zoffany (IRE)—Scarlet Belle (Sir Percy) (8000)

Other Owners: The 8 Amigos, Mr E. N. Barber, R. G. Capstick, Mr A. D. Crombie, D. J. Dickson, Mr J. D. Edgar, Mr R. A. Gorrie, Mr S. T. Gorrie, Grange Park Racing Club, Mrs K. Hall, Let's Be Lucky Racing 17, Let's Be Lucky Racing 18, Let's Be Lucky Racing 19, Let's Be Lucky Racing 20, Mr A. McAvoy, RedHotGardogs, Hugh T. Redhead, Mr J. Smith, Mr P. L. Welsby.

Assistant Trainer: Harvey Bastiman

Apprentice: Phil Dennis.

28 MR BRIAN BAUGH, Audley
Postal: **Brooklands, Park Lane, Audley, Stoke-On-Trent, Staffordshire, ST7 8HR**
Contacts: **PHONE (01782) 706222 MOBILE (07547) 495236**
E-MAIL bpjbaugh@aol.com

1 **DAVID'S BEAUTY (IRE)**, 6, b m Kodiac—Thaisy (USA) **Mr G. B. Hignett**
2 **WHISPERING SOUL (IRE)**, 6, b m Majestic Missile (IRE)—Belle of The Blues (IRE) **Mr G. B. Hignett**

THREE-YEAR-OLDS

3 **NORTH KOREA (IRE)**, b f Bungle Inthejungle—Betty Fontaine (IRE) **Mr G. B. Hignett**
4 **SHESADABBER**, b f Heeraat (IRE)—Saorocain (IRE) **Mr G. B. Hignett**

Assistant Trainer: S Potts

29 MR RALPH BECKETT, Andover
Postal: **Kimpton Down Stables, Kimpton, Andover, Hampshire, SP11 8QQ**
Contacts: **PHONE (01264) 772278 MOBILE (07802) 219022**
E-MAIL trainer@rbeckett.com

1 **AIR PILOT**, 10, b g Zamindar (USA)—Countess Sybil (IRE) **Lady Cobham**
2 **AKVAVERA**, 4, ch f Leroidesanimaux (BRZ)—Akdarena **Miss K. Rausing**
3 **ANOTHER BOY**, 6, ch g Paco Boy (IRE)—Kurtanella **Mrs Philip Snow & Partners**
4 **BATTERED**, 5, b g Foxwedge (AUS)—Swan Wings **King Power Racing Co Ltd**
5 **BLAZING SADDLES**, 4, b g High Chaparral (IRE)—Desert Sage **Mr J. H. Richmond-Watson**
6 **BLIZZARD**, 4, b f Medicean—Moretta Blanche **Absolute Solvents Ltd**
7 **CECCHINI (IRE)**, 4, br f Rip Van Winkle (IRE)—Urban Daydream (IRE) **Mr P. D. Savill**
8 **CLIFFS OF DOONEEN (IRE)**, 4, ch g Galileo (IRE)—Devoted To You (IRE) **The Anagram Partnership**
9 **DAZZLING ROCK (IRE)**, 4, ch g Rock of Gibraltar (IRE)—
Dazzling Light (UAE) **Pickford Hill Partnership, Late Mr R Roberts**
10 **DI FEDE (IRE)**, 4, b f Shamardal (USA)—Dibiya (IRE) **Mr Robert Ng**
11 **DIOCLES OF ROME (IRE)**, 4, b g Holy Roman Emperor (IRE)—Serisia (FR) **Mrs Philip Snow & Partners**
12 **DOLPHIN VISTA (IRE)**, 6, b g Zoffany (IRE)—Fiordiligi **Mr Y. Nasib**
13 **FRENCH RIVIERA (IRE)**, 4, b f Intello (GER)—Ecume du Jour (FR) **Chris Humber**
14 **HERE AND NOW**, 5, b g Dansili—Look Here **The Hon R. J. Arculli**
15 **MITCHUM SWAGGER**, 7, b g Paco Boy (IRE)—Dont Dili Dali **The Anagram Partnership**
16 **RICHENZA (FR)**, 4, b f Holy Roman Emperor (IRE)—Nantha (IRE) **Mrs Lynn Turner & Mr Guy Brook**
17 **ROCK EAGLE**, 4, ch g Teofilo (IRE)—Highland Shot **Mr J. C. Smith**
18 **STEAMING (IRE)**, 5, b g Rail Link—Dazzling Day **GC Hartigan, ADG Oldrey & GHC Wakefield**
19 **TAUREAN STAR (IRE)**, 6, b g Elnadim (USA)—Marhaba **Mr R. A. Pegum**
20 **THIMBLEWEED**, 4, b f Teofilo (IRE)—Prairie Flower (IRE) **Mr J. H. Richmond-Watson**
21 **TIME CHANGE**, 4, ch f Dutch Art—Time Honoured **Mr R. Barnett**
22 **VICTORY CHIME (IRE)**, 4, b g Campanologist (USA)—Patuca **Mr A. Nevin**

THREE-YEAR-OLDS

23 **ALOE VERA**, b f Invincible Spirit (IRE)—Almiranta **Miss K. Rausing**
24 **ANTONIA DE VEGA (IRE)**, b f Lope de Vega (IRE)—Witches Brew (IRE) **Waverley Racing**
25 **ARCADIENNE**, ch f Leroidesanimaux (BRZ)—Archduchess **Miss K. Rausing**
26 **BIOMETRIC**, b c Bated Breath—Bionic **Mr K. Abdullah**
27 **BRASCA**, ch g Nathaniel (IRE)—Regalline (IRE) **Frank Brady & Brian Scanlon**
28 **BURIRAM (IRE)**, b g Reliable Man—Wild Step (GER) **King Power Racing Co Ltd**
29 **CABARITA**, ch f Leroidesanimaux (BRZ)—Catadupa **Miss K. Rausing**
30 **CHALEUR**, b f Dansili—Lilyfire (USA) **Mr K. Abdullah**
31 **CHARTERED**, b f Frankel—Time Saved **Mr R. Barnett**
32 **CITY MASTER**, br g Mastercraftsman (IRE)—City Girl (IRE) **Mr J. C. Smith**
33 **COPAL**, b g Dark Angel (IRE)—Mirabilis (USA) **Mr K. Abdullah**
34 **DANCING VEGA (IRE)**, ch f Lope de Vega (IRE)—We Can Say It Now (AUS) **Waverley Racing**
35 **DAVE DEXTER**, b g Stimulation (IRE)—Blue Crest (FR) **Mrs Philip Snow & Partners I**
36 **DESIROUS**, b f Kingman—Emulous **Mr K. Abdullah**
37 **DOBRIANKA**, ch f Sea The Stars (IRE)—Topaze Blanche (USA) **H.H. Sheikh Mohammed Bin Khalifa Al Thani**
38 **FANCY DRESS (IRE)**, ro f Mastercraftsman (IRE)—What Style (IRE) **Kennet Valley Thoroughbreds III**
39 **FEARLESS WARRIOR (FR)**, ch c Sea The Stars (IRE)—
Mambo Light (USA) **Qatar Racing Ltd & Mr Kin Hung Kei**
40 **FELICIANA DE VEGA**, b f Lope de Vega (IRE)—Along Came Casey (IRE) **Waverley Racing**
41 **FRAGRANT BELLE**, ch f Sir Percy—Palace Princess (FR) **Mr Robert Ng**

MR RALPH BECKETT - Continued

42 **FUTURE INVESTMENT**, b g Mount Nelson—Shenir **R.N.J. Partnership**
43 **GLANCE**, b f Dansili—Look So **Mr J. H. Richmond-Watson**
44 **GUILDHALL**, b g Cityscape—Ecstasy **Mr A. D. G. Oldrey & Mr G. C. Hartigan**
45 **HEAVENLY TALE (IRE)**, b f Shamardal (USA)—Angels Story (IRE) **Qatar Racing Limited**
46 **HEREBY (IRE)**, b f Pivotal—Look Here **Mr J. H. Richmond-Watson**
47 **INNOCENT (IRE)**, b f Cape Cross (IRE)—Pirans Rock (IRE) **Highclere T'bred Racing - 5 Hertford Street Elite**
48 **ISABELLA BRANT (FR)**, gr f Mastercraftsman (IRE)—Walk In Beauty (IRE) **Merriebelle Irish Farm Limited**
49 **JAMES PARK WOODS (IRE)**, b g Australia—Happy Holly (IRE) **Quantum Leap Racing IV**
50 **JUNIUS BRUTUS (FR)**, ch g Cockney Rebel (IRE)—Tricked **King Power Racing Co Ltd**
51 **KASUKU**, b f Delegator—Hobby **Larksborough Stud Limited**
52 **LARA (IRE)**, b f Camelot—La Spezia (IRE) **Mr M. H. Dixon & Mount Coote Estate**
53 **LOCH LADY**, b f Camelot—Highland Shot **Mr J. C. Smith**
54 **LOPE SCHOLAR (IRE)**, b f Lope de Vega (IRE)—Varsity **Waverley Racing**
55 **MANUELA DE VEGA (IRE)**, b f Lope de Vega (IRE)—Roscoff (IRE) **Waverley Racing**
56 **MARLOWE ROSE (IRE)**, b f Camelot—Gameday **P Stokes, T & G Pritchard-Gordon**
57 **MISTY**, b f Oasis Dream—Ceilidh House **Mr J. H. Richmond-Watson**
58 **MOON KING (FR)**, br g Sea The Moon (GER)—Maraba (IRE) **What Asham Partnership**
59 **MRS IVY**, ch f Champs Elysees—Just Wood (FR) **Make A Circle I**
60 **MY DEAR FRIEND**, b g Kodiac—Time Honoured **King Power Racing Co Ltd**
61 **NETTE ROUSSE (GER)**, ch f Mastercraftsman (IRE)—
                                         Nina Celebre (IRE) **H.H. Sheikh Mohammed Bin Khalifa Al Thani**
62 **NIVALDO (IRE)**, b c Archipenko (USA)—Nocturne (GER) **Quantum Leap Racing II**
63 **NOBLE MUSIC (GER)**, b f Sea The Moon (GER)—Noble Lady (GER) **Mrs Emma Kennedy**
64 **OYDIS**, b f Nathaniel (IRE)—Opera Dancer **Mr J. C. Smith**
65 **PHILONIKIA**, b f Kingman—Colima (IRE) **Mr & Mrs David Aykroyd**
66 **PRINCESS SALAMAH (IRE)**, ch f Australia—Dubai Media (CAN) **Ahmad Al Shaikh**
67 **RECONDITE (IRE)**, b c Acclamation—Aquarius Star (IRE) **Mr K. Abdullah**
68 **REPULSE BAY (IRE)**, b f Dark Angel (IRE)—Soxy Doxy (IRE) **Mr Sutong Pan**
69 **b f Born To Sea (IRE)**—Rosy Mantle **Nigel & Carolyn Elwes**
70 **ROVING MISSION (USA)**, ch f Noble Mission—Preferential **Mr K. Abdullah**
71 **ROWLAND WARD**, b c Sea The Stars (IRE)—Honor Bound **H.H. Sheikh Mohammed Bin Khalifa Al Thani**
72 **SAM COOKE (IRE)**, b c Pour Moi (IRE)—Saturday Girl **Chelsea Thoroughbreds - Wonderful World**
73 **SAND SHARE**, br f Oasis Dream—Shared Account **Mr K. Abdullah**
74 **SCINTILLATING**, b f Siyouni (FR)—Photo Flash (IRE) **Highclere Thoroughbred Racing - Floors**
75 **SHAMISEN**, ch f Toronado (IRE)—Abunai **Mr Isa Salman**
76 **SKYMAX (GER)**, b g Maxios—Set Dreams (FR) **Bermuda Thoroughbred Racing Limited**
77 **SNOW IN SPRING**, b g Oasis Dream—Khione **The Outlaws**
78 **SPEED KING**, b c Kingman—Speed Cop **Mr J. C. Smith**
79 **SPICE OF LIFE**, b f Sea The Stars (IRE)—So In Love **Miss K. Rausing**
80 **STORMWAVE (IRE)**, b c Dalakhani (IRE)—Celtic Slipper (IRE) **Mr Abdulla Al Khalifa**
81 **TEODORA DE VEGA (IRE)**, b f Lope de Vega (IRE)—Applauded (IRE) **Waverley Racing**
82 **TIGERSKIN**, ch c Nathaniel (IRE)—Jamboretta (IRE) **Mr A. D. G. Oldrey & Mr G. C. Hartigan**
83 **WAN CHAI (USA)**, b c Pour Moi (IRE)—Dansette **Mr Sutong Pan**
84 **WHEREWITHAL**, b c Lope de Vega (IRE)—Banks Hill **Mr K. Abdullah**
85 **WILD ABANDON**, b f Kingman—Sant Elena **The Eclipse Partnership**
86 **WINGREEN (IRE)**, ch f Lope de Vega (IRE)—Relation Alexander (IRE) **Mr Isa Salman**

TWO-YEAR-OLDS

87 Ch f 6/3 Camacho—Adoring (IRE) (One Cool Cat (USA)) (100000) **Mr Guy Brook**
88 B c 16/2 Poet's Voice—Affaire de Coeur (Dalakhani (IRE)) (1428) **ADC Bloodstock**
89 Br f 22/2 New Approach (IRE)—
         Al Baidaa (Exceed And Excel (AUS)) (150000) **Highclere T'Bred Racing-Rosie Swale Pope**
90 **ALBAFLORA**, gr f 11/2 Muharaar—Almiranta (Galileo (IRE)) **Miss K. Rausing**
91 Ch f 4/2 Lope de Vega (IRE)—Annie's Fortune (IRE) (Montjeu (IRE)) (38000) **Waverley Racing**
92 **ARABIAN DREAM**, b f 30/1 Oasis Dream—Arabesque (Zafonic (USA)) **Mr K. Abdullah**
93 B f 10/2 Siyouni (FR)—Ascot Lady (IRE) (Spinning World (USA)) (109565) **Mr N. Martin**
94 B f 4/2 Noble Mission—Bee Brave (Rail Link) (30000) **Mrs Catherine Dallas & High Valley Thoroughbreds**
95 **CALATRAVA (IRE)**, b f 13/2 Havana Gold (IRE)—Intizara (Dansili) **Chris Humber**
96 **CHAMADE**, b f 26/3 Sepoy (AUS)—Colima (IRE) (Authorized (IRE)) **Mr & Mrs David Aykroyd**
97 **CRISPINA**, b f 11/5 Kingman—Dawn of Empire (USA) (Empire Maker (USA)) **Mr K. Abdullah**
98 B f 22/2 Holy Roman Emperor (IRE)—Dame d'honneur (IRE) (Teofilo) (50568) **Westerberg Limited**
99 **DEFT**, ch f 7/4 Dubawi (IRE)—Prowess (IRE) (Peintre Celebre (USA)) **Mr J. L. Rowsell & Mr M. H. Dixon**
100 **DUTCH SCHULTZ**, b c 13/3 Golden Horn—Karpina (Pivotal) (65000) **Chelsea Thoroughbreds Ltd**
101 B f 2/4 Camelot—Empress of France (USA) (Storm Cat (USA)) **H.H. Sheikh Mohammed Bin Khalifa Al Thani**
102 B c 18/5 Kyllachy—Flylowflylong (IRE) (Danetime (IRE)) (37000) **Richard Milner & Partners**

MR RALPH BECKETT - Continued

103 **GOLDEN CYGNET**, b f 2/4 Cable Bay (IRE)—
　　　　　　　　Dark Swan (IRE) (Zamindar (USA)) **Prince of Wales & Duchess of Cornwall**
104 **GOODWOOD REBEL (IRE)**, b c 24/1 Dandy Man (IRE)—
　　　　　　　　Our Valkyrie (IRE) (High Chaparral (IRE)) (30000) **Goodwood Racehorse Owners Group Limited**
105 **GRAIN OF SENSE (IRE)**, ch c 30/4 Teofilo (IRE)—Grain of Truth (Gulch (USA)) (68000) **Clarendon Partnership**
106 B c 14/2 Siyouni (FR)—Graphic Guest (Dutch Art) (80000) **Mr R. A. Pegum**
107 B c 28/4 Zoffany (IRE)—Highland Shot (Selkirk (USA)) **Mr J. C. Smith**
108 B c 8/5 Dandy Man (IRE)—Hold On Tight (IRE) (Hernando (FR)) **Millenium Madness**
109 B c 16/3 Dansili—Honor Bound (Authorized (IRE)) **H.H. Sheikh Mohammed Bin Khalifa Al Thani**
110 **ICE STATION ZEBRA**, b f 29/1 Showcasing—Moretta Blanche (Dansili) **Mr P. K. Gardner**
111 B f 25/1 Australia—Ignis Away (FR) (Gold Away (IRE)) (185419) **Qatar Racing Limited**
112 **IMPATIENT**, b c 17/1 More Than Ready (USA)—Regardez (Champs Elysees) **Mr J. H. Richmond-Watson**
113 **JACKSONIAN**, ch c 22/4 Frankel—Kalima (Kahyasi) **Mr K. Abdullah**
114 **KINROSS**, b c 6/5 Kingman—Ceilidh House (Selkirk (USA)) **Mr J. H. Richmond-Watson**
115 B f 26/2 Charm Spirit (IRE)—Lady Dragon (IRE) (Galileo (IRE)) **Qatar Racing Limited**
116 **LUCANDER (IRE)**, b g 21/3 Footstepsinthesand—
　　　　　　　　Lady Sefton (Oratorio (IRE)) (28000) **Mrs M. E. Slade & Mr & Mrs B. Ohlsson**
117 B f 3/4 Lope de Vega (IRE)—Lunar Phase (IRE) (Galileo (IRE)) (65000) **Waverley Racing**
118 B f 15/2 Lope de Vega (IRE)—Majenta (IRE) (Marju (IRE)) (35000) **Waverley Racing**
119 Ch f 21/4 Lope de Vega (IRE)—Mamma Morton (IRE) (Elnadim (USA)) (30000) **Mr R. Cornelius**
120 **MASCAT**, ch c 17/2 Zoffany (IRE)—Critical Acclaim (Peintre Celebre (USA)) (80000) **Mr Y. Nasib**
121 **MAXIMILIUS (GER)**, br c 11/4 Soldier Hollow—
　　　　　　　　Macuna (Acatenango (GER)) (23598) **Mrs L. Mann & Mr N. Attenborough**
122 **MERIDIANA**, b f 24/2 Galileo (IRE)—Midday (Oasis Dream) **Mr K. Abdullah**
123 B c 27/1 Al Kazeem—Midnight Dance (IRE) (Danehill Dancer (IRE)) **Mr J. C. Smith**
124 B f 11/4 Muhaarar—Najam (Singspiel (IRE)) (95000) **Westerberg Limited**
125 **NEWBOLT (IRE)**, gr c 3/2 Bated Breath—Nirva (IRE) (Verglas (IRE)) **Mr A. D. G. Oldrey & Mr G. C. Hartigan**
126 Ch c 21/2 Lope de Vega (IRE)—Paraphernalia (IRE) (Dalakhani (IRE)) (21069) **Pickford Hill Partnership**
127 B f 4/4 Dunaden (FR)—Pearl Princess (FR) (Astronomer Royal (USA)) **Qatar Racing Limited**
128 B f 10/4 Fastnet Rock (AUS)—Pure Song (Singspiel (IRE)) **Mr R. Barnett**
129 Gr f 30/3 Lope de Vega (IRE)—Safiyna (FR) (Sinndar (IRE)) (100000) **Waverley Racing**
130 Br c 8/3 Kendargent (FR)—Save Me The Waltz (FR) (Halling (USA)) (65000) **Highclere Thoroughbred Racing**
131 B f 4/3 Iffraaj—Scent of Roses (IRE) (Invincible Spirit (IRE)) (75000) **Frank Brady**
132 B c 12/3 Kodiac—Scholarly (Authorized (IRE)) (100000) **Quantum Leap Racing VIII**
133 Ch c 19/4 Exceed And Excel (AUS)—Snoqualmie Girl (IRE) (Montjeu (IRE)) **Mr J. C. Smith**
134 **SPRING TO MIND**, b f 24/3 Archipenko—Soft Morning (Pivotal) **Miss K. Rausing**
135 **STAGIAIRE**, b f 20/4 Sea The Moon (GER)—So In Love (Smart Strike (CAN)) **Miss K. Rausing**
136 **SUMMIT REACH**, b c 28/3 Dansili—Casual (Nayef (USA)) **Mr K. Abdullah**
137 B f 21/3 Zoffany (IRE)—Time Honoured (Sadler's Wells (USA)) (38000) **Mr R. Barnett**
138 **TOMFRE**, b c 12/4 Cable Bay (IRE)—Kurtanella (Pastoral Pursuits) (571) **Mrs Philip Snow & Partners**
139 **TREFOIL**, b f 11/2 Teofilo (IRE)—Prairie Flower (IRE) (Zieten (USA)) **Mr J. H. Richmond-Watson**
140 **VAPE**, gr c 1/4 Dark Angel (IRE)—Puff (IRE) (Camacho) **Mr & Mrs David Aykroyd**
141 B f 20/2 Declaration of War (USA)—Wiener Valkyrie (Shamardal (USA)) **The Eclipse Partnership**
142 **WITHIN REACH**, b f 23/4 Oasis Dream—Grasped (Zamindar (USA)) **Mr K. Abdullah**

Other Owners: H.R.H. The Prince Of Wales, Duchess of Cornwall, 5 Hertford Street Racing Club, Mr A. R. Adams, Mr N. B. Attenborough, Mr G. C. B. Brook, Mr D. W. Dennis, Mrs C. P. Elwes, Mr N. R. Elwes, N. J. Forman Hardy, Mr J. A. Glover, Highclere Nominated Partner Limited, Highclere Thoroughbred Racing Ltd, Mr R. S. Hoskins, Mr R. Hull, Mrs L. Mann, Mr N. Martin, Mr K. McAuliffe, Mrs K. J. Morton, N. Skinner, Miss B. A. Snow, Mrs J. I. Snow, Mrs L. Turner.

Assistant Trainers: Adam Kite, Mark Marris

Jockey (flat): Harry Bentley, Richard Kingscote, Oisin Murphy. **Apprentice:** Charlotte Bennett, Emma Wilkinson.

---

30 **MR MICHAEL BELL, Newmarket**
Postal: **Fitzroy House, Newmarket, Suffolk, CB8 0JT**
Contacts: **PHONE** (01638) 666567 **FAX** (01638) 668000 **MOBILE** (07802) 264514
E-MAIL office@fitzroyhouse.co.uk **WEBSITE** www.michaelbellracing.co.uk

1 **ARABIAN JAZZ (IRE)**, 4, b f Red Jazz (USA)—Queen of Rap (IRE) **Ontoawinner, K Stewart & Partner**
2 **ARTARMON (IRE)**, 4, b g So You Think (NZ)—Aljumar (IRE) **OTI Racing 1**
3 **BIG ORANGE**, 8, b g Duke of Marmalade (IRE)—Miss Brown To You (IRE) **W. J. and T. C. O. Gredley**
4 **FABRICATE**, 7, b g Makfi—Flight of Fancy **Her Majesty The Queen**
5 **FIRE BRIGADE**, 5, b g Firebreak—Island Rhapsody **The Fitzrovians**
6 **GEETANJALI (IRE)**, 4, b f Roderic O'Connor (IRE)—Scylla Cadeaux (IRE) **Mr Hugo Merry**

MR MICHAEL BELL - Continued

7 **INDIA**, 4, b f Poet's Voice—Miss Brown To You (IRE) **W. J. and T. C. O. Gredley**
8 **NEW SHOW (IRE)**, 4, ch g New Approach (IRE)—Music Show (IRE) **Mr Edward J. Ware**
9 **PLAIT**, 4, ch f Bated Breath—Quiff **Mrs Michael Bell**
10 **SWISS STORM**, 5, b g Frankel—Swiss Lake (USA) **Lordship Stud**

THREE-YEAR-OLDS

11 **ALLMANKIND**, b c Sea The Moon (GER)—Wemyss Bay **W. J. and T. C. O. Gredley**
12 **ANY SMILE (IRE)**, b f Zoffany (IRE)—Bahja (USA) **Thurloe Thoroughbreds XL VI & Partners**
13 **APERITIF**, b f Pivotal—Swiss Dream **Lordship Stud**
14 **ARTAIR (IRE)**, b g Kodiac—Bonnie Lesley (IRE) **Secular Stagnation & Partner**
15 **BABBO'S BOY (IRE)**, gr c Mastercraftsman (IRE)—Bunood (IRE) **Amo Racing Limited**
16 **BALLADEER**, b g Poet's Voice—Diamond Run **Mascalls Stud**
17 **BIGHEARTED**, ch f Farhh—Bianca Nera **Mr M. E. Perlman**
18 **CRIMSON KISS (IRE)**, ch f Sepoy (AUS)—Crimson Year (USA) **Sheikh Marwan Al Maktoum**
19 **DINAH WASHINGTON (IRE)**, ch f Australia—Gainful (USA) **Chelsea Thoroughbreds-Mad About the Boy 1**
20 **DUBAI PHILOSOPHER (FR)**, b c Tamayuz—Elopa (GER) **Ahmad Al Shaikh**
21 **EAGLES BY DAY (IRE)**, b c Sea The Stars (IRE)—Missunited (IRE) **Clipper Logistics**
22 **EIGHTSOME REEL**, b c Iffraaj—Set To Music (IRE) **Her Majesty The Queen**
23 **EMIRATES EMPIRE (IRE)**, b c Authorized (IRE)—Ana Shababiya (IRE) **Ahmad Al Shaikh**
24 **EVA MARIA**, b f Sea The Stars (IRE)—Whazzat **W. J. and T. C. O. Gredley**
25 **HAPPY HIKER (IRE)**, b f Dalakhani (IRE)—Travelling Light (USA) **Sir Edmund Loder**
26 **HEARTBREAK HOTEL (IRE)**, gr f Le Havre (IRE)—Daliana **Mr C. Wright & The Hon Mrs J.M. Corbett**
27 **HEATHERDOWN (IRE)**, b g Morpheus—Hapipi **The Heatherdonians**
28 **JAMES WATT (IRE)**, b g Morpheus—Tomintoul Singer (IRE) **Men Fae the Clyde**
29 **L'UN DEUX TROIS (IRE)**, gr c Mastercraftsman (IRE)—Moment Juste **Mrs G. Rowland-Clark & Mr Timmy Hyde**
30 **LADY ARIA**, b f Kodiac—Dot Hill **Amo Racing Limited**
31 B f Dark Angel (IRE)—Little Audio (IRE) **Clipper Logistics**
32 **LOGIE BAIRD (IRE)**, b g Mastercraftsman (IRE)—Strategy **Mr James Barnett & Mrs P. Shanahan**
33 **LUCKY TURN (IRE)**, b f Zoffany (IRE)—Lucky Spin **Mrs I. Corbani**
34 **MANIC MONDAY (USA)**, b f Declaration of War (USA)—Bohemian Dance (IRE) **Mr C. Wright & Miss E Asprey**
35 **MONTJEU'S LADY**, b f Motivator—Clizia (IRE) **Bartisan Racing Ltd**
36 **NAHEMA (IRE)**, b f Dubawi (IRE)—Sariska **Lady Bamford**
37 **ONEBABA (IRE)**, ch c No Nay Never (USA)—Enharmonic (USA) **Amo Racing Limited**
38 **PLATFORM NINETEEN (IRE)**, ch g Australia—Susan Stroman **The Royal Ascot Racing Club**
39 **POETRY**, b f Kingman—Swiss Diva **Lordship Stud**
40 **PORCELAIN GIRL (IRE)**, ch f Exceed And Excel (AUS)—Dresden Doll (USA) **Sheikh Marwan Al Maktoum**
41 **POWER OF LIFE (USA)**, b br g Hat Trick (JPN)—Asuncion (USA) **Mrs I. Corbani**
42 **PRETTY POLLYANNA**, b f Oasis Dream—Unex Mona Lisa **W. J. and T. C. O. Gredley**
43 **RAJ MARTA**, b f Kingman—Behkara (IRE) **Lady Bamford**
44 **RAPTURE (FR)**, ch f Rachel—Rosa Bonheur (USA) **Clipper Logistics**
45 **REGULAR**, ch g Exceed And Excel (AUS)—Humdrum **Her Majesty The Queen**
46 **ROBERT FITZROY (IRE)**, b g Big Bad Bob (IRE)—Semiquaver (IRE) **The Fitzrovians 2**
47 **STAGE PLAY (IRE)**, gr f Oasis Dream—Boastful (IRE) **Clipper Logistics**
48 **STARLIGHT**, b f Iffraaj—Ighraa (IRE) **Mr Edward J. Ware**
49 **SWISS PEAK**, b g Swiss Spirit—Easy To Love (USA) **Wayne & Sarah Dale & Lordship Stud**
50 **TAMOK (IRE)**, b f Australia—Anklet (USA) **Amo Racing Limited**
51 **TERESHKOVA**, b f Sea The Moon (GER)—Fanny Squeers **W. J. and T. C. O. Gredley**
52 **THELONIOUS**, b c Sea The Moon (GER)—Miss Chaussini (IRE) **W. J. and T. C. O. Gredley**
53 **THOMAS CUBITT (FR)**, b c Youmzain (IRE)—Helsinka (FR) **Men Fae the Clyde**
54 **WHIMSICAL DREAM**, b f Oasis Dream—Whim **Bartisan Racing Ltd**
55 **YOUTHFUL**, b c Shamardal (USA)—Good Hope **Her Majesty The Queen**

TWO-YEAR-OLDS

56 **ANNO MAXIMO (GER)**, b c 28/2 Maxios—Queen's Hall (Singspiel (IRE)) (16856) **OTI Racing**
57 B c 10/3 Gutaifan (IRE)—Bali Breeze (IRE) (Common Grounds) (88495) **Mr Edward J. Ware**
58 **BE IN VERSE**, b f 7/3 Sepoy (AUS)—Dansante (Champs Elysees) **W. J. and T. C. O. Gredley**
59 B f 2/4 Kingman—Because (IRE) (Sadler's Wells (USA)) **Lady Bamford**
60 B f 5/2 Archipenko (USA)—Bipartisan (Bahamian Bounty) **Mr M. E. Perlman**
61 **BRAZEN SAFA**, b f 5/2 Brazen Beau (AUS)—Insaaf (Averti (IRE)) (19047) **Ontoawinner 9 & Partner**
62 **BY JOVE**, b c 5/2 Nathaniel (IRE)—Calima Breeze (Oasis Dream) (42000) **Sarah & Wayne Dale 2**
63 **BY MY SIDE (IRE)**, ch f 19/2 Siyouni (FR)—Fill My Heart (IRE) (Peintre Celebre (USA)) **Mr S. Hanson**
64 **CHOSEN STAR**, ch f 2/3 Dubawi (IRE)—Yodelling (USA) (Medaglia d'oro (USA)) **Her Majesty The Queen**
65 **CLOUD DRIFT**, b c 29/3 Toronado (IRE)—Humdrum (Dr Fong (USA)) **Her Majesty The Queen**
66 B c 22/3 Oasis Dream—Coconut Kreek (Pivotal) **Lady Bamford**
67 **CRAYLANDS**, b f 13/3 Golden Horn—Madame Defarge (IRE) (Motivator) **W. J. & T. C. O. Gredley**

MR MICHAEL BELL - Continued

68 **DEBT OF HONOUR,** b c 3/4 Kyllachy—Capacious (Nayef (USA)) (85000) **W. J. and T. C. O. Gredley**
69 Ch f 26/2 Mukhadram—Diavana (FR) (Pivotal) **Wood Hall Stud Limited**
70 **DUTCH PAINTING,** b f 3/4 Dutch Art—Lisiere (IRE) (Excellent Art) (70000) **Mr R. A. Green**
71 Ch f 14/4 Frankel—Eva's Request (IRE) (Soviet Star (USA)) **Lady Bamford**
72 **FANTAST (GER),** b c 22/3 Maxios—Four Roses (IRE) (Darshaan) (60000) **Patrick & Scott Bryceland**
73 **FORMALITY,** b c 7/3 Frankel—Silver Mirage (Oasis Dream) **Her Majesty The Queen**
74 B c 19/4 Make Believe—French Fern (IRE) (Royal Applause) (55000) **Nick Bradley Racing & Ballylinch Stud**
75 **FRYERNS,** b f 15/3 Helmet (AUS)—Beyond Fashion (Motivator) **W. J. & T. C. O. Gredley**
76 **GOOD TRY,** b f 4/3 Iffraaj—Good Hope (Cape Cross (IRE)) **Her Majesty The Queen**
77 **HIGH SHINE,** b f 27/3 Paco Boy (IRE)—Hypoteneuse (IRE) (Sadler's Wells (USA)) **Her Majesty The Queen**
78 Ch c 2/4 Dandy Man (IRE)—Imelda Mayhem (Byron) (46354) **Middleham Park Racing XVII & Partner**
79 **INDIFFERENCE,** b c 22/2 Kingman—Bark (IRE) (Galileo (IRE)) **W. J. and T. C. O. Gredley**
80 B g 27/3 Champs Elysees—Iridescence (Dutch Art) (48000) **Mr Edward J. Ware**
81 Ch f 24/2 Exceed And Excel (AUS)—
          Kiss Me Goodbye (Raven's Pass (USA)) (85000) **Thurloe Thoroughbred XL VIII & Partner**
82 **LEYDA (IRE),** b f 26/4 Camelot—Moment Juste (Pivotal) (60000) **Wood Hall Stud Limited**
83 Ch c 30/3 Hot Streak (IRE)—Lomapamar (Nashwan (USA)) **Mascalls Stud**
84 **LORD WARBURTON (IRE),** ch c 10/5 Zoffany (IRE)—
          Portrait of A Lady (IRE) (Peintre Celebre (USA)) (33712) **The Fitzrovians 3**
85 **LYDFORD,** b c 17/2 Fastnet Rock (AUS)—Miss Brown To You (IRE) (Fasliyev (USA)) **W. J. and T. C. O. Gredley**
86 **MAXI BOY,** b c 18/1 Oasis Dream—Lavender And Lace (Barathea (IRE)) (380000) **Amo Racing Limited**
87 **MR KIKI (IRE),** b c 2/3 No Nay Never (USA)—Jacquelin Jag (Fayruz) (450000) **Amo Racing Limited**
88 **NEVENDON,** b c 21/4 Nathaniel (IRE)—Unex Mona Lisa (Shamardal (USA)) **W. J. and T. C. O. Gredley**
89 B f 18/5 Galileo (IRE)—Nijoom Dubai (Noverre (USA)) **Mrs Paul Shanahan**
90 **OTAGO,** b c 26/1 Cable Bay (IRE)—Spinning Top (Alzao (USA)) **Her Majesty The Queen**
91 B c 28/4 Tamayuz—Red Halo (IRE) (Galileo (IRE)) (200000) **Mr Edward J. Ware**
92 B gr c 1/3 Dark Angel (IRE)—Sarita (Galileo (IRE)) **Lady Bamford**
93 **SCHERZO,** b f 14/4 Golden Horn—Labise (IRE) (Azamour (IRE)) **W. J. & T. C. O. Gredley**
94 **SCULPTURESQUE,** b f 24/1 Mastercraftsman (IRE)—Diamond Bangle (Galileo (IRE)) **W. J. & T. C. O. Gredley**
95 **SHE'S AMAZING,** ch f 22/2 Showcasing—
          Nandiga (USA) (Bernardini (USA)) (65000) **Eight Investment Holdings Limited**
96 B f 21/1 No Nay Never (USA)—
          Shelley Beach (Danehill Dancer (IRE)) (650000) **George Bolton & Lady Sheila Stables LLC**
97 **SPARKLING OLLY (IRE),** b f 23/4 Gleneagles (IRE)—
          Sogno Verde (IRE) (Green Desert (USA)) (300000) **Amo Racing Limited**
98 **STEPNEY CAUSEWAY,** b c 21/3 New Approach (IRE)—
          Wake Up Call (Noverre (USA)) (100000) **W. J. and T. C. O. Gredley**
99 **STONE CIRCLE (IRE),** ch c 28/4 No Nay Never (USA)—
          Candlehill Girl (IRE) (Shamardal (USA)) (42140) **The Fitzrovians 3**
100 B f 6/1 Gutaifan (IRE)—Tamarisk (GER) (Selkirk (USA)) (66666) **Mr Christopher Wright & Mr A. C. Elliott**
101 **THELMA TODD (IRE),** ch f 29/4 Australia—
          Sugar House (USA) (Distorted Humor (USA)) (70000) **Chelsea Thoroughbreds - Los Angeles**
102 B c 16/2 Authorized (IRE)—Tocqueville (FR) (Numerous (USA)) (17699) **Secular Stagnation**
103 B c 27/3 Bungle Inthejungle—Universal Circus (Imperial Dancer) (9523) **Mr Christopher Wright & Mr David Kilburn**
104 **WELSH BACK,** b br f 30/3 Harbour Watch (IRE)—Clifton Dancer (Fraam) (15238) **The Fitzrovians 3**
105 B br f 12/3 Street Sense (USA)—Win McCool (USA) (Giant's Causeway (USA)) (239858) **Mrs Paul Shanahan**
106 **ZMILE,** b f 15/4 Medaglia d'oro (USA)—Cay Dancer (Danehill Dancer (IRE)) (150000) **W. J. and T. C. O. Gredley**

Assistant Trainer: Nick Bell

Jockey (flat): Jamie Spencer, Louis Steward, Hayley Turner. **Apprentice:** Joe Bradnam, Sara Del Fabbro, Cameron Noble.

31	**MR JAMES BENNETT, Wantage** Postal: **2 Filley Alley, Letcombe Bassett, Wantage, Oxfordshire, OX12 9LT** Contacts: **PHONE (01235) 762163 MOBILE (07771) 523076** E-MAIL jbennett345@btinternet.com

1 **GONZAGA,** 4, b g Oasis Dream—Symposia **Miss J. C. Blackwell**
2 **THE LAST MELON,** 7, ch g Sir Percy—Step Fast (USA) **Miss J. C. Blackwell**

Assistant Trainer: Miss J. Blackwell

Jockey (flat): Racheal Kneller. **Jockey (NH):** David Bass.

32   MR ALAN BERRY, Cockerham

Postal: **Moss Side Racing Stables, Crimbles Lane, Cockerham, Lancashire, LA2 0ES**
Contacts: **PHONE (01524) 791179 MOBILE (07880) 553515**
E-MAIL berryracing@hotmail.com

1 **CRAIGIE ROSE (IRE)**, 4, b f Distant Peak (IRE)—Martha's Way **Mr P. J. Rands**
2 **ECONOMIC CRISIS (IRE)**, 10, ch m Excellent Art—Try The Air (IRE) **William Burns & Alan Berry**
3 **I'LL BE GOOD**, 10, b g Red Clubs (IRE)—Willisa **Mr A. Berry**
4 **JORDAURA**, 13, br g Primo Valentino (IRE)—Christina's Dream **Mr A. Berry**
5 4, B f Lilbourne Lad (IRE)—Kasalla (IRE) **Mr P. J. Rands**
6 **KIRKBY'S PHANTOM**, 5, gr m Sayif (IRE)—Demolition Jo **Kirkby Lonsdale Racing**
7 **LEANNES LADY (IRE)**, 7, b m Ask—Wizzy (IRE) **Mr A. Berry**
8 **ONE FOR BRAD (IRE)**, 4, b f Watar (IRE)—Our Jaffa (IRE) **Kirkby Lonsdale Racing**
9 **PLASTIKI**, 10, b g Oasis Dream—Dayrose **Mr A. Berry**
10 **RAISE A BILLION**, 8, b g Major Cadeaux—Romantic Destiny **Mr P. J. Rands**
11 **RED HOT FUSION (IRE)**, 5, b h Kodiac—Unfortunate **Mr S. J. Allen**
12 **ROMAN TIMES (IRE)**, 6, b m Holy Roman Emperor—Timeless Dream **Mr A. Berry**
13 **ZIZUM**, 4, ch g Showcasing—Proud Duchess (IRE) **A Parr & A Berry**

THREE-YEAR-OLDS

14 B f Slade Power (IRE)—Ekhraaj (USA)
15 **JUSTICE SHALLOW (FR)**, ch g Shakespearean (IRE)—Try The Air (IRE) **T. W. Blane**
16 **LIBERTY DIVA (IRE)**, b f Palavicini (USA)—Alpine Mysteries (IRE) **A Parr & A Berry**
17 B f Alhebayeb (IRE)—Ribald
18 **THE FLUTER (IRE)**, b c Kodiac—Fujara **A Parr & A Berry**

Other Owners: W. Burns, A. B. Parr, Mr P. Stephenson, G. R. Taylor.

Assistant Trainer: John A. Quinn

33   MR JOHN BERRY, Newmarket

Postal: **Beverley House Stables, Exeter Road, Newmarket, Suffolk, CB8 8LR**
Contacts: **PHONE (01638) 660663**
E-MAIL john@beverleyhousestables.com WEBSITE www.beverleyhousestables.com

1 **ALSAMARA**, 4, b f New Approach (IRE)—Altitude **Mr John Berry**
2 5, B g Joe Bear—Artistic Belle (IRE) **Mrs G. A. Olive**
3 **DAS KAPITAL**, 4, b g Cityscape—Narla **The Geezers**
4 **DEAR ALIX**, 4, b g Schiaparelli (GER)—Desiree (IRE) **Mrs E. L. Berry**
5 **DELATITE**, 7, b g Schiaparelli (GER)—Desiree (IRE) **The Beverley House Stables Partnership**
6 **DERVISH**, 5, b g Cacique (IRE)—Doggerbank (IRE) **The Sisters Of Mercy**
7 **FREE BIRD**, 4, b f Phoenix Reach (IRE)—Love Supreme (IRE) **The Free Birds**
8 **HOPE IS HIGH**, 6, b m Sir Percy—Altitude **Emma Berry & John Berry**
9 **KONIGIN**, 4, b f Shamardal (USA)—Kitty Wells **Mr K. T. Yap**
10 **KRYPTOS**, 5, b g Cacique (IRE)—Posteritas (USA) **Mr A. W. Fordham**
11 **ROY ROCKET (FR)**, 9, gr g Layman (USA)—Minnie's Mystery (FR) **McCarthy & Berry**
12 **SACRED SPRITE**, 4, b f Nathaniel (IRE)—Lively Sprite **Mr K. T. Yap**
13 **SOLITARY SISTER (IRE)**, 5, br m Cockney Rebel (IRE)—Sweet Afton (IRE) **The Sisters Of Mercy**
14 **SUSSEX GIRL**, 5, ch m Compton Place—Palinisa (FR) **Mr D. Tunmore & Mr John Berry**
15 **THE ROCKET PARK (IRE)**, 6, b g Rock of Gibraltar (IRE)—Snowpalm **L. C. Wadey**

THREE-YEAR-OLDS

16 **DEREHAM**, b g Sir Percy—Desiree (IRE) **Mrs E. L. Berry**
17 **ETHICS BOY (FR)**, ch g Anodin (IRE)—Ethics Girl (IRE) **1997 Partnership & John Berry**
18 **LA PARISIENNE**, b f Champs Elysees—Gale Green **P. J. & Mrs J. P. Haycock**
19 **LOVING PEARL**, b f Dunaden (FR)—Forever Loved **Mr A. W. Fordham**

TWO-YEAR-OLDS

20 B f 3/4 Gregorian (IRE)—Forever Loved (Deploy) (3000)
21 B g 24/4 Nayef (USA)—Sweet Child O'mine (Singspiel (IRE)) (1000) **EERC**

MR JOHN BERRY - Continued

22 **THE SIMPLE TRUTH (FR)**, gr g 17/3 Rajsaman (FR)—
Minnie's Mystery (FR) (Highest Honor (FR)) (4214) **Mr A. W. Fordham**

Other Owners: The 1997 Partnership, Mr & Mrs D. Collings, Mrs A. Flaherty, Mrs B. Fordham, Mr S. Fordham, Mr B. Granahan, P J. Haycock, Mrs J. P. Haycock, Mr M. Hillyard, Mr N. Hilsden, Mr R. W. Huggins, Mr A. Mayne, Miss H. Mayne, Miss L. I. McCarthy, Mr S. McCormick, Mr & Mrs B. Moule, Mr E. Mullarkey, Mr T. O'Rourke, Mrs M. L. Parry, Mr C. Plant, Mr D. Punshon, Mr D. Regan, Mr R. Shergold, Mr B. M. Sherwin, Mr R. Sims, Ms L. Sinden, Mr P. Steele-Mortimer, Mr L. Stratton, Mr S. J. N. Sweeting, Mr J. Targett, Mr M. Tidmarsh, Mr I. Walton.

Jockey (flat): Nicola Currie, John Egan, Josephine Gordon. **Jockey (NH):** Will Kennedy, Jack Quinlan.
Amateur: Mr R. Birkett.

34
MR JOHN A. BERRY, Blackwater
Postal: Ballyroe, Blackwater, Enniscorthy, Co. Wexford, Ireland
Contacts: PHONE (00353) 53 91 27205 MOBILE (00353) 86 2557537
E-MAIL johnaberry@eircom.net

1 **ARTIC QUEST (IRE)**, 7, ch g Trans Island—Back The Queen (IRE) **J. A. Berry**
2 **CADDY SHACK (IRE)**, 5, br m Arcadio (GER)—Hot Or What (IRE) **Mr J. Berry**
3 **CARPOOL (IRE)**, 5, b m Mahler—Buslane (IRE) **Anna Berry**
4 **CATCH MY DRIFT (IRE)**, 10, ch g Subtle Power (IRE)—Deliga Lady (IRE) **J. Berry**
5 **COURT GLORY (IRE)**, 6, b m Court Cave (IRE)—Ad Gloria (IRE) **Emma Berry**
6 **DAY DAY (IRE)**, 9, b m Hurricane Run (IRE)—Mem O'rees **J. P. McManus**
7 **FUZZBUSTER (IRE)**, 5, b g Sans Frontieres (IRE)—Five Trix **P. Laffen**
8 **LE RUESKI (IRE)**, 5, b g September Storm (GER)—Calimesa (IRE) **J. Berry**
9 **STORMY WATAR (IRE)**, 6, b g Watar (IRE)—Calm Luso (IRE) **J. Berry**
10 **TAKE FIVE (IRE)**, 6, b g Arakan (USA)—World of Ballet (IRE) **J. Berry**

Assistant Trainer: Mr J. P. Berry

Amateur: Mr J. P. Berry.

35
MR JOHN BEST, Sittingbourne
Postal: Eyehorn Farm, Munsgore Lane, Borden, Sittingbourne, Kent, ME9 8JU
Contacts: MOBILE (07889) 362154
E-MAIL john.best@johnbestracing.com WEBSITE www.johnbestracing.com

1 **AFRICAN BLESSING**, 6, ch g Mount Nelson—Bella Beguine **Mr J. O. C. Tomkins**
2 **BANTA BAY**, 5, b g Kheleyf (USA)—Atnab (USA) **Jones, Fuller & Paine**
3 **BERRAHRI (IRE)**, 8, b g Bahri (USA)—Band of Colour (IRE) **White Turf Racing UK**
4 **CASA COMIGO (IRE)**, 4, b c Cape Cross (IRE)—Belanoiva (IRE) **Mr S. D. Malcolm**
5 **EDDYSTONE ROCK (IRE)**, 7, ch g Rock of Gibraltar (IRE)—Bayberry (UAE) **Curtis, Malt & Williams**
6 **FEARLESS LAD (IRE)**, 9, b g Excellent Art—Souffle **Mrs J. O. Jones**
7 **GLENYS THE MENACE (FR)**, 5, b m American Post—Elle S'voyait Deja (USA) **Curtis, Malt & Jenkins**
8 **HIORNE TOWER (FR)**, 8, b g Poliglote—Hierarchie (FR) **Mrs J. O. Jones**
9 **MALT TEASER (FR)**, 5, ch g Muhtathir—Abondante (USA) **Ms C Hart & Curtis & Williams Bloodstock**
10 **MOSSKETEER**, 4, b g Moss Vale (IRE)—Gracilia (FR) **Lingfield Park Owners Group 2016 (LPOG 2016)**
11 **MULLARKEY**, 5, b g Mullionmileanhour (IRE)—Hannah's Dream (IRE) **Thomson & Partners**
12 **PENDO**, 8, b g Denounce—Abundant **Athena Partnership**
13 **PLANTADREAM**, 4, b g Planteur (IRE)—Phantom Ridge (IRE) **H. J. Jarvis**
14 **SALVE DEL RIO (IRE)**, 4, b c Rio de La Plata (USA)—Salve Aurora (GER) **Mark Curtis & Mike Stanley**
15 **SEAQUINN**, 4, b f Equiano (FR)—Marine Girl **Harris & Beckett**
16 **TARTARIA**, 13, b m Oasis Dream—Habariya (IRE) **Mr N. Dyshaev**
17 **TOO MANY SHOTS**, 5, b g Mullionmileanhour (IRE)—Neissa (USA) **TMS & Beckett**

THREE-YEAR-OLDS

18 **CACHACA**, b f Foxwedge (AUS)—Elounta **Laura Malcolm & Partners**
19 **ELMEJOR (IRE)**, b c Xtension (IRE)—Lyca Ballerina **Layezy Racing Owners Club**
20 **FOR RICHARD**, b g Muhtathir—Retainage (USA) **Mr & Mrs Coleman**
21 **GANADOR (IRE)**, b c Zebedee—Duchess of Foxland (IRE) **Layezy Racing Owners Club**
22 **IGNATIUS (IRE)**, b c Casamento (IRE)—Free Lance (IRE) **Keaveney & Butcher**
23 **MOLIVALIENTE (USA)**, ro c The Factor (USA)—Bee Brave **Layezy Racing Owners Club**
24 **OTRACHICA (IRE)**, ch f Camacho—Endless Peace (IRE) **Layezy Racing Owners Club**

MR JOHN BEST - Continued

25 PENTIMENTO, b c Garswood—M'selle (IRE) **Walter & Geraldine Paine**
26 PRIONSA (IRE), b c Roderic O'Connor (IRE)—Lovingit (IRE) **Hucking Horses V**
27 TIPPERARY JACK (USA), b c Violence (USA)—Indian Miss (USA) **Curtis & Tomkins**
28 TORBELLINO, b f Maxios—Tiny Smile (IRE) **Layezy Racing Owners Club**
29 TOROCHICA, ch f Toronado (IRE)—Biased **Layezy Racing Owners Club**

TWO-YEAR-OLDS

30 B f 23/5 Helmet (AUS)—Balletlou (IRE) (Peintre Celebre (USA)) **Mr S. D. Malcolm**
31 BOBS LAD, b c 15/4 Casamento (IRE)—Foxie Girl (Virtual) **Mrs J. O. Jones**
32 B c 2/3 Casamento (IRE)—Elounta (Dubawi (IRE)) **Mr S. D. Malcolm**
33 B c 21/1 Garswood—French Accent (Elnadim (USA)) **TMS & Beckett**
34 PINATAR (IRE), b c 24/2 Holy Roman Emperor (IRE)—
                         Burn The Breeze (IRE) (Beat Hollow) (57142) **Layezy Racing Owners Club**
35 B f 24/3 Casamento (IRE)—Queen Ranavola (USA) (Medaglia d'oro (USA))
36 QUIMERICO, b c 3/2 Due Diligence (USA)—
                         Peyto Princess (Bold Arrangement) (23000) **Layezy Racing Owners Club**
37 Ch f 16/5 Triplicity—Triplicity (Three Valleys (USA)) **Lingfield Park Owners Group 2019**
38 ZAGAN, gr c 2/5 Dark Angel (IRE)—La Mere Germaine (IRE) (Indian Ridge) **Layezy Racing Owners Club**

Other Owners: Mr P. I. Beckett, Mr J. R. Best, Mr P. Butcher, Mr J. A. Coleman, Mrs J. Coleman, Mr M. B. Curtis, Curtis & Williams Bloodstock, Fuller & Paine, Mr A. Harris, Mr G. R. Jones, Mr A. Keaveney, Mr M. Keaveney, Mrs L. C. G. Malcolm, Mr R. C. Malt, Mr W. G. Paine, Ms C. Rice, Mr M. Stanley, Stanley Best & Williams, Miss H. J. Williams.

Assistant Trainer: Michelle Brister

---

36 MRS SUZI BEST, Lewes

Postal: **The Bungalow, Grandstand Stables, The Old Racecourse, Lewes, East Sussex, BN7 1UR**
Contacts: **MOBILE (07804) 487296**
E-MAIL sbestracing@yahoo.com

1 ANNAJEMIMA, 5, b m Firebreak—Leaping Flame (USA) **Mr J. J. Callaghan**
2 ASHAREDMOMENT, 4, b f Swiss Spirit—Shared Moment (IRE) **Mr L. Best**
3 BALLESTEROS, 10, ch g Tomba—Flamenco Dancer **Jack Callaghan & Christopher Dillon**
4 ECHO BRAVA, 9, gr g Proclamation (IRE)—Snake Skin **F.A. O'Sullivan&thefat Jockeypartnership**
5 GENEROUS JACK, 10, ch g Generous (IRE)—Yosna (FR) **Ne-Chance**
6 GRANGEROSIE (IRE), 6, b m Court Cave (IRE)—Comings (IRE) **Milldean Racing Syndicate**
7 LONDON GLORY, 6, b g Archipenko (USA)—Reflected Image (IRE) **Jack Callaghan & Christopher Dillon**
8 MARIA'S CHOICE (IRE), 10, b g Oratorio—Amathusia **Mr P. J. Arrow**
9 MILLDEAN SILVA (IRE), 6, ch m Presenting—Impudent (IRE) **Milldean Racing Syndicate**
10 MUSICAL COMEDY, 8, b g Royal Applause—Spinning Top **Jack Callaghan & Christopher Dillon**
11 NAUTICAL HAVEN, 5, b g Harbour Watch—Mania (IRE) **Milldean Racing Syndicate**
12 NEW STREET (IRE), 8, gr g Acclamation—New Deal **Mr J. J. Callaghan**
13 OUTRATH (IRE), 9, b g Captain Rio—Silver Grouse (IRE) **Mr A. R. Coupland**
14 PLANETOID (IRE), 11, b g Galileo (IRE)—Palmeraie (USA) **Planetoid Partnership**
15 RED CHARMER (IRE), 9, b g Red Clubs—Golden Charm (IRE) **Mr J. J. Callaghan**
16 RED ORATOR, 10, ch g Osorio (GER)—Red Roses Story (FR) **Mr L. Best**
17 SIX GUN SERENADE (IRE), 8, b g Kalanisi (IRE)—Zenaide (IRE) **Mr J. J. Callaghan**
18 SLOWFOOT (GER), 11, b h Hernando (FR)—Simply Red (GER) **Mr Philip Arrow & Mr Chris Dillon**
19 THATS MY RABBIT (IRE), 10, b g Heron Island (IRE)—Minnie Turbo (IRE) **Mr J. J. Callaghan**

THREE-YEAR-OLDS

20 MILLDEAN FELIX (IRE), br g Red Jazz (USA)—Plausabelle **Milldean Racing Syndicate**
21 MILLDEAN PANTHER, b g Mayson—Silver Halo **Milldean Racing Syndicate**

Other Owners: Mr C. J. Dillon, Mr J. Donnelly, Mr D. Edmonston, Mr M. Hilton, Mr N. N. Kane, Miss F. O'Sullivan, Mr B Phillpott, Mr I. R. Steadman.

Assistant Trainer: Mr Tom Best

37
MISS HARRIET BETHELL, Hull
Postal: **Waverley House, Main Street, Long Riston, Hull, North Humberside, HU11 5JF**
E-MAIL **harrietbethell@hotmail.co.uk**

1 **LOPES DANCER (IRE)**, 7, b g Lope de Vega (IRE)—Ballet Dancer (IRE) **W. A. Bethell**
2 **MISCHIEVIOUS MAX (IRE)**, 6, ch g Dubai Destination (USA)—Saabga (USA) **W. A. Bethell**
3 **MY PAINTER (IRE)**, 8, br m Jeremy (USA)—Last Cry (FR) **W. A. Bethell**
4 **NEWBERRY NEW (IRE)**, 7, b g Kodiac—Sunblush (UAE) **W. A. Bethell**
5 **STEEL HELMET (IRE)**, 5, ch g Helmet (AUS)—Marine City (JPN) **W. A. Bethell**
6 **SUMNER BEACH**, 5, ch g Aqlaam—Cosmic Song **Mr K. Brown**
7 **VALENTINO BOY (IRE)**, 5, b g Bated Breath—Capistrano Day (USA) **W. A. Bethell**

Jockey (flat): Josephine Gordon, Alistair Rawlinson. **Jockey (NH):** Danny Cook, Connor King.

38
MR JAMES BETHELL, Middleham
Postal: **Thorngill, Coverham, Middleham, North Yorkshire, DL8 4TJ**
Contacts: PHONE **(01969) 640360** FAX **(01969) 640360** MOBILE **(07831) 683528**
E-MAIL **james@bethellracing.com** WEBSITE **www.bethellracing.com**

1 **CALL ME MADAM**, 4, b f Passing Glance—Shazana **R. F. Gibbons**
2 **FAST AND FURIOUS (IRE)**, 6, b g Rock of Gibraltar (IRE)—Ocean Talent (USA) **Mr A. Buckingham**
3 **HELLO BOB**, 4, ch f Cityscape—Maid of Perth **R. F. Gibbons**
4 **HOWBAAR (USA)**, 8, b g Lonhro (AUS)—Going Day (USA) **Mr J. A. Tabet**
5 **JESSINAMILLION**, 5, b g Mine (IRE)—Miss Apricot **Culture Club**
6 **MUDAWWAN (IRE)**, 5, b g Invincible Spirit (IRE)—Louve Sacree (USA) **Clarendon Thoroughbred Racing**
7 **PORTLEDGE (IRE)**, 5, b g Acclamation—Off Chance **Mr A. Buckingham**
8 **RICH AGAIN (IRE)**, 10, b g Amadeus Wolf—Fully Fashioned (IRE) **Mr Richard T. Vickers Partnership**
9 **STRAWBERRYANDCREAM**, 4, ch f Cityscape—Miss Apricot **Mrs James Bethell & Partner**
10 **ULSHAW BRIDGE (IRE)**, 4, b g High Chaparral (IRE)—Sharaarah (IRE) **Geoffrey van Cutsem & Partners**

THREE-YEAR-OLDS
11 **CONAGLEN**, b c Toronado (IRE)—Infamous Angel **Mr P. Hibbert-Foy & Partners**
12 **DOUBLE HONOUR**, b c Garswood—Snake's Head **Mr J. E. Dance**
13 **EDGEWOOD**, b c Garswood—Heskin (IRE) **Mr D. W. Armstrong**
14 B f Garswood—Gerash (FR) **Mr D. W. Armstrong**
15 **HESSLEWOOD (IRE)**, b g Slade Power (IRE)—Rochitta (USA) **Clarendon Thoroughbred Racing**
16 **MOSS GILL (IRE)**, b g No Nay Never (USA)—Sharaarah (IRE) **G Van Cutsem & Partner**
17 **RICH APPROACH (IRE)**, b g Dawn Approach (IRE)—Kiss Me Goodbye **The Vickers & Clark Racing Partnership**
18 **TIE A YELLOWRIBBON**, gr f Poet's Voice—Silver Games (IRE) **Chris Wright & the Hon Mrs J M Corbett**
19 **TUCSON**, b c Lawman (FR)—Bruxcalina (IRE) **Mr D R Kilburn & Mr A N Horncastle**
20 **WELL FUNDED (IRE)**, b f Camelot—Malikayah (IRE) **Clarendon Thoroughbred Racing**
21 **WINTON**, b g Harbour Watch (IRE)—Arctic Song **J. Carrick & Clarendon Thoroughbred Racing**

TWO-YEAR-OLDS
22 **EAGLE'S FOOT**, b c 2/5 Eagle (IRE)—Carmens Fate (Cape Cross (IRE)) (32000) **The Eagle's Foot Syndicate**

Other Owners: Mr J. D. Bethell, Mrs S. Bethell, Mr J. Carrick, Mr M. Clark, The Hon Mrs C. Corbett, Exors of the Late P. Dixon, Mr P. M. L. Hibbert-Foy, Mr A. N. Horncastle, T. Hyde, D. Kilburn, The Earl of R. L. Ronaldshay, Mr M. J. Rozenmbroek, R. T. Vickers, Mr D. Y. Vickers, Mr C. N. Wright, Mr G. N. van Cutsem.

Assistant Trainer: Edward Bethell

39
MR GEORGE BEWLEY, Appleby-In-Westmorland
Postal: **Jerusalem Farm, Colby, Appleby-In-Westmorland, Cumbria, CA16 6BB**
Contacts: PHONE **(01768) 353003** MOBILE **(07704) 924783**
E-MAIL **bewleyracing@outlook.com** WEBSITE **www.georgebewleyracing.co.uk**

1 **ALLEZ COOL (IRE)**, 10, ch g Flemensfirth (USA)—La Fisarmonica (IRE) **G. T. Bewley**
2 **ARCANJA (IRE)**, 5, gr g Arcadio (GER)—Nanja Monja (IRE) **J. Wade**
3 **CLASSICAL MILANO (IRE)**, 8, b g Milan—Miss Baden (IRE) **Victoria Bewley, John Gibson & E G Tunstall**
4 **CLONDAW FIXER (IRE)**, 7, b g Court Cave (IRE)—The Millers Tale (IRE) **G. T. Bewley**
5 **DIPPIN AND DIVING (IRE)**, 6, b g Kalanisi—Supreme Dipper (IRE) **J. Wade**
6 **IAN'S GIFT (IRE)**, 6, b g Brian Boru—Cindy's Fancy (IRE) **Miss V. F. Bewley**

MR GEORGE BEWLEY - Continued

7 **INNIS SHANNON (IRE)**, 9, br m Stowaway—Put On Hold (IRE) **Mrs Lesley Bewley & Mr John Gibson**
8 **KENNEDYS FIELD**, 6, b g Multiplex—Supreme Lady (IRE) **Victoria Bewley & Lizzy Annett**
9 **LAWTOP LEGEND (IRE)**, 7, b g Milan—Nolagh Supreme (IRE) **Miss V. F. Bewley**
10 **MAH MATE BOB (IRE)**, 7, b g Mahler—Bobset Leader (IRE) **J. Wade**
11 **MAHLER SUPREME (IRE)**, 5, b g Mahler—Site Alite (IRE) **Miss M. D. Myco**
12 8, Ro m Fair Mix (IRE)—Miss Mattie Ross **Mrs E. Annett**
13 **ONDERUN (IRE)**, 10, b g Flemensfirth (USA)—Warts And All (IRE) **Southdean Racing Club**
14 **OUR MORRIS (IRE)**, 8, b g Milan—Broken Gale (IRE) **Mr R Fisher & Bewley**
15 **OUTBACK BLUE**, 6, gr g Aussie Rules (USA)—Beautiful Lady (IRE) **Mrs C. J. Todd**
16 **REIGN BACK DANCER (IRE)**, 5, b g Jeremy (USA)—Back The Queen (IRE) **Miss M. D. Myco**
17 **ROBIN DU ROI (IRE)**, 6, b g Doyen (IRE)—Regle d'or (FR) **G. T. Bewley**
18 **ROYAL SALUTE**, 9, br g Flemensfirth (USA)—Loxhill Lady **E G Tunstall, L Davidson & W Richardson**
19 **SAMBA TIME**, 7, gr m Black Sam Bellamy (IRE)—Tikk Tokk **Miss V. F. Bewley**
20 **SAVOY COURT (IRE)**, 8, b g Robin des Champs (FR)—North Star Poly (IRE) **Eales , Gillies & Hewitt**
21 **SEVENBALLS OF FIRE (IRE)**, 10, b g Milan—Leadamurraydance (IRE) **JGS Partnership**
22 **SKA RIDGE**, 7, b g Distant Peak (IRE)—Tandawizi **J. Wade**
23 **SUNNY DESTINATION (IRE)**, 7, b g Dubai Destination (USA)—Railway House (IRE) **Mr Alan Udale & Bewley**
24 **WAR AT SEA (IRE)**, 5, gr g Mastercraftsman (IRE)—Swirling (IRE) **G. T. Bewley**

Other Owners: Mr S. J. Baird, Mr G. Baird, Mrs L. Bewley, Mr L. J. Davidson, Mr K. F. Eales, Mr R. A. Fisher, Mr J. H. Gibson, Mr M. C. Gillies, Gillies & Hewitt, Mr J. H. Graham, Mr A. G. Hewitt, Mr W. Richardson, Mr E. G. Tunstall, Mr A. Udale.

Jockey (NH): Jonathon Bewley, Colm McCormack, Craig Nichol.

---

40 | **MRS PIPPA BICKERTON, Almington**
Postal: **Almington House, Pinfold Lane, Almington, Market Drayton, Shropshire, TF9 2QR**
Contacts: **MOBILE (07966) 441001**

1 **TROPICAL SUNSHINE (IRE)**, 11, b g Bachelor Duke (USA)—Tropical Coral (IRE) **Mrs P. F. Bickerton**

---

41 | **MR SAEED BIN SUROOR, Newmarket**
Postal: **Godolphin Office, Snailwell Road, Newmarket, Suffolk, CB8 7YE**
Contacts: **PHONE (01638) 569956**
WEBSITE www.godolphin.com

1 **ASOOF**, 4, b f Dubawi (IRE)—Lady's Purse
2 **BEAUVAIS (IRE)**, 4, ch c New Approach (IRE)—Marie de Medici (USA)
3 **BEDOUIN'S STORY**, 4, b g Farhh—Time Crystal (IRE)
4 **BENBATL**, 5, b h Dubawi (IRE)—Nahrain
5 **BEST SOLUTION (IRE)**, 5, b h Kodiac—Al Andalyya (USA)
6 **BIG CHALLENGE**, 5, ch g Sea The Stars (IRE)—Something Mon (USA)
7 **BIN BATTUTA**, 5, ch h Dubawi (IRE)—Land of Dreams
8 **DESERT FIRE (IRE)**, 4, b c Cape Cross (IRE)—Crystal House (CHI)
9 **DESERT FROST (IRE)**, 5, b g Dark Angel (IRE)—Layla Jamil (IRE)
10 **DREAM CASTLE**, 5, b g Frankel—Sand Vixen
11 **GAME STARTER (IRE)**, 5, b h Dubawi (IRE)—Opera Cloak (IRE)
12 **GIFTS OF GOLD**, 4, b g Invincible Spirit (IRE)—Sanna Bay (IRE)
13 **GLASSY WATERS (USA)**, 5, ch h Distorted Humor (USA)—Captivating Lass (USA)
14 **GREAT ORDER (USA)**, 6, b br g Distorted Humor (USA)—Michita (USA)
15 **HIGH END**, 5, b br g Dubawi (IRE)—Crystal Music (USA)
16 **JALAAD (IRE)**, 4, b g Kodiac—Surrey Storm
17 **LAIETH**, 4, b g Dubawi (IRE)—First City
18 **LESHLAA (USA)**, 5, ch h Street Cry (IRE)—Vine Street (IRE)
19 **MAJOR PARTNERSHIP (IRE)**, 4, gr c Iffraaj—Roystonea
20 **MIDNIGHT MEETING (IRE)**, 4, b c Dubawi (IRE)—Inner Secret (USA)
21 **MOUNTAIN HUNTER (USA)**, 5, b g Lonhro (AUS)—Tamarillo
22 **NATIONAL ARMY**, 4, b c Dubawi (IRE)—Silk Blossom (IRE)
23 **RACE DAY**, 6, ch g Dubawi (IRE)—Nadia
24 **RACING HISTORY (IRE)**, 7, b h Pivotal—Gonbarda (GER)
25 **REACTION TIME**, 4, b c Dubawi (IRE)—Cloudspin (USA)
26 **RED GALILEO**, 8, b g Dubawi (IRE)—Ivory Gala (FR)

MR SAEED BIN SUROOR - Continued

27 **SILENT ATTACK**, 6, b g Dream Ahead (USA)—Chanterelle (FR)
28 **SILVER RIVER**, 5, gr g Tamayuz—Tashelka (FR)
29 **STEALTH FIGHTER (IRE)**, 4, b g Kodiac—Green Chorus (IRE)
30 **TEAM DECISION (IRE)**, 4, ch c Teofilo (IRE)—Precipitous (IRE)
31 **TEAM TALK**, 6, b g Teofilo (IRE)—Native Blue
32 **THUNDER SNOW (IRE)**, 5, b h Helmet (AUS)—Eastern Joy
33 **TOP SCORE**, 5, br g Hard Spun (USA)—Windsor County (USA)
34 **VERY TALENTED**, 6, b g Invincible Spirit (IRE)—Crystal House (CHI)
35 **VICTORY WAVE (USA)**, 5, ch m Distorted Humor (USA)—Angel Craft (USA)
36 **VOLCANIC SKY**, 4, b c Street Cry (IRE)—Short Skirt
37 **WELSH LORD**, 4, gr g Dark Angel (IRE)—Welsh Angel
38 **YATTWEE (USA)**, 6, b br g Hard Spun (USA)—Alzerra (UAE)
39 **ZAHEE (IRE)**, 4, b c Iffraaj—Havin' A Good Time (IRE)

THREE-YEAR-OLDS

40 **AL MIKDAM (USA)**, ch g City Zip (USA)—Brattothecore (CAN)
41 **AL MUREIB (IRE)**, ch g Dubawi (IRE)—Lava Flow (IRE)
42 **AUTUMN LEAF (IRE)**, b f Shamardal (USA)—Beautiful Forest
43 **BURJ**, b g Dansili—Dysphonia (AUS)
44 **DESERT SECRET**, ch c Pivotal—Secret Keeper
45 **DIAMOND OASIS**, ch f Iffraaj—Belonging
46 **DISTANT IMAGE (IRE)**, b f Exceed And Excel (AUS)—Sander Camillo (USA)
47 **DREAM LOCATION**, b f Invincible Spirit (IRE)—Siyaadah
48 **DUBAI BEAUTY (IRE)**, b f Frankel—Minidress
49 **DUBAI BLUE (USA)**, b f More Than Ready (USA)—Speckled (USA)
50 **DUBAI FALCON (IRE)**, b c Teofilo (IRE)—Star Blossom (USA)
51 **DUBAI FUTURE**, b c Dubawi (IRE)—Anjaz (USA)
52 **DUBAI ICE (USA)**, ch f More Than Ready (USA)—Cableknit (USA)
53 **DUBAI LEGACY (USA)**, b c Discreet Cat (USA)—Atsana (USA)
54 **DUBAI LUXURY**, b f Teofilo (IRE)—Isobel Archer
55 **DUBAI TRADITION (USA)**, b c Medaglia d'oro (USA)—Wavering (IRE)
56 **DUBAI TREASURE**, b c Dubawi (IRE)—Surprise Moment (IRE)
57 **DUBAI VIEW (IRE)**, b f Pivotal—Gonbarda (GER)
58 **ESTIHDAAF**, b br c Arch (USA)—Enrichment (USA)
59 **FALATHAAT (USA)**, ch f Union Rags (USA)—Mezah (USA)
60 **FIRST SMILE**, ch f Teofilo (IRE)—Calipatria
61 **FUTURE KING**, b c Invincible Spirit (IRE)—Floristry
62 **GENTLE LOOK**, ch g Dubawi (IRE)—Rosewater (IRE)
63 **GHALY**, ch c Dubawi (IRE)—Hanky Panky (IRE)
64 **GLOBAL HEAT (IRE)**, b g Toronado (IRE)—Raskutani
65 **GLOBAL HUNTER (IRE)**, b c Kodiac—Romie's Kastett (GER)
66 **GREAT EXAMPLE**, b c Cape Cross (IRE)—Gower Song
67 **HAWAFEZ (IRE)**, ch f Shamardal (USA)—Devotee (USA)
68 **HOME CITY (IRE)**, gr f Exceed And Excel (AUS)—Asi Siempre (USA)
69 **ICE CAVE (IRE)**, ch c Shamardal (USA)—La Collina (IRE)
70 **ICE CLIMBER**, b c Teofilo (IRE)—Chan Tong (BRZ)
71 **JUMEIRAH ONE**, b c Dawn Approach (IRE)—Bulbul (IRE)
72 **LABIBA**, b c Dubawi (IRE)—Scatina (IRE)
73 **LAND OF LEGENDS (IRE)**, b br c Iffraaj—Homily
74 **LOST IN TIME (IRE)**, b c Raven's Pass (USA)—Prussian
75 **MADKHAL (USA)**, ch c Distorted Humor (USA)—Almurra (USA)
76 **MAGIC IMAGE**, ch f Dubawi (IRE)—White Rose (GER)
77 **MAJALAAT (IRE)**, b c New Approach (IRE)—Fawaayed (IRE)
78 **MAQBOOLA (USA)**, b f Tamayuz—Asiya (USA)
79 **MAWAHIB (IRE)**, ch f New Approach (IRE)—Violante (USA)
80 **MAWLOOD (IRE)**, b br c Dawn Approach (IRE)—Kalaatah (USA)
81 **MAWSOOF (USA)**, b c Distorted Humor (USA)—Tafaneen (USA)
82 **MEQDAM (IRE)**, ch c Dubawi (IRE)—Scatter Dice (USA)
83 **MILITARY TACTIC (IRE)**, b c Iffraaj—Lunar Spirit
84 **MOHAREB**, b c Delegator—Irrational
85 **MOMENT OF SILENCE (IRE)**, b f Slade Power (IRE)—Sleeping Beauty (IRE)
86 **MONS STAR (IRE)**, b c Sea The Stars (IRE)—Something Mon (USA)
87 **MUTAFAWWIG**, b c Oasis Dream—Reunite (IRE)
88 **NAJIB (IRE)**, b g Invincible Spirit (IRE)—Angel's Tears
89 **NEW TERRITORY**, b c Lope de Vega (IRE)—High Heel Sneakers

MR SAEED BIN SUROOR - Continued

90 **NSNAS (IRE)**, b c Bated Breath—Burn The Breeze (IRE)
91 **PERFECT NUMBER**, b f Cape Cross (IRE)—Wizara (IRE)
92 **PERFECT WINTER (IRE)**, b f Invincible Spirit (IRE)—Heartily (IRE)
93 **PROMISE OF SUCCESS**, b f Dansili—Summer School (IRE)
94 **QUIET NOTE**, b f Invincible Spirit (IRE)—Lady Marian (GER)
95 **ROYAL MARINE (IRE)**, b c Raven's Pass (USA)—Inner Secret (USA)
96 **ROYAL MEETING (IRE)**, b c Invincible Spirit (IRE)—Rock Opera (SAF)
97 **SEARCH FOR LIGHT (IRE)**, gr f New Approach (IRE)—Fire Blaze (IRE)
98 **SENDEED (IRE)**, b c Shamardal (USA)—Petrushka (IRE)
99 **SHAMEKH (IRE)**, br g Sea The Stars (IRE)—Martine's Spirit (IRE)
100 **SILENT HUNTER (IRE)**, b c Dutch Art—Yellow Rosebud (IRE)
101 **SNOW STORM (IRE)**, b c Slade Power (IRE)—Snowdrops
102 **SPECIAL DESIGN (IRE)**, ch f Shamardal (USA)—Raphinae
103 **SWIFT ROSE (IRE)**, b f Invincible Spirit (IRE)—Tulips (IRE)
104 **WESAM (IRE)**, b c Slade Power (IRE)—Many Colours
105 **WHITE MOUNTAIN (IRE)**, b f Raven's Pass (USA)—Mujarah (IRE)
106 **WILD ANIMAL**, b c Kingman—Epic Similie

TWO-YEAR-OLDS

107 **ARABIAN ROMANCE (IRE)**, b f 25/2 No Nay Never (USA)—Cabelo (IRE) (Azamour (IRE)) (88495)
108 **ARABIC CHARM (IRE)**, b f 21/2 Exceed And Excel (AUS)—Fond Words (IRE) (Shamardal (USA))
109 **ARABIC WELCOME (IRE)**, b br c 29/1 Shamardal (USA)—Bint Almatar (USA) (Kingmambo (USA))
110 **ARMY SERGEANT (IRE)**, b c 15/3 Teofilo (IRE)—Emboss (IRE) (Cape Cross (IRE))
111 **BACK FROM DUBAI (IRE)**, b c 4/2 Exceed And Excel (AUS)—Emirates Rewards (Dubawi (IRE))
112 **BASIC BEAUTY (IRE)**, b f 30/4 Dark Angel (IRE)—Rahiyah (Rahy (USA))
113 **BEAUTIFUL SCENERY (IRE)**, b f 14/5 Shamardal (USA)—Mont Etoile (IRE) (Montjeu (IRE))
114 **BIG CITY**, b c 3/4 Zoffany (IRE)—Anipa (Sea The Stars (IRE)) (80000)
115 **BIG MEETING (IRE)**, b c 30/4 Shamardal (USA)—Beta (Selkirk (USA))
116 **BLUE FLAME (IRE)**, gr b c 14/5 Dark Angel (IRE)—Bluefire (Distorted Humor (USA))
117 **BRILLIANT LIGHT**, b c 6/2 Sea The Stars (IRE)—Flame of Gibraltar (IRE) (Rock of Gibraltar (IRE))
118 **CLOUDY WATERS**, b f 13/4 Shamardal (USA)—Peacoat (Doyen (IRE))
119 **COLOUR IMAGE (IRE)**, b c 2/3 Kodiac—Chroussa (IRE) (Holy Roman Emperor (IRE)) (250000)
120 **CREEK HORIZON**, b c 29/4 Invincible Spirit (IRE)—Satin Kiss (USA) (Seeking The Gold (USA))
121 **DARK COLOURS (IRE)**, b f 6/5 Night of Thunder (IRE)—Calando (USA) (Storm Cat (USA))
122 **DARK OF NIGHT (IRE)**, gr c 31/3 Dark Angel (IRE)—Moonvoy (Cape Cross (IRE)) (155000)
123 **DEEP SNOW**, b f 26/3 Bated Breath—Polar Circle (USA) (Royal Academy (USA)) (80000)
124 **DESERT DESTINATION (IRE)**, b c 28/4 Night of Thunder (IRE)—Scarlett Rose (Royal Applause) (90000)
125 **DUBAI LOVE**, b f 5/3 Night of Thunder (IRE)—Devotion (IRE) (Dylan Thomas (IRE))
126 **DUBAI MIRAGE (IRE)**, ch c 5/4 Dubawi (IRE)—Calipatria (Shamardal (USA))
127 **DUBAI QUALITY (IRE)**, ch f 8/2 Dubawi (IRE)—Local Time (Invincible Spirit (IRE))
128 **DUBAI ROMANCE (IRE)**, ch f 24/4 Dubawi (IRE)—Gracefield (USA) (Storm Cat (USA))
129 **DUBAI SOUQ (IRE)**, b c 19/2 Dubawi (IRE)—Balsamine (IRE) (Street Cry (IRE))
130 **EGYPTIAN KING**, b c 18/4 Iffraaj—Viola d'amour (IRE) (Teofilo (IRE)) (125000)
131 **FEEL THE MOMENT**, b f 15/5 Invincible Spirit (IRE)—Michita (USA) (Dynaformer (USA))
132 **FESTIVAL OF COLOUR (IRE)**, b c 7/3 Kodiac—Redmaven (IRE) (Teofilo (IRE)) (250000)
133 **FIRST TARGET**, b c 21/1 Showcasing—Excelette (IRE) (Exceed And Excel (AUS)) (150000)
134 **FIRST VIEW (IRE)**, b c 1/3 Exceed And Excel (AUS)—Love Charm (Singspiel (IRE))
135 **FRESH SNOW (IRE)**, b gr f 27/4 Dark Angel (IRE)—Snow Rose (USA) (Elusive Quality (USA))
136 Ch f 13/3 New Approach (IRE)—Ghasabah (Dansili)
137 **GLOBAL IMAGE**, ch c 7/3 Exceed And Excel (AUS)—Margravine (AUS) (King's Best (USA))
138 **GOOD REASON**, gr f 16/4 Dark Angel (IRE)—Sander Camillo (USA) (Dixie Union (USA))
139 **GREAT IMAGE (IRE)**, b c 19/1 Exceed And Excel (AUS)—Beautiful Forest (Nayef (USA))
140 **HATTA MOUNTAINS (IRE)**, b c 4/3 Society Rock (IRE)—Shehila (USA) (Zamindar (USA)) (180000)
141 B c 1/2 Dubawi (IRE)—Hawaafez (Nayef (USA))
142 **HEARTOFTHEEMPIRE**, b c 15/4 Exceed And Excel (AUS)—Victorian Beauty (USA) (Rahy (USA))
143 **HISTORIC (IRE)**, b br c 8/5 Shamardal (USA)—Galician (Redoute's Choice (AUS))
144 **ISLAND FALCON (IRE)**, b c 25/1 Dark Angel (IRE)—Relation Alexander (IRE) (Dandy Man (IRE)) (300000)
145 B c 27/3 Shamardal (USA)—Jilnaar (IRE) (Dansili)
146 Ch c 23/3 Raven's Pass (USA)—Kalaatah (USA) (Dynaformer (USA))
147 **LASER SHOW (IRE)**, ch c 24/2 New Approach (IRE)—Entertains (AUS) (Street Cry (IRE))
148 B c 3/3 Night of Thunder (IRE)—Linda Radlett (IRE) (Manduro (GER))
149 **LIVE YOUR DREAM (IRE)**, b c 28/2 Iffraaj—Dream Book (Sea The Stars (IRE))
150 **LONG TRADITION (IRE)**, b c 6/5 Shamardal (USA)—Irish History (IRE) (Dubawi (IRE))
151 **MAKING HISTORY (IRE)**, b c 13/3 Dubawi (IRE)—Important Time (IRE) (Oasis Dream)
152 **MOVING LIGHT (IRE)**, ch c 22/3 Night of Thunder (IRE)—North East Bay (USA) (Prospect Bay (CAN)) (151706)

MR SAEED BIN SUROOR - Continued

153 **NATION'S BEAUTY (IRE)**, gr f 8/4 Dark Angel (IRE)—Nahoodh (IRE) (Clodovil (IRE))
154 **NEXT VICTORY (IRE)**, b f 2/4 Exceed And Excel (AUS)—Miss Lucifer (FR) (Noverre (USA))
155 **ONE COLOUR (IRE)**, b br c 12/2 Brazen Beau (AUS)—My Lucky Liz (IRE) (Exceed And Excel (AUS)) (66666)
156 **OPEN ROAD**, b c 9/3 Showcasing—Shembara (FR) (Dylan Thomas (IRE)) (200000)
157 **PERFECT ARCH (IRE)**, b c 15/4 Dawn Approach (IRE)—Willow Beck (Shamardal (USA)) (92709)
158 **PERFECT BALANCE (IRE)**, ch f 2/2 Dubawi (IRE)—Key To Peace (IRE) (Kheleyf (USA))
159 **PICTURE FRAME**, b f 12/2 Showcasing—Hello Glory (Zamindar (USA)) (190000)
160 **PLATINUM STAR (IRE)**, b c 22/2 Lope de Vega (IRE)—Toquette (IRE) (Acclamation) (150000)
161 **POWERFUL WORLD (IRE)**, b c 11/2 Exceed And Excel (AUS)—New Style (USA) (Street Cry (IRE))
162 **QUEEN OF THE SEA (IRE)**, b f 19/3 Sea The Stars (IRE)—Knyazhna (IRE) (Montjeu (IRE)) (400000)
163 **QUIET PLACE (IRE)**, b f 18/3 Kodiac—Need You Now (IRE) (Kheleyf (USA)) (300000)
164 B f 20/4 Dawn Approach (IRE)—Rawaaq (Invincible Spirit (IRE))
165 **REAL WORLD (IRE)**, b c 14/3 Dark Angel (IRE)—Nafura (Dubawi (IRE))
166 **ROYAL ARRIVAL (IRE)**, b br c 3/5 Shamardal (USA)—Rock Opera (SAF) (Lecture (USA))
167 **ROYAL KISS (IRE)**, b f 14/4 Teofilo (IRE)—Prussian (Dubai Destination (USA))
168 **SEA BAY**, b f 16/3 Iffraaj—Welsh Anthem (Singspiel (IRE))
169 **SECRET MOMENT (IRE)**, b c 12/5 Exceed And Excel (AUS)—Devotee (USA) (Elusive Quality (USA))
170 **SHAPE THE FUTURE (GER)**, ch c 28/3 Rock of Gibraltar (IRE)—Suzanita (IRE) (Lomitas) (48883)
171 **SILENT ESCAPE (IRE)**, ch f 2/4 New Approach (IRE)—Rosewater (IRE) (Pivotal)
172 **STAND STRONG (IRE)**, b c 12/3 No Nay Never (USA)—Hurricane Emma (USA) (Mr Greeley (USA)) (400000)
173 **STAND TALL**, b c 31/1 Sepoy (AUS)—Vitoria (IRE) (Exceed And Excel (AUS))
174 **STUNNING BEAUTY (IRE)**, ch f 25/4 Shamardal (USA)—Short Skirt (Diktat)
175 **SUMMER HOUSE**, ch f 6/2 Lope de Vega (IRE)—Soon (IRE) (Galileo (IRE)) (220000)
176 **SWISS VALLEY (IRE)**, gr f 4/2 Dark Angel (IRE)—Warshah (IRE) (Shamardal (USA)) (140000)
177 B c 13/5 Teofilo (IRE)—Thaahira (USA) (Dynaformer (USA))
178 **TOMOUH (IRE)**, b f 30/3 Dubawi (IRE)—Sundrop (JPN) (Sunday Silence (USA))
179 **TOMOUH DUBAI (IRE)**, ch f 14/4 Dubawi (IRE)—West Wind (Machiavellian (USA))
180 **VALLEY MIST**, b f 9/4 New Approach (IRE)—Bitter Lake (USA) (Halling (USA))
181 Ch f 6/4 Mukhadram—Wahgah (USA) (Distorted Humor (USA))
182 **WARM SUNSET (IRE)**, b f 18/2 Oasis Dream—Predicted (Dansili) (200000)
183 **WILD PLACE (IRE)**, b c 22/3 Gleneagles (IRE)—No Explaining (IRE) (Azamour (IRE)) (190000)
184 B c 27/4 Teofilo (IRE)—Yanabeeaa (USA) (Street Cry (IRE))

---

42 | **MRS EMMA BISHOP, Cheltenham**
Postal: **Brockhill, Naunton, Cheltenham, Gloucestershire, GL54 3BA**
Contacts: FAX **(01451) 850199** MOBILE **(07887) 845970**
E-MAIL **emmabishopracing@hotmail.co.uk** WEBSITE **www.emmabishopracing.com**

1 **ARQUEBUSIER (FR)**, 9, br g Discover d'auteuil (FR)—Djurjura (FR) **Mr R. Foulquies**
2 **BAJARDO (IRE)**, 11, b g Jammaal—Bit of Peace (IRE) **Mrs J. Arnold**
3 **BRINESTINE (USA)**, 10, b g Bernstein (USA)—Miss Zafonic (FR) **Brians Buddies**
4 **CHURCH HALL (IRE)**, 11, b g Craigsteel—Island Religion (IRE) **Mrs J. Arnold**
5 **GLANCE BACK**, 8, b g Passing Glance—Roberta Back (IRE) **Select Racing Club & Mrs M J Arnold**
6 **MACKSVILLE (IRE)**, 6, gr g Mastercraftsman (IRE)—Fairest of All (IRE)
7 **SHEEZA LEGEND**, 5, b m Midnight Legend—Roberta Back (IRE) **Mrs J. Arnold**
8 **SNOWELL (IRE)**, 12, b g Well Chosen—Snow Water (IRE) **Mrs E. J. Bishop**
9 **STAAR (IRE)**, 5, b g Sea The Stars (IRE)—Bitooh **Mrs E. J. Bishop**

THREE-YEAR-OLDS

10 Br f Passing Glance—Roberta Back (IRE)

Other Owners: Mrs M. J. Arnold, Mr M. J. Arnold, Mrs E. J. Bishop, www.Select-Racing-Club.co.uk.

---

43 | **MR FRANK BISHOP, Kidderminster**
Postal: **Parkside, Blakeshall, Wolverley, Kidderminster, Worcestershire, DY11 5XW**
Contacts: MOBILE **(07900) 407647**

1 **BIDAAYA (IRE)**, 6, b m Naaqoos—Alzaroof (USA) **Mr N. A. J. Walley Mr F Bishop**
2 **LUCKIE GEORGE**, 4, b g Mazameer (IRE)—Ernie's Girl **Mr M. P. Bishop**
3 **UNONOTHINJONSNOW**, 5, b g Arakan (USA)—Kleio **Mr F. A. Bishop**
4 **WILLSY**, 6, b g Sakhee's Secret—Blakeshall Rose **Mr M. P. Bishop**

MR FRANK BISHOP - Continued

THREE-YEAR-OLDS

5 **EMPTY PROMISES,** b c Mazameer (IRE)—Rathlin Sound **Mr F. A. Bishop**
6 **INVERARITY,** b c Mazameer (IRE)—Tripti (IRE) **Mr M. P. Bishop**

Other Owners: Mr N. A. J. Walley.

<table>
<tr><td>44</td><td>

MR KEVIN BISHOP, Bridgwater
Postal: **Barford Park Stables, Spaxton, Bridgwater, Somerset, TA5 1AF**
Contacts: **PHONE/FAX (01278) 671437 MOBILE (07816) 837610**
E-MAIL hevbishop@hotmail.com

</td></tr>
</table>

1 **BULFIN ISLAND (IRE),** 10, b g Milan—Tournore Court (IRE) **Mr B. V. Lund**
2 **COOLANURE (IRE),** 10, b m Portrait Gallery (IRE)—Aiguille (IRE) **Mr B. V. Lund**
3 **GLENFINN HALL,** 4, br g Mawatheeq (USA)—Hallingdal (UAE) **Mr D. Phillips**
4 **INSUFFICIENT FUNDS (IRE),** 9, b g Bach (IRE)—Peace Time Beauty (IRE) **Mr B. V. Lund**
5 **JUST GO FOR IT,** 6, b m Passing Glance—Just Jasmine **Mr S. G. Atkinson**
6 **JUST SPOT,** 12, ch m Baryshnikov (AUS)—Just Jasmine **K. Bishop**
7 **LETS GO DUTCHESS,** 9, b m Helissio (FR)—Lets Go Dutch **K. Bishop**
8 **MACCA'S STOWAWAY (IRE),** 6, b m Stowaway—Julies Vic (IRE) **Mr B. V. Lund**
9 **SOMERSET JEM,** 10, b g Sir Harry Lewis (USA)—Monger Lane **Slabs & Lucan**
10 **THE GREAT RAYMONDO,** 7, b g Passing Glance—Fantasy Parkes **Slabs & Lucan**
11 **WINGSOFREDEMPTION (IRE),** 7, br m Winged Love (IRE)—Lady Oakwell (IRE) **Mr B. V. Lund**

THREE-YEAR-OLDS

12 **FLAMING RED,** ch f Phenomena—Just Puddie **Mr M. R. Cook**

Other Owners: Miss S. Macey, C. J. Macey.

Assistant Trainer: Heather Bishop

Amateur: Mr Conor Smith.

<table>
<tr><td>45</td><td>

MISS LINDA BLACKFORD, Tiverton
Postal: **Shortlane Stables, Rackenford, Tiverton, Devon, EX16 8EH**
Contacts: **PHONE (01884) 881589 MOBILE (07887) 947832**
E-MAIL overthelast@outlook.com WEBSITE www.overthelast.com

</td></tr>
</table>

1 **ACROSS THE PARK (IRE),** 5, b g Presenting—Miss Baresi (IRE) **Easylife Partnership**
2 **CELTIC STYLE (IRE),** 6, b m Craigsteel—Kissangel (IRE) **Over The Last Racing**
3 **KAYF CHARMER,** 9, b m Kayf Tara—Silver Charmer **Mrs V. W. Jones & Mr B. P. Jones**
4 **LADY WETHERED (IRE),** 7, br m Westerner—Vics Miller (IRE) **Mr M. P. Beer**
5 **MOUNTAIN OF MOURNE (IRE),** 10, ch g Mountain High (IRE)—Katies Native (IRE) **Over The Last Racing**
6 **POET'S REFLECTION (IRE),** 4, b f Dylan Thomas (IRE)—
                                Lola's Reflection **Mr D. Cocks & Mrs S. Livesey-van Dorst**
7 **ROWLEY PARK (IRE),** 6, b g Golan (IRE)—Atomic Winner (IRE) **The Rowley Partnership**
8 **ROYAL CHIEFTAIN (IRE),** 9, b g Beneficial—Jensharandsue (IRE) **Over The Last Racing**
9 **STEEL EXPRESS (IRE),** 7, b g Craigsteel—Assidua (IRE) **Mrs Susan Quick**
10 **THATS YER MAN (IRE),** 11, ch g Marignan (USA)—Glengarra Princess **Over The Last Racing**

Other Owners: Miss L. A. Blackford, Mr H. Bray, Mr D. J. Cocks, Mrs V. W. Jones, B. P. Jones, Mrs S. H. Livesey-Van Dorst, Mr M. J. Vanstone, Mr B. Woolfenden.

Assistant Trainer: M. J. Vanstone

Jockey (NH): James Best, Micheal Nolan, Nick Scholfield. **Conditional:** Sean Houlihan.

46 **MR ALAN BLACKMORE, Hertford**
Postal: 'Chasers', Stockings Lane, Little Berkhamsted, Hertford
Contacts: **PHONE (01707) 875060 MOBILE (07803) 711453**

1 **COCKER**, 7, b g Shirocco (GER)—Treble Heights (IRE) **A. G. Blackmore**
2 **OCCASIONALLY YOURS (IRE)**, 15, b g Moscow Society (USA)—Kristina's Lady (IRE) **A. G. Blackmore**

Assistant Trainer: Mrs P. M. Blackmore

Jockey (NH): Marc Goldstein. **Amateur:** Miss Tabitha Worsley.

---

47 **MR MICHAEL BLAKE, Trowbridge**
Postal: Staverton Farm, Trowbridge, Wiltshire, BA14 6PE
Contacts: **PHONE (01225) 782327 MOBILE (07971) 675180**
E-MAIL mblakestavertonfarm@btinternet.com WEBSITE www.michaelblakeracing.co.uk

1 **BIG JERRY**, 6, b g Fair Mix (IRE)—Bathwick Annie **H. M. W. Clifford**
2 **BLUE HARMONY**, 4, b f Bahamian Bounty—Fascination Street (IRE) **Mr F. Tieman**
3 **BOUNTY PURSUIT**, 7, b g Pastoral Pursuits—Poyle Dee Dee **Racing For A Cause**
4 **BROADWAY DREAMS**, 5, b g Oasis Dream—Rosa Eglanteria **The Moonlighters**
5 **CHAMPS DE REVES**, 4, b g Champs Elysees—Joyeaux **Staverton Owners Group**
6 **COOLE CODY (IRE)**, 8, b g Dubai Destination (USA)—Run For Cover (IRE) **H. M. W. Clifford**
7 **DESTINYS CHOICE (IRE)**, 6, b m Dubai Destination (USA)—Leader's Hall (IRE)
8 **DOUBLY CLEVER (IRE)**, 7, ch g Iffraaj—Smartest (IRE) **The Moonlighters**
9 **EXCELLENT TEAM**, 7, b g Teofilo (IRE)—Seradim **Mrs J. M. Haines**
10 **HURRICANE ARCADIO (IRE)**, 5, b g Arcadio (GER)—Back To Favour (IRE) **Mr A. D. Potts**
11 **INIESTA (IRE)**, 8, b g Galileo (IRE)—Red Evie (IRE) **Troughers Independant Traders**
12 **MOUCHEE (IRE)**, 4, b g Zebedee—Nashaat **Mr J. Holt**
13 **ROYAL KING (IRE)**, 4, b g Teofilo (IRE)—Imperialistic Diva (IRE) **Mr J. Holt**
14 **TIS FANTASTIC (FR)**, 4, gr g Montmartre (FR)—Anadara (FR) **The Moonlighters**
15 **TWO SAMS (IRE)**, 6, b g Dubai Destination (USA)—Hello Louise (IRE) **Mr I. F. Gosden**
16 **WAITINONASUNNYDAY (IRE)**, 6, gr g Tikkanen (USA)—Coppenagh Lady (IRE) **West Wilts Hockey Lads**

Other Owners: M. J. Blake, Mrs S. E. Blake, Mr R. C. Butcher, Mrs V. A. Butcher, Mrs J. L. Godwin, Mrs B. A. Sugg.

Assistant Trainer: Sharon Blake (07812) 599904

---

48 **MR MICHAEL BLANSHARD, Upper Lambourn**
Postal: Lethrones Stables, Upper Lambourn, Hungerford, Berkshire, RG17 8QP
Contacts: **PHONE (01488) 71091 FAX (01488) 73497 MOBILE (07785) 370093**
E-MAIL blanshard.racing@btconnect.com WEBSITE www.michaelblanshard.com

1 **ACCOMPLICE**, 5, b m Sakhee's Secret—Witness **The Reignmakers**
2 **EVADALA (FR)**, 4, b f Evasive—Song of India **Ms E. A. Judd**
3 **FAMOUS DYNASTY (IRE)**, 5, b g Famous Name—Daffodil Walk (IRE) **Lady E Mays Smith & Partners**
4 **FEEL THE VIBES**, 5, b g Medicean—Apple Dumpling **The Reignmakers**
5 **IVANHOE**, 9, b g Haafhd—Marysienka **The Ivanhoe Partnership**
6 **MRS BENSON (IRE)**, 4, ch f Rip Van Winkle (IRE)—Ebble **R. P. B. Michaelson**
7 **PENNEYS HUN (IRE)**, 6, b g Arakan (USA)—De Street (IRE) **Lady E. Mays-Smith**
8 **PHOBOS**, 4, b f Intello (GER)—Jolie Etoile (USA) **Lady E. Mays-Smith**

THREE-YEAR-OLDS

9 **CELESTIAL**, b f Motivator—Celebrity **Windmill Racing Ii**
10 **MILISTORM**, b f Sepoy (AUS)—Oasis Breeze **Mr V. G. Ward**
11 **MOON ARTIST (FR)**, b f Archipenko (USA)—Moonavvara (IRE) **Moon Artist Partnership**
12 **SUPREME CHANCE**, b c Delegator—Avon Supreme **B. C. Oakley**
13 **TAZ**, b gr g Aussie Rules (USA)—Island Rhapsody **The Reignmakers**
14 **VINO ROSSO (IRE)**, b f Zebedee—Fonseca (IRE) **The Reignmakers**
15 **WILBERFORCE**, ch g Equiano (FR)—Lily In Pink **The Reignmakers**

TWO-YEAR-OLDS

16 Ch f 18/2 Showcasing—Blaugrana (IRE) (Exceed And Excel (AUS))
17 B f 8/2 Camacho—Jessie K (Compton Place)

MR MICHAEL BLANSHARD - Continued

18 Ch f 16/3 Footstepsinthesand—Landale (Raven's Pass (USA))
19 MRS LANE (IRE), ch f 2/5 Raven's Pass (USA)—

                 Arizona Sun (IRE) (Spinning World (USA)) (16000) **B. Michaelson**
20 B f 15/2 G Force (IRE)—Of Course Darling (Dalakhani (IRE)) (800) **The Reignmakers**
21 B f 1/3 Due Diligence (USA)—Sunny York (IRE) (Vale of York (IRE)) (6000)

Other Owners: Mr S. Beccle, Mr M. Blanshard, Mr D. Cannings, Mrs Emma Clarke, Mr M. Else, Dr Andrew Gay, A. J. J. Gompertz, Mr B. M. Gordon, Mr W. L. Hill, Mr D. M. James, Mr S. J. Jenkins, Mrs Fiona Marner, Lady Eliza Mays-Smith, Mr Brian Mitchell, Mr M. J. Prescott, Mr Nick Price, Mr J. P. Repard, Mr M. Stokes.

---

49 MISS GILLIAN BOANAS, Saltburn
Postal: **Groundhill Farm, Lingdale, Saltburn-By-The-Sea, Cleveland, TS12 3HD**
Contacts: **MOBILE (07976) 280154**
E-MAIL gillianboanas@aol.com

1 **BRAVE SPARTACUS (IRE)**, 13, b g Spartacus (IRE)—Peaches Polly **Miss G. L. Boanas**
2 **BROCTUNE RED**, 4, ch g Haafhd—Fairlie **Mrs M. B. Thwaites**
3 **CLOGHOUGE BOY (IRE)**, 9, b g Westerner—Back To Cloghoge (IRE) **Miss G. L. Boanas**
4 **CRIXUS'S ESCAPE (IRE)**, 6, ch g Beneficial—Tierneys Choice (IRE) **Mr R. Collins**
5 **GREAT COLACI**, 6, b g Sulamani (IRE)—Fairlie **Rug, Grub & Pub Partnership**
6 4, B g Getaway (GER)—Initforthecrack (IRE) **Mr R. Collins**
7 **JUST CALL ME AL (IRE)**, 6, br g Presenting—Tonaphuca Girl (IRE) **M.B.Thwaites G Boanas G Halder**
8 4, Ch g Black Sam Bellamy (IRE)—La Calinda **Tees Components Ltd**
9 **LOCH LINNHE**, 7, b g Tobougg (IRE)—Quistaquay **Miss G. L. Boanas**
10 **MADINAT**, 5, ch g Haafhd—Let It Be **Miss G. L. Boanas**
11 **NOBEL ROSE**, 5, ch m Sholokhov—Florarossa **Miss G. L. Boanas**
12 **PENNY BLAK**, 6, ch g Black Sam Bellamy—Pennys Pride (IRE) **Sir Ian Good & Mr C Anderson**
13 **QUIET PENNY**, 5, b m Sholokhov—Pennys Pride (IRE) **Reveley Farms**
14 **ROCK N'STONES (IRE)**, 8, b g Stowaway—Rock Abbey (IRE) **Miss G. L. Boanas**
15 **ST ANDREWS (IRE)**, 6, ch g Rip Van Winkle (IRE)—Stellavera (FR) **Mr John Coates Mr Richard Smith**
16 **SULTANS HERO**, 6, b g Sulamani (IRE)—Fairlie **The Lingdale Optimists & Miss G Boanas**
17 **SULTANS PRIDE**, 7, b g Sulamani (IRE)—Pennys Pride (IRE) **Reveley Racing 1 & Partner**
18 **SWEET VINETTA**, 5, gr m Fair Mix (IRE)—Vinetta **The Supreme Partnership**
19 **TEESCOMPONENTS LAD**, 6, b g Midnight Legend—Northern Native (IRE) **Tees Components Ltd**
20 **TETRAITES STYLE (IRE)**, 7, b g Court Cave (IRE)—Kilmessan (IRE) **Mr R. Collins**
21 **WALTZ DARLING (IRE)**, 11, b g Iffraaj—Aljafliyah **Mrs M B Thwaites & Mr M E Foxton**
22 **WATCHING OVER**, 5, b m Schiaparelli (GER)—Nobratinetta (FR) **Mrs M B Thwaites & Mr M E Foxton**

Other Owners: Mr T. Alderson, C. Anderson, Mrs M. A. Bauckham, Mrs C. M. Baxter, J. W. Coates, Mr A. Collins, Mr M. Cressey, M. E. Foxton, Sir Ian Good, Mr B. W. Goodall, D. A. Green, Mr G. S. Halder, The Lingdale Optimists, Mr K. S. Matthews, Mr A. J. Rae, D. C. Renton, Reveley Racing 1, R. V. Smith, D. Wild.

---

50 MR JIM BOLGER, Carlow
Postal: **Glebe House, Coolcullen, Carlow, Ireland**
Contacts: **PHONE (00353) 56 4443150 (00353) 56 4443158 FAX (00353) 56 4443256**
E-MAIL racing@jsb.ie

1 **ACTIVE APPROACH**, 4, ch f New Approach (IRE)—Saoirse Abu (USA) **Mrs J. S. Bolger**
2 **CHANGE OF VELOCITY**, 4, b g Teofilo (IRE)—Tiffilia (IRE) **Godolphin**
3 **CLONGOWES (IRE)**, 5, b g New Approach (IRE)—Punctilious **Godolphin**
4 **COME AT DAWN (IRE)**, 4, ch f Dawn Approach (IRE)—Luminaria (IRE) **Mrs J. S. Bolger**
5 **DAWN DELIVERS**, 4, ch f Dawn Approach (IRE)—Siyasa (USA) **Godolphin**
6 **LUCEITA (IRE)**, 4, ch f Dawn Approach (IRE)—Lura (USA) **Godolphin**
7 **MIRACULUM (IRE)**, 4, b f Teofilo (IRE)—Manayer (IRE) **Mrs J. S. Bolger**
8 **NATIONAL SECURITY (IRE)**, 4, ch c Teofilo (IRE)—Halla Siamsa (IRE) **Godolphin**
9 **NEW TO TOWN (IRE)**, 4, b f New Approach (IRE)—Tiffed (USA) **Mrs J. S. Bolger**
10 **NORMANDEL (FR)**, 5, b m Le Havre (IRE)—Lidana (IRE) **Ballylinch Stud**
11 **SMART LIVING (IRE)**, 4, b c Teofilo (IRE)—Ard Fheis (IRE) **Godolphin**
12 **SMASH WILLIAMS (IRE)**, 4, b g Fracas (IRE)—Take Flight (IRE) **Military Syndicate**
13 **SOLAR WAVE (IRE)**, 4, b f Vocalised (USA)—Solar Outburst (IRE) **Mrs J. S. Bolger**
14 **THEOBALD (IRE)**, 4, ch c Teofilo (IRE)—Sanaara (USA) **Mrs J. S. Bolger**

MR JIM BOLGER - Continued

15 **TWILIGHT PAYMENT (IRE)**, 6, b g Teofilo (IRE)—Dream On Buddy (IRE) **Mrs J. S. Bolger**
16 **VERBAL DEXTERITY (IRE)**, 4, b c Vocalised (USA)—Lonrach (IRE) **Mrs J. S. Bolger**

THREE-YEAR-OLDS

17 **AISLING GHEAR (IRE)**, b f Dream Ahead (USA)—Prudent Approach (IRE) **Mrs J. S. Bolger**
18 **ALL AMERICAN (IRE)**, b g Vocalised (USA)—Tiffed (USA) **Mrs J. S. Bolger**
19 **ALMOST DAWN (IRE)**, ch c New Approach (IRE)—Hymn of The Dawn (USA) **Mrs J. S. Bolger**
20 **AMBITIOUS APPROACH (IRE)**, b c Dawn Approach (IRE)—Estizbaal **Mrs J. S. Bolger**
21 **BANDIUC EILE (IRE)**, b f New Approach (IRE)—Dream On Buddy (IRE) **Mrs J. S. Bolger**
22 **BOLD APPROACH (IRE)**, b c Dawn Approach (IRE)—Excuse Me (USA) **Rectory Road Holdings**
23 **CERRO BAYO (IRE)**, b f Dansili—Villarrica (USA) **Godolphin**
24 **CLOSER NOW (IRE)**, b f New Approach (IRE)—Tiffilia (IRE) **Mrs J. S. Bolger**
25 **COPIA VERBORUM (IRE)**, b c Vocalised (USA)—Gold Focus (IRE) **Mrs J. S. Bolger**
26 **CUBAN HOPE (IRE)**, b c Teofilo (IRE)—Dochas Is Gra (IRE) **Mrs J. S. Bolger**
27 **CUBAN SURFER (IRE)**, b f Teofilo (IRE)—My Girl Sophie (USA) **Mrs J. S. Bolger**
28 **DAWN OF DAY (IRE)**, b f Dawn Approach (IRE)—Ard Fheis (IRE) **Mrs J. S. Bolger**
29 **FERRUM**, b c Sea The Moon (GER)—Claiomh Solais (IRE) **Mrs J. S. Bolger**
30 **FULVIO (USA)**, b g Bernardini (USA)—Lacadena (USA) **China Horse Club**
31 **GEOLAI (IRE)**, ch f New Approach (IRE)—Maria Lee (IRE) **Mrs J. S. Bolger**
32 **GIROLAMO (IRE)**, ch c Dawn Approach (IRE)—Dublin Six (IRE) **Mrs J. S. Bolger**
33 **GUARANTEED (IRE)**, b c Teofilo (IRE)—Gearanai (USA) **Mrs J. S. Bolger**
34 **HARRIET TUBMAN (IRE)**, ch f Dubawi (IRE)—Saoirse Abu (IRE) **Godolphin**
35 **KILKENNY CAT (IRE)**, b br c Teofilo (IRE)—Vincennes **Godolphin**
36 **LAETHANTA SAOIRE (IRE)**, ch f New Approach (IRE)—Saoire **Mrs J. S. Bolger**
37 **LEAGAN GAEILGE (IRE)**, b f Vocalised (USA)—Feile Bride (IRE) **Mrs J. S. Bolger**
38 **LOUGHMORE (IRE)**, b c Shamardal (USA)—Lailani **Godolphin**
39 **MAKE ME SWAY (IRE)**, b f Teofilo (IRE)—Sway Me Now (USA) **Mrs J. S. Bolger**
40 **MATER MATUTA (IRE)**, ch f Dawn Approach (IRE)—Morning Bell **Godolphin**
41 **MOTHER VINCENT (IRE)**, b f Vocalised (USA)—Teolane (IRE) **Mrs J. S. Bolger**
42 **NATIONAL IDENTITY (IRE)**, b f New Approach (IRE)—Irish Question (USA) **Mrs J. S. Bolger**
43 **NEWS ANCHOR (IRE)**, ch c New Approach (IRE)—Halla Na Saoire (IRE) **Mrs J. S. Bolger**
44 **NOVUS ADITUS (IRE)**, b c Teofilo (IRE)—Novel Approach (IRE) **Mrs J. S. Bolger**
45 **OICHE RE GEALAI (IRE)**, ch f Dawn Approach (IRE)—Oiche Ghealai (IRE) **Mrs J. S. Bolger**
46 **OPERATIC EXPORT (IRE)**, b f Vocalised (USA)—Teofolina (IRE) **Mrs J. S. Bolger**
47 **PAISTIUL (IRE)**, ch f Dawn Approach (IRE)—Pastilla (USA) **Mrs J. S. Bolger**
48 **REPETITIO (IRE)**, b c Pour Moi (IRE)—Fionnuar (IRE) **Mrs J. S. Bolger**
49 **SLANEY SAND (IRE)**, ch c Dawn Approach (IRE)—Scribonia (USA) **Mrs J. S. Bolger**
50 **SMART FLIES (IRE)**, ch f Dawn Approach (IRE)—Take Flight (IRE) **Mrs J. S. Bolger**
51 **SOLAR WIND (IRE)**, ch c Dawn Approach (IRE)—Solar Outburst (IRE) **Mrs J. S. Bolger**
52 **SON OF BEAUTY (IRE)**, b g Vocalised (USA)—Sunset Beauty (IRE) **Patrick Bolger**
53 **THE HALL (IRE)**, ch c Teofilo (IRE)—Halla Siamsa (IRE) **Mrs J. S. Bolger**
54 **TIDAL ACTION (IRE)**, b f Cape Cross (IRE)—Attasliyah (IRE) **Mrs J. S. Bolger**
55 **TRACKER SAGA (IRE)**, b c Vocalised (USA)—Gold Mirage (IRE) **Mrs J. S. Bolger**
56 **TROSSACHS**, ch c New Approach (IRE)—Falls of Lora (IRE) **Godolphin**
57 **VERBAL POWDER (IRE)**, b f Vocalised (USA)—Global Reach (USA) **Mrs J. S. Bolger**
58 **VERBALISE (IRE)**, b f Vocalised (USA)—Lonrach (IRE) **Mrs June Judd**
59 **VIATICUS (IRE)**, b c Teofilo (IRE)—Toirneach (USA) **Mrs J. S. Bolger**
60 **VOCATUS (IRE)**, b c Vocalised (USA)—Beyond Intensity (IRE) **Mrs J. S. Bolger**
61 **WESTERN DAWN (IRE)**, b c Dawn Approach (IRE)—Yes Oh Yes (USA) **Mrs J. S. Bolger**
62 **WEXFORD DAWN (IRE)**, ch c Dawn Approach (IRE)—Beyond Compare (IRE) **Mrs J. S. Bolger**
63 **WHIRLPOOL**, b f New Approach (IRE)—Tidespring (IRE) **Godolphin**

TWO-YEAR-OLDS

64 **AGITARE (IRE)**, ch c 12/3 Teofilo (IRE)—Sway Me Now (USA) (Speightstown (USA)) **Mrs J. S. Bolger**
65 **AISEIRIGH (IRE)**, b c 29/4 Teofilo (IRE)—Aiseiri (IRE) (Rock of Gibraltar (IRE)) **Mrs J. S. Bolger**
66 **ANCESTRY (IRE)**, b c 18/2 Dawn Approach (IRE)—Historian (Pennekamp (USA)) **Godolphin**
67 **APPROACH THE LINE (IRE)**, ch f 9/2 Fracas (IRE)—Ionsai Nua (IRE) (New Approach (IRE)) **Mrs J. S. Bolger**
68 **ARDLEANNTA (IRE)**, b f 24/1 Dawn Approach (IRE)—Ardnosach (IRE) (Teofilo (IRE)) **Mrs J. S. Bolger**
69 **ASSURANCE (IRE)**, b f 12/3 Teofilo (IRE)—Gearanai (USA) (Toccet (USA)) **Mrs J. S. Bolger**
70 **AUMA (IRE)**, b f 25/2 Teofilo (IRE)—Khazina (USA) (Kingmambo (USA)) **Mrs J. S. Bolger**
71 **BELLS OF TIME (IRE)**, b f 29/4 New Approach (IRE)—Ard Fheis (IRE) (Lil's Boy (USA)) **Mrs J. S. Bolger**
72 **BENIGNATAS (IRE)**, b f 24/3 Fracas (IRE)—Saintly Hertfield (USA) (Saint Ballado (CAN)) **Mrs J. S. Bolger**
73 **BEYOND HAPPY (IRE)**, b c 5/4 Fastnet Rock (AUS)—Beyond Compare (IRE) (Galileo (IRE)) **Mrs J. S. Bolger**
74 **BREACA AN LAE (IRE)**, b f 19/2 Fracas (IRE)—Danemarque (AUS) (Danehill (USA)) (2527) **Mrs J. S. Bolger**

MR JIM BOLGER - Continued

75 **BREAKING NEWS (IRE)**, b f 2/3 Dawn Approach (IRE)—
Excuse Me (USA) (Distorted Humor (USA)) **Mrs J. S. Bolger**
76 **CEAD SOLAS (IRE)**, b f 30/1 Dawn Approach (IRE)—Star Street (IRE) (Lawman (FR)) **Mrs J. S. Bolger**
77 **CHRISTIANE (IRE)**, b f 27/4 Fracas (IRE)—Arminta (USA) (Afleet Alex (USA)) **Mrs J. S. Bolger**
78 **CITY SHADE (IRE)**, b f 16/5 Teofilo (IRE)—City Square (IRE) (Lawman (FR)) (29498) **Mrs J. S. Bolger**
79 **CIVIL DAWN (IRE)**, b c 23/2 Dawn Approach (IRE)—Legal Farce (IRE) (Lawman (FR)) **Mrs J. S. Bolger**
80 **CRE NA COILLE (IRE)**, b f 16/4 Dawn Approach (IRE)—Imeall Na Speire (USA) (Galileo (IRE)) **Mrs J. S. Bolger**
81 **DANCILA (IRE)**, b c 12/2 Teofilo (IRE)—Empress of Rome (IRE) (Holy Roman Emperor (IRE)) **Mrs J. S. Bolger**
82 **DAWN VISTA (IRE)**, ch c 24/3 Dawn Approach (IRE)—Maoineach (USA) (Congaree (USA)) **Mrs J. S. Bolger**
83 **DAYLIGHT COME (IRE)**, ch c 10/4 Dawn Approach (IRE)—Oiche Ghealai (IRE) (Galileo (IRE)) **Mrs J. S. Bolger**
84 **DELECTATIO (IRE)**, b f 12/2 Dawn Approach (IRE)—Tamra Delight (USA) (Diesis) **Mrs J. S. Bolger**
85 **EUPHEMISM (IRE)**, ch f 10/4 Dawn Approach (IRE)—Innuendo (IRE) (Caerleon (USA)) **Godolphin**
86 **FEMINISTA (IRE)**, ch f 7/2 Dawn Approach (IRE)—My Fere Lady (USA) (Mr Greeley (USA)) **Mrs J. S. Bolger**
87 **FISCAL RULES (IRE)**, b c 12/5 Make Believe—Gold Mirage (IRE) (Galileo (IRE)) **Mrs J. S. Bolger**
88 **FOX TERRIER (IRE)**, b c 28/1 Dawn Approach (IRE)—Sand Vixen (Dubawi (IRE)) **Godolphin**
89 **FRAINSE (IRE)**, b f 27/4 Fracas (IRE)—Saoire (Pivotal) **Mrs J. S. Bolger**
90 **FRAOCHAN (IRE)**, ch f 20/4 Fracas (IRE)—Attasliyah (IRE) (Marju (IRE)) **Mrs J. S. Bolger**
91 **FRATERCULUS (IRE)**, ch c 14/2 Teofilo (IRE)—Sanaara (USA) (Anabaa (USA)) **Mrs J. S. Bolger**
92 **FRONT PAGING (IRE)**, b c 12/5 Lawman (FR)—Solas Na Greine (IRE) (Galileo (IRE)) **Mrs J. S. Bolger**
93 **GAELIC SUNDAY (IRE)**, b f 7/2 Intense Focus (USA)—
Lonrach (IRE) (Holy Roman Emperor (IRE)) **Mrs J. S. Bolger**
94 **GEOMETRICAL (IRE)**, ch c 26/3 Dawn Approach (IRE)—
Symmetrical (USA) (Unbridled's Song (USA)) **Mrs J. S. Bolger**
95 **GLOBAL CROSSING (IRE)**, b f 3/2 Fastnet Rock (AUS)—Global Reach (IRE) (Galileo (IRE)) **Mrs J. S. Bolger**
96 **GOLD ALLURE (IRE)**, b f 15/4 Fracas (IRE)—Gold Focus (IRE) (Intense Focus (USA)) (10113) **Mrs J. S. Bolger**
97 **GOLD MOVER (IRE)**, b f 10/4 Fracas (IRE)—Foinse (IRE) (Teofilo (IRE)) **Mrs J. S. Bolger**
98 **HEMINA (IRE)**, b f 8/2 Intense Focus (USA)—Manger Square (IRE) (Danehill (USA)) **Mrs J. S. Bolger**
99 **HIGH LAKE (IRE)**, ch f 21/2 Fracas (IRE)—Teolane (IRE) (Teofilo (IRE)) **Mrs J. S. Bolger**
100 **HISTORIC HEART (IRE)**, ch c 24/3 Fracas (IRE)—Irish Question (IRE) (Giant's Causeway (USA)) **Mrs J. S. Bolger**
101 **HOOK HEAD (IRE)**, b c 4/5 Fastnet Rock (AUS)—
Dance Troupe (Rainbow Quest (USA)) (150000) **Mrs J. S. Bolger**
102 **INSTANCIA (IRE)**, b f 18/2 Dawn Approach (IRE)—Estiqbaal (Oasis Dream) **Mrs J. S. Bolger**
103 **IVY AVENUE (IRE)**, ch f 30/4 Ivawood (IRE)—
Dance Avenue (IRE) (Sadler's Wells (USA)) (1684) **Mrs Patricia O'Rourke**
104 **LEGAL POMP (IRE)**, b c 16/2 Lawman (FR)—Halla Na Saoire (IRE) (Teofilo (IRE)) **Mrs J. S. Bolger**
105 **LEGAL REFORM (IRE)**, b c 18/2 Lawman (FR)—Amhrasach (IRE) (Teofilo (IRE)) **Mrs J. S. Bolger**
106 **LEGAL THRILLER (IRE)**, b f 30/3 Lawman (FR)—Starland (IRE) (Galileo (IRE)) **Mrs J. S. Bolger**
107 **LETTER AT DAWN (IRE)**, b c 5/4 Dawn Approach (IRE)—Christmas Letter (IRE) (Galileo (IRE)) **Mrs J. S. Bolger**
108 **LOCAL FOCUS (IRE)**, b f 8/2 Intense Focus (USA)—Stair An Damhsa (IRE) (Teofilo (IRE)) **Mrs J. S. Bolger**
109 **LUMINITA (IRE)**, ch f 26/1 New Approach (IRE)—Luminaria (IRE) (Danehill (USA)) **Godolphin**
110 **MCCABE (IRE)**, ch c 25/4 New Approach (IRE)—Fields of May (IRE) (Intense Focus (USA)) **Mrs J. S. Bolger**
111 **MOMENTS LINGER (IRE)**, b f 10/3 Dawn Approach (IRE)—Vocal Nation (IRE) (Vocalised (USA)) **Mrs J. S. Bolger**
112 **MOVING (IRE)**, b c 1/4 Gleneagles (IRE)—National Swagger (IRE) (Giant's Causeway (USA)) **Mrs J. S. Bolger**
113 **NATIONAL ASSET (IRE)**, b c 12/5 Teofilo (IRE)—Taisce Naisiunta (IRE) (Lawman (FR)) **Mrs J. S. Bolger**
114 **OUT AT DAWN (IRE)**, b f 9/2 Dawn Approach (IRE)—Tiz The Whiz (USA) (Tiznow (USA)) **Mrs J. S. Bolger**
115 **OUT FROM DAWN (IRE)**, b c 6/3 Dawn Approach (IRE)—Beachaire (CAN) (Speightstown (USA)) **Mrs J. S. Bolger**
116 **OUT TOGETHER (IRE)**, ch f 16/2 Fracas (IRE)—Something Graceful (Galileo (IRE)) **Godolphin**
117 **PASO DOBLE (IRE)**, b br c 18/4 Dawn Approach (IRE)—Baila Me (GER) (Samum (GER)) **Mrs J. S. Bolger**
118 **PATH TO FAME (IRE)**, ch c 18/5 Teofilo (IRE)—Cailiuil (IRE) (New Approach (IRE)) **Mrs J. S. Bolger**
119 **PEAT MOSS (IRE)**, b c 24/3 Fracas (IRE)—Dancing On Turf (IRE) (Dalakhani (IRE)) **Mrs J. S. Bolger**
120 **PERMAFROST (IRE)**, ch f 20/2 Dawn Approach (IRE)—Snow Powder (IRE) (Raven's Pass (USA)) **Godolphin**
121 **PILITA (IRE)**, b f 17/5 Fracas (IRE)—Manayer (IRE) (Sadler's Wells (USA)) **Mrs J. S. Bolger**
122 **PLEASANT SLANEY (IRE)**, b f 3/2 Gleneagles (IRE)—Tirghra (IRE) (Teofilo (IRE)) **Mrs J. S. Bolger**
123 **POSTER CHILD (IRE)**, b f 20/2 Fracas (IRE)—Rachida (IRE) (Hurricane Run (IRE)) **Mrs J. S. Bolger**
124 **RADICAL APPROACH (IRE)**, b c 1/2 Dawn Approach (IRE)—
Dochas Is Gra (IRE) (High Chaparral (IRE)) **Mrs J. S. Bolger**
125 **RELAXING MODE (IRE)**, ch f 18/4 Fracas (IRE)—Napping (USA) (Danzig (USA)) **Mrs J. S. Bolger**
126 **REPUBLIC (IRE)**, gr c 13/3 Dark Angel (IRE)—Saoirse Abu (USA) (Mr Greeley (USA)) **Godolphin**
127 **RURAL ISOLATION (IRE)**, ch c 28/5 Teofilo (IRE)—Holla Siamsa (IRE) (Montjeu (IRE)) **Mrs J. S. Bolger**
128 **SAILING SOUTH (IRE)**, ch f 14/5 Teofilo (IRE)—Twin Sails (IRE) (Boston Harbor (USA)) **Mrs J. S. Bolger**
129 **SASTA (IRE)**, b f 26/1 Dawn Approach (IRE)—Sasamh (IRE) (Lawman (FR)) **Mrs J. S. Bolger**
130 **SAVVY RULER (USA)**, b c 9/4 Street Boss (USA)—
Unbridled Treasure (USA) (Unbridled's Song (USA)) **Mrs J. S. Bolger**
131 **SELF ASSESSED (IRE)**, b c 4/3 Fracas (IRE)—Viennese Opera (IRE) (Pour Moi (IRE)) **Mrs J. S. Bolger**
132 **SHEER BRAVADO (IRE)**, b c 3/3 Fracas (IRE)—Dushlan (IRE) (New Approach (IRE)) **Mrs J. S. Bolger**

MR JIM BOLGER - Continued

133 **SLANEY EAST (IRE)**, b f 2/4 New Approach (IRE)—Maria Lee (IRE) (Rock of Gibraltar (IRE)) **Mrs J. S. Bolger**
134 **SLANEY RIVER (IRE)**, b c 19/5 Teofilo (IRE)—Gilded Butterfly (USA) (Tapit (USA)) **Mrs J. S. Bolger**
135 **SMART PHONE (IRE)**, b f 28/4 New Approach (IRE)—My Call (Shamardal (USA)) **Godolphin**
136 **SNASTA (IRE)**, b f 1/5 Dawn Approach (IRE)—Snas (USA) (Bernstein (USA)) **Mrs J. S. Bolger**
137 **SOINEANTA (IRE)**, b f 5/2 Intense Focus (USA)—Fionnuar (IRE) (Teofilo (IRE)) **Mrs J. S. Bolger**
138 **SOLAR SYSTEM (IRE)**, ch c 2/3 Dawn Approach (IRE)—Solar Outburst (IRE) (Galileo (IRE)) **Mrs J. S. Bolger**
139 **SPARKLING APPROACH (IRE)**, ch f 21/1 New Approach (IRE)—
                                  Gleigeal (USA) (Mr Greeley (USA)) **Mrs J. S. Bolger**
140 **SPATIAL PLAN (IRE)**, b c 5/3 Teofilo (IRE)—Yes Oh Yes (USA) (Gone West (USA)) **Mrs J. S. Bolger**
141 **SUPPORT RODERICK (IRE)**, b c 7/3 Roderic O'Connor (IRE)—
                                  Vocal Support (IRE) (Vocalised (USA)) **Mrs J. S. Bolger**
142 **SWEEPING APPROACH (IRE)**, b f 14/3 New Approach (IRE)—
                                  Hymn of The Dawn (USA) (Phone Trick (USA)) **Mrs J. S. Bolger**
143 **TEJANO (IRE)**, ch f 22/3 Teofilo (IRE)—Country Music (Street Cry (IRE)) **Godolphin**
144 **TEXTUS RECEPTUS (IRE)**, b c 28/5 Australia—Ceist Eile (IRE) (Noverre (USA)) **Mrs J. S. Bolger**
145 **THEOCRAT (IRE)**, b c 5/3 Teofilo (IRE)—Novel Approach (IRE) (New Approach (IRE)) **Mrs J. S. Bolger**
146 **THEOPHILE (IRE)**, ch f 29/5 Teofilo (IRE)—Precipitous (IRE) (Indian Ridge) **Mrs J. S. Bolger**
147 **TOTAL RETHINK (IRE)**, b c 15/4 Teofilo (IRE)—Georgie Hyde (Yeats (IRE)) **Mrs J. S. Bolger**
148 **TRADING UP (IRE)**, ch c 5/3 Fracas (IRE)—Deontas (IRE) (Teofilo (IRE)) **Mrs J. S. Bolger**
149 **UP WITH THE PLAY (IRE)**, b c 2/4 Fracas (IRE)—Alertness (IRE) (Teofilo (IRE)) **Mrs J. S. Bolger**
150 **VERBAL FLUENCY (IRE)**, b f 29/4 Vocalised (USA)—Stitch Night (IRE) (Whipper (USA)) **Mrs J. S. Bolger**
151 **WEXFORD GOLD (IRE)**, b f 1/2 Fastnet Rock (AUS)—
                                  Beyond Intensity (IRE) (Intense Focus (USA)) **Mrs J. S. Bolger**

Other Owners: Mr John Corcoran, Eclipse Thoroughbreds Partners LLC, Ennistown Stud.

Jockey (flat): R. P. Cleary, Kevin Manning, R. P. Whelan. **Apprentice:** Gavin Ryan, William Byrne, Luke McAteer.

51	**MRS MYRIAM BOLLACK-BADEL, Lamorlaye** Postal: **20 Rue Blanche, 60260 Lamorlaye, France** Contacts: FAX **(0033) 3442 13367** MOBILE **(0033) 6108 09347** E-MAIL myriam.bollack@gmail.com WEBSITE www.myriam-bollack.com

1 **ARDEATINA**, 4, ch f Harbour Watch (IRE)—May West **F. de Chatelperron**
2 **AVEC LAURA**, 6, ch h Manduro (GER)—Sign of Life **Mme M. Bollack-Badel**
3 **ESPALDINHA (FR)**, 4, b f George Vancouver (USA)—Bidart (FR) **Jean Smolen**
4 **GLORIA**, 4, gr f Showcasing—Go East (GER) **Philippe Ezri**
5 **ROYAL PRIZE**, 9, ch g Nayef (USA)—Spot Prize (USA) **M. Bollack**
6 **SECRET LADY**, 5, b m Arcano (IRE)—Lady McBeth (IRE) **J. C. Smith**

THREE-YEAR-OLDS

7 **FLIGHT COMMAND (FR)**, ch c Norse Dancer (IRE)—Angel Wing **J. C. Smith**
8 **GREEN SIREN (FR)**, ch f Siyouni (FR)—Green Speed (FR) **J. C. Smith**
9 **ICE LADY (FR)**, b f Norse Dancer (IRE)—Ice Missile **J. C. Smith**
10 **NI CHAUD NI FROID (FR)**, ch f Norse Dancer (IRE)—Numerologie (FR) **Alain Badel**
11 **PRINCE KERALI (FR)**, b c Sinndar (IRE)—Perpetual Glory **Ecurie Noel Forgeard**
12 **RENEGADE (FR)**, ch c Motivator—Cinders' Prize **J. C. Smith**
13 **RIALTOR (FR)**, b g Motivator—Sambala (IRE) **Ecurie Noel Forgeard**
14 **SHADY SHAM (IRE)**, br f Shamardal (USA)—Shamdara (IRE) **Mr A Smurfit**
15 **SINGSTREET (FR)**, b c Evasive—Sinnderelle (FR) **Ecurie Noel Forgeard**
16 **ZEITUNG (FR)**, ch c Literato (FR)—Zython (FR) **Zeitung Partnership**

TWO-YEAR-OLDS

17 **GREEN SPIRIT (FR)**, b g 25/3 Charm Spirit (IRE)—Green Speed (FR) (Green Tune (USA)) **J. C. Smith**
18 **PASSEFONTAINE (FR)**, b f 17/3 Wootton Bassett—Perpetual Glory (Dansili) **Ecurie Noel Forgeard**
19 **SALINAS GRANDE (FR)**, b f 16/4 Muhtathir—Sinnderelle (FR) (Sinndar (IRE)) **Ecurie Noel Forgeard**
20 Ch f 27/4 Al Kazeem—Tete Orange (Pastoral Pursuits) (13000) **Benoit Chalmel**
21 **ZELOTE (FR)**, b g 23/3 Literato (FR)—Zython (FR) (Kabool) **Benoit Chalmel**

Assistant Trainer: Alain Badel

52 MR MARTIN BOSLEY, Chalfont St Giles

Postal: **Bowstridge Farm, Bowstridge Lane, Chalfont St. Giles, Buckinghamshire, HP8 4RF**
Contacts: **PHONE (01494) 875533 MOBILE (07778) 938040**
E-MAIL martin@martinbosley.com WEBSITE www.martinbosleyracing.com

1 **ASK JILLY**, 6, b m Passing Glance—Heebie Jeebie **Mrs E. A. Prowting**
2 **CATHEADANS FURY**, 5, ch m Firebreak—Dualagi **Bayard Racing**
3 **CATHEADANS GIFT**, 4, ch f Major Cadeaux—Dualagi **Bayard Racing**
4 **CHAMPION CHASE (FR)**, 7, b g Voix du Nord (FR)—Darling Frisco (FR) **Mr M. R. Bosley**
5 **EXCEEDING POWER**, 8, b g Exceed And Excel (AUS)—Extreme Beauty (USA) **The Chalfonts**
6 **HELFIRE**, 6, b m Archipenko (USA)—Relkida **Deborah Collett & M. J. Watson**
7 4, B g Cape Blanco (IRE)—Imbudo (AUS) **David Stenning**
8 **MIDNIGHT JITTERBUG**, 7, b g Midnight Legend—Heebie Jeebie **Mrs E. A. Prowting**
9 **NAWAR**, 4, b g Henrythenavigator (USA)—Nouriya **Quartet Racing**
10 **OLYMPIC LEGEND (IRE)**, 5, ch g Choisir (AUS)—Margaret's Dream (IRE) **M.A.S.A.**
11 **ZEFFERINO**, 5, ch g Frankel—Turama **J. Carey**

THREE-YEAR-OLDS

12 **CATHEADANS FIYAH**, b f Firebreak—Dualagi **Bayard Racing**
13 **LOVING LIFE (IRE)**, b f Society Rock (IRE)—Edelfa (IRE) **N. Bashir, N. Dearman, R. Ridout**

TWO-YEAR-OLDS

14 B c 13/2 Delegator—Dualagi (Royal Applause) **Bayard Racing**

Other Owners: Mr M. R. Bosley, Mr G. H. Carson, Mrs D. Collett, Mr J. R. Hazeldine, Mr A. Randle, Mr M. J. Watson, Mrs K. Whitaker.

53 MR MARCO BOTTI, Newmarket

Postal: **Prestige Place, Snailwell Road, Newmarket, Suffolk, CB8 7DP**
Contacts: **PHONE (01638) 662416 FAX (01638) 662417 MOBILE (07775) 803007**
E-MAIL office@marcobotti.co.uk WEBSITE www.marcobotti.co.uk

1 **AL ASEF**, 4, br c Kyllachy—Hot Reply **Mr R. El Youssef**
2 **AL HAMDANY (IRE)**, 5, b g Kodiac—Easy Times **AlMohamediya Racing**
3 **AL REEH (IRE)**, 5, br g Invincible Spirit (IRE)—Dffra (IRE) **Mr R. El Youssef**
4 **AMERICAN ENDEAVOUR (USA)**, 4, ch f Distorted Humor (USA)—
Crazy Party (USA) **A J Suited & Gute Freunde Partnership**
5 **AZZECCAGARBUGLI (IRE)**, 6, b h Kodiac—Consultant Stylist (IRE) **Scuderia Effevi SRL**
6 **CASINA DI NOTTE (IRE)**, 5, ch g Casamento (IRE)—Nightswimmer (IRE) **Mrs L. Botti**
7 **CROWNED EAGLE**, 5, b g Oasis Dream—Gull Wing (IRE) **Excel Racing & Les Boyer**
8 **DOMAGNANO (IRE)**, 4, b c Planteur (IRE)—Daloisi (FR) **Ambrosiana Racing & Partner**
9 **ELENORA DELIGHT**, 4, b f Dansili—Missy O' Gwaun (IRE) **Les Boyer Partnership**
10 **GALACTIC SPIRIT**, 4, ch g Dutch Art—Gino's Spirits **Newsells Park Stud & Partner**
11 **HEEYAM**, 4, b f Invincible Spirit (IRE)—Shalwa **Sheikh M. B. K. Al Maktoum**
12 **HOULTON**, 4, ch g Declaration of War (USA)—Greek Goddess (IRE) **Fabtive**
13 **JELLMOOD**, 4, b g Acclamation—Emotif (ARG) **Scuderia Blueberry S.R.L. & Partner 2**
14 **NORTH FACE (IRE)**, 4, b c Declaration of War (USA)—Queen Titi (IRE) **Mr R. Bruni**
15 **PETTIFOGGER (IRE)**, 4, b g Lope de Vega (IRE)—Desert Version **Scuderia Effevi SRL**
16 **TOFAN**, 4, ch c Helmet (AUS)—Countermarch **Mr R. El Youssef**
17 **WILD HACKED (USA)**, 6, b h Lemon Drop Kid (USA)—Dance Pass (IRE) **Sheikh K. A. I. S. Al Khalifa**
18 **YUSRA**, 4, b f Invincible Spirit (IRE)—Munyatee (ARG) **Sheikh M. B. K. Al Maktoum**

THREE-YEAR-OLDS

19 B c Rock of Gibraltar (IRE)—Amwaj (IRE) **Mr M. Al Naemi**
20 **BE LIKE ME (IRE)**, b f Helmet (AUS)—Bint Malyana (IRE) **Ambrosiana Racing & Partner**
21 B c Mainsail—Better Chance (IRE) **Mr M. Al Naemi**
22 **BIG DADDY KANE**, b c Sea The Moon (GER)—Soft Morning **K. Sohi & Partners**
23 **BRANDON (FR)**, b g Showcasing—Be Released (IRE) **Mr Manfredini, Mr J Allison & Mr D Fass**
24 **BREATH OF SPRING (IRE)**, br c Bated Breath—Welcome Spring (IRE) **Excel Racing & Partner**
25 **CASH**, b c Australia—Que Puntual (ARG) **E. I. Mack**
26 **DARK MIRACLE (IRE)**, b c Mukhadram—Eolith **Mr H. Szabo**
27 **DI MATTEO**, b f Bated Breath—Pantile **Mr C. J. Murfitt & Partner**
28 **DON JUPP (USA)**, b c More Than Ready (USA)—Dame Ellen (USA) **Gute Freunde Partnership**

MR MARCO BOTTI - Continued

29 **DORCHESTER,** b f Lope de Vega (IRE)—Cloud Line **Excel Racing & Les Boyer**
30 **ECLITTICA (IRE),** b f Pour Moi (IRE)—Ekta **La Tesa SPA**
31 **EESHA MY FLOWER (USA),** b f English Channel (USA)—Bella Bandita (USA) **K Sohi & Partner**
32 **EMILY'S SEA (IRE),** b f Born To Sea (IRE)—See Emily Play (IRE) **Fabfive & Partner**
33 **EMMA POINT (USA),** ch f Point of Entry (USA)—Emma Darling (USA) **Mr R. Bruni**
34 **FARES ALPHA (USA),** gr ro g Exchange Rate (USA)—Relampago Azul (USA) **Mr W. Moraes**
35 **FARES KODIAC (IRE),** b c Kodiac—Artemis (IRE) **Mr W. Moraes**
36 **FARES POET (IRE),** b c Poet's Voice—Moon Over Water (IRE) **Mr W. Moraes**
37 **GEIZY TEIZY (IRE),** b f Lawman (FR)—For Joy **Nick Bradley Racing 30 & Sohi & Partner**
38 **GUROOR,** ch f Lope de Vega (IRE)—Shalwa **Sheikh M. B. K. Al Maktoum**
39 **HOORIYA,** b f Dark Angel (IRE)—Jellwa (IRE) **Sheikh M. B. K. Al Maktoum**
40 **IMPRESSIONABLE,** b f Exceed And Excel (AUS)—Appealing (IRE) **Miss Y. M. G. Jacques**
41 **INTELDREAM,** b g Intello (GER)—Libys Dream (IRE) **Mr R Bruni & Partner**
42 **KODIAC LASS (IRE),** b f Kodiac—Awwal Malika (USA) **Heart of the South Racing 107 & Partner**
43 **LADY SCHANNELL (IRE),** b f Teofilo (IRE)—Royal Guinevere **Nick Bradley Racing 27 & Sohi & Partner**
44 **LATIN KNIGHT,** b c Sea The Stars (IRE)—Latin Love (IRE) **Heart of the South Racing 112**
45 **LUCIPHERUS (IRE),** b g Dark Angel (IRE)—Nitya (FR) **Mr Manfredini & Partner**
46 **MANDY THE ONE,** b f War Command (USA)—Paradise Place **Dr Marwan Koukash & Partners**
47 **MARIA MAGDALENA (IRE),** b f Battle of Marengo (IRE)—Few Words **Mr A. Marconi**
48 **MI MANCHI (IRE),** b f Sea The Moon (GER)—Carraigoona (IRE) **Fabfive**
49 **NATHANIELHAWTHORNE,** ch c Nathaniel (IRE)—Gino's Spirits **Team Valor LLC**
50 **NAVADIR (JPN),** b f Deep Impact (JPN)—Zumoorooda (AUS) **Sheikh M. B. K. Al Maktoum**
51 **OLIVETO (FR),** b c Wootton Bassett—Lemon Twist (IRE) **Middleham Park Racing XCI & Les Boyer**
52 **PERFECIMPERFECTION (IRE),** b f Camelot—Sunbird **Mr R Bruni & Partner**
53 **RAISE THE CLOUDS,** b f Kyllachy—Fersah (USA) **Scuderia Archi Romani & Partner**
54 **RAMBALDI (IRE),** b g Rip Van Winkle (IRE)—Shorana (IRE) **Mr Abbas Alalawi & Partner**
55 B c Quality Road (USA)—Rhagori **Mr R. El Youssef**
56 **ROMA BANGKOK,** b c Mount Nelson—Magika **Fabfive & Partner**
57 **SCENESETTER (IRE),** gr f Shamardal (USA)—Freezy (IRE) **Miss Y. M. G. Jacques**
58 **SENSAZIONE BOY,** b c Paco Boy (IRE)—Exceed Sensazione **Scuderia Blueberry SRL**
59 **SERAPHIM,** gr f Dark Angel (IRE)—Moma Lee **Excel Racing & Partner**
60 **SHALEELA'S DREAM,** b g Oasis Dream—Shaleela (IRE) **Scuderia Blueberry SRL**
61 **SOMETHING BLOND (IRE),** ch f Olympic Glory (IRE)—Broadway Duchess (IRE) **Scuderia Archi Romani**
62 **SONJA HENIE (IRE),** b f Exceed And Excel (AUS)—Cold Cold Woman **Team Valor LLC**
63 **SWEET CELEBRATION (IRE),** b f Excelebration (IRE)—Snow Dust **Ventura Racing 5 & Partner**
64 **THUNDEROAD,** b g Street Sense (USA)—Royal Crystal (USA) **Mr Manfredini & Partner**
65 **UNDERCOLOURS (IRE),** b c Excelebration (IRE)—Puddles (FR) **Scuderia Archi Romani & Partner**
66 **WILLKOMMEN,** b c Epaulette (AUS)—Weeza (IRE) **Mrs L. Botti**
67 **WITHOUTDESTINATION,** b g Epaulette (AUS)—Where I Be **Fabfive**

TWO-YEAR-OLDS

68 B f 3/4 Deep Impact (JPN)—Amanee (AUS) (Pivotal) **Sheikh M. B. K. Al Maktoum**
69 B f 7/5 Golden Horn—Biz Bar (Tobougg (IRE)) (70000) **The Honorable Earle I. Mack & Mr Giovanni Parri**
70 **CADEO,** br c 26/3 Raven's Pass (USA)—
　　　　　　　　　　　　　Waldena (USA) (Storm Cat (USA)) (25283) **Ambrosiana Racing & Partner**
71 B c 28/4 Iffraaj—Cats Eyes (Echo of Light) (17000) **Mr Manfredini & Partner**
72 B br c 16/4 Verrazano (USA)—Don't Stop to Shop (USA) (Unbridled's Song (USA)) (21164)
73 Ch f 4/4 Roderic O'Connor (IRE)—Donatia (Shamardal (USA)) (42000)
74 **DONO,** b c 16/3 Mayson—Dan Loose Daughter (Sakhee (USA)) (33712) **Scuderia Blueberry S.R.L. & Partner 2**
75 **FAIR MAN,** b c 14/2 Kingman—Fair Dubawi (Dubawi (IRE)) **Scuderia Blueberry SRL**
76 B f 5/2 Raven's Pass (USA)—Fair Nashwan (Nashwan (USA)) (32000) **Scuderia Blueberry SRL**
77 **FAIRMET,** b f 31/1 Helmet (AUS)—Fairdal (Shamardal (USA)) **Scuderia Blueberry SRL**
78 **FAIRY LACHY,** b f 26/4 Kyllachy—Fairy Oasis (Oasis Dream) **Scuderia Blueberry SRL**
79 Ch f 27/3 Camacho—Fiancee (IRE) (Pivotal) (42000)
80 **FOLLIA,** b f 16/2 Toronado—Filona (IRE) (Motivator) **Scuderia Blueberry SRL**
81 **HABIT ROUGE,** b c 12/4 Helmet (AUS)—
　　　　　　　　　　　　　Hurricane Harriet (Bertolini (USA)) (16856) **Ambrosiana Racing & Partner**
82 Gr c 7/2 Cable Bay (IRE)—High Tan (High Chaparral (IRE)) (18541)
83 B c 18/1 Lemon Drop Kid (USA)—
　　　　　　　　　　　　　La Reine Lionne (USA) (Leroidesanimaux (BRZ)) (52910) **The Honorable Earle I. Mack & Partner**
84 **LETHAL SHADOW,** b c 16/3 Lethal Force (IRE)—
　　　　　　　　　　　　　Danehill Shadow (IRE) (Danehill Dancer (IRE)) **Scuderia Blueberry S.R.L. & Partner 2**
85 B c 23/3 Casamento (IRE)—Magika (Dubawi (IRE)) **Les Boyer Partnership**
86 B c 26/4 Gleneagles (IRE)—Native Picture (IRE) (Kodiac) (40000)

MR MARCO BOTTI - Continued

87 **NO NAY BELLA (IRE)**, b f 12/4 No Nay Never (USA)—
  Illuminating Dream (IRE) (High Chaparral (IRE)) (32026) **Middleham Park Racing CXXI & Partners**
88 B f 24/4 Lope de Vega (IRE)—Red Boots (IRE) (Verglas (IRE)) (42000)
89 B f 11/4 Dabirsim (FR)—Salona (GER) (Lord of England (GER)) (29498)
90 **SUAVIDAD (IRE)**, b f 7/4 Mukhadram—
  Delicatezza (Danehill Dancer (IRE)) (7000) **Ambrosiana Racing & Partner**
91 B f 19/2 Bated Breath—Symposia (Galileo (IRE)) (21912)
92 **ZERO LIMITS**, gr ro c 29/3 Outstrip—Mpumalanga (Observatory (USA)) (10000) **Mrs L. Botti**

Other Owners: A J Suited Partnership, Mr P. C. Aberg, Mrs E. Adamski, Mr P. Agostini, Mrs E. Agostini, Sheikh N. Al Khalifa, Sheikh N. M. H. Al Khalifa, Mr A. Alalawi, Mr J. Allison, Jonny Allison & David Fass, Ambrosiana Racing, Mr C. Austin, Mr A. Baragiola, Miss E. M. Baragiola, Mr L. Biffi, Mr N. Bradley, Mr T. Denham, Excel Racing, Mr D. V. Fass, Mr P. Fisher, Mr P. Harper, Mrs E. F. Harte, Heart of the South Racing 107, Miss S. Holden, Dr M. B. Q. S. Koukash, Mr G. Manfredini, Middleham Park Racing CXXI, Middleham Park Racing XCI, Mr T. Muller, Mr C. J. Murfitt, Newsells Park Stud Limited, Mr J. M. Nicholson, Nick Bradley Racing 27, Nick Bradley Racing 30, T. S. Palin, Mr R. B. Patel, Mr J. R. Penny, Mr C. Pizarro, M. Prince, Mr K. Sohi, Ventura Racing 5.

Assistant Trainers: Lucie Botti, Karen Parris

Apprentice: Gabriele Malune, Marc Monaghan.

54	**MR DARAGH BOURKE, Lockerbie** Postal: **Cherrybank, Waterbeck, Lockerbie, Dumfries and Galloway, DG11 3EY** Contacts: **MOBILE (07495) 948493**

1 **BATTLE HARD (IRE)**, 7, ch g Presenting—Erintante (IRE) **Mr S. Lowther**
2 **CARRY ON SCORPION (IRE)**, 6, b g Scorpion (IRE)—All My Judges **Mrs L. J. McLeod**
3 **COLORADO GOLD**, 6, ch m Beat Hollow—Crevamoy (IRE) **Distillery Stud**
4 **GOLDEN CHANCER**, 5, b g Gold Well—Princess Oriane (IRE)
5 **METRO BOULOT DODO (IRE)**, 6, br g Robin des Champs (FR)—Lizzy Langtry (IRE) **Mrs K. Cole**
6 **PADDY THE PANDA (IRE)**, 4, b g Flemensfirth (USA)—Pandorama Lady (IRE) **Mr S. Lowther**
7 **PADS (IRE)**, 9, b g Luso—Augusta Victoria **Mr Scott Lowther & Mr Gavin Hamilton**
8 **RELKWOOD (IRE)**, 9, gr g Beneficial—Rose Wood **Mr S. Lowther**
9 **SCHLIPF**, 6, b g Supreme Sound—Zahara Joy **A. B. Graham**

Other Owners: Mr G. Hamilton, Mrs Margaret Robinson, R. Robinson.

55	**MR PETER BOWEN, Haverfordwest** Postal: **Yet-Y-Rhug, Letterston, Haverfordwest, Pembrokeshire, SA62 5TB** Contacts: **PHONE (01348) 840486 FAX (01348) 840486 MOBILE (07811) 111234** E-MAIL info@peterbowenracing.com WEBSITE www.peterbowenracing.com

1 **ALF 'N' DOR (IRE)**, 8, ch g Flemensfirth (USA)—Greenflag Princess (IRE) **The Hedonists & Karen Bowen**
2 **ATOMIC RUMBLE (IRE)**, 6, b g Oscar (IRE)—Atomic Betty (IRE) **Mr C. B. Compton & Mrs Karen Bowen**
3 **AWESOMEDESTINATION (IRE)**, 6, ch g Dubai Destination (USA)—
  Don't Be Bleu (IRE) **Peter Bowen Racing Club**
4 **BANG BANG ROSIE (IRE)**, 7, b m Stowaway—Restless Dreams (IRE) **Mr C. B. Compton**
5 **BEGGAR'S WISHES (IRE)**, 8, b g Oscar (IRE)—Strong Wishes (IRE) **Roddy Owen & Paul Fullagar**
6 **BUACHAILL ALAINN (IRE)**, 12, b g Oscar (IRE)—Bottle A Knock (IRE) **Roddy Owen & Paul Fullagar**
7 **CANDY BURG (FR)**, 6, b g Sageburg (IRE)—Candinie (USA) **H Jones & M Bowen**
8 **CODESHARE**, 7, b g Dansili—Clepsydra **Roy & Louise Swinburne**
9 **COUGAR'S GOLD (IRE)**, 8, b g Oscar (IRE)—Top Her Up (IRE) **Mr W. E. V. Harries**
10 **CRUISING BYE**, 13, b g Alflora (IRE)—Althrey Flame (IRE) **F. Lloyd**
11 **DOTTIES DILEMA (IRE)**, 11, b g Pierre—Tellarue (IRE) **Mr A. R. E. Morgan**
12 **DR DUNRAVEN**, 8, b g Dr Massini (IRE)—Bajan Girl (FR) **Peter Bowen Racing Club**
13 **DR ROBIN (IRE)**, 9, b g Robin des Pres (FR)—Inter Alia (IRE) **David Robbins & Karen Bowen**
14 **DRIFT ROCK**, 5, ch g Malinas (GER)—Araucaria (IRE) **Amanda & Patrick Bancroft**
15 **EASY BUCKS**, 4, b g Getaway—Tushana (GER) **Mr M. B. Bowen**
16 **EQUUS DANCER (IRE)**, 5, b g Jeremy (USA)—Celtic Cailin (IRE) **Roddy Owen & Paul Fullagar**

MR PETER BOWEN - Continued

17 **FORTUNES HIDING (IRE)**, 6, b g Beat Hollow—Sambre (FR) **Roddy Owen & Paul Fullagar**
18 **FRANCKY DU BERLAIS (FR)**, 6, b g Saint des Saints (FR)—Legende du Luy (FR) **Roddy Owen & Paul Fullagar**
19 **GENERAL ALLENBY**, 5, b g Medicean—Cat Hunter **D. Cohen**
20 **GENERAL MALARKEY (IRE)**, 7, b g Scorpion (IRE)—Andreas Benefit (IRE) **Baker, Dodd, Cooke & Heler**
21 **GET AN OSCAR (IRE)**, 5, ch m Getaway (GER)—Lady Perspex (IRE) **Peter Bowen Racing Club**
22 **HENLLAN HARRI (IRE)**, 11, br g King's Theatre (IRE)—Told You So (IRE) **Mr W. E. V. Harries**
23 **HENRYVILLE**, 11, b g Generous (IRE)—Aquavita **Roddy Owen & Paul Fullagar**
24 **HILLARY VIEW (IRE)**, 7, b g Court Cave—Tearaway Lady (IRE) **Mr J. A. Martin**
25 **JEANNOT DE NONANT (FR)**, 7, ch g Full of Gold (FR)—Jolie Puce (FR) **Oi Digital Ltd & R & L Swinburne**
26 **JUDGE EARLE (IRE)**, 7, b g Court Cave—Louis's Teffia (IRE) **G. J. Morris**
27 **LANDOFSMILES (IRE)**, 6, b g Beneficial—Sadie Supreme (IRE) **Miss Jayne Brace & Mr Gwyn Brace**
28 **LEAVING HOME (IRE)**, 6, b g Getaway (GER)—Snuff (FR) **Mrs N. Unsworth**
29 **LEMON NOT LIME**, 5, ch m Black Sam Bellamy (IRE)—Glacial Missile (IRE) **Roddy Owen & Paul Fullagar**
30 **LORD BRYAN (IRE)**, 8, b g Brian Boru—Run Cat (IRE) **Miss Jayne Brace & Mr Gwyn Brace**
31 **LORD NAPIER (IRE)**, 6, b g Galileo (IRE)—Jacqueline (IND) **F. Lloyd**
32 **MAC TOTTIE**, 6, b g Midnight Legend—Tot of The Knar **Steve & Jackie Fleetham**
33 **MINELLA DADDY (IRE)**, 9, b g Flemensfirth (USA)—Old Moon (IRE) **Roddy Owen & Paul Fullagar**
34 **MON ELDORADO (FR)**, 7, b g Gentlewave (IRE)—Miryea (IRE) **Walters Plant Hire & James & Jean Potter**
35 **MONTANNA**, 5, ch g Notnowcato—Asi (USA) **F. Lloyd**
36 **MORE BUCK's (IRE)**, 9, ch g Presenting—Buck's Blue (FR) **P Duffy, D Semmens, V Williams & M Bowen**
37 **ONTOPOFTHEWORLD (IRE)**, 10, ch g Desert King (IRE)—Zaffre (IRE) **Saith O Ni & Karen Bowen**
38 **PEARL SWAN (IRE)**, 11, b g Gentlewave (IRE)—Swanson (USA) **Roddy Owen & Paul Fullagar**
39 **PLAY THE ACE (IRE)**, 10, b br g Scorpion (IRE)—Henris Blaze (IRE) **Roddy Owen & Paul Fullagar**
40 **POINT OF DEPARTURE (IRE)**, 8, b g Mahler—Miranda's Lace (IRE) **F. Lloyd**
41 **POTTERS STORY**, 7, b g Kayf Tara—Lily Potter **James & Jean Potter**
42 **ROLLING MAUL (IRE)**, 11, b g Oscar (IRE)—Water Sports (IRE) **Roddy Owen & Paul Fullagar**
43 **RONS DREAM**, 9, b m Kayf Tara—Empress of Light **Stepney Girls**
44 **RUPERRA TOM**, 11, b g Kayf Tara—Cathy's Dream (IRE) **Mr T. J. Rees**
45 **SCENEMAKER**, 6, b g Stowaway—Kilmac Princess (IRE) **Mr A. R. E. Morgan**
46 **STATUARIO**, 4, b g Helmet (AUS)—Cat Hunter **Mr Michael G Cohen & Mr David Cohen**
47 **THE LION ROARS (IRE)**, 5, br g Let The Lion Roar—Definite Blue (IRE) **Mr & Mrs Paul & Clare Rooney**
48 **VIENS CHERCHER (IRE)**, 8, b g Milan—La Zingarella (IRE) **Ednyfed & Elizabeth Morgan**

Other Owners: Mr J. B. Baker, P. A. Bancroft, Mrs A. Bancroft, Mr B. G. Bowen, P Bowen, Mrs K. Bowen, D. G. Brace, Miss M. J. Brace, Mr M. Cohen, Mr P. G. Cooke, Mrs D. Cossey, Mr G. T. G. Dodd, Mr D. P. Duffy, Paul Duffy, David Semmens, Viv Williams, Mrs J. Fleetham, Mr S. Fleetham, P. G. Fullagar, The Hedonists, Mr M. J. Heler, Mr H. Jones, Mr E. O. Morgan, Mrs E. Morgan, Oi Digital Limited, R. R. Owen, B. S. Port, Mrs M. J. Potter, Mr J. E. Potter, S. D. Reeve, D. J. Robbins, Mr P. A. Rooney, Mrs C. Rooney, Mr D. M. Semmens, Mrs L. T. Swinburne, R. D. J. Swinburne, Walters Plant Hire Ltd.

Assistant Trainers: Karen Bowen, Michael Bowen

Jockey (NH): Sean Bowen. **Conditional:** James Bowen.

---

56 **MR ROY BOWRING, Edwinstowe**
Postal: Fir Tree Farm, Edwinstowe, Mansfield, Nottinghamshire, NG21 9JG
Contacts: **PHONE** (01623) 822451 **MOBILE** (07973) 712942
E-MAIL srbowring@outlook.com

1 **ACE MASTER**, 11, ch g Ballet Master (USA)—Ace Maite **S. R. Bowring**
2 **DECISION MAKER (IRE)**, 5, b g Iffraaj—Consensus (IRE) **K. Nicholls**
3 **EXCEL MATE**, 5, ch m Captain Gerrard (IRE)—Exceedingly Good (IRE) **S. R. Bowring**
4 **FIRST EXCEL**, 7, ch g First Trump—Exceedingly Good (IRE) **S. R. Bowring**
5 **FOOLAAD**, 8, ch g Exceed And Excel (AUS)—Zayn Zen **K. Nicholls**
6 **HIGHLIFE FLYER**, 4, b g Medicean—Floating **S. R. Bowring**
7 **JEAN EXCELS**, 4, b f Captain Gerrard (IRE)—Exceedingly Good (IRE) **S. R. Bowring**
8 **LITTLE CHOOSEY**, 9, ch m Cadeaux Genereux—Little Nymph **Mr K. Nicholls & Mr S. R. Bowring**
9 **MASTER OF SONG**, 12, ch g Ballet Master (USA)—Ocean Song **S. R. Bowring**
10 **MEN UNITED (FR)**, 6, b g Acclamation—Moore's Melody (IRE) **S. R. Bowring**
11 **NINE ELMS (USA)**, 4, ch g Street Cry (IRE)—Nawaiet (USA) **K. Nicholls**

57 MR JIM BOYLE, Epsom
Postal: **South Hatch Stables, Burgh Heath Road, Epsom, Surrey, KT17 4LX**
Contacts: **PHONE (01372) 748800 FAX (01372) 739410 MOBILE (07719) 554147**
E-MAIL info@jamesboyle.co.uk & jimboylesec@hotmail.co.uk (Secretary)
WEBSITE www.jamesboyle.co.uk

1 **AMARETTO**, 4, b g Kyllachy—Dan Loose Daughter **A. B. Pope**
2 **BABY GAL**, 5, b m Royal Applause—Our Gal **Inside Track Racing Club**
3 **BECKY SHARP**, 4, b f Foxwedge (AUS)—Perfect Practice **Harrier Racing 1**
4 **DUKE OF NORTH (IRE)**, 7, b g Danehill Dancer (IRE)—Althea Rose (IRE) **The Paddock Space Partnership**
5 **EXEC CHEF (IRE)**, 4, ch g Excelebration (IRE)—Donnelly's Hollow (IRE) **Inside Track Racing Club**
6 **FIRST QUEST (USA)**, 5, b g First Defence (USA)—Dixie Quest (USA) **The Waterboys**
7 **FOLLOWING BREEZE (IRE)**, 4, b f Kodiac—Xaloc (IRE) **Dr P. Wilson**
8 **HATEYA (IRE)**, 4, b f Footstepsinthesand—Selfsame (USA) **Inside Track Racing Club**
9 **KNOCKOUT BLOW**, 4, b g Lethal Force (IRE)—Elidore **Mr M. B. Spence**
10 **NOBLE EXPRESSION**, 4, b g Sir Percy—Disposition **The Waterboys**
11 **PEACE PREVAILS**, 4, ch f Declaration of War (USA)—Miss Mediator (USA) **The King John Partnership**
12 **QUICK RECOVERY**, 4, gr f Lethal Force (IRE)—Lisiere (IRE) **The 'In Recovery' Partnership**

THREE-YEAR-OLDS

13 **ANGELS CHANT**, b f Gregorian (IRE)—Divine Pamina (IRE) **Sir D. J. Prosser**
14 **FANNY CHENAL**, b f Kodiac—Maakrah **Mr H. E. Wigan**
15 **ISLE OF WOLVES**, b g Nathaniel (IRE)—L'ile Aux Loups (IRE) **Inside Track Racing Club**
16 **POETIC MOTION**, b f Toronado (IRE)—Sonnetation (IRE) **The 'In Recovery' Partnership**
17 **SHINING**, b f Lethal Force (IRE)—Spring Clean (FR) **The Clean Sweep Partnership**

TWO-YEAR-OLDS

18 **ANGELS ROC**, b c 18/5 Roderic O'Connor (IRE)—Divine Pamina (IRE) (Dark Angel (IRE)) **Sir D. J. Prosser**
19 **BEAT THE HEAT**, b c 7/3 Hot Streak (IRE)—Touriga (Cape Cross (IRE)) (30000) **Inside Track Racing Club**

Other Owners: Mr K. Booth, Mrs P. Boyle, Mr J. R. Boyle, A. J. Chambers, M. C. Cook, Mr A. C. Elliott, A. P. Grinter, Ms J. E. Harrison, Mr J. Hillier, Mr P. O. Mooney, Mr A. J. R. Moseley, Mr R. O'Dwyer, Mr E. Sames, Mr P. A. Taylor.

58 MR RICHARD BRABAZON, The Curragh
Postal: **Rangers Lodge, The Curragh, Co. Kildare, Ireland**
Contacts: **MOBILE 00353 (0) 87 2515626**
E-MAIL richardbrabazon@eircom.net WEBSITE www.richardbrabazon.ie

1 **FIGURE IT OUT (IRE)**, 4, ch f Arcano (IRE)—Doubt (IRE) **Richard Brabazon**
2 **HAYYEL (IRE)**, 4, b f Dark Angel (IRE)—Ravissante (IRE) **Celbridge Estates**
3 **KORBOUS (IRE)**, 10, ch g Choisir (AUS)—Puppet Play (IRE) **Mrs F. D. McAuley**
4 **WATERBOY (IRE)**, 5, gr g Stormy River (FR)—Happy (JPN) **David Moran / Richard Brabazon**

59 MR DAVID BRACE, Bridgend
Postal: **Llanmihangel Farm, Pyle, Bridgend, Mid Glamorgan, CF33 6RL**
Contacts: **PHONE (01656) 742313**

1 **BRACHO**, 7, b g Dr Massini (IRE)—Branston Lily **D. Brace**
2 **COLORADO DOC**, 8, b g Dr Massini (IRE)—First Royal (GER) **D. Brace**
3 **COMMANCHE CHEIF**, 6, b g Dr Massini (IRE)—Commanche Token (IRE) **D. Brace**
4 **DELKANTRA (IRE)**, 9, b g Putra Pekan—Delheim (IRE) **D. Brace**
5 **KIT CASEY (IRE)**, 9, b g Robin des Pres (FR)—An Culainn Beag (IRE) **D. Brace**
6 **LADY VERONICA**, 6, ch m Martaline—Vineuil (FR) **D. Brace**
7 **MITEBEALL FORLUCK**, 11, b g Westerner—Iborga (FR) **D. Brace**
8 **PATSIO (IRE)**, 11, b g Moscow Society (USA)—Supreme Favour (IRE) **D. Brace**
9 **PINK EYED PEDRO**, 8, b g Dr Massini (IRE)—Poacher's Paddy (IRE) **D. Brace**
10 **ROBIN DES PEOPLE (IRE)**, 9, br g Robin des Pres (FR)—Zelea (IRE) **D. Brace**
11 **WILCOX AND CO**, 5, b g Dr Massini (IRE)—Betty The Bog **D. Brace**
12 **WILLIAM MONEY (IRE)**, 12, b g Cloudings (IRE)—All of A Kind (IRE) **D. Brace**

Assistant Trainer: Robbie Llewellyn

Conditional: Connor Brace.

60 MR MILTON BRADLEY, Chepstow
Postal: **Meads Farm, Sedbury Park, Chepstow, Gwent, NP16 7HN**
Contacts: **PHONE (01291) 622486 FAX (01291) 626939**

1 **ALFIE'S ANGEL (IRE)**, 5, b g Dark Angel (IRE)—Penolva (IRE) E. A. Hayward
2 **AULD SOD (IRE)**, 6, b g Court Cave (IRE)—Didn't You Know (FR) Mr C. A. H. Tilley
3 **BURAUQ**, 7, b g Kyllachy—Riccoche (IRE) D. Smith
4 **COMPTON PRINCE**, 10, ch g Compton Place—Malelane (IRE) E. A. Hayward
5 **ENGLISHMAN**, 9, b g Royal Applause—Tesary E. A. Hayward
6 **INDIAN AFFAIR**, 9, br h Sleeping Indian—Rare Fling (USA) J. M. Bradley
7 **JAZRI**, 8, b g Myboycharlie (IRE)—Read Federica J. M. Bradley
8 **MOSTASHREQAH**, 6, ch m Equiano (FR)—China Cherub J. M. Bradley
9 **MURAAQEB**, 5, b g Nathaniel (IRE)—Tesary E. A. Hayward
10 **PRANCEABOOTTHETOON (IRE)**, 4, ch c Sir Prancealot (IRE)—Cabopino (IRE) E. A. Hayward
11 **RAPID RISE (IRE)**, 5, b g Fast Company (IRE)—French Doll (IRE) Mr M. G. Ridley
12 **RISING SUNSHINE (IRE)**, 6, b g Dark Angel (IRE)—Little Audio (IRE) Mr P. Banfield & Mr J. M. Bradley
13 **TEMPLE ROAD (IRE)**, 11, b g Street Cry (IRE)—Sugarhoneybaby (IRE) J. M. Bradley
14 **UNSUSPECTED GIRL (IRE)**, 6, b m Rip Van Winkle (IRE)—Sweet Sioux J. M. Bradley

THREE-YEAR-OLDS
15 **SPRING HOLLY (IRE)**, b f Zebedee—Blue Holly (IRE) E. A. Hayward
16 **TINTERN SPIRIT (IRE)**, b f Swiss Spirit—Tintern D. Smith (Saul) & J M Bradley
17 **WYE BOTHER (IRE)**, b f Born To Sea (IRE)—Enchantment E. A. Hayward
18 **YFENNI (IRE)**, ch f Dutch Art—Paisley E. A. Hayward

Other Owners: Mr Philip Banfield, Mr J. M. Bradley.

Jockey (flat): Tom Marquand, Luke Morris, Franny Norton. **Apprentice:** Kerrie Raybould.

61 MR MARK BRADSTOCK, Wantage
Postal: **Old Manor Stables, Foresters Lane, Letcombe Bassett, Wantage, Oxfordshire, OX12 9NB**
Contacts: **PHONE (01235) 760780 (01235) 760754 MOBILE (07887) 686697**
E-MAIL mark.bradstock@btconnect.com WEBSITE www.markbradstockracing.co.uk

1 **BENDY BOW**, 4, br g Malinas (GER)—Maid of Oaksey The BB Partnership
2 **COJACK (IRE)**, 7, b g Presenting—In The Waves (IRE) M. F. Bradstock
3 **CONEYGREE (IRE)**, 12, b g Karinga Bay—Plaid Maid (IRE) The Max Partnership
4 **DOWN TO THE SEA (FR)**, 5, ch g No Risk At All (FR)—Majoritaire (FR) Cracker and Smodge Partnership
5 **EGLANTIER (FR)**, 5, b g Bonbon Rose (FR)—Kyalami (FR) Cracker and Smodge Partnership
6 **FLINTHAM**, 10, b g Kayf Tara—Plaid Maid (IRE) The Rasher Partnership
7 **HAYLEY BELLE (IRE)**, 8, b m Flemensfirth (USA)—Tart of Tipp (IRE) Mr P. B. T. Armitage
8 **I'M HERE (IRE)**, 6, ch g Hurricane Run (IRE)—Is It Here (IRE) M. F. Bradstock
9 **JAISALMER (IRE)**, 7, b g Jeremy (USA)—Shara (IRE) The Jeremy Partnership
10 **JAKAMANI**, 5, b g Sulamani (IRE)—Kentford Grebe Miss C Fordham & Mr C Vernon
11 5, Gr g Multiplex—Linen Line
12 **MIN TIKY (IRE)**, 7, b m King's Theatre (IRE)—Kon Tiky (FR) Kiki Partnership
13 **PEDDLER (IRE)**, 5, b g Scorpion (IRE)—Don't Waste It (IRE) Peddler Partnership
14 **ROBERT'S STAR (IRE)**, 9, b g Oscar (IRE)—Halona North Star Partnership
15 **STEP BACK (IRE)**, 9, ch g Indian River (FR)—Stepitoutmary (IRE) Cracker and Smodge Partnership
16 **STOOP LEAD (IRE)**, 5, b g Jeremy (USA)—The Only Girl (IRE) Outside Cards

Other Owners: Mr P. I. Armitage, Mrs A. L. Bell-Simmonds, Mrs L. Burgess, Mrs S. Crean, Lady Dundas, Miss C. Fordham, Mr D. King, Miss A. C. Loveng, Mr J. B. G. Macleod, Dr P. M. Milligan, Lord P. Oaksey, Lady Oaksey, Mr J. Reilly, Mrs S. Robinson, M. S. Tamburro, Mr R. W. Tyrrell, C. A. Vernon, A. M. Waller.

Assistant Trainer: Sara Bradstock

Jockey (NH): Nico De Boinville.

62 MR BARRY BRENNAN, Lambourn
Postal: **2 Rockfel Road, Lambourn, Hungerford, Berkshire, RG17 8NG**
Contacts: **MOBILE (07907) 529780**
E-MAIL **barrybrennan2@hotmail.co.uk** WEBSITE **www.barrybrennanracing.co.uk**

1 AVONMORE, 6, gr m Fair Mix (IRE)—Glenda Lough (IRE) **M. J. Hills**
2 HOPE'S WISHES, 9, b m Kayf Tara—Otarie (FR) **M. J. Hills**
3 LIGHTENTERTAINMENT (IRE), 11, b g King's Theatre (IRE)—Dochas Supreme (IRE) **D. R. T. Gibbons**
4 ROSE OF DUBAI, 6, b m Dubai Destination (USA)—Daraz Rose (IRE) **F. J. Brennan**
5 SAUCYSIOUX, 9, b m Tobougg (IRE)—Mohican Pass **F. J. Brennan**
6 THE LADY RULES, 5, ch m Native Ruler—Lady Author **M. T. Hughes**
7 ULYSSES (GER), 5, b g Sinndar (IRE)—Ungarin (GER) **D. R. T. Gibbons**

63 MISS RHONA BREWIS, Belford
Postal: **Chester Hill, Belford, Northumberland, NE70 7EF**
Contacts: **PHONE (01668) 213239/213281**

1 CLOVELLY, 9, b m Midnight Legend—Chantilly Rose **Miss R. G. Brewis**

64 MR JOHN BRIDGER, Liphook
Postal: **Upper Hatch Farm, Liphook, Hampshire, GU30 7EL**
Contacts: **PHONE (01428) 722528 MOBILE (07785) 716614**
E-MAIL **jbridger@sky.com**

1 AEGEAN LEGEND, 4, b g Mayson—Aegean Mystery **Mr J. J. Bridger**
2 ARCTIC FLOWER (IRE), 6, gr m Roderic O'Connor (IRE)—Just In Love (FR) **Mr & Mrs K. Finch**
3 BETSALOTTIE, 6, gr g Aqlaam—Si Belle (IRE) **Mr J. J. Bridger**
4 DEER SONG, 6, b g Piccolo—Turkish Delight **The Deer's Hut**
5 DELICATE KISS, 5, b m Delegator—Desert Kiss **DBD Partnership**
6 FAIRY MIST (IRE), 12, b g Oratorio (IRE)—Prealpina (IRE) **Mr J. J. Bridger**
7 FIRENZE ROSA (IRE), 4, b f Zebedee—Our Nana Rose (IRE) **Mr & Mrs K. Finch**
8 FLOWING CLARETS, 6, ch m Pastoral Pursuits—Flying Clarets (IRE) **Wood Marshall Bridger**
9 FLYING SAKHEE, 6, b m Sakhee's Secret—Sister Moonshine **D Higgs J J Bridger**
10 LIVE DANGEROUSLY, 9, b g Zamindar (USA)—Desert Lynx (IRE) **W. A. Wood**
11 PETTOCHSIDE, 10, b g Refuse To Bend (IRE)—Clear Impression (IRE) **Mr P. Cook**
12 PHAROH JAKE, 11, ch g Piccolo—Rose Amber **Mr J J Bridger Mrs J Stamp**
13 PORTO FERRO (IRE), 5, b m Arcano (IRE)—Sassari (IRE) **Mr J. J. Bridger**
14 SHIFTING STAR (IRE), 14, ch g Night Shift (USA)—Ahshado **Night Shadow Syndicate**
15 TIME TO ROCK, 4, b g Olden Times—Five Bells (IRE) **Mr M J Evans & Mr T M Jones**

THREE-YEAR-OLDS

16 AEGEAN MIST, ch f Mayson—Aegean Shadow **Theobalds Stud**
17 DARK IMPULSE (IRE), b ro g Dark Angel (IRE)—Invincible Me (IRE) **Mr & Mrs K. Finch**
18 PINCTADA, b f Finjaan—Oyster (IRE) **Mr J. J. Bridger**
19 SHADOW FORCE, gr f Lethal Force (IRE)—Night Premiere (IRE) **Mr & Mrs K. Finch**
20 STARCHANT, b f Gregorian (IRE)—Aegean Mystery **Mr J. J. Bridger**

TWO-YEAR-OLDS

21 Br f 27/4 Clodovil (IRE)—Coy (IRE) (Danehill (USA)) (1500) **Rachel Cook**
22 Gr g 16/3 Gregorian (IRE)—Dandoony (Byron) **Theobalds Stud**
23 HOPE BAY (IRE), b f 25/1 Camelot—Summer Bliss (Green Desert (USA)) (2000) **Mr & Mrs K. Finch**
24 KAHPEHLO, b f 8/4 Helmet (AUS)—Anosti (Act One) (1500) **Mr & Mrs K. Finch**
25 RUBEE FORTY, b f 9/2 Lethal Force (IRE)—Desert Kiss (Cape Cross (IRE)) (2000) **Mrs D. Ellison**
26 SEA MYSTERY, b f 1/5 Gregorian (IRE)—Aegean Mystery (Dr Fong (USA)) (800) **Mystery Partnership**

Other Owners: Mr J. E. Burrows, Mrs D. A. Ellison, Mr M. J. Evans, Mrs D. Finch, K. Finch, Mr D. G. Higgs, T. M. Jones, Mr F. R. Northcott, Mr B. Olkowicz, Exors of the Late Mr G. K. Panos, K. Panos, Mrs J. M. Stamp, Mrs D. Stewart.

Assistant Trainer: Rachel Cook

65 MR DAVID BRIDGWATER, Stow-on-the-Wold

Postal: **Wyck Hill Farm, Wyck Hill, Stow-on-the-Wold, Cheltenham, Gloucestershire, GL54 1HT**
Contacts: **PHONE** (01451) 830349 **FAX** (01451) 830349 **MOBILE** (07831) 635817
E-MAIL sales@bridgwaterracing.co.uk **WEBSITE** www.bridgwaterracing.co.uk

1 **ACCORD (IRE)**, 9, b g Arcadio (GER)—Detente **Mr J. H. Furlong**
2 **BELMONT PARK (FR)**, 8, br g Al Namix (FR)—Goldoulyssa (FR) **Terry & Sarah Amos**
3 **BUBLE (IRE)**, 10, b g Milan—Glorious Moments (IRE) **Mrs Mary Bridgwater & Mr & Mrs Chenery**
4 **CAMAPLU (FR)**, 7, gr m Turgeon (USA)—Line Tzigane (FR) **Terry & Sarah Amos**
5 **COMOTION (FR)**, 4, b g Kapgarde (FR)—Second Emotion (FR) **Terry & Sarah Amos**
6 **CYBALKO (FR)**, 6, b g Balko (FR)—Cybertina (FR) **Terry & Sarah Amos**
7 **DAME DU SOIR (FR)**, 6, br m Axxos (GER)—Kassing (FR) **Cwb Plus 1 Partnership**
8 **DOWNLOADTHEAPP (IRE)**, 6, b g Definite Article—Chase A Dream (IRE) **Mr G. J. Burrow**
9 **EDGAR (GER)**, 9, b g Big Shuffle (USA)—Estella (GER) **K J McCourt & Partners**
10 **ENRICHISSANT (FR)**, 5, b br g Speedmaster (GER)—Quibble (FR) **Simon & Liz Hunt**
11 **FORT GABRIEL (FR)**, 8, ch g Ange Gabriel (FR)—Forge Neuve (FR) **CWB Plus 2 Partnership**
12 **FRENCH PIECE**, 5, ch g Alkaased (USA)—Aster (IRE) **P. J. Cave**
13 **FUKUTO (FR)**, 4, b g Cokoriko (FR)—Hargaux de Saisy (FR) **Simon Hunt & Bob Wilson**
14 **JOT'EM DOWN (IRE)**, 8, b g Kalanisi (IRE)—Shuil A Hocht (IRE) **Mr S. Hunt**
15 **KEEL OVER**, 8, b g Gamut (IRE)—Kayf Keel **Taymar Racing**
16 **LITTLE RICH (IRE)**, 4, b g Arakan—Brioney (IRE) **D. G. Bridgwater**
17 **MUILEAN NA MADOG (IRE)**, 8, b g Papal Bull—Truly Precious (IRE) **CWB Partnership**
18 **NO APPROVAL (IRE)**, 6, b g Approve (IRE)—Night Cam (IRE) **The Happy Horse Partnership**
19 **NOBLE SAFFRON**, 4, br g Trans Island—Renada **Mrs J. A. Chenery & Mr R. J. Chenery**
20 **OPECHEE (IRE)**, 8, b g Robin des Champs (FR)—Falcons Gift (IRE) **AM Bostock DG Bostock**
21 **ORCHESTRATED (IRE)**, 8, b g Mahler—Rose Island **Feasibility Limited**
22 **PIRATE SAM**, 4, b g Black Sam Bellamy (IRE)—Teenero **JA & RJ Chenery & Partners**
23 **RUBY DU BERLAIS**, 5, br m Beat All (USA)—Marina du Berlais (FR) **Building Bridgies**
24 **SHAJI**, 4, b g Exceed And Excel (AUS)—Eclaircie (IRE) **The Happy Horse Partnership**
25 **THE TIN MINER (IRE)**, 8, br g Presenting—Sidalcea (IRE) **Simon & Liz Hunt**
26 **UTILITY (GER)**, 8, b g Yeats (IRE)—Ungarin (GER) **Tim & Sue Payton**
27 **WAHWONAISA**, 7, b g Kalanisi (IRE)—Clandestine **AM Bostock DG Bostock**
28 **WENCESLAUS (GER)**, 7, b g Tiger Hill (IRE)—Warrior Czarina (USA) **Deauville Daze Partnership**
29 **ZEPHYROS (GER)**, 8, br g Areion (GER)—Zandra (GER) **MMG Racing**

THREE-YEAR-OLDS

30 **GAIA VALLIS (FR)**, b f Saint des Saints (FR)—Toccata Vallis (FR) **David Bridgwater Racing**
31 B g Balko (FR)—Golden Firebird (IRE) **Mr S. Hunt**
32 **IN A TIZZ (FR)**, b br f Nicaron (GER)—Line Tzigane (FR) **Terry & Sarah Amos**
33 **MAKTAY**, b g Makfi—Cinta **Taymar Racing**
34 **MEBA FISTA (FR)**, b g No Risk At All (FR)—Argovie (FR) **Mr S. Hunt**
35 **URANUS DES BORDES (FR)**, b g Kapgarde (FR)—Queen des Bordes (FR) **Mr S. Hunt**

TWO-YEAR-OLDS

36 B c 11/4 Authorized (IRE)—Ahdaaf (USA) (Bahri (USA)) (13485) **Mr S. Hunt**
37 B c 22/3 Diamond Boy (FR)—Lazoukine (FR) (Astarabad (USA)) (6742) **Mr S. Hunt**
38 **SAQUEBOUTE (FR)**, b f 4/5 Slickly Royal (FR)—Grande Cavale (FR) (Ballingarry (IRE)) **Mr S. Hunt**

Other Owners: Mrs S. P. Amos, T. P. Amos, Mrs C. H. Borghoff, D. G. Bostock, Mrs A. M. Bostock, R. J. Brennan, Mrs
A. Bridgwater, Mr R. J. Chenery, Mrs J. A. Chenery, Mr G. J. Clarkson, Mrs A. Field, Mr A. Gunn, Miss L. M. Haywood, Mr
M. V. Hill, Mrs E. A. Hunt, Mr K. J. McCourt, Mrs S. Payton, Mr T. J. Payton, Mr A. R. Pigott, Mr A. Smelt, Mr M.
Wilkinson, Mr R. Wilson.

Assistant Trainer: Mrs Lucy K. Bridgwater

Jockey (NH): Tom Scudamore. **Conditional:** Daniel Hiskett, Callum McKinnes. **Apprentice:** Poppy Bridgwater.

66 MR MARK BRISBOURNE, Nesscliffe

Postal: **Ness Strange Stables, Great Ness, Nesscliffe, Shrewsbury, Shropshire, SY4 2LE**
Contacts: **PHONE** (01743) 741599 **MOBILE** (07803) 019651

1 **BELABOUR**, 6, b g Bernardini (USA)—Criticism **W. M. Brisbourne**
2 **CLIVE CLIFTON (IRE)**, 6, b g Wootton Bassett—Dearest Daisy **Mr P Clifton**
3 **ICE CANYON**, 5, b g Raven's Pass (USA)—Picture Hat (USA) **Mr Derek & Mrs Marie Dean**
4 **MANFADH (IRE)**, 4, b g Iffraaj—Asiya (USA) **Mr Derek & Mrs Marie Dean**

MR MARK BRISBOURNE - Continued

5 **QAYED (CAN)**, 4, b g Blame (USA)—Endless Journey (USA) **Mr Derek & Mrs Marie Dean**
6 **STORM LIGHTNING**, 10, b g Exceed And Excel (AUS)—All For Laura **Law Abiding Citizens**

Other Owners: A. J. Banton, D. Dean, Mrs M. Dean, Mr A. Pitt, Zen Racing.

Jockey (flat): Liam Jones, Shane Kelly, Eoin Walsh. **Jockey (NH):** Robert Dunne. **Apprentice:** Charlie Bennett.
Amateur: Miss Becky Brisbourne.

---

67   MR ROBYN BRISLAND, Newark
Postal: **Mill Top Equestrian Centre, Danethorpe, Newark, Notts.**
Contacts: **MOBILE (07771) 656081**
E-MAIL robbris@me.com

1 4, B f Arcano (IRE)—Alexander Duchess (IRE)
2 **APACHE BLAZE**, 4, b f Champs Elysees—Polar Circle (USA) **Ferrybank Properties Limited**
3 **ATALANTA QUEEN**, 4, b f Canford Cliffs (IRE)—Champagne Aerial (IRE) **Ferrybank Properties Limited**
4 **BEAUTIFUL ARTIST (USA)**, 4, b f Lonhro (AUS)—She's A Beauty (USA) **Mrs Jo Brisland**
5 **COLD FIRE (IRE)**, 6, ch g Frozen Power (IRE)—Eleanor Eloise (USA) **Dallas Racing & Partners**
6 **COLD HARBOUR**, 4, b g North Light (IRE)—Pilcomayo (IRE) **Mrs Jackie Cornwell & Mrs Jo Brisland**
7 **COMPASS POINT**, 4, b c Helmet (AUS)—Takarna (IRE) **Mrs J. A. Cornwell**
8 4, B f Foxwedge (AUS)—Eleanor Eloise (USA) **Mrs J. A. Cornwell**
9 **HARBOUR QUAY**, 5, b g Foxwedge (AUS)—Whatcameoverme (USA) **Mrs J. A. Cornwell**
10 **HARBOUR STORM**, 4, br g Sayif (IRE)—Minette **Mrs J. A. Cornwell**
11 **KATIE GALE**, 9, b m Shirocco (GER)—Karla June **Ferrybank Properties Limited**
12 **LIZ'S DREAM**, 6, b m Dick Turpin (IRE)—Whatcameoverme (USA) **Mrs J. A. Cornwell**
13 4, Ch f Dandy Man (IRE)—Masakira (IRE)
14 4, Ch f Dawn Approach (IRE)—Mountain Law (USA) **Mrs J. A. Cornwell**
15 **NAVAJO STAR (IRE)**, 5, b m Mastercraftsman (IRE)—Champagne Aerial (IRE) **Ferrybank Properties Limited**
16 **NINETEENRBO'MALLEY**, 7, b g Beat All (USA)—My Nora (IRE) **Mr E. O'Malley**
17 **PURBECK GEM**, 5, ch m Sakhee's Secret—Porcelana (IRE) **Mrs J. A. Cornwell**
18 **REEDWAY (IRE)**, 6, ch g Intikhab (USA)—Mistress Bailey **Mrs J. A. Cornwell**
19 4, B f Foxwedge (AUS)—Roshina (IRE) **Mrs J. A. Cornwell**
20 **WHIRL ME ROUND**, 5, ch g Piccolo—Give Her A Whirl **Dallas Racing and Partners**

THREE-YEAR-OLDS
21 B g Bungle Inthejungle—Cuiseach (IRE)
22 **INOSANTO**, b g Charm Spirit (IRE)—Astromagick **The Rogues Gallery Two**
23 B f Battle of Marengo (IRE)—Merle **Mrs J. A. Cornwell**
24 **OBLATE**, b f Epaulette (AUS)—Lady Benedicte (IRE) **Houghton Bloodstock**
25 B g Gregorian (IRE)—Sea Whisper **Mrs J. A. Cornwell**
26 Gr c Gregorian (IRE)—Takarna (IRE) **Mrs J. A. Cornwell**

TWO-YEAR-OLDS
27 Ch c 4/3 Anjaal—Abbotsfield (IRE) (Sakhee's Secret) (1500)
28 B f 4/3 Toronado (IRE)—Anna's Vision (IRE) (Invincible Spirit (IRE)) (2380)
29 B c 19/2 Sayif (IRE)—Bahie (Authorized (IRE)) (1600)
30 B c 5/5 Anjaal—Bank On Black (IRE) (Big Bad Bob (IRE)) (3370)
31 B f 17/2 Bungle Inthejungle—Blacke Forest (Manduro (GER))
32 Gr f 30/1 Lethal Force (IRE)—Chatalong (IRE) (Invincible Spirit (IRE)) **Mrs A. L. Heayns**
33 B c 28/1 Mayson—Cut The Cackle (IRE) (Danetime (IRE))
34 B f 9/2 Gregorian (IRE)—Dubawi's Spirit (IRE) (Dubawi (IRE)) (1500)
35 B c 25/3 Due Diligence (USA)—Midnight Pearl (USA) (Woodman (USA)) (2380)
36 B c 25/4 Helmet (AUS)—Millsini (Rossini (USA)) (3200)
37 Ch f 25/4 Power—Moynsha Lady (IRE) (Namid) (952)
38 B f 21/3 Dawn Approach (IRE)—Patience Alexander (IRE) (Kodiac) (25000) **Ferrybank Properties Limited**
39 B c 15/4 Alhebayeb (IRE)—Regal Kiss (King's Best (USA)) (1904)
40 Ch f 26/2 Anjaal—Sea Regatta (IRE) (Hurricane Run (USA)) (571) **Mrs J. A. Cornwell**
41 Ch f 14/3 Mayson—Sea Whisper (Compton Place) **Mrs J. A. Cornwell**
42 B c 11/5 Mayson—The Lady Lapwing (Mark of Esteem (IRE)) (1904)
43 B f 14/2 Paco Boy (IRE)—Ziefhd (Haafhd) (1904)

Other Owners: Mr T. P. Clover, Dallas Racing, Mr A. R. Elliott, Mr M. A. Glassett, Mr O. Robinson.

Jockey (flat): Martin Harley, Luke Morris.

68 **MR ANTONY BRITTAIN, Warthill**
Postal: **Northgate Lodge, Warthill, York, YO19 5XR**
Contacts: **PHONE (01759) 371472 FAX (01759) 372915**
E-MAIL email@antonybrittain.co.uk WEBSITE www.antonybrittain.co.uk

1 ANOTHER ANGEL (IRE), 5, b g Dark Angel (IRE)—Kermana (IRE) **Mr Antony Brittain**
2 BEATBYBEATBYBEAT, 6, ch m Poet's Voice—Beat As One **Mr Antony Brittain**
3 CANFORD BAY (IRE), 5, b g Canford Cliffs (IRE)—Maundays Bay (IRE) **Northgate Racing**
4 CAPLA DEMON, 4, b g Kodiac—Namu **Northgate Grey**
5 FRENCH, 6, ch m Monsieur Bond (IRE)—Guadaloup **Mr Antony Brittain**
6 GREY DESTINY, 9, gr g Desideratum—Mother Corrigan (IRE) **Mr Antony Brittain**
7 HUSSAR BALLAD (USA), 10, b g Hard Spun (USA)—Country Melody (USA) **Mr Antony Brittain**
8 INTERNATIONAL LAW, 5, gr g Exceed And Excel (AUS)—Cruel Sea (USA) **John Jarvis & Partner**
9 LUCKY LODGE, 9, b g Lucky Story (USA)—Melandre **Mr Antony Brittain**
10 MUTABAAHY (IRE), 4, b g Oasis Dream—Habaayib **Daren McCreary & Partner**
11 NUTOPIA, 4, b f Monsieur Bond (IRE)—Caranbola **Mr Antony Brittain**
12 PERCEIVED, 7, ch m Sir Percy—New Light **Mr Antony Brittain**
13 PUCHITA (IRE), 4, b f Acclamation—Violet Ballerina (IRE) **Mr Antony Brittain**
14 QAARAAT, 4, b g Acclamation—Ladyship **Mr Antony Brittain**
15 SOOQAAN, 8, bl g Naaqoos—Dream Day (FR) **Mr Antony Brittain**
16 TATHMEEN (IRE), 4, b g Exceed And Excel (AUS)—Deyaar (USA) **Mr Antony Brittain**
17 THAWRY, 4, b g Iffraaj—Salacia (IRE) **Mr Antony Brittain**
18 TRAVELLER (FR), 5, b g Henrythenavigator (USA)—Nantes (GER) **John Jarvis & Partner**

THREE-YEAR-OLDS

19 FOOTBALL FRIEND, ch g Monsieur Bond (IRE)—Mozayada (USA) **Mr Antony Brittain**
20 KLIPPERTY KLOPP, ch g Monsieur Bond (IRE)—First Harmony **Mr Antony Brittain**
21 KLOPP, b f Monsieur Bond (IRE)—Caranbola **Mr Antony Brittain**
22 ONE ONE SEVEN (IRE), b g Arcano (IRE)—Maany (USA) **John Jarvis & Partner**

TWO-YEAR-OLDS

23 Ch g 14/4 Monsieur Bond (IRE)—Mozayada (USA) (Street Cry (IRE))
24 B f 26/1 Elzaam (AUS)—Rien Ne Vas Plus (IRE) (Oasis Dream)
25 B g 24/3 Monsieur Bond (IRE)—Sea Crest (Xaar)
26 B g 23/3 Cable Bay (IRE)—Stresa (Pivotal) **Mr Antony Brittain**

Other Owners: Mr J. Jarvis, Mr A. Jarvis, Mr Daren McCreary.

Jockey (flat): Cam Hardie.

69 **MRS JULIA BROOKE, Middleham**
Postal: **Brough Farm, Middleham, Leyburn, North Yorkshire, DL8 4SG**
Contacts: **MOBILE (07776) 186581**
E-MAIL jb@juliabrookeracing.com

1 ASHES CORNER (IRE), 9, b g Marienbard (IRE)—Up Thyne Girl (IRE) **Mr B. Platts & Mr P. Platts**
2 COPT HILL, 11, b g Avonbridge—Lalique (IRE) **John & Billy Platts**
3 EMMA BEAG (IRE), 8, b m Westerner—Emma Jane (IRE) **Mrs J. A. Brooke**
4 FIDDLERS BOW (IRE), 10, b g Whitmore's Conn (USA)—
Soraleda (IRE) **MT Buckley & Brough Farm Racing Partners**
5 GLOBETROTTER (IRE), 5, ch g Helmet (AUS)—Shimna **Sowray Brothers**
6 MIDNIGHT WALK (IRE), 9, b m Oscar (IRE)—Lady Belvedere (IRE) **Mrs Mary Sadler & Billy Platts**
7 PETE SO HIGH (GER), 5, b g High Chaparral (USA)—Paulaya (GER) **Mrs J. A. Brooke**
8 PIAZON, 8, br g Striking Ambition—Colonel's Daughter **The Body Warmers**
9 TOMORROW'S LEGEND, 9, b g Midnight Legend—Colvada **Mrs M. Hatfield & Mrs S. Kramer**
10 TRUE ROMANCE (IRE), 5, gr g Mastercraftsman (IRE)—Full of Love (IRE) **Mr K. S. Ward**
11 VASCO D'YCY (FR), 10, b g Equerry (USA)—Ingrid des Mottes (FR) **Mr K. S. Ward**
12 WEAPON OF CHOICE (IRE), 11, b g Iffraaj—Tullawadgeen (IRE) **Mrs J. A. Brooke**

THREE-YEAR-OLDS

13 TRIPLE ONE (IRE), ch g Toronado (IRE)—Dutch Diamond **Mrs J. A. Brooke**

Other Owners: Brough Farm Racing Partnership, Mr M. T. Buckley, Mrs M. Hatfield, Mrs S. Kramer, Mr W. N. Platts, Mr P. Platts, Mr J. Platts, Mrs M. Sadler, Mr S. A. Sowray.

---

70 **LADY SUSAN BROOKE, Llandrindod Wells**
Postal: **Tyn-y-Berth Farm, Dolau, Llandrindod Wells, Powys, LD1 5TW**
Contacts: **PHONE (01597) 851190 MOBILE (07977) 114834**
E-MAIL suebrooke@live.co.uk

1 **ASTIGOS (FR)**, 12, b br g Trempolino (USA)—Astonishing (BRZ) **Lady Brooke**
2 **BOXER BEAT (IRE)**, 12, b g Xaar—Pantoufle **Lady Brooke**
3 **MIDNIGHT MAKEOVER**, 5, b m Midnight Legend—Makeover **Lady Brooke**
4 **RIVER PURPLE**, 12, b g Bollin Eric—Cerise Bleue (FR) **Lady Brooke**
5 **SPOCK (FR)**, 14, b g Lost World (IRE)—Quark Top (FR) **Lady Brooke**
6 **STARCROSSED**, 7, b g Cape Cross (IRE)—Gretna **Lady Brooke**
7 **VINNIE RED (IRE)**, 10, ch g Vinnie Roe (IRE)—Conzara (IRE) **Lady Brooke**

Assistant Trainer: Lorna Brooke (07786) 962911

Amateur: Miss Lorna Brooke.

---

71 **MR ROY BROTHERTON, Pershore**
Postal: **Mill End Racing Stables, Netherton Road, Elmley Castle, Pershore, Worcestershire, WR10 3JF**
Contacts: **PHONE/FAX (01386) 710772 MOBILE (07970) 877280**

1 **CNOC SION (IRE)**, 9, b g Gold Well—Bondi Babe (IRE) **Jan Carpenter & Bill Young**
2 **DEADLY ACCURATE**, 4, br g Lethal Force (IRE)—Riccoche (IRE) **R. Brotherton**
3 **DEISE VU (IRE)**, 11, b g Brian Boru—Deise Dreamer (IRE) **Elmley Queen**
4 **DRAGON GIRL (IRE)**, 4, ch f Dragon Pulse (IRE)—Raise Your Spirits (IRE) **Mrs C. A. Newman**
5 **DUN BAY CREEK**, 8, b g Dubai Destination (USA)—Over It
6 **FILAMENT OF GOLD (USA)**, 8, b g Street Cry (IRE)—Raw Silk (USA) **Mr M. A. Geobey**
7 **FILBERT STREET**, 4, ch g Poet's Voice—Tinnarinka **R. Brotherton**
8 **MAMNOON (IRE)**, 6, b g Cape Cross (IRE)—Masaafat **Mr M. A. Geobey**
9 **MR FRANKIE**, 8, b g Sleeping Indian—Shes Minnie **R. Brotherton**
10 **RITAS LEGACY**, 5, b g Passing Glance—Rita's Rock Ape **Jan Carpenter & Bill Young**

Other Owners: Mrs J. A. Carpenter, Mr N. A. Lavender Jones, Mr M. A. Savage, Mr B. K. C. Young.

Assistant Trainer: Justin Brotherton

Jockey (NH): Jamie Moore.

---

72 **MR ALAN BROWN, Malton**
Postal: **Lilac Farm, Yedingham, Malton, North Yorkshire, YO17 8SS**
Contacts: **PHONE (01944) 728090 MOBILE (07970) 672845**
E-MAIL ad.brown@hotmail.co.uk WEBSITE www.alanbrownracing.co.uk

1 **ATRAFAN (IRE)**, 5, b g Atraf—Up Front (IRE) **Mr F. E. Reay**
2 **POPPY IN THE WIND**, 7, b m Piccolo—Vintage Steps (IRE) **Mrs M Doherty & Mr A D Brown**

THREE-YEAR-OLDS

3 **BLACKCURRENT**, b g Kuroshio (AUS)—Mamounia (IRE) **Burton Agnes Bloodstock**
4 **INITIAL APPROACH (IRE)**, b f Dawn Approach (IRE)—Coquette Noire (IRE) **A. D. Brown**
5 **WEARRAAH (IRE)**, b g Heeraat (IRE)—Hoof's So Lucky **Rangers Racing Syndicate**

TWO-YEAR-OLDS

6 B g 19/3 Harbour Watch (IRE)—Dareesha (IRE) (Naaqoos) (3000) **G. Morrill**
7 B g 1/3 Sleeping Indian—Medam (Medicean) **The Hon Mrs E. S. Cunliffe-Lister**
8 B g 12/2 Gregorian (IRE)—Miss Mohawk (IRE) (Hawk Wing (USA)) **Mrs M. A. Doherty**
9 Gr g 5/5 Ruler of The World (IRE)—Silver Halo (Paris House) **A. D. Brown**

Other Owners: Mrs M. C. Coltman, Mr I. Stewart.

73 **MR ANDI BROWN, Newmarket**
Postal: **Southfields Stables, Hamilton Road, Newmarket, Suffolk, CB8 7JQ**
Contacts: **PHONE (01638) 669652 FAX (01638) 669652 MOBILE (07980) 393263**
E-MAIL southfieldsstables@btinternet.com WEBSITE www.southfieldsstables.co.uk

1 CAMINO, 6, b m Equiano (FR)—Juncea **In For A Penny In For A Pound**
2 KIRTLING, 8, gr g Araafa (IRE)—Cape Maya **Faith Hope and Charity**
3 TIMSSAAH, 4, b g Showcasing—Swan Wings **Miss L. J. Knocker**

Other Owners: A. S. Brown.

Assistant Trainer: Miss Linsey Knocker

74 **MR DAVID BROWN, Whitby**
Postal: **6 Linden Lane, Newholm, Whitby, North Yorkshire, YO21 3QX**
Contacts: **PHONE (01636) 613793 MOBILE (07889) 132931**
E-MAIL david@davidbrownracing.com

1 JONBOY, 4, b g Delegator—Cavallo da Corsa **Mr R. Hull**

THREE-YEAR-OLDS

2 ASCOT DREAMER, ch f Kyllachy—Skirrid
3 FITZY, b g Epaulette (AUS)—Zagarock **Mr R. Hull**
4 GRAYBOY, gr g Aussie Rules (USA)—Grace Hull **Mr R. Hull**
5 GUPTA, b g Equiano (FR)—Lanai (IRE) **Mr R. Hull**
6 LENNYBE, b g Epaulette (AUS)—Destiny of A Diva **Mr R. Hull**

TWO-YEAR-OLDS

7 Ch c 27/4 Coach House (IRE)—Beauty Pageant (IRE) (Bahamian Bounty)
8 CRUISING, b g 23/3 Helmet (AUS)—Lanai (IRE) (Camacho) **Mr R. Hull**
9 B f 14/4 Hellvelyn—Katie Elder (FR) (High Chaparral (IRE))
10 NORTHERN CHARM, b f 10/2 Equiano (FR)—Grace Hull (Piccolo) **Mr R. Hull**

Assistant Trainer: Dushyant Dooyea

Jockey (flat): Tom Eaves, Philip Makin.

75 **MISS MICHELLE BRYANT, Lewes**
Postal: **Bevern Bridge Farm Cottage, South Chailey, Lewes, East Sussex, BN8 4QH**
Contacts: **PHONE/FAX (01273) 400638 MOBILE (07976) 217542**
E-MAIL bear_2009@live.co.uk

1 ELUSIVE COWBOY (USA), 6, ch g Elusive Quality (USA)—
Sarmad (USA) **Miss M P Bryant, David & Eileen Bryant**
2 RON WAVERLY (IRE), 9, ch g Haatef (USA)—Mermaid Beach **Miss M P Bryant, David & Eileen Bryant**

Other Owners: Mrs E. Bryant, Mr D. Bryant.

Amateur: Miss M. P. Bryant.

76 **MRS KATE BUCKETT, Bishops Waltham**
Postal: **Woodlocks Down Farm, Upham, Bishops Waltham, Hampshire, SO32 1JN**
Contacts: **PHONE (01962) 777557**

1 BATTLEOFTHESOMME (IRE), 6, b g Mountain High (IRE)—Shannon Pearl (IRE) **Mrs K. A. Buckett**
2 BOARDWALK EMPIRE (IRE), 12, b g Overbury (IRE)—Mighty Mandy (IRE) **Mrs K. A. Buckett**
3 TRACTOR FRED (IRE), 5, br g Curtain Time (IRE)—Bonny Blackdoe (IRE) **Mrs K. A. Buckett**
4 UPHAM RUNNING (IRE), 11, b g Definite Article—Tara Brooch (IRE) **Mrs K. A. Buckett**

77 | **MR BOB BUCKLER, Bridgwater**
Postal: Gibb Hill, Courtway, Spaxton, Bridgwater, Somerset, TA5 1DR
Contacts: **PHONE (01278) 671268 MOBILE (07785) 773957**
E-MAIL rbuckler@btconnect.com WEBSITE www.robertbucklerracing.co.uk

1 **ALL KINGS (IRE)**, 10, b g Milan—Rilmount (IRE) **Avalon Surfacing & Construction Co Ltd**
2 **BALLYEGAN (IRE)**, 14, b g Saddlers' Hall (IRE)—Knapping Princess (IRE) **R. H. Buckler**
3 **CUSHUISH**, 6, b m Yeats (IRE)—My Petra **R. H. Buckler**
4 **FLOWING CADENZA**, 5, b m Yeats (IRE)—Over The Flow **Mrs H. R. Dunn**
5 **GIBB HILL**, 5, ch g Frozen Fire (GER)—River Reine (IRE) **Mrs D Gamble & R H Buckler**
6 **HOO BALLY DIVA (IRE)**, 8, b m Scorpion (IRE)—Dr Sandra (IRE) **Golden Cap**
7 **ITALIAN RIVER**, 7, b g Milan—Over The Flow **Mrs Heather Dunn & Mrs Trollope-Bellew**
8 **KNIGHT OFTHE REALM**, 10, b g Kayf Tara—Flow **Mrs H. R. Dunn**
9 **MIZZ MOONDANCE**, 4, b f Yeats (IRE)—Mizzurka **Golden Cap**
10 **OYSTER PERCH**, 5, b m Yeats (IRE)—Dudeen (IRE) **Mr M. W. Pendarves**
11 **REGAL FLOW**, 12, b g Erhaab (USA)—Flow **Mrs H. R. Dunn**
12 **4**, B f Frozen Fire (GER)—River Reine (IRE) **4 Gals and a Filly**
13 **UNWIN VC**, 5, ch g Black Sam Bellamy (IRE)—Becky B **Golden Cap**

Other Owners: Mr N. Elliott, Mrs D. R. Gamble, Mrs H. E. Shane, Mrs A. C. Trollope-Bellew.

Head Lad: Giles Scott (07774) 033246

Conditional: Sean Houlihan.

78 | **MR DAI BURCHELL, Ebbw Vale**
Postal: Drysiog Farm, Briery Hill, Ebbw Vale, Gwent, NP23 6BU
Contacts: **PHONE (01495) 302551 MOBILE (07980) 482860**

1 **BLUE TOP**, 10, b g Millkom—Pompey Blue **B. M. G. Group**
2 **CLEARLY CAPABLE (IRE)**, 10, b g Benamado (USA)—Spout Road (IRE) **W. D. Burchell**
3 **COOPERESS**, 6, b m Sixties Icon—Vilnius **J. Parfitt**
4 **FACT FLOW (IRE)**, 10, br g Whitmore's Conn (USA)—Beaver Run (IRE) **The Bill & Ben Partnership**
5 **FOLIES BERGERES**, 4, ch f Champs Elysees—May Fox **W. D. Burchell**
6 **FURIOUSLY FAST (IRE)**, 7, b g Fast Company (IRE)—Agouti **Exors of the Late C. J. Friel**
7 **MOLLYOW (IRE)**, 11, ch m Iceman—Corryvreckan (IRE) **J. Parfitt**
8 **ZORLU (IRE)**, 6, b g Invincible Spirit (IRE)—Special Assignment (USA) **Mr T. G. Williams**

Other Owners: Mr P. G. Amos, Mr T. G. Brooks, Mr W. R. A. Davies, Mrs A. Davies.

Assistant Trainer: Ruth Burchell.

Jockey (flat): Hollie Doyle. **Jockey (NH):** Robert Dunne, Alan Johns. **Conditional:** Jordan Nailor.
Amateur: Miss Jodie Hughes.

79 | **MR K. R. BURKE, Leyburn**
Postal: Spigot Lodge, Middleham, Leyburn, North Yorkshire, DL8 4TL
Contacts: **PHONE (01969) 625088 FAX (01969) 625099 MOBILE (07778) 458777**
E-MAIL karl@karlburke.co.uk WEBSITE www.karlburke.co.uk

1 **ANGEL PALANAS**, 5, b g Mayson—Scottish Exile (IRE) **Mr Mark Bates & Mrs E Burke**
2 **BARON RUN**, 9, ch g Bertolini (USA)—Bhima **Mr Eric Burke & Partner**
3 **BORN TO BE ALIVE (FR)**, 5, b g Born To Sea (IRE)—Yaria (IRE) **Mr T Dykes & Mrs E Burke**
4 **CROWN VALLARY (FR)**, 4, b f Manduro (GER)—Troiecat (FR) **Ontoawinner, Mr R McKeown & E Burke**
5 **DOUBLE REFLECTION**, 4, b f Showcasing—Green And Bleue **Ontoawinner, SDH, James Pak & E Burke**
6 **FRONTLINE PHANTOM (IRE)**, 12, b g Noverre (USA)—Daisy Hill **Mr Eric Burke & Partner**
7 **GOLDEN GUIDE**, 4, b f Havana Gold (IRE)—Blonde (IRE) **Mrs E. M. Burke**
8 **GUVENOR'S CHOICE (IRE)**, 4, ro g Intikhab (USA)—Exempt **Mr I McInnes, Dr M Glaze & E Burke**
9 **HELEN SHERBET**, 4, br f Makfi—Clifton Dancer **S Lock, J Craft & E Burke**
10 **KELLY'S DINO (FR)**, 6, b g Doctor Dino (FR)—Sabolienne (FR) **Mr Liam Kelly & Mrs E Burke**
11 **LAURENS (FR)**, 4, b f Siyouni (FR)—Recambe (USA) **Mr J. E. Dance**
12 **LORD OBERON**, 4, b g Mayson—Fairy Shoes **Mr D J MacKay & Mrs E Burke**
13 **MADE OF HONOUR (IRE)**, 5, ch m Casamento (IRE)—Bonne **Ontoawinner, Mr D Mackay & Mrs E Burke**
14 **MAMETZ WOOD (IRE)**, 4, b g Elzaam (AUS)—Shaanbar (IRE) **Ontoawinner 14, James Pak & Mrs E Burke**
15 **MAYFAIR ROCK (IRE)**, 4, ch f Society Rock (IRE)—Tara Too (IRE) **The Tara Five**

MR K. R. BURKE - Continued

16 **MOUNT ARARAT (IRE)**, 4, b g Sea The Stars (IRE)—Divine Authority (IRE) **Mr H Strecker & Mrs E Burke**
17 **RAYDIANCE**, 4, b g Mayson—Iridescence **Ontoawinner 14 & Mrs E Burke**
18 **SHAKDARA (USA)**, 4, b f Street Cry (IRE)—Shankardeh (IRE) **Mr H. J. Strecker**
19 **SUNDAY PROSPECT (FR)**, 5, ch g Sunday Break (JPN)—
Green Shadow (FR) **Owners For Owners: Sunday Prospect**
20 **THUNDER BUDDY**, 4, b g Mayson—Inchcoonan **Mrs E. M. Burke**
21 **WIND STORM**, 4, b f Holy Roman Emperor (IRE)—Imperialistic (IRE) **Mr R. Peel**
22 **YOU'RE FIRED (IRE)**, 8, b g Firebreak—My Sweet Georgia (IRE) **Hope Eden Racing Ltd & Mrs E Burke**

THREE-YEAR-OLDS

23 **ABSOLUTIO (FR)**, b g Kendargent (FR)—La Joie (FR) **S. P. C. Woods**
24 **AGENT SMITH (IRE)**, b g Morpheus—Sand N Sea (IRE) **High Moor Racing 4**
25 **ANGELIC MOTION (FR)**, b f Australia—Tipperary Honor (FR) **Mr J. E. Dance**
26 **ASTRO JAKK (IRE)**, b g Zoffany (IRE)—By The Edge (IRE) **Mr J. E. Dance**
27 **BARASTI DANCER (IRE)**, gr g Helmet (AUS)—My Girl Lisa (USA) **Ontoawinner 9 & Mrs E Burke**
28 **BEAUTIFUL GESTURE**, ch f Shamardal (USA)—Viola da Braccio (IRE) **Mr H. J. Strecker**
29 **CHAINS OF LOVE (IRE)**, b f Society Rock (IRE)—Sportsticketing (IRE) **Ontoawinner 9 & Mrs E Burke**
30 **COLLECT CALL (IRE)**, b g Kodiac—Payphone **Mr H Strecker,A F O'Callaghan & E Burke**
31 **DANCING BALLERINA (IRE)**, b f Es Que Love—Vexatious (IRE) **Mrs E. M. Burke**
32 **DAWN BLAZE**, ch g Dawn Approach (IRE)—Danat Al Atheer **Hambleton Racing Ltd XXXV & E Burke**
33 **DIVINITY**, b f Dutch Art—Elysian **Cheveley Park Stud Limited**
34 **EXALTED ANGEL (IRE)**, b c Dark Angel (IRE)—Hurryupharriet (IRE) **Pau-Perth Partnership & Mrs E Burke**
35 **FFLUR**, b f Lethal Force (IRE)—Exceedingly **Mr A. Gray**
36 **FOX FEARLESS**, b g Camelot—Silent Music (IRE) **King Power Racing Co Ltd**
37 **GEORGE HASTINGS**, gr g Gregorian (IRE)—Pachanga **Middleham Park Racing LXXXIX & E Burke**
38 **HAREEM QUEEN (IRE)**, gr f Dark Angel (IRE)—Dulcian (IRE) **Mr J. E. Dance**
39 **HARPERELLE**, ch f Burwaaz—She's So Pretty (IRE) **Hope Eden Racing Ltd & Mrs E Burke**
40 **HAVANA OOH NA NA**, ch g Havana Gold (IRE)—Blanc de Chine (IRE) **The Havana Ooh Na Na Partnership**
41 **HIGH CONTRAST**, b g Kingman—Parisi **Mr J. E. Dance**
42 **HURRICANE HERO (IRE)**, b g George Vancouver (USA)—Memoire (FR) **Hambleton Racing Ltd III & E Burke**
43 **KADAR (USA)**, b br c Scat Daddy (USA)—Kaloura (IRE) **Phoenix Thoroughbred Limited**
44 **KENICA (IRE)**, b f Camelot—Za'hara (IRE) **The Something Syndicate**
45 **KIPPER THE RED**, b g Farhh—Windlass (IRE) **Nick Bradley Racing 17 & Sohi & E Burke**
46 **KODI KING (IRE)**, b g Kodiac—Throne **Titanium Racing Club & Mrs E Burke**
47 **KODURO**, b f Kodiac—Affability (IRE) **Mr J. E. Dance**
48 **LITTLE LINDA (FR)**, ch f Manduro (GER)—Jolie Laide (IRE) **Ontoawinner, SDH Project Services Ltd 1**
49 **LITTLE KIM**, b f Garswood—Primo Lady **Nick Bradley Racing 35 & Sohi & E Burke**
50 **MAKTHECAT (FR)**, b g Makfi—Troiecat **Ontoawinner 14 & Mrs E Burke**
51 **MARDLE**, ch g Mukhadram—Hoh Chi Min **Ontoawinner 14 & Mrs E Burke**
52 **MILAGRE DA VIDA (IRE)**, b f Bated Breath—Eucharist (IRE) **Mr J. E. Dance**
53 **MISTRESS OF LOVE (USA)**, b f Scat Daddy (USA)—Beloveda (USA) **Phoenix Thoroughbred Limited**
54 **MONSIEUR PIQUER (FR)**, ch g French Fifteen (FR)—Madeenh (FR) **Middleham Park Racing LXXIII & E Burke**
55 **OVER THE GUNS (IRE)**, b g Garswood—Princess Rose **King Power Racing Co Ltd**
56 **PARALLEL WORLD (IRE)**, b g Morpheus—Miss Glitters (IRE) **Ontoawinner, SDH Project Services Ltd 1**
57 **POWER PLAYER**, b g Slade Power—Varnish **K. A. Dasmal**
58 **PRAXIDICE**, b f Toronado (IRE)—Cross My Heart **Ontoawinner, Mr R McKeown & E Burke**
59 **REFLECTED (IRE)**, bl f Excelebration (IRE)—Yin **Ontoawinner 14 & Mrs E Burke**
60 **REQUIREMENT**, b f Charm Spirit (IRE)—Bijou A Moi **Mr J. E. Dance**
61 **ROBOTIQUE DANSEUR (FR)**, b f Siyouni (FR)—Dawn To Dance (IRE) **Mr J. E. Dance**
62 **SABAI SABAI (IRE)**, b f Shamardal (USA)—Semayyel (IRE) **King Power Racing Co Ltd**
63 **SECRET FOOTSTEPS (IRE)**, br g Footstepsinthesand—Secret Friend (IRE) **Ontoawinner 14 & Mrs E Burke**
64 **SELF ASSESSMENT (IRE)**, b g Elzaam (AUS)—Little Miss Diva (IRE) **Hold Your Horses Racing & Mrs E Burke**
65 **SENSE OF DIRECTION (IRE)**, b f Kodiac—One Giant Leap (IRE) **Mr H. J. Strecker**
66 **SERENGETI SONG (IRE)**, b g Poet's Voice—African Plains **Hambleton Racing Ltd III & E Burke**
67 **SHALLOW HAL**, b c Mayson—Bazelle **Ontoawinner 14 & Mrs E Burke**
68 **SIMON'S SMILE (FR)**, b g Anodin (IRE)—Nebraska (FR) **Nick Bradley Racing 16 & Sohi and Burke**
69 B f Slade Power—Slope **Mr J. E. Dance**
70 **SO HI STORM (IRE)**, b g Holy Roman Emperor (IRE)—
Great Joy (IRE) **Nick Bradley Racing 33 & Sohi & E Burke**
71 **SWEET DREAMER**, br f Harbour Watch (IRE)—Unasuming (IRE) **Mrs M. Ryan**
72 **SYLVIACLIFFS (FR)**, b f George Vancouver (USA)—Sienna Bella **The Mount Racing Club & Mrs E Burke**
73 **TRUE MASON**, b c Mayson—Marysienka **K. A. Dasmal**

MR K. R. BURKE - Continued

TWO-YEAR-OLDS

74 B f 1/5 Fastnet Rock (AUS)—Absolute Music (USA) (Consolidator (USA)) (29498) **Ontoawinner 14**
75 B c 13/2 Sir Percy—All In Green (IRE) (Diamond Green (FR)) (33712) **Hold Your Horses Racing & Mrs E Burke**
76 B c 8/4 Invincible Spirit (IRE)—Ana Luna (Dream Well (IRE)) (160134)
77 ANGEL OF THE GLEN (FR), b f 22/1 Gleneagles (IRE)—
Archangel Gabriel (USA) (Arch (USA)) (143278) **Hunscote Stud**
78 B c 9/2 Dandy Man (IRE)—Archetypal (IRE) (Cape Cross (IRE)) (29498)
79 B f 28/4 Dandy Man (IRE)—Aunt Nicola (Reel Buddy (USA)) (60682) **Tweenhills Fillies & Mrs E Burke**
80 BARACCA ROCKS, b f 9/3 Society Rock (IRE)—
Fortune Hunter (FR) (High Chaparral (IRE)) (47619) **Redvers, Keller, Bradley & Burke**
81 Ch f 5/4 Australia—Boast (Most Welcome)
82 B c 6/5 Mayson—Bruni Heinke (IRE) (Dutch Art) **Mr D. W. Armstrong**
83 B f 20/4 Kingman—Centime (Royal Applause) (35000)
84 CONSTITUTIONAL (IRE), b c 19/3 Society Rock (IRE)—
Last Hooray (Royal Applause) (49523) **Owners For Owners & Mrs E Burke**
85 CONVENE (IRE), b c 10/5 Kodiac—Altogether (IRE) (King's Best (USA)) **Cheveley Park Stud Limited**
86 Br c 23/2 Society Rock (IRE)—Deliziosa (IRE) (Iffraaj) (49523) **Mr J. E. Dance**
87 DREAM DESIGN, b f 15/3 Invincible Spirit (IRE)—Distinctive (Tobougg (IRE)) **Mr & Mrs G. Middlebrook**
88 DUBAI STATION, b c 19/2 Brazen Beau (AUS)—Princess Guest (IRE) (Iffraaj) (30000) **Ahmad AlShaikh & Co**
89 Ch c 23/4 Zoffany (IRE)—Executrix (Oasis Dream) (50000) **Mr Liam Kelly & Mrs E Burke**
90 B f 11/5 Kodiac—Fifth Avenue Doll (USA) (Marquetry (USA)) (32000) **Nick Bradley 28, A O'Callaghan & Burke**
91 FINERY, b f 2/3 Al Kazeem—Elysian (Galileo (IRE)) **Cheveley Park Stud Limited**
92 B c 20/2 Night of Thunder (IRE)—First Party (Royal Applause) (43826) **Mr H Strecker & Mrs E Burke**
93 B c 1/4 Declaration of War (USA)—
Funny Bay (USA) (Medaglia d'oro (USA)) (48883) **Hope Eden Racing Ltd & Mrs E Burke**
94 GIN GEMBRE (FR), ch c 1/2 Dandy Man (IRE)—
Repechage (FR) (Gold Away (IRE)) (20227) **Mr D Whittaker & Mrs E Burke**
95 GOOSE LIGHTNING, gr c 4/2 Lethal Force (IRE)—
Florett (IRE) (Holy Roman Emperor (IRE)) (15238) **Hambleton Racing Ltd XXXV & E Burke**
96 GRAVITY FORCE, b c 19/1 Fountain of Youth (IRE)—Itsinthestars (Zoffany (IRE)) **Bearstone Stud Limited**
97 GRIMBOLD, b c 21/2 Kyllachy—Breve (Observatory (USA)) (33712) **Mr H. J. Strecker**
98 GUIPURE, ch f 5/4 Dutch Art—Interlace (Pivotal) **Cheveley Park Stud Limited**
99 B f 17/2 Fulbright—Heavenly River (IRE) (Stormy River (FR)) (6741) **Mrs E. M. Burke**
100 B c 1/3 Hallowed Crown (AUS)—Hflah (IRE) (Dubawi (IRE)) (24761) **Nick Bradley Racing 2 & Mrs E Burke**
101 B c 31/1 Invincible Spirit (IRE)—Highleaf (Pivotal) **Mr D. W. Armstrong**
102 B c 13/2 Anjaal—Ho Hey (Paco Boy (IRE)) (6666)
103 HOY LAKE, b c 27/4 Gutaifan (IRE)—
Flames To Dust (GER) (Oasis Dream) (12857) **Nick Bradley Racing 5 & Mrs E Burke**
104 B c 8/2 Siyouni (FR)—Hurryupharriet (IRE) (Camacho) (134850)
105 B c 7/4 Sepoy—Isola Verde (Oasis Dream) (48000) **K. A. Dasmal**
106 B f 21/2 Exceed And Excel (AUS)—Janina (Namid) (34000) **Mr J Laughton & Mrs E Burke**
107 LADY LATTE (IRE), b f 22/4 Anjaal—Cappuccino (IRE) (Mujadil (USA)) (38000) **Mr Mo Charge & Mrs E Burke**
108 LADYLEYS BELUGA, b f 14/1 Showcasing—Terse (Dansili) (28000) **Ontoawinner 14 & Mrs E Burke**
109 LIGHT THE FUSE (IRE), b c 22/1 Dandy Man (IRE)—Mandhooma (Oasis Dream) (40000) **J. C. Fretwell**
110 B c 23/3 Dandy Man (IRE)—Loud Applause (Royal Applause) (40000) **Ontoawinner, Strecker & Burke**
111 B c 11/2 Mayson—Lydiate (IRE) (Acclamation) (57142) **King Power Racing Co Ltd**
112 MACHO TIME (IRE), b c 7/4 Camacho—Galeaza (Galileo (IRE)) (76190) **J. C. Fretwell**
113 MACHO TOUCH (IRE), b f 10/2 Camacho—
Hint of Red (IRE) (Fast Company (IRE)) (58996) **Pau - Perth Partnership**
114 B c 12/5 Fountain of Youth (IRE)—Mad Annie (USA) (Anabaa (USA)) (15238)
115 B c 17/4 Siyouni (FR)—Madonna Dell'orto (Montjeu (IRE)) (220000) **Mr F. Gillespie**
116 Ch f 13/3 Kyllachy—My Propeller (IRE) (Holy Roman Emperor (IRE)) (28000) **J. Barton**
117 B gr f 3/4 Gregorian (IRE)—Mysterious Girl (IRE) (Teofilo (IRE)) (10476) **Titanium Racing Club**
118 B c 28/4 Requinto (IRE)—Narva (USA) (Grand Slam (USA)) (61904) **Ontoawinner, Strecker & Burke**
119 NEVER IN PARIS (IRE), b f 2/3 No Nay Never (USA)—
Meeting In Paris (IRE) (Dutch Art) (30952) **Ontoawinner, A Marsh & E Burke**
120 B c 15/4 Muhaarar—Persario (Bishop of Cashel) (80000)
121 B c 16/3 Ivawood (IRE)—Precautionary (Green Desert (USA)) (17142) **Ontoawinner 14 & Mrs E Burke**
122 QUEENOFTHECLYDE (IRE), ch f 12/4 Dandy Man (IRE)—
Coconut Kisses (Bahamian Bounty) (37926) **Men Fae the Clyde & E Burke**
123 Ch c 16/3 Garswood—Regal Riband (Fantastic Light (USA)) (33333)
124 B f 7/4 Exceed And Excel (AUS)—Shepherdia (IRE) (Pivotal) (75853) **King Power Racing Co Ltd**
125 SOLEMN PLEDGE, b f 1/3 Showcasing—
Lovers' Vows (Dubawi (IRE)) (55000) **Pau-Perth Partnership & Mrs E Burke**

MR K. R. BURKE - Continued

126 B c 12/3 Rock of Gibraltar (IRE)—
Special Miss (Authorized (IRE)) (30000) **Mr Tim Dykes & Hope Eden Racing Ltd**
127 SPEED DATING (FR), gr c 25/2 Outstrip—
Sign Your Name (GER) (Areion (GER)) (31184) **Pau - Perth Partnership**
128 SPRING BLOOM, ch c 23/2 Power—Almond Branches (Dutch Art) (9523) **J. C. Fretwell**
129 B c 15/2 Zebedee—Sweet'n Sassy (IRE) (Grand Lodge (USA)) (8849) **Mrs E. M. Burke**
130 WOKE (IRE), b br f 14/3 Showcasing—Analysis (Dubai Destination (USA)) (37926) **Mr H. J. Strecker**

Other Owners: Mr A. A. Al Shaikh, A. Al Shaikh, Mr D. C. Bacon, Mr M. Bates, Mr N. Bradley, Mrs S. Bridge, Mrs C. Brown, C. Bryce, Mr S. Bryceland, Mr P. Bryceland, Miss K. Buckle, Mr E. J. Burke, Mr M. Charge, Mr J. P. Craft, Mr T. Dal, Mr P. K. Davis, Mr P. Doughty, Mr T. J. Dykes, Mr A. N. Eaton, Dr C. I. Emmerson, Dr M. E. Glaze, Hambleton Racing Ltd, Hambleton Racing Ltd XXXIII, Hambleton Racing Ltd XXXV, Hold Your Horses Racing, Miss S. Holden, Mr G. W. Holden, Hope Eden Racing Limited, Mrs J. Hughes, Mr E. J. Hughes, Mrs B. M. Keller, Mr L. Kelly, R. Kent, Mr J. Laughton, Mr S. Lock, The Countess Of Lonsdale, Mr D. J. MacKay, Mr A. R. W. Marsh, I. McInnes, Mr R. C. McKeown, Mrs L. A. Middlebrook, Mr G. Middlebrook, Middleham Park Racing LXXIII, Middleham Park Racing LXXXIX, Mount Racing Club, Nick Bradley Racing 16, Nick Bradley Racing 17, Nick Bradley Racing 2, Nick Bradley Racing 28, Nick Bradley Racing 33, Nick Bradley Racing 35, Nick Bradley Racing 5, Miss M. A. O Brien, Mr N. J. O'Brien, A. F. O'Callaghan, Ontoawinner 14, Ontoawinner, Ontoawinner 9, Ontoawinner, SDH Project Services Ltd, Owners for Owners Constitutional, Ontoawinner, SDH, James Pak, James Pak, T. S. Palin, M. Prince, Mr A. S. Pritchard, Mr D. Redvers, Mr G. A. Shields, Mrs L. A. Smith, Mr S. Smith, A. Stennett, Mr S. R. H. Turner, Tweenhills Fillies, Mr D. J. Whittaker.

Assistant Trainers: Mrs Elaine Burke, Lucy Burke, Kelly Burke, Joe O'Gorman

Jockey (flat): Ben Curtis, Clifford Lee, P. J. McDonald. **Apprentice:** Jonathan Fisher, Rhona Pindar.

80

MR KEIRAN BURKE, Sturminster Newton
Postal: **Rudge Hill Farm, Rivers Corner, Sturminster Newton, Dorset**
Contacts: **MOBILE (07855) 860993**

1 BOUGGIETOPIECES, 9, b g Tobougg (IRE)—Bonnet's Pieces **K B Racing**
2 5, Br g Presenting—Catcherinscratcher (IRE) **K B Racing**
3 EVERLANES, 6, br m Shirocco (GER)—Good Thinking **Barrow Hill**
4 GAMBLING GAMUT (IRE), 7, ch g Gamut (IRE)—Red Promise (IRE) **Mr J. Burley**
5 JULLY LES BUXY, 9, b m Black Sam Bellamy (IRE)—Jadidh **Mr M. S. Rose**
6 KALABEE (IRE), 4, b g Kalanisi (IRE)—American Honey (IRE) **Mr James Burley & Mr John Rees**
7 MINE'S A PINT, 7, b g Network (GER)—Ryme Bere (FR) **K B Racing**
8 MR MAGILL (FR), 7, b g Hamairi (IRE)—Marie Cuddy (IRE) **K B Racing**
9 4, Ch f Norse Dancer (IRE)—Pull The Wool (IRE) **The Lamb Inn - Pethy**
10 PUTDECASHONTHEDASH (IRE), 6, b g Doyen (IRE)—Be My Adelina (IRE) **K B Racing**

Other Owners: Mr K. M. F. Burke, Mr J. Rees, Miss E. Rogers, R. L. Squire, Mrs S. L. Tizzard, R. G. Tizzard.

81

MR HUGH BURNS, Alnwick
Postal: **Rose Cottage, Hedgeley Hall, Powburn, Alnwick, Northumberland, NE66 4HZ**
Contacts: PHONE **(01665) 578647** MOBILE **(07503) 539571**
E-MAIL hughburns123@hotmail.co.uk

1 CLABARE, 8, b g Proclamation (IRE)—Choral Singer **Mr H. Burns**
2 COMBUSTIBLE GIRL (IRE), 6, b m Craigsteel—Slaney Legacy (IRE) **Mr H. Burns**
3 COUNTRY DELIGHTS (IRE), 6, b m Mahler (IRE)—Nadwell (IRE) **Mr H. Burns**
4 6, B m Brian Boru—Flagship Queen (USA) **Mr H. Burns**
5 7, B m Brian Boru—Indian Love (FR) **Mr H. Burns**
6 6, Gr m Double Eclipse (IRE)—Leavemealoneawhile (IRE) **Mr H. Burns**
7 MYLITTLEOULBUDDY (IRE), 6, br m Darsi (FR)—She Will Return (IRE) **Mr H. Burns**
8 SLANEY CRAIGLEGACY (IRE), 7, b m Craigsteel—Slaney Legacy (IRE) **Mr H. Burns**
9 ZAMBEZI TIGER (IRE), 10, b g Tiger Hill (IRE)—Johannesburg Cat (USA) **Mr H. Burns**

82 MR OWEN BURROWS, Lambourn

Postal: Kingwood House Stables Ltd, Lambourn Woodlands, Hungerford, Berkshire, RG17 7RS
Contacts: **PHONE (01488) 73144**

1 **ALFARQAD (USA)**, 4, b br g War Front (USA)—Love And Pride (USA) **Mr Hamdan Al Maktoum**
2 **AZALY (IRE)**, 5, ch g Sepoy (AUS)—Azzoom (IRE) **Mr Hamdan Al Maktoum**
3 **EHTIRAAS**, 6, b g Oasis Dream—Kareemah (USA) **Mr Hamdan Al Maktoum**
4 **ELWAZIR**, 4, ch c Frankel—Dash To The Front **Mr Hamdan Al Maktoum**
5 **ENJAZAAT**, 4, b g Acclamation—Miliika **Mr Hamdan Al Maktoum**
6 **HABUB (USA)**, 4, b c War Front (USA)—Sweet Lulu (USA) **Mr Hamdan Al Maktoum**
7 **KASBAAN**, 4, br g Dansili—Aghareed (USA) **Mr Hamdan Al Maktoum**
8 **KITAABAAT**, 4, b g Dansili—Ausus (USA) **Mr Hamdan Al Maktoum**
9 **LARAAIB (IRE)**, 5, b h Pivotal—Sahool **Mr Hamdan Al Maktoum**
10 **MAFAAHEEM (IRE)**, 5, b g Shamardal (USA)—Hammiya (IRE) **Mr Hamdan Al Maktoum**
11 **MIZAAH (IRE)**, 6, b g Invincible Spirit (IRE)—Miss Beabea (IRE) **Mr Hamdan Al Maktoum**
12 **MOTARAABET**, 4, b g Dansili—Hawaafez **Mr Hamdan Al Maktoum**
13 **MUTAAQEB**, 4, b c Invincible Spirit (IRE)—Mejala (IRE) **Mr Hamdan Al Maktoum**
14 **QULOOB**, 5, b g New Approach (IRE)—Jadhwah **Mr Hamdan Al Maktoum**
15 **SAWWAAH**, 4, b c New Approach (IRE)—Mudaaraah **Mr Hamdan Al Maktoum**
16 **SHABAABY**, 4, b g Kyllachy—On The Brink **Mr Hamdan Al Maktoum**
17 **TABDEED**, 4, ch c Havana Gold (IRE)—Puzzled (IRE) **Mr Hamdan Al Maktoum**
18 **WADILSAFA**, 4, b c Frankel—Rumoush (USA) **Mr Hamdan Al Maktoum**

THREE-YEAR-OLDS

19 **ALMAHHA**, b f Sea The Moon (GER)—Anqooda (USA) **Mr Hamdan Al Maktoum**
20 **ALMOKHTAAR (USA)**, b g War Front (USA)—Fascinating (USA) **Mr Hamdan Al Maktoum**
21 **ALNASEEM**, ch f Shamardal (USA)—Arwaah (IRE) **Mr Hamdan Al Maktoum**
22 **AMJAADY (USA)**, b g War Front (USA)—Prize Catch (USA) **Mr Hamdan Al Maktoum**
23 **BAALBEK (USA)**, b c Elusive Quality (USA)—Nasmatt **Sheikh Ahmed Al Maktoum**
24 **BAASEM (USA)**, ch g New Approach (IRE)—Ausus (USA) **Mr Hamdan Al Maktoum**
25 **BADAYEL (IRE)**, ch c Havana Gold (IRE)—Raggiante (IRE) **Mr Hamdan Al Maktoum**
26 **BARAAJEEL**, b c Kodiac—Madany (IRE) **Mr Hamdan Al Maktoum**
27 **BUSTAAN (USA)**, b f Distorted Humor (USA)—Aryaamm (IRE) **Sheikh Ahmed Al Maktoum**
28 **DAMLAJ**, b c Shamardal (USA)—Mahaatheer (IRE) **Mr Hamdan Al Maktoum**
29 **DAWAAM (USA)**, b c Kitten's Joy (USA)—Nereid (USA) **Mr Hamdan Al Maktoum**
30 **DAWAAWEEN (IRE)**, ch f Poet's Voice—Ghandoorah (USA) **Mr Hamdan Al Maktoum**
31 **EDAARAH**, b f Dawn Approach (IRE)—Estidraaj (USA) **Mr Hamdan Al Maktoum**
32 **EDRAAK (IRE)**, b br c Elzaam (AUS)—So Blissful (IRE) **Mr Hamdan Al Maktoum**
33 **EITHAAR**, b f Kingman—Hathrah (IRE) **Mr Hamdan Al Maktoum**
34 **FURQAAN (IRE)**, b f Dark Angel (IRE)—Surrey Storm **Mr Hamdan Al Maktoum**
35 **HADHWAH (IRE)**, b f Shamardal (USA)—Umseyat (USA) **Mr Hamdan Al Maktoum**
36 **HASSAAD**, b f Kodiac—Samaah (IRE) **Mr Hamdan Al Maktoum**
37 **HINDAAM (USA)**, b f Arch (USA)—Saraama (USA) **Mr Hamdan Al Maktoum**
38 **JOMROK**, b f Mukhadram—Shadow Dancing **Mr Hamdan Al Maktoum**
39 **MOTFAEL (IRE)**, b c Invincible Spirit (IRE)—Fidelite (IRE) **Sheikh Ahmed Al Maktoum**
40 **MUHAARAR'S NEPHEW**, b c Mukhadram—Rufoof **Mr Hadi Al Tajir**
41 **MULTAMIS (IRE)**, gr g Charm Spirit (IRE)—Dabista (IRE) **Mr Hamdan Al Maktoum**
42 **MURAAD (IRE)**, gr g Dark Angel (IRE)—Hidden Girl (IRE) **Mr Hamdan Al Maktoum**
43 **OJOOBA**, b f Dubawi (IRE)—Rumoush (USA) **Mr Hamdan Al Maktoum**
44 **RAHEEB (IRE)**, b f Kodiac—Dream Date (IRE) **Mr Hamdan Al Maktoum**
45 **RAJWAA**, gr f Dark Angel (IRE)—The Thrill Is Gone **Mr Hamdan Al Maktoum**
46 **SHARQEYYA (IRE)**, b f Oasis Dream—Daymooma **Mr Hamdan Al Maktoum**
47 **TAJAWOZ (USA)**, b c War Front (USA)—Stanwyck (USA) **Mr Hamdan Al Maktoum**
48 **TANQEEB**, b g Garswood—Oasis Mirage **Mr Hamdan Al Maktoum**
49 **TATWEEJ**, b f Invincible Spirit (IRE)—Beach Frolic **Mr Hamdan Al Maktoum**
50 **USTATH**, ch c Exceed And Excel (AUS)—Adorn **Mr Hamdan Al Maktoum**
51 **WATHEERAH (USA)**, b f Dubawi (IRE)—Atayeb (USA) **Mr Hamdan Al Maktoum**

TWO-YEAR-OLDS

52 Ch c 16/2 Le Havre (IRE)—Adjudicate (Dansili) **Mr Hamdan Al Maktoum**
53 B c 2/4 Sea The Stars (IRE)—Aghareed (Kingmambo (USA)) **Mr Hamdan Al Maktoum**
54 B c 5/2 Muhaarar—Alexander Goldrun (IRE) (Gold Away (IRE)) (500000) **Mr Hamdan Al Maktoum**
55 B f 20/3 Night of Thunder (IRE)—Ameerat (Mark of Esteem (IRE)) **Sheikh Ahmed Al Maktoum**
56 B c 4/2 Mukhadram—Anqooda (USA) (Oasis Dream) **Mr Hamdan Al Maktoum**
57 B c 12/2 Sir Prancealot (IRE)—Araajmh (USA) (Street Cry (IRE)) (80952) **Mr Hamdan Al Maktoum**

MR OWEN BURROWS - Continued

58 Ch c 24/3 Mukhadram—Arwaah (IRE) (Dalakhani (IRE)) **Mr Hamdan Al Maktoum**
59 B f 5/3 The Factor (USA)—Atayeb (USA) (Rahy (USA)) **Mr Hamdan Al Maktoum**
60 Ch f 12/2 Kitten's Joy (USA)—Ausus (USA) (Invasor (ARG)) **Mr Hamdan Al Maktoum**
61 Ch f 9/2 Showcasing—Bright Glow (Exceed And Excel (AUS)) (185000) **Mr Hamdan Al Maktoum**
62 B c 11/2 Gutaifan (IRE)—Cape Factor (IRE) (Oratorio (IRE)) (200000) **Sheikh Ahmed Al Maktoum**
63 B c 14/3 Invincible Spirit (IRE)—Cuis Ghaire (IRE) (Galileo (IRE)) **Mr Hamdan Al Maktoum**
64 Gr c 3/2 Dark Angel (IRE)—Cut No Ice (IRE) (Verglas (IRE)) (200000) **Mr Hamdan Al Maktoum**
65 B c 27/1 Pivotal—Ejadah (IRE) (Clodovil (IRE)) **Mr Hamdan Al Maktoum**
66 Ch c 16/2 Speightstown—Elraazy (USA) (Malibu Moon (USA)) **Mr Hamdan Al Maktoum**
67 B c 12/2 Invincible Spirit (IRE)—Fawaayed (IRE) (Singspiel (IRE)) **Mr Hamdan Al Maktoum**
68 B f 1/5 Oasis Dream—Goleta (IRE) (Royal Applause) (280000) **Mr Hamdan Al Maktoum**
69 Ch c 24/5 Slade Power (IRE)—Jathaabeh (Nashwan (USA)) **Sheikh Ahmed Al Maktoum**
70 B c 22/5 Make Believe—Lady Shanghai (IRE) (Alhaarth (IRE)) (210000) **Sheikh Ahmed Al Maktoum**
71 B c 5/2 Temple City (USA)—Malibu Pier (USA) (Malibu Moon (USA)) (134038) **Mr Hamdan Al Maktoum**
72 B c 21/4 Lope de Vega (IRE)—Mickleberry (IRE) (Desert Style (IRE)) (230000) **Mr Hamdan Al Maktoum**
73 B br c 17/3 Gutaifan (IRE)—Mimisel (Selkirk (USA)) (75000) **Sheikh Ahmed Al Maktoum**
74 B f 9/4 Muhaarar—Mudaaraah (Cape Cross) (IRE) **Mr Hamdan Al Maktoum**
75 B c 23/2 Golden Horn—Mudawanah (Dansili) **Mr Hamdan Al Maktoum**
76 B c 19/2 Frankel—Munasara (USA) (Bernardini (USA)) **Mr Hamdan Al Maktoum**
77 Ch f 21/2 Animal Kingdom (USA)—Nasmatt (Danehill (USA)) **Sheikh Ahmed Al Maktoum**
78 B c 21/2 Invincible Spirit (IRE)—Natagora (FR) (Divine Light (JPN)) **Mr Hamdan Al Maktoum**
79 Ch f 22/3 Night of Thunder (IRE)—Oriental Melody (IRE) (Sakhee (USA)) **Mr Hadi Al Tajir**
80 B f 3/4 Dansili—Rasmeyaa (IRE) (New Approach (IRE)) **Mr Hamdan Al Maktoum**
81 B f 22/4 Dansili—Rewaaya (IRE) (Authorized (IRE)) **Mr Hamdan Al Maktoum**
82 B f 5/5 Dansili—Rumoush (USA) (Rahy (USA)) **Mr Hamdan Al Maktoum**
83 B c 4/3 Teofilo (IRE)—Saifaana (USA) (Street Cry (IRE)) **Mr Hamdan Al Maktoum**
84 B br c 27/3 Golden Horn—Time Being (Zamindar (USA)) (220000) **Mr Hamdan Al Maktoum**
85 Ch c 28/4 Animal Kingdom (USA)—Uroobah (USA) (Dynaformer (USA)) **Mr Hamdan Al Maktoum**
86 Ch f 24/2 Speightstown—Wonderful (IRE) (Galileo (IRE)) **Mr Hamdan Al Maktoum**
87 B c 28/4 Oasis Dream—Zahoo (IRE) (Nayef (USA)) **Mr Hamdan Al Maktoum**
88 B f 30/4 Casamento (IRE)—Zahrat Dubai (Unfuwain (USA)) **Sheikh Ahmed Al Maktoum**

Assistant Trainer: Robert McDowall

---

83 MR JOHN BUTLER, Newmarket
Postal: **The Cottage, Charnwood Stables, Hamilton Road, Newmarket, Suffolk, CB8 7JQ**
Contacts: **MOBILE (07764) 999743**
E-MAIL johnbutler1@btinternet.com

1 **AMHERST ROCK**, 5, ch g Exceed And Excel (AUS)—Frigid **Mr J. Ramadhan**
2 **AVARCHIE (FR)**, 5, b g Kentucky Dynamite (USA)—Teatime (FR) **Mr J. Butler**
3 **BOUDRY (FR)**, 8, b g Crossharbour—Lavande (FR) **L. M. Power**
4 **CAT ROYALE (IRE)**, 6, b g Lilbourne Lad (IRE)—Call This Cat (IRE) **Whiterok Ltd**
5 **CONNEMARA QUEEN**, 6, ch m Major Cadeaux—Cashleen (USA) **Mr J. Butler**
6 **DELEYLL**, 5, ch g Sepoy (AUS)—Strings **Tramore Tree**
7 **FALCAO (IRE)**, 7, br g Majestic Missile (IRE)—Cafe Lassere (USA) **Power Geneva Ltd**
8 **GENUINE APPROVAL (IRE)**, 6, ch m Approve (IRE)—Genuinely (IRE) **Madeira Racing**
9 **HAVEONEYERSELF (IRE)**, 4, b c Requinto (IRE)—Charismas Birthday (IRE) **Partnership Terminated**
10 **KATALAN (GER)**, 6, b g Adlerflug (GER)—Kalla **Miss A. Haynes**
11 **KING CRIMSON**, 7, ch g Captain Gerrard (IRE)—Elegant Lady **Power Geneva Ltd**
12 **MIME DANCE**, 8, b g Notnowcato—Encore My Love **Whiterok Ltd**
13 **OUR KIM (IRE)**, 5, b g Lawman (FR)—Kayd Kodaun (IRE) **Exors of the Late S. Brown**
14 **PINCHPOINT (IRE)**, 4, ch g Exceleration (IRE)—Al Amlah (USA) **C Benham/ D Whitford/ L Quinn/ K Quinn**
15 **SAYEDAATI SAADATI (IRE)**, 6, b g Montjeu (IRE)—Guessing (USA) **Miss A. Haynes**
16 **SPECULATOR**, 7, gr g Bahamian Bounty—Swift Dispersal **Power Geneva Ltd**
17 **SPRYT (IRE)**, 7, b g Invincible Spirit (IRE)—Out of Thanks (IRE) **Mr J. Butler**
18 **TIGER LYON (USA)**, 4, b g Kitten's Joy (USA)—Hold It (USA) **Mr J. Butler**
19 **TIME TO SEA (IRE)**, 5, b g Born To Sea (IRE)—Eastern Glow **C Benham/ D Whitford/ L Quinn/ K Quinn**
20 **TOOFI (FR)**, 8, b g Henrythenavigator (USA)—Silver Bark **Northumbria Leisure Ltd**
21 **WARRIOR GODDESS (IRE)**, 4, b f Henrythenavigator (USA)—Azenzar **Mr J. Butler**
22 **ZAIN ARION (IRE)**, 6, b m Danehill Dancer (IRE)—Shaanara (IRE) **Mr A. Al Banwan**

MR JOHN BUTLER - Continued

THREE-YEAR-OLDS
23 **NABVUTIKA (IRE)**, b f Poet's Voice—Elope (GER) **Mr B. J. Lewis**
24 **NIGHT CLOSURE**, b g Royal Applause—Easter Diva (IRE) **K. J. Quinn**

Other Owners: Mr C. F. Benham, Mrs S. Horne, Mr L. M. Quinn, K. Quinn/ C. Benham, Mr D. L. Whitford.

Assistant Trainer: Alice Haynes (07585) 558717

84
MR PADDY BUTLER, Lewes
Postal: **Homewood Gate Racing Stables, Novington Lane, East Chiltington, Lewes, East Sussex, BN7 3AU**
Contacts: **PHONE/FAX (01273) 890124 MOBILE (07973) 873846**
E-MAIL homewoodgate@aol.com

1 **AEGEUS (IRE)**, 6, b g Shamardal (USA)—Magna Graecia (IRE) **Homewoodgate Racing Club**
2 **ALL OR NOTHIN (IRE)**, 10, b g Majestic Missile (IRE)—
      Lady Peculiar (CAN) **Miss M P Bryant, David & Eileen Bryant**
3 **ESTIBDAAD (IRE)**, 9, b g Haafhd (USA)—Star of Siligo (USA) **Miss M. P. Bryant**
4 **FLOWERS ON VENUS (IRE)**, 7, ch g Raven's Pass (USA)—Chelsea Rose (IRE) **Miss M. P. Bryant**
5 **HARAZ (IRE)**, 6, b g Acclamation—Hanakiyya (IRE) **Christopher W Wilson & Partner**
6 **JAMHOORI**, 11, b h Tiger Hill (IRE)—Tanasie **Mrs A. M. Cooperwhite**
7 **MERCERS**, 5, b m Piccolo—Ivory's Joy **Homewoodgate Racing Club**
8 **MY LORD**, 11, br g Ishiguro (USA)—Lady Smith **Miss M. P. Bryant**
9 **OFFICER DRIVEL (IRE)**, 8, b g Captain Rio—Spiritville (IRE) **Mr R. D. Sarin**

THREE-YEAR-OLDS
10 **GLORY STREET**, ch c Resplendent Glory (IRE)—Quality Street **Mr D. M. Whatmough & Mrs E. Lucey-Butler**
11 **ON THE BOB**, b g Big Bad Bob (IRE)—Favourite Girl (IRE) **Mrs A. M. Cooperwhite**

Other Owners: Mr D. Bryant, Mrs E. Bryant, Mrs E. Lucey-Butler, Mr D. M. Whatmough, C. W. Wilson.

Assistant Trainer: Mrs E Lucey-Butler

Amateur: Miss M. Bryant, Miss J. Oliver.

85
MRS BARBARA BUTTERWORTH, Appleby
Postal: **Bolton Mill, Bolton, Appleby-in-Westmorland, Cumbria, CA16 6AL**
Contacts: **PHONE (01768) 361363 MOBILE (07778) 104118**

1 **AGE OF GLORY**, 10, b g Zamindar (USA)—Fleeting Moon **Miss E. Butterworth**
2 **BROTHER SCOTT**, 12, b g Kirkwall—Crimson Shower **Miss E. Butterworth**
3 **CHERRY PRINCESS**, 9, gr m Act One—Francia **Mrs B. Butterworth**
4 **MINNIE MILAN (IRE)**, 10, b m Milan—Shiminnie (IRE) **Miss E. Butterworth**
5 **PERSEID (IRE)**, 9, br g Robin des Pres (FR)—Cowanstown Miss (IRE) **Mrs B. Butterworth**
6 **SNOWED IN (IRE)**, 10, gr g Dark Angel (IRE)—Spinning Gold **Miss E. Butterworth**

Assistant Trainer: Miss Elizabeth Butterworth

Jockey (NH): Sean Quinlan.

86
MISS LOUISE CABBLE, Bridgwater
Postal: **Rowden Farm, Spaxton, Bridgwater, Somerset, TA5 1DF**
Contacts: **MOBILE (07703) 045260**

1 **JUST TARA**, 7, b m Kayf Tara—Rising Bell **A. G. Fear**
2 **SPICY FRUITY (IRE)**, 9, b g Fruits of Love (USA)—Rocksham (IRE) **A. G. Fear**

87 MISS JULIE CAMACHO, Malton

Postal: **Star Cottage, Welham Road, Norton, Malton, North Yorkshire, YO17 9QE**
Contacts: **PHONE (01653) 696205 FAX (01653) 696205 MOBILE (07779) 318135 / (07950) 356440**
E-MAIL julie@jacracing.co.uk WEBSITE www.juliecamacho.com

1 **BILL CODY (IRE)**, 4, b g Declaration of War (USA)—Call This Cat (IRE) **Judy & Richard Peck**
2 **BURTONWOOD**, 7, b g Acclamation—Green Poppy **Judy & Richard Peck & Partner**
3 **CHOSEN MATE**, 5, b g Intikhab (USA)—Panoptic **The Kirkham Partnership**
4 **DEANSGATE (IRE)**, 6, b g Dandy Man (IRE)—Romarca (IRE) **Axom LXIII**
5 **DREAM MOUNT (IRE)**, 4, b g Dream Ahead (USA)—Mistify (IRE) **J. Allison, B Ahkong & Partner**
6 **DREAMOFDISCOVERY (IRE)**, 5, b g Henrythenavigator (USA)—Dreamwriter (USA) **Miss J. A. Camacho**
7 **I KNOW HOW (IRE)**, 4, b g Epaulette (AUS)—Blue Crystal (IRE) **Judy & Richard Peck & Partner**
8 **JUDICIAL (IRE)**, 7, b g Iffraaj—Marlinka **Elite Racing Club**
9 **LATHOM**, 6, b g Compton Place—Wigan Lane
10 **MAJESTIC STONE (IRE)**, 5, b g Casamento (IRE)—Pretty Majestic (IRE) **Majestic Stone Partnership**
11 **MAKANAH**, 4, b g Mayson—Diane's Choice **Axom LXXI**
12 **MYTHICAL SPIRIT (IRE)**, 5, b m Dragon Pulse (IRE)—Call This Cat (IRE) **Judy & Richard Peck & Partner**
13 **PACO ESCOSTAR**, 4, ch f Paco Boy (IRE)—Shesastar **Miss J. A. Camacho**
14 **PARIS DIXIE**, 4, b f Champs Elysees—Last of The Dixies **G. B. Turnbull Ltd**
15 **QUEENS CARE (IRE)**, 4, b f Born To Sea (IRE)—Athlumney Dancer **G. B. Turnbull Ltd**
16 **ROLL ON RORY**, 6, b g Mullionmileanhour (IRE)—Fangfoss Girls **P Adams,J Sutton,T Wickins,JHetherington**
17 **ROYAL PROSPECT (IRE)**, 4, b g Thewayyouare (USA)—Jillian (USA) **Mr & Mrs G. Turnbull**
18 **SANTAFIORA**, 5, b m Poet's Voice—Acquifer **Judy & Richard Peck & Partner**
19 **SPIRIT OF WEDZA (IRE)**, 7, b g Footstepsinthesand—Sampers (IRE) **Owners Group 005**
20 **THIS IS WENDY**, 6, b m Multiplex—This Is Us (IRE) **Mr Nigel Leadbeater Mrs Val Leadbeater**

THREE-YEAR-OLDS

21 **I'LL BE BRIEF**, b f Epaulette (AUS)—Shesastar **Miss J. A. Camacho**
22 **KODIAC DANCER (IRE)**, b f Kodiac—Kaiulani (IRE) **Mr & Mrs G. Turnbull**
23 **LORETTA (IRE)**, b f Iffraaj—Marlinka **Elite Racing Club**
24 **LORTON**, b f Sepoy (AUS)—Oilinda **G. B. Turnbull Ltd**
25 **MARVEL**, b g Poet's Voice—Baralinka (IRE) **Owners Group 010**
26 **MEA CULPA (IRE)**, b g Dandy Man (IRE)—La Dama Boba (IRE) **Miss J. A. Camacho**
27 **WILLOW BROOK**, ch f Sepoy (AUS)—Portland River (FR) **Miss J. A. Camacho**

TWO-YEAR-OLDS

28 **ADMIRAL PERCY**, ch c 29/4 Sir Percy—Oceans Apart (Desert Prince (IRE)) **Owners Group 003**
29 **LATTERHEAD (IRE)**, b f 18/4 Raven's Pass (USA)—Sequined (USA) (Street Cry (IRE)) (32000) **G B Turnbull & Julie Camacho**
30 **LOW FELL**, b f 23/2 Make Believe—
　　　　Never Change (IRE) (New Approach (IRE)) (15000) **G B Turnbull & Julie Camacho**
31 **PROCLAIMER**, b c 1/4 Free Eagle (IRE)—Pious (Bishop of Cashel) (36000) **Owners Group 033**

Other Owners: Mr P. Adams, Mr B. Ahkong, Mr J. Allison, Axom Ltd, Mr R. E. Dean, Mr D. Downie, Mr J. Hetherington, Mr A. J. Hill, Mr B. M. Hillier, Mrs V. A. Leadbeater, Mr N. G. Leadbeater, Miss M. Noden, Mr R. S. Peck, Mrs J. M. Peck, Mrs R. E. Pritchard, Mrs D. J. Rush, Mr J. Sutton, Mr G. Turnbull, Mrs S. E. Turnbull, Mr C. Verity, Mr T. Wickins.

Assistant Trainer: Mr S. Brown

---

88 MR MARK CAMPION, Malton

Postal: **Whitewell House Stables, Whitewall, Malton, North Yorkshire, YO17 9EH**
Contacts: **PHONE (01653) 692729 FAX (01653) 600066 MOBILE (07973) 178311**
E-MAIL info@markcampion-racing.com WEBSITE www.markcampion-racing.com

1 **ASK SHANROE (IRE)**, 7, b g Ask—Lady Quesada (IRE)
2 **BIDDY BE (IRE)**, 6, b m Stowaway—Ballyoscar (IRE)
3 **CIVIL ENSIGN (FR)**, 5, b g Rob Roy (USA)—Petillante Royale (FR)
4 **KNIGHT IN ARMOUR (IRE)**, 4, b g Camelot—Madeira Mist (IRE)
5 **MELDRUM WAY (IRE)**, 6, b g Getaway (GER)—Meldrum Hall (IRE)
6 **MOUNTAIN RAPID (IRE)**, 7, ch m Getaway (GER)—Founding Daughter (IRE)
7 8, Ch g Proclamation (IRE)—Tish Too
8 **TROIS BON AMIS (IRE)**, 5, gr g Lilbourne Lad (IRE)—Vanozza (FR)

Assistant Trainer: Mrs F. Campion

89 MS JENNIE CANDLISH, Leek
Postal: **Basford Grange Farm, Basford, Leek, Staffordshire, ST13 7ET**
Contacts: PHONE **(07889) 413639 (07976) 825134** FAX **(01538) 360324**
E-MAIL **jenniecandlish@yahoo.co.uk** WEBSITE **www.jenniecandlishracing.co.uk**

1 **AENGUS (IRE)**, 9, b g Robin des Champs (FR)—Which Thistle (IRE) **Mr A. J. Baxter**
2 **ANNEBELLE (IRE)**, 4, b f Jeremy (USA)—Garryduff Eile (IRE) **Mr B. J. Hall**
3 **AQUA LIBRE**, 6, b m Aqlaam—Be Free **Mrs D. Hopkins**
4 **ARTHUR'S REUBEN**, 6, b g Malinas (GER)—Ambitious Annie **Mr A. J. White**
5 **BEEVES (IRE)**, 12, b g Portrait Gallery (IRE)—Camas North (IRE) **Mr & Mrs Paul & Clare Rooney**
6 **BIG TIME DANCER (IRE)**, 6, b g Zoffany (IRE)—Final Opinion (IRE) **Andy Bell Anna Noble Arnie Flower**
7 **BRYDEN BOY (IRE)**, 9, b g Craigsteel—Cailin Vic Mo Cri (IRE) **Alan Baxter & Brian Hall**
8 **CANADIAN GEORGE (FR)**, 4, b g George Vancouver (USA)—Connaissance (IRE) **Mr A. J. Baxter**
9 **COSHESTON**, 6, ch g Black Sam Bellamy (IRE)—Rare Ruby (IRE) **Mrs J. M. Ratcliff**
10 **DOMESTIC DIVA (IRE)**, 8, b m Definite Article—Keep It Local (IRE) **Mrs G. Hennessy**
11 **FOR JIM (IRE)**, 7, gr g Milan—Dromhale Lady (IRE) **Ms J. Candlish**
12 **FORTIFIED BAY (IRE)**, 7, b g Makfi—Divergence (USA) **Mr & Mrs Paul & Clare Rooney**
13 **GRANVILLE ISLAND (IRE)**, 12, b g Flemensfirth (USA)—Fox Glen **Mr P. & Mrs G. A. Clarke**
14 **GROVE SILVER**, 10, gr g Gamut (IRE)—Cobbler's Well (IRE) **Mr A. J. Baxter**
15 **OUTCROP (IRE)**, 5, b g Rock of Gibraltar (IRE)—Desert Sage **Alan Baxter & Brian Hall**
16 **PALOMA ROSA**, 5, b m Native Ruler—Moonlight Babe (USA) **Mr K. Dove**
17 **QUICK PICK (IRE)**, 8, b g Vinnie Roe (IRE)—Oscars Arrow (IRE) **4 Left Footers & A Blewnose**
18 **RED GIANT (IRE)**, 8, ch g Beneficial—Barrack Star (IRE) **Mr V. A. Healy**
19 **SHOW PALACE**, 6, ch g Showcasing—Palais Polaire **Mr P. & Mrs G. A. Clarke**
20 **SHOWEM SILVER**, 8, b g Winged Love (IRE)—Swap Shop (IRE) **Mr V. A. Healy**
21 **SLEEPY HAVEN (IRE)**, 9, b g Indian Haven—High Society Girl (IRE) **Mr A. J. Baxter**
22 **SPIRIT OF HALE (IRE)**, 8, ch g Stowaway—Roseboreen (IRE) **Mrs A. V. Hall**
23 **SPLASH THE CASH (IRE)**, 6, b m Scorpion (IRE)—Goldfeather (IRE) **Alan Baxter & Terry Hastie**
24 **STAR ASCENDING (IRE)**, 7, ch g Thousand Words—Sakaka **Mr P. Wright-Bevans**
25 **STOP TALKING (IRE)**, 7, b m Gamut (IRE)—Miss Snapdragon (IRE) **Anthony,Barrett,Baxter,Budd,Deane,Lloyd**
26 4, B f Yeats (IRE)—Stratosphere
27 **SUNSHINEANDBUBBLES**, 6, b m Multiplex—Dockside Strike **Amazing Racing**
28 **TANARPINO**, 6, b g Tobougg (IRE)—Got Tune (FR) **Mr P. & Mrs G. A. Clarke**
29 **THEFLYINGPORTRAIT (IRE)**, 10, gr g Portrait Gallery (IRE)—Skule Hill Lass (IRE) **The Mere Partnership**
30 **TOMMY THE RASCAL**, 9, b g Multiplex—Tina Gee **Mr A. J. White**
31 **WESTERN DIXIE (IRE)**, 5, b m Westerner—Flame of Dixie (IRE) **Annie Hall & Jennie Candlish**
32 **WINTERLUDE (IRE)**, 9, b g Street Cry (IRE)—New Morning (IRE) **Brian Verinder & Alan Baxter**
33 **ZOLFO (IRE)**, 7, gr g Cloudings (IRE)—Hardy Lamb (IRE) **Matt Barrett & Alan Baxter**

THREE-YEAR-OLDS
34 **MOOR TOP**, b g Garswood—Light Hearted **Mr P. & Mrs G. A. Clarke**
35 **OZARK**, b f Archipenko (USA)—Shimoni **Mr J. C. Williams**

Other Owners: Mr D. S. Allan, Mr M. Barrett, Mrs P. M. Beardmore, Mr A. Bell, Mr P. Clarke, Mrs G. A. Clarke, Mr S. A. Flower, Mr T. Hastie, Mr P. McKeown, Mrs A. M. Noble, Mr P. A. Rooney, Mrs C. Rooney, Mrs P. A. Smith, Mr B. W. Verinder, J. White.

Assistant Trainer: Alan O'Keeffe

Jockey (flat): Joe Fanning, Tom Queally. **Jockey (NH):** Sean Quinlan. **Conditional:** Jonjo O'Neill.

90 MR HENRY CANDY, Wantage
Postal: **Kingstone Warren, Wantage, Oxfordshire, OX12 9QF**
Contacts: PHONE **(01367) 820276 / 820514** FAX **(01367) 820500** MOBILE **(07836) 211264**
E-MAIL **henrycandy@btconnect.com**

1 **BIRD OF WONDER**, 4, b gr g Hellvelyn—Phoenix Rising **Henry D. N. B. Candy**
2 **CLAUDINE (IRE)**, 4, b f Zoffany (IRE)—Hamalka (IRE) **Henry Candy & Partners III**
3 **CUBAN SPIRIT (IRE)**, 4, b g Harbour Watch (IRE)—Madam Mojito (USA) **Candy, Pritchard & Thomas**
4 **EULA VARNER**, 5, b m Showcasing—Tremelo Pointe (IRE) **Andrew Whitlock Racing Ltd**
5 **GOSCOTE**, 4, ch f Pivotal—Gosbeck **Major M. G. Wyatt**
6 **GREAT MIDGE**, 4, b g Kyllachy—Super Midge **E. Penser**

MR HENRY CANDY - Continued

7 **GREENSIDE**, 8, b g Dubawi (IRE)—Katrina (IRE) **Clayton, Frost, Kebell & Turner**
8 **I CAN (IRE)**, 4, b g So You Think (NZ)—Walk On Water **Bloomsbury Stud**
9 **KATIE LEE (IRE)**, 4, b f Camacho—Katherine Lee (IRE) **M D Poland & H Candy**
10 **LET RIP (IRE)**, 5, b g Rip Van Winkle (IRE)—Al Ihsan (IRE) **P. G. Jacobs**
11 **LIMATO (IRE)**, 7, b g Tagula (IRE)—Come April **P. G. Jacobs**
12 **MADELEINE BOND**, 5, ch m Monsieur Bond (IRE)—Spin A Wish **Candy, Pritchard & Thomas**
13 **OLAUDAH**, 5, b g Equiano (FR)—Bookiesindexdotnet **Mr A. Davis**
14 **ORD RIVER**, 4, b f Intello (GER)—Free Offer **The Earl Cadogan**
15 **ORNAMENTAL**, 4, b g Iffraaj—Tulipe Rose (FR) **Mr A. S. F. Frost**
16 **PAST MASTER**, 6, gr g Mastercraftsman (IRE)—Millestan (IRE) **Mr D B Clark/Mr A R Bentall/Mr H Candy**
17 **QUEEN OF TIME**, 5, b m Harbour Watch—Black Belt Shopper (IRE) **First Of Many**
18 **RAINCALL**, 4, b f Pivotal—Lone Rock (AUS) **Rockcliffe Stud**
19 **REBECCA ROCKS**, 5, b m Exceed And Excel (AUS)—Rebecca Rolfe **Hunscote Stud**
20 **SOVEREIGN DUKE (GER)**, 4, b g Jukebox Jury (IRE)—Shadow Queen (GER) **One Too Many Partners**
21 **THRAVE**, 4, b g Sir Percy—Feis Ceoil (IRE) **T. Barr**
22 **VERVE (IRE)**, 4, b br f Epaulette (AUS)—Onomatomania (USA) **Mr C. M. Humber**
23 **VIBRANT CHORDS**, 6, b g Poet's Voice—Lovely Thought **P. G. Jacobs**

THREE-YEAR-OLDS

24 **ADONIJAH**, b c Sea The Stars (IRE)—Meeznah (USA) **T. Barr**
25 **ALFRED BOUCHER**, gr g Aussie Rules (USA)—Policy Term (USA) **Mr R. Allcock**
26 **ALL RIGHT**, b f Intello (GER)—Alice Alleyne (IRE) **Major M. G. Wyatt**
27 **BORDER WARRIOR**, b g Sir Percy—Cheviot Heights **Simon Broke & Partners**
28 **CAMACHINO (IRE)**, ch g Camacho—Pashmina (IRE) **Thurloe Thoroughbreds XLV**
29 **CANAL ROCKS**, br g Aussie Rules (USA)—In Secret **The Earl Cadogan**
30 **FOUR FEET (IRE)**, b g Harbour Watch (IRE)—Royal Connection **Henry D. N. B. Candy**
31 **IFTON**, b c Iffraaj—Flambeau **Major M. G. Wyatt**
32 **KURIOUS**, b f Kuroshio (AUS)—Easy To Imagine (USA) **Hot To Trot Racing 1**
33 **LA LUNE**, ch f Champs Elysees—Moonlight Mystery **Alizeti Partners, Clive & Pamela Brandon**
34 **LONICERA**, gr f Lethal Force (IRE)—Puya **Girsonfield Ltd**
35 **MAIDEN CASTLE**, b g Nayef (USA)—Danae **Girsonfield Ltd**
36 **NEFARIOUS (IRE)**, ro c Zebedee—Tellelle (IRE) **Mr A. Davis**
37 **QUARRY BEACH**, b f Dutch Art—Free Offer **The Earl Cadogan**
38 **SALVE ETOILES (IRE)**, b f Sea The Stars (IRE)—Salve Diana (GER) **Hunscote Stud**
39 **SEASCAPE (IRE)**, b f Sea The Moon (GER)—Feis Ceoil (IRE) **Mr R. Allcock**
40 **SOLDIER'S SON**, b g Epaulette (AUS)—Elsie's Orphan **Henry D. N. B. Candy**
41 **TWILIGHTING**, b f Kyllachy—Night Affair **Six Too Many**
42 **WORD OF HONOUR**, b g Showcasing—Veiled Intrigue

TWO-YEAR-OLDS

43 B f 24/4 Kodiac—Anne Bonney (Jade Robbery) (USA) (160000) **Cheveley Park Stud Limited**
44 B f 12/1 Al Kazeem—Avessia (Averti (IRE)) (34285) **P. G. Jacobs**
45 **BESIDES**, ch f 23/1 Zoffany (IRE)—Beshayer (FR) (Galileo (IRE)) **Major M. G. Wyatt**
46 **CANDLEMAS**, b f 1/2 Mukhadram—Candoluminescence (Dansili) (8000) **Henry D. N. B. Candy**
47 B f 31/3 Acclamation—Cape Violet (IRE) (Cape Cross (IRE)) (11799) **Andrew Davis**
48 Ch c 4/4 Anjaal—Emma Dora (IRE) (Medaglia d'oro (USA)) (14285) **Andrew Davis**
49 **EXPEDIENT (IRE)**, b c 12/3 Kyllachy—Mabinia (IRE) (Cape Cross (IRE)) **Cheveley Park Stud Limited**
50 **HONORE DAUMIER (IRE)**, b c 5/4 Lawman (FR)—Feis Ceoil (IRE) (Key of Luck (USA)) **Mr R. Allcock**
51 Ch f 13/3 Cityscape—In Your Time (Dalakhani (IRE)) **Hunscote Stud**
52 B c 3/2 Anjaal—La Chita Bonita (IRE) (Verglas (IRE)) (7000) **Henry D. N. B. Candy**
53 **LIGHT BAY**, b f 16/3 Cable Bay (IRE)—Key Light (Acclamation) (4761) **Mr H Candy & Mrs D Blackburn**
54 **POWER PACKED**, b f 17/4 Slade Power (IRE)—Piping Dream (Approve (IRE)) (4761) **Henry D. N. B. Candy**
55 **PUBLICISE**, b f 15/3 Dream Ahead (USA)—Furbelow (Pivotal) **Cheveley Park Stud Limited**
56 B f 31/3 Champs Elysees—Puya (Kris) **Girsonfield Ltd**
57 B f 31/3 Cable Bay—Quiet Protest (USA) (Kingmambo (USA)) **Andrew Davis**
58 **RAT N MOUSE (IRE)**, gr f 17/4 Gutaifan (IRE)—
                  Rhythm And Rhyme (IRE) (Elnadim (USA)) (7619) **Henry D. N. B. Candy**
59 B f 4/4 Hot Streak (IRE)—Respondez (Oasis Dream) (15238) **The Earl Cadogan**
60 **ROCK ACADEMY (IRE)**, b c 8/2 Lope de Vega (IRE)—
                  Zippy Rock (IRE) (Fastnet Rock (AUS)) **Cheveley Park Stud Limited**
61 B f 22/4 Sea The Stars (IRE)—Step Lightly (IRE) (Danehill Dancer (IRE)) (27000) **Andrew Davis**

MR HENRY CANDY - Continued

62 WOODCOCK (IRE), gr g 18/3 Gutaifan (IRE)—
Tooley Woods (IRE) (Cape Cross (IRE)) (8000) **Henry D. N. B. Candy**

Other Owners: Mr A. Acloque, Mr A. R. Bentall, Mrs M. J. Blackburn, S. W. S. Broke, D. B. Clark, S. C. R. Clayton, Mrs S. A. Dixon, Mr D. J. Erwin, Mr R. C. Farquhar, Mr R. S. Hoskins, J. B. Inverdale, Mr J. Kebell, Mr B. W. Keswick, Mr S. L. Keswick, T. J. Le Blanc-Smith, L. Lillingston, Mr R. L. Maynard, Mr D. W. W. Norris, Mr O. J. W. Pawle, Mr G. R. Pickett, Mr M. D. Poland, Mrs C. M. Poland, Mr R. Pritchard, Mrs L. A. Smith, Mr S. Smith, Mrs J. M. Snowball, Mr J. A. B. Stafford, Mr G. A. Thomas.

Assistant Trainer: Amy Scott

MR GRANT CANN, Bath
Postal: **Park Field, Hall Lane, Lower Hamswell, Bath, Gloucestershire, BA1 9DE**
Contacts: **PHONE (01225) 891674 MOBILE (07968) 271118**

1 **BERTIE MY BOY (IRE)**, 10, b g Millenary—Slievemhuire (IRE) **J. G. Cann**
2 **CADEAU DU BRESIL (FR)**, 7, b g Blue Bresil (FR)—Melanie du Chenet (FR) **J. G. Cann**
3 **GOOSEN MAVERICK (IRE)**, 8, b g Morozov (USA)—Bonny River (IRE) **J. G. Cann**
4 **HOW'S MY FRIEND**, 14, b g Karinga Bay—Friendly Lady **The Hussey's Hustlers**
5 **I'M IN CHARGE**, 13, b g Rakaposhi King—Cloudy Pearl **J. G. Cann**
6 **JOHN DANIELL**, 14, b g Overbury (IRE)—Hottentot **The Hussey's Hustlers**
7 **QUEEN OF THE COURT (IRE)**, 6, b m Court Cave (IRE)—Waydale Hill **J. G. Cann**
8 **SAVE THE PENNIES (IRE)**, 8, ch m Shantou (USA)—Penny Fiction (IRE) **J. G. Cann**

Other Owners: Miss A. M. Bush.

MR DON CANTILLON, Newmarket
Postal: **63 Exeter Road, Newmarket, Suffolk, CB8 8LP**
Contacts: **PHONE (01638) 668507 MOBILE (07709) 377601**

1 **BLAME ME FOREVER (USA)**, 4, b f Blame (USA)—Empress Josephine (USA) **Fabfive**
2 **HUNTSMANS JOG (IRE)**, 5, b g Milan—Faucon **D. E. Cantillon**
3 **I'M BRITISH**, 6, b g Aqlaam—Libritish **Mr R. Favarulo**
4 **NAVARRA PRINCESS (IRE)**, 4, b f Intense Focus (USA)—Navarra Queen **D. E. Cantillon**
5 **WHATS NOT TO LIKE (GER)**, 8, b g Saddex—Wild Girl (GER) **D. E. Cantillon**

Other Owners: Mr L. Biffi, Mrs L. Botti.

MRS RUTH CARR, Stillington
Postal: **Mowbray House Farm, Easingwold Road, Stillington, York, North Yorkshire, YO61 1LT**
Contacts: **PHONE (01347) 823776 (home) (01347) 821683 (yard) MOBILE (07721) 926772**
E-MAIL ruth@ruthcarrracing.co.uk WEBSITE www.ruthcarrracing.co.uk

1 **ABUSHAMAH (IRE)**, 8, b g Nayef (USA)—Adaala (USA) **Grange Park Racing VIII & Mrs R Carr**
2 **ADVENTUREMAN**, 7, b g Kyllachy—Constitute (USA) **The Venturers & Mrs R Carr**
3 **BE PERFECT (IRE)**, 10, b g Street Cry (IRE)—Binya (GER) **The Beer Stalkers & Ruth Carr**
4 **BOBBY JOE LEG**, 5, ch g Pastoral Pursuits—China Cherub **Mrs A. Clark**
5 **CARDAW LILY (IRE)**, 4, b f Lawman (FR)—Chervil **British Racing Club**
6 **CHAPLIN BAY (IRE)**, 7, b g Fastnet Rock (AUS)—
Green Castle (IRE) **Miss B Houlston, Mrs M Chapman & Mrs R Carr**
7 **COSMIC CHATTER**, 9, b g Paris House—Paradise Eve **Grange Park Racing VII**
8 **CUPID'S ARROW (IRE)**, 5, b g Majestic Missile (IRE)—Kiss And Don'tell (USA) **Miss Vanessa Church**
9 **DANISH DUKE (IRE)**, 8, ch g Duke of Marmalade (IRE)—Bridge Note (USA) **Mr Michael Hill**
10 **ERASTUS**, 4, b g Swiss Spirit—Blakeshall Rose **Mr Michael Hill**
11 **EXPLAIN**, 7, ch g Kyllachy—Descriptive (IRE) **The Beer Stalkers & Ruth Carr**
12 **FINAL FRONTIER (IRE)**, 6, b g Dream Ahead (USA)—Polly Perkins (IRE) **V. Khosla**
13 **FOXTROT KNIGHT**, 7, b g Kyllachy—Rustam **Grange Park Racing XIII & Ruth Carr**
14 **FOXY REBEL**, 5, ch g Cockney Rebel (IRE)—Foxholes Lodge **Mr G. Scruton & Mr D. Williamson**
15 **FUEL INJECTION**, 8, gr g Pastoral Pursuits—Smart Hostess **Mrs M. E. Verity**
16 **GUNMAKER (IRE)**, 5, b g Canford Cliffs (IRE)—Can Dance **Gibirish Syndicate**
17 **IMPULSIVE FORCE (IRE)**, 4, gr g Lethal Force (IRE)—A Mind of Her Own (IRE) **Mr P. K. Spencer**

MRS RUTH CARR - Continued

18 **INDIAN WARRIOR,** 4, b g Sepoy (AUS)—Night Gypsy **Mrs R. A. Carr**
19 **INTENSE PLEASURE (IRE),** 4, b g Sepoy (AUS)—
                    Promesse de L'aube (FR) **Escrick Environmental Services & R Carr**
20 **KATHEEFA (USA),** 5, gr g Street Cry (IRE)—Wid (USA) **Grange Park Racing XIV & Ruth Carr**
21 **KHAZAF,** 4, b g Dawn Approach (IRE)—Winds of Time (IRE) **Mrs R. A. Carr**
22 **KIBAAR,** 7, b g Pastoral Pursuits—Ashes (IRE) **Mrs S Hibbert & Mrs R Carr**
23 **KING OF NAPLES,** 6, b g Excellent Art—Avon Lady **The Beer Stalkers & Ruth Carr**
24 **LEXINGTON PLACE,** 9, ch g Compton Place—Elidore **Mrs Marion Chapman & Mrs Ruth A. Carr**
25 **LOULIN,** 4, ch g Exceed And Excel (AUS)—Wimple (USA) **G. Murray**
26 **MAGICAL EFFECT (IRE),** 7, ch g New Approach (IRE)—Purple Glow (IRE) **Miss Vanessa Church**
27 **MAKOFITWHATYOUWILL,** 4, b g Makfi—Frequent **John Greaves & Richard Willcock**
28 **MARCELLA,** 4, b f Showcasing—Cool In The Shade **Mrs M. E. Verity**
29 **MESHARDAL (GER),** 9, b g Shamardal (USA)—Melody Fair (IRE) **The Hollinbridge Partnership & Ruth Carr**
30 **MURAADEF,** 4, b g Kodiac—Dominatrix **Mr Michael Hill**
31 **MUTAMADED (IRE),** 6, b g Arcano (IRE)—Sahaayeb (IRE) **The Bottom Liners & Mrs R. Carr**
32 **MUTANAASEQ (IRE),** 4, ch g Red Jazz (USA)—Indaba (IRE) **The Bottom Liners & Mrs R. Carr**
33 **MUTARAKEZ (IRE),** 7, ch g Fast Company (IRE)—Nightswimmer (IRE) **The Bottom Liners & Paul Saxton**
34 **ORIENTAL SPLENDOUR (IRE),** 7, br g Strategic Prince—Asian Lady **Mr J. A. Swinburne & Mrs Ruth A. Carr**
35 **OWER FLY,** 6, b g Pastoral Pursuits—Contrary Mary **Paul Saxton & The Bottom Liners**
36 **PIPERS NOTE,** 9, ch g Piccolo—Madam Valentine **Cragg Wood Racing**
37 **POINT OF HONOUR (IRE),** 4, b g Lope de Vega (IRE)—Shamayel **Dennis Clayton & James Binks**
38 **POYLE VINNIE,** 9, b g Piccolo—Poyle Dee Dee **Formulated Polymer Products Ltd**
39 **RACQUET,** 6, br g Pastoral Pursuits—Billie Jean **Reach For The Moon & Mrs R Carr**
40 **RADJASH,** 5, b g Shamardal (USA)—White Moonstone (USA) **The Beer Stalkers & Ruth Carr**
41 **RAFFLE KING (IRE),** 5, b g Kodiac—Tap The Dot (IRE) **6 Bit Racing**
42 **SKITO SOLDIER,** 4, b g Sepoy (AUS)—Kotsi (IRE) **G Scruton, D Williamson & R Carr**
43 **SUREYOUTOLDME (IRE),** 5, ch g Tamayuz—Place de Moscou (IRE) **Mr Michael Hill**
44 **SUWAAN (IRE),** 5, ch g Exceed And Excel (AUS)—Janina **Mr J. A. Swinburne & Mrs Ruth A. Carr**
45 **TADAANY (IRE),** 7, b g Acclamation—Park Haven (IRE) **Grange Park Racing Club & Ruth Carr**
46 **VALLARTA (IRE),** 9, b g Footstepsinthesand—Mexican Miss (IRE) **Mr D Renton & Mrs R Carr**
47 **VERDIGRIS (IRE),** 4, b f Intense Focus (USA)—Nimboo (USA) **Ms G. F. Khosla**
48 **WASM,** 5, ch g Exceed And Excel (AUS)—Finchley **Ged Martin Nick & Mrs R Carr**
49 **ZEBULON (IRE),** 5, gr g Zebedee—Novelina (IRE) **Bruce Jamieson, Barbara Dean, Ruth Carr**

THREE-YEAR-OLDS

50 **FABULOUS VIEW (FR),** b f Intello (GER)—I'm So Glad **N. Chapman**
51 **GLORYELLA,** b f Yorgunnabelucky (USA)—Ceiriog Valley
52 **MARK'S CHOICE (IRE),** b g Bungle Inthejungle—Ramamara (IRE) **Cragg Wood Racing**

TWO-YEAR-OLDS

53 B f 11/4 Hot Streak (IRE)—Steal The Curtain (Royal Applause) (5000) **Mr J Berry, Mrs M Chapman, Mrs R Carr**

Other Owners: The Beer Stalkers, J. Berry, J. Binks, The Bottom Liners, T. J. E. Brereton, Mrs M. Chapman, Miss V. A. Church, Mr D. G. Clayton, Mr A. D. Crombie, Mrs B. I. Dean, Mr C. Dufferwiel, Mr F. H. Eales, Escrick Environmental Services Ltd, Mrs B. S. Fowler, Mr R. J. Fowler, Ged Martin Nick, Grange Park Racing Club, Grange Park Racing VIII, Grange Park Racing X1V, Grange Park Racing XIII, Mr J. A. Greaves, J. P. Hames, Mr A. R. G. Harris, Mrs S. Hibbert, Michael Hill, Hollinbridge Partnership, Miss B. J. Houlston, Dr K. Howard, Mrs P. Howard, Mr A. B. Jamieson, Mr P. D. Kelly, Mr P. Newell, R J H Limited, Racing Club Ltd, D. C. Renton, A. Riaz, Mr P. A. Saxton, Mr G. Scruton, Mr G. A. Shields, Mr T. J. Snaith, Mr E. T. Surr, Mr J. A. Swinburne, Mr R. Willcock, Mr D. J. Williamson, Mr R. W. Wilson.

Assistant Trainer: Mrs M. Chapman

Jockey (flat): Jack Garritty, James Sullivan. **Amateur:** Miss Emily Bullock.

---

94 MR DECLAN CARROLL, Malton

Postal: **Santry Stables, Langton Road, Norton, Malton, North Yorkshire, YO17 9PZ**
Contacts: MOBILE **(07801) 553779**
E-MAIL **declancarrollracing@gmail.com**

1 **ABEL HANDY (IRE),** 4, b g Arcano (IRE)—Belle Isle **Mr F. Gillespie**
2 **BEA RYAN (IRE),** 4, b f Dream Ahead (USA)—Kimola (IRE) **Mr S. P. Ryan**
3 **BEE MACHINE (IRE),** 4, b g Footstepsinthesand—Lady Royale **Mrs S. A. Bryan**
4 **BOLD SPIRIT,** 8, b g Invincible Spirit (IRE)—Far Shores (USA) **Mrs S. A. Bryan**
5 **FRENCH HEROINE,** 4, b f Redoute's Choice (AUS)—Hasaiyda (IRE) **Clipper Group Holdings Ltd**

MR DECLAN CARROLL - Continued

6 **GOD WILLING**, 8, b g Arch (USA)—Bourbon Ball (USA) **C. H. Stephenson**
7 **HONEY GG**, 4, b f Mayson—Local Fancy **The Commissioning Team**
8 **JUSTANOTHERBOTTLE (IRE)**, 5, ch g Intense Focus (USA)—Duchess K (IRE) **Mr Steve Ryan & Mr M J Tedham**
9 **MACHREE (IRE)**, 4, b f Lord Shanakill (USA)—Faleena (IRE) **Yenilecas Syndicate**
10 **MOTAHASSEN (IRE)**, 5, b g Lonhro (AUS)—Journalist (IRE) **Mrs S. A. Bryan**
11 **MUSHARRIF**, 7, b g Arcano (IRE)—Cefira (USA) **Ray Flegg & John Bousfield**
12 **MUSIC SEEKER (IRE)**, 5, b g Henrythenavigator (USA)—Danehill Music (IRE) **Mrs S. A. Bryan**
13 **PINDARIC**, 5, ch g Poet's Voice—Hunter's Fortune (USA) **Highgreen Partnership**
14 **ROCK SOUND (IRE)**, 4, ch g Lope de Vega (IRE)—Thoughtless Moment (IRE) **The Bramblers**
15 **SAIGON CITY**, 9, b g Mount Nelson—Hoh Chi Min **C H Stephenson,Tate,Flegg & Bousfield**
16 **SHAWAAMEKH**, 5, b g Born To Sea (IRE)—Frances Stuart (IRE) **Highgreen Partnership**
17 **SHEARIAN**, 9, b g Royal Applause—Regal Asset (USA) **Mrs S. A. Bryan**

THREE-YEAR-OLDS

18 **ALOTABOTTLE**, ch g Mukhadram—Lady Tabitha (IRE) **Gordon Bulloch & Steve Ryan**
19 **DEEBEE**, ch c Dawn Approach (IRE)—Tooraweenah **Mr S. P. Ryan**
20 **HOUSE DEPOSIT**, ch g Sepoy (AUS)—Rosaceous **Lewis Ryan & Gordon Bulloch**
21 **JACKAMUNDO (FR)**, b g Fast Company (IRE)—Luxie (IRE) **Mr D. Fantom**
22 **JEM SCUTTLE (USA)**, ch c City Zip (USA)—Elegantly Wild (USA) **Mr F. Gillespie**
23 **LANGHOLM (IRE)**, b g Dark Angel (IRE)—Pindrop **Mr Steve Ryan & Mr M J Tedham**
24 **RAYPETEAFTERME**, ch g Harbour Watch (IRE)—Trump Street **Ray Flegg & John Bousfield**
25 **SEANJOHNSILVER (IRE)**, ch g Power—Fulminata (IRE) **Mr D. J. O'Reilly**
26 **SOMMER KATZE (FR)**, b g Sommerabend—Forward Feline (USA) **Mr F. Gillespie**
27 **TOBEEORNOTTOBEE**, ch c Coach House (IRE)—Lady Le Quesne (IRE) **Ray Flegg, John Bousfield & Steve Ryan**

TWO-YEAR-OLDS

28 B c 5/4 Hot Streak (IRE)—Belle Isle (Pastoral Pursuits) (45000) **Mr Frank Gillespie**
29 B c 15/3 Hot Streak (IRE)—
    Heliograph (Ishiguru (USA)) (5899) **Terry Johnston, Gordon Bulloch, John Blackburn & Andy Turton**
30 **LEOCH**, ch c 20/2 Hot Streak (IRE)—
    Acquiesced (IRE) (Refuse To Bend (IRE)) (42000) **Mr Gordon Bulloch & Shaun Hardcastle**
31 Ch c 12/2 Pivotal—Russian Heroine (Invincible Spirit (IRE)) (62000) **Mr Steve Ryan**

Other Owners: Mr S. R. Bean, Mr H. J. Bousfield, Mr G. Bulloch, R. J. Flegg, Mr E. H. M. Frost, Mrs Y. Lavin, Mrs L. Maher, Mrs N. McDonnell, Mr A. Middlehurst, Ms C. Mulrennan, Ms S. O'Dowd, J. Richardson, Mr L. Ryan, Mr D. Tate, Mr M. J. Tedham, D. Wilson.

Apprentice: Jessica Anderson, Paige Hopper, Cian Macredmond, Zak Wheatley.

95
MR TONY CARROLL, Cropthorne
Postal: **Mill House Racing, Cropthorne, Pershore, Worcs**
Contacts: **PHONE (01386) 861020 FAX (01386) 861628 MOBILE (07770) 472431**
E-MAIL a.w.carroll@btconnect.com WEBSITE www.awcarroll.co.uk

1 **ADMIRALE ART (IRE)**, 9, b g Excellent Art—Demi Voix **Mr D. S. G. Morgan**
2 **AFFAIRE D'HONNEUR (FR)**, 8, ch g Shirocco (GER)—Affaire de Moeurs (FR) **South Yorkshire Racing**
3 **ALCANAR (USA)**, 6, ch g Teofilo (IRE)—Badalona **Contubernium Racing**
4 **ALLIGATOR**, 5, ch g Sepoy (AUS)—See You Later **Neville Statham & Family**
5 **ALTAIRA**, 8, b g Dubawi (IRE)—Peach Pearl **Mrs S. R. Keable**
6 **ASTONE MAN (FR)**, 5, gr h Rajsaman (FR)—Astonia (FR) **Mr S. N. A. Al Romaithi**
7 **BALTIC PRINCE (IRE)**, 9, b g Baltic King—Brunswick **Mr A. Mills**
8 **BE MY SEA (IRE)**, 8, b g Sea The Stars (IRE)—Bitooh **L. T. Cheshire**
9 **BLACK BUBLE (IRE)**, 6, b g Valanour (IRE)—Miss Bubble Rose (FR) **Northway Lodge Racing**
10 **BLISTERING DANCER (IRE)**, 9, b g Moss Vale (IRE)—Datura **Mrs E. Madden**
11 **BOOM THE GROOM (IRE)**, 8, b g Kodiac—Ecco Mi (IRE) **Mr B. J. Millen**
12 **BROTHER IN ARMS (IRE)**, 5, b g Kodiac—Cool Cousin (IRE) **Cover Point Racing**
13 **BUTTERFIELD (IRE)**, 6, b g Fastnet Rock (AUS)—Cozzene's Angel (USA) **Shropshire Wolves**
14 **CHETAN**, 7, b g Alfred Nobel (IRE)—Island Music (IRE) **L Judd T Stamp J Hardcastle R Miles**
15 **CHIEF SITTINGBULL**, 6, ch g Indian Haven—Saharan Song (IRE) **Mr A. A. Byrne**
16 **CLOUD NINE (IRE)**, 6, b m Sakhee (USA)—Heaven **Wedgewood Estates**
17 **CREATIVE TALENT (IRE)**, 7, br g Mastercraftsman (IRE)—Pitrizzia **The Rebelle Boys**
18 **DE VEGAS KID (IRE)**, 5, ch g Lope de Vega (IRE)—Fravolina (USA) **The Rebelle Boys**
19 **DOC SPORTELLO (IRE)**, 7, b g Majestic Missile (IRE)—Queen of Silk (IRE) **Mr W. G. Nixon**

MR TONY CARROLL - Continued

20 **EESHA SAYS (IRE)**, 4, b f Fast Company (IRE)—Admire The View (IRE) **Mr A. W. Carroll**
21 **ESSAKA (IRE)**, 7, b g Equiano (FR)—Dream Vision (USA) **Mrs J. Carrington**
22 **FALCON CLIFFS (IRE)**, 5, b m Canford Cliffs (IRE)—Circle (IRE) **Mr A A Byrne & Mr Mark Wellbelove**
23 **FORESEE (GER)**, 6, b g Sea The Stars (IRE)—Four Roses (IRE) **Millen & Cooke**
24 **FRANK COOL**, 6, b g Royal Applause—Queen of Heaven (USA) **Wedgewood Estates**
25 **FRANTICAL**, 7, b g Observatory (USA)—Quest For Freedom **Mr J. M. Wall**
26 **FRENCH KISS (IRE)**, 4, b g French Fifteen (FR)—Ms Cordelia (USA) **CCCP Syndicate**
27 **GLOBAL STYLE (IRE)**, 4, b g Nathaniel (IRE)—Danaskaya (IRE) **Curry House Corner & Partner**
28 **GRACIE STANSFIELD**, 5, ch m Peintre Celebre (USA)—Ex Gracia **Surefire Racing**
29 **HAPPY ESCAPE**, 5, b m Delegator—Saharan Song (IRE) **Mr A. A. Byrne**
30 **HENRY CROFT**, 6, b g Dubawi (IRE)—Karen's Caper (USA) **Mr B. J. Millen**
31 **ILHABELA FACT**, 5, b gr h High Chaparral (USA)—Ilhabela (IRE) **Cooke & Millen**
32 **IMBUCATO**, 5, b g Paco Boy (IRE)—L'invitata **Mr D. Page**
33 **JEREMY'S JET (IRE)**, 8, b g Jeremy (USA)—Double Vie (IRE) **Mrs P. J. Clark**
34 **KATH'S BOY (IRE)**, 5, b g Bushranger (IRE)—Elayoon (USA) **Mr C. J. Wheeler**
35 **KINGSTON (GER)**, 10, br g Dylan Thomas (IRE)—Katy Carr **Three Counties Racing**
36 **LONE VOICE (IRE)**, 4, b g Poet's Voice—Zain Joy (CAN) **Mr M. B. Clarke**
37 **LONG CALL**, 6, b g Authorized (IRE)—Gacequita (URU) **Mr A. A. Byrne**
38 **MADRINHO (IRE)**, 6, ch g Frozen Power (IRE)—Perfectly Clear (USA) **Mr A. Mills**
39 **MAN OF THE NORTH**, 6, b g And Beyond (IRE)—Latin Beauty (IRE) **Last Day Racing Partnership**
40 **MISTER MUSIC**, 10, b g Singspiel (IRE)—Sierra **Mr A Sergent & Partner**
41 **MISTERCOBAR (FR)**, 7, b g Nicobar—Miss Decca (FR) **The Wayward Pilgrims**
42 **MRS TODD**, 5, b m Foxwedge (AUS)—Orange Pip **Lady Whent**
43 **NELSON RIVER**, 4, b g Mount Nelson—I Say (IRE) **CCCP Syndicate**
44 **OCEAN BENTLEY (IRE)**, 7, b g Amadeus Wolf—Bentley's Bush (IRE) **Mr A. W. Carroll**
45 **OEIL DE TIGRE (FR)**, 8, b g Footstepsinthesand—Suerte **Mr A. W. Carroll**
46 **PACO DAWN**, 5, ch m Paco Boy (IRE)—First Dawn **Mayden Stud**
47 **POETIC FORCE (IRE)**, 5, ch g Lope de Vega (IRE)—Obligada (IRE) **Mr S. Barton**
48 **POUR LA VICTOIRE (IRE)**, 9, b g Antonius Pius (USA)—Lady Lucia (IRE) **Curry House Corner & Partner**
49 **PRAIRIE TOWN (IRE)**, 8, b g High Chaparral (USA)—Lake Baino **Cooke & Millen**
50 **PREROGATIVE (IRE)**, 5, b g Rock of Gibraltar (IRE)—Tedarshana **Six Pack**
51 **PROMINNA**, 9, ch g Proclamation (IRE)—Minnina (IRE) **Mayden Stud**
52 **RED ALERT**, 5, b g Sleeping Indian—Red Sovereign **Mr A. A. Byrne**
53 **RIVER DART (IRE)**, 7, ch g Dutch Art—Sky Galaxy (IRE) **Mr B. J. Millen**
54 **ROUDRAPOUR (FR)**, 4, gr g Redoute's Choice (AUS)—Rosanara (FR) **Three Counties Racing**
55 **SCRAFTON**, 8, b g Leporello (IRE)—Some Diva **Mrs P. J. Clark**
56 **SCREAMING GEMINI (IRE)**, 5, b g Shamardal (USA)—Littlefeather (IRE) **Mr W. Y. C. Leung**
57 **SILVERTURNSTOGOLD**, 4, ch g Equiano (FR)—Saharan Song (IRE) **Mr A. A. Byrne**
58 **SIR JAMIE**, 6, ch g Monsieur Bond (IRE)—First Dawn **Mayden Stud**
59 **SPIRITOFTOMINTOUL**, 10, gr g Authorized (IRE)—Diamond Line (FR) **The Sunday Players**
60 **STAR ATTRACTION (FR)**, 4, b f Orpen (USA)—Heaven **Wedgewood Estates**
61 **SUGAR PLUM FAIRY**, 4, ch f Halling (USA)—Atyaab **Wedgewood Estates**
62 **SUNI DANCER**, 8, b m Captain Gerrard (IRE)—Sunisa (IRE) **Mr I. Furlong**
63 **TEMUR KHAN**, 4, br g Dansili—Slink **Mrs H. Hogben**
64 **TIME MEDICEAN**, 13, gr g Medicean—Ribbons And Bows (IRE) **Mr A. W. Carroll**
65 **TONI'S A STAR**, 7, b m Avonbridge—Canina **A Star Recruitment Limited**
66 **TRAVELLERS JOY**, 4, b f Equiano (FR)—Travelling **Longview Stud & Bloodstock Ltd**
67 **UPAVON**, 9, b g Avonbridge—Blaina **Mr D. Morgan and Mr K. J. Parris**
68 **VIVE LE ROI (IRE)**, 8, b g Robin des Pres—Cappard View **Surefire Racing**
69 **WINDSORLOT (IRE)**, 6, ch g Windsor Knot (IRE)—Majestic Jenny (IRE) **SF Racing Club**

THREE-YEAR-OLDS

70 **AWA BOMBA**, b g Heeraat (IRE)—Nut (IRE) **Mrs K. L. Morgan**
71 B f Kyllachy—Femme de Fer **Wedgewood Estates**
72 **FLOURISHABLE**, ch f Equiano (FR)—Choral Rhythm (IRE) **Longview Stud & Bloodstock Ltd**
73 **FORMALLY**, ch c Showcasing—Adaptability **Longview Stud & Bloodstock Ltd**
74 **FREE GIFT**, b c Makfi—Aldeburgh Music (USA) **Mr A. A. Byrne**
75 **FREEDREAMS**, b f Born To Sea (IRE)—Sinaadi (IRE) **Longview Stud & Bloodstock Ltd**
76 **IRIS'S SPIRIT**, b f Sayif (IRE)—Dubawi's Spirit (IRE) **Mill House Racing Syndicate**
77 **RECON MISSION (IRE)**, b c Kodiac—Ermine Ruby **Mr B. J. Millen**
78 **SECOND COLLECTION**, b f Delegator—Quelle Affaire **Mr A. A. Byrne**
79 **UNDER CURFEW**, ch g Stimulation (IRE)—Thicket **Mr M. J. Wellbelove**
80 **URBAN HIGHWAY (IRE)**, ch g Kodiac—Viking Fair **Millen & Partner**

MR TONY CARROLL - Continued

TWO-YEAR-OLDS

81 **BLUE VENTURE,** b f 20/3 Bated Breath—Blue Goddess (IRE) (Blues Traveller (IRE)) **G. A. Wilson**

Other Owners: Mr J. Babb, Mr J. A. Barber, Mr D. R. Blake, Mr R. Buckland, Mr C. E. Carroll, Mr M. S. Cooke, Curry House Corner, Mr J. R. Daniell, Mrs D. S. Dewhurst, J. A. Dewhurst, Mr E. A. Dupont, Mrs E. M. Juckes, Mr B. Kelleher, Mr R. J. Lanchbury, Mr J. Lawrence, Mr J. McMahon, Mr K. R. Miles, Mr R. J. Millen, Mr M. Nichol, Mr K. J. Parris, Dr A. D. Rogers, Mr N. Scanlan, Mr R. Sealey, Mr A. W. Sergent, R. Simpson, Mr A. P Stamp, Mr W. N. Standeven, Mr N. J. Statham, Mrs P. Statham, Mr L. C. Thomas, Mr A. N. Waters, Mr S. F. Whitehouse.

Jockey (flat): George Downing. **Jockey (NH):** Lee Edwards. **Conditional:** Josh Hamer.

MR TONY CARSON, Newmarket
Postal: **Cedar Lodge Racing Stables, Hamilton Road, Newmarket, Suffolk, CB8 0NQ**
Contacts: **PHONE (01638) 660947 MOBILE (07837) 601867**
E-MAIL southgatestables@outlook.com

1 **CAINHOE STAR,** 6, ch g Pivotal—Celeste **Hugh & Mindi Byrne & W H Carson**
2 **CURIOUS FOX,** 6, b m Bertolini (USA)—Doric Lady **Carson, Francis, Ghauri & Percy**
3 4, B f Cityscape—Divea **W. H. Carson**
4 **FRICKA,** 6, b m Sulamani (IRE)—Distant Florin **Mr C. T. Dennett**
5 **GULLAND ROCK,** 8, b g Exceed And Excel (AUS)—Sacre Coeur **W. F. H. Carson**
6 **TUNDRA,** 5, b m Bated Breath—Tanouma (USA) **W. F. H. Carson**

THREE-YEAR-OLDS

7 **DEERFOOT,** ch g Archipenko (USA)—Danceatdusk **Mr C. T. Dennett**
8 **KETTS HILL,** b g Mayson—Grapes Hill **Mr C. T. Dennett**

TWO-YEAR-OLDS

9 **DAME DENALI,** b f 24/3 Casamento (IRE)—Doric Lady (Kyllachy) (7500) **Dennett, Cammeron, Francis, Heart**
10 Ch f 20/4 Cityscape—Munchkin (Tiger Hill (IRE)) (761) **Willie Carson Racing Club**
11 Ch f 18/3 Harbour Watch (IRE)—Sula Two (Sulamani (IRE)) **Mr R. Prince**
12 B f 25/4 Canford Cliffs (IRE)—Tea Cup (Danehill Dancer (IRE)) (2857) **Willie Carson Racing Club**

Other Owners: Mrs M. D. Byrne, Mr H. M. Byrne, Mr Mike Francis, Mr Andy Percy.

Assistant Trainer: Graham Carson

Jockey (flat): William Carson. **Amateur:** Mr Graham Carson.

MR LEE CARTER, Epsom
Postal: **The Old Yard, Clear Height Stables, Epsom, Surrey, KT18 5LB**
Contacts: **PHONE (01372) 740878 FAX (01372) 740898 MOBILE (07539) 354819**
E-MAIL leecarterracing@aol.co.uk WEBSITE www.leecarterracing.com

1 **ART OF SWING (IRE),** 7, b g Excellent Art—Shahmina (IRE) **Fairview Racing**
2 **GERRY THE GLOVER (IRE),** 7, b g Approve (IRE)—Umlani (IRE) **N. Boyce**
3 **GLADDEN (IRE),** 4, ch f Teofilo (IRE)—Ballantrae (IRE) **Ewell Never Know**
4 **GOLD CLUB,** 8, b g Multiplex—Oceana Blue **Tattenham Corner Racing IV**
5 **KING TORUS (IRE),** 11, b g Oratorio—Dipterous (IRE) **Mr J. J. Smith**
6 **ROSS RAITH ROVER,** 6, b g Oasis Dream—Baqah (IRE) **Mr K. Tollick**
7 **SHYRON,** 8, b g Byron—Coconut Shy **Mr J. J. Smith**
8 **TABLA,** 7, b m Rail Link—Questa Nova **Mr J. J. Smith**
9 **THE WARRIOR (IRE),** 7, b g Exceed And Excel (AUS)—Aymara **Mr K. Tollick**
10 **TREBLE CLEF,** 4, b g Helmet (AUS)—Musical Key **Mrs K. T. Carter**

THREE-YEAR-OLDS

11 **LUCACHANGRETTA (IRE),** b c Alhebayeb (IRE)—Sally Is The Boss (IRE) **Sterling Racing**

Other Owners: Mr C. J. Anderson, Mr T. Dowling, Mr J. D. A. Gordon, Mr A. J. Parish, Mr D. J. Pentney, Mr S. J. Robinson.

98 MR BEN CASE, Banbury
Postal: **Wardington Gate Farm, Edgcote, Banbury, Oxfordshire, OX17 1AG**
Contacts: **PHONE (01295) 750959 FAX (01295) 758840 MOBILE (07808) 061223**
E-MAIL info@bencaseracing.com WEBSITE www.bencaseracing.com

1 **BOSTON T PARTY**, 4, b g Declaration of War (USA)—Sri Kandi **Case Racing Partnership**
2 **CODED MESSAGE**, 6, b m Oscar (IRE)—Ring Back (IRE) **Mrs A. P. B. Allen**
3 **CROCO BAY (IRE)**, 12, b g Croco Rouge (IRE)—April Thistle (IRE) **Lady Jane Grosvenor**
4 **DASH OF BLUE**, 4, b g Great Pretender (IRE)—Madame Bleue **Mrs A. P. B. Allen**
5 **DORADO DOLLAR (IRE)**, 5, ch g Golden Lariat (USA)—Stability Treaty (IRE) **Batchelor, Murray, Wright**
6 **FIRST DRIFT**, 8, ch g Generous (IRE)—Supreme Cove **Mrs C. Kendrick**
7 **FREE TRAVEL (IRE)**, 8, b g Stowaway—Janet Lindup **Mr T W Moore & Mrs Wendy Moore**
8 **GRACEFUL LEGEND**, 8, b m Midnight Legend—Clover Green (IRE) **Mrs A. P. B. Allen**
9 4, Br g Great Pretender (IRE)—High Benefit (IRE) **Mrs C. Kendrick**
10 **HUGO'S REFLECTION (IRE)**, 7, b g Robin des Champs (FR)—Dawn Court **Mrs S. R. Bailey**
11 4, B f Midnight Legend—Hymn To Love (FR)
12 **J'AI FROID (IRE)**, 6, b g Flemensfirth (USA)—Park Wave (IRE) **Mrs K. Bromley**
13 **KILBREW BOY (IRE)**, 6, b g Stowaway—Bean Ki Moon (IRE) **Lady Jane Grosvenor**
14 **KINGS TEMPTATION**, 7, b g King's Theatre (IRE)—Temptation (FR) **Lady Jane Grosvenor**
15 **MEGABOOST (IRE)**, 6, b m Court Cave (IRE)—Sweetasanu (IRE) **T W Moore & Mrs C Kendrick**
16 **MONAR ROSE**, 7, b m Yeats (IRE)—Rhapsody Rose **Mrs A. P. B. Allen**
17 **OSKI (IRE)**, 7, b g Oscar (IRE)—Mossville (FR) **Mrs C. Kendrick**
18 **PRESENTING RIO (IRE)**, 6, b m Presenting—Oh My Rubie (GER) **Wardington Hopefuls**
19 **PRINCESS ROXY**, 6, ch m Midnight Legend—Royal Roxy (IRE) **Swanee River Partnership**
20 **PULP FICTION (IRE)**, 7, b g Robin des Champs (FR)—Bean Ki Moon (IRE) **N. S. Hutley**
21 4, B g Westerner—Quel Bleu (IRE) **Case Racing Partnership**
22 **RATFACEMCDOUGALL (IRE)**, 6, b g Robin des Champs (FR)—Milano Bay (IRE) **Mrs C. Kendrick**
23 **ROCCO'S REFLECTION**, 5, ch g Shirocco (GER)—Twoy's Reflection **Rocco's Team**
24 **SHANTY ALLEY**, 5, b g Shantou (USA)—Alexander Road (IRE) **Jerry Wright Adam Lucock Patricia Murray**
25 **SHARP GETAWAY (IRE)**, 7, b g Getaway (GER)—Thanks Noel (IRE) **Mrs C. Kendrick**
26 **SHEILA TANIST (IRE)**, 6, b m Court Cave (IRE)—Douglas Park (IRE) **Case Racing Partnership**
27 **SILENT ENCORE (IRE)**, 7, ch g Curtain Time (IRE)—What Can I Say (IRE) **North & South Racing Partnership**
28 **TAKEMEOUT FREDDIE (IRE)**, 5, ch g Doyen (IRE)—Me No Puppet **Mrs C. Kendrick**
29 **TEMPLEPARK**, 6, b g Phoenix Reach (IRE)—Kenny's Dream **Mrs C. Kendrick**
30 **THEMANFROM MINELLA (IRE)**, 10, b g Shantou (USA)—Bobomy (IRE) **Mrs C. Kendrick**
31 **WHENITCOMESTOIT (IRE)**, 5, b g Arcadio (GER)—Funny Thing **D. P. Walsh**
32 **WISECRACKER**, 6, br g Sageburg (IRE)—Folie Lointaine (FR) **Lady Jane Grosvenor**

THREE-YEAR-OLDS

33 B f Califet (FR)—Clover Green (IRE) **Mrs A. P. B. Allen**
34 Ch g Gentlewave (IRE)—Ring Back (IRE) **Mrs A. P. B. Allen**

TWO-YEAR-OLDS

35 Ch f 13/4 Intello (GER)—Bertie's Best (King's Best (USA)) (12000) **Mrs A. D. Bourne**

Other Owners: Mrs C. J. C. Bailey, Mr D. Baines, C. Beaumont, N. Biggs, Mr T. Boylan, Mrs A. Case, Mr A. Case, Mrs S. Case, Mr C K Crossley Cooke, Mr Gary F. Davies, J. English, A. Gladden, E. Gladden, Mr Adrian Gregory, P Grindlay, S. Hardman, R. Harper, J. Harrison, S. Harrison, Mrs A. Hawkins, Mrs M. Howlett, R. Howlett, J. Hulse, C. Ilsley, B. Joice, Mrs Carolyn Kendrick, J. Leadbeater, H. Loggin, Mr Adam Lucock, A. Lush, P Meads, E. Middleton, Mrs Wendy Moore, Mr T. W. Moore, Miss Pat Murray, G. Nicholson, C. Nixey, J. Nowell-Smith, M. Okninski, D. Payne, K. Perrem, B. Port, J. Shaw, Mr R. I. Sims, Mrs F. Sims, D. Smith, I. Smith, J. Sullivan, D. Turberville, Mr D. P. Walsh, Mr Jerry Wright.

Jockey (NH): Daryl Jacob, Kielan Woods. **Conditional:** Max Kendrick. **Amateur:** Mr Charlie Case.

99 MR PATRICK CHAMINGS, Basingstoke
Postal: **Inhurst Farm Stables, Baughurst, Tadley, Hampshire, RG26 5JS**
Contacts: **PHONE (01189) 814494 FAX (01189) 820454 MOBILE (07831) 360970**
E-MAIL chamingsracing@talk21.com

1 **CHARLES MOLSON**, 8, b g Monsieur Bond (IRE)—Arculinge **Trolley Action**
2 **DOURADO (IRE)**, 5, b h Dark Angel (IRE)—Skehana (IRE) **Mrs A. J. Chandris**
3 **DREAMING OF PARIS**, 5, b m Oasis Dream—Parisi **Mrs A. J. Chandris**
4 **GHEPARDO**, 4, b f Havana Gold (IRE)—Clincher **The Foxford House Partnership**
5 **HAABIS (USA)**, 6, b g Super Saver (USA)—Raise Fee (USA) **Mr I. Beach**

MR PATRICK CHAMINGS - Continued

6 **HARLEQUIN ROSE (IRE)**, 5, ch m Dutch Art—Miss Chaussini (IRE) **G E Bassett & P R Chamings**
7 **HIGHWAY BESS**, 4, br f Dick Turpin (IRE)—Bob's Princess **The Foxford House Partnership**
8 **MISTER FREEZE (IRE)**, 5, ch g Frozen Power (IRE)—Beacon of Hope (IRE) **G N Hunt, G E Bassett**
9 **PERFECT CHALLENGE**, 4, b f Equiano (FR)—Bassinet (USA) **Belinda Wickens Dr B Drew P Chamings**
10 **POLLYISSIMO**, 4, ch f Nathaniel (IRE)—Fleurissimo **Dr C A Barnett & Partners**
11 **REGAL MISS**, 7, b m Royal Applause—Pretty Miss **The Foxford House Partnership**
12 **SCOTTISH GLEN**, 13, ch g Kyllachy—Dance For Fun **The Foxford House Partnership**
13 **SEABORN (IRE)**, 5, b g Born To Sea (IRE)—Next To The Top **Mr I. Beach**
14 **SPANISH STAR (IRE)**, 4, b g Requinto (IRE)—Rancho Star (IRE) **Shirley Symonds & Fred Camis**
15 **WHAT A WELCOME**, 5, ch g Nathaniel (IRE)—Hometime **Mrs K Meredith and Partners**

THREE-YEAR-OLDS

16 **HARBOUR TIMES (IRE)**, br f Harbour Watch (IRE)—Elegant Times (IRE) **Shirley Symonds & Fred Camis**
17 **JE M'EN FOUS**, b f Rock of Gibraltar (IRE)—Katya Kabanova **Wedgewood Estates**
18 **OPPORTUNE MOMENT (IRE)**, b g Slade Power (IRE)—Carry On Katie (USA) **Symonds, Camis & Fitchett**

Other Owners: Dr C. A. Barnett, Mr G. E. Bassett, F. D. Camis, Mr P. R. Chamings, Dr S. B. Drew, Mr D. P. Fitchett, Mr R. S. Hoskins, Mr G. N. Hunt, Mr C. Lloyd-Davies, Mrs K. J. Meredith, The Select Racing Club Limited, Mr M. R. Stewart, Mrs S. A. Symonds, K. W. Tyrrell, Vivaux La France, Mrs B. C. Wickens, Mr W. Womersley, Mr T. Wootton.

Assistant Trainer: Phillippa Chamings

---

100 MR MICK CHANNON, West Ilsley
Postal: **West Ilsley Stables, West Ilsley, Newbury, Berkshire, RG20 7AE**
Contacts: **PHONE (01635) 281166 FAX (01635) 281177**
E-MAIL mick@mick-channon.co.uk WEBSITE www.mickchannon.tv

1 **BANKSY'S ART**, 4, b g Sixties Icon—Outside Art **Mrs Janet Evans & Partners**
2 **BARD OF BRITTANY**, 5, b g Sayif (IRE)—Lily Le Braz **M. R. Channon**
3 **BEER WITH THE BOYS**, 4, b g Nathaniel (IRE)—Bathilde (IRE) **G. D. P. Materna**
4 **BILLY RAY**, 4, b c Sixties Icon—Fiumicino **Mr P. Trant**
5 **CARAVELA (IRE)**, 5, b m Henrythenavigator (USA)—Stella Point (IRE) **Jon & Julia Aisbitt**
6 **CHARMING GUEST (IRE)**, 4, b f Kodiac—Na Zdorovie
7 **DAN'S DREAM**, 4, br f Cityscape—Royal Ffanci **Hunscote Stud Ltd**
8 **DIAMOND DOUGAL (IRE)**, 4, b g Zebedee—Blue Saphire **Insignia Racing (Flag)**
9 **EDEN ROSE**, 4, b f Dansili—Gallic Star (IRE) **Jon & Julia Aisbitt**
10 **FANNIE BY GASLIGHT**, 4, b f Sixties Icon—Inffiraaj (IRE) **Aston Bloodstock**
11 **FITZWILLY**, 9, b g Sixties Icon—Canadian Capers **Mr Peter Taplin & Partner**
12 **GLEN FORSA (IRE)**, 7, b g Mahler—Outback Ivy **Mr T. P. Radford**
13 **HARRY CALLAHAN (IRE)**, 4, b g Dutch Art—Sovana (IRE) **Chelsea Thoroughbreds - Dirty Harry**
14 **HATS OFF TO LARRY**, 5, b g Sixties Icon—Highland Jig **Mr T Radford & Partner**
15 **HELVETIAN**, 4, b g Swiss Spirit—Lucky Dip **Box 41**
16 **HEYDOUR (IRE)**, 6, br g Presenting—Our Lucky Venture (IRE) **Mr T. P. Radford**
17 **HOLD THE NOTE (IRE)**, 5, b g Jeremy (USA)—Keys Hope (IRE) **Mr T. P. Radford**
18 **INDICIA**, 4, b f Bated Breath—Indication **Mr J. M. Mitchell**
19 **KOEMAN**, 5, b g Dutch Art—Angelic Note (IRE) **Taplin & Bunney Partnership**
20 **MAKSAB (IRE)**, 4, b br c Makfi—Azeema (IRE)
21 **MISTER WHITAKER (IRE)**, 7, b g Court Cave (IRE)—Benbradagh Vard (IRE) **Mr T. P. Radford**
22 **OCTOBER STORM**, 6, br g Shirocco (GER)—Cyber Star **Jon & Julia Aisbitt**
23 **PATTIE**, 5, ch m Sixties Icon—Excellent Day (IRE) **M. R. Channon**
24 **POUCOR**, 4, b g Pour Moi (IRE)—Corinium **Mr & Mrs D. D. Clee**
25 **ROSE CROWN**, 5, b m New Approach (IRE)—Silver Touch (IRE) **Miss I. G. Channon**
26 **SOCIAL BUTTERFLY (IRE)**, 4, gr f Clodovil (IRE)—Bank On Black (IRE) **Mrs T. Burns**
27 **TOROSAY CASTLE**, 4, b g Kayf Tara—Aneyeforaneye (IRE) **Mr T. P. Radford**
28 **TRICKSY SPIRIT**, 4, b f Lethal Force (IRE)—Spritzeria **Mr J Mitchell**
29 **VAILLANCE**, 4, gr g Sinndar (IRE)—Vayasa (FR) **M. R. Channon**
30 **WESTBROOK BERTIE**, 4, b g Sixties Icon—Evanesce **The Further Folly Partnership 1**
31 **ZOLTAN VARGA**, 5, b g Sayif (IRE)—Mar Blue (IRE) **M. R. Channon**

THREE-YEAR-OLDS

32 **ABUJA (IRE)**, b f Society Rock (IRE)—Liscoa (IRE) **Mr Peter Taplin & Partner**
33 **ADAMANTLY (IRE)**, b f Elzaam (AUS)—Ladytown (IRE) **M. R. Channon**
34 **AFTER JOHN**, b g Dutch Art—Rosacara **Mrs John Lee, Alf Heaney, Alec Tuckerman**
35 **AIR FORCE AMY**, ch f Sixties Icon—Madame Hoi (IRE) **Norman Court Stud**

MR MICK CHANNON - Continued

36 **ARCADIAN ROCKS (IRE),** b g Society Rock (IRE)—Spirit of Success **John & Zoe Webster**
37 **ASPIRING DIVA,** b f Sepoy (AUS)—Spritzeria **M. R. Channon**
38 **AZOR AHAI,** b g Sixties Icon—Good Morning Lady **M. R. Channon**
39 **BACK O' THE NET (IRE),** b c Nathaniel (IRE)—Junia Tepzia (IRE) **The Wilsley Partnership**
40 **BARBILL (IRE),** b c Zebedee—Fiuise (IRE) **Mrs S. G. Bunney**
41 **BUNGLE BROWN SUGAR (IRE),** br f Bungle Inthejungle—
    Splashofchocolate (IRE) **Mr Christopher Wright, Miss Holly Wright, Mrs Chloe Forsyth**
42 **CERTAIN LAD,** b g Clodovil (IRE)—Chelsey Jayne (IRE) **Mr C. R. Hirst**
43 **CHAIRMANOFTHEBOARD (IRE),** b c Slade Power (IRE)—Bound Copy (USA) **David Kilburn, David Hudd & Chris Wright**
44 **CHERRY COLA,** ch f Sixties Icon—Rose Cheval (USA) **Mr Peter Taplin & Partner**
45 **CHYNNA,** gr f Gregorian (IRE)—Natalie Jay **M. R. Channon**
46 **CITY WANDERER (IRE),** b g Kodiac—Viletta (GER) **George Materna & Roger Badley**
47 **COTUBANAMA,** b f Heeraat (IRE)—Saona Island **Mr J Widdows & Partner**
48 **CRYSTAL TIARA,** b f Gregorian (IRE)—Petaluma **The Sweet Partnership**
49 **DANCE OF DESTINY,** b f Mukhadram—Classical Dancer **M. R. Channon**
50 **DANCING JO,** b c Mazameer (IRE)—Remix (IRE) **R.E.F.Ten**
51 **DEAR MIRIAM (IRE),** b f Acclamation—Phillippa (IRE) **Mr T. P. Radford**
52 **EARL OF HARROW,** b g Sixties Icon—The Screamer (IRE) **Mr Peter Taplin & Partner**
53 Br f Moohaajim (IRE)—Easee On (IRE)
54 **EQUIPPED,** b f Equiano (FR)—Marjong **Mr J. L. Marsden**
55 **EVIE MAY,** b f Excelebration (IRE)—Visanilla (FR) **Barry Walters Catering**
56 **FLASH TAFF,** b c Rip Van Winkle (IRE)—Miss Lahar **Barry Walters Catering**
57 **GOSPEL,** b f Holy Roman Emperor (IRE)—Heavenly Sound **Mrs M V Magnier Mrs J Magnier Mrs P Shanahan**
58 **I'LLETYOUGONOW,** b f Bated Breath—Upskittled **Mrs J P E Cunningham & Mr G M Cunningham**
59 **JUNGLE INTHEBUNGLE (IRE),** ch g Bungle Inthejungle—Princess Banu **Mrs T. Burns**
60 **JUNGLE JUICE (IRE),** b f Bungle Inthejungle—Riymaisa (IRE) **Insignia Racing (Ribbon)**
61 **KARALINI (IRE),** b f Es Que Love (IRE)—Lucky Leigh **Mrs John Lee, Alf Heaney, Alec Tuckerman**
62 **KINKS,** b g Sixties Icon—Crazee Diamond **David Hudd, Chris Wright & Ann Black**
63 Ch f Presenting—Lakaam **Mr E. Spurrier**
64 **LIMELIGHTER,** b g Harbour Watch (IRE)—Steal The Curtain **M. R. Channon**
65 **LORD HOWARD (IRE),** b g Havana Gold (IRE)—Lady Gabrielle (IRE) **M. R. Channon**
66 **MODERN MILLIE,** b f Sixties Icon—Hairspray **Norman Court Stud**
67 **PATCHOULI,** b f Sixties Icon—Inffiraaj (IRE) **M. R. Channon**
68 **QUIRKY GERTIE (IRE),** b f Fast Company—Acushladear (IRE) **The Endless Folly Partnership**
69 **RAKASTAVA (IRE),** bl gr g Clodovil—Shemissa (IRE) **Box 41**
70 **SEVERANCE,** b c Nathaniel (IRE)—Decorative (IRE) **Mr J Turner & the Megsons**
71 **SOCIETY GUEST (IRE),** b f Society Rock (IRE)—Bronze Baby (USA) **John Guest Racing Ltd**
72 **STORTING,** b c Iffraaj—Stella Point (IRE) **Jon & Julia Aisbitt**
73 B f Cityscape—Stylos Ecossais
74 **SWINGING JEAN,** b f Sixties Icon—Shrimpton **M. R. Channon**
75 **SWISS PHILLY,** b f Cacique (IRE)—Vespasia **Insignia Racing (Ribbon)**
76 **TWO BLONDES (IRE),** ch g Dragon Pulse (IRE)—Itaya (IRE) **Mr J. Turner**
77 **VALENTINO SUNRISE,** b g Sixties Icon—Leleyf (IRE) **P. Taplin**
78 **VENUSTA (IRE),** b f Medicean—Grevillea (IRE) **Mr N. J. Hitchins**

TWO-YEAR-OLDS

79 B f 3/5 Bungle Inthejungle—Ajig Dancer (Niniski (USA)) (5899) **Mrs T. Burns**
80 B f 18/4 Gleneagles (IRE)—Al Manaal (Echo of Light)
81 Br c 2/4 Gregorian (IRE)—Altona (IRE) (Redback) **Bastian Family**
82 B f 18/2 Gregorian (IRE)—Amahoro (Sixties Icon) **Dave & Gill Hedley**
83 Gr f 29/1 Gutaifan (IRE)—Best New Show (IRE) (Clodovil (IRE)) (21069)
84 B f 27/2 Harbour Watch (IRE)—Blue Beacon (Fantastic Light (USA)) (10000) **Mrs Nicola Murray**
85 B f 20/3 Sixties Icon—Bridie Ffrench (Bahamian Bounty) (571)
86 Br c 31/3 Footstepsinthesand—Crazee Diamond (Rock of Gibraltar (IRE))
87 **DALANIJUJO (IRE),** ch f 20/4 Night of Thunder (IRE)—Kiss From A Rose (Compton Place) (60000) **C. Hirst**
88 **DECORA (IRE),** ch f 6/3 Conduit (IRE)—Grevillea (IRE) (Admiralofthefleet (USA)) **Mr N. J. Hitchins**
89 B c 21/3 Anjaal—Defensive Boast (USA) (El Gran Senor (USA)) (12642)
90 B c 4/3 Roderic O'Connor (IRE)—Desert Morning (IRE) (Pivotal) **W. Carson**
91 **DONNA RAY,** b f 9/5 Sixties Icon—Fiumicino (Danehill Dancer (IRE)) **Norman Court Stud**
92 B c 20/3 Sixties Icon—Dozen (FR) (Mastercraftsman (IRE))
93 Ch f 1/3 Bated Breath—Effie B (Sixties Icon) **Bastian Family**
94 Gr f 19/2 Sixties Icon—El Che (Winker Watson) (571) **Mr P Taplin & Partner**
95 B gr c 20/4 Al Kazeem—Enaitch (IRE) (New Approach (IRE)) **D D & Mrs J P Clee**
96 **ERIKA ROE,** ch f 15/2 Hot Streak (IRE)—Acts of Folly (SPA) (King's Best (USA)) (22000) **Ted Voute**
97 B c 19/3 Heeraat (IRE)—Evanesce (Lujain (USA)) **Dave & Gill Hedley**

MR MICK CHANNON - Continued

 98 B c 14/2 Gregorian (IRE)—Exentricity (Paco Boy (IRE)) (3809)
 99 B f 11/3 Sixties Icon—Fading Away (Fraam) (571) **Mr P. Taplin**
100 Ch g 3/3 Starspangledbanner (AUS)—Fanditha (IRE) (Danehill Dancer (IRE)) (38095)
101 B f 12/2 Sixties Icon—Follow The Faith (Piccolo) (571)
102 B f 12/4 Kodiac—Fonseca (IRE) (Red Clubs (IRE)) (38000) **Tails Partnership**
103 B f 28/2 Elusive City (USA)—Gallice (IRE) (Fuisse (FR)) (30000) **Allen, Porter, Voute Partnership**
104 Ch c 18/3 Bungle Inthejungle—Grotta Del Fauno (IRE) (Galileo (IRE)) (13062)
105 B c 29/3 Roderic O'Connor (IRE)—Hail Shower (IRE) (Red Clubs (IRE)) (1684) **Hunscote Stud**
106 Ch g 29/4 Anjaal—Hazardous (Night Shift (USA)) (15170)
107 B f 19/4 Sixties Icon—Hi Note (Acclamation) (1142)
108 Br c 12/3 Footstepsinthesand—High Society Girl (IRE) (Key of Luck (USA)) (18541)
109 B c 21/3 Dutch Art—Hot Secret (Sakhee's Secret) (24761)
110 **HUNDRED ISLES (IRE),** b c 20/2 Fastnet Rock (AUS)—Gallic Star (IRE) (Galileo (IRE)) **Jon & Julia Aisbitt**
111 B f 4/3 Sixties Icon—Ificaniwill (IRE) (Mastercraftsman (IRE))
112 Gr g 7/3 Gregorian (IRE)—Just Violet (Sixties Icon) (2857)
113 B c 27/2 Bungle Inthejungle—Kidmeforever (Piccolo) (13333) **Mr C Wright & W Carson**
114 Gr c 13/3 Gregorian (IRE)—La Gifted (Fraam)
115 B f 29/1 Australia—Lady Lahar (Fraam) **Barry Walters Catering**
116 Br f 28/3 Kayf Tara—Lakaam (Danzero (AUS)) **Mr T Radford**
117 Ch f 4/3 Equiano (FR)—Linda (FR) (Tamayuz) (24761)
118 Ch c 7/4 Anjaal—Malekat Jamal (IRE) (Dutch Art) (45000)
119 B f 7/3 Camelot—Mare Imbrium (USA) (Mr Greeley (USA)) **Barry Walters Catering**
120 B br f 13/3 Gleneagles (IRE)—Miss Lahar (Clodovil (IRE)) (30000) **Barry Walters Catering**
121 B c 29/3 Captain Gerrard (IRE)—Mistic Magic (IRE) (Orpen (USA))
122 B c 28/5 Captain Gerrard (IRE)—Natalie Jay (Ballacashtal (CAN))
123 **NOW I'M A BELIEVER,** b f 30/3 Gregorian (IRE)—Alpha Spirit (Sixties Icon) **Mr T. P. Radford**
124 Br c 8/2 Brazen Beau (AUS)—Our Gal (Kyllachy) (30341)
125 B c 20/4 Captain Gerrard (IRE)—Outside Art (Excellent Art) (1428) **Mrs Janet Evans & Partners**
126 B f 24/4 Heeraat (IRE)—Pacches (IRE) (Clodovil (IRE))
127 B f 20/3 Free Eagle (IRE)—Pesse (IRE) (Eagle Eyed (USA)) (1500)
128 Ch f 16/2 Paco Boy (IRE)—Pose (IRE) (Acclamation) (13000)
129 Br c 9/4 Sixties Icon—Potternello (IRE) (Captain Marvelous (IRE))
130 B c 17/3 Anjaal—Princess Banu (Oasis Dream) (14285) **Mrs T. Burns**
131 B c 25/2 Sidestep (AUS)—Question (USA) (Coronado's Quest (USA)) (32000) **Box 41**
132 **RHYME SCHEME (IRE),** b f 8/2 Poet's Voice—Tidal Moon (Sea The Stars (IRE)) **Jon & Julia Aisbitt**
133 B f 28/3 Le Havre (IRE)—Riot of Colour (Excellent Art) (35000)
134 B c 6/3 Fountain of Youth (IRE)—Rough Courte (Clodovil (IRE))
135 B f 22/3 Cable Bay (IRE)—Royal Ffanci (Royal Applause) **Hunscote Stud**
136 B c 6/2 Slade Power (IRE)—Sahaayef (IRE) (Mawatheeq (USA)) (60000)
137 Ch f 1/3 Sixties Icon—Shadows Ofthenight (IRE) (Fastnet Rock (AUS))
138 B c 15/2 Sir Prancealot (IRE)—Shoshoni Wind (Sleeping Indian) (36190)
139 Ch c 21/3 Harbour Watch (IRE)—Shrimpton (Cadeaux Genereux)
140 B f 24/2 Kingman—Silca Chiave (Pivotal) (40000) **Aldridge Racing Partnership**
141 Ch f 17/3 Nathaniel (IRE)—Solita (USA) (Thunder Gulch (USA)) (5000)
142 B f 31/5 Captain Gerrard (IRE)—Stella Rise (IRE) (Dutch Art) **Mr R Windridge**
143 B c 19/4 Harbour Watch (IRE)—Sweet Coconut (Bahamian Bounty) (23598) **Wayne Clifford**
144 B f 14/3 Captain Gerrard (IRE)—Symboline (Royal Applause)
145 B f 5/4 Sixties Icon—Tanojin (IRE) (Thousand Words) **Norman Court Stud**
146 B c 1/4 Nathaniel (IRE)—Tesary (Danehill (USA)) (10000)
147 B c 19/4 Camacho—Ushindi (IRE) (Montjeu (USA)) (39000)
148 B c 15/3 Captain Gerrard (IRE)—Vilnius (Imperial Dancer) (952)
149 B f 10/3 Sixties Icon—Wansdyke Lass (Josr Algarhoud (IRE)) **Norman Court Stud**
150 Br c 14/4 Camacho—When Not Iff (IRE) (Iffraaj) (28000)
151 **WILLIAMWILBERFORCE,** b c 31/1 Dream Ahead (USA)—
                                                    Isabella Bird (Invincible Spirit (IRE)) **Jon & Julia Aisbitt**
152 B f 2/3 Kodiac—Windy Lane (Dubai Destination (USA)) (62857) **Mr J. Turner**
153 B f 10/2 Requinto (IRE)—Yasmeena (USA) (Mr Greeley (USA)) (50568) **C. Hirst**

Other Owners: J. R. Aisbitt, Mrs J. M. Aisbitt, Mr K. M. Al-Mudhaf, Mr M. J. Al-Qatami, Mr T. J. Allen, Mr R. Badley, Mrs A. C. Black, Box 41 Racing, Mrs Susan Bunney, Chelsea Thoroughbreds Ltd, D. D. Clee, Mrs J. P. Clee, Mrs J. P. E. Cunningham, Mr G. M. Cunningham, Mrs J. A. Evans, R. E. Fowler, Mrs G. H. Hedley, Mr D. L. Hudd, Insignia Racing Limited, Mrs A. M. Jones, Mr A. S. L. Leader, Mrs J. Magnier, Mrs M. V. Magnier, Mr George Materna, Mr A. P. Megson, Mrs J. Megson, The Megsons, Mrs L. M. Shanahan, Mrs T. G. Trant, Mrs Z. J. Webster, Mr J. Webster, J. H. Widdows, Mr C. N. Wright.

Assistant Trainers: Jack Channon, Paul Morkan

101 **MR MICHAEL CHAPMAN, Market Rasen**
Postal: **Woodlands Racing Stables, Woodlands Lane, Willingham Road, Market Rasen, Lincolnshire, LN8 3RE**
Contacts: **PHONE/FAX (01673) 843663 MOBILE (07971) 940087**
E-MAIL woodlands.stables@btconnect.com WEBSITE www.woodlandsracingstables.co.uk

1 **DUC DE SEVILLE (IRE)**, 7, b g Duke of Marmalade (IRE)—Splendid (IRE) **Mrs M. M. Chapman**
2 **FOUR MILE BEACH**, 6, gr g Dalakhani (IRE)—Rappel **Mrs M. M. Chapman**
3 **L'ES FREMANTLE (FR)**, 8, b g Orpen (USA)—Grand Design **Mr G. Nolan**
4 **LUDUAMF (IRE)**, 5, ch g Tamayuz—Aphorism **Mrs M. M. Chapman**
5 **MONZINO (USA)**, 11, b br g More Than Ready (USA)—Tasso's Magic Roo (USA) **Mrs M. M. Chapman**
6 **NOLANS HOTSPUR (IRE)**, 7, b g Bushranger (IRE)—Cayambe (IRE) **Mr G. Nolan**
7 **PORT LAIRGE**, 9, b g Pastoral Pursuits—Stylish Clare (IRE) **Mrs M. M. Chapman**
8 **STRIKING NIGELLA**, 9, b m Striking Ambition—Fiona Fox **F. A. Dickinson**
9 **TAYARAT (IRE)**, 14, b g Noverre (USA)—Sincere (IRE) **Mrs M. M. Chapman**
10 **THE SOCIETY MAN (IRE)**, 12, ch g Moscow Society (USA)—Redruth (IRE) **Mrs M. M. Chapman**
11 **VOLCANIC JACK (IRE)**, 11, b g Kodiac—Rosaria Panatta (IRE) **Mrs M. M. Chapman**

Assistant Trainer: Mrs M. Chapman

102 **MR RYAN CHAPMAN, St Columb**
Postal: **Trembleath Farm, St. Columb, Cornwall, TR9 6DP**

1 **APAROL (IRE)**, 6, b h Peintre Celebre (USA)—Abbasharjah (GER) **R. G. Chapman**
2 **AUTUMN HILL (IRE)**, 6, b m Cloudings (IRE)—Elmside (IRE) **R. G. Chapman**
3 **DOCTOR THEA**, 6, b m Multiplex—Kallithea (IRE) **R. G. Chapman**

103 **MR FABRICE CHAPPET, Chantilly**
Postal: **29 Avenue de Joinville, 60500 Chantilly, France**
Contacts: **PHONE 33 (0) 3 44210300**
E-MAIL chappet-secretariat@orange.fr WEBSITE www.chappetracing.com

1 **AL MALHOUF (IRE)**, 4, ch c Dutch Art—Lady Eclair (IRE) **S. B. Al Kuwari**
2 **ALBA POWER (IRE)**, 4, b g Fast Company (IRE)—Shehila (IRE) **F. J. Carmichael**
3 **BROAFIELD (IRE)**, 4, b g Kodiac—Avril Rose (IRE) **A. G. Kavanagh**
4 **INTELLOGENT (IRE)**, 4, ch c Intello (GER)—Nuit Polaire (IRE) **F. J. Carmichael**
5 **KEN COLT (IRE)**, 4, b g Kendargent (FR)—Velvet Revolver (IRE) **Roy Racing Ltd**
6 **KING OF DARKNESS (FR)**, 4, b g Le Havre (IRE)—Eleona (GER) **F. J. Carmichael**
7 **MADE TO LEAD (FR)**, 4, b f Linngari (IRE)—Magic Artiste (FR) **S. Lellouche**
8 **POUR LIBRANNO (IRE)**, 4, b f Pour Moi (IRE)—Bella Vento **O. J. McDowell**
9 **ROC ANGEL (FR)**, 5, ch g Rock of Gibraltar (IRE)—Forewarned (IRE) **A. Gilibert**
10 **SILVERY MIST (FR)**, 4, gr f Stormy River (FR)—Misty Heights **Roy Racing Ltd**
11 **SON CESIO (FR)**, 8, b h Zafeen (FR)—Slitana (IRE) **S. Vidal**
12 **TROPICAL PRINCESS (FR)**, 4, b f Dabirsim (FR)—Tropical Pearl (GER) **Ecurie Normandie Pur Sang**

THREE-YEAR-OLDS

13 **ADIRONDACK (IRE)**, b c Kodiac—Kikonga **Ecurie des Charmes**
14 **AL ARESH (FR)**, b c Footstepsinthesand—Itasca (FR) **Al Shaqab Racing**
15 **AL MARROUNA (FR)**, b f Olympic Glory (IRE)—Seeharn (IRE) **Al Shaqab Racing**
16 **ALORS QUOI (IRE)**, b f Siyouni (FR)—Zeiting (FR) **A. M. Hayes**
17 **ALWAJBA (IRE)**, ch f Siyouni (FR)—Calahorra (FR) **Al Shaqab Racing**
18 B f Olympic Glory (IRE)—Bella Vento **O. J. McDowell**
19 **BLISS FOR EVER (FR)**, b c Slickly (FR)—Marital Bliss (FR) **H. de Pracomtal**
20 **BLUE CUP (IRE)**, gr c Kendargent (FR)—Hunter Forward (AUS) **M. Watt**
21 **CICCIA (FR)**, gr f Diamond Green (FR)—Ninka (FR) **A. Gilibert**
22 **COMPIEGNE (FR)**, b c Siyouni (FR)—Lady's Secret (IRE) **A. Gilibert**
23 **COOKILAYONE (FR)**, gr f Rajsaman (FR)—Saroushka (FR) **B. Dublanchet**
24 **DORIANA GRAY (FR)**, gr f Le Havre (IRE)—Doriana (FR) **D. Hazan**
25 **DUTCH WONDER (IRE)**, b f Dutch Art—Wonderous Light (IRE) **R. Shaykhutdinov**
26 **ECHELLE DU LEVANT (IRE)**, b f Dabirsim (FR)—Elnadwa (USA) **G. Algranti**
27 **FERSEN (FR)**, b g Rajsaman (FR)—Mahiladipa (FR) **J. A. Zay**

MR FABRICE CHAPPET - Continued

28 **FILS DE LUNE (FR),** b g Camelot—Full Snow Moon (USA) **L. Disaro**
29 **FUSEE D'OR (FR),** br c Equiano (FR)—Kathy's Rocket (USA) **Malih L. Al Basti**
30 **GLYSANDRINE (IRE),** b f Dabirsim (FR)—Gloomy Sunday (FR) **Ecurie Normandie Pur Sang**
31 **GRAZZIA (FR),** b f Rock of Gibraltar (IRE)—Green Ridge (FR) **Haras de Beauvoir**
32 **HONGBAO (FR),** ch g Literato (FR)—Bairgaine (FR) **F. Chappet**
33 **IDOLES DES JEUNES (FR),** b f Helmet (AUS)—Akka **K. M. Al Attiyah**
34 **INATTENDU (FR),** b c Anodin (IRE)—Suama (FR) **F. Chappet**
35 **INFOX (FR),** b c Reliable Man—Seltitude (IRE) **A. Gilibert**
36 **JUNGLE SPEED (FR),** b c Bungle Inthejungle—Velvet Revolver (IRE) **Roy Racing Ltd**
37 **KILFRUSH MEMORIES (FR),** b c Shakespearean (IRE)—Elusive Lily **S. Vidal**
38 **LITTLE FOLLY (FR),** b f Literato (FR)—Folle Dingue (FR) **X. Doumen**
39 **MACKLIN (FR),** b c Masked Marvel—Orlena (USA) **J. Studd**
40 **MASLOUB (FR),** b g Olympic Glory (FR)—Marla (GER) **Al Shaqab Racing**
41 **NOOR SAHARA (IRE),** b f Lope de Vega (IRE)—By Invitation (USA) **Ecurie J. L. Bouchard**
42 **NOXARENO (GER),** b c Maxios—Nobilissima (GER) **Ecurie Normandie Pur Sang**
43 **OLYMPIC LIGHT (FR),** b f Olympic Glory (FR)—Atlantic Light **Roy Racing Ltd**
44 **OLYMPIC STAR (FR),** ch c Olympic Glory (FR)—Sapfo (FR) **Al Shaqab Racing**
45 **OMBRA MIA (IRE),** b f Olympic Glory (FR)—Mad Existence (USA) **A. G. Kavanagh**
46 **OVER THE MOON (IRE),** b f Invincible Spirit (IRE)—Hit The Sky (IRE) **A. M. Hayes**
47 **PIVOINE ROSE (FR),** b f Cacique (IRE)—Palme Royale (IRE) **Bloodstock Agency Ltd**
48 **PIZZICATO (ITY),** b g Dabirsim (FR)—Resaca (GER) **A. Gilibert**
49 **POPINJAY (FR),** ch c Dawn Approach (IRE)—Extreme Green **G. Algranti**
50 **PRIMERAVEZ (IRE),** b f Dark Angel (IRE)—Evening Frost (IRE) **A. G. Kavanagh**
51 **REALITYHACKING (FR),** b g Bungle Inthejungle—You Got The Love **SCEA Haras du Ma**
52 **REY PELAYO (FR),** b c Wootton Bassett—Darkova (USA) **Haras d'Etreham**
53 **ROCQUES (FR),** b f Lawman (FR)—Regina Mundi (IRE) **G. Augustin-Normand**
54 **SALMON PLEASE (FR),** gr c Rajsaman (FR)—Midnight Flash (IRE) **H. de Pracomtal**
55 **SAN HUBERTO (IRE),** b c Speightstown (USA)—Sediciosa (IRE) **M. Lagasse**
56 **SEPPELTSFIELD (IRE),** b c Raven's Pass (USA)—Petit Calva (FR) **A. G. Kavanagh**
57 **SERIOUS ANGEL (FR),** gr c Dark Angel (IRE)—Serious Dowth (IRE) **Haras de Beauvoir**
58 **SHELTER (IRE),** b f Le Havre (IRE)—Peut Etre (IRE) **A. M. Hayes**
59 **SIMPLICITY (FR),** b f Casamento (IRE)—Sleek Gold **A. Jathiere**
60 **SKYWARD (FR),** b c Camelot—Shakeyourbody (USA) **A. Curty**
61 B f Violence (USA)—Storm City Blues (USA) **A. Gilibert**
62 **SUFYAAN (FR),** b g Olympic Glory (IRE)—Footsteppy (IRE) **Al Shaqab Racing**
63 **SURVOLTEE (GER),** b f Helmet (AUS)—Silver Face (FR) **A. Gilibert**
64 **VAIANA (USA),** b f Violence (USA)—Premiere Creation (FR) **Haras de Beauvoir**
65 **VISORANA (FR),** b f Rock of Gibraltar (IRE)—Visinada (IRE) **Haras de Beauvoir**

TWO-YEAR-OLDS

66 Ch c 16/3 Le Havre (IRE)—Abyssinie (IRE) (Danehill Dancer (IRE)) (92709) **Al Shaqab Racing**
67 B f 14/2 Atreides (USA)—Appearance (USA) (Harlington (USA)) (24691) **A. Gilibert**
68 B f 29/1 Lawman (FR)—Babacora (FR) (Indian Ridge) (42140) **A. Gilibert**
69 B f 2/3 Dabirsim (FR)—Baiadera (GER) (Tertullian (USA)) (13485) **Ecurie Normandie Pur Sang**
70 B c 24/4 Anodin (IRE)—Bella Vento (Shirocco (GER)) **O. J. McDowell**
71 B f 1/1 Iffraaj—Bernie's Moon (USA) (Bernstein (USA)) (39612) **R. Shaykhutdinov**
72 B c 26/3 Dabirsim (FR)—Celesteville (IRE) (Elusive City (USA)) (8428) **Ecurie Normandie Pur Sang**
73 B f 1/4 Invincible Spirit (IRE)—Celestina Agostino (USA) (Street Cry (IRE)) (151706) **Cofinvest**
74 B f 7/2 Temple City (USA)—Chiquita Picosa (USA) (Congaree (USA)) (109565) **Ecurie J. L. Bouchard**
75 B f 6/4 Anodin (IRE)—Cosquillas (IRE) (Selkirk (USA)) (26970) **A. Jathiere**
76 Ch f 16/2 Gleneagles (IRE)—Daltiana (FR) (Selkirk (USA)) (52254) **A. Gilibert**
77 B c 23/3 War Command (USA)—Dance Toupie (FR) (Dansili) (29498) **A. Gilibert**
78 **ELEA CHOPE (FR),** b f 15/2 Panis (USA)—Eyes of War (FR) (Muhaymin (USA)) (18541) **G. Augustin-Normand**
79 B br f 1/4 Gleneagles (IRE)—Elitiste (IRE) (Danehill Dancer (IRE)) (42140) **F. Bianco**
80 B c 20/2 Hurricane Cat (USA)—Elusive Lily (Elusive City (USA)) **S. Vidal**
81 **FRILLY BOLERO (FR),** gr f 17/4 Kendargent (FR)—Hunter Forward (AUS) (Galileo (IRE)) **M. Watt**
82 B c 4/5 Charm Spirit (IRE)—Full Snow Moon (USA) (Vindication (USA)) **L. Disaro**
83 B c 7/4 Zebedee—Gloomy Sunday (FR) (Singspiel (IRE)) **Ecurie Normandie Pur Sang**
84 Gr f 27/4 Anodin (IRE)—Green Media (FR) (Green Tune (USA)) (63211) **Ecurie J. L. Bouchard**
85 **HELIOS DES SOURCES (FR),** bl c 22/3 Pedro The Great (USA)—Mofa Bere (FR) (Saumarez) (54782) **L. Powell**
86 B f 27/4 Teofilo (IRE)—Holly Polly (GER) (Dylan Thomas (IRE)) (50568) **A. Gilibert**
87 **JARNAC (FR),** b f 23/1 Siyouni (FR)—Optica (FR) (Hernando (FR)) (96923) **H. de Pracomtal**
88 B c 4/4 Olympic Glory (IRE)—Jeu de Vivre (IRE) (Montjeu (IRE)) (46354) **Al Shaqab Racing**
89 **KAPSALIANA (FR),** b f 3/5 Wootton Bassett—Age of Refinement (IRE) (Pivotal) (43826) **Ecurie Vivaldi**
90 **KRAQUANTE,** b f 10/3 Bated Breath—Desert Image (Beat Hollow) (46354) **Ecurie Vivaldi**

MR FABRICE CHAPPET - Continued

91 MAGIC ATTITUDE, b f 29/3 Galileo (IRE)—Margot Did (IRE) (Exceed And Excel (AUS)) (716392)
92 MASANIVA (USA), b f 10/4 American Pharoah (USA)—Fiji Moon (USA) (Indian Charlie (USA)) **Haras d'Etreham**
93 B f 26/3 Wootton Bassett—Melilot (FR) (Elusive City (USA)) (63211) **H. Guy**
94 MOON DREAM (IRE), b c 16/4 Dream Ahead (USA)—Lune Rose (High Chaparral (IRE)) (58997) **Ecurie Vivaldi**
95 NEHOU (FR), b c 5/4 Rajsaman (FR)—Noce (FR) (Le Havre (IRE)) **G. Augustin-Normand**
96 Ch f 2/3 Declaration of War (USA)—Night Song (Oasis Dream) (50568) **A. Gilibert**
97 OCEAN SLEW (FR), b c 27/4 Galiway—Atlantic Slew (FR) (Helissio (FR)) (22756) **G. Pariente**
98 PISANELLO (IRE), b c 28/2 Raven's Pass (USA)—
Painting (Peintre Celebre (USA)) (50568) **Haras d'Etreham**
99 Ch c 30/4 Siyouni (FR)—Ponte Sanangelo (FR) (Authorized (IRE)) (46354) **H. Guy**
100 B c 6/3 Ivawood (IRE)—Quickstep Queen (Royal Applause) **F. J. Carmichael**
101 B c 11/3 Acclamation—Regina Mundi (IRE) (Montjeu (IRE)) (126422) **P. Nataf**
102 ROLLEVILLE (FR), ch f 5/4 Rock of Gibraltar (IRE)—Racemate (Hurricane Run (IRE)) **G. Augustin-Normand**
103 B c 30/3 Siyouni (FR)—Rumored (USA) (Royal Academy (USA)) (252844) **Al Shaqab Racing**
104 Gr c 26/4 Wootton Bassett—Sabloniere (FR) (Verglas (IRE)) (92709) **Ecurie J. L. Bouchard**
105 B f 17/3 Camelot—Sandy Light (IRE) (Footstepsinthesand) **D. Malingue**
106 B c 10/3 Outstrip—Sarvana (IRE) (Dubai Destination (USA)) (50568) **Ecurie J. L. Bouchard**
107 B f 2/2 Dabirsim (FR)—Simply Lady (FR) (Simplex (FR)) (11799) **Ecurie Normandie Pur Sang**
108 B c 18/4 Charm Spirit (IRE)—Ski Lift (Pivotal) (63211) **Al Shaqab Racing**
109 B f 5/3 Camacho—Song of Time (IRE) (Kheleyf (USA)) (109565) **G. Algranti**
110 B f 1/1 Muhaarar—Soudanaise (IRE) (Peintre Celebre (USA)) (25284) **Ecurie J. L. Bouchard**
111 SPEAK OF THE DEVIL (FR), b f 13/5 Wootton Bassett—Moranda (FR) (Indian Rocket) (52254) **R. Shaykhutdinov**
112 CH f 25/4 Siyouni (FR)—Special Gift (FR) (New Approach (IRE)) (185419) **Meridian International**
113 B c 9/2 Intello (GER)—Stumpy (Lawman (FR)) (71639) **A. Gilibert**
114 B c 10/3 Muhtathir—Suama (FR) (Monsun (GER)) **A. Gilibert**
115 B f 19/2 Olympic Glory (IRE)—Superstition (IRE) (Kutub (IRE)) (37926) **R. Simmons**
116 B f 13/5 Zoffany (IRE)—Sweet Dreams Baby (IRE) (Montjeu (IRE)) (25283) **A. Gilibert**
117 Ch c 13/2 No Nay Never (USA)—Via Lattea (IRE) (Teofilo (IRE)) (134850) **Al Shaqab Racing**
118 B f 13/3 Dark Angel (IRE)—Wonderous Light (IRE) (Montjeu (IRE)) (290000) **R. Shaykhutdinov**
119 ZADAR (FR), bl f 27/1 Wootton Bassett—Zanyeva (IRE) (Oasis Dream) **Riviera Equine**
120 B f 19/2 Lawman (FR)—Zardaka (IRE) (Zamindar (USA)) **San Paolo Agri Stud**

---

104 MS JANE CHAPPLE-HYAM, Newmarket
Postal: Rose Cottage, The Street, Dalham, Newmarket, Suffolk, CB8 8TF
Contacts: PHONE (01638) 500451 FAX (01638) 661335 MOBILE (07899) 000555
E-MAIL janechapplehyam@hotmail.co.uk / janechapplehyamracing@outlook.com

1 AMBIENT (IRE), 4, b g Born To Sea (IRE)—Undulant Way **Jane Chapple-Hyam & Essex Racing Club**
2 AMOURICE (IRE), 4, b f Authorized (IRE)—Amancaya (GER) **Jane Chapple-Hyam & Essex Racing Club**
3 CIRCUS COUTURE (IRE), 3, ch h Intikhab (USA)—Bois Joli (IRE) **Jane Chapple-Hyam & Bryan Hirst**
4 DALGARNO (IRE), 6, b h Sea The Stars (IRE)—Jakonda (USA) **Mrs F. J. Carmichael**
5 EHMAJ (JPN), 4, b c Empire Maker (USA)—Upward Spiral **Bryan Hirst & Jane Chapple-Hyam**
6 EXTRODINAIR, 4, b g Captain Gerrard (IRE)—Mindfulness **Jakes Family**
7 MOCHALOV, 4, b g Denounce—Awesome Asset **Ms J. F. Chapple-Hyam**
8 SCHINDLERS ARK (IRE), 5, gr g Exchange Rate (USA)—Sweet Science (USA) **Jane Chapple-Hyam**
9 STAMFORD RAFFLES, 6, b g Champs Elysees—Romantic Retreat **Jane Chapple-Hyam & Bryan Hirst**
10 SUZI'S CONNOISSEUR, 8, b g Art Connoisseur (IRE)—Suzi Spends (IRE) **Ms J. F. Chapple-Hyam**
11 UBER COOL (IRE), 5, b g Born To Sea (IRE)—My Uptown Girl **Fiona Carmichael & Jane Chapple-Hyam**
12 UNABATED (IRE), 5, b g Bated Breath—Elhareer (IRE) **Ms J. F. Chapple-Hyam**

THREE-YEAR-OLDS

13 BALTIC MOON (GER), b c Sea The Moon (GER)—Baltic Gift **Heike Bischoff**
14 BULLINGTON BOY (FR), b c Canford Cliffs (IRE)—Borgia Gold (IRE) **Mr Bryan Hirst**
15 CRAZY DAISY, b f Gregorian (IRE)—Darling Daisy **Mrs P. A. Scott-Dunn**
16 FLAUNT IT (IRE), b f Mukhadram—Labisa (IRE) **Mrs F. J. Carmichael**
17 LOVE SO DEEP (JPN), b f Deep Impact (JPN)—Soinlovewithyou (USA) **Swettenham Stud Australia**
18 MELBURNIAN, b g Hallucinate (USA)—Bedouin Bride (USA) **Jane Chapple-Hyam**
19 PUSHMI PULLYU (IRE), b f Roderic O'Connor (IRE)—Russian Rave **Mrs Jane Chapple-Hyam**
20 SLOWPOKE RODRIGUEZ (IRE), b g Fast Company (IRE)—
Spring Will Come (IRE) **Albc Ltd & Jane Chapple-Hyam**
21 SUNG CHOI BAO, b f Casamento (IRE)—Six Diamonds **B Hirst, J Chapple-Hyam, S Bryant**

MS JANE CHAPPLE-HYAM - Continued

TWO-YEAR-OLDS

22 B c 16/4 Bated Breath—Garden Row (IRE) (Invincible Spirit (IRE)) (46000) **Mr Gordon Li**
23 **LINCOLN BRIGHT (IRE),** b c 30/3 Lope de Vega (IRE)—Night Fairy (IRE) (Danehill (USA)) (60000) **Mr Gordon Li**
24 **MASTER ROCCO (IRE),** ch c 25/2 Dawn Approach (IRE)—
                                                    Mama Rocco (Shirocco (GER)) (25000) **Mrs A. Cantillon**
25 B c 4/3 War Command (USA)—Pianola (USA) (Arch (USA)) (22000) **Look Partnership**
26 B f 12/2 Lawman (FR)—Tell Mum (Marju (IRE)) (16000)
27 B c 14/4 Dylan Thomas (IRE)—Till Dawn (Kheleyf (USA)) (16856) **Abenakian Partnership**
28 Gr c 18/4 Mukhadram—Tipping Over (IRE) (Aussie Rules (USA)) (16856) **Tipping Over Partnership**

Other Owners: Albc Ltd, Ed Bishop, Simon Brewster, Amanda Brudenell, Miss S. Bryant, Essex Racing Club, Abi Harrison, Susannah Hawkes, Sandra Hughes, Mrs T. M. A. Jakes, Mr J. C. Jakes, David Keating, John Keegan, Anna Martin, Mr A. J. McCabe, Iain Nixon, Charles Peate, Mrs Joan Root, Mr Barry Root, Mr A. C. Timms, Mr Matthew Timms, Emma Youngman.

Assistant Trainer: Abigail Harrison.

Apprentice: Ray Dawson.

---

105 MR PETER CHAPPLE-HYAM, Newmarket
Postal: St Gatien Stables, All Saints Road, Newmarket, Suffolk, CB8 8HJ
Contacts: PHONE: (01638) 560827

1 **DEJA (FR),** 4, b c Youmzain (IRE)—Atarfe (IRE) **Phoenix Thoroughbred Limited**
2 **FIVETWOEIGHT,** 5, b h Kyllachy—Super Midge **Mr R. El Youssef**
3 **JUST BRILLIANT (IRE),** 4, b c Lope de Vega (IRE)—Mauresmo (IRE) **Mr P. Makin**
4 **MARTINENGO (IRE),** 4, b c Elusive Pimpernel (USA)—Albiatra (USA) **Eledy SRL**

THREE-YEAR-OLDS

5 **AL ANAAB (FR),** b f Style Vendome (FR)—Lucky For Me (USA)
6 **KVETUSCHKA,** gr ro f Mastercraftsman (IRE)—Signella **Woodcote Stud Ltd**
7 **MITHAYEL STYLE (FR),** b f Style Vendome (FR)—Tis Mighty (IRE)
8 **SH BOOM,** b f War Command (USA)—Nouvelle Lune **Mr J G Davis & Star Pointe Ltd**
9 **YOU LITTLE RIPPER (IRE),** b c Rip Van Winkle (IRE)—Sahara Sky (IRE) **Mr P. Makin**

Other Owners: J. G. Davis, Star Pointe Ltd.

---

106 MR ROGER CHARLTON, Beckhampton
Postal: Beckhampton House, Marlborough, Wiltshire, SN8 1QR
Contacts: OFFICE (01672) 539533 HOME (01672) 539330 FAX (01672) 539456
MOBILE (07710) 784511
E-MAIL office@beckhamptonstables.com WEBSITE www.rogercharlton.com

1 **ASPETAR (FR),** 4, b g Al Kazeem—Bella Qatara (IRE) **H.H. Sheikh Mohammed bin Khalifa Al-Thani**
2 **BLAKENEY POINT,** 6, b g Sir Percy—Cartoon **Axom**
3 **BLUE MIST,** 4, ch g Makfi—Namaskar **K. Abdullah**
4 **BREATHLESS TIMES,** 4, b g Bated Breath—Bea Menace (USA) **Sheikh Juma Dalmook Al Maktoum**
5 **EXTRA ELUSIVE,** 4, ch c Mastercraftsman (IRE)—Nessina (USA) **Blue Diamond Stud Farm (UK) Ltd**
6 **FORBIDDEN PLANET,** 4, b c Pivotal—Aiming **Kingwood Stud**
7 **GALILEO SILVER (IRE),** 4, gr g Galileo (IRE)—Famous (IRE) **Walters Plant Hire & James & Jean Potter**
8 **HERCULEAN,** 4, ch g Frankel—African Rose **K. Abdullah**
9 **LOGAN'S CHOICE,** 4, b g Redoute's Choice (AUS)—Bright Morning (USA) **Paul Hearson**
10 **MAKZEEM,** 6, b g Makfi—Kazeem **D. J. Deer**
11 **POLISH,** 4, b g Teofilo (IRE)—Polygon (USA) **Exors of The Late Lady Rothschild**
12 **PROJECTION,** 6, b g Acclamation—Spotlight **Royal Ascot Racing Club**
13 **SARACENE (IRE),** 4, ch f Dubawi (IRE)—Samba Brazil (GER) **H.H. Sheikh Mohammed bin Khalifa Al-Thani**
14 **SAVAANAH (IRE),** 4, b f Olden Times—Tanouma (USA) **Prince A. A. Faisal**
15 **TRUE DESTINY,** 4, ch g Mastercraftsman (IRE)—Holy Dazzle **H.R.H. Sultan Ahmad Shah**
16 **WITHHOLD,** 6, b g Champs Elysees—Coming Back **Tony Bloom**

MR ROGER CHARLTON - Continued

THREE-YEAR-OLDS

17 **BASILISK (USA)**, ch c Speightstown (USA)—Treat Gently **K. Abdullah**
18 **BLOWING DIXIE**, b g Dubawi (IRE)—Time Control **Merry Fox Stud**
19 **CAMBRIC**, ch f Australia—Poplin **D. J. Deer**
20 **CASUAL REPLY**, b f Frankel—Passing Parade **Merry Fox Stud**
21 **CHOP CHOP (IRE)**, b f Rip Van Winkle (IRE)—Mince **Exors of The Late Lady Rothschild**
22 **COCHISE**, b g Intello (GER)—Ship's Biscuit **Philip Newton**
23 **CREATIONIST (USA)**, b c Noble Mission—Bargain Blitz (USA) **Nick Bradley Racing 38 & Sohi**
24 **CRISTIELLE**, b f Australia—Nouriya **Blue Diamond Stud Farm (UK) Ltd**
25 **DOUBLY BEAUTIFUL (IRE)**, ch g Born To Sea (IRE)—Bella Bella (IRE) **Mr Paul Inglett**
26 **EXCELLENT MAGIC**, ch f Exceed And Excel (AUS)—Magic Nymph (IRE) **Sheikh Juma Dalmook Al Maktoum**
27 **FASHION'S STAR (IRE)**, ch f Sea The Stars (IRE)—Ninas Terz (GER) **Mr Andrew Rosen**
28 **FIELDS OF DREAMS**, b g Champs Elysees—Dylanesque **Mr Frank McAleavy**
29 **GREAT BEAR**, b c Dansili—Great Heavens **Kincorth Investments**
30 B f Cape Cross (IRE)—Habita (IRE) **D. J. Deer**
31 **HAWA BLADI (IRE)**, ch c Sea The Stars (IRE)—Gentle On My Mind (IRE) **Prince A. A. Faisal**
32 **HEADMAN**, b c Kingman—Deliberate **K. Abdullah**
33 **IL CAPITANO (FR)**, ch c Dawn Approach (IRE)—Manyara **Kingwood Stud**
34 **IMHOTEP**, b c Kingman—African Rose **K. Abdullah**
35 **IMPERIUM (IRE)**, ch c Frankel—Ramruma (USA) **Weston, Brook Farm & Bromfield**
36 **INFUSE (IRE)**, b f Lope de Vega (IRE)—Fusion (IRE) **The Duke of Roxburghe & William Wyatt**
37 **JUNIOR RIP (IRE)**, b g Rip Van Winkle (IRE)—Sarawati (IRE) **Nick Bradley Racing 19**
38 **LADY ADELAIDE (IRE)**, b f Australia—Confusion (FR) **Fishdance Ltd**
39 **LADY RASHA**, b c Dansili—Nessina (USA) **Blue Diamond Stud Farm (UK) Ltd**
40 **MIDPORT (IRE)**, b g Dabirsim (FR)—Monspa **Inglett & Hearson**
41 **MISTER MERLIN**, gr g Dark Angel (IRE)—Rosehill Artist (IRE) **Paul Inglett and Simon de Zoete**
42 **MOJAVE**, b c Dream Ahead (USA)—Desert Image **K. Abdullah**
43 **MOMKIN (IRE)**, b c Bated Breath—Contradict **Prince A. A. Faisal**
44 **MUBARIZ**, b c Dansili—Could It Be (IRE) **H.H. Sheikh Mohammed bin Khalifa Al-Thani**
45 **MYSTIQUESTAR (IRE)**, b f Sea The Stars (IRE)—Magique (IRE) **Yvonne Jacques**
46 **OLYMPIC FIGHTER (IRE)**, b g Teofilo (IRE)—Rosa Muscosa (USA) **Sheikh Juma Dalmook Al Maktoum**
47 **ORCHIDIA (IRE)**, ch f Bated Breath—New Orchid (USA) **Glentree Pastoral Pty Ltd**
48 **PENSEE**, b f Dansili—Fleur de Cactus (IRE) **H.H. Sheikh Mohammed bin Khalifa Al-Thani**
49 **QARASU (IRE)**, br c Le Havre (IRE)—Bella Qatara (IRE) **H.H. Sheikh Mohammed bin Khalifa Al-Thani**
50 **RED IMPRESSION**, gr f Dark Angel (IRE)—Purissima (USA) **K. Abdullah**
51 **ROYAL STAR (IRE)**, b f Sea The Stars (IRE)—Altesse Imperiale (IRE) **D. J. Deer**
52 **SAILING (GER)**, b f Lope de Vega (IRE)—Sail (IRE) **K. Abdullah**
53 **SHE'S APPLES (IRE)**, b f Redoute's Choice (AUS)—Steal The Show (NZ) **Bloomsbury Stud**
54 **SKYMAN**, b g Mukhadram—Skyrider (IRE) **Paul Inglett and Simon de Zoete**
55 **SO HI CARDI (IRE)**, b f So You Think (NZ)—Zongoraora (IRE) **Nick Bradley Racing 14**
56 **TAMACHAN**, b f Camelot—Marmalade Cat **A. E. Oppenheimer**
57 **TAVUS (IRE)**, b g Pour Moi (IRE)—La Persiana **Tony Bloom**
58 **TEMPUS**, b c Kingman—Passage of Time **K. Abdullah**
59 **THORN**, b g Dansili—Thistle Bird **Exors of The Late Lady Rothschild**
60 **TOTAL COMMITMENT (IRE)**, b c Exceed And Excel (AUS)—Crysdal **Brook Farm Bloodstock**
61 **WEST NEWTON**, b c Kitten's Joy (USA)—Queen's Prize **Her Majesty The Queen**
62 **WILD CAT**, ch f Nathaniel (IRE)—Desert Tigress (USA) **Kincorth Investments**
63 **YIMKIN (IRE)**, b f Kingman—Orpha **Prince A. A. Faisal**
64 **YOUNG MERLIN (IRE)**, b g Camelot—Zelloof (IRE) **Daniel MacAuliffe & Anoj Don**

TWO-YEAR-OLDS

65 B c 1/3 Sea The Moon (GER)—All Hallows (IRE) (Dalakhani (IRE)) (71639) **Paul & Clare Rooney**
66 B c 11/4 Le Havre (IRE)—Aspire (IRE) (Authorized (IRE)) **Paul & Clare Rooney**
67 B f 13/3 Footstepsinthesand—Bella Qatara (IRE) (Dansili) **H.H. Sheikh Mohammed bin Khalifa Al-Thani**
68 B c 2/4 Helmet (AUS)—Blue Butterfly (Kyllachy) (85000) **Beckhampton Racing**
69 B f 9/4 Dawn Approach (IRE)—Bristol Fashion (Dansili) **N. Bradley Racing**
70 **BULLFINCH**, b c 18/2 Kodiac—Thistle Bird (Selkirk (USA)) **Exors of The Late Lady Rothschild**
71 **CHOREOGRAPH**, b c 25/1 Dansili—Across The Floor (Oasis Dream) **K. Abdullah**
72 **CODE OF CONDUCT**, b c 10/4 Siyouni (FR)—Sequence (IRE) (Selkirk (USA)) **Her Majesty The Queen**
73 **COLONEL MORDAUNT (IRE)**, b c 28/2 Zoffany (IRE)—Temptress (IRE) (Shirocco (GER)) **A. Bengough, M. Hammond**
74 **CONSCIOUS**, b c 11/5 Oasis Dream—Deliberate (King's Best) **K. Abdullah**
75 B c 3/3 Dansili—Could It Be (IRE) (Galileo (IRE)) **H.H. Sheikh Mohammed bin Khalifa Al-Thani**
76 **DANCING APPROACH**, b c 14/3 Camelot—Dream Approach (IRE) (New Approach) **Fishdance Ltd**
77 **DANCING HARRY (IRE)**, b c 9/2 Camelot—Poisson d'or (Cape Cross) **Fishdance Ltd**
78 Gr f 18/2 Due Diligence (USA)—Dolly Colman (IRE) (Diamond Green (FR)) **Hot To Trot**

MR ROGER CHARLTON - Continued

79 **EVENING SUN,** b c 24/3 Muhaarar—Fiery Sunset (Galileo (IRE)) **Her Majesty The Queen**
80 B c 2/3 Invincible Spirit (IRE)—Ferevia (IRE) (Motivator) **H. H. Sheikh Mohammed bin Khalifa Al-Thani**
81 B c 28/4 Dubawi (IRE)—Flotilla (FR) (Mizzen Mast (USA)) **H.H. Sheikh Mohammed bin Khalifa Al-Thani**
82 B f 27/1 Gleneagles (IRE)—Fondly (IRE) (Dansili) (30000) **Mildmay Racing & D. H. Caslon**
83 **GRIMSTHORPE CASTLE,** b c 13/2 Dawn Approach (IRE)—
                        Willoughby (IRE) (Oasis Dream) **Exors Of The Late Lady Rothschild**
84 Ch c 17/2 Pivotal—Hala Hala (IRE) (Invincible Spirit (IRE)) (40033) **Brook Farm Bloodstock**
85 B f 5/3 Gleneagles (IRE)—Happy Holly (IRE) (Holy Roman Emperor (IRE)) **Hunscote Stud**
86 **HARVEST HOME,** b c 9/4 Zoffany (IRE)—
                        Harvest Queen (IRE) (Spinning World (USA)) **Exors Of The Late Lady Rothschild**
87 **HEXAGON (IRE),** b c 28/2 Acclamation—Somerset Falls (UAE) (Red Ransom (USA)) (75000) **Owners Group**
88 **IBIZA,** b f 21/2 Sepoy (AUS)—Hi Calypso (IRE) (In The Wings) **Philip Newton**
89 B f 5/2 Sepoy (AUS)—It's My Time (Green Desert (USA)) (46000) **Dr Jamal Ahmadzadeh**
90 **ITS A GIVEN,** ch f 31/1 Bated Breath—Emergency (Dr Fong (USA)) **K. Abdullah**
91 **IVADREAM,** b c 24/3 Ivawood (IRE)—Midnight Fling (Groom Dancer (USA)) **S. Emmett**
92 **MAURIMO,** b f 8/3 Kingman—Lynnwood Chase (USA) (Horse Chestnut (SAF)) **Beaufort Syndicate**
93 **MOSEY (IRE),** ch f 17/4 Dream Ahead (USA)—Mince (Medicean) **Exors Of The Late Lady Rothschild**
94 **NIGHT RANGER,** br c 16/2 Dansili—Sleep Walk (Oasis Dream) **K. Abdullah**
95 B f 5/4 Al Kazeem—Perfect Practice (Medicean) (25000) **Dr Bridget Drew & D H Caslon**
96 **POCKET SQUARE,** ch f 14/2 Night of Thunder (IRE)—Shared Account (Dansili) **K. Abdullah**
97 Ch c 27/2 Zoffany—Princess Loulou (IRE) (Pivotal) (80000) **Blue Diamond Stud Farm (UK) Ltd**
98 B f 17/4 Poet's Voice—Random Success (IRE) (Shamardal) (1904) **Beckhampton / Inglett**
99 B f 30/4 War Front (USA)—Royal Decree (USA) (Street Cry (IRE)) (385000) **Mr Andrew Rosen**
100 **SCHMOOZIE (IRE),** b f 1/3 Zoffany—Steal The Show (NZ) (High Chaparral (IRE)) **Bloomsbury Stud**
101 **SELECTO,** b c 26/3 Paco Boy (IRE)—Telescopic (Galileo (IRE)) **Daniel Hunt**
102 Gr f 24/2 Bated Breath—Serenity Spa (Excellent Art) **Seasons Holidays**
103 B c 21/2 Kodiac—Shamankiyna (FR) (Azamour (IRE)) (70000) **de Zoete, Inglett and Jones**
104 **SUN BEAR,** b f 17/4 Dubawi (IRE)—Great Heavens (Galileo (IRE)) **Exors Of The Late Lady Rothschild**
105 **TACITLY,** b f 22/2 Dubawi (IRE)—Timepiece (Zamindar (USA)) **K. Abdullah**
106 B f 9/3 Cable Bay (IRE)—Triton Dance (IRE) (Hector Protector (USA)) (55000) **Axom**
107 B c 16/2 Mukhadram—Victory Garden (New Approach (IRE)) (22000) **Dr Jamal Ahmadzadeh**
108 Gr c 30/1 Mastercraftsman (IRE)—Woodland Scene (IRE) (Act One) (90000) **Blue Diamond Stud Farm (UK) Ltd**

Assistant Trainer: Harry Charlton. **Pupil Assistant:** Ben James

Jockey (flat): Jason Watson, Adam McNamara.

---

107 **MR HARRY CHISMAN, Stow-on-the-Wold**
Postal: **25 Coachmans Court, Station Road, Moreton-In-Marsh, Gloucestershire, GL56 0DE**
Contacts: **PHONE (07787) 516723**
WEBSITE www.harrychisman.co.uk

1 **ALL RILED UP,** 11, b m Dr Massini (IRE)—Martha Reilly (IRE) **P Baker D Wood M Flint D Welch**
2 **FOYLESIDEVIEW (IRE),** 7, b g Dark Angel (IRE)—Showerproof **P Baker W Summers**
3 **ITSUPFORGRABSNOW (IRE),** 4, b f Footstepsinthesand—Rye Rhythm (IRE) **Mr T. Gaden**
4 **LEGENDOIRE (IRE),** 5, b g Fast Company (IRE)—Last Shaambles (IRE) **Steven Kirkland David Welch**

Other Owners: Mr P. M. Baker, Mr Harry Chisman, Mr Michael Flint, Mr S. Kirkland, Miss W. Summers, Mr D. Welch, Mr Duncan Wood.

Assistant Trainer: G. Charles-Jones

---

108 **MR NICOLAS CLEMENT, Chantilly**
Postal: **37, Avenue de Joinville, 60500 Chantilly, France**
Contacts: **PHONE (0033) 3445 75960 MOBILE (0033) 6072 34640**
E-MAIL office@nicolasclement.com WEBSITE www.nicolasclement.com

1 **L'AMI PIERROT,** 4, b br g Invincible Spirit (IRE)—Green Swallow (FR)
2 **LOUTRO,** 4, b g Leroidesanimaux (BRZ)—Air Kiss
3 **NOW WE CAN,** 10, b g Martillo (GER)—Notre Dame (GER)
4 **RISE AND DINE (FR),** 4, gr g Authorized (IRE)—Here She Comes (FR)
5 **SEXYFISH (FR),** 4, b g Authorized (IRE)—Honorable Love
6 **TRAWANGANE (FR),** 5, ch m Dutch Art—On The Line (FR)

MR NICOLAS CLEMENT - Continued

THREE-YEAR-OLDS

7 **ABABEEL (FR)**, b f Dansili—Light Up My Life (IRE)
8 **ADELINE (IRE)**, b f War Command (USA)—Madhulika (FR)
9 **ARIKI**, gr f Dark Angel (IRE)—Steer By The Stars (IRE)
10 **AT PEACE (IRE)**, b f Australia—Cherrington (IRE)
11 **BOPEDRO (FR)**, b c Pedro The Great (USA)—Breizh Touch (FR)
12 **BRAINEY BAXTER (USA)**, b f Lemon Drop Kid (USA)—Tustarta (USA)
13 **CALA VIOLINA (FR)**, b f Lope de Vega (IRE)—Aigue Marine
14 **CAPE GENTLEMAN (IRE)**, ch g Champs Elysees—Hawaiian Heat (IRE)
15 **CELESTISSIME (FR)**, b f Camelot—Keegsquaw (IRE)
16 **COME BACK TO ME (IRE)**, ch f Zoffany (IRE)—Serengeti Day (USA)
17 **CONFETTI (FR)**, b c Myboycharlie (IRE)—You Or No One (IRE)
18 **COPACABANA ROSE (FR)**, ch f Lope de Vega (IRE)—Miss Cato
19 **DANS LA LUNE (FR)**, b f Le Havre (IRE)—Wevanella (FR)
20 **GO LADY (GER)**, b f Soldier Hollow—Gondola (FR)
21 **GOLDEN IBIS (FR)**, b f Medaglia d'oro (USA)—Emerald Star
22 **HERE COMES SUMMER (FR)**, b c Sommerabend—Mahyara (FR)
23 **HINEMOA (FR)**, ch f Tamayuz—Leah Claire (IRE)
24 **KIWIANA**, b f Kodiac—Redskin Dancer (IRE)
25 **MAECENAS (FR)**, b c Motivator—Masaya (SWI)
26 **MENTHE PASTILLE (FR)**, b f Style Vendome (FR)—Age of Refinement (IRE)
27 **MICHELE DEL GRECO (IRE)**, gr c Reliable Man—Mirabile Dictu (IRE)
28 **MISS ME (GER)**, b f Footstepsinthesand—Miss Lady (GER)
29 **NATIONAL INTEREST (FR)**, b c Muhtathir—Neumark (GER)
30 **NORTHSHORE (FR)**, ch c Australia—Reine des Plages (IRE)
31 B c Lope de Vega (IRE)—Pearly Avenue
32 **PERONNE (FR)**, b c Vespone—Porza (FR)
33 **PLACE PASDELOUP (FR)**, b f Motivator—Statia (FR)
34 **POETIC DIVA (FR)**, b f Poet's Voice—Academic Angel (USA)
35 **PUISQUE (FR)**, b c Tin Horse—Lestia (FR)
36 **REINE DE VITESSE (FR)**, b f Wootton Bassett—Vitesse Superieure
37 **RELIABLE SON (FR)**, b c Reliable Man—Hot Fudge (SWE)
38 **SINGING TOWER (FR)**, ch f Siyouni (FR)—La Tour Rouge
39 **SO UNIQUE (FR)**, ch f Siyouni (FR)—Trully Blessed (FR)
40 **SPEEDEVA (FR)**, b f Evasive—Tangaspeed (FR)
41 **STACCATO (IRE)**, ch f Raven's Pass (USA)—Snake Dancer (IRE)
42 **URSUS ARCTOS (IRE)**, b c Kodiac—Bikini Babe (IRE)
43 **VANILLA GOLD (IRE)**, b f No Nay Never (USA)—Miss Childrey (IRE)
44 **WONDERMENT (IRE)**, b f Camelot—Wiwilia

TWO-YEAR-OLDS

45 B f 21/3 Oasis Dream—Aigue Marine (Galileo (IRE)) (193847)
46 Ch c 7/3 Lope de Vega (IRE)—Alkania (Dalakhani (IRE)) (71639)
47 B f 25/2 Style Vendome (FR)—Almaardiyah (IRE) (High Chaparral (IRE))
48 **AMBRE (FR)**, b f 12/2 Dabirsim (FR)—Teoris (IRE) (Bachelor Duke (USA)) (53940)
49 B f 3/1 Kodiac—Cabaret (IRE) (Galileo (IRE)) (80067)
50 B c 3/3 Olympic Glory (IRE)—Cheam Ksah (IRE) (Hurricane Run (IRE)) (29498)
51 B f 27/1 Intello (GER)—Colonialiste (IRE) (Lord of England (GER)) (63211)
52 B f 22/4 Soldier Hollow—Douala (Dubawi (IRE)) (36241)
53 **HAVANA BOUND**, ch f 20/4 Havana Gold (IRE)—Exceedingly Rare (IRE) (Lope de Vega (IRE)) (88495)
54 B f 20/1 Intello (GER)—La Pedrera (IRE) (Danehill Dancer (IRE)) (35398)
55 B f 6/4 Youmzain (IRE)—La Tour Rouge (Monsun (GER))
56 B f 26/1 Dark Angel (IRE)—Lady Tiana (Sir Percy) (147492)
57 B c 7/3 Sea The Moon (GER)—Neumark (GER) (High Chaparral (IRE))
58 B f 28/3 Gleneagles (IRE)—Nuit Polaire (FR) (Kheleyf (USA)) (337126)
59 B f 14/4 Wootton Bassett—On The Line (FR) (Green Tune (USA)) (67425)
60 B f 16/4 Thewayyouare (USA)—Ormita (GER) (Acatenango (GER)) (10113)
61 Ch f 13/2 Sea The Stars (IRE)—Padmini (Tiger Hill (IRE)) (100000)
62 **PRIVATE ROMANCE (IRE)**, ch f 21/3 Siyouni (FR)—Private Eye (FR) (American Post)
63 Ch c 3/4 Makfi—Sapfo (FR) (Peintre Celebre (USA)) (22756)

Jockey (flat): Sebastien Maillot, Stephane Pasquier. **Apprentice:** Laura Grosso, Alexandre Lecocq, Thomas Truillier.

109 MR TOM CLOVER, Newmarket

Postal: **Saville House Stables, St Mary's Square, Newmarket, Suffolk, CB8 0HZ**
Contacts: **PHONE (07795) 834960 (01638) 660055**
E-MAIL thomaspwclover@gmail.com WEBSITE www.tomcloverracing.com

1 **BALGAIR**, 5, ch g Foxwedge (AUS)—Glencal **Exors of the Late Mr J. T. Habershon-Butcher**
2 **CASTLE TALBOT (IRE)**, 7, b g Rock of Gibraltar (IRE)—Louve Sacree (USA) **Mrs J. I. Clover**
3 **CHEER THE TITLE (IRE)**, 4, b g Acclamation—Galistic (IRE) **D Proos & F H Lee**
4 **DARING GUEST (IRE)**, 5, b g Fast Company (IRE)—Balm **Mrs G. A. S. Jarvis**
5 **GO FOX**, 4, ch g Foxwedge (AUS)—Bling Bling (IRE) **R & S Marchant, C Holmes & G Jarvis**
6 **HUNNI**, 4, b f Captain Gerrard (IRE)—Lady O Malley (IRE) **The Hunni Partnership**
7 **LE MAHARAJAH (FR)**, 4, b g Cacique (IRE)—Sign of Life **Mr Raj Matharu & Egerton House Racing**
8 **ONE FINE MORNING**, 13, ch g Generous (IRE)—Flagship Princess (IRE) **Mr C. Clover**
9 **PHEIDIPPIDES**, 4, ch g Sepoy (AUS)—Bounty Box **Dr O. Rangabashyam**
10 **PIVELLO**, 4, ch g Intello (GER)—Pivotting **The Pivello Partnership**
11 **VIENTO DE CONDOR (IRE)**, 4, b g Dragon Pulse (IRE)—Polska (USA) **Dr O. Rangabashyam**

THREE-YEAR-OLDS

12 **AZTEC LADY (IRE)**, b f Magician (IRE)—Fierce Fawn (USA) **The Rogues Gallery Two**
13 **BROUGHTONS RUBY**, b f Harbour Watch (IRE)—Broughtons Jewel (IRE) **Broughton Thermal Insulations**
14 **BROUGHTONS VIEW**, ch g Harbour Watch (IRE)—Sunpearl **Broughton Thermal Insulations**
15 **CELSIUS (IRE)**, ch c Dragon Pulse (IRE)—Grecian Artisan (IRE) **J. Collins, C. Fahy & S. Piper**
16 **CHARACTERISTIC (IRE)**, ch g Casamento (IRE)—Stunned Silence (USA) **H Moorhead, C Fahy & J Collins**
17 **CHENG GONG**, b g Archipenko (USA)—Kinetica **R & S Marchant, D Fawdon & G Jarvis**
18 **CRIMEWAVE (IRE)**, b g Teofilo (IRE)—Crossover **The Rogues Gallery Two**
19 **DAWN AFFAIR**, b f Dawn Approach (IRE)—Dubai Affair **Bearstone Stud Limited**
20 **ESTRANGED (IRE)**, b f Morpheus—Compton Girl **Mrs Z. Wentworth**
21 **GYPSY SPIRIT**, b f Gregorian (IRE)—Romany Gypsy **The Gypsy Spirit Partnership**
22 **HANBURY DREAMS**, b f Heeraat (IRE)—Lady O Malley (IRE) **B Keane & S Nugent**
23 **HOLY KINGDOM (IRE)**, gr c Australia—Cable (USA) **The Rogues Gallery Two**
24 **MOHOGANY**, b g Foxwedge (AUS)—Jadeamie **The Rogues Gallery Two**
25 **MONSIEUR LAMBRAYS**, b g Champs Elysees—
Windermere Island **Exors of the Late Mr J. T. Habershon-Butcher**
26 **PLISSKEN**, b f Bated Breath—Blast Furnace (IRE) **Chasemore Farm LLP**
27 **RAJMAN**, ch c Zoffany (IRE)—Mutheera **Mr R. S. Matharu**
28 **RECONNAISSANCE**, b g Lope de Vega (IRE)—Victrix Ludorum (USA) **K. A. Dasmal**
29 **TRU GRIT (IRE)**, b g Acclamation—Qalahari (IRE) **The Rogues Gallery Two**
30 **TULLOONA**, b g Coach House (IRE)—Minnola **Mr C. F. E. Hill**

TWO-YEAR-OLDS

31 **AFRA KADABRA (IRE)**, b c 15/3 Australia—Allegrezza (Sir Percy) (30000) **K. A. Dasmal**
32 **ALIANNE**, b f 15/1 Worthadd (IRE)—Alboretta (Hernando (FR)) **Miss K. Rausing**
33 B c 5/4 Casamento (IRE)—Craighall (Dubawi (IRE)) (6000)
34 **EAGLESGLEN**, b c 6/4 Gleneagles (IRE)—Coquet (Sir Percy) (42000) **The Rogues Gallery Two**
35 B f 3/3 Dream Ahead (USA)—Grandmas Dream (Kyllachy) (6500) **The Shimplingthorne Syndicate**
36 Gr c 2/5 Henrythenavigator (USA)—Jillolini (Bertolini (USA)) (10476) **Mr J. Sumsion**
37 **ORLAGH**, b f 24/3 Fountain of Youth (IRE)—
Big Sky (Fastnet Rock (AUS)) (14285) **K Fischer, P Green & K Hughes**
38 **QAF**, b c 15/1 Brazen Beau (AUS)—Camelopardalis (Tobougg (IRE)) (19000) **Ben Spiers & Adam Signy**
39 **RAJAN**, b c 13/2 Fountain of Youth (IRE)—
Dayville (USA) (Dayjur (USA)) (24761) **Raj Matharu & Suresh Sivagnanam**
40 **RAJGURU**, ch c 15/4 Dutch Art—Gakalina (IRE) (Galileo (IRE)) (11000) **Mr R. S. Matharu**
41 B c 19/2 Pivotal—Superior Charm (USA) (Elusive Quality (USA)) (45000) **Mr A. A. Albuainain**

Other Owners: Mr T. P. Clover, Mr J. A. Collins, Mr A. R. Elliott, Mr C. J. Fahy, Mr D. Fawdon, Mrs S. Hamilton, Mr A. M. H. Heald, M. G. H. Heald, Mrs M. E. Holdcroft, Mr C. R. Holmes, Mrs A. H. Jordan, Mr B. A. Keane, Mr F. H. Lee, Mr S. Marchant, Mr R. P. Marchant, Mr S. Nugent, Mr S. J. Piper, D. M. Proos, Mr A. Signy, Mr S. Sivagnanam, Mr B. P. J. Spiers.

110 **MR DENIS COAKLEY, West Ilsley**
Postal: Keeper's Stables, West Ilsley, Newbury, Berkshire, RG20 7AH
Contacts: **PHONE** (01635) 281622 **MOBILE** (07768) 658056
E-MAIL racing@deniscoakley.com **WEBSITE** www.deniscoakley.com

1 BRILLIANT RIPOSTE, 4, b g Rip Van Winkle (IRE)—Waldena (USA) **Mrs B. Coakley**
2 DESSIE'S DIAMOND (IRE), 5, b g Dubai Destination (USA)—Diamond Katie (IRE) **Mr T. A. Killoran**
3 ELECTRIC LANDLADY (IRE), 4, b f Red Jazz (USA)—Margie (IRE) **PMC Syndicate**
4 GIVEPEACEACHANCE, 4, b f Declaration of War (USA)—Mount Crystal (IRE) **Chris van Hoorn Racing**
5 HORS DE COMBAT, 8, ch g Mount Nelson—Maid For Winning (USA) **Chris van Hoorn Racing**
6 KEEPER'S CHOICE (IRE), 5, ch m Intikhab (USA)—Crossing **Keeper's 12**
7 KING CALYPSO, 8, ch g Sir Percy—Rosa de Mi Corazon (USA)
8 LILY OF YEAR (FR), 4, b f Siyouni (FR)—Arpagone (FR) **Mr J. G. Mountford**
9 POWER HOME (IRE), 5, ch m Power—Ascendancy **Poachers' Dozen**
10 SAUMUR, 7, b m Mawatheeq (USA)—Sparkling Montjeu (IRE) **Sparkling Partners**
11 SHEILA'S ROCK (IRE), 5, b m Fastnet Rock (AUS)—Crystal Curling (IRE) **R. J. Styles**
12 STAFFA (IRE), 6, b m Rock of Gibraltar (IRE)—Gabriellina Klon (IRE) **Mrs B. Coakley**
13 SWEET CHARITY, 4, b f Mount Nelson—Fanny May **Chris van Hoorn Racing**
14 TIAR NA NOG (IRE), 7, b m Ask—Carmencita **Mrs U. M. Loughrey**
15 VANITY VANITY (USA), 4, ch f Kitten's Joy (USA)—Blue Grass Music (USA) **Chris van Hoorn Racing**

THREE-YEAR-OLDS

16 BARTIMAEUS (IRE), b g Nathaniel (IRE)—Zora Seas (IRE) **West Ilsley Racing**
17 ROCKSTAR MAX (GER), b g Maxios—Remote Romance (USA) **Melbourne 10 Racing**
18 SARI MAREIS, b f Toronado (IRE)—Fanny May **Chris van Hoorn Racing**
19 SHEILA'S SHOWCASE, b c Showcasing—Loreto Rose **R. J. Styles**
20 SONNETINA, b f Poet's Voice—Tebee's Oasis **The Good Mixers**
21 STAR COMMAND (IRE), b f War Command (USA)—Megaspiel **Bramble Syndicate**
22 B g Swiss Spirit—Velma Kelly **R. J. Styles**

TWO-YEAR-OLDS

23 MY SHEILA (IRE), b f 10/1 Australia—Dorothy B (IRE) (Fastnet Rock (AUS)) (40000) **R. J. Styles**
24 Ch f 24/4 Dawn Approach (IRE)—Sacred Aspect (IRE) (Haatef (USA)) (20000) **Sparkling Partners**
25 B f 20/3 Cable Bay (IRE)—Tamara Moon (IRE) (Acclamation) (5714)

Other Owners: Mr R. J. Barnes, Mrs C. J. Barratt, Mr I. J. Barratt, Mr A. P. Bloor, R. J. Bolam, J. C. Kerr, Mr P. G. A. MacKenzie-Charrington, J. G. Ross, Miss A. D. Swift, Mr C. T. van Hoorn.

111 **MR PAUL COLE, Whatcombe**
Postal: Whatcombe Estate, Whatcombe, Wantage, Oxfordshire, OX12 9NW
Contacts: **PHONE** (01488) 638433 **FAX** (01488) 638609
E-MAIL admin@paulcole.co.uk **WEBSITE** www.paulcole.co.uk

1 ARCTIC SEA, 5, b br g Oasis Dream—Rainbow Dancing **P. F. I. Cole Ltd**
2 BARON BOLT, 6, br g Kheleyf (USA)—Scarlet Royal **Asprey Wright Asprey Pjl Wilcock & Snook**
3 MEDIEVAL (IRE), 5, b g Kodiac—Quickstyx **Mrs F. H. Hay**
4 PLUNGER, 4, ch g Helmet (AUS)—Percolator **A. H. Robinson**
5 ROTHERWICK BANNER, 7, ch g Starspangledbanner (AUS)—Pivotalia (IRE) **P. F. I. Cole Ltd**
6 ZORAYA (FR), 4, b f Zoffany (IRE)—Aztec Queen **The Fairy Story Partnership**

THREE-YEAR-OLDS

7 ARISTOMACHOS (IRE), b c War Command (USA)—Carolines Secret **C. Shiacolas**
8 CELTIC CLASSIC (IRE), b g Cacique (IRE)—Dabtiyra (IRE) **Evans Wright Asprey Pjl Snook & Wilcock**
9 COOL REFLECTION (IRE), b c Showcasing—Miss Lacey (IRE) **Mrs F. H. Hay**
10 DUKE OF HAZZARD (FR), b c Lope de Vega (IRE)—With Your Spirit (FR) **P. F. I. Cole Ltd**
11 HAZE, b f Oasis Dream—Dorelia (IRE) **Denford Stud Limited**
12 HIGH COMMISSIONER (IRE), ch c Australia—Winesong (IRE) **Mrs F. H. Hay**
13 LI KUI, br c Poet's Voice—Lily Again **Hurun Racing**
14 MAJESTIC DAWN (IRE), ch c Dawn Approach (IRE)—Jolie Chanson (FR) **Green & Norman**
15 MERCENARY ROSE (IRE), b f Sepoy (AUS)—Hulcote Rose (IRE) **Mr F. P. Stella**
16 NGUNI, ch f Mount Nelson—Flashbang **A. H. Robinson**
17 OLIVER HARDY, b c Foxwedge (AUS)—Astrantia **Chelsea Thoroughbreds Mrs Sophie Magnier**
18 PARISH POET (IRE), ch f Lope de Vega (IRE)—Tinaheely (IRE) **Mr F. P. Stella**

MR PAUL COLE - Continued

19 **PHYSICS (IRE),** b c Acclamation—Precipitous (IRE) **Mrs F. H. Hay**
20 **PTARMIGAN,** gr f Mastercraftsman (IRE)—Arabescatta **Denford Stud Limited**
21 **RIVER DAWN,** ch c Dawn Approach (IRE)—Echo River (USA) **Mrs F. H. Hay**
22 **SASSOON,** ch c Poet's Voice—Seradim **The Fairy Story Partnership**
23 **SHATTERING (IRE),** b g Zoffany (IRE)—Lexy May (USA) **P. F. I. Cole Ltd**
24 **SHIR KHAN,** ch c Leroidesanimaux (BRZ)—Sterling Sound (USA) **Arbib, Robinson & Cole**
25 **SO STRICTLY,** b c So You Think (NZ)—Salsa Steps (IRE) **Ben & Sir Martyn Arbib**

TWO-YEAR-OLDS

26 **ATLANTIC CROSSING (IRE),** b c 10/2 Mukhadram—
　　　　　　Ghizlaan (USA) (Seeking The Gold (USA)) (55000) **Christopher Wright & David Kilburn**
27 B c 12/3 New Approach (IRE)—Harlem Dancer (Dr Devious (IRE)) (45000) **C. Shiacolas**
28 Ch c 17/2 Mastercraftsman (IRE)—Irish Song (FR) (Singspiel (IRE)) (37926) **Mrs F. H. Hay**
29 **MASTER SPY (IRE),** gr c 20/4 Mastercraftsman (IRE)—
　　　　　　Stealth Bolt (USA) (Stormy Atlantic (USA)) (21069) **Arbib, Robinson & Cole**
30 B c 31/3 War Command (USA)—Newyearresolution (USA) (Arch (USA)) (5000) **P. F. I. Cole Ltd**
31 B f 25/3 Kingman—Pink Damsel (IRE) (Galileo (IRE)) **Mrs F. H. Hay**
32 B c 17/4 Gleneagles (IRE)—Pink Symphony (Montjeu (IRE)) **Mrs F. H. Hay**
33 B c 1/4 Heeraat (IRE)—Radio Gaga (Multiplex) (20000) **P. F. I. Cole Ltd**
34 B c 11/5 War Command (USA)—Rochitta (USA) (Arch (USA)) (45000)
35 B c 5/3 Mukhadram—Springlike (IRE) (Acclamation) (58000) **Asprey Wright Evans Pjl Wilcock & Snook**
36 **STERLING STAMP (IRE),** b c 7/3 Teofilo (IRE)—Aneedah (IRE) (Invincible Spirit (IRE)) (6000)

Other Owners: Mr B. G. Arbib, M. Arbib, Miss Emily Charlotte Asprey, Mr G. Baker, Mrs C. E. S. Baker, T. M. Bird, Chelsea Thoroughbreds Ltd, Mr P. F. I. Cole, Sir C Evans, E. R. Goodwin, Mrs J. Green, D. Kilburn, Mrs S. C. Magnier, Mr C. S. Norman, Miss C. S. Scott-Balls, Mrs V. M. Snook, Mr N. Wilcock, Mr C. N. Wright.

Assistant Trainer: Oliver Cole

---

112 **MR PAUL COLLINS, Saltburn-By-The-Sea**
Postal: **1 Longthwaite Close, Skelton-In-Cleveland, Saltburn-By-The-Sea, Cleveland, TS12 2WP**
Contacts: **MOBILE (07779) 794684**

1 **DICA (FR),** 13, ch g Kapgarde (FR)—Easy World (FR) **Mr P. Collins**
2 **GIFT IN TIME (IRE),** 4, b g Society Rock (IRE)—Gift of Time **Mr P. Collins**
3 **SOLID STRIKE,** 11, b g Sir Harry Lewis (USA)—Solid Land (FR) **Mr P. Collins**

THREE-YEAR-OLDS

4 **SAOIRSE ROSE,** b f Monsieur Bond (IRE)—Mad Jazz **Mr P. Collins**

---

113 **MR STUART COLTHERD, Selkirk**
Postal: **Clarilawmuir Farm, Selkirk, Selkirkshire, TD7 4QA**
Contacts: **PHONE (01750) 21251 FAX (01750) 21251 MOBILE (07801) 398199**
E-MAIL wscoltherd@gmail.com

1 **ACHILL ROAD BOY (IRE),** 10, b g Morozov (USA)—
　　　　　　Presenting Katie (IRE) **Farming Army Newitt Flannigan Findlater**
2 **ASH PARK (IRE),** 11, b g Milan—Distant Gale (IRE) **Coltherd McDougal**
3 **AVONDHU PEARL (IRE),** 8, ch m Beneficial—Ballinapierce Lady (IRE) **Jeffrey Hall Martino Mitchell Cawkwell**
4 **BUDARRI,** 6, b g Supreme Sound—Amtaar **Cruikshank Coltherd**
5 **CAPTAIN REDBEARD (IRE),** 10, b g Bach (IRE)—Diesel Dancer (IRE) **W. S. Coltherd**
6 **CASIMIR DU CLOS (FR),** 7, b g Blue Bresil (FR)—
　　　　　　Cyrienne du Maine (FR) **Newitt Flannigan Scott Gillie Swinton**
7 **CHANCEANOTHERFIVE (IRE),** 7, b g Dubai Destination (USA)—Ryhall (IRE) **Mr R. McCulloch**
8 **FAIRLEE GRACE,** 8, b m Fair Mix (IRE)—Halo Flora **J. L. Gledson**
9 **FELIX MENDELSSOHN (IRE),** 8, b g Galileo (IRE)—Ice Queen (IRE) **Shire Dreamers**
10 **GET HELP (IRE),** 6, b g Gold Well—Present Abbey (IRE)
11 **GRAYSTOWN (IRE),** 7, b g Well Chosen—Temple Girl (IRE) **The Farming Army**
12 **LEONASISLAND (IRE),** 7, b g Trans Island—Ashanti Dancer (IRE) **Shiel Rutherford**
13 **MRS VONN (IRE),** 7, b m Scorpion (IRE)—Mrs Ritchie **Mercer Campbell Stanners**

MR STUART COLTHERD - Continued

14 **POOKIE PEKAN (IRE)**, 6, b g Putra Pekan—Shii-Take's Girl **W. S. Coltherd**
15 **WARENDORF (FR)**, 6, b g Speedmaster (GER)—Hyllisia (FR) **Howard Coltherd Flannigan Newitt**

Other Owners: Mr D. T. Campbell, Mr S. F. Cawkwell, Mr N. J. Cruikshank, Mrs G. De Martino, Mr G. Findlater, Mr R. Flannigan, Mr I. R. Flannigan, Mr E. Gillie, Mr D. A. Gray, Mr I. Hall, Mr G. P. Howard, J. B. Jeffrey, Mr M. G. M. MacDonald, Mr G. McDougal, Mr K. Mercer, Mr I. A. J. Mitchell, Mrs S. C. Newitt, Mr D. Reive, Mrs D. Rutherford, Mr M. J. Scott, Mr S. Shiel, Mrs J. Shiel, Mr S. A. Shiel, Mr M. Stanners, Mr S. Swinton.

Conditional: Sam Coltherd.

---

114 | **MR SEAN CONWAY, Lutterworth**
Postal: **Home Farm, Shawell Lane, Cotesbach, Lutterworth, Leicestershire, LE17 4HR**
Contacts: **MOBILE (07879) 066901**

1 **AERO MAJESTIC (IRE)**, 6, b g Arcadio (GER)—So Pretty (IRE) **Mr S. Conway**
2 **AIR GLIDER (IRE)**, 9, b g Mountain High (IRE)—California Blue (FR) **Mr S. Conway**
3 **ATLANTIC BREAKER (IRE)**, 9, b g Broadway Flyer (USA)—Alder Hall (IRE) **Mr S. Conway**
4 **BAMBI DU NOYER (FR)**, 8, b br g Sageburg (IRE)—Zouk Wood (USA) **Mr S. Conway**
5 **DR MOLONEY (IRE)**, 12, b g Dr Massini (IRE)—Solal Queen **Mr S. Conway**
6 **FLABELLO (IRE)**, 9, br g Publisher (USA)—Uptodate (IRE) **Mr S. Conway**
7 **MULLAGHBOY (IRE)**, 8, b g Beneficial—Mellowthemoonlight (IRE) **Mr S. Conway**
8 **OLIVER'S ISLAND (IRE)**, 7, b g Milan—Leading Rank (IRE) **Mr S. Conway**
9 **RECIPROCITY**, 4, br gr f Mastercraftsman (IRE)—Cleide da Silva (USA) **Mr S. Conway**
10 **SKILLED**, 8, b g Mastercraftsman (IRE)—Treacle (USA) **Mr S. Conway**
11 **TUNNEL CREEK**, 7, b g Tobougg (IRE)—Free Offer **Mr S. Conway**

Amateur: Mr Philip Armson.

---

115 | **MRS SUSAN CORBETT, Otterburn**
Postal: **Girsonfield, Otterburn, Newcastle upon Tyne, Tyne and Wear, NE19 1NT**
Contacts: **PHONE (01830) 520771 FAX (01830) 520771 MOBILE (07713) 651215**
E-MAIL **girsonfield@outlook.com** WEBSITE **www.girsonfield.co.uk**

1 **AMARONE GENTLEMAN (IRE)**, 7, b g Oscar (IRE)—Tigrera (IRE) **Mr T. H. J. Green**
2 **BAHRIKATE**, 6, b m Bahri (USA)—Dispol Katie **Mr L. P. Richards**
3 **DARCEY'S PENNY**, 6, b m Bahri (USA)—Penteli **Castle View Racing**
4 **EBONY ROSE**, 7, br m Kalanisi (IRE)—Cogolie (FR) **The Nelson Racing Club**
5 **FOREWARNING**, 5, b g Cacique (IRE)—Buffering **Ms J. E. Maggs**
6 **GOWANBUSTER**, 4, b g Bahri (USA)—Aahgowangowan (IRE) **Hassle-Free Racing**
7 **HARLEYS MAX**, 10, b g Winged Love (IRE)—Researcher **Girsonfield Racing Club**
8 **HARRISONS PROMISE**, 7, b m Westerner—Hello My Lovely **Mr W. F. Corbett**
9 **HEARTASIA**, 8, b m Danehill Dancer (IRE)—Big Heart **Corbett & McMahon**
10 **LUCKY WIND (IRE)**, 5, ch g Grandera (IRE)—Florida Onyx (IRE) **David & Ros Chapman**
11 **LUVLY BOY BLUE**, 8, b g Blueprint (IRE)—Mellouise **C. R. Green**
12 **MAGNUM (IRE)**, 6, gr g Lawman (FR)—Coventina (IRE) **Mr T. H. J. Green**
13 **MAMDOOD (IRE)**, 5, gr g Clodovil (IRE)—Fact **Mr T. H. J. Green**
14 **MORNING WITH IVAN (IRE)**, 9, b m Ivan Denisovich (IRE)—Grinneas (IRE) **Mr L. P. Richards**
15 **MR KITE**, 8, b g Sixties Icon—Mar Blue (FR) **TWT Racing Club 2**
16 **MY BROWN EYED GIRL**, 6, b m Ferrule (IRE)—Chalosse **Mr G. Satchwell**
17 **REIVERS LODGE**, 7, b m Black Sam Bellamy (IRE)—Crystal Princess (IRE) **Mr F. W. W. Chapman**
18 **RIPONIAN**, 9, ch g Trade Fair—Dispol Katie **Girsonfield Racing Club**
19 **RUSSIANTOM (IRE)**, 8, b m Dylan Thomas (IRE)—Russian Roubles (IRE) **Mr T. H. J. Green**
20 **SATIS HOUSE**, 5, b m Mullionmileanhour (IRE)—Ex Mill Lady **Castle View Racing**
21 **STANARLEY PIC**, 8, b g Piccolo—Harlestone Lady **Mrs S. Corbett**
22 **SUTTON WAY**, 7, b m Bahri (USA)—Kates Own **J. B. Wharf**
23 **TOMMYCOLE**, 4, b g Native Ruler—Tancred Miss **Mr G. Restorick**
24 **WATAGUDDO**, 9, ch m Abzu—Whitegatesprincess (IRE) **C. R. Green**
25 **WOR VERGE**, 6, b g Virtual—Hanover Gate **The Goodfellow Partnership**

MRS SUSAN CORBETT - Continued

THREE-YEAR-OLDS

26 KYROC (IRE), br f Society Rock (IRE)—Dispol Kylie (IRE) **Mr F. W. W. Chapman**

Other Owners: Mrs Ros Chapman, Mr David Chapman, Mr D. J. Clarke, Mr W. F. Corbett, Mrs Susan Corbett, Ms Rose Enright, Mr M. D. Foden, Mr Gavin Foley, Mr I. Galletley, Exors of the Late Mr John Goodfellow, Mr Shaun Humphries, Miss H. M. McMahon, Mrs J. Pringle, Mr Les Waugh.

Assistant Trainer: Mr J. Corbett

Conditional: James Corbett. **Amateur:** Mr Ross Wilson.

116
MR JOHN CORNWALL, Melton Mowbray
Postal: **April Cottage, Pasture Lane, Hose, Melton Mowbray, Leicestershire, LE14 4LB**
Contacts: **PHONE (01664) 444453 FAX (01664) 444754 MOBILE (07939) 557091**
E-MAIL johncornwall7@gmail.com

1 THAT'S THE DEAL (IRE), 15, b br g Turtle Island (IRE)—Sister Swing **Mr J. R. Cornwall**
2 THE JUGOPOLIST (IRE), 12, b g Oscar (IRE)—Chance My Native (IRE) **Mr J. R. Cornwall**
3 TORRENT DES MOTTES (FR), 8, gr g Montmartre (FR)—Wavy (FR) **Mr J. R. Cornwall**

117
MR JAKE COULSON, Heaton
Postal: **Bent End Farm, Bearda Hill Racing, Heaton, Macclesfield, Cheshire, SK11 0SJ**
Contacts: **MOBILE (07460) 471492**
E-MAIL beardahillracing@gmail.com

1 GOLD PATROL (IRE), 11, b g Gold Well—One Love (IRE) **Mr N. Carter**
2 HUNGRYHERO (IRE), 8, b g Scorpion (IRE)—Princess Perk (IRE) **Mr N. Carter**
3 MAKEYAMINDUPMAIZ, 5, gr m Geordieland (FR)—Pems Gift **Mr N. Carter**
4 OSCAR VESPASIAN (IRE), 11, b g Oscar (IRE)—Quinnsboro Native (IRE) **Mr N. Carter**

Assistant Trainer: Sarah Carter

118
MISS JACQUELINE COWARD, Sheriff Hutton
Postal: **Low Moor Farm, Dalby, Yorkshire, YO60 6PF**
Contacts: **PHONE (01653) 628995**

1 COVIGLIA (IRE), 5, gr g Invincible Spirit (IRE)—Bright Snow (USA) **Mr John Blackburn Racing**
2 INTANGIBLE STAR, 4, b g Sea The Stars (IRE)—Wosaita **M. W. Easterby**
3 PROCIDA, 7, b m Myboycharlie (IRE)—On The Brink **Mr E. C. Wilkin**
4 SLEDMERE, 4, b g Hellvelyn—Oriel Bank (IRE) **Mrs S. E. Mason**
5 TAPIS LIBRE, 11, b g Librettist (USA)—Stella Manuela (FR) **The Laura Mason Syndicate**

Other Owners: Mr J. N. Blackburn.

119
MR ROBERT COWELL, Newmarket
Postal: **Bottisham Heath Stud, Six Mile Bottom, Newmarket, Suffolk, CB8 0TT**
Contacts: **PHONE (01638) 570330 MOBILE (07785) 512463**
E-MAIL robert@robertcowellracing.co.uk WEBSITE www.robertcowellracing.co.uk

1 BECKER, 4, b g Delegator—Mosa Mine **Mrs Morley, R Penney & A Rix**
2 BLUE DE VEGA (GER), 6, b g Lope de Vega (IRE)—Burning Heights (GER) **Mrs M. J. Morley**
3 BURFORD BROWN, 4, br g Swiss Spirit—Sareb (FR) **The Ever Hopeful Partnership**
4 COWBOY SOLDIER (IRE), 4, b g Kodiac—Urgele (FR) **Mrs F. H. Hay**
5 DOLLAR VALUE (USA), 4, gr g Exchange Rate (USA)—Makoma (USA) **K. A. Dasmal**
6 DUBAI SILK, 4, ch f Helmet (AUS)—Silken Express (IRE) **Malih L. Al Basti**
7 ENCORE D'OR, 7, b g Oasis Dream—Entente Cordiale (IRE) **Mrs Morley, G Johnson & Newsells Park Stud**
8 GLOBAL APPLAUSE, 5, b h Mayson—Crown (IRE) **Dr J. Hon**
9 GLOBAL EXCEED, 4, b g Exceed And Excel (AUS)—Blue Maiden **Dr J. Hon**
10 GRANDFATHER TOM, 4, b g Kheleyf (USA)—Kassuta **Mr J. Sargeant**

MR ROBERT COWELL - Continued

11 **GREEN DOOR (IRE)**, 8, b g Camacho—Inourhearts (IRE) **Mrs A Henry & Partner**
12 **HADDAF (IRE)**, 4, b g Dawn Approach (IRE)—Deveron (USA) **Mr T. W. Morley**
13 **INDIAN TINKER**, 10, b g Sleeping Indian—Breakfast Creek **Bottisham Heath Stud**
14 **JUMIRA BRIDGE**, 4, b g Invincible Spirit (IRE)—Zykina **Mrs M. J. Morley**
15 **JUSTICE LADY (IRE)**, 6, br m Dream Ahead (USA)—Celestial Dream (IRE) **Mr R. Ng**
16 **L'AGE D'OR**, 4, b f Iffraaj—Goleta (IRE) **C. Humphris**
17 **LEO MINOR (USA)**, 5, b g War Front—Kissed (IRE) **Mr T. W. Morley**
18 **ONE LAST NIGHT (IRE)**, 4, ch f Elusive Quality (USA)—Danuta (USA)
19 **OSSESSIONE (FR)**, 4, b f Motivator—Royal Fantasy (IRE) **C. Humphris**
20 **PEACE DREAMER (IRE)**, 5, b m Sir Prancealot (IRE)—See Nuala (IRE) **Mrs J. Hadida**
21 **RAUCOUS**, 6, b g Dream Ahead (USA)—Shyrl **Mr T. W. Morley**
22 **STAND FIRM (IRE)**, 4, b g Kodiac—Refuse To Give Up (IRE) **Mr T. W. Morley**
23 **TIME ZONE**, 5, b g Kheleyf (USA)—Be Joyful (IRE) **Mr W. J. S. Prosser**
24 **VICTORS LADY (IRE)**, 4, b f Society Rock (IRE)—Novat (IRE) **Mr P. Hunt**
25 **VICTORY ANGEL**, 5, b g Acclamation—Golden Shadow (IRE) **Z. A. Galadari**
26 **VISIONARY (IRE)**, 5, b g Dream Ahead (USA)—Avodale (IRE) **K. A. Dasmal**
27 **WARSAW ROAD (IRE)**, 5, ch g Zebedee—Warda **Mr T. W. Morley**
28 **ZAMJAR**, 5, b g Exceed And Excel (AUS)—Cloud's End **Mrs M. J. Morley**

THREE-YEAR-OLDS

29 **ADAM TILER (USA)**, b g Justin Phillip (USA)—Moneygrabber (USA) **Mr T. W. Morley**
30 **AWARDED**, b f Swiss Spirit—Royal Award **J Sargeant, B Rose & Partner**
31 **BALLISTIC (IRE)**, b g Kodiac—Pale Orchid (IRE) **Mrs F. H. Hay**
32 **BLAME ROBERTA (USA)**, b f Blame (USA)—Royal Parisian **K. A. Dasmal**
33 **BRIGADIER**, ch g Sepoy (AUS)—Nasheej (USA) **Malih L. Al Basti**
34 **BUDAIYA FORT (IRE)**, b g Kodiac—Knapton Hill **AlMohamediya Racing**
35 **CAUSEWAY BAY (IRE)**, b f Kodiac—Dance Bid **Mr S. Pan**
36 **FAVRE (USA)**, ch c Munnings (USA)—Ice Crystal (USA) **Phoenix Thoroughbred Limited**
37 **FINCH HATTON**, b f Showcasing—Fifty (IRE) **Mrs F. H. Hay**
38 **FLY LIGHTLY**, b c Dawn Approach (IRE)—Step Lightly (IRE) **Mr N. Al Habtoor**
39 **GLOBAL MYTH (USA)**, b c Scat Daddy (USA)—Excelente (IRE) **Dr J. Hon**
40 **GOOD ANSWER**, b c Iffraaj—Cool Question **Malih L. Al Basti**
41 **HOOFLEPUFF (IRE)**, b c Gale Force Ten—Hflah (IRE) **The Cool Silk Partnership**
42 **KHAFOOQ**, b g Kodiac—Al Manaal **Mrs M. J. Morley**
43 **MAID MILLIE**, b f Dream Ahead (USA)—Maid A Million **K. A. Dasmal**
44 **MISS GRADENKO**, b f Foxwedge (AUS)—Instructress **Chelsea Thoroughbreds & Partner**
45 **MISS PRESIDENT**, b f Oasis Dream—Madam President **Malih L. Al Basti**
46 **POCKET DYNAMO (USA)**, b br c Dialed In (USA)—Little Bit Tiny (USA) **Phoenix Thoroughbred Limited**
47 **QUIET WATERS (IRE)**, ch f Society Rock (IRE)—Smart Bounty **Malih L. Al Basti**
48 **REEVES**, b g Tamayuz—Mania (IRE) **Mrs F. H. Hay**
49 **ROCKET ACTION**, b c Toronado (IRE)—Winning Express (IRE) **Mr R. Ng**
50 **SIR OX (USA)**, b g Oxbow (USA)—Lady Melesi (USA) **K. A. Dasmal**
51 **SO HI SPEED (USA)**, b g Central Banker (USA)—
          Quietly Elegant (USA) **Nick Bradley Racing 21 & Sohi & Partner**
52 **STORM BLITZ (IRE)**, b c Dandy Man (IRE)—Stormy View (USA) **Mrs M. J. Morley**
53 **SWELL SONG**, ch f Kyllachy—Racina **Southcott Racing**
54 **TOMSHALFBROTHER**, b c Sir Percy—Kassuta **Mr J. Sargeant**
55 B f Maxios—Tosca (GER) **Strawberry Fields Stud & Partner**
56 **TURQUOISE FRIENDLY**, b c Holy Roman Emperor (IRE)—Cry Freedom (IRE) **Mr H. K. Tang**
57 **VIKIVAKI (USA)**, ch f Congrats (USA)—Smart Dancer (USA) **Mr T. W. Morley**

TWO-YEAR-OLDS

58 Ch c 21/3 Lethal Force (IRE)—Agony And Ecstasy (Captain Rio) (1904) **Mr W. J. S. Prosser**
59 Ch f 19/4 More Than Ready (USA)—Alb (Pulpit (USA)) (45855) **Mr T. W. Morley**
60 B br c 27/3 Daredevil (USA)—Awesome Mama (USA) (Awesome Again (CAN)) (45855) **Sheikh Sultan**
61 B c 24/1 Dialed In (USA)—Chu and You (You and I (USA)) (56437) **Mr T. W. Morley**
62 **COCONUT SUGAR (IRE)**, b f 8/3 Gutaifan (IRE)—Murrieta (Docksider (USA)) (12000) **Mr Neil Simpson**
63 B c 1/5 Lethal Force (IRE)—Gladiatrix (Compton Place) (15238) **Mr W. J. S. Prosser**
64 B f 20/2 Muhaarar—Jellwa (IRE) (Iffraaj) (38000) **Malih L. Al Basti**
65 B f 14/4 Midnight Lute (USA)—Lady of Akita (Fantastic Light (USA)) (42328) **Sheikh Sultan**
66 B f 1/2 Trappe Shot (USA)—Lexi Morgan (USA) (Arch (USA)) (29629) **Mr T. W. Morley**
67 **LOTTIE MARIE**, ch f 24/4 Intello (GER)—Heavenly Dawn (Pivotal) **Cheveley Park Stud**
68 **LOVE NOT MONEY**, b f 29/3 Dawn Approach (IRE)—
          Maggie Lou (IRE) (Red Ransom (USA)) (800) **Mr Neil Simpson**
69 Ch f 2/3 Poet's Voice—Most Tempting (Showcasing) **Most Tempting Club**

MR ROBERT COWELL - Continued

70 B c 12/3 Outstrip—Mudammara (IRE) (Dubawi (IRE)) (11428)
71 B c 28/4 Intrinsic—One Moment (Notnowcato) **Bottisham Heath Stud**
72 Ch f 29/3 Dream Ahead (USA)—Path of Peace (Rock of Gibraltar (IRE)) (40000) **Mr M. Foulger**
73 **ROYAL APPOINTMENT,** b c 5/2 Pivotal—Royal Seal (Dansili) **Cheveley Park Stud**
74 Ch f 22/1 Intrinsic—She's So Pretty (IRE) (Grand Lodge (USA)) (4761) **Malih L. Al Basti**
75 B br c 12/3 Kitten's Joy (USA)—Stone Hope (USA) (Grindstone (USA)) (85000) **Mr K. Dasmal**
76 **TAKE IT THUNDER (IRE),** b c 7/5 Night of Thunder (IRE)—Al Nassa (USA) (Bernardini (USA)) **Nasser Al Habtoor**
77 **TELL ME THUNDER (IRE),** ch c 28/4 Night of Thunder (IRE)—
                                  International Love (IRE) (Manduro (GER)) **Nasser Al Habtoor**
78 **UNRESTRAINED,** ch f 23/2 Lethal Force (IRE)—Effusive (Starspangledbanner (AUS)) **Cheveley Park Stud**
79 B br f 13/2 Karakontie (JPN)—War Clan (War Front (USA)) **Mrs F. H. Hay**
80 Ch f 30/3 Sepoy (AUS)—Whatizzit (Galileo (IRE)) (8000) **Mr W. J. S. Prosser**
81 Br c 10/2 Blame (USA)—Whenthetimeisright (IRE) (Devil His Due (USA)) (31746) **Mr K. Dasmal**
82 Br c 24/5 Dark Angel (IRE)—Winning Express (IRE) (Camacho) **Mr Robert Ng**

Other Owners: Sheikh N. M. H. Al Khalifa, Sheikh N. M. H. Al Khalifa, Mr N. Bradley, Mr A. Chapman, Chelsea Thoroughbreds - Miss Gradenko, Chelsea Thoroughbreds Ltd, Mr R. M. H. Cowell, Mrs A. C. Finster, Mr P. Harper, Mrs A. Henry, Miss S. Holden, Mr G. M. C. Johnson, Newsells Park Stud Limited, Nick Bradley Racing 21, Mr R. C. Penney, Mr A. J. Rix, G. F. L. Robinson, Miss B. Rose, Strawberry Fields Stud, P. Swann, Mrs B. E. Wilkinson, Mr R. R. Wright.

Assistant Trainer: Mr Ross Studholme

Apprentice: Eoin Walsh.

---

120 | **MR CLIVE COX, Hungerford**
Postal: **Beechdown Farm, Sheepdrove Road, Lambourn, Hungerford, Berkshire, RG17 7UN**
Contacts: **OFFICE** (01488) 72072 **FAX** (01488) 73500 **MOBILE** (07740) 630521
E-MAIL clive@clivecox.com **WEBSITE** www.clivecox.com

1   **AL JELLABY,** 4, b g Exceed And Excel (AUS)—Dolphina (USA) **AlMohamediya Racing**
2   **BOBBY WHEELER (IRE),** 6, b g Pivotal—Regal Rose **Mr P. N. Ridgers**
3   **COME ON COME ON (IRE),** 5, br g Lord Shanakill (USA)—Maridiyna (IRE) **Paul & Clare Rooney**
4   **EXISTENTIAL (IRE),** 4, br f Lethal Force (IRE)—Fascination (IRE) **Mr J Shack & Mr G Barnard**
5   **GET BACK GET BACK (IRE),** 4, b g Lord Shanakill (USA)—Bawaakeer (USA) **Paul & Clare Rooney**
6   **GRAPHITE STORM,** 5, gr g Delegator—Ice Haven (IRE) **Mrs Olive Shaw**
7   **GREY GALLEON (USA),** 5, gr g Mizzen Mast (USA)—Floresta (USA) **BA Racing & R G Levin**
8   **HIT THE BEAT,** 4, br f Fast Company (IRE)—Dance Express (IRE) **Clive Cox Racing Ltd**
9   **HULCOTE,** 4, b f Frankel—Polly's Mark (IRE) **The Kathryn Stud**
10 **KICK ON KICK ON,** 4, b c Swiss Spirit—Catmint **Paul & Clare Rooney**
11 **KING'S SLIPPER,** 4, b g Leroidesanimaux (BRZ)—Last Slipper **D B Clark & A R Bentall**
12 **LETHAL LUNCH,** 4, gr g Lethal Force (IRE)—Pin Cushion **The Rat Pack Partnership 2017**
13 **LILBOURNE STAR (IRE),** 4, b g Lilbourne Lad (IRE)—Make Amends (IRE) **The Fifth Amendment**
14 **LITTLE MISS LILLY,** 4, b f Lethal Force (IRE)—Malilla (IRE) **Clive Cox Racing Ltd**
15 **LITTLE PALAVER,** 7, b g Showcasing—Little Nymph **Mr T. H. S. Fox**
16 **LOUIE DE PALMA,** 7, b g Pastoral Pursuits—Tahirah **Mr P. N. Ridgers**
17 **NOW CHILDREN (IRE),** 5, ch h Dragon Pulse (IRE)—Toberanthawn (IRE) **Paul & Clare Rooney**
18 **PERFECT REFUGE,** 4, gr f Champs Elysees—Perfect Haven **Hants & Herts**
19 **PETRASTAR,** 4, b g Passing Glance—Petrarchick (USA) **Mr Peter Horrocks**
20 **SALUTE THE SOLDIER (GER),** 4, br g Sepoy (AUS)—
                                  Street Fire (IRE) **Mr & Mrs P Hargreaves & Mr A D Spence**
21 **SHEPHERD MARKET (IRE),** 4, b f Reckless Abandon—Shepherdia (IRE) **Windmill Racing**
22 **SILCA MISTRESS,** 4, ch f Dutch Art—Strictly Silca **Windmill Racing II**
23 **SNAZZY JAZZY (IRE),** 4, b c Red Jazz (USA)—Bulrushes **Mrs Olive Shaw**
24 **STAND N DELIVER,** 5, b g Dick Turpin (IRE)—Drifting Gold **Martin C. Oliver**
25 **TAMERLANE (IRE),** 4, b g Dark Angel (IRE)—Coy (IRE) **AlMohamediya Racing**
26 **TIS MARVELLOUS,** 5, b g Harbour Watch (IRE)—Mythicism **Miss J. Deadman & Mr S. Barrow**

THREE-YEAR-OLDS

27 **AIGIARNE (IRE),** b f Helmet (AUS)—Golden Shine **AlMohamediya Racing**
28 **APRIL WINE,** b f Charm Spirit (IRE)—Nandiga (USA) **C. V. Wentworth**
29 **BOURBON EDITION (USA),** ch f Distorted Humor (USA)—Salonsun (GER) **Bourbon Lane Stable**
30 **CRACKIN DREAM (IRE),** b c Oasis Dream—Gothic Dance **Mrs Olive Shaw**
31 **DARGEL (IRE),** b c Dark Angel (IRE)—Lady Duxyana **Mr Trevor Fox**
32 **DARK POET,** b c Lethal Force (IRE)—Poetic Dancer **Mr A. G. Craddock**

MR CLIVE COX - Continued

33 **DARK SHADOW (IRE)**, gr g Dark Angel (IRE)—Djinni (IRE) **Mr J. Goddard**
34 **DESIGNATED**, ch f Dutch Art—Entitled **Cheveley Park Stud**
35 **ELIGIBLE (IRE)**, b c Dark Angel (IRE)—Secrets Away (IRE) **Mr Alan Spence**
36 **GABRIELA LAURA**, b f Swiss Spirit—Tintac **Mr M. A. Collins**
37 **GETCHAGETCHAGETCHA**, b c Champs Elysees—Paella **Paul & Clare Rooney**
38 **GLOBAL PROSPECTOR (USA)**, b br c Scat Daddy (USA)—Alegendinmyownmind **Dr Johnny Hon**
39 **GLORIOUS EMARATY (FR)**, b c George Vancouver (USA)—Ascot Glory **A. Al Shaikh**
40 **GOLDEN FORCE**, b g Lethal Force (IRE)—Malilla (IRE) **Racegoers Club Owners Group**
41 **GRISONS (FR)**, b c Iffraaj—Fig Roll **China Horse Club International Limited**
42 **GUIDING SPIRIT (IRE)**, b c Zebedee—Miss Smilla **The Zebbs**
43 **HEARTWARMING**, b f Showcasing—Place In My Heart **Hot To Trot Racing**
44 **HERITAGE**, b f Garswood—Inheritance **Cheveley Park Stud**
45 **HEY HO LET'S GO**, b c Dream Ahead (USA)—Lookslikeanangel **Carmel Stud**
46 **HOUSE OF KINGS (IRE)**, b c Camelot—Celestial Bow (IRE) **Martin McHale, Mrs T Burns and Partner**
47 **JUST THE MAN (FR)**, b c Rajsaman (FR)—Yachtclubgenoa (IRE) **Paul & Clare Rooney**
48 **KONCHEK**, bl c Lethal Force (IRE)—Soar **AlMohamediya Racing**
49 **LETHAL LOVER**, b f Lethal Force (IRE)—Sadaharu (FR) **Kennet Valley Thoroughbreds VI**
50 **LETHAL MISSILE (IRE)**, b g Lethal Force (IRE)—Lostintheclouds **B Allen, G Hill & N Wagland**
51 **MANANA CHICA (IRE)**, b f Kodiac—Bayalika (IRE) **Mr Martin McHale & Partners**
52 **MARTIN KING**, b c Oasis Dream—I'm A Dreamer (IRE) **China Horse Club International Limited**
53 **MEGHAN SPARKLE (IRE)**, b f Showcasing—Poppet's Lovein **Mr P. N. Ridgers**
54 **MOLLY BLAKE**, b f Bated Breath—Park Melody (IRE) **Mr P. N. Ridgers**
55 **MYKINDOFSUNSHINE (IRE)**, gr g Zebedee—Silk Fan (IRE) **Miss J. Deadman & Mr S. Barrow**
56 **NOBLE FOX**, b g Foxwedge (AUS)—Woolfall Rose **Cox's Foxes**
57 **PERFECT SHOWDANCE**, ch f Showcasing—Perfect Star **Dr Bridget Drew & Mr Ian Brown**
58 **POUR ME A DRINK**, ch c Nathaniel (IRE)—Euroceleb (IRE) **Paul & Clare Rooney**
59 **PRESUMPTIVE**, gr f Lethal Force (IRE)—Regal Heiress **Cheveley Park Stud**
60 **PURE AS GOLD**, b f Kingman—Sewards Folly **Mr Martin McHale & Partners**
61 **REBECKE (IRE)**, b f Camacho—Ibecke **Mr P. N. Ridgers**
62 **RED ARMADA (IRE)**, b c Invincible Spirit (IRE)—Alumni **China Horse Club International Limited**
63 **RED FEDORA**, b f Lethal Force (IRE)—Red Turban **Cheveley Park Stud**
64 **RED ROMANCE**, ch f Dutch Art—Semblance **Clipper Logistics**
65 **REGAL AMBITION**, ch f Pivotal—Regal Salute **Cheveley Park Stud**
66 **REIGNING ICE**, br f Xtension (IRE)—Ice Haven (IRE) **Mrs Olive Shaw**
67 **REMEMBERING YOU (IRE)**, b f Es Que Love (IRE)—Tallassee **Phillip Cove & GB Horseracing**
68 **RETICENT ANGEL (IRE)**, ro f Dark Angel (IRE)—Sioduil (IRE) **Mr N. I. O'Callaghan**
69 **SACRED WARNER (IRE)**, b g Holy Roman Emperor (IRE)—Alerted (IRE) **Ernst Holding AB**
70 **SHADES OF BLUE (IRE)**, br f Kodiac—Enjoyable (IRE) **Miss A. Jones**
71 **SWEET POEM**, b f Poet's Voice—Three Sugars (AUS) **Mrs Olivia Hoare & Simon de Zoete**
72 **SWIFT AND SURE (IRE)**, ch f Exceed And Excel (AUS)—Leopard Hunt (USA) **Mildmay Racing & D. H. Caslon**
73 **TREORCHY**, b g Bated Breath—Welsh Anthem **Malih L. Al Basti**
74 **UNCERTAIN SMILE (IRE)**, b f Bungle Inthejungle—Witnessed **S R Hope & S W Barrow**
75 **VASILIEV**, ch c Dutch Art—Barynya **Cheveley Park Stud**
76 **VENTURE (IRE)**, b c Showcasing—Starfly (IRE) **Malih L. Al Basti**
77 **WE'VE GOT THE LOVE (IRE)**, b f Charm Spirit (IRE)—Olympic Medal **S R Hope & S W Barrow**
78 **WELCOMING (FR)**, b f No Nay Never (USA)—Love Over Gold (FR) **Tactful Finance Limited**
79 **WISE COUNSEL**, b c Invincible Spirit (IRE)—Noozhah **Clipper Logistics**

TWO-YEAR-OLDS

80 **ATMOSPHERIC**, b f 30/4 Night of Thunder (IRE)—Havergate (Dansili) (36000) **Tactful Finance Limited**
81 Ch c 14/2 Excelebration (IRE)—Avomcic (IRE) (Avonbridge) (36190) **Alderson Burke Francis**
82 Gr c 1/3 Society Rock (IRE)—Chiara Wells (IRE) (Refuse To Bend (IRE)) (84280) **Mr P. N. Ridgers**
83 **COMPANY MINX**, gr f 1/4 Fast Company (IRE)—Ice Haven (IRE) (Verglas (IRE)) **Mrs Olive Shaw**
84 **DUBAI AVENUE (IRE)**, b c 8/4 Bated Breath—Starfly (IRE) (Invincible Spirit (IRE)) (20227) **A. Al Shaikh**
85 **EMIRATES CURRENCY**, b c 1/5 Muhaarar—Loulwa (IRE) (Montjeu (IRE)) (65000) **A. Al Shaikh**
86 **ENDOWMENT**, b f 8/4 Garswood—Inheritance (Oasis Dream) **Cheveley Park Stud**
87 Ch c 12/2 Lethal Force (IRE)—Entreat (Pivotal) (61904) **AlMohamediya Racing**
88 B f 21/2 Free Eagle (IRE)—Indian Maiden (IRE) (Indian Ridge) (30000) **A Syndicate**
89 B c 7/4 Cacique (IRE)—Jubilant Queen (Kyllachy) (68000) **Alderson Burke Francis**
90 Ch c 26/2 Anjaal—Just Devine (IRE) (Montjeu (IRE)) (100000) **Carmel Stud**
91 **JUST MAY**, br f 31/1 Lethal Force (IRE)—Milly's Gift (Trade Fair) **Ken Lock Racing**
92 **LADY FANDITHA (IRE)**, b f 22/1 Kodiac—Lady Ro (Showcasing) (52380) **Mr P. N. Ridgers**
93 B f 14/3 Due Diligence (USA)—Littlemisssunshine (IRE) (Oasis Dream) **Main Line Racing**
94 B f 2/4 Muhaarar—Lonely Ahead (USA) (Rahy (USA)) (78000) **Mr A D Spence & Mr M B Spence**
95 **MAHALA BAY**, b br c 9/3 Fountain of Youth (IRE)—Catmint (Piccolo) (47619) **Mr T. H. S. Fox**

MR CLIVE COX - Continued

96 B gr f 15/4 Outstrip—Makara (Lion Cavern (USA)) (23000) **Dr Bridget Drew**
97 B gr f 7/3 Lethal Force (IRE)—Malilla (IRE) (Red Clubs (IRE)) **Clive Cox Racing Ltd**
98 Ch f 20/4 Dream Ahead (USA)—Nullarbor Sky (IRE) (Aussie Rules (USA)) **AlMohamediya Racing**
99 Ch c 8/2 Dutch Art—Osipova (Makfi) (55000) **Mr Alan Spence**
100 B c 19/4 Due Diligence (USA)—Our Faye (College Chapel) (33333) **Miss J. Deadman & Mr S. Barrow**
101 B f 9/2 Nathaniel (IRE)—Packed House (Azamour (IRE)) (37926) **Mrs V. Burke & Mrs B. Miles**
102 Ch c 3/4 Anjaal—Petite Georgia (IRE) (Camacho) (6742) **Mr J. Goddard**
103 B c 18/3 Dragon Pulse (IRE)—Place That Face (Compton Place) (26970) **A Syndicate**
104 Ch c 4/3 Lethal Force (IRE)—Poetic Dancer (Byron) **Mr Alan G. Craddock**
105 B f 31/3 No Nay Never (USA)—Sanadaat (Green Desert (USA)) (92709) **Charmaine Li**
106 B c 13/4 Bated Breath—So Belle (Singspiel (IRE)) (72000) **AlMohamediya Racing**
107 B f 6/4 Pivotal—Synergy (FR) (Victory Note (USA)) **Mr Andrew L. Cohen**
108 B c 14/4 Camacho—The Hermitage (IRE) (Kheleyf (USA)) (65000) **AlMohamediya Racing**
109 TIGER ZONE (IRE), b c 1/3 Society Rock (IRE)—
Shalabina (Nayef (USA)) (57142) **Miss J. Deadman & Mr S. Barrow**
110 B c 12/3 Starspangledbanner (AUS)—Torentosa (FR) (Oasis Dream) (170000) **Carmel Stud**
111 B c 17/2 Acclamation—Vanity's Girl (Compton Place) (50000) **AlMohamediya Racing**
112 VELETA, ch f 28/4 Dutch Art—Barynya (Pivotal) **Cheveley Park Stud**
113 Ch f 19/2 Slade Power (IRE)—Wanting (IRE) (Acclamation) **Mr Andrew L. Cohen**
114 WHISPERING LEAVES (IRE), b f 8/1 Acclamation—
Djinni (IRE) (Invincible Spirit (IRE)) (16013) **JT & KM Thomas**

Other Owners: HH Shaikh Nader Mohamed Al Khalifa, Sheikh Nooh Al Khalifa, Mr Peter Alderson, Miss Barbara Allen, BA Racing, G. M. Barnard, Mr Stephen W. Barrow, Mr A. R. Bentall, Mr Paul Blaydon, Mr Ian M. Brown, Mr D. J. Burke, Mrs T. Burns, D. H. Caslon, D. B. Clark, Mr Phillip Cove, Mr C. G. Cox, Mrs T. L. Cox, Miss C. E. Davies, Mr Simon de Zoete, Miss Julie Deadman, Dr Bridget Drew & Partners, Mr N. R. R. Drew, Miss Pippa Drew, Mr Mike Francis, GB Horseracing, Mr L. R. A. Godfrey, Mr P. J. Grimes, Mr S. Harding, Mr P. K. Hargreaves, Mrs R. J. Hargreaves, Mr and Mrs P Hargreaves, Mr Peter Harper, C. J. Harper, Mr S. Hill, Mr Geoff Hill, Mrs Olivia Hoare, Mr S. R. Hope, Mr R. S. Hoskins, Mr D. M. James, Mr Michael Johnson, Mrs S. Kelly, Mr John Law, Mr Richard Levin, Mrs Christian Marner, Lady Eliza Mays-Smith, Mr M. McHale, Mildmay Racing, P. H. Morgan, Mrs M. E. Morgan, Mr N. Patsalides, Mr P. T. Robinson, Mrs C. Rooney, Mr P. A. Rooney, Mr P. J. Scargill, Mr J. Shack, Mr M. B. Spence, The Hot To Trot Syndicate, Mr J. T. Thomas, Mrs K. M. Thomas, Mr Nigel Wagland.

Jockey (flat): Hector Crouch, Adam Kirby. **Apprentice:** Amelia Glass.

---

121 MR TONY COYLE, Norton
Postal: **Long Row Stables, Beverley Road, Norton, Malton, North Yorkshire, YO17 9PJ**
Contacts: **MOBILE (07976) 621425**
E-MAIL tonycoyleracing@hotmail.co.uk

1 BEMPTON CLIFFS (IRE), 4, gr g Canford Cliffs (IRE)—Grand Lili **Mr A. C. Coyle**
2 FLOWER POWER, 8, br m Bollin Eric—Floral Rhapsody **Ms M. H. Matheson**
3 LITTLE PIPPIN, 6, b m Sir Percy—Lady Le Quesne (IRE) **Mr A. C. Coyle**
4 MAUREB (IRE), 7, br m Excellent Art—Almost Blue (USA) **Mr A. C. Coyle**
5 NEWGATE DUCHESS, 5, b m Haafhd—Arctic Queen **W. P. S. Johnson**
6 4, Ch f Malinas (GER)—Sharwakom (IRE) **Mr A. C. Coyle**

THREE-YEAR-OLDS
7 ABIE'S HOLLOW, b g Harbour Watch (IRE)—Cesseras (IRE) **Tony Coyle, John Walsh**
8 ARE YOU LOCKING UP, b f Born To Sea (IRE)—Copper Penny **Coyle, Milburn, Kench**
9 BABY MAUREB (IRE), br f Canford Cliffs (IRE)—Almost Blue (USA) **Mr A. C. Coyle**
10 BROKEN SPEAR, b g Pastoral Pursuits—My Pretty Girl **Morecool Racing**
11 EY UP ITS MICK, b g Milk It Mick—Silky Silence **Mrs M. Lingwood**
12 GOOD LOOKER (IRE), ch c Zoffany (IRE)—Looker **Coyle, Bishop, Bland, Quayle**
13 NEWGATE ANGEL, b f Heeraat (IRE)—Rio's Girl **W. P. S. Johnson**
14 SWISS LADY, b f Swiss Spirit—Hasten (USA) **Mr A. C. Coyle**
15 B f Dick Turpin (IRE)—Tarneem (USA)

Other Owners: Mr D. F. L. Bishop, Mr S. Bland, Mr N. M. Kench, Mr I. Milburn, Mrs S. M. Quayle, Mr M. Sykes, Mr J. Walsh.

Jockey (flat): Barry McHugh.

122 MR RAY CRAGGS, Sedgefield
Postal: **East Close Farm, Sedgefield, Stockton-On-Tees, Cleveland, TS21 3HW**
Contacts: **PHONE (01740) 620239 FAX (01740) 623476**

1 **AMOURI CHIEF,** 5, b g Sleeping Indian—Tour d'amour (IRE) **R. Craggs**
2 **AMOURI GLEAM,** 4, b f Arabian Gleam—Tour d'amour (IRE) **R. Craggs**
3 **CORAL QUEEN,** 8, b m Desideratum—Queen's Lodge (IRE) **R. Craggs**
4 **GALLEY CAT,** 4, ch f Sleeping Indian—Celestial Welcome
5 **GLASGOW,** 9, gr g Verglas (IRE)—Miss St Tropez **R. Craggs**
6 **GRANNY ROZ,** 5, b m Bahamian Bounty—Hulcote Rose (IRE) **R. Craggs**
7 **PARK HOUSE,** 10, b g Tillerman—Rasin Luck **R. Craggs**
8 **QUAY QUEST,** 5, ch g Shami—Quay Four (IRE) **R. Craggs**
9 **SHAMITSAR,** 5, b g Shami—Tsarina Louise **R. Craggs**
10 **TARA TIARA,** 7, b m Kayf Tara—Royal Roxy (IRE) **R. Craggs**
11 **WELL I NEVER,** 7, b g Josr Algarhoud (IRE)—Tour d'amour (IRE) **R. Craggs**

THREE-YEAR-OLDS
12 **AMELIA R (IRE),** b f Zoffany (IRE)—Xaloc (IRE) **R. Craggs**
13 **AMOURIE,** ch f Haafhd—Tour d'amour (IRE) **R. Craggs**

Assistant Trainer: Miss J N Craggs

---

123 MR PETER CRATE, Dorking
Postal: **Springfield Farm, Parkgate Road, Newdigate, Dorking, Surrey, RH5 5DZ**
Contacts: **MOBILE (07775) 821560**
E-MAIL peterdcrate@jandjfranks.com

1 **SANDFRANKSKIPSGO,** 10, ch g Piccolo—Alhufoof (USA) **P. D. Crate**
2 **SKIP TO MY LOU,** 4, b f Foxwedge (AUS)—Alhufoof (USA) **P. D. Crate**

TWO-YEAR-OLDS
3 Ch c 25/3 Starspangledbanner (AUS)—Supreme Quest (Exceed And Excel (AUS)) **P. D. Crate**

Jockey (flat): Shane Kelly. **Amateur:** Mr George Crate.

---

124 MR SIMON CRISFORD, Newmarket
Postal: **Kremlin House Stables, Fordham Road, Newmarket, Suffolk, CB8 7AQ**
Contacts: **PHONE (01638) 662661**
E-MAIL office@crisfordracing.com WEBSITE Instagram: crisford_racing Twitter: @crisfordracing

1 **AFRICAN RIDE,** 5, b h Candy Ride (ARG)—Paiota Falls (USA)
2 **ALWASMIYA,** 4, b f Kyllachy—Miss Bunter
3 **BOBBY K (IRE),** 4, br g Dabirsim (FR)—Shanjia (GER)
4 **CENTURY DREAM (IRE),** 5, b h Cape Cross (IRE)—Salacia (IRE)
5 **GLOBAL CONQUEROR,** 4, b g Dubawi (IRE)—Nargys (IRE)
6 **HONEY MAN (IRE),** 4, ch g Dawn Approach (IRE)—Whisp (GER)
7 **HOW FAR (IRE),** 4, b c Kodiac—Akuna Magic (IRE)
8 **IRON DOVE (IRE),** 4, gr f Dark Angel (IRE)—I'm So Glad
9 **MOKARRIS (USA),** 5, b br h More Than Ready (USA)—Limonar (IRE)
10 **MORDIN (IRE),** 5, b g Invincible Spirit (IRE)—Bryanstown (IRE)
11 **MUTAFANI,** 4, b c Exceed And Excel (AUS)—Hokkaido
12 **NOBLEMAN'S NEST,** 4, br g Poet's Voice—Tamzin
13 **OSTILIO,** 4, ch c New Approach (IRE)—Reem Three
14 **OUTBOX,** 4, b g Frankel—Emirates Queen
15 **PERSIAN SUN,** 4, b g Dansili—Khor Sheed
16 **RED MIST,** 4, b c Frankel—Red Dune (IRE)
17 **REGAL DIRECTOR (IRE),** 4, b g New Approach (IRE)—Dubai Queen (USA)
18 **SAROOG,** 5, b g Nathaniel (IRE)—Bahama Bay (GER)
19 **SHARP SUITED,** 4, b g Dansili—Appearance
20 **SMART CHAMPION,** 4, b g Teofilo (IRE)—Soryah (IRE)

MR SIMON CRISFORD - Continued

THREE-YEAR-OLDS

21 **AKWAAN (IRE),** b c Camacho—Saytara (IRE)
22 **ALDANA,** b f Slade Power (IRE)—Bright Glow
23 **ALNADIR (USA),** ch g Noble Mission—Sarah's Secret (USA)
24 **ALUQAIR (IRE),** b c Kodiac—Morethanafeeling (IRE)
25 **ANGEL OF FREEDOM,** b f Dark Angel—Angelic Air
26 **APPROACH THE CITY (IRE),** b c New Approach (IRE)—First City
27 **ARISTOCRATIC LADY (IRE),** b f Invincible Spirit (IRE)—Dubai Queen (USA)
28 **BUNIANN (IRE),** b c Tamayuz—Darajaat (USA)
29 **CAPE CAVALLI (IRE),** b c Cape Cross (IRE)—Matauri Pearl (IRE)
30 **CHANCE,** ch c Lope de Vega (IRE)—Harem Lady (FR)
31 **CLASSIC DESIGN (IRE),** b g Pivotal—Fashion Line (IRE)
32 **COOL EXHIBIT,** b c Showcasing—Frigid
33 **DESERT MISSION (IRE),** b f Shamardal (USA)—Jathabah (IRE)
34 **DOUBLE KODIAC (IRE),** b g Kodiac—Via Lattea (IRE)
35 **DREAMING AWAY (IRE),** b f Shamardal (USA)—Dreaming Beauty
36 **EBBRAAM,** b f Teofilo (IRE)—Oojooba
37 **EDEN GARDENS (IRE),** ch g Mukhadram—Showerproof
38 **EL GUMRYAH (IRE),** b f No Nay Never (USA)—Dancing Shoes (IRE)
39 **IMPERIAL CHARM,** b f Dubawi (IRE)—Reem Three
40 **ISOCRATES (USA),** b c Dansili—I Am Beautiful (IRE)
41 **JASH (IRE),** b c Kodiac—Miss Azeza
42 **KAREENA KAPOOR (USA),** ch f More Than Ready (USA)—Tabreed
43 **KUNG FU,** b c Kingman—Cubanita
44 **LOCAL AFFAIR,** ch f Teofilo (IRE)—Local Spirit (USA)
45 **MAAMORA (IRE),** b f Dubawi (IRE)—Zoowraa
46 **MAKE A WISH (IRE),** ch f No Nay Never (USA)—Saturn Girl (IRE)
47 **MANNAAL (IRE),** b f Dubawi (IRE)—Soraaya (IRE)
48 **MANNGUY,** b c Oasis Dream—Galaxy Highflyer
49 **MASAAQAAT (USA),** b f Quality Road (USA)—Mufajaah (USA)
50 **MOFAAJI,** ch c Animal Kingdom (USA)—My Dubai (IRE)
51 **NEESAAN,** b f New Approach (IRE)—Red Dune (IRE)
52 **PERSIAN BEAUTY (IRE),** b f Dubawi (IRE)—Zeeba (IRE)
53 **RUN FAST (IRE),** b f Shamardal (USA)—Prime Run
54 **SAFFRAN (IRE),** b g Teofilo (IRE)—Oriental Step (IRE)
55 **SAY THE WORD,** b g Authorized (IRE)—Soryah (IRE)
56 **SHAMA'S FIRST,** ch f Exceed And Excel (AUS)—Shama's Crown (IRE)
57 **SIAM DAWN (IRE),** b c Dawn Approach (IRE)—Tea Cup
58 **SPORTING CHANCE,** b c Kodiac—Elpida (USA)
59 **STAGING POST (IRE),** b c Cape Cross (IRE)—Buntingford (IRE)
60 **STARRY EYES (USA),** ch f Animal Kingdom (USA)—Starship Elusive (USA)
61 B g Camelot—Trapeze
62 **TROLIUS (IRE),** b g Cape Cross (IRE)—Trikala (IRE)
63 **TURN 'N TWIRL (USA),** b f Twirling Candy (USA)—Kind Turn (USA)
64 **TURNTABLE,** b g Pivotal—Masarah (IRE)
65 **VISIONARA,** b f Kingman—State Treasure (USA)
66 **WALLAA,** b f Dawn Approach (IRE)—Shuhra (IRE)
67 **WATERFRONT (IRE),** b g Cape Cross (IRE)—Bright Water
68 **WISE RULER,** ch g Dawn Approach (IRE)—Bint Almukhtar (IRE)

TWO-YEAR-OLDS

69 B f 22/3 Golden Horn—Anaamil (IRE) (Darshaan)
70 **ANJAH (IRE),** b c 31/3 Kodiac—Terhaab (USA) (Elusive Quality (USA))
71 B c 9/1 Charm Spirit (IRE)—Aquarelliste (FR) (Danehill (USA)) (100000)
72 B f 2/4 Night of Thunder (IRE)—Badalona (Cape Cross (IRE))
73 B f 11/3 New Approach (IRE)—Badminton (Zieten (USA))
74 Ch f 29/3 No Nay Never (USA)—Beta Tauri (USA) (Oasis Dream) (72000)
75 **BRIGHT VIEW (IRE),** b f 18/4 Siyouni (FR)—Quilting (USA) (King's Best (USA))
76 B c 13/4 Siyouni (FR)—Cape Magic (IRE) (Cape Cross (IRE)) (40000)
77 B f 8/4 Footstepsinthesand—Cordial (Oasis Dream) (62000)
78 Ch f 6/5 Slade Power (IRE)—Crimson Year (USA) (Dubai Millennium)
79 B f 31/1 Iffraaj—Dance Awhile (IRE) (Kodiac)
80 B f 7/2 Sea The Stars (IRE)—Elision (IRE) (Samum (GER)) (40000)
81 **FANTAIL,** b f 17/3 Zoffany (IRE)—Red Fantasy (IRE) (High Chaparral (IRE)) (75000)
82 Ch f 3/3 Dawn Approach (IRE)—Fashion Line (IRE) (Cape Cross (IRE))

MR SIMON CRISFORD - Continued

83 B c 21/5 New Approach (IRE)—Feedyah (USA) (Street Cry (IRE))
84 FINEST SOUND (IRE), b c 15/2 Exceed And Excel (AUS)—Amplifier (Dubawi (IRE))
85 B c 1/3 More Than Ready (USA)—Hijaab (USA) (Tiznow (USA))
86 B f 15/2 Zoffany (IRE)—Kittens (Marju (IRE)) (75853)
87 B c 28/4 Invincible Spirit (IRE)—Liberating (Iffraaj) (160000)
88 Gr f 19/2 More Than Ready (USA)—Lismore (USA) (Tiznow (USA)) (300000)
89 Ch c 14/2 Starspangledbanner (AUS)—Lorient (Champs Elysees) (100000)
90 MAESTRO STICK, b c 5/4 Frankel—Moon Sister (IRE) (Cadeaux Genereux)
91 MAJESTIC JEWEL, b f 4/5 Kingman—Soryah (IRE) (Shamardal (USA))
92 B f 21/1 Night of Thunder (IRE)—Many Colours (Green Desert (USA)) (36190)
93 B c 13/2 Siyouni (FR)—Melbourne Shuffle (USA) (Street Cry (IRE)) (202275)
94 B g 12/4 Kodiac—Mitre Peak (Shamardal (USA)) (80952)
95 ONE IDEA, gr b c 19/4 Dubawi (IRE)—Rose Diamond (IRE) (Daylami (IRE))
96 Gr c 7/2 Lope de Vega (IRE)—Partita (Montjeu (IRE)) (140000)
97 B f 17/4 Kodiac—Pivotal Era (Pivotal) (180000)
98 B c 28/3 Dawn Approach (IRE)—Qareenah (USA) (Arch (USA))
99 Br c 22/2 Dream Ahead (USA)—Rahlah (Dansili) (52000)
100 B f 7/4 Dubawi (IRE)—Red Dune (IRE) (Red Ransom (USA))
101 Gr ro f 4/4 The Factor (USA)—Smitten (USA) (Tapit (USA)) (52910)
102 B f 19/3 Dark Angel (IRE)—Soraaya (IRE) (Elnadim (USA))
103 Ch f 14/1 Lope de Vega (IRE)—Starring Guest (IRE) (Teofilo (IRE)) (185419)
104 B f 11/3 First Defence (USA)—Supposition (Dansili) (84280)
105 B c 14/2 Exceed And Excel (AUS)—Tazffin (IRE) (Iffraaj)
106 TRACHELIUM, b f 21/3 Pivotal—Salacia (IRE) (Echo of Light)
107 B c 7/3 Dawn Approach (IRE)—Turmalin (IRE) (Dalakhani (IRE))
108 B c 30/3 Shamardal (USA)—Twilight Sky (Authorized (IRE)) (150000)
109 B c 3/2 Muhaarar—Vanishing Grey (IRE) (Verglas (IRE)) (350000)
110 WISE GLORY (IRE), b c 13/3 Muhaarar—Bint Almukhtar (IRE) (Halling (USA))
111 WITHOUT A FIGHT (IRE), b c 29/1 Teofilo (IRE)—Khor Sheed (Dubawi (IRE))

---

125 **MR GAVIN CROMWELL, Co. Meath**
Postal: **Danestown, Balrath, Navan, Co. Meath, Ireland**
Contacts: **MOBILE (00353) 86 2693388**
E-MAIL admin@gavincromwellracing.com WEBSITE www.gavincromwellracing.com

1 A PLACE APART (IRE), 5, b g Power—Simadartha (USA) **Peter Michael**
2 AASLEAGH DAWN (IRE), 6, b m Milan—Aasleagh Lady (IRE) **Rollx Syndicate**
3 AINMISFEARR (IRE), 4, b f Famous Name—Virevolle (FR) **Brunabonne Syndicate**
4 BENTHAM (IRE), 5, b g Jeremy (USA)—Detonante (IRE) **Brendan Higgins, Conor Irwin, Willie Murphy**
5 BIDDY THE BOSS (IRE), 6, b m Doyen (IRE)—Thiarnathoir (IRE) **Kilbrien's Syndicate**
6 BLUE HEATHER (IRE), 5, b m Doyen (IRE)—Limavady (IRE) **Finbar O'Reilly**
7 BOTTOMLESS PIT (IRE), 5, b h Scorpion (IRE)—Clonleigh Lady (IRE) **John Keegan**
8 BREX DRAGO (ITY), 7, b g Mujahid (USA)—Shibuni's Thea (IRE) **Marhan Construction**
9 BRISK TEMPO (FR), 4, b g Dabirsim (FR)—Allegro Vivace (FR) **Eoin Hughes**
10 CALLTHEBARMAN (IRE), 5, b g Lord Shanakill (USA)—African Scene (IRE) **Killian McDonnell**
11 CAPTAIN COURAGEOUS (IRE), 6, b g Canford Cliffs (IRE)—Annacloy Pearl (IRE) **Running In Heels Syndicate**
12 CIAO (IRE), 4, ch f Lord Shanakill (USA)—Selouma (FR) **Martin Hannon**
13 CLASH OF D TITANS (IRE), 6, b g Gold Well—Give Us A Look (IRE) **Swans High Stool Syndicate**
14 CLASSICAL ROSE, 7, b m Amadeus Wolf—Monaazalah (IRE) **Tony Cromwell**
15 DARVER STAR (IRE), 7, b g Kalanisi (IRE)—Maggies Oscar (IRE) **SSP Number Two Syndicate**
16 DEBURRAFIELD (IRE), 6, b br g Kalanisi (IRE)—Santa's Girl (IRE) **Enda Kerley**
17 EJAYTEEKAY, 6, b m Big Bad Bob (IRE)—Lovely Dream (IRE) **Brian Poots**
18 ESPOIR D'ALLEN (FR), 5, b g Voix du Nord (FR)—Quadanse (FR) **J. P. McManus**
19 GETAFLYER (IRE), 6, b g Getaway (GER)—Knapping Princess (IRE) **P. McGuiness, Willie Murphy**
20 ILIKEDWAYURTHINKIN (IRE), 5, b g Yeats (IRE)—Sway (FR) **Mr J. P. McManus**
21 IT HAS TO BE (IRE), 8, b g Kalanisi (IRE)—Amathea (FR) **Old Pals Syndicate**
22 JEREMYS FLAME (IRE), 5, b m Jeremy (USA)—Supreme Beneficial (IRE) **Flushfarm Syndicate**
23 LADY CAMELOT (IRE), 4, b f Camelot—Queen Jock (USA) **G. Bourke**
24 LADY ISCHIA (IRE), 7, b m Getaway (GER)—Summer Flight (FR) **James O'Rourke**
25 LEVER DU SOLEIL (FR), 4, b g Le Havre (IRE)—Morning Dust (IRE) **Sunshine Partnership (Pat McGuinness)**
26 POLITICAL POLICY (IRE), 8, b g Bushranger (IRE)—Alexander Express (IRE) **F. Lynch Snr**
27 PROSPECTUS, 6, b g Sakhee (USA)—Some Sunny Day **McAlpine Syndicate**
28 PUNTERS POET (IRE), 4, b c Urban Poet (USA)—Eritrea **Keith Brazil**

MR GAVIN CROMWELL - Continued

29 **RAZ DE MAREE (FR),** 14, ch g Shaanmer (IRE)—Diyala III (FR) **James Swan**
30 **SPADES ARE TRUMPS (IRE),** 6, b g Yeats (IRE)—Sway (FR) **J. P. McManus**

THREE-YEAR-OLDS

31 **AUGAR,** b c Garswood—Authoritative **Yard**

Other Owners: Darren Cahill, J. D. Cotton, Mrs B. Cotton, Tony Gannon, JRM Racing Syndicate, Hans Krebs, Mr E. W. Lee, John Lynch, Mac Fitz Partnership (Paul Louis), Pub and Grub Syndicate, Sams Snug Syndicate, Turlough Blessing, Mr E. F. Vaughan.

Assistant Trainer: Ger Fox

Jockey (flat): Gary Carroll. **Jockey (NH):** Ger Fox, Andrew Lynch. **Conditional:** Breen Kane, Conor McNamara. **Apprentice:** Conor Heavey. **Amateur:** Mr Anthony Fox, Mr Corey McGivern.

126
MR ANDREW CROOK, Leyburn
Postal: Ashgill Stables (Yard 2), Tupgill Park, Coverham, Middleham, North Yorkshire, DL8 4TJ
Contacts: **PHONE** (01969) 640303 **MOBILE** (07764) 158899
E-MAIL andycrookracing@gmail.com **WEBSITE** www.andrewcrookracing.co.uk

1 **ALONG CAME THEO (IRE),** 9, b g Vertical Speed (FR)—Kachina (IRE) **The 100 Club**
2 **CRAKEHALL LAD (IRE),** 8, ch g Manduro (GER)—My Uptown Girl **Mrs K. M. Savage**
3 5, B g Malinas (GER)—Cute N You Know It **Mr Saxby**
4 **CYRANO STAR (FR),** 7, gr g Martaline—Quezac du Boulay (FR) **Leeds Plywood & Doors Ltd**
5 **EARLY BOY (FR),** 8, b g Early March—Eclat de Rose (FR) **R. P. E. Berry**
6 **EMPORTEPARLAFOULE (FR),** 5, gr g Smadoun (FR)—Sempiternelle (FR) **Mr D. Carter**
7 5, B g Sholokhov (IRE)—Good Shine (IRE) **David Carter**
8 **HIGH ANXIETY,** 5, ch m Bated Breath—Odense (USA) **Mrs S. J. Beddis**
9 **IDEAL ANGEL (IRE),** 5, b g Dark Angel (IRE)—Irishstone (IRE) **Mr D. Carter**
10 **K O KENNY,** 8, b g Apple Tree (FR)—Cool Island (IRE) **Mr K. Heilbron**
11 **LADY BABS,** 5, br m Malinas (GER)—Jontys'lass **Ashgill Stud**
12 **LORD FRANKLIN,** 10, ch g Iceman—Zell (IRE) **The 100 Club**
13 4, B f Sholokhov (IRE)—Manorville (IRE) **R. P. E. Berry**
14 **MONTELIMAR,** 4, b f Raven's Pass (USA)—Mascarene (USA) **Jolly Boys Racing Club**
15 **RACEMAKER,** 5, b g Stimulation (IRE)—Sophies Heart **Mrs H. Sinclair**
16 **ROBERTTOWN ROSE (IRE),** 6, b m Milan—Windfola (FR) **Mr S. J. Padgett**

THREE-YEAR-OLDS

17 **HEY JAZZY LADY (IRE),** b f Red Jazz (USA)—First Bunting (IRE) **Miss M. Hodgson**
18 **JAGERBOND,** ch g Monsieur Bond (IRE)—Velvet Jaguar **Mrs Christine Hopper & Carl Chapman**
19 B f Universal (IRE)—Jontys'lass **Ashgill Stud**
20 **PINKIE PIE (IRE),** b f Tagula (IRE)—Bidable **Jolly Boy's Racing Club**

Other Owners: Mr R. Boswell, Mr Dave Carter, Mr Carl Chapman, Mr D. Chapman, Mrs C. M. Clarke, Miss A. Crook, Foulrice Park Racing Limited, Miss D. Gabbitas, Mrs Christine Hopper, Mr P. T. Midgley, Mr R. Parks, Mr J. Saxby, Mr Ruairi Stirling, Mr Colin Stirling, Miss Maiti Stirling, Mr Tom Wooldridge.

Assistant Trainer: Amy Crook

Jockey (flat): Jason Hart, Kevin Stott. **Jockey (NH):** Will Kennedy, Adam Nicol. **Amateur:** Mr Charlie Todd.

127
MR KEN CUNNINGHAM-BROWN, Stockbridge
Postal: Danebury Place, Stockbridge, Hampshire, SO20 6JX
Contacts: **PHONE** (01264) 781061 **FAX** (01264) 781061 **MOBILE** (07802) 500059
E-MAIL kcb@danebury.co.uk

1 **ALLOFMELOVESALLOFU,** 5, ch g Sakhee's Secret—La Palma **Danebury Racing Stables**
2 **AYE AYE SKIPPER (IRE),** 9, b g Captain Marvelous (IRE)—Queenfisher **Mr J. F. Pearl**
3 **BULLETPROOF (IRE),** 13, b g Wareed (IRE)—Laura's Native (IRE) **Danebury Racing Stables & David Henery**
4 **DRACARYS,** 4, b g Sepoy (AUS)—Fen Guest **Danebury Racing Stables**
5 **INDIAN CHARLIE,** 7, b m Compton Place—Emerald Fire **Danebury Racing Stables**
6 **LOVING YOUR WORK,** 8, b g Royal Applause—Time Crystal (IRE) **Danebury Racing Stables**
7 **MISS GERONIMO,** 7, b m Hellvelyn—Churn Dat Butter (USA) **Danebury Racing Stables**
8 **RED TYCOON (IRE),** 7, b g Acclamation—Rugged Up (IRE) **Mr D. F. Henery**

MR KEN CUNNINGHAM-BROWN - Continued

9 **SECRET STRIKER**, 7, ch m Sakhee's Secret—Silver Purse **Danebury Racing Stables**
10 **SUFI**, 5, ch g Pivotal—Basanti (USA) **Mr J. F. Pearl**
11 **VINCENZO COCCOTTI (USA)**, 7, gr ro g Speightstown (USA)—Ocean Colors (USA) **Mr D. F. Henery**
12 **WASEEM FARIS (IRE)**, 10, b g Exceed And Excel (AUS)—Kissing Time **Danebury Racing Stables**

THREE-YEAR-OLDS

13 **CAUTHEN (IRE)**, b g Dandy Man (IRE)—Chellalla **David Henery & Lee Turland**
14 **LUCKY LOU (IRE)**, b f Most Improved (IRE)—Bessie Lou **Danebury Racing Stables**
15 **QUEMONDA**, ch f Mount Nelson—Quesada (IRE) **Mrs E. A. Bass**

Other Owners: Mr K. Cunningham-Brown, Mrs V. E. Cunningham-Brown, L. R. Turland.

Assistant Trainer: Tony Charlton

---

128 **MR SEAN CURRAN, Swindon**
Postal: Twelve Oaks, Lechlade Road, Highworth, Swindon, Wiltshire, SN6 7QR
Contacts: **MOBILE (07774) 146169**

1 **ALL YOURS (FR)**, 8, ch g Halling (USA)—Fontaine Riant (FR) **Power Geneva Ltd**
2 **GOOD MAN HUGHIE (IRE)**, 10, ch g Flemensfirth (USA)—Good Dawn (IRE) **Power Geneva Ltd**
3 **IS IT OFF (IRE)**, 4, b g Clodovil (IRE)—French Doll (IRE) **Power Geneva Ltd**
4 **RIGHTDOWNTHEMIDDLE (IRE)**, 11, b g Oscar (IRE)—Alternative Route (IRE) **Power Geneva Ltd**

---

129 **MISS REBECCA CURTIS, Newport**
Postal: Fforest Farm, Newport, Pembrokeshire, SA42 0UG
Contacts: **PHONE (01348) 811489 MOBILE (07970) 710690**
E-MAIL rebcurtis@hotmail.com

1 **ABSOLUTE POWER**, 8, b g Flemensfirth (USA)—Crystal Ballerina (IRE) **Mark Sherwood & Spencer Gammond**
2 **ANAX (IRE)**, 5, b g Oscar (IRE)—Limetree Leader (IRE) **Mr N. D. Morris**
3 **CUBAO (IRE)**, 5, b g Fame And Glory—Rematch (IRE) **Primus Partners**
4 **CWYNAR**, 4, b f Kodiac—Modern Art **Mr N. D. Morris**
5 **DROVERS LANE (IRE)**, 7, b g Oscar (IRE)—Minnie Turbo (IRE) **Hyde Hill Moran Outhart & Trembath**
6 **FINANCIAL OUTCOME (IRE)**, 6, b g Financial Reward (IRE)—Catriona's Mare (IRE) **Ccorz Partners**
7 **FLERE IMSAHO (IRE)**, 4, b g Kodiac—Florida City (IRE) **Mr N. D. Morris**
8 **FULL TIME PARTY (IRE)**, 6, b g Milan—Native Singer (IRE) **Miss R. Curtis**
9 **GEORDIE DES CHAMPS (IRE)**, 8, br g Robin des Champs (FR)—Kilcoleman Lady (IRE) **Mr J. P. McManus**
10 **JOE FARRELL (IRE)**, 10, b g Presenting—Luck of The Deise (IRE) **M Sherwood, N Morris & R Curtis**
11 **JOUEUR BRESILIEN (FR)**, 7, b g Fuisse (FR)—Fille du Bresil (FR) **Inthewayboy Group**
12 **JUST A THOUGHT (IRE)**, 7, ch m Stowaway—Carrig Lucy (IRE) **Hyde, Outhart, Moran & Hill**
13 **LEGENDS GOLD (IRE)**, 5, b m Gold Well—Fu's Legend (IRE) **Lockett,Hyde,Mountford,Bishop&Outhart**
14 **LIBBY T VALANCE (IRE)**, 8, b m Scorpion (IRE)—Dipp In The Dark (IRE) **Mr A. McIver**
15 **LISNAGAR OSCAR (IRE)**, 6, b g Oscar (IRE)—Asta Belle (FR) **Racing For Fun**
16 **MINELLA BOBO (IRE)**, 6, gr g Oscar (IRE)—Line Kendie (FR) **Moran, Outhart, McDermott, Hyde & Hill**
17 **O'FAOLAINS BOY (IRE)**, 12, b g Oscar (IRE)—Lisa's Storm (IRE) **Hyde, Roddis, Outhart, Hill & Curtis**
18 **RELENTLESS DREAMER (IRE)**, 10, br g Kayf Tara—Full of Elegance (FR) **Mr N. D. Morris**
19 **RUTHLESS ARTICLE (IRE)**, 6, b g Definite Article—Lady Kamando **Mr M. A. Sherwood**
20 **SUMMER NAME (IRE)**, 7, b g Duke of Marmalade (IRE)—Summer's Eve **Miss R. Curtis**
21 **SUNSET SHOWDOWN (IRE)**, 6, b g Flemensfirth (USA)—Sunset Queen (IRE) **Mr J. P. McManus**
22 **WAYFINDER (IRE)**, 5, br g Shantou (USA)—Sibury (IRE)

Other Owners: Mr D. J. Bishop, Mr A. R. Clerkson, Mr J. Conyers, Mr M. Davis, Fishlake Commercial Motors Ltd, Mr G. S. Gammond, Mr I. Glendenning, Mr N. Goulden, M. Hill, Mr R. Hyde, Mr R. J. Line, Mrs C. M. Lockett, Mr D. P. McDermott, Mr B. Merrett, Ms J. A. Moran, Mrs K. M. Mountford, Mr W. J. O'Reilly, Mr J. P. O'Reilly, A. J. Outhart, Mr D. Paish, Mr N. M. Roddis, Mr A. Spencer, Mr C. R. Trembath, D. C. Zeffman.

Assistant Trainer: Paul Sheldrake

130 MISS HELEN CUTHBERT, Brampton
Postal: **Woodlands, Cowranbridge, How Mill, Brampton, Cumbria, CA8 9LH**
Contacts: **PHONE (01228) 560822 MOBILE (07879) 634494**
E-MAIL **cuthbertracing@gmail.com**

1 RED FOREVER, 8, ch g Major Cadeaux—Spindara (IRE) **Mrs J. Cuthbert**
2 YAIR HILL (IRE), 11, b g Selkirk (USA)—Conspiracy **Mrs J. Cuthbert**

131 MR PAUL D'ARCY, Newmarket
Postal: **Charnwood Stables, Hamilton Road, Newmarket, Suffolk, CB8 7JQ**
Contacts: **PHONE (01638) 662000 MOBILE (07768) 807653**
E-MAIL **pauldarcyracingltd@gmail.com** WEBSITE **www.pauldarcyracing.com**

1 BRIGAND, 4, b g Dick Turpin (IRE)—Juncea **Power Geneva Ltd**
2 COME ON DAVE (IRE), 10, b g Red Clubs (IRE)—Desert Sprite (IRE) **Royale Racing Syndicate**
3 FACE LIKE THUNDER, 4, b g Passing Glance—Violet's Walk **Whiterok Ltd**
4 INAAM (IRE), 6, b g Camacho—Duckmore Bay (IRE) **Tramore Tree**
5 JOYFUL DREAM (IRE), 5, ch m Dream Ahead (USA)—Tearsforjoy (USA) **Mr G. Dolan**
6 MARTINEO, 4, b g Declaration of War (USA)—Woodland Scene (IRE) **Power Geneva Ltd**
7 MOUNT CLESHAR, 5, b g Mount Nelson—Resal (IRE) **Mr P. A. Cafferty**
8 PECHEURS DE PERLES (IRE), 5, b g Pour Moi (IRE)—Annacloy Pearl (IRE) **Northumbria Leisure Ltd**
9 PUSHKIN MUSEUM (IRE), 8, gr g Soviet Star (USA)—Chaste **Tramore Tree**
10 RED INVADER (IRE), 9, b g Red Clubs (IRE)—Tifariti (USA) **Power Geneva Ltd**
11 RUBY GATES (IRE), 6, b m Avonbridge—Wild Academy (IRE) **Mr D. James**
12 SOAR ABOVE, 4, b g Lethal Force (IRE)—Soar **Mr J. Butler**
13 SPRING LOADED (IRE), 7, gr g Zebedee—Nisriyna (IRE) **Rowley Racing**
14 UNFORGIVING MINUTE, 8, b g Cape Cross (IRE)—Ada River **Power Geneva Ltd**
15 WANEEN (IRE), 6, b g Approve (IRE)—Million All Day (IRE) **Power Geneva Ltd**
16 WELOOF (FR), 5, b g Redoute's Choice (AUS)—Peinted Song (USA) **Tramore Tree**

THREE-YEAR-OLDS

17 DOLLY DUPREE, b f Poet's Voice—Meddle **Mr K. Snell**
18 ZEEBAD (IRE), gr g Zebedee—Love Intrigue (IRE) **Jan Harris Racing**

TWO-YEAR-OLDS

19 B c 26/2 Sepoy (AUS)—Nurai (Danehill Dancer (IRE)) **Mr K. Snell**

Other Owners: Mr P. W. D'Arcy, Mrs S. I. D'Arcy, Mrs M. Doyle, Mr A. Fellowes, Mrs J. Harris, L. M. Power, Mr D. M. Standring.

Assistant Trainer: Sue D'Arcy

132 MR LUKE DACE, Billingshurst
Postal: **Copped Hall Farm and Stud, Okehurst House, Okehurst Lane, Billingshurst, West Sussex, RH14 9HR**
Contacts: **FAX (01403) 612176 MOBILE (07949) 401085**
E-MAIL **lukedace@yahoo.co.uk** WEBSITE **www.lukedace.co.uk**

1 MADDI, 4, b f Foxwedge (AUS)—Sulis Minerva (IRE) **R. L. Page**
2 RAVENOUS, 8, b g Raven's Pass (USA)—Supereva (IRE) **I Farminer,Hilary&C Barrett,Farminer Dev**
3 THE SECRETS OUT, 5, bl g Sakhee's Secret—Brooksby **Mr G. Collacott**

THREE-YEAR-OLDS

4 SUSSEX SPIRIT, b f Swiss Spirit—Hip Hip Hooray **The Sussex Partnership**

Other Owners: Mr C. Barrett, Mrs H. A. Barrett, L. A. Dace, Mrs L. J. Dace, Mr I. E. J. Farminer, Farminer Developments Ltd.

Assistant Trainer: Mrs L Dace

133 **MR KEITH DALGLEISH, Carluke**
Postal: **Belstane Racing Stables, Carluke, Lanarkshire, ML8 5HN**
Contacts: **PHONE (01555) 773335**
E-MAIL dalgleish.racing@outlook.com

1 **ALABANZA**, 4, b g Big Bad Bob (IRE)—Tahfeez (IRE) **Mr R. C. Hyndman**
2 **ALFIE'S CHOICE (IRE)**, 7, b g Shantou (USA)—Bally Bolshoi (IRE) **Mr & Mrs Paul & Clare Rooney**
3 **ALRIGHT SUNSHINE (IRE)**, 4, b g Casamento (IRE)—Miss Gibraltar **Mr & Mrs Paul & Clare Rooney**
4 **BEAST OF BELSTANE**, 4, b g Pivotal—Miss Corniche **Straightline Bloodstock**
5 **BEST TO COME (IRE)**, 6, b g Stowaway—Nippy Nora (IRE) **Mr & Mrs Paul & Clare Rooney**
6 **BROKEN WINGS (IRE)**, 4, b f Canford Cliffs (IRE)—Moss Top (IRE) **Middleham Park Racing LXXVII**
7 **CHICA BUENA (IRE)**, 4, b f Thewayyouare (USA)—Easter Parade **Straightline Bloodstock**
8 **CHOOKIE DUNEDIN**, 4, b g Epaulette (AUS)—Lady of Windsor (IRE) **Raeburn Brick Limited**
9 **CORTON LAD**, 9, b g Refuse To Bend (IRE)—Kelucia (IRE) **Mr J. J. Hutton**
10 **CORTON LASS**, 4, gr f Showcasing—Elbow Beach **Mr J. J. Hutton**
11 4, B c Tobougg (IRE)—Crack The Kicker (IRE)
12 **CRAZY TORNADO (IRE)**, 6, b g Big Bad Bob (IRE)—All Day (CHI) **Mr J. K. McGarrity**
13 **CUCKOO'S CALLING**, 5, b m So You Think (NZ)—Sinndarina (FR) **Straightline Bloodstock**
14 **DESERT POINT (FR)**, 7, b g Le Havre (FR)—Bonne Mere (FR) **Straightline Bloodstock**
15 **DRAGON MOUNTAIN**, 4, b g Sir Percy—Rouge Dancer **Mr J S Morrison**
16 **EL HOMBRE**, 5, ch g Camacho—Nigella **Weldspec Glasgow Limited**
17 **ENEKO (FR)**, 5, bl g Laverock (IRE)—Kaline Collonges (FR) **Straightline Bloodstock**
18 **EYE OF THE STORM (IRE)**, 9, ch g Galileo (IRE)—Mohican Princess **Mr J S Morrison**
19 **EYREBORN (IRE)**, 5, b m Born To Sea (IRE)—Eyrecourt (IRE) **Ayr Racecourse Club**
20 **FIRTH OF THE CLYDE**, 14, b g Flemensfirth (USA)—Miss Nel **R. H. Goldie**
21 **FOREVER A LADY (IRE)**, 6, b m Dark Angel (IRE)—Unicamp **Mr J. K. McGarrity**
22 **GENNADY (IRE)**, 5, b g Arakan (USA)—Topathistle **Straightline Bloodstock**
23 **GLENGARRY**, 6, b g Monsieur Bond (IRE)—Lady McBeth (IRE) **Mrs J. M. MacPherson**
24 **GLORIOUS LADY (IRE)**, 5, b m Fame And Glory—Lady Secret (FR) **Straightline Bloodstock**
25 **GOLD OPERA (IRE)**, 10, b g Gold Well—Flute Opera (IRE) **Straightline Bloodstock**
26 **GOLDENCARD (IRE)**, 6, b g Golden Lariat—Flemensfirth Lady (IRE) **The Gilbert's & Mr Campbell**
27 **HANDSOME BOB (IRE)**, 4, b g Most Improved (IRE)—Beautiful Dreamer **Weldspec Glasgow Limited**
28 **HAVANA GO**, 4, ch g Havana Gold (IRE)—Stagecoach Jade (IRE) **Letsbuyahorse5 - Rp, Jm, Dvdh, Bm, Km**
29 **HIGHWAY COMPANION (IRE)**, 5, b g Milan—Niffyrann (FR) **Weldspec Glasgow Limited**
30 **HOME BEFORE DUSK**, 4, b g Medicean—Flylowflylong (IRE) **Mr G. R. Leckie**
31 **I'M IMPROVING (IRE)**, 4, b g Most Improved (IRE)—Shebelia (GER) **Mr & Mrs Paul & Clare Rooney**
32 **I'M TO BLAME (IRE)**, 5, b g Winged Love (IRE)—Swap Shop (IRE) **Mr & Mrs Paul & Clare Rooney**
33 **ICONIC CODE**, 4, ch f Sixties Icon—Silca Key **Sir Ian Good & Mr C Anderson**
34 **JACOB BLACK**, 8, b g Amadeus Wolf—First Eclipse (IRE) **Mr J. K. McGarrity**
35 **L'AIR DU VENT (FR)**, 5, b g Coastal Path—Bleu Perle (FR) **Straightline Bloodstock**
36 **LOMU (IRE)**, 5, ch g Dandy Man (IRE)—Miss Me **S. J. Macdonald**
37 **MAC N CHEESE (IRE)**, 9, b g Milan—Fox Burrow (IRE) **Straightline Bloodstock**
38 **MAULESDEN MAY (IRE)**, 6, b m Dark Angel (IRE)—Jemima's Art **The County Set (Two)**
39 **MI CAPRICHO (IRE)**, 4, b g Elzaam (AUS)—Mavemacullen (IRE) **Prestige Thoroughbred Racing**
40 **MIRSAALE**, 9, ch g Sir Percy—String Quartet (IRE) **Mr J Fyffe**
41 **MISS BEAR BEACH (IRE)**, 4, b f Choisir (AUS)—Whitegate Way **Middleham Park Racing CXV**
42 **MIXBOY (FR)**, 9, gr g Fragrant Mix (IRE)—Leston Girl (FR) **Mr & Mrs Paul & Clare Rooney**
43 **MONSIEUR CO (FR)**, 6, b g Turgeon (USA)—Cayras Style (FR) **The Gilbert's & Mr Campbell**
44 **MORTICIA**, 4, b f Dandy Man (IRE)—Diksie Dancer **Weldspec Glasgow Limited**
45 **MRS DAVIES (IRE)**, 5, b m Court Cave (IRE)—Bandelaro (IRE)
46 **MURPHY'S LAW (IRE)**, 5, b g Gold Well—Balleen Rose (IRE)
47 **NEVER BE ENOUGH**, 4, ch f Sir Percy—Camp Fire (IRE) **Straightline Bloodstock**
48 **NEW FRONTIER (IRE)**, 5, b g Sans Frontieres (IRE)—Line Jade (FR) **Straightline Bloodstock**
49 **NICEANDEASY (IRE)**, 6, b g Kalanisi (IRE)—High Priestess (IRE) **Straightline Bloodstock**
50 **ONE NIGHT IN MILAN (IRE)**, 6, b g Milan—Native Mo (IRE) **The Gilbert's & Mr Campbell**
51 **PRINCE KAYF**, 5, b g Kayf Tara—Annie's Answer (IRE) **Straightline Bloodstock**
52 4, B g Fame And Glory—Printing Polly (IRE) **Mr & Mrs Paul & Clare Rooney**
53 **QASR**, 5, b g Excelebration (IRE)—Blur **Weldspec Glasgow Limited**
54 **SAINT EQUIANO**, 5, b g Equiano (FR)—St Athan **Mr & Mrs Paul & Clare Rooney**
55 **SEBASTIAN'S WISH (IRE)**, 6, b g Aqlaam—Swish (GER) **Two Goldfish & A Balloon**
56 **SENOR LOMBARDY (IRE)**, 6, b g Milan—Killoughey Babe (IRE) **Straightline Bloodstock**
57 **SHPADOINKLE DAY (IRE)**, 4, ch g Champs Elysees—Idle Chatter (IRE) **Mr G. R. Leckie**
58 **SIDI ISMAEL (FR)**, 5, b g Great Pretender—Tetouane (FR) **Straightline Bloodstock**
59 **SOLDIER'S MINUTE**, 4, b g Raven's Pass (USA)—Hadba (IRE) **Weldspec Glasgow Limited**
60 **SPARK OF WAR (IRE)**, 4, b g Declaration of War (USA)—Acts of Grace (USA) **Mr F. Brady**
61 **SPORTING PRESS (IRE)**, 6, b g Flemensfirth (USA)—Rudy Renata (IRE) **Straightline Bloodstock**

MR KEITH DALGLEISH - Continued

62 **TAXMEIFYOUCAN (IRE)**, 5, b g Beat Hollow—Accounting **Straightline Bloodstock**
63 **THE VOCALIST**, 7, b m Recharge (IRE)—Ivy Edith **Straightline Bloodstock**
64 **TOMMY DOCC (IRE)**, 7, b g Thewayyouare (USA)—Liturgy (IRE) **Mr R. Docherty**
65 **TONICNGIN (FR)**, 5, b g Irish Wells (FR)—Kahipiroska (FR) **Thats My Boys**
66 **TOUGH REMEDY**, 4, b g Tough As Nails (IRE)—Remediate (USA) **Titanium Racing Club**
67 **TRIANGLE ROCK (IRE)**, 6, b g Stowaway—Lucy Cooper (IRE) **The Gilbert's & Mr Campbell**
68 **UNIVERSAL GLEAM**, 4, b g Sir Percy—Mookhlesa **Weldspec Glasgow Limited**
69 **UPTOWN FUNK (IRE)**, 5, b g Galileo (IRE)—All's Forgotten (USA) **Mr J. Fyffe**
70 **VALKENBURG**, 4, b g Dutch Art—Balamana (FR) **The Gilbert's & Mr Campbell**
71 **WHAT'S THE STORY**, 5, b g Harbour Watch (IRE)—Spring Fashion (IRE) **Weldspec Glasgow Limited**

THREE-YEAR-OLDS

72 B g Alhebayeb (IRE)—Al Amlah (USA)
73 **BEECHWOOD IZZY (IRE)**, b f Dandy Man (IRE)—Rugged Up (IRE) **Middleham Park Racing LII**
74 **BEECHWOOD JUDE (FR)**, b g War Command (USA)—Ponte Sanangelo (FR) **Middleham Park Racing LXXXIV**
75 **BOSTON GEORGE (IRE)**, b c Raven's Pass (USA)—Her Own Kind (JPN) **Weldspec Glasgow Limited**
76 **BRAHMA KAMAL**, b c Equiano (FR)—Midnight Flower (IRE)
77 **CABALLERO (IRE)**, ch c Camacho—Dame d'honneur (IRE) **Weldspec Glasgow Limited**
78 **CAUSTIC LOVE (IRE)**, b f Fast Company (IRE)—Moss Top (IRE) **Weldspec Glasgow Limited**
79 **DARK LOCHNAGAR (USA)**, b c Australia—Virginia Waters (USA) **Weldspec Glasgow Limited**
80 **DIAMONIQUE**, b f Kyllachy—Al Joudha (FR) **Weldspec Glasgow Limited**
81 **EPONA**, b f Epaulette (AUS)—Jackline **From the Front Racing & Partner**
82 **EURO IMPLOSION (IRE)**, b g Battle of Marengo (IRE)—Mikes Baby (IRE) **Mr J S Morrison**
83 **EURO NO MORE (IRE)**, b f Kodiac—Gerobies Girl (USA) **Mr J S Morrison**
84 **FOR HEAVEN'S SAKE (FR)**, b f Wootton Bassett—Joyce (GER) **Middleham Park Racing CXI**
85 **FRANK'S LAW**, b g Orientor—Berberana (IRE) **Mr J. Fyffe**
86 **FRIENDLY ADVICE (IRE)**, ch g Orientor—Secret Advice **A. R. M. Galbraith**
87 **FUENTE (IRE)**, ch c Havana Gold (IRE)—Bounty Box **The Fuente Partnership**
88 **GOMETRA GINTY (IRE)**, b f Morpheus—Silver Cache (USA) **Mr K. W. Dalgleish**
89 **HOWZER BLACK (IRE)**, b g Requinto (IRE)—Mattinata **Middleham Park Racing LXXVI**
90 **I COULD DO BETTER (IRE)**, b g Canford Cliffs—Shebelia (GER) **Mr & Mrs Paul & Clare Rooney**
91 **IRON MIKE**, gr g Gregorian (IRE)—Regal Velvet **Weldspec Glasgow Limited**
92 **JEAN MERCI (IRE)**, b g Panis (USA)—Fabulatrice (FR) **Straightline Bloodstock**
93 **LET ME BE (IRE)**, b g Gale Force Ten—Peryzat (IRE) **Mr & Mrs Paul & Clare Rooney**
94 **LEXINGTON PALM (IRE)**, b f Elzaam (AUS)—Easter Girl **Middleham Park Racing LXXV**
95 B c Battle of Marengo (IRE)—Misrepresent (USA) **Weldspec Glasgow Limited**
96 **NORTHERN SOCIETY (IRE)**, b f Camacho—La Estatua **John Kelly, John McNeill & Alan Johnston**
97 **RED BOND (IRE)**, b c Red Jazz (USA)—Faithfulbond (IRE) **Middleham Park Racing XXVII**
98 **SUMMER DAYDREAM (IRE)**, b f Footstepsinthesand—Summer Dream (IRE) **Mr R. Docherty**
99 **THEATRE OF WAR (IRE)**, b g War Command (USA)—Final Opinion (IRE) **Campbell, Cull, Gilbert & Mackenzie**
100 **THREE CASTLES**, b c Zoffany—Fountain of Honour (IRE) **W. M. Johnstone**
101 B c Noble Mission—Winendynme (USA) **Weldspec Glasgow Limited**
102 **WOODSIDE WONDER**, br c Camacho—Cambridge Duchess **Middleham Park Racing XIV**

TWO-YEAR-OLDS

103 Ch c 7/3 Lethal Force (IRE)—Dutch Heiress (Dutch Art) (28571) **Mrs J. M. MacPherson**
104 B c 13/2 Hot Streak (IRE)—Enchanted Princess (Royal Applause) (30476) **Mr & Mrs Paul & Clare Rooney**
105 B c 14/2 Fountain of Youth (IRE)—Hip Flask (Motivator) (18000) **Mrs J. M. MacPherson**
106 B c 27/1 Kendargent (FR)—Really Lovely (Galileo (IRE)) **Mr & Mrs Paul & Clare Rooney**
107 B c 3/3 Champs Elysees—Sojitzen (FR) (Great Journey (JPN)) (46354) **Mr & Mrs Paul & Clare Rooney**
108 Ch c 27/3 Dragon Pulse (IRE)—Veronica Falls (Medicean) (71428) **Mr & Mrs Paul & Clare Rooney**

Other Owners: C. Anderson, Mr K. P. Bucas, Mr W. Burke, A. Cadger, Mr J. J. Campbell, Mr R. Cull, Mr J. E. Dance, Mr D. Duncan, Equus I, Mr S. Franks, From The Front Racing, Mr A. N. Gargan, Mr R. P. Gilbert, Richard & Katherine Gilbert, Mrs K. E. Gilbert, G. Godsman, Sir Ian Good, E. D. Haggart, Mr A. W. Henderson, Mr A. Johnston, Keith Dalgleish Racing Limited, Mr J. Kelly, Mr J. S. Lessells, Robert Macgregor, Mrs P. M. Mackenzie, Mr K. McFarlane, Mr B. McLaughlin, Mr J. McLaughlin, Mr J. McNeill, Mr J. M. Mcintyre, Mr M. G. Mellor, Miss M. A. O Brien, T. S. Palin, D. F. Powell, M. Prince, Mr R. Provan, Mr S. C. Reay, Mr P. A. Rooney, Mrs C. Rooney, Mr A. Savage, A. W. Sinclair, Miss M. M. Smith, Straightline Construction Ltd, Mr P. P. Thorman, Mr D. A. Walker, Western Meeting Club Ltd, Mr D. P. van der Hoeven.

Assistant Trainer: Kevin Dalgleish

Conditional: Callum Bewley. **Apprentice:** Rowan Scott.

134 **MR HENRY DALY, Ludlow**
Postal: Trainer did not wish details of his string to appear

135 **MR PHILLIP DANDO, Peterston-Super-Ely**
Postal: **Springfield Court, Peterston-Super-Ely, Cardiff, South Glamorgan, CF5 6LG**
Contacts: **PHONE (01446) 760012 MOBILE (07872) 965395**

1 BEAU HAZE, 6, b g Black Sam Bellamy (IRE)—Bella Haze **P. C. Dando**
2 DRIFTWOOD HAZE, 11, b g Nomadic Way (USA)—Kristal Haze **P. C. Dando**
3 HARRY HAZE, 7, b g Dr Massini (IRE)—Gypsy Haze **Mr Phillip Dando & Mr Anthony Brown**
4 IFANDABUT (IRE), 7, b g Scorpion (IRE)—Native Wonder (IRE) **The Gambling Cousins**
5 MOONTRIPPER, 10, b m Doyen (IRE)—Moon Spinner **Mr H. A. Brown**
6 RIVER HAZE, 9, b g Lucarno (USA)—Kristal Haze **P. C. Dando**

Other Owners: Mrs D. Hill, Mr T. B. James.

Assistant Trainer: Mrs Rebecca Davies

136 **MR VICTOR DARTNALL, Barnstaple**
Postal: **Higher Shutscombe Farm, Charles, Brayford, Barnstaple, Devon, EX32 7PU**
Contacts: **PHONE (01598) 710280 FAX (01598) 710708 MOBILE (07974) 374272**
E-MAIL **victordartnall@gmail.com** WEBSITE **www.victordartnallracing.com**

1 ADMIRAL'S SECRET, 8, b g Kayf Tara—Bobs Bay (IRE) **The Whacko Partnership**
2 BINDON LANE, 5, b g Arvico (FR)—Cuckoo Lane (IRE) **Mrs E. S. Weld**
3 BOLVING (IRE), 8, b g Stowaway—Kiniohio (FR) **Mrs C. M. Barber**
4 DANCING SHADOW (IRE), 10, br g Craigsteel—Be My Shadow (IRE) **The Dancing Shadows**
5 EXMOOR MIST (IRE), 11, gr g Kayf Tara—Chita's Flora **Exmoor Mist Partnership**
6 FISHERMANS COVE (IRE), 5, b g Getaway (GER)—Toscar (GER) **G. D. Hake**
7 GET WISHING (IRE), 7, b g Getaway (GER)—Third Wish (IRE) **Edge Of Exmoor**
8 HALDON HILL (IRE), 6, b g Mahler—Qui Plus Est (FR) **Mr J. P. McManus**
9 HELUVAGOOD, 7, b g Helissio (FR)—Cape Siren **Mr Dennis & Mr Mark Blight**
10 HOWARDIAN HILLS (IRE), 6, b g Vale of York (IRE)—Handsome Anna (IRE) **Mrs C Carter & Mr V Dartnall**
11 ISTANBUL PASHA (IRE), 4, ch g Fast Company—Red Red Rose **Mr V. R. A. Dartnall**
12 MAHLER'S FIRST (IRE), 7, b g Mahler—Fridays Folly (IRE) **First Brayford Partnership**
13 MINNIE ESCAPE, 7, b m Getaway (GER)—Minnie Hill (IRE) **The Second Brayford Partnership**
14 RIVER BRAY (IRE), 6, ch g Arakan (USA)—Cill Fhearga (IRE) **The River Bray Syndicate**
15 RUN TO MILAN (IRE), 7, b g Milan—Run Supreme (IRE) **Barber, Birchenough, De Wilde**
16 SHUTSCOMBE HILL, 7, b g Arvico (FR)—Storm Kitten (IRE) **Edge Of Exmoor**
17 SWEET ADARE (IRE), 6, b m Getaway (GER)—The Adare Woman (IRE) **G. D. Hake**
18 UT MAJEUR AULMES (FR), 11, ch g Northern Park (USA)—My Wish Aulmes (FR) **Mrs S. De Wilde**

Other Owners: Mrs K. Birchenough, Mr D. P. Blight, Mr M. Blight, Ms F. M. Carter, Ms C. Carter, Mrs P. Cunliffe, Mr B. C. Dallyn, Mrs J. Dartnall, Mr G. Dartnall, Miss Alison Delve, Mr J. Edelman, N. P. Haley, Mrs S. M. Hall, Mr C. W. M. Herbert, Mr M. E. Nicholls, Mr M. W. Richards, Mr P. A. Roberts, Mrs T. M. Scott, Mr L. Singleton, A. P. Staple.

Assistant Trainer: G. A. Dartnall

137 **MR TOM DASCOMBE, Malpas**
Postal: **Manor House Stables, Malpas, Cheshire, SY14 8AD**
Contacts: **PHONE (01948) 820485 FAX (01948) 820495 MOBILE (07973) 511664**
E-MAIL **tom@manorhousestables.com** WEBSITE **www.manorhousestables.com**

1 ARCANADA (IRE), 6, ch g Arcano (IRE)—Bond Deal (IRE) **The Arcanada Partnership**
2 CALDER PRINCE (IRE), 6, gr g Dark Angel (IRE)—Flame of Ireland (IRE) **Mr P. G. Birbeck**
3 CELESTIAL FORCE (IRE), 4, b g Sea The Stars (IRE)—Aquarelle Bleue **Mr J. E. Dance**
4 CHAI CHAI (IRE), 4, b g Zoffany (IRE)—Flamenco Red **King Power Racing Co Ltd**
5 CHARLIE D (USA), 4, b g Animal Kingdom (USA)—Ocicat (USA) **Mr D. R. Passant & Mr T. Dascombe**
6 DOCTOR SARDONICUS, 8, ch g Medicean—Never A Doubt **C. V. Wentworth**
7 DRAGONS TAIL (IRE), 4, b c Dragon Pulse (IRE)—Mastoora (IRE) **Goss Hyden Jones Owen Chasemore**

MR TOM DASCOMBE - Continued

8 EPAULEMENT (IRE), 4, b g Epaulette (AUS)—Little Whisper (IRE) **Deva Racing Epaulette Partnership**
9 FINNISTON FARM, 4, b g Helmet (AUS)—Logic **Godel Technologies Europe Limited**
10 FIRE DIAMOND, 6, b g Firebreak—Diapason (IRE) **Mr J. D. Brown**
11 KACHY, 6, b h Kyllachy—Dubai Bounty **Mr D. J. Lowe**
12 MICKEY (IRE), 6, b g Zoffany (IRE)—Enchantment **Mrs Janet Lowe & Mr Tom Dascombe**
13 PROSCHEMA (IRE), 4, ch g Declaration of War (USA)—Notable **Empire State Racing Partnership**
14 REFLEKTOR (IRE), 6, ch g Bahamian Bounty—Baby Bunting **David Lowe & Miss Amber Lowe**
15 SHA LA LA LA LEE, 4, b g Helmet (AUS)—Shamara (IRE) **Nigel and Sharon Mather & Charles Ledigo**
16 THIS GIRL, 4, b f Nathaniel (IRE)—Fibou (USA) **Mr D. J. Lowe**

THREE-YEAR-OLDS

17 ANGEL ALEXANDER (IRE), b c Dark Angel (IRE)—Majestic Alexander (IRE) **Birbeck Mound Trowbridge & Owen**
18 ARTHUR KITT, b c Camelot—Ceiling Kitty **Chasemore Farm LLP**
19 ARTISTIC STREAK, b f New Approach (IRE)—Artisti **David & Carol Shaw**
20 Ch f Lope de Vega (IRE)—Ballymore Celebre (IRE) **Mr J. E. Dance**
21 BARRISTAN THE BOLD, b c Excelebration (IRE)—Cradle of Life (IRE) **Chasemore Farm & Mr Kevin Costello**
22 DARK ENVOY (IRE), gr c Dark Angel (IRE)—Moonvoy **Mr D. R. Passant**
23 DONTHOLDYOURBREATH (IRE), ch f Bated Breath—Don't Tell Mary (IRE) **Keith & Mary Trowbridge**
24 DROGON (IRE), b c Zoffany (IRE)—Flames To Dust (GER) **APCC Limited**
25 FINOAH (IRE), b g Kodiac—Burstingdalak (IRE) **Alan & Sue Cronshaw & Peter Birbeck**
26 FLIGHTY ALMIGHTY, b f Elusive Quality (USA)—Wall of Sound **Chasemore Farm LLP**
27 FRANKADORE (IRE), ch c Frankel—Adoration (USA) **Clyne Dance Mound**
28 GREAT SCOT, b c Requinto (IRE)—La Rosiere (USA) **Empire State Racing Partnership**
29 GUANDI (USA), ch c Declaration of War (USA)—Hoh Buzzard (IRE) **Empire State Racing Partnership**
30 ICONIC CHOICE, ch f Sixties Icon—Adorable Choice (IRE) **Mr J. D. Brown**
31 JACKSTAR (IRE), gr c Dark Angel (IRE)—Starbright (IRE) **Mrs C. L. Ingram**
32 JONAH JONES (IRE), b c No Nay Never (USA)—Conniption (IRE) **Mr D. Ward**
33 KATIESHEIDINLISA, b f Camelot—Spritza (IRE) **Mr D.R Passant & Hefin Williams**
34 LIBERATION DAY, b g Iffraaj—Welsh Cake **FDCHoldings Nolan RCG Rutherford**
35 LOLA'S THEME, gr f Iffraaj—Lady's Art (FR) **David Lowe & Russell Jones**
36 METATRON (IRE), gr c Dark Angel (IRE)—Orikawa (FR) **Burns Smyth Studholme**
37 MOGSY (IRE), br g Dandy Man (IRE)—Dictatrice (FR) **Satchell Moran Solicitors**
38 NAVIGATE BY STARS (IRE), br f Sea The Stars (IRE)—Bitooh **The Wilmshurst Partnership**
39 RAJINSKY (IRE), b c Zoffany (IRE)—Pink Moon (IRE) **Egerton House Racing**
40 RED DRAGONESS (IRE), ch f Dragon Pulse (IRE)—Salydora (FR) **Roofing Consultants Group**
41 SHE CAN BOOGIE (IRE), b f Dandy Man (IRE)—Disko (IRE) **Mike Nolan & Partner**
42 SIR VICTOR (IRE), b c Sir Prancealot (IRE)—Victoria Lodge (USA) **Deva Racing Sir Prancealot P/ship**
43 SLOWMO (IRE), b c Kodiac—Motion Lass **Chasemore Farm LLP & Owen Promotions Ltd**
44 SMOKI SMOKA (IRE), ch g Dragon Pulse (IRE)—Creating Speed (IRE) **Duncan, Dunnington & Shaw**
45 WILD EDRIC, ch c Equiano (FR)—Lady Red Oak **Mr D. R. Passant**
46 ZOFFEE, b g Zoffany (IRE)—Mount Crystal (IRE) **Mr A. E. Peterson**

TWO-YEAR-OLDS

47 Gr c 16/4 Alhebayeb (IRE)—Annouska (IRE) (Ad Valorem (USA)) **Manor House Stables LLP**
48 Ch c 15/4 Dragon Pulse (IRE)—Balaagha (USA) (Mr Greeley (USA)) (42140) **Manor House Stables LLP**
49 B f 17/4 Muhaarar—Baldovina (Tale of The Cat (USA)) **King Power Racing Co Ltd**
50 BRAD THE BRIEF, b gr c 7/3 Dutch Art—Kenzadargent (FR) (Kendargent (FR)) **Chasemore Farm LLP**
51 B c 13/4 Kodiac—Brazilian Bride (IRE) (Pivotal) (63210) **King Power Racing Co Ltd**
52 BROOKSIDE BANNER (IRE), ch f 18/2 Starspangledbanner (AUS)—
            Akrivi (Tobougg (IRE)) (63211) **Mr S. Burns**
53 Br c 11/1 Society Rock (IRE)—Cape Karli (IRE) (Cape Cross (IRE)) (43826) **Manor House Stables LLP**
54 B f 11/4 Camelot—Conniption (IRE) (Danehill Dancer (IRE)) (63211) **Mr D. Ward**
55 B f 9/4 Brazen Beau (AUS)—Coz I Do (Pivotal) (3000) **Chasemore Farm LLP**
56 DANA FOREVER (IRE), b f 19/2 Requinto (IRE)—
            Positive Step (Footstepsinthesand) (52380) **Miss S. Y. D. Goh**
57 B c 3/3 Muhaarar—Dubai Bounty (Dubai Destination (USA)) (100000) **Mr D. R. Passant**
58 B c 1/4 Kodiac—Escapism (IRE) (Iffraaj) (80000) **Manor House Stables LLP**
59 B f 16/4 Kodiac—Esterlina (IRE) (Highest Honor (FR)) **Chasemore Farm LLP**
60 B c 12/3 Dragon Pulse (IRE)—Glen Ginnie (IRE) (Red Clubs (IRE)) (49523) **Middleham Park Racing C**
61 GLOBAL ORCHID (IRE), b f 6/2 Showcasing—Law Keeper (IRE) (Lawman (FR)) (70190) **Dr J. Hon**
62 GODFATHER (IRE), ch c 10/3 Night of Thunder (IRE)—Aqlaam Vision (Aqlaam) (80000) **Miss S. Y. D. Goh**
63 GRIV GIRL (IRE), b f 22/2 Starspangledbanner (AUS)—Grivele (IRE) (El Prado (IRE)) (62000) **Mr J. M. Kirkland**
64 HIGH FLYING BIRD (FR), b f 12/2 Reliable Man—
            Supernova Heights (IRE) (Oasis Dream) (33712) **The High Flying Bird Partnership**
65 HOT HEELS, ch c 24/4 Hot Streak (IRE)—Poulaine Bleue (Bertolini (USA)) (22756) **Fox Trotters**

MR TOM DASCOMBE - Continued

66 B c 25/3 Fountain of Youth (IRE)—La Rosiere (USA) (Mr Greeley (USA)) **Empire State Racing Partnership**
67 B c 13/4 Bated Breath—Laber Ildut (IRE) (Whipper (USA)) (45714) **More Turf Racing**
68 **LOVABLE CHOICE,** ch f 20/2 Sixties Icon—Adorable Choice (IRE) (Choisir (AUS)) **Mr J. D. Brown**
69 B c 23/2 Dandy Man (IRE)—Mad About The Girl (IRE) (Excellent Art) (761) **Owen Promotions Limited**
70 B c 2/4 Requinto (IRE)—Mattinata (Tiger Hill (IRE)) (37926) **Manor House Stables LLP**
71 **ME AND MR JONES,** b c 18/4 Brazen Beau (AUS)—
                                   Posy Fossil (USA) (Malibu Moon (USA)) (33333) **Mr R. Jones**
72 B c 3/4 Ivawood (IRE)—Mirror Image (Acclamation) (38095) **Manor House Stables LLP**
73 Ch f 28/1 Make Believe—Miss Lucy Jane (Aqlaam) (33333) **Peter Birbeck & Rachel Dawson**
74 B f 21/2 Dandy Man (IRE)—New Romantic (Singspiel (IRE)) (22857) **Mr R. Jones**
75 B f 17/4 Lawman (FR)—Paddy Again (IRE) (Moss Vale (IRE)) (25284) **Mike Nolan & John Abbey**
76 Ch f 2/3 Declaration of War (USA)—
                                   Parisian Affair (USA) (Mr Greeley (USA)) (50568) **Empire State Racing Partnership**
77 B c 20/4 Epaulette (AUS)—Party Feet (IRE) (Noverre (USA)) (15238) **Mr M. Edwards**
78 B c 15/4 Society Rock (IRE)—Perfect Pose (IRE) (Amadeus Wolf) (45714) **Manor House Stables LLP**
79 Ch f 17/3 No Nay Never (USA)—Princess Patsky (USA) (Mr Greeley (USA)) (47619) **More Turf Racing**
80 B c 21/3 Due Diligence (USA)—Queens Park (FR) (King's Best (USA)) **Mr & Mrs R. Scott**
81 Ch g 10/4 Dragon Pulse (IRE)—Raktina (Polish Precedent) (11428) **Michael Owen Racing Club**
82 **SHE'S A UNICORN,** b f 23/4 Garswood—Shatter (IRE) (Mr Greeley (USA)) (4761) **Mr T. G. Dascombe**
83 **SHEVCHENKO PARK (IRE),** b c 12/3 Epaulette (AUS)—
                                   Compton Girl (Compton Place) (29498) **Nolan O'Halloran Satchell & Partner**
84 B c 8/3 Dabirsim (FR)—
                    Shining Glory (GER) (Konigstiger (GER)) (71639) **K. Trowbridge, P. Radcliffe & P. Birbeck**
85 B gr c 18/4 Brazen Beau (AUS)—Silver Grey (IRE) (Chineur (FR)) (67000) **Manor House Stables LLP**
86 B f 31/3 Golden Horn—Simonetta (IRE) (Lil's Boy (USA)) (65739) **Mr D. Ward**
87 B f 1/3 Outstrip—Singing Field (IRE) (Singspiel (IRE)) (29498) **Manor House Stables LLP**
88 B c 4/4 Heeraat (IRE)—Trixie Malone (Ishiguru (USA)) (19047) **Manor House Stables LLP**
89 B c 1/3 Cappella Sansevero—Varnay (Machiavellian (USA)) (57142) **Mr J. E. Dance**
90 B f 13/2 Kingman—Wall of Sound (Singspiel (IRE)) **Chasemore Farm LLP**

Other Owners: J. E. Abbey, Mrs Sandra G. E. Arkwright, Major P. W. F. Arkwright, Mr N. B. Attenborough, Mrs A. Biles, Mrs J. E. Black, A. W. Black, Mr G. Bouch, Mr N. Clyne, Mr P. G. Cooke, Mrs F. H. B. Cork, Mr J. F. P. Cork, Mr K. Costello, Alan & Sue Cronshaw, Mr A. Cronshaw, Mrs S. P. Cronshaw, Mr R. S. Dawson, Mr D. Duncan, Mr C. Dunnington, FDC Holdings Ltd, Mr M. D. Foster, Mrs J. Foster, Mr G. S. Goss, Mr A. M. H. Heald, M. G. H. Heald, Mrs L. C. Hyden, Mr G. Jones, Mr C. Ledigo, Miss A. J. Lowe, Mrs J. Lowe, Mrs S. E. Mather, Mr N. P. Mather, Mrs J. P. Melia, Mr T. J. Moran, Mr S. N. Mound, M. F. Nolan, Mr M. O'Halloran, Mr L. T. Owen, Mr M.J Owen, T. S. Palin, M. Prince, Mr P. Radcliffe, L. M. Rutherford, Mr M. Satchell, R. Scott, Mrs P. M. Scott, Mr D. M. Shaw, Mrs C. A. Shaw, Mr M. Smyth, Mr D. Studholme, K. P. Trowbridge, Mrs M. C. Trowbridge, Mr H. Williams, Mr C. J. Wilmshurst, Mr M. Wilmshurst.

Assistant Trainer: Colin Gorman

Jockey (flat): Richard Kingscote. **Apprentice:** Elisha Whittington. **Amateur:** Miss Alyson Deniel.

---

138 **MR TRISTAN DAVIDSON, Carlisle**
Postal: Bellmount, Laversdale, Irthington, Carlisle, Cumbria, CA6 4PS
Contacts: **MOBILE (07789) 684290**

1 **ALPINE PASS,** 5, b g Sir Percy—In The Pink (IRE) **Ben Greenslade, David McCrone & J Dixon**
2 **ASKGARMOR (IRE),** 7, b g Ask—Karmatair (IRE) **E G Tunstall, The Not Very Likely Lads**
3 **CHICORIA (IRE),** 10, ch g Presenting—Coco Girl **Carlisle Poker Club & Mr P S Nicholson**
4 **CHINGACHGOOK,** 4, b g Al Kazeem—Natty Bumppo (IRE) **Mr W. A. Tinkler**
5 **DRAMATIC MOMENT,** 4, ch f Helmet (AUS)—
                                   Distant Drama (USA) **Ben Greenslade David McCrone & L Cameron**
6 **INCHCOLM (IRE),** 9, br g Presenting—Rose of Inchiquin (IRE) **SprayClad UK**
7 **JUSTATENNER,** 8, b g Northern Legend—Shelayly (IRE) **The Whartons**
8 **LA CUMPARSITA (IRE),** 5, b m Papal Bull—Silk Slippers **Ben Greenslade, David McCrone & J Dixon**
9 **LOSTOCK HALL (IRE),** 7, b g Lord Shanakill (USA)—Cannikin (IRE) **Ben Greenslade & David McCrone**
10 **NELSON ROAD (IRE),** 6, b g Mount Nelson—Merciful (IRE) **Ben Greenslade, David McCrone & J Dixon**
11 **RUBENESQUE (IRE),** 7, b m Getaway (GER)—Shouette (IRE) **Ben Greenslade & David McCrone**
12 **SELFCONTROL (IRE),** 8, b br g Al Namix (FR)—L'ascension (USA) **Carlisle Poker Club & Mr P S Nicholson**

Other Owners: L Cameron, Carlisle Poker Club, Mr J. Dixon, Mr L. Ellison, Mr Gary Etheridge, Mr Ben Greenslade, Mr Dean Lamonby, Mr D. L. McCrone, Mr P. S. Nicholson, Mr J. Reay, Mr W. A. Tinkler, Mr E. G. Tunstall, Mrs Joyce Wharton, Mr T. Wharton, Mr Eddie Wharton.

Conditional: Harry Reed.

139 MR JOHN DAVIES, Darlington
Postal: **Denton Grange, Piercebridge, Darlington, County Durham, DL2 3TZ**
Contacts: **PHONE (01325) 374366 MOBILE (07746) 292782**
E-MAIL johndavieshorses@live.co.uk WEBSITE www.johndaviesracing.com

1 **ALFRED RICHARDSON,** 5, ch g Dapper—Vera Richardson (IRE) **K Kirkup & J Davies**
2 **CRIMSON SKIES (IRE),** 4, ch f Declaration of War (USA)—Emily Blake (IRE) **The Red and White Stripes**
3 **IM DAPPER TOO,** 8, b g Dapper—Lonely One **Mr C. W. Davies**
4 **MAJOR ROWAN,** 8, b g Captain Gerrard (IRE)—Julie's Gift **J. J. Davies**
5 **MANGO CHUTNEY,** 6, b g Sleeping Indian—Crimson Topaz **The Sexy Fish Partnership**
6 **MR COOL CASH,** 7, b g Firebreak—Cashleen (USA) **Mr I. Lawson**
7 **MY NAME IS RIO (IRE),** 9, ch g Captain Rio—Walk In My Shadow (IRE) **K. Kirkup**
8 **PETITIONER (IRE),** 5, b g Dansili—Reflective (USA) **Mr C. J. Mooney**
9 4, B f Mount Nelson—Sambarina (IRE) **J. J. Davies**

THREE-YEAR-OLDS

10 **GATESY (IRE),** gr g Swiss Spirit—Firoza (FR) **Ms D. Nicholson**
11 **HAPPY HANNAH (IRE),** ch f Gale Force Ten—Sli Na Fiarana **Ms D. Nicholson**
12 **HIGHJACKED,** b g Dick Turpin (IRE)—Vera Richardson (IRE) **K Kirkup & J Davies**
13 **TSCHUSS,** b f Toronado (IRE)—Rosa Bud **The Maroon Stud**

TWO-YEAR-OLDS

14 Ch c 17/3 Intrinsic—Angelic Kitten (IRE) (One Cool Cat (USA)) **J. J. Davies**
15 B c 21/4 Helmet (AUS)—Emily Blake (IRE) (Lend A Hand) **Mr & Mrs R. Scott**
16 B c 12/4 Lethal Force (IRE)—Tamalain (USA) (Royal Academy (USA)) **Mr & Mrs R. Scott**
17 Ch c 18/3 Casamento (IRE)—Tamara Bay (Selkirk (USA)) **Mr & Mrs R Scott & J Davies**

Other Owners: Mr K. Borrett, L. L. Dickman, Mr A. Dickman, Mr P. Dunnill, R. Scott, Mrs P. M. Scott, Mr P. Taylor.

140 MISS SARAH-JAYNE DAVIES, Leominster
Postal: **The Upper Withers, Hundred Lane, Kimbolton, Leominster, Herefordshire, HR6 0HZ**
Contacts: **PHONE (01584) 711780 MOBILE (07779) 797079**
E-MAIL sjdracing@live.co.uk WEBSITE www.sjdracing.co.uk

1 **ACCESSALLAREAS (IRE),** 14, ch g Swift Gulliver (IRE)—Arushofgold (IRE) **Withers Winners**
2 **ALBERT GEORGE,** 5, ch g Paco Boy (IRE)—Avonrose
3 **ARVICO'S LIGHT,** 5, b g Arvico (FR)—Miss Lightning **Mrs S. M. Davies**
4 **BENSON,** 4, b g Beat Hollow—Karla June **Pump & Plant Services Ltd**
5 **CAMLAD KINGFISHER,** 7, ch g Sulamani (IRE)—Val de Fleurie (GER) **Mrs C. J. Davies**
6 **CODDINGTON BANKS,** 7, b m Fair Mix (IRE)—Coddington Girl **Miss H. S. Chapman**
7 **DEADLY APPROACH,** 8, b g New Approach (IRE)—Speirbhean (IRE) **Quadriga Racing**
8 **FAIR TO DREAM,** 6, b g Fair Mix (IRE)—Sahara's Dream **K. E. Stait**
9 **HEREFORDSHIRE,** 11, b g Beneficial—Handmemy Moneydown (IRE) **Mr M. A. Fothergill**
10 **HIGGS,** 6, b g Scorpion (IRE)—Captain Supreme (IRE) **Pump & Plant Services Ltd**
11 **LAST CHANCE PADDY (USA),** 5, gr g Paddy O'prado (USA)—Mizzcan'tbewrong (USA) **Miss S. J. Davies**
12 **PEMBROKE HOUSE,** 12, gr g Terimon—Bon Coeur **Sarah-Jayne Davies & Steve Mace**
13 **PEPPERDEW (USA),** 5, ch g Street Cry (IRE)—Spice Island (USA) **Pump & Plant Services Ltd**
14 **ROYAL ACT,** 7, br g Royal Anthem (USA)—Native's Return (IRE) **Moorland Racing**
15 **SALAZAR (IRE),** 4, ch g Raven's Pass (USA)—Queen Padme (IRE) **Miss N. Thompson**
16 **SAM CHISOLM (IRE),** 6, br g Getaway (GER)—
    Undecided Hall (IRE) **S Mace, P Whilock, M Hammond & D Cotton**
17 **SECRET MELODY,** 6, b g Sakhee's Secret—Montjeu's Melody (IRE) **Moorland Racing & Mark Hammond**
18 **SOLDIER OF WAR (USA),** 4, b g War Front (USA)—Praise (USA) **Pump & Plant Services Ltd**
19 **SPANISH STARLING,** 7, b g Fantastic Spain (USA)—Clarice Starling **Mr A. J. Gough**

Other Owners: Mr D. Cotton, Mr M. J. Hammond, S. A. Mace, Mrs A. M. Mace, Mrs C. Tucker, Mr J. F. Vincent, Mr P. R. Whilock.

Jockey (NH): James Davies. **Conditional:** Ben Godfrey. **Amateur:** Miss Tabitha Worsley.

141
MISS JO DAVIS, East Garston
Postal: **1 Parson Close Stables, School Lane, East Garston, Hungerford, Berkshire, RG17 7HR**
Contacts: **PHONE (01488) 649977 FAX (01488) 649977 MOBILE (07879) 811535**
E-MAIL davisjo_007@hotmail.com WEBSITE www.jodavisracing.com

1 BOND DO TIGRAO, 4, b c Monsieur Bond (IRE)—Bahama Bay **Angela Ford**
2 GALLIC DESTINY (IRE), 8, b g Champs Elysees—Cross Your Fingers (USA) **Mrs P. M. Brown**
3 IT'S FOR ALAN, 6, b g Multiplex—Miss Keck **Tony Worth & Vic Bedley**
4 JOHN BISCUIT (IRE), 8, b g Hawk Wing (USA)—Princess Magdalena **Mrs P. M. Brown**
5 KEN'S WELL (IRE), 8, b g Trans Island—Tiergarten (IRE) **Mrs P. M. Brown**
6 MARMONT, 6, ch g Winker Watson—Five Bells (IRE) **Miss J. S. Davis**
7 MINIATURE DAFFODIL (IRE), 4, b g Thewayyouare (USA)—Queen of Stars (USA) **TheseGirlsCan Racing Club**
8 MR FITZROY (IRE), 9, ch g Kyllachy—Reputable **Mrs P. M. Brown**
9 OSCARS LEADER (IRE), 6, b g Oscar (IRE)—Lead'er Inn (IRE) **J. L. Marriott**
10 SAGGAZZA, 5, b g Schiaparelli (GER)—Wee Dinns (IRE) **Mrs P. M. Brown**
11 STAR FOOT (IRE), 8, b g Soviet Star (USA)—On The Backfoot (IRE) **J. L. Marriott**
12 THE BIG YIN, 5, ch g Malinas (GER)—Bright Spangle (IRE) **Maggie Davis & Jo Davis**
13 TOUCHY SUBJECT (IRE), 6, br g Tikkanen (USA)—Legal Lodge (IRE) **J. L. Marriott**

THREE-YEAR-OLDS
14 B f Epaulette (AUS)—No Frills (IRE) **Mrs P. M. Brown**

Other Owners: V. R. Bedley, Mrs M. A. Davis, Mr A. G. Worth.

Assistant Trainer: Gregg Whitehead

142
MISS LOUISE DAVIS, Stafford
Postal: **The Stables, Hillcrest, Bradley Lane, Levedale, Stafford, Staffordshire, ST18 9AH**
Contacts: **MOBILE (07940) 923452**

1 BRIDGE OF SIGHS, 7, ch g Avonbridge—Ashantiana **Miss L. V. Davis**
2 CALLING DES BLINS (FR), 7, b m Konig Turf (GER)—Quelye des Blins (FR) **Miss L. V. Davis**
3 PHOBIAPHILIAC (IRE), 8, b g Beneficial—Denys Eyre (IRE) **Miss L. V. Davis**
4 RED DEVIL LADS (IRE), 10, b g Beneficial—Welsh Sitara (IRE) **Miss L. V. Davis**
5 SALLA, 5, b m Foxwedge (AUS)—Sahara Sunshine **Miss L. V. Davis**
6 SARPECH (IRE), 8, b g Sea The Stars (IRE)—Sadima (IRE) **Miss L. V. Davis**
7 SPADER (IRE), 6, b g Jeremy (USA)—Poulkovo (IRE) **Miss L. V. Davis**
8 TENNESSEE BELLE, 5, b m Teofilo (IRE)—Dixie Belle **Miss L. V. Davis**

Assistant Trainer: Jason Freeman

143
MISS ZOE DAVISON, East Grinstead
Postal: **Shovelstrode Racing Stables, Shovelstrode Lane, Ashurstwood, East Grinstead, West Sussex, RH19 3PN**
Contacts: **PHONE (01342) 300319 MOBILE (07970) 839357 & (07812) 007554**
E-MAIL andy01031976@yahoo.co.uk WEBSITE www.shovelstroderacing.co.uk

1 BRANDY CROSS (IRE), 5, b g Le Fou (IRE)—Glenquin (IRE) **Surefire Racing**
2 BROTHER BENNETT (FR), 9, gr g Martaline—La Gaminerie (FR) **The Secret Circle**
3 CLONDAW ROBIN (IRE), 6, ch g Robin des Champs (FR)—Old Town Queen (IRE) **The Plum Merchants**
4 DEVIOUS DICKS DAME, 4, b f Dick Turpin (IRE)—Bridal White **The Secret Circle Racing Club**
5 DYLANSEOGHAN (IRE), 10, b g Pierre—Sabbatical (IRE) **The Lump O'Clock Syndicate**
6 FINNEGAN'S GARDEN (IRE), 10, b g Definite Article—Tri Folene (FR) **Mr K. Corke**
7 GLORIOUS BORU (IRE), 8, b g Brian Boru—Sea Off The Gales (IRE) **Eventmasters Racing**
8 GUSTAV (IRE), 9, b g Mahler—Pakaradyssa (FR) **The Plum Merchants**
9 HARRY HAZARD, 5, b g Schiaparelli (GER)—Eveon (IRE) **Mr A. Lewers**
10 IMPULSIVE LEADER (IRE), 6, b m Westerner—Impulsive Ita (IRE) **Mr K. Corke**
11 KILINAKIN (IRE), 9, ch g Definite Article—Topanberry (IRE) **The Lump O'Clock Syndicate**
12 KING OF THE SHARKS (IRE), 6, b g Flemensfirth (USA)—Kings Rose (IRE) **Go Faster Syndicate**
13 MAISY BELLE (IRE), 4, b m Westerner—Sabbiosa (IRE) **The Secret Circle Racing Club**
14 O'RAHILLY (IRE), 7, b g Aristotle (IRE)—Linoora (IRE) **The Secret Circle Racing Club**
15 OPEN HANDED, 4, b g Sakhee (USA)—Naemi (GER) **Mrs K. Meekins**
16 PETE'S CHOICE (IRE), 6, b br g Arcadio (GER)—Definite Design (IRE) **Jokulhlaup Syndicate**

MISS ZOE DAVISON - Continued

17 THE GAME IS A FOOT (IRE), 12, b g Oscar (IRE)—Cooksgrove Rosie (IRE) **The Secret Circle Racing Club**
18 THE GOLDEN HOUR (IRE), 9, b m Gold Well—Kirktonmoor Katie (IRE) **Mr N. D. Sharp**
19 VENETIAN PROPOSAL (IRE), 5, b m Fast Company (IRE)—Ide Say (IRE) **Mr D. Shaw**
20 WATAR ALLSTAR (IRE), 5, ch g Watar (IRE)—All Star Lady (IRE) **Mr D. Shaw**
21 WINDY BOTTOM (IRE), 8, b m Milan—Swinley Bottom (IRE) **The Lump Oclock the Secret Circle**

Other Owners: Mr J. A. Barber, S. J. Clare, Mr A. C. Clift, Miss Z. C. Davison, Mr A. J. Irvine, Mr V. Lewis, Mr S. R. McInnes, T. M. Santry, Mr E. J. N. Sheasby, Mrs D. Sheasby, Mr A. N. Waters.

Assistant Trainer: A. Irvine.

---

144 **MR ANTHONY DAY, Hinckley**
Postal: **Wolvey Fields Farm, Coalpit Lane, Wolvey, Hinckley, Leicestershire, LE10 3HD**

1 CHARMING LAD (IRE), 14, b g Dushyantor (USA)—Glens Lady (IRE) **Mrs K. D. Day**
2 DANNY'S STAR, 8, b g Winged Love (IRE)—Corcullentra Lass (IRE) **Mrs K. D. Day**
3 MY ANCHOR, 8, b g Mount Nelson—War Shanty **Mrs K. D. Day**
4 SOUND THE BUGLE, 9, b g Overbury (IRE)—Fusion of Tunes **Mrs K. D. Day**
5 STRIPE OF HONOUR (IRE), 6, b g Court Cave—Miss Top (IRE) **Mrs K. D. Day**

---

145 **MR WILLIAM DE BEST-TURNER, Calne**
Postal: **8 North End, Calne, Wiltshire, SN11 9DQ**
Contacts: PHONE (01249) 811944 HOME (01249) 813850 MOBILE (07977) 910779
E-MAIL debestracing@hotmail.co.uk

1 CALGARY TIGER, 4, b g Tiger Groom—Sachiko **W. de Best-Turner**
2 CHICAGO SOCKS, 9, b h Catcher In The Rye (IRE)—Sachiko **W. de Best-Turner**
3 NELSON'S HILL, 9, b g Mount Nelson—Regal Step **Debestracing**
4 PIXELATIT, 4, b f Dream Eater (IRE)—Spartaculous **Debestracing**
5 TIGER PRINT, 4, b f Tiger Groom—Maylan (IRE)

TWO-YEAR-OLDS

6 B f 8/4 Phenomena—Spartaculous (Spartacus (IRE))
7 Ch f 2/5 Arvico (FR)—Sterling Moll (Lord of Men)

Other Owners: Miss S J Slade, Mr W. de Best-Turner.

Assistant Trainer: Mrs I. De Best

---

146 **MR ED DE GILES, Ledbury**
Postal: **Lilly Hall Farm, Little Marcle, Ledbury, Herefordshire, HR8 2LD**
Contacts: PHONE (01531) 637369 MOBILE (07811) 388345
E-MAIL ed@eddegilesracing.com WEBSITE www.eddegilesracing.com

1 AKAVIT (IRE), 7, b g Vale of York (IRE)—Along Came Molly **Simon Treacher & Partner**
2 BOMBASTIC (IRE), 4, ch g Raven's Pass (USA)—Star of The West **The Philistines**
3 BOMBERO (IRE), 5, b g Dragon Pulse (IRE)—Mathool (IRE) **Woodham Walter Partnership**
4 5, B m Mount Nelson—Candle **Mr E. B. de Giles**
5 CLASSIFIED (IRE), 5, b m Lope de Vega (IRE)—Crossbreeze (USA) **Tight Lines Partnership**
6 COACHELLA (IRE), 5, gr g Kyllachy—Indian Belle (IRE) **Clarissa Casdagli & Partners**
7 COOLSPIN (IRE), 4, b f Teofilo (IRE)—Ocean Silk (USA) **Tight Lines Partnership**
8 DELIRIUM (IRE), 5, b m Tamayuz—Coeur de La Mer (IRE) **Tight Lines Partnership**
9 FITZROVIA, 4, br g Poet's Voice—Pompey Girl **Simon Treacher & Clarissa Casdagli**
10 INCUS, 6, b g Bertolini (USA)—Cloudchaser (IRE) **Mrs Yvonne Fleet & Partner**
11 LESANTI, 5, b g Royal Applause—Kammaan **The LAM Partnership**
12 ORANGE SUIT (IRE), 4, b c Declaration of War (USA)—Guantanamera (IRE) **Tight Lines Partnership**
13 PIKE CORNER CROSS (IRE), 7, b g Cape Cross (IRE)—Smart Coco (USA) **Mrs Yvonne Fleet & Partner**
14 PLENTY IN THE TANK (IRE), 4, b g Champs Elysees—Lunathea (IRE) **Simon Treacher & Partner**
15 QUANTUM DOT (IRE), 8, ch g Exceed And Excel (AUS)—Jeed (IRE) **Mrs Yvonne Fleet & Partner**
16 ROAR (IRE), 5, b g Pour Moi (IRE)—Evening Rushour (IRE) **P Inglett, J Basquill & E Frost**

MR ED DE GILES - Continued

17 **SALSA VERDE (IRE)**, 4, b g Canford Cliffs (IRE)—Bridal Dance (IRE) **John Manser & Simon Treacher**
18 **SEXY BEAST**, 4, b c Teofilo (IRE)—Wadaat **Tight Lines Partnership**
19 **SWANTON BLUE (IRE)**, 6, b g Kodiac—Cabopino (IRE) **Mr E. B. de Giles**
20 **SWEETEST SMILE (IRE)**, 4, b f Champs Elysees—Scorn (USA) **The LAM Partnership**
21 **TENEDOS**, 4, b g High Chaparral (IRE)—Garanciere (FR) **Star Sports Bloodstock**
22 **TREACHEROUS**, 5, b g Paco Boy (IRE)—Black Baroness **Woodham Walter Partnership**
23 **WIND IN MY SAILS**, 7, b g Footstepsinthesand—Dylanesque **Mr P. J. Manser**
24 **ZAMORANO (IRE)**, 7, b m Teofilo (IRE)—Petit Calva (FR) **Mr E. B. de Giles**
25 **ZLATAN (IRE)**, 6, b g Dark Angel (IRE)—Guard Hill (USA) **Casdagli & Partners**

THREE-YEAR-OLDS

26 **BACON'S REBELLION**, b c Nathaniel (IRE)—Linda (FR) **Carrington & Cunningham**
27 **CORRIDA DE TOROS (IRE)**, b c Lope de Vega (IRE)—The Shrew **Mr E. B. de Giles**
28 **FRANCISCO BAY**, b c Paco Boy (IRE)—Lucky Breeze (IRE) **Mr C. C. Shand Kydd & Partner**
29 **MAERCHENGARTEN**, b f Bated Breath—Kammaan **The LAM Partnership**
30 **THE FURROWS END**, bl g Proclamation (IRE)—Chalosse **Sharron & Robert Colvin**

TWO-YEAR-OLDS

31 Ch f 10/3 Night of Thunder (IRE)—Broadway Duchess (IRE) (New Approach (IRE)) (50000) **The LAM Partnership**
32 **FLIPPANCE**, b f 7/4 Toronado (IRE)—Fantastic Santanyi (Fantastic Light (USA)) **R. Mathew**
33 Br g 26/3 Gutaifan (IRE)—Inca Trail (USA) (Royal Academy (USA))

Other Owners: Mr J. M. Basquill, Mr J. P. Carrington, Mrs C. R. Casdagli, Mr S. N. Champ, Mrs S. Colvin, R. Colvin, Ms A. P. M. Cunningham, Mrs Y. Fleet, Dr M. F. Ford, Mr E. H. M. Frost, Mr J. C. Golder, Mr D. J. Haddrell, Mr G. A. Holmes, Mr P. Inglett, Mr B. Keith, Mr T. D. J. Marshall, Ms L. M. Mulcahy, Mr P. R. Sercombe, C. C. Shand Kydd, Mr S. Treacher, A. J. Viall, Mrs C. R. de Giles.

---

147 MR GEOFFREY DEACON, Compton
Postal: **Hamilton Stables, Hockham Road, Compton, Newbury, Berkshire, RG20 6QJ**
Contacts: **MOBILE (07967) 626757**
E-MAIL geoffdeacon@aol.com WEBSITE www.geoffreydeacontraining.com

1 **CAPTAIN RYAN**, 8, b g Captain Gerrard (IRE)—Ryan's Quest (IRE) **Mr R. J. Douglas**
2 **HELLEBERRY**, 5, gr m Hellvelyn—Elderberry **Mara Racing**
3 **HONEY BOO**, 6, ch m Tobougg (IRE)—Queen of The Bees (IRE) **Mrs S. A. Roe**
4 **MIRROR MAGIC**, 4, br f Nathaniel (IRE)—Mirror Effect (IRE) **Stuart McPhee & Partner**
5 **MOON TRIP**, 10, b g Cape Cross (IRE)—Fading Light **The Moon Trip Partnership**
6 **PICKET LINE**, 7, b g Multiplex—Dockside Strike **Homegrown Partnership**
7 **RAHMAH (IRE)**, 7, b g Vale of York (IRE)—Sweet Home Alabama (IRE) **Mr P. D. Cundell and Partner**
8 **SUITSUS**, 8, b g Virtual—Point Perfect **Suitsus Partnership**
9 **SUTTONWOOD SALLY**, 5, b m Delegator—Hip Hip Hooray **Mr R. J. Douglas**
10 **WOGGLE (IRE)**, 4, ch f Camacho—Radio Wave **Hearty Racing**

THREE-YEAR-OLDS

11 **FROSTY TERN**, gr f Aussie Rules (USA)—Frosty Welcome (USA) **Mr R. J. Douglas**
12 **MISREAD**, ch f Nayef (USA)—Widescreen (USA) **Compton Racing Club**

TWO-YEAR-OLDS

13 Ch f 23/3 Anjaal—Allegrissimo (IRE) (Redback) (841) **Mr G. Deacon**

Other Owners: Mr M. V. Aram, Mr E. A. Bolton, Business Moves Group Ltd, P. D. Cundell, Mr F. Hearty, R. Kent, Mr P. M. Lafford, Miss L. McGrath, Mr S. K. McPhee, Mr A. R. Pittman, Mr J. Wakefield.

Assistant Trainer: Sally Duckett

148 MR DAVID DENNIS, Hanley Swan

Postal: **Tyre Hill Racing Stables, Hanley Swan, Worcester, Worcestershire, WR8 0EQ**
Contacts: **PHONE (01684) 310565 MOBILE (07867) 974880**
E-MAIL **david@daviddennistrainer.co.uk** WEBSITE **www.ddracing.co.uk**

1 **ADAMS STAR (IRE)**, 4, b g Mahler—Pepelina (IRE) **The Adam's Star Syndicate**
2 4, B f Presenting—Aguida (FR) **Mrs Emma Stewart & Partner**
3 **AUBIS PARK (FR)**, 4, b f Walk In The Park (IRE)—Aubisquinette (FR) **Prof L. P. Hardwick**
4 **BLACKMILL (IRE)**, 8, b g Kalanisi (IRE)—Lady of The Mill (IRE) **Mrs J. Hitchings**
5 **BROKEN QUEST (IRE)**, 7, b g Ask—Broken Thought (IRE) **Wright Morgan Ltd & Partner**
6 **BRUNEL WOODS (IRE)**, 7, b g Oscar (IRE)—Golden Bay **The Dobbin Club & Favourites Racing 7**
7 **CANDID COASTGUARD**, 4, ch g Harbour Watch (IRE)—Honesty Pays **Tyre Hill Farm Ltd**
8 **CYCLOP (IRE)**, 8, b g King's Theatre (IRE)—Tasmani (FR) **DD Racing & Professor L P Hardwick**
9 **DANECASE**, 6, ch g Showcasing—Yding (IRE) **Professor L P Hardwick & Partner**
10 **DEAUVILLE DANCER (IRE)**, 8, b g Tamayuz—Mathool (IRE) **Favourites Racing (Syndication) Ltd 10**
11 **DONATELLO MAIL (FR)**, 6, ch g Zambezi Sun—Kestrel Mail (FR) **Mrs J. Rees & Professor L P Hardwick**
12 **DONTCOUNTURCHIKENS (IRE)**, 5, b g Getaway (GER)—Stormy Breeze (IRE) **Clan McNeil**
13 **FINAL NUDGE (IRE)**, 10, b g Kayf Tara—Another Shot (IRE) **Corbett Stud**
14 **FLYING VERSE**, 7, b g Yeats (IRE)—Flight Sequence **Dr C. A. Barnett & Partner**
15 **GETAWAY HONEY (IRE)**, 7, ch m Getaway (GER)—Knappogue Honey (IRE) **Taylormaid**
16 **GLASSBOY (IRE)**, 4, br g Avonbridge—Encore du Cristal (USA) **Four Blokes Ltd**
17 **HAHADI (IRE)**, 7, ch g Getaway (GER)—Derrygowna Lord (IRE) **Legacy Racing**
18 4, B g Arctic Cosmos (USA)—Hardy Lamb (IRE) **Mrs J. Rees**
19 **INDY FIVE (IRE)**, 9, b g Vertical Speed (FR)—Beesplease (IRE) **The Dobbin Club**
20 **INNISFREE LAD (IRE)**, 7, b g Yeats (IRE)—Tasmani (FR) **Rees, Hardwick, Vaughan, Allum & Saville**
21 **KINGFAST (IRE)**, 4, b g Fast Company (IRE)—Monarchy (IRE) **Mr G. Saville, Mr G. Brandrick & Partner**
22 **KRACQUER**, 5, ch g Schiaparelli (GER)—Norma Hill **Mr G. Lloyd**
23 **LUCKY JIM**, 8, b g Lucky Story (USA)—Lateralle (IRE) **DD Racing & Professor L P Hardwick 2**
24 **MAKE GOOD (IRE)**, 4, b g Fast Company (IRE)—Rectify (IRE) **Clan McNeil**
25 **MARQUIS OF CARABAS (IRE)**, 9, b br g Hurricane Run (IRE)—Miss Otis Regrets (IRE) **Favourites Racing Ltd**
26 **MR WASHINGTON (IRE)**, 6, b g Vinnie Roe (IRE)—Anna Bird (IRE) **Mrs J. Hitchings**
27 **MY SOCIETY (IRE)**, 4, b g Society Rock (IRE)—Greek Easter (IRE) **Mr A. Killoran & Partners**
28 **NIGHTBOATTOCLYRO**, 5, ch g Sulamani (IRE)—Wychwood Legend **Kevin, Anne & Mark Glastonbury**
29 **NORSE LIGHT**, 8, ch g Norse Dancer (IRE)—Dimelight **The David Dennis Racing Club**
30 **NOTHING MAN (IRE)**, 5, b g Ask—Holly Gaga (IRE) **Mrs J. Rees**
31 4, Br g Jeremy (USA)—Phantom Waters **Tyre Hill Farm Ltd**
32 **PILOT WINGS (IRE)**, 4, b g Epaulette (AUS)—Intaglia (GER) **Green lighting Ltd**
33 **ROMAN FLIGHT (IRE)**, 11, b g Antonius Pius (USA)—Flight Sequence **Favourites Racing Ltd**
34 **SCHNABEL (IRE)**, 7, b g Ask—Velsatis (IRE) **Professor L P Hardwick & Partner**
35 **SHANTY TOWN (IRE)**, 10, b g Zagreb (USA)—Rapsan (IRE) **Mrs E. C. Stewart**
36 **SHELDON COOPER (IRE)**, 6, b g Excellent Art—Lapis Lazuli **The Dobbin Club**
37 **SPENCER LEA (IRE)**, 11, b g Overbury (IRE)—Castanet **Mrs C. Davis**
38 **SWISSAL (IRE)**, 4, b g Swiss Spirit—Al Gharrafa **Scott Wilson & Tyre Hill Farm Ltd**
39 **VEILED SECRET (IRE)**, 5, b g Teofilo (IRE)—Seven Veils (IRE) **Clan McNeil**
40 4, B g Mahler—Venusorserena (IRE) **Mrs J. Rees**
41 **ZEE MAN (FR)**, 5, b g Soldier of Fortune (IRE)—Sky High Flyer **Mr B. D. Vaughan**

Other Owners: Mr R. Allum, Mr M. J. S. Cockburn, Mr D. R. Dennis, Mr D. W. Doolittle, Favourites Racing (Syndication) 14, Favourites Racing (Syndication) Ltd, Favourites Racing (Syndication) Ltd 7, Miss T. A. Fulcher, Mrs A. J. Glastonbury, Mr K. J. Glastonbury, Kevin & Anne Glastonbury, Mr M. Glastonbury, J. R. Hall, Mr M. N. Higgs, M. Hingley, Mr A. R. Hitchings, Mr T. A. Killoran, Mr J. McNeil, Mr P. J. McNeil, Mr G. A. S. Saville, Mrs Ann Taylor, Mr S. A. Wilson.

149 MR TIM DENNIS, Bude

Postal: **Thorne Farm, Bude, Cornwall, EX23 0LU**

1 **STORM SALLY (IRE)**, 6, br m September Storm (GER)—Gaelic River (IRE) **Mrs J. E. Dennis**

150 MR ROBIN DICKIN, Alcester
Postal: Hill Farm, Park Lane, Great Alne, Alcester, Warwickshire, B49 6HS
Contacts: MOBILE (07979) 518593 / (07979) 518594
E-MAIL claire@robindickinracing.org.uk WEBSITE www.robindickinracing.org.uk

1 ALL IS GOOD (IRE), 7, b g Scorpion (IRE)—Peinture Rose (IRE) **The Tricksters & The Goodies**
2 ANTI COOL (IRE), 10, b g Heron Island (IRE)—Youngborogal (IRE) **EPDS Racing Partnership 10**
3 BALLY LAGAN (IRE), 11, gr g Kalanisi (IRE)—Rose Palma (FR) **Park Lane Partnership**
4 BLAZING GOLD, 6, b m Fair Mix (IRE)—Playing With Fire (IRE) **Mrs A. L. Merry**
5 BOB MAXWELL (IRE), 5, b g Big Bad Bob (IRE)—Catching Stars (IRE) **Just 4 Fun**
6 CHEER'S DELBOY (IRE), 6, ch g Golan (IRE)—Lindy Lou **Just 4 Fun Partnership**
7 DONTMINDDBOYS (IRE), 10, gr g Portrait Gallery (IRE)—Native Ocean (IRE) **EPDS Racing Partnership 7**
8 FUTURE BOY (IRE), 7, b g Beneficial—Money Clip (IRE) **Mrs C. M. Dickin**
9 GALACTIC POWER (IRE), 9, ch g Gamut (IRE)—Celtic Peace (IRE) **EPDS Racing Twitterati Partnership**
10 LA FILLE FRANCAISE (FR), 6, b m Kapgarde (FR)—Pondimari (FR) **Mrs Louise Merry & Mrs Julia Venvell**
11 LARA TROT (IRE), 7, b m Scorpion (IRE)—Honour Own (IRE) **The Trotters**
12 MR PALMTREE (IRE), 6, gr g Robin des Pres (FR)—Mattys Joy (IRE) **The Cocoa Nuts & the Tricksters**
13 NOMINATION GAME (IRE), 8, b g Oscar (IRE)—Tiarella (IRE) **John Nicholls (Trading) Ltd**
14 ONEIDA TRIBE (IRE), 10, b g Turtle Island (IRE)—Glory Queen (IRE) **John Nicholls (Trading) Ltd**
15 SCORPION SEA (IRE), 8, b m Scorpion (IRE)—Peinture Rose (IRE) **NHRE Racing Club**
16 SOME FINISH (IRE), 5, b g Kayf Tara—Kylie Kaprice (GER) **Mrs C Dickin & The Some Finish Partners**
17 STORMING HARRY, 7, ch g Assertive—Miss Pebbles (IRE) **Mr Nigel Thick**
18 TARA WELL (IRE), 9, b m Kayf Tara—Miss Baden (IRE) **NHRE Racing Club**
19 THE LION MAN (IRE), 9, b g Let The Lion Roar—Just Smart (IRE) **Mrs M A Cooper & Mr J R Cooper**
20 THOMAS CRAPPER, 12, b g Tamure (IRE)—Mollycarrs Gambul **Apis.uk.com**
21 THREE BULLET GATE (IRE), 6, b g Touch of Land (FR)—Brave Hope (IRE) **The Point Of Attack Partnership**
22 TWYCROSS WARRIOR, 7, b g Cockney Rebel (IRE)—Gaelic Roulette (IRE) **Graham & Lynn Knight**
23 VOCALISER (IRE), 7, b g Vocalised (USA)—Bring Back Matron (IRE) **The Songsters**
24 WONDERGIRL (IRE), 5, b m Court Cave (IRE)—Young Elodie (FR) **Nic Allen**

THREE-YEAR-OLDS

25 B g Native Ruler—Dancing Daffodil **Mrs C M Dickin**

Other Owners: Mr H. Brown, Mr R. A. Cockrell, Mrs M. A. Cooper, J. R. Cooper, Mrs C. M. Dickin, Mr C. J. Dickin, Mr M. F. FitzGerald, The Goodies, Mr R. L. Henderson, D. J. Hern, Mr S. P. J. Kirby, Mrs A. L. Merry, Mr J. S. Porter, Mr T. P. Poulson, Mr J. R. Powell, Miss T. Sloan, The Tricksters, Miss H. Turner, Mrs J. C. Venvell, Mr L. M. Weinstein.

Assistant Trainer: Claire Dickin

Jockey (NH): James Nixon, Charlie Poste, Jack Quinlan. **Conditional:** Ceris Biddle, Miss Tabitha Worsley.

151 MR JOHN DIXON, Carlisle
Postal: Moorend, Thursby, Carlisle, Cumbria, CA5 6QP
Contacts: PHONE (01228) 711019

1 BALLELA'S DREAM, 5, b m Josr Algarhoud (IRE)—Ballela Road (IRE) **Mrs S. F. Dixon**
2 CAPTAIN ZEBO (IRE), 7, b g Brian Boru—Waydale Hill **Mrs S. F. Dixon**
3 PISTOL (IRE), 10, b g High Chaparral (IRE)—Alinea (USA) **Mrs S. F. Dixon**
4 PRESENCE FELT (IRE), 11, br g Heron Island (IRE)—Faeroe Isle (IRE) **Mrs S. F. Dixon**

Amateur: Mr J. J. Dixon.

152 MR SCOTT DIXON, Retford
Postal: Haygarth House Stud, Haygarth House, Babworth, Retford, Nottinghamshire, DN22 8ES
Contacts: PHONE (01777) 869300 (01777) 869079/701818 FAX (01777) 869326
MOBILE (07976) 267019 E-MAIL scottdixon1987@hotmail.com / mrsyvettedixon@gmail.com
WEBSITE www.scottdixonracing.com
Trainer is to move to Southwell racecourse in Spring 2019

1 ALBERT BOY (IRE), 6, ch g Falco (USA)—Trumbaka (IRE) **Mr J. Radford**
2 BEST TAMAYUZ, 8, ch g Tamayuz—Pink Ivory **Winning Connections Racing**
3 BOBBY'S CHARM (USA), 4, b g Shanghai Bobby (USA)—Magic Charm (USA) **The Cool Silk Partnership**
4 BOOTS AND SPURS, 10, b g Oasis Dream—Arctic Char **Mr S. E. Chappell**

MR SCOTT DIXON - Continued

5 **BREAK THE SILENCE**, 5, b g Rip Van Winkle (IRE)—In A Silent Way (IRE) **Winning Connections Racing**
6 **CHEZ VEGAS**, 6, gr g Hellvelyn—Lola Sapola (IRE) **Winning Connections Racing**
7 **CHICA DA SILVA**, 4, br f Kheleyf (USA)—Cora Pearl (IRE) **Winning Connections Racing**
8 **COISTE BODHAR (IRE)**, 8, b g Camacho—Nortolixa (FR) **The William A Robinson & Partners**
9 **CROSSE FIRE**, 7, b g Monsieur Bond (IRE)—Watersilk (IRE) **Paul J Dixon & Darren Lucas**
10 **DARK SHOT**, 6, b g Acclamation—Dark Missile **Chappell Rose & Radford**
11 **DORIES DELIGHT (IRE)**, 4, b g Dandy Man (IRE)—She's My Rock (IRE) **Mrs M. Cousins**
12 **EBITDA**, 5, b m Compton Place—Tipsy Girl **P. J. Dixon**
13 **IPCRESS FILE**, 4, ch g Sixties Icon—Solmorin **Showstoppers Racing**
14 **JAFFAR**, 4, b g Mawatheeq (USA)—Velvet Jaguar **Homecroft Wealth Racing & Partner**
15 **KATHY**, 4, b f Bated Breath—Lolita Lebron (IRE) **Ian Buckley**
16 **KRYSTALLITE**, 6, ch m Kheleyf (USA)—Chrystal Venture (IRE) **Paul J Dixon & The Chrystal Maze Ptn**
17 **LAKESKI**, 5, b m Sir Percy—Floating **Showstoppers Racing**
18 **LOVE RAT**, 4, b g Mawatheeq (USA)—Watersilk (IRE) **Jilly Cooper & Friends**
19 **MEDICI MOON**, 5, ch g Medicean—Cockney Fire **Medici Moon Partnership**
20 **NELLIE'S DANCER**, 5, b m Mount Nelson—Xaphania **Winning Connections Racing**
21 **OPTIMICKSTICKHILL**, 4, gr f Milk It Mick—Stylistickhill (IRE) **P. J. Dixon**
22 **PEARL NOIR**, 9, b g Milk It Mick—Cora Pearl (IRE) **Winning Connections Racing**
23 **PENNY DREADFUL**, 7, b m Piccolo—Trina's Pet **Sexy Six Partnership**
24 **RED DOUGLAS**, 4, ch g Sakhee (USA)—Chrystal Venture (IRE) **Paul J Dixon & The Chrystal Maze Ptn**
25 **SAMOVAR**, 4, b g Finjaan—Chrystal Venture (IRE) **Paul J Dixon & The Chrystal Maze Ptn**
26 **SANDS CHORUS**, 4, b g Footstepsinthesand—Wood Chorus **The Cool Silk Partnership**
27 **SANS SOUCI BAY**, 5, b g Medicean—Cumana Bay **Chappell Rose & Radford**
28 **SIR GEOFFREY (IRE)**, 13, b g Captain Rio—Disarm (IRE) **General Sir Geoffrey Howlett/Mr Paul J. Dixon**
29 **SOCIALITES RED**, 6, ch m Sakhee's Secret—Tipsy Girl **Winning Connections Racing**
30 **SOCIOLOGIST (FR)**, 4, gr g Society Rock (IRE)—Fabiola (GER) **Rob Massheder, A J Turton & Partners**
31 **SOLO HUNTER**, 8, b g Sleeping Indian—Night Owl **Rob Massheder, A J Turton & Partners**
32 **SUREWHYNOT (IRE)**, 5, gr m Baltic King—Lina Story **P. J. Dixon**
33 **THUNDERBELL**, 5, ch m Haafhd—Trustthunder **P. J. Dixon**
34 **THUNDERCLOUD**, 4, gr f Aussie Rules (USA)—Trustthunder **P. J. Dixon**
35 **TILLY DEVINE**, 5, gr m Aussie Rules (USA)—Cora Pearl (IRE) **Winning Connections Racing**

THREE-YEAR-OLDS

36 **BELVELLY BOY (IRE)**, b c Showcasing—Freedom Pass (USA) **Anglo Irish Partners**
37 **CHAMPAGNE MONDAYS**, ch g Milk It Mick—La Capriosa **The William A Robinson & Partners**
38 **DEIA GLORY**, b f Kyllachy—Blue Lyric **Anglo Irish Partners**

Other Owners: Mr A. D. Baker, The Chrystal Maze Partnership, Mrs Y. Dixon, Homecroft Wealth Racing, General Sir G. H. W. Howlett, Mr D. R. Lucas, Mr R. Massheder, Mr B. Pettis, Mr S. J. Piper, Mr W. A. Robinson, P. Swann, Mr A. C. Timms, Mr A. Turton, Mrs B. E. Wilkinson.

Assistant Trainer: Mr K. Locking (07835 360125)

Amateur: Mr Kevin Locking.

---

153 **MR STEVEN DIXON, Salisbury**
Postal: **Apple Tree Barn, Livery Road, Winterslow, Nr Salisbury, Wiltshire, SP5 1RJ**
Contacts: **PHONE** (01980) 862930 **MOBILE** (07771) 963011
E-MAIL sarahjdixon@hotmail.co.uk

1 **FINGAL GIRL (IRE)**, 7, ch m Thewayyouare (USA)—She's Our Girl (IRE) **Mr S. D. Dixon**
2 **I'LL BE YOUR CLOWN (IRE)**, 8, b g Aqlaam—Lady Avenger (IRE) **Mr S. D. Dixon**

Assistant Trainer: Mrs Sarah Dixon

---

154 **MRS ROSE DOBBIN, Alnwick**
Postal: **South Hazelrigg Farm, Chatton, Alnwick, Northumberland, NE66 5RZ**
Contacts: **PHONE** (01668) 215395 (office) (01668) 215151 (house) **FAX** (01668) 215114
MOBILE (07969) 993563
E-MAIL hazelriggracing1@btconnect.com **WEBSITE** www.rosedobbinracing.co.uk

1 4, B g Shantou (USA)—Accardi (IRE) **Mr & Mrs Duncan Davidson**
2 **ALONE NO MORE (IRE)**, 7, b g Gold Well—Cherry In A Hurry (IRE) **The Sea Foxes**

MRS ROSE DOBBIN - Continued

3 **ARDGLASS STAR (IRE)**, 5, b g Arctic Cosmos (USA)—Verney Roe (IRE) **Straightline Bloodstock**
4 **ATTENTION PLEASE (IRE)**, 9, b g Kalanisi (IRE)—
    Dangerous Dolly (IRE) **Mr Ronnie Jacobs & Mrs Rose Dobbin**
5 **BAKO DE LA SAULAIE (FR)**, 8, b g Balko (FR)—Krickette (FR) **Mr & Mrs Duncan Davidson**
6 **BIGIRONONHISHIP (IRE)**, 8, b g Beneficial—Portobello Lady (IRE) **Mr & Mrs Duncan Davidson**
7 **CHOSEN FLAME (IRE)**, 7, b g Well Chosen—Flaming Misty (IRE) **S & G Soils Limited**
8 **CLASSICAL SOUND (IRE)**, 7, b g Mahler—Sovienne (IRE) **M Hunter, J Matterson & R Jacobs**
9 **COOLE HALL (IRE)**, 7, b g Flemensfirth (USA)—Coole Assembly (IRE) **Mr & Mrs Duncan Davidson**
10 **DEFINITE WISDOM (IRE)**, 6, b g Definite Article—
    Wisdom And Light (IRE) **M & M Edwardson, M Hunter & J Matterson**
11 **DO NOT DISTURB (IRE)**, 6, b g Mahler—Galbertstown Run (IRE) **Mr & Mrs Duncan Davidson**
12 **DOKTOR GLAZ (FR)**, 9, b g Mount Nelson—Deviolina (IRE) **Mr & Mrs D Davidson & The Friday Lions**
13 4, B g Fame And Glory—Endless Moments (IRE) **Mr & Mrs Duncan Davidson**
14 **ENZILLERYA (FR)**, 5, b g Anzillero (GER)—Trieste (FR) **Mr & Mrs Duncan Davidson**
15 **ESPOIR MORIVIERE (FR)**, 5, ch g Saddex—Sagesse Moriviere (FR) **Straightline Bloodstock**
16 **GEORDIELANDGANGSTA**, 6, br g Geordieland (FR)—
    Dunsfold Duchess (IRE) **Mr & Mrs Davidson, C Davidson & N James**
17 **HEATHER BURNING (IRE)**, 8, b g Mountain High (IRE)—Go To Blazes (IRE) **The Friday Lions**
18 **HITMAN FRED (IRE)**, 6, b g Getaway (GER)—Garravagh Lass (IRE) **Mr & Mrs Duncan Davidson**
19 **HONOURABLE GENT**, 11, b g Gentleman's Deal—Gudasmum **Mr & Mrs Duncan Davidson**
20 **JACK DEVINE (IRE)**, 7, b g Kalanisi (IRE)—Sybil Says (IRE) **Mr & Mrs Duncan Davidson**
21 **LADY LONDON (IRE)**, 8, b m Beneficial—Torduff Storm (IRE) **Miss C. L. Jones**
22 **LE CHEVAL NOIR (IRE)**, 5, b g Le Fou (IRE)—Bonny Lass **Mr & Mrs Duncan Davidson**
23 **LE GAVROCHE (IRE)**, 6, b g Flemensfirth (USA)—Knockieran (IRE) **Mr. Ronnie Jacobs & Mr. Albert Roux**
24 4, B g Getaway (GER)—Listening (IRE) **Mr & Mrs Duncan Davidson**
25 **LOG ON (IRE)**, 8, b g Scorpion (IRE)—Go Girl (IRE) **R. Jacobs, S. Davidson, R. & T. Dobbin**
26 **MINELLA SUITE (IRE)**, 8, br g Oscar (IRE)—Ballymaguirelass (IRE) **Mr & Mrs Duncan Davidson**
27 **MONFASS (IRE)**, 8, b g Trans Island—Ajo Green (IRE) **Mrs Dobbin & The Dimhorns**
28 **PERMISSION GRANTED (IRE)**, 7, b g Oscar (IRE)—Ask The Misses (IRE) **Jacobs, Dickson & Brown**
29 **PLANET NINE (IRE)**, 7, b g Flemensfirth (USA)—Old Moon (IRE) **Mr & Mrs Duncan Davidson**
30 **PURCELL'S BRIDGE (FR)**, 12, b g Trempolino (USA)—Theatrical Lady (USA) **Mrs R. Dobbin**
31 **ROMULUS DU DONJON (IRE)**, 8, gr g Stormy River (FR)—Spring Stroll (USA) **Jacobs, Ray & Roberts**
32 **ROSEY**, 5, b m Multiplex—Rose Street (IRE) **Mr & Mrs Raymond Anderson Green**
33 **RUBY WHO (IRE)**, 7, gr g Daylami (IRE)—Lelepa (IRE) **Mr&Mrs R Houghton,T Houghton&H Gopsill**
34 **SLANELOUGH (IRE)**, 7, b g Westerner—Tango Lady (IRE) **Miss J. Matterson & Mrs D. Davidson**
35 **SMUGGLER'S STASH (IRE)**, 9, ch g Stowaway—Sweetasanu (IRE) **The Friday Lions 2**
36 **SOME REIGN (IRE)**, 8, b g Kayf Tara—Bridge Love (FR) **Mr & Mrs Duncan Davidson**
37 **STYLE NELSON (FR)**, 4, b g Mount Nelson—Ana Style (FR) **Mr & Mrs Duncan Davidson**
38 **SWEET AS CANDY (IRE)**, 7, b g Morozov (USA)—Sweet Nancy (IRE) **Mr & Mrs Duncan Davidson**
39 **THE HOLLOW CHAP (IRE)**, 5, ch g Beat Hollow—An Banog (IRE) **Mr & Mrs Duncan Davidson**
40 **TROOPER TURNBULL (IRE)**, 5, b g Arcadio (GER)—Clover Pearl (IRE) **Hunter & McKie**
41 **VINTAGE GLEN (IRE)**, 7, b g Ask—Rare Vintage (IRE) **Mrs R. Dobbin**

Other Owners: Mr E. R. Brown, D. H. Davidson, Mrs S. K. Davidson, Miss C. M. Davidson, Mr J. L. Dickson, Mr L. Dimsdale, Mr A. G. Dobbin, J. M. & Mrs M. R. Edwardson, Mrs M. R. Edwardson, J. M. Edwardson, Mr R. P. Gilbert, Ms H. Gopsill, R. A. Green, Mrs A. Green, Mr T. A. Houghton, Mrs A. M. Houghton, Mr R. Houghton, M. S. Hunter, Mr R. A. Jacobs, Mrs N. James, J. R. Jeffreys, Miss J. G. K. Matterson, Mrs V. J. McKie, Mr W. B. Ramsay, Mrs M. H. Ray, Mr R. Roberts, Mr A. H. Roux, Mr D. A. C. Spencer-Churchill, Straightline Construction Ltd.

Assistant Trainer: Tony Dobbin (07775) 680894

Jockey (NH): Craig Nichol.

---

 155 **MR ASHLEY DODGSON, Thirsk**
Postal: **Southerby House, Catton, Thirsk, North Yorkshire, YO7 4SQ**

1 **MR DEALER (IRE)**, 7, b g Mr Dinos (IRE)—Vera Glynn (IRE) **Mrs F. M. G. Dodgson**

156 MR MICHAEL DODS, Darlington

Postal: Denton Hall Farm, Piercebridge, Darlington, County Durham, DL2 3TY
Contacts: PHONE (01325) 374270 FAX (01325) 374020
MOBILE (07860) 411590/ (07773) 290830 C Dods
E-MAIL dods@michaeldodsracing.co.uk WEBSITE www.michaeldodsracing.co.uk

1 ARCAVALLO (IRE), 4, ch g Arcano (IRE)—Pashmina (IRE) **Mr P Appleton & Mrs Anne Elliott**
2 ARCHI'S AFFAIRE, 5, ch g Archipenko (USA)—Affaire d'amour **D. Neale**
3 BYRON'S CHOICE, 4, b g Poet's Voice—Byrony (IRE) **Mr Doug Graham & Mrs M Wynn-williams**
4 CAMACHO CHIEF (IRE), 4, b g Camacho—Passage To India (IRE) **Davison & Drysdale**
5 DAKOTA GOLD, 5, b g Equiano (FR)—Joyeaux **Doug Graham & Ian Davison**
6 DANIELSFLYER (IRE), 5, b g Dandy Man (IRE)—Warm Welcome **Elliott Brothers And Peacock**
7 FARHH AWAY, 4, ch g Farhh—Bukhoor (IRE) **Mrs M Wynn-williams & Mr D Neale**
8 GET KNOTTED (IRE), 7, ch g Windsor Knot (IRE)—Genuinely (IRE) **D. Neale**
9 GRINTY (IRE), 5, b g Elnadim (USA)—Fire Line **Mr J. N. Blackburn**
10 ILIKEYOUALOT (IRE), 4, b f Swiss Spirit—Timeless
11 INTENSE ROMANCE (IRE), 5, b m Intense Focus (USA)—Hedera (USA) **Mr H. M. Linsley**
12 JOHN KIRKUP, 4, ch g Assertive—Bikini **Mrs Suzanne Kirkup & Mr Kevin Kirkup**
13 KIWI BAY, 14, b g Mujahid (USA)—Bay of Plenty (FR) **Kiwi Racing**
14 MININGGOLD, 6, b m Piccolo—Rosein **Mrs C. E. Dods**
15 MOOLTAZEM (IRE), 5, b g Elzaam (AUS)—Whisper Dance (USA) **Mr M. D. Pearson**
16 MUSTAQBAL (IRE), 7, b g Invincible Spirit—Alshamatry (USA) **Denton Hall Racing Ltd**
17 PROUD ARCHI (IRE), 5, b g Archipenko (USA)—Baharah (USA) **Eagle Racing**
18 RUMSHAK (IRE), 4, ch g Arcano (IRE)—Scarlet Rosefinch **Mrs C. Dods & Mr D Stone**
19 VENTURA SECRET (IRE), 5, ch g Roderic O'Connor (IRE)—Bajan Belle (IRE) **Mr V Spinks & Partner**
20 WAHOO, 4, b g Stimulation (IRE)—Shohrah (IRE) **Mr J Blackburn & Mr A Turton**

THREE-YEAR-OLDS

21 AMAZING ALBA, ch f Helmet (AUS)—Silcasue **Mr F. Lowe**
22 BEAUFORT (IRE), b g Zoffany (IRE)—Change Course **Mr Peter Appleton & Mr M. J. K. Dods**
23 BILLY NO MATES (IRE), b g Clodovil (IRE)—Sabaidee (IRE) **Mr J Sagar & Mr M Dods**
24 BULLION BOSS (IRE), b g War Command (USA)—Gold Bubbles (USA) **Tullpark Limited**
25 BUMBLEDOM, br g Epaulette (AUS)—Miaplacidus (IRE) **Mr G Thompson & Mr M Dods**
26 CASANNA (IRE), b f Casamento (IRE)—Monroe **Derek McNamara & Pat Cahill**
27 CHARLIE'S BOY (IRE), b g Poet's Voice—Royal Sister Two (IRE) **Sekura Trade Frames Ltd**
28 COCO MOTION (IRE), b g Es Que Love (IRE)—Beguiler **Mr D. Stone**
29 DANCIN BOY, br g Gregorian (IRE)—La Gifted **Mr R. R. D. Saunders**
30 DUTCH PURSUIT (IRE), b g Canford Cliffs (IRE)—Dansili Dutch (IRE) **Mr & Mrs G. Turnball**
31 EPAULINI, b g Epaulette (AUS)—Baylini **Top Dog Racing**
32 FLINT HILL, ch g Excelebration (IRE)—Modify **Mr T. P. Curry**
33 GALE FORCE MAYA, ch f Gale Force Ten—Parabola **Mr F. Lowe**
34 GENERAL MISCHIEF (IRE), b g Dream Ahead (USA)—Dorothy Parker (IRE) **Denton Hall Racing Ltd**
35 KOLOSSUS, ch g Assertive—Bikini **K. Kirkup**
36 LITTLEBITOFMAGIC, b g Phoenix Reach (IRE)—Magic Echo **F. Watson**
37 MECCA'S GIFT (IRE), b f Dark Angel (IRE)—Frizzante **Mr David T J Metcalfe & Mr M J K Dods**
38 MUSICAL SKY, ch f Mayson—Sky Wonder **Bolton Grange**
39 MYRMIDONS (IRE), ch g Casamento (IRE)—Allegrissimo (IRE) **Mr D. Stone**
40 QUE AMORO (IRE), b f Es Que Love (IRE)—Onomatomania (USA) **Mr P Appleton & Mrs Anne Elliott**
41 RIDE THE MONKEY (IRE), b g Bungle Inthejungle—EileenIilian **Dunham Trading Ltd**
42 SPIRITUAL COMMAND (IRE), b g War Command (USA)—Emeralds Spirit (IRE) **Mr T Scothern Racing**
43 TRANSPENNINE GOLD, gr g Gregorian (IRE)—Perfect Cover (IRE) **Transpennine Partnership**

TWO-YEAR-OLDS

44 AMERICA FIRST (IRE), gr c 29/1 Le Havre (IRE)—
Aglaia (IRE) (Invincible Spirit (IRE)) (14327) **Bardsley, Hyde & Tattersall**
45 ARCH MOON, b c 27/1 Sea The Moon (GER)—
Archduchess (Archipenko (USA)) (21913) **Mr Allan Mcluckie & Mr M. J. K. Dods**
46 BAY FILLY ROLLA, b f 9/2 Showcasing—Memoria (Teofilo (IRE)) **The Storm Again Syndicate**
47 BEAUTRIX, b f 9/3 Brazen Beau (AUS)—Dartrix (Dutch Art) **Osbaldeston/Cure/Knox Partnership**
48 B c 11/2 Battle of Marengo (IRE)—Dubaya (Dubawi (IRE)) (33712) **Rjh Ltd & D Stone**
49 B c 6/3 Archipenko (USA)—Florentia (Medicean) (41000) **Mr D Neale & Mr D Stone**
50 B c 29/4 Due Diligence (USA)—Frequent (Three Valleys (USA)) (36000) **Mr P Appleton & Mrs Anne Elliott**
51 B g 28/4 Lethal Force (IRE)—Joyeaux (Mark of Esteem (IRE)) (11000) **Mr Doug Graham & Mr Ian Davison**
52 B c 22/3 Camacho—Kimola (King's Theatre (IRE)) (58997) **Mr & Mrs Paul & Clare Rooney**
53 PEARL STREAM, b f 14/1 Fountain of Youth (IRE)—Seaperle (Firebreak) **Bearstone Stud Limited**

MR MICHAEL DODS - Continued

54 **ROAD RAGE (IRE)**, b c 27/3 Requinto (IRE)—
        Grid Lock (IRE) (Van Nistelrooy (USA)) (52380) **Merchants and Missionaries**
55 Ch c 4/5 Dragon Pulse (IRE)—Salydora (FR) (Peintre Celebre (USA)) (26126) **Mr D. Stone**
56 **SHADOW LEADER**, b c 4/4 Equiano (FR)—
        Midnight M (Green Desert (USA)) (47619) **Merchants and Missionaries**
57 B c 3/4 Bungle Inthejungle—Shamiya (IRE) (Acclamation) (10956) **K. Kirkup**
58 **SPARKLING BREEZE**, ch g 7/3 Coach House (IRE)—African Breeze (Atraf) (6000) **Mrs C Hewitson, Mr M Dods**
59 Gr f 20/4 Dark Angel (IRE)—
        Strait Power (Rock of Gibraltar (IRE)) (29523) **Mr D W Armstrong & Mr M J K Dods**
60 **TROUBADOR (IRE)**, gr g 31/3 Poet's Voice—
        Eastern Destiny (Dubai Destination (USA)) (10000) **Mr J Sagar & Mr S Lowthian**
61 **TWIST OF HAY**, b f 18/3 Showcasing—Spinatrix (Diktat) (11428) **Mr J. A. Knox and Mrs M. A. Knox**
62 **UNIFIER**, b c 23/1 Showcasing—Miss Chicane (Refuse To Bend (IRE)) (38095) **Brook Stud**
63 Ch f 28/1 Hot Streak (IRE)—
        Vintage Steps (IRE) (Bahamian Bounty) (18000) **Mr David T J Metcalfe & Mr M J K Dods**
64 **WHITE COPPER**, br gr f 28/1 Outstrip—Native Nickel (IRE) (Be My Native (USA)) **The Storm Again Syndicate**

Other Owners: Mr P. Appleton, Mr D. W. Armstrong, Mr C. Banister, Mr D. A. Bardsley, D. C. Batey, Mr I. Bennett, Mr P. Cahill, Mr J. Cockcroft, Mr M. R. Cure, Mr Ian Davison, M. J. K. Dods, Mr A. Drysdale, J. M. Elliott, Mrs A. E. Elliott, Cr R. Elliott, J. A. Ellis, Miss E. A. Ellis, Facility Solutions Management Limited, J. W. Fullick, R. T. Goodes, Mr D. R. Graham, Mrs C. M. Hewitson, Mr G. Hyde, Mrs S. Kirkup, Mr J. A. Knox, Mrs M. A. Knox, W. S. D. Lamb, Mr S. R. Lowthian, Mr A. McLuckie, Mr D. McNamara, D. T. J. Metcalfe, Mr S. Osbaldeston, Mrs S. Peacock, R J H Limited, D. G. Raffel, Mr P. A. Rooney, Mrs C. Rooney, Mr J. Sagar, T. A. Scothern, Mr S. R. Skinns, V. J. Spinks, Mr B. Stewart, Mr M. W. Syme, G. Tattersall, Mr G. C. Thompson, Mr W. A. Tinkler, Mr G. Turnbull, Mrs S. E. Turnbull, Mr A. Turton, D. Watts, Mr G. W. Witheford, D. G. A. E. Woods, Mr E. W. J. Woods, Mrs M. Wynn-Williams.

Assistant Trainer: Carole Dods, **Head Lads:** Steve Alderson (07533) 401887, David Dickenson

Jockey (flat): Connor Beasley, Paul Mulrennan, Callum Rodriguez. **Apprentice:** Paula Muir.
Amateur: Miss Sophie Dods, Miss Chloe Dods, Miss Rachel Taylor.

---

157 | **MR CONOR DORE, Frampton Fen**
Postal: **Barford Farm, Swineshead Road, Frampton Fen, Boston, Lincolnshire, PE20 1SG**
Contacts: **PHONE (01775) 822747 MOBILE (07984) 609170**
E-MAIL dores@supanet.com

1 **COLLODI (GER)**, 10, b g Konigstiger (GER)—Codera (GER) **A. N. Page**
2 **HURRICANE RITA (FR)**, 9, gr m Sagamix (FR)—Madonna da Rossi **Barford Farm**
3 **INDIAN REEL (FR)**, 9, b f Indian River (FR)—Ceilidh Dancer **McHugh & Beckford**
4 **MULSANNE CHASE**, 5, b g Sixties Icon—Hot Pursuits **Mr M. Fitzsimons**

THREE-YEAR-OLDS

5 **QUEEN EMILY**, b f Toronado (IRE)—Daysiwaay (IRE) **Mrs L. J. Marsh**
6 **ROMANY ROSE (IRE)**, b f Requinto (IRE)—Five Star Maria (IRE) **Mrs J. W. Lamley**

Other Owners: Mr T. Beckford, Mr C. R. Dore, Mr C. McHugh.

---

158 | **MR SIMON DOW, Epsom**
Postal: **Clear Height Stable, Derby Stables Road, Epsom, Surrey, KT18 5LB**
Contacts: **PHONE (01372) 721490 MOBILE (07860) 800109**
E-MAIL simon@simondow.co.uk WEBSITE www.simondow.co.uk Twitter: @SimonDowRacing

1 **ALBISHR (IRE)**, 4, gr g Clodovil (IRE)—Casual Remark (IRE) **Mr R. J. Moss**
2 **BOBBY BISCUIT (USA)**, 4, b c Scat Daddy (USA)—Poupee Flash (USA) **Mr D. Brennan**
3 **BROGANS BAY (IRE)**, 4, b f Born To Sea (IRE)—Sister Sylvia **R. A. Murray-Obodynski**
4 **CHACACHACARE (IRE)**, 4, b g Power—Half-Hitch (USA) **Chua, Ong, Dow**
5 **CHICA DE LA NOCHE**, 5, b m Teofilo (IRE)—Welsh Cake **Mr R. J. Moss**
6 **CORAZON ESPINADO (IRE)**, 4, b c Iffraaj—Three Decades (IRE) **Mr R. J. Moss**
7 **EL BORRACHO (IRE)**, 4, br g Society Rock (IRE)—Flame of Hibernia (IRE) **Mr R. J. Moss**
8 **EMENEM**, 5, b g Sir Percy—Kahalah (IRE) **Mr R. J. Moss**
9 **LE TORRENT**, 7, ch g Sir Percy—Cinnas Ransom **P. G. Jacobs**
10 **MONT KIARA (FR)**, 6, b g Kendargent (FR)—Xaarienne **Mr C. G. J. Chua**
11 **MR SCARAMANGA**, 5, b h Sir Percy—Lulla **Mr R. J. Moss**

MR SIMON DOW - Continued

12 **PRINCE ROCK (IRE)**, 4, ch g Society Rock (IRE)—She's A Queen (IRE) **Mr M. McAllister**
13 **REGAL GAIT (IRE)**, 6, b g Tagula (IRE)—Babylonian **P. G. Jacobs**
14 **ROUNDABOUT MAGIC (IRE)**, 5, ch h Zebedee—Cayo Largo (IRE) **Six Mile Hill Racing**
15 **SARGENTO**, 4, b g Dick Turpin (IRE)—Vezere (USA) **Mr R. J. Moss**
16 **SPARKALOT**, 5, br g Bated Breath—Three Wrens (IRE) **Robert Moss, H Redknapp**
17 **SUBLIMINAL**, 4, b c Arcano (IRE)—Rare Virtue (USA) **Mr M. McAllister**
18 **VENTRILOQUIST**, 7, ch g New Approach (IRE)—Illusion **Mr C. G. J. Chua**
19 **WESTERN DYNAMISME (FR)**, 4, b f Manduro (GER)—Western Hope (IRE) **Malcolm & Alicia Aldis**

THREE-YEAR-OLDS

20 **BRENBAR (USA)**, b br c Scat Daddy (USA)—Pretty Elusive (USA) **Mr Damien Brennan**
21 **DELCIA**, br f Delegator—Fiducia **Mr Paul G. Jacobs**
22 **PACIFICADORA (USA)**, b br f Declaration of War (USA)—Rau Breck (USA) **Mr R. J. Moss**
23 **QUE QUIERES (USA)**, b c Bernardini (USA)—Christine Daae (USA) **Mr R. J. Moss**
24 **RECUERDAME (USA)**, b g The Factor (USA)—B R's Girl (USA) **Mr R. J. Moss**
25 **TE AMO TE AMO**, b c Kyllachy—Caption **Mr R. J. Moss**
26 **THORA (IRE)**, b f Iffraaj—Authora (IRE) **Woodcote Stud Ltd**

TWO-YEAR-OLDS

27 **BEAT THE BREEZE**, gr ro c 13/2 Outstrip—Tranquil Flight (Oasis Dream) (10476) **Mr Simon Caunce**
28 **HEADLEY GEORGE (IRE)**, b c 22/4 Due Diligence (USA)—
　　　　　　　　　　　　　Silent Secret (IRE) (Dubai Destination (USA)) (40000) **Mr M. J. Convey**
29 **HECTOR LOZA**, b c 18/3 Kodiac—Queen Sarra (Shamardal (USA)) (55000) **Mr Robert Moss**
30 **LEGENDARY GRACE**, b f 29/3 Multiplex—Fairyinthewind (IRE) (Indian Haven) **Mr R. J. Delnevo**
31 **MADAM HASHTAG**, b f 8/1 Zebedee—Stinky Socks (IRE) (Footstepsinthesand) (6666) **Mr Nick Hawkins**
32 **MUNGO'S QUEST (IRE)**, ch c 2/4 Sir Prancealot (IRE)—
　　　　　　　　　　　　　Sheila Blige (Zamindar (USA)) (6666) **C & J Cooley. D & M Sorrell. K Jones**
33 **SAN QUIRICO**, b g 13/2 Outstrip—Fiducia (Lawman (FR)) (952) **Mr Paul G. Jacobs**
34 B c 11/2 Al Kazeem—Selka (FR) (Selkirk (USA)) (10000)
35 B f 19/2 Toronado (IRE)—Vezere (USA) (Point Given (USA)) **Mr Robert Moss**

Other Owners: Mr J. C. G. Chua, Mr Colin Cooley, Mr Jordon Cooley, Mr S. Dow, Ken Jones, Mr C. K. Ong, Ms S. A. Snell, David Sorrell, Mary Sorrell.

159	**MR CHRIS DOWN, Cullompton** Postal: Upton, Cullompton, Devon, EX15 1RA Contacts: **PHONE** (01884) 33097 **FAX** (01884) 33097 **MOBILE** (07828) 021232 **E-MAIL** cjdownracing@gmail.com

1 **ANIS DES MALBERAUX (FR)**, 9, b g Reste Tranquille (FR)—Scavenger (FR) **Little Loxbrook Babes and Bays**
2 **ARCTIC FOOTPRINT**, 5, br m Blueprint (IRE)—Arctic Flow **Mrs H. R. Dunn**
3 **BILLY MY BOY**, 10, b g Volochine (IRE)—Key West (FR) **Mr J. B. Radford**
4 **BROADCLYST (IRE)**, 7, b g Ask—Broadcast **Mrs S. M. Trump**
5 **CHAMPAGNE IDEAS (IRE)**, 6, b g Acambaro (GER)—Charannah (IRE) **Upton Racing 2**
6 **CULM COUNSELLOR**, 10, ch g Erhaab (USA)—Miss Counsel **Culm Valley Racing**
7 **FOXY ACT**, 8, ch m Act One—Brown Fox (FR) **C. J. Down**
8 **GAELIC FLOW**, 8, ch g With The Flow (USA)—Gaelic Lime **The Jack High Racing Partnership**
9 5, Ch m Shantou (USA)—Kingara **C. J. Down**
10 **LADIES DANCING**, 13, b g Royal Applause—Queen of Dance (IRE) **C. J. Down**
11 **MAX FORTE (IRE)**, 9, br g Indian River (FR)—Brook Forte **P Holland,JT Measures,MA Kerr,V Holland**
12 **MONDA'S LEGACY**, 6, b m Tamure (IRE)—Monda **Kittymore Racing**
13 **MOTTS CROSS (IRE)**, 8, b g Scorpion (IRE)—Rainy Season (IRE) **Mrs S. M. Trump**
14 **PAHASKA (GER)**, 6, b m Saddex—Pacific Sun (GER) **P Holland,JT Measures,MA Kerr,V Holland**
15 **SCRUPULEUX (FR)**, 8, b g Laveron—Rouge Folie (FR) **Mrs M. Trueman & Mr A O'Neill**
16 **STARLIT NIGHT**, 7, b m Nayef (USA)—Perfect Night **C. J. Down**

Other Owners: H. J. W. Davies, Mr N. D. Elliott, Mrs J. Elliott, Mrs V. Holland, P. D. Holland, Ms M. A. Kerr, Mrs G. H. Leeves, Mrs H. M. Luscombe, Mr D. Luscombe, Mr J. T. Measures, Mr A. G. O'Neill, Mrs M. Trueman, Mr N. Vanstone.

Jockey (NH): James Davies.

160 **MR CLIVE DREW, Rampton**
Postal: Fox End Stables, 83 King Street, Rampton, Cambridgeshire, CB24 8QD
Contacts: **PHONE/FAX** (01954) 250772 **MOBILE** (07917) 718127
E-MAIL polly.drew@googlemail.com

1 **HIGHCASTLE (IRE)**, 4, b g High Chaparral (IRE)—Green Castle (IRE) **C. Drew**
2 **MAISON BRILLET (IRE)**, 12, b g Pyrus (USA)—Stormchaser (IRE) **C. Drew**
3 **MONSIEUR ROYALE**, 9, ch g Monsieur Bond (IRE)—Bond Royale **C. Drew**

TWO-YEAR-OLDS

4 B c 21/2 Sixties Icon—Hallo Sexy (Halling (USA))

Assistant Trainer: Miss Polly Drew

---

161 **MR DAVID W. DRINKWATER, Redmarley**
Postal: Chapel Farm, Chapel Lane, Redmarley, Gloucester, Gloucestershire, GL19 3JF
Contacts: **PHONE** (07766) 011007 (07973) 193771
E-MAIL drinkys35@outlook.com

1 **ASHPAN SAM**, 10, b g Firebreak—Sweet Patoopie **R Tudor Holdings Limited**
2 **DEAR BRUIN (IRE)**, 7, b m Kodiac—Namu **R Tudor Holdings Limited**
3 **DLTRIPLESEVEN (IRE)**, 6, gr g Dark Angel (IRE)—Namu **R Tudor Holdings Limited**
4 **MAHNA MAHNA (IRE)**, 5, b g Kodiac—Namu **R Tudor Holdings Limited**
5 **MISS DUSKY DIVA (IRE)**, 7, gr m Verglas (IRE)—Dispol Veleta **R Tudor Holdings Limited**

Assistant Trainer: Rachel Tudor

Jockey (flat): William Carson. **Jockey (NH):** Nico De Boinville.

---

162 **MR SAMUEL DRINKWATER, Strensham**
Postal: The Granary, Twyning Road, Strensham, Worcester, Worcestershire, WR8 9LH
Contacts: **MOBILE** (07747) 444633
E-MAIL samdrinkwater@gmail.com

1 **BIGCHEXTOCASH (IRE)**, 7, b g Stowaway—Monakeeba (IRE) **The Railway children**
2 **BILLY HICKS**, 8, b g Kayf Tara—Michelle's Ella (IRE) **P. Drinkwater**
3 **CHATELIER (FR)**, 7, ch g Network (GER)—Elza III (FR) **The Lucky Seven**
4 **FIRST DU CHARMIL (FR)**, 7, ch g Ballingarry (IRE)—Famous Member (FR) **Mr N T Griffith & H M Haddock**
5 **GALLIC GEORDIE**, 6, b g Geordieland (FR)—Je Ne Sais Plus (FR) **Kevin & Anne Glastonbury**
6 **GENERAL CONSENSUS**, 7, br g Black Sam Bellamy (IRE)—Charlottes Webb (IRE) **Mrs K. Drinkwater**
7 **HAVE THIS FOR NOW (IRE)**, 6, b g Daylami (IRE)—Annas Theatre **Mick Coulson & Colin Poore**
8 4, B g Yeats (IRE)—Honey Rosie (IRE) **P. Drinkwater**
9 **HOWLING MILAN (IRE)**, 5, b g Milan—Fantasia Filly (IRE) **Strensham Stragglers**
10 **KAUTO LINGARRY (FR)**, 7, ch g Ballingarry (IRE)—Kauto Luisa (FR) **Mrs J. Drinkwater**
11 7, B g Black Sam Bellamy (IRE)—Mimi Equal **Mr K. Kane**
12 **PRAY FOR A RAINBOW**, 8, b g Rainbow High—Blackchurch Lass (IRE) **Kevin & Anne Glastonbury**
13 **RIGHT ON ROY**, 9, b g Double Trigger—One Wild Night **Mr R. E. Bailey**
14 **RUSSIAN SERVICE**, 7, b g Robin des Champs (FR)—Just Kate **Mr S. J. Mattick**
15 **SERGEANT BRODY**, 8, ch g Black Sam Bellamy (IRE)—Ardent Bride **Mrs K. Drinkwater**
16 **SOME CAN DANCE (IRE)**, 6, b g Gold Well—Rocella (GER) **Richard Bailey & Mr D P Drinkwater**
17 **TOP DECISION (IRE)**, 6, ch g Beneficial—Great Decision (IRE) **Prestbury Racing Club**

Other Owners: Mr M. Ball, R. J. Clarke, Mr M. D. Coulson, Mr D. P. Drinkwater, Mrs A. J. Glastonbury, Mr K. J. Glastonbury, Mr N. Griffith, Mrs H. M. Haddock, C. D. Massey, Mr M. Pearse, Mr C. W. D. Poore, Mr N. J. Witts-Hewinson.

163 MISS JACKIE DU PLESSIS, Saltash
Postal: **Burell Farm, Longlands, Saltash, Cornwall, PL12 4QH**
Contacts: **PHONE (01752) 842362 MOBILE (07970) 871505**
E-MAIL ziggerson@aol.com

1 CORNELIUS SOCKS (IRE), 9, b g Asian Heights—Delightful Choice (IRE) **Miss J. M. du Plessis**
2 ERICAS LAD, 8, b g Mutazayid (IRE)—Kingsmill Quay **Miss J. M. du Plessis**
3 LADY KINGSMILL, 8, b m Bandmaster (USA)—Kingsmill Lake **Miss J. M. du Plessis**
4 LEGEND LADY, 8, b m Midnight Legend—Aoninch **The Cornish Barmies**
5 NIGHT GENERATION (GER), 7, ch g Sholokhov (IRE)—
                 Night Woman (GER) **Jackie Du Plessis & Sarah Pridham**
6 RUPERT VALENTINO, 6, b g Schiaparelli (GER)—Magic Valentine **The Cornish Barmies**
7 SEA PRESENT (IRE), 7, b m Presenting—Nautical Lady (IRE) **Miss J. M. du Plessis**
8 ST ERNEY, 8, ch g Kadastrof (FR)—Ticket To The Moon **Miss J. M. du Plessis**
9 THEATRE MIX, 6, gr m Fair Mix (IRE)—Theatre Diva (IRE) **Miss J. M. du Plessis**

Other Owners: Miss S. Pridham.

164 MRS ANN DUFFIELD, Leyburn
Postal: **Sun Hill Racing Stables, Sun Hill Farm, Constable Burton, Leyburn,
North Yorkshire, DL8 5RL**
Contacts: **PHONE (01677) 450303 FAX (01677) 450993 MOBILE (07802) 496332**
E-MAIL ann@annduffield.co.uk WEBSITE www.annduffield.co.uk

1 ANTICIPATE (IRE), 4, b g Yeats (IRE)—Princess Minnie **Mr T Ingham & Partner**
2 ARNOLD, 5, b g Equiano (FR)—Azurinta (IRE) **Dj & Sa Shewring, D Marshall, F Fantoni**
3 BIBBIDIBOBBIDIBOO (IRE), 4, b f Red Jazz (USA)—Provence **Ms J. F. Bianco**
4 CAPE HILL COTTER (FR), 4, b f Dabirsim (FR)—Nelly Dean **Middleham Park Racing XCVI**
5 CHANT (IRE), 9, b g Oratorio (IRE)—Akarita (IRE) **Mrs Ann Starkie & Mrs I. Starkie**
6 COTTON SOCKS (IRE), 4, b g Dream Ahead (USA)—Kartella (IRE) **Mrs Ann Starkie & Partner**
7 CUPPACOCO, 4, b f Stimulation (IRE)—Glen Molly (IRE) **Mrs C. A. Gledhill**
8 GORSE (IRE), 4, b g Zebedee—Golden Flower **The Duchess of Sutherland**
9 HIGHLY FOCUSSED (IRE), 5, b g Intense Focus (USA)—Mood Indigo (IRE) **The Duchess of Sutherland**
10 MISS BATES, 5, b m Holy Roman Emperor (IRE)—Jane Austen (IRE) **The Duchess of Sutherland**
11 NIFTY NIECE (IRE), 5, gr m Zebedee—Hasty Harriet (IRE) **The Duchess of Sutherland**
12 NINEPIN BOWLER, 5, b g Rip Van Winkle (IRE)—Smooth As Silk (IRE) **Ramscove Ltd**
13 PEACH PAVLOVA (IRE), 5, b m Elzaam (AUS)—Zvezda (USA) **E & R Stott**
14 ROSINA, 6, b m Showcasing—Mondovi **Ms J. F. Bianco**
15 SUNHILL LAD (IRE), 4, gr g Lilbourne Lad (IRE)—Gris Ladera (IRE) **Mr Alan Court & Partner**
16 TROOP, 4, gr g Lethal Force (IRE)—Bendis (GER) **Dj & Sa Shewring, L Patterson**
17 UNCLE CHARLIE (IRE), 5, b g Vale of York (IRE)—Velvet Kiss (IRE) **Mr David Barker & Partner**

THREE-YEAR-OLDS

18 HEARTSTRING, br f Slade Power (IRE)—The Terrier **DGA Racing Limited**
19 MISS SABINA, ch f Mayson—Some Diva **Mr S. Bradley**
20 SILS MARIA, gr f Swiss Spirit—Snow Cover **Solo Syndicate**
21 SWIFT INTRIGUE (IRE), b f Roderic O'Connor (IRE)—Fleeting Affair (USA) **Mr Joe Richardson & Partner**
22 YOU LITTLE BEAUTY, b f Stimulation (IRE)—Ziefhd **Mrs A. Duffield**

TWO-YEAR-OLDS

23 B f 27/2 Swiss Spirit—Annie Kenney (Showcasing) **Inspire Racing Club**
24 CHARMORE, b f 5/2 Swiss Spirit—Caramelita (Deportivo) (761)
25 GAINSBORO GREY, gr c 1/3 Archipenko (USA)—
              Albacocca (With Approval (CAN)) (11000) **Mr Ian Farrington & Partner**
26 B f 20/4 Swiss Spirit—Houri (IRE) (Alhaarth (IRE))
27 QUERCUS (IRE), b c 11/3 Nayef (USA)—Dufoof (IRE) (Shamardal (USA)) (26000) **Mrs C. A. Gledhill**
28 B c 2/5 Fast Company (IRE)—Saralea (FR) (Sillery (USA)) (5714)
29 WARNE'S ARMY, b f 30/3 Fast Company (IRE)—Euro Empire (USA) (Bartok (IRE)) (36190) **DGA Racing Limited**

Other Owners: D. K. Barker, Mr A. Court, Mr F. Fantoni, Mr I. J. Farrington, Mr T. S. Ingham, Inspire Racing Club Ltd, Mr D. A. Marshall, T. S. Palin, Mr L. S. Patterson, M. Prince, Mr J. Richardson, Mrs S. A. Shewring, Mr D. J. Shewring, Mrs I. L. A. Starkie, Mrs A. Starkie, Miss R. Stott, Miss E. Stott.

165 MR BRENDAN W. DUKE, The Curragh
Postal: **Fenway House, Pollardstown, Curragh, Co. Kildare, Ireland**
Contacts: **MOBILE (00353) 85 8189724**

1 **CLAIOMH GEAL**, 4, ch f Leroidesanimaux (BRZ)—Claiomh Solais (IRE) **Mrs Jackie Bolger**
2 **LET THE HEIRS WALK (IRE)**, 5, b g Vocalised (USA)—Heir Today (IRE) **Mrs Jackie Bolger**
3 **PUNCH BAG (IRE)**, 8, ch g Teofilo (IRE)—Heir Today (IRE) **Martin Hayes, Peter Slezak**
4 **QUI BONO (IRE)**, 8, gr g Beneficial—Dream Witness (FR) **Brendan W Duke Racing**
5 **ULURU PARK (IRE)**, 4, b f So You Think (NZ)—I'm Sheikra (IRE) **Brendan W. Duke & Mrs Linda Rodriguez**
6 **VOCAL QUEEN (IRE)**, 4, b f Vocalised (USA)—Silver Queen **Mrs Jackie Bolger**
7 **VOLATILE LADY (IRE)**, 4, b f Vocalised (USA)—Astralai (IRE) **Mrs Jackie Bolger**

THREE-YEAR-OLDS
8 **CLEMENCIA (IRE)**, b g Pour Moi (IRE)—Cleofila (IRE) **Mrs Jackie Bolger**
9 **EARLY VOICE (IRE)**, b g Vocalised (USA)—Maidin Moch (IRE) **Mrs Jackie Bolger**
10 **MACKEN (IRE)**, b c Kendargent (FR)—Salorina (USA) **Macken Partnership**
11 B g Mustameet (USA)—Old Phobie (IRE) **Patrick Brennan**
12 **PRIDE OF PIMLICO (IRE)**, ch g Casamento (IRE)—Casina Valadier (IRE) **Martin Hayes & Peter Slezak**
13 **THAM LUANG (IRE)**, b c Arcano (IRE)—Katoom (IRE) **MrJ Houston & Desmond Strain**
14 **VOCAL DUKE (IRE)**, b g Vocalised (USA)—Heir Today (IRE) **Mrs Jackie Bolger**

TWO-YEAR-OLDS
15 B c 25/4 Raven's Pass (USA)—Brazilian Spirit (IRE) (Invincible Spirit (IRE)) **The Fenway Syndicate**
16 **MADE IN PIMLICO (IRE)**, ch c 2/3 Dragon Pulse (IRE)—
Runway Giant (USA) (Giant's Causeway (USA)) **The Fenway Syndicate**
17 B f 18/3 Ivawood (IRE)—Pearl Blue (IRE) (Exceed And Excel (AUS)) (7584) **Brendan W. Duke Racing**
18 B f 17/2 Free Eagle (IRE)—Poplar Close (IRE) (Canford Cliffs (IRE)) **The Fenway Syndicate**
19 **VALUE CHAIN**, gr c 13/3 Garswood—Actionplatinum (IRE) (Act One) (16856) **Mrs Jackie Bolger**
20 **VERITE (GER)**, br f 2/4 Earl of Tinsdal (GER)—
Vareze (Duke of Marmalade (IRE)) (4214) **Suzanne Zollinger & Partners**

Jockey (flat): Rory Cleary, Kevin Manning, Ronan Whelan. **Jockey (NH):** Andrew Lynch. **Apprentice:** Daniel Redmond.

166 MR IAN DUNCAN, Coylton
Postal: **Sandhill Farm, Coylton, Ayr, Ayrshire, KA6 6HE**
Contacts: **PHONE (01292) 571118 FAX (01292) 571118 MOBILE (07731) 473668**
E-MAIL jennyclose86@googlemail.com

1 **ABRACH ROAD**, 4, ch c Supreme Sound—Belfast Central (IRE) **Mr A. J. R. Lilley**
2 **BALLYHACKAMORE**, 6, b br m Oscar (IRE)—Za Beau (IRE) **Dr S. Sinclair**
3 **CIARABELLA (IRE)**, 6, b m Gold Well—Fancy Fashion (IRE) **Miss J. Girasoli**
4 **CYPRUS AVENUE**, 7, b m Kayf Tara—Za Beau (IRE) **Dr S. Sinclair**
5 **FINAGHY AYR (IRE)**, 11, ch g Lahib (USA)—Ali Ankah (IRE) **Ronnie Lilley, Boyce, Mitchell & Payne**
6 **IMPERIAL PRINCE (IRE)**, 10, b g Subtle Power—Satco Rose (IRE) **Mr A. J. R. Lilley**
7 **JESSIEMAC (IRE)**, 5, br m Sholokhov (IRE)—All Our Blessings (IRE) **Alan & Barry Macdonald**
8 **LARGY PROSPECT (IRE)**, 7, b g Stowaway—Thrilling Prospect (IRE) **I. A. Duncan**
9 **OLLISU LAD (IRE)**, 10, b g Westerner—Nick's Jule (IRE) **I. A. Duncan**
10 **PORTSTORM**, 4, b g Shirocco (GER)—Viva Victoria **Gregg, Lilley & Davidson**

Other Owners: Mr J. Boyce, Mr C. Davidson, Mr A. L. Gregg, Mr B. Macdonald, Mr A. Macdonald, Mr D. Mitchell, Mr J. Payne.

167 MR NIGEL DUNGER, Pulborough
Postal: **17 Allfrey Plat, Pulborough, West Sussex, RH20 2BU**
Contacts: **PHONE (07494) 344167 MOBILE (07790) 631962**
E-MAIL debdunger05@gmail.com

1 **HIER ENCORE (FR)**, 7, ch g Kentucky Dynamite (USA)—Hierarchie (FR) **N. A. Dunger**
2 **THAT'S EXACTLY (IRE)**, 10, ch m Bach (IRE)—Maracana (IRE) **N. A. Dunger**

Assistant Trainer: Mrs D Dunger

168 MR ED DUNLOP, Newmarket

Postal: **La Grange Stables, Fordham Road, Newmarket, Suffolk, CB8 7AA**
Contacts: **PHONE (01638) 661998 FAX (01638) 667394 MOBILE (07785) 328537**
E-MAIL **edunlop@eddunloptracing.co.uk** WEBSITE **www.edunlop.com**

1 **ALTERNATIVE FACT**, 4, b g Dalakhani (IRE)—O Fourlunda
2 **AMAZING RED (IRE)**, 6, b g Teofilo (IRE)—Artisia (IRE)
3 **BAASHA**, 4, b g Havana Gold (IRE)—Tawaasul
4 **BAWAADER (IRE)**, 4, gr g Dark Angel (IRE)—Aspen Falls (IRE)
5 **CUE'S FOLLY**, 4, b f Nathaniel (IRE)—Island Odyssey
6 **DAGUENEAU (IRE)**, 4, b g Champs Elysees—Bright Enough
7 **DARK RED (IRE)**, 7, gr g Dark Angel (IRE)—Essexford (IRE)
8 **GLOBAL ART**, 4, b g Dutch Art—Constant Dream
9 **GLOBAL GIANT**, 4, b c Shamardal (USA)—Aniseed (IRE)
10 **GLOBAL HUMOR (USA)**, 4, b g Distorted Humor (USA)—In Bloom (USA)
11 **GOTTARDO (IRE)**, 4, b g Choisir (AUS)—Chantarella (IRE)
12 **GRANDSCAPE**, 4, b g Lemon Drop Kid (USA)—Unnatural (USA)
13 **MELODIES**, 4, ch f Iffraaj—Singersongwriter
14 **MR GENT (IRE)**, 4, br g Society Rock (IRE)—Furnival (USA)
15 **PERLA BLANCA (USA)**, 5, gr m Dalakhani (IRE)—Trend Line (IRE)
16 **RED VERDON (USA)**, 6, ch g Lemon Drop Kid (USA)—Porto Marmay (IRE)
17 **SIR GNET (IRE)**, 5, b g Galileo (IRE)—Ecoutila (IRE)
18 **SPORTING TIMES**, 5, ch g Sir Percy—Queen of Iceni

THREE-YEAR-OLDS

19 **ACHAEUS (GER)**, b c Tertullian (USA)—Anatola (GER)
20 **ALAMEERY**, b c Kingman—Zacheta
21 **ALWISAAM (IRE)**, gr g Dark Angel (IRE)—Jo Bo Bo (IRE)
22 **ARCTIC SPIRIT**, b f Intello (GER)—Tahirah
23 **DANCINGWITHWOLVES (IRE)**, b g Footstepsinthesand—Clodovina (IRE)
24 **GLOBAL ACCLAMATION**, b g Acclamation—High Luminosity (USA)
25 **GLOBAL COMMAND (IRE)**, b g War Command (USA)—Parsley (IRE)
26 **GLOBAL DESTINATION (IRE)**, b c Slade Power (IRE)—Silk Trail
27 **GLOBAL EXPRESS**, ch c New Approach (IRE)—All For Laura
28 **GLOBAL FREEDOM**, b c Maxios—Modesty's Way (USA)
29 **GLOBAL GIFT (FR)**, b g Invincible Spirit (IRE)—Special Gift (IRE)
30 **GLOBAL LIGHT (IRE)**, b f Excelebration—Lucina
31 **GLOBAL ROCK (FR)**, b c Siyouni (FR)—Baino Rock (FR)
32 **GLOBAL WARNING**, b c Poet's Voice—Persario
33 **HELIAN (IRE)**, b c Shamardal (USA)—Amathia (IRE)
34 **HOMESICK BOY (IRE)**, b g Data Link (USA)—Don't Cry For Me (USA)
35 **INSPIRATIONAL (IRE)**, b f Slade Power (IRE)—Refuse To Give Up (IRE)
36 **JABALALY (IRE)**, b c Moohaajim (IRE)—Bahati (IRE)
37 **MAP OF AUSTRALIA**, ch c Australia—Map of Heaven
38 **MAQAADEER**, b c Mukhadram—Burnt Fingers (IRE)
39 **MAWSOOL (IRE)**, b g Kodiac—Habaayib
40 **MAY JUNE (IRE)**, b f Mukhadram—Subsequently (FR)
41 **PERIQUE**, b g Cacique (IRE)—Meetyouthere (IRE)
42 **RAINBOW SPIRIT**, b f Charm Spirit (IRE)—Navajo Rainbow
43 **RED SECRET (CAN)**, b c Lemon Drop Kid (USA)—Parley (USA)
44 **REDDIAC (IRE)**, b g Kodiac—Margarita (IRE)
45 **ROCA MAGICA**, b f Garswood—Marigay's Magic
46 **ROXY ART (IRE)**, ch f Dutch Art—Chicago Girl (IRE)
47 **SAN DIACO (IRE)**, gr g Kodiac—Cland di San Jore (IRE)
48 **SAN SEBASTIAN (IRE)**, b c Iffraaj—Invincible Cara (IRE)
49 B c Wootton Bassett—Scarlet Sonnet (IRE)
50 **SHAWAAHEQ (IRE)**, b g Tamayuz—Jabhaat (USA)
51 B br f Medaglia d'oro (USA)—Strathnaver
52 **TORO DORADO (IRE)**, b g Toronado (IRE)—Rawoof (IRE)
53 **TRIPLE GENIUS (IRE)**, b g Mastercraftsman (IRE)—Three Moons (IRE)
54 **VALENCE**, b c Oasis Dream—Independence
55 **VENEDEGAR (IRE)**, b g Dubawi (IRE)—Cara Fantasy (IRE)
56 **YES CAN DO (USA)**, b f No Nay Never (USA)—Sheba's Humor (USA)

MR ED DUNLOP - Continued

TWO-YEAR-OLDS

57 AHDAB (IRE), b c 21/4 Shamardal (USA)—Habaayib (Royal Applause)
58 AHLAN SAYIDATY, b f 4/4 Fast Company (IRE)—Michelle Shift (Night Shift (USA)) (7000)
59 AYSAR (IRE), b c 19/1 Sir Prancealot (IRE)—Yajala (Fasliyev (USA)) (160000)
60 BIANCA CASTAFIORE (FR), b f 30/3 Dabirsim (FR)—Faviva (USA) (Storm Cat (USA)) (30341)
61 Ch f 22/1 Showcasing—Bronte Sister (IRE) (Acclamation) (42000)
62 B f 9/3 Toronado (IRE)—Burnt Fingers (IRE) (Kheleyf (USA)) (6500)
63 B c 25/3 Brazen Beau (AUS)—Eclaircie (IRE) (Thunder Gulch (USA)) (85714)
64 ENOSI (FR), ch c 24/2 Champs Elysees—Frasque (IRE) (Iffraaj) (63211)
65 FEISTY GAL (IRE), b f 5/3 Invincible Spirit (IRE)—Bobbie Soxer (IRE) (Pivotal)
66 B c 6/4 Roderic O'Connor (IRE)—Hector's Girl (Hector Protector (USA)) (50000)
67 B c 4/3 The Factor (USA)—Ishraak (USA) (Sahm (USA))
68 B c 12/3 Kingman—Lady Linda (USA) (Torrential (USA)) (300000)
69 B f 23/4 Gleneagles (IRE)—Liberally (IRE) (Statue of Liberty (USA)) (75000)
70 MAYSONG, ch c 16/3 Mayson—Aldeburgh Music (IRE) (In The Wings) (32026)
71 B c 10/3 Tamayuz—Nassaakh (Cape Cross (IRE)) (10000)
72 OWHATANIGHT, gr c 23/2 Night of Thunder (IRE)—White Wedding (IRE) (Green Desert (USA)) (155000)
73 PLUNKETT, b c 17/3 Gleneagles (IRE)—Aragella (IRE) (Oasis Dream) (10000)
74 Gr f 21/3 Poet's Voice—Reaching Ahead (USA) (Mizzen Mast (USA)) (35000)
75 RED CELEBRE (IRE), ch c 24/3 Teofilo (IRE)—Artisia (IRE) (Peintre Celebre (USA)) (65000)
76 RED FOR ALL, b c 30/3 Muhaarar—All For Laura (Cadeaux Genereux) (140000)
77 B c 10/4 Kodiac—Slatey Hen (IRE) (Acclamation) (125000)
78 VIRGIN SNOW, b f 12/3 Gleneagles (IRE)—Snow Fairy (IRE) (Intikhab (USA))

Owners: Mr Hamdan Al Maktoum, Ahmad Al Shaikh, Mr Austin Allison, The Hon R J Arculli, Mr N B Attenborough, Mr Stephen W Barrow, Mr Geoffrey Bishop, Mr & Mrs R Bourne, Mrs Emma Capon, Cliveden Stud, Mrs Gillian Cotton, Mr Alan Cronshaw, The Countess of Derby, Mrs Edward Dunlop, Exors of the Late Mr J L Dunlop, Mr R P Foden, Mr Andrew Gemmell, Global Group Lifestyle and Sports Club, Mr Jeremy Gompertz, Mr T Henderson, Mr David Hicken, Philippa Higgins, Mr Dennis Hill, Dr Johnny Hon, Mrs S R Hope, Mr S F Hui, Ms Helian Jianru, Mr E W Lee, Mr Ralph Marshall, Mr M J Meacock, Mr Patrick Milmo, Mr Trevor Milner, Mr A M Mitchell, Mr Mark Newcombe, Mrs Georgina Newcombe, Mr Paul Nightingale, The Old Etonian Racing Syndicate, O T I Racing, Mr Bill Paton, Mr Brian Plows, Mr Malcolm Plows, Mrs Janice Quy, Lady Ritblat, Mr David Roberts, Mrs Susan Roy, Mrs C L Smith, Mr Richard Smith, Mr Colin Snowdon, St Albans Bloodstock Limited, Mrs I H Stewart-Brown, Mrs A M Sturges, Mr Christopher Symons, Mr Andrew White, Mrs Julie White, Mr Michael Wilmshurst, Mr Ken Wilson, Windflower Overseas Holdings Inc, Mr W P Wyatt, Mr Yin Yue, Mr Quentin Zheng.

Assistant Trainer: Victoria Hayter

Amateur: Miss Sophie Smith.

---

169 **MR HARRY DUNLOP, Lambourn**
Postal: **Windsor House Stables, Crowle Road, Lambourn, Hungerford, Berkshire, RG17 8NR**
Contacts: PHONE **(01488) 73584** MOBILE **(07880) 791895**
E-MAIL info@harrydunlopracing.com WEBSITE www.harrydunlopracing.com

1 COASTAL CYCLONE, 5, b g Canford Cliffs (IRE)—Seasonal Cross **Malcolm & Alicia Aldis**
2 FIGHTING IRISH (IRE), 4, b c Camelot—Quixotic **Daniel MacAuliffe & Anoj Don**
3 JACKFINBAR (FR), 4, b c Whipper (USA)—Anna Simona (GER) **Haven't A Pot**
4 KHAZIX (IRE), 4, b g Al Kazeem—Burlesque Star (IRE) **Kingwood Stud Management Co Ltd**
5 KNIGHT TO BEHOLD (IRE), 4, b c Sea The Stars (IRE)—Angel of The Gwaun (IRE) **Mr L. N. Jones**
6 LOOKING FOR CARL, 4, b g Lope de Vega (IRE)—Dam Beautiful **Haven't A Pot**
7 PIRATE KING, 4, br c Farhh—Generous Diana **Daniel MacAuliffe & Anoj Don**
8 ROBIN OF NAVAN (FR), 6, ch h American Post—Cloghran (FR) **Haven't A Pot & Richard Foden**

THREE-YEAR-OLDS

9 BALLET RED, ch f Rio de La Plata (USA)—Beriosova (FR) **The Ascot 9**
10 BLACK ABBEY (FR), bl g Hannouma (IRE)—Alta Stima (IRE) **Daniel MacAuliffe & Anoj Don**
11 BROOKLYN BOY, b c Camelot—Tan Tan **Daniel MacAuliffe & Anoj Don**
12 CRACKAWAY (FR), b c Whipper (USA)—Ellary (FR) **Elwes Moore Scandrett & Wynne-morgan**
13 CRANEUR, ch g Showcasing—Paris Winds (IRE) **Be Hopeful Partnership**
14 FREA, b f Sea The Moon (GER)—Patronella (IRE) **Kingwood Stud Management Co Ltd**
15 GOLDINO BELLO (FR), b c Anodin (IRE)—Valse Legere (FR) **Daniel MacAuliffe & Anoj Don**
16 LADY ELYSIA, ch f Champs Elysees—Lost In Lucca **The Nigel Bennett Partnership**
17 LEVANTER (FR), b f Rock of Gibraltar (IRE)—Seasonal Cross **Malcolm & Alicia Aldis**

MR HARRY DUNLOP - Continued

18 **MISS GARGAR**, b f Garswood—Verge (IRE) **British Racing Club**
19 **OOFY PROSSER (IRE)**, br g Tough As Nails (IRE)—Choir Lady (IRE) **The Megsons**
20 **RIVERINA**, ch f Australia—Peace Palace **Hambro, Westerberg & Partners**

TWO-YEAR-OLDS

21 B f 8/5 Style Vendome (FR)—Aljafliyah (Halling (USA)) (13485) **Hoskins de Zoete, Lewis & Nutting**
22 **ANGEL ON HIGH (IRE)**, b c 9/4 Dark Angel (IRE)—
      Angel of The Gwaun (IRE) (Sadler's Wells (USA)) **Mr L. N. Jones**
23 B c 31/3 American Post—Atarfe (IRE) (Anabaa (USA)) (63211) **Haven't A Pot, D. Macauliffe & Anoj Don**
24 B f 4/3 Siyouni (FR)—Bearlita (GER) (Lomitas) (71639) **Mrs S. M. Roy**
25 **CAPTAIN HADDOCK (IRE)**, b c 5/2 Make Believe—
      Kayd Kodaun (IRE) (Traditionally (USA)) (12000) **Mrs Susan Roy & Partner**
26 **CASSIDY JO (IRE)**, b f 23/3 Golden Horn—Roses For The Lady (IRE) (Sadler's Wells (USA)) **Mr L. N. Jones**
27 **GENTLEMAN AT ARMS (IRE)**, b c 5/5 Reliable Man—
      Sworn Sold (GER) (Soldier Hollow) (25000) **Be Hopeful (2) & Fair Salinia Ltd**
28 B f 8/2 Hurricane Run (IRE)—Hungry Heart (IRE) (Hawk Wing (USA)) (33712) **Mr E. Mudge**
29 B f 26/2 Epaulette (AUS)—Joyful Risk (IRE) (Kheleyf (USA))
30 B f 17/2 Golden Horn—Lady Penko (IRE) (Archipenko (USA)) (80000) **Haven't A Pot & Ballylinch Stud**
31 B g 16/4 Stormy River (FR)—Lemon Twist (Marju (IRE)) (25284) **Hambro von Opel**
32 **LONDON CALLING (ITY)**, ch c 20/4 Kingston Hill—Senhall (Halling (USA)) (17277) **Friends of John Dunlop**
33 **LOST EMPIRE (IRE)**, b c 6/3 Footstepsinthesand—
      Ballerina Rose (Duke of Marmalade (IRE)) (42140) **Mr L. N. Jones**
34 B g 10/4 Holy Roman Emperor (IRE)—
      Miss Topsy Turvy (IRE) (Mr Greeley (USA)) (674) **Windflower Overseas Holdings Inc**
35 **RAGTIME SALLY**, b f 29/3 Iffraaj—Honky Tonk Sally (Dansili) (50000) **Whsp & Mrs Maitland-Jones**
36 **SAFFRON LANE**, b f 13/4 Mukhadram—Sabreon (Caerleon (USA)) **Velocity Racing**
37 B c 9/3 Intello (GER)—Savoie (FR) (Anabaa (USA)) (64896) **Daniel MacAuliffe & Anoj Don**
38 **VULCAN (IRE)**, b c 22/2 Free Eagle—Quixotic (Pivotal) **The 2 Under Partnership**
39 Br g 10/5 Montmartre (FR)—Water Feature (Dansili) (20000) **Mr Erik Penser & The Duchess of Bedford**

Other Owners: Mrs S. Abbott, Mrs A. Aldis, Mr M. S. Aldis, Ballylinch Stud, Be Hopeful (2), Mrs J. K. Bennett, Mr N. A. Bennett, Mr A. C. Culumbarapitiyage Don, Mrs C. A. M. Dunlop, H. J. L. Dunlop, Mr N. R. Elwes, R. P. Foden, Mr R. J. Fowler, Mrs B. S. Fowler, Mr G. Freeman, Mr K. C. Freeman, Lady C. Guise, Mr R. Hambro, S. A. Hanson, Mr D. A. Kirby, Mr D. P. MacAuliffe, Mrs J. F. Maitland-Jones, Mrs J. Megson, Mr A. P. Megson, Ph Milmo, Mr J. Moore, Racing Club Ltd, Mr L. C. Reed, Mr N. S. Scandrett, Westerberg Limited, The Windsor House Stables Partnership, Mr D. A. Woodley, Mr D. Wynne-Morgan.

Pupil Assistant: Rachel Davies

---

170 MRS ALEXANDRA DUNN, Wellington
Postal: **The Gallops, West Buckland, Wellington, Somerset, TA21 9LE**
Contacts: **MOBILE (07738) 512924**
WEBSITE www.alexandradunnracing.com

1 **ARGUS (IRE)**, 7, b g Rip Van Winkle (IRE)—Steel Princess (IRE) **Mr N. McCloskey**
2 **AZARI**, 7, b g Azamour (IRE)—Atasari (IRE) **B.B.S. & Lot 51**
3 **BLACK NARCISSUS (IRE)**, 10, b m Westerner—Arcanum (IRE) **Team Dunn**
4 **BLACKWATER BRAMBLE (IRE)**, 8, b g King's Theatre (IRE)—Don't Be Upset (IRE) **Mrs K. R. Smith-Maxwell**
5 **BROKE AWAY (IRE)**, 7, br m Stowaway—Not Broke Yet (IRE) **Staplegrove Racing**
6 **CHAMPAGNEFOROSCAR (IRE)**, 5, b m Oscar (IRE)—Creaking Step (IRE) **Exe Valley Racing**
7 **CHASING HEADLIGHTS (IRE)**, 7, b g Getaway (GER)—Could Do **S. Towens & W.B.B.**
8 **CHORUS OF LIES**, 7, b g Teofilo (IRE)—Cherry Orchard (IRE) **Dave Arthur & W.B.B.**
9 **COMPTON ABBEY**, 5, b m Compton Place—Bolsena (USA) **Team Dunn**
10 **COOL MACAVITY (IRE)**, 11, b g One Cool Cat (USA)—Cause Celebre (IRE) **West Buckland Bloodstock Ltd**
11 **CORRUPTION**, 5, b m Malinas (GER)—Blue Ride (IRE) **Four Quarters**
12 **CRY WOLF**, 6, ch g Street Cry (IRE)—Love Charm **W.B.B. & G.J. Daly**
13 **DE LITTLE ENGINE (IRE)**, 5, ch g Power—Reveuse de Jour (IRE) **Equinox Racing & Team Dunn**
14 **DIAMOND REFLECTION (IRE)**, 7, b g Oasis Dream—Briolette (IRE) **Team Dunn**
15 **ENMESHING**, 6, ch g Mastercraftsman (IRE)—Yacht Club (USA) **The Crafty Six & W. B. B.**
16 **ENVOLE TOI (FR)**, 5, b g Enrique—Orphee de Vonnas (FR) **Sir P. Austin Bt**
17 **FOXY LASS**, 5, b m Foxwedge (AUS)—Domitia **Team Dunn**
18 **FRENCH MIX (USA)**, 5, b m Dalakhani (USA)—Alharmina **Mrs R. Welch**
19 **GANG WARFARE**, 8, b g Medicean—Light Impact (IRE) **Gangbusters**
20 **GENI JOHNSON (IRE)**, 7, b m Mountain High (IRE)—Garrymorris (IRE) **West Buckland Bloodstock Ltd**

MRS ALEXANDRA DUNN - Continued

21 **GOONJIM (IRE)**, 8, ch g Beneficial—Clogga Native (IRE) **The Profile Partnership**
22 **GUARACHA**, 8, ch g Halling (USA)—Pachanga **West Buckland Bloodstock Ltd**
23 **HILL FORT**, 9, ch g Pivotal—Cairns (UAE) **The Profile Partnership 2**
24 **HOW ABOUT IT (IRE)**, 10, b g Kayf Tara—Midnight Gift (IRE) **Mrs K. R. Smith-Maxwell**
25 **ICONIC BOY**, 4, b g Cape Cross (IRE)—Snoqualmie Girl (IRE) **West Buckland Bloodstock Ltd**
26 **JUPITER**, 4, b g Finjaan—Medicea Sidera **Team Dunn & W.B.B.**
27 **MINELLA VOUCHER**, 8, b g King's Theatre (IRE)—All Rise (GER) **Blue Blood Syndications & W. B. B.**
28 **POLO THE MUMM (FR)**, 9, b g Great Journey (JPN)—Maido (FR) **Mrs R. Welch**
29 **PUNKAWALLAH**, 5, ch g Sepoy (AUS)—Max One Two Three (IRE) **Mrs R. Welch**
30 **RAMBLOW**, 6, b m Notnowcato—Nsx **West Buckland Bloodstock Ltd**
31 **REGULATOR (IRE)**, 4, b g Acclamation—Rasana **West Buckland Bloodstock Ltd**
32 **RESHAAN (IRE)**, 4, b g Dark Angel (IRE)—Bluebell (IRE) **Ms L. L. Clune**
33 **SANDRO BOTTICELLI (IRE)**, 7, b g Galileo (IRE)—Ask For The Moon (IRE) **The Primaveras**
34 **SHINGHARI (IRE)**, 7, br g Cape Cross (IRE)—Sindiyma (IRE) **West Buckland Bloodstock Ltd**
35 **SIGRID NANSEN**, 4, b f Cityscape—Hail Shower (IRE) **West Buckland Bloodstock Ltd**
36 **SPINY NORMAN**, 6, b g Malinas (GER)—Helen Wood **The Time Enough Stud Partnership**
37 **SPRING STEEL (IRE)**, 10, b g Dushyantor (USA)—Fieldtown (IRE) **N Berbillion & West Buckland Bloodstock**
38 **SWEET OBSESSION (IRE)**, 7, b m Getaway (GER)—Dual Obsession **A Game Pair**
39 **SWIFT CRUSADOR**, 8, b g Kayf Tara—Goldenswift (IRE) **Mr & Mrs William Rucker**
40 **TACTICAL MANOEUVRE (IRE)**, 8, b g Marienbard (IRE)—Pride O'fleet (IRE) **The Tacticians**
41 **THAHAB IFRAJ (IRE)**, 6, ch g Frozen Power (IRE)—Penny Rouge (IRE) **The Dunnitalls**
42 **TRUCKERS TANGLE (IRE)**, 7, b g Tajraasi—Lodge Tangle (IRE) **Blue Blood Syndications & W. B. B.**
43 **TSUNDOKU (IRE)**, 8, ch m Medicean—Toberanthawn (IRE) **Dave Arthur & W.B.B.**
44 **TULSA JACK (IRE)**, 10, b g Urban Ocean (FR)—Jessica's Pet (IRE) **The Dunn Club**
45 **VENTURA BLUES**, 5, b br m Bated Breath—Salmon Rose (IRE) **Middleham Park Racing VI**
46 **WESTERNER OCEAN (IRE)**, 7, gr m Westerner—Silver Proverb **Team Dunn**
47 **WINGED EXPRESS (IRE)**, 10, b g Winged Love (IRE)—Zaffaran Express (IRE) **West Buckland Bloodstock Ltd**

Other Owners: Mr D. R. Arthur, Mrs Y. Bennett, Mr C. Bennett, Mr N. Berbillion, Blue Blood Syndications, The Crafty Six, G. J. Daly, Mrs A. Dunn, Equinox Racing, Mr V. P Finn, Mr D. J. Fitzgerald, Mr B. J. Greening, Mr S. Hill, Lot 51, T. S. Palin, M. Prince, M. J. Rowe, W. J. Rucker, Mrs A. Rucker, Miss R. J. Smith-Maxwell, Mr S. J. Studley, Mr N. Towens, Mr T. Wheatley, Mrs C. M. Wheatley, Mr A. G. S. Wiltshire, Mr R. G. Wiltshire, Mrs J. Winfield, Mr S. W. H. Winfield.

171 MRS CHRISTINE DUNNETT, Norwich
Postal: **College Farm, Hingham, Norwich, Norfolk, NR9 4PP**
Contacts: **PHONE (01953) 850596 MOBILE (07775) 793523**
E-MAIL christine@christinedunnett.com WEBSITE www.christinedunnett.com

1 **AGENT OF FORTUNE**, 4, ch f Kheleyf (USA)—Royal Bloom (IRE) **Mr A. Machin & Mrs C. Dunnett**
2 **ARRYZONA**, 8, b g Phoenix Reach (IRE)—Southwarknewsflash **Christine Dunnett Racing (Arryzona)**
3 **BEATISA**, 5, b m Intikhab (USA)—Bea Menace (USA) **One For All**
4 **CLASSIC FLYER**, 7, b g Stimulation (IRE)—Tranquil Flight **Christine Dunnett Racing (Arryzona)**
5 **COACH MONTANA (IRE)**, 10, b g Proud Citizen (USA)—Market Day
6 **COLLEGE KING**, 4, b g Baltic King—Flaming Telepath **Christine Dunnett Racing (Arryzona)**
7 **DANZOE (IRE)**, 12, br g Kheleyf (USA)—Fiaba **Mrs C. A. Dunnett**
8 **DROP KICK MURPHI (IRE)**, 4, b g Sir Prancealot (IRE)—Rindiseyda (IRE) **Mr T. Milner**
9 **FATA MORGANA**, 4, b f Society Rock (IRE)—Life's A Whirl **College Farm Stud**
10 **GIVE US A BELLE (IRE)**, 10, b g Kheleyf (USA)—Bajan Belle (IRE) **Mr F Butler & Mrs C Dunnett**
11 **HIDDEN DREAM (IRE)**, 4, b f Casamento (IRE)—Anything (IRE) **Machin, Milner, Sparkes & Dunnett**
12 **JONATHANS GIRL**, 4, b f Equiano (FR)—Jewelled **Jonathan Butcher & Christine Dunnett**
13 **KRAKA (IRE)**, 4, b g Dark Angel (IRE)—Manuelita Rose (ITY) **Team Kraka**
14 **ONE FOR ALL**, 6, b g Pivotal—Midpoint (USA) **Partnership Terminated**
15 **PATIENCEISAVIRTUE**, 4, b f Libranno—Patience **Mr P. D. West**
16 **PERCY TOPLIS**, 5, b g Kheleyf (USA)—West Lorne (USA) **Mrs C. A. Dunnett**
17 **PROUD KATE**, 5, b m Proud Citizen (USA)—Oceans Apart **The Executors of Mr A & Mrs K Barnard**
18 **RATHEALY (IRE)**, 8, b g Baltic King—Baltic Belle (IRE) **Mr P. D. West**
19 **RIPPER STREET (IRE)**, 5, b g Big Bad Bob (IRE)—Caster Sugar (USA) **Mr T. Milner**
20 **SHYARCH**, 5, b g Archipenko (USA)—Coconut Shy **Mr P. D. West**
21 **SHYJACK**, 4, ch g Archipenko (USA)—Coconut Shy **Mr F. G. Butler**

MRS CHRISTINE DUNNETT - Continued

THREE-YEAR-OLDS

22 **FORGOTTEN GIRL**, b f Sir Prancealot (IRE)—College Doll **College Farm Stud**
23 **MAZMERIZE**, b g Mazameer (IRE)—Patience **Mr P. Amey**
24 **SECRET TREATIES**, b f Heeraat (IRE)—Honky Tonk Queen (USA) **Mr A. Machin & Mrs C. Dunnett**

TWO-YEAR-OLDS

25 **CUBAN**, b c 7/5 Havana Gold (IRE)—Dignify (IRE) (Rainbow Quest (USA)) (3000) **Mr P. Eggett**
26 **KATES STAR**, b f 1/2 Casamento (IRE)—Naady (Mawatheeq (USA))
27 **LAST DAYS OF MAY**, gr ro f 5/4 Outstrip—Fenella Rose (Compton Place) (3000) **Machin & Eggett**

Other Owners: Exors of the Late Mrs K. M. Barnard, Exors of the Late Mr A. Barnard, Mr D. G. Burt, Mr J. G. Butcher, Mr A. S. Machin, Mr G. R. Price, Mr E. N. Sparkes.

---

172 MR SEAMUS DURACK, Upper Lambourn
Postal: **The Croft Stables, Upper Lambourn, Hungerford, Berkshire, RG17 8QH**
Contacts: **PHONE (01488) 491480 MOBILE (07770) 537971**
E-MAIL sd.111@btinternet.com WEBSITE www.seamusdurack.com

1 **ALFREDO (IRE)**, 7, ch g Arcano (IRE)—Western Sky **Mr Stephen Tucker & Mr Keith Mcintosh**
2 **APEX PREDATOR (IRE)**, 4, b g Acclamation—Key Girl (IRE) **Mrs A. Cowley**
3 **CAYIRLI (FR)**, 7, b g Medicean—Clarinda (FR) **S. P. Tucker**
4 **MAKAARIM**, 5, b g Tamayuz—Dubawi Cheetah (IRE) **Miss S. J. Beddoes**
5 **NICELY DONE (IRE)**, 6, b m Mahler—Rare Dollar (IRE) **Looksarnteverything Partnership**
6 **PARA MIO (IRE)**, 4, b c Pour Moi (IRE)—Malaspina (IRE) **Tucker Stafford & McCormack**
7 **PIPES OF PEACE (IRE)**, 5, b g Galileo (IRE)—Coachella **Egan Waste Services Ltd**
8 **SEAPORT**, 8, ch g Champs Elysees—Cochin (USA) **Mrs Pao, Mr Stafford & Mr Tucker**
9 4, B g Holy Roman Emperor (IRE)—Summer Bliss **Miss S. J. Beddoes**
10 **THE SWAGMAN (USA)**, 5, ch g Galileo (IRE)—Ventura **Clan McNeil**
11 **ZENITH ONE (IRE)**, 4, br g Footstepsinthesand—Gemini Diamond (IRE) **Mrs A. Cowley**

THREE-YEAR-OLDS

12 **FAST ART (IRE)**, b c Fast Company (IRE)—Poulkovo (IRE) **Mr & Mrs A Archer & Mr & Mrs M Leonard**
13 **HIERONYMUS**, b c Dutch Art—Sleek **Mrs Pao, Mr Stafford & Mr Tucker**
14 B c Bungle Inthejungle—Kannon
15 **LA ROCA DEL FUEGO (IRE)**, br c Rock of Gibraltar (IRE)—Reign (IRE) **Mr M. D. Drake**
16 **SET POINT CHARLIE (IRE)**, b c Holy Roman Emperor (IRE)—Love Thirty **Mrs Pao, Mr Stafford & Mr Tucker**

Other Owners: Mrs J. Archer, Mr A. Archer, Mr S. J. Lee, Mr M. A. Leonard, Mrs M. E. Leonard, E. McCormack, Mr K. R. McIntosh, Mr P. J. McNeil, Mr J. McNeil, Mrs A. Pao, Mr D. Parkinson, Mr N. J. Stafford.

Assistant Trainer: Sam Beddoes

---

173 MISS CLAIRE DYSON, Evesham
Postal: **Froglands Stud Farm, Froglands Lane, Cleeve Prior, Evesham, Worcestershire, WR11 8LB**
Contacts: **PHONE (07803) 720183 (01789) 774000 FAX (01789) 774000**
E-MAIL cdyson@live.co.uk WEBSITE www.clairedysonracing.co.uk

1 **CLASSIC TUNE**, 9, b g Scorpion (IRE)—Classic Fantasy **D. J. Dyson**
2 **CLASSULA**, 7, b g Sulamani (IRE)—Classic Fantasy **D. J. Dyson**
3 **CLASSY AFAIR**, 5, b m Fair Mix (IRE)—Classic Fantasy **Mr B. D. Vaughan**
4 **HOLY CROSS (IRE)**, 8, b g Yeats (IRE)—Bleu Ciel Et Blanc (FR) **FSF Racing**
5 **JOHNNY OG**, 10, b g Flemensfirth (USA)—Mrs Roberts **I. K. Pardy & D. J. Pardy**
6 **MIDNIGHT OWLE**, 9, ch g Midnight Legend—Owlesbury Dream (IRE) **FSF Racing**
7 **MINELLA STYLE (IRE)**, 9, b g King's Theatre (IRE)—Rose of The Erne (IRE) **Mr G. T. Sainsbury**
8 **PASSAM**, 7, b g Black Sam Bellamy (IRE)—One Wild Night **FSF Racing**
9 **PERSIAN DELIGHT**, 9, b g Lucarno (USA)—Persian Walk (FR) **Miss C. Dyson**
10 5, B m Passing Glance—Qualitee **FSF Racing**
11 **ROYAL REEF (IRE)**, 7, b g Duke of Marmalade (IRE)—Bintalreef (USA) **Mr M. P. Hammond**
12 **STILL A DREAM**, 6, b g Sulamani (IRE)—Owlesbury Dream (IRE) **D. J. Dyson**

Other Owners: Mr D. J. Pardy, Mr I. K. Pardy.

Jockey (NH): David Noonan. **Conditional:** Charlie Hammond.

174 MR SIMON EARLE, Sutton Veny
Postal: **The Lower Barn, The Beeches Farm, Deverill Road, Sutton Veny, Wiltshire, BA12 7BY**
Contacts: **PHONE (01985) 840450 FAX (01985) 840450 MOBILE (07850) 350116**
E-MAIL simonearleracing@btinternet.com WEBSITE www.simonearleracing.co.uk

1 **GOLDEN HOUR (USA)**, 5, b g Medaglia d'oro (USA)—Morrow **R. L. Dacombe**
2 **KAVANAGHS CORNER (IRE)**, 10, b g Coroner (IRE)—Annacarney (IRE) **Mrs B. O'Flynn**
3 5, B g Sakhee (USA)—Madame Mozaik (USA) **Mr S. A. Earle**
4 **THE LACEMAKER**, 5, b m Dutch Art—Sospel **Mrs Dawn Scott**
5 **WATER RAIL**, 10, b g Manipulator (IRE)—Madame Mozaik (USA) **Mr S. A. Earle**

175 MR MICHAEL EASTERBY, Sheriff Hutton
Postal: **New House Farm, Sheriff Hutton, York, North Yorkshire, YO60 6TN**
Contacts: **PHONE (01347) 878368 FAX (01347) 878204 MOBILE (07831) 347481**
E-MAIL enquiries@mickeasterby.co.uk WEBSITE www.mickeasterby-racing.co.uk

1 **AGAR'S PLOUGH**, 4, ch g Dutch Art—Cloud's End **J. Blackburn & L. Fowell**
2 **AIRGLOW (IRE)**, 4, b g Invincible Spirit (IRE)—Pearl Grey **Mr S Davis & Mr S Hull**
3 **ALBERT'S BACK**, 5, b g Champs Elysees—Neath **Golden Ratio P'ship, Mr S Winter & Mr J Blackburn**
4 **ALDRETH**, 8, b g Champs Elysees—Rowan Flower (IRE) **Mr A. Morse & Stittenham Racing**
5 **ARROWTOWN**, 7, b m Rail Link—Protectress **S Hollings L Folwell S Hull M Bannister**
6 **ASTRAEA**, 4, b f Cityscape—Rapid Revalation (USA) **Mrs Linda Folwell Racing**
7 **BALLYMOUNT**, 4, ch g Cityscape—Symphony Star (IRE) **Winter Straghalis Fielding Hollings Hull**
8 **BARTON MILLS**, 4, b g Iffraaj—Balladonia **Harry Easterby Racing**
9 **BOSHAM**, 9, b g Shamardal (USA)—Awwal Malika (USA) **P. Easterby**
10 **BOWSON FRED**, 7, b g Monsieur Bond (IRE)—Bow Bridge **Mrs A. Jarvis**
11 **CAPTON**, 6, b g Cape Cross (IRE)—Flavian **Irrational Group & J Blackburn**
12 **CHASMA**, 9, b m Kayf Tara—Luneray (FR) **Mr N W A Bannister & Mr S A Lewis Racing**
13 **CHOOSEY (IRE)**, 4, ch g Choisir (AUS)—Petit Chou (IRE) **K Wreglesworth**
14 **DAHIK (IRE)**, 4, ch g Society Rock (IRE)—Bishop's Lake **Mr A. Saha**
15 **DARKANDSTORMY**, 4, b f Hurricane Run (IRE)—Unquenchable (USA) **Mr J Blackburn, Mr S Winter & Mr H Cram**
16 **DECIMA (IRE)**, 5, b m Dream Ahead (USA)—Snowtime (IRE) **W H & Mrs J A Tinning & Mrs C Wallis**
17 **DESERT DREAM**, 5, b g Oasis Dream—Rosika **Harry Easterby Racing**
18 **ENLIGHTEN**, 5, b g Kayf Tara—Rapturous **R S Cockerill (farms) Ltd Racing**
19 **FLIGHT OFFICER**, 8, b g New Approach (IRE)—Danuta (USA) **Imperial Racing Partnership No.8**
20 **FLYMETOTHESTARS**, 6, b g Sea The Stars (IRE)—Precious Gem (IRE) **Middleham Park Racing**
21 **FURZE LADY**, 4, b f Dick Turpin (IRE)—Baymist **Mrs Linda Folwell Racing**
22 **GANBEI**, 13, ch g Lomitas—Native Ring (FR) **Mr N. W. A. Bannister**
23 **GULF OF POETS**, 7, b g Oasis Dream—Sandglass **Mr J Blackburn Mr A Pollock Mr A Turton**
24 **HARVEST DAY**, 4, b f Harbour Watch (IRE)—Miss Wells (IRE) **Mrs C E Mason & Partner**
25 **HOLIDAY MAGIC (IRE)**, 8, gr g Dark Angel (IRE)—Win Cash (IRE) **Mr A. Saha**
26 **IMPERIAL STATE**, 6, b g Holy Roman Emperor (IRE)—Seldemosa **Mrs L Folwell J Blackburn & S Winter**
27 **ITLAAQ**, 13, b g Alhaarth (IRE)—Hathrah **M. W. Easterby**
28 **KALK BAY (IRE)**, 12, b g Hawk Wing (USA)—Politesse (USA) **Mrs Linda Folwell Racing**
29 **KANNAPOLIS (IRE)**, 4, b g Makfi—Alta Definizione (IRE) **Mr A Stott & Mr E Brook**
30 **KINDLY**, 6, b m Kyllachy—Touching (IRE) **M Blades, S Hull & S Hollings**
31 **LA RAV (IRE)**, 4, b g Footstepsinthesand—Swift Acclaim (IRE) **S Davis, S Hull & B Hoggarth**
32 **LUZUM (IRE)**, 4, b g Epaulette (AUS)—Empress Ella (IRE) **Winter Straghalis Mason Hollings & Hull**
33 **MAGIC CITY (IRE)**, 10, b g Elusive City (USA)—Annmarie's Magic (IRE) **A Turton J Blackburn & Mrs L Folwell**
34 **MALDONADO (FR)**, 5, ch g Rio de La Plata (USA)—Spanish Winner (USA) **Mr A. Saha**
35 **MANON**, 5, b m Malinas (GER)—La Creole (FR) **Mr N Wrigley, Mrs J Lukas & Mr B Guerin**
36 **MANZIL (IRE)**, 4, ch g Bated Breath—Pointed Arch (IRE) **Imperial Blackburn Saha Sh Df & Sh**
37 **PERFECT PASTURE**, 9, b g Pastoral Pursuits—Word Perfect **S Hull & S Hollings**
38 **QAFFAAL (USA)**, 8, b g Street Cry (USA)—Wasseema (USA) **Calam & Holdsworth & Laura Mason Synd**
39 **QAWAMEES (IRE)**, 4, b g Exceed And Excel (AUS)—Jabhaat (USA) **Irrational Group & J Blackburn**
40 **QUICK LOOK**, 6, b g Kheleyf (USA)—Weqaar (USA) **Golden Ratio, Hull, Hollings & Winter**
41 **RAPID APPLAUSE**, 7, b g Royal Applause—Madam Ninette **Folwell Morse Mulryan Winter & Cram**
42 **ROLLADICE**, 4, ch g Bated Breath—Selkirk Sky **A Pollock and J Blackburn**
43 **ROLLER**, 6, b g Rail Link—Buffering **Irkroy Racing & Mr Andrew Pollock**
44 **ROYCANO**, 9, ch g Lucarno (USA)—Royal Distant (USA) **Mr M. J. R. Bannister/Stittenham Racing**
45 **SAINTS AND SINNERS (IRE)**, 11, b g Gold Well—How Provincial (IRE) **Mr N Wrigley & Mrs J Lukas**
46 **SAM'S GUNNER**, 6, ch g Black Sam Bellamy (IRE)—Falcon's Gunner **Falcon's Line Ltd**
47 **SELECTION (FR)**, 6, ch g Siyouni (FR)—Perspective (FR) **Mr S Davis & Mr S Hull**

MR MICHAEL EASTERBY - Continued

48 **SPACE WAR,** 12, b g Elusive City (USA)—Princess Luna (GER) **The Laura Mason Syndicate**
49 **STAR ARCHER,** 5, b g Champs Elysees—Postale **S Hull, J Blackburn**
50 **STEEL CITY,** 11, gr g Act One—Serraval (FR) **J. T. Brown**
51 **SUNNYSIDE LADY,** 4, ch f Kheleyf (USA)—Skiddaw Wolf **J. R. Wills**
52 **SWANSWAY,** 6, ch g Showcasing—Spring Stroll (USA) **W. H. & Mrs J. A. Tinning**
53 **TORRID,** 8, ch g Three Valleys (USA)—Western Appeal (USA) **J Blackburn & Mrs A Bartram**
54 **TOWN HEAD,** 6, ch g Archipenko (USA)—Forever Loved **Mr M. J. R. Bannister/Stittenham Racing**
55 **UNCLE BOBBY,** 8, ch g Avonbridge—Aunt Hilda **M W Easterby**
56 **UP TEN DOWN TWO (IRE),** 10, b g Hurricane Run (IRE)—Darabela (IRE) **Mrs C Daurge Racing**
57 **WELD AL EMARAT,** 7, b g Dubawi (IRE)—Spirit of Dubai (IRE) **Imperial Racing Partnership No.8**
58 **WHERE'S JEFF,** 4, b g Haafhd—Piece of Magic **A G Pollock, Golden Ratio & Jolly Boys**

THREE-YEAR-OLDS

59 **ABWAB (IRE),** b g Teofilo (IRE)—Alaia (IRE) **Mr S Winter**
60 **ARCHON,** ch g Lope de Vega (IRE)—Date With Destiny (IRE) **Mr B. Padgett**
61 **BOREAS DUKE,** b g Rip Van Winkle (IRE)—Amalna **Sheep As A Lamb Syndicate**
62 **BRANDY SPIRIT,** b g Charm Spirit (IRE)—B Berry Brandy (USA) **Mr A. H. L. Zheng**
63 Ch g Pivotal—Dream Play (IRE) **Mr Alan Zheng & Stittenham Racing**
64 **ELYSIAN FLAME,** ch g Champs Elysees—Combustible (IRE) **Mr J Blackburn & Imperial Racing P'ship**
65 B br c Havana Gold (IRE)—Fine Lady **M Blades & S Hull**
66 B g Lope de Vega (IRE)—Forces of Darkness (IRE) **Imperial Racing P'Ship & Mr J Blackburn**
67 **GANTON EAGLE,** b g Poet's Voice—Our Faye **Mr S Davis, Mr S Hull & Mrs L Folwell**
68 **GEORGE RIDSDALE,** ch g Ruler of The World (IRE)—
                                                Cape Rising (IRE) **Mr J Blackburn & Imperial Racing P'ship**
69 **HALF FULL,** ch g Monsieur Bond (IRE)—Choral Singer **Blackburn Turton Blades Hollings & Hull**
70 **IT'S ALL GUCCI,** ch g Equiano (FR)—Faldal **Mr S Davis, Mr S Hull & Mrs L Folwell**
71 **JOE THE BEAU,** ch g Mukhadram—Divine Power **Mr B Padgett Racing**
72 **KIMBERLEY GIRL,** b f Heeraat (IRE)—Black Baccara **Mr Stewart A Lewis Racing**
73 **LADY LAVINIA,** b f Burwaaz—El Molino Blanco **David Scott & Co Ltd & Partner**
74 **MAJOR SNUGFIT,** ch g Ruler of The World (IRE)—Bridle Belle **Mr A Greenwood & Mr S Windle**
75 **MELGATE MAGIC,** ch g Harbour Watch (IRE)—Corn Rigs **B Hoggarth & D Scott Pattern Makers Ltd**
76 **MELGATE MAJEURE,** br g Lethal Force (IRE)—Ambrix (IRE) **Bernard Hoggarth Racing**
77 **NO BILLS,** ch f Mayson—Brave Mave **Mr J. Munroe**
78 **NO DRESS REHEARSAL,** b f Cityscape—Sailing Days **Mrs E. A. Cyzer**
79 **SHALL WE BEGIN (IRE),** ch f Bungle Inthejungle—Shone Island (IRE) **Mr G. McMullan**
80 **SHE'S AWAKE,** b f Iffraaj—Porthcawl **The Laura Mason Syndicate**
81 **SOCRU (IRE),** b g Kodiac—Hemaris (IRE) **Winter Blackburn Lm Syn Cram Mb Sh & Sh**
82 **SOFT SUMMER RAIN,** ch f Champs Elysees—Modern Art **J Blackburn & Imperial Racing**
83 **TABOU BEACH BOY,** b g Mukhadram—Illandrane (IRE) **E. A. Brook**
84 **UH OH CHONGO,** ch g Monsieur Bond (IRE)—Champagne Katie **Reg Bond & John Blackburn**

TWO-YEAR-OLDS

85 B f 17/3 Iffraaj—Aetna (Indesatchel (IRE)) **Mr B Padgett**
86 B c 8/5 Fastnet Rock (AUS)—Angelic Note (IRE) (Excellent Art) **J Sissons & B Sangster**
87 Ch c 23/2 Casamento (IRE)—Be Lucky (Kyllachy) (7619) **J Sissons & B Sangster**
88 B c 9/2 Harbour Watch (IRE)—Beldale Memory (IRE) (Camacho) (28571) **J Blackburn & Mrs J Lukas**
89 B f 15/3 Casamento (IRE)—Bow Bridge (Bertolini (USA)) **Mrs A Jarvis**
90 Gr c 24/3 Piccolo—Cherrycombe-Row (Classic Cliche (IRE)) (42857) **Harry Easterby Racing**
91 Ch c 4/3 Cityscape—Croeso Cariad (Most Welcome) **J Blackburn**
92 B c 29/1 Intrinsic—Danehill Dazzler (IRE) (Danehill Dancer (IRE)) (5714) **Intrinsic Syndicate**
93 B f 4/3 Coach House (IRE)—El Molino Blanco (Royal Applause) (4761) **Mr D Scott**
94 B c 1/2 Archipenko (USA)—Eminencia (Sadler's Wells (USA)) **Imperial Racing & J Blackburn**
95 Ch c 18/2 Equiano (FR)—Ewenny (Warrshan (USA)) (24761) **Evora Construction & D Scott**
96 B c 4/2 Harbour Watch (IRE)—Gadfly (Galileo (IRE)) **Harry Easterby Racing**
97 Br g 4/4 Garswood—Handsome Molly (Halling (USA)) (7000) **Rosyground Stud**
98 B c 22/3 Fountain of Youth (IRE)—Harryana To (Compton Place) (14285) **S Hull, S Hollings & S Davis**
99 B f 4/4 Mukhadram—How Fortunate (Haafhd) (5000) **Rosyground Stud**
100 **IVORY COMMAND (IRE),** b g 20/2 War Command (USA)—
                                                Haute Volta (FR) (Grape Tree Road) (16000) **Gay & Peter Hartley**
101 B f 16/3 Helmet (AUS)—Kibenga (Oasis Dream) (7619) **Mrs J Lukas & Laura Mason Syndicate**
102 B c 4/3 Fulbright—Kotdiji (Mtoto) (20000) **J Blackburn & S Winter**
103 B c 20/3 Dabirsim (FR)—Madonna Incognito (USA) (El Prado (IRE)) (12000) **S Davis & S Hull**
104 B c 20/3 Archipenko (USA)—Medaille d'or (With Approval (CAN)) **Imoerial Racing**
105 Ch gr f 9/3 Monsieur Bond (IRE)—Poetic Verse (Byron) **Mr J Blackburn**
106 **RING OF GOLD,** b g 23/3 Havana Gold (IRE)—Pitter Patter (Nayef (USA)) (8000) **Gay & Peter Hartley**

MR MICHAEL EASTERBY - Continued

107 SEA OF SHADOWS, ch f 6/2 Sea The Stars (IRE)—Pink Opaque (Nayef (USA)) (800) **Sea of Shadows Synd**
108 Ch c 13/3 New Approach (IRE)—Sudfah (USA) (Unbridled's Song (USA)) (10000) **A Stott & Mrs J Lukas**
109 B c 20/4 Equiano (FR)—The Clan Macdonald (Intikhab (USA)) (761) **S Hull & S Hollings**

Other Owners: Mr M. J. R. Bannister, Mr N. W. A. Bannister, A. Barney, Mrs Ann Bartram, Mr A. G. Black, Mr J. N. Blackburn, Chris Blackburn, Mr Michael Blades, Andrew Bluck, Mr R. C. Bond, Mr J. E. Bray, Mr E. A. Brook, Mr Michael Burrows, Mr T. Calam, Mr D. Chapman, Mr Carl Chapman, S. Charman, Mr A. Courtine, Mr H. A. A. Cram, Mrs Christine Daurge, David Scott and Co (Pattern Makers) Ltd, Mr Steve Davis, Mr J. Douglas, Mr M. W. Easterby, Mr Harry Peter Easterby, Mr Peter Easterby, H. Fell, Mr Dean Fielding, Mrs S. Folwell, Miss D. Gabbitas, Mr A. G. Greenwood, Mr B. Guerin, Mr Bernard Hoggarth, Mr P Holdsworth, Mr S. A. Hollings, Mr Steve Hull, Imperial Racing Partnership, Jolly Boys Racing Club, Jeff Kemp, The Laura Mason Syndicate, Mr Stewart Lewis, David Lonsdale, Mrs Julia Lukas, Mrs C. E. Mason, Jason McIvor, Mr A. Morse, Mr L. Mulryan, Mrs J. Norris, Mr B. Padgett, Mr R. Parks, Mr A. G. Pollock, Mr M. J. Pryce, R. S. Cockerill (Farms) Ltd, Miss Michelle Robinson, Mr Ian A. Robinson, Mr A. Saha, Mr Clive Sigsworth, Stittenham Racing, Mr A. F. Stott, Mr Chris Straghalis, Michael Taylor, Mrs J. A. Tinning, Mr W. H. Tinning, Sharon Tomlinson, Tom Turner, Mr Andrew Turton, Mrs C. Wallis, Peter Wilson, Simon.A.Windle, Mr S. J. Winter, Mr N. H. T. Wrigley, Mr Alan Zheng.

Assistant Trainer: D. M. Easterby

Jockey (flat): Nathan Evans, Paul Mulrennan, James Sullivan. **Jockey (NH):** Harry Bannister. **Apprentice:** Josh Quinn. **Amateur:** Miss S. Brotherton, Miss Joanna Mason.

---

176 MR TIM EASTERBY, Malton
Postal: **Habton Grange, Great Habton, Malton, North Yorkshire, YO17 6TY**
Contacts: **PHONE (01653) 668566 FAX (01653) 668621**
E-MAIL easterby@btconnect.com WEBSITE www.timeasterby.co.uk

1 AASHEQ (IRE), 6, b g Dubawi (IRE)—Beach Bunny (IRE) **Ryedale Partners No1**
2 AFANDEM (IRE), 5, b g Vale of York (IRE)—Al Mahmeya **Reality Partnerships XI**
3 AIRPLANE (IRE), 4, b g Pour Moi (IRE)—Abyssinie (IRE) **Mr M. Stewart**
4 AIYA (IRE), 4, ch g Declaration of War (USA)—Flamingo Sea (USA) **King Power Racing Co Ltd**
5 AL ERAYG (IRE), 6, b g Oasis Dream—Vallee des Reves (USA) **Reality Partnerships III**
6 ALICE LISLE, 5, ch m Flemensfirth (USA)—Twilight Affair **Ryedale Partners No 4**
7 APPOINTED, 5, b m Delegator—Celestial Harmony **Mr M. J. Macleod & Partner**
8 ATTENTION SEAKER, 9, b m Bollin Eric—Pay Attention **Ryedale Partners No 6**
9 BOLLIN ACE, 8, b g Bollin Eric—Bollin Annabel **Ryedale Partners No 3**
10 4, B f Multiplex—Bollin Annabel **Habton Farms**
11 BOLLIN JOAN, 4, b f Mount Nelson—Bollin Greta **N Arton, P Hebdon, R Taylor & Prtnr**
12 BOLLIN TED, 5, b g Haafhd—Bollin Greta **Mr Neil Arton & Partner**
13 BOSSIPOP, 6, ch g Assertive—Opopmil (IRE) **A. R. Turnbull**
14 BREATHABLE, 4, b g Bated Breath—Cassique Lady (IRE) **Mr B Guerin Mr J Westoll & Habton Farms**
15 BROTHER MCGONAGALL, 5, b r Equiano (FR)—Anatase **Reality Partnerships VI**
16 COMPUTABLE, 5, ch g Compton Place—Kummel Excess (IRE) **Mr B Guerin Mrs E J Wills & Habton Farms**
17 CONTREBASSE, 4, b g Champs Elysees—Viola da Braccio (IRE) **The Harmonious Lot & Partner**
18 COPPER KNIGHT (IRE), 5, b g Sir Prancealot (IRE)—Mystic Dream **Ventura Racing (Copper) & Partner**
19 DANCE KING, 3, ch g Danehill Dancer (IRE)—One So Wonderful **Mr Ambrose Turnbull & Partner**
20 DEW POND, 7, b g Motivator—Rutland Water (IRE) **Ashfield Caravan Park**
21 DUKE OF YORKSHIRE, 9, b g Duke of Marmalade (IRE)—Dame Edith (FR) **Habton Farms**
22 EAST STREET REVUE, 6, ch g Pastoral Pursuits—Revue Princess (IRE) **Mr S. A. Heley & Partner**
23 EMERALD CLIFFS (IRE), 4, b f Canford Cliffs (IRE)—Emeralds Spirit (IRE) **T. A. Scothern**
24 EXCELLENT TIMES, 4, b f Excelebration (IRE)—Al Janadeirya **Times Of Wigan Ltd**
25 EXCESSABLE, 6, ch g Sakhee's Secret—Kummel Excess (IRE) **Mr B Guerin & Habton Farms**
26 FLYING PURSUIT, 6, ch g Pastoral Pursuits—Choisette **Ontoawinner, M Hulin & Partner**
27 FOREST FUSION (IRE), 5, b g Flemensfirth (USA)—Qui Plus Est (FR) **The Hon Mrs E. J. Wills**
28 GARDEN OASIS, 4, b g Excelebration (IRE)—Queen Arabella **Habton Farms**
29 GHAYYAR (IRE), 5, b g Power—Al Ihtithar (IRE) **CDM Developments (North West) Ltd & Ptr**
30 GIVE IT SOME TEDDY, 5, b g Bahamian Bounty—Croeso Cariad **Mr T. J. Hemmings**
31 GLEN MOOAR (IRE), 5, b g Presenting—Supreme Serenade (IRE) **Mr T. J. Hemmings**
32 GLENCADAM GLORY, 5, b g Nathaniel (IRE)—Lady Grace (IRE) **Habton Farms**
33 GOGO BALOO, 7, b m Schiaparelli (GER)—Tarabaloo **R. W. Metcalfe**
34 GOLDEN APOLLO, 5, ch g Pivotal—Elan **Mr David Scott & Partner**
35 GULLANE ONE (IRE), 4, ch g Dream Ahead (USA)—Shamsalmaidan (IRE) **Mount Pleasant Racing**
36 4, B g Desideratum—Gwyre (IRE) **Habton Farms**
37 HAWK HIGH (IRE), 9, b g High Chaparral (IRE)—Septembers Hawk (IRE) **Mr T. J. Hemmings**
38 HYPERFOCUS (IRE), 5, b br g Intense Focus (USA)—Jouel (FR) **Ryedale Partners No 14**

MR TIM EASTERBY - Continued

39 **ICEFALL (IRE)**, 6, b g Frozen Power (IRE)—Silvertine (IRE) **Ryedale Partners No. 10**
40 **IWASTHEFUTUREONCE (IRE)**, 6, b g Fruits of Love (USA)—Ruthy Lukey (IRE) **Ryedale Partners No 11**
41 **JUST HISS**, 6, b g Lawman (FR)—Feather Boa (IRE) **The Sandmoor Partnership**
42 **KENNY THE CAPTAIN (IRE)**, 8, ch g Captain Rio—Kelso Magic (USA) **Reality Partnerships V**
43 **KHAMRY**, 6, b g Poet's Voice—Poppets Sweetlove **Habton Farms**
44 **MADAM CLOUD (IRE)**, 6, gr m Cloudings (IRE)—Model Girl **Mr T. J. Hemmings**
45 **MELTING (IRE)**, 4, b g Epaulette (AUS)—Ice On Fire **Habton Farms**
46 **MIDNIGHT MALIBU (IRE)**, 6, b m Poet's Voice—Midnight Martini **Mr D. A. West & Partner**
47 **MIKMAK**, 6, b g Makfi—Rakata (USA) **K J Racing**
48 **MILL RACE KING (IRE)**, 6, b g Scorpion (IRE)—Oso Special **Reality Partnerships IX**
49 **MISCHIEF MANAGED (IRE)**, 5, ch g Tagula (IRE)—Cape Clear **Dubelem (Racing) Limited**
50 **MOUNTAIN HAWK (IRE)**, 7, b g Mountain High (IRE)—Septembers Hawk (IRE) **Mr T. J. Hemmings**
51 **MR GREENLIGHT**, 4, b g Bahamian Bounty—Nos Da **R. Taylor & Mr P. Hebdon**
52 **MR MAXX (IRE)**, 4, b c Cape Cross (IRE)—Mirror Image **Mr M. O' Mahony**
53 **MUKHAYYAM**, 7, b g Dark Angel (IRE)—Caster Sugar (USA) **Mr T. A. Scothern & Partner**
54 **MULTELLIE**, 7, b g Multiplex—Bollin Nellie **Mr David Scott & Partner**
55 **MURAABIT**, 7, ch g Makfi—Ho Hi The Moon (IRE) **Major Sir E. Brook & Mr A Stott**
56 **MUSIC SOCIETY (IRE)**, 4, gr g Society Rock (IRE)—Absolutely Cool (IRE) **Habton Farms**
57 **MY REWARD**, 7, b g Rail Link—Tarot Card **Mr M. J. Macleod**
58 **NEW LOOK (FR)**, 4, b g Style Vendome (FR)—Tara's Force (IRE)
59 **NUNS WALK**, 5, ch m Sleeping Indian—Dance Card **Mr Ambrose Turnbull & Partner**
60 **ORION'S BOW**, 8, ch g Pivotal—Heavenly Ray (USA) **Mr T. J. Swiers**
61 **OUR CHARLIE BROWN**, 5, b g American Post—Cordoba **Ontoawinner, SDH Project Services Ltd 2**
62 **PAROLE (IRE)**, 7, ch g Mastercraftsman (IRE)—Leniency (USA) **The Senators**
63 **PARYS MOUNTAIN (IRE)**, 5, gr g Dark Angel (IRE)—Muzdaan (IRE) **Reality Partnerships XII**
64 **POET'S DAWN**, 4, ch g Poet's Voice—Dudley Queen (IRE) **Mr Timothy O'Gram & Partner**
65 **PUPPETONASTRING**, 4, b f Sixties Icon—Valbuena (IRE) **David Lumley & Prtnr**
66 **RADIO SOURCE (IRE)**, 4, ch g Raven's Pass (USA)—Roshanak (IRE) **A. R. Turnbull**
67 **RANDY PIKE (IRE)**, 9, b g Mahler—Niamh's Leader (IRE) **Reality Partnerships II**
68 **REASSURANCE**, 4, b f Champs Elysees—Timely Words **Habton Farms**
69 **REGAL MIRAGE (IRE)**, 5, ch g Aqlaam—Alzaroof (USA) **Ryedale Partners No 7**
70 **RELIGHT MY FIRE**, 9, ch g Firebreak—Making Music **J. Gill**
71 **RELKADAM (FR)**, 5, b g Muhtathir—Gloirez (FR) **Ryedale Partners No 12**
72 **RUX RUXX (IRE)**, 4, b f Dark Angel (IRE)—Lady Duxyana **King Power Racing Co Ltd**
73 **SHAIYEM (IRE)**, 6, b g Starspangledbanner (AUS)—Shaanbar (IRE) **Habton Farms**
74 **SHERIFF GARRETT (IRE)**, 5, b g Lawman (FR)—Few Are Chosen (IRE) **Ontoawinner 10 & Partner 4**
75 **SHORTBACKANDSIDES (IRE)**, 4, b g Fast Company (IRE)—Whatagoodcatch (IRE) **Habton Farms**
76 **SILVER STARLIGHT**, 4, gr f Showcasing—Pendulum **Reality Partnerships I**
77 **SILVERY MOON (IRE)**, 12, gr g Verglas (IRE)—Starry Night **Mrs D Stevens & Partner**
78 **STAXTON**, 4, b g Equiano (FR)—Snake's Head **Ontoawinner 10 & Partner**
79 **STING IN HIS TAIL (IRE)**, 6, b g Scorpion (IRE)—Glory Queen (IRE) **Mrs E J Wills & Partner**
80 **STORM AHEAD (IRE)**, 6, b g Iffraaj—Loose Julie (IRE) **A. R. Turnbull**
81 **STORMIN TOM (IRE)**, 7, b g Dylan Thomas (IRE)—She Storm (IRE) **Three Jolly Farmers**
82 **SUITCASE 'N' TAXI**, 5, br g Major Cadeaux—Finalize **Ontoawinner 10 & Partner 3**
83 **SUPAULETTE (IRE)**, 4, b f Epaulette (AUS)—Supreme Spirit (USA) **Mr Ambrose Turnbull & Partner**
84 **SUPER KID**, 7, b g Exceed And Excel (AUS)—Crimson Year (USA) **Mr M. J. Macleod**
85 **SURRENDER**, 4, b g Sixties Icon—Mango Music **Reality Partnerships II**
86 **TARA FORCE**, 5, b m Kayf Tara—Whizz Back (IRE) **Reality Partnerships VIII**
87 **TRAVEL LIGHTLY**, 4, b f Showcasing—Upton Seas **E. A. Brook**
88 **VERY FIRST TIME**, 7, b g Champs Elysees—Like A Virgin (IRE) **Mr T. J. Hemmings**
89 **VIVE LA DIFFERENCE (IRE)**, 5, b g Holy Roman Emperor (IRE)—Galaxie Sud (USA) **Ryedale Partners No 5**

THREE-YEAR-OLDS

90 **AGRAVAIN**, b g Camelot—Pivotal Lady **Mr & Mrs G. Turnbull**
91 **AMADEUS GREY (IRE)**, gr g Zebedee—Benedicte (IRE) **Ontoawinner 10 & Partner**
92 **ARLETTA STAR**, b f Bated Breath—Winifred Jo **Mr M. J. Macleod**
93 **AUTUMN FLIGHT (IRE)**, b g Dandy Man (IRE)—Swallow Falls (IRE) **Mr Ambrose Turnbull & Partner**
94 **BOLL WEEVIL**, b g Delegator—Royal Punch **Habton Farms**
95 Ch c Haafhd—Bollin Nellie **Habton Farms**
96 **CAWTHORNE LAD**, ch g Coach House (IRE)—Upton Seas **E. A. Brook**
97 **CUBA RUBA**, ch g Havana Gold (IRE)—Diksie Dancer **Reality Partnerships Xiii**
98 **DREAM HOUSE**, b g Coach House (IRE)—Kummel Excess (IRE) **Ontoawinner, SDH Project Services Ltd 2**
99 **DREAM OF HONOUR (IRE)**, b g Dream Ahead (USA)—Pernica **Mr & Mrs J. D. Cotton**
100 **DREAMSELLER (IRE)**, ch g Dream Ahead (USA)—Picture of Lily **Ryedale Partners No. 2**
101 **FLO JO'S GIRL**, b gr f Mastercraftsman (IRE)—Portraitofmylove (IRE) **Habton Farms**

MR TIM EASTERBY - Continued

102 **FORCETORECKON**, b f Lethal Force (IRE)—Barleycorn Lady (IRE) **Mr B Valentine & Partner**
103 **GEORGE'S LAW**, b g Lawman (FR)—Despatch **Habton Farms**
104 **GOLDEN PARADE**, ch g Pivotal—Fondled **Mr David Scott & Partner**
105 **GREMOBOY**, ch g Mayson—Largo (IRE) **Gremot Racing**
106 **GREY BERRY (IRE)**, gr f Alhebayeb (IRE)—Ur Secret Is Safe (IRE) **Mr E. A. Al Afoo**
107 **GRIMSDYKE**, b g Firebreak—Katie Boo (IRE) **Mr J. F. Bowers**
108 **HARD KNOCK LIFE**, b g Dream Ahead (USA)—Little Annie **Ventura Racing 3 & Partner**
109 **HIGHWAYGREY**, b g Dick Turpin (IRE)—Maybeagrey **Reality Partnerships VII**
110 **IDEAL OPTION (IRE)**, ch g Camacho—Practicallyperfect (IRE) **Middleham Park LXIX & Partner**
111 **JUNIORS FANTASY (IRE)**, b g War Command (USA)—Natural Choice **Reality Partnerships IV**
112 **LADY CALCARIA**, b f Mayson—Ride The Wind **Ontoawinner 10 & Partner**
113 **LOOK OUT LOUIS**, b g Harbour Watch (IRE)—Perfect Act **Habton Farms**
114 **MAC AILEY**, ch g Firebreak—Rosabee (IRE) **Dubelem (racing) Limited & Partner**
115 B g Paco Boy (IRE)—Mini Driver **Habton Farms**
116 **NEIGH LASS**, b f Raven's Pass (USA)—Fidelio's Miracle (USA) **Mr & Mrs Lamplough & Partner**
117 **NEILETA**, b g Epaulette (AUS)—Neila (GER) **Habton Farms**
118 **OBEE JO (IRE)**, b c Kodiac—Maleha (IRE) **Mrs Joanne Boxcer & Partner**
119 **OFF PISTE**, gr g Reliable Man—Hamloola **Qatar Racing Ltd & Ptnr**
120 **ONE TO GO**, gr g Champs Elysees—Tina's Spirit (IRE) **Mr B Valentine & Partner**
121 **PERFECT SWISS**, b g Swiss Spirit—Perfect Practice **Habton Farms**
122 **RAQUELLE (IRE)**, b f Requinto (IRE)—Zuccini Wind (IRE) **Reality Partnerships X**
123 **RENT'S DEW (IRE)**, b g Shirocco (GER)—Rutland Water (IRE) **Ashfield Caravan Park**
124 B f Mayson—Sand And Deliver
125 **SDH DREAM TEAM**, b g Epaulette (AUS)—Donatia **Ontoawinner, SDH Project Services Ltd 2**
126 **SE GREEN**, b f Sepoy (AUS)—Nos Da **R. Taylor & Mr P. Hebdon**
127 B g Pastoral Pursuits (IRE)—Sea Flower (IRE) **Habton Farms**
128 **SEPARABLE**, ch g Sepoy (AUS)—Poyle Meg **Mr B Guerin & Habton Farms**
129 B g Ruler Of The World (IRE)—Shakeeba (IRE) **Habton Farms**
130 B g Nathaniel (IRE)—Sister Sylvia **CDM Developments (North West) Ltd & Ptr**
131 **STEELY SPIRIT (IRE)**, gr g Invincible Spirit (IRE)—Syamantaka (IRE) **Mrs T Burns & Partner**
132 **SWHISKEY**, b g Swiss Spirit—Glittering Prize (UAE) **Ontoawinner 10**
133 **THE GREY ZEBEDEE**, gr g Zebedee—Nippy (FR) **The Geordie Boys & Partner**
134 **TIMETODOCK**, b g Harbour Watch (IRE)—Unwrapit (USA) **Mr E. A. Brook & Partner**
135 **UGO GREGORY**, br g Gregorian (IRE)—Raajis (IRE) **Mr F. Gillespie**
136 **UNCLE NORMAN (FR)**, ch g Havana Gold (IRE)—Holy Moly (USA) **Mr J. R. Saville**
137 **VINTAGE BRUT**, b c Dick Turpin (IRE)—Traditionelle **King Power Racing Co Ltd**

TWO-YEAR-OLDS

138 **ART POWER (IRE)**, gr c 4/5 Dark Angel (IRE)—
        Evening Time (IRE) (Keltos (FR)) (92709) **King Power Racing Co Ltd**
139 B f 26/3 Champs Elysees—Astral Weeks (Sea The Stars (IRE)) (13484) **Reality Partnerships XV**
140 B f 7/2 Helmet (AUS)—Barqeyya (IRE) (Shamardal (USA)) (8095) **Habton Farms**
141 B f 15/2 Cityscape—Beautifulwildthing (Mount Nelson) (15000) **Mr M. J. Macleod**
142 B c 6/2 Mazameer (IRE)—Cassique Lady (IRE) (Langfuhr (CAN)) (25000) **Habton Farms**
143 B f 23/1 Kodiac—Charlie Em (Kheleyf (USA)) (104761) **Mr D. W. Armstrong**
144 **ELIXIR SKY**, b f 30/1 Fountain of Youth (IRE)—
        Millinsky (USA) (Stravinsky (USA)) (4800) **Bearstone Stud Limited**
145 **EMERALD SWALK (IRE)**, gr c 6/5 Zebedee—
        Telegraphy (IRE) (Giant's Causeway (USA)) (15000) **Mrs Joanne Boxcer & Partner**
146 B f 28/1 Ivawood (IRE)—Enliven (Dansili) (3809) **Habton Farms**
147 **EXPRESSIONS**, b f 18/4 Fountain of Youth (IRE)—Punchie (Lucky Story (USA)) (5000) **Bearstone Stud Limited**
148 Ch c 16/5 Le Havre (IRE)—Four Green (FR) (Green Tune (USA)) (17000) **Ryedale Partners No 13**
149 B c 25/2 Tagula (IRE)—Fritta Mista (IRE) (Linamix (FR)) (17142) **Habton Farms**
150 B f 17/3 Harbour Watch (IRE)—Hamloola (Red Ransom (USA)) (1500) **Habton Farms**
151 B c 18/4 Camacho—Hawajib (FR) (Elusive City (USA)) (4761) **Habton Farms**
152 B c 4/5 Kitten's Joy (USA)—He Loves Me More (USA) (More Than Ready (USA)) **Habton Farms**
153 B c 21/3 Camacho—La Estatua (Lope de Vega (IRE)) (6000) **Ryedale Partners No 8**
154 B c 15/3 Camacho—Labisa (IRE) (High Chaparral (IRE)) (13333) **Habton Farms**
155 **LAMPANG**, b c 9/3 Dandy Man (IRE)—
        Black Mascara (IRE) (Authorized (IRE)) (109523) **King Power Racing Co Ltd**
156 B f 12/4 Society Rock (IRE)—Lywaan (USA) (Fantastic Light (USA)) (10000) **Reality Partnerships XIV**
157 **MIDNIGHT MIMOSA (IRE)**, ch f 28/3 Anjaal—Miss Prim (Case Law) (19047) **Mr D. A. West & Partner**
158 Br gr c 2/4 Lethal Force (IRE)—Miliika (Green Desert (USA)) (13000) **Reality Partnerships XVI**
159 B f 22/3 Showcasing—Music In Exile (Diesis) (15238) **Habton Farms**
160 B c 6/3 Sir Prancealot (IRE)—Mystic Dream (Oasis Dream) (23809) **Ventura Racing 9 & Partner**

MR TIM EASTERBY - Continued

161 B c 28/3 War Command (USA)—Never Lose (Diktat) (20000) **Ryedale Partners No.15**
162 B c 11/2 Equiano (FR)—Nos Da (Cape Cross) (IRE) (9523) **Ontoawinner 10 & Partner**
163 B c 23/1 Heeraat (IRE)—Otrooha (IRE) (Oasis Dream) (14285) **Habton Farms**
164 B c 20/2 Helmet (AUS)—Royal Circles (Royal Applause) (20952) **Habton Farms**
165 B c 14/3 Finjaan—Samerous (FR) (Generous) (IRE)) **Mr M. J. Macleod**
166 B c 20/1 Gutaifan (IRE)—Scent of Summer (USA) (Rock Hard Ten (USA)) (28000) **Reality Partnerships**
167 B c 17/4 Mustajeeb—Shemriyna (IRE) (King of Kings (IRE)) **Habton Farms**
168 B f 12/4 Cable Bay (IRE)—Siena Gold (Key of Luck (USA)) (4761) **Habton Farms**
169 Gr f 8/3 Due Diligence (USA)—Skiing (Sakhee's Secret) (9523) **Habton Farms**
170 B c 10/3 Slade Power (IRE)—Sloane Square (Teofilo (IRE)) (28571) **Ontoawinner 10 & Partner**
171 Ch c 4/2 Cityscape—Speedy Utmost Meg (Medicean) (15000) **Mr M. J. Macleod**
172 Ch c 14/3 Shooting To Win (AUS)—Spirit of Success (Invincible Spirit (IRE)) (1904) **Habton Farms**
173 B f 23/1 Dandy Man (IRE)—Storyline (IRE) (Kodiac) (6666) **Mr Godfrey Horsford & Partner**
174 B c 30/4 Mayson—Tabrina (IRE) (Fasliyev (USA)) (22000) **Italia Keogh & Partner**
175 B c 4/3 Fountain of Youth (IRE)—Today's The Day (Alhaarth (IRE)) (5714) **Mr J Ball, Mr A Hodkinson & Mr P Malley**
176 B f 23/1 Firebreak—Traditionelle (Indesatchel (IRE)) (5714) **Ontoawinner 10 & Partner**
177 TWO SOX, b c 13/3 Nathaniel (IRE)—Anna Sophia (USA) (Oasis Dream) (11000) **Mr D Whittaker & Partner**
178 B c 25/3 Mukhadram—Umthoulah (IRE) (Unfuwain (USA)) (7000) **Habton Farms**
179 Gr c 28/3 Lethal Force (IRE)—Unasuming (IRE) (Orpen (USA)) (12000) **Habton Farms**
180 B f 22/2 Make Believe—Zerka (Invincible Spirit (IRE)) (7619) **Mr D Botterill & Lady Marchwood**

Other Owners: Armstrong Richardson & Co Ltd, Mr N. F. Arton, Mr J. Ball, Mr D. R. Botterill, Mrs J. Boxcer, Mr S. Bridge, Mr S. N. Bulmer, Mrs T. Burns, J. Buzzeo, CDM Developments (North West) Limited, J. D. Cotton, Mrs B. Cotton, Mr T. Denham, Mr T. D. Easterby, Mrs S. J. Easterby, Mr G. Fox, The Geordie Boys, A. J. J. Gompertz, Mr J. H. Green, Mrs K. E. Green, Mr B. M. P. R. Guerin, Mr P. F. Hebdon, S. A. Heley, Mr A. S. Hodkinson, G. Horsford, Mr M. A. S. Hulin, Mr N. E. M. Jones, Miss I. Keogh, Mrs D. Lamplough, D. B. Lamplough, Mr David John Lumley, Mr P. Malley, Lady S. K. Marchwood, Martyn Macleod Racing, Middleham Park Racing LXIX, P. H. Milmo, Mr J. E. Mott, Mrs J. M. Mott, Mr J. Mounsey, Mr P. E. Nodding, Mr N. J. O'Brien, T. J. O'Gram, Ontoawinner, SDH Project Services Ltd, T. S. Palin, Mr M. Pearson, Mr J. Preston, M. Prince, Qatar Racing Limited, Mr A. H. Raby, Mr S. V. Rutter, D. Scott, Mrs D. Stevens, Mr A. F. Stott, Mr R. Taylor, Mr G. Turnbull, Mrs S. E. Turnbull, Miss S. J. Turner, Mr B. Valentine, Ventura Racing 3, Ventura Racing 9, D. A. West, Mr James Westoll, Mr D. J. Whittaker.

Jockey (flat): Rachel Richardson. **Amateur:** Mr W. Easterby.

MR BRIAN ECKLEY, Brecon
Postal: **Closcedi Farm, Llanspyddid, Brecon, Powys, LD3 8NS**
Contacts: PHONE **(01874) 622422** MOBILE **(07891) 445409**
E-MAIL **brian.eckley@live.co.uk**

1 JAUNTY SORIA, 6, ch m Malinas (GER)—Jaunty Spirit **B. J. Eckley**
2 4, B c Norse Dancer (IRE)—Jaunty Spirit
3 JAUNTY VELOCITY, 6, b m Sulamani (IRE)—Jaunty Walk **B. J. Eckley**
4 4, B f Norse Dancer (IRE)—Jaunty Walk
5 LIBERTY BELLA, 5, b m Librettist (USA)—Classy Crewella **B. J. Eckley**
6 4, B c Norse Dancer (IRE)—Timeforagin
7 TIMEFORASPIN, 5, b g Librettist (USA)—Timeforagin **B. J. Eckley**

MR ROBERT EDDERY, Newmarket
Postal: **Robert Eddery Racing, Heywood Place Stables, Hamilton Road, Newmarket, Suffolk, CB8 7JQ**
Contacts: PHONE **(01638) 428001** MOBILE **(07938) 898455**
E-MAIL **info@robertedderyracing.com** WEBSITE **www.robbertedderyracing.com**

1 COLWOOD, 5, ch g Champs Elysees—La Colline (GER) **R. J. Creese**
2 COUNTRY'N'WESTERN (FR), 7, b g Samum (GER)—Cracking Melody **Mr C. R. Eddery**
3 EQUIMOU, 5, ch m Equiano (FR)—Culture Queen **E. S. Phillips**
4 FIERY BREATH, 4, br g Bated Breath—Sunset Kitty (USA) **E. S. Phillips**
5 GRACEFUL LADY, 6, b m Sixties Icon—Leitzu (IRE) **Graham & Lynn Knight**
6 SEVENTII, 5, b m Medicean—Lowndes **Graham & Lynn Knight**
7 TYNECASTLE PARK, 6, b g Sea The Stars (IRE)—So Silk **Ian Anderson & Robert Eddery**

MR ROBERT EDDERY - Continued

THREE-YEAR-OLDS

8 **ALBAN'S DREAM**, gr ro f Lethal Force (IRE)—Piping Dream (IRE) **Graham & Lynn Knight & Pamela Aitken**
9 **ELSIE VIOLET (IRE)**, ch f Gale Force Ten—Kuaicoss (IRE) **E. S. Phillips**
10 **FARUMP**, b gr f Zebedee—Grey Again **E. S. Phillips**
11 **NATIVE SILVER**, gr c Olympic Glory (IRE)—Kendorova (IRE) **Pamela Aitken & Julia Rayment**

TWO-YEAR-OLDS

12 B c 7/4 Sepoy (AUS)—Dream Day (Oasis Dream) (5000)
13 **EEVILYNN DREW**, b c 30/3 Epaulette (AUS)—Halicardia (Halling (USA)) (1500) **Graham & Lynn Knight**

Other Owners: Mrs Pam Aitken, Mr Ian Anderson (Edinburgh), Mr Robert Eddery, Mrs L. C. Knight, Mr G. Knight, Mrs J. M. Rayment.

Jockey (flat): Andrea Atzeni. **Apprentice:** Darragh Keenan. **Amateur:** Mr George Eddery.

| 179 | **MR STUART EDMUNDS**, Newport Pagnell |

Postal: **6 Fences Farm**, Tyringham, Newport Pagnell, Buckinghamshire, MK16 9EN
Contacts: **PHONE** (01908) 611406 Office (01908) 611369 FAX (01908) 611255
MOBILE (07778) 782591
E-MAIL Trishandstu@aol.com

1 **A LITTLE CHAOS (IRE)**, 5, b m Yeats (IRE)—Marias Dream (IRE) **The Garratt Family**
2 **BLACKFINCH**, 4, ch g Black Sam Bellamy (IRE)—Grassfinch **Exors of the Late Mr P. D. Robeson**
3 **CLASSIC BEN (IRE)**, 6, b g Beneficial—Dark Daisy (IRE) **The Lavendon Partnership**
4 **CLONDAW NATIVE (IRE)**, 7, b g Golan (IRE)—Great Outlook (IRE) **KTDA Consultancy Limited**
5 **EARLSHILL (IRE)**, 8, b g Milan—Mrs Marples (IRE) **The Horwoods Partnership**
6 **FAR BIHOUE (FR)**, 4, bl g Konig Turf (GER)—Vann Bihouee (FR) **Far Bihoue Partnership**
7 **FIGARELLA BORGET (FR)**, 4, b f Network (GER)—Kashima (FR) **Nick Brown Racing**
8 **GETAWAY MIXIE (IRE)**, 6, b m Getaway (GER)—Mixie The Pixie (IRE) **The Tyringham Partnership**
9 **GO MILLIE GO (IRE)**, 6, b m Milan—Another Present (IRE) **The Chicheley Partnership**
10 **HAVANA HERMANO (IRE)**, 5, b g Flemensfirth (USA)—Senorita Rumbalita **The Golf Victor Charlie Syndicate**
11 **HEPIJEU (FR)**, 8, b g Palace Episode (USA)—Helenjeu **Mr D. & Mrs H. Woodhall**
12 **HILLCREST FIRE (IRE)**, 5, b m Fast Company (IRE)—Firecrest (USA) **Mr J. Humberstone**
13 **JODIES JEM**, 9, br g Kheleyf (USA)—First Approval **Mrs R. L. Banks**
14 **KLARE CASTLE**, 7, b g Black Sam Bellamy (IRE)—Always Forgiving **Mr D. Sutherland**
15 **LAND LEAGUE (IRE)**, 8, b g Touch of Land (FR)—Be My Sunset (IRE) **Nick Brown Racing**
16 **LILLY'S ARC (IRE)**, 5, b m Arcadio (GER)—Eye And Ear (IRE) **Nick Brown Racing**
17 **MARIA'S BENEFIT (IRE)**, 7, b m Beneficial—Youngborogal (IRE) **Mr P. D. Wells**
18 **MISTER MIYAGI (IRE)**, 10, b g Zagreb (USA)—Muckle Flugga (IRE) **Ben Turner & Jay Tabb**
19 **MOLLY CHILDERS (IRE)**, 7, b m Stowaway—Hushaby (IRE) **The Ravenstone Partnership**
20 **NOW MCGINTY (IRE)**, 5, b g Stowaway—Western Whisper (IRE) **The Garratt Family**
21 **OUR BUBBA (IRE)**, 5, b g Scorpion (IRE)—Lady Marnay (IRE) **The Sharnbrook Partnership**
22 **PINE WARBLER**, 10, b g Pilsudski (IRE)—Cetti's Warbler **Exors of the Late Mr P. D. Robeson**
23 **PULL TOGETHER (IRE)**, 7, b g Curtain Time (IRE)—Whos To Know (IRE) **The Oakley Partnership**
24 **QUEENOHEARTS (IRE)**, 6, ch m Flemensfirth (USA)—Chars (IRE) **The Sherington Partnership**
25 **RED ROYALIST**, 5, b g Royal Applause—Scarlet Royal **Mrs R. L. Banks**
26 **SAN SEB (GER)**, 4, br g Mamool (IRE)—Sunshine Story (IRE) **Riverport Racehorse Association**
27 **SECRET GETAWAY (IRE)**, 5, ch m Getaway (GER)—Good Tune (IRE) **Horwood Harriers Partnership**
28 **THECLOCKISTICKING (IRE)**, 7, br g Gamut (IRE)—Curragheen (IRE) **Asphalt Reinforcement Services Ltd**
29 **VINEGAR HILL**, 10, b g Kayf Tara—Broughton Melody **Theshouldhavehadabiggerbudgetgroup**
30 **WOLF OF WINDLESHAM (IRE)**, 7, ch g Mastercraftsman (IRE)—Al Amlah (USA) **M. W. Lawrence**

THREE-YEAR-OLDS

31 **DUNEFINCH**, b g Dunaden (FR)—Grassfinch **Exors of the Late Mr P. D. Robeson**
32 **MARSH WREN**, b f Schiaparelli (GER)—Carolina Wren **Exors of the Late Mr P. D. Robeson**

Other Owners: Mr H. F. Bowley, Mr N. J. Brown, Mr A. C. Garratt, Mrs A. A. Garratt, Mr S. Shepherd, A. G. Sim, Mr J. A. Tabb, Mr S. E. Tate, Mr B. H. Turner, Mr S. J. Winter, D. M. Woodhall, Mrs H. C. L. Woodhall, D. Yates.

Assistant Trainer: Miss Harriet Edmunds

180   MR GORDON EDWARDS, Minehead

Postal: **Summering, Wheddon Cross, Minehead, Somerset, TA24 7AT**
Contacts: **PHONE (01643) 831549 FAX (01643) 831549 MOBILE (07970) 059297**
E-MAIL angelaedwards549@gmail.com

1 **IN ARREARS (IRE)**, 7, b m Beneficial—Gullet Dawn (IRE) **G. F. Edwards**
2 **SHANANN STAR (IRE)**, 13, br m Anshan—Baile An Droichid (IRE) **G. F. Edwards**

Amateur: Mr D. Edwards.

181   MISS LUCINDA EGERTON, Malton

Postal: **Flint Hall, Brawby, Malton, North Yorkshire, YO17 6PZ**
Contacts: **PHONE (01944) 768233 MOBILE (07900) 458666**
E-MAIL lucy@legertonracing.co.uk WEBSITE www.legertonracing.co.uk

1 **BETTY PETCH**, 5, ch m Schiaparelli (GER)—Perchance To Dream **Northern Belles**
2 **BOLLIN LINE**, 12, b g Bollin Eric—Leading Line **Reassuringly Racy Club**
3 **CAMANCHE GREY (IRE)**, 8, gr g Camacho—Sense of Greeting (IRE) **Mrs C. Sampson**
4 **DRAGONFLI**, 7, b g Revoque (IRE)—Chiddingfold Chick **Northern Belles**
5 **DREAM ON DREAMER (IRE)**, 5, b m Dream Ahead (USA)—Marula (IRE) **Reassuringly Racy Club**
6 **DUTCH MELODY**, 5, b m Dutch Art—Mystic Melody (IRE) **Miss L. Egerton**
7 **ENDLESS CREDIT (IRE)**, 9, b g High Chaparral (IRE)—Pay The Bank **Mike and Eileen Newbould**
8 **FIXED ASSET**, 7, b g Dr Massini (IRE)—Sharayna **Miss L. Egerton**
9 **MERRION ROW (IRE)**, 11, b g Milan—Diklers Dante (IRE) **Miss L. Egerton**
10 **MIDDLESCENCE (IRE)**, 5, ch g Lope de Vega (IRE)—Silesian (IRE) **Reassuringly Racy Club**
11 **OROBAS (IRE)**, 7, b g Dark Angel (IRE)—Miss Mujadil (IRE) **Northern Belles**
12 **PATIENCE TONY (IRE)**, 8, b g Windsor Knot (IRE)—Johar Jamal (IRE) **P. Robinson, D. Woodhead & L. Egerton**
13 **PICTURE YOUR DREAM**, 4, ch f Kheleyf (USA)—Another Sunset **B. Dunn**
14 **SHANDON (IRE)**, 4, b g Big Bad Bob (IRE)—Rum Raisin **Reassuringly Racy Club**
15 **ST GEORGE'S OVAL (IRE)**, 6, b g Milan—Lisselton Lady (IRE) **Miss L. Egerton**
16 **VENT DE FORCE (IRE)**, 8, b g Hurricane Run (IRE)—Capriolla **Northern Belles**
17 **WELSH RAREBIT (IRE)**, 6, b g Dylan Thomas (IRE)—Chelsey Jayne (IRE) **P Robinson & J Gill**
18 **WHISPER A WORD (IRE)**, 5, ch m Bated Breath—Affability (IRE) **J. Gill**

Other Owners: Mrs C. M. Egerton, Mrs E. E. Newbould, Mr J. M. Newbould, Mrs R. Robinson, Mr P. Robinson, Mr D. A. Woodhead.

182   MISS CLARE ELLAM, Market Drayton

Postal: **Lostford Manor Stables, Mickley, Tern Hill, Market Drayton, Shropshire, TF9 3QW**
Contacts: **MOBILE (07974) 075042**
E-MAIL clareellam@btinternet.com WEBSITE www.clareellamracing.com

1 **ARCHIE STEVENS**, 9, b g Pastoral Pursuits—Miss Wells (IRE) **Miss Clare L. Ellam**
2 **ARCHIPENTURA**, 7, b m Archipenko (USA)—Bookiesindex Girl (IRE) **Mr R. P. Clarke**
3 **BARNAY**, 4, b g Nayef (USA)—Barnezet (GR) **D. Ashbrook**
4 **CLICK AND COLLECT**, 7, b g Humbel (USA)—Galena (GER) **D. Ashbrook**
5 **FREE BOUNTY**, 6, b g Dick Turpin (IRE)—Native Ring (FR) **Mr R. P. Clarke**
6 **FRIENDS DON'T ASK**, 4, b g Champs Elysees—Kintyre **Mr R. P. Clarke**
7 **KHELEYF'S GIRL**, 4, br f Kheleyf (USA)—Handsome Molly **Miss Clare L. Ellam**
8 **PADDOCKS LOUNGE (IRE)**, 12, b g Oscar (IRE)—Sister Rosza (IRE) **Miss Clare L. Ellam**
9 **SIMAFAR (IRE)**, 5, b g Makfi—Simawa (IRE) **Miss Clare L. Ellam**
10 **SPORTING MILAN (IRE)**, 8, b g Milan—Sports Leader (IRE) **The Double Six Racing Partnership**

Other Owners: Mr M. Lenton.

Assistant Trainer: Amy Myatt

183   MR GORDON ELLIOTT, Co. Meath

Postal: **Cullentra House, Longwood, Co. Meath, Ireland, A83 XF20**
Contacts: PHONE **(00353) 46 9555051 MOBILE (00353) 86 2495453**
E-MAIL office@gordonelliottracing.com WEBSITE www.gordonelliottracing.com

1 **A TOI PHIL (FR)**, 9, b g Day Flight—Lucidrile (FR)
2 **ABACADABRAS (FR)**, 5, b g Davidoff (GER)—Cadoubelle des As (FR)
3 **ACRONYM (IRE)**, 6, b g Flemensfirth (USA)—Turtle Lamp (IRE)
4 **ALLEE BLEUE (FR)**, 9, ch g Mount Nelson—Murrieta
5 **ALPHA DES OBEAUX (FR)**, 9, b g Saddler Maker (IRE)—Omega des Obeaux (FR)
6 **ALPHA INDI (FR)**, 8, b br g Oscar (IRE)—High Park Lady (FR)
7 **ANGE D'OR JAVILEX (FR)**, 9, b g Puit d'or (IRE)—Ixia de Menil (FR)
8 **APPLE'S JADE (FR)**, 7, b m Saddler Maker (IRE)—Apple's For Ever (FR)
9 **ARION SKY (IRE)**, 5, b m Jeremy (USA)—Dream Function (IRE)
10 **ASKARI**, 6, b g Sea The Stars (IRE)—Loulwa (IRE)
11 **AUTHORIZO (FR)**, 4, b g Authorized (IRE)—Street Lightning (IRE)
12 **AXIOMATIC (IRE)**, 5, b g Milan—Thegoodwans Sister (IRE)
13 **BABY TWIG (FR)**, 8, b m Network (GER)—Natty Twigy (FR)
14 **BACK BAR (IRE)**, 7, b br g Brian Boru—Howrwedoin (IRE)
15 **BALAGAN**, 4, b g Great Pretender (IRE)—Lovely Origny (FR)
16 **BALL D'ARC (FR)**, 8, b g Network (GER)—Pretty Moon (FR)
17 **BARRA (FR)**, 8, b m Vendangeur (IRE)—Oasaka (FR)
18 **BATTLEOVERDOYEN (IRE)**, 6, b g Doyen—Battle Over (IRE)
19 **BEN DUNDEE (IRE)**, 7, ch g Beneficial—Miss Dundee (IRE)
20 **BLACK TEARS**, 5, b m Jeremy (USA)—Our Girl Salley (IRE)
21 **BLESS THE WINGS (IRE)**, 14, b g Winged Love (IRE)—Silva Venture (IRE)
22 **BLOW BY BLOW (IRE)**, 8, ch g Robin des Champs (FR)—Shean Rose (IRE)
23 **BOOT CAMP (IRE)**, 6, br g Milan—Derravaragh Native (IRE)
24 **BORICE (FR)**, 8, b g Network (GER)—Judice (FR)
25 **BRELADE**, 7, b g Presenting—Polivalente (FR)
26 **BURREN LIFE (IRE)**, 7, br g Pelder (IRE)—Burren Valley (IRE)
27 **CAMPEADOR (FR)**, 7, gr g Gris de Gris (IRE)—Royale Union (FR)
28 **CARA'S WAY (IRE)**, 6, br m Robin des Champs (FR)—Dare To Venture (IRE)
29 **CARTER MCKAY (IRE)**, 8, gr g Martaline—Saxona (FR)
30 **CARTWRIGHT**, 6, b g High Chaparral (IRE)—One So Marvellous
31 **CATS FOR CASH (IRE)**, 5, gr g Mahler—Harvard Girl (IRE)
32 **CECIL CORBETT**, 12, b g Bollin Eric—Cadoutene (FR)
33 **CHAMPAGNE CLASSIC (IRE)**, 8, b g Stowaway—Classical Rachel (IRE)
34 **CHIEF JUSTICE**, 4, b g Acclamation—Freedom Pass (USA)
35 **COEUR DE BEAUCHENE (FR)**, 7, br g Peer Gynt (JPN)—Iris de Beauchene (FR)
36 **COEUR SUBLIME (IRE)**, 4, b g Elusive Pimpernel (USA)—Love Knot (IRE)
37 **COLUMN OF FIRE (IRE)**, 5, b g Robin des Champs (FR)—Ghillie's Bay (IRE)
38 **COMMANDER OF FLEET (IRE)**, 5, b g Fame And Glory—Coonagh Cross (IRE)
39 **COMMENTARIOLUS (IRE)**, 5, b g Frankel—Apsara (FR)
40 **COOL GETAWAY (IRE)**, 7, b g Getaway (GER)—Coolnacarriga (IRE)
41 **COUNT SIMON (IRE)**, 5, b g Rip Van Winkle (IRE)—Wedding Gake (IRE)
42 **CRACKING SMART (FR)**, 7, b g Great Pretender (IRE)—Maya du Frene (FR)
43 **CREADAN BELLE (IRE)**, 6, b m Vinnie Roe (IRE)—Aliceaneileen (IRE)
44 **CUBOMANIA (IRE)**, 6, gr ro g Halling (USA)—Surrealism
45 **DALLAS DES PICTONS (FR)**, 6, b g Spanish Moon (USA)—Nadia des Pictons (FR)
46 **DAYLIGHT KATIE (IRE)**, 6, b m Bonbon Rose (FR)—Sirani (FR)
47 **DE PLOTTING SHED (IRE)**, 9, b g Beneficial—Lady Willmurt (IRE)
48 **DEFI BLEU (FR)**, 6, b g Saddler Maker (IRE)—Glycine Bleue (FR)
49 **DELTA WORK (FR)**, 6, br g Network (GER)—Robbe (FR)
50 **DESTIN D'AJONC (FR)**, 6, b g Martaline—Fleur d'ajonc (FR)
51 **DIAMOND CAUCHOIS (FR)**, 8, b g Crillon (FR)—Diamond Turtle (FR)
52 **DIAMOND TURF (FR)**, 6, b g Diamond Boy (FR)—Lovely Turf (FR)
53 **DINARIA DES OBEAUX (FR)**, 6, b m Saddler Maker (IRE)—Indiana Jaune (FR)
54 **DINONS (FR)**, 6, b g Balko (FR)—Beni Abbes (FR)
55 **DOCTOR PHOENIX (IRE)**, 11, br g Dr Massini (IRE)—Lowroad Cross (IRE)
56 **DON POLI (IRE)**, 10, b g Poliglote—Dalamine (FR)
57 **DORTMUND PARK (FR)**, 6, b g Great Pretender (IRE)—Qena (FR)
58 **DOUNIKOS (FR)**, 8, b g Smadoun (FR)—Baby Sitter (FR)
59 **DUCA DE THAIX (FR)**, 6, b g Voix du Nord (FR)—Nouca de Thaix (FR)
60 **EDENE D'ARC (FR)**, 5, b m Maresca Sorrento (FR)—Pretty Moon (FR)
61 **EMPIRE BURLEQUE (IRE)**, 7, b g Cape Cross (IRE)—Mowazana (IRE)

MR GORDON ELLIOTT - Continued

62 **ENNEMI PUBLIC (FR)**, 5, b g Network (GER)—Jacady (FR)
63 **ENVOI ALLEN (FR)**, 5, b g Muhtathir—Reaction (FR)
64 **ENZANI (IRE)**, 8, b g Cape Cross (IRE)—Eytarna (IRE)
65 **ERRATIC PATH (IRE)**, 5, b g Elusive Pimpernel (USA)—Berg Bahn (IRE)
66 **ESHTIAAL (USA)**, 9, b g Dynaformer (USA)—Enfiraaj (USA)
67 **EXTRAPOLATE (IRE)**, 6, ch g Muhtathir—Sahabah (USA)
68 **FAGAN**, 9, ro g Fair Mix (IRE)—Northwood May
69 **FALAK (IRE)**, 6, b g Teofilo (IRE)—Family (IRE)
70 **FARCLAS (FR)**, 5, gr g Jukebox Jury (IRE)—Floriana (GER)
71 **FEEL MY PULSE (IRE)**, 5, b g Stowaway—Zenaide (IRE)
72 **FELIX DESJY (FR)**, 6, ch g Maresca Sorrento (FR)—Lamadoun (FR)
73 **FINAL LIST (IRE)**, 5, ch g Doyen (IRE)—Lady Goldilocks (IRE)
74 **FLAWLESS ESCAPE**, 6, gr g Sagamix (FR)—Sainte Kadette (FR)
75 **FLAXEN FLARE (IRE)**, 10, ch g Windsor Knot (IRE)—Golden Angel (USA)
76 **FOLSOM BLUE (IRE)**, 12, b g Old Vic—Spirit Leader (IRE)
77 **FOOLS AND KINGS**, 5, b br g Sakhee (USA)—Mookhlesa
78 **FURY ROAD (IRE)**, 5, b g Stowaway—Molly Duffy (IRE)
79 **GALVIN (IRE)**, 5, b g Gold Well—Burren Moonshine (IRE)
80 **GENERAL PRINCIPLE (IRE)**, 10, b g Gold Well—How Provincial (IRE)
81 **GER'S LAD (IRE)**, 7, b g Kalanisi (IRE)—Mill Lady (IRE)
82 **GETAWAY JOHN (IRE)**, 6, ch g Getaway (GER)—Present Your Own (IRE)
83 **GIRLEY TALK (IRE)**, 6, ch m Whitmore's Conn (USA)—Fallacy
84 **GLENLOE (IRE)**, 8, br g Kayf Tara—Mandys Native (IRE)
85 **GLOBAL JACKPOT (IRE)**, 6, b g Flying Legend (USA)—A Fistful of Euros
86 **GRAINEYHILL (IRE)**, 8, b g Craigsteel—Inca Hill (IRE)
87 **GREAT VIZIER**, 4, b g Sir Percy—Special Green (FR)
88 **GREY EXCHANGE**, 6, gr g Apple Tree (FR)—Pems Gift
89 **GUN DIGGER (IRE)**, 7, ch g Stowaway—Booley Bay (IRE)
90 **HARDLINE (IRE)**, 7, b g Arcadio (GER)—Hidden Reserve (IRE)
91 **INVINCIBLE CAVE (IRE)**, 6, b g Court Cave (IRE)—Bespoke Baby (IRE)
92 **ISLE OF DESTINY (IRE)**, 6, b m Gold Well—Young Amelie (IRE)
93 **ITS ALL GUESSWORK (IRE)**, 7, b g Mahler—La Lambertine (FR)
94 **JAUNTY WARRIOR**, 7, b g Lucarno (USA)—Jaunty Walk
95 **JURY DUTY (IRE)**, 8, b g Well Chosen—Swan Heart (IRE)
96 **KAYF THOU**, 8, br g Kayf Tara—Labelthou (IRE)
97 **KISS ME KAYF (IRE)**, 6, b m Kayf Tara—Volverta (FR)
98 **KURAKA**, 5, b g Cacique (IRE)—Puzzling
99 **LACKANEEN LEADER (IRE)**, 7, b m Oscar (IRE)—Shandora (IRE)
100 **LADY V (IRE)**, 5, b m Jeremy (USA)—Daly (IRE)
101 **LAST MINUTE MAN (IRE)**, 7, b g Yeats (IRE)—Ella Watson (IRE)
102 **LETHAL STEPS**, 4, gr g Lethal Force (IRE)—Tanda Tula (IRE)
103 **LORD SCOUNDREL (IRE)**, 10, b g Presenting—Noble Choice
104 **MAJOR MITCHELL (IRE)**, 6, b g Gold Well—Cooper's Rose (IRE)
105 **MALA BEACH (IRE)**, 11, b g Beneficial—Peppardstown (IRE)
106 **MENGLI KHAN (IRE)**, 6, b g Lope de Vega (IRE)—Danielli (IRE)
107 **MICK JAZZ (FR)**, 8, b g Blue Bresil (FR)—Mick Maya (FR)
108 **MIDNIGHT ESCAPE (IRE)**, 7, b g Milan—Special Case (IRE)
109 **MINELLA TILL DAWN (IRE)**, 7, br g Shantou (USA)—Have At It (IRE)
110 **MIRACLE IN MEDINAH (IRE)**, 8, b g Milan—Annaghbrack (IRE)
111 **MISSY TATA (FR)**, 7, b m Astarabad (USA)—Queen Running (FR)
112 **MITCHOUKA (FR)**, 5, b g Creachadoir (IRE)—Minnaloushe (FR)
113 **MONATOMIC (IRE)**, 6, b g Arcadio (GER)—Star Island (IRE)
114 **MONBEG NOTORIOUS (IRE)**, 8, b g Milan—Borleagh Princess (IRE)
115 **MONITION (IRE)**, 6, b g Stowaway—Forever Bubbles (IRE)
116 **MONKSHOOD (IRE)**, 7, br g Stowaway—Flirthing Around (IRE)
117 **MORATORIUM (IRE)**, 6, b g Presenting—Shuil Oilean (IRE)
118 **MR LINGO (IRE)**, 6, b g Curtain Time (IRE)—Pharlingo (IRE)
119 **MRS LOVETT (IRE)**, 6, ch m Sir Percy—Madame Boulangere
120 **NEARLY MAN (FR)**, 6, b g Turgeon (USA)—La Loute (FR)
121 **NED STARK (IRE)**, 11, b g Wolfe Tone (IRE)—Last Moon (IRE)
122 **NOBLE ENDEAVOR (IRE)**, 10, b g Flemensfirth (USA)—Old Moon (IRE)
123 **OSMOTIC (IRE)**, 6, b g Fracas (IRE)—Miss Pickering (IRE)
124 **OUT SAM**, 10, b g Multiplex—Tintera (IRE)
125 **OUTLANDER (IRE)**, 11, b g Stowaway—Western Whisper (IRE)
126 **PALLASATOR**, 10, b g Motivator—Ela Athena

MR GORDON ELLIOTT - Continued

127 **PAT'S OSCAR (IRE)**, 8, b m Oscar (IRE)—Coming Home (FR)
128 **PERCY (IRE)**, 5, b gr g Kodiac—Bysshe
129 **POLI ROI (FR)**, 7, b g Poliglote—Belle du Roi (FR)
130 **POORMANS HILL (IRE)**, 8, ch g Stowaway—Sharps Express (IRE)
131 **PRESENT IN COURT (IRE)**, 6, b g Court Cave (IRE)—Present Line (IRE)
132 **PRESENTING JULIO (IRE)**, 11, b g Presenting—Ouro Preto
133 **PRINCE OF SCARS (IRE)**, 9, b g Flemensfirth (USA)—Spirit Leader (IRE)
134 **RAKHINE STATE (IRE)**, 6, b g Arakan (USA)—Oiselina (FR)
135 **RAVENHILL (IRE)**, 9, b g Winged Love (IRE)—Rhythm Hill (IRE)
136 **ROARING BULL (IRE)**, 6, b g Milan—Gift of Freedom (IRE)
137 **ROBIN DES MANA (IRE)**, 8, br g Robin des Pres (FR)—Kokopelli Mana (IRE)
138 **ROGUE ANGEL (IRE)**, 11, b g Presenting—Carrigeen Kohleria (IRE)
139 **RUN WILD FRED (IRE)**, 5, ch g Shantou (USA)—Talkin Madam (IRE)
140 **SAFFRON AND GREY (IRE)**, 6, br g Robin des Champs (FR)—Tambourine Davis (FR)
141 **SAMCRO (IRE)**, 7, ch g Germany (USA)—Dun Dun (IRE)
142 **SANTANA PLESSIS (FR)**, 5, b g Saint des Saints (FR)—La Passeroie (FR)
143 **SAVANNAH STORM (IRE)**, 6, b g Dubawi (IRE)—Savannah Belle
144 **SHATTERED LOVE (IRE)**, 8, b m Yeats (IRE)—Tracker
145 **SIR CARNO (FR)**, 6, ch g Lucarno (USA)—Orlana (FR)
146 **SIRE DU BERLAIS (FR)**, 7, b g Poliglote—Royale Athenia (FR)
147 **SMILING ELIZA (IRE)**, 4, b f Rock of Gibraltar (IRE)—Gift Dancer
148 **SPACE CADET (IRE)**, 9, b g Flemensfirth (USA)—Shuil A Hocht (IRE)
149 **SQUOUATEUR (FR)**, 8, gr g Martaline—Samansonnienne (FR)
150 **STEAMBOAT QUAY (IRE)**, 8, b g Milan—Sunny Native (IRE)
151 **STOOSHIE (IRE)**, 6, b g Fracas (IRE)—Misty Native (IRE)
152 **SUTTON MANOR (IRE)**, 8, b g Gold Well—Nighty Bless (IRE)
153 **SUTTON PLACE (IRE)**, 8, b g Mahler—Glebe Beauty (IRE)
154 **SWINGBRIDGE (IRE)**, 11, b g Milan—Creative Approach (IRE)
155 **SYNOPSIS**, 7, b m Azamour (IRE)—Censored
156 **TAKEITTOTHELIMITS (IRE)**, 7, br m Stowaway—A Plus Ma Puce (FR)
157 **TAPENADE (IRE)**, 5, br g Scorpion (IRE)—Corravilla (IRE)
158 **THE BIG LENSE (IRE)**, 6, b g Court Cave (IRE)—Megans Joy (IRE)
159 **THE GAME CHANGER (IRE)**, 10, b g Arcadio (GER)—Gilt Ridden (IRE)
160 **THE STORYTELLER (IRE)**, 8, ch g Shantou (USA)—Bally Bolshoi (IRE)
161 **TIGER ROLL (IRE)**, 9, b g Authorized (IRE)—Swiss Roll (IRE)
162 **TIMIYAN (USA)**, 8, b g Ghostzapper (USA)—Timarwa (IRE)
163 **TINTANGLE (IRE)**, 6, b m Yeats (IRE)—Connaught Hall (IRE)
164 **TOMBSTONE (IRE)**, 9, ch g Robin des Champs (FR)—Connaught Hall (IRE)
165 **TOUCH BASE (IRE)**, 7, b g Robin des Champs (FR)—Badawi Street
166 **TYCOON PRINCE (IRE)**, 9, b g Trans Island—Downtown Train (IRE)
167 **UCELLO CONTI (FR)**, 11, b g Martaline—Gazelle Lulu (FR)
168 **VEINARD (FR)**, 10, ch g Shaanmer (IRE)—Ombline (FR)
169 **VISION D'HONNEUR (FR)**, 5, b g Vision d'etat (FR)—Hembra (FR)
170 **WARLIKE INTENT (IRE)**, 7, ch g Stowaway—Native Mistress (IRE)
171 **WESTERN COMMAND (IRE)**, 7, b g Westerner—Mighty Millie (IRE)
172 **WOODS WELL (IRE)**, 8, ch g Fleetwood (IRE)—Millbrook Marble (IRE)

Assistant Trainers: Ian Amond, Keith Donoghue, Davy Condon

Jockey (flat): Declan McDonagh. **Jockey (NH):** Jack Kennedy, Davy Russell. **Amateur:** Mr Jamie Codd, Miss Lisa O'Neill.

---

184 | **MISS JOEY ELLIS, Newmarket**
Postal: Georgia House Stud, Bradley Road, Burrough Green, Newmarket, Suffolk, CB8 9NH
Contacts: PHONE (07827) 316360
E-MAIL georgiahousestud@btinternet.com

1 **ALICE'S PLACE**, 4, ch f Compton Place—Just Alice **Mrs A. B. Ellis**
2 **BELLMAID**, 4, b f Champs Elysees—Never Enough (GER) **Mrs A. B. Ellis**
3 **FIFTYSHADESOFNEIGH (IRE)**, 4, b f Sleeping Indian—Sceilin (IRE) **Mrs A. B. Ellis**
4 **HOW'S LUCY**, 5, b m Approve (IRE)—Murielle **Mrs A. B. Ellis**
5 **MARBOOH (IRE)**, 6, b g Dark Angel (IRE)—Muluk (IRE) **Mrs A. B. Ellis**
6 **TWILIGHT CAPER**, 4, ch f Captain Gerrard (IRE)—Blades Princess **Georgia House Racing Club**

MISS JOEY ELLIS - Continued

THREE-YEAR-OLDS

7 **BREATHTAKING VIEW,** b f Bated Breath—Morning View (USA) **Mr B. S. F. Edwards**
8 **DOUGAL BUG,** b g Compton Place—Apple Sauce **Mrs A. B. Ellis**
9 **JIMMY BERKELEY,** b g Epaulette (AUS)—Topflight Princess **Mrs A. B. Ellis**
10 **MISCHIEF MAKER,** b f Epaulette (AUS)—Just Alice **Mrs A. B. Ellis**
11 **QUINTANA ROO,** b f Coach House (IRE)—Elegant Pursuit **Mrs A. B. Ellis**
12 **RAINBOW PANACEA,** b c Monsieur Bond (IRE)—Parsonagehotelyork (IRE) **Mrs A. B. Ellis**

Other Owners: Miss J. B. Ellis.

Assistant Trainer: Angela Ellis.

Jockey (flat): Stevie Donohoe. **Apprentice:** Rosie Jessop.

---

185 MR BRIAN ELLISON, Malton
Postal: **Spring Cottage Stables, Langton Road, Norton, Malton, North Yorkshire, YO17 9PY**
Contacts: **OFFICE** (01653) 690004 **FAX** (01653) 690008 **MOBILE** (07785) 747426
E-MAIL office@brianellisonracing.co.uk **WEBSITE** www.brianellisonracing.co.uk

1 **AHORSEWITHNONAME,** 4, b f Cacique (IRE)—Sea of Galilee **Mr D. J. Burke & Mr P Alderson**
2 **APTERIX (FR),** 9, b g Day Flight—Ohe Les Aulmes (FR) **Brian Ellison Racing Club & Mr P Boyle**
3 **ARCHIVE (FR),** 9, b g Sulamani (IRE)—Royale Dorothy (FR) **Brian Ellison Racing Club**
4 **BAL DE RIO (FR),** 6, b g Vertigineux (FR)—Baldoranic (FR) **Phil & Julie Martin**
5 **BALLYCRYSTAL (IRE),** 8, b g Oscar (IRE)—Musical Madam (IRE) **Phil & Julie Martin**
6 **BALLYVIC BORU (IRE),** 7, b g Brian Boru—Thedoublede (IRE) **Mr P J Martin & Partner**
7 **BARON DE MIDLETON (IRE),** 6, b g Brian Boru—Present Climate (IRE) **Phil & Julie Martin**
8 **BARRYS JACK (IRE),** 9, b g Well Chosen—Theatre Fool (IRE) **D Gilbert, M Lawrence, A Bruce**
9 **BASILDON,** 4, b g Champs Elysees—Casual **D Gilbert, M Lawrence, A Bruce**
10 **BE KOOL (IRE),** 6, b g Approve (IRE)—Accounting **Miss J. J. Bell**
11 **BORDEAUX BILL (IRE),** 8, b g Craigsteel—Laura Croft (IRE) **Julie & Phil Martin**
12 **BURN SOME DUST (IRE),** 4, b g Shirocco (GER)—Chilly Filly (IRE) **Mr D. R. Gilbert**
13 **CHATEAU MARMONT (IRE),** 6, b g Flemensfirth (USA)—Sliabh Geal Gcua (IRE) **Phil & Julie Martin**
14 **CONTRE TOUS (FR),** 7, b g Forestier (FR)—Orphee de Vonnas (FR) **Personal Racehorse Owners 2**
15 **CRACKDELOUST (FR),** 7, b g Daramsar (FR)—Magic Rose (FR) **Phil & Julie Martin**
16 **DEFINITLY RED (IRE),** 10, ch g Definite Article—The Red Wench (IRE) **Phil & Julie Martin**
17 **EYES OF A TIGER (IRE),** 8, ch g Golan—Backtothekingsnest (IRE) **Phil & Julie Martin**
18 **FAIR LOCH,** 11, gr g Fair Mix (IRE)—Ardentinny **Julie & Phil Martin**
19 **FERRY ALL (FR),** 4, ch g No Risk At All (FR)—Ohe Les Aulmes (FR) **Phil & Julie Martin**
20 **FIRST FLIGHT (IRE),** 8, b g Invincible Spirit (IRE)—First of Many **Koo's Racing Club**
21 **FOREST BIHAN (FR),** 8, ch g Forestier (FR)—Katell Bihan (FR) **Phil & Julie Martin**
22 **INSTANT REPLAY (IRE),** 7, ch g Fruits of Love (USA)—Ding Dong Belle **Phil & Julie Martin**
23 **LITTLE JO,** 5, b g Major Cadeaux—Discoed **Mr Ian & Tom Pallas & The Mackem 2**
24 **LUCKY ROBIN (IRE),** 7, ch g Mister Fotis (USA)—Bewilderment (IRE) **Brian Ellison Racing Club**
25 **MONSIEUR JIMMY,** 7, ch g Monsieur Bond (IRE)—Artistic License (IRE) **Ms Z. Hatcher**
26 **NEW LIST,** 6, ch g Pivotal—Angel's Tears **S & S Racing & Partner**
27 **NIETZSCHE,** 6, ch g Poet's Voice—Ganga (IRE) **D Gilbert, M Lawrence, A Bruce, G Wills**
28 **NORTHERN QUEEN (IRE),** 4, gr f Dark Angel (IRE)—
Queen Bodicea (IRE) **Northern Water Services & Graham Lund**
29 **NORTHGATE LAD (IRE),** 7, b g Dark Angel (IRE)—Canosa (IRE) **Julie & Phil Martin**
30 **PEA SHOOTER,** 10, b g Piccolo—Sparkling Eyes **Mrs A. M. Mallinson**
31 **PICKETT'S CHARGE,** 6, b g Clodovil (IRE)—Chelsea Morning (USA) **Brian Ellison Racing Club**
32 **PISTOL PARK (FR),** 8, b g Poliglote—Pistolera (GER) **Brian's Mates**
33 **RANSKILL ROAD (IRE),** 4, b g Jeremy (USA)—Tarziyma (IRE) **Julie & Phil Martin**
34 **RAVENHILL ROAD (IRE),** 8, ch g Exit To Nowhere (USA)—Zaffarella (IRE) **Phil & Julie Martin**
35 **ROYAL FLAG,** 9, b g New Approach (IRE)—Gonbarda (GER) **Dean Woodhouse & Brian Ellison**
36 **SAM'S ADVENTURE,** 7, b g Black Sam Bellamy (IRE)—My Adventure (IRE) **Julie & Phil Martin**
37 **SEAMOUR (IRE),** 8, b g Azamour (IRE)—Chifney Rush (IRE) **Phil & Julie Martin**
38 **SECRET PASSENGER (IRE),** 6, ch g Stowaway—Mtpockets (IRE) **Brian Ellison Racing Club**
39 **SIANNES STAR (IRE),** 6, b g Arakan (USA)—Musical Madam (IRE) **Julie & Phil Martin**
40 **SKYVA,** 4, b g Dick Turpin (IRE)—Skylla **Facts & Figures**
41 **SMART TALK (IRE),** 9, b m Hubbly Bubbly—Belon Breeze (IRE) **Julie & Phil Martin**
42 **SNOOKERED (IRE),** 5, b g Born To Sea (IRE)—Secret Quest **Brian Ellison Racing Club**
43 **SOLDIER BLUE (FR),** 5, ch g Sepoy (AUS)—Kocooning (IRE) **S & S Racing**

MR BRIAN ELLISON - Continued

44 **SUGARLOAF MOUNTAIN (IRE)**, 6, b g Fastnet Rock (AUS)—
Cherry Hinton **Andy Bell Anna Noble Arnie Flower 1**
45 **THE KING OF MAY (FR)**, 5, b g High Rock (IRE)—Waltzing (IRE) **Phil & Julie Martin**
46 **THECORNISHBARRON (IRE)**, 7, b g Bushranger (IRE)—Tripudium (IRE) **Melton Mowbray Bowls Club**
47 **TICKERTY BOO (IRE)**, 7, gr m Tikkanen (USA)—La Fille d'or (IRE) **Julie & Phil Martin**
48 **WEAKFIELD (IRE)**, 6, b g Court Cave (IRE)—Thats The Lot (IRE) **Phil & Julie Martin**
49 **WINDSOR AVENUE (IRE)**, 7, b g Winged Love (IRE)—Zaffarella (IRE) **Phil & Julie Martin**

THREE-YEAR-OLDS

50 **ARRIBA DE TODA (IRE)**, b g Gale Force Ten—Luxuria (IRE) **Brian Ellison Racing Club**
51 **BISCUIT QUEEN**, br f Harbour Watch (IRE)—Ginger Cookie **Brian Ellison Racing Club**
52 **CHAMPAGNE CLOUDS**, b g Equiano (FR)—Procession **Brian Ellison Racing Club**
53 **DRAGONS HEART**, b f Captain Gerrard (IRE)—Striking Cat **Brian Ellison Racing Club**
54 B c Multiplex—Gagajulu **Mrs D. F. Robe**
55 **IDENTITY CRISIS**, b f Mayson—Dance Card **Brian Ellison Racing Club**
56 **LITTLE LEGS**, b f Captain Gerrard (IRE)—Livia Drusilla (IRE) **Brian Ellison Racing Club**
57 **PEARL OF QATAR**, gr f Footstepsinthesand—Musical Molly (IRE) **Mrs J. A. Martin**
58 **QUICKLY DOES IT**, b f Havana Gold—Mylington Maid **Ne-Chance**
59 **WHISKEY AND WATER**, b g Harbour Watch (IRE)—Bahamamia **D Gilbert, M Lawrence, A Bruce**

TWO-YEAR-OLDS

60 **CHAMPAGNE VICTORY (IRE)**, b f 26/3 Bungle Inthejungle—
Golittlebadgirl (USA) (Giant's Causeway (USA)) (5899) **One For the Road & Partner 1**
61 **GRANDMA**, b f 22/3 Mayson—Livia Drusilla (IRE) (Holy Roman Emperor (IRE)) **Brian Ellison Racing Club**
62 **HAVANA BROWN**, br c 8/3 Delegator—Striking Cat (Striking Ambition) **Brian Ellison Racing Club**
63 **KATSONIS (IRE)**, b c 10/3 Ivawood (IRE)—Livadiya (IRE) (Shernazar) (13484) **S & S Racing & Partner**
64 **NEVER SAID NOTHING (IRE)**, b c 27/3 Hallowed Crown (AUS)—
Semiquaver (Mark of Esteem (IRE)) (5899) **Mr A. N. Brooke Rankin**
65 **NORTHERN GRACE**, ch f 30/3 Helmet (AUS)—Amelia Grace (IRE) (Starspangledbanner (AUS)) **Brian Ellison Racing Club**
66 **PUNXSUTAWNEY PHIL (IRE)**, b c 5/2 Shirocco (GER)—Chilly Filly (Montjeu (IRE)) **Mr D. R. Gilbert**
67 B c 13/4 Camacho—Reina de Luz (IRE) (Echo of Light) (5056) **Mr K. Brown**
68 B c 22/1 French Navy—Siphon Melody (USA) (Siphon (BRZ)) (8571)
69 **SOMBRA DE MOLLYS**, gr f 12/4 Mayson—Musical Molly (IRE) (Mastercraftsman (IRE)) **Julie & Phil Martin**
70 Gr f 23/2 Camacho—Stone Roses (IRE) (Zebedee) (9270) **S & S Racing & Partner**
71 B c 12/5 Camacho—Vita Mia (Central Park (IRE)) (10476) **Mr K. Brown**

Other Owners: P. S. Alderson, Mr A. Bell, Mr P. Boyle, Mr A. Bruce, Mr D. J. Burke, Mrs C. L. Ellison, Mr Brian Ellison, Mr S. A. Flower, J. P. Hames, Mr C. S. Heaps, Mr M. Hilton, Mr S. T. Hoare, Mr N. N. Kane, Mr P. D. Laidler, Mr M. Lawrence, Mr G. Lund, Mr N. P. Lyons, Mr P. J. Martin, Mrs A. M. Noble, Northern Water Services Limited, One For The Road, Mr G. Pickering, Mr B. Robe, Mr P. A. Saxton, Mr R. J. T. Smillie, Mr P. M. Stacey, Mr K. J. Strangeway, Mr R. Watson, Mr G. Wills, Mr D. Woodhouse.

Assistant Trainer: Jessica Bell, Mobile (07939) 480860

Jockey (flat): Ben Curtis. **Jockey (NH):** Henry Brooke, Danny Cook, Brian Hughes. **Conditional:** Nathan Moscrop.
Apprentice: Ben Robinson.

---

186 **MR DAVID ELSWORTH, Newmarket**
Postal: **Kings Yard, Egerton House Stables, Cambridge Road, Newmarket, Suffolk, CB8 0TH**
Contacts: **PHONE (01638) 665511 FAX (01638) 665310 MOBILE (07540) 750424**
E-MAIL office@drcelsworth.com

1 **BRANCASTER (IRE)**, 5, ch g Casamento (IRE)—Makheelah **C Benham/ D Whitford/ L Quinn/ K Quinn**
2 **DASH OF SPICE**, 5, br h Teofilo (IRE)—Dashiba **J. C. Smith**
3 **DESERT SKYLINE (IRE)**, 5, ch g Tamayuz—Diamond Tango (FR) **C Benham/ D Whitford/ L Quinn/ K Quinn**
4 **ENTANGLING (IRE)**, 5, b g Fastnet Rock (AUS)—Question Times **Mr B. C. M. Wong**
5 **FARHHMOREEXCITING**, 4, ch g Farhh—Something Exciting
6 **LADY DANCEALOT (IRE)**, 4, b f Sir Prancealot (IRE)—Mayorstone (IRE) **K. J. Quinn**
7 **MAIN STREET**, 4, b g Street Cry (IRE)—My Special J's (USA) **King Power Racing Co Ltd**
8 **MASTER THE WORLD (IRE)**, 8, gr g Mastercraftsman (IRE)—Zadalla **K. Quinn/ C. Benham**
9 **MISS HERITAGE (IRE)**, 5, b m Pour Moi (IRE)—Haretha (IRE) **Mark Venus & David Elsworth**
10 **RIPP ORF (IRE)**, 5, b g Rip Van Winkle (IRE)—Barzah (IRE) **C Benham/ D Whitford/ L Quinn/ K Quinn**
11 **SIR DANCEALOT (IRE)**, 5, b g Sir Prancealot (IRE)—
Majesty's Dancer (IRE) **C Benham/ D Whitford/ L Quinn/ K Quinn**

MR DAVID ELSWORTH - Continued

THREE-YEAR-OLDS
12 **AIDE MEMOIRE (IRE)**, b f Rip Van Winkle (IRE)—Bessichka **Mr J. D. Manley**
13 **ARABIAN KING**, ch c New Approach (IRE)—Barshiba (IRE) **J. C. Smith**
14 **DANDHU**, ch f Dandy Man (IRE)—Polhdu **Hadopa, ISM, Elsworth & Coughlan**
15 **DARWIN DREAM**, b g Australia—Snoqualmie Girl (IRE) **J. C. Smith**
16 **HARRY THE NORSEMAN**, ch c Norse Dancer (IRE)—Titled Lady **Elsworth & Nettlefold**
17 **MARTINI MAGIC**, ch f Norse Dancer (IRE)—Premier Prize **J. C. Smith**
18 **MIRACLES TAKE TIME**, b gr f Gregorian (IRE)—Noble Nova
19 **NO NONSENSE**, b c Acclamation—Gift of Music (IRE) **J. C. Smith**
20 **POOR AULD PADDY**, b c Swiss Spirit—Moment In The Sun **The Boys From Roscommon Syndicate**
21 **REDEMPTIVE**, b f Royal Applause—Hope And Fortune (IRE) **K. J. Quinn**
22 **SONGKRAN (IRE)**, b c Slade Power (IRE)—Choose Me (IRE) **King Power Racing Co Ltd**
23 **TARGET ZONE**, ch c Champs Elysees—Sailors Path **G. B. Partnership**
24 **TOP FOX**, b c Frankel—Lady Linda (USA) **King Power Racing Co Ltd**

TWO-YEAR-OLDS
25 B c 18/2 Australia—Anna Karenina (USA) (Atticus (USA)) (71639) **K Quinn / C Benham / L Quinn / D Whitford**
26 B c 6/4 Dutch Art—
          Bonnie Brae (Mujahid (USA)) (50000) **K Quinn / C Benham / L Quinn / D Whitford / D Elsworth**
27 B c 11/4 Norse Dancer (IRE)—Cascades (IRE) (Montjeu (IRE)) **J. C. Smith**
28 B r c 23/1 Dubawi (IRE)—Cocktail Queen (IRE) (Motivator) **J. C. Smith**
29 B c 12/3 Acclamation—Dashiba (Dashing Blade) **J. C. Smith**
30 B f 17/2 Al Kazeem—Easter Diva (IRE) (Dansili) **K Quinn / C Benham / L Quinn / D Whitford**
31 B c 15/4 Camelot—Fraulein (Acatenango (GER)) (92709) **King Power Racing Co Ltd**
32 B c 13/4 Holy Roman Emperor (IRE)—Gift of Music (IRE) (Cadeaux Genereux) **J. C. Smith**
33 O'REILLY'S PASS, b c 22/2 Australia—Dynaglow (USA) (Dynaformer (USA))
34 B f 31/3 New Approach (IRE)—Porthcawl (Singspiel (IRE)) (30000) **D. R. C. Elsworth**
35 RED SHELLEY, b f 26/3 Sir Percy—Rouge Dancer (Elusive City (USA)) (52000) **Mrs A. Coughlan**
36 RUSSIAN DANCER, b c 20/4 Toronado (IRE)—Russian Rhapsody (Cosmonaut) **Mr Derek Price**
37 THE TURPINATOR, b c 20/2 Canford Cliffs (IRE)—Bessichka (Exceed And Excel (AUS)) **Mr John Manly**
38 B f 18/2 Mukhadram—Xtrasensory (Royal Applause) **Hot To Trot Racing**

Other Owners: Mr Chris Benham, Mrs Anne Coughlan, Mr D. R. C. Elsworth, Mr M. G. H. Heald, Mr Andrew Heald, Mr Shane Higgins, Mr Gerard Higgins, Mr Julian Nettlefold, Mr Kevin Quinn, Mr Leo Quinn, Mr M. Venus, Mr D. Whitford.

Amateur: Mr George Eddery.

---

187 MISS SARA ENDER, Malton
Postal: **Swallows Barn, East Heslerton, Malton, North Yorkshire, YO17 8RN**
Contacts: **MOBILE (07983) 462314**
E-MAIL seeequineservices@hotmail.com WEBSITE www.nevilleender.wix.com/enderracing

1 **BOLD PRINCE RUPERT (IRE)**, 9, b g Royal Anthem (USA)—Fortune And Favour (IRE) **Mr N. P. Ender**
2 **DURLINGTON (FR)**, 6, ch g Montmartre (FR)—Dalyonne (FR) **Mr N. P. Ender**
3 **GREY MONK (IRE)**, 11, br g Alderbrook—Thats The Bother (IRE) **Mr N. P. Ender**
4 **IVOR THE FOX**, 7, b g Sakhee (USA)—Florie **Mr N. P. Ender**
5 **MISTER KALANISI (IRE)**, 10, b g Kalanisi (IRE)—Maxis Girl (IRE) **Mr N. P. Ender**
6 **MOORLANDS MIST**, 12, gr g Fair Mix—Sandford Springs (USA) **Mr N. P. Ender**
7 **NORTHANDSOUTH (IRE)**, 9, ch g Spadoun (FR)—Ennel Lady (IRE) **Mr N. P. Ender**

Assistant Trainer: Mr Neville Ender

---

188 MRS SAM ENGLAND, Guiseley
Postal: **Brentwood, Manor Farm, Guiseley, Leeds, West Yorkshire, LS20 8EW**
Contacts: **MOBILE (07921) 003155**

1 **ASK PADDY (IRE)**, 7, ch g Ask—Dalzenia (FR) **Gremot Racing 2**
2 **BARATINEUR (FR)**, 8, ch g Vendangeur (IRE)—Olmantina (FR) **Mr M. J. D. Matthews**
3 **BRAAVOS**, 8, br g Presenting—Tatanka (IRE) **Simon & Angela Gillie**
4 **CHEF D'OEUVRE (FR)**, 8, b g Martaline—Kostroma (FR) **The Sandmoor Partnership 2**
5 **CHOOCHOOBUGALOO**, 7, b m Rail Link—Charmante Femme **Sam England Racing Club**
6 **DRUMOCHTER**, 5, br m Bated Breath—Dixey **Mowbray Park**

MRS SAM ENGLAND - Continued

7 **GATACRE STREET**, 7, b g Lucarno (USA)—Sherry Darling (IRE) **Mr & Mrs G. E. Pickering**
8 **GOLD RUNNER (IRE)**, 7, b m Gold Well—Copper Coast (IRE) **Itsnotabadlife**
9 **KILMACALLOGUE BAY**, 13, b g Karinga Bay—Wahiba Reason (IRE) **Mr R. D. Potter**
10 **KING'S COINAGE (IRE)**, 5, b g Holy Roman Emperor (IRE)—Seducing (IRE) **Cragg Wood Racing**
11 **MAGIC OF MILAN (IRE)**, 6, b m Milan—Laughing Lesa (IRE) **On the Road Again**
12 **MANICMAN (IRE)**, 5, ch g Getaway (GER)—Quinsborohall (IRE)
13 **MANWELL (IRE)**, 9, b g Gold Well—Roborette (FR) **Sam England Racing Club**
14 **MURCHISON RIVER**, 5, b g Medicean—Free Offer **The Atkin Partnership**
15 **MY LIEGE (IRE)**, 8, b g Marienbard (IRE)—Smashing Leader (IRE) **Worcester Racing Club**
16 **MY RENAISSANCE**, 9, b br g Medicean—Lebenstanz **Lynne Pearson, Diane Mulcahy & Partners**
17 **NEAR KETTERING**, 5, ch g Medicean—Where's Broughton **Redivivus Racing**
18 **NINEPOINTSIXTHREE**, 9, b g Bertolini (USA)—Armada Grove **Mr G. Smith**
19 **PICCALILLI PIE**, 5, b m Weetman's Weigh (IRE)—Piece of Pie **Mrs J. Pighills**
20 **THE LINKSMAN (IRE)**, 7, b g Westerner—Lost Link (IRE) **Mrs S. A. England**
21 **WINDY WRITER (IRE)**, 9, br g Rudimentary (USA)—Hardabout (IRE) **Guess What Racing**
22 **WISHFULL DREAMING**, 8, ch g Alflora (IRE)—Poussetiere Deux (FR) **Mr J C England and Valerie Beattie**

Other Owners: T. J. Atkin, J. A. Atkin, Mr M. V. Atkinson, Mr P. H. Ayre, Mrs V. A. Beattie, J. R. Bewley, Mr J. Birtles, Mr D. Brooks, Mr A. J. Cooper, Crowd Racing Partnership, Mr T. K. Davis, Mrs J. E. Drake, Mr R. Drye, Mr G. G. Edwards, Mr J. C. England, Mr G. Fox, Mr D. N. French, Mr S. P. Gillie, Mrs A. Gillie, Mr J. H. Green, M. P. Hill, Mrs P. Howard, Dr K. Howard, Mr I. Janotta, Mr C. McKenna, Mrs S. J. McKenna, Mr J. E. Mott, Mrs D. Mulcahy, Mrs L. E. Pearson, Mr G. E. Pickering, Mrs P. Pickering, Mr M. J. Roche, Miss H. Webster, Mr J. J. Wilkinson.

Jockey (NH): Jonathan England.

---

189 **MR JAMES EUSTACE, Newmarket**
Postal: **Park Lodge Stables, Park Lane, Newmarket, Suffolk, CB8 8AX**
Contacts: **PHONE (01638) 664277 FAX (01638) 664156 MOBILE (07802) 243764**
E-MAIL jameseustace@tiscali.co.uk **WEBSITE www.jameseustace.com**

1 **APACHE SONG**, 6, ch m Mount Nelson—Pantita **Mr Andrew Mcgladdery & Mrs James Eustace**
2 **CAPTAIN FELIX**, 7, b g Captain Gerrard (IRE)—Sweet Applause (IRE) **Mr M. Bartram**
3 **COVERHAM (IRE)**, 5, b g Bated Breath—Mark Too (IRE) **Blue Peter Racing 15**
4 **DEBACLE**, 6, b g Bach (IRE)—De Blanc (IRE) **J. P. Hancock**
5 **DIRECTORY**, 4, b g Oasis Dream—Minority **Blue Peter Racing 16**
6 **ENVOY**, 5, gr g Delegator—La Gessa **Mrs G. R. Eustace**
7 **GLENDUN (USA)**, 5, b g First Defence (USA)—La Mina (USA) **The MacDougall Two**
8 **HIGHFALUTING (IRE)**, 5, b g High Chaparral (IRE)—Walk On Water **D. H. Batten**
9 **LONGSIDE**, 7, b g Oasis Dream—Hypoteneuse (IRE) **Mrs G. R. Eustace**
10 **NEXT TRAIN'S GONE**, 6, b g Rail Link—Coh Sho No **Mr Harold Nass**
11 **NORDIC FLIGHT**, 4, b g Norse Dancer—Winged Diva (IRE) **J. C. Smith**
12 **SEE THE CITY (IRE)**, 5, b g Lawman (FR)—Cedar Sea (IRE) **The MacDougall Two**
13 **WIND PLACE AND SHO**, 7, b g Shirocco (GER)—Coh Sho No **Mr Harold Nass**

THREE-YEAR-OLDS

14 **MAJOR BLUE**, b g Delegator—Bahama Blue **J. C. Smith**
15 **MENDOZA (IRE)**, ch g Zebedee—Strange Magic (IRE) **The MacDougall Two**
16 **PERIPHERIQUE**, ch f Champs Elysees—Somersault (IRE) **Mr G. N. Carstairs**
17 **POSTIE**, b f Medicean—Postage Stampe **Major M. G. Wyatt**
18 **REASONED (IRE)**, ch f Intello (GER)—Do The Honours (IRE) **Park Lodge Racing**
19 **SIBLE HEDINGHAM**, ch f Rip Van Winkle (IRE)—Emily Blake (IRE) **Mr & Mrs R Scott & Mrs James Eustace**
20 **STERLING PRICE**, b g War Command (USA)—Chantry **Scott, Rushby, Charter**

TWO-YEAR-OLDS

21 B f 30/4 Cable Bay (IRE)—Bahama Blue (Bahamian Bounty) **J. C. Smith**
22 **FORT NELSON**, b c 6/4 Mount Nelson—Iron Butterfly (Shirocco (GER)) **Mr. Harold Nass & Partner**
23 **PEARLY REDD**, b f 4/5 Heeraat (IRE)—Lady O Malley (IRE) (Oratorio (IRE)) **Sherin & Rod Lloyd**
24 **WINDY COVE**, b f 15/2 Lawman (FR)—Gale Green (Galileo (IRE)) **Major M. G. Wyatt**

Other Owners: Mr R. P. Abel, Mr D. F. Ballheimer, Mrs B. J. Carter, P. F. Charter, Mr B. M. Cimmering, C. Z. Curtis, Mr T. E. Dyke, Mr J. M. P. Eustace, Mr A. C. Frost, Mr S. J. Gibson, Mrs J. A. Gibson, Mrs L. R. Lawson, Mrs S. A. Lloyd, R. E. Lloyd, Mr A. J. McGladdery, H. D. Nass, Mr I. L. Rushby, R. Scott, Mr & Mrs R. Scott, Mrs P. M. Scott, Mrs K. J. Smith, Mr R. J. Uzupris.

190 MR DAVID EVANS, Abergavenny

Postal: Ty Derlwyn Farm, Pandy, Abergavenny, Monmouthshire, NP7 8DR
Contacts: PHONE (01873) 890837 (07834) 834775 E. Evans FAX (01873) 890837
MOBILE (07860) 668499
E-MAIL pdevansracing@btinternet.com WEBSITE www.pdevansracing.co.uk

1 AMOR FATI (IRE), 4, b g Zoffany (IRE)—Roman Love (IRE) **Miss C. Gannon**
2 ANIF (IRE), 5, b g Cape Cross (IRE)—Cadenza (FR) **Dave & Emma Evans**
3 ATHASSEL, 10, ch g Dalakhani (IRE)—Hope Island (IRE) **Mrs E. Evans**
4 ATLETICO (IRE), 7, b g Kodiac—Queenofthefairies **Mr K McCabe & Mr P D Evans**
5 BARBARA VILLIERS, 4, b f Champs Elysees—Frances Stuart (IRE) **Mickley Stud & Mrs A O'Sullivan**
6 BOATRACE (IRE), 4, ch g Camacho—Shamarlane **Mrs I. M. Folkes**
7 BOND ANGEL, 4, gr f Monsieur Bond (IRE)—Angel Grigio **M. W. Lawrence**
8 BROCKEY RISE (IRE), 4, ch g Zebedee—Age of Diplomacy **John Abbey & Emma Evans**
9 ESSENAITCH (IRE), 6, b g Zoffany—Karlisse (IRE) **Spiers & Hartwell Ltd & Mrs E. Evans**
10 GIVE EM A CLUMP (IRE), 4, br g Camacho—Pixie's Blue (IRE) **Dave & Emma Evans**
11 GRACIOUS JOHN (IRE), 6, b g Baltic King—Dorn Hill **T. Reffell**
12 HERM (IRE), 5, b g Bushranger (IRE)—School Holidays (USA) **T. H. Gallienne**
13 JOEGOGO (IRE), 4, b g Approve (IRE)—Joyfullness (USA) **H. M. W. Clifford**
14 KODI KOH (IRE), 4, b f Kodiac—Laywaan (USA) **Mrs I. M. Folkes**
15 KODILINE (IRE), 5, b g Kodiac—Kris Spring **Mrs E. Evans**
16 LOS CAMACHOS (IRE), 4, b g Camacho—Illuminise (IRE) **Mrs Penny Keble White & Emma Evans**
17 MIDNIGHT GUEST (IRE), 4, b f Acclamation—Midnight Martini **Mrs R. L. Dawson**
18 MR TOP HAT, 4, b g Helmet (AUS)—Tut (IRE) **Mr B McCabe & Mrs E Evans**
19 SARK (IRE), 6, b g Zoffany—Breezeway (IRE) **T. H. Gallienne**
20 SATCHVILLE FLYER, 8, ch g Compton Place—Palinisa (FR) **Dave & Emma Evans**
21 SCOFFLAW, 5, b g Foxwedge (AUS)—Belle des Airs (IRE) **John Abbey & Emma Evans**
22 SEA FOX (IRE), 5, b g Kodiac—City Maiden (USA) **Eric Griffiths & P D Evans**
23 SONNETIST, 5, b g Poet's Voice—Society Rose **H. M. W. Clifford**
24 THE ESTABLISHMENT, 4, b g Exceed And Excel (AUS)—Sweet Coincidence **Power Geneva Ltd & Partner**
25 THE GROOVE, 6, b g Azamour (IRE)—Dance East **Dave & Emma Evans**

THREE-YEAR-OLDS

26 ANONYMOUS BLONDE, b f Toronado (IRE)—Angus Newz **Mrs R. L. Dawson**
27 DERRY BOY, b g Havana Gold (IRE)—Steppe By Steppe **Mr & Mrs Paul & Clare Rooney**
28 ELEGANT LOVE, b f Delegator—Lovellian **H. M. W. Clifford**
29 ISABELLA RED (IRE), b f Dark Angel (IRE)—Littlepromisedland (IRE) **Mrs E. Evans**
30 B br c Hat Trick (JPN)—Island Escape (USA)
31 LIHOU, ch c Mayson—Kodiac Island **T. H. Gallienne**
32 MADE IN LEWISHAM (IRE), b g Morpheus—River Beau (IRE) **Mrs I. M. Folkes**
33 NOT SO SHY, b f Heeraat (IRE)—Littlemisstutti (IRE) **R. Kent**
34 PETERS PUDDING (IRE), ch g Fast Company (IRE)—Whats For Pudding (IRE) **Dave & Emma Evans**
35 TSARMINA (IRE), B f Ruler of The World (IRE)—Caelis
36 TWPSYN (IRE), b g Es Que Love (IRE)—Gold Blended (IRE) **Rob Emmanuelle, T Burns & P D Evans**

TWO-YEAR-OLDS

37 B c 6/4 Baltic King—Cayambe (IRE) (Selkirk (USA)) (6741)
38 B c 24/2 Acclamation—Chances Are (IRE) (Dandy Man (IRE)) (19047) **H. M. W. Clifford**
39 CHASANDA, ch f 23/4 Footstepsinthesand—Miss Chamanda (IRE) (Choisir (AUS)) **Mr E. A. R. Morgans**
40 B f 1/4 Gutaifan (IRE)—Classic Style (IRE) (Desert Style (IRE)) (12642)
41 B c 13/3 Bungle Inthejungle—Fig Digliani (IRE) (Fasliyev (USA)) (3370) **Mr J. A. Wilcox**
42 B f 10/4 Baltic King—Gilded Verse (Act One) **P. D. Evans**
43 Gr ro f 24/4 Toronado (IRE)—Indian Dumaani (Indian Ridge) (17000) **T. H. Gallienne**
44 B c 5/2 Kodiac—Khaimah (Nayef (USA)) (16013) **D. E. Edwards**
45 LILI WEN FACH (IRE), gr f 16/2 Gregorian (IRE)—
                                      Zuzinia (IRE) (Mujadil (USA)) (11904) **Mr Rob Emmanuelle & Dave Evans**
46 B f 8/2 Heeraat (IRE)—Littlemisstutti (IRE) (Noverre (USA)) (4761)
47 B c 17/4 Alhebayeb (IRE)—Luvmedo (IRE) (One Cool Cat (USA)) (15000) **H. M. W. Clifford**
48 B c 20/3 Heeraat (IRE)—Madam Mojito (USA) (Smart Strike (USA)) (2528)
49 Ch c 10/5 Starspangledbanner (AUS)—Moriches (IRE) (Alhaarth (IRE)) (5000)
50 B c 10/4 Elzaam (AUS)—Mountain Glow (Araafa (IRE)) (6741) **Dukes Head Racing**
51 Ch f 16/2 Camacho—Nurture (IRE) (Bachelor Duke) (8427)
52 Br c 23/1 Ivawood (IRE)—Sharp Applause (IRE) (Royal Applause) (3370) **Mr E. R. Griffiths**
53 SPIRITULIST, b c 17/4 Fountain of Youth (IRE)—Spirit Glance (Invincible Spirit (IRE))
54 B c 19/4 Sir Prancealot (IRE)—Startori (Vettori (IRE)) (7163) **Dukes Head Racing**

MR DAVID EVANS - Continued

55 B f 4/4 War Command (USA)—Tides (Bahamian Bounty) (7163) **Mrs E. Evans**
56 Ch c 21/3 Kyllachy—Tweety Pie (IRE) (Rock of Gibraltar (IRE)) (6741)
57 Ch c 19/4 Helmet (AUS)—Windlass (IRE) (Teofilo (IRE)) (2528)
58 B c 23/2 Baltic King—Zeeoneandonly (IRE) (Zebedee) **Mr E. R. Griffiths**

Other Owners: J. E. Abbey, Mrs T. Burns, J. L. Collins, Mr P. G. Dalton, Mr R. Emmanuel, Mrs P. Keble-White, Mr K. McCabe, Mr B. McCabe, Mrs A. M. O'Sullivan, Power Geneva Ltd, Mrs C. Rooney, Mr P. A. Rooney, Spiers & Hartwell Ltd.

Assistant Trainer: Mrs Emma Evans

Jockey (flat): Fran Berry, John Egan. **Apprentice:** Katherine Begley. **Amateur:** Miss E. McKenzie.

---

191 **MR JAMES EVANS, Worcester**
Postal: Stone Farm, Broadwas, Worcester, Worcestershire, WR6 5NE
Contacts: **MOBILE (07813) 166430**
E-MAIL herbie_evans@hotmail.com WEBSITE www.hjamesevans.co.uk

1 AMIRAL COLLONGES (FR), 9, ch g Dom Alco (FR)—Idole Collonges (FR) **Mr S. D. Faiers**
2 COMPADRE (IRE), 8, b g Yeats (IRE)—Jolivia (FR) **Mr B. W. Preece**
3 CONNETABLE (FR), 7, b g Saint des Saints (FR)—Montbresia (FR) **Elegant Clutter & Mr S D Faiers**
4 CROESO CYMRAEG, 5, b g Dick Turpin (IRE)—Croeso Cusan **Mr R. R. Evans**
5 FRENCH DE GUYE (FR), 4, gr g Lord du Sud (FR)—Kasibelle de Guye (FR) **Elegant Clutter & Mr S D Faiers**
6 FRIENDSHIP BAY, 15, b g Midnight Legend—Friendly Fairy **Mrs J. Evans**
7 LORD GETAWAY (IRE), 7, b g Getaway (GER)—Terre d'orient (FR) **Mr B. W. Preece**
8 MALINDI BAY (IRE), 6, b m Malinas (GER)—La Grande Villez (FR) **Mr S. D. Faiers**
9 MOSSING, 7, b m Passing Glance—Missy Moscow (IRE) **James Evans Racing & the Gmw Syndicate**
10 NOBEL LEADER (IRE), 9, b g Alflora (IRE)—Ben Roseler (IRE) **Mr S. D. Faiers**
11 OKMYWAY, 6, br m Passing Glance—Highlight Girl **Mr T. P. Hitchman**
12 OPTIMISTIC BIAS (IRE), 10, b g Sayarshan (FR)—Dashers Folly (IRE) **Elegant Clutter Ltd**
13 PRINCE OF STEAL (IRE), 9, b g Craigsteel—Princess Gloria (IRE) **The Cheltenham Flyers**
14 SANDS COVE (IRE), 12, b g Flemensfirth (USA)—Lillies Bordello (IRE) **James Evans & The Harlequins Racing**
15 SHARAINA, 5, b m Yorgunnabelucky (USA)—Sharbasia (IRE)

Other Owners: Mr H. J. Evans, Mr N. Goodger, The Harlequins Racing, International Plywood (Importers) Ltd, Mr A. J. Pidgeon, Mr P. M. Smith, The GMW Syndicate.

Assistant Trainer: Mrs Jane Evans

Amateur: Miss Emma Yardley.

---

192 **MRS MARY EVANS, Haverfordwest**
Postal: Hengoed, Clabeston Road, Haverfordwest, Dyfed, SA63 4QL
Contacts: **PHONE (01437) 731336**

1 HOLD COURT (IRE), 12, br g Court Cave (IRE)—Tipsy Miss (IRE) **Mary & Billy Evans**

Other Owners: W. J. Evans, Mrs M. Evans.

Assistant Trainer: W J Evans

---

193 **MRS NIKKI EVANS, Abergavenny**
Postal: Penbiddle Farm, Penbidwal, Pandy, Abergavenny, Gwent, NP7 8EA
Contacts: **(01873) 890957 FAX (01873) 890957 MOBILE (07977) 753437**
E-MAIL nikki@penbiddle.fsnet.co.uk WEBSITE www.nikki-evans-racing.co.uk

1 AGREEMENT (IRE), 9, b g Galileo (IRE)—Cozzene's Angel (USA) **Nikki Evans Racing**
2 ALLOW DALLOW (IRE), 12, b g Gold Well—Russland (GER) **Mr J. Berry**
3 ALMONTASER (FR), 5, ch g Manduro—Mamitador **Mrs N. S. Evans**
4 ANTON CHIGURH, 10, b g Oasis Dream—Barathiki **Mr Matt Watkinson & Dare To Dream Racing**
5 ARISTOCLES, 6, b g High Chaparral (IRE)—Amathusia **East Grinstead Scaffolding**
6 ATLANTIC SUNSHINE, 4, b f Fight Club (GER)—Atlantic Lady (GER) **Nikki Evans Racing**
7 CANADIAN ROYAL, 5, b g Royal Applause—Emily Carr (IRE) **Dare To Dream Racing**
8 CARNAGE, 4, b g Holy Roman Emperor (IRE)—Sylvestris (IRE) **Mr J. Berry**

MRS NIKKI EVANS - Continued

9 **CAVIAR ROYALE**, 4, b g Royal Applause—Precious Secret (IRE) **Mrs M. E. Gittings-Watts**
10 **CHICAGO SCHOOL (IRE)**, 6, ch g Approve (IRE)—Ms Sasha Malia (IRE) **Mrs D. C. Scott**
11 **CRIMSON PRINCESS**, 4, ch f Sayif (IRE)—Crimson Queen **Mr A. T. L. Clayton**
12 **LATE SHIPMENT**, 8, b g Authorized (IRE)—Time Over **Mrs M. E. Gittings-Watts**
13 **LITTLE FOLKE**, 8, gr m Sagamix (FR)—Little Choice (IRE) **Mr R. Sparks**
14 **MAROC**, 9, b g Rock of Gibraltar (IRE)—Zietory **Dare To Dream Racing**
15 **OUTBACK TRAVELLER (IRE)**, 8, b g Bushranger (IRE)—Blue Holly (IRE) **Mr J. Berry**
16 **PACO FILLY**, 5, b m Paco Boy (IRE)—Respectfilly **Mr G. M. Jones**
17 **POLKADOT PRINCESS (IRE)**, 5, b m Sir Prancealot (IRE)—Miriam's Song **L Gibbs & Nikki Evans Racing**
18 **SKYLARK LADY (IRE)**, 6, ch m Tamayuz—Allegrissimo (IRE) **Mrs M. E. Gittings-Watts**
19 **SUE BE IT (IRE)**, 8, b m Presenting—Runaround Sue **Hanford's Chemist Ltd**
20 **TAKBEER (IRE)**, 7, b g Aqlaam—Precious Secret (IRE) **Mrs M. E. Gittings-Watts**
21 **TIME FOR CHAMPERS (IRE)**, 9, b m Robin des Champs (FR)—Someone Told Me (IRE) **Hanford's Chemist Ltd**
22 **TURNBURY**, 8, b g Azamour (IRE)—Scottish Heights (IRE) **Dare To Dream Racing**
23 **WHAT A SCORCHER**, 8, b m Authorized (IRE)—Street Fire (IRE) **Mrs M. E. Gittings-Watts**

THREE-YEAR-OLDS

24 **LUCKY SEVERN**, b g Mazameer (IRE)—Los Organos (IRE) **Severn Bridge Racing**

Other Owners: P. T. Evans, Mr L. R. Gibbs, Mr I. Sharrock, Mr W. Smith, Mr A. N. Waters, Mr M. Watkinson.

Assistant Trainer: Mr P. T. Evans

---

194 | **MR JAMES EWART, Langholm**
Postal: **James Ewart Racing Limited, Craig Farm, Westerkirk, Langholm, Dumfriesshire, DG13 0NZ**
Contacts: **PHONE** (01387) 370707 **MOBILE** (07786) 995073
E-MAIL office@jeracing.co.uk **WEBSITE** www.jamesewarttracing.com

1 **APACHE VALLEY**, 4, b f Sleeping Indian—Vallani (IRE) **The Craig Farm Syndicate**
2 **AQUITAINE BOY (FR)**, 4, b g Walk In The Park (IRE)—Dolce Vita Yug **Mrs J. E. Dodd**
3 **ARISTO DU PLESSIS (FR)**, 9, b g Voix du Nord (FR)—J'aime (FR) **Mrs J. E. Dodd**
4 **ASCOT DE BRUYERE (FR)**, 9, b br g Kapgarde (FR)—Quid de Neuville (FR) **The Steel Bonnets**
5 **BERING UPSUN**, 8, b g And Beyond (IRE)—Bering Up (IRE) **The Craig Farm Syndicate**
6 **BINGO D'OLIVATE (FR)**, 8, b g Laverock (IRE)—Ombrelle de L'orme (FR) **The Craig Farm Syndicate**
7 **BLUEFORTYTWO**, 6, gr g Overbury (IRE)—Celine Message **Leeds Plywood & Doors Ltd**
8 **BULLION (FR)**, 6, ch g Full of Gold (FR)—Ryde (FR) **Mrs Hugh Fraser**
9 **CA LE FERRA (FR)**, 9, b g Turgeon (USA)—Branceilles (FR) **Mr J. Ewart**
10 **CALIX DELAFAYETTE (FR)**, 7, b g Caballo Raptor (CAN)—Obepinedelafayette (FR) **Mrs J. E. Dodd**
11 **CELLAR VIE**, 5, gr g Tikkanen (USA)—Branceilles (FR) **Mr J. Ewart**
12 **CHARMANT (FR)**, 7, b g Balko (FR)—Ravissante (FR) **Mr A Phillips & Mr&Mrs Sperling**
13 **CIVIL UNREST (IRE)**, 13, ch g Blueprint—Yore (IRE) **Ancrum ,Cfs, Carruthers, Palmer**
14 **COCHISEE**, 5, gr g Tikkanen (USA)—Pocahontas (FR) **N. M. L. Ewart**
15 **DUNLY (FR)**, 8, b g Gris de Gris (IRE)—Octavine du Meix (FR) **Mrs J. E. Dodd**
16 **EMPIRE DE MAULDE (FR)**, 5, b g Spanish Moon (USA)—Ondine de Brejoux (FR) **Mr J. Ewart**
17 **ETTILA DE SIVOLA (FR)**, 5, gr g Noroit (GER)—Wild Rose Bloom (FR) **Kesson,Phillips,Humbert,Ogilvie**
18 **FAST SCENIC (FR)**, 4, b br g Brave Mansonnien (FR)—Scenaria (IRE) **Mrs J. E. Dodd**
19 **FEETRONIE DE KERVI (FR)**, 4, b f No Risk At All (FR)—Malandra **Mr N Ewart & Mrs Drew**
20 **FOR THREE (IRE)**, 5, b g Pour Moi (USA)—Asmaa (USA) **The Craig Farm Syndicate**
21 **FOSTERED PHIL (IRE)**, 5, b br g Arcadio (GER)—Knock Na Shee (IRE) **N. M. L. Ewart**
22 **FOXEY**, 4, b g Foxwedge (AUS)—Blue Lyric **Mr M. J. James**
23 **GROUND CONTROL (FR)**, 5, b g Al Namix (FR)—Gobeline (FR) **Mr J. Ewart**
24 **HONOURARY GIFT (FR)**, 6, b g City Honours (USA)—Zaffalong (IRE) **Ewart,Phillips,Elliot**
25 **I AM DANDY (IRE)**, 4, b g Dandy Man (IRE)—Acushladear (IRE) **The Craig Farm Syndicate**
26 **INTO THE BREACH (FR)**, 6, b g Al Namix (FR)—Arvicaya **N. M. L. Ewart**
27 **IT'S NEVER ENOUGH**, 5, b g Equiano (FR)—Swynford Pleasure **J. D. Gordon**
28 **JASSAS (FR)**, 7, ch g Fuisse (FR)—Sylverina (FR) **Mrs J. E. Dodd**
29 **LEADING SCORE (IRE)**, 9, b g Scorpion (IRE)—Leading Rank (IRE) **Palmer & Graham**
30 **LOOK NOW**, 6, b g Observatory (USA)—One For Philip **The Craig Farm Syndicate**
31 **LORD WISHES (IRE)**, 12, b g Milan—Strong Wishes (IRE) **Leeds Plywood & Doors Ltd**
32 **LYCIDAS (GER)**, 10, b g Zamindar (USA)—La Felicita **J. D. Gordon**
33 **MUHTAMAR (FR)**, 4, ch g Muhtathir—Martalina (FR) **Mrs J. E. Dodd**
34 **MULLION DREAMS**, 5, b g Mullionmleanhour (IRE)—High Meadow Rose **Mr D. S. Hogg**
35 **MULTIPEDE**, 7, b g Multiplex—Playful Lady **Mrs Hugh Fraser**
36 **NIKGARDE (FR)**, 4, b g Kapgarde (FR)—Nikoline (FR) **Mrs J. E. Dodd**

MR JAMES EWART - Continued

37 **SAO MAXENCE (FR)**, 6, b g Saint des Saints (FR)—Primadona (FR) **Mrs J. E. Dodd**
38 **SLEEP IN FIRST (FR)**, 13, b br g Sleeping Car (FR)—First Union (FR) **First Sleepers, Craig Farm**
39 **THE MAESTRO (IRE)**, 5, b g Doyen (IRE)—Myown (IRE) **J. D. Gordon**
40 **TORTUGA BAY**, 5, b m Sulamani (IRE)—Empress of Light **Mrs Hugh Fraser**
41 **UEUETEOTL (FR)**, 11, gr g Tikkanen (USA)—Azturk (FR) **Dodd & Graham**
42 **UNDISPUTED (FR)**, 5, gr g Al Namix (FR)—Arvicaya **M. J. James**

THREE-YEAR-OLDS

43 **GOOD LORD TIEP (FR)**, gr g Lord du Sud (FR)—Sacree Tiepy (FR) **Mrs J. E. Dodd**
44 **KARISMATIK (FR)**, b g Kap Rock (FR)—Crack d'emble (FR) **N. M. L. Ewart**

TWO-YEAR-OLDS

45 **IT'S ENOUGH**, b g 12/3 Multiplex—High Meadow Girl (Pursuit of Love) **Mrs B. J. Ewart**

Other Owners: Mr J. D. Allen, Mr R. Carruthers, Mrs L. J. Drew, Mr J. J. Elliot, W. Graham, Mrs A. G. Humbert, Dr C. M. Kesson, Mr A. Kirkpatrick, Mr P. M. Ogilvie, Dr R. A. Palmer, Mrs J. D. Percy, Mr A. M. Phillips, Mr D. I. Rolinson, Mr R. E. Smith, Mrs J. Sperling, Mr N. A. Sperling, Mr D. R. Stanhope.

Assistant Trainer: Briony Ewart

Conditional: Steven Fox.

---

195 MR LES EYRE, Beverley
Postal: Ivy House Stables, Main Street, Catwick, Beverley, North Humberside, HU17 5PJ
Contacts: MOBILE (07864) 677444
E-MAIL leseyreracing@hotmail.co.uk

1 **COSMIC RAY**, 7, b g Phoenix Reach (IRE)—Beat Seven **Mrs M. A. Cooke**
2 **COTE D'AZUR**, 6, ch g Champs Elysees—Florentia **Billy Parker & Steven Parker**
3 **DAWAALEEB (USA)**, 5, b g Invincible Spirit (IRE)—Plaza (USA) **Billy Parker & Steven Parker**
4 **DETACHMENT**, 6, b g Motivator—Argumentative **Mr M. Moulds**
5 **GOLDEN GUEST**, 5, ch g Bated Breath—Si Belle (IRE) **Mr R. Peel**
6 **HIGHLY SPRUNG (IRE)**, 6, b g Zebedee—Miss Donovan **Mr A Turton & Dr V Webb**
7 **HILBOROUGH**, 4, b g Makfi—Ambrix (IRE) **Les Eyre Racing Partnership I**
8 **INTENSE STYLE (IRE)**, 7, ch g Intense Focus (USA)—Style Queen (IRE) **RP Racing Ltd**
9 **ISLAND FLAME (IRE)**, 6, b m Kodiac—Noble Flame (IRE) **Billy Parker & Steven Parker**
10 **MAKE ON MADAM (IRE)**, 7, b m Captain Rio—Rye (IRE) **Partnership Terminated**
11 **MORETTI (IRE)**, 4, b f Requinto (IRE)—Hassaya (IRE) **Mr J. L. Eyre**
12 **PLAY IT COOL (IRE)**, 5, b g Medicean—Grecian Dancer **RP Racing Ltd**
13 **QUEEN OF KALAHARI**, 4, b f Lethal Force (IRE)—Aromatherapy **Billy Parker & John Blackburn**
14 **RONNIE THE ROOSTER**, 5, b g Captain Gerrard (IRE)—Piranha (IRE) **J A Campbell & A Tattersall**
15 **SANDRA'S SECRET (IRE)**, 6, gr m Zebedee—Good For Her **Sunpak Racing**
16 **TIDAL SURGE (IRE)**, 4, ch f Showcasing—Oke Bay **Mr J. L. Eyre**
17 **VALLEY OF FIRE**, 7, b g Firebreak—Charlie Girl **Billy Parker & Steven Parker**
18 **VAN GERWEN**, 6, ch g Bahamian Bounty—Disco Ball **Sunpak Racing**

THREE-YEAR-OLDS

19 **ALISIA R (IRE)**, b f Holy Roman Emperor (IRE)—Shamrock Lady (IRE) **Mr M. J. Rozenbroek**
20 **AMBER ROCK (USA)**, b g Australia—Amber Isle (USA) **RP Racing Ltd**
21 **BUNGLE BILLY (IRE)**, b g Bungle Inthejungle—Testa Unica (ITY) **Personal Racehorse Owners**
22 **YORKSHIRE FLYER (IRE)**, b g Cape Cross (IRE)—Moonlight Wish (IRE) **RP Racing Ltd**

TWO-YEAR-OLDS

23 **STRICTLY SANDRA (IRE)**, b f 30/3 Iffraaj—Dance Club (IRE) (Fasliyev (USA)) (18000) **Sunpak Racing**
24 B c 6/5 Zoffany (IRE)—Xaloc (IRE) (Shirocco (GER)) (25000) **Mr M. J. Rozenbroek**

Other Owners: Mr J. N. Blackburn, Mr J. A. Campbell, Mr T. S. Ely, Mr C. S. Heaps, Mr S. Parker, Mr B. Parker, A. Tattersall, Mr B. L. Thompson, Mr A. Turton, Dr V. Webb, Mrs S. J. Yates, Mr A. Yates.

Assistant Trainer: Tracy Johnson

196 MR RICHARD FAHEY, Malton

Postal: RF Racing Ltd, Mews House, Musley Bank, Malton, North Yorkshire, YO17 6TD
Contacts: **PHONE (01653) 698915 FAX (01653) 699735 MOBILE (07713) 478079**
E-MAIL enquiries@richardfahey.com WEBSITE www.richardfahey.com

1 **ALJADY (FR)**, 4, b g Bated Breath—No Truth (IRE) **Al Shaqab Racing UK Limited**
2 **ANDOK (IRE)**, 5, b g Elzaam (AUS)—My Causeway Dream (IRE) **Mr N. O'Keeffe**
3 **BENGALI BOYS (IRE)**, 4, gr g Clodovil (IRE)—Caherassdotcom **Bardsley, Hyde & Tattersall**
4 **BILLY BOND**, 7, b g Monsieur Bond (IRE)—Princess Cocoa (IRE) **Mr & Mrs P. Ashton**
5 **BOUNDSY (IRE)**, 5, ch g Dandy Man (IRE)—Chiba (UAE) **Kevin Mercer & Partner**
6 **BRIAN THE SNAIL (IRE)**, 5, gr g Zebedee—Sweet Irish **Dr Marwan Koukash**
7 **CALVADOS SPIRIT**, 6, b g Invincible Spirit—Putois Peace **Aidan J Ryan & Partner**
8 **CAMEO STAR (IRE)**, 4, ch g Camacho—Passionforfashion (IRE) **Let's Go Racing 2**
9 **CLAIRE UNDERWOOD (IRE)**, 4, b f Declaration of War (USA)—Sindjara (USA) **The Parker Partnership**
10 **CROWNTHORPE**, 4, b g Monsieur Bond (IRE)—Normandy Maid **Richard Fahey Ebor Racing Club Ltd**
11 **DANEHILL DESERT (IRE)**, 4, b g Clodovil (IRE)—Misplace (IRE) **Percy/Green Racing**
12 **DARK DEVIL (IRE)**, 6, gr g Dark Angel (IRE)—Ride For Roses (IRE) **Dr M. B. Q. S. Koukash**
13 **DAZE OUT (IRE)**, 4, b f Acclamation—Maid To Order (IRE) **Johnson, Thornton, Thwaites**
14 **DOSE**, 6, b m Teofilo (IRE)—Prescription **Richard Fahey Ebor Racing Club Ltd**
15 **DUBAI ACCLAIM (IRE)**, 4, b g Acclamation—Bahati (IRE) **S & G Clayton**
16 **EXHORT**, 4, ch f Dutch Art—Entreat **Cheveley Park Stud Limited**
17 **FOOL FOR YOU (IRE)**, 4, b f Lawman (FR)—Bosphorus Queen (IRE) **Mr J. E. Dance**
18 **FOREST RANGER (IRE)**, 5, b g Lawman (FR)—Alava (IRE) **Mrs H. Steel**
19 **FURZIG**, 8, b g Monsieur Bond (IRE)—Princess Cocoa (IRE) **Mr & Mrs P. Ashton**
20 **GABRIAL (IRE)**, 10, b g Dark Angel (IRE)—Guajira (FR) **Dr M. B. Q. S. Koukash**
21 **GABRIAL THE DEVIL (IRE)**, 4, b g Epaulette (AUS)—Grasshoppergreen (IRE) **Dr M. B. Q. S. Koukash**
22 **GABRIAL THE SAINT (IRE)**, 4, ch g Society Rock (IRE)—Green Briar **Dr M. B. Q. S. Koukash**
23 **GABRIAL THE TIGER (IRE)**, 7, b g Kodiac—Invincible **Dr M. B. Q. S. Koukash**
24 **GABRIALS CENTURION (IRE)**, 4, b g Society Rock (IRE)—Flamanda **Dr M. B. Q. S. Koukash**
25 **GALLIPOLI (IRE)**, 6, b g Compton Place—Altadena Lady (IRE) **P. Timmins**
26 **GEORGE BOWEN (IRE)**, 7, gr g Dark Angel (IRE)—Midnight Oasis **M. A. Scaife**
27 **GIN IN THE INN (IRE)**, 6, b g Alfred Nobel (IRE)—Nose One's Way (IRE) **Mr D. Hardman & Mrs S. Hardman**
28 **GREAT PROSPECTOR (IRE)**, 4, b g Elzaam (AUS)—Guana (IRE) **Mr & Mrs J. D. Cotton**
29 **GRISE LIGHTNING (FR)**, 4, gr f Wootton Bassett—Tenepia (FR) **Middleham Park Racing CXIX**
30 **GROWL**, 7, b g Oasis Dream—Desert Tigress (USA) **Dr M. B. Q. S. Koukash**
31 **INDOMENEO**, 4, b g Piccolo—Cherrycombe-Row **Middleham Park Racing LX**
32 **INTERNATIONAL MAN**, 4, b g Epaulette (AUS)—Right Answer **P. D. Smith Holdings Ltd**
33 **INVIOLABLE SPIRIT (IRE)**, 4, b g Zebedee—Mediska **Bardsley, Hyde & Tattersall**
34 **KIMBERELLA**, 9, b g Kyllachy—Gleam of Light (IRE) **Mr C. J. Titcomb**
35 **KNOWING GLANCE (IRE)**, 4, b g Kodiac—Shauna's Princess (IRE) **Richard Fahey Ebor Racing Club Ltd**
36 **LA SIOUX (IRE)**, 5, ch m Casamento (IRE)—Dakota Sioux (IRE) **Mrs U. Towell**
37 **LUCKY LUCKY MAN (IRE)**, 4, gr g Clodovil (IRE)—Regrette Rien (IRE) **The Musley Bank Partnership & Partner**
38 **LUIS VAZ DE TORRES (IRE)**, 7, b g Tagula (IRE)—Tekhania (IRE) **Lets Go Racing 1**
39 **MAGGIES ANGEL (IRE)**, 4, b f Dark Angel (IRE)—Last Bid **P. D. Smith Holdings Ltd**
40 **MR LUPTON (IRE)**, 6, ch g Elnadim (USA)—Chiloe Wigeon (IRE) **Mr N. D. Kershaw & Partner**
41 **ODDS ON OLI**, 4, b g Camelot—Red Blooded Woman (USA) **Mr Mike Browne & Mrs Dee Howe 1**
42 **ORIENT EXPRESS**, 4, b g Orientor—Midnight Dynamo **Ewan & Anna Hyslop**
43 **PADDY POWER (IRE)**, 6, ch g Pivotal—Rag Top (IRE) **M Scaife & R A Fahey**
44 **PENWORTHAM (IRE)**, 6, b g Dandy Man (IRE)—Portofino Bay (IRE) **Dr M. B. Q. S. Koukash**
45 **POWERALLIED (IRE)**, 6, b g Camacho—Kaplinsky (USA) **Dr M. B. Q. S. Koukash**
46 **REQUINTO DAWN (IRE)**, 4, b g Requinto (IRE)—Till Dawn (IRE) **The Phoenix Racing C.O. & Partner**
47 **RIGHT ACTION**, 5, b g Dandy Man (IRE)—Rockaby Baby (IRE) **Middleham Park Racing LVII & Partner**
48 **ROYAL CONNOISSEUR (IRE)**, 8, b g Art Connoisseur (IRE)—Valferno (IRE) **Morebrooke Limited**
49 **ROYAL COSMIC**, 5, b m Wootton Bassett—Cosmic Case **The Cosmic Cases**
50 **SANDS OF MALI (FR)**, 4, b c Panis (USA)—Kadiania (FR) **The Cool Silk Partnership**
51 **SAXONROAD BOY (USA)**, 4, b g Mastercraftsman (IRE)—Good Strike (USA) **Mr Darren Barton & Partner**
52 **SEMPRE PRESTO (IRE)**, 4, b f Nathaniel (IRE)—Flandre (USA) **Mrs H. Steel**
53 **SHAZZAB (IRE)**, 4, b f Elzaam (AUS)—Ceylon Round (FR) **Mr D. N. Barton**
54 **SHOWMETHEDOUGH**, 4, ch g Showcasing—Silver Purse **Dr M. B. Q. S. Koukash**
55 **SOCIETY RED**, 5, ch g Arcano (IRE)—Idonea (CAN) **Mr M. J. Macleod**
56 **SOSIAN**, 4, b f Showcasing—Leonica **H. J. P. Farr**
57 **STARLIGHT ROMANCE**, 5, b m Excelebration (IRE)—Takizada (IRE) **Mrs H. Steel**
58 **STEWARDESS (IRE)**, 4, gr f Dandy Man (IRE)—Smart Hostess **Five Plus One Syndicate**
59 **THE GOODS**, 4, b g Orientor—Vanessa Bell (IRE) **Ewan & Anna Hyslop**
60 **THE RIGHT CHOICE (IRE)**, 4, ch g Choisir (AUS)—Expedience (USA) **The Fairweather Foursome**

MR RICHARD FAHEY - Continued

61 **THIRD TIME LUCKY (IRE)**, 7, gr g Clodovil (IRE)—Speckled Hen (IRE) **The Musley Bank Partnership & Partner**
62 **VENTURA GOLD (IRE)**, 4, b g Red Jazz (USA)—Desert Shine (IRE) **Middleham Park Racing XLVIII & Partner**
63 **VERA DRAKE (FR)**, 4, ch f Footstepsinthesand—Venetian Beauty (USA) **Richard Fahey Ebor Racing Club Ltd**
64 **WINDSOR CROSS (IRE)**, 4, gr g Camacho—Lizzy's Township (USA) **Richard Fahey Ebor Racing Club Ltd**
65 **WIRRAL GIRL (IRE)**, 4, b f Kodiac—Ursula (IRE) **Richard Fahey Ebor Racing Club Ltd**
66 **WITHERNSEA (IRE)**, 8, b g Dark Angel (IRE)—Charlene Lacy (IRE) **Withernsea Thoroughbred Ltd & Partner**
67 **ZIP ALONG (IRE)**, 4, b f Iffraaj—Wizz Up (IRE) **S. Ali**

THREE-YEAR-OLDS

68 **ABSOLUTE DREAM (IRE)**, ch g Dream Ahead (USA)—Absolute Diamond **S & G Clayton**
69 **ALLEN A DALE (IRE)**, br c Kyllachy—Wood Chorus **H. J. P. Farr**
70 **AMBERSAND (IRE)**, b f Footstepsinthesand—Miss Sally (IRE) **Mrs H. Steel**
71 **ANGEL SARAH (IRE)**, b f Dark Angel (IRE)—Padma **P. D. Smith Holdings Ltd**
72 **ARCHIES LAD**, b g Lawman (FR)—Stirring Ballad **Mark Barlow & Partner**
73 **BARONIAL PRIDE**, b g Mayson—Trust Fund Babe (IRE) **Nick Bradley Racing 20 & Partner**
74 **BATAAR (IRE)**, b g Acclamation—Elusive Laurence (IRE) **AlMohamediya Racing**
75 **BENJI**, b c Magician (IRE)—Penny Sixpence (FR) **Withernsea Thoroughbred Limited**
76 **BERESFORD (IRE)**, b c Arcano (IRE)—Carrauntoohil (IRE) **Mr Kenneth MacPherson**
77 **BOBBY SHAFT**, b g Garswood—She Mystifies **Nick Bradley Racing 4 & Sohi**
78 **CADEAU D'AMOUR (IRE)**, b g Camacho—Perfect Pose (IRE) **Middleham Park Racing LXX**
79 **CALL HIM AL (IRE)**, b g Alhebayeb (IRE)—Exempt **CBWS & Partner**
80 **CAMBER**, b g Garswood—Topflightcoolracer **Highclere Thoroughbred Racing - Ganton**
81 **CHARMING KID**, b c Charm Spirit (IRE)—Child Bride (USA) **The Cool Silk Partnership**
82 **COOLAGH FOREST (IRE)**, b c Elzaam (AUS)—Ekagra **Mr A. Harte**
83 **COOLAGH MAGIC**, b c Sepoy (AUS)—Miliika **Mr A. Harte**
84 **COSMIC LAW (IRE)**, b g No Nay Never (USA)—Dhamma (USA) **Mr J. E. Dance**
85 **CRITICAL VOLTAGE (IRE)**, b c Dark Angel (IRE)—Elektra Marino **Mr J. E. Dance**
86 **DEFENCE TREATY (IRE)**, b c Dandy Man (IRE)—Just Like Ivy (CAN) **Clipper Group Holdings Ltd**
87 **DORIS BLEASEDALE (IRE)**, b f Intikhab (USA)—Sheba Five (USA) **Richard Fahey Ebor Racing Club Ltd**
88 **ETERNAL ROMANTIC**, ch g Nathaniel (IRE)—Romantic Settings **Mr Mel Roberts & Ms Nicola Meese 1**
89 **FAIRY STORIES**, b f Mayson—Fairy Shoes **Richard Fahey Ebor Racing Club Ltd**
90 **FANTASTIC MS FOX**, b f Foxwedge (AUS)—Cracking Lass (IRE) **Mr Mel Roberts & Ms Nicola Meese 1**
91 **FIREWATER**, ch g Monsieur Bond (IRE)—Spirit Na Heireann (IRE) **Mrs H. Steel**
92 **FORTUNATE MOVE**, b f Heeraat (IRE)—Fortunately **Titanium Racing Club**
93 **GABRIAL THE ONE (IRE)**, b g Zoffany (IRE)—Guilia **Dr M. B. Q. S. Koukash**
94 **GABRIAL THE WIRE**, b g Garswood—Nightunderthestars **Dr M. B. Q. S. Koukash**
95 **GET THE RHYTHM**, b c Garswood—Star Kodiak (IRE) **P. Timmins & A. Rhodes Haulage**
96 **GINGER MAX**, b c Garswood—Miss Bunter **Withernsea Thoroughbred Ltd & Partner**
97 **GRIGGY (IRE)**, b c Dandy Man (IRE)—Joint Destiny (IRE) **Tramore Tree**
98 **GUNNISON**, b g Mayson—Kinkajou **Mr A. B. Phipps**
99 **HARRYJOEJOE**, b g Iffraaj—Salutare (IRE) **Amie Canham I**
100 **INTERNATIONAL GUY (IRE)**, b g Alhebayeb (IRE)—America Alone **P. D. Smith Holdings Ltd**
101 **IRREVERENT**, b c Iffraaj—Royal Rascal **Mr & Mrs N. Wrigley**
102 **ISLAND GREETING (IRE)**, b f Kodiac—Sweet'n Sassy (IRE) **Mr R. A. Fahey**
103 **IT'LLCOMEIN (FR)**, b g Wootton Bassett—L'hommee (FR) **Middleham Park Racing LXXV & Partner**
104 **IVORY CHARM**, b f Charm Spirit (IRE)—Ivory Gala (FR) **Mr J. E. Dance**
105 **JAZZ HANDS (IRE)**, b g Red Jazz (USA)—Ishimagic **Mr Mike Browne & Mrs Dee Howe**
106 **JIMMY GREENHOUGH (IRE)**, gr g Dream Ahead (USA)—Expedience (USA) **Withernsea Thoroughbred Limited**
107 **JUNGLE SECRET (IRE)**, ch f Bungle Inthejungle—Secret Circle **The Secret O'Circle Syndicate**
108 **KENSINGTON ART**, b g Dutch Art—Lady Luachmhar (IRE) **Mrs H. Steel**
109 **KINGSON (IRE)**, b g Kingman—Gaditana **Mr & Mrs P Ashton & Partner**
110 **LIGHTNING ATTACK**, b g Lethal Force (IRE)—Afrodita (IRE) **P. Timmins**
111 **MADAME VITESSE (FR)**, b f Vertigineux (FR)—Do I Worry (FR) **Middleham Park Racing XV**
112 **MENIN GATE (IRE)**, gr g Farhh—Telegraphy (USA) **A Long Long Way To Run**
113 **METALLIC BLACK**, br g Bated Breath—Silken Express (IRE) **Malih L. Al Basti**
114 **MICRONIZE (IRE)**, b c Dream Ahead (USA)—Marmaria (SPA) **Nick Bradley Racing 43 & Partner**
115 **MR BUTTONS (IRE)**, b c Elzaam (AUS)—Clann Force **Richard Fahey Ebor Racing Club Ltd**
116 **MR DIAMOND (IRE)**, b g Bated Breath—Diamond Lass (IRE) **Amie Canham I**
117 **MRS HOO (IRE)**, b f Lawman (FR)—Wingspan (USA) **Richard Fahey Ebor Racing Club Ltd**
118 **NICKI'S ANGEL (IRE)**, gr f Dark Angel (IRE)—Titova **P. D. Smith Holdings Ltd**
119 **NOBLE PROSPECTOR (IRE)**, b g Elzaam (AUS)—Seraphina (IRE) **J. D. Cotton**
120 **PACINO**, b g Heeraat (IRE)—Ringtail (USA) **Dr M. B. Q. S. Koukash**
121 **PICCOTHEPACK**, b f Piccolo—Cards **Middleham Park Racing CXX**
122 **PLUMETTE**, b f Compton Place—Belatorio (IRE) **Titanium Racing Club**
123 **POSH PERFECT**, gr f Showcasing—Pinch of Posh (IRE) **Mr N. Hartery**

MR RICHARD FAHEY - Continued

124 **PRIMEIRO BOY (IRE)**, gr g Zebedee—House of Roses **Bardsley, Hyde & Tattersall**
125 **RED HOT (FR)**, b f Siyouni (FR)—Green China (FR) **Clipper Group Holdings Ltd**
126 **ROBEAM (IRE)**, b g Helmet (AUS)—Secret Flame **Amie Canham I**
127 **SABRE**, b c Mayson—Crinkle (IRE) **Mrs J. M. MacPherson**
128 **SEVEN FOR A POUND (USA)**, b g Scat Daddy (USA)—Gimlet Witha Twist (USA) **Dtr Racing Group**
129 **SHARP BREATH**, b f Bated Breath—First Approval **Percy Green Racing 3 & Partner**
130 **SHOW ME A SUNSET**, b c Showcasing—Sunrise Star **The Cool Silk Partnership**
131 **SILVER DUST (IRE)**, gr g Clodovil (IRE)—Silesian (IRE) **The Far Corner Partnership**
132 **SOCIETY QUEEN (IRE)**, b f Society Rock (IRE)—Passion Fruit **Mrs H. Steel**
133 **SOOTABILITY (IRE)**, br f Camelot—Balaagha (USA) **Mrs H. Steel**
134 **SPONTANEOUS FUN**, gr f Lethal Force (IRE)—Code Cracker **Mr P. K. Spencer**
135 **UNCLEBY**, ch g Paco Boy (IRE)—Kunegunda **The Earl Of Halifax**
136 **VENTURA BAY (IRE)**, b g Dragon Pulse—Meduse Bleu **Middleham Park Racing LXXIV & Partner**
137 **VENTURA OCEAN (IRE)**, b g Raven's Pass (USA)—Tranquil Spirit (IRE) **Middleham Park Racing Xix & Partner**
138 **WAR TIGER (USA)**, b c War Front (USA)—Quarter Moon (IRE) **Mrs R. Henry**
139 **WASNTEXPECTINGTHAT**, b g Foxwedge (AUS)—Carsulae (IRE) **Good Bad Ugly & Deaf**
140 **ZIP**, ro c Kyllachy—Flycatcher (IRE) **The Knavesmire Partnership**

Trainer did not supply details of his two-year-olds.

Other Owners: A. Rhodes (Haulage) Limited, Sheikh N. M. H. Al Khalifa, Sheikh N. Al Khalifa, Mr T. Alderson, Mr P. Ashton, Mrs S. Ashton, Mr D. A. Bardsley, Mr M. Barlow, Mr A. D. Barraclough, Mr D. Bowen, Mr N. Bradley, Mr S. D. Bradley, Mr S. Bridge, M. F. Browne, I. T. Buchanan, Mr T. Burns, CBWS Partnership, Ms A. Canham-White, Mr J. P. Carr, Mrs M. Clark-Wright, Mr S. W. Clayton, Mrs G. A. Clayton, E. Coll, Mr S. C. Corbett, A. E. Corbett, Mrs B. Cotton, Mr M. Cressey, Mr G. D. Cuthbert, Mrs C. Daurge, Miss C. E. Davies, B. D. Drinkall, Mr S. Ellis, Farranamanagh, M. J. Feneron, Mrs H. J. Fitzsimons, Mr B. W. Goodall, J. D. Gordon, T. C. O. Gredley, W. J. Gredley, D. A. Green, The Countess of Halifax, Mr D. A. Hardman, Mrs S. J. Hardman, Mr P. Harper, Mr D. J. Harrison, K. Hart, R. J. Hart, Mr R. Hayes, Mr G. P. Henderson, Highclere Thoroughbred Racing Ltd, Mrs M. E. Holdcroft, Miss S. Holden, Mr D. Holgate, Mrs D. Howe, Mr D. Hoyle, Mr K. W. Hubery, Mrs L. J. Huddlestone, Mr G. Hyde, Mr E. W. Hyslop, Ms A. Hyslop, Mr R. F. Johnson, Mr N. D. Kershaw, Mr S. A. Kershaw, Mr D. M. Knaggs, M. A. Leatham, P. J. Longstaff, Mr P. D. Macintosh, Mrs J. E. Malcolmson, Mr F. McGovern, Ms N. Meese, Mr K. J. Mercer, Middleham Park Racing CXVI, Middleham Park Racing LXXIV, Middleham Park Racing LXXXV, Middleham Park Racing XIX, Middleham Park Racing XLVIII, Mr M. Morrissey, Mrs A. Morrissey, Mrs M. S. Nelson, Mrs J. E. Newett, Nick Bradley Racing 20, Nick Bradley Racing 36, Nick Bradley Racing 40, Nick Bradley Racing 43, Mrs K. Nolan, Mrs J. Norris, Miss M. A. O Brien, Mr N. J. O'Brien, Mr R. O'Callaghan, A. F. O'Callaghan, Mr C. M. O'Neill, Ontoawinner 8, Mr A. R. Owen, T. S. Palin, Percy Green Racing 3, The Phoenix Racing C.O., L. M. Power, M. Prince, Mr J. Rhodes, Mr M. Roberts, Mr Mel Roberts & Ms Nicola Meese, Mr A. J. Ryan, J. Struth, Mr R. Sutcliffe, P. Swann, A. Tattersall, Mr D. M. Tempest, Mr P. Thompkins, Mr R. Thornton, Mr C. Thwaites, Ventura Racing 10, G. M. L. Weaver, Mr J. M. Wicks, D. Wild, Mrs B. E. Wilkinson, Mr M. K. Williams, Mrs V. A. Wrigley.

Assistant Trainers: Robin O'Ryan, Jessica McLernon.

Jockey (flat): Tony Hamilton, Paul Hanagan, Paddy Mathers, Barry McHugh, Jack Garritty, David Nolan. **Jockey (NH):** Brian Hughes. **Conditional:** Jamie Hamilton. **Apprentice:** Sean Davis, Connor Murtagh, Sebastian Woods.

---

197 | MR CHRIS FAIRHURST, Middleham

Postal: **Glasgow House, Middleham, Leyburn, North Yorkshire, DL8 4QG**
Contacts: **PHONE/FAX** (01969) 622039 **MOBILE** (07889) 410840
E-MAIL cfairhurst@tiscali.co.uk

1 **BENADALID**, 4, b g Assertive—Gambatte **Mrs S. France**
2 **FLORENZA**, 6, b m Haafhd—Danzatrice **980 Racing**
3 **KATY ROYAL**, 7, b m King's Theatre (IRE)—Water Stratford (IRE) **Hugh T. Redhead**
4 **RED TORNADO (FR)**, 7, ch g Dr Fong (USA)—Encircle (USA) **Richard III Partnership**
5 **SIXTIES STAR**, 5, b g Sixties Icon—Songbook **Mrs A. M. Leggett**
6 **THE ARMED MAN**, 6, b g Misu Bond (IRE)—Accamelia **Mrs C. Arnold**
7 **THE GINGERBREADMAN**, 4, b g Misu Bond (IRE)—Accamelia **Mrs C. Arnold**

THREE-YEAR-OLDS

8 **FEEBI**, b f Pour Moi (IRE)—Scorn (USA) **Mr A. Davies**

TWO-YEAR-OLDS

9 **LASTING LEGACY**, gr f 14/4 Lethal Force (IRE)—
Araminte (One Cool Cat (USA)) (50000) **Exors of the Late Mrs L. Peacock**

MR CHRIS FAIRHURST - Continued

10 **TOP ATTRACTION,** b c 5/2 Fountain of Youth (IRE)—
                        Symphonic Dancer (USA) (Smart Strike (CAN)) (3000) **The PQD Partnership**
11 **VELMA,** b f 24/4 Fast Company (IRE)—Valoria (Hernando (FR)) (4500) **Mr A. Davies**
Other Owners: Mrs Angela Mary Leggett, Mr Hugh T. Redhead, Mr R. Todd, Mr M. D. Tozer, Mr J. M. Tozer.

---

198   MR JAMES R. FANSHAWE, Newmarket
Postal: **Pegasus Stables, Snailwell Road, Newmarket, Suffolk, CB8 7DJ**
Contacts: **PHONE** (01638) 664525 **FAX** (01638) 664523
E-MAIL james@jamesfanshawe.com
WEBSITE www.jamesfanshawe.com / www.fredarcherracing.com

1 **ASTROSPEED (IRE),** 4, ch g Choisir (AUS)—Angel Stevens (IRE) **Dragon Gate**
2 **BEAUTY SALON,** 4, b f Dutch Art—Albisola (IRE) **Clipper Logistics**
3 **BOMBYX,** 4, ch g Sir Percy—Bombazine (IRE) **Mr & Mrs A. E. Pakenham**
4 **CHETWYND ABBEY,** 4, b f Nathaniel (IRE)—Chetwynd (IRE) **Mr G. S. Shropshire**
5 **CUILLIN (USA),** 4, b f Arch (USA)—Zahrah (USA) **Dr J. P. Ryan**
6 **ENVISAGING (IRE),** 5, b g Zoffany (IRE)—Star of Stars (IRE) **Fred Archer Racing - Ormonde**
7 **ENZEMBLE (IRE),** 4, b g Zoffany (IRE)—Fifer (IRE) **Mr Ben C. M. Wong**
8 **FLAMING MARVEL (IRE),** 5, b g Redoute's Choice (AUS)—Flame of Hestia (IRE) **Merry Fox Stud Limited**
9 **HARRY'S BAR,** 4, ch g Exceed And Excel (AUS)—Firenze **Jan & Peter Hopper**
10 **HIGHER POWER,** 7, b g Rip Van Winkle (IRE)—Lady Stardust **Mrs Martin Armstrong**
11 **INDIAN TYGRESS,** 4, b f Sepoy (AUS)—Persario **Elizabeth Grundy & Rosie Manning**
12 **INSURGENCE,** 4, ch g Sepoy (AUS)—Isis (USA) **Dr Catherine Wills & Frederik Tylicki**
13 **LADY BERGAMOT (FR),** 5, gr m Mastercraftsman (IRE)—Mahima (FR) **Andrew & Julia Turner**
14 **LILYPAD (IRE),** 4, b f New Approach (IRE)—Vow **Mrs A. M. Swinburn**
15 **LORD GEORGE (IRE),** 6, gr g Sir Percy—Mahima (FR) **Fred Archer Racing - Bend Or**
16 **MAINSAIL ATLANTIC (USA),** 4, b c Speightstown (USA)—Minakshi (FR) **Mrs Amelie Ehrnrooth**
17 **MASTER ARCHER (IRE),** 5, gr g Mastercraftsman (IRE)—Kinigi (IRE) **Fred Archer Racing - Atlantic**
18 **MERCHANT OF VENICE,** 4, b g Bated Breath—Isola Verde **Mr & Mrs P. Hopper, Mr & Mrs M. Morris**
19 **MORE THAN MORE (USA),** 4, b f More Than Ready (USA)—Donamour (USA) **Mr Malih L. Al Basti**
20 **PRAXEDIS,** 4, b f Dutch Art—Angel Song **Mr P. S. Ryan**
21 **PREENING,** 4, b f Dutch Art—Striving (IRE) **Cheveley Park Stud**
22 **SLEEPING (USA),** 4, ch g Teofilo (IRE)—Flame of Hestia (IRE) **Merry Fox Stud Limited**
23 **SOCIETY PRINCE (IRE),** 4, b g Society Rock—Princess Atoosa (USA) **Fred Archer Racing - Melton**
24 **SPANISH ARCHER (IRE),** 4, b g Lope de Vega (IRE)—Parcelle Perdue (FR) **Fred Archer Racing - Iroquois**
25 **SPORTING BILL (IRE),** 4, b g Society Rock—Pandoras Secret (IRE) **Mr Simon Gibson**
26 **THE PINTO KID (FR),** 4, b g High Chaparral (IRE)—Lake Palace **Fred Archer Racing - Bruce**
27 **THE TIN MAN,** 7, b g Equiano (FR)—Persario **Fred Archer Racing - Ormonde**
28 **TIGER EYE (IRE),** 4, b f Frankel—Crystal Gaze (IRE) **Qatar Racing Ltd**
29 **VISOR,** 4, b g Helmet (AUS)—Entitlement **Dr Catherine Wills & Frederik Tylicki**

THREE-YEAR-OLDS

30 **ARCHER'S DREAM (IRE),** b f Dream Ahead (USA)—
                    Badr Al Badoor (IRE) **Fred Archer Racing - Wheel of Fortune**
31 **AUDARYA (FR),** b f Wootton Bassett—Green Bananas (FR) **Mrs A. M. Swinburn**
32 **AVENUE FOCH,** b c Champs Elysees—Kindu **Fittocks Stud**
33 **CANASTA,** b f Charm Spirit (IRE)—Morzine **Elite Racing Club**
34 **CARNIVAL ROSE,** b f Harbour Watch (IRE)—Gypsy Carnival **Evelyn, Duchess of Sutherland**
35 **DURRELL,** b c Animal Kingdom (USA)—Royal Order (USA) **Silver, Steed, Gambini & Venice Consulting**
36 **ENTRUSTING,** b c Nathaniel (IRE)—Royal Empress (IRE) **Mr Ben C. M. Wong**
37 **EXCELLED (IRE),** b f Exceed And Excel (AUS)—Elle Woods (IRE) **Fred Archer Racing - Spinaway**
38 **GASLIGHT,** br f Aussie Rules (USA)—Isis (USA) **Dr Catherine Wills**
39 **GRACIE,** b f Champs Elysees—Fallen From Grace **Normandie Stud Ltd**
40 **KEEP ME COMPANY (IRE),** b c Fast Company (IRE)—Chirkova (USA) **Mrs A. M. Swinburn**
41 **KEYHAVEN,** b f Raven's Pass (USA)—New Forest **Elite Racing Club**
42 **KIRSTENBOSCH,** b f Mount Nelson—Kassiyra (IRE) **Fittocks Stud**
43 **KNOWING,** b g Pour Moi (IRE)—Wedding Speech (IRE) **Mr Gary Marney**
44 **LADY MASCARA,** b f Cacique (IRE)—Avon Lady **Helena Springfield Ltd**
45 **NORMA,** ch f New Approach (IRE)—Deirdre **Normandie Stud Ltd**
46 **OLYMPIC CONQUEROR (IRE),** b g Olympic Glory (IRE)—Queen's Conquer **The Cool Silk Partnership**
47 **PAMPER,** b f Lethal Force (IRE)—Cosseted **Cheveley Park Stud**
48 **PONDUS,** b c Sea The Moon (GER)—Diablerette **Mr Hubert John Strecker**

MR JAMES R. FANSHAWE - Continued

49 **RAINING FIRE (IRE)**, ch g Kitten's Joy (USA)—Flame of Hestia (IRE) **Merry Fox Stud Limited**
50 **REINE MAGNIFIQUE (FR)**, ch f Excelebration (IRE)—Mahima (FR) **Andrew & Julia Turner**
51 **SELINO**, b g Champs Elysees—Air Kiss **Dr Catherine Wills**
52 **SINCERITY**, b f Iffraaj—Affinity **Elite Racing Club**
53 **SKERRYVORE**, ch g Toronado (IRE)—Succinct **Dr Catherine Wills**
54 **STORM APPROACHING**, b f Dawn Approach (IRE)—Dubai Cyclone (USA) **Mr Mohamed Obaida**
55 **SWEET PROMISE**, b f Intello (GER)—Penny Rose **Mr A. Boyd-Rochfort**
56 **VIBRANCE**, b f Nathaniel (IRE)—Park Crystal (IRE) **Cheveley Park Stud**
57 **VIDEO DIVA (IRE)**, b f Camelot—Caught On Camera **Helena Springfield Ltd**

TWO-YEAR-OLDS

58 **COBNUT (IRE)**, b c 13/4 Oasis Dream—Alsace Lorraine (IRE) (Giant's Causeway (USA)) **Merry Fox Stud Limited**
59 **AMICABLE**, br gr f 28/4 Dutch Art—Likeable (Dalakhani (IRE)) **Helena Springfield Ltd**
60 **BAY WATCHING**, ch c 26/1 Hunter's Light (IRE)—Tropicana Bay (Oasis Dream) **Helena Springfield Ltd**
61 B f 29/1 Intrinsic—Cara's Delight (AUS) (Fusaichi Pegasus (USA)) (1904) **Mr Malih L. Al Basti**
62 B f 17/4 Camelot—Causeway Queen (IRE) (Giant's Causeway (USA)) (90000) **King Power Racing Co Ltd**
63 **COBNUT (IRE)**, b c 29/5 Kodiac—Macadamia (IRE) (Classic Cliche (IRE)) **Lord Vestey**
64 B f 2/2 Dutch Art—Cosseted (Pivotal) **Cheveley Park Stud**
65 **COUSIN ROSAURA**, b f 26/3 Nathaniel (IRE)—
                                    Czarna Roza (Polish Precedent (USA)) **Evelyn, Duchess of Sutherland**
66 B c 19/1 Nathaniel (IRE)—Definition (FR) (Dunkerque (FR)) (4214) **Dragon Gate**
67 B f 16/3 Bated Breath—Esteemable (Nayef (USA)) **Mrs C. R. Philipson**
68 Ch f 24/2 Iffraaj—Firenze (Efisio) **Jan & Peter Hopper**
69 **FLOWER OF SCOTLAND**, b f 2/3 Gleneagles (IRE)—Seal of Approval (Authorized (IRE)) **Mr T. R. G. Vestey**
70 **FLYING WEST**, b g 6/3 Free Eagle (IRE)—West of The Moon (Pivotal) **Cheveley Park Stud**
71 **FORTULTOUS**, b g 20/2 Camelot—Operettist (Singspiel (IRE)) **Mr Les Ward**
72 **GREYCOAT**, gr c 28/3 Lethal Force (IRE)—Scarlet Royal (Red Ransom (USA)) (60000) **Chris Van Hoorn Racing**
73 Ch c 1/2 Lope de Vega (IRE)—Jam Jar (Duke of Marmalade (IRE)) (120000) **Mrs A. M. Swinburn**
74 B f 15/4 Oasis Dream—Millennium Star (IRE) (High Chaparral (IRE)) (22000) **Fittocks Stud**
75 **PENPAL (IRE)**, b f 12/3 Invincible Spirit (IRE)—
                                    French Friend (IRE) (Teofilo (IRE)) (46354) **Fred Archer Racing - Janette**
76 **PIAZZA NAVONA**, b f 21/4 Dutch Art—Field of Miracles (IRE) (Galileo (IRE)) **Cheveley Park Stud**
77 **RAINBIRD**, gr f 10/3 Oasis Dream—Pocket Watch (Pivotal) **Mr S. Stuckey**
78 **SECOND SLIP (IRE)**, b c 11/5 Lope de Vega (IRE)—
                                    Arkadina (IRE) (Danehill (USA)) (60000) **Merry Fox Stud Limited**
79 B f 3/5 Intrinsic—Sensible Way (USA) (Street Sense (USA)) **Mr Malih L. Al Basti**
80 B c 17/3 Charm Spirit (IRE)—Shendaya (FR) (Danehill Dancer (IRE)) (50000) **Fred Archer Racing - Paradox**
81 **SHOWUTOO**, ch f 21/2 Showcasing—Sinaadi (IRE) (Kyllachy) **Mr Les Ward**
82 **TILLY FRANKL**, b f 14/3 Frankel—Ribbons (Manduro (GER)) (300000) **Fred Archer Racing - Lonely**
83 **TOM HART**, b c 20/2 Dunaden (FR)—Ellingham (IRE) (Bushranger (IRE)) **Mary Benjafield & Terry Hart**
84 **VIOLA (IRE)**, b f 1/3 Lope de Vega (IRE)—Sistine (Dubai Destination (USA)) **Elite Racing Club**

Other Owners: Mr Geoffrey Baber, Mrs Denise Beetles, Mrs Mary Benjafield, Mrs Tina Blockley, Mr John Bodie, The Hon Mrs Penny Butler, Mr Isidore Carivalis, Mrs Emma Coutts, Mr Alex Davidson, Mrs Olivia Davidson, Mr Roy Eady, Mr Nigel Elwes, Mrs Georgie Fanshawe, Mr Brian Fanshawe, Mrs Libby Fanshawe, Mr Tony Francis, Mrs Susan French, Mr G. Gambini, Mr Colin Gilbert, Mr Haydn Gott, Mr Robert Grove, Mr Terry Hart, Mr Tony Hill, Mr A. J. Hill, Mrs Sue Human, Mr Mike King, Mrs Sarah King, Mrs Jenny King, Mr Arne Korsbakken, Mrs Sue Law, Mr Bill Lemon, Mr Niall Lynch, Mr Dan Marney, Mr A. A. Massen, Mr Simon Massen, Mrs Elizabeth Meads, Miss M. Noden, Miss M. Noden, Mr Gordon Papworth, Mr Ian Pittaway, Mr Bill Rogerson, Mrs Pat Rowley, Mr William Russell, Mr David Russell, Mrs Sarah Russell, Mr Ulf Ryden, Ms Hermione Scrope, Mr Roger Shelton, Mrs Angie Silver, Mr P. Silver, Mr Nigel Smith, Mr G. Steed, Mr Rob Stevens, Mr Richard Stevens, Miss A.D. Swift, Mr Peter Tarrant, Mrs Gilly Thompson, Mrs Tam Murray Thriepland, Mr Tom Trew Smith, Venice Consulting S.A., The Lady Vestey, Mrs Janet Walker, Mrs Sue Willson.

Assistant Trainer: Kevin Philippart De Foy

---

199 | **MR JOHNNY FARRELLY, Midford**
Postal: **Upper Twinhoe Farm, Midford, Bath, Avon, BA2 8QX**
Contacts: **PHONE (01278) 671782 MOBILE (07811) 113363**

1 **AHEAD OF THE GAME (IRE)**, 5, b g Westerner—Kildea Cailin (IRE) **Mr & Mrs Paul & Clare Rooney**
2 **ALI THE HUNTER (IRE)**, 6, ch m Papal Bull—Polish Spring (IRE) **Monday Boys Partnership**
3 **AMBRE DES MARAIS (FR)**, 9, ch m Network (GER)—Fee des Marais (FR) **Monday Boys Partnership**
4 **AND THE NEW (IRE)**, 8, b g Kalanisi (IRE)—Wheredidthemoneygo (IRE) **Mr P. A. Randall**
5 **BATHWICK BRAVE (IRE)**, 12, b g Westerner—Dorans Grove **Mr J. Farrelly**

MR JOHNNY FARRELLY - Continued

6 BERMEO (IRE), 8, b g Definite Article—Miss Blueyes (IRE) **Mr R. E. Stuart-Jervis**
7 BIG PICTURE, 7, b g Recharge (IRE)—Just Jenny (IRE) **Mr J. McMahon**
8 BILLY TWO TONGUES, 11, b g Heron Island (IRE)—Ranahinch (IRE) **Mrs G. Morgan**
9 CONNA CROSS (IRE), 8, b g Lecroix (GER)—Country Time (IRE) **Hanford's Chemist Ltd**
10 CROWN HILL (IRE), 9, b g Definite Article—Silver Prayer (IRE) **Hanford's Chemist Ltd**
11 D'PINESFLYER (IRE), 7, b m Westerner—Diskretion (GER) **Mr J. McMahon**
12 FOOL TO CRY (IRE), 6, ch m Fast Company (IRE)—Islandagore (IRE) **Mr J. Farrelly**
13 GINGILI, 9, b g Beat All (USA)—Gentian **Mr J. Farrelly**
14 HELL OF A LADY, 5, gr m Hellvelyn—Lady Killer (IRE) **Mr J. Farrelly**
15 KALASKADESMILLEY, 8, b g Myboycharlie (IRE)—Congressional (IRE) **C. Cheesman**
16 KIE (IRE), 11, b g Old Vic—Asura (GER) **Mr J. Farrelly**
17 LADY MAKFI (IRE), 7, b m Makfi—Dulcet Tones (IRE) **Mr J. McMahon**
18 LAKE SHORE DRIVE, 7, b g Thewayyouare (USA)—Labrusca **Mr P. M. Tosh**
19 LOVE THE LEADER (IRE), 11, b g Fruits of Love (USA)—Suelena (IRE) **Hanford's Chemist Ltd**
20 MARVELLOUS MONTY (IRE), 9, br m Oscar (IRE)—Montys Miss (IRE) **Hanford's Chemist Ltd**
21 MR LANDO, 10, b g Shirocco (GER)—Capitana (GER) **The Lansdowners**
22 ORMSKIRK, 6, gr g Hellvelyn—River Song (USA) **Mrs G. Morgan**
23 POLISHED ROCK (IRE), 9, ch g Rock of Gibraltar (IRE)—Where We Left Off **Mr J. McMahon**
24 PORTRAIT KING (IRE), 14, gr g Portrait Gallery (IRE)—Storm Queen (IRE) **Mr J. Farrelly**
25 ROBINROYALE (IRE), 8, b g Robin des Champs (FR)—Rosafi (IRE) **Mrs G. Morgan**
26 SANDFORD CASTLE (IRE), 9, b g Norwich—Pegs Polly (IRE) **Live The Life**
27 SEHAYLI (IRE), 6, b g Iffraaj—Quaich **Mr P. M. Tosh**
28 SPARKLING DAWN, 7, gr m Sulamani (IRE)—Clotted Cream (USA) **Live The Life - Atlas**
29 SPORTING BOY (IRE), 11, b g Barathea (IRE)—Sportsticketing (USA) **H. M. W. Clifford**
30 SPRING STORM, 7, b m Morozov (USA)—Presenting Gayle (IRE) **Mr D. J. Adams**
31 VALSE AU TAILLONS (FR), 6, b m Montmartre (FR)—Eyaelle (FR) **Hanford's Chemist Ltd**
32 VICTORY MILL, 9, b br g King's Theatre (IRE)—Full of Surprises (IRE) **Mr J. Farrelly**
33 WESTERN SUNRISE (IRE), 10, b m Westerner—Presenting Gayle (IRE) **Mr D. J. Adams**
34 WINTER SPICE (IRE), 8, gr g Verglas—Summer Spice (IRE) **Mrs E. A. Heal**
35 ZERO GRAND (IRE), 8, b g Thousand Words—Ellistown Lady (IRE) **H. M. W. Clifford**

Other Owners: J. F. Baldwin, Mr P. Duffy, Mr D. Goodman, Mr G. R. Heapy, Mr P. A. Rooney, Mrs C. Rooney, Mr T. Rowsell, R. T. Wilkins.

200 MS DEBORAH FAULKNER, Chepstow
Postal: Craig-Y-Ceiliog Farm, Bettws, Newport, Gwent, NP20 7AE

1 ACLASSAGOLD (IRE), 6, b g Gold Well—Midnight Classic (IRE) **T. P. Faulkner**
2 BEALLANDENDALL (IRE), 11, b g Beneficial—Railstown Lady (IRE) **Ms D. C. Faulkner**
3 COURTINTHEMIDDLE (IRE), 8, b g Court Cave (IRE)—Kilmessan (IRE) **T. P. Faulkner**
4 GOLDANBLEU (IRE), 6, b g Gold Well—Lisa Bleu (IRE) **T. P. Faulkner**
5 GUN SHY (IRE), 11, b g Norwich—Debbies Scud (IRE) **T. P. Faulkner**
6 OUTSMARTIN (IRE), 7, b br g Marienbard (IRE)—Fair Gina (IRE) **T. P. Faulkner**
7 POLYMATH (IRE), 8, ch g Stowaway—Godlylady **T. P. Faulkner**
8 SPIN THE BEAT, 9, b g Beat All (USA)—Little Red Spider **Ms D. C. Faulkner**
9 STANZA BOY (IRE), 7, b g Stowaway—Lisa Bleu (IRE) **T. P. Faulkner**
10 THOMAS CROWN (IRE), 5, b g Helmet (AUS)—Picture of Lily **T. P. Faulkner**
11 WELSBY (IRE), 7, b g Gold Well—Stonehouse (IRE) **T. P. Faulkner**

201 MISS JULIA FEILDEN, Newmarket
Postal: Harraton Stud, Laceys Lane, Exning, Newmarket, Suffolk, CB8 7HW
Contacts: MOBILE (07974) 817694
E-MAIL juliafeilden@gmail.com WEBSITE www.juliafeildenracing.com

1 BOXATRICKS (IRE), 4, b g Arakan (USA)—Million To One (IRE) **Million To One Partnership**
2 CANDESTA (USA), 9, b g First Defence (USA)—Wandesta **Mrs J. E. Lambert**
3 CASEY BANTER, 4, b br f Holy Roman Emperor (IRE)—
Sinister Ruckus (USA) **Newmarket Equine Tours Racing Club**
4 GAS MONKEY, 4, b g Cityscape—Bavarica **Newmarket Equine Tours Racing Club**
5 GO ON GAL (IRE), 6, b m Approve (IRE)—Jeritza **Go On Gal Partnership**
6 LIMERICK LORD (IRE), 7, b g Lord Shanakill (USA)—Hollow Green (IRE) **Steve Clarke & Partner**

MISS JULIA FEILDEN - Continued

7 **LULU STAR (IRE)**, 4, b f Oasis Dream—Jeanie Johnston (IRE) **T. Healy**
8 **MAAZEL (IRE)**, 5, b g Elzaam (AUS)—Laylati (IRE) **Newmarket Equine Tours Racing Club**
9 **MAJESTIC MOON (IRE)**, 9, b g Majestic Missile (IRE)—Gala Style (IRE) **Ahamed Farook & Partners**
10 **OCEANUS (IRE)**, 5, b g Born To Sea (IRE)—Alkhawarah (USA) **Good Company Partnership**
11 **OUD METHA BRIDGE (IRE)**, 5, ch g Helmet (AUS)—Central Force **In It To Win Partnership**
12 **SEA SHACK**, 5, b g Equiano (FR)—Folly Bridge **Koya Equine**
13 **SIR FRED (IRE)**, 4, gr g Born To Sea (IRE)—Diamond Line (FR) **Mrs C. T. Bushnell**
14 **SPANISH MANE (IRE)**, 4, b f Havana Gold (IRE)—Kiva **Stowstowquickquickstow Partnership**
15 **TALLULAH'S QUEST (IRE)**, 5, b m Tagula (IRE)—Sarin Dubhe (IRE) **The Sultans of Speed**
16 **TELEKINETIC**, 4, b f Champs Elysees—Kinetix **T. Healy**
17 **TERRI RULES (IRE)**, 4, b f Camacho—Hawaiian Storm **Newmarket Equine Tours Racing Club**
18 **WILSON (IRE)**, 4, b g Born To Sea (IRE)—Alkhawarah (USA) **Adrian Sparks & Partners**

THREE-YEAR-OLDS

19 **APPROVE THE DREAM (IRE)**, ch g Approve (IRE)—Jacquotte (IRE) **Harraton Hopefuls**
20 **DELL'S BOY**, b c Epaulette (AUS)—Bushy Dell (IRE) **Newmarket Equine Tours Racing Club**
21 **HIGHWAY ROBBERY**, gr g Dick Turpin (IRE)—Minty Fox **Mrs C. T. Bushnell**
22 **I'M BRIAN**, b g Sepoy (AUS)—Emily Carr (IRE) **Mrs J. E. Lambert**
23 **NEW EXPO (IRE)**, ch g New Approach (IRE)—Anayid **The Strategists**
24 **PAINTBALL WIZARD (IRE)**, ch g Mastercraftsman (IRE)—Dance Avenue (IRE) **Carol Bushnell & Partners**
25 **RAHA**, b f Mukhadram—Cefira (USA) **Ahamed Farook & Partner**
26 B f Camacho—Seven Sing (USA) **Newmarket Equine Tours Racing Club**
27 **TARAKONA (IRE)**, ch f Dragon Pulse (IRE)—Callherhome (IRE) **The Bucketeers**
28 **WAR EMPRESS (IRE)**, b f War Command (USA)—Alice Rose (IRE) **Jen Cullen**
29 **WINTER SNOWDROP (IRE)**, gr f War Command (USA)—Morning Jewel (IRE) **Mrs C. T. Bushnell**

TWO-YEAR-OLDS

30 **LILY BONNETTE**, ch f 5/4 Helmet (AUS)—Wish You Luck (Dubai Destination (USA)) (3000) **Syndicate**
31 **RIDE AND PREJUDICE**, b f 17/4 Casamento (IRE)—
    Emma's Gift (IRE) (Aussie Rules (USA)) **Mrs Emma Raffan & Mr Michael Raffan**
32 **VALLETTA SUNSET**, b c 21/4 Casamento (IRE)—
    Sunset Kitty (USA) (Gone West (USA)) **Steve Clarke & Partners 3**

Other Owners: Mr R. Birkett, Mr J. Birkett, Mr S. Clarke, Mr David Haddrell, Mr Chris Page, Mr Eddie Partridge, Mr M. I. Raffan, Mrs E. M. Raffan, Mr R. Weston, Mr O. A. Wideson, Mr R. Wright.

Assistant Trainer: Ross Birkett

Jockey (flat): Shelley Birkett. **Amateur:** Mr R. Birkett, Mr Sam Feilden.

202	**MR ROGER FELL**, Nawton

202

MR ROGER FELL, Nawton

Postal: **Arthington Barn House, Highfield Lane, Nawton, York, North Yorkshire, YO62 7TU**
Contacts: PHONE **(01439) 770184**
E-MAIL rogerfellracing@gmail.com WEBSITE www.rogerfell.co.uk

1 **AD LIBITUM**, 4, b g Elusive Quality (USA)—Sarmad (USA) **The Roses Partnership & R G Fell**
2 **ADMIRALITY**, 5, b g Mount Nelson—Dialma (USA) **Ventura Racing & Partners**
3 **AL OZZDI**, 4, b g Acclamation—Zibeling (IRE) **Northern Marking Ltd & Partners**
4 **BEADLAM (IRE)**, 6, ch m Frozen Power (IRE)—Pivotal Role **Arthington Barn Racing**
5 **BENARAS (USA)**, 4, b f Gio Ponti (USA)—Brocatelle **Mr & Mrs G. Turnbull**
6 **BURNT SUGAR (IRE)**, 7, b g Lope de Vega (IRE)—Lady Livius **Middleham Park Racing XL & Partner**
7 **CLUB WEXFORD (IRE)**, 8, b g Lawman (FR)—Masnada (IRE) **Mr C. J. Varley**
8 **COCKALORUM (IRE)**, 4, b g Cape Cross—Opinionated **R. G. Fell & Henry Dean**
9 **COUNT MONTECRISTO (FR)**, 7, b g Siyouni (FR)—Blackberry Pie (USA) **Ventura Racing (monty) & Partner**
10 **CROSS SWORDS**, 4, b g Invincible Spirit (IRE)—The First of May Crew & Partner
11 **DAAWY (IRE)**, 5, ch g Teofilo (IRE)—Juno Marlowe (IRE) **Hollowdean**
12 **DAPPER MAN (IRE)**, 5, b g Dandy Man (IRE)—Gist (IRE) **Colne Valley Racing & Partner**
13 **DOMMERSEN (IRE)**, 6, ch g Dutch Art—Kelowna (IRE) **Middleham Park Racing (x) & Partner**
14 **ELIXSOFT (IRE)**, 4, b f Elzaam (AUS)—Grandegrandegrande (IRE) **Middleham Park Racing CXIII & Partner**
15 **ELUSIVE HEIGHTS (IRE)**, 6, b g Elusive Pimpernel (USA)—
    Berg Bahn (IRE) **Middleham Park Racing LXI & Partner 2**
16 **FARD**, 4, b g Dutch Art—Rose Blossom **Northern Marking Ltd & Partners**
17 **GLOBAL SPIRIT**, 4, b g Invincible Spirit (IRE)—Centime **Mr R. G. Fell & Ian White**

MR ROGER FELL - Continued

18 **GUARDIA SVIZZERA (IRE)**, 5, b g Holy Roman Emperor (IRE)—
Winged Harriet (IRE) **Ventura Racing 7 & Partner**
19 **HAROME (IRE)**, 5, ch g Bahamian Bounty—Clytha **Middleham Park Racing Lxxi & Partner**
20 **HAWAAM (IRE)**, 4, b g Swiss Spirit—Anne Bonney **Arcane Racing Partnership**
21 **INNER CIRCLE (IRE)**, 5, b g Choisir (AUS)—Eternity Ring **Middleham Park Racing LXXII & Partner**
22 **KUPA RIVER (IRE)**, 5, b g Big Bad Bob (IRE)—Lamanka Lass (USA) **Ventura Racing 6 & Partner**
23 **MUATADEL (IRE)**, 6, b g Exceed And Excel (AUS)—Rose Blossom **Mr R. G. Fell**
24 **MULLIGATAWNY (IRE)**, 6, b g Lope de Vega (IRE)—Wild Whim (IRE) **Middleham Park Racing LI & Partner**
25 **MUNTADAB (IRE)**, 7, b g Invincible Spirit (IRE)—Chibola (ARG) **Fell & High Hopes Partnership**
26 **MUQARRED (USA)**, 7, b br g Speightstown (USA)—Bawaara (FR) **Mr R. G. Fell**
27 **NAJASHEE (IRE)**, 5, gr g Invincible Spirit (IRE)—Tonnara (IRE) **Mr R. G. Fell**
28 **PIONEERING (IRE)**, 5, b g Shamardal (USA)—Oregon Trail (USA) **Ebor Racing Club VI**
29 **PRESIDENTIAL (IRE)**, 5, b g Invincible Spirit (IRE)—Poetical (IRE) **Nick Bradley Racing 3,Ian White &partner**
30 **ROUSAYAN (IRE)**, 8, b g Invincible Spirit (IRE)—Rose Quartz **The Roses Partnership**
31 **TADAAWOL (IRE)**, 5, b g Kyllachy—Bright Edge **Fell, Hamilton & Smeaton**
32 **TAMREER (IRE)**, 4, ch f New Approach (IRE)—Reyaadah **Mr R. G. Fell**
33 **WATHEER (IRE)**, 4, ch g Leroidesanimaux (BRZ)—Sunset Shore **Middleham Park Racing Ciii & Partner**
34 **ZIHAAM (IRE)**, 5, ch g Dutch Art—Hymnsheet **Nick Bradley Racing 29 & Partner**
35 **ZODIAKOS (IRE)**, 6, b g Kodiac—Zonic **Mr C Varley & Mr R G Fell**
36 **ZYLAN (IRE)**, 7, ch g Kyllachy—Belgique (IRE) **Mr R. G. Fell**

THREE-YEAR-OLDS

37 **DANCING MOUNTAIN (IRE)**, b f Kodiac—Pearl Mountain (IRE) **Arthington Barn Racing**
38 **GEOGRAPHY TEACHER (IRE)**, b g Bungle Inthejungle—Magical Bupers (IRE) **Northern Marking Ltd & Partners**
39 **KODI DREAM**, b g Coach House (IRE)—Gumhrear (IRE) **Nick Bradley & Partner**
40 B f Holy Roman Emperor (IRE)—Lady Chaparral **Mr& Mrs G. Turnbull**
41 **LADY MAYHEM (IRE)**, b f Zebedee—Novelina (IRE) **Mr R. G. Fell**
42 **MONTALVAN (IRE)**, ch g Lope de Vega (IRE)—Shermeen (IRE) **High Hopes & Partner**
43 **MY BOY LEWIS (IRE)**, b g Dandy Man (IRE)—Flamelet (USA) **Fell & Salthouse**
44 **SLAITHWAITE (IRE)**, br g Society Rock (IRE)—Wild Whim (IRE) **Colne Valley Racing & Partner**
45 **SMEATON (IRE)**, b g Sir Prancealot (IRE)—Sunny Harbor (IRE) **Mr R.G. Fell & Mr K Hamilton**
46 **TAILS I WIN (CAN)**, b f Shanghai Bobby (USA)—Beshairt (USA) **Nick Bradley Racing 16 & Partner**
47 **THE GABBA (IRE)**, b g Vocalised (USA)—Style Queen (IRE) **Mr S Greenhalgh & Northern Marking Ltd**
48 **TWO FOR THREE (IRE)**, b g Dawn Approach (IRE)—Antique (IRE) **Mr R. G. Fell**
49 **YOLO AGAIN (IRE)**, b f Toronado (IRE)—Suite (USA) **Nick Bradley Racing 28**

Other Owners: Mr P. Bamford, Mr J. M. Binns, Mr N. Bradley, Mr Lester Christie, Colne Valley Racing, Mr H. T. H. Dean, Mr T. Denham, Mr B. Fellows, Mr A. Franks, S. Franks, Mr M. P. Glass, Mr S. Greenhalgh, Mr Karl Hamilton, Miss S. Holden, Dr John Hollowood, Mr Tony Kelvin, Mr P. M. Lockwood, Middleham Park Racing CIII, Middleham Park Racing CXIII, Middleham Park Racing LI, Middleham Park Racing LXI, Middleham Park Racing LXXI, Middleham Park Racing LXXII, Middleham Park Racing X, Middleham Park Racing XL, Nick Bradley Racing 16, Nick Bradley Racing 29, Nick Bradley Racing 3, Northern Marking Ltd, Mr T. S. Palin, Mr M. Prince, The Roses Partnership, Mr W. J. Salthouse, Mr Robert Smeaton, Mr David Smith, Mr Michael Taylor, Mr Geoffrey Turnbull, Mrs S. E. Turnbull, Mr C. Varley, Ventura Racing 6, Ventura Racing 7, Mr K. Walton, Mr Ian White.

Assistant Trainer: Sean Murray

Jockey (flat): Ben Curtis, Tony Hamilton. **Apprentice:** Keelan Baker, Ben Sanderson.
Amateur: Ms Rosie Haworth, Ms Debra Hutchinson.

---

203 **MR CHARLIE FELLOWES, Newmarket**
Postal: St. Gatien Cottage, Vicarage Road, Newmarket, Suffolk, CB8 8HP
Contacts: PHONE (01638) 666948 MOBILE (07968) 499596
E-MAIL charlie@charliefellowesracing.co.uk WEBSITE www.charliefellowesracing.co.uk

1 **ALEXANDRIA**, 4, gr f Oasis Dream—Amarillo Starlight (IRE) **OTI Racing**
2 **BUBBLY**, 4, b f Excelebration (IRE)—Baralinka (IRE) **Elite Racing Club**
3 **BUCKLAND BEAU**, 8, b g Rock of Gibraltar (IRE)—Heavenly Whisper (IRE) **Mr P. S. McNally**
4 **BUCKLAND BOY (IRE)**, 4, b g Bated Breath—Rancho Montoya (IRE) **Mr P. S. McNally**
5 **CAPLA JAIPUR**, 4, ch g Sepoy (AUS)—Parthenos **Joe Soiza & Mason Soiza**
6 **CARNWENNAN (IRE)**, 4, b g Cacique (IRE)—Slieve Mish **Vincent Kong**
7 **CHIEFOFCHIEFS**, 6, b g Royal Applause—Danvers **M. L. Ayers**
8 **ESCALATOR**, 4, br g Cape Cross (IRE)—Sayyedati Symphony (USA) **Mr S. M. bel Obaida**
9 **FREEROLLING**, 4, ch g Exceed And Excel (AUS)—Overturned **Three Of A Kind**

MR CHARLIE FELLOWES - Continued

10 IN DEMAND (IRE), 4, b g Dalakhani (IRE)—Fleur de Cactus (IRE) **The Yes Men**
11 JEREMIAH, 4, ch g Kheleyf (USA)—Tessie **M. L. Ayers**
12 LADY OF ARAN (IRE), 4, b f Sir Prancealot (IRE)—Tipperary Boutique (IRE) **Bengough, Horsford & Capon**
13 MIA TESORO (IRE), 6, b m Danehill Dancer (IRE)—Souter's Sister (IRE) **Mr D. Pearson**
14 PRINCE OF ARRAN, 6, b g Shirocco (GER)—Storming Sioux **Mr S. M. bel Obaida**
15 RAMSBURY, 4, b g Dansili—Disco Volante **A. E. Oppenheimer**
16 TREASURE ME, 4, b f Poet's Voice—Treasured Dream **Daniel MacAuliffe & Anoj Don**
17 WISE FOX, 4, gr g Foxwedge (AUS)—Daheeya

THREE-YEAR-OLDS

18 CAVALRY PARK, b c Epaulette (AUS)—Sarah Park (IRE) **Never So Bold - Aquino**
19 CIRCLE OF STARS (IRE), b g Magician (IRE)—Stars Above Me **Elite Racing Club**
20 CRIMEAN QUEEN, b f Iffraaj—Victoria Cross (IRE) **Mr A. E. Oppenheimer**
21 DIVINE GIFT (IRE), b g Nathaniel (IRE)—Souter's Sister (IRE) **Mr Deron Pearson**
22 GARRYOWEN, b g Garswood—Lomapamar **Mrs Emma Capon**
23 GIBRALTARIAN (IRE), b f War Command (USA)—Star of Gibraltar **Normandie Stud Ltd**
24 HIGH ABOVE, b f Australia—Gertrude Gray (IRE) **Lady Bamford**
25 I AM MAGICAL, b f Declaration of War (USA)—Lady Wingshot (IRE) **Pearson, Magnier & Shanahan**
26 ISANGO, b f Dansili—Incheni (IRE) **Mr A. E. Oppenheimer**
27 JACK BERRY HOUSE, b g Harbour Watch (IRE)—Dularame (IRE) **Mr S. M. Kwok**
28 KING OTTOKAR (FR), b c Motivator—Treasure (FR) **Mrs S. M. Roy**
29 LADY AMELIA, b f Lope de Vega (IRE)—Amelia May **Mr A. E. Oppenheimer**
30 LADY DAUPHIN (IRE), b f Bungle Inthejungle—Chateau Dauphin (USA) **The Johnson's**
31 LOCK SEVENTEEN (USA), b c Kitten's Joy (USA)—Spirit Line (USA) **Mr P O'Callaghan**
32 LORD HALIFAX (IRE), b g Famous Name—Neutral **Never So Bold - Aquino**
33 MAID FOR LIFE, b f Nathaniel (IRE)—Dream To Be Maid **Normandie Stud Ltd**
34 MANKAYAN (IRE), b c Intello (GER)—Angelic Note (IRE) **Dahab Racing**
35 MANTON WARRIOR (IRE), b g War Command (USA)—Kotdiji **Second Chancers**
36 MAYFAIR POMPETTE (FR), ch f Toronado (IRE)—Tipsy Me **Joe Soiza & Mason Soiza**
37 MAYFAIR SPIRIT (IRE), b g Charm Spirit (IRE)—Sassy Gal (IRE) **Mr J. Soiza**
38 MOON SWIFT, b f Sea The Moon (GER)—Parisette **Mr P & Mrs S Homewood**
39 PENTLAND LAD (IRE), b g Camacho—First Lady (IRE) **GG Thoroughbreds VIII**
40 RUDY LEWIS (IRE), b c Exceleration (USA)—Bless You **Chelsea Thoroughbreds & Martin Hughes 1**
41 RUM BABA, ch c New Approach (IRE)—Soft Centre **Normandie Stud Ltd**
42 SCORCHED BREATH, b g Bated Breath—Danvers **Joe Soiza & Charlie Fellowes**
43 SECOND SIGHT, b c Showcasing—Dream Vision (USA) **Mr Philip Booth & Friends**
44 SHOW THE WORLD, ch g Showcasing—Moving Sea (IRE) **Never So Bold & Sohi**
45 SMOKE ON THE WATER, ch c Iffraaj—Fullaah (IRE) **Chris Wright and Emily Asprey**
46 TANZERIN (IRE), b f Dansili—Seolan (IRE) **Mr D. Pearson**
47 THANKS BE, ch f Mukhadram—Out of Thanks (IRE) **Mrs Emma Capon**
48 TULFARRIS, b c Zoffany (IRE)—Eurolink Raindance (IRE) **Dahab Racing**
49 URBAN SCENE, b f Cityscape—Fashionable Gal (IRE) **Mr John Webb**

TWO-YEAR-OLDS

50 B f 30/3 Exceed And Excel (AUS)—Airline Hostess (IRE) (Sadler's Wells (USA)) (35000) **Crispin Estates Ltd**
51 B f 6/3 Gleneagles (IRE)—All's Forgotten (USA) (Darshaan) **Lady Bamford**
52 B c 7/5 Sir Prancealot (IRE)—Caffe Latte (IRE) (Seattle Dancer (USA)) (16856) **Sohi, Clark & Moore**
53 Ch f 12/3 Lethal Force (IRE)—
         Confusing (Refuse To Bend (IRE)) (12000) **GG Thoroughbreds, Whatton Manor Stud, Mrs D Beetles & Mrs J King**
54 B f 3/3 Shamardal (USA)—Dubian To (IRE) (Sea The Stars (IRE)) (50000) **Mr Mohamed Obaida**
55 B c 21/4 Kingston Hill—Gwen Lady Byron (IRE) (Dandy Man (IRE)) (22756) **Perry Joyce & Charlie Fellowes**
56 B c 25/2 Teofilo (IRE)—Hana Lina (Oasis Dream) (120000) **Crispin Estates Ltd**
57 B c 12/2 Mayson—Height of Vanity (IRE) (Erhaab (USA)) (55000) **Hey Pal Syndicate**
58 B f 21/2 Mukhadram—Miss Rimex (IRE) (Ezzoud (IRE)) (8428) **Dun Lee**
59 B c 4/4 Bated Breath—Modesty's Way (USA) (Giant's Causeway (USA)) (202275) **Mr S. M. Kwok**
60 B br f 25/3 Poet's Voice—Monasada (Nayef (USA)) (27000) **JCK Partnership**
61 B c 8/4 Fastnet Rock (AUS)—Mount Crystal (IRE) (Montjeu (IRE)) (200000) **Crispin Estates Ltd**
62 Ch c 24/3 Society Rock (IRE)—Neutrina (IRE) (Hector Protector (USA)) (36190) **Lady De Ramsey**
63 Ch c 22/2 Starspangledbanner (AUS)—Obligada (IRE) (Beat Hollow) (66666) **Daniel MacAuliffe & Anoj Don**
64 ONASSIS (IRE), b f 20/2 Dubawi (IRE)—Jacqueline Quest (Rock of Gibraltar (IRE)) (200000)
65 B c 11/3 Kyllachy—Partly Sunny (Alhaarth (IRE)) (65000) **Dun Lee**
66 B f 3/3 Nathaniel (IRE)—Queen's Dream (IRE) (Oasis Dream) (13000)
67 Br c 8/2 Gutaifan (IRE)—Rayon Rouge (IRE) (Manduro (GER)) (17142) **Mr M. B. Hughes**
68 B f 6/3 Camelot—Zamzama (IRE) (Shamardal (USA)) (90000) **Crispin Estates Ltd**

MR CHARLIE FELLOWES - Continued

Other Owners: Mr J. M. Basquill, Mr O. S. W. Bell, Mr A. N. C. Bengough, Mr C. Bird, Mr C. Bloor, D. Boorer, Mr P. Booth, T. P. Bostwick, Mrs G. P. Bostwick, Mr S. P. Capon, Mr A. C. Culumbarapitiyage Don, Mrs L. Cumani, Mr C. H. Fellowes, Mrs B. S. Fowler, Mr J. R. Fowler, Mr E. H. M. Frost, Mr G. Gill, Mr N. Griffith, Mr A. J. Hill, G. Horsford, Mr G. Johnson, Mr M. J. Johnson, Mr G. Johnson, Mr D. P. MacAuliffe, Miss N. Noden, Mr C. Pigram, Racing Club Ltd, Mrs P. Roche, Mr M. R. Soiza, Mr M. B. Spence, Ms S. Vrska.

Jockey (flat): Stevie Donohoe. **Apprentice:** Aled Beech.

---

204 **MR DOMINIC FFRENCH DAVIS, Lambourn**
Postal: **College House, 3 Oxford Street, Lambourn, Hungerford, Berkshire, RG17 8XP**
Contacts: **73675 Home (01488) 72342 FAX (01488) 73675 MOBILE (07831) 118764**
E-MAIL ffrenchdavis@btinternet.com WEBSITE www.ffrenchdavis.com

1 ANONYMOUS JOHN (IRE), 7, gr g Baltic King—Helibel (IRE) **Mr R. F. Haynes**
2 CHERRIES AT DAWN (IRE), 4, ch f Dawn Approach (IRE)—Cherry Orchard (IRE) **Mr R. F. Haynes**
3 COSMIC LANDSCAPE, 4, b c Lawman (FR)—Dancingintheclouds (IRE) **Kingwood Stud Management Co Ltd**
4 COSMOGYRAL (IRE), 4, b f Camelot—Fanditha (IRE) **Kingwood Stud Management Co Ltd**
5 DISTANT APPLAUSE (IRE), 4, b g Acclamation—Spacecraft (USA) **S. J. Edwards**
6 EMMPARA, 5, ch g Black Sam Bellamy (IRE)—Maria Antonia (IRE) **Mr D. White**
7 INDEED, 4, b c Showcasing—Argumentative **Marchwood Recycling Ltd**
8 MIDNIGHT MOOD, 6, b m Aqlaam—Inflammable **D. J. S. Ffrench Davis**
9 MONDAY CLUB, 6, ch g Strategic Prince—Support Fund (IRE) **Faber, Ffrench Davis & Taylor**
10 REALT OR (IRE), 6, b g Gold Well—Starventure (IRE) **David White & Dean Gibbs**
11 SMART GETAWAY (IRE), 7, b m Getaway (GER)—Legendsofthefall (IRE) **D. J. S. Ffrench Davis**
12 WHATTHEBUTLERSAW (IRE), 10, br g Arcadio (GER)—
　　　　　　　　　　　　　　　　　　　　Phar From Men (IRE) **Mrs P Ffrench Davis & Mr D Ffrench Davis**

TWO-YEAR-OLDS

13 B c 23/4 Equiano (FR)—If I Were A Boy (IRE) (Invincible Spirit (IRE)) (571) **Mr R. F. Haynes**

Other Owners: Mr E. S. G. Faber, Mrs P. Ffrench Davis, Mr D. Gibbs, Mrs J. E. Taylor.

Assistant Trainer: Avery Ffrench Davis

Jockey (NH): Mark Grant.

---

205 **MR GUISEPPE FIERRO, Hednesford**
Postal: **Brook House, Rawnsley Road, Hednesford, Cannock, Staffordshire, WS12 1RB**
Contacts: **HOME/YARD (01543) 879611 MOBILE (07976) 321468**

1 JUST LIKE BETH, 11, b m Proclamation (IRE)—Just Beth **G. Fierro**
2 LITTLE DOTTY, 10, br m Erhaab (USA)—Marsh Marigold **G. Fierro**
3 RAMBLING RIVER, 8, b g Revoque (IRE)—Just Beth **G. Fierro**
4 SUNDANCE BOY, 10, gr g Proclamation (IRE)—Just Beth **G. Fierro**

Assistant Trainer: M Fierro

---

206 **MRS MARJORIE FIFE, Stillington**
Postal: **White Thorn Farm, Stillington, Easingwold, York, YO61 1LT**
Contacts: **PHONE (01347) 822012 MOBILE (07890) 075217**
E-MAIL wfife10416@aol.com

1 AFRICAN FRIEND (IRE), 6, b g Equiano (FR)—Fontanally Springs (IRE) **Mr S. W. Gunn**
2 ALLNITE (IRE), 4, b g Arcano (IRE)—Paint The Town (IRE) **Mr L. A. Bellman**
3 B FIFTY TWO (IRE), 10, br g Dark Angel (IRE)—Petite Maxine **Fat Badger Racing**
4 BIG BRAVE BOB, 4, br g Big Bad Bob (IRE)—Namaadhej (USA) **Biddestone Racing XIII**
5 BLUE MEDICI, 5, b g Medicean—Bluebelle **Mr L. A. Bellman**
6 CLASSIC SENIORITY, 7, b g Kyllachy—Dramatic Solo **HuggyMac Racing**
7 ENNJAAZ (IRE), 5, b g Poet's Voice—Hall Hee (IRE) **Mr R. W. Fife**
8 LORD COOPER, 5, b g Sir Percy—Zooming (IRE) **Lads Of The Summer Wine**
9 LUV U WHATEVER, 9, b g Needwood Blade—Lady Suesanne (IRE) **Mr T. W. Fife**

MRS MARJORIE FIFE - Continued

10 MUIRSHEEN DURKIN, 5, b g Fastnet Rock (AUS)—Be My Queen (IRE) **Mr T. W. Fife**
11 MY AMIGO, 6, gr g Stimulation (IRE)—Blue Crest (FR) **Mr R. W. Fife**
12 ROBOT BOY (IRE), 9, ch g Shamardal (USA)—Pivotal's Princess (IRE) **Mr Laurence O'Kane & Paul Murphy**
13 RULER OF THE NILE, 7, b g Exceed And Excel (AUS)—Dinka Raja (USA) **Equinox Racing**
14 SCENERY, ch g Elnadim (USA)—Widescreen (USA) **Mrs M. Turner**
15 SQUIRE, 8, b g Teofilo (IRE)—Most Charming (FR) **Mr T. W. Fife**
16 TOMMY HALLINAN (IRE), 5, b g Intense Focus (USA)—Bowstring (IRE) **Mr P. J. Vogt**

THREE-YEAR-OLDS

17 DANCING SPEED (IRE), br c Dandy Man (IRE)—Air Maze **Dragon Gate Development Limited**
18 DIXIELAND (IRE), b g Red Jazz (USA)—Signora Lina (IRE) **Mr Chris Giles & Sullivan Bloodstock Ltd**
19 RODNEY AFTER DAVE (IRE), b g Intense Focus (USA)—Ceol Cois Tine (IRE) **Equinox Racing**

Other Owners: Mr C. Bennett, Mrs G. P. Bostwick, T. P. Bostwick, Mr C. M. Giles, Mr D. J. Haddrell, Harrowgate Bloodstock Ltd, Mr A. Huggins, Mr J. Mcalpine, Mr P. A. Murphy, L. G. O'Kane, Sullivan Bloodstock Limited.

---

207 | **MR TIM FITZGERALD**, Malton
Postal: Norton Grange, Norton, Malton, North Yorkshire, YO17 9EA
Contacts: OFFICE (01653) 228456 MOBILE (07950) 356437
E-MAIL fitzgeraldracing@hotmail.com

1 COMPETENT, 7, b g Compton Place—Pantita **Dukes Racing 1**
2 HE'S MAGIC, 8, b g Court Masterpiece—Lady Magician **Mrs M. Lingwood**
3 MOLLY WHUPPIE, 6, br m Beat Hollow—Daisies Adventure (IRE) **Mr D. J. Sturdy**
4 NOBUTTABOY (IRE), 8, b g Darsi (FR)—Buckalong (IRE) **Mr D. J. Sturdy**
5 WOULD YOU BYPASS (IRE), 6, br m Vinnie Roe (IRE)—Academy Hall (IRE)

Other Owners: Mrs K. Dukes, O. R. Dukes.

---

208 | **MR JOHN FLINT**, Bridgend
Postal: Woodland Lodge, Waunbant Road, Kenfig Hill, Bridgend, Mid Glamorgan, CF33 6FF
Contacts: FAX (01656) 744347 MOBILE (07581) 428173
E-MAIL johnflint900@gmail.com WEBSITE www.johnflintracing.com

1 AIR OF YORK (IRE), 7, b g Vale of York (IRE)—State Secret **Mrs L. A. Cullimore**
2 AMATEUR (IRE), 6, ch g Giant's Causeway (USA)—Adja (IRE) **Burnham Plastering & Drylining Ltd**
3 ARIAN (IRE), 7, b m King's Theatre (IRE)—Brave Betsy (IRE) **Mr D. M. Mathias**
4 AYLA'S EMPEROR, 10, b m Holy Roman Emperor (IRE)—Ayla (IRE) **Mr L. H. & Mrs T. Evans**
5 BAZ'S BOY, 6, b g Compton Place—Spunger **Partnership Terminated**
6 CARP KID (IRE), 4, b g Lope de Vega (IRE)—Homegrown (IRE) **JACK Racing**
7 CILLIAN'S WELL (IRE), 9, b g Trans Island—Live A Lot (IRE) **Belly's Heroes & P D Thomas**
8 COOLING, 5, b m Firebreak—Esplanade **Miss S. Carter**
9 COURT DUTY (IRE), 7, b g Court Cave (IRE)—Easter Duties (IRE) **Davies & Price**
10 CRINDLE CARR (IRE), 5, ch g Compton Place—Arley Hall **J. L. Flint**
11 DE BEAU TANT, 4, b f Delegator—Miss Beaudacious (IRE) **Mrs C. C. Diamond**
12 EBEN DUBAI (IRE), 7, b g New Approach (IRE)—Eldalil **J. L. Flint**
13 EDDIEMAURICE (IRE), 8, ch g Captain Rio—Annals **Mr D. M. Mathias**
14 ENGLISH PALE (IRE), 6, b g Elusive Pimpernel (USA)—Terme Cay (USA) **Westerwood (WG) Global Limited**
15 FIELD OF VISION (IRE), 6, b g Pastoral Pursuits—Grand Design **Paul Duffy, David Semmens, Viv Williams**
16 I AM PLASTERED, 4, b g Midnight Legend—One For Joules (IRE) **Burnham Plastering & Drylining Ltd**
17 JUST MARTHA, 4, b f Sepoy—Porthcawl **Mr D. A. Poole**
18 JUST RIGHT, 4, ch f Medicean—Rightside **Mr D. A. Poole**
19 KAYF MOSS, 11, b g Kayf Tara—Madam Mosso **Mr L. H. & Mrs T. Evans**
20 KHISMET, 6, b m Kheleyf (USA)—Bisaat (USA) **Mr D. M. Mathias**
21 LAC SACRE (FR), 10, b g Bering—Lady Glorieuse (FR) **Mr L. H. & Mrs T. Evans**
22 LOVE AND BE LOVED, 5, b m Lawman (FR)—Rightside **J. L. Flint**
23 NATIVE SOLDIER (IRE), 5, b g Sepoy (AUS)—Electra Star **J. L. Flint**
24 OUTER SPACE, 8, b g Acclamation—Venoge (IRE) **Corbsinger thoroughbreds**
25 PACOFILHA, 5, b m Paco Boy (IRE)—Seradim **Burnham Plastering & Drylining Ltd**
26 PASTAMAKESUFASTER, 4, b f Multiplex—Sopran Cross (ITY) **Katchar Racing**
27 TRAVIS BICKLE (IRE), 8, b g Sky Mesa (USA)—Out of Woods (USA) **Mr D. M. Mathias**

MR JOHN FLINT - Continued

28 WINKLEMANN (IRE), 7, br g Rip Van Winkle (IRE)—Kykuit (IRE) **Mr D. M. Mathias**
29 WITH PLEASURE, 6, b g Poet's Voice—With Fascination (USA) **Burnham Plastering & Drylining Ltd**

Other Owners: Mr P. D. Bell, Belly's Heroes, R. A. Davies, Mr D. P. Duffy, Mrs T. Evans, Mr L. H. Evans, Miss R. Grensinger, Mrs K. H. L. Mills, Mr A. G. Price, Mr S. A. Raymond, Mrs T. J. Raymond, Mr D. M. Semmens, P. D. Thomas.

Assistant Trainer: Mrs Martine Louise Flint (07968) 044487

Jockey (NH): Rhys Flint.

---

209 **MR DAVID FLOOD, Swindon**
Postal: **15 High Street, Chiseldon, Swindon, Wiltshire, SN4 0NG**
Contacts: **PHONE (07919) 340619**
E-MAIL **davidflood1@hotmail.co.uk**

1 BAZOOKA (IRE), 8, b g Camacho—Janadam (IRE) **Mrs A. Cowley**
2 DU CHATELIER (FR), 6, ch g Network (GER)—Elza III (FR) **Flood Family Racing Limited**
3 KENDERGARTEN KOP (IRE), 4, ch g Kendargent (FR)—Elsa T (IRE) **Mrs A. Cowley**
4 STOPDWORLDNLETMEOF, 5, b g Piccolo—Dilli Dancer **Flood Family Racing Limited**

THREE-YEAR-OLDS

5 ACCREDITED, b f Archipenko (USA)—Saltpetre (IRE) **Mrs A. Cowley**

---

210 **MR STEVE FLOOK, Leominster**
Postal: **The Granary Stables, Downwood Farm, Shobdon, Leominster, Herefordshire, HR6 9NH**
Contacts: **MOBILE (07811) 511566**
E-MAIL **lwallace@btinternet.com**

1 BLACKJACKTENNESSEE, 5, b g Fair Mix (IRE)—No Virtue **S. M. Flook**
2 DEMOPHON, 5, b g Oasis Dream—Galatee (FR) **S. M. Flook**
3 GIRL POWRE, 4, br f Great Pretender (IRE)—Annieegan **Miss L. Wallace**
4 GOLD HUNTER (IRE), 9, b g Invincible Spirit (IRE)—Goldthroat (IRE) **Chasing Charlie Syndicate**
5 HIGHLAND LIFE, 9, b m Trans Island—High Life **Mr F. J. A. Morgan**
6 HIGHLAND WAY, 5, b m Getaway (GER)—High Life **Mr F. J. A. Morgan**
7 KNIGHT COMMANDER, 6, br g Sir Percy—Jardin **Foxhunters In Mind**
8 MON GARCON FRANKIE, 7, ch g Sulamani (IRE)—Rhetorique (FR) **Mrs S. E. Vaughan**
9 SHOVEL IT ON (IRE), 4, br g Elusive Pimpernel (USA)—Fitrah (IRE) **S. M. Flook**
10 SILVER MAN, 12, gr g Silver Patriarch (IRE)—Another Mans Cause (FR) **T. J. Wardle**

Other Owners: Mr P. E. Jones.

Assistant Trainer: Lynn Wallace

---

211 **MR TONY FORBES, Uttoxeter**
Postal: **Hill House Farm, Poppits Lane, Stramshall, Uttoxeter, Staffordshire, ST14 5EX**
Contacts: **PHONE (01889) 562722 MOBILE (07967) 246571**
E-MAIL **tony@thimble.net**

1 BENISSIMO (IRE), 9, b g Beneficial—Fennor Rose (IRE) **Mr A. L. Forbes**
2 BERTIE MOON, 9, b g Bertolini (USA)—Fleeting Moon **Mr A. L. Forbes**
3 TINGO IN THE TALE (IRE), 10, b g Oratorio (IRE)—Sunlit Skies **Mr A. L. Forbes**

Assistant Trainer: Mr Tim Eley

212 **MRS PAM FORD, Hereford**
Postal: **Stone House Stables, Preston Wynne, Hereford, Herefordshire, HR1 3PB**
Contacts: **HOME/FAX (01432) 820604 MOBILE (07733) 152051**
E-MAIL **pam_ford@hotmail.co.uk**

1 **DIGI (IRE)**, 6, b m Baltic King—Lorena (IRE) **Mrs V. A. M. Dutton**
2 **KING FRANK**, 6, b h Fantastic Spain (USA)—Elegant Accord (IRE)

Assistant Trainer: Mr K Ford

---

213 **MRS RICHENDA FORD, Blandford Forum**
Postal: **Garlands Farm, The Common, Okeford Fitzpaine, Blandford Forum, Dorset, DT11 0RT**
Contacts: **MOBILE (07800) 634846**
E-MAIL **richendasnook@hotmail.co.uk WEBSITE www.richendafordracing.co.uk**

1 **DONT BE ROBIN (IRE)**, 7, b g Robin des Pres (FR)—Rainbow Times (IRE) **Mr & Mrs K. B. Snook**
2 **HURRY HENRY (IRE)**, 10, b g Blueprint (IRE)—Tower Princess (IRE) **Mr & Mrs K. B. Snook**
3 **MONKEY HARRIS (IRE)**, 7, b g Oscar (IRE)—Benefit Ball (IRE) **Mr & Mrs K. B. Snook**
4 **SHANROE SMOOCH (IRE)**, 6, b g Ask—Lady Quesada (IRE) **Mr & Mrs K. B. Snook**
5 **SUSTAINABLE STAR (IRE)**, 8, gr g Winged Love (IRE)—Fooling Around (IRE) **Mr & Mrs K. B. Snook**

Other Owners: Mrs M. Snook, K. B. Snook.

---

214 **MR BRIAN FORSEY, Taunton**
Postal: **Three Oaks, Ash Priors, Taunton, Somerset, TA4 3NQ**
Contacts: **PHONE (01823) 433914 MOBILE (07747) 392760**
E-MAIL **forsey2001@yahoo.com**

1 **BARISTA (IRE)**, 11, b g Titus Livius (FR)—Cappuccino (IRE) **Three Oaks Racing & Mrs P Bosley**
2 **DROPZONE (USA)**, 10, b g Smart Strike (CAN)—Dalisay (IRE) **Mr Alan Stevens & Mr Brian Forsey**
3 **EDDIES PEARL (IRE)**, 9, b m Craigsteel—Florida Bay (IRE) **Mrs S. Smyth-Ribeiro**
4 **GEORGIEZAR**, 6, ch m Winker Watson—Quaker Parrot **Mr K. C. Jago**
5 **RUNAIOCHT (IRE)**, 9, ch g Teofilo (IRE)—Julie Girl (USA) **Mrs C. E. E. Turner**
6 **THE IBBSTER (IRE)**, 9, b g Shantou (USA)—Annalisa (IRE) **Mrs S. Smyth-Ribeiro**

Other Owners: Mrs P. Bosley, Mr B. Forsey, Mr A. Stevens.

Assistant Trainer: Mrs Elizabeth Chatfield

---

215 **MISS SANDY FORSTER, Kelso**
Postal: **Halterburn Head, Yetholm, Kelso, Roxburghshire, TD5 8PP**
Contacts: **PHONE/FAX (01573) 420615 FAX (01573) 420615**
MOBILE (07880) 727877 or (07976) 587315
E-MAIL **clivestorey@btinternet.com**

1 **CHARLIE SNOW ANGEL**, 10, b g Overbury (IRE)—Sister Seven (IRE) **C. Storey**
2 **CLAUD AND GOLDIE (IRE)**, 10, ch g Portrait Gallery (IRE)—Glacial Jewel (IRE) **The Border Racers**
3 **FLYING DISMOUNT (IRE)**, 6, b g St Jovite (USA)—Posh Posy (IRE) **Dave Skeldon & Sandy Forster**
4 **KITTY FISHER (IRE)**, 9, b m Scorpion (IRE)—Luck of The Deise (IRE) **Mrs A. Long**
5 **LASTIN' MEMORIES**, 7, b g Overbury (IRE)—Dusky Dante (IRE) **Dave Skeldon & Sandy Forster**
6 **LISSEN TO THE LADY (IRE)**, 5, b m Fame And Glory—Liss Rua (IRE) **Mr M. H. Walton**
7 **LOWANBEHOLD (IRE)**, 12, gr g Cloudings (IRE)—Marble Quest (IRE) **C. Storey**

Other Owners: Miss Sandra Forster, Mr D. Skeldon, Mr C. Storey.

Assistant Trainer: C. Storey

Conditional: Tommy Dowson, Thomas Wilmott. **Amateur:** Miss J. Walton.

216 MISS JOANNE FOSTER, Ilkley
Postal: **Brookleigh Farm, Burley Road, Menston, Ilkley, West Yorkshire, LS29 6NS**
Contacts: **PHONE (07980) 301808 MOBILE (07980) 301808**
E-MAIL info@jofosterracing.co.uk WEBSITE www.jofosterracing.co.uk

1 **CANNY STYLE**, 6, b m Canford Cliffs (IRE)—Stylish One (IRE) **The Golden Syndicate**
2 **CHASE THE WIND (IRE)**, 10, ch g Spadoun (FR)—Asfreeasthewind (IRE) **Mr J. Nixon**
3 **FLEMISH MAID (IRE)**, 7, b m Flemensfirth (USA)—Lucy May (IRE) **Miss J. E. Foster**
4 **FRANKIE BALLOU (IRE)**, 10, br g Norwich—One Up (IRE) **The Yorkshire Racing Partnership**
5 **HOUNDSCOURT (IRE)**, 12, b g Court Cave (IRE)—Broken Rein (IRE) **The Berry Syndicate**
6 **LAMMTURNER (IRE)**, 7, b m Brian Boru—Deploy Or Die (IRE) **Mr E. C. Wilkin**
7 **LEOPARD (IRE)**, 5, b g Iffraaj—Appletreemagic (IRE) **Mad For Fun & Partners (2)**
8 **SIGURD (GER)**, 7, ch g Sholokhov (IRE)—Sky News (GER) **Mrs E. A. Verity**
9 **TWO HOOTS (IRE)**, 8, gr g Tikkanen (USA)—Supreme Beneficial (IRE) **Reign It In 2**

Other Owners: Mr J. Batty, Mr J. Berry, Mr David Ellis, Mr C. Finn, Miss J. E. Foster, Mr P. Foster, Mr S. A. Hollings, Mrs Christine Potter, Mr Matt Roche, Mr Peter Thompson.

Assistant Trainer: P. Foster

Jockey (NH): Henry Brooke, Danny Cook. **Amateur:** Miss Becky Smith.

217 MR JIMMY FOX, Marlborough
Postal: **Highlands Farm Stables, Herridge, Collingbourne Ducis, Marlborough, Wiltshire, SN8 3EG**
Contacts: **PHONE (01264) 850218 (07931) 724358 MOBILE (07702) 880010**
E-MAIL jcfoxtrainer@aol.com

1 **ACT ACCORDINGLY**, 6, gr g Sagamix (FR)—Anns Girl **Mrs J. A. Cleary**
2 **AMY KANE**, 5, b m Excelebration (IRE)—Be Free **Mr C. Fiford**
3 **BILLY STAR**, 4, b g Sixties Icon—Appreciative **Sugar Syndicate**
4 **CAPTAIN MARMALADE (IRE)**, 7, gr g Duke of Marmalade (IRE)—Elisium **Lord Mutton Racing Partnership**
5 **GRACEFUL JAMES (IRE)**, 6, ch g Rock of Gibraltar (IRE)—Little Miss Gracie **Abacus Employment Services Ltd**
6 **GRACIOUS GEORGE**, 9, b g Oratorio (IRE)—Little Miss Gracie **Highlands Farm Racing Partnership**
7 **MILLIE MAY**, 5, b m Sixties Icon—Maydream **The Dancing Partners**
8 **PURPLE PADDY**, 4, b g Swiss Spirit—Stunning In Purple (IRE) **Mrs B. A. Fuller**
9 **SWEET AND DANDY (IRE)**, 4, b f Dandy Man (IRE)—Translator (IRE) **Mrs S. J. Fox**
10 **WILD FLOWER (IRE)**, 7, b m Approve (IRE)—Midsummernitedream (GER) **Mrs S. J. Fox**

THREE-YEAR-OLDS

11 **LADY MAZIE (IRE)**, ch f Excelebration (IRE)—Blessing Box **Sugar Syndicate**
12 **PURPLE TOMMY**, ch c Assertive—Stunning In Purple (IRE) **Abacus Employment Services Ltd**

Other Owners: Mr M. Dolnik, Mrs E. Estall, Mr D. S. Estall, Mr P. Ondrcka.

Assistant Trainer: Sarah-Jane Fox

218 MISS SUZZANNE FRANCE, Norton on Derwent
Postal: **Cheesecake Hill House, Highfield, Beverley Road, Norton on Derwent, North Yorkshire, YO17 9PJ**
Contacts: **PHONE (01653) 691947 FAX (01653) 691947 MOBILE (07904) 117531**
E-MAIL suzzanne@newstartracing.co.uk WEBSITE www.suzzannefranceracing.com / www.new-startracing.co.uk

1 **ABERDONIAN**, 5, b g Royal Applause—Delaware Dancer (IRE) **Miss Kate Dobb & Mr Stuart Dobb**
2 **AD VITAM (IRE)**, 11, ch g Ad Valorem (USA)—Love Sonnet **Newstart Partnership**
3 **LUATH**, 6, ch g Archipenko (USA)—Delaware Dancer (IRE) **Miss Kate Dobb & Mr Stuart Dobb**
4 **MOUNTAIN OF STARS (IRE)**, 4, b g Equiano (FR)—Ivory Silk **Stuart Dobb & Kate Dobb**
5 **STAMP DUTY (IRE)**, 11, b g Ad Valorem (USA)—Lothian Lass (IRE) **Newstart Partnership**

Other Owners: Mr Stuart Dobb, Miss K. M. Dobb, Mrs P. France.

Assistant Trainer: Mr Aaron James

219 MR DEREK FRANKLAND, Brackley
Postal: **Springfields, Mixbury, Brackley, Northamptonshire, NN13 5RR**
Contacts: **FAX (01280) 847334 MOBILE (07763) 020406**
E-MAIL **dsfrankland@aol.com**

1 CANNY TOM (IRE), 9, b g Jimble (FR)—Tombazaan (IRE) **Mr D. S. Frankland**
2 DREAM EMPRESS, 6, gr m Naaqoos—Daheeya **Mr D. S. Frankland & Mr D. J. Trott**
3 STINGGREY (IRE), 6, gr g Scorpion (IRE)—Northinn Lady (IRE) **Mr D. S. Frankland & Mr D. J. Trott**

Other Owners: D. S. Frankland, Mr D. J. Trott.

220 MR JAMES FROST, Buckfastleigh
Postal: **Hawson Stables, Buckfastleigh, Devon, TQ11 0HP**
Contacts: **YARD (01364) 642267 HOME (01364) 642332 FAX (01364) 643182**
MOBILE (07860) 220229
E-MAIL **info@frostracingclub.co.uk**

1 ATLANTIC GREY (IRE), 6, gr g Acambaro (GER)—Clooney Eile (IRE) **Mr T. Saye**
2 BOGOSS DU PERRET (FR), 8, b br g Malinas (GER)—Lady Paques (FR) **Mrs J. Bury**
3 FINDUSATGORCOMBE, 7, b g Tobougg (IRE)—Seemma **Mr P. R. Meaden**
4 GILLY GRACE, 9, b m Morpeth—Miss Grace **Frost Racing Club**
5 ICE KONIG (FR), 10, gr g Epalo (GER)—Isarwelle (GER) **Frost Racing Club**
6 KRISTJANO (GER), 7, b g Nayef (USA)—Kalahari Dancer **Mr T. Saye**
7 LEGEND OF ZORRO (IRE), 6, ch g Touch of Land (FR)—Wotaglen (IRE) **G. D. Thompson**
8 LION OF LACKABANE (IRE), 8, b g Welsh Lion (IRE)—Lackabane Julie (IRE) **Frost Racing Club**
9 MONET MOOR, 10, b m Morpeth—Miracle Monarch **Frost Racing Club**
10 QUINTO, 9, ch g Desideratum—Cruz Santa **Frost Racing Club**
11 SILVER QUAY (IRE), 7, gr g Dark Angel (IRE)—She Runs (FR) **C & Mrs A Jones**
12 TRIPLE CHIEF (IRE), 8, b br g High Chaparral (IRE)—Trebles (IRE) **G. D. Thompson**

Other Owners: J. D. Frost, Mrs J. A. Jones, Mr C. Jones, Mr B. A. G. Robarts.

Assistant Trainer: G. Frost

Conditional: Bryony Frost.

221 MR KEVIN FROST, Butterton
Postal: **Butterton Racing Stables, Park Road, Butterton, Newcastle, Staffordshire, ST5 4DZ**
Contacts: **(07748) 873092 MOBILE (07919) 370081**
E-MAIL **info@kevinfrostracing.co.uk** WEBSITE **www.kevinfrostracing.co.uk**

1 ALL SET TO GO (IRE), 8, gr g Verglas (IRE)—Firecrest (IRE) **C & D Racing**
2 ARROWZONE, 8, b g Iffraaj—Donna Giovanna **Robert Greenwood Racing**
3 BHODI (IRE), 4, b g Dark Angel (IRE)—Modesty's Way (USA)
4 BORN TO REASON (IRE), 5, b g Born To Sea (IRE)—Laureldean Lady (IRE) **D. S. Lovatt**
5 CALVINIST, 6, b g Holy Roman Emperor (IRE)—Sharp Relief (IRE) **Mr M. G. Roberts**
6 CARACAS, 5, b g Cacique (IRE)—Bourbonella **Mr K. Frost**
7 CHIEFTAIN'S CHOICE (IRE), 10, b g King's Theatre (IRE)—
Fairy Native (IRE) **Curzon House Partnership & Friends**
8 COTTINGHAM, 4, b g Dalakhani (IRE)—Echelon **Mr S Petty & Partner**
9 DOC PENFRO, 7, b g Dr Massini (IRE)—Prescelli (IRE) **Doc Redemption**
10 DOCTOR WONDERFUL, 4, ch g Medicean—Wonderful Desert **Mr K. Frost**
11 DOCUMENTING, 6, b g Zamindar (USA)—Namaskar **Bgc Racing & M.A. Humphreys**
12 FRANCIS XAVIER (IRE), 5, b g High Chaparral (IRE)—Missionary Hymn (USA) **Curzon House Partnership**
13 GHAZAN (IRE), 4, ch c Iffraaj—Sweet Firebird (IRE) **Robert Greenwood Racing & M.A. Humphreys**
14 HURRICANE DYLAN (IRE), 5, b g Brian Boru—Definetly Sarah (IRE) **Mr J. Stimpson**
15 LIFEBOAT (IRE), 4, b g Born To Sea (IRE)—Mrs Seek **Mr R. Ward**
16 MASKED IDENTITY, 4, b g Intello (GER)—Red Bloom **D. S. Lovatt**
17 MY BROTHER MIKE (IRE), 5, b g Bated Breath—Coming Back **Mr J. Stimpson**
18 MY TOWN CHICAGO (USA), 4, b c Medaglia d'oro (USA)—Say You Will (IRE) **Mr J. Stimpson**
19 PERSHING, 4, b g Mount Nelson—La Gandilie (FR) **Mr D. M. Forrester**
20 POPPY JAG (IRE), 4, b f Kodiac—Jacquelin Jag (IRE) **Curzon House Partnership**
21 REDEMPTION SONG (IRE), 7, gr m Mastercraftsman (IRE)—Humilis (IRE) **Doc Redemption**
22 SCOFFSMAN, 4, b g Dansili—Purissima (USA) **David & Jan Mead**

MR KEVIN FROST - Continued

23 **SHAMLAN (IRE)**, 7, br g Shamardal (USA)—Atamana (IRE) **Robert Greenwood Racing & Wayne Smith**
24 **SHELFORD (IRE)**, 10, b g Galileo (IRE)—Lyrical **Mrs A. Frost**
25 **SHOWDANCE KID**, 5, b g Showcasing—Maid To Dance **Mr K. Frost**
26 **SINGULAR QUEST**, 7, ch g Dalakhani (IRE)—Singuliere (IRE) **Mr D. Mead**
27 **STEAL THE SCENE (IRE)**, 7, b g Lord Shanakill (USA)—Namoos (USA) **Curzon House Partnership & Friends**
28 **TARBEYAH (IRE)**, 4, ch f Teofilo (IRE)—Shamtari (IRE) **Robert Greenwood Racing**
29 **THE THROSTLES**, 4, b g Poet's Voice—Stylish Dream (USA) **Bgc Racing & Trisha Keane**
30 **TORONTO SOUND**, 5, b g Aussie Rules (USA)—Caribana **V7 International Ltd & Partner**

THREE-YEAR-OLDS

31 **PERUVIAN SUMMER (IRE)**, ch c Lope de Vega (IRE)—Need You Now (IRE) **Mr J. Stimpson**
32 **RED SKY IN SPAIN**, ch c Iffraaj—Adonesque (IRE) **Mr J. Stimpson**

TWO-YEAR-OLDS

33 B c 9/4 Fountain of Youth (IRE)—Apache Glory (USA) (Cherokee Run (USA)) **Mr J. Stimpson**
34 Ch c 13/3 Mukhadram—Farletti (Royal Applause) (6000) **Mr D. Mead**
35 Bl c 10/3 Gregorian (IRE)—Reel Cool (Reel Buddy (USA)) **Mr J. Stimpson**
36 B c 24/3 Pastoral Pursuits—Topflight Princess (Cockney Rebel (IRE)) **Mrs A. Frost**
37 B c 5/5 Roderic O'Connor (IRE)—Waitingonacloud (In The Wings) (800) **Mrs A. Frost**

Other Owners: BGC Racing, Mr D. L. Coles, Mr S. W. Dunn, Mr R. J. Greenwood, Mr M. A. Humphreys, Mr H. Jones, Miss J. Jones, Ms T. Keane, Mr D. L'Honore, Mrs J. A. Mead, Mr J. H. Mills, Mrs M. A. Moore, Mr C. Owen, Mr S. Petty, Mr W. L. B. Smith, V7 International Limited.

Jockey (NH): Brian Hughes.

---

222 **MR HUGO FROUD, Bruton**
Postal: **Redlynch Farm, Redlynch, Nr Bruton, Somerset, BA10 0NH**
Contacts: **MOBILE (07590) 413550**
E-MAIL hugo.froud@hugofroudracing.com WEBSITE www.hugofroudracing.com

1 **GIFT FROM GOD**, 6, b g Teofilo (IRE)—Piffling **The Gift From God Syndicate**
2 **LADY LYDIA (IRE)**, 8, b m Kheleyf (USA)—Piece Unique **The Lady Lydia Syndicate**
3 10, B m General Gambul—Vitinsel

Other Owners: P. E. Froud, Mr H. C. Froud.

---

223 **MR HARRY FRY, Seaborough**
Postal: **Flat 1, Manor Farm, Seaborough, Beaminster, Dorset, DT8 3QY**
Contacts: **PHONE (01308) 868192 FAX (01308) 867512**
E-MAIL info@harryfryracing.com WEBSITE www.harryfryracing.com

1 **ACTING LASS (IRE)**, 8, b g King's Theatre (IRE)—Darrens Lass (IRE) **Nigel & Barbara Collison**
2 **AIR HORSE ONE**, 8, gr g Mountain High (IRE)—Whisky Rose (IRE) **The Dons**
3 **AMERICAN (FR)**, 9, b g Malinas (GER)—Grande Sultane (FR) **The Jago Family Partnership**
4 **AMERICAN GIGOLO**, 7, b g Azamour (IRE)—Sadie Thompson (IRE) **Mr D. A. Olver**
5 **ANY DRAMA (IRE)**, 8, b g Gamut (IRE)—Oak Lodge (IRE) **N. G. Cooper**
6 **AQUILA SKY (IRE)**, 4, b g Arcadio (GER)—Starventure **The Jago Family Partnership**
7 **ARCTIC ROSE (GER)**, 4, b f Pastorius (GER)—Adelma (GER) **Holt, Robinson, Macnabb, Clark, Weedon**
8 **ART OF PAYROLL (GER)**, 10, b g Shirocco (GER)—Anna Maria (GER) **Bishopsgate Syndicate**
9 **AS I SEE IT**, 7, b g King's Theatre (IRE)—Chomba Womba (IRE) **Mrs D. J. Goodall**
10 4, B g Shantou (USA)—Baby Lenson (IRE)
11 **BAGS GROOVE (IRE)**, 8, b g Oscar (IRE)—Golden Moment (IRE) **M. Pescod**
12 **BILLY MERRIOTT (IRE)**, 13, b g Dr Massini (IRE)—Hurricane Bella (IRE) **G. D. Taylor**
13 **BLACK MISCHIEF**, 7, b g Black Sam Bellamy (IRE)—Miss Mitch (IRE) **Tom Chadney and Friends**
14 **BULLIONAIRE (IRE)**, 6, b g Gold Well—Dontcallerthat (IRE) **Phil Fry & Charlie Walker -Osborne House**
15 **CAPTAIN DRAKE (IRE)**, 6, b g Getaway (GER)—Julika (GER) **Gary Stevens & Brian & Sandy Lambert**
16 **CARIBERT (FR)**, 6, b g Ballingarry (IRE)—Cardamine (FR) **Charlie Walker & Phil Fry -Osborne House**
17 **CHALONNIAL (FR)**, 7, ch g Protektor (GER)—Kissmirial (FR) **N. G. Cooper**
18 **CHETSFORD WATER (IRE)**, 5, b m Yeats (IRE)—Courting Jenny **Somerset Racing**
19 **DALILA DU SEUIL (FR)**, 6, gr m Bachir (IRE)—Misery (FR) **Mr J. P. McManus**
20 **DASHING OSCAR (IRE)**, 9, b g Oscar (IRE)—Be My Leader (IRE) **Andy & Sharon Measham**

MR HARRY FRY - Continued

21 **DEADRINGERFORLOVE**, 5, b m Black Sam Bellamy (IRE)—
La Perrotine (FR) **Mayoh, Callan, Beese & the Dennys**
22 **DEFINITELYANOSCAR (IRE)**, 6, b m Oscar (IRE)—Bobs Article (IRE) **Jago & Taylor**
23 **ELEANOROFAQUITAINE (IRE)**, 6, b m Flemensfirth (USA)—
Misty Heather (IRE) **Dolan-Abrahams & Fry Families**
24 **GAMEFACE (IRE)**, 5, b g Oscar (IRE)—Queensland Bay **Mr J. P. McManus**
25 **GEORGE VALENTINE (FR)**, 4, b g George Vancouver (USA)—Yes My Love (FR) **A Holt, J Robinson, A Taylor**
26 **GET IN THE QUEUE**, 5, b g Mount Nelson—Amarullah (FR) **Mr & Mrs Paul & Clare Rooney**
27 **GOFORTHECRAIC (IRE)**, 6, b g Arcadio (GER)—
Valin Thyne (IRE) **Holt Macnabb Clark Jeffrey Milton Robinson**
28 **GOLDEN BIRTHDAY (FR)**, 8, b g Poliglote—Gold Or Silver (FR) **G. C. Stevens**
29 **GOODNITESWEETHEART**, 8, b m Midnight Legend—Over To Charlie **The Twelfth Man Partnership III**
30 **GREEN DOLPHIN (IRE)**, 5, b g Oscar (IRE)—Shamrock Miss (IRE) **M. Pescod**
31 **HELL'S KITCHEN**, 8, b g Robin des Champs (FR)—Mille Et Une (FR) **Mr J. P. McManus**
32 **IF THE CAP FITS (IRE)**, 7, b g Milan—Derravaragh Sayra (IRE) **Mr & Mrs Paul & Clare Rooney**
33 **IMPERIAL ESPRIT (IRE)**, 5, b g Scorpion (IRE)—Shesourpresent (IRE) **Imperial Racing Partnership 2016**
34 **ISHKHARA LADY**, 5, b m Scorpion (IRE)—Loxhill Lady **The Horse Flys Partnership**
35 **JEREMIAH JAMES (IRE)**, 5, b g Jeremy (USA)—Lougholly Native (IRE) **Dr Caroline Fry & Susie Dilhorne**
36 **JOLLY'S CRACKED IT (FR)**, 10, b g Astarabad (USA)—Jolly Harbour **GDM Partnership**
37 **JUST A STING (IRE)**, 7, b g Scorpion (IRE)—Shanann Lady (IRE) **Nigel & Barbara Collison**
38 **KING ROLAND (IRE)**, 5, br g Stowaway—Kiltiernan Robin (IRE) **Masterson Holdings Limited**
39 **LAND OF OUR DREAMS**, 5, gr m Geordieland (FR)—Dream Leader (IRE) **J. P. Blakeney**
40 4, B g Asian Heights—Leahs Joy (IRE) **Mrs C. Fry**
41 **LEGENDE DE MINUIT**, 5, br g Midnight Legend—Chilla Cilla **The Eyre Family**
42 **LIGHTLY SQUEEZE**, 5, b g Poet's Voice—Zuleika Dobson **J Davies, G Brown & P Govier**
43 **LOQUACIOUS LADY (IRE)**, 5, b m Milan—Jennifers Diary (IRE) **Hot To Trot Jumping**
44 **MANTOVANI (IRE)**, 4, b g High Chaparral (IRE)—Ripley (GER) **Mahon Racing**
45 **MILLBANK FLYER (IRE)**, 4, b g Milan—The Last Bank (IRE) **The Jago Family Partnership**
46 **MILLE SUSSURRI (IRE)**, 4, b g Milan—Silent Whisper (IRE) **The Jago Family Partnership**
47 **MINELLA AWARDS (IRE)**, 8, b g Oscar (IRE)—Montys Miss (IRE) **Masterson Holdings Limited**
48 **MISTERTON**, 8, gr g Sagamix (FR)—Mighty Splash **Wilkin, Orr, Boileau and Sim**
49 **MISTY WHISKY**, 5, gr m Stowaway—Whisky Rose (IRE) **Distillery Stud**
50 **MOMELLA (IRE)**, 7, ch m Sholokhov (IRE)—Missing Link (IRE) **Holt, Clark, Macnabb, Nugent & Robinson**
51 **OLYMPIC ODYSSEY**, 4, b g Camelot—Field of Hope (IRE) **Masterson Holdings Limited**
52 **ONEFORTHEROADTOM**, 6, gr g Fair Mix (IRE)—Ifni du Luc (FR) **Mr J. P. McManus**
53 **OPENING BATSMAN (IRE)**, 13, b g Morozov (USA)—Jolly Signal (IRE) **The Twelfth Man Partnership**
54 **OUTOFTHISWORLD (IRE)**, 6, b br m Shantou (USA)—Mystic Masie (IRE) **Chasing Gold Limited**
55 **OVER TO SAM**, 8, b g Black Sam Bellamy (IRE)—Lady Brig **The Jago Family Partnership**
56 **OVERTOWN EXPRESS (IRE)**, 11, b g Overbury (IRE)—Black Secret **Lorna Squire & Richard Metherell**
57 **PHOENIX WAY (IRE)**, 5, b g Stowaway—Arcuate **Mr J. P. McManus**
58 **POGO I AM**, 5, b m Passing Glance—Orbital Orchid **Sandie & David Newton**
59 **PRESS GANG**, 6, b g Mount Nelson—Rutba **Mr D. A. Olver**
60 **REALITY BITES (IRE)**, 8, b g Mahler—Seeds of Doubt (IRE) **Masterson Holdings Limited**
61 **ROSEMARY RUSSET**, 7, b m Midnight Legend—Apple Days **Somerset Racing**
62 **RUBY BEAR (IRE)**, 5, b g Gold Well—Noble Nell (IRE) **Brian & Sandy Lambert**
63 **RUFIO**, 5, b g Schiaparelli (GER)—Mole End **The Lost Boys**
64 **SAM I (FR)**, 6, gr g Lord du Sud (FR)—Blue Girl Star (FR) **Seuss Racing**
65 **SAMARQUAND**, 5, b g Malinas (GER)—Samandara (FR) **Charlie Walker & Phil Fry -Osborne House**
66 **SECRET DOOR (IRE)**, 8, b m Stowaway—Cellar Door (IRE) **Thornton, Gibbs, Cameron & Fry**
67 **SEROSEVSKY (IRE)**, 6, b g Morozov (USA)—Be My Rainbow (IRE) **Brian & Sandy Lambert**
68 **SIR IVAN**, 9, b g Midnight Legend—Tisho **The Eyre Family**
69 **SOUND WALL (IRE)**, 4, b g Milan—Wall of Silence (IRE) **C. C. Walker**
70 **SPACE ODDITY (FR)**, 8, br g Al Namix (FR)—Schoune (FR) **The Rate Chasers**
71 **STEEL BOB (IRE)**, 7, b g Craigsteel—Lady Kamando **Bob and Friends**
72 **SUPERB STORY (IRE)**, 8, b g Duke of Marmalade (IRE)—
Yes My Love (FR) **A Holt, J Robinson, A Taylor & S Miller**
73 **THE BIG STING (IRE)**, 4, b g Scorpion (IRE)—Glory Queen (IRE) **C. C. Walker**
74 **THE JITTERBUG**, 6, b g Sulamani (IRE)—She Likes To Boogy (IRE) **Twelfth Man Partnership 5**
75 **THE LAST SAMURI (IRE)**, 11, ch g Flemensfirth (USA)—Howaboutthis (IRE) **Mr & Mrs Paul & Clare Rooney**
76 **TOODLEPIP (IRE)**, 5, b m Robin des Champs (FR)—Shannon Theatre (IRE) **Mrs J. A. Thomas**
77 4, B g Fame And Glory—Trabrega Bay (IRE)
78 **UNOWHATIMEANHARRY**, 11, b g Sir Harry Lewis (USA)—Red Nose Lady **Mr J. P. McManus**
79 **VIVANT POEME (FR)**, 10, b g Early March—Hasta Manana (FR) **Andy & Sharon Measham**
80 **WHATAKNIGHT**, 10, b g Midnight Legend—What A Mover **J. M. Dare, T. Hamlin, J. W. Snook**
81 **WHITE HART LADY (IRE)**, 5, b m Doyen (IRE)—Hats And Heels (IRE) **Chasing Gold Limited**

MR HARRY FRY - Continued

82 **WHITEHOTCHILLIFILI (IRE)**, 5, b m Milan—Mhuire Na Gale (IRE) **Chasing Gold Limited**
83 **WINNINGSEVERYTHING (IRE)**, 5, b g Flemensfirth (USA)—Baliya (IRE) **Mr & Mrs Paul & Clare Rooney**
84 **WINSTON C (IRE)**, 5, b g Rip Van Winkle (IRE)—Pitrizza (IRE) **C. V. Wentworth**
85 **WOTZIZNAME (IRE)**, 9, b g Fruits of Love (USA)—Native Beau (IRE) **Mr C. J. Horton**

THREE-YEAR-OLDS

86 **BURROWS TREAT (FR)**, b f Muhtathir—La Vie de Boitron (FR)
87 **GENTLEMAN KAP (FR)**, b g Kapgarde—Sabuelle (FR)

TWO-YEAR-OLDS

88 **SECRET PROPHET (IRE)**, b g 12/3 Lucky Speed (IRE)—Grangeclare Rhythm (IRE) (Lord Americo)

Other Owners: Mr J. D. Beese, Mr C. Blackburn, Mrs H. L. Boileau, P. H. Boss, G. S. Brown, Mr I. P. Callan, Mrs S. Cameron, Mr D. M. Cameron, Mrs V. J. Chadney, Mr T. H. Chadney, G. Charlesworth, Mr D. Charlesworth, Mr C. N. Clark, Mr N. Collison, Mrs B. Collison, Mr J. M. Dare, Mr J. Davies, R. B. Denny, D. J. B. Denny, Mr M. R. Dentten, Viscountess S. J. Dilhorne, Mrs P. E. Dolan-Abrahams, Mr E. J. Dolan-Abrahams, Mrs C. A. Eyre, Mr H. Eyre, Miss R. E. Eyre, Mr C. G. S. Eyre, R. P. Fry, Dr C. E. Fry, R. A. Fry, Mr R. Gibbs, Mr P. F. Govier, T. Hamlin, Mr A. G. Hipgrave, Mr A. Holt, Mr R. S. Hoskins, Mr P. J. A. Jago, Miss M. L. A. Jago, Mr F. C. A. Jago, Mrs J. L. Jago, Miss A. Jeffrey, Mrs J. K. Keech, Mr I. N. Kingham, Mr B. Lambert, Mr I. Macnabb, Mr D. Magrath, Mr R. F. Magrath, Mr D. J. Mahon, Dr B. Mayoh, Mr G. W. McCausland, Mr T. F. McGowan, Mr A. R. Measham, Mrs S. M. Measham, R. J. Metherell, R. P. B. Michaelson, Mr S. R. Miller, Mr C. J. Milton, Mr P. A. Munnelly, Mrs J. S. Newton, Mr D. Newton, Mr J. P. Nugent, Mrs S. Orr, Mr A. D. Polson, Mr M. Powell, Mr I. Robinson, Mr J. D. Robinson, R. Robinson, Mrs Margaret Robinson, Mrs C. Rooney, Mr P. A. Rooney, A. G. Sim, Mr M. Smith, J. W. Snook, Mrs L. Squire, Miss M. L. Taylor, Mr A. Taylor, Mr A. J. Taylor, Mr G. M. Thornton, Mr J. P. G. Turner, Mr J. Weedon, Mr T. Wheatley, Mr R. C. Wilkin.

Assistant Trainers: Ciara Fry, Mike Legg

Jockey (NH): Noel Fehily, Niall P. Madden. **Conditional:** Kieron Edgar. **Amateur:** Mr M. Legg, Miss A. B. O'Connor.

---

224 **MISS CAROLINE FRYER, Wymondham**
Postal: **Browick Hall Cottage, Browick Road, Wymondham, Norfolk, NR18 9RB**
Contacts: **PHONE (01953) 601257 MOBILE (07768) 056076**
E-MAIL caroline@carolinefryerracing.co.uk / c.fryer528@btinternet.com
WEBSITE www.carolinefryerracing.co.uk

1 **GOODNIGHT CHARLIE**, 9, gr m Midnight Legend—Over To Charlie **Miss C. Fryer**
2 **MIDNIGHT BLISS**, 9, b m Midnight Legend—Violet Elizabeth **Miss C. Fryer**
3 **RIDDLESTOWN (IRE)**, 12, b g Cloudings (IRE)—Gandi's Dream (IRE) **Mr J. D. Ward**
4 **SCHAP**, 7, ch m Schiaparelli (GER)—Royal Keel **Miss C. Fryer**
5 **VOLCAN SURPRISE (FR)**, 11, b g Dom Alco (FR)—Invitee Surprise (FR) **Miss C. Fryer**

---

225 **MR IVAN FURTADO, Newark**
Postal: **The Old Stables, Averham Park Farm, Averham, Newark, Nottinghamshire, NG23 5RU**
Contacts: **MOBILE (07783) 520746**
E-MAIL ivanfurtado@hotmail.co.uk

1 **AFRICAN SHOWGIRL**, 6, ch m Showcasing—Georgie The Fourth (IRE) **Miss V. Ohlidalova**
2 **ALBA DEL SOLE (IRE)**, 4, b f Dandy Man (IRE)—Winterwell (USA) **The Uxbridge Road Syndicate**
3 **ANIMATED HERO**, 6, b g Sakhee's Secret—Society (IRE) **Mr D. H. Slater**
4 **AVAGO JOSH**, 5, ch g Aqlaam—Heart Stopping (USA) **The Giggle Factor Partnership**
5 **BLACKLOOKS (IRE)**, 4, b g Society Rock (IRE)—Mosaique Beauty (IRE) **J. L. Marriott**
6 **BLUE CANDY**, 4, b c Bahamian Bounty—Sally Can Wait **Mr K. Sohi**
7 **BORN IN THORNE**, 6, b m Haafhd—Royal Nashkova **Mr N. P. Sennett**
8 **CAPTAIN DION**, 6, gr g Equiano (FR)—Bandanna **Mr T. R. B. T. A. Shah**
9 **COX BAZAR (FR)**, 5, b g Nombre Premier—Dame de Montlebeau (FR) **Mr C. Hodgson**
10 **DIAMOND PURSUIT**, 4, b f Pastoral Pursuits—Broughtons Jewel (IRE) **From The Front Racing**
11 **DONCASTER STAR**, 4, b f Doncaster Rover (USA)—Pucker Up **Miss B. Griffiths**
12 **ESKIMO POINT (IRE)**, 7, ch g Lope de Vega (IRE)—Diamond Star (USA) **Layezy Racing Owners Club**
13 **ESME KATE (IRE)**, 4, b f Arch—Francisca (USA) **Timms, Timms & McCabe**
14 **ETERNAL SUN**, 4, b f Mayson—Golden Dirham **Mrs S Nicholls Mrs R J Mitchell**
15 **FLORA TRISTAN**, 4, ch f Zoffany (IRE)—Red Roxanne **The Giggle Factor Partnership**
16 **FLY TRUE**, 6, b m Raven's Pass (USA)—Have Faith (IRE) **Stuart Dobb & Kate Dobb**

MR IVAN FURTADO - Continued

17 **FOLLOWTHESTEPS (IRE)**, 4, b g Footstepsinthesand—Excellent Mariner (IRE) **J. L. Marriott**
18 **ILLUSTRISSIME (USA)**, 6, b g Mizzen Mast (USA)—Ghost Friendly (USA) **Mr C. Hodgson**
19 **INEXES**, 7, gr g Exceed And Excel (AUS)—Likeable **21st Century Racing**
20 **IRISH CHARM (FR)**, 5, b h Siyouni (FR)—Danclare (USA) **The Giggle Factor Partnership**
21 **KINGS HIGHWAY (IRE)**, 4, b c Shamardal (USA)—Bimini **Layezy Racing Owners Club**
22 **LAW EQUITY (FR)**, 8, b br g Lawman (FR)—Basse Besogne (FR) **Mr D. H. Slater**
23 **LOOSE CHIPPINGS (IRE)**, 5, b g Rock of Gibraltar (IRE)—Karjera (IRE) **Mr J. Melo**
24 **MALASPINA (ITY)**, 7, b m Pounced (USA)—Modern Goddess (USA) **The Giggle Factor Partnership**
25 **MEDAHIM (IRE)**, 5, b g Kodiac—Novel Fun (IRE) **J. C. Fretwell**
26 **MURDANOVA (IRE)**, 6, gr g Zebedee—Agnista (IRE) **Mr P. Slater**
27 **MUTAWAARY (IRE)**, 5, b g Shamardal (USA)—Shuhra (IRE) **Mr A. H. Malik**
28 **NORMAL EQUILIBRIUM**, 9, b g Elnadim (USA)—Acicula (IRE) **J. L. Marriott**
29 **ROMAN DE BRUT (IRE)**, 7, ch g Rock of Gibraltar (IRE)—Nesmeh (USA) **Mr P. Slater**
30 **RULED BY THE MOON**, 5, b g Mawatheeq (USA)—Hallingdal (UAE) **The Giggle Factor Partnership**
31 **SHEILA'S TREAT (IRE)**, 6, b g Frozen Power (IRE)—Bonny Rose **Mr D. Maniatis**
32 **SIR OTTOMAN (FR)**, 6, b g Excellent Art—Hali Layali **Mr C. Hodgson**
33 **SKI BLAST**, 8, ch g Three Valleys (USA)—Chasing Stars **The Giggle Factor Partnership**
34 **SWORD EXCEED (GER)**, 5, b g Exceed And Excel (AUS)—
                                            Sword Roche (GER) **21st Century Racing & Nigel Sennett**
35 **TAGLE (IRE)**, 4, b g Requinto (IRE)—Beginners Luck (IRE) **Sohi & Sohi**
36 **ZAEEM**, 10, b g Echo of Light—Across (ARG) **21st Century Racing & Nigel Sennett**

THREE-YEAR-OLDS

37 **ANYTHINGISPOSSIBLE**, b f Born To Sea (IRE)—Be Amazing (IRE) **The Giggle Factor Partnership**
38 **CRAZY SPIN**, b f Epaulette (AUS)—George's Gift **The Giggle Factor Partnership**
39 **EESHA'S SMILE (IRE)**, ch f Toronado (IRE)—Lamentation **Mr K. Sohi**
40 **ELOQUENT STYLE (IRE)**, b c Dandy Man (IRE)—Eloquent Rose (IRE) **The Giggle Factor Partnership**
41 **GAZTON**, b g Equiano (FR)—Duchess of Seville **Layezy Racing Owners Club**
42 **GENNARO (IRE)**, b g Harbour Watch (IRE)—Buzkashi (IRE) **Sohi & Sohi**
43 **GHOST BUY (FR)**, b c Orpen (USA)—Nantha (IRE) **John Marriott & Giggle Factor**
44 **HECTOR'S HERE**, b c Cityscape—L'addition **John Marriott & Giggle Factor**
45 B f Pastoral Pursuits—Jocasta Dawn **The Giggle Factor Partnership**
46 **LITTLE BUSTARD (IRE)**, b f Roderic O'Connor (IRE)—Liturgy (IRE) **The Giggle Factor Partnership**
47 **MELISSA (FR)**, ch f Evasive—Snow Jasmine (IRE) **J. L. Marriott**
48 **MENINA ATREVIDA**, ch f Nayef (USA)—Delaware Dancer (IRE) **Stuart Dobb & Kate Dobb**
49 **MUNHAMEK**, b g Dark Angel (IRE)—Cadenza (FR) **J. C. Fretwell**
50 **NETTLE PEGGY**, b f Toronado (IRE)—Wise Melody **The Giggle Factor Partnership**
51 **QUEEN OF BRADGATE**, b f Compton Place—Russian Ruby (FR) **J Crossfield & Giggle Factor Partnership**
52 **RUM LAD**, b g Heeraat (IRE)—Madam Mojito (USA) **Dalwhinnie Bloodstock Limited**
53 **SCANDINAVIAN LADY (IRE)**, b f Swiss Spirit—Azzurra du Caprio (IRE) **The Giggle Factor Partnership**
54 **SOPHIA'S PRINCESS**, ch f Coach House (IRE)—Rosa Luxemburg **Miss B. Griffiths**
55 **SPARKLEALOT (IRE)**, b c Sir Prancealot (IRE)—Monsusu (IRE) **J. L. Marriott**
56 **VEE MAN TEN**, b c Mayson—Sadiigah **Mr K. Sohi**
57 **WONTGETFOOLEDAGEN (IRE)**, b g Zebedee—No Way (IRE) **Mr D. H. Slater**

TWO-YEAR-OLDS

58 B c 12/2 Epaulette (AUS)—Corryvreckan (IRE) (Night Shift (USA)) (6190) **From The Front Racing**
59 B f 1/5 Heeraat (IRE)—Dockside Strike (Docksider (USA))
60 Ch c 2/4 Dawn Approach (IRE)—Learned Friend (GER) (Seeking The Gold (USA)) **Sohi & Sohi**
61 B f 25/2 Alhebayeb (IRE)—Mosa Mine (Exceed And Excel (AUS)) (1619) **The Giggle Factor Partnership**
62 Ch f 7/2 Dawn Approach (IRE)—Neuquen (IRE) (Rock of Gibraltar (IRE)) (42000) **J. L. Marriott**
63 Ch c 4/2 Camacho—Queenie Keen (IRE) (Refuse To Bend (IRE)) (28571) **BGC Racing**
64 B f 7/4 Mayson—Raajis (IRE) (Dark Angel (IRE)) (2500) **The Giggle Factor Partnership**
65 Ch c 19/2 Tagula (IRE)—Raseel (Aqlaam) (2380) **From The Front Racing**
66 B c 16/3 Toronado (IRE)—Rotunda (Pivotal) (800) **The Giggle Factor Partnership**
67 B f 21/1 War Command (USA)—Shegotloose (USA) (Dynaformer (USA)) (3000) **The Giggle Factor Partnership**
68 **STAY CALM (IRE)**, b c 2/5 Epaulette (AUS)—Emerald Peace (IRE) (Green Desert (USA)) (22755) **J. C. Fretwell**
69 B f 10/4 Slade Power (IRE)—Weood (IRE) (Dubawi (USA)) (3500) **The Giggle Factor Partnership**

Other Owners: Mr J. R. Best, Mrs B. Catterall, A. W. Catterall, Mr J. A. Crossfield, Mr J. Danaher, Mr S. Dobb, Miss K. M. Dobb, Mr S. Franks, Mr A. N. Gargan, Mr G. Goonan, Mr J. R. Holt, Mr A. J. McCabe, Mrs R. J. Mitchell, Mrs S. E. Nicholls, Mr J. Sohi, Mr M. Stanley, Mr A. C. Timms, Mr M. E. Timms, Mr R. Ward.

226 **MR JOHN GALLAGHER, Moreton-In-Marsh**
Postal: **Grove Farm, Chastleton, Moreton-In-Marsh, Gloucestershire, GL56 0SZ**
Contacts: PHONE **(01608) 674492** MOBILE **(07780) 972663**
E-MAIL **john@gallagherracing.com** WEBSITE **www.gallagherracing.com**

1 **BAHAMIAN SUNRISE**, 7, ch g Bahamian Bounty—Tagula Sunrise (IRE) **Caveat Emptor Partnership**
2 **BELLA'S VENTURE**, 6, gr m Hellvelyn—Fayre Bella **John Gallagher**
3 **GOWER GOLD**, 4, b f Mayson—Mistressofthelake (IRE) **John Gallagher**
4 **GREEN POWER**, 4, b g Kheleyf (USA)—Hakuraa (IRE) **Nino's Partnership**
5 **ILEY BOY**, 5, b g Delegator—Menha **J & L Wetherald - M & M Glover**
6 **JUNOESQUE**, 5, b m Virtual—Snake Skin **The Juniper Racing Club Ltd**
7 **LADWEB**, 9, ch g Bertolini (USA)—Adweb **The Juniper Racing Club & Andrew Bell**
8 **MAJOR PUSEY**, 7, ch g Major Cadeaux—Pusey Street Lady **C. R. Marks (Banbury)**
9 **OOLOGIST**, 8, gr g Proclamation (IRE)—Orchid's Silver **Mr Charles Stone & Mr Trevor Beeches**
10 **QUENCH DOLLY**, 5, gr m Hellvelyn—Hollybell **Quench Racing Partnership**
11 **RIVAS ROB ROY**, 4, ch g Archipenko (USA)—Rivas Rhapsody (IRE) **Mr T. J. F. Smith**

THREE-YEAR-OLDS

12 **BLUE BATTALION**, ch g Cityscape—Hollybell **Mr R. Little**
13 **FOXY FEMME**, ch f Foxwedge (AUS)—Pusey Street Vale **Mrs C. R. Clifford**
14 **MAHUIKA**, b f Firebreak—Adweb **The Juniper Racing Club & Andrew Bell**
15 **MAID FROM THE MIST**, gr f Hellvelyn—Ball Burst (IRE) **M. C. S. D. Racing Partnership**
16 **SALLY HOPE**, ch f Coach House (IRE)—First Term
17 **SWISS MISS**, b f Swiss Spirit—Miss Meticulous **The LAM Partnership**
18 **TARRZAN (IRE)**, b br g Bungle Inthejungle—Susiescot (IRE) **C. R. Marks (Banbury)**
19 **TOMAHAWK RIDGE (IRE)**, gr g Alhebayeb (IRE)—Low Cut Affair (IRE) **Max Europe Limited**

TWO-YEAR-OLDS

20 **LADY ILEY**, b f 2/5 Equiano (FR)—Hollybell (Beveled (USA)) **C. R. Marks (Banbury)**
21 B c 25/2 Due Diligence (USA)—Miss Meticulous (Bahamian Bounty) (10000) **The LAM Partnership**
22 **SARAS HOPE**, b c 20/4 Swiss Spirit—Rivas Rhapsody (IRE) (Hawk Wing (USA)) **John Gallagher**

Other Owners: Mr T. A. Beeches, Mr A. Bell, Mr B. Downard, Dr M. F. Ford, Mrs A. J. Forde, Ms M. E. Glover, M. P. Glover, Mr M. W. Goodall, Mr J. N. Greenley, Mr C. F. Little, J. F. Long, Mrs B. A. Long, Mrs M. B. McClean, B. J. McClean, Ms L. M. Mulcahy, Mr M. Preedy, Mr M. T. Rigby, Mr C. Stone, Mr J. A. Wetherald, Mrs L. T. Wetherald.

Assistant Trainer: Mrs R. J. Gallagher

227 **MR THOMAS GALLAGHER, Borehamwood**
Postal: **5 Old Priory Park, Old London Road, St. Albans, Hertfordshire, AL1 1QF**
Contacts: MOBILE: **(07786) 025427** Email: **Thomasgallagher77@hotmail.com**

1 **AH WELL (IRE)**, 7, b g Gold Well—Valentina Gaye (IRE) **Mr J. J. Reddington**
2 **BEEPEECEE**, 5, b g Henrythenavigator (USA)—Roedean (IRE) **Mr J. J. Reddington**
3 **BOLAND'S MILL (IRE)**, 7, b g Winged Love (IRE)—Madam Rocher (IRE) **Mr J. J. Reddington**
4 **DOM GARO CATELINE (FR)**, 6, b g Ungaro (GER)—Dame Jaune (FR) **Mr J. J. Reddington**
5 6, B g Dahjee (USA)—Exit Stage Left (IRE) **Mr J. J. Reddington**
6 **LOSTIN A FOG (IRE)**, 7, ch m Mahler—Spirit Rock (IRE) **Mr J. J. Reddington**
7 **MOUNTAIN SO HIGH (IRE)**, 6, b g Mountain High—Marigier (IRE) **Mr J. J. Reddington**
8 **MR HARP (IRE)**, 6, b g Court Cave—Chapel Wood Lady (IRE) **Mr J. J. Reddington**
9 **MR RAJ (IRE)**, 11, b g Oscar (IRE)—Chapel Wood Lady (IRE) **Mr J. J. Reddington**
10 **TOP MAN TIM (IRE)**, 12, b g Flemensfirth (USA)—Wont Change (IRE) **Mr J. J. Reddington**
11 4, Gr g Carlotamix (FR)—Whisky (IRE) **Mr J. J. Reddington**

228 MRS ILKA GANSERA-LÉVÊQUE, Newmarket
Postal: **Saint Wendreds, Hamilton Road, Newmarket, Suffolk, CB8 7JQ**
Contacts: **PHONE (01638) 454973 MOBILE (07855) 532072**
E-MAIL **office@gansera-leveque.com** WEBSITE **www.gansera-leveque.com**

1 RISING SEAS, 4, b g Mount Nelson—Puya **Mrs I. Gansera-Leveque**

THREE-YEAR-OLDS
2 AWESOMEDUDE, ch c Australia—Millevini (IRE) **Mr Y. L. A. Lee**
3 B c Born To Sea (IRE)—Disposition **M. J. Caddy**
4 JUST ONCE, b f Holy Roman Emperor (IRE)—Nur Jahan (IRE) **Mr I. Sze**
5 MELO PEARL, ch f Paco Boy (IRE)—Jewelled **M & M Franklin**
6 MOUDALLAL, b f Poet's Voice—Elhaam (IRE) **Saleh Al Homaizi & Imad Al Sagar**
7 MYSTIC DRAGON, ch f Intello (GER)—Portrait **Mr S. P. Hussain**
8 OBSESSION FOR GOLD (IRE), b c Acclamation—Campfire Glow (IRE) **Mr J. P. Kok**
9 RIVIERA NIGHTS, b c Kingman—Turama

TWO-YEAR-OLDS
10 B f 19/2 Night of Thunder (IRE)—Mystic Melody (IRE) (Montjeu (IRE)) (48040)

Other Owners: Mr I. H. Al Sagar, Mrs M. G. Franklin, Mr M. Franklin, Saleh Al Homaizi.

Assistant Trainer: Stephane Lévêque

---

229 MRS SUSAN GARDNER, Longdown
Postal: **Woodhayes Farm, Longdown, Exeter**
Contacts: **PHONE/FAX (01392) 811213 MOBILE (07936) 380492**
E-MAIL **woodhayesstudfarm@btinternet.com** WEBSITE **www.suegardnerracing.co.uk**

1 ATAGUISEAMIX (FR), 6, b g Al Namix (FR)—Olafane (FR) **Mr D. V. Gardner**
2 BREDON HILL LAD, 12, ch g Kirkwall—Persian Clover **Mr & Mrs R W & Mrs J M Mitchell**
3 BREDON HILL LEO, 7, b g Sulamani (IRE)—Persian Clover **Mr & Mrs R W & Mrs J M Mitchell**
4 COBY NINE (IRE), 6, b g Arcadio (GER)—Timing **Mr J. F. Panvert**
5 COEUR BLIMEY (IRE), 8, b br g Winged Love (IRE)—Eastender **Keith Harris & Tom Gardner**
6 EDDY, 10, b g Exit To Nowhere (USA)—Sharway Lady **Mr J. F. Panvert**
7 ENDLESS FLIGHT (IRE), 5, b g Winged Love (IRE)—Lady Oakwell (IRE) **Mr D. V. Gardner**
8 HERE'S HERBIE, 11, b g Classic Cliche (IRE)—Tyre Hill Lilly **Mr P. A. Tylor & Mr D V Gardner**
9 INDIAN HARBOUR, 6, b g Indian Haven—Hawait Al Barr **Harris,Wheeler,Brooke,Gardner**
10 NORDENFELT (IRE), 6, b g Lilbourne Lad (IRE)—There With Me (USA) **Mr D. V. Gardner**
11 ONLY GORGEOUS (IRE), 10, b g Vertical Speed (FR)—
                                                   Pure Beautiful (IRE) **Miss Jane Edgar & Mr D. V. Gardner**
12 TEA TIME FRED, 10, b g Kayf Tara—Darjeeling (IRE) **Mr D. V. Gardner**
13 TEA TIME ON MARS, 7, ch g Schiaparelli (GER)—Darjeeling (IRE) **Mrs B. Russell & Mr D. V. Gardner**
14 TRANS EXPRESS (IRE), 9, br g Trans Island—Hazel Fastrack **Mr D. V. Gardner**
15 WOULDUADAMANDEVEIT (IRE), 6, b g Stowaway—Figlette **Keith Harris & Tom Gardner**

Other Owners: Mr J. J. Brooke, Miss Jane Edgar, Mr T. A. Gardner, Mr D. V. Gardner, Mr K. T. Harris, R. W. Mitchell, Mrs J. M. Mitchell, Mrs B. A. Russell, P. A. Tylor, Mr N. J. Wheeler.

Assistant Trainer: D. V. Gardner

Jockey (NH): Lucy Gardner, Micheal Nolan.

---

230 MRS ROSEMARY GASSON, Banbury
Postal: **Alkerton Grounds, Balscote, Banbury, Oxfordshire, OX15 6JS**
Contacts: **PHONE (01295) 730248 MOBILE (07769) 798430**
E-MAIL **arb@aqf.myzen.co.uk**

1 BIGNORM (IRE), 7, b g Mahler—Merry Heart (IRE) **Mrs R. Gasson**
2 DESERT DE BRUYERE (FR), 6, b g Great Pretender (IRE)—Quid de Neuville (FR) **Mrs R. Gasson**
3 DRAGON KHAN (IRE), 10, b g Dr Fong (USA)—Desert Magic (IRE) **Mrs R. Gasson**
4 FREEDOM CHIMES, 5, b g Champs Elysees—Ombre **Mrs R. Gasson**
5 IRISH OCTAVE (IRE), 9, b g Gamut (IRE)—Fairytaleofnewyork (IRE) **Mrs R. Gasson**
6 JUSTTHEGREY (IRE), 7, gr g Getaway (GER)—Line White (FR) **Mrs R. Gasson**

MRS ROSEMARY GASSON - Continued

7 **MR MCGUINESS (IRE)**, 9, b g Kalanisi (IRE)—Maig Mandy (IRE) **Mrs R. Gasson**
8 **SCARTARE (IRE)**, 8, br g Trans Island—La Speziana (IRE) **Mrs R. Gasson**

Jockey (NH): Ben Poste.

---

231 MR PAUL GEORGE, Crediton
Postal: **Higher Eastington, Lapford, Crediton, Devon, EX17 6NE**
Contacts: MOBILE **(07733) 171112**
E-MAIL **paul.george1@icloud.com** WEBSITE **www.paulgeorgeracing.co.uk**

Trainer also operates a satellite stable in Bouce, France. Some horses may switch between yards.

1 **AUNTIE NEILA**, 4, ch f Intikhab (USA)—Storm Quest **Mr M. J. Hocking**
2 4, Ch g Stimulation (IRE)—Belle de Nuit (IRE)
3 **COUNTERFEIT**, 4, b f Iffraaj—Money Note **E Foster, , M Ashton & K George**
4 **ESSGEE NICS (IRE)**, 6, b g Fairly Ransom (USA)—Vannuccis Daughter (IRE) **S Nicholls & Wackey Racers**
5 **FAIRWAY TO HEAVEN (IRE)**, 10, b g Jeremy (USA)—Luggala (IRE) **Miss K. M. George**
6 **KODIAC HARBOUR (IRE)**, 4, b g Kodiac—Operissimo **Mr M. J. Hocking**
7 **NETLEY ABBEY**, 5, b g Myboycharlie (IRE)—Ana Style (FR) **Henacre Racing Club Ltd**
8 **POLLY'S GOLD (IRE)**, 4, ch f Havana Gold (IRE)—Keyta Bonita (IRE) **Wackey Racers Harefield**
9 **PRINCESS WAY (IRE)**, 5, gr m Zebedee—Stef's Girl (IRE) **Mr D. W. Renfree**
10 **SECRET RETURN (IRE)**, 6, ch m Roderic O'Connor (IRE)—Quick Return **Karen George**
11 **SIMON THE GREAT**, 6, b g Great Palm (USA)—Miss Royello **Mrs V. James**
12 **SPIRITUAL STAR (IRE)**, 10, b g Soviet Star (USA)—Million Spirits (USA) **Wackey Racers Harefield**
13 **THE AWESOME ALICE (IRE)**, 5, b m Mawatheeq (USA)—Amourallis (IRE) **The Black Type Partnership**
14 **ZAPATEADO**, 4, b f Zoffany (IRE)—Ziggy Zaggy **Edward Foster & Karen George**

THREE-YEAR-OLDS
15 **BRINKLEYS KATIE**, ch f New Approach (IRE)—Opera Gloves (IRE) **R Brinkley E Foster A Parr K George**
16 **BUG BOY (IRE)**, b g Big Bad Bob (IRE)—Velvetina (IRE) **P. J. H. George**
17 B c Dunaden (FR)—Caribbean Star **R Brinkley & P George**
18 B f Pastoral Pursuits—Cassie's Choice (IRE)
19 **COUTTS DE VILLE**, ch f Dawn Approach (IRE)—Samdaniya **A Coutts & K George**
20 **HALLE'S HARBOUR**, ch f Harbour Watch (IRE)—Clifton Dancer **D. Boddy, E Foster & Karen George**
21 **KNIGHTSHAYES**, ch f Mukhadram—Today's The Day **Henacre Racing Club Ltd**
22 **LIPPY LADY (IRE)**, b f Bungle Inthejungle—Sayrah **Miss K. M. George**
23 B g Nayef (USA)—Panoptic
24 **SEA OF MARENGO (IRE)**, b g Battle of Marengo (IRE)—Margie (IRE) **Mrs V. James**

TWO-YEAR-OLDS
25 Ch f 3/3 Iffraaj—Annawi (Dubawi (IRE)) (2500)
26 B g 20/1 Camelot—Annina (Singspiel (IRE)) (11000)
27 B f 27/4 Royal Anthem (USA)—Apsara (Groom Dancer (USA))
28 **DEREK LE GRAND**, b c 19/3 Mukhadram—Duo de Choc (IRE) (Manduro (GER)) (10000) **Mrs V. James**
29 B c 24/3 Heeraat (IRE)—Lexington Rose (Captain Gerrard (IRE)) (6742)

Other Owners: Mr M. Ashton, Mr D. Boddy, Mr R. R. Brinkley, Mr Andrew Bull, Mr A. Coutts, Mr E. Foster, Mr S. G. Nicholls, Mr J. O'Hara, Mr R. N. Olsen, A. B. Parr, Mr D. Wood.

Assistant Trainer: Cassie Haughton

Apprentice: Rhiain Ingram.

---

232 MR TOM GEORGE, Slad
Postal: **Down Farm, Slad, Stroud, Gloucestershire, GL6 7QE**
Contacts: PHONE **(01452) 814267** MOBILE **(07850) 793483**
E-MAIL **tom@trgeorge.com** WEBSITE **www.tomgeorgeracing.co.uk**

1 **ACTIVIAL (FR)**, 9, gr g Lord du Sud (FR)—Kissmirial (FR) **R. S. Brookhouse**
2 **AGAMEMMON (IRE)**, 7, b g Getaway (GER)—Oscar Road (IRE) **Mr N T Griffith & H M Haddock**
3 **AIR NAVIGATOR (IRE)**, 8, b g Yeats (IRE)—Lox Lane (IRE) **Lady N. F. Cobham**
4 **ALWAYS ON THE RUN (IRE)**, 9, br g Robin des Pres (FR)—Kerrys Cottage (IRE) **Mr T. George**

MR TOM GEORGE - Continued

5 **ANOTHER STOWAWAY (IRE)**, 7, b g Stowaway—Another Pet (IRE) **H Stephen Smith & Family Gabbertas**
6 **BABY KING (IRE)**, 10, b g Ivan Denisovich (IRE)—Burn Baby Burn (IRE) **About Two Weeks**
7 **BALLADAME (FR)**, 4, b f Ballingarry (IRE)—Summer (FR) **Lord & Lady Harrington**
8 **BALLON ONABUDGET (IRE)**, 6, b g Arcadio (GER)—Little Present (IRE) **Duffy, Rea, Keelan**
9 **BANISH (USA)**, 6, b g Smart Strike (CAN)—Beyond Our Reach (IRE) **Mr H. F. Birtles**
10 **BATTLE OF SHILOH (IRE)**, 10, b g Shantou (USA)—Realt Na Ruise (IRE) **Mr & Mrs Paul & Clare Rooney**
11 **BIG WINDMILL (IRE)**, 8, b g Stowaway—Neighbours Wager (IRE) **Mr D. W. Brookes**
12 **BLACK OP (IRE)**, 8, br g Sandmason—Afar Story (IRE) **R. S. Brookhouse**
13 **BLUE N YELLOW (IRE)**, 6, b g Jeremy (USA)—Bluemamba (USA) **R. S. Brookhouse**
14 **BOAGRIUS (IRE)**, 7, ch g Beneficial—Greenhall Rambler (IRE) **The MerseyClyde Partnership**
15 **BORN TO STING (IRE)**, 6, b g Scorpion (IRE)—Hatch Away (IRE) **Tom Chadney, John Moynihan, Tom Keelan**
16 **BOYHOOD (IRE)**, 8, b g Oscar (IRE)—Glen Dubh (IRE) **H Stephen Smith & The Gabbertas Family**
17 **BRANDON HILL (IRE)**, 11, b g Beneficial—Annesbanker (IRE) **Mr N T Griffith & H M Haddock**
18 **BRAVENTARA**, 8, b m Kayf Tara—L'aventure (FR) **Mr C. J. Harriman**
19 **BUCK'S BIN'S (FR)**, 5, b g Khalkevi (IRE)—Buck's Bravo (FR) **R. S. Brookhouse**
20 **BUN DORAN (IRE)**, 8, b g Shantou (USA)—Village Queen (IRE) **Crossed Fingers Partnership**
21 **CASA TALL (FR)**, 5, b g No Risk At All (FR)—Gribouille Parcs (FR) **Racing Ventures, Sharon, Dermot & David**
22 **CERNUNNOS (FR)**, 9, b g Della Francesca (USA)—Jackette (USA) **Mr J. P. McManus**
23 **CHAMPAGNE CITY**, 6, ch g Tobougg (IRE)—City of Angels **R. S. Brookhouse**
24 **CLONDAW CASTLE (IRE)**, 7, b g Oscar (IRE)—Lohort Castle (IRE) **J French, D McDermott, S Nelson, T Syder**
25 **COME ON TEDDY (IRE)**, 5, b g Fame And Glory—Theatre View (IRE) **Mr N T Griffith & H M Haddock**
26 **CONNECT FOUR**, 5, b g Midnight Legend—Sovereignsflagship (IRE) **Mr S. W. Clarke & Sisters**
27 **COPPER WEST (IRE)**, 8, b g Westerner—Printing Copper (IRE) **The MerseyClyde Partnership**
28 **CRUISEAWEIGH (IRE)**, 8, b g Oscar (IRE)—Triptoshan (IRE) **Mr S. W. Clarke**
29 **DARLING DU LARGE (FR)**, 6, b m Kapgarde (FR)—Dissidente (FR) **Mr S. W. Clarke**
30 **DOCTOR DEX (IRE)**, 6, b g Oscar (IRE)—Larnalee (IRE) **Crossed Fingers Partnership**
31 **DOUBLE SHUFFLE (IRE)**, 9, b g Milan—Fiddlers Bar (IRE) **Crossed Fingers Partnership**
32 **DRILL BABY DRILL**, 8, b m Black Sam Bellamy (IRE)—Tulipa (POL) **Sharon Nelson & Thoroughbred Ladies**
33 **DRUMLEE SUNSET (IRE)**, 9, br g Royal Anthem (USA)—Be My Sunset (IRE) **R. S. Brookhouse**
34 **EASY WOOD (FR)**, 5, gr g Martaline—Ball of Wood (FR) **Beesley, McDermott, Smith, Trembath**
35 **ENEMY COAST AHEAD**, 5, b g Malinas (GER)—Penang Princess **McNeill Family Ltd**
36 **ESPOIR DE TEILLEE (FR)**, 7, b g Martaline—Belle de Lyphard (FR) **R. S. Brookhouse**
37 **FANFAN DU SEUIL (FR)**, 4, b g Racinger (FR)—Nina du Seuil (FR) **Crossed Fingers Partnership**
38 **FARO DE KERSER (FR)**, 4, b g Ungaro—Nuit de Kerser (FR) **The Twenty One Club**
39 **FEARLESS FRACAS (IRE)**, 5, b g Fracas (IRE)—Mayo Mystique (IRE) **R. S. Brookhouse**
40 **FONTLEY HOUSE (IRE)**, 7, ch g Getaway (GER)—
Down Town Cork (IRE) **Colin Perry, Alan Waller & John Lawson**
41 **FORGOT TO ASK (IRE)**, 7, b g Ask—Lady Transcend (IRE) **Miss J. A. Hoskins**
42 **FORGOTTEN GOLD (IRE)**, 13, b g Dr Massini (IRE)—Ardnataggle (IRE) **Mr T. George**
43 **GET RHYTHM (IRE)**, 9, b g Kayf Tara—Ninna Nanna (FR) **Miss J. A. Hoskins**
44 **GOD'S OWN (IRE)**, 11, b g Oscar (IRE)—Dantes Term (IRE) **Crossed Fingers Partnership**
45 **GOOD MAN JIM (FR)**, 6, gr g Martaline—Precious Lucy (FR) **R. S. Brookhouse**
46 **GORSKY ISLAND**, 11, b g Turtle Island (IRE)—Belle Magello (FR) **Silkword Racing Partnership**
47 **IS A REAL CHAMP (IRE)**, 5, ch g Getaway (GER)—Siobhans Charm (IRE) **McNeill Family Ltd**
48 **KK LEXION (IRE)**, 8, b g Flemensfirth (USA)—Kiloradante (IRE) **Perry, Lawson, Waller, Rea, McDermott**
49 **LEG LOCK LUKE (IRE)**, 9, b g Indian River (FR)—Delirious Tantrum (IRE) **J. T. Warner**
50 **MANOFTHEMOMENT (IRE)**, 5, br g Jeremy (USA)—Endless Ambition (IRE) **James Longley & Charles Tatnall**
51 **MASSINI MAN**, 6, b g Dr Massini (IRE)—Alleged To Rhyme (IRE) **Mrs E. A. Fletcher**
52 **MINELLA FOR ME (IRE)**, 9, b g King's Theatre (IRE)—Irish Mystics (IRE) **Mr S. W. Clarke**
53 **MISS NIGHT OWL (IRE)**, 9, ch m Midnight Legend—Moylisacar **Capt & Mrs J. A. Capt & Mrs John George**
54 4, B g Jeremy (USA)—Miss Vic Lovin (IRE) **Mr & Mrs Paul & Clare Rooney**
55 **MOSS ON THE MILL**, 4, br g Overbury (IRE)—Mimis Bonnet (FR) **Mr R. T. Cornock**
56 **MY STORY (IRE)**, 7, b g Court Cave (IRE)—Holloden (IRE) **R. S. Brookhouse**
57 **MZUZU (IRE)**, 7, b g Oscar (IRE)—Tempest Hill (IRE) **Mr N T Griffith & H M Haddock**
58 **NET DE TREVE (IRE)**, 6, b g Network (GER)—Dame de Treve (FR) **O'Donohoe, Cavanagh, Robinson, Nelson**
59 **NOW LOOK AT ME (IRE)**, 5, ch g Shantou (USA)—Similan (IRE) **Mr & Mrs Paul & Clare Rooney**
60 **OTTER MOON (IRE)**, 7, b g Midnight Legend—Highland Dawn **Somerset Racing**
61 **ROCK ON ROCCO (IRE)**, 5, b g Shirocco (GER)—Katalina **R. S. Brookhouse**
62 **ROCKLANDER (IRE)**, 10, b g Oscar (IRE)—Rua Lass (IRE) **Mr D O'Donohoe, J Cavanagh, S Nelson**
63 **SANDYMOUNT (IRE)**, 8, b g Yeats (IRE)—Flaiha (FR) **D O'Donohoe, S Nelson, J Cavanagh**
64 **SEDDON (IRE)**, 6, b g Stowaway—Andreas Benefit (IRE) **McNeill Family Ltd**
65 **SHAMILAN (IRE)**, 6, b g Milan—Shatani (IRE) **Mr N T Griffith & H M Haddock**
66 **SINGLEFARMPAYMENT**, 9, b g Milan—Crevamoy (IRE) **Mr N T Griffith & H M Haddock**
67 **SMOKING JACKET (IRE)**, 9, b g Beneficial—Unalaska (IRE) **Vicki Robinson & James Williams**
68 **SMUGGLER'S BLUES (IRE)**, 7, b g Yeats (IRE)—Rosy de Cyborg (FR) **Mr N T Griffith & H M Haddock**

MR TOM GEORGE - Continued

69 **SONG SAA**, 9, b m Midnight Legend—Mystere (IRE) **Sharon C. Nelson & Georgie McGrath**
70 **STAMP YOUR FEET (IRE)**, 7, b g Galileo (IRE)—Nausicaa (USA) **Mr J. P. McManus**
71 **STOP THE WORLD (IRE)**, 6, b g Oscar (IRE)—Coolsilver (IRE) **McNeill Family Ltd**
72 **SUMKINDOFKING (IRE)**, 8, br g King's Theatre (IRE)—Shannon Rose (IRE) **Mr D. W. Fox**
73 **SUMMERVILLE BOY (IRE)**, 7, b g Sandmason—Suny House **R. S. Brookhouse**
74 **SUPER SID (IRE)**, 7, b g Westerner—Super Sammy **Mr N T Griffith & H M Haddock**
75 **THE BIG BITE (IRE)**, 6, b g Scorpion (IRE)—Thanks Noel (IRE) **Mr N T Griffith & H M Haddock**
76 **THE WORLDS END (IRE)**, 8, b g Stowaway—Bright Sprite (IRE) **McNeill Family Ltd**
77 **TRIBESMANS GLORY (IRE)**, 5, b g Jeremy (USA)—
　　　　　　　　　　　　　　　　　　　Benecash (IRE) **T Keelan,J Moynihan,S Nelson,D O'Donohoe**
78 **VALSEUR DU GRANVAL (FR)**, 10, b g Della Francesca (USA)—
　　　　　　　　　　　　　　　　　　　La Grande Vallee (FR) **D Thompson & The Magic Ten**
79 4, B g Aizavoski (IRE)—Victory Run (IRE) **O'Donohoe, Cavanagh, Robinson, Nelson**
80 **WESTERN WAVE (FR)**, 7, b g Westerner—Kaprissima (FR) **Somerset Racing**
81 **WHATCOLOURISHE (IRE)**, 6, br m Ask—Ardnataggle (IRE) **Mr N T Griffith & H M Haddock**
82 **WILD WEST WIND (IRE)**, 10, b g Westerner—Mhuire Na Gale (IRE) **Mr S. W. Clarke**
83 **ZOUTOISE (FR)**, 4, b f Enrique—Belle Yepa (FR) **P. E. Atkinson**

Other Owners: Mr M. Beesley, Mr Andrew Brown, Mr Peter Burslem, Mr J. Cavanagh, Mr Simon W. Clarke, Mr J. M. Fawbert, Mr J. French, Mrs Virginia Gabbertas, Mrs S. Gabbertas, Mr R. K. Gabbertas, Mr Mark Gabbertas, Capt. J. A. George, Mrs C. M. George, Mrs S. P. George, Mr N. Griffith, Heather Haddock, Lady Harrington, The Earl of Harrington, Miss Julie Hoskins, Mr T. Keelan, Mr John B. Lawson, Mr James Timothy Chapman Longley, Mr David McDermott, Mrs Georgie McGrath, Ms J. Moran, Mr John Moynihan, Mrs Sharon C. Nelson, Mr D. J. O'Donohoe, Mr Tony Outhart, Mr Colin Perry, Racing Ventures 2014, Mr David Rea, Ms Vicki Robinson, Mrs C. Rooney, Mr P A. Rooney, Mr P. Ryan, Mr R. Stephen Smith, Mr Andy Smith, Tim Syder, Mr Charles Ronald Spencer Tatnall, Mr Dave Thompson, Thoroughbred Ladies, Mr C. R. Trembath, Mr R. F. Tromans, Mr Alan Waller, Mr Richard Wilkin, Mr James S. Williams, Mr Nicholas Williamson.

Assistant Trainers: John Cullinan, Ciaran McKee

Jockey (NH): Paddy Brennan, Jonathon Burke, Ciaran Gethings, Adrian Heskin. **Amateur:** Mr Noel George.

---

233 | MR NICK GIFFORD, Findon
Postal: **The Downs, Stable Lane, Findon, West Sussex, BN14 0RT**
Contacts: OFFICE (01903) 872226 MOBILE (07940) 518077
E-MAIL downs.stables@btconnect.com WEBSITE www.nickgiffordracing.co.uk

1 **ALKA STEP (IRE)**, 8, gr g Alkaadhem—D'bibbys Step (IRE) **Mr J E Burrows & Mrs V C Burrows**
2 4, B br g Westerner—Baladiva (IRE)
3 **BELARGUS (FR)**, 4, b g Authorized (IRE)—Belga Wood (USA) **Mr J. P. McManus**
4 **BLACK LIGHTNING (IRE)**, 6, br g Whitmore's Conn (USA)—Annie May (IRE) **D. G. Trangmar**
5 **BROWN BEAR (IRE)**, 8, b g Yeats (IRE)—Moray Firth (UAE) **The Bear Necessities**
6 **CANYOURINGMEBACK (IRE)**, 7, b br g Robin des Pres (FR)—Hunters Bar (IRE) **Mr T. C. McKeever**
7 4, B g Alkaadhem—Castle Hope (IRE)
8 **CORAL LADE (IRE)**, 4, b g Shirocco (GER)—Gli Gli (IRE) **Project Mars Racing Partnership**
9 4, B g Yeats (IRE)—Crowning Virtue (IRE)
10 **DELTA ROSE (IRE)**, 5, br m Robin des Champs (FR)—Cruising Katie (IRE) **J. R. Hulme**
11 **DIDTHEYLEAVEUOUTTO (IRE)**, 6, ch g Presenting—Pretty Puttens (IRE) **Mr J. P. McManus**
12 **FAIRWAY FREDDY (IRE)**, 6, b g Elusive Pimpernel (USA)—Silent Supreme (IRE) **New Gold Dream**
13 **FLIBINIGHT (IRE)**, 4, b f Getaway (GER)—Fern Bird (IRE)
14 **FLY NUMBER ONE (IRE)**, 5, b g Oscar (IRE)—Kahysera **Mr J Kyle & Mr G Brooks**
15 **GIVE HIM TIME**, 8, b g Kalanisi (IRE)—Delayed (FR) **Mrs T. J. Stone-Brown**
16 **GLEN ROCCO (IRE)**, 8, ch g Shirocco (GER)—Adees Dancer **J Kyle, G Mason, D Stevens**
17 **HAWKERLAND (IRE)**, 6, b g Sea The Stars (IRE)—Zarara (USA) **The Willow & Bridle Partnership**
18 **LADY TALLULAH (IRE)**, 5, b m September Storm (GER)—Music School (IRE) **The South Downs Partnership**
19 **MYSTIC DREAMER (IRE)**, 5, b m Sans Frontieres—Free Dreamer (FR) **Nick Gifford Racing Club**
20 **NOTRE AMI (IRE)**, 8, br g Kalanisi (IRE)—Shuilan (IRE) **The Morpheus Partnership**
21 **ODEN**, 5, ch g Lope de Vega (IRE)—Dashing (IRE) **Mrs S. Cotty**
22 **PADDY'S POEM**, 8, b g Proclamation (IRE)—Ashleys Realm (IRE) **Mrs T. J. Stone-Brown**
23 **PARTY ROYAL**, 9, b g Royal Applause—Voliere **Coldunell Limited**
24 **SNOWY OSCAR (IRE)**, 6, b g Oscar (IRE)—Reedsbuck (FR) **Mr M. K. O'Shea**
25 **SOLAR GLORY (IRE)**, 5, b g Fame And Glory—Cashalass (IRE) **Glory Boys**
26 4, B br f Yeats (IRE)—Spring Baloo (IRE) **Nick Gifford Racing Club**
27 **THE MIGHTY DON (IRE)**, 7, ch g Shantou (USA)—Flying Answer (IRE) **Golden Rose Partnership**
28 **THEO'S CHARM (IRE)**, 9, b g Presenting—Kates Charm (IRE) **Mr M. K. O'Shea**

MR NICK GIFFORD - Continued

Other Owners: Mr W. A. T. Beer, Mrs S. A. Beer, Mr A. T. Beer, Mrs L. Bowtell, Mr J. P. M. Bowtell, Mr G. F. Brooks, Mr J. E. Burrows, Mrs V. C. Burrows, Mr E. M. P. Clark, Mr M. T. Forbes-Wood, Mrs C. A. Foster, Mrs R. E. Gifford, Mr A. Goldsmith, Mr M. Hogan, Mr J. A. M. Johnson, Mr C. Killeen, Mr J. Kyle, Mr R. Lawrie, G. A. Mason, Mr M. A. C. Rudd, Mr D. J. Stevens, Mr M. J. Tracey, Mr P. R. Tymms, Mr R. Walker, Mrs L. Wolfe.

Jockey (NH): Leighton Aspell, Tom Cannon.

---

234   MR MARK GILLARD, Blandford Forum
Postal: **Hawkes Field Farm, Hilton, Blandford Forum, Dorset, DT11 0DN**
Contacts: PHONE **(01258) 881111** MOBILE **(07970) 700605**
E-MAIL **Mark@thegillards.co.uk** WEBSITE **www.markgillardracing.com**

1 **AVITHOS**, 9, b m Kayf Tara—Digyourheelsin (IRE) **Mr N J McMullan & Mr T Winzer**
2 **CORSECOMBE**, 7, ch g Norse Dancer (IRE)—Digyourheelsin (IRE) **Miss Kay Russell**
3 **DARTMOOR GIRL (IRE)**, 5, b m So You Think (NZ)—Preveza (FR) **Mr B. R. Rudman**
4 **FINISHER (USA)**, 4, br g Street Cry (IRE)—Morena (PER) **Mrs P. M. R. Gillard**
5 **GOLDEN FOOTSTEPS (IRE)**, 4, b f Footstepsinthesand—Contemplate **Mr S. Hosie**
6 **INDIGO STAMP**, 8, b g Rainbow High—Philatelic Lady (IRE) **N. J. McMullan & S. H. Bryant**
7 **KARL MARX (IRE)**, 9, b g Red Clubs (IRE)—Brillano (FR) **Mr S. Bartlett**
8 **KINGSTON MIMOSA**, 7, b g Kheleyf (USA)—Derartu (AUS) **Mrs P. M. R. Gillard**
9 **L'ATTESA (IRE)**, 10, b g Kalanisi (IRE)—Tara Brooch (IRE) **Mr S. J. Garnett**
10 **NO NO CARDINAL (IRE)**, 10, ch g Touch of Land (FR)—Four Moons (IRE) **T. J. C. Seegar**
11 **NOT GOING OUT (IRE)**, 5, ch g Doyen (IRE)—Alannico **Mr S. Hosie**
12 **POWERFUL SOCIETY (IRE)**, 4, b f Power—Society Gal (IRE) **Mr S. Hosie**
13 **TEMASEK STAR (IRE)**, 8, b g Soviet Star (USA)—Crazy About You (IRE) **Mr S. Hosie**
14 **TOP BEAK (IRE)**, 6, b g Lawman (FR)—Tree Tops **Mr S. Hosie**
15 **TOUCH SCREEN (IRE)**, 9, b g Touch of Land (FR)—Capard Lady (IRE) **T. L. Morshead**
16 **VANDERBILT (IRE)**, 5, ch g Intense Focus (USA)—Star of The West **Tjc Seegar & Stephen Hosie**

TWO-YEAR-OLDS

17 B f 19/4 Casamento (IRE)—Enchanting Smile (FR) (Rakti) **Kay Russell**

Other Owners: Mr Steve Bryant, Mr N. J. McMullan, Mr T. J. C. Seegar, Mr T. Winzer.

Assistant Trainer: Pippa Grace

Jockey (NH): James Davies. **Amateur:** Mr Fergus Gillard, Mr Theo Gillard.

---

235   MR JAMES GIVEN, Willoughton
Postal: **Mount House Stables, Long Lane, Willoughton, Gainsborough, Lincolnshire, DN21 5SQ**
Contacts: PHONE **(01427) 667618** FAX **(01427) 667734** MOBILE **(07801) 100496**
E-MAIL **james@jamesgivenracing.com** WEBSITE **www.jamesgivenracing.com**

1 **BLYTON LASS**, 4, ch f Havana Gold (IRE)—Cesseras (IRE) **Mr A. Clarke**
2 **COOL SPIRIT**, 4, b g Swiss Spirit—Marmot Bay (IRE) **The Cool Silk Partnership**
3 **G EYE JOE**, 4, ch g Lethal Force (IRE)—Winifred Jo **The Cool Silk Partnership**
4 **INDIANAPOLIS (IRE)**, 4, b c Galileo (IRE)—Adoration (USA) **Mr A. Owen**
5 **POPPY MAY**, 5, b m Zoffany (IRE)—Lara Amelia (IRE) **Team Given 1**
6 **REACTIVE**, 4, ch g Cityscape—Hollowina **Mr P. Onslow**
7 **ROYAL BAJAN (USA)**, 11, gr ro g Speightstown (USA)—Crown You (USA) **The Cool Silk Partnership**

THREE-YEAR-OLDS

8 **ALICIA DARCY (IRE)**, b f Sir Prancealot (IRE)—Ballet of Doha (IRE) **The Cool Silk Partnership**
9 **CUBAN SUN**, b f Havana Gold (IRE)—Sunseek **Mr C. G. Rowles Nicholson**
10 **FAROL**, br f Kuroshio (AUS)—Spate Rise **Peter Onslow & Ingram Racing**
11 **GARSBAY**, ch c Garswood—Marmot Bay (IRE) **The Cool Silk Partnership**
12 **GINVINCIBLE**, gr f Zebedee—Gone Sailing **Roy Tozer & Team Given 2**
13 **LETHAL LAURA**, ch f Lethal Force (IRE)—Laurena (GER) **C. G. Rowles Nicholson**
14 **MENDELEEV**, b g Hellvelyn—Wightgold **Mullin, Goddard & Enid's Army**
15 **ORANGE BLOSSOM**, ch f Showcasing—Satsuma **The Cool Silk Partnership**
16 **OUT OF ANGELS (IRE)**, b f Dark Angel (IRE)—Extricate (IRE) **The Cool Silk Partnership**
17 **PIPOCA**, ch f Archipenko (USA)—Trick Or Treat **Mr P. Onslow**
18 **ROYAL SANDS (FR)**, b br c Dabirsim (FR)—Agent Mimi (FR) **The Cool Silk Partnership**

MR JAMES GIVEN - Continued

19 **RUSSIAN RUM**, b g Archipenko (USA)—Bebe de Cham **Lovely Bubbly Racing**
20 **SANTANA SLEW**, gr f Gregorian (IRE)—Saratoga Slew (IRE) **Dachel Stud**
21 **SISTER OF THE SIGN (IRE)**, b f Kodiac—Summer Magic (IRE) **The Cool Silk Partnership**
22 **THE LAST UNICORN**, b c Bated Breath—Rohlindi **The Cool Silk Partnership**
23 **TUNKY**, gr f Gregorian (IRE)—Alushta **Mrs Stephanie Oliver & Mr Ron Spore**

TWO-YEAR-OLDS

24 **CALLIPYGIAN**, b f 16/4 Magician (IRE)—Soft Drink (USA) (Lemon Drop Kid (USA)) (10000)
25 **DASHING ROGER**, b c 18/4 Fast Company (IRE)—
                     Croeso Cusan (Diktat) (761) **Mrs Stephanie Oliver & Mr Ron Spore**
26 **GREY EMINENCE**, gr c 6/3 Outstrip—
                 Laurena (GER) (Acatenango (GER)) (6666) **Mrs Stephanie Oliver & Mr Ron Spore**
27 B f 16/3 Lethal Force (IRE)—Inyordreams (Teofilo (IRE)) **Apple Tree Stud**
28 B f 19/3 Mount Nelson—Katy Nowaitee (Komaite (USA)) (10000) **Team Given 3**
29 **MONSARAZ**, b c 10/4 Cityscape—Rattleyurjewellery (Royal Applause) **Mr P. Onslow**
30 **RED MAHARANI**, ch f 1/2 Sepoy (AUS)—Vintage Gardenia (Selkirk (USA)) (10000) **Mr P. Venner**
31 **ROYAL LIGHTNING**, b f 7/3 Hot Streak (IRE)—Royal Obsession (IRE) (Val Royal (FR)) (9000)
32 **SIR CHARLES PUNCH**, b c 26/1 Sir Percy—Russian Punch (Archipenko (USA)) **Lovely Bubbly Racing**
33 Ch f 12/2 Garswood—Sweet Power (Pivotal) **Dachel Stud**
34 B f 18/4 Poet's Voice—Tia Mia (Dr Fong (USA))

Other Owners: Mr S. C. Applebee, Mrs D. Dunkley, P. J. Dunkley, James Given, Mrs C. Goddard, Mr P. A. Horton, Ingram Racing, Mr I. Jackson, O. H. Kingsley, Mr J. Mullin, Mrs R. J. Norman, Dr M. J. O'Brien, Mrs S. Oliver, R. C. Spore, P. Swann, Team Given 2, Mr R. C. L. Tozer, Mrs B. E. Wilkinson.

---

236 **MR JIM GOLDIE, Glasgow**
Postal: **Libo Hill Farm, Uplawmoor, Glasgow, Lanarkshire, G78 4BA**
Contacts: **PHONE (01505) 850212 MOBILE (07778) 241522**
WEBSITE www.jimgoldieracing.com

1 4, B f Shirocco (GER)—Another Shot (IRE)
2 4, Ch g Rock of Gibraltar (IRE)—Belle Rebelle (IRE)
3 **BRENDAN (IRE)**, 6, b g Elnadim (USA)—My **Ayr Racecourse Club**
4 **BURMESE BLAZER (IRE)**, 4, b br g Arakan (USA)—Sr Puss (IRE) **Johnnie Delta Racing**
5 4, B f Shirocco (GER)—Catcherinscratcher (IRE)
6 **COUNTY FAIR**, 5, b g Nayef (USA)—Village Fete **Mr & Mrs Raymond Anderson Green**
7 **DOON STAR**, 4, b f Sulamani (IRE)—La Vecchia Scuola (IRE) **Mrs V. C. Macdonald**
8 **ELITE ICON**, 5, b g Sixties Icon—Sailing Days **Johnnie Delta Racing**
9 **EMPLOYER (IRE)**, 4, b g Camelot—Close Regards (IRE) **Mr J. Fyffe**
10 **GET OUT THE GATE (IRE)**, 6, b g Mahler—Chartani (IRE) **Jim Fyffe & Stacey McQueen**
11 **HUGOIGO**, 5, b g Sulamani (IRE)—Gargoyle Girl **Johnnie Delta Racing**
12 **INSURPLUS (IRE)**, 6, b g Bushranger (IRE)—Emly Express (IRE) **Mr & Mrs G Grant & Partner**
13 **JESSIE ALLAN (IRE)**, 8, b m Bushranger (IRE)—Ishimagic **Mr R. W. C. McLachlan**
14 **LORD OF THE GLEN**, 4, b g Orientor—Glenlini **Musselburgh Lunch Club**
15 **LOUD AND CLEAR**, 8, b g Dalakhani (IRE)—Whispering Blues (IRE) **Mr & Mrs Philip C. Smith**
16 **NANJOE**, 4, b f Helmet (AUS)—Hanella (IRE) **Frank & Annette Brady**
17 **NICHOLAS T**, 7, b g Rail Link—Thorntoun Piccolo **Mr J. S. Goldie**
18 **ONE LAST HUG**, 4, b g Orientor—Gargoyle Girl **The Reluctant Suitor's**
19 **ORIENTAL LILLY**, 5, ch m Orientor—Eternal Instinct **Johnnie Delta Racing**
20 **PAMMI**, 5, b g Poet's Voice—Bright Girl (IRE) **Mr James Callow & Mr J. S. Goldie**
21 **PRIMO'S COMET**, 4, b g Orientor—Primo Heights **The Reluctant Suitor's**
22 **REMMY D (IRE)**, 4, b g Lawman (FR)—Evening Time (IRE) **Whitestonecliffe Racing Partnership**
23 **RESTIVE (IRE)**, 6, b g Rip Van Winkle (IRE)—I Hearyou Knocking (IRE) **Johnnie Delta Racing**
24 **RIOJA DAY (IRE)**, 9, b g Red Clubs (IRE)—Dai E Dai (USA) **Ayrshire Racing & Partner**
25 **SARVI**, 4, br f Intello (GER)—Crystal Swan (IRE) **Mr James Fyffe & Mr Scott Fyffe**
26 **SCOTS SONNET**, 5, b g Poet's Voice—Jabbara (IRE) **W. M. Johnstone**
27 **SIR CHAUVELIN**, 7, b g Authorized (IRE)—Jabbara (IRE) **Mr J. Fyffe, Mrs M. Craig, Mr G. Thomson**
28 **STAR CRACKER (IRE)**, 7, ch g Starspangledbanner (AUS)—Champagne Cracker **Mr G E Adams & Mr J S Goldie**
29 **STRATHY**, 6, b g Mount Nelson—Rose Street (IRE) **Mr James Callow & Mr J. S. Goldie**
30 **STRONG STEPS**, 7, b g Aqlaam—Wunders Dream (IRE) **Mrs M Craig & Mr G Adams**
31 **TESTA ROSSA (IRE)**, 9, b g Oratorio (IRE)—Red Rita (IRE) **Mr & Mrs Gordon Grant**
32 **THEGLASGOWWARRIOR**, 5, b g Sir Percy—Sweet Cando (IRE) **Mrs L. B. K. Bone**

MR JIM GOLDIE - Continued

33 **THORNTOUN LADY (USA)**, 9, b m Henrythenavigator (USA)—Valery Lady (ARG) **Mrs M. Craig & Mr J. S. Goldie**
34 **TIGER JIM**, 9, b g Tiger Hill (IRE)—Quintrell **Johnnie Delta Racing**
35 **TOMMY G**, 6, ch g Makfi—Primo Heights **Johnnie Delta Racing**

THREE-YEAR-OLDS

36 **BALMUICK (IRE)**, br g So You Think (NZ)—Full of Love (IRE) **T. Barr**
37 **CALL ME GINGER**, ch g Orientor—Primo Heights **Johnnie Delta Racing**
38 B g Orientor—Gargoyle Girl
39 B g Orientor—Glenlini
40 B f Kayf Tara—La Vecchia Scuola (IRE) **The Reluctant Suitor's**
41 **SOUND OF IONA**, ch f Orientor—Eternal Instinct **Mr & Mrs G Grant & the Reluctant Suitors**

TWO-YEAR-OLDS

42 Ch c 23/3 Poet's Voice—Miss Anneliese (IRE) (Mastercraftsman (IRE)) **W. M. Johnstone**
43 Ch c 25/3 Casamento (IRE)—Spirit of The Sea (IRE) (Invincible Spirit (IRE)) **W. M. Johnstone**

Other Owners: Mr G. Adams, Mr N. Boyle, Mrs A. Brady, Mr F. Brady, Mr J. R. Callow, Mrs M. Craig, Mr J. Frew, Mr S. Fyffe, Mrs D. I. Goldie, Mr G. R. Grant, Mrs C. H. Grant, Mrs A. Green, R. A. Green, P. Hampshire, Mr G. R. McGladery, Mr D. W. McIntyre, Miss S. McQueen, Mr P. C. Smith, Mrs J. W. Smith, G. M. Thomson, Mr G. T. Wallace, Western Meeting Club Ltd.

Assistant Trainers: James Goldie, George Goldie

Jockey (flat): P. J. McDonald. **Conditional:** Callum Bewley. **Apprentice:** Phil Dennis.

---

237 MR STEVE GOLLINGS, Louth
Postal: **Highfield House, Scamblesby, Louth, Lincolnshire, LN11 9XT**
Contacts: **YARD** (01507) 343204 **HOME/FAX** (01507) 343213 **MOBILE** (07860) 218910
E-MAIL stevegollings@aol.com WEBSITE www.stevegollings.com

1 **BOREAGH LASS (IRE)**, 4, b f Fast Company (IRE)—Jalasaat (USA) **North Yorkshire Bloodstock Racing**
2 **CAGED LIGHTNING (IRE)**, 9, b g Haatef (USA)—Rainbow Melody (IRE) **Northern Bloodstock Racing**
3 **ESPECIALLY SO**, 4, b g So You Think (NZ)—Behra (IRE) **Mr P. S. Walter**
4 **HANDIWORK**, 9, ch g Motivator—Spinning Top **Mr C. A. Johnstone**
5 **MOLTEN LAVA (IRE)**, 7, b g Rock of Gibraltar (IRE)—Skehana (IRE) **David & Ros Chapman**
6 **NEVADA**, 6, gr g Proclamation (IRE)—La Columbina **Northern Bloodstock Racing**
7 **ROCOCO STYLE**, 6, b m Shirocco (GER)—Akdara (IRE) **Tensational**
8 **TROOPINGTHECOLOUR**, 13, b g Nayef (USA)—Hyperspectra **Mrs Jayne M. Gollings**
9 **WITH HINDSIGHT (IRE)**, 11, b g Ad Valorem (USA)—Lady From Limerick (IRE) **Northern Bloodstock Racing**
10 **ZAMOYSKI**, 9, ch g Dutch Art—Speech **P Taiano, N Gollings, S Powell**

THREE-YEAR-OLDS

11 **ASPIRE TOWER (IRE)**, b g Born To Sea (IRE)—Red Planet **North Yorkshire B'stock & B. McNeill**

Other Owners: Mr G. Barot, Mrs B. Blair, Mr D. O. Chapman, Mrs R. M. H. Chapman, S. Gollings, Miss N. J. Gollings, Mr B. McNeill, Mr S. T. Powell, Mr P. G. Taiano.

Assistant Trainer: Mrs J M Gollings

---

238 MR CHRIS GORDON, Winchester
Postal: **Morestead Farm Stables, Morestead, Winchester, Hampshire, SO21 1JD**
Contacts: **PHONE** (01962) 712774 **FAX** (01962) 712774 **MOBILE** (07713) 082392
E-MAIL chrisgordon68@hotmail.co.uk WEBSITE www.chrisgordonracing.com

1 5, B m Indian Haven—Alexandra S (IRE)
2 **BADDESLEY KNIGHT (IRE)**, 6, b g Doyen (IRE)—Grangeclare Rhythm (IRE) **Mr Richard & Mrs Carol Cheshire**
3 **BADDESLEY PRINCE (IRE)**, 5, b g Doyen (IRE)—Norabella (IRE) **Mr Richard & Mrs Carol Cheshire**
4 **BALLYHEIGUE BAY (IRE)**, 12, b g Rudimentary (USA)—Terinka (IRE) **E. J. Farrant**
5 **BE DARING (FR)**, 8, gr g Dom Alco (FR)—Quinine (FR) **Gilbert & Gamble**
6 **CADMAR**, 5, b g Shirocco (GER)—Raitera (FR) **Mr Richard & Mrs Carol Cheshire**
7 **COMMANCHE RED (IRE)**, 6, ch g Mahler—Auntie Bob **Mr Richard & Mrs Carol Cheshire**
8 4, B g Stowaway—Currently In Milan (IRE) **Mr D. S. Dennis**
9 **DESIREMOI D'AUTHIE (FR)**, 6, b g Cachet Noir (USA)—Toietmoi d'authie (FR) **Mr D. S. Dennis**

MR CHRIS GORDON - Continued

10 **DON'T TELL GEORGE (FR)**, 6, b g Enrique—Anowa (FR) **Mrs K. Digweed**
11 4, B f Winged Love (IRE)—Gill Hall Lady **C. E. Gordon**
12 **HAREFIELD (IRE)**, 6, b g Doyen (IRE)—Bobbi's Venture (IRE) **Mr A. Charity**
13 **HIGHWAY ONE O ONE (IRE)**, 7, br g Stowaway—High Accord (IRE) **A. C. Ward-Thomas**
14 **HIGHWAY ONE O TWO (IRE)**, 4, b br g Shirocco (GER)—Supreme Dreamer (IRE) **A. C. Ward-Thomas**
15 **HIT THE HIGHWAY (IRE)**, 10, b g Pierre—Highway Belle (IRE) **Team ABC**
16 **HOWLONGISAFOOT (IRE)**, 10, b g Beneficial—Miss Vic (IRE) **Mr D. S. Dennis**
17 **ITSONLYROCKNROLL (IRE)**, 7, ch g Shantou (USA)—Compelled (IRE) **The Select Syndicate**
18 **JIMMY**, 6, ch g Norse Dancer (IRE)—Isintshelovely (IRE) **L. Gilbert**
19 **JUMPING JACK (IRE)**, 5, b g Sir Prancealot (IRE)—She's A Character **Broadsword Group Ltd**
20 4, Ch g Mahler—Kilbarry Cliche (IRE) **Broadsword Group Ltd**
21 **KING CNUT (FR)**, 5, ch g Kentucky Dynamite (USA)—Makadane **Mr D. S. Dennis**
22 4, B g Sans Frontieres (IRE)—Lady Nelson (IRE) **Mrs N. Morris**
23 **LOVES DESTINATION**, 8, b m Dubai Destination (USA)—Bijou Love (IRE) **Chris Gordon Racing Club**
24 **MAQUISARD (FR)**, 7, ch g Creachadoir (IRE)—Gioiosa Marea (IRE) **M. K. George**
25 **MAROCCHINO**, 6, gr g Tikkanen (USA)—Mocha (FR) **Mr A. P. Finden**
26 **MELLOW BEN (IRE)**, 6, b g Beneficial—Mellowthemoonlight (IRE) **Broadsword Group Ltd**
27 **MOROMAC (IRE)**, 5, b g Morozov (USA)—My Bay Lady **Party People**
28 4, Br g Mountain High (IRE)—Mrs Bukay (IRE) **Mrs J. L. Gordon**
29 **ON THE SLOPES**, 5, b g Librettist (IRE)—Dalriath **Skill Scaffolding Ltd**
30 **ONLY MONEY (IRE)**, 5, ch g Getaway (GER)—Kings Diva (IRE) **Mr E. Barker**
31 **POMPEY CHIMES (IRE)**, 4, b g Big Bad Bob (IRE)—Zamarelle **M. K. George**
32 **RAMORE WILL (IRE)**, 8, gr g Tikkanen (USA)—Gill Hall Lady **E. J. Farrant**
33 **REALLYRADICAL (IRE)**, 6, b g Insatiable (IRE)—Glenogra Cailin (IRE) **Mrs B. I. Chantler**
34 **SEAWEED (IRE)**, 7, b g Winged Love (IRE)—Grangeclare Rhythm (IRE) **Chris Gordon Racing Club**
35 **SHUT THE BOX (IRE)**, 5, ch g Doyen (IRE)—Bond Holder (IRE) **The Shut The Box Syndicate**
36 **SING OUR LOUD (IRE)**, 4, b g Vocalised (USA)—Tus Maith (IRE) **Mrs Susan Neville & Mr Mike George**
37 **SKY FULL OF STARS (IRE)**, 9, b g Mahler—Gold Flo (IRE) **Gilbert & Gamble**
38 **TARA BRIDGE**, 11, b g Kayf Tara—Annie Greenlaw **B. J. Champion**
39 **TELEGRAPH PLACE (IRE)**, 6, br g Yeats (IRE)—Sea Skate (USA) **Mr Roger Alwen Mrs Heather Alwen**
40 4, B br g Doyen (IRE)—Tropical Ocean (IRE) **Mr R. Cheshire**
41 **VICENZO MIO (FR)**, 9, b g Corri Piano (FR)—Sweet Valrose (FR) **Mr D. S. Dennis**
42 **VOLPONE JELOIS (FR)**, 6, gr g Vol de Nuit—Jenne Jelois (FR) **David Maxwell Racing Limited**
43 **YAMUNA RIVER**, 4, b f Foxwedge (AUS)—Harryana To **Ms E. J. Southall**

THREE-YEAR-OLDS

44 B f Doyen (IRE)—Grangeclare Rhythm (IRE) **C. E. Gordon**

Other Owners: Mr R. N. Alwen, Mrs H. J. Alwen, Mrs F. A. Axel-Berg, Mr L. W. Axel-Berg, Mrs Sarah Bullen, Mrs C. L. Cheshire, Miss R. S. S. Cooper, W. E. Enticknap, Mr J. M. Gamble, Mr S. C. Hobbs, Mrs S. C. Neville, Mr R. M. Venn.

Assistant Trainer: Jenny Gordon

Jockey (NH): Tom Cannon.

239 **MR JOHN GOSDEN, Newmarket**
Postal: **Clarehaven, Bury Road, Newmarket, Suffolk, CB8 7BY**
Contacts: **PHONE (01638) 565400 FAX (01638) 565401**
E-MAIL **jhmg@johngosden.com**

1 **BEN VRACKIE**, 4, b c Frankel—Kinnaird (IRE)
2 **CORELLI (USA)**, 4, b c Point of Entry (USA)—Vignette (USA)
3 **CORONET**, 5, gr m Dubawi (IRE)—Approach
4 **COURT HOUSE (IRE)**, 4, b c Dawn Approach (IRE)—Crossanza (IRE)
5 **CROSSED BATON**, 4, b c Dansili—Sacred Shield
6 **DREAMFIELD**, 5, b h Oasis Dream—Izzi Top
7 **EMBLAZONED (IRE)**, 4, b c Invincible Spirit (IRE)—Sendmylovetorose
8 **ENABLE**, 5, b m Nathaniel (IRE)—Concentric
9 **ENBIHAAR (IRE)**, 4, b f Redoute's Choice (AUS)—Chanterelle (FR)
10 **ERDOGAN**, 5, b h Frankel—Dar Re Mi
11 **FIRST ELEVEN**, 4, b c Frankel—Zenda
12 **HAMEEM**, 4, b f Teofilo (IRE)—Tres Ravi (GER)
13 **HIGHGARDEN**, 4, b f Nathaniel (IRE)—Regalline (IRE)
14 **LAH TI DAR**, 4, b f Dubawi (IRE)—Dar Re Mi

MR JOHN GOSDEN - Continued

15 **MILITARY LAW**, 4, b g Dubawi (IRE)—Marine Bleue (IRE)
16 **OSCAR'S RIDGE (IRE)**, 4, b c Galileo (IRE)—Posterity (IRE)
17 **ROYAL LINE**, 5, ch h Dubawi (IRE)—Melikah (IRE)
18 **STAR OF BENGAL**, 4, b c Oasis Dream—Stage Presence (IRE)
19 **STRADIVARIUS (IRE)**, 5, ch h Sea The Stars (IRE)—Private Life (FR)
20 **STREAM OF STARS**, 4, b g Sea The Stars (IRE)—Precious Gem (IRE)
21 **STYLEHUNTER**, 4, ch c Raven's Pass (USA)—Sunday Bess (JPN)
22 **WEEKENDER**, 5, b g Frankel—Very Good News (USA)
23 **WISSAHICKON (USA)**, 4, ch c Tapit (USA)—No Matter What (USA)
24 **WITHOUT PAROLE**, 4, b c Frankel—Without You Babe (USA)

THREE-YEAR-OLDS

25 **ALFAATIK**, b c Sea The Stars (IRE)—Biz Bar
26 **ALMASHRIQ (USA)**, b c War Front (USA)—Theyskens' Theory (USA)
27 **ALNORAS**, b f Kingman—Kareemah (IRE)
28 **ALRAJAA**, b c Dubawi (IRE)—Ethaara
29 **AMBLING (IRE)**, b f Lope de Vega (IRE)—Royale Danehill (IRE)
30 **AMMANNATI (IRE)**, b f Galileo (IRE)—Acoma (USA)
31 **ANAPURNA**, b f Frankel—Dash To The Top
32 **ANGEL'S HIDEAWAY (IRE)**, gr f Dark Angel (IRE)—The Hermitage (IRE)
33 **ARABIST**, b c Invincible Spirit (IRE)—Highest
34 **ASAATIER (USA)**, b f War Front (USA)—Spring In The Air (CAN)
35 **AZANO**, b c Oasis Dream—Azanara (IRE)
36 **BATTLE FOR GLORY (USA)**, b c War Front (USA)—Immortal Verse (IRE)
37 **BEATBOXER (USA)**, b c Scat Daddy (USA)—Thmoruplathlesupay (USA)
38 **BEGUILE**, gr f Pivotal—Infatuate
39 **BLADESMITH (IRE)**, ch c Mastercraftsman (IRE)—Annabelle Ja (FR)
40 **CALYX**, b c Kingman—Helleborine
41 **CASANOVA**, b c Frankel—Karen's Caper (USA)
42 **CHANDERI**, ch f Dubawi (IRE)—Silk Sari
43 **CONFIDE**, b c Lope de Vega (IRE)—Confidential Lady
44 **COPPER AND FIVE**, ch c Paco Boy (IRE)—Peachez
45 **COZI BAY**, gr f Kingman—Cozy Maria (USA)
46 **DAARIK (IRE)**, b c Tamayuz—Whip And Win (FR)
47 **DAMON RUNYON**, b c Charm Spirit (IRE)—Tawaasul
48 **DUBAI WARRIOR**, b c Dansili—Mahbooba (AUS)
49 **DUNEFLOWER (IRE)**, b f Dubawi (IRE)—Desert Blossom (IRE)
50 **EL MISK**, b c Dansili—Igugu (AUS)
51 **ELISHEBA (IRE)**, b f Australia—Laugh Out Loud
52 **ENTITLE**, b f Dansili—Concentric
53 **FABULIST**, b f Dubawi (IRE)—Melodramatic (IRE)
54 **FALAISE (USA)**, br f War Front (USA)—La Conseillante (USA)
55 **FALSEHOOD (IRE)**, gr c Kingman—Half Truth (IRE)
56 **FANFARONADE (USA)**, gr f Exchange Rate (USA)—Fanzine (USA)
57 **FANNY LOGAN (IRE)**, b f Sea The Stars (IRE)—Linda Radlett (IRE)
58 **FIGHTWITHME (IRE)**, b c Shamardal (USA)—Music Show (IRE)
59 **FINESPUN (IRE)**, b f Sea The Stars (IRE)—Gossamer
60 **FIRST IN LINE**, ch c New Approach (IRE)—Hidden Hope
61 **FLY THE FLAG**, gr f Australia—Approach
62 **FOREST OF DEAN**, b c Iffraaj—Forest Crown
63 **FRANZ KAFKA (IRE)**, ch c Dubawi (IRE)—Kailani
64 **FRISELLA**, b f Frankel—Panzanella
65 **GANTIER**, b g Frankel—Kid Gloves
66 **GENTLEWOMAN (IRE)**, b f Shamardal (USA)—Satin Kiss (USA)
67 **GODHEAD**, b c Charm Spirit (IRE)—Hello Glory
68 **GOLD STICK (IRE)**, b c Dubawi (IRE)—Gamilati
69 **GOOD TIDINGS (FR)**, b c Teofilo (IRE)—Nouvelle Bonne (FR)
70 **HANDMAIDEN**, b f Invincible Spirit (IRE)—Zabeel Park (USA)
71 **HARROVIAN**, b c Leroidesanimaux (BRZ)—Alma Mater
72 **HARRY HOTSPUR (IRE)**, b g Dubawi (IRE)—Hawsa (USA)
73 **HONEST ALBERT**, ch c Sepoy (AUS)—Mini Mosa
74 **HUMANITARIAN (USA)**, b c Noble Mission—Sharbat (USA)
75 **INFERENCE**, b f Intello (GER)—Dublino (USA)
76 **INFORMED FRONT (USA)**, gr c War Front (USA)—Informed Decision (USA)

MR JOHN GOSDEN - Continued

77 **INTRICATE**, b f Showcasing—Last Slipper
78 **JADEERAH**, b f Frankel—Maqaasid
79 **JAHAFIL**, b f Kingman—Taghrooda
80 **KESIA (IRE)**, ch f Australia—Caserta
81 **KICK ON**, b c Charm Spirit—Marika
82 **KIMBLEWICK (IRE)**, b f Iffraaj—Kiyra Wells (IRE)
83 **KING OF COMEDY (IRE)**, b c Kingman—Stage Presence (IRE)
84 **KOSCIUSZKO (IRE)**, b c Australia—Nobilis
85 **LADY LAWYER (USA)**, b f Blame (USA)—Profess (USA)
86 **LITIGIOUS**, b f Lawman (FR)—Field of Miracles (IRE)
87 **LOGICIAN**, gr c Frankel—Scuffle
88 **LONG BEACH**, b f Iffraaj—Pacifica Highway (USA)
89 **LORD NORTH (IRE)**, b c Dubawi (IRE)—Najoum (USA)
90 **LORD TENNYSON**, b c Poet's Voice—Poppet's Passion
91 **MAGICAL RHYTHMS (USA)**, br f Pioneerof the Nile (USA)—Nayarra (IRE)
92 **MAKE MY DAY (IRE)**, b c Galileo (IRE)—Posset
93 **MARHABA MILLIAR (IRE)**, b c Kodiac—Lady of The Desert (USA)
94 **MARIA DANILOVA (IRE)**, b f Galileo (IRE)—Dank
95 **MARY SOMERVILLE**, ch f Galileo (IRE)—Maureen (IRE)
96 **MAXIMUM EFFECT**, ch f Iffraaj—Dubai Bounty
97 **MEHDAAYIH**, b f Frankel—Sayyedati Symphony (USA)
98 **MERRY VALE**, b f Intello (GER)—Monturani (IRE)
99 **MERRY YARN (IRE)**, ch c Galileo (IRE)—Posterity (IRE)
100 **MILLICENT FAWCETT**, b f Kingman—Mainstay
101 **MISS MOROCCO**, b f Nathaniel (IRE)—Morocco Moon
102 **MOUSER (USA)**, gr ro g Kitten's Joy (USA)—Cozzy Street (USA)
103 **MUCHLY**, b f Iffraaj—Ego
104 **NAZEEF**, b f Invincible Spirit (IRE)—Handassa
105 **NEW ANGEL**, ch f New Approach (IRE)—Angel Terrace (USA)
106 **NEW JAZZ (USA)**, ch f Scat Daddy (USA)—Seanchai (USA)
107 **NEW KING**, b c Frankel—Marine Bleue (IRE)
108 **NONCHALANCE**, b f Dubawi (IRE)—Tearless
109 **PENNYWHISTLE (IRE)**, b f Iffraaj—Folk Melody (IRE)
110 **PIANISSIMO**, b c Teofilo (IRE)—Perfect Note
111 **PRIVATE SECRETARY**, b c Kingman—Intrigued
112 **PROMISSORY (IRE)**, b f Dubawi (IRE)—Seal of Approval
113 **QUEEN OF MAYFAIR**, b f Dubawi (IRE)—Wonder Why (GER)
114 **REPAUPO (USA)**, b c Quality Road (USA)—No Matter What (USA)
115 **ROYAL FAMILY (FR)**, b f Frankel—Crafty (AUS)
116 **SEVERNAYA (IRE)**, b f Dubawi (IRE)—Zibelina (IRE)
117 **SHAMBOLIC (IRE)**, b f Shamardal (USA)—Comic (IRE)
118 **SHE'S GOT YOU**, b f Kingman—Without You Babe (USA)
119 **SHERIFFMUIR (USA)**, b c War Front (USA)—Lerici (USA)
120 **SILENT SPIRIT**, b c Charm Spirit (IRE)—No Song
121 **SO HIGH**, ch c Nathaniel (IRE)—Fugitive Angel (USA)
122 **SPANISH ARIA**, b f Lope de Vega (IRE)—Woodland Aria
123 **SPARKLE ROLL (FR)**, gr f Kingman—Ysoldina (FR)
124 **STAR CATCHER**, b f Sea The Stars (IRE)—Lynnwood Chase (USA)
125 **STRATIFICATION (USA)**, ch f Australia—Rags To Riches (USA)
126 **SUAKIN (IRE)**, b f Motivator—Adeste
127 **SUCELLUS**, b c Dansili—Primevere (IRE)
128 **SWIFT WING**, ch c Pivotal—Gull Wing (IRE)
129 **TACITURN**, b g Dubawi (IRE)—Silent Moment (USA)
130 **TAHNEED (IRE)**, b f War Front (USA)—Auld Alliance (IRE)
131 **TEA DANCING**, b f Dubawi (IRE)—Princesse Dansante (IRE)
132 **TEREBELLUM (IRE)**, b f Sea The Stars (IRE)—Marvada (IRE)
133 **TO THE MOON**, b f Sea The Stars (IRE)—Ladys First
134 **TOO DARN HOT**, b c Dubawi (IRE)—Dar Re Mi
135 **TRAVEL ON**, b c Lope de Vega (IRE)—Teeky
136 **TURGENEV**, b c Dubawi (IRE)—Tasaday (IRE)
137 **VALENTINE'S DAY (IRE)**, b f Galileo (IRE)—L'amour de Ma Vie (USA)
138 **VANDELLA (IRE)**, b f Invincible Spirit (IRE)—Lady Livius (IRE)
139 **WALDSTERN**, ch c Sea The Stars (IRE)—Waldlerche
140 **WHIMBREL (IRE)**, gr f Dark Angel (IRE)—Seagull (IRE)
141 **WHITE COAT**, b c Dansili—Clinical

MR JOHN GOSDEN - Continued

142 **WILL OF IRON,** b c Invincible Spirit (IRE)—Astronomy Domine
143 **WIRRAWAY (USA),** ch c Australia—Fly Past
144 **WORLD'S FAIR,** ch f Showcasing—Coplow
145 **YURI GAGARIN,** ch c Sea The Moon (GER)—Soviet Terms

Trainer did not supply details of his two-year-olds.

Jockey (flat): L. Dettori, Kieran O'Neill, Nicky Mackay, Robert Havlin.

---

240 **MRS HARRIET GRAHAM, Jedburgh**
Postal: **Strip End, Jedburgh, Roxburghshire, TD8 6NE**
Contacts: **PHONE (01835) 840354 MOBILE (07843) 380401**
E-MAIL hgrahamracing@aol.com

1 **AYE RIGHT (IRE),** 6, b g Yeats (IRE)—Gaybric (IRE) **Mr G. F. Adam**
2 **BELL OFTHE BONGATE (IRE),** 5, b m Sakhee (USA)—Peace Lily **Mr M McGovern & Partner**
3 **BIG CHEVIOT,** 4, br g Bollin Eric—Miss Quickly (IRE) **H G Racing**
4 **RHYMERS STONE,** 11, b g Desideratum—Salu **Mr G. F. Adam**
5 **ROCKET MAN RODNEY,** 6, b g Black Sam Bellamy (IRE)—Miss Quickly (IRE) **H G Racing**

THREE-YEAR-OLDS

6 B f Black Sam Bellamy (IRE)—Minimum **H G Racing**

Other Owners: Mrs H. O. Graham, Mr R. D. Graham, Mr. M. J. McGovern.

Assistant Trainer: R D Graham

Conditional: Callum Bewley, Tommy Dowson.

---

241 **MR CHRIS GRANT, Billingham**
Postal: **Low Burntoft Farm, Wolviston, Billingham, Cleveland, TS22 5PD**
Contacts: **PHONE (01740) 644054 MOBILE (07860) 577998**
E-MAIL chrisgrantracing@gmail.com WEBSITE www.chrisgrantracing.co.uk

1 **ACDC (IRE),** 9, b g King's Theatre (IRE)—Always Alert (IRE) **D&D Armstrong Limited**
2 **ASK CAITLIN (IRE),** 5, b m Ask—Bold Cailin (IRE) **Mrs H. N. Eubank**
3 **ASKMEWHY (IRE),** 5, b g Ask—Grey Clouds **Mr T. J. Hemmings**
4 **BARFLY (IRE),** 5, gr g Fair Mix (IRE)—Just Smokie **D&D Armstrong Limited**
5 **BLUNDER BUSS (IRE),** 6, b g Court Cave (IRE)—Shantou Rose (IRE) **D&D Armstrong Limited**
6 **BROADWAY BELLE,** 9, b m Lucarno (USA)—Theatre Belle **Mrs M Nicholas & Chris Grant**
7 **CASTLE ON A CLOUD (IRE),** 8, b g Flemensfirth (USA)—Ifyoucouldseemenow (IRE) **C. Grant**
8 **DONNA'S DIAMOND (IRE),** 10, gr g Cloudings (IRE)—Inish Bofin (IRE) **D&D Armstrong Limited**
9 **DONNAS DREAM (IRE),** 6, b m Kalanisi (IRE)—Gerarda (IRE) **D&D Armstrong Limited**
10 **DOTHRAKI PRINCE,** 5, b g Sulamani (IRE)—Crystal Princess (IRE) **C. Grant**
11 **DRUMS OF WAR (IRE),** 7, b g Youmzain (IRE)—Min Asl Wafi (IRE) **J. Wade**
12 **EXPRESSTIME (IRE),** 6, b m Scorpion (IRE)—Glenair Dante (IRE) **D&D Armstrong Limited**
13 **GEORGIE BEAR,** 5, gr m Proclamation (IRE)—Glen Clova **G. F. White**
14 **GREEBA,** 5, ch g Getaway (GER)—Ladyday Lady **Mr T. J. Hemmings**
15 **HARRY THE POTTER,** 6, b g Sulamani (IRE)—Glen Clova **G. F. White**
16 **HEY BOB (IRE),** 7, br g Big Bad Bob (IRE)—Bounty Star (IRE) **Miss Alison P. Lee & Mr Chris Grant**
17 **JINKAMAN,** 5, b g Black Sam Bellamy (IRE)—Lady Jinks **Miss A. P. Lee**
18 **JO CASHFLOW (IRE),** 5, b m Getaway (GER)—Mary Kate O'brien **C. Grant**
19 **KALANITI (IRE),** 8, b m Kalanisi (IRE)—Miss Twinkletoes (IRE) **Mrs S. Sunter**
20 **KNOCKKING (IRE),** 5, b g Baltic King—Lady of Knock (IRE) **C. Grant**
21 **OUTNUMBERED (IRE),** 6, b g Stowaway—Back Market Lass **Mr N. E. M. Jones**
22 **PIECEOFTHEACTION (IRE),** 6, br g Oscar (IRE)—Homebird (IRE) **G. F. White**
23 **REAPLEE,** 6, ch g Recharge (IRE)—Chant de L'aube (FR) **Miss A. P. Lee**
24 **RED OCHRE,** 6, b g Virtual—Red Hibiscus **C. Grant**
25 **RED REMINDER,** 5, b m Mount Nelson—Red Hibiscus **Miss S. J. Turner**
26 **SALVEN,** 6, b g Presenting—Montefolene (IRE) **D. Mossop**
27 **SHEPHERD STORM (IRE),** 9, b g September Storm (GER)—Clerhane Belle (IRE) **J. Wade**
28 **SLANEMORE HILL (IRE),** 7, br g Court Cave (IRE)—Goodonyou-Polly (IRE) **The Hon Mrs D. J. Faulkner**
29 **STORMY RECEPTION (IRE),** 5, b m September Storm (GER)—Mandalus Lady (IRE) **Mrs S. Sunter**

MR CHRIS GRANT - Continued

30 **TAKING AIM (IRE)**, 7, b g Acambaro (GER)—Sharp Missile (IRE) **C. Grant**
31 **THEATRE ACT**, 8, ch m Act One—Theatre Belle **Division Bell Partnership**
32 **THEATRE LEGEND**, 6, b g Midnight Legend—Theatre Belle **Division Bell Partnership**
33 **ZAKETY ZAK**, 8, b g Overbury (IRE)—Jeanne d'arc **Mr D. M. Wordsworth**

Other Owners: T. Cunningham, A. Meale, Mrs M. Nicholas, A. D. Wright.

Assistant Trainer: Mrs S. Grant

Jockey (NH): Brian Hughes. **Conditional:** Callum Bewley.

---

242 | **MR JAMES GRASSICK, Cheltenham**
Postal: Dryfield Farm, Cleeve Hill, Cheltenham, Gloucestershire, GL54 5AG
Contacts: **MOBILE (07976) 779623**

1 **ISOBEL BLEU**, 4, b f Arvico (FR)—Applepie Lady (IRE) **J. R. Grassick**
2 **LADY NATASHA (IRE)**, 6, b m Alfred Nobel (IRE)—Hot To Rock (IRE) **J. R. Grassick**
3 4, B f Arvico (FR)—Pechaubar (FR) **J. R. Grassick**
4 **VALENTINE MIST (IRE)**, 7, b m Vale of York (IRE)—Silvertine (IRE) **J. R. Grassick**
5 **WAYWARD SUN (IRE)**, 8, b g Double Eclipse (IRE)—Mahonrun (IRE) **J. R. Grassick**

---

243 | **MR MICHAEL GRASSICK, The Curragh**
Postal: Fenpark House, Pollardstown, Curragh, Co. Kildare, Ireland
Contacts: **MOBILE (00353) 86 3648829**
E-MAIL michaelgrassick1@gmail.com WEBSITE www.michaelcgrassick.com

1 **KING OF ARAN (IRE)**, 12, b br g Val Royal (FR)—Innishmore (IRE) **M. C. Grassick**
2 **SILVRETTA SCHWARZ (IRE)**, 4, b br f Silver Frost (IRE)—Perruche Grise (FR) **Lets Feel Good Syndicate**
3 **TEXAS ROCK (IRE)**, 8, b g Rock of Gibraltar (IRE)—Vestavia (IRE) **J. Keeling**
4 **VARTANO (IRE)**, 5, br g Rock of Gibraltar (IRE)—Vestavia (IRE) **Roisin Walshe**
5 **VERHOYEN**, 4, b g Piccolo—Memory Lane **P. Cullen**

THREE-YEAR-OLDS

6 **BERRY GIRL (IRE)**, b f Slade Power (IRE)—Blueberry Gal (IRE) **J. Keeling**
7 Ch f Arakan (USA)—Blaenavon **Chris Grassick**
8 **CACTUS TREE (IRE)**, b f Camelot—Limetree Lady **T. Geary**
9 **EMILY GRACE (IRE)**, b f Elzaam (AUS)—Showmesomething (IRE) **P. Cullen**
10 **INDY SYSTEM (IRE)**, gr f Raven's Pass (USA)—Perruche Grise (FR) **T. Geary**
11 **LIVE SHOW (IRE)**, ch c Excelebration (IRE)—Livia Galilei (IRE) **M. C. Grassick**
12 B c Henrythenavigator (USA)—Only Exception (IRE) **Roisin Walshe**
13 **SEVENADAY**, b g Charm Spirit (IRE)—Vintage Gardenia **J Keeling**

TWO-YEAR-OLDS

14 Ch f 19/4 Rock of Gibraltar (IRE)—Blaenavon (Cadeaux Genereux) **Partnership**
15 B c 5/4 Raven's Pass (USA)—Blueberry Gal (IRE) (Bushranger (IRE)) (3370) **J. Keeling**
16 **MUSICAL MEMORIES**, b f 29/1 Piccolo—Memory Lane (With Approval (CAN)) **Miss K. Rausing**
17 B f 31/3 Elusive Pimpernel (USA)—Princess Nicole (IRE) (Alhaarth (IRE)) (841) **M. C. Grassick**
18 B c 23/5 Elzaam (AUS)—Showmesomething (IRE) (Mujadil (USA)) (3792) **P. Cullen**
19 Ch c 21/1 Leroidesanimaux (BRZ)—Stellaire (Archipenko (USA)) (4635) **P. O'Reilly**
20 B c 10/3 Dragon Pulse (IRE)—Vanitycase (IRE) (Editor's Note (USA)) **J. Keeling**

Assistant Trainer: David Flynn

Jockey (flat): W J Lee, Niall McCullagh. **Jockey (NH):** Danny Mullins.

---

244 | **MR CARROLL GRAY, Bridgwater**
Postal: The Little Glen, Peartwater Road, Spaxton, Bridgwater, Somerset, TA5 1DG
Contacts: **MOBILE (07989) 768163**

1 **ARTHUR'S QUEEN (FR)**, 8, b m Soldier of Fortune (IRE)—Tintagel **Mr R. J. Napper & Mr S Reeves**
2 **BELLAMY'S GREY**, 7, gr g Black Sam Bellamy (IRE)—Lambrini Queen **Riverdance Consortium 2**

MR CARROLL GRAY - Continued

3 **BERTIE BORU (IRE)**, 12, b g Brian Boru—Sleeven Lady **Unity Farm Holiday Centre Ltd**
4 **CAUTIOUS KATE (IRE)**, 12, b m Witness Box (USA)—Cautious Leader **Mr L & Mrs J Waring**
5 **TIS WONDERFUL (IRE)**, 5, b g Casamento (IRE)—Cosenza **Riverdance Consortium 3**

Other Owners: Mr M. J. Colenutt, Mr R. Napper, Mr S. Reeves, Mrs J. Waring, Mr L. Waring, Mr M. Wright.

Assistant Trainer: Mrs C. M. L. Gray

Jockey (NH): Micheal Nolan.

---

245 MR WARREN GREATREX, Upper Lambourn
Postal: Uplands, Upper Lambourn, Hungerford. Berkshire, RG17 8QH
Contacts: **PHONE** (01488) 670279 **FAX** (01488) 72193 **MOBILE** (07920) 039114
E-MAIL info@wgreatrexracing.com **WEBSITE** www.wgreatrexracing.com

1 4, B g Martalaine—Ailette **Mr W. J. Greatrex**
2 **ANOTHER EMOTION (FR)**, 7, gr g Turgeon (USA)—Line Perle (FR) **Mr Terry Warner & the McNeill Family**
3 **ARTICLE FIFTY (IRE)**, 6, b g Doyen (IRE)—Annie Go (IRE) **Swanee River Partnership**
4 **ATTEST**, 6, b g Cacique (IRE)—Change Course **Bolingbroke Bartram Flatt Molony Sutton**
5 **AURELLO**, 5, b m Kayf Tara—Haudello (FR) **Little Lodge Farm & Warren Greatrex**
6 **BAILARICO (IRE)**, 5, b g Dubawi (IRE)—Baila Me (GER) **Fitorfat Racing**
7 4, B g Yeats (IRE)—Belsalsa (FR) **Mr W. J. Greatrex**
8 **BLUBERRY HIGH (IRE)**, 5, b m Getaway (GER)—Blu Louisiana (IRE) **Mr W. J. Greatrex**
9 **BOB MAHLER (IRE)**, 7, b g Mahler—Cooladurragh (IRE) **Bolingbroke, Bunch, Howard & Sutton**
10 **BODES WELL (IRE)**, 4, b g Rock of Gibraltar (IRE)—Gypsie Queen (IRE) **Warren Greatrex Club**
11 **BOITE (IRE)**, 9, b g Authorized (IRE)—Albiatra (USA) **Mrs T. J. Stone-Brown**
12 **BRIGHT TOMORROW (IRE)**, 8, b g Robin des Pres (FR)—Gweedara (IRE) **Confex Racing For Charity**
13 **CAHILL (IRE)**, 7, b g Lawman (FR)—Malaspina (IRE) **Mr R. J. Vibert**
14 **CARNSPINDLE (IRE)**, 7, b m Ask—Whistling Gypse (IRE) **Fitorfat1 Racing**
15 4, B g Mahler—Coumhall (IRE) **Mr L. A. Bolingbroke**
16 **DANCINGWITH STORMS (IRE)**, 5, ch g New Approach—Mad About You (IRE) **Jadobry Management Ltd**
17 **DICOSIMO (IRE)**, 8, b g Laveron—Coralisse Royale (FR) **Mrs Jill Eynon & Mr Robin Eynon**
18 **DON DES FOSSES (FR)**, 6, b g Denham Red (FR)—Sara des Fosses (FR) **Glassex Holdings Ltd**
19 **DON'T ASK (IRE)**, 6, b m Ask—Outback Ivy (IRE) **Walters Plant Hire & James & Jean Potter**
20 **DRUMLEE WATAR (IRE)**, 6, ch g Watar (IRE)—Dolly of Dublin (IRE) **Bryan Drew & Friends/ Swanee River**
21 **ECTOR (FR)**, 5, b g Coastal Path—Evane (FR) **McNeill Family Ltd**
22 **EMITOM (IRE)**, 5, b g Gold Well—Avenging Angel (IRE) **The Spero Partnership Ltd**
23 **ENCORE CHAMPS (IRE)**, 5, b g Robin des Champs (FR)—
                                    Dani California **Bryan Drew/ Swanee River Partnership**
24 **ESCORT'NAMIX (FR)**, 6, b m Al Namix (FR)—Escortee (FR) **Mr N. Earls**
25 **EVRON (FR)**, 5, b g Secret Singer (FR)—Rive Droite (FR) **Mr Simon Munir & Mr Isaac Souede**
26 **GANGSTER (FR)**, 9, ch g Green Tune (USA)—Dahlia's Krissy (USA) **Mr W. J. Greatrex**
27 4, B g Jeremy (USA)—Golden Summer (IRE) **McNeill Family and Prodec Networks Ltd**
28 **GREAT RETURN**, 6, b g New Approach—Under the Rainbow **Fitorfat Racing**
29 **GROUNDUNDERREPAIR (IRE)**, 8, b g Milan—Discerning Air **Fleming Helyar & Sutton**
30 **HILLARY JOHN (IRE)**, 8, ch g Gamut (IRE)—Dar Dar Supreme **Warren Greatrex Club**
31 **INDIAN HERCULES (IRE)**, 7, b br g Whitmore's Conn (USA)—Carrawaystick (IRE) **Excel Racing**
32 **INFLUENTIAL LADY (IRE)**, 5, b m Doyen (IRE)—Lady Zephyr (IRE) **Lease Terminated**
33 **INVISIBLE CLOUDS (IRE)**, 6, gr g Cloudings (IRE)—Go My Dream **Mr T. J. Hemmings**
34 **JACKSON HILL (IRE)**, 5, b g Jeremy (USA)—Definite Leader (IRE) **Mr T. J. Hemmings**
35 **JAMMIN MASTERS (IRE)**, 8, b g Sinndar (IRE)—Zara Million (ITY) **No Dramas**
36 **KEEPER HILL (IRE)**, 8, b g Westerner—You Take Care (IRE) **McNeill Family Ltd**
37 **KEMBLE'S CASCADE (IRE)**, 4, b g Kalanisi (IRE)—Beauty Star (IRE) **A. W. K. Merriam**
38 **KYLLACHY GALA**, 6, b g Kyllachy—Tenuta di Gala (IRE) **Excel Racing & Lee Bolingbroke**
39 **LA BAGUE AU ROI (FR)**, 8, b m Doctor Dino (FR)—
                                    Alliance Royale (FR) **Mrs Julien Turner & Mr Andrew Merriam**
40 **LITTLE JACK**, 5, b g Malinas (GER)—Persian Forest **Jadobry Management Ltd**
41 **LOVENORMONEY (IRE)**, 8, br g Winged Love (IRE)—Dixies Gem (IRE) **Mr T. D. J. Syder**
42 **MADAM MALINA**, 5, b m Malinas (GER)—Madam Jolie (IRE) **Bolingbroke Da Mata Molony & Sutton**
43 **MAHLERVOUS (IRE)**, 6, b g Mahler—Brook Style (IRE) **The Marvellous Partnership**
44 **MAITREE EXPRESS**, 5, br g Malinas (GER)—Shatabdi (IRE) **Mr R. B. Waley-Cohen**
45 **MARTHA BRAE**, 4, b f Shirocco (GER)—Harringay **Mrs R. I. Vaughan**
46 **MASTER CARD**, 6, ch g Presenting—Subtlity **Shropshire Wanderers**
47 **MINELLA EXAMINER (IRE)**, 6, b g Beat Hollow—Bold Fire **Bolingbroke, Spero, Richards & Friends**
48 **MISS HONEY RYDER (IRE)**, 6, b m Stowaway—Seesea (IRE) **The Albatross Club**

MR WARREN GREATREX - Continued

49 MISSED APPROACH (IRE), 9, b g Golan (IRE)—Polly's Dream (IRE) **Alan & Andrew Turner**
50 MULCAHYS HILL (IRE), 7, b g Brian Boru—Belsalsa (FR) **McNeill Family and Prodec Networks Ltd**
51 MYTHICAL PRINCE (IRE), 7, b g Beneficial—Conker Nails (IRE) **Mr L. A. Bolingbroke**
52 NOBLE QUEST, 7, b g Kalanisi (IRE)—Katlana **Mrs R. I. Vaughan**
53 NORTH STAR OSCAR (IRE), 5, b g Oscar (IRE)—
North Star Poly (IRE) **Walters Plant Hire & James & Jean Potter**
54 4, B f Great Pretender (IRE)—One Gulp **Swanee River Partnership**
55 PENN LANE (IRE), 8, b g Scorpion (IRE)—Belsalsa (FR) **Alan & Andrew Turner**
56 4, B g Westerner—Pepsi Starlet (IRE)
57 PETTICOAT TAILS, 7, b m Presenting—Theatre Girl **Wynnstay Wanderers**
58 PRINTING DOLLARS, 6, b m Doyen (IRE)—Printing Polly (IRE) **Mr R. B. Waley-Cohen**
59 RITUAL OF SENSES (IRE), 9, b g Milan—Nonnetia (FR) **Lady Lloyd- Webber, Cavanagh & Egerton**
60 ROCCOWITHLOVE, 5, b g Shirocco (GER)—Love Train **Grech & Parkin**
61 ROCK MY STYLE (IRE), 7, b g Marienbard (IRE)—Meara Trasna (IRE) **Alan & Andrew Turner**
62 ROSE OF CIMARRON (IRE), 6, b m Westerner—Sharp Single (IRE) **The Munificent Seven**
63 SANDHURST LAD (IRE), 8, b g Presenting—Off She Goes (IRE) **Nigel & Barbara Collison**
64 SARIM (IRE), 4, b g Declaration of War (USA)—Silver Star **Warren Greatrex Club**
65 STAR OF LANKA (IRE), 5, b g Zoffany (IRE)—Indian Bounty **J&r Eynon,Little,Roberts,Dowley&turner**
66 TALKTOMENOW, 5, b g Shirocco (GER)—Sweet Stormy (IRE) **Mr T. D. J. Syder**
67 THE WOLF (FR), 5, ch g Kapgarde (FR)—Ges (FR) **McNeill Family and Prodec Networks Ltd**
68 THEATRE TERRITORY (IRE), 9, b m King's Theatre—Specifiedrisk (IRE) **Mr R. B. Waley-Cohen**
69 TOBY MAGUIRE (IRE), 6, b g Darsi (FR)—Minnie Maguire (IRE) **Charles Levinson & Alexia Robinson**
70 TOP OF THE CHARTS (FR), 5, b g Great Pretender (IRE)—
Precious Lucy (FR) **McNeill Family and Prodec Networks Ltd**
71 TOP ROCK TALULA (IRE), 4, b f Lord Shanakill (USA)—Spirit Watch (IRE) **Fitorfat Racing**
72 TURN FOR RIO (IRE), 6, b br g Getaway (GER)—Rio Trio (IRE) **Million in Mind Partnership**
73 WESTERN RYDER (IRE), 7, b g Westerner—Seesea (IRE) **Albatross Club/Bryan Drew & Friends**
74 YOUNG LIEUTENANT (IRE), 5, b g Robin des Champs (FR)—Be My Gesture (IRE) **Mrs S. M. Drysdale**

Other Owners: R. K. Aston, Mr C. Austin, J. Baldwin, Mr M. Bartram, J. R. Bayer, Mr T. E. Boylan, A. R. Bromley, Bryan Drew and Friends, Mrs P. M. Bunch, Mr J. P. Cavanagh, N. J. Chamberlain, Mrs J. S. Chugg, Mr R. D. Chugg, Mr N. Collison, Mrs B. Collison, Mr C. K. Crossley Cooke, Mr J. P Da Mata, Mr K. J. Dowley, Mr B. J. C. Drew, G. K. Duncan, Mr C. R. Egerton, R. A. F. Eynon, Mrs J. M. Eynon, Mr P Fisher, Mr S. R. Fisher, Mrs G. Fisher, Mr D. R. Flatt, Mrs D. J. Fleming, Mr T. R. Gittins, G. F. Goode, Mr C. M. Grech, R. A. Green, Mr M. W. Gregory, Mr M. Helyar, Mr G. P. Howard, S. Hurst, James & Jean Potter, Dr C. M. Levinson, Mr S. M. Little, Little Roberts Dowley & Turner, Lady Lloyd-Webber, Mrs J. M. Minton, Mr W. D. C. Minton, Mr P. Molony, S. E. Munir, Mrs D. C. Nicholson, Palatinate Thoroughbred Racing Limited, Mr S. J. Parkin, Mr S. J. Piper, Mr N. Pogmore, Mrs M. J. Potter, Mr J. E. Potter, Prodec Networks Ltd, Mr J. Ratcliffe, Mr A. W. Richards, Mr D. A. Roberts, Ms A. Robinson, Mr S. R. Roper, Mr W. L. Smith, Mr I. Souede, Mrs K. A. Stuart, Mr C. J. Sutton, Mr A. R. Turner, Mr A. M. Turner, Mr J. S. E. Turner, Mr D. A. Turner, Mrs N. C. Turner, Walters Plant Hire Ltd, J. T. Warner, Mrs N. White, I. F. White.

Assistant Trainer: Olly Kozak **Head Lads:** Trigger Plunkett, Ian Yeates

Jockey (flat): Edward Greatrex. **Jockey (NH):** Adrian Heskin, Daryl Jacob, Richard Johnson, Gavin Sheehan, Andrew Tinkler. **Conditional:** Ben Hicks, Harry Teal. **Apprentice:** Thomas Greatrex. **Amateur:** Mr A Elias, Mr L Spencer.

---

246 **MR OLIVER GREENALL, Malpas**
Postal: Stockton Hall Farm, Oldcastle, Malpas, Cheshire, SY14 7AE
Contacts: PHONE (01948) 861207 MOBILE (07771) 571000
E-MAIL ocg@stocktonhall.co.uk WEBSITE www.olivergreenall.co.uk

1 ABSOLUTE JAFFA, 4, ch f Lucarno (USA)—Reverse Swing **Astbury, Hewitt & Hockenhull**
2 ACE VENTURA, 4, b g Mayson—Ventura Highway **Hardscrabble**
3 AKILAYA (IRE), 4, b f Getaway (GER)—Akilara (IRE) **D. M. W. Hodgkiss**
4 ARCTIC ROAD, 6, b g Flemensfirth (USA)—Arctic Actress **Mr J. F. Wilson**
5 ASKING QUESTIONS (IRE), 7, b g Ask—Just Sara (IRE) **Salmon Racing**
6 BLUE BALLERINA (IRE), 5, br m Fame And Glory—
Peinture Rose (IRE) **P Nolan, T Nolan, P Norbury, P Daresbury**
7 BOSSINEY BAY (IRE), 4, b f Camelot—Ursula Minor (IRE) **Mr O. C. Greenall**
8 CAVE TOP (IRE), 7, b g Court Cave—Cyrils Top Girl (IRE) **Lord Daresbury & Jocelyn Rosenburg**
9 COISA BLANCO (IRE), 6, b g Jeremy (USA)—Moon Legend (USA) **S.Evason,A.Clarke,R.Hewitt & O.Greenall**
10 COURT IN MATERA (IRE), 5, b g Court Cave (IRE)—
Orador Sur Glane (IRE) **Daresbury,Macechern,Hewitt&lee Baldwin**
11 DEBROUILLARD (FR), 6, b g Irish Wells (FR)—Indecise (FR) **Burns Smyth Studholme**
12 DESERT STING, 10, b g Scorpion (IRE)—Skipcarl (IRE) **Mrs B Bostock & Mr P Cartmell**

MR OLIVER GREENALL - Continued

13 **HELF (IRE)**, 5, b g Helmet (AUS)—Causeway Song (USA) **Hewitt & Ocg Racing Club**
14 **KATEBIRD (IRE)**, 5, gr m Dark Angel (IRE)—She Basic (IRE) **Mrs J. P. Rosenberg**
15 **LATE ROMANTIC (IRE)**, 9, b g Mahler—Mere Gaye (IRE) **Spitalized Racing**
16 **LESKINFERE (IRE)**, 6, b g Darsi (FR)—Taipans Girl (IRE) **Racing Spirit Leskinfere Owners Group**
17 **LORD COUNTY (FR)**, 5, gr g Lord du Sud (FR)—County County (FR) **E. A. Brook**
18 **LUCKY LOVER BOY (IRE)**, 4, b g Teofilo (IRE)—Mayonga (IRE) **Mr O. C. Greenall**
19 **MID DAY GUN (IRE)**, 6, ch g Robin des Champs (FR)—Crackin' Liss (IRE) **Evason, Dodd, Hewitt & Walsh**
20 **MISS DELIGHTED (IRE)**, 6, b m Getaway (GER)—
                            Abhainn Ri (IRE) **Arkwright Blum Michaelson Onions Daresbury**
21 **MR YOUNG (FR)**, 5, ch g Mr Sidney (USA)—Young Majesty (USA) **Mr D. C. Mercer**
22 **NEVER A WORD (USA)**, 5, br g Lonhro (AUS)—Janetstickettocats (USA) **Mr G. Dewhurst**
23 **OMOTESANDO**, 9, b g Street Cry (IRE)—Punctilious **P. G. Evans**
24 **SHADY CHARACTER**, 6, b g Malinas (GER)—Shady Anne **Jocelyn Rosenberg & Roger Weatherby**
25 **SHOTGUN SALLY (IRE)**, 6, b m Milan—Awesome Miracle (IRE) **Cheshire Racing**
26 **STRONG RESEMBLANCE (IRE)**, 8, b g Tikkanen (USA)—Shenamar (IRE) **Oliver's Army**
27 **TIM ROCCO (GER)**, 7, ch g Doyen (IRE)—Timbalada (GER) **The Tim Rocco Partnership**
28 **TWOTWOTHREE (IRE)**, 6, b g Shantou (USA)—Sibury (IRE) **Evason, Hewitt, Michaelson & Walsh**
29 **VEREINA**, 4, b f Universal (IRE)—Lady de La Vega (FR) **Oliver Greenall Racing Club**
30 **ZALVADOS (FR)**, 6, ch g Soldier of Fortune (IRE)—Zariyana (IRE) **Mr D. C. Mercer**

THREE-YEAR-OLDS

31 **MI LADDO (IRE)**, b gr g Lilbourne Lad (IRE)—Fritta Mista (IRE) **The Two Greys Syndicate**

Other Owners: Mrs Sandra G. E. Arkwright, Mr D. J. Astbury, Mrs J. L. Baldwin, Mr W. B. B. Blum Gentilomo, Mrs B. A. Bostock, Mr S. Burns, Mr P. Cartmell, Mr A. Clarke, Mr S. A. Coxon, Lord Daresbury, Mr K. J. Dodd, Mr S. Evason, Mr E. Glassonbury, R. J. Hewitt, P. D. Hockenhull, Mr M. J. Jones, Mr M. H. Lampton, Mr K. R. Lawton, Gavin MacEchern, R. P. B. Michaelson, Mr T. Nolan, Mr P. Nolan, C. P. Norbury, Mr A. W. Onions, Mrs Lynn Salmon, Mr M. W. Salmon, Mr D. B. Salmon, Mr M. Smyth, Mr J. E. Stockton, Mr D. Studholme, Mr S. M. Walsh, Mr R. N. Weatherby.

Assistant Trainer: J. Guerriero

---

247 **MR TOM GRETTON, Inkberrow**
Postal: C/o Gretton & Co Ltd, Middle Bouts Farm, Bouts Lane, Inkberrow, Worcester
Contacts: PHONE (01386) 792240 FAX (01386) 792472 MOBILE (07866) 116928
E-MAIL tomgretton@hotmail.co.uk WEBSITE www.tomgrettonracing.com

1 **BAGAN**, 5, ch g Sulamani (IRE)—Aunt Rita (IRE) **Tom Gretton Racing Club**
2 **INCERTAINE**, 6, b m Milan—La Dame Brune (FR) **Mr J. R. Hynes**
3 **JIGCLEANINGUS (IRE)**, 6, b g Ask—Vocative (GER) **Mr B. P. Keogh**
4 **JIMMY'S SISTER**, 6, b m Denounce—Sementina (USA) **Ownaracehorse Ltd & Mr T. R. Gretton**
5 **KAUTO RIKO (FR)**, 8, b g Ballingarry (IRE)—Kauto Relstar (FR) **Mr & Mrs J.Dale & Partners**
6 **KEPPEL ISLE (IRE)**, 10, b g Heron Island (IRE)—Wadi Khaled (FR) **Tom Gretton Racing Club**
7 **LASSANA ANGEL**, 5, b m High Chaparral (IRE)—Diara Angel (IRE) **Ownaracehorse Ltd & Mr T. R. Gretton**
8 **LICKPENNY LARRY**, 8, gr g Sagamix (FR)—Myriah (IRE) **Mr A. S. Clarke**
9 **LITTLE JIMMY**, 12, br g Passing Glance—Sementina (USA) **Tom Gretton Racing & Ownaracehorse Ltd**
10 **OENOPHILE (GER)**, 4, b f Mamool (IRE)—Ormita (GER) **4 Of Us and partner**
11 **SHAW'S DILEMMA**, 5, bl m Sakhee (USA)—Donastrela (USA) **Mr B. P. Keogh**
12 **SNOW RESCUE (IRE)**, 7, gr g Stowaway—Annilogs Palm (IRE) **Ian Powell & Ownaracehorse Ltd**
13 **VIVA LA VEGA**, 5, b m Sulamani (IRE)—Lady de La Vega (FR) **Edwards, Richards & Ray**
14 **YOURHOLIDAYISOVER (IRE)**, 12, ch g Sulamani (IRE)—Whitehaven **G1 Racing Club Ltd**

Other Owners: 4 Of Us, Mr J. W. Dale, Mrs J. S. Dale, Mr B. Dennehy, Mr J. P. Edwards, Mrs L. Gretton, T. R. Gretton, Ownaracehorse Ltd, Mr G. C. Parkins, Mr I. Powell, Mr T. Rees.

Assistant Trainer: Laura Gretton (07789) 754806

---

248 **MR DAVID C. GRIFFITHS, Bawtry**
Postal: Martin Hall, Martin Common, Bawtry, Doncaster, South Yorkshire, DN10 6DA
Contacts: PHONE (01302) 714247 MOBILE (07816) 924621
E-MAIL davidgriffiths250@hotmail.com WEBSITE www.davidgriffithsracing.co.uk

1 **ARCHIMEDES (IRE)**, 6, b g Invincible Spirit (IRE)—Waveband **Ladies & The Tramps**
2 **CYFLYMDER (IRE)**, 13, b g Mujadil (USA)—Nashwan Star (IRE) **Mr D. C. Griffiths**

MR DAVID C. GRIFFITHS - Continued

3 **DUKE OF FIRENZE**, 10, ch g Pivotal—Nannina **Adlam,Damary-Thompson,Wilson,Griffiths**
4 **KILLER QUEEN**, 4, b f Havana Gold (IRE)—Radio Gaga **R. Kent**
5 **LUCKY BEGGAR (IRE)**, 9, gr g Verglas (IRE)—Lucky Clio (IRE) **Eros Bloodstock**
6 **MAGIC PULSE (IRE)**, 4, b f Dragon Pulse (IRE)—Invincible Magic (IRE) **Mr C. Buckingham**
7 **MYSTICAL MOON (IRE)**, 4, ch f Excelebration (IRE)—Boast **Wentdale Limited & Partner**
8 **ORNATE**, 6, b g Bahamian Bounty—Adorn **Kings Road Racing Partnership**
9 **PEARL ACCLAIM (IRE)**, 9, b g Acclamation—With Colour **Ontoawinner 2 & Partner**
10 **RED CYMBAL**, 4, b g Pivotal—Red Baton **Mr C. Buckingham**
11 **SANDYTOWN (IRE)**, 4, b g Tamayuz—Wild Ways **Quinn & Co**
12 **STAR OF VALOUR (IRE)**, 4, b g Invincible Spirit (IRE)—Birthstone **Mr C. Buckingham**
13 **TAVENER**, 7, b g Exceed And Excel (AUS)—Sea Chorus **Baker, Hensby, Longden, Baker**
14 **WARRIOR'S VALLEY**, 4, b g Mayson—Sand And Deliver **Mr N Davies, Mr D Clarke & Eros**

THREE-YEAR-OLDS

15 **ARTHUR SHELBY**, ch g Arakan (USA)—Ambonnay **The Count On Arthur Racing Club & 1**
16 **BAWTRY LADY**, b f Epaulette (AUS)—Precious Secret (IRE) **Mr D. C. Griffiths**

Other Owners: Mr J. P. Adlam, Mr R. Baker, Mr D. J. Clarke, Miss H. A. Damary-Thompson, Mr G. Davidoff, Mr N. J. Davies, Mrs S. E. Griffiths, Mr G. D. Hensby, K&J Bloodstock Ltd, Mr A. R. Lavender, Mr N. J. O'Brien, Mr P. S. Quinn, Mr J. Slater, The Count on Arthur Racing Club, Wentdale Limited, Mr L. Wilson.

Assistant Trainer: Mrs S. E. Griffiths

---

249 **MR SIRRELL GRIFFITHS, Carmarthen**
Postal: **Rwyth Farm, Nantgaredig, Carmarthen, Dyfed, SA32 7LG**
Contacts: **PHONE (01267) 290321/290120**

1 **COUSIN RITA**, 7, b m Black Sam Bellamy (IRE)—Aunt Rita (IRE) **S. G. Griffiths**
2 **LORD EDWARD (IRE)**, 7, b g Scorpion (IRE)—Schwarzina (IRE) **S. G. Griffiths**

Assistant Trainer: Martyn Roger Griffiths

---

250 **MRS DIANA GRISSELL, Robertsbridge**
Postal: **Brightling Park, Robertsbridge, East Sussex, TN32 5HH**
Contacts: **PHONE (01424) 838241 MOBILE (07950) 312610**
E-MAIL digrissell@aol.com WEBSITE www.brightlingpark.com

1 **CANYOUHEARMENOW (IRE)**, 8, b g Trans Island—First of April (IRE) **Mr P.S.Wardle & Mr.J.N.Allen**
2 **DOWNE MILKING LANE**, 5, b g Fair Mix (IRE)—Downe Payment (IRE) **Gardie Grissell & Mrs E.A.Lynch**
3 **EOS (FR)**, 5, gr m Martaline—Oreli (FR) **Mr J. B. Robinson**
4 **GRAYHAWK (IRE)**, 9, gr g Kalanisi (IRE)—Saddler Regal (IRE) **Mrs C. V. Wedmore**
5 **HERE I AM (IRE)**, 12, b g Presenting—The Last Bank (IRE) **Nigel & Barbara Collison**
6 **MICKIEBLUEEYES (IRE)**, 7, b g Dilshaan—Killerig Park **Mr K. M. Dilworth**
7 **MILTON**, 7, br g Nomadic Way (USA)—Jesmund **Ms C. A. Lacey**
8 **WRITINGSONTHEWALL (IRE)**, 8, ch g Vinnie Roe (IRE)—Saddlers Eve (IRE) **Mr R. Mackenzie**

Other Owners: Mr J. N. Allen, Mrs B. Collison, Mr N. Collison, D. M. Grissell, Mrs E. E. A. Lynch, P. S. Wardle.

Assistant Trainer: Paul Hacking

Jockey (NH): Marc Goldstein. **Amateur:** Mr O. Wedmore.

---

251 **MR JOHN GROUCOTT, Much Wenlock**
Postal: **Dairy Cottage, Bourton, Much Wenlock, Shropshire, TF13 6QD**
Contacts: **PHONE (01746) 785603**

1 **BATTLEBRAVE (IRE)**, 6, b g Fracas (IRE)—Silly Mille (IRE) **Mrs B. Clarke**
2 **DARK SAPPHIRE**, 5, b m Malinas (GER)—Sunnyland **Mrs C. Craig**
3 **EL SCORPIO (IRE)**, 7, b g Scorpion (IRE)—El Monica (IRE) **Mrs B. Clarke**
4 **HAPPY NEWS**, 6, gr m Fair Mix (IRE)—Welcome News **Mrs C. L. Shaw**
5 **HEAVENLY PROMISE (IRE)**, 8, ch m Presenting—Ambrosia's Promise (IRE) **Geoff Hubbard Racing**
6 **JESSIE LIGHTFOOT (IRE)**, 5, b m Yeats (IRE)—Needle Doll (IRE) **Mr E. C. Parkes**

MR JOHN GROUCOTT - Continued

7 **LADY RED OAK**, 8, ch m Medicean—Nuit Sans Fin (FR) **Mr D. R. Passant**
8 **MIDNIGHT TARGET**, 9, b m Midnight Legend—Right On Target (IRE) **Mr E. P. Parkes**
9 **MUSE OF FIRE (IRE)**, 5, b g Getaway (GER)—Maria Sophia (IRE) **C. J. Tipton**
10 **NEWERA**, 7, ch g Makfi—Coming Home **Mr D. R. Passant**
11 **OVERAWED**, 8, b m Overbury (IRE)—Alleged To Rhyme (IRE) **Mrs E. A. Fletcher**
12 **PEARLESQUE (FR)**, 7, gr m Martaline—Anazeem (IRE) **J. B. Groucott**
13 **QUASI (IRE)**, 7, ch g Presenting—Pink Mist (IRE) **Mr D. R. Passant**
14 **ROSIERITA**, 5, b m Black Sam Bellamy (IRE)—Mtilly **Mrs B. Clarke**
15 **SHININSTAR (IRE)**, 10, b g Westerner—Shiny Button **Mrs B. Clarke**
16 **SIDSTEEL (IRE)**, 8, b g Craigsteel—Clare Hogan (IRE) **Mrs B. Clarke**
17 **STAR OF RORY (IRE)**, 5, b g Born To Sea (IRE)—Dame Alicia (IRE) **Mr D. R. Passant & Hefin Williams**
18 **THE TOOJUMPA**, 6, b m Midnight Legend—Sunnyland **Lord C. D. Harrison**
19 **TRUCKERS HIGHWAY**, 10, b g Rudimentary (USA)—Countessdee (IRE) **C. J. Tipton**

THREE-YEAR-OLDS

20 B f Schiaparelli (GER)—Sunnyland

Other Owners: Mr J. E. H. Reader, Mrs J. Reader, Mr H. Williams.

---

252 **MR RAE GUEST, Newmarket**
Postal: **Chestnut Tree Stables, Hamilton Road, Newmarket, Suffolk, CB8 0NY**
Contacts: **PHONE (01638) 661508 FAX (01638) 667317 MOBILE (07711) 301095**
E-MAIL raeguest@raeguest.com WEBSITE www.raeguest.com

1 **ALASKAN BAY (IRE)**, 4, b f Kodiac—Party Appeal (USA) **Mr P. A. Sakal**
2 **DANCE LEGEND**, 4, b f Camelot—Syvilla **Mr T. J. Cooper**
3 **ETERNAL DESTINY**, 4, b f Poet's Voice—Mrs Mogg **4G Racing Ltd**
4 **KACHUMBA**, 4, b f Mayson—Native Nickel (IRE) **The Bucket List Racing Syndicate**
5 **MIDNIGHTLY**, 5, b m Acclamation—Midnight Shift (IRE) **Bradmill Meats Ltd**
6 **MINORIA**, 4, ch f Harbour Watch (IRE)—Mina **C. J. Mills**
7 **MINUTY**, 4, b f Acclamation—Million Faces **C. J. Mills**
8 **MIRZA**, 12, b g Oasis Dream—Millyant **C. J. Mills**
9 **ROMAN SPINNER**, 4, ch f Intikhab (USA)—Pompeia **Reprobates Too**
10 **SALT WHISTLE BAY (IRE)**, 5, b g Royal Applause—Quantum (IRE) **The Hightailers & Rae Guest**
11 **SHOW STEALER**, 6, ch m Showcasing—Winifred Jo **Mr C. S. Joseph**
12 **THE EAGLE'S NEST (IRE)**, 5, ch g Lope de Vega (IRE)—Follow My Lead **The Eagle Has Landed**
13 **WALLFLOWER (IRE)**, 4, b f Thewayyouare—Gaselee **Paul Smith & Rae Guest**

THREE-YEAR-OLDS

14 **BRICKLEBRIT**, ch f Sir Percy—Blush's Gift **Mr E. F. Albert**
15 **DEPTFORD MICK (IRE)**, br g Bated Breath—Be Joyful (IRE) **Purple & Yellow**
16 **DUPIONI (IRE)**, ch f Siyouni (FR)—Kincob (USA) **A. P. Rogers**
17 **ECSTASEA (IRE)**, b f Born To Sea (IRE)—Rhapsodize **The Reprobates**
18 **FASHIONESQUE (IRE)**, b f Fast Company (IRE)—Featherlight **Miss V. Markowiak**
19 **LAND OF WINTER (FR)**, b g Camelot—Gaselee (USA) **Paul Smith & Rae Guest**
20 **MOUNTAIN DOG**, b c Mount Nelson—The Blue Dog (IRE) **Mr R. W. Carson**
21 B f Bated Breath—Ruffled **Mr C. J. Murfitt**
22 B f Roderic O'Connor—Salsa Brava (IRE) **G. F. L. Robinson**

TWO-YEAR-OLDS

23 **DREAMBOAT GIRL (IRE)**, b f 5/2 Dream Ahead (USA)—
    Junia Tepzia (IRE) (Rock of Gibraltar (IRE)) (6000) **The Storm Again Syndicate**
24 B f 27/3 Cityscape—Lady Gabrielle (IRE) (Dansili) (7000) **Mr R. Guest**
25 B f 25/3 Golden Horn—Morzine (Miswaki (USA)) (12000) **RGRL Syndicate 2**
26 B f 15/3 War Command (USA)—Na Zdorovie (Cockney Rebel (IRE)) (16000) **RGRL Syndicate 2**
27 **ROSA GOLD**, b f 24/1 Havana Gold—Rosa Grace (Lomitas) (16000) **Mr E. P. Duggan**
28 Gr f 6/2 Gutaifan (IRE)—Sveva (IRE) (Danehill Dancer (IRE)) (9000) **RGRL Syndicate 2**

Other Owners: Mr A. P. Davies, J. W. Fullick, R. T. Goodes, The Hightailers, Mr R. H. Jennings, Mrs L. M. Lambert, D. G. Raffel, Mr P. J. Smith, Mr B. Stewart, Mr D. J. Willis, Mrs H. M. Worboys, J. R. Worboys.

253 MR RICHARD GUEST, Ingmanthorpe

Postal: **Ingmanthorpe Racing Stables, Ingmanthorpe Grange Farm, Ingmanthorpe, Wetherby, West Yorkshire, LS22 5HL**
Contacts: **PHONE 0800 2988088 (07715) 516072 (07713) 132577 MOBILE (07715) 516071**
E-MAIL **enquiries@richardguestracing.co.uk** WEBSITE **www.richardguestracing.co.uk**

1 **AMBITIOUS ICARUS**, 10, b g Striking Ambition—Nesting Box **Mrs A. Guest**
2 **BREATHOFFRESHAIR**, 5, b g Bated Breath—Stormy Weather **Mr R. C. Guest**
3 **EXCHEQUER (IRE)**, 8, ch g Exceed And Excel (AUS)—Tara's Force **A. R. Barnes**
4 **FOXRUSH TAKE TIME (FR)**, 4, b g Showcasing—Stranded **Mrs C N Clayton & Partner**
5 **ISNTSHESOMETHING**, 7, br m Assertive—Princess Almora **Mr C. J. Penney**
6 **LADY JOANNA VASSA (IRE)**, 6, ch m Equiano (FR)—Lady Natilda **Mrs A. Guest**
7 **LASTMANLASTROUND (IRE)**, 6, b g Azamour (IRE)—Lastroseofsummer (IRE) **Mr R. C. Guest**
8 **LOUGH SALT (IRE)**, 8, b g Brian Boru—Castlehill Lady (IRE) **Mr J Toes & Mr J O'Loan**
9 **MR POTTER**, 6, ch g Assertive—Enclave (USA) **A. Turton, A. Rhodes & Mrs Alison Guest**
10 **MY GIRL MAISIE (IRE)**, 5, b m Fast Company (IRE)—Queen Al Andalous (IRE) **Mr R. C. Guest**
11 **OUTLAW TORN (IRE)**, 10, ch g Iffraaj—Touch And Love (IRE) **Mr J Toes & Mr J O'Loan**
12 **TELLOVOI (IRE)**, 11, b g Indian Haven—Kloonlara (IRE) **The Captain Scooby Syndicate**
13 **UDONTDODOU**, 6, b g Fastnet Rock (AUS)—Forever Times **Mrs A. Guest**
14 **WHATWOULDYOUKNOW**, 4, b g Lope de Vega (IRE)—Holamo (IRE) **Dearing Plastics Ltd & Partner**

THREE-YEAR-OLDS

15 **JIMMY KRANKYAR (USA)**, gr ro g Exchange Rate (USA)—Lastroseofsummer (IRE) **Mrs W. Burdett**
16 **TREASURED COMPANY (IRE)**, b g Fast Company (IRE)—Lady's Locket (IRE) **Mrs A. Guest**

TWO-YEAR-OLDS

17 Pt c 10/5 Angrove Spottedick—Charlemagne Diva (Holy Roman Emperor (IRE)) **Mr C. J. Penney**

Other Owners: Mrs C. N. Clayton, Dearing Plastics Ltd, Mr John O'Loan, Mr A. Rhodes, Mr J. Toes, Mr A. Turton.

254 MS POLLY GUNDRY, Ottery St Mary

Postal: **Holcombe Brook, Holcombe Lane, Ottery St Mary, Devon, EX11 1PH**
Contacts: **PHONE (01404) 811181 MOBILE (07932) 780621**
E-MAIL **pollygundrytraining@live.co.uk** WEBSITE **www.pollygundrytraining.co.uk**

1 **BIG TIME FRANK (IRE)**, 8, b g Bienamado (USA)—Pure Spirit (IRE) **N Allen & P Bowler**
2 **CREM FRESH**, 5, b m Malinas (GER)—Clotted Cream (USA) **Mrs P. Walker**
3 **DANSEUR DU LARGE (FR)**, 6, gr g Martaline—Antagua (FR) **Lady Dulverton**
4 **DAWSON CITY**, 10, b g Midnight Legend—Running For Annie **Ian Payne & Kim Franklin**
5 **HOLD ME TIGHT (IRE)**, 5, b g Zoffany (IRE)—All Embracing (IRE) **Mrs W. J. Jarrett**
6 **MAUNA KEA (IRE)**, 7, b g Mountain High (IRE)—The Bench (IRE) **Mr M. James**
7 **MOOR FREEDOM**, 6, b m Beat Hollow—Line Freedom (FR) **The Moor Freedom Partnership**
8 **SIR DYLAN**, 10, b g Dylan Thomas (IRE)—Monteleone (IRE) **M James & S Jarrett**
9 **SWINCOMBE SCORCHIO**, 9, b g Scorpion (IRE)—Lady Felix **Holcombe Hopefuls**
10 **WHIZZ BANG**, 7, b m Schiaparelli (GER)—Whizz Back (IRE) **R. Mathew**

Other Owners: Mr N. G. Allen, Mr P. O. Bowler, Miss K. M. Franklin, T. A. F. Frost, Mr S. H. Jarrett, Mrs E. A. Kelvin-Hughes, R. J. Maggs, Mr I. T. Payne, Mrs E. D. Shepherd.

Assistant Trainer: Edward Walker

Jockey (NH): James Best, Nick Schofield. **Amateur:** Mr William Biddick.

255 MR WILLIAM HAGGAS, Newmarket

Postal: **Somerville Lodge, Fordham Road, Newmarket, Suffolk, CB8 7AA**
Contacts: **PHONE (01638) 667013 FAX (01638) 660534 MOBILE (07860) 282281**
E-MAIL **william@somerville-lodge.co.uk** WEBSITE **www.somerville-lodge.co.uk**

1 **ADDEYBB (IRE)**, 5, ch g Pivotal—Bush Cat (USA) **Sheikh Ahmed Al Maktoum**
2 **ADORABLE (IRE)**, 4, b f Kodiac—Caffe Latte **Barnane Stud Ltd**
3 **AL MUFFRIH (IRE)**, 4, b g Sea The Stars (IRE)—Scarlet And Gold (IRE) **Sheikh Juma Dalmook Al Maktoum**
4 **ALEXANA**, 4, b f Al Kazeem—Dolores **Normandie Stud Ltd**
5 **ALLIEYF**, 4, b g New Approach (IRE)—Sajjhaa **Sheikh Ahmed Al Maktoum**

MR WILLIAM HAGGAS - Continued

6 **AWESOMETANK**, 4, br f Intense Focus (USA)—Janey Muddles (IRE) **Mr Lee Yuk Lun Alan**
7 **BEAUTY FILLY**, 4, b f Invincible Spirit (IRE)—Miss Delila (USA) **Sheikh Juma Dalmook Al Maktoum**
8 **BESHAAYIR**, 4, b f Iffraaj—Bahia Breeze **Sheikh Rashid Dalmook Al Maktoum**
9 **BIG KITTEN (USA)**, 4, ch g Kitten's Joy (USA)—Queen Martha (USA) **Hussain Alabbas Lootah**
10 **CANFORD HEIGHTS (IRE)**, 4, b g Canford Cliffs (IRE)—Highindi **Mr & Mrs Ian Beard**
11 **DRAMATIC QUEEN**, 4, ch f Kitten's Joy (USA)—

Midnight Music (IRE) **Sheikh Juma Dalmook Al Maktoum**
12 **ISLAND OF LIFE (USA)**, 5, b m Dubawi (IRE)—Pimpernel (IRE) **Hamer, Hawkes & Hellin**
13 **KLASSIQUE**, 4, b f Galileo (IRE)—Chachamaidee (IRE) **Yvonne Jacques**
14 **MAGICAL SIGHT**, 4, b c Sea The Stars (IRE)—Sentaril **Lael Stable**
15 **MANKIB**, 5, ch h Tamayuz—Natagora (FR) **Mr Hamdan Al Maktoum**
16 **MOJITO (IRE)**, 5, b g Requinto (IRE)—Narva (USA) **Carmichael Jennings**
17 **MUTHMIR (IRE)**, 9, b g Invincible Spirit (IRE)—Fairy of the Night (IRE) **Mr Hamdan Al Maktoum**
18 **MY LORD AND MASTER (IRE)**, 4, ch c Mastercraftsman (IRE)—Affability (IRE) **Mr Tim Bridge**
19 **NAQAAWA (IRE)**, 4, b f Shamardal (USA)—Hammiya (IRE) **Yvonne Jacques**
20 **NICKLAUS**, 4, ch g Exceed And Excel (AUS)—Nianga (GER) **Highclere Thoroughbred Racing**
21 **NKOSIKAZI**, 4, gr f Cape Cross (IRE)—Whatami **Scotney/Symonds/Fisher**
22 **ONE MASTER**, 5, b m Fastnet Rock (AUS)—Enticing (IRE) **Lael Stable**
23 **ORIGINAL CHOICE (IRE)**, 5, ch g Dragon Pulse (IRE)—Belle Watling (IRE) **Mr Albert Goodman**
24 **PRETTY BABY (IRE)**, 4, b f Orpen (USA)—Premiere Danseuse **Sheikh Rashid Dalmook Al Maktoum**
25 **RAHEEN HOUSE (IRE)**, 5, b g Sea The Stars (IRE)—Jumooh **Mr J. L. Day**
26 **SEA OF CLASS (IRE)**, 4, ch f Sea The Stars (IRE)—Holy Moon (IRE) **Sunderland Holding Inc.**
27 **SENIORITY**, 5, ch g Dubawi (IRE)—Anna Palariva (IRE) **Her Majesty The Queen**
28 **SOLAR GOLD (IRE)**, 4, b f Sea The Stars (IRE)—Jessica's Dream (IRE) **Cayton Park Stud Ltd**
29 **UMMALNAR**, 4, ch f Shamardal (USA)—Royal Secrets (IRE) **Mohammed Jaber**
30 **VICTORY BOND**, 6, b g Medicean—Antebellum (FR) **Duke Of Bedford**
31 **YOUNG RASCAL (FR)**, 4, b c Intello (GER)—Rock My Soul (IRE) **Mr B. Kantor**

THREE-YEAR-OLDS

32 **AL HADEER (USA)**, b c War Front (USA)—Storybook (UAE) **Mr Hamdan Al Maktoum**
33 **ALBAWAADY (USA)**, ch f More Than Ready (USA)—Mujannada (USA) **Mr Hamdan Al Maktoum**
34 **APLOMB (IRE)**, b g Lope de Vega (IRE)—Mickleberry (IRE) **Fiona Carmichael**
35 **AQUASTAR (IRE)**, b g Sea The Stars (IRE)—Chiosina (IRE) **Fiona Carmichael**
36 **ASCENDED (IRE)**, gr f Dark Angel (IRE)—Mamma Morton (IRE) **Mr & Mrs M. Morris**
37 **AWE**, b c Bated Breath—On Her Way **China Horse Club**
38 **BAIDDEA (IRE)**, b f Dubawi (IRE)—Ferdoos **Sheikh Ahmed Al Maktoum**
39 **BAILEYA (IRE)**, b f Cacique (IRE)—Desert Bloom (IRE) **O.T.I. Racing**
40 **BIBLIC (IRE)**, b f New Approach (IRE)—Savannah Belle **Graham Smith-Bernal**
41 **BOERHAN**, b c Sea The Stars (IRE)—Greenisland (IRE) **Sheikh Ahmed Al Maktoum**
42 **BREAK OF DAY**, b f Shamardal (USA)—Dawn Glory **Her Majesty The Queen**
43 **CELTIC MANOR (IRE)**, b g Dandy Man (IRE)—Celtic Lynn (IRE) **Sheikh Rashid Dalmook Al Maktoum**
44 **COUP DE GOLD (IRE)**, br g Maxios—Astroglia (USA) **Sunderland Holding Inc.**
45 **CRISTAL BREEZE (IRE)**, b g Gale Force Ten—Sapphire Spray (IRE) **Roberts/Green/Savidge/Whittal-Williams**
46 **CRITICAL TIME**, b f Pivotal—Winds of Time (IRE) **Mr & Mrs R. Scott**
47 **CRYSTAL TRIBE (IRE)**, b c Dansili—Crystal Music (USA) **Lord Lloyd-Webber**
48 **CURRENT OPTION (IRE)**, b c Camelot—Coppertop (IRE) **Mr B. Kantor**
49 **DAL HORRISGLE**, b g Nathaniel (IRE)—Dalvina **St Albans Bloodstock Limited**
50 **DALAALAAT (IRE)**, b c Kingman—Gile Na Greine (IRE) **Mr Hamdan Al Maktoum**
51 **DESERT CARAVAN**, b g Oasis Dream—Sequence (IRE) **Her Majesty The Queen**
52 **DESERT ICON (FR)**, b c Sea The Stars (IRE)—Plume Rose **Sheikh Juma Dalmook Al Maktoum**
53 **DESTINATION**, b g Mukhadram—Danehill Destiny **Cheveley Park Stud**
54 **EXOPTABLE**, b gr f Dark Angel (IRE)—Executrix **Cheveley Park Stud**
55 **FAIR STAR (IRE)**, b c Sea The Stars (IRE)—Night Fairy (IRE) **Sunderland Holding Inc.**
56 **FANAAR (IRE)**, b g Dark Angel (IRE)—Inca Trail (USA) **Mr Hamdan Al Maktoum**
57 **FAYLAQ**, b c Dubawi (IRE)—Danedream (GER) **Mr Hamdan Al Maktoum**
58 **FIVE DIAMONDS**, b f Mukhadram—Felwah **Khalil Al Sayegh**
59 **FLAREPATH**, b f Exceed And Excel (AUS)—Fiery Sunset **Her Majesty The Queen**
60 **FRANKELLINA**, ch f Frankel—Our Obsession (IRE) **Mr A. E. Oppenheimer**
61 **GHAZIYAH**, gr f Galileo (IRE)—Fork Lightning (USA) **Sheikh Juma Dalmook Al Maktoum**
62 **HALLALULU**, br f Kyllachy—Cat O' Nine Tails **Mohammed Jaber**
63 **HAMISH**, b g Motivator—Tweed **Mr B. Haggas**
64 **HIDDEN MESSAGE (USA)**, b br f Scat Daddy (USA)—Secret Charm (IRE) **Qatar Racing Ltd**
65 **ICE GALA**, b f Invincible Spirit (IRE)—Ice Palace **Cheveley Park Stud**
66 **INCREDULOUS**, b f Intello (GER)—Fantasize **Cheveley Park Stud**
67 **INSANDI (FR)**, b g Anodin (IRE)—Insan Mala (IRE) **Sunderland Holding Inc.**

MR WILLIAM HAGGAS - Continued

68 **IT HAD TO BE YOU**, b c Frankel—Fallen For You **Normandie Stud Ltd**
69 **JAHBATH**, b c Mukhadram—Oulianovsk (IRE) **Mr Hamdan Al Maktoum**
70 **JUST BENJAMIN**, b c Epaulette (AUS)—Desert Royalty (IRE) **Ian & Christine Beard**
71 **KENTUCKY KINGDOM (IRE)**, b c Camacho—Venetian Rhapsody (IRE) **Abdulla Al Mansoori**
72 **KODIAC PRIDE**, b g Kodiac—Queen of Mean **Sheikh Rashid Dalmook Al Maktoum**
73 **LISTEN TO THE WIND (IRE)**, b f Toronado (IRE)—Henties Bay (IRE) **Sheikh Rashid Dalmook Al Maktoum**
74 **LUXOR**, b c Oasis Dream—Eminently **Highclere Thoroughbred Racing**
75 **MAGNETIC CHARM**, b f Exceed And Excel (AUS)—Monday Show (USA) **Her Majesty The Queen**
76 **MAJAALIS (FR)**, b c Invincible Spirit (IRE)—High Surf (USA) **Mr Hamdan Al Maktoum**
77 **MAKTABBA**, b f Dansili—Mudaaraah **Mr Hamdan Al Maktoum**
78 **MAQSAD (FR)**, b f Siyouni (FR)—Amerique (IRE) **Mr Hamdan Al Maktoum**
79 **MARMARR**, b f Dubawi (IRE)—Anaamil (IRE) **Sheikh Ahmed Al Maktoum**
80 **MOFTRIS**, b c Iffraaj—Baheeja **Sheikh Ahmed Al Maktoum**
81 **MONICA SHERIFF**, b f Lawman (FR)—Require **Duke Of Devonshire**
82 **MONTZAR**, b c Dansili—Nahrain **Sheikh Ahmed Al Maktoum**
83 **NAHAARR (IRE)**, b c Dark Angel (IRE)—Charlotte Rua (IRE) **Sheikh Ahmed Al Maktoum**
84 **NARINA (IRE)**, b f Rip Van Winkle (IRE)—Savanna Days (IRE) **Jon & Julia Aisbitt**
85 **ORIGINAIRE (IRE)**, b c Zoffany (IRE)—Polly Perkins (IRE) **China Horse Club**
86 **PABLO ESCOBARR (IRE)**, b c Galileo (IRE)—Bewitched (IRE) **Hussain Alabbas Lootah**
87 **PAY COURT**, b f Motivator—Courting **Cheveley Park Stud**
88 **PEARL JAM**, br f Showcasing—Dance Pearl **Mr & Mrs M. Morris**
89 **POLITICISE (IRE)**, b g Camelot—Politesse (USA) **Mr B. Kantor**
90 **RAINBOW HEART (IRE)**, b f Born To Sea (IRE)—Sea of Heartbreak (IRE) **Sunderland Holding Inc.**
91 **REIMS**, b f Invincible Spirit (IRE)—Riberac **Mr & Mrs G. Middlebrook**
92 **SEA OF FAITH (IRE)**, b f Sea The Stars (IRE)—Jumooh **Sunderland Holding Inc.**
93 **SEA OF REALITY (IRE)**, b f Born To Sea (IRE)—Girouette (IRE) **Sunderland Holding Inc.**
94 **SEA WINGS**, ch c Sea The Stars (IRE)—Infallible **Cheveley Park Stud**
95 **SENZA LIMITI (IRE)**, ch c Lope de Vega (IRE)—Senza Rete (IRE) **Simon Munir & Isaac Souede**
96 **SHREWDNESS**, br f Lawman (FR)—Shama (IRE) **Her Majesty The Queen**
97 **SINJAARI (IRE)**, b c Camelot—Heavenly Song (IRE) **Mohammed Jaber**
98 **SKARDU (IRE)**, ch c Shamardal (USA)—Diala (IRE) **Abdulla Al Khalifa**
99 **SMARTER (IRE)**, gr ro g Dark Angel (IRE)—Coquette Rouge (IRE) **Sheikh Ahmed Al Maktoum**
100 **SOFT COVER**, b br f Shamardal (USA)—Sentaril **Lael Stable**
101 **SOLOIST (IRE)**, b f Camelot—Ayshea **Highclere Thoroughbred Racing**
102 **SPACE WALK**, b c Galileo (IRE)—Memory (IRE) **Her Majesty The Queen**
103 **SPARKLE IN HIS EYE**, ch c Sea The Stars (IRE)—Nyarhini **Mr A. E. Oppenheimer**
104 **SPOTTON (IRE)**, b c Tamayuz—Farbenspiel (IRE) **Sheikh Ahmed Al Maktoum**
105 **SWANSDOWN**, ch f Dubawi (IRE)—Pongee **Fittocks Stud**
106 **SWISS AIR**, b f Oasis Dream—Swiss Lake (USA) **Lordship Stud**
107 **TAPISSERIE**, ch f Le Havre (FR)—Miss Work of Art **Mr Isa Salman**
108 **THE NIGHT WATCH**, b g Dutch Art—Scarlet Runner **Tom Wilson & Colne Valley Stud**
109 **TWO BIDS**, b c Dalakhani (IRE)—Echelon **Sheikh Ahmed Al Maktoum**
110 **WANNIE MAE (IRE)**, ch f Australia—Wurflinge (GER) **Bjande Minde-Minde**
111 **WHISPERING BEAUTY (USA)**, b br f Arch—She's A Beauty (USA) **Ms A. Gigliola da Silva**
112 **WOODS (IRE)**, b c Garswood—Flare of Firelight (USA) **Kemal Kurt**
113 **YOUARESTAR**, b c Sea The Stars (IRE)—Alumna (USA) **Mohammed Jaber**

TWO-YEAR-OLDS

114 **ABERFFRAW**, ch c 1/3 Exceed And Excel (AUS)—Nahab (Selkirk (USA)) (80000) **Julie & David Martin**
115 **ADORNMENT**, b f 5/4 Kodiac—Adorn (Kyllachy) **Cheveley Park Stud**
116 **AL TARMAAH (IRE)**, b c 12/4 Muhaarar—
How's She Cuttin' (IRE) (Shinko Forest (IRE)) (350000) **Mr Hamdan Al Maktoum**
117 B f 11/3 Invincible Spirit (IRE)—Alaata (USA) (Smart Strike (CAN)) **Mr Hamdan Al Maktoum**
118 B c 26/3 Gleneagles (IRE)—Alive Alive Oh (Duke of Marmalade (IRE)) (117993) **HRH Prince Faisal Bin Khaled**
119 B f 21/1 Zoffany (IRE)—Allez Y (IRE) (Rip Van Winkle (IRE)) (100000) **Highclere Thoroughbred Racing**
120 **AMETIST**, ch c 25/3 Dutch Art—Zykina (Pivotal) **Cheveley Park Stud**
121 B c 1/2 Oasis Dream—Ananas (Nayef (USA)) **Her Majesty The Queen**
122 **AWARD SCHEME**, b f 22/2 Siyouni (FR)—Queen's Prize (Dansili) **Her Majesty The Queen**
123 B f 12/2 Pivotal—Baheeja (Dubawi (IRE)) **Sheikh Ahmed Al Maktoum**
124 B f 29/3 Muhaarar—Ballymore Celebre (IRE) (Peintre Celebre (USA)) (92000) **Hussain Alabbas Lootah**
125 **BECADA (IRE)**, b f 14/2 Camacho—Woodcock Moon (Kyllachy) (66666) **Mr Isa Salman**
126 B c 28/2 Showcasing—Belatorio (IRE) (Oratorio (IRE)) (180000) **Sheikh Ahmed Al Maktoum**
127 B c 23/2 Wootton Bassett—Belova (IRE) (Soviet Star (USA)) (200000) **Sheikh Ahmed Al Maktoum**
128 **BLUE DAWN**, b f 26/2 Oasis Dream—Blue Waltz (Pivotal) **Fittocks Stud**
129 B c 25/1 Invincible Spirit (IRE)—Blue Paraiba (IRE) (Sea The Stars (IRE)) **Sunderland Holding Inc.**

MR WILLIAM HAGGAS - Continued

130 **BORN A KING**, b c 4/2 Frankel—Fairwater (USA) (Empire Maker (USA)) **Faisal Meshrf Alqahtani**
131 B f 26/2 Camelot—Brown Diamond (IRE) (Fastnet Rock (AUS)) (130000) **Sheikh Juma Dalmook Al Maktoum**
132 **BRYN DU**, b c 18/2 Ivawood (IRE)—Caption (Motivator) (60000) **Julie & David Martin**
133 **CHORAL WORK**, b f 27/1 Nathaniel (IRE)—Chapel Choir (Dalakhani (IRE)) **Cheveley Park Stud**
134 B c 29/1 Cable Bay (IRE)—Coin A Phrase (Dubawi (IRE)) (142857) **Mr Hamdan Al Maktoum**
135 B f 5/4 Poet's Voice—Diala (IRE) (Iffraaj) **Abdulla Al Khalifa**
136 **DUSTY DREAM**, b f 14/4 Dubawi (IRE)—Memory (IRE) (Danehill Dancer (IRE)) **Her Majesty The Queen**
137 B c 25/4 Kodiac—Enticing (IRE) (Pivotal) **Lael Stable**
138 B f 25/2 Dubawi (IRE)—Ethaara (Green Desert (USA)) **Mr Hamdan Al Maktoum**
139 B c 20/4 Lope de Vega (IRE)—Froglet (Shaamit (IRE)) **Mr B. Haggas**
140 **FUNDTANK**, b f 12/3 Frankel—Millevini (IRE) (Hawk Wing (USA)) **Mr Lee Yuk Lun Alan**
141 B c 22/1 Galileo (IRE)—Giofra (Dansili) (269700) **Hussain Alabbas Lootah**
142 **GRANNY'S ECLIPSE (IRE)**, b f 7/4 Shamardal (USA)—
                Crown of Diamonds (USA) (Distorted Humor (USA)) (100000) **Barnane Stud Ltd**
143 B c 22/1 Tonalist (USA)—Happy Face (USA) (Exchange Rate (USA)) (84656) **HRH Prince Faisal Bin Khaled**
144 B f 19/3 Intello (GER)—Hawraa (Dansili) **Mr Hamdan Al Maktoum**
145 B f 8/4 Golden Horn—Hikari (IRE) (Galileo (IRE)) (150000) **Hussain Alabbas Lootah**
146 **ICE SPRITE**, ch f 4/3 Zoffany (IRE)—Queen of Ice (Selkirk (USA)) **Cheveley Park Stud**
147 **JOHAN**, b c 4/3 Zoffany (IRE)—Sandreamer (IRE) (Oasis Dream) **Jon & Julia Aisbitt**
148 **KEW PALACE**, b f 2/2 Kingman—Shama (IRE) (Danehill Dancer (IRE)) **Her Majesty The Queen**
149 B f 23/5 Kodiac—Khazeena (Oasis Dream) **Mr Hamdan Al Maktoum**
150 B c 7/3 Camelot—Kikonga (Danehill Dancer (IRE)) (115000) **Saeed Suhail**
151 B c 3/3 Sea The Stars (IRE)—Kitcara (Shamardal (USA)) (300000) **Mr Hamdan Al Maktoum**
152 B c 30/4 Kodiac—Lady Lucia (IRE) (Royal Applause) (231773) **Mr Hamdan Al Maktoum**
153 **LAMORNA**, b f 21/1 Oasis Dream—Golden Laughter (USA) (Bernardini (USA)) (90000) **Graham Smith-Bernal**
154 B f 29/3 Kodiac—Lough Mewn (IRE) (Woodman (USA)) (65000) **Liam Sheridan**
155 B c 18/2 Equiano (FR)—Love And Cherish (IRE) (Excellent Art) (115000) **Saeed Suhail**
156 B gr c 14/2 Muhaarar—Majmu (AUS) (Redoute's Choice (AUS)) **Mr Hamdan Al Maktoum**
157 B f 24/3 Galileo (IRE)—Maureen (IRE) (Holy Roman Emperor (IRE)) (442477) **Qatar Racing Ltd**
158 B f 21/3 Oasis Dream—Midnight Thoughts (USA) (Henrythenavigator (USA)) **Apple Tree Stud**
159 B c 4/2 Acclamation—Miss Gibraltar (Rock of Gibraltar (IRE)) (142857) **Hussain Alabbas Lootah**
160 B f 14/4 Iffraaj—Modeyra (Shamardal (USA)) **Sheikh Ahmed Al Maktoum**
161 B c 3/5 Australia—My Fairy (IRE) (Sea The Stars (IRE)) **Sunderland Holding Inc.**
162 B c 12/2 Dubawi (IRE)—My Titania (IRE) (Sea The Stars (IRE)) **Sunderland Holding Inc.**
163 Ch c 28/2 Free Eagle (IRE)—Nebraas (Green Desert (USA)) (337125) **Mr Hamdan Al Maktoum**
164 B f 24/2 Tamayuz—Nozhar (IRE) (Iffraaj) **Mr Hamdan Al Maktoum**
165 B c 10/3 Teofilo (IRE)—Off Chance (Olden Times) (80000) **Royal Ascot Racing Club**
166 B f 9/3 Dubawi (IRE)—Oojooba (Monsun (GER)) **Sheikh Ahmed Al Maktoum**
167 Ch c 26/3 Exceed And Excel (AUS)—Peeress (Pivotal) **Cheveley Park Stud**
168 **PENYSARN (IRE)**, b f 9/2 Camacho—Kindling (Dr Fong (USA)) (48000) **Julie & David Martin**
169 B f 25/2 Kodiac—Pilates (Shamardal (USA)) (130000) **Mr Hamdan Al Maktoum**
170 B c 18/2 War Front (USA)—Pin Up (IRE) (Lookin At Lucky (USA)) (846560) **Mr Hamdan Al Maktoum**
171 **PORTRAY**, b c 30/3 Dubawi (IRE)—Placidia (IRE) (Sea The Stars (IRE)) **Her Majesty The Queen**
172 **PRETTY PICKLE (IRE)**, b f 14/4 Born To Sea (IRE)—
                Onomatomania (USA) (Mr Greeley (USA)) (23598) **Mr Tim Bridge**
173 B f 26/3 Iffraaj—Pussycat Lips (IRE) (Holy Roman Emperor (IRE)) (92709) **Qatar Racing Ltd**
174 B f 17/4 Muhaarar—Queenofthefairies (Pivotal) (925000) **Mr Hamdan Al Maktoum**
175 B c 16/3 Intello (GER)—Red Bloom (Selkirk (USA)) **Cheveley Park Stud**
176 B c 10/3 Lord Kanaloa (JPN)—Ripples Maid (Dansili) **Qatar Racing Ltd**
177 B c 12/3 Australia—Rock of Ridd (IRE) (Antonius Pius (USA)) (206489) **Bjande Minde-Minde**
178 B f 25/2 Invincible Spirit (IRE)—Sajjhaa (King's Best (USA)) **Sheikh Ahmed Al Maktoum**
179 Ch c 25/1 Lope de Vega (IRE)—Saraha (Dansili) **Mr Hamdan Al Maktoum**
180 **SEA MOOD (FR)**, b f 14/3 Siyouni (FR)—
                Upbeat Mood (USA) (Mizzen Mast (USA)) (150000) **Highclere Thoroughbred Racing**
181 B f 17/3 Invincible Spirit (IRE)—Sea of Heartbreak (IRE) (Rock of Gibraltar (IRE)) **Sunderland Holding Inc.**
182 **SEA TROUT REACH (IRE)**, ch c 1/4 Mukhadram—Caelica (IRE) (Sea The Stars (IRE)) (37083) **Mr Tim Bridge**
183 B c 27/2 Gleneagles (IRE)—Sentaril (Danehill Dancer (IRE)) **Lael Stable**
184 B f 2/2 Invincible Spirit (IRE)—Shargeyih (Shamardal (USA)) **Mr Hamdan Al Maktoum**
185 Ch f 25/1 Frankel—Sortita (GER) (Monsun (GER)) **Mr Hamdan Al Maktoum**
186 **SOUND MIXER**, b f 19/2 Cable Bay (IRE)—Medley (Danehill Dancer (IRE)) **Her Majesty The Queen**
187 **ST IVES**, b c 1/3 Cable Bay (IRE)—Galaktea (IRE) (Statue of Liberty (USA)) (85714) **Graham Smith-Bernal**
188 Ch f 18/2 Pivotal—Suelita (Dutch Art) (425000) **Cheveley Park Stud**
189 B c 5/2 Zoffany (IRE)—Superstar Leo (IRE) (College Chapel) **Lael Stable**
190 Br c 16/4 Society Rock—Tara Too (IRE) (Danetime (IRE)) (130000) **Sheikh Ahmed Al Maktoum**
191 B f 25/2 Galileo (IRE)—Timbuktu (IRE) (Fastnet Rock (AUS)) (220000) **Apple Tree Stud**

MR WILLIAM HAGGAS - Continued

192 B f 8/2 Champs Elysees—Undress (IRE) (Dalakhani (IRE)) **Mr B. Haggas**
193 B f 2/5 Dutch Art—Vallado (IRE) (Clodovil (IRE)) **Wood Hall Stud Limited**
194 B c 16/3 Acclamation—Vastitas (IRE) (Green Desert (USA)) (160000) **Mr Hamdan Al Maktoum**
195 VEGA'S ANGEL, b f 19/4 Lope de Vega (IRE)—Lily's Angel (IRE) (Dark Angel (IRE)) **Cheveley Park Stud**
196 B f 30/4 Dark Angel (IRE)—Vine Street (IRE) (Singspiel (IRE)) **Sheikh Ahmed Al Maktoum**
197 B f 15/2 Dark Angel (IRE)—Wiltshire Life (IRE) (Camacho) (142857) **Cheveley Park Stud**
198 WINDOW, b c 6/5 Showcasing—Blancmange (Montjeu (IRE)) **Mr B. Haggas**
199 WITH REASON, ch f 6/3 Frankel—Eminently (Exceed And Excel (AUS)) (650000) **Mr & Mrs G. Middlebrook**

Other Owners: Mrs J. M. Aisbitt, J. R. Aisbitt, Mrs C. Beard, Mr I. Beard, P. J. Dunkley, Mrs D. Dunkley, Highclere Thoroughbred Racing Ltd, Mrs G. S. Jackson, Mr R. Jackson, Mrs J. M. T. Martin, D. R. Martin, Mrs L. A. Middlebrook, Mr G. Middlebrook, Mrs P. M. Scott, R. Scott, Somerville Lodge Limited.

Assistant Trainers: Harry Eustace, Josh Hamer, Ben Morris

Apprentice: Georgia Cox, Cieran Fallon, Gianluca Sanna.

---

256 **MR ALEX HALES, Edgecote**
Postal: **Trafford Bridge Stables, Edgecote, Banbury, Oxfordshire, OX17 1AG**
Contacts: **PHONE (01295) 660131 FAX (01295) 660128 MOBILE (07771) 511652**
E-MAIL **alex@alexhalesracing.co.uk** WEBSITE **www.alexhalesracing.co.uk**

1 BIG JIM, 10, b g Revoque (IRE)—Chilly Squaw (IRE) **Gumbrills Racing Partnership**
2 CEARA BE (IRE), 6, b m Oscar (IRE)—Pearl's A Singer (IRE) **Mr P. J. Byrne**
3 DANDILION (IRE), 6, b m Dandy Man (IRE)—Free Angel (USA) **The Golden Horse Racing Club**
4 DARTAGNAN LE DUN (FR), 6, b g Kapgarde (FR)—Silvazeyra (IRE) **All For One And One For All**
5 DUEL AT DAWN (IRE), 9, b g Presenting—Phillis Hill **The Duel At Dawn Partnership**
6 EMILY WEBB, 4, b f Franklins Gardens—Lofaire (IRE) **Mr R Hunt & Mr T J Acott**
7 FLORRIE KNOX (IRE), 6, gr g Gold Well—Miss Orphan (FR) **The Fortune Hunters**
8 FLOW AWAY (IRE), 5, br m Stowaway—Water Rock **Mr N Rodway & Partner**
9 FOR PLEASURE (IRE), 4, ch g Excelebration (IRE)—Darsan (IRE) **Premier Plastering (UK) Limited**
10 HUNTSMAN SON (IRE), 9, b g Millenary—Daly Lady (IRE) **C. W. Booth**
11 INDIAN NATIVE (IRE), 9, b m Oscar (IRE)—Roman Native (IRE) **C. W. Booth**
12 JIMMI CHEW (IRE), 6, br g Jimble (FR)—Katie Baby (IRE) **Mr B. E. Brackenbury**
13 JUST MARVIN (IRE), 6, b g Atraf—Gailybay Ellen (IRE)
14 L'ANE FOU (IRE), 9, b m Robin des Pres (FR)—Katcharto Lady (IRE) **Mr R. J. B. Brown**
15 MAGGIES LEGEND, 6, b m Midnight Legend—Very Special One (IRE) **Gumbrills Racing Partnership**
16 METHAG (FR), 6, b m Pour Moi (IRE)—Kyria **The One For Us**
17 MILLERS BANK, 5, b g Passing Glance—It Doesn't Matter **Mr S. Bocking**
18 MINELLAFORLEISURE (IRE), 11, br g King's Theatre (IRE)—Dame Foraine (FR) **The Patient Partnership**
19 MOUNTAIN RANGER (IRE), 7, b g Mountain High (IRE)—Oscareen (IRE) **The Golden Horse Racing Club**
20 PANKO (IRE), 6, b g Iffraaj—Engraving **S Mullaney, S Brown, D & V Jones**
21 4, ch f Shirocco (GER)—Phillis Hill **Equinox Racing**
22 ROUGH NIGHT (IRE), 6, b g Doyen (IRE)—Sunny Bob (IRE) **Miss P. M. Morris**
23 ROYAL SUNDAY (FR), 5, gr g Never On Sunday (FR)—Royale Malaisie (FR) **Old Stoics Racing Club 2**
24 RUNNING WOLF (IRE), 8, b g Amadeus Wolf—Monet's Lady (IRE) **The Wolfgangers**
25 SAFARHI, 4, b g Farhh—Swarm (IRE) **The Barbury Lions**
26 SHAZZAMATAZ (IRE), 7, br m Presenting—Dame O'neill (IRE) **Edging Ahead**
27 SMOOTH STEPPER, 10, b g Alflora (IRE)—Jazzy Refrain (IRE) **Mr B. E. Brackenbury**
28 STACEY SUE (IRE), 6, b m Robin des Champs (FR)—Antonia Hall (IRE) **The The Backburners**
29 STEPOVER, 8, b m Midnight Legend—Ring Back (IRE) **Mrs A. P. B. Allen**
30 TAKE TWO, 10, b g Act One—Lac Marmot (FR) **Edging Ahead**
31 THE DRONE (IRE), 8, b br g Mahler—Liberess (IRE) **Gumbrills Racing Partnership**
32 THE OTMOOR POET, 6, b g Yeats (IRE)—Kristalette (IRE) **The of Ten Partnership & Equinox Racing**
33 TINKER TIME (IRE), 11, b g Turtle Island (IRE)—Gypsys Girl (IRE) **Mr B. E. Brackenbury**
34 TOPPER THORNTON (IRE), 10, ch g Double Eclipse (IRE)—Gailybay Ellen (IRE) **Old Stoic Racing Club**
35 TOWER OF ALLEN (IRE), 8, b g Beneficial—Baile An Droichid (IRE) **The Hexagon Racing Partnership**
36 ULTIMATUM DU ROY (FR), 11, b g Brier Creek (USA)—La Fleur du Roy (FR) **Mrs A. P. B. Allen**

THREE-YEAR-OLDS

37 ES QUE MAGIC (IRE), b g Es Que Love (IRE)—Itzakindamagic (IRE) **Mr A. M. Hales**

MR ALEX HALES - Continued

TWO-YEAR-OLDS

38 GONE IN SIXTY, b g 15/3 Sixties Icon—Gib (IRE) (Rock of Gibraltar (IRE)) **The Golden Horse Racing Club**

Other Owners: Mr T. J. Acott, Miss S. A. Baxter, Mr C. Bennett, Mr S. Brown, Miss S. E. Burnell, Mrs K. A. Fry, J. S. C. Fry, Mr D. F. Hill, Mr C. R. B. Hunt, Mr H. Kimbell, Alan King, Ms L. Langford, R. E. Morris-Adams, The Of-Ten Racing Partnership, Mr N. Rodway, Mrs H. Steele, Mr B. Tait, Mrs C. Taylor, Mrs J. Wood, Mr C. J. Woods.

---

257 | **MR MICHAEL HALFORD, Kildare**
Postal: **Copper Beech Stables, Doneaney, Kildangan Road, Kildare, Co. Kildare, Ireland**
Contacts: **PHONE (00 353) 45 526119 FAX (00 353) 45 526157 MOBILE (00 353) 87 2579204**
E-MAIL info@michaelhalford.com WEBSITE www.michaelhalford.com

1 **AHLAN BIL ZAIN (FR),** 5, b br g Elusive City (USA)—Fall View **Mr R McNally**
2 **ARCANEARS (IRE),** 4, b g Arcano (IRE)—Ondeafears (IRE) **Mrs C. Roper**
3 **CASTLE GUEST (IRE),** 10, b g Rock of Gibraltar (IRE)—Castelletto **Mr P Rooney**
4 **GOUGANE BARRA (USA),** 5, b br g First Defence (USA)—Beiramar (IRE) **Mr P Rooney**
5 **KATIYMANN (IRE),** 7, b g Shamardal (USA)—Katiyra (IRE) **Mr P Rooney**
6 **LADY DE VESCI (IRE),** 6, ch m Approve (IRE)—La Bandola (GER) **Mr F Sommer**
7 **LUNA'S LUCK (IRE),** 5, b g Vale of York (IRE)—Over The Tylery (IRE) **Mr J Matthews**
8 **MASSIF CENTRAL (IRE),** 5, b g Arcano (IRE)—Melaaya (USA) **Mr P Rooney**
9 **MISS SNOSSYBOOTS (IRE),** 5, ch m Rip Van Winkle (IRE)—Nick's Nikita (IRE) **Mr N Hartery**
10 **SPIRIT OF BIG BANG (IRE),** 4, b g Intikhab (USA)—Crossing **Mr E Koh**
11 **SURROUNDING (IRE),** 6, b m Lilbourne Lad (IRE)—Roundabout Girl (IRE) **Mr P E I Newell**
12 **TIRMIZI (FR),** 6, b g Sea The Stars (IRE)—Timabiyra (IRE) **Mr P Rooney**

THREE-YEAR-OLDS

13 **ALAKAHAN (IRE),** ch c Motivator—Aliyama (IRE) **H. H. Aga Khan**
14 **BALEFIRE (IRE),** b c Shamardal (USA)—Patent Joy (IRE) **Godolphin**
15 **BEETHOVEN'S GAL,** b f Iffraaj—Apasionata Sonata (USA) **Mr F McGovern**
16 **CARTESIENNE (IRE),** ch f Pivotal—Modern Ideals **Godolphin**
17 **DEFINING BATTLE (IRE),** gr c Lope de Vega (IRE)—Royal Fortune (IRE) **Mrs W O'Leary**
18 **DILLYGASS (IRE),** b f Requinto (IRE)—Sandbox Two (IRE) **Mrs C Roper**
19 **ELIZABETH WAY (IRE),** ch f Frankel—Maids Causeway (IRE) **Godolphin**
20 **FLAMBOYANT FLING (IRE),** b f Dandy Man (IRE)—Breathless Kiss (USA) **Mr P Byrne**
21 **GARABANDAL (USA),** gr ro f Orb (USA)—Bestowal (USA) **Rollx Syndicate**
22 **GRUFALO (IRE),** ch g Bungle Inthejungle—Park Approach (IRE) **Mr R McNally**
23 **HAMARIYNA (IRE),** b f Sea The Moon (GER)—Hanakiyya (IRE) **H. H. Aga Khan**
24 **HAZRAN (IRE),** b c Lope de Vega (IRE)—Hazaraba (IRE) **H. H. Aga Khan**
25 **ISOSCELES (IRE),** b c Rulership (JPN)—Triple Pirouette (USA) **Godolphin**
26 **KALANOURA (IRE),** b f Casamento (IRE)—Kaladena (USA) **H. H. Aga Khan**
27 **KARAKHAN (IRE),** b c So You Think (NZ)—Karawana (IRE) **H. H. Aga Khan**
28 **KARASI (IRE),** ch c Excelebration (IRE)—Kerisa (IRE) **H. H. Aga Khan**
29 **KERLA (IRE),** b f Zoffany (IRE)—Kerania (IRE) **H. H. Aga Khan**
30 **LIBRAS POWER (IRE),** b f Slade Power (IRE)—Buffalo Berry (IRE) **Mr Y Zhang**
31 **MAGIC SHUFFLE (IRE),** b c Ruler of The World (IRE)—Himiko (IRE) **Mr T. Kimura**
32 **MALVOLIO (IRE),** ch c Farhh—Philae (USA) **Godolphin**
33 **METAL MAN (IRE),** ch c Australia—Nick's Nikita (IRE) **Mr N Hartery**
34 **MOUNEERA (IRE),** ch f Dawn Approach (IRE)—Mouramara (IRE) **H. H. Aga Khan**
35 **PEARLMAN,** ch c Nathaniel (IRE)—Lurina (IRE) **Godolphin**
36 **PLAYA DEL PUENTE (IRE),** br c Elzaam (AUS)—Playamongthestars (AUS) **Copper Beech Racing Partnership**
37 **RAYOUNPOUR (IRE),** b c Cape Cross (IRE)—Rayna (IRE) **H. H. Aga Khan**
38 **RIYAZA (IRE),** gr f Dark Angel (IRE)—Riyaba (IRE) **H. H. Aga Khan**
39 **SAGITTARIAN WIND,** b f Iffraaj—Bahia Breeze **Mr Y Zhang**
40 **SENDMYLOVETOYOU (IRE),** b f Invincible Spirit (IRE)—Sendmylovetorose **Mr M Enright**
41 **SHAMIYAN (IRE),** b c Lope de Vega (IRE)—Shamooda (IRE) **H. H. Aga Khan**
42 **SHENNAN (IRE),** ch c Rip Van Winkle (IRE)—Shebella (IRE) **H. H. Aga Khan**
43 **SIMSIR (IRE),** b c Zoffany (IRE)—Simawa (IRE) **H. H. Aga Khan**
44 **SKY SEVEN (IRE),** ch c Helmet (AUS)—Ready When You Are (IRE) **Mr N Askar**
45 **SONAIYLA (IRE),** gr f Dark Angel (IRE)—Sinaniya (USA) **H. H. Aga Khan**
46 **SPELGA,** b g Sir Percy—Emma's Gift (IRE) **Mr P Rooney**
47 **SUCCEEDANDSURPASS (IRE),** b c Exceed And Excel (AUS)—Sequined (USA) **Mr D Cantillon**
48 **TAKE SILK (IRE),** b f Shamardal (USA)—Raw Silk (USA) **Godolphin**
49 **TIFFINDELL (IRE),** ch f Raven's Pass (USA)—Nadia **Godolphin**

MR MICHAEL HALFORD - Continued

50 **TOTAL RECHARGE (IRE)**, br c Power—Money Penny (ITY) **Copper Beech Racing Syndicate**
51 **WILD MUSTANG (IRE)**, b c Invincible Spirit (IRE)—Propaganda (IRE) **Mr E Koh**
52 **ZEYDABAD (IRE)**, b g Camelot—Zerkeriya (IRE) **H. H. Aga Khan**

TWO-YEAR-OLDS

53 B c 21/2 Ruler of The World (IRE)—Aliyfa (IRE) (Spinning World (USA)) **H. H. Aga Khan**
54 Ch c 16/2 Footstepsinthesand—Diylawa (IRE) (Mastercraftsman (IRE)) **H. H. Aga Khan**
55 Bl c 9/2 Gutaifan (IRE)—Gerash (FR) (Layman (USA)) (43825) **Mr S Ma**
56 B c 29/4 Clodovil (IRE)—Hattie Jacques (Sixties Icon) (15170) **Copper Beech Racing Partnership**
57 B c 31/3 Mastercraftsman (IRE)—Hazaraba (IRE) (Oasis Dream) **H. H. Aga Khan**
58 Gr f 19/2 Mastercraftsman (IRE)—Kalabaya (IRE) (Sinndar (IRE)) **H. H. Aga Khan**
59 B c 10/5 War Command (USA)—Kaladena (IRE) (Daylami (IRE)) **H. H. Aga Khan**
60 Ch c 4/3 Siyouni (FR)—Karawana (IRE) (King's Best (USA)) **H. H. Aga Khan**
61 B f 5/3 Free Eagle (IRE)—Kastania (USA) (Gone West (USA)) **H. H. Aga Khan**
62 Ch c 24/4 Champs Elysees (IRE)—Kerisa (IRE) (Azamour (IRE)) **H. H. Aga Khan**
63 B c 29/4 Born To Sea (IRE)—Lidaya (USA) (Elusive Quality (USA)) **H. H. Aga Khan**
64 Ch f 2/4 Shamardal (USA)—Modern Ideals (New Approach (IRE)) **Godolphin**
65 B f 8/2 Lope de Vega (IRE)—Paimpolaise (IRE) (Priolo (USA)) **Mr M Enright**
66 Ch f 14/4 Exceed And Excel (AUS)—Philae (USA) (Seeking The Gold (USA)) **Godolphin**
67 B f 17/4 Shamardal (USA)—Pimpernel (IRE) (Invincible Spirit (IRE)) **Godolphin**
68 Ch c 15/3 Outstrip—Quinine (Dark Angel (IRE)) (15000) **Copper Beech Racing Syndicate**
69 Br f 29/1 Sea The Stars (IRE)—Raydara (IRE) (Rock of Gibraltar (IRE)) **H. H. Aga Khan**
70 **SATIN SLIPPER (IRE)**, b f 28/3 Camacho—Slipper Orchid (IRE) (Verglas (IRE)) **Mrs C Roper**
71 B c 22/4 Camacho—Shamardyh (IRE) (Shamardal (USA)) (33712) **Copper Beech Racing Syndicate**
72 Ch c 3/2 Raven's Pass (USA)—Sharp Crisp Air (IRE) (Danehill Dancer (IRE)) (10113) **Mrs L Halford**
73 B f 19/4 Dark Angel (IRE)—Silca's Sister (Inchinor) **Godolphin**
74 B f 17/3 Mastercraftsman (IRE)—Sinaniya (USA) (More Than Ready (USA)) **H. H. Aga Khan**
75 **SLIEVE BEARNAGH (IRE)**, b c 4/5 Zoffany (IRE)—Angels Story (IRE) (Galileo (IRE)) (38000) **Mr P Rooney**
76 Ch f 27/2 Poet's Voice—Speak Softly (JPN) (Alkaased (USA)) **Godolphin**
77 Ch f 6/3 Dubawi (IRE)—Suez (Green Desert (USA)) **Godolphin**
78 B c 23/3 Holy Roman Emperor (IRE)—Swish (GER) (Monsun (GER)) (46354) **Mr S Ma**
79 B c 11/3 Dandy Man (IRE)—Talitha Kum (IRE) (Chineur (FR)) (42140) **Copper Beech Racing Syndicate**
80 B f 23/1 Teofilo (IRE)—Winter Queen (Dubawi (IRE)) **Godolphin**
81 B c 16/3 Kodiac—Wrood (USA) (Invasor (ARG)) **Mr N Hartery**
82 B c 7/4 Raven's Pass (USA)—Zamra (IRE) (Azamour (IRE)) (12641) **Copper Beech Racing Syndicate**
83 Ch c 24/4 Nathaniel (IRE)—Zariyna (IRE) (Marju (IRE)) **H. H. Aga Khan**

Assistant Trainer: Fabian Burke

Jockey (flat): Ross Coakley, Niall McCullagh, Ronan Whelan. **Apprentice:** Adam Farraghar. **Amateur:** Mr Evan Halford.

MRS DEBRA HAMER, Carmarthen
258
Postal: **Bryngors Uchaf, Nantycaws, Carmarthen, Dyfed, SA32 8EY**
Contacts: **HOME (01267) 234585 MOBILE (07980) 665274**
E-MAIL hamerracing@hotmail.co.uk

1 **JAC BROWN**, 5, b g Multiplex—Do It On Dani **Mrs D. A. Hamer**
2 **LAYERTHORPE (IRE)**, 7, b bl g Vale of York (IRE)—Strobinia (IRE) **Mr C. A. Hanbury**
3 **LOOKS LIKE POWER (IRE)**, 9, ch g Spadoun (FR)—Martovic (IRE) **Mr C. A. Hanbury**
4 **MAGICAL MAN**, 12, b br g Lahib (USA)—Majestic Di (IRE) **Mr C. A. Hanbury**
5 **SUPER SCORPION (IRE)**, 9, b g Scorpion (IRE)—Nolagh Supreme (IRE) **Mrs J. M. Edmonds**
6 **TOBEFAIR**, 9, b br g Central Park (IRE)—Nan **Down The Quay Club**
7 **TOE TO TOE (IRE)**, 11, br g Presenting—Tavildara (IRE) **Palms Landscaping Limited**

Other Owners: Mr M. J. Cole, Mr A. G. Pannell.

Assistant Trainer: Mr M. P. Hamer

259 MRS ALISON HAMILTON, Hawick
Postal: **Dykes Farm House, Denholm, Hawick, Roxburghshire, TD9 8TB**
Contacts: **PHONE (01450) 870323 MOBILE (07885) 477349**
E-MAIL Alisonhamilton53@yahoo.com

1 **ASK JD (IRE)**, 6, b g Ask—Sara Cara (IRE) **J. P. G. Hamilton**
2 **DANEHILLS WELL (IRE)**, 11, b g Indian Danehill (IRE)—Collatrim Choice (IRE) **J. P. G. Hamilton**
3 **EXPRESS DES MOTTES (FR)**, 5, b g Network (GER)—
　　　　　　　　　　　　　　　　　　Uzelle des Mottes (FR) **Mr & Mrs D S Byers & Jpg Hamilton**
4 **MASTER RAJEEM (USA)**, 10, b br g Street Cry (IRE)—Rajeem **J. P. G. Hamilton**
5 **PAINTERS LAD (IRE)**, 8, b g Fruits of Love (USA)—Great Cullen (IRE) **J. P. G. Hamilton**
6 **ROYAL SUMMIT**, 8, b g Kayf Tara—Nas Na Riogh (IRE) **J. M. Nicholson**
7 **SKYHILL (IRE)**, 6, b g Gold Well—Classic Mari (IRE) **Mr & Mrs D S Byers & Jpg Hamilton**
8 **SUNSET MARQUIS (IRE)**, 8, b m Kayf Tara—Miss Abrahnovic (IRE) **J. P. G. Hamilton**
9 **THE ICE FACTOR**, 11, b g Iceman—Kiruna **J. P. G. Hamilton**
10 **TOWERBURN (IRE)**, 10, b g Cloudings (IRE)—Lady Newmill (IRE) **J. P. G. Hamilton**

Other Owners: Mr & Mrs D. S. Byers, Mrs M. J. Byers, D. S. Byers, Mrs A. C. Hamilton.

Assistant Trainer: Mr G. Hamilton

260 MRS ANN HAMILTON, Newcastle Upon Tyne
Postal: **Claywalls Farm, Capheaton, Newcastle Upon Tyne, Tyne and Wear, NE19 2BP**
Contacts: **PHONE (01830) 530219 MOBILE (07704) 670704**
E-MAIL annhamilton1952@hotmail.com

1 **LITTLE BAVINGTON**, 6, b g Strategic Prince—Vanilla Delight (IRE) **Mr I. Hamilton**
2 **NUTS WELL**, 8, b g Dylan Thomas (IRE)—Renada (IRE) **Mr I. Hamilton**
3 **POINT BREAK (IRE)**, 5, b g Westerner—Pertinent Point (IRE) **Mr I. Hamilton**

Assistant Trainer: Ian Hamilton

261 MR MICKY HAMMOND, Middleham
Postal: **Oakwood Stables, East Witton Road, Middleham, Leyburn, North Yorkshire, DL8 4PT**
Contacts: **PHONE (01969) 625223 MOBILE (07808) 572777**
E-MAIL mickyhammondracing@hotmail.com WEBSITE www.mickyhammondracing.co.uk

1 **ALDERBROOK LAD (IRE)**, 13, ch g Alderbrook—Alone Tabankulu (IRE) **Ian Barran, Rita Butler & Gemma Hogg**
2 **ART OF SUPREMACY (IRE)**, 7, b g Milan—Marble Desire (IRE) **Give Every Man His Due**
3 **ASK PADDINGTON (IRE)**, 5, ch g Ask—Dual Obsession **Mr C. Buckingham**
4 **BECKY THE THATCHER**, 6, b m Mastercraftsman (IRE)—Fairmont (IRE) **McGoldrick Racing**
5 **BLACK KETTLE (IRE)**, 9, b g Robin des Pres (FR)—Whistful Suzie (IRE) **Tasker-Brown & Partners**
6 **BLUE HUSSAR (IRE)**, 8, b g Montjeu—Metaphor (USA) **Mr Richard Howard & Mr Ben Howard**
7 **BULKOV (FR)**, 7, b g Zambezi Sun—Say Say (FR) **Finch Porter&the Deckchair Partnership**
8 **BURDIGALA (FR)**, 6, b g Way of Light (USA)—Tiara **Mrs R. Hetherington**
9 **CALIPTION**, 7, gr g Fair Mix (IRE)—Sheriff's Falcon (IRE) **The Cheltenham Trail**
10 **CANFORD THOMPSON**, 6, b g Canford Cliffs (IRE)—Sadie Thompson (IRE) **M. D. Hammond**
11 **CARALINE (FR)**, 8, b m Martaline—Vie Ta Vie (FR) **Give Every Man His Due**
12 **CHRISTMAS TWENTY (IRE)**, 9, b g Zagreb (USA)—Celestial Gale (IRE) **The Uncles**
13 **CONNECTIVE (IRE)**, 4, ch g Dubawi (IRE)—Connecting **Mr C. Buckingham**
14 **CONVIVIAL**, 4, b f Mount Nelson—Vino **Grange Park Racing XV1**
15 **CORNERSTONE LAD**, 5, b g Delegator—Chapel Corner (IRE) **Mrs B. M. Lofthouse**
16 **CORREGGIO**, 9, ch g Bertolini (USA)—Arian Da **Forty Forty Twenty**
17 **CREST**, 8, b g Kayf Tara—Maiden Voyage **Mike & Eileen Newbould, N Rust**
18 **CRYPTO (IRE)**, 5, b g Gold Well—Top Lot (IRE) **Mrs J. E. Newett**
19 **DAKOTA GREY**, 8, gr g Fair Mix (IRE)—Miss Sassi **Still Game Associates**
20 **DARK VALLEY (IRE)**, 9, b g Lend A Hand—Glorys Flame (IRE) **The Snook Family & Partner**
21 **DEDIGOUT (IRE)**, 13, b g Bob Back (USA)—Dainty Daisy (IRE) **Masters of the Hall 3**
22 **DONTDELAY (IRE)**, 9, b g Indian Danehill (IRE)—Garden Heaven (IRE) **Mrs G. Hogg**
23 **EAGER TO KNOW (IRE)**, 9, b g Sayarshan (FR)—Drew (IRE) **Tasker-Brown & Partners**
24 **ENFIN PHIL (FR)**, 5, ch g No Risk At All (FR)—Nheyranne (FR) **Randall Orchard & Partners**
25 **EX S'ELANCE (FR)**, 5, b g Saddex—Pampa Brune (FR) **The Fifty Fifty Partnership**
26 **EXCALIBUR (POL)**, 6, gr g Youmzain (IRE)—Electra Deelites **The Golden Cuckoo**

MR MICKY HAMMOND - Continued

27 **FRANK THE SLINK**, 13, b g Central Park (IRE)—Kadari **The Three Tigers**
28 **FRANKSTER (FR)**, 6, b g Equiano (FR)—Milwaukee (FR) **The Cobb Family**
29 **FULLMOON LUNA LADY (FR)**, 4, b f Spanish Moon (USA)—Question de Temps (FR) **Mr S. M. Everard**
30 **HORST (FR)**, 5, b g Soldier Hollow—Sternenkonigin (IRE) **Mr C. Buckingham**
31 **ILAYA (FR)**, 5, gr m Kapgarde (FR)—Tour Magic (FR) **The Golden Cuckoo**
32 **IT'S ALL ABOUT ME (IRE)**, 7, b m King's Theatre (IRE)—Annie Spectrim (IRE) **M.H.O.G.**
33 **JO'S GIRL (IRE)**, 4, b f Zebedee—Diamond Finesse (IRE) **Mr & Mrs I P Earnshaw**
34 **JUST CAMERON**, 12, b g Kayf Tara—Miss Fencote **Mr & Mrs P. Chapman**
35 **JUSTCALL'M JOHN (IRE)**, 5, b g Witness Box (USA)—Black N Amber (IRE) **Maybe The Last Time**
36 **JUSTFORJAMES (IRE)**, 10, b g Dr Massini (IRE)—Over The Road (IRE) **J4J Partnership**
37 **KAVORA**, 4, b f Havana Gold (IRE)—Anadiya (FR) **Mr I. Ender**
38 **KISUMU**, 7, b g High Chaparral (IRE)—Arum Lily (USA) **Tasker-Brown & Partners**
39 **KNOCKNAMONA (IRE)**, 8, b g Trans Island—Faraday Lady (IRE) **The Rat Pack Racing Club**
40 **LADY OF THE REA (IRE)**, 8, b m Scorpion (IRE)—Sonnys Girl (IRE) **Mr K. J. McNeill**
41 **LATE DATE (IRE)**, 8, b g Oscar (IRE)—Regents Ballerina (IRE) **County Set Six & Partner**
42 **LE MAITRE CHAT (USA)**, 8, b g Tale of The Cat (USA)—Bedside Story **Mr & Mrs I P Earnshaw**
43 **LEODIS (IRE)**, 7, ch g Shirocco (GER)—Leonica **A & S Associates**
44 **LESTER KRIS**, 5, b g Fame And Glory—Wood Sprite **Mr C. Buckingham**
45 **MAC CENNETIG (IRE)**, 7, b g Brian Boru—Buslane (IRE) **Mrs B. M. Lofthouse**
46 **MARVELLOUS JOE (IRE)**, 4, b g Mahler—Marvellous Dream (FR) **Mr Joe Buzzeo & Partner**
47 **MISS TOOTSY (FR)**, 6, b m Authorized (IRE)—Miss Sissy (FR) **Mrs Jennifer Hill & Mrs Samantha Toomes**
48 **NINE O THREE (IRE)**, 7, gr g Central Park (IRE)—That's My Sister (IRE) **Mr C. Buckingham**
49 **ONLY ORSENFOOLSIES**, 10, b g Trade Fair—Desert Gold (IRE) **M.H.O.G.**
50 **ONLYFOOLSOWNHORSES (IRE)**, 8, b g Presenting—Lizzy Langtry (IRE)
51 **OUR GETAWAY GIRL (IRE)**, 4, b f Getaway (GER)—Tastytimes (IRE) **The Getaway Gang**
52 **PADDLING (FR)**, 8, b g Walk In The Park (IRE)—Sea Mamaille (FR) **Masters Of The Hall 2**
53 **QUOTELINE DIRECT**, 6, ch g Sir Percy—Queen's Pudding (IRE) **JFW Properties Limited**
54 **ROCKLIFFE**, 6, b g Notnowcato—Hope Island (IRE) **R M & T Holdings Limited & Partners**
55 **ROXYFET (FR)**, 9, b g Califet (FR)—Roxalamour (FR) **Mr Samuel Sutton & Partner**
56 **RUSSIAN ROYALE**, 9, b m Royal Applause—Russian Ruby (FR) **Raypasha**
57 **SAUCY SALLY (IRE)**, 4, b f Declaration of War (USA)—

          Ardere (USA) **Mr S & Mrs D Everard, A Smith & O Weeks**
58 **SCHIEHALLION MUNRO**, 8, ch g Schiaparelli (GER)—Mrs Fawlty **Tennant, Lynch,Sharpe and Boston**
59 **SILVER TASSIE (IRE)**, 11, b g Shantou (USA)—Silver Castor (IRE) **Mr R. M. Howard**
60 **SIR RUNS A LOT**, 7, b g Sir Percy—Monjouet (IRE) **R M & T Holdings Limited & Oakwood**
61 **SQUARE VIVIANI (FR)**, 8, b g Satri (IRE)—Idria (GER) **Stephen Sugden & Ryder Sugden**
62 **STORMIN NORMAN**, 4, b g Sir Percy—Roses **The Monday Club**
63 **STRAIT RUN (IRE)**, 8, ch g Rock of Gibraltar (IRE)—Gentlemen's Guest (USA) **Littlethorpe Park Racing**
64 **STRIKE WEST (IRE)**, 7, b g Westerner—Fuel Queen (IRE) **The Multi-Taskers**
65 **SWINTON DIAMOND (IRE)**, 8, b g Dubai Destination (USA)—Absent Beauty (IRE) **Mr & Mrs I P Earnshaw**
66 **THE PINE MARTIN (IRE)**, 9, br g Kalanisi (IRE)—Regal Holly **The Rat Pack Racing Club**
67 **THE RETRIEVER (IRE)**, 4, ch g Shamardal (USA)—Silent Secret (IRE) **R M & T Holdings Limited & Partners**
68 **THE STING (IRE)**, 6, br g Scorpion (IRE)—Moon Approach (IRE) **Maybe The Last Time**
69 **THUNDER BOY (FR)**, 4, b g Haatef (USA)—Nice To Know (FR) **Mr D. Lees**
70 **TICKENWOLF (IRE)**, 9, gr g Tikkanen (USA)—Emma's Choice (IRE) **Mr G. R. Orchard & Partner**
71 **VALGOR DU RONCERAY (FR)**, 10, gr g Al Namix (FR)—Malta de Ronceray (FR) **Grey Daze In Yorkshire**
72 **WHO'S THE GUV'NOR (IRE)**, 5, b g Gold Well—Clamit Brook (IRE) **Mr & Mrs I P Earnshaw**
73 **WIG WAM WIGGLE (IRE)**, 7, b g Mahler—Last Sunrise (IRE) **Mrs Jennifer Hill & Mrs Samantha Toomes**
74 **WILD GYPSY BOY**, 4, ch g Intikhab (USA)—Sahabah (USA) **The Golden Cuckoo**
75 **WISHING WELL**, 7, b m Bahri (USA)—Amourallis (IRE) **The Pennies Dropped Partnership**
76 **WITNESS (FR)**, 10, b g Astarabad (USA)—Belle Yepa (FR) **R M & T Holdings Limited & Partners**

THREE-YEAR-OLDS

77 **BURNAGE BOY (IRE)**, b g Footstepsinthesand—Speedi Mouse **JFW Properties Limited**
78 **BURUNDI (IRE)**, b g Cape Cross (IRE)—Tralanza (IRE)
79 **DRAGONS WILL RISE (IRE)**, b g Dragon Pulse (IRE)—Jaldini (IRE) **The Golden Cuckoo**
80 **GUSTAVE AITCH (FR)**, b g Maxios—Alyssandre (IRE) **Mr J. T. Finch**
81 **IRV (IRE)**, ch g Zoffany (IRE)—Marion Antoinette (IRE) **I. M. Lynch**
82 **B g f Alhebayeb (IRE)—Kowara (IRE) **Mrs N. McGrath**
83 **OUR BOY ZEUS (IRE)**, b g Morpheus—Alexander Duchess (IRE) **Deckchair Syn & Jen Hill,Samantha Toomes**
84 **THE RUTLAND REBEL (IRE)**, b g Delegator—Do Disturb (IRE) **Stephen Sugden & Ryder Sugden**

TWO-YEAR-OLDS

85 Ch f 4/3 Ruler of The World (IRE)—Twelfth Night (IRE) (Namid) (4761)

MR MICKY HAMMOND - Continued

Other Owners: I. J. Barran, R. P. E. Berry, Mr A. Bradley, Mrs M. A. Butler, J. Buzzeo, Mrs J. Chapman, Mr P. W. Chapman, Mrs J. Cobb, Mr S. J. M. Cobb, Mr A. D. Crombie, Mr R. Doak, Mr I. P. Earnshaw, Mrs J. Earnshaw, Mrs D. S. Everard, G. Godsman, Mr R. Green, Mr D. A. Harrison, Mr J. A. Hill, Mrs J. Hill, Mr L. Horvath, Mr B. R. Howard, J. M. Hughes, Mr D. Hymas, Mrs A. Kane, Mr R. J. Longley, Mr R. Manners, Mr J. M. Newbould, Mrs E. E. Newbould, G. R. Orchard, Mr J. Pettit, Mr A. M. Phillips, Mr E. Price, R M & T Holdings Limited, Mr J. Reid, Mr N. J. Rust, Mr A. Savage, Mr C. M. Sharpe, A. W. Sinclair, Mr A. Smith, Mr T. Snook, Mrs V. M. Snook, The Snook Family, Mr A. Stainton, Mr R. Sugden, Mr S. Sugden, Mr S. Sutton, Mr J. Tasker-Brown, Mr J. E. Tennant, The Deckchair Syndicate, Mrs S. Toomes, Mr A. Walsh, Mr K. Ward, O. R. Weeks.

Assistant Trainer: Mrs. G. Hogg (07809) 428117

Jockey (NH): Alain Cawley, Joe Colliver. **Conditional:** Billy Garritty, Finian O'Toole. **Apprentice:** Lauren Steade. **Amateur:** Miss R. Smith.

---

262   **MR GARY HANMER, Tattenhall**
Postal: **Church Farm, Harthill Lane, Harthill, Tattenhall, Chester, Cheshire, CH3 9LQ**
Contacts: **MOBILE (07737) 181165**

1 **ARCTIC VALLEY (IRE)**, 5, b g Arctic Cosmos (USA)—Grangevalley Gold (IRE) **The Ed-chester Partnership**
2 4, B g Yeats (IRE)—Consultation (IRE) **Mrs M. D. Ritson**
3 **DEE LANE (IRE)**, 6, br g Oscar (IRE)—Royal Robin (IRE) **The Deeside Partnership**
4 **HIGH COUNSEL (IRE)**, 10, br g Presenting—The Bench (IRE) **Herongate Racers**
5 **KNOCKNAGOSHEL (IRE)**, 6, b g Kalanisi (IRE)—Granny Clark (IRE) **Knock Knock Syndicate**
6 **LOCH GARMAN ARIS (IRE)**, 9, b g Jammaal—See Em Aime (IRE) **Exors of Late George Brookes & Family**
7 **O'GRADY'S BOY (IRE)**, 8, b g Kalanisi (IRE)—Jemima Jay (IRE)
8 **ORO REBELDE**, 6, b g Cockney Rebel (IRE)—Corsa All Oro (USA) **P. S. Burke**
9 **OSCAR NOMINATION (IRE)**, 7, b g Getaway (GER)—Nightofthe Oscars (IRE) **The Deeside Partnership**
10 **PACKETTOTHERAFTERS (IRE)**, 10, b g Craigsteel—Darazari River (IRE) **The Tunstall Green Partnership**
11 **STEEL WAVE (IRE)**, 9, br g Craigsteel—Musical Waves (IRE) **The Tunstall Green Partnership**
12 **WHAT A LAUGH**, 14, ch g Kayf Tara—Just For A Laugh **Mr S. P. Edkins**

Other Owners: Mrs S. Archdale, G. E. Brookes, Mr L. Felstead, M. E. Green, Mr J. F. Hales, Mrs F. M. Midwood, J. M. Tomlinson, Mr N. P. Tunstall, Mr G. J. Winchester.

---

263   **MR RICHARD HANNON, Marlborough**
Postal: **Herridge Racing Stables, Herridge, Collingbourne Ducis, Wiltshire, SN8 3EG**
Contacts: **PHONE (01264) 850254 FAX (01264) 850076**
E-MAIL kevin@richardhannonracing.co.uk WEBSITE www.richardhannonracing.co.uk

1 **AL BARG (IRE)**, 4, b g Acclamation—Miss Hawai (FR)
2 **BLANCHEFLEUR (IRE)**, 4, b f Camelot—Portrait of A Lady (IRE)
3 **BREXITMEANSBREXIT**, 4, b f Helmet (AUS)—Lady Scarlett
4 **BURIDAN (FR)**, 4, b g Choisir (AUS)—Lady McKell (IRE)
5 **DANEHILL KODIAC (IRE)**, 6, b h Kodiac—Meadow
6 **DRAKEFELL (IRE)**, 4, b c Canford Cliffs (IRE)—Cake (IRE)
7 **ELYSIUM DREAM**, 4, b f Champs Elysees—Dream of Wunders
8 **EMBOUR (IRE)**, 4, b g Acclamation—Carpet Lady (IRE)
9 **MR TYRRELL (IRE)**, 5, b g Helmet (AUS)—Rocking
10 **MUSHTAQ (IRE)**, 4, b g Zoffany (IRE)—Iamfine (IRE)
11 **NAHHAM (IRE)**, 4, b g Dawn Approach (IRE)—Anna's Rock (IRE)
12 **OH THIS IS US (IRE)**, 6, b h Acclamation—Shamwari Lodge (IRE)
13 **QAYSAR (FR)**, 4, b g Choisir (AUS)—Coco Demure (IRE)
14 **RAYMOND TUSK (IRE)**, 4, b c High Chaparral (IRE)—Dancing Shoes (IRE)
15 **RED STARLIGHT**, 4, br f Pivotal—Star Chart (IRE)
16 **REPTON (IRE)**, 5, b g Zebedee—African Moonlight (UAE)
17 **ROCKSHINE**, 5, b m Fastnet Rock (AUS)—Shine Like A Star
18 **RUM RUNNER**, 4, b c Havana Gold (IRE)—Thermopylae
19 **SECOND PAGE**, 5, b g Harbour Watch (IRE)—Almunia (IRE)
20 **TANGLED (IRE)**, 4, b g Society Rock (IRE)—Open Verse (USA)
21 **TOMILY (IRE)**, 5, b g Canford Cliffs (IRE)—Cake (IRE)
22 **WAHASH (IRE)**, 5, gr g Dark Angel (IRE)—Delira (IRE)
23 **WAR GLORY (IRE)**, 6, b g Canford Cliffs (IRE)—Attracted To You (IRE)

MR RICHARD HANNON - Continued

THREE-YEAR-OLDS

24 **AIM POWER (IRE)**, gr f Zebedee—Montefino (IRE)
25 **AIR BENDER**, b c Garswood—Swanky Lady
26 **AL MESSILA**, b f Toronado (IRE)—Rose Blossom
27 **ALHAKMAH (IRE)**, b f No Nay Never (USA)—Hureya (USA)
28 **ALLOCATOR (FR)**, b c Kendargent (FR)—Vezina (FR)
29 **AMOROUSLY (IRE)**, b f Australia—Know Me Love Me (IRE)
30 **AUBRETIA (IRE)**, ch f Poet's Voice—Abilene
31 **BADER**, b c Elusive City (USA)—Golbahar (IRE)
32 **BEAT LE BON (FR)**, b c Wootton Bassett—Frida La Blonde (FR)
33 **BEECHWOOD JAMES (FR)**, b c Sunday Break (JPN)—Mururoa (FR)
34 **BIG BABY BULL (IRE)**, ch c Tagula (IRE)—Grotta Del Fauno (IRE)
35 **BINT SOGHAAN**, b f Dark Angel (IRE)—Deyaar (USA)
36 **BOITRON (FR)**, b c Le Havre (IRE)—Belliflore (FR)
37 **BRIAN EPSTEIN (IRE)**, b c Dark Angel (IRE)—Jewel In The Sand (IRE)
38 **CANTON QUEEN (IRE)**, b f Shamardal (USA)—Hana Lina
39 **CHATHAM HOUSE**, gr c Dark Angel (IRE)—Timely
40 **COME ON LEICESTER (IRE)**, b f Kodiac—Graphic Guest
41 **CRACKING SPEED (IRE)**, gr c Alhebayeb (IRE)—Summer Glow (IRE)
42 **CROQUETA (IRE)**, b f Camacho—Oatcake
43 **CROWN OF FLOWERS**, ch f Garswood—Ring of Love
44 **DAYS OF GLORY (CAN)**, b c Scat Daddy (USA)—Charming Thunder (USA)
45 **DIRTY RASCAL (IRE)**, b c Acclamation—Refusetolisten (IRE)
46 **DOUGHAN ALB**, b c Havana Gold (IRE)—Sandtime (IRE)
47 **DRAGON SUN**, ch g Pivotal—Moon Sister (IRE)
48 **EDDIE COCHRAN (IRE)**, bl c Society Rock (IRE)—Crossreadh (USA)
49 **EMBRACE THE MOMENT (IRE)**, b f Le Havre (IRE)—Kithonia (FR)
50 **ENCHANTED LINDA**, b f Charm Spirit (IRE)—Enchanted Princess
51 **EQUAL SUM**, br f Paco Boy (IRE)—Hypoteneuse (IRE)
52 **EXTREME (IRE)**, br c No Nay Never (USA)—Mixed Blessing
53 **FLOATING ARTIST**, b c Nathaniel (IRE)—Miss Kenton (IRE)
54 **FLYING DRAGON (FR)**, b g War Command (USA)—Histoire de Jouer (FR)
55 **FOX CHAMPION (IRE)**, b c Kodiac—Folegandros Island (FR)
56 **FOX HAPPY (IRE)**, b c Showcasing—Roo
57 **FOX KASPER**, ch g Society Rock (IRE)—Easy Times
58 **FOX POWER (IRE)**, gr c Dark Angel (IRE)—Zenella
59 **GLORIOUS DANE (IRE)**, b g Olympic Glory (IRE)—Kaminari (IRE)
60 **GLORY**, b c Olympic Glory (IRE)—Updated (FR)
61 **GOOD LUCK FOX (IRE)**, b c Society Rock (IRE)—Violet Ballerina (IRE)
62 **HAAYEM (FR)**, b c Olympic Glory (IRE)—Almaardiyah (IRE)
63 **HE'ZANARAB (IRE)**, b c Footstepsinthesand—Ziggy's Secret
64 **HERMOCRATES (FR)**, b c Farhh—Little Shambles
65 **HUA HIN (IRE)**, ch c Dandy Man (IRE)—Midnight Oasis
66 **IFREET (QA)**, ch c Toronado (IRE)—Bella Varenna (IRE)
67 **IN THE COVE (IRE)**, b c Footstepsinthesand—Vatrouchka (USA)
68 **JADELLA WILLFIN (FR)**, gr f Tin Horse (IRE)—Sienna May (USA)
69 **JUNGLE WARFARE (IRE)**, ch c Bungle Inthejungle—Fanditha (IRE)
70 **KING OF CHANGE**, b c Farhh—Salacia (IRE)
71 **KUWAIT CURRENCY (USA)**, ch c Kitten's Joy (USA)—Thebignbadestbunny (USA)
72 **LEROY LEROY**, b c Compton Place—Small Fortune
73 **LEXINGTON WARLORD**, b g War Command (USA)—Archina (IRE)
74 **MAGICAL WISH (IRE)**, b c Heeraat (IRE)—Tomintoul Magic (IRE)
75 **MAHBOB (IRE)**, b c Toronado (IRE)—Lily Link
76 **MASARU**, b c Lethal Force (IRE)—Spontaneity (IRE)
77 **MICHIGAN BLUE (IRE)**, b f War Command (USA)—Regency Girl (IRE)
78 **MOLAAHETH**, b c Heeraat (IRE)—All Fur Coat
79 **MORDRED (IRE)**, b c Camelot—Endure (IRE)
80 **MOTAFAAWIT (IRE)**, b br g Intikhab (USA)—Rayaheen
81 **NAUGHTY RASCAL (IRE)**, ch c Kyllachy—Gerika (FR)
82 **OSHO**, b c Oasis Dream—Maid of Killeen (IRE)
83 **OUZO**, b c Charm Spirit (IRE)—Miss Meltemi (IRE)
84 **PRODUCTION**, b g Oasis Dream—Pure Excellence
85 **PURBECK HILLS (IRE)**, b c Oasis Dream—Albisola (IRE)
86 **QUICK**, b f Olympic Glory (IRE)—The Giving Tree (IRE)
87 **REAL SMOOTH (IRE)**, b c Teofilo (IRE)—Amber Silk (IRE)

MR RICHARD HANNON - Continued

- 88 **RITCHIE VALENS (IRE)**, ch c Helmet (AUS)—Miss Cape (IRE)
- 89 **ROLLICKING (IRE)**, b f Holy Roman Emperor (IRE)—Maghzaa (IRE)
- 90 **ROONG ROONG (IRE)**, gr f Dark Angel (IRE)—Cut No Ice (IRE)
- 91 **SHAMKHA (IRE)**, b f Teofilo (IRE)—Shivaree
- 92 **SIRINAPHA (IRE)**, b c Alhebayeb (IRE)—Sassari (IRE)
- 93 **STAR OF WAR (USA)**, b f Declaration of War (USA)—Sunshine For Life (USA)
- 94 **STAR TERMS**, ch f Sea The Stars (IRE)—Best Terms
- 95 **SUMMA FORCE (IRE)**, b c Gale Force Ten—Queen Myrine (IRE)
- 96 **TIME FOR BED (IRE)**, b f Zebedee—Violet Flame (IRE)
- 97 **TOPICAL**, b g Toronado (IRE)—Star Value (IRE)
- 98 **TYPHOON TEN (IRE)**, b c Slade Power (IRE)—Cake (IRE)
- 99 **URBAN ICON**, b c Cityscape—Fauran (IRE)
- 100 **VENTURA GLORY**, b f Olympic Glory (IRE)—Fringe Success (IRE)
- 101 **VENTURA ISLAND (FR)**, b f Le Havre (IRE)—Sun Seeker (IRE)
- 102 **WALKINTHESAND (IRE)**, b c Footstepsinthesand—Masseera (IRE)
- 103 **WAREEDA (IRE)**, b f War Command (USA)—Areeda (IRE)
- 104 **WARSASH (IRE)**, b f War Command (USA)—Deora De
- 105 **WATAN**, ch c Toronado (IRE)—Shotgun Gulch (USA)
- 106 **WATER DIVINER (IRE)**, b c Bungle Inthejungle—Khayrat (IRE)
- 107 **WEDDING DATE**, b f Dandy Man (IRE)—Fiancee (IRE)
- 108 **WELL DONE FOX**, b c Acclamation—Excelette (IRE)
- 109 **YESTAAHEL**, b c Footstepsinthesand—Azenzar

TWO-YEAR-OLDS

- 110 **AFRO BLUE (IRE)**, b c 21/2 Oasis Dream—Najraan (Cadeaux Genereux) (50000)
- 111 B c 8/2 Dark Angel (IRE)—Age of Chivalry (IRE) (Invincible Spirit (IRE)) (161904)
- 112 Br c 12/2 Gutaifan (IRE)—Aja (IRE) (Excellent Art) (38095)
- 113 **AL HAAMY (IRE)**, b c 16/5 Shamardal (USA)—Sharedah (IRE) (Pivotal)
- 114 **AL NAMIR (IRE)**, b c 23/4 Shamardal (USA)—Rayaheen (Nayef (USA))
- 115 **ALMUERZO LOCO (IRE)**, gr c 2/5 Zebedee—Chica Loca (FR) (American Post) (33712)
- 116 **ALWAYS FEARLESS (IRE)**, ch c 9/4 Camacho—Zenella (Kyllachy) (270000)
- 117 B c 21/3 Due Diligence (USA)—Amazed (Clantime) (95000)
- 118 B c 4/2 Dabirsim (FR)—Amazing Bounty (FR) (Tertullian (USA)) (82595)
- 119 B f 15/1 Kodiac—Ambiguous (Kheleyf (USA)) (80000)
- 120 B c 8/4 Clodovil (IRE)—Apostrophe (IRE) (Barathea (IRE)) (38095)
- 121 **ATTENDOLO (IRE)**, b c 29/4 Raven's Pass (USA)—Summer Dream (IRE) (Oasis Dream) (63211)
- 122 **AUDIO**, b c 16/3 Equiano (FR)—Naayla (IRE) (Invincible Spirit (IRE)) (24000)
- 123 B c 23/3 Canford Cliffs (IRE)—Azharia (Oasis Dream) (3809)
- 124 **BACCHALOT (IRE)**, b f 11/4 Sir Prancealot (IRE)—Bacchanalia (IRE) (Blues Traveller (IRE)) (12000)
- 125 Gr c 3/4 Gutaifan (IRE)—Beguiler (Refuse To Bend (IRE)) (71428)
- 126 **BIG WING (IRE)**, b br c 12/3 Free Eagle (IRE)—Orafinitis (IRE) (Oratorio (IRE)) (60000)
- 127 B f 16/3 Frankel—Biscaya Bay (Dansili) (230000)
- 128 B c 26/2 Dandy Man (IRE)—Boca Dancer (IRE) (Indian Ridge) (20952)
- 129 Br c 28/2 Dream Ahead (USA)—Body Beautiful (IRE) (Big Bad Bob (IRE)) (43825)
- 130 B f 14/3 Canford Cliffs (IRE)—Cake (IRE) (Acclamation)
- 131 B c 28/4 Red Jazz (USA)—Ceylon Round (FR) (Royal Applause) (15000)
- 132 B f 9/2 Kodiac—Cherrington (IRE) (Lope de Vega (IRE))
- 133 **CLOAK OF SPIRITS (IRE)**, b f 4/2 Invincible Spirit (IRE)—Pivotique (Pivotal)
- 134 B f 2/3 Kodiac—Coquette Rouge (IRE) (Croco Rouge (IRE)) (150000)
- 135 **COUNT OF AMAZONIA (IRE)**, b c 15/2 Lope de Vega (IRE)—Queen Myrine (IRE) (Oratorio (IRE)) (160000)
- 136 B f 28/3 Camacho—Cover Girl (IRE) (Common Grounds) (122207)
- 137 **DARK LADY**, b gr f 9/4 Dark Angel (IRE)—Ladyship (Oasis Dream)
- 138 Ch c 11/4 Paco Boy (IRE)—Dark Quest (Rainbow Quest (USA)) (4500)
- 139 B f 21/1 Havana Gold (IRE)—Dark Reckoning (Equiano (FR))
- 140 **DESERT PALMS**, b c 6/3 Oasis Dream—Be My Gal (Galileo (IRE)) (320000)
- 141 B f 13/2 Kodiac—Dhuma (Falco (USA)) (120000)
- 142 B f 7/3 Due Diligence (USA)—Diapason (IRE) (Mull of Kintyre (USA)) (15000)
- 143 **DIVINE COVEY**, gr f 4/4 Dark Angel (IRE)—Pack Together (Paco Boy (IRE))
- 144 **DONTCALLMEJUNIOR (IRE)**, b f 28/2 Holy Roman Emperor (IRE)—Layla's Red Devil (IRE) (Dalakhani (IRE))
- 145 **DR AVERY (FR)**, b c 10/3 Dabirsim (FR)—Fox Force Five (IRE) (Araafa (IRE)) (75853)
- 146 **DREAMY RASCAL (IRE)**, b f 21/3 Dream Ahead (USA)—Emirates Challenge (IRE) (Cape Cross (IRE)) (18000)
- 147 B c 24/3 Zoffany (IRE)—Dress Rehearsal (IRE) (Galileo (IRE)) (80000)
- 148 B c 20/2 Gutaifan (IRE)—Dust Flicker (Suave Dancer (USA)) (140000)
- 149 B f 20/4 Kodiac—Ebtisama (USA) (Kingmambo (USA))
- 150 **ELEGANT ERIN (IRE)**, b f 18/3 Dandy Man (IRE)—Eriniya (IRE) (Acclamation) (17699)

MR RICHARD HANNON - Continued

151 Br c 20/2 No Nay Never (USA)—Emeralds Spirit (IRE) (Rock of Gibraltar (IRE)) (45000)
152 B c 3/2 Dark Angel (IRE)—Encore View (Oasis Dream) (45714)
153 B c 2/3 Dubawi (IRE)—Estidraaj (USA) (Medaglia d'oro (USA))
154 **EXHIBIT (IRE),** b f 5/5 Showcasing—Timely (Pivotal)
155 **FROZEN WATERS (IRE),** ch c 24/3 No Nay Never (USA)—Whitefall (USA) (Street Cry (IRE)) (320000)
156 B c 31/3 No Nay Never (USA)—Gems (Haafhd) (250000)
157 Bl gr c 6/3 Outstrip—Gennie Bond (Pivotal) (1142)
158 **GOOD JOB POWER (IRE),** b c 4/3 Acclamation—Thousandfold (USA) (Giant's Causeway (USA)) (109565)
159 B f 3/3 Cable Bay (IRE)—Grand Depart (Royal Applause) (17000)
160 **GRINLING (IRE),** b c 23/3 Mastercraftsman (IRE)—Gravitation (Galileo (IRE))
161 B c 1/1 Zoffany (IRE)—Heliocentric (FR) (Galileo (IRE)) (42140)
162 **HERMANO BELLO (FR),** b c 5/2 Youmzain (IRE)—Pasaquina (GER) (Acatenango (GER)) (33712)
163 B f 18/3 Dutch Art—Holberg Suite (Azamour (IRE)) (35000)
164 B f 29/4 Dandy Man (IRE)—Hucking Hot (Desert Prince (IRE)) (40000)
165 B c 29/3 Zebedee—Imtidaad (USA) (Lemon Drop Kid (USA)) (15000)
166 **INEXPLICABLE (IRE),** b gr c 20/2 Dark Angel (IRE)—Bikini Babe (IRE) (Montjeu (IRE))
167 **INQUIZITIVE,** b f 2/4 Fountain of Youth (IRE)—Quiz Show (Primo Dominie)
168 **IVOR,** b g 19/2 Iffraaj—Ligeia (Rail Link)
169 **JACK RUBY (IRE),** b c 25/2 Havana Gold (IRE)—Make Me Blush (IRE) (Makfi) (52380)
170 B c 6/2 Brazen Beau (AUS)—Jaiyana (Dansili) (50000)
171 B f 27/2 Showcasing—Jeanie Johnston (IRE) (One Cool Cat (USA)) (26970)
172 **JEN'S LAD (IRE),** b c 26/1 Dandy Man (IRE)—Strawberry Queen (Dr Fong (USA)) (80952)
173 **KEEP IT BRIEF,** b c 24/1 Muhaarar—Brevity (USA) (Street Cry (IRE)) (100000)
174 B f 21/3 Cityscape—L'addition (Exceed And Excel (AUS))
175 B c 26/2 Oasis Dream—La Petite Reine (Galileo (IRE))
176 B c 20/1 Hot Streak (IRE)—Lahqa (IRE) (Tamayuz) (59047)
177 B f 25/1 Hallowed Crown (AUS)—Lauren's Girl (IRE) (Bushranger (IRE)) (52254)
178 B f 6/2 Gutaifan (IRE)—Lillebonne (FR) (Danehill Dancer (IRE)) (54782)
179 B f 1/2 Gregorian (IRE)—Limousine (Beat Hollow) (14285)
180 Ch c 27/4 Camacho—Little Audio (IRE) (Shamardal (USA)) (31428)
181 **LITTLE BIRD (IRE),** b f 27/4 Free Eagle (IRE)—Burma Star (Shamardal (USA)) (8427)
182 Ch c 2/2 Zoffany (IRE)—Loch Ma Naire (IRE) (Galileo (IRE)) (55000)
183 **LOST EDEN (IRE),** b c 7/3 Sea The Stars (IRE)—Ghostflower (IRE) (Dansili) (168562)
184 B f 22/2 Dark Angel (IRE)—Lottie Dod (IRE) (Invincible Spirit (IRE)) (33333)
185 **LOVE LOVE,** b f 10/3 Kodiac—Perfect Blessings (IRE) (Kheleyf (USA)) (600000)
186 **LOVE POWERFUL (IRE),** b f 20/3 Gutaifan (IRE)—Montefino (Shamardal (USA)) (303413)
187 B c 31/1 Mastercraftsman (IRE)—Loved (IRE) (Galileo (IRE)) (130000)
188 B c 30/4 Harbour Watch (IRE)—Lucina (Machiavellian (USA)) (34285)
189 **LYRIC GOLD,** b c 19/4 Dubawi (IRE)—The Sound of Music (IRE) (Galileo (IRE))
190 **MAFIA POWER,** b c 13/3 Gleneagles (IRE)—Rivara (Red Ransom (USA)) (200000)
191 **MAMBO NIGHTS (IRE),** b c 18/2 Havana Gold (IRE)—Inez (Dai Jin) (250000)
192 B f 10/2 Dabirsim (FR)—Mamusella (FR) (Invincible Spirit (IRE)) (67425)
193 **MAN OF THE NIGHT (FR),** b c 6/2 Night of Thunder (USA)—Mandheera (USA) (Bernardini (USA)) (294985)
194 **MANIGORDO (IRE),** b br c 12/4 Kitten's Joy (USA)—Cutting Edge (USA) (Silver Deputy (CAN)) (50568)
195 B c 9/3 Sir Percy—Maria Kristina (FR) (Footstepsinthesand) (40000)
196 **MARK OF GOLD,** b c 12/5 Golden Horn—Polly's Mark (IRE) (Mark of Esteem (IRE)) (220000)
197 Gr c 9/2 Toronado (IRE)—Match Point (FR) (Verglas (IRE)) (80952)
198 **MAYELLA,** b f 19/1 Mayson—Cardrona (Selkirk (USA))
199 **MIRAZ (IRE),** b c 1/4 Kodiac—Summer Blues (USA) (Summer Bird (USA)) (38000)
200 B c 7/4 Zebedee—Monsusu (IRE) (Montjeu (IRE)) (21070)
201 **MUMS TIPPLE (IRE),** ch c 26/2 Footstepsinthesand—Colomone Cross (IRE) (Xaar) (42857)
202 B c 16/3 Epaulette (AUS)—My Uptown Girl (Dubai Destination (USA)) (34285)
203 B c 8/2 Brazen Beau (AUS)—Netta (IRE) (Barathea (IRE)) (47000)
204 Br f 6/3 Dandy Man (IRE)—New Magic (IRE) (Statue of Liberty (USA)) (61904)
205 **NO SHOW (IRE),** ch c 21/4 Showcasing—Innocent Air (Galileo (IRE)) (92709)
206 **NORTHERN SUN (IRE),** b c 1/3 Showcasing—Solstice (Dubawi (IRE)) (92709)
207 Gr ro f 28/4 Gutaifan (IRE)—Novel Fun (IRE) (Noverre (USA)) (16856)
208 **NUGGET,** b c 26/3 Siyouni (FR)—Gemstone (IRE) (Galileo (IRE)) (85714)
209 **ON PARADE,** b g 21/3 Paco Boy (IRE)—Flash of Gold (Darshaan)
210 B c 19/2 Kodiac—Open Verse (USA) (Black Minnaloushe (USA)) (114285)
211 B c 2/3 War Command (USA)—Outshine (Exceed And Excel (AUS)) (15000)
212 **PARTRIDGE (IRE),** b f 6/3 Zoffany (IRE)—Lasilia (IRE) (Acclamation) (126421)
213 **PHOTOGRAPH (IRE),** b c 11/1 Kodiac—Supreme Occasion (IRE) (Teofilo (IRE)) (85000)
214 **PRINCE CASPIAN,** b c 2/2 Muhaarar—Riskit Fora Biskit (IRE) (Kodiac) (70000)
215 Gr f 5/4 Gutaifan (IRE)—Rahaala (IRE) (Indian Ridge) (42857)

MR RICHARD HANNON - Continued

216 B c 23/4 Free Eagle (IRE)—Regalline (IRE) (Green Desert (USA)) (150000)
217 **ROCKY DREAMS,** b c 21/2 Muhaarar—Mrs Greeley (Mr Greeley (USA)) (300000)
218 Ch c 16/4 Sepoy (AUS)—Samdaniya (Machiavellian (USA)) (65000)
219 **SEADANCE,** b c 28/4 Harbour Watch (IRE)—Sand Dancer (IRE) (Footstepsinthesand) (30000)
220 B f 22/1 Acclamation—Semaral (IRE) (High Chaparral (IRE)) (57000)
221 **SEPARATE,** b f 19/3 Cable Bay (IRE)—Miss Moses (USA) (Gulch (USA)) (28571)
222 B c 24/4 Ivawood (IRE)—Serenata (IRE) (Oratorio (IRE)) (30476)
223 B c 11/3 Night of Thunder (IRE)—Shama's Song (Teofilo (IRE)) (88495)
224 Ch f 10/4 Night of Thunder (IRE)—Silent Serenade (Bertolini (USA)) (37000)
225 **SKY POWER (IRE),** b c 25/2 Fastnet Rock (AUS)—Dame Blanche (IRE) (Be My Guest (USA)) (450000)
226 Ch c 29/4 Zebedee—Smokey Ryder (Bertolini (USA)) (22756)
227 B c 13/2 Harbour Watch (IRE)—Sorella Bella (IRE) (Clodovil (IRE)) (55000)
228 Bc 7/4 Night of Thunder (IRE)—Sparkling Smile (IRE) (Cape Cross (IRE)) (115000)
229 B c 1/3 Canford Cliffs (IRE)—Spinning Lucy (IRE) (Spinning World (USA))
230 B f 4/5 Kodiac—Spritza (IRE) (Spectrum (IRE))
231 **SRI SENE POWER (IRE),** b f 2/2 Dark Angel (IRE)—Fanciful Dancer (Groom Dancer (USA)) (600000)
232 B c 18/1 Zoffany (IRE)—Stor Mo Chroi (IRE) (Montjeu (IRE)) (65739)
233 B c 27/3 Society Rock (IRE)—Sunny Days (IRE) (Areion (GER)) (200000)
234 Ch c 22/1 Mastercraftsman (IRE)—Tendency (IRE) (Galileo (IRE)) (150000)
235 B f 30/1 Orpen (USA)—Tengeline (FR) (Cardoun (FR)) (21070)
236 **THE SEVENTH DAY,** b c 11/3 Siyouni (FR)—Mad Existence (IRE) (Val Royal (USA)) (300000)
237 **THREAT (IRE),** ch c 19/2 Footstepsinthesand—Flare of Firelight (USA) (Birdstone (USA))
238 B c 2/5 Charm Spirit (IRE)—Tocopilla (FR) (Medaaly) (70000)
239 **TODAY POWER (IRE),** b c 20/2 Dark Angel (IRE)—Todegica (Giant's Causeway (USA)) (210702)
240 **TOP CLASS ANGEL (IRE),** b f 25/1 Dark Angel (IRE)—Expensive Date (Monsieur Bond (IRE)) (202275)
241 **TOTAL PERFECTION (IRE),** br c 14/3 Fountain of Youth (IRE)—Day By Day (Kyllachy) (25284)
242 Ch f 17/3 Anjaal—Trading Places (Dansili) (10013)
243 Ch f 26/2 Equiano (FR)—Updated (FR) (New Approach (IRE)) (26666)
244 B c 22/3 Le Havre (USA)—Vassaria (IRE) (Rock of Gibraltar (IRE)) (50000)
245 **VINTAGE RASCAL (FR),** b c 17/2 Nathaniel (IRE)—Irish Vintage (FR) (Loup Solitaire (USA)) (22756)
246 Ch c 8/4 Intello (GER)—Vivacity (Trempolino (USA)) (54782)
247 **WHAT AN ANGEL,** br gr c 8/3 Dark Angel (IRE)—Mary Boleyn (IRE) (King's Best (USA)) (70000)
248 **WHISPER NOT,** b c 13/3 Poet's Voice—Poyle Meg (Dansili) (16856)
249 **WIN WIN POWER (IRE),** b c 7/3 Exceed And Excel (AUS)—Spesialta (Indian Ridge) (200000)
250 **WINTER HALO (IRE),** b f 28/1 Dark Angel (IRE)—Snowy Peak (Pivotal) (219131)
251 **WRITTEN BROADCAST (IRE),** gr c 15/3 Gutaifan (IRE)—Teeline (IRE) (Exceed And Excel (AUS)) (126421)
252 B c 3/3 Gutaifan (IRE)—Xema (Danehill (USA)) (95238)

Assistant Trainer: Tom Ward

Jockey (flat): Tom Marquand, Sean Levey, Hollie Doyle, Rossa Ryan. **Apprentice:** Mark Crehan, Seamus Cronin, Thore Hammer Hansen, Emma Taff.

264	**MR GEOFFREY HARKER, Thirsk**

Postal: Stockhill Green, York Rd, Thirkelby, Thirsk, North Yorkshire, YO7 3AS
Contacts: PHONE (01845) 501117 FAX (01845) 501614 MOBILE (07803) 116412/(07930) 125544
E-MAIL gandjhome@aol.com WEBSITE www.geoffharkerracing.com

1 **EXTRASOLAR,** 9, b g Exceed And Excel (AUS)—Amicable Terms **The Twelve Minimum Partnership**
2 **MAMBILA (FR),** 5, b g Rio de La Plata (USA)—Maka (FR) **Paddy Downes,Bill Green & Phil Harker**
3 **ROUE DE CHARRETTE,** 4, ch f Champs Elysees—Somersault **Mrs S. Dwyer**
4 **ROYAL LIBERTY,** 4, b g Acclamation—Anadolu (IRE) **P. I. Harker**
5 **SCOTTISH SUMMIT (IRE),** 6, b g Shamardal (USA)—Scottish Stage (IRE) **Sterling Racing & Geoff Harker**
6 **SHAMAHEART (IRE),** 9, b g Shamardal (USA)—Encouragement **A. S. Ward**
7 **WENTWORTH FALLS,** 7, gr g Dansili—Strawberry Morn (CAN) **Mr G. A. Harker**

Other Owners: Mr H. G. Bryson, Mr P. Downes, Mr W. Green, Mr J. P. Noble, Mr A. J. Parish, Mr D. J. Pentney, Mr S. J. Robinson, Sterling Racing.

Assistant Trainer: Jenny Harker

Jockey (NH): W. T. Kennedy.

265 **MR RICHARD HARPER, Banbury**
Postal: **Home Farm, Kings Sutton, Banbury, Oxfordshire, OX17 3RS**
Contacts: **PHONE (01295) 810997 FAX (01295) 812787 MOBILE (07970) 223481**
E-MAIL rharper@freeuk.com

1 BRERETON (IRE), 8, b g Kalanisi (IRE)—Westgrove Berry (IRE) **R. C. Harper**
2 JUST SKITTLES (IRE), 11, b g Storming Home—Miss Roberto (IRE) **R. C. Harper**
3 POYNTZPASS (IRE), 9, ch g Gamut (IRE)—Play Trix (IRE) **R. C. Harper**
4 THOMAS BLOSSOM (IRE), 9, b g Dylan Thomas (IRE)—Woman Secret (IRE) **R. C. Harper**

Assistant Trainer: C. Harper

266 **MRS JESSICA HARRINGTON, Kildare**
Postal: **Commonstown Stud, Moone, Co. Kildare, Ireland**
Contacts: **PHONE (00353) 5986 24153 MOBILE (00353) 8725 66129**
E-MAIL jessica@jessicaharringtonracing.com WEBSITE www.jessicaharringtonracing.com

1 A SIZING NETWORK (FR), 9, ch g Network (GER)—Gemma (FR) **Ann & Alan Potts Ltd**
2 ABOVE AND BEYOND (FR), 4, gr g Al Namix (FR)—Comohio (FR) **Robcour**
3 ALLETRIX (IRE), 6, b m Flemensfirth (USA)—Miracle Trix (IRE) **Ms Sally Rowley-Williams**
4 ANOTHER BARNEY (IRE), 6, br g Scorpion (IRE)—Roseabel (IRE) **Robcour**
5 ASHDALE BOB (IRE), 4, b g Shantou (USA)—Ceol Rua (IRE) **Diarmuid Horgan**
6 BERTONI (IRE), 5, b g Shirocco (GER)—Lovely Star (IRE) **Roberto Rea**
7 BIT OF BANTER (IRE), 4, b f Big Bad Bob (IRE)—Armoise **A Blessing In Disguise Partnership**
8 BOHO (IRE), 4, br g Big Bad Bob (IRE)—Are You Mine (IRE) **Anamoine Ltd**
9 BRICK BY BRICK (IRE), 4, b g Big Bad Bob (IRE)—Pivka **Anamoine Ltd**
10 CHARCOR (IRE), 5, b g Choisir (AUS)—Sanadaat **Mr John O'Hagan**
11 CITY BALLERINA (IRE), 4, b f Rip Van Winkle (IRE)—Vanity (IRE)
12 CLOSE SHAVE (IRE), 8, b g Presenting—Knock Down (IRE) **Mr J P McManus**
13 COMMANDER LADY (IRE), 4, b f Yeats (IRE)—Shuil Aris (IRE) **Jim Mulcahy**
14 CONRON (IRE), 5, b g Mastercraftsman (IRE)—Numbers Game **Mr John O'Hagan**
15 COROMANDEL LADY (IRE), 5, b m Milan—Katie's Cracker **Mount Temple Three Racing Syndicate**
16 DISCORDANTLY (IRE), 5, b g Salutino (GER)—Collinstown Queen (IRE) **Odd Fellows**
17 EARL OF DESMOND (IRE), 4, ch g Presenting—Gemini Lucy (IRE) **Westerwood Global Ltd**
18 ECHO PARK (IRE), 4, br f Elusive Pimpernel (USA)—Pershaan (IRE) **Anamoine Ltd**
19 EMILY MOON (IRE), 5, b m Beneficial—Wood Lily (IRE) **Mr Philip Myerscough**
20 ENVIOUS EDITOR (IRE), 5, b br g Aizavoski (IRE)—Moll The Rol (IRE) **Robcour**
21 EUPHORIQUE (FR), 5, b g Secret Singer (FR)—Nanny (FR) **Mrs A Frost**
22 EXIT POLL (IRE), 5, b g Elusive Pimpernel (USA)—Carolobrian (IRE)
23 EXTRASENSORY (IRE), 4, b f Arcano (IRE)—Kindest **Mr George Hartigan and Commonstown Racing Stables**
24 FORGE MEADOW (IRE), 7, b m Beneficial—Ballys Baby (IRE) **Mr Joe Doyle**
25 FRENCH STEPS (IRE), 6, b g Schiaparelli (GER)—La Perrotine (FR) **Niall Kennelly**
26 GOD KNOWS WHY (IRE), 4, b g Oscar (IRE)—Ballys Baby (IRE) **Joe Doyle**
27 GOT TRUMPED (IRE), 4, b g Mahler—Madam President **David Reid Scott**
28 HELIERS BAY (IRE), 5, ch m Flemensfirth (USA)—Now Its My Turn (IRE) **The Flyers Syndicate**
29 HOTEL DU NORD (FR), 6, b g Voix du Nord (FR)—Iu Mi Nao (IRE) **Mr Vimal Khosla**
30 HYPERDRIVE (IRE), 5, ch g Mastercraftsman (IRE)—Dromod Mour (IRE) **Mr Vimal Khosla**
31 IMPACT FACTOR (IRE), 7, b g Flemensfirth (USA)—Hello Kitty (IRE) **Robcour**
32 JACK FIASCO, 6, b g Black Sam Bellamy (IRE)—Damascena (GER) **Mr Sam Watson**
33 JELARA (IRE), 5, b m Milan—Jeree (IRE) **Mr Gerard McGrath**
34 JELONA (IRE), 4, b f Milan—Jeree (IRE) **Mr Gerard McGrath**
35 JETEZ (IRE), 6, b g Getaway (GER)—Miss Squiff (IRE) **Mr Gerard McGrath**
36 JETT (IRE), 8, b g Flemensfirth (USA)—La Noire (IRE) **Mr Gerard McGrath**
37 JETZ (IRE), 7, b g Flemensfirth (USA)—Miss Squiff (IRE) **Mr Gerard McGrath**
38 JEZKI (IRE), 11, b g Milan—La Noire (IRE) **Mr J P McManus**
39 JEZUKI (IRE), 4, b f Flemensfirth (USA)—Miss Squiff (IRE) **Mr Gerard McGrath**
40 JUNGLE JUNCTION (IRE), 4, br g Elusive Pimpernel (USA)—Consignia (IRE) **Mrs A Frost and Mrs G Galvin**
41 LIGHT THAT (IRE), 7, b g Echo of Light—Tucum (IRE) **The Flyers Syndicate**
42 LONG MARCH (IRE), 4, b g Bellamy Road (USA)—Magnifica (USA) **Kai Chan Tan**
43 LOVE AND WISHES (IRE), 7, b br g Winged Love (IRE)—Dixies Gem (IRE)
44 LYNWOOD GOLD (IRE), 4, gr ro g Mastercraftsman (IRE)—Witch of Fife (USA) **Robcour**
45 MADISON TO MONROE (IRE), 6, ro g Presenting—Caltra Princess (IRE) **Ann & Alan Potts Ltd**
46 MAGIC OF LIGHT (IRE), 8, b m Flemensfirth (USA)—Quest of Passion (FR) **Ann & Alan Potts Ltd**
47 MAGNUM (IRE), 6, b g Westerner—Anshan Bay (IRE) **Pat Rabbitt**

MRS JESSICA HARRINGTON - Continued

48 **MARSHALL JENNINGS (IRE)**, 7, b g Lawman (FR)—Zuniga's Date (USA) **Westward Bloodstock Ltd**
49 **MINNIE HAHA (FR)**, 4, gr f Style Vendome (FR)—Claveria (FR) **Mr Gerry Byrne**
50 **MITCHELL ONE (IRE)**, 5, ch g Le Fou (IRE)—Wrensboro (IRE) **Pam Sweeney**
51 **MOONSHINE BAY (IRE)**, 6, b g Milan—Chantoue Royale (IRE) **Ann & Alan Potts Ltd**
52 **MOROSINI (FR)**, 4, b g Martaline—Iris du Berlais (FR) **Mr J P McManus**
53 **NEVERUSHACON (IRE)**, 8, b g Echo of Light—Lily Beth (IRE) **David Reid Scott**
54 **NOT MANY LEFT (IRE)**, 6, b g Oscar (IRE)—Lasado (IRE) **Robcour**
55 **PAPAL PEARL (IRE)**, 4, b f Doyen (IRE)—Johnsons Coat (IRE) **Joe Doyle**
56 **PERES ET FILS (IRE)**, 5, br g Stowaway—Allthewhile (IRE) **Lynch Bages, Samac Ltd and Robcour**
57 **PERSIAN LION (IRE)**, 4, ch g Leroidesanimaux (BRZ)—Persian Memories (IRE) **Anamoine Ltd**
58 **POLISHED STEEL (IRE)**, 5, b g Jeremy (USA)—Chaperoned (IRE) **Mr Joe O'Flaherty**
59 **PRESS CONFERENCE (IRE)**, 6, b g Getaway (GER)—Beautiful Tune (FR) **Robcour**
60 **RAPID RESPONSE (FR)**, 5, br m Network (GER)—La Grande Villez (FR) **Ann & Alan Potts Ltd**
61 **ROBIN DES SIVOLA (IRE)**, 5, b m Robin des Champs (FR)—Falcons Gift (IRE) **Jim Mulcahy**
62 **ROCK THE WORLD (IRE)**, 11, b g Orpen (USA)—Sue N Win (IRE)
63 **ROVETTA (FR)**, 5, b m So You Think (NZ)—Rosa Brett (ITY) **The Long Wait Partnership**
64 **SANDYMOUNT DUKE (IRE)**, 10, b g Hernando (FR)—Joleah (IRE) **Mr Ron Wood**
65 **SIZING JOHN**, 9, b g Midnight Legend—La Perrotine (FR) **Ann & Alan Potts Ltd**
66 **SIZING POTTSIE (IRE)**, 5, b g Kapgarde (FR)—Line Salsa (FR) **Ann & Alan Potts Ltd**
67 **SPOKEN FOR (IRE)**, 5, b g Fame And Glory—Princess Susan (IRE) **Orpendale**
68 **ST BRELADES BAY (IRE)**, 7, b g Camacho—Tides **Commonstown Racing Stables**
69 **STILL STANDING (IRE)**, 4, ch c Mastercraftsman (IRE)—Il Palazzo (USA) **Anamoine Ltd**
70 **SUPASUNDAE**, 9, b g Galileo (IRE)—Distinctive Look (IRE) **Ann & Alan Potts Ltd**
71 **THE GABBY CABBY (IRE)**, 4, b g Stowaway—Coca's Lady (IRE) **Neil Durkan, Liam Durkan and Danny Durkan**
72 **THE HOLY ONE (IRE)**, 6, b g Court Cave—Vickate (IRE) **Mr David Bobbett**
73 **THE KING (IRE)**, 4, ch c Mastercraftsman (IRE)—Catch The Moon (IRE) **Millhouse LLC**
74 **THEGOAHEADMAN (IRE)**, 5, br g Jeremy (USA)—Little Luv (IRE) **Rainbow Gems Syndicate**
75 **UP'N'OVER (IRE)**, 5, b g Flemensfirth (USA)—Cut 'n' Run (IRE) **Mr Elder Scouller**
76 **WALK TO FREEDOM (IRE)**, 9, br g Arcadio (GER)—Carryonharriet (IRE) **Whole Of The Moone Syndicate**
77 **WHIRLING DERVISH**, 4, b c Camelot—Synergy (FR) **Millhouse LLC**
78 **WHISPERINTHEBREEZE**, 6, gr ro g Kayf Tara—Silver Spinner **Ann & Alan Potts Ltd**
79 **WHYDAH**, 5, gr g Black Sam Bellamy (IRE)—Talk The Talk **Mr G Ruddock**
80 **WINGS LIKE ARION (IRE)**, 7, b m Beneficial—Fruits de Mer (IRE) **Mr G Ruddock**
81 **WOODLAND OPERA (IRE)**, 9, br g Robin des Champs (FR)—
Opera Hat (IRE) **Mrs Diana Cooper, Mrs Valerie Cooper and Mrs Carolyn Waters**

THREE-YEAR-OLDS

82 **AYE AYE CAPT'N (IRE)**, b c Charm Spirit (IRE)—Cristal Fashion (IRE) **Mr Jim McDonald**
83 **BAR ROOM BORE (IRE)**, b g Big Bad Bob—Alayna (IRE) **Anamoine Ltd**
84 **BELLAKRIS (IRE)**, br f Scat Daddy (USA)—Akris Queen (USA) **Sally Rowley-Williams**
85 **BELLE CORA (IRE)**, gr f Zebedee—Ctesiphon (USA)
86 **BODAK (IRE)**, b f Kodiac—Arty Crafty (USA) **Bill Crager and Paul Hondros**
87 **BOSTON BRUIN (IRE)**, b c Kodiac—Sovana (IRE) **Millhouse LLC**
88 **BUILDING BRIDGES (IRE)**, br c New Approach (IRE)—City On Sea (IRE) **P K Cooper**
89 **CALLING TIME (IRE)**, b f Camelot—
Timeless Call (IRE) **Diana Cooper, P K Cooper and Ronchalon Ireland Partnership**
90 **CASE IN POINT (IRE)**, b c Showcasing—Golden Legacy (IRE) **The Long Wait Partnership**
91 **CHICAS AMIGAS (IRE)**, b f Dragon Pulse—Veronica Falls **Qatar Racing Ltd**
92 **CHOCOLATE MUSIC (IRE)**, br f Dark Angel (IRE)—Speedy Sonata (USA) **The Long Wait Partnership**
93 **CLAIM THE LADY (IRE)**, b c Acclamation—Always The Lady **The Long Wait Partnership**
94 **DALI'S DREAM (IRE)**, b f Tamayuz—Mags Rock (IRE)
95 **DAME KYTELER (IRE)**, b f Acclamation—Irish Flower (IRE) **Nore Racing & Mr Adolf Schneider**
96 **DRAGON ROLL (IRE)**, ch f Dragon Pulse—Blue Dune **Magic Cap Stables LLC**
97 **FANCY FEAT (IRE)**, b f Rajj (IRE)—Royal Jelly **Mr Jim Nicholson**
98 **FLASH GORDON (IRE)**, b c Kodiac—Oasis Sunset (IRE) **Westward Bloodstock Ltd**
99 **FOR YOUR EYES (IRE)**, b f Iffraaj—Armoise **Flaxman Stables Ireland Ltd**
100 **KLUTE (IRE)**, br c Kodiac—Fonda (USA) **The Long Wait Partnership**
101 **LADY ARONA (IRE)**, b f Big Bad Bob (IRE)—Analysis
102 **LARGER THAN LIFE (GER)**, b c Camelot—La Vinchina (GER) **Millhouse LLC**
103 **MALLACOOTA (IRE)**, b f Australia—Mauralakana (FR) **Mr Robert Scarborough**
104 **MARFA LIGHTS (IRE)**, b f Galileo (IRE)—Moment In Time (IRE) **Frank Fahy**
105 **MARSHALL LAW (IRE)**, b c Bated Breath—Art of Dance **Magic Cap Stables LLC**
106 **MORPHO BLUE (IRE)**, b f Mastercraftsman (IRE)—Butterfly Blue (IRE) **D Nagle and Roncon**
107 **MR SECRETARY (IRE)**, b c Sea The Stars (IRE)—Oui Say Oui (IRE) **Millhouse LLC**
108 **PLANET VENUS (IRE)**, b f Mastercraftsman (IRE)—Transhumance (IRE) **Course Investment Corporation**

MRS JESSICA HARRINGTON - Continued

109 **PLEASURABLE (IRE)**, b f Camelot—Notable **Alan Cooper, George Hills, Elaine Lawlor and Others**
110 **POCOTALIGO**, b c Helmet (AUS)—Pizzarra **Millhouse LLC**
111 **PULSE OF SHANGHAI (IRE)**, b g Dragon Pulse (IRE)—Emsiyah (USA) **Milltown Stud and Dr Kai Chah Tan**
112 **PURSUIT OF MAGIC (IRE)**, b f Kingman—Three Mysteries (IRE) **Course Investment Corporation**
113 **SERVALAN (IRE)**, b f No Nay Never (USA)—Catch The Eye (IRE) **Mr Vimal Khosla**
114 **SNEAKY SNOOZE (IRE)**, b f Exceed And Excel (AUS)—
                                            Crossanza (IRE) **Miss Margaret Davin, Mrs Ramona Morris and Mr Richie Galway**
115 **SUTTER (IRE)**, b c Dubawi (IRE)—Snowgal (IRE) **Jon S. Kelly**
116 **SWEET DIME**, b f Toronado (IRE)—
           Rainbow's Edge **Ronchalon Ireland Partnership, Mr Russell Jones, Ms Suzi Prichard-Jones and Others**
117 **TIMEMAKESITFINE (IRE)**, b f Lope de Vega (IRE)—Better Be Mine (IRE) **Anamoine Ltd**
118 **TORREADOR**, b c Toronado (IRE)—Pompey Girl
119 **TRETHIAS**, b f Invincible Spirit (IRE)—Evita **Stonethorn Stud Farm Ltd**
120 **WEAVING SILK (IRE)**, b f Mastercraftsman (IRE)—Apparel (IRE) **Nore Racing & Mr David Magnier**
121 **XCITE (IRE)**, b f Kingman—Recite (JPN)

TWO-YEAR-OLDS

122 **ALBIGNA (IRE)**, ch f 20/3 Zoffany (IRE)—Freedonia (Selkirk (USA)) **Niarchos Family**
123 **ALLEZ ALLEZ ALLEZ (IRE)**, b f 20/2 Invincible Spirit (IRE)—Growling (IRE) (Celtic Swing) (105351) **Robcour**
124 **ALPINE STAR (IRE)**, ch f 24/3 Sea The Moon (GER)—Alpha Lupi (IRE) (Rahy (USA)) **Niarchos Family**
125 **ANTHEM (IRE)**, ch f 12/2 Australia—Muwakada (USA) (Elusive Quality (USA)) **Jon S. Kelly**
126 B c 25/4 Golden Horn—Astonishing (IRE) (Galileo (IRE)) (550000) **The Long Wait Partnership**
127 B f 13/3 Kyllachy—Attachee de Presse (IRE) (Danehill (USA)) (56468) **Roddy Ryan**
128 B f 14/1 Hot Streak (IRE)—
            Breedj (IRE) (Acclamation) (74167) **Russell Jones, Suzi Prichard-Jones, P K Cooper and Others**
129 **BUT YOU SAID (IRE)**, b f 20/3 No Nay Never (USA)—San Macchia (Rock of Gibraltar (IRE)) (75853) **Robcour**
130 B c 4/3 Exceed And Excel (AUS)—
            Causeway Lass (AUS) (Giant's Causeway (USA)) **Yulong Investments Australia PTY Ltd**
131 B c 19/3 Fast Company (IRE)—Erebis (Green Desert (USA)) (15170) **Yulong Investments Australia PTY Ltd**
132 Ch g 16/4 Mastercraftsman (IRE)—Excellent Mariner (IRE) (Henrythenavigator (USA)) (1011) **P K Cooper**
133 Ch f 5/3 Showcasing—Fair Sailing (IRE) (Docksider (USA)) (202275) **Stonestreet Stables LLC**
134 **FREE SOLO (IRE)**, ch c 4/2 Showcasing—Amuser (IRE) (Galileo (IRE)) **Niarchos Family**
135 **GIBSON DESERT**, b c 9/3 Australia—Namaadhej (USA) (Swain (IRE)) (52000) **Alpha Racing**
136 **GRANTED (IRE)**, ch c 11/5 Starspangledbanner (AUS)—Green Castle (IRE) (Indian Ridge) **Stonethorn Stud Farm Ltd**
137 **GRIZZLY (IRE)**, b c 24/4 Kodiac—Savannah Poppy (Statue of Liberty (USA)) (95000) **Alpha Racing**
138 **HA'PENNY BRIDGE (IRE)**, ch f 30/1 Tamayuz—
           Diminuir (IRE) (Raven's Pass (USA)) (32026) **Its All About The Girls**
139 **HINT OF STARS (IRE)**, ch c 14/4 Sea The Stars (IRE)—
           Rosenreihe (IRE) (Catcher In The Rye (IRE)) (115000) **Jon S. Kelly**
140 **IN THE PRESENT (USA)**, b f 26/4 Karakontie (JPN)—
           Dreams of Fire (USA) (Dynaformer (USA)) **Flaxman Stables Ireland Ltd**
141 B g 23/2 Mastercraftsman (IRE)—Invincible Cara (IRE) (Invincible Spirit (IRE)) (674) **Anamoine Ltd**
142 **INVINCIBLE DIVA (IRE)**, br f 25/2 Invincible Spirit (IRE)—Lulawin (Kyllachy) **Jon S. Kelly**
143 **IRISH MASTER (IRE)**, gr ro c 8/4 Mastercraftsman (IRE)—Selva Real (Royal Applause) (280000) **Jon S. Kelly**
144 **KATIE BO KAT**, b f 24/2 Muhaarar—Infamous Angel (Exceed And Excel (AUS)) (20000) **Alpha Racing**
145 **LIAR LIAR (IRE)**, b c 17/2 Dream Ahead (USA)—Rubileo (Galileo (USA)) (26970) **Alpha Racing**
146 **MERRY POPPINS (GER)**, gr f 8/4 Authorized (IRE)—Manita (IRE) (Peintre Celebre (USA)) (13485) **Robcour**
147 **MUTINY (IRE)**, ch f 29/4 Sepoy (AUS)—Lashkaal (Teofilo (IRE)) (15170) **Its All About The Girls**
148 B f 10/4 Australia—Nimboo (USA) (Lemon Drop Kid (USA)) (25283) **Mr Vimal Khosla**
149 **NOPE (IRE)**, b f 9/3 No Nay Never (USA)—Bright Sapphire (IRE) (Galileo (IRE)) (135000) **Alpha Racing**
150 **OCEAN MONARCH (IRE)**, b c 29/3 Bungle Inthejungle—Spinning Ruby (Pivotal) (52254) **Alpha Racing**
151 Gr c 11/4 Mastercraftsman (IRE)—Purple Glow (IRE) (Orientate (USA)) (100000) **Millhouse LLC**
152 **RECALL THE SHOW**, ch c 26/4 Showcasing—Rappel (Royal Applause) (88495) **Alpha Racing**
153 B c 2/4 Kodiac—Roger Sez (IRE) (Red Clubs (IRE)) (95000) **Millhouse LLC**
154 Br f 18/2 Canford Cliffs (IRE)—Rub A Dub Dub (Falbrav (IRE))
155 Br gr c 21/2 Maxios—Sandy Cay (USA) (Mizzen Mast (USA)) **Jon S. Kelly**
156 B f 22/3 No Nay Never (USA)—Sarawati (IRE) (Haafhd) (50568) **Yulong Investments Australia PTY Ltd**
157 **SECRET STASH (IRE)**, b f 3/3 Mukhadram—
           Poppet's Lovein (Lomitas) (29498) **Justin Carty/Richie Galway/ Sue Ann Kaia**
158 B br f 29/1 Ivawood (IRE)—
           Siesta Time (Oasis Dream) (17699) **Suzi Prichard-Jones, Commonstown Racing Stables and Russell Jones**
159 B f 9/3 War Command (USA)—
           Sonning Rose (IRE) (Hawk Wing (USA)) (12641) **Yulong Investments Australia PTY Ltd**
160 **TOORA LOORA**, ch f 21/1 Nathaniel (IRE)—Victoria Regina (IRE) (Mastercraftsman (IRE)) **Jon S. Kelly**
161 **UNKNOWN PLEASURES (IRE)**, b f 13/4 Zoffany (IRE)—Three Mysteries (IRE) (Linamix (FR)) **Niarchos Family**

MRS JESSICA HARRINGTON - Continued

162 B f 19/2 Acclamation—Urban Daydream (IRE) (Oasis Dream) **Peter Savill**
163 Ch f 1/3 Sepoy (AUS)—Wojha (IRE) (Pivotal) (41000) **Alpha Racing**
164 YA BEAUTY, b f 13/4 Muhaarar—Long Face (USA) (Whywhywhy (USA)) (85000) **Alpha Racing**
165 YA YA BABY (IRE), b f 21/3 Hallowed Crown (AUS)—
                                    Standout (FR) (Robellino (USA)) (32026) **Its All About The Girls**
166 B f 27/1 Poet's Voice—
                          Zaaqya (Nayef (USA)) (46354) **J Hennessy, Robcour and Commonstown Racing Stables**

Assistant Trainers: Miss Kate Harrington, Eamonn Leigh

---

267 MISS GRACE HARRIS, Shirenewton
Postal: White House, Shirenewton, Chepstow, Gwent, NP16 6AQ
Contacts: **MOBILE (07912) 359425**
E-MAIL gracehharris90@gmail.com WEBSITE www.graceharrisracing.com

1 BOUTAN, 6, gr m Tobougg (IRE)—High Tan **Mrs S. M. Maine**
2 BUNGEE JUMP (IRE), 4, b f Canford Cliffs (IRE)—Starchy **Mr Ronald Davies & Mrs Candida Davies**
3 FIELD EXHIBITION (IRE), 9, b m Great Exhibition (USA)—Leefield Rose (IRE) **Mr C. Johnston**
4 GRAMS AND OUNCES, 12, b g Royal Applause—Ashdown Princess (IRE) **Grace Harris Racing**
5 HALF NELSON, 4, ch g Mount Nelson—Maria Antonia (IRE) **Mrs Elaine Tate & Partner**
6 KARAKORAM, 4, b g Excelebration (IRE)—Portrait **Grace Harris Racing**
7 MAGUIRE'S GLEN (IRE), 11, b g Craigsteel—Next Venture (IRE) **Grace Harris Racing**
8 MOOROVERTHEBRIDGE, 5, b m Avonbridge—Spennymoor (IRE) **Grace Harris Racing**
9 NEARLY FAMOUS, 6, b m Rip Van Winkle (IRE)—Ermena **Brendon Sabin & Partner**
10 PADDY THE OSCAR (IRE), 16, b g Oscar (IRE)—Parsonage **Michelle Harris & Deberah Lawton**
11 TALLY'S SONG, 6, b m Piccolo—Talamahana **Paul & Ann de Weck**
12 TUSCANY (IRE), 5, ch g Poet's Voice—Avril Rose (IRE) **Grace Harris Racing**
13 YET ANOTHER (IRE), 4, b g High Chaparral (IRE)—Elaflaak (USA) **Mrs S. M. Maine**

THREE-YEAR-OLDS

14 MYSTICAL JADEITE, b g Finjaan—Striking Pose (IRE) **Mr B. M. Cakebread**

Other Owners: Mr R. I. D. Davies, Mrs C. M. Davies, Mrs A. De Weck, Ms M. Harris, Miss G. Harris, Mrs D. L. S. Lawton, Mr B. Sabin, Mrs E. Tate, P. L. de Weck.

Assistant Trainer: Michelle Harris (07789) 003545

Jockey (NH): Liam Heard.

---

268 MR MILTON HARRIS, Warminster
Postal: The Beeches, Deverill Road, Sutton Veny, Warminster, Wiltshire, BA12 7BY
Contacts: **MOBILE (07879) 634308**

1 AMERICAN LIFE (FR), 12, b br g American Post—Poplife (FR) **American Life Partnership**
2 AWAY FOR SLATES (IRE), 9, b g Arcadio (GER)—Rumi **Mrs D. Dewbery**
3 CAFE AU LAIT (GER), 9, b g Nicaron (GER)—Cariera (GER) **Faithful Followers**
4 FUTURE SECURITY (IRE), 10, ch g Dalakhani (IRE)—Schust Madame (IRE) **Faithful Followers**
5 JACAMAR (GER), 4, b g Maxios—Juvena (GER) **Pegasus Bloodstock Limited**
6 JANUS (IRE), 4, b g Rock of Gibraltar (IRE)—Jardina (GER) **Pegasus Bloodstock Limited**
7 LOS CERRITOS (SWI), 7, ch g Dr Fong (USA)—La Coruna (SWI) **Emdells Limited**
8 MAGIC RIVER (IRE), 8, ch g Indian River (FR)—All Magic (IRE) **Emdells Limited**
9 QUARRY LAMI (IRE), 8, gr g Daylami (IRE)—Lady Leila (IRE) **Quarry Lami Partnership**
10 QUARRY WIZARD (IRE), 9, b g Trans Island—Hazel Green (IRE) **Mrs D. J. Brown & Mrs D. Dewbery**
11 RIVIERE ARGENTEE (FR), 5, gr m Hurricane Cat (USA)—River Trebor (USA) **Mrs D. Dewbery**
12 STIMULATING SONG, 4, ch g Stimulation (IRE)—Choral Singer **Pegasus Bloodstock Limited**
13 THE MISTRESS (IRE), 4, b m Kalanisi (IRE)—Sonnerschien (IRE) **Emdells Limited**
14 WESTERN MORNING (IRE), 6, b g Westerner—Gweedara (IRE) **Faithful Followers**
15 ZAMBINO (GER), 4, b g It's Gino (GER)—Zamba (GER) **Pegasus Bloodstock Limited**

THREE-YEAR-OLDS

16 B g Yeats (IRE)—Va'vite (IRE) **Mrs D. Dewbery**

MR MILTON HARRIS - Continued

TWO-YEAR-OLDS

17 B c 8/5 Yeats (IRE)—Va'vite (IRE) (Vinnie Roe (IRE))

Other Owners: Mrs S. E. Brown, Dr J. D. Dalton, Lord Daresbury, Mr G. MacDonald, Mr J. P. Naylor, Mrs L. Winrow-Campbell.

---

269 **MR RONALD HARRIS, Chepstow**
Postal: **Ridge House Stables, Earlswood, Chepstow, Monmouthshire, NP16 6AN**
Contacts: PHONE (01291) 641689 FAX (01291) 641258 MOBILE (07831) 770899
E-MAIL ridgehousestables.ltd@btinternet.com WEBSITE www.ronharrisracing.co.uk

1 **ALRIGHT DAVE**, 4, ch g Frozen Power (IRE)—Crazy Hazy (IRE) **Mrs A. Jones**
2 **ARIZONA SNOW**, 7, b g Phoenix Reach (IRE)—Calgary **Ridge House Stables Ltd**
3 **BENTAYGA BOY**, 4, gr g Hellvelyn—Lady Mango (IRE) **Ridge House Stables Ltd**
4 **BROADHAVEN HONEY (IRE)**, 5, b m Harbour Watch (IRE)—
Honeymead (IRE) **M Doocey, S Doocey & P J Doocey**
5 **CASTANEA**, 7, ch g Pivotal—Invitee **Ridge House Stables Ltd**
6 **CORPORAL MADDOX**, 12, b g Royal Applause—Noble View (USA) **Ridge House Stables Ltd**
7 **DIAMOND VINE (IRE)**, 11, b g Diamond Green (FR)—Glasnas Giant **Ridge House Stables Ltd**
8 **EQUALLY FAST**, 7, b g Equiano (FR)—Fabulously Fast (USA) **Ridge House Stables Ltd**
9 **EYMET**, 7, b m Avonbridge—Emma Peel **Mrs D. M. Barker**
10 **FANTASY JUSTIFIER (IRE)**, 8, b g Arakan (USA)—Grandel **Ridge House Stables Ltd**
11 **FETHIYE BOY**, 5, br g Pastoral Pursuits—Ocean Blaze **Ridge House Stables Ltd**
12 **GLAM'SELLE**, 5, b m Elnadim (USA)—Town And Gown **Robert & Nina Bailey**
13 **GLAMOROUS DREAM (IRE)**, 4, b f Dark Angel (IRE)—Glamorous Air (IRE) **Robert & Nina Bailey**
14 **GLAMOROUS ROCKET (IRE)**, 4, gr f Dark Angel (IRE)—Glamorous Spirit (IRE) **Robert & Nina Bailey**
15 **JUST GLAMOROUS (IRE)**, 6, ch g Arcano (IRE)—Glamorous Air (IRE) **Robert & Nina Bailey**
16 **KYLLACHY DRAGON (IRE)**, 4, b g Dragon Pulse (IRE)—Lafayette (GER) **Mr S. R. Middleton**
17 **LADY MANGO (IRE)**, 11, ch m Bahamian Bounty—Opera
18 **LIGHT FROM MARS**, 14, gr g Fantastic Light (USA)—Hylandra (USA) **Ridge House Stables Ltd**
19 **LIGHT OF ATHENA (IRE)**, 5, b m Doyen (IRE)—Reflecting (IRE) **Mrs D. Titmus**
20 **MAJESTIC HERO (IRE)**, 7, b g Majestic Missile (IRE)—Xena (IRE) **Mrs Jackie Jarrett & Ridge House Stables**
21 **MARGARET BAKER**, 9, b m Windsor Castle—Daisy Leigh
22 **PEACE SEEKER**, 11, b g Oasis Dream—Mina **Ridge House Stables Ltd**
23 **POWERFUL DREAM (IRE)**, 6, b m Frozen Power (IRE)—Noble View (USA) **Ridge House Stables Ltd**
24 **RAIN WIND AND FIRE (USA)**, 7, ch g Eskendereya (USA)—Call Mariah (USA) **Ridge House Stables Ltd**
25 **RUPERTCAMBELLBLACK (IRE)**, 5, b g Canford Cliffs (IRE)—Negotiate **Ridge House Stables Ltd**
26 **SECRET POTION**, 5, b g Stimulation (IRE)—Fiancee (IRE) **RHS Ltd, Mr R Fox, Mr P Charter**
27 **SELENA ROSE**, 6, b m Stimulation (IRE)—Dot Hill **Mr D. A. Evans**
28 **TEXAN NOMAD**, 7, ch g Nomadic Way (USA)—Texas Belle (IRE) **Mr J. W. Miles**
29 **THE DALEY EXPRESS (IRE)**, 5, b g Elzaam (AUS)—Seraphina (IRE) **The W.H.O. Society**
30 **TICKTOCKS**, 4, b f Stimulation (IRE)—Thicket **Ridge House Stables Ltd**
31 **TOP COP**, 10, b g Acclamation—Speed Cop **Ridge House Stables Ltd**
32 **UNDER THE COVERS**, 6, b m Stimulation (IRE)—Sakha **Ridge House Stables Ltd**
33 **UNION ROSE**, 7, b g Stimulation (IRE)—Dot Hill **Mr D. A. Evans**
34 **VINCENTTI (IRE)**, 9, b g Invincible Spirit (IRE)—Bint Al Balad (IRE) **Robert & Nina Bailey**
35 **VIOLA PARK**, 5, b g Aqlaam—Violette **Mr John & Margaret Hatherell & RHS Ltd**

THREE-YEAR-OLDS

36 **BROADHAVEN DREAM (IRE)**, b c Dream Ahead (USA)—Queen Grace (IRE) **M Doocey, S Doocey & P J Doocey**
37 **BROTHER BENTLEY**, gr c Hellvelyn—Lady Mango (IRE) **Ridge House Stables Ltd**
38 **CLEVEDON (IRE)**, br g Bungle Inthejungle—Sandy Smile (IRE) **J. A. Gent**
39 **COUNTRY ROSE (IRE)**, b f Bungle Inthejungle—Fitrah (IRE) **Mrs J. Jarrett**
40 **ELZAAM'S DREAM (IRE)**, b f Elzaam (AUS)—Alinda (IRE)
41 **EYE OF THE WATER (IRE)**, b g Lilbourne Lad (IRE)—Desert Location **Mr M. E. Wright**
42 **ROCKY PARK**, b g Foxwedge (AUS)—Violette **Mr John & Margaret Hatherell & RHS Ltd**
43 **SMOKEY'S ANGEL (IRE)**, b f Alhebayeb (IRE)—Smokey Ryder **Ridge House Stables Ltd**
44 **THEGREYVTRAIN**, gr f Coach House (IRE)—Debutante Blues (USA) **Ridge House Stables Ltd**

Other Owners: R. M. Bailey, Mrs J. H. Bailey, P. F. Charter, Mr S. Doocey, Mr M. A. Doocey, Mr P. J. Doocey, Mr R. S. Fox, Mrs M. E. Hatherell, Mr R. A. J. Hatherell, Mr D. Thomas.

Jockey (flat): Luke Morris.

270 MR SHAUN HARRIS, Worksop
Postal: **Pinewood Stables, Carburton, Worksop, Nottinghamshire, S80 3BT**
Contacts: **PHONE (01909) 470936 FAX (01909) 470936 MOBILE (07768) 950460**
E-MAIL **shaunharrisracing@yahoo.com** WEBSITE **www.shaunharrisracing.co.uk**

1 **ALLLEEDSAREN'TWE,** 4, b g Havana Gold (IRE)—Minnola **Dallas Racing**
2 **AZA RUN (IRE),** 9, b g Hurricane Run (IRE)—Aza Wish (IRE) **Miss G. H. Ward**
3 **CHATEAU CHINON (FR),** 7, b g Dream Well (FR)—Liesse de Marbeuf (FR) **Miss G. H. Ward**
4 **DOLPHIN VILLAGE (IRE),** 9, b g Cape Cross (IRE)—Reform Act (USA) **Nottinghamshire Racing**
5 **HARBOUR SUNRISE,** 4, b f Harbour Watch (IRE)—Nairobi (IRE) **Mr C. Harris**
6 **HEAR THE CHIMES,** 10, b g Midnight Legend—Severn Air **Miss G. H. Ward**
7 **MAJOR MUSCARI (IRE),** 11, ch g Exceed And Excel (AUS)—Muscari **J. Morris**
8 **QUICK MONET (IRE),** 6, b g Excellent Art—Clinging Vine (USA) **J. Morris**
9 **ROY'S LEGACY,** 10, b h Phoenix Reach (IRE)—Chocolada **Notts Racing, S A Harris & S Rowley**
10 **SAVLAD,** 4, b g Delegator—Dubai Legend **D. & S. L. Tanker Transport Limited**
11 **VANILLA BREEZE,** 5, b m Trans Island—Vanilla Delight (IRE) **C A Harris & Peter Dawson**

THREE-YEAR-OLDS

12 **PHOEBE AGNES,** b f Phoenix Reach (IRE)—Medam **Burton Agnes Bloodstock**

Other Owners: Mrs M. C. Coltman, The Hon Mrs E. S. Cunliffe-Lister, P. G. Dawson, Mr M. A. Glassett, S. A. Harris, Mr S. Rowley.

Assistant Trainer: Miss G. H. Ward

271 MISS LISA HARRISON, Wigton
Postal: **Cobble Hall, Aldoth, Nr Silloth, Cumbria, CA7 4NE**
Contacts: **PHONE (01697) 361753 FAX (01697) 342250 MOBILE (07725) 535554**
E-MAIL **lisa@daharrison.co.uk**

1 **GREEN ZONE (IRE),** 8, b g Bushranger (IRE)—Incense **T Hunter & D A Harrison Racing**
2 **INSTINGTIVE (IRE),** 8, b g Scorpion (IRE)—Fully Focused (IRE) **D A Harrison & Abbadis Racing & Thompson**
3 **MILEVA ROLLER,** 7, b m Multiplex—Alikat (IRE) **Mr E. Chapman**
4 **MUWALLA,** 12, b g Bahri (USA)—Easy Sunshine (IRE) **Bell Bridge Racing**
5 **PRESENTED (IRE),** 12, ch g Presenting—Rustic Court (IRE) **Abbadis Racing & D A Harrison Racing**
6 **SOLWAY AVA,** 6, b m Overbury (IRE)—Solway Sunset **D A Harrison Racing**
7 **SOLWAY BERRY,** 8, b m Overbury (IRE)—Solway Rose **D A Harrison Racing**
8 **SOLWAY LARK,** 8, b g Beat All (USA)—Solway Larkin (IRE) **D A Harrison & Abbadis Racing & Hunter**
9 **SOLWAY LIZZIE,** 7, ch m Tobougg (IRE)—Solway Rose **D A Harrison Racing**
10 **SOLWAY SPIRIT,** 6, b g Overbury (IRE)—Notadandy **Mr & Mrs Batey**
11 **SOLWAY SUNNY,** 7, b m Double Trigger (IRE)—Solway Sunset **D A Harrison Racing**

Other Owners: Abbadis Racing Club, Mrs A. E. Batey, Mr K. D. Batey, Mrs F. H. Crone, Mr D. Gillespie, Mr J. D. Graves, Miss L. Harrison, Mr W. H. Harrison, Mr R. A. Harrison, Exors of the Late Mr David A. Harrison, Mr T. Hunter, R. E. Jackson, Mr J. H. Monkhouse, Mrs L. Monkhouse, Mr K. V. Thompson.

272 MR BEN HASLAM, Middleham
Postal: **Castle Barn Cottage, Castle Hill, Middleham, Leyburn, North Yorkshire, DL8 4QW**
Contacts: **PHONE (01969) 624351 MOBILE (07764) 411660**
E-MAIL **office@benhaslamracing.com** WEBSITE **www.benhaslamracing.com**

1 **BLINDINGLY (GER),** 4, br g Shamardal (USA)—Boccassini (GER) **Mr J. P. McManus**
2 **BOUVREUIL (FR),** 8, b g Saddler Maker (IRE)—Madame Lys (FR) **Mr J. P. McManus**
3 **CALL THE COPS (IRE),** 10, b g Presenting—Ballygill Heights (IRE) **Mr J. P. McManus**
4 **CASH AGAIN (FR),** 7, br g Great Pretender (IRE)—Jeu de Lune (FR) **Mr J. P. McManus**
5 **CASTLE HILL CASSIE (IRE),** 5, ch m Casamento (IRE)—Angel Bright (IRE) **D.Howden, S.Lock & D.Redvers**
6 **CHERRY OAK (IRE),** 4, b f Society Rock (IRE)—Blue Holly (IRE) **Ontoawinner, D Shapiro & Mrs J Feeney**
7 **DEMI SANG (FR),** 6, b g Gris de Gris (IRE)—Morvandelle (FR) **Mr J. P. McManus**
8 **DISPLAYING AMBER,** 4, ch f Showcasing—Amber Lane **Middleham Park Racing**
9 **ELYSEE STAR,** 4, b f Champs Elysees—Alushta **Go Alfresco Racing Partners**
10 **EPEIUS (IRE),** 6, b g Arakan (USA)—Gilda Lilly (USA) **Ben Haslam Racing Syndicate**
11 **EVER SO MUCH (IRE),** 10, b g Westerner—Beautiful World (IRE) **Mr J. P. McManus**
12 **FIRST BREATH,** 4, b g Bated Breath—Miss Rimex (IRE) **Ben Haslam Racing Syndicate**

MR BEN HASLAM - Continued

13 **FUNKADELIC**, 4, ch g Dandy Man (IRE)—Cape Elizabeth (IRE) **South Yorkshire Racing, M. Buckley & M. Cook**
14 **HASANOANDA**, 4, b g Champs Elysees—Indian Mystery (IRE) **Mrs C. Barclay**
15 **LORD CAPRIO (IRE)**, 4, b g Lord Shanakill (USA)—
Azzurra du Caprio (IRE) **Blue Lion Racing IX, J McCullagh, D Morland & Mrs C Barclay**
16 **MANAMITE (FR)**, 6, b g Kentucky Dynamite (USA)—Masaya (SWI) **Mr J. P. McManus**
17 **MELODY OF SCOTLAND (FR)**, 5, b m Youmzain (IRE)—This Melody (FR) **Mr J. P. McManus**
18 **MUSBAQ (USA)**, 4, b g Union Rags (USA)—Eraada **Champagne Charlies Club**
19 **PORRIMA (IRE)**, 4, gr f Morocco (USA)—El Morocco (USA) **D Shapiro, Mrs J Feeney & J Feeney**
20 **PRANCING OSCAR (IRE)**, 5, b g Sir Prancealot (IRE)—
Beguiler **Middleham Park Racing & Mrs E Fox-Andrews**
21 **REY LOOPY (IRE)**, 5, b g Lope de Vega (IRE)—Al Basar (USA) **Mr Daniel Shapiro & Mrs C Barclay**
22 **ROCK ON FRUITY (IRE)**, 10, b g Fruits of Love (USA)—Sancta Miria (IRE) **Mr J. P. McManus**
23 **THE BULL (IRE)**, 4, ch g Camacho—Zarara (USA) **Excel Racing, D Shapiro & N McGarry**

THREE-YEAR-OLDS

24 **BLACK KRAKEN**, b c Battle of Marengo (IRE)—Stereo Love (FR) **D Shapiro & C Connochie**
25 **BLAZING DREAMS (IRE)**, b g Morpheus—Pure Folly (IRE) **Champagne Charlies Club & Mrs E Fox-Andrews**
26 **CALEVADE (IRE)**, gr g Gregorian (IRE)—Avoidance (USA) **K Nicol, D Shapiro, Mrs A Haslam & P Wood**
27 **FORTAMOUR (IRE)**, b c Es Que Love (IRE)—Kathy Sun (IRE) **Ben Haslam Racing Syndicate**
28 **NATALEENA (IRE)**, b f Nathaniel (IRE)—
Hayyona **M Cook, K Nicol, M Rees, J Milner, D Shapiro & Mrs J Feeney**
29 **PINARELLA (FR)**, ch f Kendargent (FR)—Ponte di Legno (FR) **Ontoawinner & K Nicol**
30 **RITCHIE STAR (IRE)**, b g Lilbourne Lad (IRE)—Array of Stars (USA) **Mr R. A. Tocher**
31 **SANDRET (IRE)**, b g Zebedee—Sava Sunset (IRE) **Ben Haslam Racing Syndicate**

TWO-YEAR-OLDS

32 **AIDEN'S DELIGHT (IRE)**, b c 7/4 Dandy Man (IRE)—Bonne (Namid) (21904) **Mrs C. Barclay**
33 Ch c 4/3 Casamento (IRE)—
Ansina (USA) (Distant View (USA)) (15238) **Mrs C. Barclay & Middleham Park Racing**
34 **EMILY'S DELIGHT (IRE)**, ch f 24/2 Anjaal—Masela (IRE) (Medicean) (24761) **Mrs C. Barclay**
35 B c 16/3 Casamento (IRE)—Promise You (Teofilo (IRE)) **D Shapiro**
36 B f 19/4 Battle of Marengo (IRE)—
Saldenaera (GER) (Areion (GER)) (9523) **South Yorkshire Racing & Mrs C Barclay**

Other Owners: Mr Charlie Austin, Mr Simon Bridge, Mr M. T. Buckley, Champagne Charlies Club, Mr E. A. Dupont, Excel Racing, Mrs J. M. Feeney, Mr John S. Feeney, Mr David Ian Firth, Mr P. Fisher, Mr Craig Harrison, Mrs Anne Haslam, Mr David Howden, Mr Steve Lock, Mrs L. McGarry, Middleham Park Racing XVIII, Mrs S. Milner, Mr K. Nicol, Mr N. J. O'Brien, Ontoawinner, Mr T. S. Palin, Mr M. Prince, Mr David Redvers, Mr M. Rees, Mr Daniel Shapiro, South Yorkshire Racing, Mr W. N. Standeven, Mr Peter Taylor, Mr Geoff Wilson, Mr Philip Gordon Wood, Mr R. Young.

Assistant Trainer: Alice Haslam

---

273 MR NIGEL HAWKE, Tiverton
Postal: **Thorne Farm, Stoodleigh, Tiverton, Devon, EX16 9QG**
Contacts: **PHONE (01884) 881666 MOBILE (07769) 295839**
E-MAIL nigel@thornefarmracingltd.co.uk WEBSITE www.nigelhawkethornefarmracing.co.uk

1 **ALMINAR (IRE)**, 6, b g Arakan (USA)—Classic Magic (IRE) **Mr M. J. Phillips**
2 **BALLYMAGROARTY BOY (IRE)**, 6, b g Milan—Glazed Storm (IRE) **Nigel Hawke Racing Club & Partners**
3 **BELLA BEAU (IRE)**, 4, b f Jeremy—Bella Patrice (IRE) **Mark Phillips**
4 **CALIN DU BRIZAIS (FR)**, 8, b g Loup Solitaire (USA)—Caline du Brizais (FR) **Pearce Bros Partnership**
5 **CAMRON DE CHAILLAC (FR)**, 7, br g Laverock (IRE)—Hadeel **Mr R. Lane**
6 **FARMER BOY (IRE)**, 6, b g Scorpion (IRE)—Absent Beauty (IRE) **Mrs K. Hawke & Mr W. Simms**
7 **FLINTS LEGACY**, 7, gr m Sagamix (FR)—Luneray (FR) **Partnership Registration Req**
8 **GREYBOUGG**, 10, gr g Tobougg (IRE)—Kildee Lass **Di Vincenzo, Capps, Smith & Partner**
9 **HARTLAND QUAY (IRE)**, 4, b g Arcadio (GER)—Regents Ballerina (IRE) **Mr Richard Weeks & Partner**
10 **HEART OF KERNOW (IRE)**, 7, b g Fruits of Love (USA)—Rathturtin Brief (IRE) **Mrs K. Hawke & Mr W. Simms**
11 **JOHANOS (FR)**, 8, ch g Limnos (JPN)—Madame Johann (FR) **Mark Phillips, Mrs Pumphrey & Partners**
12 **KAPITALL**, 4, b f Kapgarde (FR)—Doubly Guest **Mr R Weeks & Jimmy & Toots Partnership**
13 **KENDELU (IRE)**, 4, b g Yeats (IRE)—Supreme Baloo (IRE) **Ken & Della Neilson & Partners**
14 **LAMH AR LAMH (IRE)**, 5, ch m Teofilo (IRE)—Tintreach (CAN) **Mr M. J. Martin**
15 **LE MUSEE (FR)**, 6, b g Galileo (IRE)—Delicieuse Lady **Dragonfly Racing**
16 **LORD BALLIM (FR)**, 9, ch g Balko (FR)—Lady Pauline (FR) **Mr Jeff W. Hall, Mrs K.Hawke, Mr William Simms**
17 **MALINA OCARINA**, 4, b f Malinas (GER)—Ocarina Davis (FR) **Mr & Mrs C Glover**

MR NIGEL HAWKE - Continued

18 **MEAD VALE**, 6, ch g Schiaparelli (GER)—Devon Peasant **Nigel Hawke Racing Club & Partners**
19 **NACHI FALLS**, 6, ch g New Approach (IRE)—Lakuta (IRE) **Bryant, McMullan, Phillips & Partner**
20 **NIKAP (FR)**, 5, b m Kapgarde (FR)—Nika Glitters (FR) **Kapinhand**
21 **ONBOARD**, 4, gr g Dalakhani (IRE)—Emplane (USA) **Onboard Partners**
22 **PEARL ROYALE (IRE)**, 7, b m Robin des Champs (FR)—
                                                Dartmeet (IRE) **Air Cdre & Mrs M R Hallam & Mark Phillips**
23 **PHOENIX FIREBIRD**, 6, b m Flying Legend (USA)—Flamebird (IRE) **Air Cdre Hallam & Mrs Martin Hallam**
24 **POINT N SHOOT (IRE)**, 8, b g Broadway Flyer (USA)—Ali's Dipper (IRE) **Mr J A Vowles & Partners**
25 **SAPPHIRE NOIRE (IRE)**, 6, b m Shantou (USA)—Cool Cool (FR) **Mr Steve Winfield & Partner**
26 **SIENNA ROYALE (IRE)**, 5, b m Sholokhov (IRE)—Dartmeet (IRE) **Air Cdre Hallam & Mrs Martin Hallam**
27 **SIN SIN (IRE)**, 5, b m Intense Focus (USA)—Saor Sinn (IRE) **Mrs K. Hawke & Mr W. Simms**
28 **SLAYING THE DRAGON (IRE)**, 6, ch g Notnowcato—Empress Charlotte **Bestwork Racing**
29 **SOME DETAIL (IRE)**, 5, b g Getaway (GER)—You Should Know Me (IRE) **Milltown Racing**
30 **SPEREDEK (FR)**, 8, b br g Kapgarde (FR)—Sendamagic (FR) **Kapinhand**
31 **SPERONIMO (FR)**, 7, b g Diamond Green (FR)—Spepita (FR) **Pearce Bros Partnership**
32 **SPINOLO**, 4, b g Piccolo—Spinning Coin **Mr Sandy Evans & Partner**
33 **STORMY BLUES**, 5, b g Sepoy (AUS)—Miss Brown To You (IRE) **Mr M. J. Phillips**
34 **TANRUDY (IRE)**, 5, b g Presenting—Come In Moscow (IRE) **Mark J Phillips & Mrs A B Walker**
35 **THE BOOLA BEE (IRE)**, 6, b m Arcadio (GER)—Hy Kate (IRE) **Mr R. Lane**
36 **VERBITUDE (IRE)**, 4, b c Vocalised (USA)—Bring Back Matron (IRE) **John White & Anne Underhill**
37 **WISE GARDEN (FR)**, 4, b f Kapgarde (FR)—Fabulous Wisdom (FR)

THREE-YEAR-OLDS

38 **GUARDIA TOP (FR)**, b f Top Trip—Jour de Chance (FR) **Thorne Farm Racing**
39 **GWENNOLINE (FR)**, gr f Balko (FR)—Ugoline (FR) **Thorne Farm Racing**
40 B f Gentlewave (IRE)—Ocarina Davis (FR) **Thorne Farm Racing**
41 **POLA CHANCE (FR)**, gr f Boris de Deauville (IRE)—Take A Chance (FR) **Thorne Farm Racing**
42 B c Norse Dancer (IRE)—Sedgemoor Classact (IRE) **Thorne Farm Racing**

TWO-YEAR-OLDS

43 B f 22/4 Blue Bresil (FR)—Ocarina Davis (FR) (Ballingarry (IRE))
44 B f 17/5 Blue Bresil (FR)—Sedgemoor Classact (IRE) (Exit To Nowhere (USA)) **Thorne Farm Racing**

Other Owners: Mr M. Bevan, Mrs Kate Brain, Mr Steve Bryant, Mr M. Capps, Mr Marcus Di-Vincenzo, Mr P.A. Docker, Mr S. A. Evans, Mr F. G. Flanagan, Mrs K. J. Glover, Mr C. S. Glover, Mr J. H. Gumbley, Mr Jeff W. Hall, Mrs M. R. Hallam, Air Cdre M. R. Hallam, Mrs K. Hawke, Mr N. J. Hawke, Mr Martin Hill, Mrs D. M. Hill, Mr T. B. James, Mrs H. Jefferies, Jimmy & Toots Partnership, Mr N. J. McMullan, Mr Ken Neilson, The Nigel Hawke Racing Club, Mr David Pearce, Mrs Marguerite Pumphrey, Mr William Simms, Mrs Denise E. Smith, Mrs A. Underhill, Mr J. A. Vowles, Mrs A. B. Walker, Mr Richard Weeks, Mr A. J. White, Mr S. W. H. Winfield.

Assistant Trainers: Katherine Hawke, Edward Buckley

Jockey (NH): Sean Bowen, Tom Cannon, Danny Cook, David Noonan. **Conditional:** Tom Buckley. **Amateur:** Mr Kieran Buckley.

---

274 **MR MICHAEL HAWKER, Chippenham**
Postal: **Battens Farm, Allington, Chippenham, Wiltshire, SN14 6LT**

1 **BETTY BATTENS**, 6, ch m Tobougg (IRE)—Where's My Slave (IRE) **Mr M. R. E. Hawker**
2 **LEMONADE DRINKER**, 6, gr g Fair Mix (IRE)—Sheknowsyouknow **Mr M. R. E. Hawker**
3 **MORTENS LEAM**, 7, b g Sulamani (IRE)—Bonnet's Pieces **Mr M. R. E. Hawker**

---

275 **MR RICHARD HAWKER, Frome**
Postal: **Rode Farm, Rode, Bath, Somerset, BA11 6QQ**
Contacts: **PHONE (01373) 831479**

1 **GENTLEMAN FARMER**, 7, ch g Tobougg (IRE)—Sweet Shooter **R. G. B. Hawker**
2 **KILCREA BRIDGE**, 8, b g Kayf Tara—Ballyhoo (IRE) **Mr W. Rowles**
3 **PARLOUR MAID**, 8, gr m Dr Massini (IRE)—Charliebob **Rolling Aces**

MR RICHARD HAWKER - Continued

    4 **PENGO'S BOY,** 10, gr g Proclamation (IRE)—Homeoftheclassics **Mrs P. J. Pengelly**
    5 **REGAL FLUTE,** 7, b m Schiaparelli (GER)—Regal Music **Mrs P. R. Stocker**

Other Owners: Mr J. Bartram.

---

276   **MR JONATHAN HAYNES, Brampton**
Postal: **Cleugh Head, Low Row, Brampton, Cumbria, CA8 2JB**
Contacts: **PHONE (01697) 746253 MOBILE (07771) 511471**

    1 **BERTIELICIOUS,** 11, b g And Beyond (IRE)—Pennepoint **J. C. Haynes**
    2 **BEYONDTEMPTATION,** 11, ch m And Beyond (IRE)—Tempted (IRE) **J. C. Haynes**
    3 **BEYONDTHEFLAME,** 9, b m And Beyond (IRE)—Flame of Zara **J. C. Haynes**
    4 **DOROTHY'S FLAME,** 7, ch m Black Sam Bellamy (IRE)—Flame of Zara **J. C. Haynes**

---

277   **MISS GAIL HAYWOOD, Moretonhampstead**
Postal: **Stacombe Farm, Doccombe, Moretonhampstead, Newton Abbot, Devon, TQ13 8SS**
Contacts: **PHONE (01647) 440826**
E-MAIL gail@gghracing.com WEBSITE www.gghracing.com

    1 **AMOUR D'OR,** 8, b m Winged Love (IRE)—Diletia **Haywood's Heroes**
    2 **CHICA RAPIDA,** 7, ch m Paco Boy (IRE)—Tora Bora **Mrs J. Bland**
    3 **DANCING GREY,** 6, gr m Dream Eater (IRE)—State of Grace **Mrs J B Floyd-Walker & Mrs J Oliver**
    4 **FLEUR DU WELD,** 11, ch m Weld—Midnight Walker **Mrs J. B. Floyd-Walker**
    5 **RICHARDOFDOCCOMBE (IRE),** 13, b g Heron Island (IRE)—Strike Again (IRE) **Phillip & Mary Creese**
    6 **RUSSIAN'S LEGACY,** 9, b m Kayf Tara—Ruby Star (IRE) **Miss G. G. Haywood**
    7 **SECRET PALACE,** 7, ch m Pastoral Pursuits—Some Sunny Day **Phillip & Mary Creese**
    8 **ZULU,** 5, b g Cockney Rebel (IRE)—Pantita **Haywood's Heroes**

Other Owners: Mr P. V. Creese, Mrs S. M. Creese, Mrs J. B. Floyd-Walker, Mr M. J. Haywood, Miss G. G. Haywood, Mrs M. O'Sullivan, Ms V. O'Sullivan, Mr J. Oliver.

Jockey (NH): David Noonan. **Conditional:** Kieron Edgar. **Amateur:** Miss Sioned Whittle.

---

278   **MR PETER HEDGER, Hook**
Postal: **2 Channel View, St Peter's Road, North Hayling Island, Hampshire, PO11 0RT**
Contacts: **PHONE (02392) 463161 MOBILE (07860) 209448**
E-MAIL hedgerlaura@hotmail.com

    1 **C'EST NO MOUR (GER),** 6, b g Champs Elysees—C'est L'Amour (GER) **Mr D. Wilbrey**
    2 **CONTINUUM,** 10, b br g Dansili—Clepsydra **P C F Racing Ltd**
    3 **FRANCO'S SECRET,** 8, b g Sakhee's Secret—Veronica Franco **P C F Racing Ltd**
    4 **MEDBURN CUTLER,** 9, ch g Zafeen (FR)—Tiegs (IRE) **Mr E. L. Evans**
    5 **MR MAC,** 5, b g Makfi—Veronica Franco **P C F Racing Ltd**
    6 **SHACKLED N DRAWN (USA),** 7, b g Candy Ride (ARG)—
                               Cajun Flash (USA) **Ron Smith Recycling Ltd/Mr P. R. Hedger**
    7 **SILENT ECHO,** 5, b g Oasis Dream—Quiet **P C F Racing Ltd**
    8 **TRALEE HILLS,** 5, b g Mount Nelson—Distant Waters **P C F Racing Ltd**
    9 **WHIPCRACKAWAY (IRE),** 10, b g Whipper (USA)—Former Drama (USA) **Mr P. R. Hedger & P C F Racing Ltd**

THREE-YEAR-OLDS

   10 **SISTER'S ACT,** b f Equiano (FR)—Sister Guru **Mr P. R. Hedger & P C F Racing Ltd**

TWO-YEAR-OLDS

   11 B f 21/3 Finjaan—Afro (Araafa (IRE)) **P C F Racing Ltd**

Other Owners: P. R. Hedger, Ron Smith Recycling Ltd.

Jockey (flat): Charles Bishop. **Jockey (NH):** Leighton Aspell.

279 MR NICKY HENDERSON, Lambourn

Postal: **Seven Barrows, Lambourn, Hungerford, Berkshire, RG17 8UH**
Contacts: **PHONE (01488) 72259 MOBILE (07774) 608168**
E-MAIL njh@njhenderson.com

1 **ADJALI (GER)**, 4, b g Kamsin (GER)—Anabasis (GER) **Mr Simon Munir & Mr Isaac Souede**
2 **ALLART (IRE)**, 5, b g Shantou (USA)—The Adare Woman (IRE) **R. A. Bartlett**
3 **ALPH (IRE)**, 5, b g Gold Well—She's Our Banker (IRE) **Mrs P. J. Pugh**
4 **ALTIOR (IRE)**, 9, b g High Chaparral (IRE)—Monte Solaro (IRE) **Mrs P. J. Pugh**
5 **ANGELS BREATH (IRE)**, 5, gr g Shantou (USA)—Mystic Masie (IRE) **Walters Plant Hire & Ronnie Bartlett**
6 **APPLE'S SHAKIRA (FR)**, 5, b m Saddler Maker (IRE)—Apple's For Ever (FR) **Mr J. P. McManus**
7 **ARCADIAN PEARL (IRE)**, 4, br g Arcadio (GER)—Grangeclare Pearl (IRE) **Biddestone Racing XVII**
8 **ARTURUS (IRE)**, 4, b g Camelot—Scandisk (IRE) **Mr J. Turner**
9 **BALLYCAINES (IRE)**, 4, ch g Finsceal Fior (IRE)—Annamanamoux (USA) **Mr A. Davis**
10 **BARBADOS BLUE (IRE)**, 5, b m Getaway (GER)—Buck's Blue (FR) **Crimbourne Stud**
11 **BEAT THAT (IRE)**, 11, b g Milan—Knotted Midge (IRE) **M. A. C. Buckley**
12 **BEFORE MIDNIGHT**, 6, ch g Midnight Legend—Lady Samantha **Walters Plant Hire & James & Jean Potter**
13 **BEWARE THE BEAR (IRE)**, 9, b g Shantou (USA)—Native Bid (IRE) **G. B. Barlow**
14 **BEYONDTHESTORM (IRE)**, 6, b g Flemensfirth (USA)—Blue Gale (IRE) **Cheveley Park Stud Limited**
15 **BIRCHDALE (IRE)**, 5, b g Jeremy (USA)—Onewayortheother (IRE) **Mr J. P. McManus**
16 **BOLD RECORD (IRE)**, 5, b g Fame And Glory—Shop Dj (IRE) **R. M. Kirkland**
17 **BRAIN POWER (IRE)**, 8, b g Kalanisi—Blonde Ambition (IRE) **M. A. C. Buckley**
18 **BRAVE EAGLE (IRE)**, 7, b g Yeats (IRE)—Sinful Pleasure (IRE) **R. M. Kirkland**
19 **BURBANK (IRE)**, 7, b g Yeats—Spring Swoon (FR) **Mr T. J. Hemmings**
20 **BURROWS EDGE (FR)**, 6, b g Martaline—La Vie de Boitron (FR) **M. A. C. Buckley**
21 **BUVEUR D'AIR (FR)**, 8, b g Crillon (FR)—History (FR) **Mr J. P. McManus**
22 **CALL ME LORD (FR)**, 6, b br g Slickly (FR)—Sosa (GER) **Mr Simon Munir & Mr Isaac Souede**
23 **CAPTAIN WOODIE (IRE)**, 7, b g Presenting—Lasado (IRE) **Middleham Park Racing LXXX**
24 **CASABLANCA MIX (FR)**, 7, ch m Shirocco (GER)—Latitude (FR) **E. R. Hanbury**
25 **CHAMP (IRE)**, 7, b g King's Theatre (IRE)—China Sky (IRE) **Mr J. P. McManus**
26 **CHAMPAGNE MYSTERY (IRE)**, 5, b g Shantou (USA)—Spanker **Mr T. J. Hemmings**
27 **CHAMPAGNE PLATINUM (IRE)**, 5, gr g Stowaway—Saffron Holly (IRE) **Mr J. P. McManus**
28 **CHANTRY HOUSE (IRE)**, 5, br g Yeats (IRE)—The Last Bank (IRE) **Mr J. P. McManus**
29 **CHAPARRAL PRINCE (IRE)**, 4, b g High Chaparral (IRE)—Snow Gretel (IRE) **Mr & Mrs J. D. Cotton**
30 **CHARLI PARCS (FR)**, 6, b g Anabaa Blue—Ella Parcs (FR) **Mr J. P. McManus**
31 **CHEF DES OBEAUX (FR)**, 7, b g Saddler Maker (IRE)—O Dame de Gene (FR) **Sullivan Bloodstock Limited**
32 **CHIVES**, 5, b g Sulamani (IRE)—Ceilidh Royal **Mrs Rita Brown**
33 **CLARENDON STREET (IRE)**, 6, b g Court Cave—Carrigeen Kalmia (IRE) **Owners Group 028**
34 **COLONIAL DREAMS (IRE)**, 7, b g Westerner—Dochas Supreme (IRE) **C. N. Barnes**
35 **COMMANDER MILLER**, 5, b g Shirocco (GER)—Milliegait **HP Racing Commander Miller**
36 **CORRANY (IRE)**, 5, br g Court Cave (IRE)—Time For An Audit **Mr T. J. Hemmings**
37 **COUNTISTER (FR)**, 7, b m Smadoun (FR)—Tistairly (FR) **Mr J. P. McManus**
38 **CULTIVATOR**, 8, b g Alflora (IRE)—Angie Marinie **Kimmins Family & Friends**
39 **DAPHNE DU CLOS (FR)**, 6, b m Spanish Moon (USA)—Katarina du Clos (FR) **Sullivan Bloodstock Limited**
40 **DARIUS DES BOIS (FR)**, 6, b g Great Pretender (IRE)—Palafixe (FR) **Sullivan Bloodstock Limited**
41 **DIAMOND ROSE (IRE)**, 4, ch g Imperial Monarch (IRE)—River Clyde (IRE) **Jockey Club Ownership (SW 2018)**
42 **DICKIE DIVER (IRE)**, 6, b g Gold Well—Merry Excuse (IRE) **Mr J. P. McManus**
43 **DIEU BENISSE (FR)**, 6, b m Blue Bresil—Flowerfull (FR) **Seven Barrows Limited**
44 **DIVINE SPEAR (IRE)**, 8, b g Oscar (IRE)—Testaway (IRE) **Middleham Park Racing LXII**
45 **DOUX PRETENDER (FR)**, 6, b g Great Pretender (IRE)—Lynnka (FR) **Sullivan Bloodstock Limited**
46 **DOWNTOWN GETAWAY (IRE)**, 6, b g Getaway (GER)—Shang A Lang (IRE) **T. F. P.**
47 **DRAGON D'ESTRUVAL (FR)**, 6, b g Enrique—Rose d'estruval (FR) **Mr Simon Munir & Mr Isaac Souede**
48 **DREAM DU GRAND VAL (FR)**, 6, b g Puit d'or (FR)—Apple Mille (FR) **Million in Mind Partnership**
49 **DU DESTIN (FR)**, 6, gr g Fuisse (FR)—Parenthese (FR) **Middleham Park Racing V**
50 **DUKE DEBARRY (IRE)**, 8, b g Presenting—Blue Dante (IRE) **Middleham Park Racing CIX**
51 **EL KALDOUN (FR)**, 5, b g Special Kaldoun (FR)—Kermesse d'estruval (FR) **Middleham Park Racing CIV**
52 **ELUSIVE BELLE (IRE)**, 5, b m Elusive Pimpernel (USA)—Soviet Belle (IRE) **Mr R. B. Waley-Cohen**
53 **EPATANTE (FR)**, 5, b m No Risk At All (FR)—Kadjara (FR) **Mr J. P. McManus**
54 **FALCO BLITZ (IRE)**, 5, b g Falco (USA)—Ignited **Axom LXXVII**
55 **FATHER JOHN (FR)**, 4, b g Secret Singer (FR)—Oudette (FR) **Middleham Park Racing CVII**
56 **FELONY (FR)**, 4, b g Getaway (GER)—Sparkling Gem (IRE) **Highland Thoroughbred Racing - Getaway**
57 **FOLLOW THE BEAR (IRE)**, 7, b g King's Theatre (IRE)—Mrs Dempsey (IRE) **G. B. Barlow**
58 **FOREVER FIELD (IRE)**, 9, b g Beneficial—Sarahs Reunion (IRE) **R. M. Kirkland**
59 **FOXWORTHY**, 7, b g Yeats (IRE)—Candy Creek (IRE) **Mr & Mrs R. G. Kelvin-Hughes**
60 **FRENCH CRUSADER (FR)**, 6, b g Kapgarde (FR)—Largesse (FR) **R. M. Kirkland**
61 **FRUCTINE (FR)**, 4, b f Saint des Saints (FR)—Platine (FR) **Mr J. P. McManus**

MR NICKY HENDERSON - Continued

62 **FUGITIVES DRIFT (IRE)**, 4, b g Yeats (IRE)—Shebeganit (IRE) **HP Racing Fugitives Drift**
63 **FULL BORE (IRE)**, 6, b g Milan—Senora Snoopy (IRE) **The Albatross Club**
64 **FUSIL RAFFLES (FR)**, 4, b g Saint des Saints (FR)—Tali des Obeaux (FR) **Mr Simon Munir & Mr Isaac Souede**
65 **GALLAHERS CROSS (IRE)**, 7, b g Getaway (GER)—Raheen Lady (IRE) **Grech & Parkin**
66 **GANACHE (IRE)**, 6, b g Scorpion (IRE)—Spring Baloo (IRE) **Mr T. J. Hemmings**
67 **GOLD PRESENT (IRE)**, 9, br g Presenting—Ouro Preto **Mr & Mrs J. D. Cotton**
68 **GUNNERY (FR)**, 6, ch g Le Havre (IRE)—Loup The Loup (FR) **Mrs F. H. Hay**
69 **HAMILTON'S FANTASY**, 4, b f Mount Nelson—Romantic Dream **Her Majesty The Queen**
70 **HAUL AWAY (IRE)**, 6, b g Stowaway—Lisacul Queen (IRE) **R. M. Kirkland**
71 **HEATSTROKE (IRE)**, 7, b g Galileo (IRE)—Walklikeanegyptian (IRE) **Mrs F. H. Hay**
72 **HUMPHREY BOGART (IRE)**, 6, b g Tagula (IRE)—Hazarama (IRE) **Chelsea Thoroughbreds - Malteses Falcon**
73 **I CAN'T EXPLAIN (IRE)**, 6, b g Getaway (GER)—Dr Sandra (IRE) **Julie & David F Martin & Dan Hall**
74 **IGOR**, 6, b g Presenting—Stravinsky Dance **M Hankin, C Noell, MenHolding, R Waley-Cohen**
75 **INTERCONNECTED**, 5, br g Network (GER)—R de Rien Sivola (FR) **Grech & Parkin**
76 **ITALIAN SUMMER**, 4, br f Milan—Midsummer Magic **Her Majesty The Queen**
77 **JACK SHARP (IRE)**, 4, b br g Scorpion (IRE)—That's Amazing (IRE) **Walters Plant Hire & James & Jean Potter**
78 **JANIKA (FR)**, 6, b g Saddler Maker (IRE)—Majaka (FR) **Mr Simon Munir & Mr Isaac Souede**
79 **JEN'S BOY (IRE)**, 5, b g Malinas (GER)—Friendly Craic (IRE) **Middleham Park Racing CV & Jen Errington**
80 **JENKINS (IRE)**, 7, b g Azamour (IRE)—Aladiyna (IRE) **Pump & Plant Services Ltd**
81 **JOSSES HILL (IRE)**, 11, b g Winged Love (IRE)—Credora Storm **Mr Alan Spence**
82 **KEEN ON**, 5, b g Kayf Tara—Romantic Dream **Her Majesty The Queen**
83 **KILCREA VALE (IRE)**, 9, b g Beneficial—Inflation (IRE) **Mr Alan Spence**
84 **KINGS RYDE (IRE)**, 7, b g King's Theatre (IRE)—Ryde Back **Miss R. C. Tregaskes**
85 **KNOWN (IRE)**, 5, b g Fame And Glory—Aasleagh Lady (IRE) **The Rose & Thistle Partnership**
86 **KUPATANA (IRE)**, 6, b m Westerner—Kildea Cailin (IRE) **Grech & Parkin**
87 **LA HULPE (FR)**, 5, ch m No Risk At All (FR)—Belle Yepa (FR) **Walters Plant Hire & James & Jean Potter**
88 **LASKADINE (FR)**, 4, b f Martaline—Laskadoun (FR) **Mr J. P. McManus**
89 **LAUGHING LUIS**, 5, b g Authorized (IRE)—Leitzu (IRE) **J. C. Sillett**
90 **LISHEEN CASTLE (IRE)**, 4, b g Most Improved (IRE)—Mafaaza (USA) **Elite Racing Club**
91 **LOMACHENKO (IRE)**, 5, ch g Sans Frontieres (IRE)—
                                    Midnight Orchid (IRE) **Mr Simon Munir & Mr Isaac Souede**
92 **LOUGH DERG SPIRIT (IRE)**, 7, b g Westerner—Sno-Cat Lady (IRE) **Grech & Parkin**
93 **LOUGHFAIR**, 5, gr g Fair Mix (FR)—Glenda Lough (IRE) **T. J. Whitley**
94 **LOVEHERANDLEAVEHER (IRE)**, 7, b br m Winged Love (IRE)—Rowdy Exit (IRE) **Mr Alan Spence**
95 **LUST FOR GLORY (IRE)**, 6, b m Getaway (GER)—Maisie Presenting (IRE) **Grech & Parkin**
96 **LYNDSAYS LAD**, 6, b g Kayf Tara—Ceilidh Royal **Mrs R. H. Brown**
97 **MALACHITE**, 6, gr g Malinas (GER)—Kali **Mr D. H. Low**
98 **MALTON ROSE (IRE)**, 8, b g Milan—Pharney Fox (IRE) **Galopp Syndicate Ltd**
99 **MARCEL DEBRUXELLES (FR)**, 7, b g Librettist (USA)—Forcaster (FR) **Mr P. Van Belle**
100 **MARIE'S ROCK (IRE)**, 4, b br f Milan—By The Hour (IRE) **Middleham Park Racing XLII**
101 **MIGHT BITE (IRE)**, 10, b g Scorpion (IRE)—Knotted Midge (IRE) **The Knot Again Partnership**
102 **MILL GREEN (IRE)**, 7, b g Black Sam Bellamy (IRE)—Ceilidh Royal **Mrs R. H. Brown**
103 **MISTER FISHER (IRE)**, 5, b g Jeremy (USA)—That's Amazing (IRE) **James & Jean Potter**
104 **MONBEG LEGEND (IRE)**, 9, b g Midnight Legend—Reverse Swing **Eventmasters Racing**
105 4, B g Milan—Monte Solaro (FR) **Mrs John Magnier**
106 **MORNING VICAR (IRE)**, 6, b g Beneficial—Mary's Little Vic (IRE) **The Parishioners**
107 **MR WHIPPED (IRE)**, 6, br g Beneficial—Dyrick Daybreak (IRE) **Grech & Parkin**
108 **MR WOODY (IRE)**, 5, b g Shantou (USA)—She's On The Case (IRE) **Mrs E. C. Roberts**
109 **NEW MOON (FR)**, 5, b g Kapgarde (FR)—Not Lost (FR) **Walters Plant Hire & James & Jean Potter**
110 **NO HIDING PLACE (IRE)**, 6, b g Stowaway—Subtle Gem (IRE) **HP Racing No Hiding Place**
111 **NONESUCH (IRE)**, 5, b m Shirocco (GER)—N'avoue Jamais (FR) **Mr R. B. Waley-Cohen**
112 **O CONNELL STREET (IRE)**, 5, b g Fame And Glory—Victorine (GER) **Magniers/ Mrs P Shanahan/justin Carthy**
113 **O O SEVEN (IRE)**, 9, b g Flemensfirth (USA)—Kestral Heights (IRE) **C. O. P. Hanbury**
114 **OK CORRAL (IRE)**, 9, b g Mahler—Acoola (IRE) **Mr J. P. McManus**
115 **ON THE BLIND SIDE (IRE)**, 7, b g Stowaway—Such A Set Up (IRE) **Mr Alan Spence**
116 **PACIFIC DE BAUNE (FR)**, 6, gr g Al Namix (FR)—Perle De Baune (FR) **Mr & Mrs Sandy Orr**
117 **PALIXANDRE (FR)**, 5, b g Kapgarde (FR)—Palmeriade (FR) **Mrs S. Ricci**
118 **PENTLAND HILLS (IRE)**, 4, b g Motivator—Elle Galante (GER) **Owners Group 031**
119 4, B g Jeremy (USA)—Peratus (IRE) **International Plywood (Importers) Ltd**
120 **PIPESMOKER (FR)**, 4, b g Authorized (IRE)—Pisa (GER) **Lady Dulverton**
121 **PISTOL WHIPPED (IRE)**, 5, b g Beneficial—Holiday Time (IRE) **Mr A. Speelman & Mr M. Speelman**
122 **PRECIOUS CARGO (IRE)**, 6, b g Yeats (IRE)—Kilbarry Classic (IRE) **T. Barr**
123 **PYM (IRE)**, 6, b g Stowaway—Liss Rua (IRE) **Mrs P. J. Pugh**
124 **RAISING THE BAR (IRE)**, 7, b g Kalanisi (IRE)—Cool Quest (IRE) **The Bartenders**
125 **RATHER BE (IRE)**, 8, b g Oscar (IRE)—Irish Wedding (IRE) **Matt & Lauren Morgan**

MR NICKY HENDERSON - Continued

126 **RATHHILL (IRE)**, 6, b g Getaway (GER)—Bella Venezia (IRE) **Mr J. P. McManus**
127 4, B f Fame And Glory—Real Papoose (IRE) **International Plywood (Importers) Ltd**
128 **REIGNING SUPREME (IRE)**, 8, b g Presenting—Gli Gli (IRE) **M. A. C. Buckley**
129 **RIVER WYLDE (IRE)**, 8, b g Oscar (IRE)—Clarin River (IRE) **Grech & Parkin**
130 **ROYAL REEL**, 6, ch g Shirocco (GER)—Close Harmony **Mrs R. H. Brown**
131 **ROYAL RUBY**, 7, b g Yeats (IRE)—Close Harmony **Mrs R. H. Brown**
132 **SANTINI**, 7, b g Milan—Tinagoodnight (IRE) **Mr & Mrs R. G. Kelvin-Hughes**
133 **SCARPIA (IRE)**, 5, ch g Sans Frontieres (IRE)—Bunglasha Lady (IRE) **Mrs T. J. Stone-Brown**
134 **SHE MITE BITE (IRE)**, 6, b m Scorpion (IRE)—That's Moyne (IRE) **The SMBs**
135 **SHISHKIN (IRE)**, 5, b g Sholokhov (IRE)—Labarynth (IRE) **Mrs M. Donnelly**
136 **SLEIGHT OF HAND (IRE)**, 5, b g Kalanisi (IRE)—Katariya (IRE) **Michael Buckley & Mark Blandford**
137 **SON OF CAMAS (FR)**, 4, ch g Creachadoir (IRE)—Camas (FR) **Sullivan Bloodstock Ltd**
138 **SORGHATANI**, 4, b f Kayf Tara—Follow The Dream **Richard's Rascals**
139 **SOUL EMOTION (FR)**, 6, b g Martaline—Second Emotion (FR) **Mr & Mrs J. D. Cotton**
140 **STEAL A MARCH**, 4, b g Mount Nelson—Side Step **Her Majesty The Queen**
141 **STORM OF INTRIGUE (IRE)**, 7, b g Oscar (IRE)—Storminoora (IRE) **Mr Oscar Singh & Miss Priya Purewal**
142 **STYLE DE GARDE (FR)**, 5, b g Kapgarde (FR)—Anowe de Jelois (FR) **Highclere Thoroughbred Racing - Style**
143 **STYLE DE VOLE (FR)**, 4, gr g Vol de Nuit—Anowe de Jelois (FR) **Mr J. P. McManus**
144 4, B g Kayf Tara—Suave Shot **Trevor and Linda Marlow**
145 **SUNRISE RUBY (IRE)**, 5, ch m Sholokhov (IRE)—Maryota (FR) **Blunt, Breslin, Duffy, Slattery**
146 **SUNSHADE**, 6, b m Sulamani (IRE)—Spring Flight **Her Majesty The Queen**
147 **SURF WALK (IRE)**, 4, b g Born To Sea (IRE)—Meon Mix **Mr A Speelman & Mr M Speelman**
148 **TAKE IT AWAY (IRE)**, 5, b m Yeats (IRE)—Claudia's Pearl **Mr J. P. McManus**
149 **TEMPLE HIGH**, 4, b f Sulamani (IRE)—Uppermost **James & Jean Potter**
150 **TERREFORT (FR)**, 6, gr g Martaline—Vie de Reine (FR) **Mr Simon Munir & Mr Isaac Souede**
151 **THE BOTTOM BAR (IRE)**, 7, br g Stowaway—Serenade Leader (IRE) **Mr Simon Munir & Mr Isaac Souede**
152 **THEINVAL (FR)**, 9, b g Smadoun (FR)—Kinevees (FR) **Mr & Mrs Sandy Orr**
153 **THOMAS CAMPBELL**, 7, b g Yeats (IRE)—Hora **Mrs Van Geest & Mrs Kelvin Hughes**
154 **TOP NOTCH (FR)**, 8, b g Poliglote—Topira (FR) **Mr Simon Munir & Mr Isaac Souede**
155 **TRULL LA LA**, 5, ch m Flemensfirth (USA)—Chomba Womba (IRE) **The Tra La La Syndicate**
156 **TURTLE WARS (FR)**, 6, b g Turtle Bowl (IRE)—Forces Sweetheart **Sullivan Bloodstock Limited**
157 **TWIST (IRE)**, 4, b g Invincible Spirit (IRE)—Kahira (IRE) **Mr Alan Spence**
158 **VALTOR (FR)**, 10, b g Nidor (FR)—Jossca (FR) **Mr Simon Munir & Mr Isaac Souede**
159 **VEGAS BLUE (IRE)**, 4, b f Getaway (GER)—Bella Venezia (IRE) **Crimbourne Stud**
160 **VERDANA BLUE (IRE)**, 7, b m Getaway (GER)—Blue Gallery (IRE) **Crimbourne Stud**
161 **VERSATILITY**, 5, b g Yeats (IRE)—Stravinsky Dance **The Barrow Boys 2**
162 **VYTA DU ROC (FR)**, 10, gr g Lion Noir—Dolce Vyta (FR) **Mr Simon Munir & Mr Isaac Souede**
163 **WALLACE SPIRIT (FR)**, 6, gr g Le Havre (IRE)—In Love New (FR) **Mr & Mrs Sandy Orr**
164 **WE HAVE A DREAM (FR)**, 5, b g Martaline—Sweet Dance (FR) **Mr Simon Munir & Mr Isaac Souede**
165 **WELSH SAINT (FR)**, 5, b g Saint des Saints (FR)—Minirose (FR) **Walters Plant Hire & James & Jean Potter**
166 **WENYERREADYFREDDIE (IRE)**, 8, ch g Beneficial—Ware It Vic (IRE) **Mr M. Landau & Mr J. Lightfoot**
167 **WHATSWRONGWITHYOU (IRE)**, 8, ch g Bienamado (USA)—
Greenfield Noora (IRE) **5 Hertford Street Racing Club**
168 **WILLIAM HENRY (IRE)**, 9, b g King's Theatre (IRE)—Cincuenta (IRE) **Walters Plant Hire Ltd**
169 **WITH DISCRETION (IRE)**, 8, b m Tiger Hill (IRE)—Discreet **Bloomsbury Stud**
170 **YELLOW DOCKETS (IRE)**, 7, ch m Getaway (GER)—Soft Skin (IRE) **Grech & Parkin**

Other Owners: Axom Ltd, Mr M. R. Blandford, Mr L. J. Blunt, L. Breslin, A. R. Bromley, Mr J. Carthy, Ms H. Corderoy, J. D. Cotton, Mrs B. Cotton, Mr M. R. Dodd, Mr D. Downie, Mr J. B. Duffy, G. F. Goode, Mr C. M. Grech, D. A. Hall, N. J. Henderson, Highclere Nominated Partner Limited, Highclere Thoroughbred Racing Ltd, Mr A. J. Hill, Mr B. M. Hillier, J. F. Jarvis, Mrs E. A. Kelvin-Hughes, R. G. Kelvin-Hughes, Mr M. B. J. Kimmins, Mr C. Kimmins, M. R. Landau, Mr J. L. Lightfoot, Mrs E. Magnier, Mr J. P. Magnier, D. R. Martin, Mr P Martin, Mrs J. M. T. Martin, Mr W. D. C. Minton, Mrs L. K. Morgan, M. Morgan, S. E. Munir, Mrs D. C. Nicholson, Miss M. Noden, Mr J. A. M. Orr, Mrs C. R. Orr, Palatinate Thoroughbred Racing Limited, T. S. Palin, Mrs M. Parker, Mr C. M. Parker, Mr S. J. Parkin, Mr S. R. C. Philip, W. H. Ponsonby, Mrs M. J. Potter, Mr J. E. Potter, Brig C. K. Price, M. Prince, Miss P. Purewal, Mrs L. M. Shanahan, Mrs D. Sheasby, Mr E. J. N. Sheasby, Mr A. Singh, Mr W. Slattery, Mr I. Souede, Anthony Speelman, Mr M. Speelman, Mrs G. D. V. Van Geest, Mr R. J. Whatford, Mr S. Williams.

Jockey (NH): James Bowen, James Bowen, Nico De Boinville, Barry Geraghty, Jeremiah McGrath.
Conditional: Ned Curtis, Alan Doyle.

280 MR PAUL HENDERSON, Whitsbury

Postal: **1 Manor Farm Cottage, Whitsbury, Fordingbridge, Hampshire, SP6 3QP**
Contacts: **PHONE** (01725) 518113 **FAX** (01725) 518113 **MOBILE** (07958) 482213
E-MAIL phendersonracing@gmail.com

1 **ABBEY STREET (IRE)**, 8, b g Asian Heights—Cnocbui Cailin (IRE) **Mr and Mrs J Baigent**
2 **AMRON KALI (IRE)**, 9, b m Kalanisi (IRE)—Glacial Snowboard (IRE) **Mareildar Racing Part 1**
3 **BIG MAN CLARENCE (IRE)**, 8, b g Golden Tornado (IRE)—Glens Lady (IRE) **Pittville Park**
4 **CROSSLEY TENDER**, 6, b g Sulamani (IRE)—Slow Starter (IRE) **Hawkings Harding Pearson Pyatt Willis**
5 **DOITFORTHEVILLAGE (IRE)**, 10, b g Turtle Island (IRE)—Last Chance Lady (IRE) **The Rockbourne Partnership**
6 **DUARIGLE (IRE)**, 7, ch g Dubai Destination (USA)—
　　　　　　　　　　　　　　　　　　　Silver Valley (IRE) **A Pearson E Hawkings M Jenner P Scope**
7 **FOR CARMEL (IRE)**, 9, b g Mr Dinos (IRE)—Bobalena (IRE) **The Rockbourne Partnership**
8 **GOOD MAN VINNIE (IRE)**, 8, ch g Vinnie Roe (IRE)—Pellerossa (IRE) **Sarah Habib & Ed Hawkings**
9 **HATCHET JACK (IRE)**, 7, b g Black Sam Bellamy (IRE)—
　　　　　　　　　　　　　　　　　　　Identity Parade (IRE) **A J Pearson, Mark Jenner, Ed Hawkings**
10 **KEYBOARD WARRIOR (IRE)**, 7, b g Scorpion (IRE)—Our Shelly (IRE) **Miss J. Patten**
11 **MEGALODON (IRE)**, 6, b g Getaway (GER)—Fitzgrey (IRE) **Hawkings Finch Harding Stubbs Willis**
12 **MINELLA GATHERING (IRE)**, 10, b g Old Vic—A Plus Ma Puce (FR) **Mr E. J. Hawkings**
13 **MINELLA TWEET (IRE)**, 11, b g King's Theatre—Cara Mhaith (IRE) **Michael & Tracie Willis**
14 **MIRIAM VIOLET**, 5, b m Dick Turpin (IRE)—Velvet Band **Mr J. H. W. Finch**
15 **MOUNT VESUVIUS (IRE)**, 11, b g Spartacus (IRE)—Parker's Cove (USA) **Mr R. G. Henderson**
16 **MR MULLINER (IRE)**, 10, br g Millenary—Mrs Battle (IRE) **Mr M. Day**
17 **MR SCAFF (IRE)**, 5, br g Vocalised (USA)—Nancy Rock (IRE) **M R Scaffolding Services Ltd**
18 **MR STUBBS (IRE)**, 8, b g Robin des Pres (FR)—Crystal Stream (IRE) **Miss J. Patten**
19 **POLAR LIGHT**, 4, b f Norse Dancer (IRE)—Dimelight **J. P. Duffy**
20 **PRESENT DESTINY (IRE)**, 7, b g Dubai Destination (USA)—Anns Present (IRE) **The Friday Night Club**
21 **QUESTIONATION (IRE)**, 8, b m Dubai Destination (USA)—How Is Things (IRE) **Mr and Mrs J Baigent**
22 **RAISING HOPE (IRE)**, 10, b m Turtle Island (IRE)—Jurado It Is (IRE) **Mrs J. L. Chappell**
23 **RING MINELLA (IRE)**, 8, b g King's Theatre—Ring of Water (USA) **NHRE Racing Club**
24 **RUN DON'T HIDE (IRE)**, 8, b g High Chaparral (IRE)—Right Key (IRE) **Mareildar Racing Part 1**
25 **SHAW'S CROSS (IRE)**, 7, b g Mr Dinos (IRE)—Capparoe Cross (IRE) **Mareildar Racing Part 1**
26 **SIZING SAHARA**, 11, gr g Shirocco (GER)—Aristocratique **Mr C. Clark**
27 **TALK OF THE SOUTH (IRE)**, 10, b g Milan—Smalltowntalk (IRE) **The Rockbourne Partnership**
28 **TED BACH (IRE)**, 8, b g Bach (IRE)—Rose Tanner (IRE)
29 **TREACY HOTELS BOY (IRE)**, 12, br g Overbury (IRE)—Bridgehotel Rose (IRE) **Miss J. Patten**
30 **TURBAN (FR)**, 12, b g Dom Alco (FR)—Indianabelle (FR) **The Ray Of Hope Partnership**
31 **UN BEAU ROMAN (FR)**, 11, bl g Roman Saddle (IRE)—Koukie (FR) **John H. W. Finch & The Romans**

Other Owners: Mr J. R. Baigent, Mr R. J. Galpin, Mrs S. J. Habib, Mr B. C. Harding, Mr R. L. Henderson, Mr P. F. Henderson, Mr M. E. Jenner, Mr A. Pearson, Mr J. Pyatt, Mr S. Reid, Mr P. T. Scope, J. F. R. Stainer, Mr T. J. Stubbs, Mr L. M. Weinstein, Mr L. R. Whitbread, Mrs T. J. Willis, Mr M. R. Willis.

---

281 MR MICHAEL HERRINGTON, Thirsk

Postal: **Garbutt Farm, Cold Kirby, Thirsk, North Yorkshire, YO7 2HJ**
Contacts: **MOBILE** (07855) 396858
E-MAIL info@michaelherringtonracing.co.uk **WEBSITE** www.michaelherringtonracing.co.uk

1 **DUKE COSIMO**, 9, ch g Pivotal—Nannina **Mr J. S. Herrington**
2 **JAN VAN HOOF (IRE)**, 8, b g Dutch Art—Cosenza **Mrs H. J. Lloyd-Herrington**
3 **KOMMANDER KIRKUP**, 8, ch g Assertive—Bikini **Stuart Herrington & Pete Forster**
4 **NADINE**, 4, b f Nathaniel (IRE)—Opening Ceremony (USA) **H. M. Hurst**
5 **STEELRIVER (IRE)**, 9, b g Iffraaj—Numerus Clausus (FR) **Mrs H. J. Lloyd-Herrington**
6 **STREET POET (IRE)**, 6, b g Poet's Voice—Street Star (USA) **Mrs H. J. Lloyd-Herrington**
7 **TUKHOOM (IRE)**, 6, b g Acclamation—Carioca (IRE) **M. A. Leatham**
8 **TUM TUM**, 4, ch g Dawn Approach (IRE)—Lalectra (IRE) **Mrs H. J. Lloyd-Herrington**

Other Owners: Mr David Barlow, Mr Peter Forster, Mr Stuart Herrington, Mrs H. Lloyd-Herrington.
Assistant Trainer: Helen Lloyd-Herrington

282 MR PETER HIATT, Banbury
Postal: **Six Ash Farm, Hook Norton, Banbury, Oxfordshire, OX15 5DB**
Contacts: **PHONE (01608) 737255 FAX (01608) 730641 MOBILE (07973) 751115**

1 BAASHIQ (IRE), 5, b g New Approach (IRE)—Fatanah (IRE) **P. Kelly**
2 BEAMING, 5, b m Shamardal (USA)—Connecting **Mr R G Robinson & Mr R D Robinson**
3 FARAWAY FIELDS (USA), 4, b g First Defence (USA)—Faraway Flower (USA) **Mrs S. M. Tucker**
4 MONARCH MAID, 8, b m Captain Gerrard (IRE)—Orange Lily **Mr P. W. Hiatt**
5 RAASHDY (IRE), 6, b g Intikhab (USA)—Maghya (IRE) **Mr P. W. Hiatt**
6 RAFAAF (IRE), 11, b g Royal Applause—Sciunfona (IRE) **Mr P. W. Hiatt**
7 TAKIAH, 4, b f Arcano (IRE)—Elmaam **Phil Kelly & Peter Hiatt**
8 VISIBLE LIGHT (IRE), 11, b g Shantou (USA)—Strand Lady (IRE) **Ms J. Barton**
9 WILDOMAR, 10, b g Kyllachy—Murrieta **Mr P. W. Hiatt**

THREE-YEAR-OLDS

10 BAYAANAAT, ch g Dawn Approach (IRE)—Khothry (IRE) **Jeremy Dougall & Will Watt**
11 DOUBLE COFFEE, b f Mawatheeq (USA)—Maimoona (IRE) **Mr K. L. Read**

Other Owners: Mr P. W. Hiatt, Mr Phil Kelly, Mr R. Robinson, Mr R. D. Robinson.

Assistant Trainer: Mrs E Hiatt

Jockey (flat): Luke Morris. **Amateur:** Miss M. Edden.

283 MRS LAWNEY HILL, Aston Rowant
Postal: **Woodway Farm, Aston Rowant, Watlington, Oxford, OX49 5SJ**
Contacts: **PHONE (01844) 353051 MOBILE (07769) 862648**
E-MAIL lawney@lawneyhill.co.uk WEBSITE www.lawneyhill.co.uk

1 CASPER KING (IRE), 8, b g Scorpion (IRE)—Princess Supreme (IRE) **The Casper King Partnership**
2 CLONDAW WESTIE (IRE), 8, b g Westerner—You're A Native (IRE) **Mrs D. M. Caudwell**
3 MISS MAYFAIR (IRE), 12, b m Indian Danehill (IRE)—Cocktail Party (USA) **Mr Alan Hill**
4 ROGUE DANCER (FR), 14, b g Dark Moondancer—Esperanza IV (FR) **Exors of the Late Mr M. C. Banks**
5 ROYAL IRISH HUSSAR (IRE), 9, b g Galileo (IRE)—Adjalisa (IRE) **Mrs T. J. Hill**
6 SHIMBA HILLS, 8, b g Sixties Icon—Search Party **Yeomanry Racing**
7 SUNSET SKYE, 6, b m Sea Freedom—Money Central **Yeomanry Racing**

Other Owners: Mrs Diana Clark, Edwyn Good, Mr Ian Moss, Mrs Heather Munn, Mr Nick Watts.
Jockey (NH): Aidan Coleman, Nick Scholfield.

284 MR CHARLES HILLS, Lambourn
Postal: **Wetherdown House, Lambourn, Hungerford, Berkshire, RG17 8UB**
Contacts: **PHONE (01488) 71548 FAX (01488) 72823**
E-MAIL info@charleshills.com WEBSITE www.charleshills.com

1 A MOMENTOFMADNESS, 6, b g Elnadim (USA)—Royal Blush **Tony Wechsler & Ann Plummer**
2 AFAAK, 5, b g Oasis Dream—Ghanaati (USA) **Mr Hamdan Al Maktoum**
3 AUTUMN WAR (IRE), 4, ch c Declaration of War (USA)—Autumn Leaves (FR) **Mr Chi Un Fred Ma**
4 BARTHOLOMEU DIAS, 4, b g Mount Nelson—Lady Francesca **Mr P. K. Siu**
5 BATTAASH (IRE), 5, b g Dark Angel (IRE)—Anna Law (IRE) **Mr Hamdan Al Maktoum**
6 BIN DAAHIR, 4, b g Exceed And Excel (AUS)—Beach Frolic **Mr Hamdan Al Maktoum**
7 DARK SERAPHIM (IRE), 4, b c Dark Angel (IRE)—Win Cash (IRE) **Tony Wechsler & Ann Plummer**
8 EQUILATERAL, 4, b c Equiano (FR)—Tarentaise **Mr K. Abdullah**
9 GLOBAL TANGO (IRE), 4, gr g Zebedee—Beautiful Dancer (IRE) **Dr Johnny Hon**
10 GRAPEVINE (IRE), 6, b g Lilbourne Lad (IRE)—High Vintage (IRE) **Mrs J K Powell**
11 JALLOTA, 8, b g Rock of Gibraltar (IRE)—Lady Lahar **Mrs Fitri Hay**
12 KHAWAATEM (USA), 4, ch c Smart Strike (CAN)—Charmed Gift (USA) **Mr Hamdan Al Maktoum**
13 LIVVYS DREAM (IRE), 4, b f Declaration of War (USA)—Briolette (IRE) **International Plywood (Importers) Ltd**
14 MAGICAL MEMORY (IRE), 7, gr g Zebedee—Marasem **Kennet Valley Thoroughbreds I**

MR CHARLES HILLS - Continued

15 **MOON OF BARODA (IRE)**, 4, gr g Dubawi (IRE)—Millennium Star (IRE) **Tony Wechsler & Ann Plummer**
16 **NEVER SURRENDER (IRE)**, 5, b g High Chaparral (IRE)—Meiosis (USA) **D M James, Steve Jenkins, Maurice Mogg**
17 **ORDER OF THISTLE (IRE)**, 4, b g High Chaparral (IRE)—Law of The Jungle (IRE) **Mrs Fitri Hay**
18 **PARKMILL**, 4, b g Pivotal—Lady Grace **Mr D. J. Deer**
19 **PLUTONIAN (IRE)**, 5, b g Raven's Pass—Ripalong (IRE) **Mrs Fitri Hay**
20 **REWAAYAT (IRE)**, 4, br g Pivotal—Rufoof **Mr Hamdan Al Maktoum**
21 **RIPLEY (IRE)**, 4, b f Declaration of War (USA)—La Conquerante **Mr R. J. Tufft**
22 **ROCK OF ESTONIA (IRE)**, 4, ch g Society Rock (IRE)—Estonia **Kangyu Int. Racing (HK) Ltd & Mr F Ma**
23 **SPOOF**, 4, b g Poet's Voice—Filona (IRE) **Gary & Linnet Woodward**
24 **TIME FOR A TOOT (IRE)**, 4, b f Oasis Dream—Market Forces **Mr P Winkworth**
25 **VANBRUGH (USA)**, 4, b c First Defence (USA)—Hachita (USA) **Mr K. Abdullah**
26 **WAFY (IRE)**, 4, br c Dubawi (IRE)—Ghanaati (USA) **Mr Hamdan Al Maktoum**
27 **WITH GOOD GRACE (IRE)**, 4, ch f Galileo (IRE)—
Withorwithoutyou (IRE) **Mrs J Magnier, Mr M Tabor & Mr D Smith**
28 **WUFUD**, 4, b c Dubawi (IRE)—Tahrir (IRE) **Mr Hamdan Al Maktoum**

THREE-YEAR-OLDS

29 **ALANDALOS**, b f Invincible Spirit (IRE)—Ghanaati (USA) **Mr Hamdan Al Maktoum**
30 B g Mayson—Aromatherapy **Hills Angels**
31 **ARTISTIC RIFLES (IRE)**, b c War Command (USA)—Chatham Islands (USA) **Mrs Fitri Hay**
32 B f Galileo (IRE)—Baraka (IRE)
33 **BE TOGETHER**, ch f Showcasing—Love And Cherish (IRE) **Mr B. W. Hills**
34 **BRAWNY**, b g Dark Angel (IRE)—Natty Bumppo (IRE) **Mr Hussain Alabbas Lootah**
35 **BREATH OF AIR**, b c Bated Breath—Western Appeal (USA) **Mr K. Abdullah**
36 **CAESONIA**, ch f Garswood—Agrippina **Mrs Fiona Williams**
37 **CLEMATIS (USA)**, b br f First Defence (USA)—Faraway Flower (USA) **Mr K. Abdullah**
38 **CONSPIROTOR**, b g Charm Spirit (IRE)—Royal Confidence **Mr D. M. James**
39 **COOL POSSIBILITY (IRE)**, b br c Dark Angel (IRE)—Pink Diva (IRE) **Mrs Fitri Hay**
40 **DARK JEDI (IRE)**, b c Kodiac—Whitefall (USA) **Mr Chi Un Fred Ma**
41 **DRUMNADROCHIT**, b g Coach House (IRE)—Blissamore **Mick and Janice Mariscotti**
42 **ELENA**, b f Toronado (IRE)—Red Intrigue (IRE) **Mr Jeremy Gompertz**
43 **ESCAPE THE RAIN (CAN)**, b c Magician (IRE)—Looks Like Rain **Mr P. K. Siu**
44 **FRAGRANT DAWN**, b f Iffraaj—Festivale (IRE) **Mr Abdullah Al Khalifa**
45 **GLOBAL FALCON**, ch c Siyouni (FR)—Maggi Fong **Dr Johnny Hon**
46 **GLOBAL QUALITY**, ch c No Nay Never (USA)—Dynacam (USA) **Dr Johnny Hon & Kir (hk) Ltd**
47 **GLORY FIGHTER**, b g Kyllachy—Isola Verde **KIR (HK) Ltd & Dr Johnny Hon**
48 **HEROIC**, b c Heeraat (IRE)—Aquasulis (IRE) **Mrs J K Powell**
49 **KHAADEM (IRE)**, b c Dark Angel (IRE)—White Daffodil (IRE) **Mr Hamdan Al Maktoum**
50 **KHILWAFY**, b c Mukhadram—Almass (IRE) **Mr Hamdan Al Maktoum**
51 **LYRICAL BALLAD (IRE)**, b f Dark Angel (IRE)—Iffraaj Pink (IRE) **Mrs Fitri Hay**
52 **MOONGAZER**, br f Kuroshio (AUS)—Sonnellino **Mrs Mary-Anne Parker**
53 **MOTAGALLY**, b c Swiss Spirit—Gilt Linked **Mr Hamdan Al Maktoum**
54 **MUTARAFFA (IRE)**, b g Acclamation—Excellent View **Mr Hamdan Al Maktoum**
55 **MUTAWAFFER (IRE)**, b g Kodiac—Golden Flower **Mr Hamdan Al Maktoum**
56 **NOOSHIN**, b f Declaration of War (USA)—Queen Sarra **Saleh Al Homaizi & Imad Al Sagar**
57 **NUBOUGH (IRE)**, b g Kodiac—Qawaasem (IRE) **Mr Hamdan Al Maktoum**
58 **OCEAN PARADISE**, b gr f New Approach (IRE)—Tropical Paradise (IRE) **Mr P Winkworth**
59 **PENRHOS**, b c Kodiac—Bereka **Mrs Julie Martin & David R. Martin**
60 **PHOENIX OF SPAIN (IRE)**, gr c Lope de Vega (IRE)—Lucky Clio (IRE) **Tony Wechsler & Ann Plummer**
61 **POGO (IRE)**, b c Zebedee—Cute **Gary & Linnet Woodward**
62 **QUTOB (IRE)**, b c Acclamation—When Not Iff (IRE) **Mr Hamdan Al Maktoum**
63 **RED BRAVO (IRE)**, b c Acclamation—Vision of Peace (IRE) **John C. Grant & The Hon R. J. Arculli**
64 **RHOSSILI DOWN**, b f Kingman—Exceptionelle **Mr D J Deer**
65 **RING OUT THE BELLS (IRE)**, br f Kodiac—Newlywed (IRE) **Tony Wechsler & Ann Plummer**
66 **RIQAABY (USA)**, b f New Approach (USA)—Aqsaam (USA) **Mr Hamdan Al Maktoum**
67 **RISAALA (IRE)**, b br f Mukhadram—Maayaat (USA) **Mr Hamdan Al Maktoum**
68 **SAIKUNG (IRE)**, b f Acclamation—Glitter Baby (IRE) **Kangyu International Racing (HK) Limited**
69 **SCOTTISH BLADE (IRE)**, b c Exceed And Excel (AUS)—Hecuba **Mrs Fitri Hay**
70 **SHANGHAI GRACE**, b c Kyllachy—Lavinia's Grace **Kangyu International Racing (HK) Limited**
71 **STAGEHAND**, b f Kodiac—Silent Entrance **Mr K. Abdullah**
72 **STARLIGHT RED (IRE)**, gr f Sea The Stars (IRE)—Turning Point **R.Whitehand, D.James, S.Jenkins & Partners**
73 **SUNDIATA**, b f Showcasing—Dawn of Empire (USA) **Mr K. Abdullah**
74 **SUPERSEDED (IRE)**, gr g Exceed And Excel (AUS)—Satwa Ruby (FR) **Kennet Valley Thoroughbreds IX**
75 **TABASSOR (IRE)**, ch f Raven's Pass (USA)—Thaahira (USA) **Mr Hamdan Al Maktoum**

MR CHARLES HILLS - Continued

76 **TADAABEER,** b f Dubawi (IRE)—Thakafaat (IRE) **Mr Hamdan Al Maktoum**
77 **TEMUJIN (IRE),** b c Moohaajim (IRE)—Alhena (IRE) **Mrs J K Powell**
78 **THAKAA (USA),** b f Lemon Drop Kid (USA)—Yaqeen **Mr Hamdan Al Maktoum**
79 **VINDOLANDA,** ch f Nathaniel (IRE)—Cartimandua **Mrs Fiona Williams**
80 **VITRUVIUS,** b c Zoffany (IRE)—Domitia **Mrs Fiona Williams**
81 **YNYS MON (IRE),** b c Olympic Glory (IRE)—Russian Spirit **Julie Martin & David R Martin & Partner**

TWO-YEAR-OLDS

82 Ch f 5/3 Tamayuz—Abhajat (IRE) (Lope de Vega (IRE))
83 Ch f 20/3 Kitten's Joy (USA)—Aqsaam (USA) (Dynaformer (USA))
84 B c 26/3 Zoffany (IRE)—Ardbrae Lady (Overbury (IRE)) (87000)
85 B c 5/4 Raven's Pass (USA)—Atab (IRE) (New Approach (IRE))
86 B c 15/2 Make Believe—Avizare (IRE) (Lawman (FR)) (36190)
87 B c 6/3 Dabirsim (FR)—Aziali (Equiano (FR)) (70000)
88 B c 17/4 Zebedee—Bishop's Lake (Lake Coniston (IRE)) (45000)
89 Ch f 5/2 Kitten's Joy (USA)—Bluebell (IRE) (Mastercraftsman (IRE))
90 **BRING HIM HOME (FR),** CH C 30/3 Le Havre (IRE)—Unaided (Dansili)
91 B c 18/1 Australia—Dalasyla (IRE) (Marju (IRE)) (30000)
92 **DULAS (IRE),** b c 21/3 Raven's Pass (USA)—Petit Calva (FR) (Desert King (IRE)) (60000)
93 Gr c 16/3 Dark Angel (IRE)—Enfijaar (IRE) (Invincible Spirit (IRE))
94 B c 10/4 Muhaarar—Eshaadeh (USA) (Storm Cat (USA))
95 B f 19/2 Oasis Dream—Fadhayyil (IRE) (Tamayuz)
96 **FAVOURED DESTINY (USA),** b f 3/5 Noble Mission—Faraway Flower (USA) (Distant View (USA))
97 B c 10/2 Raven's Pass (USA)—Full Moon Fever (IRE) (Azamour (IRE)) (25283)
98 B c 5/5 Sea The Stars (IRE)—Fullaah (Shamardal (USA)) (85000)
99 Ch c 29/3 Gleneagles (IRE)—Hallouella (Halling (USA)) (55000)
100 Gr f 2/4 Dark Angel (IRE)—Havin' A Good Time (IRE) (Jeremy (USA)) (84280)
101 B c 2/2 Cable Bay (IRE)—Hear My Cry (USA) (Giant's Causeway (USA)) (30000)
102 Ch f 25/2 Australia—Iffraaj Pink (IRE) (Iffraaj)
103 B c 25/3 Gleneagles (IRE)—Impressionist Art (USA) (Giant's Causeway (USA))
104 B c 13/3 Kodiac—Incessant (IRE) (Elusive Quality (USA)) (140000)
105 B c 15/3 Gutaifan (IRE)—Island Sunset (IRE) (Trans Island) (45000)
106 B f 28/3 Hot Streak (IRE)—Joshua's Princess (Danehill (USA)) (17142)
107 **KING'S KNIGHT (IRE),** b c 17/4 Dark Angel (IRE)—Oatcake (Selkirk (USA)) (75000)
108 B f 27/2 Muhaarar—Lear's Princess (USA) (Lear Fan (USA))
109 B c 19/4 Shamardal (USA)—Maayaat (USA) (Jazil (USA))
110 Ch c 28/4 Raven's Pass (USA)—Moon's Whisper (USA) (Storm Cat (USA))
111 Ch c 9/2 Bated Breath—Movementneverlies (Medicean) (57142)
112 B c 17/3 Bated Breath—Olympic Medal (Nayef (USA)) (60000)
113 B c 11/2 Kodiac—On Location (Street Cry (IRE)) (55000)
114 B f 30/4 Ivawood (IRE)—Parabola (Galileo (IRE)) (50568)
115 B c 28/1 Dark Angel (IRE)—Penny Drops (Invincible Spirit (IRE)) (160000)
116 B f 8/2 Dark Angel (IRE)—Pindrop (Exceed And Excel (AUS)) (29498)
117 Ch c 15/2 Showcasing—Puzzling (Peintre Celebre (USA)) (125000)
118 Ch f 5/1 Tamayuz—Qawaasem (IRE) (Shamardal (USA))
119 B c 4/4 Gutaifan (IRE)—Renaissance Rio (IRE) (Captain Rio) (80000)
120 B f 21/2 Dawn Approach (IRE)—Reyaadah (Tamayuz)
121 **RONDO (USA),** b c 6/4 Twirling Candy (USA)—Short Dance (USA) (Hennessy (USA))
122 B c 1/2 Free Eagle (IRE)—Rosa's Cantina (IRE) (Paco Boy (IRE)) (63210)
123 **ROYAL COMMANDO (IRE),** b c 2/2 No Nay Never (USA)—Online Alexander (IRE) (Acclamation) (125000)
124 B f 29/3 Oasis Dream—Rufoof (Zamindar (USA))
125 **RUN FOR FREEDOM,** b c 11/2 Muhaarar—Twilight Mistress (Bin Ajwaad (IRE))
126 B f 12/5 Shamardal (USA)—Shamtari (IRE) (Alhaarth (IRE))
127 Gr f 10/4 Cable Bay (IRE)—Silver Rainbow (IRE) (Starspangledbanner (AUS)) (2857)
128 **SMART CONNECTION (IRE),** b c 1/3 Dutch Art—Endless Love (IRE) (Dubai Destination (USA))
129 **SPUROFTHEMOMENT,** b f 4/4 Brazen Beau (AUS)—Royal Blush (Royal Applause) (95238)
130 Gr ro c 23/3 War Front (USA)—Tahrir (IRE) (Linamix (FR))
131 **TILSIT (USA),** b c 5/2 First Defence (USA)—Multilingual (Dansili)
132 **TOMMY DE VITO,** b c 3/4 Dandy Man (IRE)—Rohlindi (Red Ransom (USA)) (33333)
133 B f 11/2 Cable Bay (IRE)—Triple Star (Royal Applause) (59047)
134 **TWELVE DIAMONDS (IRE),** ch f 28/2 Raven's Pass (USA)—Wardat Dubai (Mawatheeq (USA))
135 Ch c 14/5 Australia—Wewantitall (Pivotal) (63210)
136 B f 23/2 Charm Spirit (IRE)—Zero Gravity (Dansili)

MR CHARLES HILLS - Continued

Other Owners: Janet Adams, Khalil Al Sayegh, N Browne, Chelsea Thoroughbreds, Zoe Donald, Dragon Gate, Ziad A Galadari, Mrs Christopher Hanbury, Mr Christopher Hanbury, George Hills, KMP Law Ltd, James Moore, Mr A. V. Nicoll, Katrina Oldham, Jason & Julie Pedder, Mrs Susan Roy, The Hon Mrs Peter Stanley, Mr R J Tufft, Sir Peter Vela, Mr Godfrey Wilson.

Assistant Trainers: Kevin Mooney, Joe Herbert. **Pupil Assistant:** Jamie Insole

Jockey (flat): Callum Shepherd. **Apprentice:** Owen Lewis.

---

285 MR MARK HOAD, Lewes
Postal: Windmill Lodge Stables, Spital Road, Lewes, East Sussex, BN7 1LS
Contacts: **PHONE** (01273) 477124/(01273) 480691 **FAX** (01273) 477124 **MOBILE** (07742) 446168
E-MAIL markhoad@aol.com

1 HURRICANE ALERT, 7, b g Showcasing—Raggle Taggle (IRE) **Mr M. R. Baldry**
2 RIANNA STAR, 6, b m Haafhd—Sayrianna **Mr B Pay**
3 SEA'S ARIA (IRE), 8, b g Sea The Stars (IRE)—Speed Song **Mrs K. B. Tester**
4 WILLSHEBETRYING, 8, b m Act One—Precedence (IRE) **G. C. Brice**

THREE-YEAR-OLDS

5 CHUTZPAH (IRE), b g Alhebayeb (IRE)—Cheeky Weeky **Mrs K. B. Tester**

---

286 MR PHILIP HOBBS, Minehead
Postal: Sandhill, Bilbrook, Minehead, Somerset, TA24 6HA
Contacts: **PHONE** (01984) 640366 **FAX** (01984) 641124 **MOBILE** (07860) 729795
E-MAIL pjhobbs@pjhobbs.com **WEBSITE** www.pjhobbs.com

1 AT ITS OWN EXPENSE (IRE), 5, ch g Arakan (USA)—Blow A Gasket (IRE) **Taunton Racecourse Owners Club**
2 ATIRELARIGO (FR), 9, b g Puit d'or (IRE)—Ouchka (FR) **Mrs K. V. Vann**
3 AWAKE AT MIDNIGHT, 7, b g Midnight Legend—Wakeful **Mrs S. L. Lloyd-Baker**
4 BALLOTIN (FR), 8, b g Enrique—Orphee de Vonnas (FR) **David Maxwell Racing Limited**
5 BALLYGOWN BAY (IRE), 6, b g Flemensfirth (USA)—Star Shuil (IRE) **Mrs J. J. Peppiatt**
6 BARBROOK STAR (IRE), 7, b g Getaway (GER)—Fille de Robin (FR) **Mrs B. A. Hitchcock**
7 BEAU DU BRIZAIS (FR), 7, gr g Kapgarde (FR)—Belle du Brizais (FR) **Mrs C. Skan**
8 BRADFORD BRIDGE (IRE), 7, b g Milan—Isis Du Berlais (FR) **Brocade Racing**
9 BROTHER TEDD, 10, gr g Kayf Tara—Neltina **Scrase Farms**
10 CAPTAINS RUN (IRE), 7, ch g Curtain Time (IRE)—Sailors Run (IRE) **Mr R. E. Halley**
11 CEDAR VALLEY (IRE), 5, b h Flemensfirth (USA)—Lunar Path (IRE) **Mrs Caren Walsh & Mrs Kathleen Quinn**
12 4, Br g Presenting—Cent Prime **Munnelly Support Services Limited**
13 CHEF D'EQUIPE (FR), 7, b g Presenting—Millesimee (FR) **David Maxwell Racing Limited**
14 CIGARISI (IRE), 7, b g Kalanisi (IRE)—Eileens Dream (IRE) **Mr R. A. S. Offer Partnership**
15 COME ON CHARLIE (FR), 7, b g Anzillero (GER)—End of Spring (FR) **Mr M. G. St Quinton**
16 COTSWOLD WAY (IRE), 6, b g Stowaway—Rosies All The Way **Miss I. D. Du Pre**
17 CROOKS PEAK, 6, b g Arcadio (GER)—Ballcrina Girl (IRE) **Mr C. A. H. Tilley**
18 DANCINGATDUNRAVEN (IRE), 6, b g Mahler—My Kit (IRE) **Let's Get Ready To Rumble Partnership**
19 DARK EPISODE, 5, b g Getaway (GER)—No Moore Bills **Louisville Syndicate Elite**
20 DEFI DU SEUIL (FR), 8, b g Voix du Nord (FR)—Quarvine du Seuil (FR) **Mr J. P. McManus**
21 DEISE ABA (IRE), 6, b g Mahler—Kit Massini (IRE) **Mr T. J. Hemmings**
22 DEMOPOLIS (FR), 5, b g Poliglote—Princess Demut (GER) **Mr J. P. McManus**
23 DIPLOMATE SIVOLA (FR), 6, ch g Noroit (GER)—None de Sivola (FR) **David Maxwell Racing Limited**
24 DOSTAL PHIL (FR), 6, b g Coastal Path—Quiphile (FR) **Mr J. P. McManus**
25 DUKE DES CHAMPS (IRE), 9, b g Robin des Champs (FR)—Ballycowan Lady (IRE) **Diana Whateley & Tim Syder**
26 EBONY GALE, 5, br g Shirocco (GER)—Glenora Gale (IRE) **Mrs J. A. S. Luff**
27 ECU DE LA NOVERIE (FR), 5, b g Linda's Lad—Quat'sous d'Or (FR) **David Maxwell Racing Limited**
28 ESPION (FR), 5, ch g Coastal Path—Toutamie (FR) **Mr Michael & Mrs Norma Tuckey**
29 ET APRES THOU (FR), 5, b g Network (GER)—Lady Thou (FR) **Dr V. M. G. Ferguson**
30 EVIDENCE DE THAIX (FR), 5, b m Network (GER)—Nacre de Thaix (FR) **Mr J. P. McManus**
31 FESTIVAL DAWN, 7, b m Kayf Tara—Keel Road (IRE) **British Racing Club**
32 FLINCK (IRE), 5, b g Fame And Glory—Princess Supreme (IRE) **R. A. Bartlett**
33 FOR GOOD MEASURE (IRE), 8, b g King's Theatre (IRE)—Afdala (IRE) **Mr J. P. McManus**
34 FROM THE HEART (IRE), 5, b g Jeremy (USA)—Zephyr Lilly (IRE) **Mr R. Whitehorn**
35 GAELIC PRINCE (FR), 7, b g Martaline—Gaelic Jane (FR) **Diana Whateley & Tim Syder**

MR PHILIP HOBBS - Continued

36 **GALA BALL (IRE)**, 9, b g Flemensfirth (USA)—Nuit des Chartreux (FR) **R. & Mrs J. E. Gibbs**
37 **GOLDEN SOVEREIGN (IRE)**, 5, b g Gold Well—Fugal Maid (IRE) **Mr L. Quinn**
38 **GOSHEVEN (IRE)**, 6, b g Presenting—Fair Choice (IRE) **The Grocer Syndicate**
39 **GUMBALL (FR)**, 5, gr g No Risk At All (FR)—Good Time Girl (FR) **J. T. Warner**
40 **HALLOWEEN HARRY (IRE)**, 6, b g Wareed (IRE)—Leteminletemout (IRE) **Mr S. P. Marsh**
41 **I'M A GAME CHANGER (IRE)**, 7, b g Arcadio (GER)—Drinadaly (IRE) **Mr & Mrs Paul & Clare Rooney**
42 **ICE COOL CHAMPS (IRE)**, 8, ch g Robin des Champs (FR)—Last of Many (IRE) **West Coast Haulage Limited**
43 **IMPERIAL PRESENCE (IRE)**, 8, ch g Presenting—Penneyrose Bay **Sir Christopher & Lady Wates**
44 **JERRYSBACK (IRE)**, 7, b g Jeremy (USA)—Get A Few Bob Back (IRE) **Mr J. P. McManus**
45 **KALOOKI (GER)**, 5, b g Martaline—Karuma (GER) **Mr A. L. Cohen**
46 **KAYF ADVENTURE**, 8, b g Kayf Tara—My Adventure (IRE) **Louisville Syndicate**
47 **KEEP MOVING (FR)**, 7, b g Linda's Lad—Keeping Gold (FR) **The Country Side**
48 **KEEP ROLLING (IRE)**, 6, ch g Mahler—Kayles Castle (IRE) **Mick Fitzgerald Racing Club**
49 4, Ch g Presenting—Kings Diva (IRE) **Mr & Mrs Paul & Clare Rooney**
50 **LARKBARROW LAD**, 6, b g Kayf Tara—Follow My Leader (IRE) **The Englands and Heywoods**
51 **LE LIGERIEN (FR)**, 6, b g Turgeon (USA)—Etoile de Loir (FR) **D. R. Churches**
52 **LITTLE MISS POET**, 7, b m Yeats (IRE)—R de Rien Sivola (FR) **Mr M. W. Pendarves**
53 **LORD DUVEEN (IRE)**, 8, br g Doyen (IRE)—Afdala (IRE) **L Field, L Cognet, J Sigler & C Walsh**
54 **MAJESTIC TOUCH (IRE)**, 8, br g Kalanisi (IRE)—Alexander Divine **N. R. A. Sutton**
55 **MASTER WORK (IRE)**, 6, b g Network (GER)—Mascarpone (FR) **Mr B K Peppiatt & Mr D R Peppiatt**
56 **MCNAMARAS BAND (IRE)**, 6, b g Getaway (GER)—Katies Pet (IRE) **Tim Syder & Dominic Burke**
57 **MELCHIOR KING (IRE)**, 5, br g Stowaway—Miss Ira Zarad (IRE) **The Brushmakers**
58 **MELEKHOV (IRE)**, 5, b g Sholokhov (IRE)—Yorkshire Girl (IRE) **Owners For Owners: Melekhov**
59 **MENDIP EXPRESS (IRE)**, 13, br g King's Theatre (IRE)—Mulberry (IRE) **David Maxwell Racing Limited**
60 **MIDNIGHT GLORY**, 7, b m Midnight Legend—Land of Glory **Mrs L. R. Lovell**
61 **MUSICAL SLAVE (IRE)**, 6, b g Getaway (GER)—Inghwung **Mr J. P. McManus**
62 **NEW MILLENNIUM (IRE)**, 6, b g Galileo (IRE)—Banquise (GER) **Mr D Symondson & Mrs L Roper**
63 **NINTH WAVE (IRE)**, 5, b g September Storm (GER)—Royale Pearl **Mr T. J. Hemmings**
64 **NO COMMENT**, 8, br g Kayf Tara—Dizzy Frizzy **Mr J. P. McManus**
65 **OAKLEY (IRE)**, 6, b g Oscar (IRE)—Tirolean Dance (IRE) **Mr T. D. J. Syder**
66 **OZZIE THE OSCAR (IRE)**, 8, b g Oscar (IRE)—Private Official (IRE) **Bradley Partnership**
67 **PERFORM (IRE)**, 10, b g King's Theatre (IRE)—Famous Lady (IRE) **Merry Old Souls**
68 **PINEAPPLE RUSH**, 6, b m Kayf Tara—Celtic Native (IRE) **Bradley Partnership**
69 **POINTED AND SHARP (IRE)**, 7, b g Scorpion (IRE)—Leamybe (IRE) **Tony Staple & George Giles**
70 **PRECIOUS BOUNTY (IRE)**, 5, b g Yeats (IRE)—Zaharath Al Bustan **Highclere T'Bred Racing-Precious Bounty**
71 **RAVEN COURT (IRE)**, 5, b g Court Cave (IRE)—Lady Kate Ellen (IRE) **Mr T. J. Hemmings**
72 **REIKERS ISLAND (IRE)**, 6, b g Yeats (IRE)—Moricana (GER) **The Hon J. R. Drummond**
73 **ROLL THE DOUGH (IRE)**, 10, b g Definite Article—High Dough (IRE) **The Kingpins**
74 **ROLLING DYLAN (IRE)**, 8, ch g Indian River (FR)—Easter Saturday (IRE) **Miss I. D. Du Pre**
75 **SAMBURU SHUJAA (FR)**, 6, b g Poliglote—Girelle (FR) **R. & Mrs J. E. Gibbs**
76 **SANDY BOY (IRE)**, 5, b g Tajraasi (USA)—Annienoora (IRE) **Mrs B. A. Hitchcock**
77 4, B br g Milan—Shatani (IRE) **Mrs J. A. S. Luff**
78 4, Br g Shirocco (GER)—She's All That (IRE) **Mrs C. Skan**
79 **SHOW ON THE ROAD**, 8, b g Flemensfirth (USA)—Roses of Picardy (IRE) **R. M. Penny**
80 **SINGAPORE SAGA**, 4, b f Midnight Legend—Kim Tian Road (IRE) **Mr D. J. Burke**
81 **SMARTY WILD**, 5, b g Fair Mix (IRE)—Blaeberry **Mr Michael & Mrs Norma Tuckey**
82 **SNEAKY FEELING (IRE)**, 7, b g Oscar (IRE)—Shuil Aris (IRE) **Syder, Whateley, Murphy, Burke**
83 **SPRINGTOWN LAKE (IRE)**, 7, b g Gamut (IRE)—Sprightly Gal (IRE) **Mr T. D. J. Syder**
84 **STEELY ADDITION (IRE)**, 7, b g Craigsteel—Blond's Addition (IRE) **Step By Step**
85 **STERNRUBIN (GER)**, 8, b g Authorized (IRE)—Sworn Mum (GER) **J. T. Warner**
86 **STORM FORCE BEN (IRE)**, 5, b g Fame And Glory—Torduff Storm (IRE) **Dr V. M. G. Ferguson**
87 **STRONG PURSUIT (IRE)**, 9, ch g Flemensfirth (USA)—Loughaderra (IRE) **Mr T. D. J. Syder**
88 4, B g Yeats (IRE)—Tempest Belle (IRE) **Mr & Mrs Paul & Clare Rooney**
89 **THAT'S A GIVEN (FR)**, 5, b g Great Pretender (IRE)—Aulne River (FR) **Mr A. L. Cohen**
90 **THYME HILL**, 5, b g Kayf Tara—Rosita Bay **The Englands and Heywoods**
91 **TIDAL FLOW**, 6, b g Black Sam Bellamy (IRE)—Mrs Philip **Brocade Racing**
92 **TRUCKERS PASS (IRE)**, 5, br g Kalanisi (IRE)—Lady Knightess (IRE) **Brocade Racing**
93 **TRUCKIN AWAY (IRE)**, 6, br g Getaway (GER)—Simons Girl (IRE) **Brocade Racing**
94 **TURANGI**, 7, b g King's Theatre (IRE)—Bold Fire **Mrs D. L. Whateley**
95 **UMNDENI (FR)**, 5, b br g Balko (FR)—Marie Royale (FR) **St Quinton, D.L. Whateley & Syder**
96 **VANGO DE VAIGE (FR)**, 6, b g Great Pretender (FR)—Yellow Park (FR) **M. Short**
97 **VICTARION (IRE)**, 7, b g Scorpion (IRE)—Gaye Preskina (IRE) **Mrs D. L. Whateley**
98 **VILLAGE VIC (IRE)**, 12, b g Old Vic—Etoile Margot (FR) **David Maxwell Racing Limited**
99 **VODKA ALL THE WAY (IRE)**, 7, b g Oscar (IRE)—Fully Focused (IRE) **Bradley Partnership**
100 **WAIHEKE**, 6, ch m Black Sam Bellamy (IRE)—Its Meant To Be **Mrs S. A. White**

MR PHILIP HOBBS - Continued

101 **WAIT FOR ME (FR)**, 9, b g Saint des Saints (FR)—Aulne River (FR) **Mr A. L. Cohen**
102 **WAR SOUND**, 10, b g Kayf Tara—Come The Dawn **The Englands and Heywoods**
103 **WHATSMEANTTOBE**, 5, b g Fair Mix (IRE)—Its Meant To Be **Mrs S. A. White**
104 **WHO'S MY JOCKEY (IRE)**, 6, b g Yeats (IRE)—Scandisk (IRE) **Mr & Mrs Paul & Clare Rooney**
105 **ZAFAR (GER)**, 4, b c Kamsin (GER)—Zambuka (FR) **Govier & Brown**
106 **ZANZA (IRE)**, 5, b g Arcadio (GER)—What A Bleu (IRE) **Louisville Syndicate Elite**
107 **ZIZANEUR (FR)**, 4, b g Planteur (IRE)—Zitana (FR) **David Maxwell Racing Limited**

Other Owners: Mrs A. E. M. Broom, Mr G. R. Broom, G. S. Brown, Mrs J. L. Buckingham, Mrs V. F. Burke, C. J. Butler, Mrs L. J. Cognet, Mr J. P. Cooper, Mr P. K. Davis, Mrs E. England, Mr A. D. England, Mr D. V. Erskine Crum, Mrs L. H. Field, Mrs B. S. Fowler, Mr R. J. Fowler, Mrs J. E. Gibbs, H. R. Gibbs, Mr G. R. Giles, Mr P. F. Govier, Mr P. Govier, Mr T. M. Hailstone, J. R Hall, Mr C. G. Hellyer, Mr A. S. Heywood, Mr A. H. Heywood, Mr M. N. Higgs, Highclere Thoroughbred Racing Ltd, Mr J. R. Holmes, Mrs J. Hughes, Mr M. J. Hyson, Mr B. R. Ingram, Miss N. Martin, H. A. Murphy, R. A. S. Offer, Mr T. E. Olver, B. K. Peppiatt, Mr J. R. Peppiatt, D. R. Peppiatt, Mr N. D. Peppiatt, Mrs K. Quinn, Racing Club Ltd, D. A. Rees, Mr P. A. Rooney, Mrs C. Rooney, Mrs L. J. Roper, Mr M. C. Sargent, N. C. Savery, Mr J. M. Scrase, Mr N. D. Scrase, Exors of the Late Mrs J. E. Scrase, Mr J. Sigler, Mr J. Simpson, Mr S. C. C. Stacey, A. P. Staple, Step By Step Supporting Independence Ltd, Mr C. Stoddart, Mr D. W. Symondson, Mrs N. Tuckey, M. J. Tuckey, A. J. Viall, C. J. M. Walker, Mrs C. J. Walsh, Mr M. D. Warner, Sir Christopher Wates, Lady G. F. Wates.

Assistant Trainer: Richard White

Jockey (NH): Richard Johnson, Micheal Nolan, Tom O'Brien. **Conditional:** Sean Houlihan. **Amateur:** Mr Tom Doggrell, Mr Ben Jones, Mr Stefan Kirwan, Mr Nathan Vergne.

---

287 **MISS CLARE HOBSON, Royston**
Postal: **The Woolpack, London Road, Reed, Royston, Hertfordshire, SG8 8BB**
Contacts: **MOBILE (07966) 734889**
E-MAIL clarehobsonracing@gmail.com

1 **BRIGHT SAFFRON**, 4, ch f Champs Elysees—Mercy Pecksniff **Smith's Wapping Partnership**
2 **DHARMA RAIN (IRE)**, 4, b f High Chaparral (IRE)—Crazy Volume (IRE) **Barry White**
3 **GOLD CLASS**, 8, ch g Firebreak—Silken Dalliance **The Fox and Duck syndicate**
4 **LOST ON YOU**, 4, b f Lord Shanakill (USA)—If Or When (IRE) **Greg Molen & Harry Hobson**
5 **OLDABBEY BRIDGE (IRE)**, 5, b g Morozov (USA)—Jacks Joy (IRE) **Rosemary Hobson**
6 **UNCLE O**, 5, gr g Fair Mix (IRE)—Clever Liz **The Fox and Duck syndicate**

Other Owners: Mr Barry White, Mrs Rosemary Hobson, Miss Clare Hobson, Mr Harry Hobson, Mr G. Molen.

Assistant Trainer: Harry Hobson

---

288 **MR RICHARD HOBSON, Little Rissington**
Postal: **Bobble Barn Farm, Little Rissington, Cheltenham, Gloucestershire, GL54 2NE**
Contacts: PHONE (01451) 820535 MOBILE (07939) 155843
E-MAIL hobson.r1@sky.com WEBSITE www.richardhobsonracing.co.uk

1 **ALLYSSON MONTERG (FR)**, 9, b g Network (GER)—Mellyssa (FR) **Mr D. W. Fox**
2 **CHIC NAME (FR)**, 7, b g Nickname (FR)—Vuelta Al Ruedo (FR) **The Boom Syndicate**
3 **DEFI SACRE (FR)**, 6, b g Network (GER)—Iowa Sacree (FR) **Mr D. W. Fox**
4 **DISCKO DES PLAGES (FR)**, 6, b g Balko (FR)—Lady des Plages (FR) **G Farr & R Hobson**
5 **ECHO WATT (FR)**, 5, gr g Fragrant Mix (IRE)—Roxane du Bois (FR) **The Boom Syndicate**
6 **EUREU DU BOULAY (FR)**, 5, b g Della Francesca (USA)—Idole du Boulay (FR) **Mr N. Allen & Mr R. Hobson**
7 **EXTRA BALD (FR)**, 5, b g Linda's Lad—Palatyne (FR) **Mr D. W. Fox**
8 **FANZIO (FR)**, 4, b g Day Flight—Tu L'as Eu (FR) **Mr R. H. Hobson**
9 **FILIPINE (FR)**, 4, gr f Network (GER)—Promo d'alienor (FR) **Mr R. H. Hobson**
10 **LORD DU MESNIL (FR)**, 6, b g Saint des Saints (FR)—Ladies Choice (FR) **Mr D. W. Fox**
11 **PETIVILLE (FR)**, 7, gr g Montmartre (FR)—Aegle (IRE) **Mr R. H. Hobson**
12 **RAMONEX (FR)**, 8, b g Saddex—Ramondia (GER) **Mr R. H. Hobson**
13 **SHANTOU FLYER (IRE)**, 9, b g Shantou (USA)—Carrigmorna Flyer (IRE) **David Maxwell Racing Limited**
14 **VALADOM (FR)**, 10, gr g Dadarissime (FR)—Laurana (FR) **Mr R. H. Hobson**

Other Owners: N. J. Allen, Mr G. C. Farr.

Assistant Trainer: Shirley Jane Becker. **Head Lad:** Dawson Lees.

Jockey (NH): James Bowen, Danny Cook. **Conditional:** Jordan Nailor, Paul O'Brien.

289 MR JOHN HODGE, Cumnock
Postal: **Corbie Lodge, Muirdyke Farm, Cumnock, Ayrshire, KA18 2SG**

1 GLORIOUS ROCKET, 5, b g Bated Breath—Up And About **J. M. C. Hodge**
2 SCRIPTURIENT (IRE), 7, ch g Arakan (USA)—Kelso Magic (USA) **J. M. C. Hodge**

290 MR RON HODGES, Somerton
Postal: **Little Orchard, George Street, Charlton Adam, Somerton, Somerset, TA11 7AS**
Contacts: **PHONE (01458) 223922 MOBILE (07770) 625846**
E-MAIL mandyhodges@btconnect.com

1 BRINGTHEHOUSEDOWN (IRE), 5, b g Royal Applause—Raskutani **Mrs S. Steele**
2 DAYLAMI KIRK (IRE), 8, b g Daylami (IRE)—Uptothefrontkirk (IRE) **P. L. Hart**
3 DAYTIME AHEAD (IRE), 8, gr m Daylami (IRE)—
Bright Times Ahead (IRE) **Mrs Jan Dare,Rj Hodges & Colin Mackenzie**
4 GENERAL GIRLING, 12, b g General Gambul—Gold Charm **The Yeovilton Flyers**
5 MET BY MOONLIGHT, 5, b m Sakhee's Secret—Starlight Walk **P. E. Axon**
6 MIDNIGHT MIDGE, 5, b g Midnight Legend—Posh Emily **A Midgley, R J Hodges**
7 MISTER MUSICMASTER, 10, b g Amadeus Wolf—Misty Eyed (IRE) **Mrs S. Clapp & Mr R. J. Hodges**

THREE-YEAR-OLDS

8 BEQUEST, b f Equiano (FR)—Bandanna **Miss R. J. Dobson**
9 LAWN MEET, b f Foxwedge (AUS)—Lane County (USA) **John Frampton & Paul Frampton**

TWO-YEAR-OLDS

10 B g 20/3 Due Diligence (USA)—Small Fortune (Anabaa (USA)) (10476) **P. E. Axon**
11 B g 13/2 Swiss Spirit—Starlight Walk (Galileo (IRE)) (15238) **P. E. Axon**

Other Owners: Mrs S. G. Clapp, Mrs Jan Dare, Mr Paul S. Frampton, Mr J. L. Frampton, Ms Jane Girling, Mr R. J. Hodges, Mr John Knight (Somerset), Mr C. Mackenzie, Mr Andrew Midgley, Mrs L. Sharpe.

291 MR HENRY HOGARTH, Stillington
Postal: **New Grange Farm, Stillington, York**
Contacts: **PHONE (01347) 811168 FAX (01347) 811168 MOBILE (07788) 777044**
E-MAIL harryhogarth@ymail.com

1 ALADDIN SANE (IRE), 5, b g Teofilo (IRE)—Aqua Aura (USA) **Hogarth Racing**
2 ALTO DES MOTTES (FR), 9, b g Dream Well (FR)—Omance (FR) **Hogarth Racing**
3 BOSS DES MOTTES (FR), 8, b g Califet (FR)—Puszta des Mottes (FR) **Hogarth Racing**
4 GRAND ENTERPRISE, 9, b g Fair Mix (IRE)—Miss Chinchilla **Hogarth Racing**
5 GRIS DE PRON (FR), 6, b g Gris de Gris (IRE)—Say Say (FR) **Hogarth Racing**
6 HATTONS HILL (IRE), 10, b g Pierre—Cluain Chaoin (IRE) **Hogarth Racing**
7 KAMIL (GER), 6, ch g Sholokhov (USA)—Kastoria (GER) **Hogarth Racing**
8 KILCULLEN LADY (IRE), 9, b m Scorpion (IRE)—Glittering Star (IRE) **Hogarth Racing**
9 MANCE RAYDER (IRE), 6, b g Flemensfirth (USA)—J'y Viens (FR) **Hogarth Racing**
10 THE BLACK SQUIRREL (IRE), 6, br g Craigsteel—Terra Lucida (IRE) **Hogarth Racing**
11 WOOD EMERY (FR), 7, b g Califet (FR)—Take Emery (FR) **Hogarth Racing**

Other Owners: Mr P. H. Hogarth, Mr H. P. Hogarth, Mr J. Hogarth, Mr J. L. Hogarth.

Assistant Trainer: Russ Garritty

Jockey (NH): Jamie Hamilton. **Conditional:** Billy Garritty. **Amateur:** Miss Emma Todd.

292 MISS SARAH HOLLINSHEAD, Upper Longdon
Postal: **Lodge Farm, Upper Longdon, Rugeley, Staffordshire, WS15 1QF**
Contacts: **PHONE (01543) 490298**

1 CASTLEREA TESS, 6, ch m Pastoral Pursuits—Zartwyda (IRE) **Mr John Graham & Sarah Hollinshead**
2 FINAL ATTACK (IRE), 8, b g Cape Cross (IRE)—Northern Melody (IRE) **N. Chapman**

MISS SARAH HOLLINSHEAD - Continued

3 **GMS PRINCE,** 4, b g Kayf Tara—Zartwyda (IRE) **Graham Brothers Racing Partnership**
4 **JENNY REN,** 4, b f Multiplex—Cherished Love (IRE) **Mr J. Gould**
5 **LOOKFORARAINBOW,** 6, b g Rainbow High—Look Here's May **The Giddy Gang**
6 **MADAME JO JO,** 4, ch f Havana Gold (IRE)—Paradise Place **David Lockwood & Fred Lockwood**
7 **MISTRESS VIZ (IRE),** 5, gr m Mastercraftsman (IRE)—Vizean (IRE) **Mr J. A. Ashley**
8 **MYSTERIOUS GLANCE,** 6, b m Cacique (IRE)—Largo (IRE) **S. L. Edwards**
9 **UNCLE BERNIE (IRE),** 9, gr g Aussie Rules (USA)—Alwiyda (USA) **Graham Brothers Racing Partnership**
10 **ZENAFIRE,** 10, b g Firebreak—Zen Garden **Mr R. J. R. Moseley**

THREE-YEAR-OLDS

11 **GMS PRINCESS,** b f Albaasil (IRE)—Zartwyda (IRE) **Graham Brothers Racing Partnership**
12 **LETHAL LOOK,** gr c Lethal Force (IRE)—Look Here's Dee **S. L. Edwards**
13 **SINNDARELLA (IRE),** b f Fast Company (IRE)—Alafzara (IRE) **Mr J. A. Ashley**
14 **WILLETT,** br g Avonbridge—Madame Elizabeth **David Lockwood & Fred Lockwood**

Other Owners: Mr A. M. Graham, Mr M. P. Graham, Mr J. R. Graham, Miss S. A. Hollinshead, Mr A. Lawrence, Mr F. M. Lockwood, D. J. Lockwood.

---

293 MRS STEPH HOLLINSHEAD, Upper Longsdon
Postal: **Deva House, Bardy Lane, Upper Longsdon, Rugeley, Staffordshire, WS15 4LJ**
Contacts: **PHONE (01543) 493656 MOBILE (07791) 385335**
E-MAIL steph_hollinshead@hotmail.co.uk WEBSITE www.stephhollinsheadracing.com

1 **ACADIAN ANGEL (IRE),** 5, b m Dark Angel (IRE)—Bon Ton Roulet **Mrs D. A. Hodson**
2 **BARNSDALE,** 6, b g Stimulation (IRE)—Seren Teg **Planters (Leicester) Limited**
3 **BELLE EN NOIR,** 7, b m Black Sam Bellamy (IRE)—Miss Holly **The Four Plus Two More Partnership**
4 **BILLIEBROOKEDIT (IRE),** 4, ch g Dragon Pulse (IRE)—Klang (IRE) **Mr Matthew & Mrs Rachael Gavin**
5 **BRIDGE OF SIGHS,** 7, ch g Avonbridge—Ashantiana **Miss L. V. Davis**
6 **CORAL CAYE,** 5, b m Pastoral Pursuits—Vermilion Creek **M. A. N. Johnson**
7 **ENCHANTING ENYA (IRE),** 4, ch f Champs Elysees—Miss Honorine (IRE) **Mr Matthew & Mrs Rachael Gavin**
8 **GRANDMA TILLY,** 4, b f Hellvelyn—Sleep Dance **Mrs D. A. Hodson**
9 **SNOOKER JIM,** 4, b g Holy Roman Emperor (IRE)—Lucia de Medici (IRE) **Mrs D. A. Hodson**
10 **STONEYFORD LANE (IRE),** 5, b g Bushranger (IRE)—Peace Talks **Ocean Four**
11 **THE GOLDEN CUE,** 4, ch g Zebedee—Khafayif (USA) **The Golden Cue Partnership**

THREE-YEAR-OLDS

12 **ALLTAMI (IRE),** b g Lethal Force (IRE)—Peace Talks **J.Howlett, S.Hughes, G. Rowley**
13 **BUMBLEKITE,** ch f Nayef (USA)—Harriet's Girl **Ray Bailey and Steph Hollinshead**
14 **CASTER SEMENYA,** gr f Albaasil (IRE)—Goldeva **Hollinshead & Pyle**
15 B f Mukhadram—Green Poppy
16 **GREGORY THE GREAT,** b c Heeraat (IRE)—Word Perfect **Mr N. S. Sweeney**
17 **LA VOIX MAGIQUE,** ch f Poet's Voice—Inaminute (IRE) **R. Bailey**
18 **MADDFOURMAGGY (IRE),** b f Heeraat (IRE)—Matron **Magg Group & Partner**
19 **TIDAL POINT (IRE),** br g Sea The Moon (GER)—Centred (IRE) **Sleeve It Ltd**
20 **TIZWOTITIZ,** b g Finjaan—Girl of The Rain (IRE) **Steph Hollinshead Racing 1**

TWO-YEAR-OLDS

21 B f 11/3 Coach House (IRE)—Circadian Rhythm (Lujain (USA)) (2500)
22 **DREAM ISLE (IRE),** b c 11/4 Tagula (IRE)—
Desert Location (Dubai Destination (USA)) (4285) **M Johnson & S C Hawkins**
23 Br f 22/3 Pastoral Pursuits—Fortunately (Forzando) (9523)
24 B g 25/3 Roderic O'Connor (IRE)—Inner Sea (USA) (Henrythenavigator (USA)) (800)
25 B f 12/4 Cable Bay (IRE)—Lady Macduff (IRE) (Iffraaj) (6500) **Mrs D. A. Hodson**
26 **RACY STACEY,** ch f 31/1 Fast Company (IRE)—
Stilettoesinthemud (IRE) (Footstepsinthesand) (761) **Mr A. C. Gray**
27 Ch g 14/2 Night of Thunder (IRE)—Yukon Girl (IRE) (Manduro (GER)) (1904)

Other Owners: Mr D. J. Carter, Mr M. Gavin, Mrs R. Gavin, Mr M. Gibbons, Mr G. Hancock, Mr A. Hawkins, Mrs S. C. Hawkins, Mr A. J. Highfield, Mrs L. A. Hollinshead, Mrs J. E. Howlett, Mr S. Hughes, R. Kent, Miss Y. Lowe, M. J. F. Pyle, Mr G. T. Rowley, Mr M. J. Upton.

Assistant Trainer: Adam Hawkins (07554) 008405

294 MR JOHN HOLT, Peckleton
Postal: Hall Farm, Church Road, Peckleton, Leicester, LE9 7RA
Contacts: PHONE/FAX (01455) 821972 MOBILE (07850) 321059
E-MAIL hallfarmracing@btconnect.com WEBSITE www.hallfarmracing.co.uk

1 GLYDER, 5, b m Camacho—Blades Princess **Jobsworth Racing**
2 MOCEAD CAPPALL, 4, b f Captain Gerrard (IRE)—All Fur Coat **Holt, Lynch, Mickley Stud**
3 NOMADRUSH, 9, b m Nomadic Way (USA)—Tanguero (IRE) **Mrs C. M. Tyler**
4 NUMBER THEORY, 11, b g Halling (USA)—Numanthia (IRE) **Mr M. S. Fonseka**
5 REBEL CAUSE (IRE), 6, b g Cockney Rebel—Happy Go Lily **J. R. Holt**
6 VICKY CRISTINA (IRE), 4, b f Arcano (IRE)—And Again (USA) **Clearthermglasssealed Units Ltd &j Holt**

THREE-YEAR-OLDS
7 LADY MONICA, b f Bated Breath—Sina (GER) **Mr M. Hollier**
8 TIGERINMYTANK, b f Heeraat (IRE)—Tiger Cub **J. R. Holt**

TWO-YEAR-OLDS
9 B f 26/4 Cappella Sansevero—Annellis (UAE) (Diesis) (841) **J. R. Holt**
10 HERRING BAY, b f 6/3 Heeraat (IRE)—Hikkaduwa (Sakhee (USA)) **Mr M. S. Fonseka**
11 B f 8/3 Sir Percy—Lady Bling (Showcasing) (800) **J. R. Holt**
12 B f 26/3 Clodovil (IRE)—Puerto Oro (IRE) (Entrepreneur) (1714)
13 B g 1/3 Casamento (IRE)—Sina (GER) (Trans Island) **J. R. Holt**

Other Owners: Cleartherm Glass Sealed Units Ltd, Mr A. A. Ford, Mr M. P. Gavin, R. Kent, Mr M. G. Lynch.

Assistant Trainer: Jessica Holt

Apprentice: Megan Ellingworth.

295 MR ANTHONY HONEYBALL, Beaminster
Postal: Potwell Farm, Mosterton, Beaminster, Dorset, DT8 3HG
Contacts: PHONE (01308) 867452 MOBILE (07815) 898569
E-MAIL anthony@ajhoneyballracing.co.uk WEBSITE www.ajhoneyballracing.co.uk

1 ACEY MILAN (IRE), 5, b g Milan—Strong Wishes (IRE) **Owners For Owners: Acey Milan**
2 AMINUTETOMIDNIGHT, 4, ch g Malinas (GER)—Eleven Fifty Nine **Geegeez.co.uk PA**
3 AUDORA, 8, b m Alflora (IRE)—Vixen Run (IRE) **British Racing Club**
4 AVOIR DE SOINS (IRE), 5, ch g Flemensfirth (USA)—Garranlea Maree (IRE) **Richard & Shirl Smith**
5 DEJA VUE (IRE), 5, b m Fame And Glory—Westgrove Berry (IRE) **Axom Ltd**
6 DROPS OF JUPITOR (IRE), 7, gr m Dylan Thomas—Fancy Intense **Mr & Mrs G Woodley**
7 DUHALLOW GESTURE (IRE), 7, b m King's Theatre (IRE)—Rare Gesture (IRE) **Galveston Partners**
8 FREE (FR), 5, b m Mr Sidney (USA)—Funny Feerie (FR) **Mr J. P. McManus**
9 GUSTAVIAN (IRE), 4, b g Mahler—Grange Oscar (IRE) **Decimus Racing I**
10 HIDEAWAY VIC (IRE), 6, b g Stowaway—Cailin Vic Mo Cri (IRE) **Michael & Angela Bone**
11 INDIAN BRAVE (IRE), 8, b g Definite Article—Fridays Folly (IRE) **Mr D. J. Bridger**
12 IT'S A LILY, 5, b m Sulamani (IRE)—It's A Discovery (IRE) **Glastonbury & Vyner-brooks Partnership**
13 JEPECK (IRE), 10, b g Westerner—Jenny's Jewel (IRE) **Mr J. M. Pike**
14 KAYF SERA SERA, 4, b f Kayf Tara—Fernello **Mr & Mrs G Woodley**
15 LE COEUR NET (FR), 7, ch g Network (GER)—Silverwood (FR) **Wessex Racing Club**
16 LILY THE PINK, 5, b m Malinas (GER)—Carrigeen Queen (IRE) **Mr P. G. Nicholas**
17 MARILYN MONROE (IRE), 6, b m Scorpion (IRE)—Go On Eileen (IRE) **Some Like It Hot**
18 MIDNIGHT CALLISTO, 4, br f Midnight Legend—Carrigeen Queen (IRE) **Ms G. S. Langford**
19 MIDNIGHT TUNE, 8, b m Midnight Legend—Harmonic Motion (IRE) **The Park Homes Syndicate**
20 MILAN IN MAY (IRE), 4, gr g Milan—Nina Fontenail (FR) **Richard & Shirl Smith**
21 MISTRESS MASSINI, 8, b m Dr Massini (IRE)—Mistress Willie **The Foundations Partnership**
22 MONT SEGUR (FR), 4, ch g French Fifteen (FR)—Vie de Reine (FR) **Men Of Stone**
23 MS PARFOIS (IRE), 8, ch m Mahler—Dolly Lewis **Mr M. R. Chapman**
24 MYSTICAL KNIGHT, 10, b g Kayf Tara—Dark Diva **Geegeez.co.uk PA**
25 NOCTURNAL MYTH, 5, b g Midnight Legend—Gan On **The Night Shifters**
26 PURE VISION (IRE), 8, b g Milan—Distillery Lane (IRE) **Mr J. P. McManus**
27 REGAL ENCORE (IRE), 11, b g King's Theatre (IRE)—Go On Eileen (IRE) **Mr J. P. McManus**
28 REPRESENTED (IRE), 6, b g Presenting—Lunar Path (IRE) **One Small Step**
29 SAM BROWN, 7, b g Black Sam Bellamy (IRE)—Cream Cracker **Mr T. C. Frost**
30 SHAPIRO, 6, b m Schiaparelli (GER)—Lady Turk (FR) **Burley, Buckingham, Chapman & Cobbett**
31 SOJOURN (IRE), 6, b g Getaway (GER)—Toscar (IRE) **Jon & Jacqueline Hughes**

MR ANTHONY HONEYBALL - Continued

32 **SOLSTICE SON**, 10, b g Haafhd—Karasta (IRE) **The Summer Solstice**
33 **SOLSTICE TWILIGHT**, 7, b m Milan—Twilight Eclipse (IRE) **Gill Langford & Dorothy Ritzema**
34 **SOULSAVER**, 7, ch g Recharge (IRE)—Lapina (IRE) **R. J. Matthews**
35 **SULLY D'OC AA (FR)**, 5, b g Konig Turf (GER)—Samarra d'oc (FR) **Mr J. P. McManus**
36 **TACENDA (IRE)**, 7, b m Flemensfirth (USA)—Tordasia (IRE) **Return Ta Senda**
37 **TARA WEST**, 5, b m Kayf Tara—West River (USA) **Decimus Racing II**
38 **TEMPLAR (IRE)**, 4, gr g Jeremy (USA)—Gaye Steel (IRE) **Ms G. S. Langford**
39 **URCA DE LIMA**, 6, b m Black Sam Bellamy (IRE)—Dame Fonteyn **R. W. Devlin**

Other Owners: Mr Jeremy Barber, Mr M. Bisogno, Mr J. F. Blackburn, Mrs A. P. Bone, Mr Michael Bone, Mrs J. L. Buckingham, Mr James Burley, Mr Jim Cannon, Mr M. R. Chapman, Mr A. J. Chapman, Mr Chris Cobbett, Mr Graham Craig, Mr P. K. Davis, Mr Ian Dickson, Mrs Belinda Fowler, Mr Rupert Fowler, Mrs Anne Glastonbury, Mr Kevin Glastonbury, Kevin & Anne Glastonbury, Mr M. S. Green, Mr Richard Guest, Mr A. Honeyball, Mr Jon Hughes, Mrs Jacqueline Hughes, Mr Eric Jones, Ms Gill Langford, Mr Peter Lloyd, Racing Club Ltd, Mrs D. J. Ritzema, Mr J. P. Romans, Mrs S A Smith, Mr R S Smith, Mr Varlien Vyner-Brooks, Mr Gary Woodley, Mrs D. Woodley.

Assistant Trainer: Rachael Honeyball (07813) 984418

Jockey (NH): Aidan Coleman, David Noonan. **Conditional:** Rex Dingle.

296	**MR PAUL HOWLING, Newmarket**
	Postal: Mulligans Yard, Cowlinge, Newmarket, Suffolk, CB8 9HP
	Contacts: MOBILE (07866) 674469

1 **ANAHLINE**, 4, b f Rail Link—Al Rayanah **Mr M. Bartram**
2 **AT YOUR SERVICE**, 5, b g Frankel—Crystal Gaze (IRE) **Chelsea Banham Pre Training ltd**
3 **ENZO (IRE)**, 4, b g Exceed And Excel (AUS)—Zamhrear **Power Geneva Ltd**
4 **FAIR POWER (IRE)**, 5, b g Power—Pitrizzia **Power Geneva Ltd**
5 **HOLY TIBER (IRE)**, 4, b f Holy Roman Emperor (IRE)—Quiet Waters (USA) **Mr M. Bartram**
6 **INDEPENDENCE DAY (IRE)**, 6, b h Dansili—Damson (IRE) **Chelsea Banham Pre Training ltd**
7 **LADY OF YORK**, 5, b m Sir Percy—Parsonagehotelyork (IRE) **Miss C. A. Calton**
8 **MAKAMBE (IRE)**, 4, gr g Dark Angel (IRE)—Pink Diva (IRE) **Mr T. F. Parrett**
9 **MIAELLA**, 4, b f Captain Gerrard (IRE)—Sweet Applause (IRE) **Mr M. Bartram**
10 **OFFICER IN COMMAND (USA)**, 13, b br g Officer (USA)—Luv to Stay n Chat (USA) **Miss C. A. Calton**
11 **SLIPALONGTREVASKIS**, 6, b g Kheleyf (USA)—Tilly's Dream **VSN Ltd**
12 **VOICE OF A LEADER (IRE)**, 8, b g Danehill Dancer (IRE)—
Thewaytosanjose (IRE) **Chelsea Banham Pre Training ltd**

THREE-YEAR-OLDS

13 **CHOCCO STAR (IRE)**, b f Lawman (FR)—Sharplaw Star **Chelsea Banham Pre Training ltd**
14 **CRAKADAWN**, ch f Excelebration (IRE)—Atacama Sunrise **Chelsea Banham Pre Training ltd**

297	**MRS JO HUGHES, Lambourn**
	Postal: Hill House Stables, Folly Road, Lambourn, Hungerford, Berkshire, RG17 8QE
	Contacts: PHONE (01488) 71444 FAX (01488) 71103 MOBILE (07900) 680189
	E-MAIL johughes3@aol.co.uk WEBSITE www.johughesracing.co.uk

1 **ALESSANDRO ALLORI (IRE)**, 4, ch g Dawn Approach (IRE)—Truly Mine (IRE) **Mrs C. C. Regalado-Gonzalez**
2 **ALLITERATION**, 4, ch g Poet's Voice—Duo de Choc (IRE) **Dalwhinnie Racing, Tim & Miranda Johnson**
3 **ALONSO CANO (IRE)**, 4, b g High Chaparral (IRE)—Awjila **Mrs C. C. Regalado-Gonzalez**
4 **CALEDONIA DUCHESS**, 6, b m Dutch Art—Granuaile O'malley (IRE) **Isla & Colin Cage**
5 **CALEDONIA LAIRD**, 8, b g Firebreak—Granuaile O'malley (IRE) **Isla & Colin Cage**
6 **CAPE GRECO (USA)**, 4, b g Cape Blanco (IRE)—High Walden (USA) **Joe Smith, Jimmy Smith, Jo Hughes**
7 **CAPTAIN KISSINGER**, 4, b g Captain Gerrard (IRE)—Nigella **Mrs J. F. Hughes**
8 **COMPASS HILL (USA)**, 7, ch g Mizzen Mast (USA)—Zamindarling (USA) **Mrs C. C. Regalado-Gonzalez**
9 **DIABLO DE ROUHET (FR)**, 6, b g Great Pretender (IRE)—
Querelle d'estruval (FR) **Business Moves Group & David White**
10 **FLOR DE SEDA (FR)**, 4, b f George Vancouver (USA)—Toile de Soie (FR) **Mrs J. F. Hughes**
11 **GET EVEN**, 4, b f Multiplex—Retaliator **Richard Kent & Jo Hughes**
12 **LEFORTOVO (FR)**, 6, b g Arcano (IRE)—Lorientaise (IRE) **Mrs C. C. Regalado-Gonzalez**
13 **PEGGY'S ANGEL**, 4, b f Captain Gerrard (IRE)—Dora's Sister (IRE) **Dalwhinnie Bloodstock Limited**

MRS JO HUGHES - Continued

14 **ROCK ICON**, 6, b g Sixties Icon—Monashee Rock (IRE) **Mr M. J. Goggin**
15 **WHITE FEATHER**, 4, ch g Bated Breath—Just Wood (FR) **J. Smith**

THREE-YEAR-OLDS

16 **ALATIA (IRE)**, b g Moohaajim (IRE)—Hatria (IRE) **Mr H S Maan & Jo Hughes**
17 **CHAMPAGNE CASTLE (IRE)**, b f Dragon Pulse (IRE)—Quiet Dream (USA) **John Wardle & Jo Hughes**
18 **CINQUAIN**, b f Poet's Voice—Duo de Choc (IRE) **Mrs J. F. Hughes**
19 **DANSEUR D'ARGENT (FR)**, gr f Le Havre (IRE)—Sardinelle (FR) **P & L Partners & Jo Hughes**
20 **GRANDEE DAISY**, ch f Sepoy (AUS)—Chili Dip **Mark Goggin & Jo Hughes**
21 **HAWK CLIFF (FR)**, b g Panis (USA)—Valse Mystique (IRE) **Mrs J. F. Hughes**
22 **JOJO (IRE)**, b f Battle of Marengo (IRE)—Swingsky (IRE) **P & L Partners**
23 **MIDGHAM**, b g Heeraat (IRE)—Kallisima **David Klein & Jo Hughes**
24 **NEFYN BEACH (IRE)**, b f Big Bad Bob (IRE)—Lucky Date (IRE) **Tim & Miranda Johnson**
25 **STAR AT MIDNIGHT**, b f Heeraat (IRE)—Intense Feeling (IRE) **John Wardle & Jo Hughes**
26 **VELVET VIXEN (IRE)**, br f Requinto (IRE)—Theebah (USA) **Tim & Miranda Johnson**

Other Owners: Business Moves Group Ltd, Mr C. J. Cage, Mrs I. Cage, Mr T. Johnson, Mrs M. Johnson, R. Kent, Mr D. A. Klein, Mr A. T. Larkin, Mr H. S. Maan, Mr G. Pickering, Mr J. D. A. Smith, T. J. Wardle, Mr D. White.

Assistant Trainer: Paul Blockley (07778 318295)

298	**MR RICHARD HUGHES, Upper Lambourn**

Postal: **Weathercock House, Upper Lambourn, Hungerford, Berkshire, RG17 8QT**
Contacts: **PHONE (01488) 71198 MOBILE (07768) 894828**
E-MAIL office@richardhughesracing.co.uk WEBSITE www.richardhughesracing.co.uk

1 **AMITIE WALTZ (FR)**, 7, b g Sinndar (IRE)—Lia Waltz (FR) **Third Time Lucky**
2 **APPENZELLER (USA)**, 4, gr g Mizzen Mast (USA)—Uforia (USA) **Mrs D J Fleming & Partner**
3 **CREEK HARBOUR (IRE)**, 4, b g Kodiac—Allegheny Creek (IRE) **Mr Richard Hughes**
4 **GEORGE OF HEARTS (FR)**, 4, gr g Kendargent (FR)—Bugie d'amore **Mr D Campbell & Mr D Waters**
5 **GETBACK IN PARIS (IRE)**, 6, ch g Galileo (IRE)—Elusive Wave (IRE) **G. B. Firmager & G. H. Firmager**
6 **GLENDEVON (USA)**, 4, ch g Scat Daddy (USA)—Flip Flop (FR) **Campbell, Clarke, Rexton & Waters**
7 **GOLD FILIGREE (IRE)**, 4, gr f Dark Angel (IRE)—Gold Lace (IRE) **Galloway, Lawrence, Merritt & Mrs Blake**
8 **HAREEQ**, 4, b c New Approach (IRE)—Fallen Star **Rashed Aldaban**
9 **HELLOVAQUEEN**, 4, gr f Hellvelyn—Regal Quest (IRE) **Mr A. F. Horsington**
10 **JACK TAYLOR (IRE)**, 4, b g Invincible Spirit (IRE)—Glory Power (IRE) **Mr Anthony Hogarth**
11 **JASHMA (IRE)**, 5, b g Power—Daganya (IRE) **M Clarke, S Geraghty, J Jeffries**
12 **KATH'S LUSTRE**, 4, b f Dick Turpin (IRE)—It's Dubai Dolly **Mr Richard Hughes**
13 **MOTAJAASID (IRE)**, 4, b g Harbour Watch (IRE)—Cape Joy (IRE) **Graham Doyle & Hazel Lawrence**
14 **MR MINERALS**, 4, b g Poet's Voice—River Song (USA) **Mr P. R. Gallagher**
15 **PTARMIGAN RIDGE**, 5, b g Kyllachy—Joshua's Princess **Mr Michael Williams**
16 **SOGHAN (IRE)**, 5, br g Cape Cross (IRE)—Quiet Dream (USA) **The Queens**
17 **STANLEY**, 6, ch g Sea The Stars (IRE)—Deirdre **Normandie Stud Ltd**

THREE-YEAR-OLDS

18 **ANTIDOTE (IRE)**, gr g Dark Angel (IRE)—Mood Indigo (IRE) **Mr Anthony Hogarth**
19 **BALLYLEMON (IRE)**, b c Champs Elysees—Athreyaa **Graham Doyle & Hazel Lawrence**
20 B g Le Havre (IRE)—Bugie d'amore **Mr Danny Waters**
21 **CANFORD DANCER**, b f Canford Cliffs (IRE)—Petite Nymphe **The Lakota Partnership & Mrs J Blake**
22 **CHARLIE ARTHUR (IRE)**, b c Slade Power (IRE)—Musical Bar (IRE) **L Turland and A Smith**
23 **COASTGUARD WATCH (FR)**, b c Olympic Glory (IRE)—Miss Hygrove (IRE) **Mr H. Robin Heffer**
24 **DANDY LAD (IRE)**, ch g Dandy Man (IRE)—Lucky Pipit **Mr Peter Crane**
25 **FINTAS**, b c Lope de Vega (IRE)—Free Rein **Sheikh Abdullah Almalek Alsabah**
26 **HARBOUR SPIRIT (FR)**, b g Charm Spirit (IRE)—Save Me The Waltz (FR) **The Heffer Syndicate**
27 **JAILBREAK (IRE)**, b c Lawman (FR)—Luminata (IRE) **Biddestone Racing II**
28 **KADIZ (IRE)**, b f Lope de Vega (IRE)—Looby Loo **The High Flyers**
29 **KENOUGHRY (FR)**, b g Kendargent (FR)—Meandra (IRE) **Mr John Henwood**
30 **KNOCKACULLION (USA)**, b c Bernardini (USA)—Vole Vole Monamour (USA) **Gallagher Bloodstock Limited**
31 **LADY MADISON (IRE)**, b f No Nay Never (USA)—Sparkling Rock (IRE) **M Clarke, P Munnelly & D Waters**
32 **LIGHT UP OUR STARS (IRE)**, ch c Rip Van Winkle (IRE)—Shine Like A Star **Dereck Boocock**
33 **LITTLE ROCK (IRE)**, b g Zebedee—Lakatoi **Mr M. H. Dixon**
34 **MARCUS AGRIPPA (USA)**, b c War Command (USA)—Aurelia **M Clarke, P Munnelly & D Waters**
35 **MISS ENIGMA (IRE)**, b f Kodiac—Mysteriousness (FR) **Sir Martyn Arbib & Everett Partnership**
36 **MORE THAN LIKELY**, b f Coach House (IRE)—Moss Likely (IRE) **H Pinniger & Peter Cook**

MR RICHARD HUGHES - Continued

37 PECORINO, ch c Intello (GER)—Puff Pastry **Normandie Stud Ltd**
38 PINK ICEBURG (IRE), b f Kodiac—Twinkling Ice (USA) **Mr Jaber Abdullah**
39 PRINCE OF ROME (IRE), gr c Lethal Force (IRE)—Garraun (IRE) **John & Jordan Lund**
40 PUZZLE, b g Paco Boy (IRE)—Appleton Drove (USA) **Her Majesty The Queen**
41 PYTILIA (USA), gr f Mizzen Mast (USA)—Infanta (IRE) **K Dhunjibhoy & Z Dhunjibhoy**
42 RAGSTONE COWBOY (IRE), b g Slade Power (IRE)—Three Decades (IRE) **Gallagher Bloodstock Limited**
43 ROCK BOTTOM, ch c Coach House (IRE)—La Tinta Bay **Mr R P Gallagher & Partner**
44 SATISFYING (IRE), b f Fast Company (IRE)—Misscomplacent **The Boys**
45 SCAT KING (IRE), b g Scat Daddy (USA)—Come To Heel (IRE) **Mr Jaber Abdullah**
46 SCATTERBRAINED (USA), ch c Scat Daddy (USA)—Cool Ghoul (USA) **H Pinniger, Peter Cook & Partner**
47 SUNSPRITE (IRE), b c Kodiac—Dutch Rose (IRE) **Mr Jaber Abdullah**
48 SWISS PRIDE (IRE), b g Swiss Spirit—Encore Encore (FR) **Mr Don Churston & Mr Ray Greatorex**
49 TOP BREEZE (IRE), b c Gale Force Ten—Shamarlane **Life's A Breeze**
50 TOROLIGHT, b g Toronado (IRE)—Tuscan Light **Mr D. Thorpe**
51 TWENTY YEARS ON, b g Rip Van Winkle (IRE)—Distinctive **HP Racing Twenty Years On**
52 UNCLE JERRY, b c Kyllachy—News Desk **Thames Boys**
53 WINTER LIGHT, ch f Bated Breath—Moonglow **Cheveley Park Stud**
54 ZERO DOUBT (GER), b g Dabirsim (FR)—Zenaat **Williams & Reddington**

TWO-YEAR-OLDS

55 B c 19/3 Kyllachy—Ardessie (Bahamian Bounty) (52380) **Mr K Lawrence & Mr P Merritt**
56 B g 2/3 Showcasing—Aristoteliciennne (IRE) (Acclamation) (42857) **Mr Peter Cook**
57 BERMUDA SCHWARTZ, gr c 17/3 Outstrip—Almaviva (IRE) (Grand Lodge (USA)) (36190) **Mr Alex Smith**
58 B c 9/3 Raven's Pass (USA)—Bold Bidder (Indesatchel (IRE)) (40000)
59 BYTHEBAY, b c 26/3 Cable Bay (IRE)—Kristollini (Bertolini (USA)) **Grace Muir & Partners**
60 CRANBERRY, ch f 1/4 Toronado (IRE)—Raymi Coya (CAN) (Van Nistelrooy (USA)) **Her Majesty The Queen**
61 DAKOTA MOON (IRE), b c 6/3 Shamardal (USA)—
    Moon Over Water (IRE) (Galileo (IRE)) (70000) **The Dakota Partnership**
62 DANDY DANCER, b c 15/2 Dandy Man (IRE)—Last of The Dixies (Halling (USA)) (48000) **John & Jordan Lund**
63 B gr f 10/3 Lethal Force (IRE)—Danehill Revival (Pivotal) **Cheveley Park Stud**
64 B f 19/2 Mukhadram—Dhuyoof (Sinndar (IRE)) **Mr Jaber Abdullah**
65 B f 26/3 Coach House (IRE)—Dolly Daydreamer (Equiano (FR)) (761) **J Magee & Partner**
66 EDEN PACE (IRE), b c 13/2 Elzaam (AUS)—
    Black Meyeden (FR) (Black Minnaloushe (USA)) (60000) **Aristotle's Elements**
67 Ch f 3/3 Night of Thunder (IRE)—Elegant Peace (IRE) (Intense Focus (USA)) (38095) **Mr Jaber Abdullah**
68 B c 18/2 Dark Angel (IRE)—Folga (Atraf) (115000) **Mr D. Waters**
69 B f 9/4 Lope de Vega (IRE)—Jewel In The Sand (IRE) (Bluebird (USA)) (78000) **Rashed Aldaban**
70 LADY LYNETTA (IRE), b f 11/3 Tamayuz—Cristal Fashion (IRE) (Jeremy (USA)) (67424) **Mr Khalifa Dasmal**
71 B c 22/4 Gutaifan (IRE)—Lathaat (Dubai Destination (USA)) (30476) **Mrs Philip Snow & Partners**
72 Ch c 11/4 Kyllachy—Light Hearted (Green Desert (USA)) (62000) **Sheikh Abdullah Almalek Alsabah**
73 MAC MCCARTHY (IRE), ch c 25/2 Anjaal—
    Kitty Softpaws (IRE) (Royal Applause) (14285) **Mr R Gander & Partner**
74 Ch c 28/4 Sea The Stars (IRE)—
    Madhulika (FR) (Marchand de Sable (USA)) (72000) **Sheikh Abdullah Almalek Alsabah**
75 B f 20/2 Dark Angel (IRE)—Magic Florence (IRE) (Zebedee) (65000) **Sheikh Abdullah Almalek Alsabah**
76 B c 1/3 Charm Spirit (IRE)—Manyara (Manduro (GER)) (65000)
77 MAORI KNIGHT (IRE), b c 19/3 Camelot—
    Chatham Islands (USA) (Elusive Quality (USA)) (69110) **White Beech Farm**
78 B f 12/4 Footstepsinthesand—Meadow (Green Desert (USA)) (50000) **Sheikh Abdullah Almalek Alsabah**
79 Ch c 30/3 Kyllachy—Modify (New Approach (IRE)) (55000) **Sheikh Abdullah Almalek Alsabah**
80 B c 3/3 Swiss Spirit—Night Premiere (IRE) (Night Shift (USA)) (800) **Rosemary Greener**
81 B c 14/5 Heeraat (IRE)—Nut (FR) (Fasliyev (USA)) **Mark Bloomfield**
82 B c 10/4 Hallowed Crown (AUS)—
    Queen Wasp (IRE) (Shamardal (USA)) (52000) **M Clarke, P Munnelly & D Waters**
83 B f 1/3 Dunkerque (FR)—Salome (FR) (Fuisse (FR)) **Mark Bloomfield**
84 Gr c 28/3 Gutaifan (IRE)—Scarlet Rosefinch (Cockney Rebel (IRE)) (20000) **Mr Jaber Abdullah**
85 B f 4/2 Toronado (IRE)—Sciolina (IRE) (Oratorio (IRE)) (27000) **The Low Flyers**
86 SO I TOLD YOU (IRE), b f 26/4 Gleneagles (IRE)—
    Nocturne (GER) (Rock of Gibraltar (IRE)) **Flaxman Stables Ireland Ltd**
87 SOUTER JOHNNIE (IRE), b c 11/3 Elzaam (AUS)—
    Too Close (IRE) (Danehill Dancer (IRE)) (26666) **The Caledonian Racing Society**
88 SWINLEY (IRE), br c 28/4 Dragon Pulse (IRE)—
    Invincibile Stella (IRE) (Invincible Spirit (IRE)) (42140) **Clarke, Devine, Hughes & Peters**
89 TAFISH (IRE), b c 10/2 War Command (USA)—Zigarra (Halling (USA)) (80066) **Mr Jaber Abdullah**
90 TWICE AS LIKELY, b f 12/3 Tamayuz—Xaphania (Sakhee (USA)) (10000) **H. Pinniger**

MR RICHARD HUGHES - Continued

91 **TYPHOON LILY (IRE)**, ch f 15/1 G Force (IRE)—
        Rise Up Lotus (IRE) (Zebedee) (30476) **Lawrence, Galloway, Dadswell, Blake**
92 B f 27/4 Morpheus—Unfortunate (Komaite (USA)) (23000)
93 Ch c 16/3 Society Rock (IRE)—Village Singer (USA) (Rahy (USA)) (11428) **Weathercock House Partnership**

Other Owners: M. Arbib, Mr D. Barrett, Mrs J. A. Blake, Mr Tim Bostwick, Mrs Gill Bostwick, Mr M. Burke, Mr D. A. Campbell, Cedar Investments Limited, Mr M. Clarke, Mr P. D. Conway, Mr J. Devine, Mr Z. K. Dhunjibhoy, Mr K. Dhunjibhoy, Mr G. J. Doyle, Mr M. M. Everett, Mr G. D. D. Everett, Mr G. B. Firmager, Mr G. H. Firmager, Mr Ivan Forster, Mr B. S. Galloway, Mr David Gallyer, R. A. Gander, Mr S. Geraghty, Mr Jon Gwyther, Mr R. Hannon, Mr James Jeffries, Mr K. Lawrence, Mr J. E. Lund, Mr Eamonn Malone, Mr P. D. Merritt, Mr M. J. Mitchell, Mrs K. J. Morton, Mr P. A. Munnelly, Mr G. O'Sullivan, Mr P. Peters, W. H. Ponsonby, Mr John Reddington, Mr A. Regan, Mr R. J. Rexton, Ms F. E. Rogers, Mr D. W. Rogers, Miss B. A. Snow, Mrs J. I. Snow, Star Pointe Ltd, Mr G. P. Triefus.

Assistant Trainer: Patrick McEwan

Jockey (flat): Shane Kelly. **Apprentice:** Finley Marsh, George Rooke.

---

299   MRS SARAH HUMPHREY, West Wratting
Postal: Yen Hall Farm, West Wratting, Cambridge, Cambridgeshire, CB21 5LP
Contacts: **PHONE (01223) 291445 MOBILE (07798) 702484**
E-MAIL sarah@yenhallfarm.com WEBSITE www.sarahhumphrey.co.uk

1 4, B f Shirocco (GER)—Academy Miss (IRE)
2 **ARCADIAN SEA (IRE)**, 5, b g Born To Sea (IRE)—Drombeg Dawn (IRE) **The Louis P Partnership**
3 **AVOCET (IRE)**, 6, b m Artie Schiller (USA)—Striking Example (USA) **The Avocet Partnership**
4 4, B g Mountain High (IRE)—Benedicta Rose (IRE)
5 **BISOUBISOU**, 7, b m Champs Elysees—Marathea (FR) **Yen Hall Farm Racing**
6 **BRECON HILL (IRE)**, 6, b g Arcano (IRE)—Bryanstown Girl (IRE) **The Brecon Hill Partnership**
7 **CALL ME TJ**, 5, b g Mawatheeq (USA)—Silver Lily (IRE) **Silver Lily Bloodstock**
8 **HIDDEN PASSAGE (IRE)**, 7, b m Stowaway—More Hope (IRE) **Mrs S. J. Humphrey**
9 **HIGHWAY STAR (FR)**, 7, b g Vision d'etat (FR)—Lyli Rose (FR) **Yen Hall Farm Racing**
10 **LEGEND TO BE**, 9, b g Midnight Legend—Pentasilea **Mrs S. J. Humphrey**
11 **LEGENDOFTHEKNIGHT**, 7, b g Midnight Legend—Pentasilea **Mrs S. J. Humphrey**
12 **LOCAL SHOW (IRE)**, 11, br g Oscar (IRE)—Loughaderra Rose (IRE) **Mrs S. J. Humphrey**
13 **PARSONAL (IRE)**, 6, b g Oscar (IRE)—Rith Ar Aghaidh (IRE) **The Friday Lunch Club**
14 **RUMBLE B (IRE)**, 5, b g Presenting—John's Eliza (IRE) **Mrs S. J. Humphrey**
15 4, Gr g Mawatheeq (USA)—Silver Lily **Silver Lily Bloodstock**
16 **STONEBRIGG LEGEND**, 7, b m Midnight Legend—Forget The Ref (IRE) **Yen Hall Farm Racing**
17 **THE HAPPY CHAPPY (IRE)**, 8, b g Flemensfirth (USA)—Native Design (IRE) **The Happy Folders**
18 **VIRNON**, 8, b g Virtual—Freedom Song **Mr M. J. Pearce**

THREE-YEAR-OLDS

19 Ch f Nayef (USA)—Kompete

TWO-YEAR-OLDS

20 Gr g 19/2 Casamento (IRE)—Little Annie (Compton Place)

Other Owners: Mr & Mrs R. Benfield, Dr R. C. Britton, Mr P. Darlington, Mr P. Denley, Mr R. Fuller, Mr L. Greenlees, Mrs S. H. Greenlees, Mr A. R. Humphrey, Mrs S. J. Humphrey, Mrs E. Reid, Mrs L. Thomas, Mr G. Thomas, Mr J. Thomas.

Assistant Trainer: Mr A. R. Humphrey

Jockey (NH): Sean Bowen, Aidan Coleman, Daryl Jacob, Nick Scholfield. **Amateur:** Mr W. Humphrey.

---

300   MR KEVIN HUNTER, Natland
Postal: Larkrigg, Natland, Cumbria, LA9 7QS
Contacts: **PHONE (01539) 560245**

1 **CATACLYSM (IRE)**, 9, b g Captain Rio—Marilaya (IRE) **J. K. Hunter**
2 **DAVID JOHN**, 8, b g Overbury (IRE)—Molly's Secret **J. K. Hunter**
3 **FAIR OAKS**, 7, gr m Fair Mix (IRE)—School Days **J. K. Hunter**

301 **MISS LAURA HURLEY, Tiverton**
Postal: Ringstone Stables, Oakford, Tiverton, Devon, EX16 9EU
Contacts: MOBILE (07999) 693322
E-MAIL lauramhurley@hotmail.com

1 CANDYMAN CAN (IRE), 9, b g Holy Roman Emperor (IRE)—Palwina (FR) **Mrs R. E. Hurley**
2 CATCHIN TIME (IRE), 11, b g Chineur (FR)—Lady Dane (IRE) **Mrs R. E. Hurley**
3 LITTLE ROBIN (IRE), 7, b br m Robin des Pres (FR)—Soi (IRE) **Mrs R. E. Hurley**

302 **MR ROGER INGRAM, Epsom**
Postal: Wendover Stables, Burgh Heath Road, Epsom, Surrey, KT17 4LX
Contacts: PHONE (01372) 748505 or (01372) 749157 FAX (01372) 748505
MOBILE (07773) 665980 / (07715) 993911
E-MAIL roger.ingram.racing@virgin.net WEBSITE www.rogeringramracing.com

1 ARGENT BLEU, 4, b g Steele Tango (USA)—Silver Marizah (IRE) **Burgh Heath Associates**
2 AWESOME ROCK (IRE), 10, ch g Rock of Gibraltar (IRE)—Dangerous Diva (IRE) **Mr M. F. Cruse**
3 CHARLIE ALPHA (IRE), 5, b g Dandy Man (IRE)—Maroussies Rock **Mr P. J. Burton**
4 CRISTAL PALLAS CAT (IRE), 4, b g Kodiac—Flower of Kent (USA) **Titan Partnership**
5 DUKES MEADOW, 8, b g Pastoral Pursuits—Figura **The Stargazers**
6 JUST AN IDEA (IRE), 5, b g Lilbourne Lad (IRE)—Emreliya (IRE) **Miss C. Swift**
7 STAY IN THE LIGHT, 4, b f Showcasing—Starlight Walk **Mr M. F. Cruse**

THREE-YEAR-OLDS

8 MISS POLLYANNA (IRE), ch f Helmet (AUS)—Ivy Batty (IRE) **Mrs Cathy Hallam & Wendover Racing**

Other Owners: Mr S. J. Appleyard, Ms C. C. Fagerstrom, Mrs C. E. Hallam, Mr D. A. Hazelton, Mrs S. Ingram, Mr R. Ingram, M. W. Joy, Mr D. Ross-Watt, Mr S. Steele.

Assistant Trainer: Sharon Ingram

Apprentice: Rhiain Ingram.

303 **MR DEAN IVORY, Radlett**
Postal: Harper Lodge Farm, Harper Lane, Radlett, Hertfordshire, WD7 7HU
Contacts: PHONE (01923) 855337 FAX (01923) 852470 MOBILE (07785) 118658
E-MAIL deanivoryracing@gmail.com WEBSITE www.deanivoryracing.co.uk

1 BADENSCOTH, 5, b g Foxwedge (AUS)—Twice Upon A Time **P. J. Skinner**
2 CLASSIC CHARM, 4, b f Rip Van Winkle (IRE)—Classic Lass **Gracelands Stud Partnership**
3 DADDY'S DAUGHTER (CAN), 4, b f Scat Daddy (USA)—Golden Stripe (CAN) **Michael & Heather Yarrow**
4 DARK MAGIC, 5, b g Invincible Spirit (IRE)—Dark Promise **Heather & Michael Yarrow**
5 DON'T LOOK DOWN, 4, gr g Aussie Rules (USA)—Miss Katmandu (IRE) **Solario Racing (Tring)**
6 DOR'S LAW, 6, b m Lawman (FR)—Law of Chance **Mrs D. A. Carter**
7 EIRENE, 4, b f Declaration of War (USA)—Za Za Zoom (USA) **Mr M. J. Yarrow**
8 ELJADDAAF (IRE), 8, b g Shamardal (USA)—Almansoora (USA) **Wentdale Ltd & Mrs L A Ivory**
9 FANTASTIC FLYER, 4, br f Harbour Watch (IRE)—Lucky Flyer **Mrs K. M. Young**
10 FIGHTING TEMERAIRE (IRE), 6, b g Invincible Spirit (IRE)—Hot Ticket (IRE) **Michael & Heather Yarrow**
11 FLAMING SPEAR (IRE), 7, ch g Lope de Vega (IRE)—Elshamms **Mr A. G. Bloom**
12 HELLO GIRL, 4, ch f Bated Breath—Elysee (IRE) **Mr A. Chapman**
13 INCREDIBLE DREAM (IRE), 6, b g Vale of York (IRE)—Finnmark **Black Star Racing**
14 KADRIZZI (FR), 6, ch g Hurricane Cat (USA)—Kadiania (FR) **Mr A Chapman & Wentdale Limited**
15 LANCELOT DU LAC (ITY), 9, b g Shamardal (USA)—Dodie Mae (USA) **Michael & Heather Yarrow**
16 LIBRISA BREEZE, 7, gr g Mount Nelson—Bruxcalina (FR) **Mr A. G. Bloom**
17 LOTHARIO, 5, gr g Dark Angel (IRE)—Kisses For Me (IRE) **Michael & Heather Yarrow**
18 LUCYMAI, 6, b m Multiplex—Miss Lesley **Mr R. Beadle**
19 NEZAR (IRE), 8, ch g Mastercraftsman (IRE)—Teddy Bears Picnic **Mrs D. A. Carter**
20 NICKY BABY (IRE), 5, gr g Dark Angel (IRE)—Moon Club (IRE) **Mrs D. A. Carter**
21 ONE COOL DADDY (USA), 4, b c Scat Daddy (USA)—Coup (USA) **Michael & Heather Yarrow**
22 OVERBECK (IRE), 4, b g Camelot—Brigid (USA) **Mr D. K. Ivory**
23 RED COSSACK (CAN), 8, ch g Rebellion—Locata (USA) **Mrs G. Thomas**
24 SHANAKILL STAR (IRE), 5, b m Lord Shanakill (USA)—Lola Rosa (IRE) **Mr B Edwards & Mr L Doolan**
25 SIR PRIZE, 4, b g Sir Percy—Three Sugars (AUS) **Michael & Heather Yarrow**

MR DEAN IVORY - Continued

26 **SIX STRINGS**, 5, b g Requinto (IRE)—Island Music (IRE) **Crown Connoisseurs**
27 **SOARING SPIRITS (IRE)**, 9, ch g Tamayuz—Follow My Lead **Mrs D. A. Carter**
28 **SPRING ROMANCE (IRE)**, 4, b br g Zebedee—Love And Devotion **Solario Racing (Berkhamsted)**
29 **STAKE ACCLAIM (IRE)**, 7, b g Acclamation—Golden Legacy (IRE) **Mr M. J. Yarrow**
30 **TANGRAMM**, 7, b br g Sakhee's Secret—Tripti (IRE) **Mr R. Beadle**
31 **THE CRUIX (IRE)**, 4, ch g Galileo (IRE)—Walklikeanegyptian (IRE) **Mr A. L. Cohen**
32 **TROPICS (USA)**, 11, ch g Speightstown (USA)—Taj Aire (USA) **Mr D. K. Ivory**
33 **VILLETTE (IRE)**, 5, b m Sixties Icon—Spinning Lucy (IRE) **Mr D. K. Ivory**
34 **WOTAMADAM**, 4, gr f Lethal Force (IRE)—Rhapsilian **Mr D. C. Mead**
35 **YIMOU (IRE)**, 4, b g Kodiac—Heroine Chic (IRE) **Mr A. L. Cohen**
36 **YOLO STAR (IRE)**, 4, br f Society Rock (IRE)—Pearly Brooks **Heather & Michael Yarrow**

THREE-YEAR-OLDS

37 **ARCHDEACON**, b g Archipenko (USA)—Akdarena **K T Ivory & Michael Yarrow**
38 **BRUYERE (FR)**, b f Exceed And Excel (AUS)—Pale Mimosa (IRE) **Heather & Michael Yarrow**
39 **CLASSIC STAR**, b g Sea The Moon (GER)—Classic Lass **Cynthia Smith & Radlett Racing**
40 **DOR'S DIAMOND**, gr g Gregorian (IRE)—Primavera **Mrs D. A. Carter**
41 **FANCY FLYER**, b g Archipenko (USA)—Lucky Flyer **Cynthia Smith & Radlett Racing**
42 **GREGORIAN GIRL**, b f Gregorian (IRE)—Jackie's Opera (FR) **Skipsey, Franks & Roper & Mr A Chapman**
43 **IVORY STAR**, b f Lethal Force (IRE)—Love Me Tender **Mr D. K. Ivory**
44 **JACK LOUIE**, ch g Mazameer (IRE)—Fleetwood Nix **Mr R. Beadle**
45 B f Epaulette (AUS)—Maisie's Moon (USA)
46 B c Shamardal (USA)—Punita (USA) **K T Ivory & Dean Ivory**
47 B f Albaasil (IRE)—Steel Breeze (IRE)
48 **SWISS CHIME**, b f Swiss Spirit—Dolly Daydreamer **K T Ivory & Mrs Valerie Hubbard**
49 **VENA D'AMORE (IRE)**, b f Exceed And Excel (AUS)—Sues Surprise (IRE) **Heather & Michael Yarrow**

TWO-YEAR-OLDS

50 **ALSUKAR**, b f 7/3 Brazen Beau (AUS)—
                            Three Sugars (AUS) (Starcraft (NZ)) (16000) **K T Ivory & Mrs Valerie Hubbard**
51 **CLASSIC DREAM (IRE)**, b f 20/2 Rock of Gibraltar (IRE)—
                            Classic Lass (Dr Fong (USA)) (2000) **Gracelands Stud Partnership**
52 **DOVER LIGHT**, ch c 29/4 Sir Prancealot (IRE)—
                            Miss Mediator (USA) (Consolidator (USA)) (22000) **K T Ivory & Mrs Valerie Hubbard**
53 **FLASHY FLYER**, ch f 23/2 Helmet (AUS)—Lucky Flyer (Lucky Story (USA)) (3500) **Gracelands Stud Partnership**
54 B c 18/3 Coach House (IRE)—Ojai (IRE) (Big Bad Bob (IRE)) (7619) **Mr A. L. Cohen**
55 B c 20/4 Garswood—Pachanga (Inchinor) (15000)

Other Owners: Mr P. A. Brend, Mr S. Calton, Dean Ivory Racing Ltd, Mr L. J. Doolan, Mr S. K. I. Double, Mr B. S. F. Edwards, Mr J. Gunnell, Mrs V. Hubbard, Mrs L. A. Ivory, K. T. Ivory, Radlett Racing, Mr N. A. Rooney, Mr D. R. Skipsey, Skipsey, Franks and Roper, Mrs C. Smith, Wentdale Limited, Mr M. E. White, Mrs H. Yarrow, R. V. Young.

Assistant Trainer: Chris Scally

Apprentice: Jack Duern.

---

304 MISS TINA JACKSON, Loftus
Postal: Tick Hill Farm, Liverton, Loftus, Saltburn, Cleveland, TS13 4TG
Contacts: **PHONE (01287) 644952 MOBILE (07774) 106906**

1 **GLACEON (IRE)**, 4, b f Zoffany (IRE)—Ihtiraam (IRE) **Peter Jeffers & Howard Thompson**
2 **GRIMTHORPE**, 8, ch g Alflora (IRE)—Sally Scally **Mr H. L. Thompson**
3 **IVORS INVOLVEMENT (IRE)**, 7, b g Amadeus Wolf—Summer Spice (IRE) **Mr H. L. Thompson**
4 **JAMIH**, 4, ch g Intello (GER)—Hannda (IRE) **Peter Jeffers & Howard Thompson**
5 **JAMIL (IRE)**, 4, b g Dansili—Havant **Peter Jeffers & Howard Thompson**
6 **JAN DE HEEM**, 9, ch g Dutch Art—Shasta **H L Thompson & D Tucker**
7 **KHITAAMY (IRE)**, 5, b g Approve (IRE)—Halliwell House **Peter Jeffers & Howard Thompson**
8 **MADAM SCULLY**, 6, ch m Flying Legend (USA)—Sally Scally **Mr H. L. Thompson**
9 **MR WIGGINS**, 7, ch g Alflora (IRE)—Winnie Wild **Miss T. Jackson**
10 **POINT OF WOODS**, 8, b g Showcasing—Romantic Myth **Mr H. L. Thompson**
11 **PURPLE HARRY**, 11, gr g Sir Harry Lewis (USA)—Ellfiedick **Mr H. L. Thompson**
12 **ROSY RYAN (IRE)**, 9, b m Tagula (IRE)—Khaydariya (IRE) **Mr H. L. Thompson**
13 **SORY**, 12, b g Sakhee (USA)—Rule Britannia **Mr H. L. Thompson**

MISS TINA JACKSON - Continued

14 **THOMAS CRANMER (USA)**, 5, b g Hard Spun (USA)—
House of Grace (USA) **Peter Jeffers & Howard Thompson**
15 **YOUNOSO**, 8, b g Alflora (IRE)—Teeno Nell **Mr H. L. Thompson**

THREE-YEAR-OLDS

16 **HAVANA BAY**, b c Havana Gold (IRE)—Bisou **Mr H. L. Thompson**

Other Owners: Mr P. Jeffers, Mr D. Tucker.

---

305 **MISS HANNAH JAMES, Malvern**
Postal: **The Merries Farm, Rye Street, Birtsmorton, Malvern, Worcestershire, WR13 6AS**

1 **JUNIOR MASSINI**, 4, b g Dr Massini (IRE)—Bach Me (IRE) **Miss H. L. James**
2 **SEE WHAT (IRE)**, 9, b m Craigsteel—See For Yourself (IRE) **Miss H. L. James**
3 **SPROGZILLA**, 10, gr m Fair Mix (IRE)—Gentle Approach **Miss H. L. James**

THREE-YEAR-OLDS

4 Gr f Phoenix Reach (IRE)—Mickie **Miss H. L. James**

---

306 **MR LEE JAMES, Malton**
Postal: **Cheesecake Hill Stables, Norton, Malton, North Yorkshire, YO17 9PJ**
Contacts: **PHONE (01653) 699466 MOBILE (07732) 556322**

1 **CRASHING WAVES**, 9, b m Dubai Destination (USA)—Palisandra (USA) **Mrs C. Lloyd James**
2 **ICONIC FIGURE (IRE)**, 6, b g Approve—Tough Chic (IRE) **L. R. James**
3 **JACKMAN**, 5, gr g Aussie Rules (USA)—Fit To Burst **Mr Ian Johnson & Partner**
4 **MA PETIT LUMIER**, 9, b g Echo of Light—Alisdanza **L. R. James**
5 **TEALS LAD**, 10, b g Kayf Tara—Derry Ann **Mr C. I. Ratcliffe**

Other Owners: Mr Ian Johnson (North Yorkshire), Mrs Carol Lloyd-James.

Assistant Trainer: Carol James

---

307 **MR IAIN JARDINE, Carrutherstown**
Postal: **Paddock House, Hetlandhill Farm, Carrutherstown, Dumfriesshire, DG1 4JX**
Contacts: **PHONE (01387) 840347 MOBILE (07738) 351232**
E-MAIL office@iainjardineracing.com WEBSITE www.iainjardineracing.com

1 **ALWAYS LION (IRE)**, 9, b g Let The Lion Roar—Addie's Choice (IRE) **Mr & Mrs Paul & Clare Rooney**
2 **ANGEL'S ENVY**, 7, b m Yeats (IRE)—Caoba **Distillery Racing Club**
3 **ANIMORE**, 6, b m Sulamani (IRE)—More Likely **Mrs A. F. Tullie**
4 **ATKINSON GRIMSHAW (FR)**, 5, ch g Rio de La Plata (USA)—Cosabawn (IRE) **Mr J. Fyffe**
5 **COLOUR CONTRAST (IRE)**, 6, b g Rock of Gibraltar (IRE)—Colour Coordinated (IRE) **Kildonan Gold Racing**
6 **COOL MIX**, 7, gr g Fair Mix (IRE)—Lucylou (IRE) **D&D Armstrong Limited**
7 **DIZOARD**, 9, b m Desideratum—Riviere **Dr R. G. Fairs**
8 **DOUBLE WHAMMY**, 13, b g Systematic—Honor Rouge (IRE) **Alex & Janet Card & Partner**
9 **EQUIDAE**, 4, ch c Equiano (FR)—Dularame (IRE) **Mr I. Jardine**
10 **FALMOUTH LIGHT (FR)**, 4, b g Cape Cross (IRE)—Wonderous Light (IRE) **Drew & Ailsa Russell**
11 **FLOOD DEFENCE (IRE)**, 5, b m Harbour Watch (IRE)—Krynica (USA) **Let's Be Lucky Racing 20**
12 **FLOWERY (IRE)**, 7, b g Millenary—Dato Vic (IRE) **Mr I. Jardine**
13 **FRAME RATE**, 4, b g Arcano (IRE)—Miss Quality (USA) **The Dregs Of Humanity & Partner**
14 **GOLDEN JEFFREY (SWI)**, 6, b g Soldier Hollow—Ange Doree (FR) **Mrs J. Tracey**
15 **GOLDEN WOLF (IRE)**, 5, b br g Big Bad Bob (IRE)—Jeunesse Doree (IRE) **The Risk Takers Partnership**
16 **HOUSE OF CARDS**, 4, b f Mayson—Neyraan **Ayr Racecourse Club**
17 **INDIAN OPERA**, 7, b m Indian Danehill (IRE)—Minouchka (FR) **Mrs P. M. Shirley-Beavan**
18 **JABBAAR**, 6, ch g Acclamation—Echelon **Let's Be Lucky Racing 11**
19 **KEEP THE RIVER**, 5, b m Scorpion (IRE)—River Alder **Kitchens Plus, Friel, Morrison & Jardine**
20 **KNIGHTLY SPIRIT**, 4, br g Dalakhani (IRE)—Elysian **Mr I. Rachid**
21 **L'INGANNO FELICE (FR)**, 9, br g Librettist (USA)—Final Overture (FR) **Mr A. Dawson & Mrs K. Campbell**

MR IAIN JARDINE - Continued

22 **LADY OF ARDVAR,** 5, b m Sulamani (IRE)—Minouchka (FR) **Mrs P. M. Shirley-Beavan**
23 **LASTOFTHECOSMICS,** 4, b g Shirocco (GER)—Cosmic Case **The Cosmic Cases**
24 **MABLE LEE (IRE),** 4, ch f Zoffany (IRE)—Mexican Milly (IRE) **Dunedin Castle Rock Partnership**
25 **MARBLE BAR,** 4, b g Makfi—Presbyterian Nun (IRE) **The Twelve Munkys**
26 **MARNIE JAMES,** 4, b g Camacho—Privy Garden (IRE) **James Property Ltd**
27 **MEARING,** 4, b g Aussie Rules (USA)—Director's Dream (IRE) **Let's Be Lucky Racing 14**
28 **MYSTICAL MAC (IRE),** 4, b g Clodovil (IRE)—Long Lost Love **Mrs V. C. Macdonald**
29 **NAKEETA,** 8, b g Sixties Icon—Easy Red (IRE) **Alex & Janet Card & Atb Ltd**
30 **NEWMARKET WARRIOR (IRE),** 8, b g Dalakhani (IRE)—Heavens Peak **Ms S A Booth & Partner**
31 **NIGHT OF GLORY,** 5, b g Sea The Stars (IRE)—Kesara **Alba-eire Syndicate & Mr Iain Jardine**
32 **PLUS JAMAIS (FR),** 12, b g Caballo Raptor (CAN)—Branceilles (FR) **A Crawford & Partner**
33 **RIVER ICON,** 7, b m Sixties Icon—River Alder **Mr M Friel & Mr T Reid**
34 **SHREWD,** 9, b g Street Sense (USA)—Cala (FR) **Mr I. Jardine**
35 **SIOUX FRONTIER (IRE),** 4, b g Excelebration (IRE)—Sioux Rising (IRE) **Let's Be Lucky Racing 23**
36 **SMUGGLERS CREEK (IRE),** 5, b g Medicean—Crystany (IRE) **Mr A. McLuckie**
37 **SO SATISFIED,** 8, b g Aqlaam—Pirouetting **Wharton, Nixon, Jardine**
38 **SOMETHING BREWING (FR),** 5, gr g Clodovil (IRE)—Talwin (IRE) **Mrs C Brown & Mr Michael Wares**
39 **SONG OF SUMMER,** 4, ch f Choisir (AUS)—Height of Summer (IRE) **Let's Be Lucky Racing 16**
40 **STONE THE CROWS,** 5, b g Cape Cross (IRE)—Stars In Your Eyes **Mr R. D. Rainey**
41 **SUPER FLORENCE (IRE),** 4, gr f Zebedee—Top of The Ridge (IRE) **Top Of The Hill Racing Club**
42 **TOKARAMORE,** 7, b m Sulamani (IRE)—More Likely **Mrs A. F. Tullie**
43 **TOMORROW'S ANGEL,** 4, ch f Teofilo (IRE)—Funday **Mr I. Jardine**
44 **TOR,** 5, ch g Orientor—Dance In The Sun **Mr I. Wilson**
45 **TRADITIONAL DANCER (IRE),** 7, b g Danehill Dancer (IRE)—Cote Quest (USA) **I. G. M. Dalgleish**
46 **TRONGATE (IRE),** 7, b g Dansant—Val Eile (IRE) **M. Sawers**
47 **VILLIERSDORP,** 4, b f Lucarno (USA)—Ballinargh Girl (IRE) **Top of the Hill Racing Club & Partner**
48 **WEE TIGER TOTS,** 5, b m Sakhee (USA)—Foxglove **Mr B. P. Keogh**
49 **YES YOU (IRE),** 5, ch m Clodovil (AUS)—Mexican Milly (IRE) **Taco Partners**

THREE-YEAR-OLDS

50 **ALEXANDER JAMES (IRE),** b g Camelot—Plying (USA) **James Property Ltd**
51 **FIVE HELMETS (IRE),** b g Helmet (AUS)—Sweet Home Alabama (IRE) **Mr B. P. Keogh**
52 **GUNNABEDUN (IRE),** gr g Gregorian (IRE)—Green Vision (IRE) **Davidson & Jardine**
53 **MUST SEE THE DOC,** b c Sea The Moon (GER)—Kong Moon (FR) **Mr & Mrs Paul & Clare Rooney**
54 **MY LITTLE ORPHAN,** b c Heeraat (IRE)—Costa Brava (IRE) **Mr & Mrs Paul & Clare Rooney**
55 **PLAY IT BY EAR (IRE),** ch c Dragon Pulse (IRE)—Seriously (FR) **Mr & Mrs Paul & Clare Rooney**
56 **SHE'ZANARAB,** ch f Orientor—Rafta (IRE) **Mr J. Fyffe**
57 **SPIRIT OF LUND (IRE),** b g Fast Company—Kyrielle **Mr R. D. Rainey**
58 **YOUNG ARCHIE,** b g Bahri (USA)—Licence To Win **Mr A. Nichol**

TWO-YEAR-OLDS

59 B f 6/4 Fastnet Rock (AUS)—Cmonbabylitemyfire (IRE) (Piccolo) **Mr I. Jardine**
60 B f 13/4 Cappella Sansevero—Feabhas (IRE) (Spectrum (IRE)) **Mr I. Jardine**
61 Ch f 20/3 Casamento (IRE)—Idyllic Star (IRE) (Choisir (AUS)) **Mrs L. Drummond**

Other Owners: Mr R. M. S. Allison, Australian Thoroughbred Bloodstock, Miss S. A. Booth, Mrs C. Brown, I. T. Buchanan, Mr C. A. Burness, Mrs K. Campbell, Mrs J. A. Card, Mr A. M. Card, Alex & Janet Card, Mr A. S. Crawford, Mr D. P. Dance, Mr G. B. Davidson, A. Dawson, Mr J. Doherty, The Dregs Of Humanity, Mr M. Friel, Mr R. J. Goodfellow, Mr R. A. Gorrie, Mr S. T. Gorrie, E. Graham, A. G. Guthrie, Mr D. T. Irving, Mr M. Johnston, Kitchens Plus Ltd, Mr D. I. B. Livingstone, Mr A. Manson, Mr S. R. Mckenzie, Mr B. Melrose, Mr R. Morrison, Mrs M. S. Nelson, Mr D. E. T. Nicholson, G. R. S. Nixon, Mr C. T. Reid, R. Robinson, Mrs C. Rooney, Mr P. A. Rooney, Mrs A. Russell, A. J. R. Russell, Mr M. P. Wares, Western Meeting Club Ltd, Mr R. E. Wharton, Mrs S. E. Williams, Mr N. Williams, Mr J. Wright.

Jockey (flat): Jamie Gormley, Callum Rodriguez. **Jockey (NH):** Conor O'Farrell.
Conditional: Ross Chapman, Bruce Lynn.

---

308   **MR WILLIAM JARVIS, Newmarket**
Postal: **Phantom House Stables, Fordham Road, Newmarket, Suffolk, CB8 7AA**
Contacts: **OFFICE (01638) 669873 HOME (01638) 662677 FAX (01638) 667328**
E-MAIL mail@williamjarvis.com WEBSITE www.williamjarvis.com

1 **ARIGATO,** 4, b g Poet's Voice—Xtrasensory **Ms E. L. Banks**
2 **CHIEF IRONSIDE,** 4, b c Lawman (FR)—Moment of Time **Mr Clive Washbourn**
3 **COLD SNAP (IRE),** 6, b g Medicean—Shivering **P. C. J. Dalby & R. D. Schuster**

MR WILLIAM JARVIS - Continued

4 **QUEEN TOMYRIS**, 4, b f Declaration of War (USA)—Caphene **Ms E. L. Banks**
5 **RAMPANT LION (IRE)**, 4, ch g Bahamian Bounty—Mamma Morton (IRE) **Dr Jim Walker**
6 **RED CHOIS (IRE)**, 5, b m Choisir (AUS)—Red Blossom **Mr Kevin Hickman**
7 **TILGHMAN (IRE)**, 4, b g Lawman (FR)—Poppet's Lovein **Mr Clive Washbourn**
8 **WIMPOLE HALL**, 6, b g Canford Cliffs (IRE)—Sparkling Eyes **Ms E. L. Banks**

THREE-YEAR-OLDS

9 **FURY AND FIRE**, b c Equiano (FR)—Luanshya **The Marine Team**
10 **GREAT SUSPENSE**, b c Bated Breath—Gimasha **Mr Clive Washbourn**
11 **HONEY LANE**, gr f Nathaniel (IRE)—All Hallows (IRE) **Mr Kevin Hickman**
12 **LADY BOWTHORPE**, b f Nathaniel (IRE)—Maglietta Fina (IRE) **Ms E. L. Banks**
13 **LESTRADE**, b c Lawman (FR)—Ninas Rainbow **Mr Clive Washbourn**
14 **MICHAELS CHOICE**, b g War Command (USA)—Todber **The Music Makers**
15 **MISS LIBERTY BELLE (AUS)**, ch f Starspangledbanner (AUS)—Alpine Belle (NZ) **Mr Kevin Hickman**
16 **NO THANKS**, b g Pour Moi (IRE)—Miss Fifty (IRE) **P. C. J. Dalby & R. D. Schuster**
17 **QUEEN CONSTANTINE (GER)**, b f Holy Roman Emperor (IRE)—Quilita (GER) **Mr Kevin Hickman**
18 **THOUGHTFULLY (IRE)**, b f Acclamation—Lovely Thought **Ms E. L. Banks**

TWO-YEAR-OLDS

19 **GALACTIC GLOW (IRE)**, b c 31/3 No Nay Never (USA)—
    Shine Like A Star (Fantastic Light (USA)) (160000) **Mr Clive Washbourn**
20 **HO LENG LUI**, b f 23/4 Hot Streak (IRE)—Sparkling Eyes (Lujain (USA)) (14000) **Dr Jim Walker**
21 B c 9/2 Lawman (FR)—Madame Vestris (IRE) (Galileo (IRE)) (24000) **Mr Rupert Villers**
22 B c 12/3 Showcasing—Moment of Time (Rainbow Quest (USA)) (57142) **MM Stables**
23 **ONE NIGHT STAND**, b c 29/4 Swiss Spirit—Tipsy Girl (Haafhd) (20000) **David Batten & Partners**
24 B f 31/1 Hot Streak (IRE)—Rate (Galileo (IRE)) (21913) **Mr Kevin Hickman**
25 **SAHARAN SHIMMER**, b c 20/4 Oasis Dream—
    Come Touch The Sun (IRE) (Fusaichi Pegasus (USA)) (70000) **Mr Clive Washbourn**
26 **SHOOT THE MOON (IRE)**, b c 16/2 Lawman (FR)—
    Luna Moon (Equiano (FR)) (50000) **P. C. J. Dalby & R. D. Schuster**
27 **UNCLE SID**, b c 4/4 Free Eagle (IRE)—Paisley (Pivotal) (10000) **Mr Danny Robinson**
28 B f 7/1 Siyouni (FR)—Wannabe Special (Galileo (IRE)) (150000) **Ms E. L. Banks**

Assistant Trainer: James Toller

309	**MISS RUTH JEFFERSON, Malton**

Postal: **Newstead Stables, Beverley Road, Norton, Malton, North Yorkshire, YO17 9PJ**
Contacts: PHONE **(01653) 697225** MOBILE **(07976) 568152**
WEBSITE www.ruthjefferson.co.uk

1 **BALLY CONOR (IRE)**, 6, b g Presenting—Soliya (FR) **Drew & Ailsa Russell**
2 **BLACK EBONY**, 5, b g Malinas (GER)—Our Ethel **The Mount Fawcus Partnership**
3 **BUSTER VALENTINE (IRE)**, 6, b g Ask—Femme du Noir (IRE) **The Mount Fawcus Partnership**
4 **CARD GAME (IRE)**, 10, b m Scorpion (IRE)—Cardona **Messrs Hales Dodd Wood & Dickinson**
5 **CYRUS KEEP (IRE)**, 6, b g Doyen (IRE)—Overbranch **Ruth Jefferson Racing Club**
6 **DOUBLE W'S (IRE)**, 9, ch g Fruits of Love (USA)—Zaffre (IRE) **Wharton & Wilson**
7 **DUBAI ANGEL (IRE)**, 8, b g Dubai Destination (USA)—Just Another Penny (IRE) **Mrs D. W. Davenport**
8 **HELLO BERTIE**, 7, b g Kayf Tara—I'm Delilah **Mr C. S. Johnston & Mr T. Ambler**
9 **HELMSLEY LAD**, 8, gr g Fair Mix (IRE)—Wuchowsen (IRE) **Derek Gennard & Gillian Gennard**
10 **JAMPOT EDDIE**, 5, ch g Sulamani—Thenford Lass (IRE) **Mrs I C Straker & Steven Key**
11 **KARAPIRO BOY**, 5, b g Arabian Gleam—Littlemiss **James Binks**
12 **LEMON T**, 6, gr g Sulamani—Altogether Now (IRE) **Miss N. R. Jefferson**
13 **MEGA YEATS (IRE)**, 5, br m Yeats (IRE)—Mega Mum (IRE) **The Mount Fawcus Partnership**
14 **NORTHERN SOUL**, 6, ch g Presenting—Our Ethel **The Northern Triangle**
15 **ONWARD ROUTE (IRE)**, 5, b g Yeats (IRE)—Just Stunning (IRE) **Mr R. Collins**
16 **RAECIUS FELIX (IRE)**, 5, ch g Stowaway—Dances With Waves (IRE) **Mr R. Collins**
17 **RETURN TICKET (IRE)**, 6, b g Getaway (GER)—Capelvenere (IRE) **Mr R. Collins**
18 **RYEDALE RACER (IRE)**, 8, b g Indian Danehill (IRE)—Jontys'lass **Derek Gennard & Gillian Gennard**
19 **SCHIAPARANNIE (IRE)**, 7, b m Schiaparelli (GER)—Annie's Answer **Can't Last Won't Last**
20 **SECRETE STREAM (IRE)**, 10, ch g Fruits of Love (USA)—Bonny River (IRE) **Mrs M. E. Dixon**
21 **SHEPHERD'S SIGHT (IRE)**, 7, b g Court Cave (IRE)—Orador Sur Glane (IRE) **Mrs S. M. Wood**
22 **SPECIAL CATCH (IRE)**, 12, b g Catcher In The Rye (IRE)—Top Quality **Newstead Racing Partnership**
23 **SUN CLOUD (IRE)**, 12, b g Cloudings (IRE)—Miss Melrose **Boundary Garage (Bury) Limited**

MISS RUTH JEFFERSON - Continued

24 **TAYZAR**, 8, b g Kayf Tara—Matilda Too (IRE) **C. D. Carr**
25 **TEMPLE MAN**, 7, b g Sulamani—Altogether Now (IRE) **Mrs I C Straker & Steven Key**
26 **WAITING PATIENTLY (IRE)**, 8, b g Flemensfirth (USA)—Rossavon (IRE) **Mr R. Collins**

Other Owners: Mr Tony Ambler, Mrs D. W. Davenport, Mrs W. J. Dickinson, Mrs J. M. Dodd, Mr D. S. Fawcus, Mrs M. W. Fawcus, Mr Derek Gennard, Mrs Gillian Gennard, Mrs J. U. Hales, Mrs Madie Jagger, Mrs S. Jefferson, Mr C. S. Johnston, Mr S. Key, Mr R. G. Makin, Mr S. Oldroyd, Mrs Ailsa Russell, Mr Drew Russell, Mrs I. C. Straker, Mr N. J. Taylor, Mr R. Wharton, Mr J. H. Wilson, Mrs A. R. Wood.

Conditional: Aiden Blakemore.

---

310 **MR J. R. JENKINS, Royston**
Postal: Kings Ride, Baldock Road, Royston, Hertfordshire, SG8 9NN
Contacts: **PHONE** (01763) 241141 (01763) 246611 **FAX** (01763) 248223 **MOBILE** (07802) 750855
E-MAIL john@johnjenkinsracing.co.uk **WEBSITE** www.johnjenkinsracing.co.uk

1 **ACE CHEETAH (USA)**, 5, b g Kitten's Joy (USA)—Imagistic (USA) **The Ace Cheetah Partnership**
2 **ACE TIME**, 5, b g Sinndar (IRE)—Desert Run (IRE) **Ms Aurelija Juskaite**
3 4, B f Hellvelyn—Artistic Liason **Mr F Qadir**
4 **BILLY'S BOOTS**, 5, ch g Winker Watson—Solmorin **Mr F. Qadir**
5 **CARVELAS (IRE)**, 10, b g Cape Cross (IRE)—Caraiyma (IRE) **Crofters Racing Syndicate**
6 4, Ch f Stimulation (IRE)—Chase The Fox **Mr F. Qadir**
7 **CHLOELLIE**, 4, b f Delegator—Caramelita **Mrs Veronica Bullard & Mrs Wendy Jenkins**
8 **CLEVER DIVYA**, 6, b m Archipenko (USA)—Clever Omneya (USA) **Ms Aurelija Juskaite**
9 **COMPTON BRAVE**, 5, b g Compton Place—Willmar (IRE) **Compton Brave Partnership**
10 **COOL ECHO**, 5, b m Mount Nelson—Ellcon (IRE) **Mr M. K. P. Turner**
11 **DALKADAM (FR)**, 8, gr g Martaline—Cadoudame (FR) **Mrs Susan Hadida**
12 **DOLLYWAGGON PIKE**, 5, b m Hellvelyn—Once Removed **Mr T. J. Turner**
13 **DURATION (IRE)**, 4, b g Champs Elysees—Fringe **Mr B. Dowling & Mr R. Stevens**
14 **FOOTSTEPSINTHERAIN (IRE)**, 9, b g Footstepsinthesand—Champagne Toni (IRE) **Mr John Joseph Smith**
15 **FREDDY WITH A Y (IRE)**, 9, b g Amadeus Wolf—Mataji (IRE) **Mrs Wendy Jenkins**
16 **KARAM ALBAARI (IRE)**, 11, b h King's Best (USA)—Lilakiya (IRE) **Mr Mark Goldstein & Mrs Wendy Jenkins**
17 **LEDBURY (IRE)**, 7, b g Lawman (FR)—Truly Magnificent (USA) **Mr John Joseph Smith**
18 **LITTLE INDIAN**, 9, b g Sleeping Indian—Once Removed **Mrs Wendy Jenkins**
19 **MOBHAM (IRE)**, 4, b c Teofilo (IRE)—Elegant Beauty **Claire Goddard & Progressive Racing**
20 **ONLY TEN PER CENT (IRE)**, 11, b g Kheleyf (USA)—Cory Everson (IRE) **Mr T. J. Turner**
21 **RAISE A LITTLE JOY**, 4, b f Pastoral Pursuits—Ray of Joy **Mr Robin Stevens**
22 **SAGA SPRINT (IRE)**, 6, b m Excellent Art—Queen of Malta (IRE)
23 **TILSWORTH LUKEY**, 6, b g Sixties Icon—Chara **Michael Ng & Phyllis Hutchins**
24 **TILSWORTH PRISCA**, 4, ch f Equiano (FR)—Ashwell Rose **Mr M. Ng**
25 **TILSWORTH ROSE**, 5, b m Pastoral Pursuits—Pallas **Mr M. Ng**
26 **TILSWORTH SAMMY**, 4, b g Mount Nelson—Chara **Mr M. Ng**
27 **WHALEWEIGH STATION**, 8, b g Zamindar (USA)—Looby Loo **Mr J. Melo**
28 **ZAHIRAH**, 5, b m Mullionmileanhour (IRE)—Numanthia (IRE) **Mr F. Qadir**
29 **ZAHRAANI**, 4, b c Mount Nelson—Mediterranean Sea (IRE) **Mr F. Qadir**

THREE-YEAR-OLDS

30 **ANGLESEY PENNY**, ch f Captain Gerrard (IRE)—Magic By Bell **Mr M. K. P. Turner**
31 B f Mayson—Ashwell Rose **Mr M. Ng**
32 B g Coach House (IRE)—Lady Bonanova (IRE) **Mr M. Ng**
33 **SHERELLA**, b f Delegator—Mediterranean Sea (IRE) **Mrs Wendy Jenkins**

TWO-YEAR-OLDS

34 B f 13/4 Delegator—Artistic Liason (Auction House (USA)) **Mr F Qadir**
35 **JORREL**, b c 30/4 Canford Cliffs (IRE)—Tamasha (Sea The Stars (IRE)) (5000) **Mrs Irene Hampson**
36 B c 24/4 Ivawood (IRE)—Lilakiya (IRE) (Dr Fong (USA))
37 B f 29/4 Cappella Sansevero—Mediterranean Sea (IRE) (Medecis) **Mrs Wendy Jenkins**
38 **SIR RODNEYREDBLOOD**, ch c 20/4 Roderic O'Connor (IRE)—
Red Blooded Woman (USA) (Red Ransom (USA)) (4285) **Mrs Claire Goddard**
39 B f 24/3 Fast Company (IRE)—Teyateyaneng (IRE) (Hawk Wing (USA)) **Mr F Qadir**

311   MR ALAN JESSOP, Chelmsford
Postal: **Flemings Farm, Warren Road, South Hanningfield, Chelmsford, Essex, CM3 8HU**
Contacts: **PHONE (01268) 710210 MOBILE (07718) 736482**

1 BLAZING GLEN (IRE), 11, ch g Beneficial—Kofiyah's Rose (IRE) **Mrs G. Jessop**
2 CHORAL BEE, 10, b m Oratorio (IRE)—Chief Bee **Mrs G. Jessop**
3 MAX MILANO (IRE), 14, b g Milan—Stellissima (IRE) **Mrs G. Jessop**
4 OUTLAW JACK (IRE), 7, b g Mr Dinos—Bonus Issue (IRE) **Mrs G. Jessop**

312   MR FERGUS JESTIN, Wigton
Postal: **Hilltop, Brocklebank, Wigton, Cumbria, CA7 8DL**
Contacts: **PHONE (01697) 478439**
E-MAIL fejestin@icloud.com

1 COOTE STREET (IRE), 11, b g Winged Love (IRE)—Unknown Quality **F. Jestin**
2 HOMBRE DE HIERRO (IRE), 11, b g Winged Love (IRE)—Dama De Seda (IRE) **F. Jestin**

313   MRS LINDA JEWELL, Maidstone
Postal: **Southfield Stables, South Lane, Sutton Valence, Maidstone, Kent, ME17 3AZ**
Contacts: **PHONE (01622) 842788 MOBILE (07856) 686657**
E-MAIL lindajewell@hotmail.com WEBSITE www.lindajewellracing.co.uk

1 BREDEN (IRE), 9, b g Shamardal (USA)—Perfect Touch (USA) **The Breden Racing Partnership**
2 CALYPSO JACK (IRE), 6, ch g Papal Bull—Miss Barbados (IRE) **Mr H J Jarvis & Mrs P Jarvis**
3 CLONUSKER (IRE), 11, b g Fasliyev (USA)—Tamburello (IRE) **Mr David Yeadon & Mrs Linda Jewell**
4 COCKNEY SEAGULL (IRE), 6, b g Watar (IRE)—Acountry Lane (IRE) **CS Partnership**
5 DEEWHY (IRE), 6, b g Papal Bull—Chanteuse de Rue (IRE) **Mr D. Yeadon**
6 DRAGON TATTOO (IRE), 4, b f Zoffany (IRE)—Geisha Lily (FR) **Valence Racing**
7 DUE SOUTH (IRE), 8, b g City Honours (USA)—Lady Shackleton (IRE) **Mrs P. Reynolds**
8 EASYONTHEEYE (IRE), 8, br m Kalanisi (IRE)—Lady Bernie (IRE) **Valence Racing**
9 HAB SAB (IRE), 7, b g Papal Bull—Tamburello (IRE) **Mr T. Betteridge**
10 ITOLDYOU (IRE), 13, ch g Salford Express (IRE)—Adisadel (IRE) **Valence Racing Too**
11 MAB DAB (IRE), 8, b g Papal Bull—Pret A Porter (UAE) **Mr T. Betteridge**
12 MADAM ANNA (IRE), 6, b m Papal Bull—Melaaya (USA) **Mr T. Betteridge**
13 MISS MALARKY (IRE), 6, b m Presenting—The Shan Gang (IRE) **Mr D. Churcher Racing**
14 MONEYSTOWN (IRE), 9, b m Touch of Land (FR)—Karinga Duff **Mr H J Jarvis & Mrs P Jarvis**
15 MR JACK (IRE), 7, ch g Papal Bull—Miss Barbados (IRE) **The Breden Racing Partnership**
16 MRS JACK (IRE), 5, ch m Papal Bull—Miss Barbados (IRE) **Mr R. Dean**
17 OUR GIRL ACORN, 5, b m Bushranger (IRE)—Dominatrix **From Little Acorns**
18 ROYAL CONCORDE (IRE), 8, br g Kalanisi (IRE)—Talinas Rose (IRE) **Mr R. B. Morton**
19 UALLRIGHTHARRY (IRE), 7, b g Craigsteel—Enchanted Valley (IRE) **Mrs S. M. Stanier**
20 WONTSTOPMENOW (IRE), 6, b g Scorpion (IRE)—Jodi (IRE) **Valence Racing Too**

THREE-YEAR-OLDS
21 INVINCIBLE SEA (IRE), b f Born To Sea (IRE)—Melaaya (USA) **Mr T. Betteridge**
22 JAZZY CARD (IRE), ch f Red Jazz (USA)—Gilda Lilly (USA) **Alex & Janet Card**

TWO-YEAR-OLDS
23 HEER ME, b f 19/3 Heeraat (USA)—Push Me (IRE) (Verglas (IRE)) **Alex & Janet Card**

Other Owners: Mr A. M. Card, Mrs J. A. Card, Mrs Lisa Felstead, Mrs S. M. Fitzjohn, Mr Malcolm Fitzjohn, Mr W. Giggins, Mrs A. P. Giggins, Miss S. E. Haughton, Mr B. J. Hensman, Mr H. J. Jarvis, Mrs P. Jarvis, Mr K. Pinder, Mr J. J. Saxton, Mr J. C. Webb, Mr R. I. B. Young.

Assistant Trainer: Karen Jewell

Jockey (flat): Robert Havlin, Robert Winston. Jockey (NH): Leighton Aspell, Tom Cannon, Tom Garner.
Conditional: Jack Sherwood. Amateur: Mr O Brophy, Mr A Comoy.

314   MR BRETT JOHNSON, Epsom

Postal: **The Durdans Stables, Chalk Lane, Epsom, Surrey, KT18 7AX**
Contacts: MOBILE **(07768) 697141**
E-MAIL **thedurdansstables@googlemail.com** WEBSITE **www.brjohnsonracing.co.uk**

1 **CAYUGA**, 10, b g Montjeu (IRE)—Ithaca (USA) **B. R. Johnson**
2 **DANGEROUS ENDS**, 5, b g Monsieur Bond (IRE)—Stolen Glance **Mr C. Westley**
3 **HERON (USA)**, 5, b g Quality Road (USA)—Dreamt **01 Racing Partnership**
4 **LACAN (IRE)**, 8, b g New Approach (IRE)—Invincible Isle (IRE) **Mr C. Westley**
5 **RAKEMATIZ**, 5, ch g Pivotal—Regal Velvet **Mr C. Westley**
6 **SHINING VALLEY (IRE)**, 5, b g Clodovil (IRE)—Shining Vale (USA) **B. R. Johnson**
7 **SPIRIT OF EPSOM**, 5, b g Captain Gerrard (IRE)—Bettina Blue (IRE) **Taylor Anderson Racing**
8 **TROOPER'S GOLD**, 5, ch g Sepoy (AUS)—Samira Gold (FR) **Mr J Daniels & Mrs A M Upsdell**
9 **VERY HONEST (IRE)**, 6, b m Poet's Voice—Cercle d'amour (USA) **Omni Colour Presentations Ltd**
10 **VIOLET'S LADS (IRE)**, 5, b m Myboycharlie (IRE)—Cape Violet (IRE) **The Savy Group**

THREE-YEAR-OLDS

11 **PRIME APPROACH (IRE)**, ch c Dawn Approach (IRE)—Remarkable Story **Mr C. Westley**
12 **RUN AFTER GENESIS (IRE)**, gr c Archipenko (USA)—She Is Great (IRE) **Mr C. Westley**

Other Owners: Mr D. I. Anderson, Mr M. Cumins, J. Daniels, Mr N. Hale, Mr S. Hills, Mr N. A. Jarvis, Mr G. Peck, Mrs S. Rutherford, Mr G. Tann, Mrs C. A. Taylor, Mr B. D. Townsend, Mrs A. M. Upsdell, Miss L. Wilde.

Assistant Trainer: Vanessa Johnson

315   MISS EVE JOHNSON HOUGHTON, Blewbury

Postal: **Woodway, Blewbury, Didcot, Oxfordshire, OX11 9EZ**
Contacts: PHONE **(01235) 850480 (01235) 850500 (Home)** FAX **(01235) 851045**
MOBILE **(07721) 622700**
E-MAIL **Eve@JohnsonHoughton.com** WEBSITE **www.JohnsonHoughton.com**

1 **ACCIDENTAL AGENT**, 5, b h Delegator—Roodle **Mrs F. M. Johnson Houghton**
2 **COUNT CALABASH (IRE)**, 5, b g Big Bad Bob (IRE)—Tinaheely (IRE) **Trish Hall & Colin Fletcher**
3 **FRANK ROGERS**, 4, b g Compton Place—Bubblina **Mrs S. J. Doyle**
4 **GIVINITSUM (SAF)**, 4, b g Lateral—Fine Hope (SAF) **Mr Norman Cheng**
5 **GORING (GER)**, 7, b g Areion (GER)—Globuli (GER) **G. C. Stevens**
6 **HEDGING (IRE)**, 5, gr ro g Mastercraftsman (IRE)—Privet (IRE) **Eden Racing Club**
7 **HYANNA**, 4, b f Champs Elysees—Highly Spiced **Mr G. C. Vibert**
8 **ICE AGE (IRE)**, 4, b g Frozen Power (IRE)—Incendio **Eden Racing III**
9 **KEY PLAYER**, 4, ch g Kheleyf (USA)—My Pretty Girl **Raw, Reeve & Wollaston**
10 **KIRKLAND FOREVER**, 5, ch m Sakhee (USA)—Maystock **Mrs M Fairbairn & Mr P Dean**
11 **LADY MARIGOLD (IRE)**, 4, b f Intense Focus (USA)—Peace Lily **The Ascot Revellers**
12 **MAGNOLIA SPRINGS (IRE)**, 4, b f Shamardal (USA)—Rainbow City (IRE) **A Rogers & Mrs S Rogers**
13 **MARY ELISE (IRE)**, 4, b f Mastercraftsman (IRE)—Je T'adore (IRE) **Elaine Chivers Racing**
14 **NEW RICH**, 9, b g Bahamian Bounty—Bling Bling (IRE) **Eden Racing Club**
15 **STATUARIO**, 4, b g Helmet (AUS)—Cat Hunter **Mr Michael G Cohen & Mr David Cohen**
16 **VIXEN (IRE)**, 5, b m Kodiac—Radio Wave **Mrs Jennifer Simpson Racing**
17 **WHAT ABOUT CARLO (FR)**, 8, b g Creachadoir (IRE)—Boccatenera (GER) **Mr A. J. Pye-Jeary**

THREE-YEAR-OLDS

18 **BELLA VITA**, gr f Aussie Rules (USA)—Garabelle (IRE) **Mrs H. B. Raw**
19 **BUCKINGHAM (IRE)**, gr g Clodovil (IRE)—Lizzy's Township (USA) **The Buckingham Partnership**
20 **CANAVESE**, ch f Mastercraftsman (IRE)—Rivara **The Chriselliam Partnership**
21 **COMPASSIONATE**, b f Charm Spirit (IRE)—Bathilde (IRE) **Minster Stud**
22 **DARYANA**, b f Dutch Art—Darysina (USA) **Lionel Godfrey & Peter Wollaston**
23 **DISRUPTOR (FR)**, ch g Siyouni (FR)—Ultradargent (FR) **Mr Simon Munir & Mr Isaac Souede**
24 **DOUBLE ESPRIT**, b g Invincible Spirit (IRE)—Nature Spirits (FR) **Simon Munir & Isaac Souede**
25 **DREAM MANOEUVRE**, b g Oasis Dream—Jostle **Mr Simon Munir & Mr Isaac Souede**
26 **FOREVER MINE**, ch f Iffraaj—Best Regards (IRE) **Brightwalton Bloodstock Limited**
27 **GAMBON (GER)**, b c Dutch Art—Guajara (GER) **Mr A. J. Pye-Jeary**

MISS EVE JOHNSON HOUGHTON - Continued

28 **GARRISON COMMANDER (IRE)**, b g Garswood—Malea (IRE) **HP Racing Garrison Commander**
29 **GIN PALACE**, b g Swiss Spirit—Regal Curtsy **Mrs Z. C. Campbell-Harris**
30 **IDEAL GRACE**, ch f Poet's Voice—Sunday Bess (JPN) **Chasemore Farm LLP**
31 **JUMEIRAH (IRE)**, b f Acclamation—Scarlet Plum **Mr S. A. K. T. A. Almuhairi**
32 **KIEFER**, gr c Pour Moi (IRE)—Dali's Grey **Aston House Stud**
33 **KWELA**, b f Kodiac—Funday **Mr & Mrs James Blyth Currie**
34 **LIVELY LYDIA**, b f Charm Spirit (IRE)—Coventina (IRE) **K. A. Dasmal**
35 **LOLITA PULIDO (IRE)**, b f Toronado (IRE)—Myth And Magic (IRE) **Galloway Page Pritchard Hobson & Thomas**
36 **LYRICAL WATERS**, b g Poet's Voice—Golden Waters **Exors of the Late Mr R. E. Crutchley**
37 **MADAME TANTZY**, b f Champs Elysees—Roodle **Mrs F. M. Johnson Houghton**
38 **MARJUBILATION (IRE)**, b f Acclamation—Meet Marhaba (IRE) **Biddestone Racing**
39 **MASTER MILLINER (IRE)**, ch c Helmet (AUS)—Aqualina (IRE) **Mrs Jennifer Simpson Racing**
40 **MISS ELSA**, b f Frozen Power (IRE)—Support Fund (IRE) **Eden Racing Club**
41 **MISS HAVANA**, b f Havana Gold (IRE)—Tamalain (USA) **L & J Perkins, N. Freeman, R & P Scott**
42 **MY STYLE (IRE)**, gr g Holy Roman Emperor (IRE)—That's My Style **The Hon Mrs J. M. Corbett & C. Wright**
43 **OBERYN MARTELL**, b g Charm Spirit (IRE)—
                                      Nickels and Dimes (IRE) **Nick Bradley Racing 32 & Sohi & Partner**
44 **PARISEAN ARTISTE (IRE)**, ch f Zoffany (IRE)—Meeting In Paris (IRE) **Mr A. R. W. Marsh**
45 **PEGASUS BRIDGE**, b g Camacho—Fire Line **HP Racing Pegasus Bridge**
46 **RESOLUTE BAY**, b f Showcasing—Confusing **Mrs Jennifer Simpson Racing**
47 **SHORTER SKIRT**, ch f Showcasing—Heading North **Hot To Trot Racing - Shorter Skirt**
48 B f Charm Spirit (IRE)—Silent Act (USA) **Mr & Mrs R. Scott**
49 **SMITH (IRE)**, ch g Dawn Approach (IRE)—Alazeya **Mr A. J. Pye-Jeary**
50 **SOMETHINGABOUTJACK (IRE)**, br c No Nay Never (USA)—City Dazzler (IRE) **Ms E. Chivers & Merlin Racing**
51 **TIN HAT (IRE)**, ch g Helmet (AUS)—Precautionary **Eden Racing IV**

TWO-YEAR-OLDS

52 **ALEZAN**, ch f 8/4 Dawn Approach (IRE)—Sarinda (Dubawi (IRE)) (38000) **Mr M. Middleton-Heath**
53 **ALLEZ SOPHIA (IRE)**, b f 25/2 Kingman—Allez Alaia (IRE) (Pivotal) **Trevor Stewart**
54 B f 25/3 Brazen Beau (AUS)—Amberley Heights (IRE) (Elnadim (USA)) **Elaine Chivers Racing**
55 **ARIASTAR (IRE)**, b f 28/1 Clodovil (IRE)—
                              Some Site (IRE) (Nayef (USA)) (21070) **The Buckingham Partnership II**
56 B c 6/2 Outstrip—Bocca Bianca (GER) (Saddex) (15170)
57 B c 9/4 Sea The Stars (IRE)—Boccassini (GER) (Artan (GER)) (55000) **K. Dasmal**
58 Gr c 4/3 Gutaifan (IRE)—Boucheron (Galileo (IRE)) (48000) **Mrs Jennifer Simpson Racing**
59 **CHAMPAGNE HIGHLIFE (GER)**, b c 6/4 Holy Roman Emperor (IRE)—
                              Casanga (IRE) (Rainbow Quest (USA)) (9000) **The Highlife Racing Club**
60 Br c 4/4 Power—Dhamma (USA) (Broad Brush (USA)) (20952)
61 **FOLIE D'AMOUR**, b f 10/2 Nathaniel (IRE)—
                          Rock Follies (Rock of Gibraltar (IRE)) (20000) **J. Cross, M. Duckham, L. Godfrey, P. Wollaston**
62 **FORGETFUL AGENT**, ch c 7/3 Anjaal—Bronze Star (Mark of Esteem (IRE)) (15000) **Miss Emily Charlotte Asprey**
63 B f 24/2 Fulbright—Garabelle (IRE) (Galileo (IRE)) **Mrs H. Raw**
64 B f 14/3 Canford Cliffs (IRE)—Garraun (IRE) (Tamayuz) (2857)
65 **GO BOB GO (IRE)**, b c 21/3 Big Bad Bob (IRE)—Fire Up (Motivator) (25000) **Mr G. J. Owen**
66 **GRACEFUL MAGIC**, gr f 13/2 Gutaifan (IRE)—Magic Escapade (IRE) (Azamour (IRE)) **The Kimber Family**
67 **HMS PRESIDENT (IRE)**, b c 6/4 Excelebration (IRE)—Dance Hall Girl (IRE) (Dansili) (32380) **HP Racing**
68 B c 20/2 Delegator—Letizia (IRE) (Tamayuz) (19047) **The Picnic Partnership**
69 Ch g 8/3 Nathaniel (IRE)—Mea Parvitas (IRE) (Oasis Dream) (3000) **Eden Club Racing**
70 **NOBLE MASQUERADE**, b c 22/2 Sir Percy—Moi Aussi (USA) (Mt Livermore (USA)) (23000) **HP Racing**
71 **ON THE BRIGHTSIDE (IRE)**, ch c 29/3 Anjaal—Kardyls Hope (IRE) (Fath (USA)) (25000) **Eden Racing**
72 Ch f 28/4 Camacho—Pashmina (IRE) (Barathea (IRE)) (26969) **Kennet Valley Thoroughbreds**
73 B f 16/4 Helmet (AUS)—Perfect Cover (IRE) (Royal Applause) (13000) **Mr Mike Slade & Partner**
74 Gr c 8/2 Dragon Pulse (IRE)—Primrose Gate (IRE) (Verglas (IRE)) (7619)
75 B f 27/3 Bated Breath—Rococoa (IRE) (Zebedee) **Elaine Chivers Racing**
76 B f 4/3 Due Diligence (USA)—Roodle (Xaar) (30000) **Mrs R F Johnson Houghton**
77 B c 18/4 New Approach (IRE)—Samya (Invincible Spirit (IRE)) (38000) **Mick and Janice Mariscotti**
78 B c 15/3 Tamayuz—Soul Custody (CAN) (Perfect Soul (IRE)) (24000) **Rogate Racing**
79 B f 7/5 Swiss Spirit—Support Fund (IRE) (Intikhab (USA)) (1904) **The Ascot Colts & Fillies Club**
80 **SWORD BEACH (IRE)**, ch c 1/4 Ivawood (IRE)—Sleeping Princess (Dalakhani (IRE)) (28571) **HP Racing**
81 **VARIOUS (IRE)**, b c 1/4 Fulbright—Miss Frangipane (IRE) (Acclamation) (15238) **G. C. Stevens**
82 **ZULU GIRL**, b f 29/4 Lethal Force (IRE)—Upskittled (Diktat) (11428) **Trish Hall & Colin Fletcher**

MISS EVE JOHNSON HOUGHTON - Continued

Other Owners: 2HotToTrot, Mr Matthew Bird, Mr A. Black, Mrs J. E. Black, Mrs James Blyth Currie, Mr James Blyth Currie, Mrs G. P. Bostwick, T. P. Bostwick, Mr N. Bradley, Mr J. A. Bryan, Mr Richard Bryan, Mr P. Buckley, Mrs E. Carson, W. F. H. Carson, Mr Andrew J. Carter, Miss Charlotte Chivers, Ms Lauren Chivers, Ms Elaine Chivers, Mr Michael Cohen, Mr David Cohen, The Hon Mrs C. Corbett, Mr R. J. Cornelius, Mr Gordon Cosburn, Mr S. Davis, Mr Paul Dean, Mrs M. Fairbairn, Mr Colin Fletcher, Mr B. Galloway, Mr L. R. A. Godfrey, Mr M. W. Gregory, Ms Trish Hall, Mr John Hobson, Miss S. Holden, Mr R. S. Hoskins, Miss E. Johnson Houghton, Mrs R. F. Johnson Houghton, Mr R. F. Johnson Houghton, Mr Colin Jones, Mr H. Kearns, L. Lillingston, Mrs Janice Mariscotti, Mr Mick Mariscotti, Mrs Jayne McWilliam, Mr S. Munir, Nick Bradley Racing 32 & Sohi, Mr M. E. Page, Mr P. D. Player, Mr Roy Pritchard, Mrs H. Raw, Mr Robert Reeve, Mrs S. M. Rogers, A. P. Rogers, Mr Robert Scott, Mrs P. M. Scott, Mr W. H. Simpson, Mrs J. I. Simpson, Mr Isaac Souede, The Stewkley Shindiggers Partnership, Mr Gerry Thomas, Mr J. R. Wallis, Mr P. Wollaston, Mr C. N. Wright.

Jockey (flat): Charles Bishop, Edward Greatrex. **Apprentice:** Georgia Dobie.

---

316 MR KENNY JOHNSON, Newcastle Upon Tyne
Postal: **Grange Farm, Newburn, Newcastle Upon Tyne, Tyne and Wear, NE15 8QA**
Contacts: **PHONE (0191) 2674464 (01388) 721813 MOBILE (07774) 131121**
E-MAIL kennyjohnson68@hotmail.co.uk WEBSITE www.johnsonracing.co.uk

1 **AFLORALDANCE**, 4, b f Westlake—Guava **R. Naylor**
2 **CAIRNSHILL (IRE)**, 8, gr g Tikkanen (USA)—Ilikeyou (IRE) **Mr K. Johnson**
3 **CLIFF BAY (IRE)**, 5, b g Elzaam (AUS)—Lost Highway (IRE) **Mr K. Comb**
4 **HARD KNOCKS (IRE)**, 9, b g Turtle Island (IRE)—
Celtic Tigress (IRE) **Mr Robert C. Whitelock/Mr Kenny Johnson**
5 **KING GOLAN (IRE)**, 8, b g Golan (IRE)—Crimson Bow (GER) **Blacklock & Partners**
6 **POLITELYSED**, 13, ch m Courteous—Allegedly Red **Partnership Terminated**
7 **STARPLEX**, 9, b g Multiplex—Turtle Bay **Mr B. J. Herron**

Other Owners: Mr I. M. Blacklock, Mrs K. Elliott, R. C. Whitelock.

---

317 MRS SUSAN JOHNSON, Madley
Postal: **Carwardine Farm, Madley, Hereford**
Contacts: **PHONE (01981) 250214 FAX (01981) 251538**

1 **THE LAST BRIDGE**, 12, b g Milan—Celtic Bridge **I. K. Johnson**

Jockey (NH): Richard Johnson.

---

318 MR MARK JOHNSTON, Middleham
Postal: **Kingsley Park, Middleham, Leyburn, North Yorkshire, DL8 4PH**
Contacts: **PHONE (01969) 622237 FAX (01969) 622484**
E-MAIL info@johnston.racing WEBSITE www.johnston.racing

1 **ADDICTED TO YOU (IRE)**, 5, ch g Medicean—Adalawa (IRE) **M. W. Graff**
2 **AUSTRIAN SCHOOL (IRE)**, 4, b c Teofilo (IRE)—Swiss Roll (IRE) **Dr J. Walker**
3 **BAGHDAD (FR)**, 4, b c Frankel—Funny Girl (IRE) **Mr M. B. H. K. Al Attiya**
4 **BAILEYS EXCELERATE (FR)**, 4, gr g Excelebration (IRE)—
Cruel Sea (USA) **G. R. Bailey Ltd (Baileys Horse Feeds)**
5 **CARDSHARP**, 4, b g Lonhro (AUS)—Pure Illusion (IRE) **Sheikh Hamdan Bin Mohammed Al Maktoum**
6 **CHARLES KINGSLEY**, 4, b c New Approach (IRE)—Kailani **Sheikh Hamdan Bin Mohammed Al Maktoum**
7 **COMMUNIQUE (IRE)**, 4, ch c Casamento (IRE)—
Midnight Line (USA) **Sheikh Hamdan Bin Mohammed Al Maktoum**
8 **DEE EX BEE**, 4, b c Farhh—Dubai Sunrise (USA) **Sheikh Hamdan Bin Mohammed Al Maktoum**
9 **DR RICHARD KIMBLE (IRE)**, 4, b g Lawman (FR)—Aoife Alainn (IRE) **Garrett J Freyne & Partner**
10 **ELARQAM**, 4, b c Frankel—Attraction **Hamdan Bin Rashid Al Maktoum**
11 **ELEGIAC**, 4, b c Farhh—Lamentation **S&d Richards, N Browne & I Boyce**
12 **FIRE FIGHTING (IRE)**, 8, b g Soldier of Fortune (IRE)—Savoie (FR) **Mr Alan Spence**
13 **FRANCOPHILIA**, 4, b f Frankel—Lady Jane Digby **Miss K. Rausing**
14 **GALITELLO**, 4, b g Intello (GER)—Coventina (IRE) **Kingsley Park 12 - Ready to Run**
15 **HIBERNICUS (IRE)**, 4, ch g Sea The Stars (IRE)—Lidanski (IRE) **Ballylinch Stud**
16 **HOCHFELD (IRE)**, 5, b g Cape Cross (IRE)—What A Charm (IRE) **Sheikh Hamdan Bin Mohammed Al Maktoum**
17 **JUNEAU (IRE)**, 4, b f Dubawi (IRE)—Snow Rose (USA) **Sheikh Hamdan Bin Mohammed Al Maktoum**

MR MARK JOHNSTON - Continued

18 **JUST WAIT (IRE)**, 4, b f Teofilo (IRE)—Winesong (IRE) **Mr A. Al Mansoori**
19 **KALAGIA (IRE)**, 4, b f Kodiac—Esuvia (IRE) **Mrs J. E. Newett**
20 **KING'S ADVICE**, 5, ch h Frankel—Queen's Logic (IRE) **Saeed Jaber**
21 **LAKE VOLTA (IRE)**, 4, b g Raven's Pass (USA)—Ghanaian (FR) **Sheikh Hamdan Bin Mohammed Al Maktoum**
22 **LUCKY DEAL**, 4, ch c Mastercraftsman (IRE)—Barter **K. F. Leung**
23 **MAKING MIRACLES**, 4, b g Pivotal—Field of Miracles (IRE) **Acorn Partnership. Brown, Parker & Scott**
24 **MASHAM STAR**, 5, b g Lawman (FR)—Croisiere (USA) **3 Batterhams and a Reay**
25 **MATTERHORN (IRE)**, 4, b c Raven's Pass (USA)—Tanaghum **Sheikh Hamdan Bin Mohammed Al Maktoum**
26 **MILDENBERGER**, 4, b c Teofilo (IRE)—Belle Josephine **Sheikh Hamdan Bin Mohammed Al Maktoum**
27 **NYALETI (IRE)**, 4, gr ro f Arch (USA)—America Nova (FR) **3 Batterhams and a Reay**
28 **OUTSIDE INSIDE (IRE)**, 4, b f Holy Roman Emperor (IRE)—Humble And Proud (IRE) **Mr G. J. Freyne**
29 **RUFUS KING**, 4, ch g Iffraaj—Mosqueras Romance **Garrett J Freyne & Partner**
30 **SHOWROOM (FR)**, 4, b g Motivator—Lemon Twist (IRE) **Highclere T'bred Racing- Nick Skelton**
31 **SUNBREAK (IRE)**, 4, b g Dawn Approach (IRE)—
                             Carry On Katie (USA) **Sheikh Hamdan Bin Mohammed Al Maktoum**
32 **THREADING (IRE)**, 4, b f Exceed And Excel (AUS)—
                             Chaquiras (USA) **Sheikh Hamdan Bin Mohammed Al Maktoum**
33 **VALE OF KENT (IRE)**, 4, b g Kodiac—Red Vale (IRE) **Sheikh Hamdan Bin Mohammed Al Maktoum**
34 **VICTORIA DRUMMOND (IRE)**, 4, b f Sea The Stars (IRE)—Rezyana (AUS) **Mr P. F. M. D. Carmo**
35 **WADACRE GIGI**, 4, gr f Martaline—Glenreef **Wadacre Stud**
36 **WATERSMEET**, 8, gr g Dansili—Under The Rainbow **Mr J. A. Barson**
37 **WINGED SPUR (IRE)**, 4, ch f Motivator—Mark of An Angel (IRE) **Kingsley Park 12**

THREE-YEAR-OLDS

38 **AL THOORAYAH (USA)**, b c Arch (USA)—Worshipper (USA) **Mr A. Al Mansoori**
39 **ANAAN (IRE)**, br c Nayef (USA)—Amjaad **Hamdan bin Rashid Al Maktoum**
40 **ANCIENT EAST (IRE)**, b f Sea The Stars (IRE)—Aquila d'oriente (ITY) **Rifa Mustang Europe Ltd**
41 **ANYONECANBEASTAR (IRE)**, ch f Showcasing—Generous Heart **Mr G. J. Freyne**
42 **ANYONECANHAVEITALL**, b g Nathaniel (IRE)—Floriade (IRE) **Mr G. J. Freyne**
43 **ARCTIC SOUND**, b c Poet's Voice—Polar Circle (USA) **Mr S. B. M. Al Qassimi**
44 **ASIAN ANGEL (IRE)**, b c Dark Angel (IRE)—Chiang Mai (IRE) **Dr J. Walker**
45 B c Jukebox Jury (IRE)—Attima **Mr Alan Spence**
46 **AUSSIE VIEW (IRE)**, b f Australia—Dingle View (IRE) **Mr A. Al Mansoori**
47 **AUTUMN PRIDE (IRE)**, b c Teofilo (IRE)—Rahiyah (USA) **Sheikh Hamdan Bin Mohammed Al Maktoum**
48 **BAY OF NAPLES (IRE)**, b c Exceed And Excel (AUS)—
                             Copperbeech (IRE) **Sheikh Hamdan Bin Mohammed Al Maktoum**
49 **BLOWN BY WIND**, b c Invincible Spirit (IRE)—Discourse (USA) **Sheikh Hamdan Bin Mohammed Al Maktoum**
50 **BO SAMRAAN (IRE)**, b c Sea The Stars (IRE)—Sassenach (IRE) **Jaber Abdullah**
51 **BORN POOR (IRE)**, ch c Champs Elysees—Biaraafa (IRE) **Mr & Mrs Paul & Clare Rooney**
52 **CAPE ISLAY (FR)**, b f Cape Cross (IRE)—Eilean Ban (USA) **N Browne, I Boyce, S Frosell & S Richards**
53 **CAPLIN**, b g Cape Cross (IRE)—Party Line **S. R. Counsell**
54 **CHANCE OF GLORY (FR)**, b c Olympic Glory (IRE)—
                             Miss Carmie (FR) **Miss D Finkler Mr A Herd & Dr P Holloway**
55 **CHAPELLI**, b f Poet's Voice—Indian Petal **Sheikh Hamdan Bin Mohammed Al Maktoum**
56 **CITY TOUR**, b c Dutch Art—Privacy Order **Mr A. Al Mansoori**
57 **COPPER ROSE (IRE)**, b f Lawman (FR)—Rose of Mooncoin (IRE) **Kingsley Park 8**
58 **COUNTRY STAR**, b f Iffraaj—Honky Tonk Sally **Sheikh Hamdan Bin Mohammed Al Maktoum**
59 **CREEK ISLAND (IRE)**, ch c Iffraaj—Jumeirah Palm Star **Mr H. R. Bin Ghedayer**
60 **DAME FREYA STARK**, ch f Leroidesanimaux (BRZ)—Lady Jane Digby **Miss K. Rausing**
61 **DARK VISION (IRE)**, b c Dream Ahead (USA)—Black Dahlia **Godolphin Management Company Ltd**
62 **DEEP INTRIGUE**, gr c Dark Angel (IRE)—Abbakova (IRE) **Clipper Group Holdings Ltd**
63 **DESERT FRIEND (IRE)**, ch c Universal (IRE)—Assabiyya (IRE) **Mr A. Menahi**
64 **DESERT LANTERN (USA)**, b f More Than Ready (USA)—
                             Shuruq (USA) **Sheikh Hamdan Bin Mohammed Al Maktoum**
65 **DIVA D (IRE)**, b f Shamardal (USA)—Say No Now (IRE) **Jane Newett & Dougie Livingston**
66 **DIVINER (IRE)**, b f Charm Spirit (IRE)—Water Fountain **Kingsley Park 8**
67 **FICTION WRITER (USA)**, b c Super Saver (USA)—
                             Peggy Jane (USA) **Sheikh Hamdan Bin Mohammed Al Maktoum**
68 **FOLLOWME FOLLOWYOU (IRE)**, b f Holy Roman Emperor (IRE)—Capall An Ibre (IRE) **Mr G. J. Freyne**
69 **FORTISSIMO (IRE)**, b g Dream Ahead (USA)—Double Diamond (FR) **John Brown, Megan Dennis & Partner**
70 **FRASER ISLAND (IRE)**, ch g Australia—Ponty Acclaim (IRE) **Mr Alan Spence**
71 **FRENCH TWIST**, ch f Animal Kingdom (USA)—Braided (USA) **Sheikh Hamdan Bin Mohammed Al Maktoum**
72 **GRAVISTAS**, b c Dansili—Gaze **China Horse Club International Limited**
73 **GRENADIER GUARD (IRE)**, ch c Australia—Another Storm (USA) **Mr J. A. Barson**
74 **HONEY BEAR (IRE)**, ch f Animal Kingdom (USA)—Ishitaki (ARG) **Sheikh Hamdan Bin Mohammed Al Maktoum**

MR MARK JOHNSTON - Continued

75 **I AM A DREAMER,** b c Dream Ahead (USA)—Alexander Ballet **Mr M. Doyle**
76 **I'LL HAVE ANOTHER (IRE),** b f Dragon Pulse (IRE)—Jessie Jane (IRE) **Mr & Mrs Paul & Clare Rooney**
77 **INDIAN SOUNDS (IRE),** b g Exceed And Excel (AUS)—Sarinda **Sheikh Hamdan Bin Mohammed Al Maktoum**
78 **JOHN BRODIE,** ch c Helmet (AUS)—Hush Money (CHI) **Sheikh Hamdan Bin Mohammed Al Maktoum**
79 **JUKEBOX JUNIOR,** gr c Jukebox Jury (IRE)—Street Fire (IRE) **Mr A.D. Spence & Mr & Mrs P.Hargreaves**
80 **KEY TO POWER,** b f Slade Power (IRE)—Key To Peace (IRE) **Sheikh Hamdan Bin Mohammed Al Maktoum**
81 **KILBARCHAN (GER),** gr f Jukebox Jury (IRE)—Kellemoi de Pepita **Dr J. Walker & Partner**
82 **KING SHAMARDAL,** b c Shamardal (USA)—Model Queen (USA) **K. F. Leung**
83 **LIVING LEGEND (IRE),** b c Camelot—Jazz Girl (IRE) **Barbara & Alick Richmond**
84 **LORD LAMINGTON,** b g Australia—Lady Eclair (IRE) **Netherfield House Stud**
85 **MAIN EDITION (IRE),** b f Zoffany (IRE)—Maine Lobster (USA) **S. Ali**
86 **MARIE'S DIAMOND (IRE),** br c Footstepsinthesand—Sindiyma (IRE) **Middleham Park Racing LXXXVI**
87 **MASSAM,** ch r Dubawi (IRE)—Shumoos (USA) **Mr A. Al Mansoori**
88 **MESSAGE,** b c Dansili—Melikah (IRE) **Sheikh Hamdan Bin Mohammed Al Maktoum**
89 **MIND THE CRACK (IRE),** b g Jukebox Jury (IRE)—Mountain Melody (GER) **Mr & Mrs Paul & Clare Rooney**
90 **MISTER CHIANG,** b c Archipenko (USA)—Robe Chinoise **The Originals**
91 **MITHMAAR (IRE),** b c Sea The Stars (IRE)—Nufoos **Hamdan Bin Rashid Al Maktoum**
92 **MONDAIN,** ch c Dubawi (IRE)—Mondalay **Sheikh Hamdan Bin Mohammed Al Maktoum**
93 **MOUNTAIN RULER,** b g Ruler of The World (IRE)—Regal Fairy (IRE) **East Layton Stud Ltd**
94 **MUSTADUN,** b c Lethal Force (IRE)—Tiger Stone **Ewan & Anna Hyslop**
95 **NATALIE'S JOY,** b f Lope de Vega (IRE)—Semaphore **Merriebelle Stable & Mr S. Chappell**
96 **NAYEF ROAD (IRE),** ch c Galileo (IRE)—Rose Bonheur **M. Obaida**
97 **NORDANO (GER),** ch c Jukebox Jury (IRE)—Navajo Queen (GER) **Mr A. Al Mansoori**
98 **OASIS PRINCE,** b c Oasis Dream—Demisemiquaver **Mr J. D. Abell**
99 **OCTAVE (IRE),** ch f Dawn Approach (IRE)—Calando (IRE) **Sheikh Hamdan Bin Mohammed Al Maktoum**
100 **PANZANO,** b g Dutch Art—Special Meaning **P. D. Savill**
101 **PERSIAN MOON (IRE),** b c Makfi—Lune Rose **Kennet Valley Thoroughbreds X**
102 **PINK FLAMINGO,** b f Dream Ahead (USA)—Naivasha **Lowther Racing & Partner**
103 **PORT OF LEITH (IRE),** b g Dark Angel (IRE)—Tender Is Thenight (IRE) **Jane Newett & Dougie Livingston**
104 **PRAIRIE SPY (IRE),** b f Sepoy (AUS)—Vista Bella **Sheikh Hamdan Bin Mohammed Al Maktoum**
105 **RED PHOENIX (IRE),** ch g Pivotal—Huma Bird **Sheikh Hamdan Bin Mohammed Al Maktoum**
106 **RICH CUMMINS,** b c Dalakhani (IRE)—Claxon **Nick Bradley Racing 18 & Sohi**
107 **ROCHESTER HOUSE (IRE),** ch c Galileo (IRE)—Kalla **John Brown & Megan Dennis**
108 **ROCK UP IN STYLE,** b g Showcasing—Flora Trevelyan **Mr B. Yeardley**
109 **ROYAL BORN (IRE),** b c Born To Sea (IRE)—Albarouche **Jaber Abdullah**
110 **SAMSTAR,** ch f Nathaniel (IRE)—Gossamer Seed (IRE) **Equinox Racing & Partner**
111 **SAPA INCA (IRE),** b f Galileo (IRE)—Inca Princess (IRE) **China Horse Club International Limited**
112 **SEDUCTIVE MOMENT (GER),** ch g Shamardal (USA)—Sexy Lady (GER) **Kingsley Park 10**
113 **SIR RON PRIESTLEY,** ch c Australia—Reckoning (IRE) **P. Dean**
114 **SKY CROSS (IRE),** b c Cape Cross (IRE)—Lil's Jessy (IRE) **Jaber Abdullah**
115 **SKY DEFENDER,** b c Farhh—Al Mahmeyah **Mr H. R. Bin Ghedayer**
116 **SMILE A MILE (IRE),** ch g Slade Power (IRE)—Bergamask (USA) **Sheikh Hamdan Bin Mohammed Al Maktoum**
117 **SPIRIT KINGDOM (USA),** ch f Animal Kingdom (USA)—
                                   Infinite Spirit (USA) **Sheikh Hamdan Bin Mohammed Al Maktoum**
118 **STONE COUGAR (USA),** ch f Kitten's Joy (USA)—
                                   Fitful Skies (IRE) **Sheikh Hamdan Bin Mohammed Al Maktoum**
119 **SUMMER MOON,** ch c Sea The Moon (GER)—Songerie **The Originals**
120 B f Iffraaj—Sweet Lilly **Mr A. Al Mansoori**
121 **TANAAWOL,** b c Dansili—Eshaadeh (USA) **Hamdan Bin Rashid Al Maktoum**
122 **THE TRADER (IRE),** ch c Mastercraftsman (IRE)—Chinese White (IRE) **A. Saeed**
123 **THEMAXWECAN (IRE),** b c Maxios—Psychometry (FR) **D. C. Livingston**
124 **TRUCKINGBY,** b g Raven's Pass—Off Chance **Trucking By Brian Yeardley**
125 **VICTORY COMMAND (IRE),** b c War Command (USA)—Aguinaga (IRE) **Kingsley Park 10**
126 **VIVID DIAMOND (IRE),** b f Cape Cross (IRE)—Pretty Diamond (IRE) **M. W. Graff**
127 **WADACRE MIMI,** ch f Mastercraftsman (IRE)—Madam Valentine **Wadacre Stud**
128 **WAR CHARIOT,** b g Slade Power (IRE)—Boadicea **Sheikh Hamdan Bin Mohammed Al Maktoum**
129 **WARNING FIRE,** b f Shamardal (USA)—Bright Beacon **Sheikh Hamdan Bin Mohammed Al Maktoum**
130 **WEST END CHARMER (IRE),** b c Nathaniel (IRE)—Solar Midnight (USA) **Martin McHale & Partner**

TWO-YEAR-OLDS

131 Ch c 28/1 Lord of England (GER)—Adalawa (IRE) (Barathea (IRE)) **M. W. Graff**
132 B c 28/4 Motivator—Alava (IRE) (Anabaa (USA)) (22000) **Mr J. D. Abell**
133 Ch c 17/1 New Approach (IRE)—Alonsoa (IRE) (Raven's Pass (USA)) (70000) **Hamdan bin Rashid Al Maktoum**
134 **ALPHA THETA,** b f 23/2 Archipenko (USA)—Alumna (USA) (Mr Greeley (USA)) **Miss K. Rausing**
135 B f 4/3 Dubawi (IRE)—Ama (USA) (Storm Cat (USA)) **Sheikh Hamdan Bin Mohammed Al Maktoum**

MR MARK JOHNSTON - Continued

136 Ch f 24/2 Lord of England (GER)—Ange Doree (FR) (Sinyar (IRE)) (4761) **M. W. Graff**
137 B c 28/3 Kodiac—Aravonian (Night Shift (USA)) (128571) **Hamdan bin Rashid Al Maktoum**
138 B c 21/3 Fountain of Youth (IRE)—Art of Gold (Excellent Art) (17142) **Kingsley Park 11**
139 B c 25/3 Canford Cliffs (IRE)—Assault On Rome (IRE) (Holy Roman Emperor (IRE)) **Mrs C. E. Budden**
140 AVENTURIERE, b f 21/2 Archipenko (USA)—Lady Jane Digby (Oasis Dream) **Miss K. Rausing**
141 BAVARDAGES (IRE), b c 31/3 Dream Ahead (USA)—Petits Potins (Verglas (IRE)) (10000) **Kingsley Park 11**
142 B c 4/4 Exceed And Excel (AUS)—Beneventa (Most Welcome) (38768) **Rob Ferguson**
143 Br f 10/3 Dark Angel (IRE)—Best Regards (IRE) (Tamayuz) (57142) **Mr John Dance**
144 B c 10/2 Camacho—Bilderberg (IRE) (Big Bad Bob (IRE)) (13485) **Mr G. J. Freyne**
145 Gr f 11/4 Sea The Stars (IRE)—Bite of The Cherry (Dalakhani (IRE)) (50568) **Jaber Abdullah**
146 B 20/3 Dawn Approach (IRE)—Brom Felinity (AUS) (Encosta de Lago (AUS)) **Mr S. Chappell**
147 B c 29/3 Karakontie (JPN)—Candy Kitty (USA) (Lemon Drop Kid (USA)) (52000) **Mr M. Doyle**
148 B c 11/3 Starspangledbanner (AUS)—Caribbean Ace (IRE) (Red Clubs (IRE)) (76190) **Mr John Dance**
149 B c 13/5 Authorized (IRE)—Caribbean Dancer (USA) (Theatrical) **Mr H. C. Hart**
150 B f 24/3 Golden Horn—Chan Tong (BRZ) (Hampstead (URU)) **Sheikh Hamdan Bin Mohammed Al Maktoum**
151 Bl c 8/3 Footstepsinthesand—Clodovina (IRE) (Rock of Gibraltar (IRE)) (10956) **Ventura Racing**
152 B c 17/2 Golden Horn—Concordia (Pivotal) **Sheikh Hamdan Bin Mohammed Al Maktoum**
153 Ch f 20/2 Lope de Vega (IRE)—Copernica (IRE) (Galileo (IRE)) (65000) **Mr Abdulla Al Mansoori**
154 Ch c 26/1 Pivotal—Coral Mist (Bahamian Bounty) (62000) **Mr Abdulla Al Mansoori**
155 Br c 29/4 Planteur (IRE)—Croisiere (IRE) (Capote (USA)) (3792) **Kingsley Park 14**
156 B f 11/5 Gleneagles (IRE)—Crossover (Cape Cross (IRE)) (15170) **Kingsley Park 11**
157 B c 12/3 Lethal Force (IRE)—Danehill Destiny (Danehill Dancer (IRE)) (23809) **Mr M. Doyle**
158 B c 20/4 Nathaniel (IRE)—Danehill Dreamer (USA) (Danehill (USA)) (20000) **T T Bloodstocks**
159 DOUGLAS FIR (IRE), b c 1/5 Australia—Danehill Music (IRE) (Danehill Dancer (IRE)) (58996) **Mr R. G. Davies**
160 DREAM TONIGHT (IRE), b f 1/4 Dream Ahead (USA)—
Jeanne Girl (IRE) (Rip Van Winkle (IRE)) (16856) **Barbara & Alick Richmond**
161 B c 21/2 Casamento (IRE)—
Dubai Sunrise (USA) (Seeking The Gold (USA)) **Sheikh Hamdan Bin Mohammed Al Maktoum**
162 Ch c 19/4 Dawn Approach (IRE)—
Dunnes River (USA) (Danzig (USA)) **Sheikh Hamdan Bin Mohammed Al Maktoum**
163 Ch f 7/3 New Approach (IRE)—Elle Shade (Shamardal (USA)) **Sheikh Hamdan Bin Mohammed Al Maktoum**
164 B c 28/2 Shamardal (USA)—Elshabakiya (IRE) (Diktat) (50000) **Jaber Abdullah**
165 Ch c 3/3 Night of Thunder (IRE)—Emreliya (IRE) (Danehill Dancer (IRE)) (62000) **Kennet Valley Thoroughbreds**
166 EXHALATION, ch f 16/3 Bated Breath—Pamushana (IRE) (Teofilo (IRE)) **East Layton Stud Ltd**
167 FLASHING APPROACH (IRE), b c 23/4 New Approach (IRE)—
Flashing Green (Green Desert (USA)) (92709) **Mr C. R. Hirst**
168 FLYLIKEANEAGLE (IRE), b c 20/3 Free Eagle (IRE)—
Dulcian (IRE) (Shamardal (USA)) (21069) **Barbara & Alick Richmond Racing**
169 B c 21/3 Kingman—Forever Times (So Factual (USA)) (70000) **Mr H. A. Lootah**
170 FRED, ch c 11/2 Frankel—Deirdre (Dubawi (IRE)) (145000) **The Burke Family**
171 B f 2/3 Golden Horn—Free Rein (Dansili) (95000) **Mr A D Spence & Mr M B Spence**
172 B f 14/2 Frankel—Gale Force (Shirocco (GER)) (130000) **Nick Bradley Racing**
173 B f 16/2 More Than Ready (USA)—Glorification (Champs Elysees) **Mr Hamdan Al Maktoum**
174 GOBI SUNSET, b c 13/3 Oasis Dream—
Dark Promise (Shamardal (USA)) (38000) **N Browne, I Boyce, S Frosell & S Richards**
175 B c 3/5 Tamayuz—Hammiya (IRE) (Darshaan) (24761) **Mr G. J. Freyne**
176 Ch f 9/2 Dubawi (IRE)—Hush Money (CHI) (Hussonet (USA)) **Sheikh Hamdan Bin Mohammed Al Maktoum**
177 B f 19/3 Rock of Gibraltar (IRE)—Idle Rich (Sky Classic (CAN)) (10113) **Mr P. D. Savill**
178 B c 24/4 Shamardal (USA)—
Illustrious Miss (USA) (Kingmambo (USA)) **Sheikh Hamdan Bin Mohammed Al Maktoum**
179 Ch c 20/2 Supplicant—Indiana Blues (Indian Ridge) **G. R. Bailey Ltd (Baileys Horse Feeds)**
180 Gr c 8/5 Dark Angel (IRE)—Inner Secret (USA) (Singspiel (IRE)) **Sheikh Hamdan Bin Mohammed Al Maktoum**
181 B c 2/3 Oasis Dream—Interception (IRE) (Raven's Pass (USA)) (34285) **Mr G. J. Freyne**
182 B c 24/1 Supplicant—Jane Jubilee (IRE) (Misbar Baileys) **G. R. Bailey Ltd (Baileys Horse Feeds)**
183 JUMBY BAY, b f 8/2 Oasis Dream—Al Joza (Mubtaker (IRE)) (40000) **Mr J. M. Brown**
184 B c 28/4 Lawman (FR)—Kalandara (IRE) (Rainbow Quest (USA)) (26000) **Ventura Racing**
185 Br c 16/4 New Approach (IRE)—Karen's Caper (USA) (War Chant (USA)) (11000) **Kingsley Park 13**
186 B f 13/3 Dream Ahead (USA)—Kartiste (IRE) (Kalanisi (IRE)) (28000) **Johnston Racing Ltd & Mr John O'Connor**
187 B gr f 20/2 Dark Angel (IRE)—Katawi (Dubawi (IRE)) **Moyns Park Stud**
188 B gr f 31/3 No Nay Never (USA)—Kawn (Cadeaux Genereux) (48883) **Paul Crowe**
189 Bl f 31/1 Maxios—La Zubia (Montjeu (IRE)) (29498) **Mrs S Russell & A M Russell**
190 B br f 22/1 Hard Spun (USA)—Lacy (GER) (Authorized (IRE)) (85000) **Mr A. Al Mansoori**
191 B c 7/4 Frankel—Lamar (IRE) (Cape Cross (IRE)) (85000) **S. Ali**
192 Br c 10/3 Golden Horn—Liber Nauticus (IRE) (Azamour (IRE)) (75000) **David & Jane Newett**
193 B f 17/2 Oasis Dream—Maid To Perfection (Sadler's Wells (USA)) (60000) **David & Jane Newett**

MR MARK JOHNSTON - Continued

194 B f 8/2 Shamardal (USA)—Majestic Manner (Dubawi (IRE)) (40000) **Saeed Jaber**
195 **MAKYON (IRE)**, b c 22/4 Make Believe—Mise (IRE) (Indian Ridge) (22000) **The Makyowners**
196 B c 25/2 Brazen Beau (AUS)—Malpas Missile (IRE) (Elusive City (USA)) (6742) **Kingsley Park 14**
197 B c 17/4 Casamento (IRE)—Mambo Rhythm (Authorized (IRE)) (9270) **Kingsley Park 14**
198 **MARGARET DUMONT (IRE)**, b f 2/3 Camelot—
Sapphire Waters (IRE) (Six Sense (JPN)) (20000) **Tactful Finance & J. Barnett**
199 B c 2/3 Exceed And Excel (AUS)—
Memorial (AUS) (Street Cry (USA)) **Sheikh Hamdan Bin Mohammed Al Maktoum**
200 B f 11/2 Dark Angel (IRE)—
Merry Jaunt (USA) (Street Sense (USA)) (45000) **Duke Of Roxburghe & Mr D. Burke 1**
201 Ch f 31/1 City Zip (USA)—
Midnight Watch (USA) (Stormy Atlantic (USA)) **Sheikh Hamdan Bin Mohammed Al Maktoum**
202 **MISTY GREY (IRE)**, b gr c 5/3 Dark Angel (IRE)—
Chinese Whisper (IRE) (Dalakhani (IRE)) (72000) **Barbara & Alick Richmond**
203 B f 20/4 Requinto (IRE)—Mocca (Sri Pekan (USA)) (25000) **Mr C. R. Hirst**
204 **MOTION**, b f 2/4 Invincible Spirit (IRE)—Attraction (Efisio) **The Duke Of Roxburghe**
205 B f 15/3 War Command (USA)—Naomh Geileis (USA) (Grand Slam (USA)) **Mrs C. E. Budden**
206 B c 10/4 Zebedee—Negotiate (Red Ransom (USA)) (31428) **Sheikh Hamdan Bin Mohammed Al Maktoum**
207 **NETIQUETTE**, ch f 7/4 Archipenko (USA)—Nimiety (Stormy Atlantic (USA)) **Miss K. Rausing**
208 B c 14/2 Fountain of Youth (IRE)—New Falcon (IRE) (New Approach (IRE)) **Bearstone Stud**
209 B c 23/4 Kodiac—Noahs Ark (IRE) (Charnwood Forest (IRE)) (35000) **P. D. Savill**
210 **NOSTALGICA**, b f 15/4 Sea The Moon (GER)—Neige d'antan (Aussie Rules (USA)) **Miss K. Rausing**
211 B br f 4/3 Temple City (USA)—
Pico Duarte (USA) (Storm Cat (USA)) **Sheikh Hamdan Bin Mohammed Al Maktoum**
212 B c 22/4 Holy Roman Emperor (IRE)—Pink Tequila (Teofilo (IRE)) **J. R. Jacobs (Newsells Park Stud)**
213 B f 22/2 Sepoy (AUS)—Plucky (Kyllachy)
214 B f 16/2 Kingman—Posteritas (USA) (Lear Fan (USA)) **G. R. Bailey Ltd (Baileys Horse Feeds)**
215 **PRAXEOLOGY (IRE)**, b c 30/3 Dark Angel (IRE)—Hartstown House (IRE) (Primo Dominie) (35000) **Dr J. Walker**
216 B c 4/3 Rock of Gibraltar (IRE)—Princess Sofia (UAE) (Pennekamp (USA)) (54782) **Dr J. Walker**
217 B f 12/5 Toronado (IRE)—Rainbow's Edge (Rainbow Quest (USA)) (6000) **Jaber Abdullah**
218 B c 17/4 Oasis Dream—Rehn's Nest (IRE) (Authorized (IRE)) (70000) **M. Obaida**
219 B c 18/2 Slade Power (IRE)—Risen Sun (Shamardal (USA)) **Sheikh Hamdan Bin Mohammed Al Maktoum**
220 B f 19/3 Toronado (IRE)—Riva Royale (Royal Applause) (9523) **Mr G. J. Freyne**
221 B c 22/3 Invincible Spirit (IRE)—Rose de France (IRE) (Diktat) (126421) **China Horse Club/Ballylinch Stud**
222 Ch f 29/3 Distorted Humor (USA)—
Sahara Wind (USA) (A P Indy (USA)) **Sheikh Hamdan Bin Mohammed Al Maktoum**
223 **SECRET SMILE (IRE)**, ch f 9/5 Exceed And Excel (AUS)—
Zam Zoom (IRE) (Dalakhani (IRE)) (22000) **Barbara & Alick Richmond**
224 Ch c 19/3 Dawn Approach (IRE)—Shanooan (USA) (English Channel (USA)) (16856) **Kingsley Park 13**
225 B f 13/3 Teofilo (IRE)—Shawanda (IRE) (Sinndar (IRE)) **Sheikh Hamdan Bin Mohammed Al Maktoum**
226 B c 5/4 Slade Power (IRE)—Shirley Blake (IRE) (Acclamation) (9270) **Kingsley Park 13**
227 B f 22/4 Golden Horn—Sibling Honour (Bernardini (USA)) **Sheikh Hamdan Bin Mohammed Al Maktoum**
228 B f 18/4 Shamardal (USA)—Silkwood (Singspiel (IRE)) **Sheikh Hamdan Bin Mohammed Al Maktoum**
229 Ch c 21/4 Footstepsinthesand—Simla Bibi (Indian Ridge) (22756) **Rob Ferguson**
230 Ch c 26/2 Night of Thunder (IRE)—
Souviens Toi (Dalakhani (IRE)) (70000) **Highclere T'Bred Racing - George Stubbs**
231 Ch f 12/4 Dark Angel (IRE)—Special Meaning (Mount Nelson) (37926) **Mr G J Freyne**
232 **SUBJECTIVIST**, b c 30/3 Teofilo (IRE)—Reckoning (Danehill Dancer (USA)) (62000) **Dr J. Walker**
233 Ch f 17/4 Slade Power (IRE)—Summer Fete (IRE) (Pivotal) **Sheikh Hamdan Bin Mohammed Al Maktoum**
234 Ch c 8/4 Australia—Super Sleuth (IRE) (Selkirk (USA)) (32000) **Jaber Abdullah**
235 B f 31/3 Elvstroem (AUS)—Three French Hens (IRE) (Elnadim (USA)) (12642) **Jaber Abdullah**
236 B f 17/3 Elusive Quality (USA)—Tourner (IRE) (Hard Spun (USA)) **Sheikh Hamdan Bin Mohammed Al Maktoum**
237 **TRINITY GIRL**, b f 11/4 Teofilo (IRE)—
Micaela's Moon (USA) (Malibu Moon (USA)) (5000) **Tactful Finance Limited**
238 B c 8/3 Dark Angel (IRE)—Utrecht (Rock of Gibraltar (IRE)) **Sheikh Hamdan Bin Mohammed Al Maktoum**
239 Ch c 10/5 Speightstown (USA)—
Vaguely Familiar (USA) (A P Indy (USA)) **Sheikh Hamdan Bin Mohammed Al Maktoum**
240 B c 23/3 Exceed And Excel (AUS)—
Vanity Rules (New Approach (IRE)) (62000) **Jane Newett & Dougie Livingston**
241 **VILLA PALOMA (IRE)**, ch f 8/4 Rock of Gibraltar (IRE)—
Ma Paloma (FR) (Highest Honor (FR)) (16190) **Mrs S. E. Rowett (Varsfontein Stud)**
242 Ch c 8/2 Shamardal (USA)—Villarrica (USA) (Selkirk (USA)) **Sheikh Hamdan Bin Mohammed Al Maktoum**
243 **VISINARI (FR)**, gr c 11/3 Dark Angel (IRE)—Visinada (IRE) (Sinndar (IRE)) (46354) **Rob Ferguson**
244 B f 12/2 Golden Horn—Vituisa (Bering) **Sheikh Hamdan Bin Mohammed Al Maktoum**
245 B f 21/4 Lope de Vega (IRE)—Vow (Motivator) (32000) **Miss D Finkler, Mr A Herd and Dr P Holloway**

MR MARK JOHNSTON - Continued

246 Br gr c 19/2 Kingman—Warling (IRE) (Montjeu (IRE)) (22000) **Mr R. S. Brookhouse**
247 B c 3/5 Invincible Spirit (IRE)—
              Windsor County (USA) (Elusive Quality (USA)) **Sheikh Hamdan Bin Mohammed Al Maktoum**
248 B br c 27/1 Street Boss (USA)—
              Wipe Out (USA) (Hard Spun (USA)) **Sheikh Hamdan Bin Mohammed Al Maktoum**
249 **WOLDGATE WOODS (IRE),** ch c 5/5 Tamayuz—
              Convent Girl (IRE) (Bishop of Cashel) (8428) **The Passionate Partnership**
250 B c 9/4 Iffraaj—Zofzig (USA) (Danzig (USA)) **Sheikh Hamdan Bin Mohammed Al Maktoum**

Other Owners: Ballylinch Stud, Mr R. Batterham, Mrs R. F. Batterham, Mr C. M. Batterham, Mr C. Bennett, Mr I. Boyce, Mr N. Bradley, Mr E. Brierley, Mrs Christine Brown, Mr J. M. Brown, John Brown & Megan Dennis, Mr N. N. Browne, Mrs Christine E. Budden, Mr Matthew Budden, Mr M. Budden, Mr D. J. Burke, Mr R. S. Chappell, China Horse Club International Limited, David Scott and Co (Pattern Makers) Ltd, Mrs Megan Dennis, Mr G. Dennis, Equinox Racing, Miss D. L. Finkler, Mr Garrett J. Freyne, Mrs Robert Frosell, Mr A. Greenhalgh, Mr and Mrs P. Hargreaves, Mr P. K. Hargreaves, Mrs R. J. Hargreaves, Mr Jason Hathorn, Mrs Fiona Hathorn, Mr Andrew Herd, Mr T. Heywood, Highclere Nominated Partner Limited, Highclere Thoroughbred Racing Ltd, Dr Peter Holloway, Mr R. S. Hoskins, Hot To Trot Racing 1, Mr R. W. Huggins, Mrs Anna Hyslop, Mr E. W. Hyslop, Mrs Deirdre Johnston, Mrs Sabina Kelly, Mrs Stephen Knight, Mrs Julie Lightbody, Mr M. Lightbody, Mr Luke Lillingston, Mr Douglas Livingston, Countess of Lonsdale, Manor Farm Stud (Rutland), Ms J. Matthews-Griffiths, Mr Martin McHale, Merriebelle Irish Farm Limited, Mrs Jane Newett, Mr T. S. Palin, Mr A. F. Parker, Mr M. Prince, Mrs J. Reay, Mr Stevie Richards, Mrs Stevie Richards, Mr A. Richmond, Barbara & Alick Richmond, Mrs Barbara Richmond, Mr G. F. L. Robinson, Mrs C. Rooney, Mr P. A. Rooney, Duke of Roxburghe, Mrs S. Russell, Mr A. M. Russell, Mr M. B. Spence, Mr A. D. Spence, Mr Brian Yeardley.

Assistant Trainers: Deirdre Johnston, Charlie Johnston, Jock Bennett

Jockey (flat): Joe Fanning, P. J. McDonald, Franny Norton. **Apprentice:** Andrew Breslin, Oli Stammers.
Amateur: Miss Emma Bedford.

---

319   MR ALAN JONES, Timbercombe
Postal: **East Harwood Farm, Timbercombe, Minehead, Somerset, TA24 7UE**
Contacts: **FAX 01633 680232 MOBILE (07901) 505064**
E-MAIL heritageracing@btconnect.com WEBSITE www.alanjonesracing.co.uk

1 4, B c Arvico (FR)—A Nun With A Gun (IRE)
2 **AGAINN DUL AGHAIDH,** 8, b g Black Sam Bellamy (IRE)—Star Ar Aghaidh (IRE) **Mr A. H. Crow**
3 4, B g Midnight Legend—Dancing Emily (IRE) **Burnham Plastering & Drylining Ltd**
4 **DUHALLOW LAD (IRE),** 7, b g Papal Bull—Macca Luna (IRE) **Burnham Plastering & Drylining Ltd**
5 6, B g Craigsteel—Glenair Lucy (IRE)
6 **I'M NOTAPARTYGIRL,** 6, b m Arvico (FR)—Lady Shirley Hunt
7 **LADY AVERY (IRE),** 7, b m Westerner—Bobs Article (IRE) **Burnham Plastering & Drylining Ltd**
8 **MA'IRE RUA (IRE),** 12, ch g Presenting—Long Acre
9 **MISSMEBUTLETMEGO,** 9, b g With The Flow (USA)—Bay Bianca (IRE) **Mr A. E. Jones**
10 **ON THE METER (IRE),** 5, b br g Eastern Anthem (IRE)—Party Belle **Premier Plastering (UK) Limited**
11 **POKARI (FR),** 7, ch g Bonbon Rose (FR)—Pokara (FR) **Mr A. E. Jones**
12 **QUALANDO (FR),** 8, b g Lando (GER)—Qualite Controlee (FR) **Mrs K. A. Stuart**
13 **STAND BY ME (FR),** 9, b g Dream Well (FR)—In Love New (FR) **Mr A. E. Jones**
14 **SUPERNOVERRE (IRE),** 13, b g Noverre (USA)—Caviare
15 **TIQUER (FR),** 11, b g Equerry (USA)—Tirenna (FR) **Burnham Plastering & Drylining Ltd**
16 **TRICKS AND TRAILS (IRE),** 6, b g Flemensfirth (USA)—Loughaneala (IRE) **Premier Plastering (UK) Limited**
17 **VETONCALL (IRE),** 7, b g Well Chosen—Miss Audacious (IRE) **Burnham Plastering & Drylining Ltd**

TWO-YEAR-OLDS
18 **COCARDIER,** b c 7/1 My Risk (FR)—Tamaline (FR) (Malinas (GER)) (3371) **Mr A. E. Jones**
19 B c 16/5 Bollin Eric—Rest And Be (IRE) (Vinnie Roe (IRE))

Assistant Trainer: Miss A. Bartelink

Jockey (NH): Richard Johnson, Paddy Brennan, Tom O' Brien.

320 MR MARTIN KEIGHLEY, Moreton-In-Marsh

Postal: **Condicote Stables, Luckley, Longborough, Moreton-In-Marsh, Gloucestershire, GL56 0RD**
Contacts: **MOBILE (07767) 472547**
E-MAIL keighleyracing@btinternet.com WEBSITE www.martinkeighley.com

1 **ACACIA DREAM (IRE)**, 5, b m Mahler—Paumafi (IRE) Oliver Ryan & Irene Mychajlyszyn
2 5, B g Kayf Tara—Aunt Harriet **Mr R. Allsop**
3 **BACK ON THE LASH**, 5, b g Malinas (GER)—Giovanna M Boothright G Lovett P Deffains
4 **BALLYMOUNTAIN BOY (IRE)**, 8, b g Mountain High (IRE)—Minoras Return (IRE) The Chameleons
5 **BEN BUIE (IRE)**, 5, br g Presenting—Change of Plan (IRE) Owners for Owners Ben Buie
6 **BIG NASTY**, 6, b g Black Sam Bellamy (IRE)—Hello My Lovely Peel Racing Club
7 **BLACK PRINCE (FR)**, 5, b g Falco (USA)—Thamara (USA) Martin Keighley Racing Club
8 **BOBBLE EMERALD (IRE)**, 11, ch g Rudimentary (USA)—Aunt Emeralds (IRE) D Bishop, C Bowkley & M Parker
9 4, B f Mahler—Bobset Leader (IRE) **Martin Keighley Racing Partnership 5**
10 **BRILLARE MOMENTO (IRE)**, 8, b m Milan—Sunshine Leader (IRE) Mr O. F. Ryan
11 4, B br g Yeats (IRE)—Change of Plan (IRE) **Owners For Owners**
12 **CHEQUERED VIEW**, 6, b m Passing Glance—Blue Plaid H.R.H. The Princess Royal
13 **CITY NEVER SLEEPS (IRE)**, 7, b g Central Park (IRE)—Goodnightmrskelly (IRE) Martin Keighley Racing Club
14 **COTSWOLD PRINCE (IRE)**, 4, b g Elzaam (AUS)—Kalinjara (IRE) Martin Keighley Racing Partnership 3
15 **CUL DE POULE**, 5, b g Multiplex—Madam Blaze Roger & Yvonne Allsop
16 **CUT AND RUN**, 6, b m Getaway (GER)—Somethinaboutmolly (IRE) Mrs Z. A. E. Tindall
17 **DEBDEN BANK**, 5, b g Cacique (IRE)—Rose Row Tyrone Hanlon & Mark Boothright
18 **ENFORCEMENT (IRE)**, 4, b g Lawman (FR)—Elodie Mr E. J. Hughes
19 **FAIRMOUNT**, 8, gr g Fair Mix (IRE)—Miss Chinchilla J B Property Investments (Midlands) Ltd
20 **FINNICK GLORY (IRE)**, 5, gr m Fame And Glory—Jeu de Dame Mrs Z. J. Stock
21 **FORECAST**, 7, ch g Observatory (USA)—New Orchid (USA) The E, G & B Partnership
22 **GOLD MOUNTAIN (IRE)**, 9, b g Gold Well—La Belle de Serk (IRE) Mr J. Burley
23 **JEANS GENIE**, 4, b gr f Kayf Tara—Aberdeen Park Mr & Mrs Chris Massey
24 **MATRAVERS**, 8, b g Oasis Dream—Maakrah Martin Keighley Racing Club
25 **MELLO YELLO**, 5, b m Milan—Fernello Hot To Trot Jumping
26 **MISS ANTIPOVA**, 7, b m Pasternak—Herballistic Batsford Stud Racing Club
27 **MOZZARO (IRE)**, 4, b g Morozov (USA)—Baraza (IRE) Owners For Owners Mozzaro
28 **MR MAFIA (IRE)**, 10, b g Zerpour (IRE)—Wizzy (IRE) Peter Boggis
29 **OSCAR WORLD (IRE)**, 7, b m Oscar (IRE)—Maresin P. R. Armour
30 **PINNACLE PEAK**, 4, b g Passing Glance—Giovanna M Boothright & G Lovett
31 **PIRATE LOOK (IRE)**, 5, b g Canford Cliffs (IRE)—Gerika (FR) The Jack Sparrow Syndicate
32 **RAVING BONKERS**, 6, ch g Notnowcato—Harriet's Girl What In Heavens Partnership
33 **REVE**, 5, b g Nathaniel (IRE)—Rouge (FR) Mr O. F. Ryan
34 **ROBSAM (IRE)**, 4, b g Mahler—Silver Set (IRE) Mr M. Capp
35 **SOLSTICE STAR**, 9, b g Kayf Tara—Clover Green (IRE) Foxtrot Racing: Solstice Star
36 **SOMEWHERE TO BE (IRE)**, 7, ch g Golan (IRE)—Somethinaboutmolly (IRE) P. R. Armour
37 **WORLD WAR (IRE)**, 5, ch g Galileo (IRE)—Jacqueline Quest (IRE) Mrs L. Jones
38 **YOUNG PHOENIX (IRE)**, 7, b g Robin des Pres (FR)—Lady Phoenix (IRE) The Four Tops

THREE-YEAR-OLDS

39 **SARASOTA STAR (IRE)**, b gr g Zebedee—Riviera Rose (IRE) Torben Dal & Jon Hughes

Other Owners: Mr J. Abernethy, Mr D. Abraham, Mrs Y. E. Allison, Mr Stuart Baikie, The Batsford Stud, Mr David Bishop, Mr P. F. Boggis, Mr M. Boothright, Mr Colin Bowkley, Mr A. Cole, Mr T. Dal, Mr P.K. Davis, Mrs C. L. Dee, Mr P. Deffains, Mr J. A. Gent, Mr J. M. Gibbs, Mr Nick Guttridge, Mr Tyrone Hanlon, Mr B. G. Hellyer, Mr R. S. Hoskins, Mr Jon Hughes, Mrs Jacqueline Hughes, Mrs B. J. Keighley, Mr W. R. Kinsey, Mr G. Lovett, Mr A. S. Martin, Mr M. Parker, Mr S. C. Prowting, Mr B. Smith, Mr Neville Statham, Mr G. M. Thornton.

Assistant Trainer: Matthew Carter

Conditional: Harry Stock. **Amateur:** Mr Paddy Berkins.

321 MR SHAUN KEIGHTLEY, Newmarket

Postal: **Flat 1, Harraton Court Stables, Church Lane, Exning, Newmarket, Suffolk, CB8 7HF**
Contacts: **PHONE (01638) 577279**

1 **BOLLIHOPE**, 7, ch g Medicean—Hazy Dancer Mr S. Lockyer
2 **CANIMAR**, 4, b f Havana Gold (IRE)—Acquifer Simon Lockyer & Tim Clark
3 **DANCE TEACHER (IRE)**, 5, ch m Lope de Vega (IRE)—Fairnilee Simon Lockyer & Tim Clark
4 **ELUSIF (IRE)**, 4, b g Elusive Quality (USA)—Appealing (IRE) Simon Lockyer & Tim Clark

MR SHAUN KEIGHTLEY - Continued

5 **JOHN JOINER**, 7, b g Captain Gerrard (IRE)—Nigella **Mrs S Lynch & Mr A Lomax**
6 **MOREMONEYMOREPARTY (IRE)**, 4, b f Epaulette (AUS)—Three Times **Mr S. Lockyer**
7 **PERFECT SOLDIER (IRE)**, 5, b g Kodiac—Independent Girl (IRE) **Simon Lockyer & Tim Clark**
8 **RAIL DANCER**, 7, b g Rail Link—Mara Dancer **Mr S. Lockyer**
9 **VOLUNTEER**, 6, b g Aqlaam—Blaenavon
10 **WARNING LIGHT**, 4, b f Lethal Force (IRE)—Cefira (USA) **Simon Lockyer & Tim Clark**

THREE-YEAR-OLDS

11 **ANGEL BLACK (IRE)**, b c Dark Angel (IRE)—Basandere (FR) **Simon Lockyer & Tim Clark**
12 **IMAGE OF THE MOON**, b f Mukhadram—Hamsat Elqamar **Simon Lockyer & Tim Clark**
13 **JUAN DE VALDES**, br gr c Exceed And Excel (AUS)—Vayasa (FR) **Mrs C. C. Regalado-Gonzalez**
14 **LOVES FIRST (IRE)**, ch g Es Que Love (IRE)—Prima **Mr S. Lockyer**
15 **MAISIE MOO**, b f Swiss Spirit—Al Hawa (USA) **Simon Lockyer & Tim Clark**
16 **SAN CARLOS**, b c Havana Gold (IRE)—Ittasal **Mrs C. C. Regalado-Gonzalez**
17 **TROUBLE SHOOTER (IRE)**, b g Delegator—Khibraat **Mr S. Lockyer**

TWO-YEAR-OLDS

18 Gr f 12/4 Casamento (IRE)—Distant Waters (Lomitas)
19 **LILKIAN**, ch c 28/3 Sepoy (AUS)—Janie Runaway (IRE) (Antonius Pius (USA)) (3809)
20 B f 12/3 Anjaal—Miss Inferno (IRE) (Tagula (IRE)) (10000) **Simon Lockyer & Tim Clark**
21 B c 30/4 Gregorian (IRE)—Shambodia (IRE) (Petardia) (3000)
22 B f 8/2 Gale Force Ten—Snowtime (IRE) (Galileo (IRE)) (10113)
23 B f 25/2 Slade Power (IRE)—Winterwell (USA) (First Defence (USA)) (1000)

Other Owners: Mr T. M. Clarke, Mr A. R. A. Lomax, Mrs S. C. Lynch.

---

322 MR CHRISTOPHER KELLETT, Lathom
Postal: **6 Canal Cottages, Ring O Bells Lane, Lathom, Ormskirk, Lancashire, L40 5TF**
Contacts: PHONE (01704) 643775 MOBILE (07966) 097989
E-MAIL CNKellett@outlook.com WEBSITE www.chriskellettracing.co.uk

1 **ARGENT KNIGHT**, 9, gr g Sir Percy—Tussah **Blythe Stables LLP**
2 **CLONDAW STORM (IRE)**, 5, gr g September Storm (GER)—Oh So Smart (IRE) **Blythe Stables LLP**
3 **KODIMOOR (IRE)**, 6, b g Kodiac—Victoria Lodge (IRE) **Blythe Stables LLP**

THREE-YEAR-OLDS

4 **BLISTERING BARNEY (IRE)**, b g Sir Prancealot (IRE)—Eternal View (IRE) **Andy Bell & Fergus Lyons**
5 **CARLOW BOY (IRE)**, b g Elzaam (AUS)—Whitershadeofpale (IRE) **Andy Bell & Fergus Lyons**
6 **DECONSO**, b g Dandy Man (IRE)—Tranquil Flight **Andy Bell & Fergus Lyons**
7 **SHOWSHUTAI**, b g Showcasing—Sleeper **Andy Bell & Fergus Lyons**

Other Owners: Mr A. J. Bell, Mrs T. Bell, Mr F. Lyons, Mrs C. Lyons, Fergus & Caroline Lyons.

---

323 MISS GAY KELLEWAY, Newmarket
Postal: **Queen Alexandra Stables, 2 Chapel Street, Exning, Newmarket, Suffolk, CB8 7HA**
Contacts: PHONE (01638) 577778 MOBILE (07974) 948768
E-MAIL gaykellewayracing@hotmail.co.uk WEBSITE www.gaykellewayracing.com

Trainer also operates a satellite stable in Chantilly, France. Some horses may switch between yards.

1 **COSMELLI (ITY)**, 6, b g Mr Vegas (IRE)—Victorian Girl (GER) **Import Racing, G. Kelleway, M. Walker**
2 **CRYSTAL DEAUVILLE (FR)**, 4, b g Equiano (FR)—Crystal Plum (IRE) **iBoxit Ltd & Partner 2**
3 **FAIRY TALE (IRE)**, 4, b g Kheleyf (USA)—Singapore Fairy (FR) **Winterbeck Manor Stud & Gay Kelleway**
4 **GLOBAL ACADEMY (IRE)**, 4, b g Zebedee—Lady Meagan (IRE) **Dr J. Hon**
5 **GLOBAL HOPE (IRE)**, 4, b g Oasis Dream—Classic Remark (IRE) **Dr J. Hon**
6 **GLOBAL ROSE (IRE)**, 4, b f Dark Angel (IRE)—Classic Falcon (IRE) **Global Group Lifestyle and Sports Club**
7 **GLOBAL WONDER (IRE)**, 4, b g Kodiac—Traveller's Tales **Dr J. Hon**
8 **LADY ALAVESA**, 4, b f Westlake—Matilda Peace **N. Scandrett & Strictly Fun Racing Club**
9 **PASTIME**, 5, b g Pastoral Pursuits—Piddies Pride (IRE) **Boston R. S. & Countrywide Classics**
10 **PURPLE ROCK (IRE)**, 7, b g Fastnet Rock (AUS)—Amethyst (IRE) **Strictly Fun Racing Club**

MISS GAY KELLEWAY - Continued

11 **ROBERO**, 7, b g Piccolo—Ceilidh Band **John Farley & Gay Kelleway**
12 **ROBSDELIGHT (IRE)**, 4, br g Harbour Watch (IRE)—Silca Boo **Mr G. Kerr**
13 **STOSUR (IRE)**, 8, b m Mount Nelson—Jules (IRE) **B. C. Oakley**
14 **TOPMEUP**, 5, ch m Mayson—Ambrix (IRE) **Mortlock & Partners**
15 **UBLA (IRE)**, 6, ch g Arcano (IRE)—Manuelita Rose (ITY) **Strictly Fun Racing Club**

THREE-YEAR-OLDS

16 **ALLSMOKEANDMIRRORS**, b g Westlake—Kodafine (IRE) **Mr M. A. Walker**
17 **BOLT N BROWN**, b f Phoenix Reach (IRE)—Beat Seven **Logistics Terminal LLP**
18 **ELIEDEN (IRE)**, b f Camacho—Ohwhatalady (IRE) **A. Parr, G. Kelleway & D. Johnson**
19 **ELITE GAY**, b f Mazameer (IRE)—Minstrell Tygeress **Mr A. P. Griffin**
20 **GLOBAL CHALLENGER**, gr g Dark Angel (IRE)—Silca Boo **Dr J. Hon**
21 **GLOBAL GODDESS (IRE)**, b f Morpheus—Church Mice (IRE) **Dr J. Hon**
22 **GLOBAL SPECTRUM**, b c Dutch Art—Lady Darshaan (IRE) **Dr J. Hon**
23 **LADY NAVARRA (IRE)**, ch f Iffraaj—Natural Flair (USA) **Rioja Racing**
24 **MOVEONUP (IRE)**, b g Zebedee—Emma Dora (IRE) **B. C. Oakley**
25 **MUKHA MAGIC**, b g Mukhadram—Sweet Lemon (IRE) **P Crook, J Moynihan, R Mortlock**
26 **PHOENIX QUEEN**, b f Phoenix Reach (IRE)—Chocolada **Winterbeck Manor Stud Ltd**
27 **SCALE FORCE**, gr g Lethal Force (IRE)—Alectrona (FR) **iBoxit Ltd**
28 **STAR TALENT (IRE)**, b g Lilbourne Lad (IRE)—High Vintage (IRE) **Craig Robertson & Gay Kelleway**

TWO-YEAR-OLDS

29 B f 12/1 War Command (USA)—Amaya (USA) (Kingmambo (USA)) (10000)
30 B f 19/4 Mayson—Highly Spiced (Cadeaux Genereux) (5714) **Premier Thoroughbred Racing Ltd**
31 **INDURO DE FONTAINE (FR)**, b c 23/3 Manduro (GER)—
                                Indian View (GER) (Spectrum (IRE)) (13485) **Miss G. M. Kelleway**
32 **THUNDERDOME (FR)**, b c 25/4 Orpen (USA)—The Lucky Bug (GER) (Dr Devious (IRE)) (3371) **iBoxit Ltd**

Other Owners: Mr M. R. Brown, Countrywide Classics Ltd, Miss P. F. Crook, Mr J. W. Farley, Mr G. A. Hodson, Impor Racing, Ms D. S. Johnson, Mr R. Mortlock, Mr D. J. Mourad, Mr J. Moynihan, Mr A. Newbold, P. R. Nodder, A. B. Parr Mr C. Robertson, Mr N. S. Scandrett, Mr I. J. Sparham, Mr P. R. Tyler.

Assistant Trainer: Anne-Sophie Crombez **Head Girl:** Liz Mullin

---

324

MRS STEF KENIRY, Middleham
Postal: **Barry Keniry Racing, Warwick Lodge, North Road, Middleham, North Yorkshire, DL8 4PB**
Contacts: **PHONE (01969) 368467**

1 **ABEL TASMAN**, 5, b g Mount Nelson—Helena Molony (IRE) **Mrs S. J. Keniry**
2 **AMY BLAIR**, 6, b g Captain Gerrard (IRE)—Shalad'or **Mrs S. J. Keniry**
3 **BETANCOURT (IRE)**, 9, ch g Refuse To Bend (IRE)—Orinoco (IRE) **Mrs S. J. Keniry**
4 **BOX AND COX**, 4, br g Harbour Watch (IRE)—Rosa Luxemburg **Mrs S. J. Keniry**
5 **CAPTAIN PUGWASH (IRE)**, 5, b g Sir Prancealot (IRE)—Liscoa (IRE) **Miss Alison Jones**
6 **DURBANVILLE**, 7, b g Black Sam Bellamy (IRE)—Kealshore Lass **Mrs S. J. Keniry**
7 **GILMER (IRE)**, 8, b g Exceed And Excel (AUS)—Cherokee Rose (IRE) **Mrs S. J. Keniry**
8 4, B g Dylan Thomas (IRE)—Handikova (IRE)
9 **HERMANUS (IRE)**, 7, ch m Golan (IRE)—Almost Trumps **Mrs S. J. Keniry**
10 **JAXLIGHT**, 7, b m Lucarno (USA)—Jaxelle (FR) **Mr J. D. King**
11 **MISSION TRIO (IRE)**, 7, b g Presenting—Miss Brandywell (IRE) **J. B. Wallwin**
12 4, B g Fair Mix (IRE)—Mobhi Boreen (IRE)
13 **OLD SALT (IRE)**, 7, b g Craigsteel—Andrea Gale (IRE) **Mr A. Kanji**
14 **RAFFERTY (IRE)**, 5, b g Arcadio (GER)—Mighty Star (IRE) **J. B. Wallwin**
15 **SPIRIT OF SARWAN (IRE)**, 5, b g Elzaam (AUS)—Hidden Heart (USA) **Mrs S. J. Keniry**
16 **TRAPPER PEAK (IRE)**, 10, b g Westerner—Banningham Blaze **Mr J. D. King**

THREE-YEAR-OLDS

17 **CHAMPYOWNEZ**, ch g Medicean—Mawjoodah **Mr D. R. Gilbert**
18 **CORMIER (IRE)**, b c Born To Sea (IRE)—Scotch Bonnet (IRE) **Mr K. J. Strangeway**
19 B g Malinas (GER)—Lily Lenor (IRE) **Dan Gilbert & Kristian Strangeway**
20 **MACS BLESSINGS**, b g Society Rock (IRE)—Lear's Crown (USA) **From the Front Racing & Stef Keniry**
21 **MISS WOW (IRE)**, B f Elusive Pimpernel (USA)—Hannah's Magic (IRE)
22 **POTENZA (IRE)**, b c Born To Sea (IRE)—Cranky Spanky (IRE) **Mr K. J. Strangeway**

MRS STEF KENIRY - Continued

TWO-YEAR-OLDS

23 Ch f 19/2 Cityscape—Ananda Kanda (USA) (Hero's Tribute (USA)) (761) **Mr K. J. Strangeway**

Other Owners: Mr S. Franks, From The Front Racing, Mr A. N. Gargan.

---

325 MR NICK KENT, Brigg
Postal: Newstead House, Newstead Priory, Cadney Road, Brigg, Lincolnshire, DN20 9HP
Contacts: PHONE (01652) 650628 MOBILE (07710) 644428
E-MAIL nick@nickkent.co.uk WEBSITE www.nickkent.co.uk

1 BENE REGINA (IRE), 7, b m Beneficial—Lareine d'anjou (FR) **BDS Pointers**
2 BOWIE (IRE), 12, br g Pelder (IRE)—La Fenice (IRE) **Cynthia Commons,Marina Kent,Nick Kent**
3 BRIGHTS PARK (IRE), 7, b g Mahler—Ellesmere (IRE) **Mr Andy Parkin, Nick Kent**
4 CATLIN, 4, b f Bollin Eric—Linen Line **Cynthia Commons, Nick Kent**
5 DUFFY ALLEN (FR), 6, b g Lucarno (USA)—Parade (FR) **Mrs M Pinney, N Kent**
6 4, B f Watar (IRE)—Durango (IRE)
7 GONALSTON CLOUD (IRE), 12, gr g Cloudings (IRE)—Roseoengus (IRE) **Mr R. J. Jackson**
8 LAHLOO, 5, b m Native Ruler—Clipper Line (USA) **Mr J. N. Kent**
9 OREGON GOLD (FR), 6, b g Confuchias (IRE)—Gold Wine (FR) **Newstead Priory Racing Club**
10 PICKNICK PARK, 7, b g Sulamani (IRE)—Eva's Edge (IRE) **Mr Andy Parkin, Nick Kent**
11 POP THE CHAMPERS (IRE), 8, b g Scorpion (IRE)—Manesbil (IRE) **C W Booth, W Wesley, N Kent**
12 THE GRINDER (IRE), 7, b g Arcadio (GER)—Bincas Beauty (IRE) **Mrs Wendy Wesley, Mr Nick Kent**
13 THEBIGCLEANUP (IRE), 7, b g Milan—Newcastlebeauty (IRE) **Mr C Booth and Mrs Wendy Wesley**
14 TIME IS HONEY (IRE), 6, ch m Rajj (IRE)—Bob's Sarah (IRE) **Nick Kent Racing Club II**

TWO-YEAR-OLDS

15 B g 17/6 Multiplex—Linen Line (Double Eclipse (IRE))
16 B f 14/4 Universal (IRE)—Saaboog (Teofilo (IRE)) **Mrs M. E. Kent**

Other Owners: Mr C. W. Booth, Mr Bob Carter, Miss C. Commons, Mrs Sheila Daubney, Mrs Dai Evans, Mrs Marina Kent, Mr Nick Kent, Mr Andy Parkin, Mrs M. A. Pinney, Mrs Wendy Wesley.

Assistant Trainer: Mrs Jane Kent.

Jockey (NH): Adam Wedge.

---

326 MR LEONARD KERR, Irvine
Postal: Annick Lodge, Irvine, Ayrshire, KA11 2AN

1 CONS AMIGO (IRE), 6, b g Blueprint (IRE)—Consproblem (IRE) **Mr A Kerr Mr L Kerr**
2 HAVANA JACK (IRE), 9, b g Westerner—Hackler Poitin (IRE) **Mrs J. A. Watts**
3 MISTERMOONBOY (IRE), 5, ch g Mister Fotis (USA)—Sister Moon (IRE) **Mr A Kerr Mr L Kerr**
4 SWORD OF FATE (IRE), 6, b g Beneficial—Beann Ard (IRE) **Mr A Kerr Mr L Kerr**

Other Owners: Mr A. M. Kerr.

---

327 MR ALAN KING, Barbury Castle
Postal: Barbury Castle Stables, Wroughton, Wiltshire, SN4 0QZ
Contacts: PHONE (01793) 815009 FAX (01793) 845080 MOBILE (07973) 461233
E-MAIL alan@alanking.biz WEBSITE www.alankingracing.co.uk

1 AKARITA LIGHTS (IRE), 5, b g Arctic Cosmos (USA)—Akarita (IRE) **Mr Allan Stennett & Mickley Stud**
2 ALSA MIX (FR), 7, gr m Al Namix (FR)—Lady Tsana (FR) **Mrs J. A. Watts**
3 ARKYN (FR), 4, ch g Champs Elysees—Fever Fever (USA) **Mr J. A. Law**
4 AWESOME ROSIE, 8, b m Midnight Legend—
Awesome Aunt (IRE) **Mrs Meacham, Withyslade & Mrs A L Davies**
5 AZZERTI (FR), 7, b g Voix du Nord (FR)—Zalagarry (FR) **McNeill Family and Prodec Networks Ltd**
6 BALLYWOOD (FR), 5, b g Ballingarry (IRE)—Miss Hollywood (FR) **Highclere Thoroughbred Racing -Ballywood**
7 BASTIEN (FR), 8, b br g Panoramic—Que du Charmil (FR) **The Sandy Lodge Syndicate**
8 4, B g Scorpion (IRE)—Be My Granny **Alan King**

MR ALAN KING - Continued

- **9 BENEAGLES (IRE)**, 7, b g Milan—Liss Rua (IRE) **Lady Horn-Smith & Godfrey Wilson**
- **10 BERINGER**, 4, b g Sea The Stars (IRE)—Edaraat (USA) **L Field, B Cognet, N Farrell, J Spack**
- **11 BIG CHIEF BENNY (IRE)**, 8, ch g Beneficial—Be Airlie (IRE) **Oitavos Partnership**
- **12 BOARD OF TRADE**, 8, ch g Black Sam Bellamy (IRE)—Realms of Gold (USA) **Ian Payne & Kim Franklin**
- **13 BRIGADE OF GUARDS (IRE)**, 5, b g Presenting—Lasado (IRE) **C Dingwall, N Farrell & J Murray**
- **14 BURREN WALK**, 4, ch f Lucarno (USA)—Persian Walk (FR) **Mr D. J. Barry**
- **15 CANELO (IRE)**, 6, ch g Mahler—Nobody's Darling (IRE) **Mr J. P. McManus**
- **16 CASPAR THE CUB (IRE)**, 4, ch g Casamento (IRE)—Esposa (IRE) **The Barbury Lions**
- **17 CHATEZ (IRE)**, 8, b g Dandy Man (IRE)—Glory Days (GER) **Mrs P. Andrews**
- **18 CHOSEN PATH (IRE)**, 6, b g Well Chosen—Karsulu (IRE) **McNeill Family and Prodec Networks Ltd**
- **19 COEUR DE LION**, 6, b g Pour Moi (IRE)—Hora **The Barbury Boys**
- **20 COGBURN**, 7, ch g Black Sam Bellamy (IRE)—Realms of Gold (USA) **Mrs Sue Welch & Alan King**
- **21 COLDITZ CASTLE (IRE)**, 5, ch g Getaway (GER)—Stowaway Sue (IRE) **Charles Dingwall & Tony Morris**
- **22 COSMEAPOLITAN**, 6, b g Mawatheeq (USA)—Cosmea **Kingston Stud**
- **23 CRACKER FACTORY**, 4, b g Poet's Voice—Pure Song **Mr Simon Munir & Mr Isaac Souede**
- **24 DELICE**, 4, b f Delegator—Perception (IRE) **Kingston Stud & David Anderson**
- **25 DEXCITE (FR)**, 8, b f gr Authorized (IRE)—Belle Alicia (FR) **Crossed Fingers Partnership**
- **26 DEYRANN DE CARJAC (FR)**, 6, b g Balko (FR)—Queyrann (FR) **Mr J. A. Law**
- **27 DINGO DOLLAR (IRE)**, 7, ch g Golden Lariat (USA)—
                                               Social Society (IRE) **M Warren J Holmes R Kidner & J Wright**
- **28 DINO VELVET (FR)**, 6, b g Naaqoos—Matgil (FR) **McNeill Family & Niall Farrell**
- **29 4**, B f Milan—Dream Lass (IRE) **Hunscote Stud**
- **30 EDWARDSTONE**, 5, b g Kayf Tara—Nothingtoloose (IRE) **Robert Abrey & Ian Thurtle**
- **31 ELGIN**, 7, b g Duke of Marmalade (IRE)—China Tea (USA) **Elite Racing Club**
- **32 ELYSEES (IRE)**, 4, ch g Champs Elysees—Queen of Tara (IRE) **Elysees Partnership**
- **33 ESCAPABILITY (IRE)**, 4, b g Excelebration (IRE)—Brief Escapade (IRE) **Alan King & Anthony Bromley**
- **34 EYES RIGHT**, 4, b f Passing Glance—Call Me A Star **Hamer & Richardson**
- **35 FIBONACCI**, 5, ch g Galileo (IRE)—Tereschenko (USA) **Mrs E. A. Prowting**
- **36 FIDUX (FR)**, 6, b g Fine Grain (JPN)—Folle Tempete (FR) **Axom LXVIII**
- **37 FIELDS OF FORTUNE**, 5, b g Champs Elysees—Widescreen (USA) **HP Racing Fields Of Fortune**
- **38 5**, B g Mountain High (IRE)—Forget The Ref (IRE) **Robert Abrey & Ian Thurtle**
- **39 FORGETTHESMALLTALK (IRE)**, 7, b g Flemensfirth (USA)—
                                               Mylane du Charmil (FR) **Tim Leadbeater & Barry Winfield**
- **40 FOURSHOES**, 4, b f Passing Glance—Peel Me A Grape **Mrs E. A. Prowting**
- **41 FRET D'ESTRUVAL (FR)**, 4, br g No Risk At All (FR)—
                                               Udine d'estruval (FR) **Mr Simon Munir & Mr Isaac Souede**
- **42 FULL GLASS (FR)**, 6, b g Diamond Green (FR)—Full Tune (FR) **Mr Simon Munir & Mr Isaac Souede**
- **43 FUSEAU (FR)**, 4, b g Barastraight—Monepopee (FR) **Michael Rembaum & Michael Tuckey**
- **44 GAVI DI GAVI (IRE)**, 4, b g Camacho—Blossom Deary (IRE) **L Field, N Farrell, B Cognet & C Trigg**
- **45 GIVEAWAY GLANCE**, 6, br m Passing Glance—Giving **Pitchall Stud Partnership**
- **46 GIVING BACK**, 5, br gr m Midnight Legend—Giving **Pitchall Stud Partnership & Mrs Pat Toye**
- **47 GIVING GLANCES**, 4, b f Passing Glance—Giving **Pitchall Stud Partnership**
- **48 GLASHA'S PEAK**, 5, b m Flemensfirth (USA)—Peggies Run **Sir Christopher Wates**
- **49 GOOD MAN PAT (IRE)**, 6, b g Gold Well—Basically Supreme (IRE) **Mr D. J. S. Sewell**
- **50 GREY DIAMOND (FR)**, 5, b g Gris de Gris (IRE)—Diamond of Diana (FR) **Walters Plant Hire Ltd**
- **51 HARAMBE**, 6, b g Malinas (GER)—Crystal Princess (IRE) **Niall Farrell & Friends**
- **52 HEREWEGO HEREWEGO (IRE)**, 8, b g Kalanisi (IRE)—Downtown Train (IRE) **Mr J. P. McManus**
- **53 HOSTILE**, 5, ch g Malinas (GER)—Skew **Alan King**
- **54 HOTTER THAN HELL (FR)**, 5, ch m No Risk At All (FR)—Ombrelle (FR) **The Devil's Advocates**
- **55 I'M A BELIEVER**, 5, b m Sixties Icon—Fascinatin Rhythm **Mr W. A. Harrison-Allan**
- **56 INN THE BULL (GER)**, 6, ch g Lope de Vega (IRE)—Ile Rousse **Loose Cannon Racing**
- **57 INNER DRIVE (IRE)**, 11, b g Heron Island (IRE)—Hingis (IRE) **McNeill Family & A King**
- **58 JABOTICABA (FR)**, 5, ch g Muhtathir—Janiceinwonderland (FR) **Owners Group 025**
- **59 JUNDERSTAND**, 4, ch f Champs Elysees—Sienna Sunset (IRE) **R. Bailey**
- **60 JUST IN TIME**, 5, b g Excelebration (IRE)—Flying Finish (IRE) **HP Racing Just In Time**
- **61 KAREZAK (IRE)**, 8, b g Azamour (IRE)—Karawana (IRE) **McNeill Family Ltd**
- **62 KERROW (IRE)**, 9, ch g Mahler—Olives Hall (IRE) **Mr T. J. Hemmings**
- **63 KIMBERLEY POINT**, 6, b m Sixties Icon—Kingara **P. E. Atkinson**
- **64 KISMAT**, 4, b f Sepoy (AUS)—Magic Destiny **R. Bailey**
- **65 KOOTENAY RIVER (IRE)**, 5, ch g Dubai Destination (USA)—Siwaara (IRE) **Mrs E. A. Prowting**
- **66 KOZIER (GER)**, 5, ch g Muhtathir—Kasumi (GER) **Alan King**
- **67 LABEL DES OBEAUX (FR)**, 8, b g Saddler Maker (IRE)—La Bessiere (FR) **David Sewell & Terry Warner**
- **68 4**, B g Yeats (IRE)—Lady Secret (FR) **Mr J. P. McManus**
- **69 LEXINGTON LAW (IRE)**, 6, b g Lawman (FR)—Tus Nua (IRE) **Middleham Park Racing XXXIX**
- **70 LISP (IRE)**, 5, ch g Poet's Voice—Hora **Mr & Mrs R. G. Kelvin-Hughes**

MR ALAN KING - Continued

71 **LONG SOCKS,** 5, ch g Notnowcato—Sienna Sunset (IRE) **R. Bailey**
72 **LORD WALSINGHAM,** 5, b g Shirocco (GER)—Glorious Twelfth (IRE) **C Dingwall, A Morris & S Kiss**
73 **LOUGH DERG ROSE (IRE),** 6, b m Stowaway—Good Looking Woman (IRE) **Simon Munir & Isaac Souede**
74 **MADIBA PASSION (FR),** 5, b g Al Namix (FR)—Birsheba (FR) **Alan King**
75 **MAHLERMADE (IRE),** 6, ch g Mahler—Double Concerto (IRE) **The Lesser Lights**
76 **MANOR PARK,** 4, b g Medicean—Jadeel **McNeill Family & Niall Farrell**
77 **MASTER BLUEYES (IRE),** 6, gr g Mastercraftsman (IRE)—Miss Blueyes (IRE) **The Legends Partnership**
78 **MESSIRE DES OBEAUX (FR),** 7, b g Saddler Maker (IRE)—Madame Lys (FR)
79 **MIA'S STORM (IRE),** 9, b m September Storm (GER)—Letitia's Gain (IRE) **The Maple Street Partnership**
80 **MICK MAESTRO (FR),** 6, b br g Air Chief Marshal (FR)—Mick Maya (FR) **Crossed Fingers Partnership**
81 **MIDNIGHT GLANCE,** 4, b g Passing Glance—Magical Legend **R. H. Kerswell**
82 **MIDNIGHT MAESTRO,** 7, b g Midnight Legend—Calaminta **Mr J. P. McManus**
83 **MIDNIGHTREFERENDUM,** 6, b m Midnight Legend—Forget The Ref (IRE) **Robert Abrey & Ian Thurtle**
84 **MILLSTONE,** 5, b g Alkaased (USA)—Stoney Path **Mrs S. C. Welch**
85 **MISS CRICK,** 8, b m Midnight Legend—Kwaheri **Mr D. J. S. Sewell**
86 **MR PUMBLECHOOK,** 5, b g Midnight Legend—Definitely Pip (IRE) **Mr D. J. S. Sewell**
87 **MYSTICAL CLOUDS (IRE),** 6, gr g Cloudings (IRE)—Silent Valley **Mr T. J. Hemmings**
88 **NEBUCHADNEZZAR (FR),** 4, b g Planteur (IRE)—Trexana **Top Brass 2**
89 **NEWTOWN BOY (IRE),** 6, b g Beneficial—Tanit Lady (IRE) **Mr & Mrs Paul & Clare Rooney**
90 **NOBBY,** 5, b g Authorized (IRE)—Magic Music (IRE) **R. Bailey**
91 **NOTACHANCE (IRE),** 5, b g Mahler—Ballybrowney Hall (IRE) **David J S Sewell & Tim Leadbeater**
92 **NYLON SPEED (IRE),** 5, b g Campanologist (USA)—Neuquen (IRE) **Axom LXXIV**
93 **OUR POWER (IRE),** 4, b g Power—Scripture (IRE) **Walters Plant Hire & James & Jean Potter**
94 **OUTOFTHEQUESTION,** 5, b g Delegator—Why Dubai (USA) **The Barbury Lions**
95 **OUTONPATROL (IRE),** 5, gr m Stowaway—Burnt Oil Babe (IRE) **McNeill Family & Niall Farrell**
96 **PADDY BOSS (IRE),** 7, ch g Gamut (IRE)—Agladora (FR) **McNeill Family Ltd**
97 **PASSING CALL,** 6, b m Passing Glance—Call Me A Legend **Pitchall Stud Partnership**
98 **PEGGIES VENTURE,** 8, b m Presenting—Peggies Run **Sir Christopher & Lady Wates**
99 **PERFECT HARMONY (IRE),** 7, b g Definite Article—Brandam Supreme (IRE) **Mrs E. A. Prowting**
100 **PERFECT PREDATOR,** 4, b g Passing Glance—Cosmea **Kingston Stud**
101 **POTTERMAN,** 6, b g Sulamani (IRE)—Polly Potter **James & Jean Potter**
102 **POTTERS VISION (IRE),** 6, b m Getaway (GER)—Peripheral Vision (IRE) **James & Jean Potter**
103 **PRAECEPS (IRE),** 4, b g Canford Cliffs (IRE)—Sliding Scale **Incipe Partnership**
104 **RAINBOW DREAMER,** 6, b g Aqlaam—Zamhrear **The Maple Street Partnership**
105 **REDICEAN,** 5, b g Medicean—Red Halo (IRE) **Cheveley Park Stud Limited**
106 **REVEREND JACOBS,** 5, b g Nathaniel (IRE)—Light Impact (IRE) **Crossed Fingers Partnership**
107 **RIVER FROST,** 7, b g Silver Frost (IRE)—River Test **Mr J. P. McManus**
108 **ROCK FORCE (IRE),** 4, b g Fastnet Rock (AUS)—Sweepstake (IRE) **Apple Tree Stud**
109 **ROCK STEADY (IRE),** 6, ch g Intikhab (USA)—Mannsara (IRE) **Owners Group 011**
110 **RUNNING CLOUD (IRE),** 4, b g Cacique (IRE)—Nimbus Star **HP Racing Running Cloud**
111 **SALMANAZAR,** 11, b g Classic Cliche (IRE)—Leroy's Sister (FR) **Top Brass Partnership**
112 **SAN RUMOLDO,** 4, ch g Malinas (GER)—Ancora (IRE) **Alan King**
113 **SCARLET DRAGON,** 6, b g Sir Percy—Welsh Angel **HP Racing Scarlet Dragon**
114 **SCEAU ROYAL (FR),** 7, b g Doctor Dino (FR)—Sandside (FR) **Mr Simon Munir & Mr Isaac Souede**
115 **SEABOROUGH (IRE),** 4, b g Born To Sea (IRE)—Nobilissima (IRE) **Nautical 5**
116 **SECOND TIME AROUND,** 7, b g Midnight Legend—Silk Rope (IRE) **Mr & Mrs R. Scott**
117 **SENIOR CITIZEN,** 6, b g Tobougg (IRE)—Mothers Help **McNeill Family Ltd**
118 **SHANNON HILL,** 5, b g Kayf Tara—Shannon Native (IRE) **Grech & Parkin**
119 **SHESHOON SONNY (FR),** 4, b g Youmzain (IRE)—Minnie's Mystery (FR) **McNeill Family & Niall Farrell**
120 **SIMPLY A LEGEND,** 10, b g Midnight Legend—Disco Danehill (IRE) **Mrs E. A. Prowting**
121 **SIR PASS I AM,** 6, b g Passing Glance—Orbital Orchid **Sandie & David Newton**
122 **SIXTY'S BELLE,** 5, b m Gold Well—Over Sixty **Mr & Mrs C. Harris**
123 **SMITH'S BAY,** 6, b g Midnight Legend—Takotna (IRE) **Ian Payne & Kim Franklin**
124 **STOCKBURN (IRE),** 6, b g Scorpion (IRE)—Hayabusa **Godfrey Keirle & Alan King**
125 **STYLISH MOMENT (IRE),** 6, b g Milan—Up The Style (IRE) **Mr T. J. Hemmings**
126 **SULA ISLAND,** 5, ch m Sulamani (IRE)—Cosmea **Kingston Stud**
127 **TALKISCHEAP (IRE),** 7, b g Getaway—Carrigmoorna Oak (IRE) **Mr C. B. J. Dingwall**
128 **TARA VIEW,** 8, b m Kayf Tara—Temptation (FR) **Mr D. J. Barry**
129 5, B g Jeremy (USA)—Teffia Gold (IRE) **Mr J. P. McManus**
130 **THE BLUES MASTER (IRE),** 5, gr g Mastercraftsman (IRE)—Catch The Blues (IRE) **HJW Partnership**
131 **THE CULL BANK (IRE),** 5, b m Yeats (IRE)—Creme d'arblay (IRE) **Mrs J. A. Watts**
132 **THE DEVILS DROP (IRE),** 6, b g Court Cave (IRE)—Concernforkillen (IRE) **Mr D. M. Mason**
133 **THE GLANCING QUEEN (IRE),** 5, b m Jeremy (USA)—Glancing (IRE) **Dingwall, Farrell, Hornsey & Murray**
134 **THE TOURARD MAN (IRE),** 13, b g Shantou (USA)—Small Iron **Mr & Mrs F Bell,N Farrell, A Marsh**
135 **THE UNIT (IRE),** 8, b g Gold Well—Sovana (FR) **International Plywood (Importers) Ltd**

MR ALAN KING - Continued

136 TIFFIN TOP, 4, gr g Oasis Dream—Mussoorie (FR) **McNeill Family Ltd**
137 TILLYTHETANK (IRE), 6, b m Stowaway—All Heart **Alan King**
138 TIMOTEO (FR), 6, b g Diamond Green (FR)—Goldnella (FR) **Million in Mind Partnership**
139 TOP TUG (IRE), 8, ch g Halling (USA)—Top Romance (IRE) **Elite Racing Club**
140 TOUR DE PARIS (IRE), 4, b g Champs Elysees—Disco Lights **HP Racing Tour de Paris**
141 VAIN GIRL, 4, b f Malinas (GER)—Line Freedom (FR) **Michael Rembaum & Michael Tuckey**
142 VALDEZ, 12, ch g Doyen (IRE)—Skew **Riverdee Stable**
143 VOIE DANS VOIE (FR), 6, br g Coastal Path—Peggy Pierji (FR) **R. & P. Scott & I. Payne & K. Franklin**
144 WALTER WHITE (FR), 4, b g Maxios—Antique Rose (GER) **Mr Simon Munir & Mr Isaac Souede**
145 WAR CHIEF, 5, ch g Aqlaam—My Colleen (USA) **Andrews Farrell King McNeill Sullivan**
146 WHO DARES WINS (IRE), 7, b g Jeremy (USA)—Savignano **HP Racing Who Dares Wins**
147 WILDE BLUE YONDER (IRE), 10, b g Oscar (IRE)—Blue Gallery (IRE) **Maybe Only Fools Have Horses**
148 WILDE SPIRIT (IRE), 5, b m Oscar (IRE)—Full of Spirit (IRE) **Mr & Mrs C. Harris**
149 WILLIAM H BONNEY, 8, b g Midnight Legend—Calamintha **Mr & Mrs R. Scott**
150 WILLIAM HUNTER, 7, b g Mawatheeq (USA)—Cosmea **Incipe Partnership**
151 YANWORTH, 9, ch g Norse Dancer (IRE)—Yota (FR) **Mr J. P. McManus**
152 YESANDNO (IRE), 6, b g Scorpion (IRE)—In Fact (IRE) **Mrs G. Meacham**
153 ZIGA BOY (FR), 10, gr g Califet (FR)—Our Ziga (FR) **Axom Ll**

THREE-YEAR-OLDS

154 AWEEDRAM (IRE), ch g Mukhadram—Invitee **McNeill Family & Niall Farrell**
155 CHICAGO DOLL, ch f Cityscape—Crooked Wood (USA) **Hunscote Stud**
156 CHICAGO GUY, ch c Cityscape—Hail Shower (IRE) **Hunscote Stud**
157 DUNKERRON, b g Kuroshio (AUS)—Triple Cee (IRE) **Ron Sullivan & Kingston Stud**
158 GREEN ETOILE, ch g Nathaniel (IRE)—Myriades d'etoiles (IRE) **Mr Simon Munir & Mr Isaac Souede**
159 GROUP STAGE (GER), b g Maxios—Good Hope (GER) **McNeill Family & Niall Farrell**
160 HUMMDINGER (FR), ch g Planteur—Interior (USA) **The Barbury Lions 4**
161 LUKE SAN, b g Excelebration (IRE)—Fantastisch (IRE) **Mrs M. C. Sweeney**
162 B f Champs Elysees—Ommadawn (IRE) **Mr & Mrs R. Scott**
163 PASSERINA, b f Coach House (IRE)—Dolcetto (IRE) **The Bacchanalians**
164 PECKINPAH (IRE), ch g Excelebration (IRE)—Melodrama (IRE) **Alan King**
165 SEPHTON, b g Shamardal (USA)—Honour **The Barbury Lions 4**
166 B g Intello (GER)—Storyland (USA) **Mr & Mrs R. Scott**
167 SUKALIA, b f Swiss Spirit—Perception (IRE) **Kingston Stud & David Anderson**
168 THE OLYMPIAN (FR), ch g Olympic Glory (IRE)—Basira (FR) **Mr J. P. McManus**
169 TRONADA, b f Toronado (IRE)—Manbaa (USA) **The Barbury Lions 4**
170 TRUESHAN (FR), b g Planteur (IRE)—Shao Line (FR) **Singula Partnership**

TWO-YEAR-OLDS

171 B c 17/3 No Nay Never (USA)—
          Duchess of Gazeley (IRE) (Halling (USA)) (43809) **Jamie Magee, A Bromley & A King**
172 B c 12/2 Harbour Watch (IRE)—
          Volkovkha (Holy Roman Emperor (IRE)) (4761) **Jamie Magee, Henry Ponsonby & Alan King**

Other Owners: Mr R. Abrey, Mr D. J. Anderson, Axom Ltd, Mr F. D. Bell, Mrs H. L. Bell, Mr David Bond, Mr P. A. Boyle, A. R. Bromley, Mr N. S. G. Bunter, Mr S. Clancy, Mr N. Clyne, Mr B. R. Cognet, Mrs A. L. Davies, Mr I. Dodds-Smith, Mr D. Downie, P. J. Dunkley, Mrs D. Dunkley, Mr N. Farrell, Mr J. M. Fawbert, Mrs L. H. Field, Mr R. S. Field, Miss K. M. Franklin, Mr A. Gemmell, G. F. Goode, Mr C. M. Grech, Mr M. Grier, Mr C. M. Hamer, Mr C. I. K. Harris, Mrs C. A. Harris, Mr D. A. Heffer, Highclere Thoroughbred Racing Ltd, Mr A. J. Hill, Mr D. F. Hill, Mr B. M. Hillier, Mrs K. Holmes, J. Holmes, Mr D. Holmes, Lady E. Horn-Smith, J. Hornsey, Mr D. J. Jackson, Mr C. S. D. James, G. F. Keirle, R. G. Kelvin-Hughes, Mrs E. A. Kelvin-Hughes, R. Kent, Mr R. A. Kidner, Mr S. J. Kiss, Mr E. T. D. Leadbeater, Mr W. P. Ledward, Mr R. M. Levitt, Mr J. Magee, Miss K. A. Marsh, Mr A. R. W. Marsh, Mr W. D. C. Minton, Mr A. A. Morris, S. E. Munir, Mr J. J. Murray, Mrs D. C. Nicholson, Miss M. Noden, Mr P. Nolan, Mr T. Nolan, T. S. Palin, Mr S. J. Parkin, Mr I. T. Payne, Miss H. Pease, W. H. Ponsonby, Mrs M. J. Potter, Mr J. E. Potter, Mr M. Prince, Prodec Networks Ltd, Mr M. J. Rembaum, Mrs S. Richardson, Mr S. J. Rogers, Mr P. A. Rooney, Mrs C. Rooney, Mrs P. M. Scott, R. Scott, Mr S. Smith, Mrs L. A. Smith, Mr I. Souede, Mrs J. A. Spack, A. Stennett, Mr R. T. Sullivan, Mr A. L. Tappin, Mr I. R. Thurtle, Mrs C. Townene, Mr M. Townroe, Mrs P. J. Toye, Mr C. G. Trigg, M. J. Tuckey, Mr O. Vaughan, Mr E. C. J. W. Walsh, J. T. Warner, Mr M. K. Warren, Lady G. F. Wates, Mr N. Williamson, G. A. Wilson, B. Winfield, J. Wright.

Assistant Trainers: Dan Horsford, Olly Stevens. **Pupil Assistant:** Robin Smith

Jockey (NH): Wayne Hutchinson. **Conditional:** Tom Bellamy, Kevin Dowling, Will Featherstone, Jamie Insole.

328 MR NEIL KING, Barbury Castle
Postal: **Upper Herdswick Farm, Barbury Castle, Swindon, Wiltshire, SN4 0QH**
Contacts: **PHONE (01793) 845011 FAX (01793) 845011 MOBILE (07880) 702325**
E-MAIL neil@neil-king.co.uk **WEBSITE** www.neil-king.co.uk

1 **BIG MEADOW (IRE),** 8, br g Marienbard (IRE)—Lakyle Lady (IRE) **Mr P. M. H. Beadles**
2 **BRANDON CASTLE,** 7, b g Dylan Thomas (IRE)—Chelsey Jayne (IRE) **Mr I. A. Low & Mr J. S. English**
3 **CANYON CITY,** 6, b g Authorized (IRE)—Colorado Dawn **A Whyte, J Bone, D Nott & B Smith**
4 **COMANCHE CHIEFTAIN (CAN),** 7, b g Broken Vow (USA)—
Platinum Preferred (CAN) **Mr B Bell, Mr T Messom & Mrs P Sturgis**
5 **CUBSWIN (IRE),** 5, b m Zamindar (USA)—Moonlight Rhapsody (IRE) **Mr D Caldwell & Mr K Lawrence**
6 **FARNE (IRE),** 5, b m Stowaway—Bonnies Island (IRE) **Blyth Currie & Royle**
7 **FFORBIDDEN LOVE,** 5, b m Fastnet Rock (AUS)—Trinkila (USA) **Mr D. S. Lee**
8 **GATEWAY TO EUROPE,** 5, b g Trans Island—Polly Doodle
9 **HOLBROOK PARK,** 9, b g Midnight Legend—Viciana **Mrs B. M. Chamberlain**
10 **IROLIN JACK,** 4, b g Bollin Eric—Aoninch **Milsom Baker Racing & Royle**
11 **KEYBOARD JOAN (IRE),** 5, b m Jeremy (USA)—
Kilcrea Present (IRE) **The Ridgeway Racing For Fun Partnership**
12 **LIL ROCKERFELLER (USA),** 8, ch g Hard Spun (USA)—Layoune (USA) **Davies Smith Govier & Brown**
13 **LITTLE MILLIE (IRE),** 7, b m Milan—Sweetbitter (FR) **Mr A Whyte, Mr T Messom & Mrs P Sturgis**
14 **LITTLE WINDMILL (IRE),** 9, ch g Mahler—Ennismore Queen (IRE) **The Ridgeway Racing For Fun Partnership**
15 **MARIENSTAR (IRE),** 8, b m Marienbard (IRE)—Starofdonickmore (IRE) **Kevin Taylor & Garry Ambrose**
16 **MERCERS COURT (IRE),** 11, b g Court Cave (IRE)—
Vikki's Dream (IRE) **David Nott, Ken Lawrence, Tim Messom**
17 **MILANSBAR (IRE),** 12, b g Milan—Ardenbar **Mr R. N. Bothway**
18 4, b g Imperial Monarch (IRE)—Mount Radhwa (IRE) **N. King**
19 **MR WOOLLEY,** 5, b g Shirocco (GER)—Evella (IRE) **Mrs H. M. Buckle**
20 **MYPLACEATMIDNIGHT,** 7, b g Midnight Legend—Zahra's Place **Mrs H. M. Buckle**
21 **NEARLY PERFECT,** 5, b g Malinas (GER)—The Lyme Volunteer (IRE) **Mr P. M. H. Beadles**
22 **OH LAND ABLOOM (IRE),** 9, b g King's Theatre (IRE)—Talinas Rose (IRE) **Milsom Baker Racing**
23 **PARISIAN AFFAIR,** 4, b f Champs Elysees—Trinkila (USA) **Mr D. S. Lee**
24 4, B f Malinas (GER)—Peggies Run
25 **PETITE JACK,** 6, ch g Champs Elysees—Pilcomayo (IRE) **Mr W. Burn**
26 **PRINCETON ROYALE (IRE),** 10, br g Royal Anthem (USA)—Shelikesitstraight (IRE) **D Nott, P Beadles, R Clarke**
27 **REGULATION (IRE),** 10, br g Danehill Dancer (IRE)—
Source of Life (IRE) **The Ridgeway Racing For Fun Partnership**
28 **SACKETT,** 8, b g Midnight Legend—Gloriana **Woodward, Laurie, Bridges & Smith**
29 **SILENT STEPS (IRE),** 8, b m Milan—Taking Silk (IRE) **The Silent Steps Partnership**
30 **SLAINE,** 5, b m Brian Boru—Flowing On **Mrs A. E. Maundrell**
31 **THE BOSS'S DREAM (IRE),** 11, b g Luso—Mrs Kick (IRE) **SLIS Ltd, Mr M Gibbons & Mr D Nott**
32 **THE KNOT IS TIED (IRE),** 4, b g Casamento (IRE)—Really Polish (USA) **Ken Lawrence & Roy Mousley**
33 **THIRD ESTATE (IRE),** 7, b g Suleiman (IRE)—Fizanni (IRE) **Lawrence, Govier & Brown**
34 **VAXALCO (FR),** 10, gr g Dom Alco (FR)—Galaxie (FR) **N. King**
35 **VENTURA MAGIC,** 4, b g Mount Nelson—Elle Desert (GER) **N. King**

Other Owners: Mr G. P. Ambrose, Mr S. R. Baker, Mr B. Bell, Mrs H. D. Blyth Currie, Mr J. Bone, Mr D. Bridges, G. S. Brown, Mr D. R. Caldwell, Mr N. J. Catterwell, Mr R. Clarke, Mr J. Davies, Mr J. S. English, Mr M. H. Gibbons, Mr P. F. Govier, Mr P. Govier, Govier & Brown, Mrs D. J. Hagenbuch, Mr R. Laurie, Mr K. Lawrence, I. A. Low, Mr T. J. Messom, Mr G. Milsom, Mr R. Mousley, Mr D. F. Nott, Mrs H. M. Royle, Mr R. W. Smith, Mrs G. S. Smith, Mr A. J. Smith, Stephen Lower Insurance Services Limited, Mr G. E. Stevenson, Mrs P. M. F. Sturgis, Mr D. A. Sutton, Mr K. A. Taylor, Mr A. A. Whyte, Mr B. Woodward.

Assistant Trainer: Richie O'Dee **Racing Secretary:** Jessica White

Jockey (NH): Wayne Hutchinson, Jack Quinlan. **Conditional:** Bryony Frost, Harry Teal. **Amateur:** Mr Jack Andrews.

329 MR PHILIP KIRBY, Richmond
Postal: **Green Oaks Farm, East Appleton, Richmond, North Yorkshire, DL10 7QE**
Contacts: **PHONE (01748) 517337 (07711) 709876 MOBILE (07984) 403558**
E-MAIL pkirbyracing@gmail.com **WEBSITE** www.philipkirbyracing.co.uk

1 **ABINGTON PARK,** 4, br g Passing Glance—Epicurean **Red Cap Racing & Clearabee Ltd**
2 **ADELPHI PRINCE,** 6, b g Schiaparelli (GER)—Cailin Na Ri (IRE) **Mr B. Brown**
3 **ANDORNS LEGACY,** 4, b f Andorn (GER)—Cayman Sound **Mr P. A. Kirby**
4 **ANIKNAM (FR),** 9, b g Nickname (FR)—Kelle Home (FR) **Mr P. A. Kirby**

MR PHILIP KIRBY - Continued

5 **ARCHIPPOS**, 6, b g Archipenko (USA)—Sparkling Clear **Well Oiled Partnership & Friend**
6 **ASUM**, 8, b g Kayf Tara—Candy Creek (IRE) **Bill Fraser & Adrian Pritchard**
7 **BAHKIT (IRE)**, 5, b g Intikhab (USA)—Pink Moon (IRE) **Mrs J. Porter**
8 **BERTIE BLAKE (IRE)**, 6, b g Beneficial—Diandrina **The Kirby Club Partnership**
9 **CARA'S WAY (IRE)**, 6, br m Robin des Champs (FR)—Dare To Venture (IRE) **Mr W. R. Kinsey**
10 **CORINDA**, 8, b m Midnight Legend—Conchita **Miss R. G. Brewis**
11 **COURTOWN OSCAR (IRE)**, 10, b g Oscar (IRE)—Courtown Bowe VII **Harbour Rose Partnership**
12 **DARES TO DREAM (IRE)**, 5, br m Beneficial—Miss McGoldrick (IRE) **Ashley & Sue Clark & Clearabee Ltd**
13 **DAZACAM**, 5, b m Camacho—Dazakhee **Mr & Mrs D. Yates**
14 **DISCAY**, 10, b g Distant Music (USA)—Caysue **John & Linda Oldroyd**
15 **FILLE D'AVIGNON (IRE)**, 4, br f Getaway (GER)—Site-Leader (IRE) **The Topspec II Partnership**
16 **FINGAL'S CAVE (IRE)**, 7, ch g Fast Company (IRE)—Indiannie Moon **RedHotGardogs**
17 **HURRICANE HUGO**, 6, b g Iktibas—Nativus (IRE) **Mr C. Watson**
18 **ICE GALLEY (IRE)**, 6, br g Galileo (IRE)—Ice Queen (IRE) **Mrs J. Sivills**
19 **ICE PYRAMID (IRE)**, 4, ch g New Approach (IRE)—Coolnagree (IRE) **Bill Fraser & Adrian Pritchard**
20 **ICONIC BELLE**, 5, ch m Sixties Icon—Five Bells (IRE) **Mr & Mrs D. Yates**
21 **IRIDESCENT RESDEV (FR)**, 4, gr f Montmartre (FR)—Feria To Bitch (FR) **Resdev Ltd**
22 **JAYCOLS STAR**, 4, ch g Medicean—A Lulu Ofa Menifee (USA) **Mrs J. Sivills**
23 **JURISTE (IRE)**, 5, b g Lawman (FR)—Green Lassy (FR) **Mrs J. Porter**
24 **KILCORAN**, 4, ch f Champs Elysees—India Spirit **Mr P. A. Kirby**
25 **KILCULLEN FLEM (IRE)**, 9, ch g Flemensfirth (USA)—
                                             Cansalrun (IRE) **David Obree David McDermott Paul Betts**
26 **L'ATTENDUE (IRE)**, 5, br m Oscar (IRE)—Triptoshan (IRE) **Mr A. D. Bradshaw**
27 **LADY BUTTONS**, 9, b m Beneficial—Lady Chapp (IRE) **Mrs J. Sivills**
28 **LADY CAMELOT (IRE)**, 4, b f Camelot—Queen Jock (USA) **Mr E. A. Bourke**
29 **LADY KYRIA (FR)**, 5, b m Holy Roman Emperor (IRE)—Segesta (IRE) **Hope Eden Racing Limited**
30 **LITTLE BRUCE (IRE)**, 7, b g Yeats (IRE)—Lady Rolfe (IRE) **The Gps Partnership**
31 **LORD ROCCOCO (FR)**, 4, b g Shirocco (GER)—Lady Chloe **The Roccoco Partnership**
32 **MAGELLAN**, 5, b g Sea The Stars (IRE)—Hector's Girl **Mr & Mrs D. Yates**
33 **MAGIC DRAGON (IRE)**, 5, b g Dragon Pulse (IRE)—Milenka (USA) **David Barlow & Lyn Rutherford**
34 **MAN OF VERVE (IRE)**, 5, b g Dandy Man (IRE)—She's Our Rock (IRE) **The Splash Of Verve Partnership**
35 **MASTER NEWTON (IRE)**, 4, br gr g Mastercraftsman (IRE)—French Friend (IRE) **Newton Racing**
36 **MIDAS MAGGIE**, 4, b f Archipenko (USA)—Algarade **The Jessies**
37 **MISSCARLETT (IRE)**, 5, b m Red Rocks (IRE)—Coimbra (USA) **Mrs J. Porter**
38 **MR CARBONATOR**, 4, b g Bated Breath—Diamond Lass (IRE) **Alan Fairhurst & David Fairhurst**
39 **NAUTICAL NITWIT (IRE)**, 10, b g Let The Lion Roar—Mrs Pugwash (IRE) **Birrafun 2**
40 **NEMEAN LION (IRE)**, 7, b g Mahler—Sandy Desert **The Well Oiled Partnership**
41 **NICELY INDEED (IRE)**, 9, b g Marienbard (IRE)—Rare Dollar (IRE) **A Jowsey & R Bainbridge**
42 **NIVEN (IRE)**, 6, b g Elusive Pimpernel (USA)—Ginger Lily (IRE) **John Birtles & Bill Allan**
43 **NORTHERN GIRL (IRE)**, 6, b m Westerner—Janebailey **Ownaracehorse & Topspec Partnership**
44 **OAK VINTAGE (IRE)**, 9, b g Fruits of Love (USA)—Brandam Supreme (IRE) **Mrs J. Porter**
45 **PENNINE CROSS**, 4, b g Shirocco (GER)—Gaspara (FR) **The Well Oiled Partnership**
46 **PULLMAN BROWN (USA)**, 7, b g Big Brown (USA)—Touch Too Much (USA) **Mr P. A. Kirby**
47 **PUMAFLOR (IRE)**, 7, b g Aussie Rules (USA)—Krasotka (IRE) **Resdev Ltd**
48 **RAYNA'S WORLD (IRE)**, 4, b f Poet's Voice—Salmon Rose (IRE) **Ace Bloodstock & Rayna Fitzgerald**
49 **RICHARD STRAUSS (IRE)**, 5, b br g Kheleyf (USA)—Symfony (IRE) **Zoe Hassall & George Hassall**
50 **ROBIN DES CHAPP (IRE)**, 4, b g Robin des Champs (FR)—Lady Chapp (IRE) **The Pinnacleplus Partnership**
51 **ROMEO BROWN**, 5, br g Yeats (IRE)—Santia **McGoldrick Racing 5 & Birrafun**
52 **SAKHEE'S CITY (FR)**, 8, b g Sakhee (USA)—A Lulu Ofa Menifee (USA) **Mrs J. Sivills**
53 **SHINE BABY SHINE**, 5, b m Aqlaam—Rosewood Belle (USA) **David Gray & P Kirby**
54 **SHOW PROMISE**, 4, b g Josr Algarhoud (IRE)—Show Potential (IRE) **The Philip Kirby Racing Partnership**
55 **SINCERELY RESDEV**, 4, br g Rock of Gibraltar (IRE)—Sincerely **Resdev Ltd**
56 4, B f Teofilo (IRE)—Skid (IRE) **Ace Bloodstock Ltd**
57 **SKIPTHESCALES (IRE)**, 7, b g Winged Love (IRE)—Waterland Gale (IRE) **Mr L. P. Richards**
58 **SOUTH SEAS (IRE)**, 5, ch g Lope de Vega (IRE)—Let It Be Me (USA) **Mr & Mrs D. Yates**
59 **STAPLEGROVE (IRE)**, 4, b g Camelot—Teddy Bears Picnic **Mr & Mrs D. Yates**
60 **STARGAZER (IRE)**, 6, b g Canford Cliffs (IRE)—Star Ruby (IRE) **Zoe Hassall & George Hassall & P Kirby**
61 **SUGGESTION**, 4, b g Dansili—Jibboom (USA) **Red Cap Racing 1**
62 **TEKIBLUE DE L'ORME (FR)**, 6, b g Blue Bresil (FR)—Tekila de l'orme (FR) **The Des Champs Partnership**
63 **THATS DIGBY**, 9, ch g Cayman Kai (IRE)—Jupiter's Fancy **Mr M. V. Coglan**
64 **THE RESDEV WAY**, 6, b g Multiplex—Lady Duxyana **Resdev Ltd**
65 **TOP VILLE BEN (IRE)**, 7, b g Beneficial—Great Decision (IRE) **Harbour Rose Partnership**
66 **TRANS DES OBEAUX**, 5, br g Trans Island—Quechua des Obeaux (FR) **R. A. Ross**
67 **WEMYSS POINT**, 7, b g Champs Elysees—Wemyss Bay **The Green Oaks Partnership**
68 **ZIG ZAG (IRE)**, 6, b g Zoffany (IRE)—Le Montrachet **Mr & Mrs R G Capstick**

MR PHILIP KIRBY - Continued

THREE-YEAR-OLDS
69 ARCHIE'S SISTER, b f Archipenko (USA)—Sparkling Clear **Well Oiled Partnership & Friend**
70 IMAJORBLUSH, ch g Mukhadram—Winter Dress **Zoe Hassall & George Hassall**
71 B c Fast Company (IRE)—Musikhani **Ace Bloodstock Ltd**
72 MY STRONG MAN (IRE), b c Authorized (IRE)—Lady Chloe **Mr & Mrs D. Yates**

Other Owners: Mr W. Allan, Mrs R. A. Bainbridge, Mr D. Barlow, Mr S. Beach, Mr J. K. Bell, The Birrafun Partnership, Mr J. Birtles, Mr D. C. Blake, Mr S. Bocking, R. G. Capstick, Mrs K. L. Capstick, Mr D. Cassidy, Mrs S. M. Clark, Mr A. G. Clark, Clearabee Limited, Mr B. J. Connolly, Mr B. H. Dolan, Mr A. Fairhurst, Mr D. H. Fairhurst, Mrs R. Fitzgerald, Mr I. Ford, W. R. Fraser, Mr J. A. Glover, Mr D. W. Gray, Mr J. D. Hanson, Mr S. Harrison, Mrs Z. L. Hassall, Mr N. A. D. Hassall, Mr G. A. Hassall, Mr W. Hayler, Miss S. R. Haynes, Mr A. Jowsey, Mrs P. R. Kirby, Mr R. J. Longley, Sir I. Magee, Mr J. Matthews, Nobaj Ltd, Mr W. D. Obree, Mr J. Oldroyd, Mrs L. M. Oldroyd, Ownaracehorse Ltd, Mr A. Pritchard, Ramscove Ltd, Red Cap Racing, Hugh T. Redhead, Mr A. J. Roberts, Mr W. G. Rolfe, L. M. Rutherford, N. Skinner, Mr J. G. R. Stent, Mr M. C. P Suddards, The Topspec Partnership, Mr C. R. Trembath, Mr L. C. Wiggins, The Wiggins Family, Mrs A. V. Yates, Mr D. Yates.

Assistant Trainer: Simon Olley

Jockey (NH): Adam Nicol. **Conditional:** Thomas Dowson. **Apprentice:** Nick Barratt-Atkin.
Amateur: Mr Henry Newcombe.

---

330 **MR SYLVESTER KIRK, Upper Lambourn**
Postal: Cedar Lodge Stables, Upper Lambourn, Hungerford, Berkshire, RG17 8QT
Contacts: PHONE (01488) 73215 FAX (01488) 670012 MOBILE (07768) 855261
E-MAIL info@sylvesterkirkracing.co.uk WEBSITE www.sylvesterkirkracing.co.uk

1 AINNE, 4, ch f Cityscape—Ayun (USA) **S. A. Kirk**
2 BUBBLE AND SQUEAK, 4, b f Mastercraftsman (IRE)—
Comeback Queen **Chris Wright,Holly Wright,Chloe Forsyth**
3 GAWDAWPALIN (IRE), 6, b g Holy Roman Emperor (IRE)—Dirtybirdie **Mr H. Balasuriya**
4 GRAVITY WAVE (IRE), 5, br g Rip Van Winkle (IRE)—Phrase **Deauville Daze Partnership**
5 MASTERS APPRENTICE (IRE), 4, ch g Mastercraftsman (IRE)—
Maghzaa (IRE) **The Old Enough To Know Better Partners**
6 SALOUEN (IRE), 5, b h Canford Cliffs—Gali Gal (IRE) **Mr H. Balasuriya**
7 SASSIE (IRE), 4, b f Rip Van Winkle (IRE)—Star of Gibraltar **Mr N. Simpson**
8 SHE BELIEVES (IRE), 4, ch f Arcano (IRE)—African Moonlight (UAE) **Marchwood Recycling Ltd**
9 THREE LITTLE BIRDS, 4, b f Dandy Man (IRE)—Oilinda **Miss A. J. Rawding**

THREE-YEAR-OLDS
10 ALTAR BOY, b c Mukhadram—Royal Whisper **S. A. Kirk**
11 ATLANTIC CITY (IRE), b g Battle of Marengo (IRE)—Autumn Tide (IRE) **S. A. Kirk**
12 BENNY AND THE JETS (IRE), ch g Showcasing—Orange Pip **Deauville Daze Partnership**
13 BREEZING, b f Garswood—Presto Levanter **Mr P Reglar & Mr R Gander**
14 HACKLE SETTER (USA), b g Noble Mission—Zaharias (USA) **Mr E. McCay**
15 HTILOMINLO, b c Zoffany (IRE)—Haven's Wave (IRE) **Mr H. Balasuriya**
16 INVINCIBLE ONE (IRE), b g Invincible Spirit (IRE)—Photophore (IRE) **Mr R. Clothier & Miss J. Gray**
17 IRENE MAY (IRE), b f Moohaajim (IRE)—Poker Hospital **Mr N. Simpson**
18 KODIAK ATTACK (IRE), b g Kodiac—Good Clodora (IRE) **Mrs J. A. Fowler**
19 MR NICE GUY (IRE), b g Nathaniel (IRE)—Three Choirs **Deauville Daze Partnership & Mr G Morrin**
20 RING CYCLE, ch g Norse Dancer (IRE)—Opera Glass **J. C. Smith**
21 ROYAL DANCER, b g Norse Dancer (IRE)—King's Siren (IRE) **Mr G. Dolan**
22 TRIBUNE, ch g Medicean—Giusina Mia (USA) **Mrs J. K. Powell**
23 WAVE WALKER, ch g Footstepsinthesand—Winged Diva (IRE) **J. C. Smith**

TWO-YEAR-OLDS
24 Ch c 8/4 Gleneagles (IRE)—Bora Blues (Peintre Celebre (USA)) (25284) **S. A. Kirk**
25 Ch f 7/2 Slade Power (IRE)—Buttercross (Zamindar (USA)) (11000) **Mr N. Simpson**
26 Br c 31/3 Kyllachy—Close To The Edge (IRE) (Iffraaj) (52000) **Marchwood Recycling Ltd**
27 B f 16/3 Brazen Beau (AUS)—Flemish School (Dutch Art) (9000) **N. Pickett**
28 Br c 22/4 Slade Power (IRE)—Knock Stars (IRE) (Soviet Star (USA)) (13485) **S. A. Kirk**
29 B f 17/4 Canford Cliffs (IRE)—Moma Lee (Duke of Marmalade (IRE)) (1200) **Homebred Racing**
30 Ch c 24/3 Australia—Natty Bumppo (IRE) (Kheleyf (USA)) (40000) **S. A. Kirk**
31 B f 5/3 Gutaifan (IRE)—Queenofthenorth (IRE) (Halling (USA)) (1000) **Mr R. Clothier & Miss J. Gray**

MR SYLVESTER KIRK - Continued

32 B c 5/4 Iffraaj—Sister Ship (Sulamani (IRE) (16000) **S. A. Kirk**
33 B c 17/3 Raven's Pass (USA)—Solva (Singspiel (IRE) (13000) **Mrs J. A. Fowler**

Other Owners: R. J. Brennan, Mr R. W. Clothier, Ms C. Forsyth, R. A. Gander, Miss J. F. Gray, Mr M. V. Hill, Mr C. McEvoy, Mr G. Morrin, Mr P W. Reglar, Mrs S. Wall, Mr C. M. Wall, Mr A. W. Wilson, Miss H. E. Wright, Mr C. N. Wright.

Assistant Trainer: Fanny Kirk

---

331 MR STUART KITTOW, Cullompton
Postal: **Haynefield Farm, Blackborough, Cullompton, Devon, EX15 2JD**
Contacts: **HOME (01823) 680183 FAX (01823) 680601 MOBILE (07714) 218921**
E-MAIL stuartkittowracing@hotmail.com WEBSITE www.stuartkittowracing.com

1 AVOCADEAU (IRE), 8, b g Lawman (FR)—Christmas Cracker (FR) **Mrs S. Clapp & Mrs L. Sharpe**
2 BEYOND EQUAL, 4, b g Kheleyf (USA)—Samasana **Stuart Wood & Partner**
3 DAGHASH, 10, b g Tiger Hill (IRE)—Zibet **Mrs P. E. Hawkings**
4 DORA'S FIELD (IRE), 6, b m Rip Van Winkle (IRE)—Rydal Mount (IRE) **R. S. E. Gifford**
5 EVERLASTING SEA, 5, b m Harbour Watch (IRE)—Doliouchka **R. S. E. Gifford**
6 FANFAN LA COLMINE (FR), 4, b g No Risk At All (FR)—Union Leto (FR) **Mr T. J. Malone**
7 FREDDY FANATAPAN, 4, b g Nathaniel (IRE)—Pan Galactic (USA) **Dr G. S. Plastow**
8 GLOWETH, 4, b f Pastoral Pursuits—Dancing Storm **M. E. Harris**
9 HOWABOUTRIGHTNOW (IRE), 4, b g Where Or When (IRE)—
                                          Suelena (IRE) **The Howaboutrightnow Partnership**
10 INCENTIVE, 5, b m Stimulation (IRE)—Folly Drove **W. S. Kittow**
11 LILY JEAN, 4, ch f Makfi—Eastern Lily (USA) **Mr S. Lock**
12 MAD ENDEAVOUR, 8, b g Muhtathir—Capefly **R. S. E. Gifford**
13 NIGHTINGALE VALLEY, 6, ch m Compton Place—Dancing Storm **M. E. Harris**
14 ROSIE LEA (FR), 6, b m Manduro (GER)—Saralea (FR) **Mr J. R. Urquhart**
15 SPIRIT OF ISHY, 4, b f Hellvelyn—Our Piccadilly (IRE) **Mrs G. R. Shire**
16 TOBOUGGALOO, 3, ch m Tobougg (IRE)—Let Alone **Dr G. S. Plastow**
17 TROTTER, 5, b g Piccolo—Vintage Steps **Mr K. B. Hodges**
18 YOUKAN (IRE), 4, b g Choisir (AUS)—Ellikan (IRE) **Mrs L. M. Francis**

THREE-YEAR-OLDS

19 MAYFAIR MADAME, ch f Mayson—Talqaa **The Swells Syndicate**
20 MISS HARRIETT, b f Arvico (FR)—Ivorsagoodun **Mr P. G. Gibbins**

TWO-YEAR-OLDS

21 B c 18/5 Gentlewave (IRE)—Arctic Magic (IRE) (Saddlers' Hall (IRE))
22 B c 6/4 Outstrip—Cape Mystery (Cape Cross (IRE)) **Mr T. J. Malone**
23 CROWDED EXPRESS, b c 20/5 Fast Company (IRE)—Dilys (Efisio) **Cushing, Boswell, Ingham & Kittow**
24 B f 2/3 Shooting To Win (AUS)—Ellikan (IRE) (Exceed And Excel (AUS)) (15238)
25 GHERKIN, b c 18/4 Coach House (IRE)—Our Piccadilly (IRE) (Piccolo) **Mrs G. R. Shire**
26 B c 23/3 Fast Company (IRE)—Jackline (Diktat) (5056) **Newton Barn Racing**
27 OHNOTANOTHERONE, b f 14/2 Camacho—Saint Lucy (Selkirk (USA)) (11428) **Mr K. B. Hodges**
28 B c 25/3 Holy Roman Emperor—Quiff (Sadler's Wells (USA)) (40000) **R. S. E. Gifford**
29 B g 3/3 Fast Company (IRE)—Sister Guru (Ishiguru (USA)) (9523)
30 WINANDER, b c 30/3 Ruler of The World (IRE)—Rydal Mount (IRE) (Cape Cross (IRE)) **R. S. E. Gifford**

Other Owners: John Boswell, Mrs S. G. Clapp, Mr H. A. Cushing, Mr A. J. Edwards, Mr A. R. Ingham, Mr S. Kittow, Mrs L. Sharpe, Mr T. P. Wilson, Mr S. C. Wood.

Assistant Trainer: Mrs Judy Kittow

---

332 MR WILLIAM KNIGHT, Angmering
Postal: **Lower Coombe Racing Stables, Angmering Park, Littlehampton, West Sussex, BN16 4EX**
Contacts: **PHONE (01903) 871188 FAX (01903) 871184 MOBILE (07770) 720828**
E-MAIL william@wknightracing.co.uk WEBSITE www.wknightracing.co.uk

1 AD VALOREM QUEEN (IRE), 4, b f Dandy Man (IRE)—Herful Schnerful **Mr A. Hetherton & Partner**
2 ARCHIMENTO, 6, ch g Archipenko (USA)—Caribana **Forever Optimists**

MR WILLIAM KNIGHT - Continued

3 **AUTHOR'S DREAM**, 6, gr g Authorized (IRE)—Spring Dream (IRE) **Mr & Mrs Conroy**
4 **GAVLAR**, 8, b g Gentlewave (IRE)—Shawhill **Canisbay Bloodstock**
5 **JACOB CATS**, 10, b g Dutch Art—Ballet **Canisbay Bloodstock**
6 **KINGSTON KURRAJONG**, 6, b g Authorized (IRE)—Kingston Acacia **Canisbay Bloodstock**
7 **N OVER J**, 4, b g Kodiac—Risk A Look **Mr A. Hetherton**
8 **NOBLE GIFT**, 9, ch g Cadeaux Genereux—Noble Penny **Canisbay Bloodstock**
9 **QUEEN OF PARIS**, 4, b f Champs Elysees—Beldarian (IRE) **Biddestone Racing XXI**
10 **SECRET ART (IRE)**, 9, ch g Excellent Art—Ivy Queen (IRE) **Art of Racing**
11 **SEINESATIONAL**, 4, b g Champs Elysees—Kibara **One Day Rodney Partnership**
12 **SOTO SIZZLER**, 4, b g Mastercraftsman (IRE)—Jalousie (IRE) **I. J. Heseltine**
13 **TESORINA**, 4, b f Lilbourne Lad (IRE)—Insieme (IRE) **Angmering Park Thoroughbreds Vi**
14 **TUSCAN PEARL**, 4, b f Medicean—Western Pearl **Mr & Mrs N. Welby**
15 **UNIT OF ASSESSMENT (IRE)**, 5, b g Dragon Pulse (IRE)—Before The Storm **Mr A. Hetherton**
16 **VELVET MORN (IRE)**, 4, b f Epaulette (AUS)—El Soprano (IRE) **Mrs S. K. Hartley**

THREE-YEAR-OLDS

17 **CHINESE ALPHABET**, b g Leroidesanimaux (BRZ)—Kesara **Mr C. K. R. Cheung**
18 **DANCING WARRIOR**, b f War Command (USA)—Corps de Ballet (IRE) **Mr T. G. Roddick**
19 **GOODWOOD SONNET (IRE)**, b g Lope de Vega (IRE)—
               Surface of Earth (USA) **Goodwood Racehorse Owners Group Limited**
20 **LOCO AMOR (IRE)**, b g Es Que Love (IRE)—Larghetto (USA) **Angmering Park Thoroughbreds V**
21 **POWER OF YOU (IRE)**, ch g Dragon Pulse (IRE)—Add Up (IRE) **W. J. Knight**
22 B f Aussie Rules (USA)—Purest **Mr & Mrs N. Welby**
23 **SEA ART**, b g Born To Sea (IRE)—Kekova **Mr T. G. Roddick**
24 **SHIFTING GOLD (IRE)**, b f Fast Company (IRE)—Elusive Gold (IRE) **Mrs Joanna Farrant & Partner**
25 **SIR BUSKER (IRE)**, b g Sir Prancealot (IRE)—Street Kitty (IRE) **Kennet Valley Thoroughbreds Xi Racing**
26 **WINTER GLEAM (IRE)**, b f Kodiac—Boo Boo Bear (IRE) **Mrs E. C. Roberts**

TWO-YEAR-OLDS

27 Br gr c 11/4 Gregorian (IRE)—Beacon Lady (Haafhd) **Chasemore Farm LLP**
28 **COMMIT NO NUISANCE (IRE)**, ch c 26/3 Ivawood (IRE)—
               Free Lance (IRE) (Grand Lodge (USA)) (9270) **G. C. Stevens**
29 B c 15/4 Sir Prancealot (IRE)—Gwyllion (USA) (Red Ransom (USA)) (19384) **Angmering Park Thoroughbreds I**
30 B c 17/3 Lope de Vega (IRE)—Kissable (IRE) (Danehill Dancer (IRE)) (30000) **Kennet Valley Thoroughbreds XIV**
31 **MR NUTHERPUTT (IRE)**, b c 15/5 Camacho—
               Right After Moyne (IRE) (Imperial Ballet (IRE)) (42000) **Seabrook Miller & Ions**
32 B c 10/3 Mukhadram—Plover (Oasis Dream) **Canisbay Bloodstock**
33 **PROGRESSIVE RATING**, br c 21/4 Bated Breath—
               Foxtrot Alpha (IRE) (Desert Prince (IRE)) (14285) **Progressive Racing & Mr A Hetherton**
34 B f 9/3 Due Diligence (USA)—Purest (Shamardal (USA)) **Mr & Mrs N Welby**
35 B c 23/3 Equiano (FR)—Royal Ivy (Mujtahid (USA)) **Canisbay Bloodstock**
36 B c 12/4 Xtension (IRE)—Sail With The Wind (Saddlers' Hall (IRE)) (5478) **Mr Y. O. Wong**
37 B c 7/5 Ivawood (IRE)—Sandbox Two (Foxhound (USA)) (12642) **Mr Y. O. Wong**
38 **SELSEY SIZZLER**, b c 4/3 Nathaniel (IRE)—Heho (Dansili) **Mr I. J. Heseltine & Mr P Winkworth**
39 B f 18/2 Sir Percy—Sweetheart Abbey (Dancing Spree (USA)) **Miss S. Bannatyne**
40 B f 23/2 Footstepsinthesand—Western Pearl (High Chaparral (IRE)) **Mr & Mrs N Welby**

Other Owners: Mr A. Black, Mrs J. E. Black, Mrs Gill Bostwick, Mr Tim Bostwick, Mr Carl Conroy, Mr N. A. Coster, Mrs Joanna Farrant, Mr P. J. Gregg, Mr I. J. Heseltine, Mr A. Hetherton, Mr R. S. Hoskins, Exors of the Late Mr Paul Jubert, Kennet Valley Thoroughbreds Xi, Mr R. F. Kilby, Mrs Emily Knight, Mr W. J. Knight, Mr Myles McBride, Progressive Racing, Mr Mike Rudd, Miss Maureen Stopher, Mr L. Stoten, Ms Linda Thompson, Mr Mark Tracey, Mrs N. J. Welby, Mr N. Welby, Mr P. Winkworth.

Assistant Trainer: Kayleigh Flower

---

333 **MR DANIEL KUBLER, Lambourn**
Postal: High View Stables, Folly Road, Lambourn, Hungerford, Berkshire, RG17 8QE
Contacts: **MOBILE (07984) 287254**
E-MAIL daniel@kublerracing.com WEBSITE www.kublerracing.com

1 **DAWN COMMANDO**, 4, ch g Dawn Approach (IRE)—Dynacam (USA) **Mr A. Stonehill**
2 **DISTINGUE**, 5, b g Sepoy (AUS)—Distinctive **Mr & Mrs G. Middlebrook**

MR DANIEL KUBLER - Continued

3 **FRONSAC**, 4, ch g Frankel—Riberac **Mr & Mrs G. Middlebrook**
4 **INVOLVED**, 4, b c Havana Gold (IRE)—Trick Or Treat **Peter Onslow & Gary Middlebrook**
5 **NOEL (IRE)**, 4, b g Requinto—Santacus (IRE) **The Noel Racing Partnership**
6 **OUTRAGE**, 7, ch g Exceed And Excel (AUS)—Ludynosa (USA) **Capture The Moment Vi**
7 **SENECA CHIEF**, 5, b g Invincible Spirit (IRE)—Albertine Rose **Mr & Mrs G. Middlebrook**
8 **TAPPITY TAP**, 4, b f Leroidesanimaux (BRZ)—Dance of Light (USA) **Mr & Mrs G. Middlebrook**

THREE-YEAR-OLDS

9 **ARISHKA (IRE)**, b f Dandy Man (IRE)—Symbol of Peace (IRE) **Crowd Racing & Diskovery Partnership Vi**
10 **BRUTE FORCE**, ch c Paco Boy (IRE)—Free Falling **A.C. Entertainment Technologies Limited**
11 **CHAMOMILE**, b f Teofilo (IRE)—Al Joza **Mr & Mrs G. Middlebrook**
12 **CHITRA**, b f Sea The Moon (GER)—Persian Star **Mr & Mrs G. Middlebrook**
13 **DON DIEGO VEGA**, b g Toronado (IRE)—Jules (IRE) **Capture The Moment V**
14 **FREESIA GOLD (IRE)**, ch f Havana Gold (IRE)—Secret Happiness **Ontoawinner Viii & Partner**
15 B f Kyllachy—Welsh Angel **Newclose Properties Ltd**
16 **ZEPHYRINA (IRE)**, b f Big Bad Bob (IRE)—Western Sky **Mr P. J. H. Whitten**

TWO-YEAR-OLDS

17 B c 20/4 Gleneagles (IRE)—Acquainted (Shamardal (USA)) (50000) **Mr & Mrs G. Middlebrook**
18 B f 28/2 Gutaifan (IRE)—Avenbury (Mount Nelson) (27619) **Mr A. Stonehill**
19 B f 30/3 Casamento (IRE)—La Donacella (Sir Percy) **Ms V. O'Sullivan**

Other Owners: Mr D. Blunt, David & Yvonne Blunt, Mrs Y. Blunt, Mr S. Bridge, Capture Syndicate, Capture Syndicate I, Crowd Racing Partnership, Diskovery Partnership Vl, Mr I. Hebbard, Mrs C. E. Kubler, Kubler Racing Ltd, Mrs S. J. McKenna, Mr C. McKenna, Mrs L. A. Middlebrook, Mr G. Middlebrook, Mr N. J. O'Brien, Mr P. Onslow, Ontoawinner, W. T. Whittle, Mr N. S. Whittle.

Assistant Trainer: Claire Kubler

334	**MR TOM LACEY, Woolhope**

Postal: **Sapness Farm, Woolhope, Herefordshire, HR1 4RG**
Contacts: **MOBILE (07768) 398604**
E-MAIL tom@cottagefield.co.uk WEBSITE www.cottagefield.co.uk

1 **ALBERTO'S DREAM**, 10, b g Fantastic Spain (USA)—Molly's Folly **Wallys Dream Syndicate**
2 **BY ORDER OF (IRE)**, 4, b g Shantou (USA)—Guydus (IRE) **Peaky Blinders**
3 **CONINGSBY**, 6, ch g Midnight Legend—Motcombe **Lady N. F. Cobham**
4 **DORKING BOY**, 5, ch g Schiaparelli (GER)—Megasue **Galloping On The South Downs Partnership**
5 **DORKING COCK (IRE)**, 5, b g Winged Love (IRE)—Kiss Jolie (FR) **Galloping On The South Downs Partnership**
6 **EN MEME TEMPS (FR)**, 5, b g Saddler Maker (IRE)—Lady Reine (FR) **Roberts, Churchward, Whittal-Williams**
7 **EQUUS AMADEUS (IRE)**, 6, b g Beat Hollow—Charade (IRE) **Galloping On The South Downs Partnership**
8 **FAIR KATE**, 5, b m Fair Mix (USA)—Silver Kate (IRE) **Roberts, Churchward, Whittal-Williams**
9 **FLASHING GLANCE**, 6, b g Passing Glance—Don And Gerry (IRE) **Barrett, Meredith, Panniers, Wilde**
10 **FLOATING ROCK (GER)**, 4, b g It's Gino (GER)—Fly Osoria (GER) **Mr T. F. Lacey**
11 **GLORY AND FORTUNE (IRE)**, 4, b g Fame And Glory—Night Heron (IRE) **Mr J. Hinds**
12 **HAZZAAR (IRE)**, 5, b g Flemensfirth (USA)—Una Sorpresa (GER) **Boultbee Brooks Ltd**
13 **HE'S A GOER (IRE)**, 5, b g Yeats (IRE)—Tessas Girl (IRE) **Mr D. Kellett**
14 **JESTER JET**, 9, br m Overbury (IRE)—Hendre Hotshot **Mrs T. P. James**
15 **JOHNBB (IRE)**, 5, b g Stowaway—Flemins Evening (IRE) **Boultbee Brooks Ltd**
16 **KATESON**, 6, gr g Black Sam Bellamy (IRE)—
                                  Silver Kate (IRE) **David M Richards and Roberts C Whittal Williams**
17 **KIMBERLITE CANDY (IRE)**, 7, b g Flemensfirth (USA)—Mandys Native (IRE) **Mr J. P. McManus**
18 **LADY CYLLA**, 4, b f Kayf Tara—Lady Samantha **Mrs M. U. B. Redvers**
19 **LAMANVER STORM**, 4, b g Geordieland (FR)—Lamanver Homerun **Dr D. Christensen**
20 **LOSSIEMOUTH**, 4, b g Makfi—First Bloom (USA) **Lady N. F. Cobham**
21 **MEEP MEEP**, 6, ch m Flemensfirth (USA)—Charming Leader (IRE) **HFT Forklifts Limited**
22 **POLYDORA (IRE)**, 7, b g Milan—Mandysway (IRE) **P. J. H. Wills & J. J. King**
23 **QURI (IRE)**, 6, b m Gold Well—Wigwam Mam (IRE) **Mr T. F. Lacey**
24 **SEBASTOPOL (IRE)**, 5, b g Fame And Glory—Knockcroghery (IRE) **Boultbee Brooks Ltd**
25 **SIR EGBERT**, 6, b g Kayf Tara—Little Miss Flora **Mrs E. M. F. Cadbury**
26 4, B g Fame And Glory—Sister Imelda (IRE) **Boultbee Brooks Ltd**
27 **SNAPDRAGON FIRE (IRE)**, 6, b g Getaway (GER)—Global Diamond (IRE) **P J King & Son**
28 **SORAYA**, 5, b m Black Sam Bellamy (IRE)—Star Ar Aghaidh (IRE) **Mrs S. M. Newell**

MR TOM LACEY - Continued

29 **THAIS TOIR (FR)**, 4, b g Diamond Boy (FR)—Scotland Act (FR) **Mr J. Hinds**
30 **THOMAS PATRICK (IRE)**, 7, b g Winged Love (IRE)—Huncheon Siss (IRE) **Mr D. Kellett**
31 **TRIOPAS (IRE)**, 7, b g Stowaway—Aine Dubh (IRE) **P J King & Son**
32 **VADO FORTE (FR)**, 6, b g Walk In The Park (IRE)—Gloire (FR) **Roberts, Churchward, Whittal-Williams**
33 **VIA DELLE VOLTE**, 4, b f Motivator—Castellina (USA) **D. J. Deer**
34 4, B g Fame And Glory—Westgrove Berry (IRE) **Boultbee Brooks Ltd**

Other Owners: Mr P. J. Andrews, Mr P. L. Barrett, Mr P. Henchoz, Mr P. A. Herbert, Mrs V. C. King, Mr J. J. King, Mr G. J. Meredith, Mr R. M. Ovel, Mr N. J. Panniers, Mr S. Powell, Mr B. Reynolds, D. M. Richards, G. A. Roberts, Mr M. C. Waddingham, Mr E. B. Whittal-Williams, Mr W. E. Wilde, Mr P. J. H. Wills.

Jockey (NH): Richard Johnson, Robert Dunne. **Amateur:** Mr Tommie O'Brien.

---

335 | MR CARLOS LAFFON-PARIAS, Chantilly
Postal: 38, Avenue du General Leclerc, 60500 Chantilly, France
E-MAIL ecuries.laffon.parias@wanadoo.fr

1 **CONTORTIONISTE**, 4, ch c Pivotal—Distortion **Wertheimer et Frere**
2 **LIPSTICK**, 4, ch c Kendargent (FR)—Soft Lips **Wertheimer et Frere**
3 **ZIYAD**, 4, b br g Rock of Gibraltar (IRE)—Arme Ancienne **Wertheimer et Frere**

THREE-YEAR-OLDS

4 **ARCMANIA (IRE)**, b f Dansili—Solemia (IRE) **Wertheimer et Frere**
5 **BENALUA**, b f Le Havre (IRE)—Ebareva (IRE) **SARL Darpat France**
6 **CARTES**, ch c Sea The Moon (GER)—Kensington Gardens **Bering SL**
7 **CORANDO**, b c Dark Angel (IRE)—Norway Cross **Al Shira'aa Farms SARL**
8 **DOSILA**, b f Galileo (IRE)—Stormina (USA) **Wertheimer et Frere**
9 **ECOLO (FR)**, b c Invincible Spirit (IRE)—Never Green (IRE) **Wertheimer et Frere**
10 **FLAMBEUR (USA)**, gr g Mizzen Mast (USA)—Flamenba (USA) **Wertheimer et Frere**
11 **GWENDOLA**, b f Oasis Dream—Gwenseb (FR) **Wertheimer et Frere**
12 **HAPPY BEAN (USA)**, bl f Medaglia d'oro (USA)—Happy Week (USA) **Wertheimer et Frere**
13 **HIMOLA (FR)**, b c Dalakhani (IRE)—Campanillas (IRE) **Partnership**
14 **ILLA ALQMAR**, ch f Lope de Vega (IRE)—Tebee **Al Shira'aa Farms SARL**
15 **INTELLINA**, b f Intello (GER)—Paiota Falls (USA) **Wertheimer et Frere**
16 **LYONS (IRE)**, ch c Australia—Light Quest (USA) **Partnership**
17 **MATEMATICA (GER)**, b f Rock of Gibraltar (IRE)—Mathematicienne (IRE) **Wertheimer et Frere**
18 **MIENGO (FR)**, b c Dalakhani (IRE)—Visiyna (FR) **Bering SL**
19 **MIRABELLE (FR)**, b f Anodin (IRE)—Minted (USA) **Wertheimer et Frere**
20 **MUTAMAKINA**, b f Nathaniel (IRE)—Joshua's Princess **Al Shira'aa Farms SARL**
21 **OYAMBRE**, b c Sea The Moon (GER)—Shemriyna (IRE) **Bering SL**
22 **PALOMBA (IRE)**, b f Lope de Vega (IRE)—Australienne (IRE) **Wertheimer et Frere**
23 **PLATANE**, ch f Le Havre (IRE)—Modestie (FR) **Wertheimer et Frere**
24 **PRAXIAS (IRE)**, gr c Iffraaj—Pearl Earrine (FR) **Partnership**
25 **RIVEN STAR (FR)**, b f Falco (USA)—Vivacity **Ecurie Skymarc Farm**
26 **ROYALIST (IRE)**, b c Intello (GER)—Royalemixa (FR) **Partnership**
27 **SAMSKARA (IRE)**, gr f Kodiac—Chiara Wells (IRE) **Al Shira'aa Farms SARL**
28 **SHAMAN (IRE)**, ch c Shamardal (USA)—Only Green (IRE) **Wertheimer et Frere**
29 **SICILIA**, br f Kingman—Palitana (USA) **Al Shira'aa Farms SARL**
30 **SOSOFT (FR)**, b c Pivotal—Soft Lips **Wertheimer et Frere**
31 **STARIFIQUE (IRE)**, ch f Sea The Stars (IRE)—Sapphire Pendant (IRE) **Wertheimer et Frere**
32 **STARMANIAC**, b c Sea The Stars (IRE)—Plumania **Wertheimer et Frere**
33 **TOO LOUD (USA)**, b f Arch (USA)—Quiet Royal (USA) **Wertheimer et Frere**
34 **TOP SPACE (USA)**, b c Speightstown (USA)—Top Order (USA) **Wertheimer et Frere**
35 **TREBUJENA (IRE)**, b f Siyouni (FR)—Freedom Flashing (USA) **SARL Darpat France**
36 **ULTIMATUM**, b c Dutch Art—Danzigaway (USA) **Wertheimer et Frere**
37 **VILLA MARINA**, b f Le Havre (IRE)—Briviesca **SARL Darpat France**
38 **VILLALAR (FR)**, b f Whipper (USA)—Highphar (FR) **SARL Darpat France**

TWO-YEAR-OLDS

39 **ALLUCINATION**, b f 29/3 Lope de Vega (IRE)—Desertiste (Green Desert (USA)) **Wertheimer et Frere**
40 **ANGELISSIMA (FR)**, gr f 21/3 Dark Angel (FR)—Foreign Tune (Invincible Spirit (IRE)) **Wertheimer et Frere**
41 **ECRIVAIN**, ch c 21/3 Lope de Vega (IRE)—
　　　　　　　　　　　　　Sapphire Pendant (IRE) (Danehill Dancer (USA)) **Wertheimer et Frere**
42 **FEMINA (IRE)**, b f 28/4 Siyouni (FR)—Legerete (USA) (Rahy (USA)) **Wertheimer et Frere**

MR CARLOS LAFFON-PARIAS - Continued

43 Gr f 18/3 Dark Angel (IRE)—Foreign Legionary (IRE) (Galileo (IRE)) (117994) **Partnership**
44 **GALAWI (IRE)**, b c 3/3 Dubawi (IRE)—Galikova (FR) (Galileo (IRE)) **Wertheimer et Frere**
45 **HOPEFUL (FR)**, b c 4/3 Motivator—Monst (IRE) (Monsun (GER)) **Wertheimer et Frere**
46 **LASY W (USA)**, b f 2/4 War Front (USA)—Zaftig (USA) (Gone West (USA)) **Wertheimer et Frere**
47 **LIPSINK (IRE)**, b c 3/3 Kodiac—Iron Lips (Iron Mask (USA)) **Wertheimer et Frere**
48 **MATELLO (FR)**, b c 6/5 Intello (GER)—Mama Lulu (USA) (Kingmambo (USA)) (50568) **Wertheimer et Frere**
49 **SEACHANGE (FR)**, b f 7/5 Siyouni (FR)—Ydillique (IRE) (Sadler's Wells (USA)) **Wertheimer et Frere**
50 **SEAMIA**, b f 11/4 Sea The Stars (IRE)—Solemia (IRE) (Poliglote) **Wertheimer et Frere**
51 **SILASTAR**, b c 14/2 Sea The Stars (IRE)—Silasol (IRE) (Monsun (GER)) **Wertheimer et Frere**
52 **SITOUTVABIEN (FR)**, b c 7/2 Golden Horn—Sefroua (USA) (Kingmambo (USA)) (168563) **Haras d'Etreham**
53 **STANZO**, ch c 8/3 Speightstown (USA)—Viva Rafaela (BRZ) (Know Heights (IRE)) **Wertheimer et Frere**
54 **TWIST (FR)**, ch c 5/3 Pivotal—Distortion (Distorted Humor (USA)) **Wertheimer et Frere**

---

336   **MR NICK LAMPARD, Marlborough**
Postal: **South Cottage, 2 The Crossroads, Clatford, Marlborough, Wiltshire, SN8 4EA**
Contacts: **PHONE (01672) 861420**

1 **FOREST LORD**, 5, b g Native Ruler—La Belle Au Bois (IRE) **N. M. Lampard**
2 **MINMORE GREY (IRE)**, 10, gr g Primary (USA)—Hopeful Memory (IRE) **N. M. Lampard**
3 **RUBY TAYLOR**, 7, b m Passing Glance—Bold Rose **N. M. Lampard**
4 **SADMA**, 10, gr g Street Cry (IRE)—Blue Dress (USA) **N. M. Lampard**

---

337   **MR DAVID LANIGAN, Newmarket**
Postal: **Rathmoy Stables, Hamilton Road, Newmarket, Suffolk, CB8 0GU**
Contacts: **PHONE (01638) 664063 MOBILE (07803) 257864**
E-MAIL david@laniganracing.co.uk WEBSITE www.laniganracing.co.uk

1 **EXCELABIT**, 4, b c Exceed And Excel (AUS)—Saaboog
2 **HEAVENS ALIGN (IRE)**, 4, b f Shamardal (USA)—Althea Rose (IRE)
3 **LEXINGTON EMPIRE**, 4, ch g Intello (GER)—Emperice (USA)
4 **LIGHT OF JOY (USA)**, 5, ch m Kitten's Joy (USA)—Light Blow (USA)
9 **WORTH WAITING**, 4, b f Bated Breath—Salutare (IRE)

THREE-YEAR-OLDS

6 **BURNING TOPIC (GER)**, b f Maxios—Burning Sunset
7 **CALIFORNICATION**, b g Epaulette (AUS)—Ermyn Express
8 **CORINTHIAN GIRL (IRE)**, ch f Raven's Pass (USA)—Elegant Beauty
9 **DEPUTY STAR**, b c Epaulette (AUS)—Starkat
10 **DREAMINGOFDIAMONDS (IRE)**, b f Alhebayeb (IRE)—Jemima's Art
11 **FAST STRIKE**, b f Champs Elysees—Al Cobra (IRE)
12 **GOLD ARCH**, b g Archipenko (USA)—Goldrenched (IRE)
13 **IRISH ART (IRE)**, b g Dutch Art—Slieve Mish (IRE)
14 **IRISH STEPS**, b f Giant's Causeway (USA)—Sarah Lynx (IRE)
15 **KNIGHTFALL**, b c Nathaniel (IRE)—Enchanted
16 **MALIKA I JAHAN (FR)**, b f Australia—Have Faith (IRE)
17 **MILLIONS MEMORIES**, b c Zoffany (IRE)—Millestan (IRE)
18 **MR CARPENTER (IRE)**, gr g Mastercraftsman (IRE)—Satwa Pearl
19 **POWERFUL STAR (IRE)**, ch f Slade Power (IRE)—Star Studded
20 **SUNSET FLASH (IRE)**, b f Mayson—Sunset Avenue (USA)
21 **TRONADOR (IRE)**, ch g Lope de Vega (IRE)—Autumn Leaves (FR)
22 **UNIVERSAL EFFECT**, b f Universal (IRE)—Saaboog

TWO-YEAR-OLDS

23 B c 12/4 Shamardal (USA)—Arabian Comet (IRE) (Dubawi (IRE)) (80000)
24 B c 15/2 Gutaifan (IRE)—C'est Ma Souer (IRE) (Oratorio (IRE)) (55000)
25 B c 9/3 Showcasing—Crossmolina (IRE) (Halling (USA))
26 B c 5/2 Gutaifan (IRE)—Galileo's Star (IRE) (Galileo (IRE)) (21000)
27 **HESSSA**, b f 12/4 Zoffany (IRE)—Ana Shababiya (IRE) (Teofilo (IRE))
28 B f 18/3 Mukhadram—Interstella (Sea The Stars (IRE)) (70000)
29 B f 2/5 Zoffany (IRE)—Jasmine Blue (IRE) (Galileo (IRE)) (68000)
30 B c 1/3 Ruler of The World (IRE)—Lady Dettoria (FR) (Vettori (IRE)) (75000)

MR DAVID LANIGAN - Continued

31 B c 7/4 Shamardal (USA)—Magical Crown (USA) (Distorted Humor (USA)) (100000)
32 B c 21/4 War Command (USA)—Pink Moon (IRE) (Namid) (10000)
33 Ch f 24/2 Sea The Stars (IRE)—Rietondale (USA) (Dynaformer (USA)) (75000)
34 B f 22/4 Free Eagle (IRE)—Satwa Pearl (Rock of Gibraltar (IRE))
35 B f 19/4 Shamardal (USA)—Say No Now (IRE) (Refuse to Bend (IRE)) (90000)
36 B f 15/4 Acclamation—Simkana (IRE) (Kalanisi (IRE)) (40000)
37 B c 15/2 Free Eagle (IRE)—Sleeping Beauty (IRE) (Oasis Dream) (70000)
38 B c 26/2 Kingman—South Atlantic (USA) (Stormy Atlantic (USA)) (58996)
39 Ch c 22/2 New Approach (IRE)—Starletina (IRE) (Sea The Stars (IRE)) (50000)
40 Gr f 10/1 Mastercraftsman (IRE)—Stars At Night (IRE) (Galileo (IRE)) (50568)
41 B f 26/2 Kendargent (FR)—West of Venus (USA) (Street Cry (IRE))
42 B f 13/5 Muhaarar—Zacheta (Polish Precedent (USA)) (55000)

Owners: Abdulla Al-Mansoori, Ahamd Abdulla Al Shaikh, Saeed H Al-Tayer, Sultan Ali, Saif Ali, S. H. Altayer, Mr Fergus Anstock, Mr Ian Black, Mr Paul Brosnan, Ms Madelaine Delaney, Diamond Racing, Flaxman Stables, Mr C A McMillan, Middleham Park, Niarchos Family, Norcroft Park Stud, Mrs M O'Malley, Promenade Bloodstock, Mr Ben Sangster, 21st Century Farms, Ventura Racing.

338	**MISS EMMA LAVELLE, Marlborough**

MISS EMMA LAVELLE, Marlborough
Postal: Bonita Racing Stables, Ogbourne Maizey, Marlborough, Wiltshire, SN8 1RY
Contacts: PHONE (01672) 511544 FAX (01672) 511544 MOBILE (07774) 993998
E-MAIL info@emmalavelle.com WEBSITE www.emmalavelle.com

1 4, B g Shantou (USA)—Backtothekingsnest (IRE) **N. Mustoe**
2 **BALIBOUR (FR),** 7, b g Policy Maker (IRE)—Saintheze (FR) **The High Altitude Partnership**
3 **BELLE EMPRESS,** 8, b m Black Sam Bellamy (IRE)—Empress of Light **Mighty Acorn Stables**
4 4, Ch c Vinnie Roe (IRE)—Bewildered (IRE) **The Bonhamie Partnership**
5 **BLUSHING RED (FR),** 5, ch g Le Havre (IRE)—Boliche **Richard Lavelle & John Crook**
6 **BOOMARANG,** 5, b g Passing Glance—Materiality **Booma Racing & Emma Fenton**
7 **BOREHAM BILL (IRE),** 7, b g Tikkanen (USA)—Crimond (IRE) **Mrs S. P. Foran**
8 **BUSTER THOMAS (IRE),** 8, b g Westerner—Awesome Miracle (IRE) **Axom LXVII**
9 **CASINO MARKETS (IRE),** 11, br g Fruits of Love (USA)—Vals Dream (IRE) **Mighty Acorn Stables**
10 **CELTIC JOY (IRE),** 6, b g Kayf Tara—No Time For Tears (IRE) **Hawksmoor Partnership**
11 **CHELSEA FLYER (IRE),** 8, b g Westerner—Aktress (IRE) **Mrs Rosemary Luck & Mrs Deirdre Walker**
12 **CLOSING CEREMONY (IRE),** 10, b g Flemensfirth (USA)—
Supreme Von Pres (IRE) **The High Altitude Partnership**
13 **DE RASHER COUNTER,** 7, b g Yeats (IRE)—Dedrunknmunky (IRE) **Makin' Bacon Partnership**
14 **DISSAVRIL (FR),** 6, gr m Balko (FR)—Odile (FR) **P. G. Jacobs**
15 **DOLLNAMIX (FR),** 8, b g Al Namix (FR)—Sleeping Doll (FR) **GDM Partnership**
16 **DOWN THE HIGHWAY (IRE),** 6, b g Duke of Marmalade (IRE)—Petit Moselle (IRE) **Thurloe 56**
17 **ENNISCOFFEY OSCAR (IRE),** 7, b g Oscar (IRE)—Enniscoffey (IRE) **The Pick 'N' Mix Partnership**
18 **FLEMCARA (IRE),** 7, b g Flemensfirth (USA)—Cara Mara (IRE) **Andy & The Frisky Fillies**
19 **FLEMINGS (IRE),** 5, b g Flemensfirth (USA)—How Is Things (IRE) **T. Syder & N. Mustoe**
20 **FONTSANTA (IRE),** 6, b g Flemensfirth (USA)—Day's Over **Mr T. D. J. Syder**
21 **FORGET ME KNOT (IRE),** 6, b m Presenting—J'y Reste (FR) **Swanbridge Bloodstock Limited**
22 **FORTIA,** 5, b m Nathaniel (IRE)—Veenwouden **Mrs C. L. Bonner**
23 **FORTUNATE GEORGE (IRE),** 9, b g Oscar (IRE)—Fine Fortune (IRE) **The George Inn Racing Syndicate**
24 **FOX APPEAL (IRE),** 12, b g Brian Boru—Lady Appeal (IRE) **The Hawk Inn Syndicate 3**
25 **FREEDOM RUN,** 6, ch m Presenting—Mathine (FR) **Bonita Racing Club**
26 **FULL IRISH (IRE),** 8, b g Flemensfirth (USA)—Miss Kettlewell (IRE) **N. Mustoe**
27 **GUNFLEET (IRE),** 7, b g Oscar (IRE)—Lady Lincon (IRE) **Mrs P. J. Travis**
28 **HAWK'S WELL (IRE),** 5, b g Yeats (IRE)—Our Song **Mrs N. Turner & Mrs E. Fenton**
29 **HIGH NOON (IRE),** 7, b g Westerner—Seymourswift **N. Mustoe**
30 **HIGHLY PRIZED,** 6, b br g Manduro (GER)—Razzle (USA)
31 **IRISH PROPHECY (IRE),** 6, b g Azamour (IRE)—Prophets Honor (FR) **N. Mustoe**
32 **JAVERT (IRE),** 10, b g Kayf Tara—Royalrova (FR) **Axom LII**
33 **JEMIMA P (IRE),** 5, b m Jeremy (USA)—Peig Alainn (IRE) **The Three A's Syndicate**
34 **JOYRIDER (IRE),** 7, b g Stowaway—Aileen Supreme (IRE) **N. Mustoe**
35 **JUNCTION FOURTEEN (IRE),** 10, b g King's Theatre (IRE)—Chevet Girl (IRE) **Martin St. Quinton & Tim Syder**
36 **JUST GONE MIDNIGHT,** 5, ch m Midnight Legend—Precious Lady **Swanbridge Bloodstock Limited**
37 **LADY MARKBY (IRE),** 8, b m Oscar (IRE)—Leitrim Bridge (IRE) **Mrs S. Metcalfe**
38 **MAJESTIC MOLL (IRE),** 7, b m King's Theatre (IRE)—Artist's Muse (IRE) **Mustoe & Lavelle**
39 **MISTY BLOOM (IRE),** 6, b m Yeats (IRE)—Misty Mountain (IRE) **Bonita Racing Club**
40 **MONTANA GREY (IRE),** 6, gr g Watar (IRE)—Wapiti Creek (IRE) **Mr R. L. Fanshawe**

MISS EMMA LAVELLE - Continued

41 **MR FENTON (IRE)**, 8, b g Trans Island—Carnagh Girl (IRE) **The Hawk Inn Syndicate**
42 4, B f Robin des Champs (FR)—Mystic Masie (IRE) **N. Mustoe & A. Gemmell**
43 **NAMIB DANCER (IRE)**, 5, b g Westerner—Derriana (IRE) **Mr A Mrs W & Dr T Davies & Mrs T Grundy**
44 **OLD RASCALS (IRE)**, 6, b g Ask—Balleen Rose (IRE) **The Optimists**
45 **PAISLEY PARK (IRE)**, 7, b g Oscar (IRE)—Presenting Shares (IRE) **Mr A. Gemmell**
46 **PAWN STAR (IRE)**, 9, b g Beneficial—Missindependence (IRE) **Hawk Inn Syndicate 5**
47 **PEMBERLEY (IRE)**, 6, b g Darsi (FR)—Eyebright (IRE) **Laurie Kimber & Partners**
48 **PRIVATE MALONE (IRE)**, 10, b g Darsi (FR)—Native Artist (IRE) **Mrs Sarah Stevens & Mr P. Mitford-Slade**
49 **PROPHETS PRAYER (IRE)**, 5, b m Azamour (IRE)—Prophets Honor (FR) **N. Mustoe**
50 **REELINGINTHEYEARS (IRE)**, 7, b g Flemensfirth (USA)—Savitha (IRE) **British Racing Club**
51 **SHANG TANG (IRE)**, 5, b g Shantou (USA)—Ballyguider Bridge (IRE) **T. Syder & N. Mustoe**
52 **SHIROCCAN ROLL**, 5, b g Shirocco (GER)—Folie Dancer **A. Gemmell**
53 **SILENT ASSISTANT (IRE)**, 5, b g Sans Frontieres (IRE)—Monanig Lass (IRE) **Lavelle, Awdry & Williams**
54 **STATISTICAL (IRE)**, 7, br g Robin des Champs (FR)—Lusty Beg (IRE) **Paley Heights Syndicate**
55 **TALENT TO AMUSE (IRE)**, 6, b m Manduro (GER)—Burn Baby Burn (IRE) **Thurloe 55**
56 **THE BUNNYMAN**, 5, b g Authorized (IRE)—Linnet (GER) **The Bonhamie Partnership**
57 **THE DOMINO EFFECT (IRE)**, 5, b g Oscar (IRE)—Lively Lass (IRE) **Mighty Acorn Stables**
58 **THE SWEENEY (IRE)**, 7, b g Oscar (IRE)—Banningham Blaze **N. Mustoe**
59 **THUNDERSTRUCK (IRE)**, 5, b g Fame And Glory—Go Sandy Go (IRE) **Mr T. D. J. Syder**
60 **TIERRA VERDE**, 8, b m Josr Algarhoud (IRE)—La Corujera **Greenlands Racing Syndicate**
61 **VENDREDI TROIS (FR)**, 10, b g Shaanmer (IRE)—Legende Sacree (FR) **Awdry, Gemmell, Pomford & Williams**
62 **VIVA VITTORIA (IRE)**, 5, b m Stowaway—La Fisarmonica (IRE) **Mr & Mrs A Millett**
63 **WATER WAGTAIL**, 12, b g Kahyasi—Kentford Grebe **D. I. Bare**
64 **WHAT A HOOT**, 5, b m Presenting—Flying Iris (IRE) **Bonita Racing Club**
65 **WOODUKHELEYFIT**, 5, b g Kheleyf (USA)—Wood Chorus **Lady S. M. O'Brien**

Other Owners: Mr C. V. Awdry, Axom Ltd, Booma Racing, Mr D. M. Bradshaw, Mr K. Casini, G. Charlesworth, Mr D. Charlesworth, Mr J. R. Crook, Mr W. P. L. Davies, Dr T. J. W. Davies, Mrs S. C. Davies, Mr D. Downie, Mr J. B. Duffy, Mrs B. S. Fowler, Mr R. J. Fowler, Mrs T. A. Grundy, Mrs N. J. Haigh, Mr S. Halpern, Mrs C. D. Halpern, Mrs S. C. Hepworth, Mr A. J. Hill, Mr R. S. Keck, Mr L. G. Kimber, Mr M. Kirkby, Miss I. G. Langton, Mr J. R. Lavelle, Mr R. J. Lavelle, Mrs A. C. Lavelle, Miss E. C. Lavelle, Mrs R. A. Luck, Mr G. P. MacIntosh, Mr A. J. Millett, Mrs A. M. Millett, P. B. Mitford-Slade, Mr P. Nicholls, Mr O. J. W. Pawle, Mr B. G. Pomford, Racing Club Ltd, K. P. Ryan, Dr M. J. Scott, Mrs V. Scott, Sir David Sieff, Mr J. Smee, Mr M. Smith, Mr M. G. St Quinton, Mr J. A. B. Stafford, Exors of the Late Mrs S. V. M. Stevens, Mrs K. M. Taylor, Mrs N. C. Turner, Mrs J. C. Verity, Mrs V. A. Villers, Mrs D. Walker, Mr J. Webb, Mr A. G. Weston, Mr P. R. Weston, Mrs P. H. Williams.

Assistant Trainer: Barry Fenton

---

339 **MR BARRY LEAVY, Stoke-on-Trent**
Postal: Cash Heath Farm, Cash Heath, Forsbrook, Stoke on Trent, ST11 9DE
Contacts: HOME/FAX (01782) 398591 MOBILE (07540) 806915
E-MAIL lauraleavy@hotmail.co.uk WEBSITE www.leavyracing.co.uk

1 **CLOCK ON TOM**, 9, b g Trade Fair—Night Owl **Mr F. W. Dronzek**
2 **DEEP RESOLVE (IRE)**, 8, b g Intense Focus (USA)—I'll Be Waiting **Mr B. Leavy**
3 **GEORGIAN FIREBIRD**, 9, b m Firebreak—Skovshoved (IRE) **Mrs E. A. Wilson**
4 **GRAND COUREUR (FR)**, 7, b br g Grand Couturier—Iris du Berlais (FR) **You Can Be Sure**
5 **HELAMIS**, 9, b m Shirocco (GER)—Alnoor (USA) **Mr D Holmes & Mr B D Leavy**
6 **INFINITI (IRE)**, 6, b m Arcano (IRE)—Seraphina (IRE) **Mr Frank Dronzek & Mrs Susan Ashford**
7 **REMEMBER NERJA (IRE)**, 5, ch m Lord Shanakill (USA)—Tequise (IRE) **Mr B. Leavy**

Other Owners: Dr Martin Booth, Dr Chris Cowell, Mr Frank Dronzek, Mr D. B. Holmes, Mr N. A. Johnson, Mr Barry Leavy, Mrs S. D. Ashford.

Assistant Trainer: Mrs L Leavy

---

340 **MISS KERRY LEE, Presteigne**
Postal: Bell House, Byton, Presteigne, Powys, LD8 2HS
Contacts: PHONE (01544) 267672 MOBILE (07968) 242663
E-MAIL kerry@kerrylee.co.uk WEBSITE www.kerrylee.co.uk

1 **ABSOLUT MAGIC**, 4, ch g Norse Dancer (IRE)—Lady Gongar **Mark E. Smith & the Magic 7**
2 **ALFIE SPINNER (IRE)**, 14, b g Alflora (IRE)—Little Red Spider **Alan Beard & Brian Beard**

MISS KERRY LEE - Continued

3 **ASKNOTWHAT (IRE)**, 8, ch g Dylan Thomas (IRE)—Princess Roseburg (USA) **In It For The Crack No.1**
4 **BISHOPS ROAD (IRE)**, 11, b g Heron Island (IRE)—Nice Resemblance (IRE) **Mr D. A. Halsall**
5 **BRIGADIER BOB (IRE)**, 6, b g Excellent Art—Plausabelle **Mark E Smith & The Excellent Dees**
6 **CINDERFELLA**, 8, gr g Sagamix (FR)—Firecracker Lady (IRE) **J.C.Harrison Lee & T.Howard Partnership**
7 **DESTINED TO SHINE (IRE)**, 7, b g Dubai Destination (USA)—Good Shine (IRE) **Campbell-mizen**
8 **DO IT FOR THY SEN (IRE)**, 5, ch g Mountain High (IRE)—Ashlings Princess (IRE) **Campbell-Mizen & R L Baker**
9 **EATON COLLINA (IRE)**, 4, b g Milan—Flowers On Sunday (IRE) **Mr & Mrs J. H. Watson**
10 **EATON HILL (IRE)**, 7, b g Yeats (IRE)—Guilt Less (FR) **Mr & Mrs J. H. Watson**
11 **FINANCIER**, 6, ch g Dubawi (IRE)—Desired **W. Roseff**
12 **GINO TRAIL (IRE)**, 12, br g Perugino (USA)—Borough Trail (IRE) **Mrs J. Smith**
13 **GREY GOLD (IRE)**, 14, gr g Strategic Choice (USA)—Grouse-N-Heather **Mrs M. A. Boden**
14 **HAPPY DIVA (IRE)**, 8, b m King's Theatre (IRE)—Megans Joy (IRE) **W. Roseff**
15 **HENRI LE BON (IRE)**, 4, b g Sea The Stars (IRE)—Speed Song **W. Roseff**
16 **JETSTREAM (IRE)**, 4, b g Galileo (IRE)—Bewitched (IRE) **Mr M. E. Smith**
17 **KINGS MONARCH (IRE)**, 6, b g Schiaparelli (GER)—Monarch's View **Miss K. Lee**
18 **KRACKATOA KING**, 11, b g Kayf Tara—Firecracker Lady (IRE) **J.C.Harrison Lee & T.Howard Partnership**
19 **KRIS SPIN (IRE)**, 11, br g Kris Kin (USA)—Auditing Empress (IRE) **Six To Five Against**
20 **MAGIC DANCER (IRE)**, 7, b g Norse Dancer (IRE)—King's Siren (IRE) **Mark E Smith & The Magic Partnership**
21 **MAGIC MUSTARD (IRE)**, 8, ch g Stowaway—Honey Mustard (IRE) **Magic Mustard Partnership**
22 **MAHARI (IRE)**, 6, b g Duke of Marmalade (IRE)—Mission Secrete (USA) **W. Roseff**
23 **MURPHY'S NAILS (IRE)**, 7, b g Milan—Definite Artist (IRE) **Bailey-Carvill Equine**
24 **PILGRIM SOUL (IRE)**, 4, b f Yeats (IRE)—Sabah **Mark E Smith & the 12 Minimum Pship**
25 **QUIETO SOL (FR)**, 8, ch g Loup Solitaire (USA)—First Wonder (FR) **The QS Trio & Mark E. Smith**
26 **SCALES (IRE)**, 13, b g Bob Back (USA)—Mrs Avery (IRE) **A Beard B Beard S Ripley**
27 **SHEAR ROCK (IRE)**, 9, b g Spadoun (FR)—Sleeping Diva (FR) **Mr M. E. Smith**
28 **SINAKAR (IRE)**, 8, br g Manduro (GER)—Siniyya (IRE) **Miss K. Lee**
29 **SIR WILL (IRE)**, 8, b g Yeats (IRE)—Tinopasa (FR) **West Coast Haulage Limited**
30 **STORM CONTROL (IRE)**, 6, b g September Storm (GER)—Double Dream (IRE) **W. Roseff**
31 **THE WELSH PADDIES (IRE)**, 7, b g Court Cave (IRE)—Masiana (IRE) **West Coast Haulage Limited**
32 **TOP GAMBLE (IRE)**, 11, ch g Presenting—Zeferina (IRE) **Walters Plant Hire & James & Jean Potter**
33 **TOWN PARKS (IRE)**, 8, b g Morozov (USA)—Outdoor Heather (IRE) **Mrs J. A. Beavan**
34 **TREE OF LIBERTY (IRE)**, 7, ch g Stowaway—The Wrens Nest (IRE) **Mr M. E. Smith**
35 **WEST COAST GLORY (IRE)**, 5, b m Fame And Glory—Turntofacethesun **West Coast Haulage Limited**
36 **ZARA HOPE (IRE)**, 8, b m Stowaway—Agua Caliente (IRE) **Mr M. E. Smith**

Other Owners: Mr R. F. Bailey, Mr R. L. Baker, Mr Alan Beard, Mr B. Beard, Mr Harry Bryson, Mr Daniel Campbell, Campbell-Mizen, Mr R. K. Carvill, The Excellent Dees, Mr G. T. Gilbert, Mr Stewart Harris, Ms J. C. Harrison-Lee, Mr R. L. C. Hartley, Mr M. R. Hawkins, Miss T. Howard, James and Jean Potter, Mr B. Knight, The Magic Partnership, Mr P. Mizen, Ms L. E. Moore, Mr M. J. Neat, Mr James Noble, Mr J. E. Potter, Mrs J. E. Potter, The QS Trio, Lady Susan Ripley, Mr Will Roseff, Mr Mark E. Smith, The Magic 7, The Twelve Minimum Partnership, Walters Plant Hire Ltd, Mr J. H. Watson, Mrs H. Watson.

Assistant Trainer: Richard Lee

Jockey (NH): Richard Johnson, Jamie Moore. **Conditional:** Richard Patrick.

---

341 MRS SOPHIE LEECH, Westbury-on-Severn
Postal: Leech Racing Limited, Tudor Racing Stables, Elton Road, Elton, Newnham, Gloucestershire, GL14 1JN
Contacts: PHONE (01452) 760691 MOBILE (07775) 874630
E-MAIL info@leechracing.co.uk WEBSITE www.leechracing.co.uk

1 **ADMIRAL SPICE (IRE)**, 4, gr g Lethal Force (IRE)—Rustam **Out Of Bounds Racing Club**
2 **ANTEROS (IRE)**, 11, b g Milan—Sovereign Star (IRE) **K. W. Bell**
3 **APPLESANDPIERRES (IRE)**, 11, b g Pierre—Cluain Chaoin (IRE) **C. J. Leech**
4 **BIRCH HILL (IRE)**, 9, b g Kalanisi (IRE)—Miss Compliance (IRE) **G. D. Thompson**
5 **BUONAROTTI BOY (IRE)**, 7, b g Galileo (IRE)—Funsie (FR) **Mr R. S. Liddington**
6 **CLONDAW CIAN (IRE)**, 9, br g Gold Well—Cocktail Bar (IRE) **Mr A. R. Purvis**
7 **DOTHRAKI RAIDER (IRE)**, 8, b g Kayf Tara—French Spice **Mr M. J. Gorman**
8 **DUN SCAITH (IRE)**, 11, b g Vinnie Roe (IRE)—Scathach (IRE) **Cheltenham Racing Club**
9 **FULL SHIFT (FR)**, 10, b g Ballingarry (IRE)—Dansia (GER) **Mr A. R. Purvis**
10 **GARO DE JUILLEY (FR)**, 7, b g Ungaro (GER)—Lucy de Juilley (FR) **G. D. Thompson**
11 **GENERAL BUX (IRE)**, 8, b g Lucarno (USA)—Cadoutene (FR) **The Scoobyless Partnership**
12 **GHOST SERGE (IRE)**, 4, gr g Zebedee—Cornakill (USA) **Mr J. T. Finch**

MRS SOPHIE LEECH - Continued

13 HAZAMAR (IRE), 6, gr g Manduro (GER)—Hazarafa (IRE) **Mike Harris Racing Club & Partner**
14 LIEUTENANT COLONEL, 10, b g Kayf Tara—Agnese **G. D. Thompson**
15 LIL LAZARUS (FR), 6, ch g Anabaa Blue—Santoria (FR) **C. J. Leech**
16 MAN OF PLENTY, 10, ch g Manduro (GER)—Credit-A-Plenty **G. D. Thompson**
17 MIDNIGHT GEM, 9, b m Midnight Legend—Barton Flower **Ms G. E. Morgan**
18 MILROW (IRE), 6, b g Tamayuz—Cannikin (IRE) **John Cocks & Roger Liddington**
19 OLD HARRY ROCKS (IRE), 7, b g Milan—Miss Baden (IRE) **G. D. Thompson**
20 4, Ch g Native Ruler—Rabbit
21 SAXO JACK (FR), 9, b g King's Best (USA)—Gamma (FR) **Mike Harris Racing Club & Partner**
22 SINFONIETTA (FR), 7, b g Sinndar (IRE)—Final Whistle (IRE) **Mr C. A. Washbourn**
23 SOIESAUVAGE (FR), 8, b m Lauro (GER)—Taffetas (FR) **Ms K. Neill & Mr W. Mackey**
24 STEPHANIE SUNSHINE (IRE), 6, b m Dubai Destination (USA)—Shyanne (IRE) **Out Of Bounds Racing Club**
25 TAMARILLO GROVE (IRE), 12, b g Cape Cross (IRE)—Tamarillo (IRE) **Cheltenham Racing Club**
26 THROCKLEY, 8, b g Passing Glance—Porcelain (IRE) **Out Of Bounds Racing Club**
27 VINCENT'S FOREVER, 6, b g Pour Moi (IRE)—Glen Rosie (IRE) **Cheltenham Racing Club**
28 WALDEN PRINCE (IRE), 12, b g Saffron Walden (FR)—Kahyasi Princess (IRE) **Mike Harris Racing Club**
29 WE'VE GOT PAYET, 5, b g Authorized (IRE)—Missoula (IRE) **Mr Steve Ashley & Mr Gary Pettit**
30 WEST WIZARD (FR), 10, b br g King's Theatre (IRE)—Queen's Diamond (GER) **J. O'Brien**
31 YASIR (USA), 11, b g Dynaformer (USA)—Khazayin (USA) **Mike Harris Racing Club**

THREE-YEAR-OLDS

32 LYSANDER BELLE (IRE), b f Exceed And Excel (AUS)—Switcher (IRE) **Mike Harris Racing Club**

Other Owners: Mr S. A. Ashley, Mr J. J. Cocks, Mr M. E. Harris, A. D. I. Harris, Mr M. D. Kilsby, Mr W. Mackey, Ms K. Neill, Mr C. Parkin, Mr G. Pettit.

Assistant Trainer: Christian Leech (07880) 788464

---

342 MISS TRACEY LEESON, Towcester
Postal: **Glebe Stables, Blakesley Heath Farm, Maidford, Northants, NN12 8HN**
Contacts: **MOBILE (07761) 537672**
E-MAIL **traceyl31@hotmail.co.uk** WEBSITE www.traceyleesonracing.co.uk

1 CEANN SIBHEAL (IRE), 10, b g Flemensfirth (USA)—Imperial Award (IRE) **The Peter Partnership**
2 JONJOELA (IRE), 8, b m Great Exhibition (USA)—Yorkshire Blade (IRE) **In The Pink Partnership**
3 OVER TO BREE, 7, b m Overbury (IRE)—Nouf **The Nap Hand Partnership**
4 RINGMOYLAN (IRE), 7, b g Mahler—La Spezania (IRE) **Buzzing Again Partnership**
5 SWILLY SUNSET, 6, b g Kyllachy—Spanish Springs (IRE) **The Nap Hand Partnership**

Other Owners: Mr M. H. Beesley, Mr D. Deveney, Mr J. L. Frampton, Mr J. D. Horgan, Miss Tracey Leeson, Mr M. E. White.

---

343 MRS SHEILA LEWIS, Brecon
Postal: **Mill Service Station, Three Cocks, Brecon, Powys, LD3 0SL**
Contacts: **PHONE (01497) 847081**
E-MAIL **sheilalewisracing1@gmail.com**

1 CHANGE UR TUNE (IRE), 7, br g Milan—Sunny Native (IRE) **Mr G. Wilson**
2 LISSYCASEY (IRE), 6, b g Rule of Law (USA)—Forever Mates (IRE) **Hopefully Not A Moose Partnership**
3 RED EMPEROR (IRE), 5, b g Holy Roman Emperor (IRE)—Rougette **Jr Jones & Dewi Evans**
4 STRANGSMILL (IRE), 10, b m Beneficial—Sweet Vale (IRE) **Mr G. Wilson**
5 STUPID CUPID (IRE), 8, b m Beneficial—Supreme Arrow (IRE) **W. B. R. Davies**
6 THE FINAL WHISTLE (IRE), 6, ch g Approve (IRE)—Fairnilee **W. B. R. Davies**
7 TRY IT SOMETIME (IRE), 11, b g Milan—Lead'er Inn (IRE) **W. B. R. Davies**
8 WAY OF THE WORLD (IRE), 8, b g Flemensfirth (USA)—Night Heron (IRE) **W. B. R. Davies**

Other Owners: Mr D. L. Evans, Mr J. R. Jones, Mr Richard Sheppard, Mr S. J. Winter.

345 MR NICK LITTMODEN, Newmarket
Postal: **Inner Yard, Brickfield Stud, Cemetery Hill, Newmarket, Suffolk CB8 7JH**
Contacts: **MOBILE (07770) 964865**
E-MAIL **nicklittmoden@icloud.com**

1 **BERRY POPPINS**, 5, b m Mawatheeq (USA)—Florie **Strawberry Fields Stud**
2 **BY RAIL**, 5, br g Rail Link—Soldata (USA) **Mr G. F. Chesneaux & Mr Nick Littmoden**
3 **CAPTAIN SPEAKING (FR)**, 4, ch g Linda's Lad—Hilliflower (FR) **We Live In Norfolk Partnership**
4 **FEARSOME**, 5, b g Makfi—Lixian **Mr G. F. Chesneaux & Mr Nick Littmoden**
5 **FIGEAC (FR)**, 5, gr g Kendargent (FR)—Faviva (USA) **Mr G. F. Chesneaux & Mr Nick Littmoden**
6 **GIOGIOBBO**, 6, b h Bahamian Bounty—Legnani **Mr G. F. Chesneaux & Mr Nick Littmoden**
7 **PACO'S PRINCE**, 4, b g Paco Boy (IRE)—Equitissa (IRE) **Stewart Turner & Amanda Wilson-Martin**
8 **PLETTENBERG GREY**, 5, gr g Sir Percy—Great White Hope (IRE) **Strawberry Fields Stud**
9 5, B br g Sulamani (IRE)—Returning **N. P. Littmoden**
10 **TAMBOURINE SAM**, 6, b g Black Sam Bellamy (IRE)—Tambourine Ridge (IRE) **Mrs E. J. Hulse**
11 **TORIANO**, 6, ch g Equiano (FR)—Ticki Tori (IRE) **Chesneaux, Hassiakos & Littmoden**

THREE-YEAR-OLDS

12 **BADGER BERRY**, b g Epaulette (AUS)—Snow Shoes **Strawberry Fields Stud**
13 **CASARUBINA (IRE)**, br f Casamento (IRE)—Mi Rubina (IRE) **Mr & Mrs J Harris**
14 **GLUTNFORPUNISHMENT**, b g Dawn Approach (IRE)—Oxsana **A. A. Goodman**
15 **GREYBYCHOICE (IRE)**, b g Dark Angel (IRE)—Khalice **A. A. Goodman**

TWO-YEAR-OLDS

16 B c 11/3 Tobougg (IRE)—Sarah Berry (First Trump) (5000) **Strawberry Fields Stud**

Other Owners: G. F. Chesneaux, Mr J. E. Harris, Mrs P. A. Harris, S. Hassiakos, Mr A. Highfield, Mr T. A. Ringer, G. F. L. Robinson, Mr S. J. A. Turner, Ms A. V. Wilson-Martin.

Jockey (NH): Jack Quinlan.

346 MR BERNARD LLEWELLYN, Bargoed
Postal: **Ffynonau Duon Farm, Pentwyn, Fochriw, Bargoed, Mid Glamorgan, CF81 9NP**
Contacts: **PHONE (01685) 841259 FAX (01685) 843838 MOBILE (07971) 233473/(07960) 151083**
E-MAIL **bernard.llewellyn@btopenworld.com**

1 **ARTY CAMPBELL (IRE)**, 9, b g Dylan Thomas (IRE)—Kincob (USA) **Mr Alex James & Mr B. J. Llewellyn**
2 **ASCOT DAY (FR)**, 5, ch g Soave (GER)—Allez Hongkong (GER) **Mr Michael Edwards & Partner**
3 **EARTHLY (USA)**, 5, ch g Spring At Last (USA)—Geographic (USA) **B. J. Llewellyn**
4 **EDGE (IRE)**, 8, b g Acclamation—Chanter **Mr D Maddocks & Partner**
5 **FILATORE (IRE)**, 10, ch g Teofilo (IRE)—Dragnet (IRE) **B. J. Llewellyn**
6 **FLANAGANS FIELD (IRE)**, 11, b g Araafa (IRE)—Zvezda (USA) **G A Security**
7 **GLOBAL THRILL**, 10, b g Big Shuffle (USA)—Goonda **Mr Alex James & Mr B. J. Llewellyn**
8 **GUARDIOLA (USA)**, 4, b g Lonhro (AUS)—Badalona **Mr Gethyn Mills & Mr B. J. Llewellyn**
9 **HANSUPFORDETROIT (IRE)**, 14, b g Zagreb (USA)—Golden Needle (IRE) **B. J. Llewellyn**
10 **MARENGO**, 8, gr g Verglas (IRE)—Cloudchaser (IRE) **Mrs Beth Williams**
11 **MUSTAAQEEM (USA)**, 7, b g Dynaformer (USA)—Wasseema (USA) **B. J. Llewellyn**
12 **NABHAN**, 7, b g Youmzain (IRE)—Danidh Dubai (IRE) **Gethyn Mills & Alex James**
13 **NEVER EQUALLED (IRE)**, 10, br g Brian Boru—Broken Thought (IRE) **Miss I. G. Tompsett**
14 **NORAB (GER)**, 8, b g Galileo (IRE)—Night Woman (GER) **B. J. Llewellyn**
15 **PETRIFY**, 9, b g Rock of Gibraltar (IRE)—Frigid **T. G. Price**
16 **SHADOW'S BOY**, 10, gr g Norse Dancer (IRE)—Inspired Role VII **G. Mills**
17 **SHADOW'S GIRL**, 7, gr m Fair Mix (IRE)—Special Beat **G. Mills**
18 **SPLASH AROUND**, 5, ch g Nathaniel (IRE)—Splashdown **G A Security**
19 **TYBIELASS**, 4, br f Fight Club (GER)—Capesarah **Mr T. Jones**

Other Owners: Mr G. Anstee, Mr M. V. Edwards, Mr A. James, Mrs E. A. Llewellyn, Mr D. P. Maddocks.

Assistant Trainer: J L Llewellyn

Jockey (flat): David Probert. **Conditional:** Sean Houlihan, Robert Williams. **Amateur:** Mr Jordan Williams.

347 MISS NATALIE LLOYD-BEAVIS, East Garston
Postal: **Parsonage Farm Stables, Newbury Road, East Garston, Hungerford, Berkshire, RG17 7ER**
Contacts: **PHONE (01488) 648347 MOBILE (07768) 117656**
E-MAIL nlbracing@gmail.com

1 DANCING DRAGON (IRE), 5, b m Dragon Pulse (IRE)—Abbeyleix Lady (IRE) **Parsonage Racing Partnership**
2 DOCTOR PARKES, 13, b g Diktat—Lucky Parkes **Parsonage Racing Partnership**
3 GENTLEMAN MOORE (IRE), 9, b g Royal Anthem (USA)—Near Dunleer (IRE) **Parsonage Racing Partnership**
4 GRANNY ANNE (IRE), 11, ch m Redback—Krayyalei (IRE) **Mr Y. T. Mehmet**
5 JAMPOWER, 4, b g Equiano (FR)—Wiki Tiki **Parsonage Racing Partnership**
6 ROSSETTI, 11, gr g Dansili—Snowdrops **Sheikh A'Leg Racing**
7 SPRING DIXIE (IRE), 7, gr m Zebedee—Dixie Jazz **Sheikh A'Leg Racing**

THREE-YEAR-OLDS

8 CARLA KOALA, b f Kuroshio (AUS)—Bold Love **Parsonage Racing Partnership**

Other Owners: Mr R. Bonney, Mrs H. M. Bonney, R. Eagle, Miss N. A. Lloyd-Beavis.

348 MR ALAN LOCKWOOD, Malton
Postal: **Fleet Cross Farm, Brawby, Malton, North Yorkshire, YO17 6QA**
Contacts: **PHONE (01751) 431796 MOBILE (07747) 002535**

1 CHRISTMAS LIGHT, 12, b m Zafeen (FR)—Arabian Dancer **A. J. Lockwood**

349 MR JOHN E. LONG, Brighton
Postal: **Southdown Stables, Bear Road, Brighton, East Sussex, BN2 6AB**
Contacts: **MOBILE (07958) 296945/(07815) 186085**
E-MAIL winalot@aol.com

1 BIGDEAL (FR), 6, gr g Montmartre (FR)—Rauxa **Mrs S. E. Colville**
2 CATIVO RAGAZZO, 4, b g Multiplex—Sea Isle **Miss M. B. Fernandes**
3 CHORAL MUSIC, 4, b f Equiano (FR)—Gospel Music **Mrs A. M. Sturges**
4 4, B g Denounce—Ela d'argent (IRE) **Mr J. King**
5 LIBBRETTA, 4, ch f Libranno—Dispol Katie **Mrs A. M. Sturges**
6 MAGICINTHEMAKING (USA), 5, br m Wildcat Heir (USA)—
Love in Bloom (USA) **Mr Martin J. Gibbs & Mr R. D. John**
7 TRUST ME BOY, 11, gr g Avonbridge—Eastern Lyric **R. Pearson & J. Pearson**

Other Owners: Mr Martin J. Gibbs, Mr R. D. John, Mr R. Pearson, Miss J. Pearson.

Assistant Trainer: Miss S Cassidy

Jockey (flat): Hollie Doyle, Robert Havlin, Franny Norton. **Jockey (NH):** Mattie Batchelor. **Apprentice:** Ellie Mackenzie.

350 MR CHARLIE LONGSDON, Chipping Norton
Postal: **Hull Farm Stables, Stratford Road, Chipping Norton, Oxfordshire, OX7 5QF**
Contacts: **PHONE (08450) 525264 FAX (08450) 525265 MOBILE (07775) 993263**
E-MAIL charlie@charlielongsdonracing.com WEBSITE www.charlielongsdonracing.com

1 A VOS GARDES (FR), 9, br g Kapgarde (FR)—Miscia Nera (FR) **Mr C. E. Longsdon**
2 ALASKA RANGE (FR), 4, b g Kapgarde (FR)—Loin de Moi (FR) **Mr A. L. Brooks**
3 BALLYDINE (IRE), 9, ch g Stowaway—Bealaha Essie (IRE) **Mr D. A. Halsall**
4 BESTWORK (FR), 8, bl g Network (GER)—Harmony (FR) **Mr R. J. Aplin**
5 CARDIGAN BAY (IRE), 6, b m Turtle Bowl (IRE)—Nan's Catch (IRE) **Birch, Djivanovic & Doel**
6 CARLOW FARMER (IRE), 6, b g Stowaway—Supreme Fivestar (IRE) **Cracker Syndicate**
7 CASTAFIORE (USA), 6, b m Street Cry (IRE)—Showlady (USA) **Slater Stockwood Nicholson Partnership**
8 CHAMPAGNE NOIR (IRE), 5, br g Stowaway—Prayuwin Drummer (IRE) **Mr T. J. Hemmings**
9 CHECKITOUT (IRE), 5, b g Salutino (GER)—Akasha (IRE) **Mills & Mason Partnership**
10 DANDRIDGE, 10, ch g Doyen (IRE)—Arantxa **Mrs J. A. Wakefield**
11 DARIYA (USA), 4, b f Include (USA)—Dubai (IRE)
12 DIGER DAUDAIE (FR), 6, b g Tiger Groom—Stone Again (FR) **Mr Richard & Mrs Susan Perkins**

MR CHARLIE LONGSDON - Continued

13 **FAITHFULNESS (IRE)**, 6, b m Robin des Champs (FR)—Ballycowan Lady (IRE) **Swanee River Partnership**
14 **FLY HOME HARRY**, 10, b g Sir Harry Lewis (USA)—Fly Home **The Charlie Longsdon Racing Club**
15 **FORTH BRIDGE**, 6, b g Bernardini (USA)—Sally Forth **Her Majesty The Queen**
16 **FROZEN MOTION**, 7, b m Black Sam Bellamy (IRE)—Katys Jools **The Four Kings**
17 **HAMMERSLY LAKE (FR)**, 11, b g Kapgarde (FR)—Loin de Moi (FR) **Mr R. J. Aplin**
18 **HEATHER SONG**, 5, b m Kayf Tara—Bella Macrae **Her Majesty The Queen**
19 **HOOT AT MIDNIGHT**, 4, b f Midnight Legend—Kahooting **Mr & Mrs N. F. Maltby**
20 **INAWHILECROCODILE (IRE)**, 4, b f Robin des Champs (FR)—Charming Present (IRE) **Lady Dulverton**
21 **JET SET (IRE)**, 7, b m Getaway (GER)—Lavender Track (IRE) **Lady Dulverton**
22 **JUST DON'T ASK (IRE)**, 7, ch g Ask—Lucys Mate (IRE) **Robert Aplin & Swanee River Partnership**
23 **JUST YOUR TYPE (IRE)**, 7, gr g Morozov (USA)—Enistar (IRE) **Mr T. Hanlon**
24 5, B m Sulamani (IRE)—Karinga Madame **R. Jenner & J. Green**
25 **KILFINICHEN BAY (IRE)**, 11, b g Westerner—Cailin Deas (IRE) **Cracker Syndicate**
26 **LADY INGLEBY**, 9, b m Multiplex—Lady Jay Jay **Mr P. Bates**
27 **LEITH HILL LAD**, 9, b g Kayf Tara—Leith Hill Star **Mr & Mrs N. F. Maltby**
28 **LEITH HILL LEGASI**, 10, b m Kahyasi—Leith Hill Star **Mr & Mrs N. F. Maltby**
29 **LISDOONVARNA LAD (IRE)**, 7, br g Westerner—Socialite Girl **Swanee River Partnership**
30 **LOCHINVER (FR)**, 5, b g American Post—Golden Gleam (IRE) **Macechern & Thornton Family & C Walsh**
31 **LOOSE CHIPS**, 13, b g Sir Harry Lewis (USA)—Worlaby Rose **Barrels Of Courage**
32 **LOUSE TALK (IRE)**, 7, b g Mahler—Foxy-Lady (IRE) **Pauling,Perkins,Kerwood,King&Williams**
33 **MACH ONE**, 5, b g Makfi—Perfect Spirit (IRE) **The Four Kings**
34 **MIDNIGHT SHOT**, 9, b g Midnight Legend—Suave Shot **Mr D. A. Halsall**
35 **MISS MOLINARI**, 5, b m Malinas (GER)—Maiden Voyage **Mr N. Davies**
36 **MONTY'S AWARD (IRE)**, 7, b g Oscar (IRE)—Montys Miss (IRE) **Mr D. A. Halsall**
37 **NIGHTFLY**, 8, br m Midnight Legend—Whichway Girl **Mrs D. P. G. Flory**
38 **NO TRUMPS**, 5, b m Black Sam Bellamy (IRE)—Magic Score **Her Majesty The Queen**
39 **OLD JEROBOAM (IRE)**, 5, b g Jeremy (USA)—Old Line (IRE) **Mr Matthew Roberts & Simon Jessel**
40 **ON RAGLAN ROAD (FR)**, 7, b g Walk In The Park (IRE)—Millessima (FR) **Five Saints Racing**
41 **ORTENZIA (IRE)**, 5, b m Lawman (FR)—Ondoyante (IRE) **Mr J. N. Greenley**
42 **OUR KAEMPFER (IRE)**, 10, b g Oscar (IRE)—Gra-Bri (IRE) **Swanee River Partnership**
43 **OUR PERCY (IRE)**, 5, b g Stowaway—Another Present (IRE) **Mr T. J. Hemmings**
44 **OVERWORKDUNDERPAID (IRE)**, 6, b g Getaway (GER)—Another Whiparound (IRE) **Mrs J. A. Wakefield**
45 **PERLE'S AN ICON**, 5, b m Sixties Icon—Kahooting **Leith Hill Chasers**
46 **PETE THE FEAT (IRE)**, 15, b g King's Theatre (IRE)—Tourist Attraction (IRE) **Don Sebastiao Partnership**
47 **PETER'S PORTRAIT (IRE)**, 6, b g Portrait Gallery (IRE)—Fancyfacia (IRE)
48 **PRESENT ENDEAVOUR (IRE)**, 4, ch g Presenting—Boragh Thyme (IRE) **The Endeavour Racing Syndicate**
49 **SAINT DALINA (FR)**, 5, b m Saint des Saints (FR)—Dalina (FR) **Mr D. A. Halsall**
50 **SHANROE IN MILAN (IRE)**, 7, b g Milan—Shanroe Scenario (IRE) **Mr D. M. Mason**
51 **SOME AMBITION (IRE)**, 6, b g Westerner—Heath Heaven **Birch, Doel & Parker-Jervis**
52 **STATE VISION (FR)**, 5, b g Vision d'etat (FR)—Dona Rez (FR) **Mr D. A. Halsall**
53 **STORM GODDESS (IRE)**, 5, br m Oscar (IRE)—Afasheen (IRE) **Don Sebastiao Partnership**
54 **STORMY MILAN (IRE)**, 6, b g Milan—Socialite Girl **The Charlie Longsdon Racing Club**
55 **THE VOLLAN (IRE)**, 5, b g Scorpion (IRE)—Print It On Lips (IRE) **Mr T. J. Hemmings**
56 **TREACKLE TART (IRE)**, 7, b m Winged Love (IRE)—Battle Over (FR) **Bradley Partnership**
57 **VIVAS (FR)**, 8, b br g Davidoff (GER)—Lavircas (FR) **Mr N. Davies**
58 **WAY OUT WEST (IRE)**, 6, b g Westerner—Rose Vic (IRE) **Mrs C Djivanovic & Mr M Rose**
59 **WESTERN MILLER (IRE)**, 8, b g Westerner—Definite Miller (IRE) **The Pantechnicons IV**
60 **WILLIE BOY (IRE)**, 8, b g Tikkanen (USA)—Pandora's Moon (IRE) **Kate & Andrew Brooks**

THREE-YEAR-OLDS

61 **THINQUE TANK**, b g So You Think (NZ)—Azharia **Mrs M. M. Fox-Pitt**

Other Owners: Mr N. M. Birch, Mr T. E. Boylan, Mrs K. L. Brooks, Mr N. A. Brown, Mr I. M. Brown, Dr M. R. Clinch, Mr C. K. Crossley Cooke, Mrs C. J. Djivanovic, Mrs R. J. Doel, P. J. Donnison, Dr S. B. Drew, Mrs A. J. Green, Ms R. A. Jenner, Mr S. R. J. Jessel, G. J. Larby, Mr C. O. A. Liverton, Gavin MacEchern, Mr N. F. Maltby, Mrs J. Maltby, Miss N. Martin, Mrs A. May, W. R. Mills, F. J. Mills, J. M. Nicholson, Mrs E. H. Parker-Jervis, Mrs J. Pauling, Mr M. A. Pausey, Mr N. S. Pearse, R. A. H. Perkins, Mrs R. S. Perkins, E. M. G. Roberts, Mr S. N. Roberts, Mr M. C. Rose, Mr J. Simpson, Mr P. J. Smith, Mr S. Spencer-Jones, Mrs S. Spencer-Jones, Mr J. Stockwood, Mrs J. Thornton, Mrs C. J. Walsh, Mr R. W. P. Weeks, Mr F. Wintle.

Jockey (NH): Jonathan Burke. **Conditional:** Paul O'Brien.

351 **MR DANIEL MARK LOUGHNANE, Kidderminster**
Postal: Rock Farm, Rock Cross, Rock, Kidderminster, Worcestershire, DY14 9SA
Contacts: MOBILE (07805) 531021

1 ARTSCAPE, 7, b g Iffraaj—Artisti **Mrs C. M. Loughnane**
2 BIG LACHIE, 5, b g Camacho—Ryan's Quest (IRE) **A Tait & G&J Fernand**
3 BOUNDERBY, 5, b g Manduro (GER)—Most Charming (FR) **Shropshire Wolves**
4 CHOCOLATE BOX (IRE), 5, b g Zoffany (IRE)—Chocolate Mauk (USA) **Racing Facades Syndicate**
5 CLASSY CAILIN (IRE), 4, b f Kodiac—Waroonga (IRE) **Mr P. Moran**
6 DARK ALLIANCE (IRE), 8, b g Dark Angel (IRE)—Alinda (IRE) **Andy Holding Speed Figures.Co.Uk**
7 DESTINYS ROCK, 4, b f Zoffany (IRE)—Special Destiny **Ladies of Rock**
8 DREAM GIFT, 4, b f Dream Eater (IRE)—Charles Bear
9 DREAM MAGIC (IRE), 5, b g Lord Shanakill (USA)—Pursuit of Passion **Mrs C. M. Loughnane**
10 ELWADI, 4, ch g Dutch Art—Caesarine (FR) **Mrs C. M. Loughnane**
11 EMBER'S GLOW, 4, ch g Sepoy (AUS)—Fading Light **T. D. Johnson**
12 GRANNY FRANKHAM, 6, b m Authorized (IRE)—Faldal **Mr R. Cooper**
13 ICE COOL CULLIS (IRE), 4, ch c Frozen Power (IRE)—Kathoe (IRE) **Shropshire Wolves**
14 ITMAKESYOUTHINK, 5, b g So You Think (NZ)—Anbella (FR) **Mr R. M. Brilley**
15 JOUST (IRE), 4, b g Iffraaj—Thawrah (IRE) **Mrs R. M. Serrell**
16 JUST FOR FEE (IRE), 5, b m Fame And Glory—Hakuna (IRE) **Concept Furniture International Limited**
17 KEHAL (IRE), 4, b f High Chaparral (IRE)—Tamazug **Mrs C. M. Loughnane**
18 LITTLE MISS KODI (IRE), 6, b m Kodiac—Sensasse (IRE) **S. & A. Mares**
19 LORD MURPHY (IRE), 6, b g Holy Roman Emperor (IRE)—Tralanza (IRE) **The Goodwooders**
20 4, B c Fast Company (IRE)—Magical Bupers (IRE)
21 MOXY MARES, 4, ch g Motivator—Privalova (IRE) **S. & A. Mares**
22 ONEFOOTINFRONT, 4, b g Sir Percy—Anaya **Mrs C. M. Loughnane**
23 PENSAX BOY, 7, b g Rail Link—Cyclone Connie **S. & A. Mares**
24 PONTBLYDDYN, 4, ch g Mount Nelson—Daring Damsel (IRE) **Mr R. M. Brilley**
25 4, Ch g Casamento (IRE)—Precious Citizen (USA)
26 RED GUNNER, 5, b g Oasis Dream—Blue Maiden **2 Counties Racing**
27 ROCK BOY GREY (IRE), 4, gr g Dark Angel (IRE)—Encore View **The Likely Lads**
28 SEBASTIANO RICCI (IRE), 4, b g Lope de Vega (IRE)—Dear Dream (IRE) **The Sebastiano Ricci Partnership**
29 SILVINGTON, 4, b g Firebreak—Millinsky (USA) **Mr M. Millicham**
30 TAKEONEFORTHETEAM, 4, b g Bahamian Bounty—Miss Bond (USA) **S. & A. Mares**
31 WALLY'S WISDOM, 7, b g Dutch Art—Faldal **Mrs C. M. Loughnane**

THREE-YEAR-OLDS

32 BOLD PRINT (IRE), b c Shamardal (USA)—Visalia (IRE) **Mr R. M. Brilley**
33 DANCING JAQUETTA (IRE), b f Camacho—Skehana (IRE) **Mr R Brilley & Mrs A Townsend**
34 DREAM MODEL (IRE), b f Dream Ahead (USA)—Twiggy's Girl **Live In Hope Partnership**
35 NANANITA (IRE), b f War Command (USA)—Causeway Queen (IRE) **S. & A. Mares**
36 PADDY'S PURSUIT (IRE), b c Pastoral Pursuits—Anaya **Ian O'Connor & Clare Loughnane**
37 PRECISION PRINCE (IRE), b c Dragon Pulse (IRE)—Little Live Wire (IRE) **Precision Facades Ltd**
38 SEAFARING GIRL (IRE), ch f Born To Sea (IRE)—Elayoon (USA) **Greens & Blues Syndicate**
39 SECRET MAGIC (IRE), b f Alhebayeb (IRE)—No Secrets (USA) **Mrs C. M. Loughnane**
40 SITTIN HANDY (IRE), ch g Helmet (AUS)—Three Times **Maximum Limit Syndicate**
41 B f Swiss Spirit—Starlight Angel (IRE) **S. & A. Mares**
42 B f Kodiac—Sugarhoneybaby (IRE)
43 SWIFT JUSTICE, b g Sixties Icon—Wansdyke Lass **Legal Marketing Ltd**

Other Owners: Mr J. Babb, Mr D. A. Cullimore, Mrs L. A. Cullimore, Mr J. Fernand, Mr G. Fernand, Mrs A. Mares, Mr S. Mares, Mr Ian O'Connor, R. Simpson, Mr A. F. Tait, Mrs A. E. Townsend.

352 **MR DAVID LOUGHNANE, Tern Hill**
Postal: Helshaw Grange, Warrant Road, Tern Hill, Shropshire
Contacts: MOBILE (07527) 173197
E-MAIL info@daveloughnaneracing.com WEBSITE www.daveloughnaneracing.com

1 APEX KING (IRE), 5, b g Kodiac—Rainbowskia (FR) **G. B. Firmager & G. H. Firmager**
2 BAHUTA ACHA, 4, b g Captain Gerrard (IRE)—Rosein **Lancashire Lads Partnership**
3 BERLIOS (IRE), 6, b g Excellent Art—Endless Peace (IRE) **Rocke & Hoyland**
4 BERLUSCA (IRE), 10, b g Holy Roman Emperor (IRE)—Shemanikha (FR) **Mr P. Ball**
5 CANDELISA (IRE), 6, br g Dream Ahead (USA)—Vasilia **Mr Dewhurst & Mr Swansbury**
6 CAREYANNE, 5, ch m Mount Nelson—Mayaar (USA) **Gentech Products Ltd**

MR DAVID LOUGHNANE - Continued

7 **CRITICAL THINKING (IRE)**, 5, b g Art Connoisseur (IRE)—Cookie Cutter (IRE) **Mr J. Rocke**
8 **FALSE ID**, 6, b g Aqlaam—Miss Dutee **Mr K. A. Percy**
9 **FUWAIRT (IRE)**, 7, b g Arcano (IRE)—Safiya Song (IRE) **Lowe, Lewis & Hoyland**
10 **HARBOUR PILOT**, 4, b c Harbour Watch (IRE)—Bountiful Girl **Ms J. A. French**
11 **HARRY FROM HAVANA**, 4, b g Havana Gold (IRE)—Devonelli (IRE) **Ms J. A. French**
12 **HIC BIBI**, 4, b f Cityscape—Real Me **Mr P. Onslow**
13 **IFTIRAAQ (IRE)**, 8, b g Muhtathir—Alzaroof (USA) **Miss H. Brookshaw**
14 **KASER (IRE)**, 4, b g Invincible Spirit (IRE)—Lethal Quality (USA) **Lowe, Lewis & Hoyland**
15 **LAST PAGE**, 4, b g Pastoral Pursuits—No Page (IRE) **Mr P. G. Harvey**
16 **MALPREEDY (IRE)**, 7, b m Mahler—Miles Apart (IRE) **Max Europe Limited**
17 **MILAN REEF**, 4, br f Famous Name—Jagapaw (IRE) **Mr M. Godfrey**
18 **RAVEN'S RAFT (IRE)**, 4, gr f Raven's Pass (USA)—Sea Drift (FR) **Mr J. Rocke**
19 **ROCKESBURY**, 4, b g Foxwedge (AUS)—Nellie Ellis (IRE) **Mr J. Rocke**
20 **SEAMSTER**, 12, ch g Pivotal—Needles And Pins (IRE) **Miss S. L. Hoyland**
21 **SHEPHERD'S PURSE**, 7, b g Pastoral Pursuits—Neyraan **Mr C. Greenall**
22 **SIGNORE PICCOLO**, 8, b g Piccolo—Piccolo Cativo **Mike and Eileen Newbould**
23 **STRINGYBARK CREEK**, 5, b g Bushranger (IRE)—Money Note **Miss S. L. Hoyland**
24 **THEODORICO (IRE)**, 6, b g Teofilo (IRE)—Yes Oh Yes (USA) **Mike and Eileen Newbould**

THREE-YEAR-OLDS

25 **BABY STEPS**, b g Paco Boy (IRE)—Stepping Out (IRE) **Mr D. J. Lowe**
26 **FAME N FORTUNE**, b g Thewayyouare (USA)—Acapella Star (IRE) **Fame n Fortune Syndicate**
27 **FAYETTA**, b f Champs Elysees—Starfan (USA) **Miss S. L. Hoyland**
28 **FIZZY FEET (IRE)**, b f Footstepsinthesand—Champagne Mistress **D Lowe & S Hoyland**
29 **KYLLACHY PRINCESS**, ch f Kyllachy—Inagh River **Mr A. Lewis**
30 B c Dark Angel (IRE)—Mythicism **Mr C. B. J. Dingwall**
31 **NAUGHTY NIGEL**, b g Cityscape—Erebis **Mr P. Onslow**
32 **PETIT POIS**, b f Havana Gold (IRE)—Bountiful Girl **Ms J. A. French**
33 **SWEET AND INNOCENT**, br f Lethal Force (IRE)—Zainda (IRE) **Ms J. A. French**
34 B g Temple City (USA)—Travel Plans **Mr G. Dewhurst**
35 **UM SHAMA (IRE)**, ch f Helmet (AUS)—Night Club **G. B. Firmager & G. H. Firmager**

TWO-YEAR-OLDS

36 B c 25/4 Dragon Pulse (IRE)—Alexia Reveuse (IRE) (Dr Devious (IRE)) (7163) **Mike and Eileen Newbould**
37 B c 25/3 Iffraaj—Bint Nayef (IRE) (Nayef (USA)) (40000) **Mike and Eileen Newbould**
38 **CROFTIE**, b c 14/4 Lethal Force (IRE)—Llyn (Dutch Art)
39 **CUPID'S BEAU**, b c 20/3 Brazen Beau (AUS)—Oilinda (Nayef (USA)) (38095) **Mr D. J. Lowe**
40 B f 28/3 Holy Roman Emperor (IRE)—Dabtiyra (IRE) (Dr Devious (IRE)) (16013) **Mike and Eileen Newbould**
41 B f 8/2 Cappella Sansevero—Dissonance (IRE) (Rossini (USA)) (5478) **Mike and Eileen Newbould**
42 **ELPHEBA (IRE)**, b f 6/4 Anjaal—Broadway Musical (Exceed And Excel (AUS)) (23809) **Mr D. J. Lowe**
43 B c 28/1 Tagula (IRE)—Eye Catching (Exceed And Excel (AUS)) (25714)
44 B f 19/3 Cappella Sansevero—Katy Daly (IRE) (Amadeus Wolf)
45 B f 8/3 Gutaifan (IRE)—Maracuja (Medicean) **Mike and Eileen Newbould**
46 B f 26/1 Due Diligence (USA)—Random (Shamardal (USA)) (17142)
47 Ch f 26/4 Night of Thunder (IRE)—Refusetolisten (IRE) (Clodovil (IRE)) (18541) **Mike and Eileen Newbould**
48 B c 29/3 Fulbright—Royal Interlude (IRE) (King's Theatre (IRE)) (20952) **Peter R Ball & Andy Lewis**
49 B f 28/1 Poet's Voice—Signorina Roseina (Captain Gerrard (IRE)) (6000)
50 Ch c 17/2 Anjaal—Yellow Trumpet (Petong) (40000) **Mike and Eileen Newbould**

Other Owners: Mr C. R. S. Black, Mr G. B. Firmager, Mr G. H. Firmager, Mr B. K. Haughey, Mr M. Keating, Mr J. M. Newbould, Mrs E. E. Newbould, Mr C. D. Swansbury, Capt J. H. Wilson.

---

353 **MR SHAUN LYCETT, Witney**
Postal: Fairspear Racing Stables, Fairspear Road, Leafield, Witney, Oxfordshire, OX29 9NT
Contacts: **PHONE** (01451) 824143 **MOBILE** (07788) 100894
E-MAIL trainer@bourtonhillracing.co.uk **WEBSITE** www.bourtonhillracing.co.uk

1 **AUMERLE**, 7, b g Authorized (IRE)—Succinct **S. Lycett**
2 **BARE NECESSITIES (IRE)**, 9, b g Sandmason—Marquante (IRE) **D Gilbert, M Lawrence, A Bruce**
3 **BOSTONIAN**, 9, b g Dubawi (IRE)—Bolshaya **Mr H E Peachey & Mr M J Snowdon**
4 **DJ HAVANA**, 4, b g Havana Gold (IRE)—Fantastic Santanyi **Worcester Racing Club**
5 **EXCELLENT PUCK (IRE)**, 9, b g Excellent Art—Puck's Castle **Bourton Racing**
6 **HALLINGS COMET**, 10, ch g Halling (USA)—Landinium (ITY) **Lord J. Blyth**

MR SHAUN LYCETT - Continued

  7 **MONSART (IRE)**, 7, gr g Echo of Light—Monet's Lady (IRE) **L & M Atkins**
  8 **PARK PADDOCKS (IRE)**, 5, b g Sea The Stars (IRE)—Dream of The Hill (IRE) **Mr D. R. Gilbert**
  9 **SCOTSBROOK NIGHT**, 6, b m Midnight Legend—Won More Night **Mr P. E. T. Price**
10 **THE KING'S STEED**, 6, b g Equiano (FR)—King's Siren (IRE) **D Gilbert, J Lancaster, G Wills**
11 **TIKANITE (IRE)**, 8, b g Tikkanen (USA)—Scented Night (IRE) **L & M Atkins**
12 **TROY DEE KNEE**, 7, b g Rainbow High—Matthew's Bridey **The Golden Boys Partnership**
13 **WEEKLY GOSSIP (IRE)**, 8, br g Kalanisi (IRE)—Mary's Little Vic (IRE) **L & M Atkins**

Other Owners: Mrs M. Atkins, Mr L. Atkins, Mr A. Bruce, Mr P Davis, Mr G. G. Edwards, M. P. Hill, Mr M. Lawrence, Mr M. Lovett, Mr H. E. Peachey, Mr M. J. Snowdon, Mr M. White.

---

354   **MR JOHN MACKIE, Church Broughton**
Postal: **The Bungalow, Barton Blount, Church Broughton, Derby**
Contacts: PHONE **(01283) 585604/585603 FAX (01283) 585603 MOBILE (07799) 145283**
E-MAIL jmackie@bartonblount.freeserve.co.uk

  1 **ANOTHER SITUATION (USA)**, 4, ch f Trappe Shot (USA)—Return The Jewel (USA) **Koya Equine**
  2 **ART ECHO**, 6, b g Art Connoisseur (IRE)—Madhaaq (IRE) **Annwell Inn Syndicate**
  3 **BARTON KNOLL**, 7, b g Midnight Legend—Barton Flower **Mr S. W. Clarke**
  4 **BERTOG**, 4, ch g Sepoy (AUS)—Lucky Token (IRE) **Mr D. Ward**
  5 **BRIDAL MARCH**, 5, ch m Casamento (IRE)—Exultate Jubilate (USA) **Derbyshire Racing III**
  6 **CALIN'S LAD**, 4, ch g Equiano (FR)—Lalina (GER) **Lycett Racing Ltd**
  7 **CUSTARD THE DRAGON**, 6, b g Kyllachy—Autumn Pearl **Derbyshire Racing**
  8 **DUKE OF ALBA (IRE)**, 4, b g Lope de Vega (IRE)—Royal Alchemist **Allstars**
  9 **EBBISHAM (IRE)**, 6, b g Holy Roman Emperor (IRE)—Balting Lass (IRE) **P. Riley**
10 **FIRE JET (IRE)**, 6, ch m Ask—Lightning Jet **Ladas**
11 **INFLEXIBALL**, 7, b m Refuse To Bend (IRE)—Sphere (IRE) **Derbyshire Racing II**
12 **JUST MILLY (IRE)**, 8, b m Milan—Out Performer (IRE) **The Mojan Partnership**
13 **KINGS ACADEMY**, 5, ch g Mayson—Intrusion **Derbyshire Racing VI**
14 **LONDON PROTOCOL (FR)**, 6, ch g Muhtathir—Troiecat (FR) **NSU Leisure & Mrs Carolyn Seymour**
15 **LUNAR JET**, 5, ch g Ask—Lightning Jet **Ladas**
16 **MANY TALES**, 7, b g Multiplex—All Three Fables **Mrs E. M. Mackie**
17 **MONKS STAND (USA)**, 5, b g More Than Ready (USA)—Return The Jewel (USA) **Koya Equine**
18 **OFF THE BEAT**, 5, ch g Black Sam Bellamy (IRE)—Off By Heart **Mrs E. M. Mackie**
19 **POLYPHONY (IRE)**, 4, b f Power—Start The Music (IRE) **Mr D. Ward**
20 **THE STALKING MOON (IRE)**, 5, b m Arcano (IRE)—Cornakill (USA) **Lycett Racing Ltd**
21 **TURANGA LEELA**, 5, ch m Paco Boy (IRE)—Sunday Bess (JPN) **Eventmasters Racing**
22 **WHATDOESNOTKILLYOU**, 5, b g Camacho—Verus Decorus (IRE) **Mr J. Deaves**

THREE-YEAR-OLDS

23 **AMBER JET (IRE)**, b f Dream Ahead (USA)—Star Jet (IRE) **Ladas**
24 **ROCK N ROLL QUEEN**, gr f Coach House (IRE)—Misty's Choice **You Betta You Betta You Bet**

Other Owners: G. Bromley, Mrs S. M. Gasch, Mr D. J. Haddrell, Mr P. Maloney, Mrs M. T. Mullin, Mr C. Mullin, NSU Leisure Ltd, Mr D. R. Penman, Mrs C. Seymour, Mr E. J. N. Sheasby, Mrs D. Sheasby, Mr M. Skellett, Sotby Farming Company Limited, Mr J. P. Whittaker.

---

355   **MR PETER MADDISON, Skewsby**
Postal: **5 West End Cottages, Skewsby, York, YO61 4SG**
Contacts: PHONE **(01347) 888385**

1 **KINGS OWN**, 5, b g Distant Peak (IRE)—Phoebe Nullis **P. Maddison**
2 **SGT BULL BERRY**, 12, b g Alflora (IRE)—Cede Nullis **P. Maddison**
3 **THE SASKATOON**, 10, b g Desideratum—Skewsby Girl **P. Maddison**

Conditional: Jamie Hamilton.

356 MR MICHAEL MADGWICK, Denmead
Postal: **Forest Farm, Forest Road, Denmead, Waterlooville, Hampshire, PO7 6UA**
Contacts: **PHONE/FAX (02392) 258313 MOBILE (07835) 964969**

1 **ACE COMBAT**, 4, b c Shamardal (USA)—Require **Los Leader**
2 **DONO DI DIO**, 4, b f Nathaniel (IRE)—Sweet Cecily (IRE) **Mr O. Lodge**
3 **ETHANDEXTER**, 4, ch g Alkaased (USA)—Miss Venice (IRE) **Sheepwash Partnership**
4 **FAMILY FORTUNES**, 5, ch g Paco Boy (IRE)—Barawin (IRE) **Los Leader**
5 **HI THERE SILVER (IRE)**, 5, gr g Clodovil (IRE)—Elaborate **Los Leader**
6 **MARGIE'S CHOICE (GER)**, 4, b f Redoute's Choice (AUS)—Margie's World (GER) **Mr G. Dixon**
7 **MISS RECYCLED**, 4, b f Royal Applause—Steel Free (IRE) **Recycled Products Limited**
8 **MULTIGIFTED**, 6, b m Multiplex—Attlongglast **Mrs L. N. Harmes**
9 **TOMMYS GEAL**, 7, b m Halling (USA)—Steel Free (IRE) **Recycled Products Limited**
10 **VLANNON**, 4, b g Captain Gerrard (IRE)—Attlongglast **M Gannon, H Vlatas, M Willis, L N Harmes**
11 **WHERE'S TOM**, 4, b g Cape Cross (IRE)—Where's Susie **Recycled Products Limited**

THREE-YEAR-OLDS

12 **ARBUCKLE**, b g Heeraat (IRE)—Attlongglast **Mrs L. N. Harmes**
13 B g Alkaased (USA)—Leading Star **M. Madgwick**

TWO-YEAR-OLDS

14 B f 8/4 Heeraat (IRE)—Attlongglast (Groom Dancer (USA)) **Mrs L. N. Harmes**
15 B g 6/5 Sixties Icon—Leading Star (Motivator) **M. Madgwick**
16 Ch g 1/5 Cappella Sansevero—Meebo (IRE) (Captain Rio) **Partnership**

Other Owners: Mrs Susan Bunney, Mr Matt Gannon, Mrs L. N. Harmes, Mr M. Madgwick, Mr Robert Oliver, Mr T. Smith, Mr Peter Taplin, Mr D. Tapper, Mr Hugh Vlatas, Mr Mark Willis.

Assistant Trainer: David Madgwick

Jockey (NH): Marc Goldstein.

357 MRS HEATHER MAIN, Wantage
Postal: **Kingston Common Farm, Kingston Lisle, Wantage, Oxfordshire, OX12 9QT**
Contacts: **PHONE (01367) 820124 FAX (01367) 820125**
E-MAIL heather.main@hotmail.com WEBSITE www.heathermainracing.com

1 **AL KOUT**, 5, gr g Oasis Dream—Honorlina (FR) **John Rylands & Wetumpka Racing**
2 **C NOTE (IRE)**, 6, b g Iffraaj—Alexander Queen (IRE) **G. C. Stevens**
3 **CAPTAIN SCOTT (IRE)**, 4, b g Tamayuz—Capriole **Mrs H. S. Main**
4 **DASHING POET**, 5, b m Poet's Voice—Millisecond **Mr M. J. Moss**
5 **GRATOT (FR)**, 4, br c Le Havre (IRE)—Absolute Lady (IRE) **D. M. Kerr**
6 **ISLAND BRAVE (IRE)**, 5, b h Zebedee—Tip the Scale (USA) **D. M. Kerr**
7 **KESWICK**, 5, b g Dansili—Marywell **Main Murphy Partnership**
8 **MARSHAL DAN (IRE)**, 4, b g Lawman (FR)—Aunt Nicola **Coxwell Partnership**
9 **MERWEB (IRE)**, 4, gr c Shamardal (USA)—Ashley Hall (USA) **Wetumpka Racing**
10 **RAKE'S PROGRESS**, 5, b g Sir Percy—Cartoon **Coxwell Partnership**

THREE-YEAR-OLDS

11 Gr g Mount Nelson—Cloud Illusions (USA)
12 **GOOD TYNE GIRL (IRE)**, gr f Requinto (IRE)—Hardy Pink (IRE) **Mrs H. Adams**
13 **ISLAND GLEN (USA)**, ch g More Than Ready (USA)—Miss Lavinia (USA) **D. M. Kerr**
14 **ISLAND REEL (IRE)**, b f Ruler of The World (IRE)—Bridge Note (USA) **D. M. Kerr**
15 **LAPIDARY**, b f Kodiac—Carved Emerald **Andrew Knott & Wetumpka Racing**
16 **MEDORAS CHILDE**, b f Nayef (USA)—Byroness **Mr & Mrs D. R. Guest**
17 **MOSTAWAA**, ch g Poet's Voice—Mumtaza **The Haroldians**
18 **PARA QUEEN (IRE)**, b f Slade Power—Dancer's Leap **Don Knott & Wetumpka Racing**
19 **PRINCE LLYR (IRE)**, b g Zoffany (IRE)—Zadalia **Llewellyn Yardley Runeckles**
20 **SONG OF THE ISLES (IRE)**, ch f Tagula (IRE)—Musicology (USA) **D. M. Kerr**

TWO-YEAR-OLDS

21 **BRAZEN ORANGE**, b c 9/5 Brazen Beau (AUS)—Dutch S (Dutch Art) **Mondial Racing & Robert Haim**
22 Gr c 30/4 Poet's Voice—Cloud Illusions (USA) (Smarty Jones (USA))

MRS HEATHER MAIN - Continued

Other Owners: J. Bernstein, Miss C. A. Green, Mr D. R. Guest, Mr R. Haim, Mr D. G. Knott, Mr A. Knott, G. I. D. Llewelyn, Sir J. A. Mactaggart, J. P. M. Main, Mondial Racing, Mr J. F. Runeckles, Mr J. M. C. Rylands, Mr M. R. Telfer.

---

358 MRS ALYSON MALZARD, Jersey
Postal: Les Etabl'yes, Grosnez Farm, St Ouen, Jersey, JE3 2AD
Contacts: MOBILE (07797) 738128
E-MAIL malzardracing@gmail.com

1 BAL AMIE (FR), 5, b g Ballingarry (IRE)—Amie Roli (FR) **Mr A. Taylor**
2 BARWICK, 11, b g Beat Hollow—Tenpence **Mr M. Watt**
3 BOWL IMPERIOR, 7, ch g Raven's Pass (USA)—Turtle Point (USA) **Geoff Somers**
4 BRAC JAG (FR), 7, b g Evasive—Bideeya (USA) **Malzard Racing**
5 CARRERA, 9, b g Sixties Icon—Aileen's Gift (IRE) **Malzard Racing**
6 COUNTRY BLUE (FR), 10, bl g Country Reel (USA)—Exica (FR) **Mr A. Taylor**
7 FLUTTERBEE, 7, b m Equiano (FR)—Dunya **Geoff Somers**
8 FOURNI (IRE), 10, ch m Rakti—Eckbeag (USA) **Ms J. Lowery**
9 HARD TO HANDEL, 7, b g Stimulation (IRE)—Melody Maker **Matt Watkinson & The Baroque Partnership**
10 HONCHO (IRE), 7, gr g Dark Angel (IRE)—Disco Lights **Sheikh A Leg Racing**
11 ICE ROYAL (IRE), 6, b g Frozen Power (IRE)—Salford Princess (IRE) **Mr A. Taylor**
12 MENDACIOUS HARPY (IRE), 8, b m Dark Angel (IRE)—Idesia (IRE) **Malzard Racing**
13 OCEAN CRYSTAL, 7, gr m Stimulation (IRE)—Crystal Gale (IRE) **Channel Highland Racing**
14 RELAXED BOY (FR), 6, b g Le Havre (IRE)—Joyce (GER) **Geoff Somers**
15 SAFIRA MENINA, 7, b m Paco Boy (IRE)—Isla Azul (IRE) **Simon & Florence Harrison-White**
16 SPANISH BOUNTY, 14, b g Bahamian Bounty—Spanish Gold **Malzard Racing**
17 WINKLEVI (FR), 4, b g Maxios—Wild Star (IRE) **Trevor & Pat Gallienne**

THREE-YEAR-OLDS
18 MY DRAMA QUEEN, b f Iffraaj—Garden Row (IRE) **Simon & Florence Harrison-White**

Jockey (NH): Mattie Batchelor. **Amateur:** Miss Michelle Hooper, Miss Victoria Malzard, Mr Freddie Tett.

---

359 MR JAMES JOSEPH MANGAN, Mallow
Postal: Curraheen, Conna, Mallow, Co. Cork, Ireland
Contacts: PHONE (00 353) (0)87 2684611

1 CASTLEBROOK (IRE), 6, b g Oscar (IRE)—Monty's Sister (IRE) **Ann & Alan Potts Ltd**
2 COWBOY DES LONG (FR), 7, gr g Konig Turf (GER)—Garde de Nuit (FR) **Darragh McDonagh**
3 MONTYS MEADOW (IRE), 11, b g Oscar (IRE)—Montys Miss (IRE) **Hanford's Chemist Ltd**
4 WINTER MAGIC (IRE), 11, b g Cloudings (IRE)—Mr K's Winterblues (IRE) **Mrs T C Kouwenberg & Nicola Kent**

Assistant Trainer: Mary Mangan

---

360 MR CHARLIE MANN, Upper Lambourn
Postal: Neardown, Upper Lambourn, Hungerford, Berkshire, RG17 8QP
Contacts: PHONE (01488) 71717 / 73118 FAX (01488) 73223 MOBILE (07721) 888333
E-MAIL charlie@charliemann.info WEBSITE www.charliemannracing.com

1 BLACKFYRE (IRE), 4, br g Redoute's Choice (AUS)—Hazarayna **Tom Segrue**
2 CABRAGH (IRE), 10, b g Old Vic—Satco Street (IRE) **Major J. G. Thorneloe**
3 CAPONE (GER), 4, br g Nathaniel (IRE)—Codera (GER) **Mr B. Kerr**
4 CODY WYOMING, 13, b g Passing Glance—Tenderfoot
5 FINANCIAL CONDUCT (IRE), 5, b g Harbour Watch (IRE)—Popolo (IRE) **The Steeple Chasers**
6 GLORVINA (IRE), 5, b m Dragon Pulse (IRE)—Hawk Dance (IRE) **Mr M. J. R. Bannister**
7 ILEWIN GEEZ, 9, ch g Generous (IRE)—Ilewin Janine (IRE)
8 IVILNOBLE (IRE), 6, b g Alfred Nobel (IRE)—Almutamore (IRE) **Mrs L. C. Taylor**
9 LEX TALIONIS (IRE), 6, b g Thewayyouare (USA)—Dawn Air (USA) **Mrs J. M. Mayo**
10 LIKE THE SOUND (IRE), 8, b g Soldier of Fortune (IRE)—Zalida (IRE) **STG Racing Partnership**
11 LITTLE MISS DARSI (IRE), 6, b m Darsi (FR)—Shaylejon (IRE) **Eventmasters Racing**
12 MORNEY WING (IRE), 10, b g Antonius Pius (USA)—Tillan Fuwain (FR) **The Steeple Chasers**
13 ORIENTAL FLAME, 6, b m Norse Dancer (IRE)—Eastern Paramour (IRE) **Mr E. S. G. Faber**

MR CHARLIE MANN - Continued

14 OSCAR CEREMONY (IRE), 8, b g Oscar (IRE)—Native Singer (IRE) **Racing Ventures 2014**
15 PICKAMIX, 8, gr g Sagamix (FR)—Star of Wonder (FR) **Racing Ventures 2014**
16 PRABENI, 4, ch g Teofilo (IRE)—Nyarhini **Mr D. W. Fox**
17 ROYALS AND REBELS (IRE), 9, b g Robin des Pres (FR)—Native Deal (IRE) **The Neardowners**
18 SID HOODIE (IRE), 5, b m Rip Van Winkle (IRE)—Universe **Mr D. G. Christian**
19 THE DARLEY LAMA (IRE), 5, b g Carlotamix (FR)—Last Sunrise (IRE) **C. J. Mann**
20 THE LINCOLN LAWYER, 4, b g Lawman (FR)—Adventure Seeker (FR) **The Neardowners**
21 THE LION DANCER (IRE), 7, b g Let The Lion Roar—Shesadoll (IRE) **The 25 Club**
22 THE OGLE GOGLE MAN (IRE), 7, b g Yeats (IRE)—Miss Otis Regrets (IRE) **The 25 Club**
23 WISHICOULD (IRE), 8, br m Asian Heights—Dark Wish (IRE) **Mr & Mrs Jim Reeve and Mrs H Kebby**
24 ZEN MASTER (IRE), 7, b g Shantou (USA)—Back Log (IRE) **The 25 Club**

Other Owners: Mr W. Brindle, Mrs H. L. Kebby, Mr Charlie Mann, Mr E. McClafferty, Mr A. J. McClafferty, Ms J. Moran, Mr Tony Outhart, Mrs Laura Reeve, Mr Jim Reeve, Mr E. J. N. Sheasby, Mrs Denise Sheasby, Mr Andy Stone, Major John Thorneloe, Mr C. R. Trembath.

Assistant Trainer: Lilly Carson

Jockey (NH): Harry Bannister, Noel Fehily. **Conditional:** Angus Cheleda.

---

361 **MR GEORGE MARGARSON, Newmarket**
Postal: **Graham Lodge, Birdcage Walk, Newmarket, Suffolk, CB8 ONE**
Contacts: **PHONE (01638) 668043 MOBILE (07860) 198303**
E-MAIL george@georgemargarson.co.uk WEBSITE www.georgemargarson.co.uk

1 BLAME CULTURE (USA), 4, b g Blame (USA)—Pearl In The Sand (IRE) **Mangiacapra, Hill, Hook Partnership**
2 CARIBBEAN SPRING (IRE), 6, b g Dark Angel (IRE)—Bogini (IRE) **Graham Lodge Partnership II**
3 PROTECTED GUEST, 4, b g Helmet (AUS)—Reem Star **John Guest Racing Ltd**
4 TECHNOLOGICAL, 4, gr c Universal (IRE)—Qeethaara (USA) **Mr A. Al Mansoori**

THREE-YEAR-OLDS

5 MODEL GUEST, ch f Showcasing—Looks All Right (IRE) **John Guest Racing Ltd**
6 PAINTED DREAM, b f Showcasing—Speed Date **Graham Lodge Partnership**
7 SPIRITED GUEST, b g Swiss Spirit—Choisette **John Guest Racing Ltd**

TWO-YEAR-OLDS

8 ALVEDA, b f 29/4 Archipenko (USA)—Alizadora (Zilzal (USA)) **Miss K. Rausing**
9 HOT DATE, b f 17/2 Hot Streak (IRE)—
                                    Speed Date (Sakhee's Secret) (5000) **Mangiacapra, Hill, Hook Partnership**
10 SHYMAY, b f 27/3 Mayson—Coconut Shy (Bahamian Bounty) **Mr F. G. Butler**

Other Owners: Mr R. Buckenham, Mr S. Hill, Mrs E. L. Hook, Mr J. G. Mangiacapra, G. G. Margarson.

Assistant Trainer: Katie Margarson

Apprentice: Jane Elliott. **Amateur:** Miss Rosie Margarson.

---

362 **MR ANDREW J. MARTIN, Chipping Norton**
Postal: **Yew Tree Barn, Hook Norton Road, Swerford, Chipping Norton, Oxfordshire, OX7 4BF**
Contacts: **PHONE (01608) 737288**

1 GLEN ROE (IRE), 11, b g Vinnie Roe (IRE)—Belgrove Girl (IRE) **A. J. Martin**
2 MIDNIGHT MUSTANG, 12, b g Midnight Legend—Mustang Molly **A. J. Martin**
3 MIGHTY MUSTANG, 9, b g Passing Glance—Mustang Molly **A. J. Martin**
4 MILITARIAN, 9, b g Kayf Tara—Mille Et Une (FR) **A. J. Martin**
5 SUNNY LEDGEND, 14, b g Midnight Legend—Swordella **A. J. Martin**
6 THISONETIME (IRE), 8, br g Kalanisi (IRE)—Dizzy's Whisper (IRE) **Farrier Jump Jets**

363 MISS NICKY MARTIN, Minehead
Postal: **Great Bradley, Withypool, Minehead, Somerset, TA24 7RS**
Contacts: PHONE (01643) 831175 MOBILE (07980) 269510
E-MAIL nickymartin3@hotmail.com

1 ACCORDING TO HARRY (IRE), 10, b g Old Vic—Cassilis (IRE) **Bradley Partnership**
2 BANG ON FRANKIE (IRE), 7, br g Kalanisi (IRE)—Shuil Abbey (IRE) **Bradley Partnership**
3 BODEKIN POINT (IRE), 8, br g Robin des Pres (FR)—Countessdee (IRE) **Bradley Partnership**
4 BRADLEY BROOK (IRE), 13, ch g Alderbrook—Mazza
5 CAN YOU BELIEVE IT (IRE), 6, br g Oscar (IRE)—Cassilis (IRE) **Bradley Partnership**
6 COLONEL CUSTARD (IRE), 6, ch g Mahler—Criaire Princess (IRE) **Bradley Partnership**
7 CUCUMBER GIN (IRE), 5, b m Oscar (IRE)—Redwood Lady (IRE) **Bradley Partnership**
8 JOG ON (IRE), 6, b g Definite Article—Azabu Juban (IRE) **Bradley Partnership**
9 MERRY MILAN (IRE), 7, b g Milan—Timerry (IRE) **Bradley Partnership**
10 OTTOS ON THE MONEY (IRE), 5, br g Robin des Champs (FR)—Lady Titanium (IRE)
11 PISTOL SHOOT (IRE), 7, b g Milan—Emesions Lady (IRE) **Bradley Partnership**
12 POISON ARROW (IRE), 5, b g Scorpion (IRE)—Lobatica (GER) **Bradley Partnership**
13 PURE VODKA, 6, b m Westerner—Fairly High (IRE)
14 SONOFTHEKING (IRE), 11, b g King's Theatre (IRE)—Nikadora (FR) **Bradley Partnership**
15 STEADY AWAY (IRE), 5, b g Fame And Glory—Inch Pride (IRE) **Bradley Partnership**
16 SYKES (IRE), 10, b g Mountain High (IRE)—Our Trick (IRE) **Bradley Partnership**
17 THE TWO AMIGOS, 7, b g Midnight Legend—As Was **Bradley Partnership**

Other Owners: Miss N. Martin, Mr J. Simpson.

364 MR CHRISTOPHER MASON, Caerwent
Postal: **Whitehall Barn, Five Lanes, Caerwent, Monmouthshire**
Contacts: PHONE (01291) 422172 FAX (01633) 666690 MOBILE (07767) 808082
E-MAIL cjmason@tiscali.co.uk

1 EDGED OUT, 9, b m Piccolo—Edge of Light **Mr Christopher and Annabelle Mason Racing**
2 MASONS BELLE, 4, b g Piccolo—Edge of Gold **Mr Christopher and Annabelle Mason Racing**

THREE-YEAR-OLDS

3 ATTY'S EDGE, b c Coach House (IRE)—Belle's Edge **International Plywood (Importers) Ltd**
4 DISEY'S EDGE, b f Harbour Watch (IRE)—Edge of Light **Int Plywood (Importers) Ltd & C Mason**
5 B f Harbour Watch (IRE)—Elidore **Mr S Bishop & Mr C Mason**
6 GILT EDGE, b f Havana Gold (IRE)—Bright Edge **Mr S Bishop & Mr C Mason**
7 B f Swiss Spirit—Sharpened Edge **Mr Christopher and Annabelle Mason Racing**

TWO-YEAR-OLDS

8 GLAMOROUS ANNA, b f 24/3 Cable Bay (IRE)—Go Glamorous (IRE) (Elnadim (USA)) **Robert & Nina Bailey**
9 B f 22/3 Cable Bay (IRE)—
    Sharpened Edge (Exceed And Excel (AUS)) **Mr Christopher and Annabelle Mason Racing**
10 B c 26/3 Harbour Watch (IRE)—
    Superior Edge (Exceed And Excel (AUS)) **Mr Christopher and Annabelle Mason Racing**

Other Owners: R. M. Bailey, Mrs J. H. Bailey, Mr S. Bishop, C. J. Mason, Exors of the Late Mrs A. L. Mason.

Assistant Trainer: Annabelle Mason

365 MRS JENNIFER MASON, Cirencester
Postal: **Manor Farm, Ablington, Bibury, Cirencester, Gloucestershire, GL7 5NY**
Contacts: PHONE (01285) 740445 MOBILE (07974) 262438
E-MAIL pwmason2002@yahoo.co.uk WEBSITE www.jennifermasonracing.com

1 ACT ALONE, 10, b g Act One—Figlette **Mason Racing Club**
2 CALL ME SID, 7, b g Schiaparelli (GER)—Zolotaya **Mr N. G. Mills**
3 DAN'S WEE MAN, 10, b g Kayf Tara—Hazel Bank Lass (IRE) **Mr G. F. Disney**
4 LOVE OF MIDNIGHT, 5, b m Midnight Legend—Love of Tara **North Park Farm Racing**
5 4, Ch g Schiaparelli (GER)—Tenderfoot **Mrs J. S. Mason**

MRS JENNIFER MASON - Continued

Other Owners: Mrs Richard Slocock.
Assistant Trainer: Mr Peter W. Mason
Amateur: Mr Peter Mason.

---

366 **MR ROBIN MATHEW, Burford**
Postal: **Church Farm, Little Barrington, Burford, Oxfordshire, OX18 4TE**
Contacts: **PHONE (01451) 844311 MOBILE (07960) 990037**

THREE-YEAR-OLDS

1 B g Mount Nelson—Behest **R. Mathew**

---

367 **MISS JANE MATHIAS, Llancarfan**
Postal: **Crosstown, Llancarfan, Vale of Glamorgan, CF62 3AD**
Contacts: **MOBILE (07779) 382727**

1 **DEFINATELY VINNIE,** 9, ch g Vinnie Roe (IRE)—Sohapara **Mrs S. E. Mathias**

---

368 **MR PHILIP MCBRIDE, Newmarket**
Postal: **Exeter House Stables, 33 Exeter Road, Newmarket, Suffolk, CB8 8LP**
Contacts: **PHONE/FAX (01638) 667841 MOBILE (07929) 265711**

1 **BOND STREET BEAU,** 4, ch g Dandy Man (IRE)—Loveleaves **Mr Chris Budgett & Mr P J McBride**
2 **PRISCILLA'S DREAM,** 4, ch f Bated Breath—Be Free **Mr Chris Massie & Partners**
3 **VAMPISH,** 4, b f Sir Percy—Falling Angel **Mr C. M. Budgett**

THREE-YEAR-OLDS

4 **CAMACHESS (IRE),** b f Camacho—Heeby Jeeby **The Narc Partnership**
5 **GONBUTNOTFORGOTTEN (FR),** b f Showcasing—Porcini **The Gonbutnotforgotten Partnership**
6 **MALLET HEAD,** b c Rajsaman (FR)—Attachee de Presse (IRE) **Miss C. McPhillips-Witt**
7 **MASAI SPIRIT,** b f Charm Spirit (IRE)—Eastern Lily **Mrs Jacqui Barrs & Mr P. J. Mcbride**
8 **MINNELLI,** ch f Showcasing—Clear Voice (USA) **Pmracing (Uk) Ltd**
9 **MOLLY MAI,** b f Mayson—Handsome Molly **The Ten Fools & A Horse Partnership**
10 **SIMBA SAMBA,** b g Leroidesanimaux (BRZ)—Rouge Dancer **Pmracing (Uk) Ltd**
11 B g Garswood—Suerte Loca (IRE) **Mr Chris Budgett & Mr P J McBride**

TWO-YEAR-OLDS

12 **ANANCY,** b f 11/1 Mukhadram—Anarchiste (Archipenko (USA)) **Miss K. Rausing**
13 B f 18/3 Kyllachy—Falling Angel (Kylian (USA)) (19047) **Serafinoagodino,C.M.Budgett,P.J.Mcbride**
14 B f 2/2 Mustajeeb—Firebelly (Nicolotte) (10000) **Pmracing (Uk) Ltd**
15 B f 23/3 Fountain of Youth (IRE)—Island Rhapsody (Bahamian Bounty) (4500) **Mr C Massie & Mr Pj McBride**
16 **POKER MASTER (IRE),** b c 25/1 Sepoy (AUS)—Three Cards (Mastercraftsman (IRE)) (8571)
17 B f 17/4 Cable Bay (IRE)—Read Federica (Fusaichi Pegasus (USA)) (5500) **Mrs Jacqui Barrs & Mr P. J. Mcbride**
18 **SHINING AITCH,** gr c 22/3 Sepoy (AUS)—Light Shine (Dansili) (4761) **Mr Howard J. Cooke & Mr P. J. Mcbride**

Other Owners: Mr S. Agodino, Mrs J. Barrs, Mr J. W. Blake, Mr A. D. Bunce, Mr G. P. Chapman, Mr H. J. Cooke, N. L. Davies, Mrs S. Hamilton, Mr C. Massie, P. J. McBride, Mr I. J. Pattle, Mr R. Wilson.

---

369 **MR DONALD MCCAIN, Cholmondeley**
Postal: **D McCain Racing Ltd, Bankhouse, Cholmondeley, Cheshire, SY14 8AL**
Contacts: **PHONE (01829) 720352/720351 MOBILE (07903) 066194**
E-MAIL info@donaldmccain.co.uk WEBSITE www.donaldmccain.co.uk

1 **ALWAYS DU CERISIER (FR),** 6, b g Apsis—Tyr Elissa (FR) **Mr P. J. Byrne**
2 **ARMATTIEKAN (IRE),** 5, b g Arakan (USA)—Serpentine Mine (IRE) **Clwydian International**
3 **ARTICHOKE HEART,** 4, b f Shantou (USA)—Seedless **R Kent & Partner**

MR DONALD MCCAIN - Continued

4 **BALLASALLA (IRE)**, 7, br g Presenting—Papoose (IRE) **Mr T. J. Hemmings**
5 **BARNABY BROOK (CAN)**, 9, b g North Light (IRE)—Mascara (USA) **D. R. McCain**
6 **BEACH BREAK**, 5, b g Cacique (IRE)—Wemyss Bay **Mr G. E. Fitzpatrick**
7 **BIRCH BANK**, 6, b g Multiplex—Dolly Duff **Birkdale Bloodstock**
8 **BIRCH VALE (IRE)**, 7, br m Presenting—Oscar Rebel (IRE) **Tim & Miranda Johnson**
9 **BLACK KEY**, 7, b g Authorized (IRE)—Pentatonic **Mr D. E. Owens**
10 **BREAKFAST (IRE)**, 4, b g Kodiac—Pride Celebre (IRE) **Mr T Leslie & Mr N Sutton**
11 **BRIGHT SIDE OFLIFE (IRE)**, 6, ch m Doyen (IRE)—Lough Lein Leader (IRE) **T. G. Leslie**
12 **BROTHER PAT**, 4, b g Muhtathir—Comtesse du Sud (FR) **The Coyne Family**
13 **CADELLIN**, 8, b g Black Sam Bellamy (IRE)—Clotted Cream (USA) **Mr R. J. Morgan**
14 **CAPMONFOR (FR)**, 6, b g Kap Rock (FR)—Fautine World (FR) **The Jockey Club Haydock Park Racing Club Ltd**
15 **CARRY ON**, 4, b g Footstepsinthesand—Evening **T. G. Leslie**
16 **CHICAGO LADY (IRE)**, 8, b m Stowaway—Gemmeus (IRE) **D. R. McCain**
17 **CHTI BALKO (FR)**, 7, gr g Balko (FR)—Ina Scoop (FR) **Mr D. Carrington**
18 **CLOUDY DREAM (IRE)**, 9, gr g Cloudings (IRE)—Run Away Dream (IRE) **Mr T. J. Hemmings**
19 **CONSTANCIO (IRE)**, 6, b g Authorized (IRE)—Senora Galilei (IRE) **Elite Racing Club**
20 **COURT JURADO (IRE)**, 5, b g Court Cave (IRE)—Glen Eile (IRE) **David & Carol Shaw**
21 **COUSIN OSCAR (IRE)**, 7, b g Oscar (IRE)—On The Jetty (IRE) **T. G. Leslie**
22 **CRAIG STAR (IRE)**, 9, b g Craigsteel—Different Dee (IRE) **Hale Racing Limited**
23 **CULMINATION**, 7, b g Beat Hollow—Apogee **Tim & Miranda Johnson**
24 **DANCEINTOTHELIGHT**, 12, gr g Dansili—Kali **Mrs S. K. McCain**
25 **DARK CONFIDANT (IRE)**, 6, b g Royal Applause—Sleek Gold **D. R. McCain**
26 **DARK SUNSET (IRE)**, 8, b m Scorpion (IRE)—Wilmott's Fancy **Bart Ryan-Beswick 1**
27 **DEAR SIRE (FR)**, 7, gr g Al Namix (FR)—Polismith (FR) **Green Day Racing**
28 **DERINTOHER YANK (IRE)**, 8, b g Dubai Destination (USA)—
  Anns Present (IRE) **Don't Tell The Wife Racing Ltd P'Ship**
29 **DERRYNANE (IRE)**, 8, b g Oscar (IRE)—Tessano Queen (IRE) **Donald McCain Racing Club**
30 **DEVITO'SREDROBIN (IRE)**, 6, b m Robin des Champs (FR)—
  Koko Rose (IRE) **Bart Ryan-Beswick & Peel Bloodstock**
31 **DOMINATING (GER)**, 5, ch g Jukebox Jury (IRE)—Dominante (GER) **ValueRacingClub.co.uk**
32 **DRY LIGHTENING (IRE)**, 5, b g Arcadio (GER)—Waydale Hill **Mr J. M. Glews**
33 **FEDERICI**, 10, b g Overbury (IRE)—Vado Via **M Four Properties Ltd**
34 **FIERCLY FORGIE (IRE)**, 6, b g Court Cave (IRE)—Bosanova Girl (IRE) **Mr A. R. Horabin**
35 **FIN AND GAME (IRE)**, 7, b g Oscar (IRE)—Miss Cilla (IRE) **T. G. Leslie**
36 **FIRST ACCOUNT**, 5, b br g Malinas (GER)—Kind Nell **Straightline Bloodstock**
37 **FLEMENS STORY (IRE)**, 8, b g Flemensfirth (USA)—Amelia Earhart (IRE) **T. G. Leslie**
38 **FRONT AT THE LAST (IRE)**, 9, b g Golan—Kilgefin Tina (IRE) **Aykroyd & Sons Limited**
39 **GAELIK COAST (FR)**, 5, br g Coastal Path—Gaelika (IRE) **T. G. Leslie**
40 **GOFFSBRIDGE GIRL (IRE)**, 6, b m Touch of Land (FR)—The Bosses Mare (IRE) **Mr M. Kelly**
41 **GOLDEN FRIDAY (IRE)**, 6, b g Gold Well—Azulada (FR) **Mr A. N. Brooke Rankin**
42 **GOLDEN INVESTMENT (IRE)**, 10, b g Gold Well—Mangan Pet (IRE) **T. G. Leslie**
43 **GRACELAND (FR)**, 7, gr m Mastercraftsman (IRE)—Jeunesse Lulu (IRE) **Mr A. Whelan**
44 **GRAY DAY (IRE)**, 8, gr g Daylami (IRE)—Carrigeen Diamond (IRE) **Dr G. M. Thelwall Jones**
45 **HANDY HOLLOW (IRE)**, 6, ch g Beat Hollow—Hesperia **Donald McCain Racing Club**
46 **HENRY'S JOY (IRE)**, 6, b g Craigsteel—Shocona (IRE) **T. G. Leslie**
47 **HILLS OF DUBAI (IRE)**, 10, ch g Dubai Destination (USA)—Mowazana (IRE) **T. G. Leslie**
48 5, B m Beat Hollow—Holme Rose **T. G. Leslie**
49 4, B g Shirocco (GER)—Holme Rose **T. G. Leslie**
50 **INK MASTER (IRE)**, 9, b g Whitmore's Conn (USA)—Welsh Connection (IRE) **Green Day Racing**
51 **ITS ALL A LARK (IRE)**, 6, b m Oscar (IRE)—Itsalark (IRE) **The Gilbert's & Mr Campbell**
52 **KATACHENKO (IRE)**, 10, b g Kutub (IRE)—Karalee (IRE) **D. R. McCain**
53 **KELKA**, 7, b m Exit To Nowhere (USA)—Scarvagh Diamond (IRE) **D&D Armstrong Limited**
54 4, B f Multiplex—Kind Heart **Don't Tell The Wife Racing Ltd**
55 **KNOCK HOUSE (IRE)**, 10, ch g Old Vic—Lady's Gesture (IRE) **T. G. Leslie**
56 **KNOCKROBIN (IRE)**, 8, b br g Robin des Pres (FR)—Tudor Style (IRE) **Deva Racing Knockrobin Partnership**
57 **LIVA (IRE)**, 4, ch g Champs Elysees—Resistance Heroine **Mr Simon Munir & Mr Isaac Souede**
58 **LOFGREN**, 8, b g Multiplex—Sherry Darling (IRE) **Mrs A. M. Lees-Jones**
59 **LORD SPRINGFIELD (IRE)**, 6, ch g Well Chosen—Super Thyne (IRE) **Straightline Bloodstock**
60 **LOUGH DERG JEWEL (IRE)**, 8, b g Oscar (IRE)—River Valley Lady (IRE) **Mrs A. E. Strang Steel**
61 **MAC O'POLO (IRE)**, 5, b g Henrythenavigator (USA)—Topka (FR) **Macguire's Bloodstock Ltd**
62 **MAHLER LAD (IRE)**, 9, b g Mahler—Sister Merenda (IRE) **T. G. Leslie**
63 **MIDDLEBROW (IRE)**, 8, b g Oscar (IRE)—O What A Girl (IRE) **T. G. Leslie**
64 **MORRAMAN (IRE)**, 6, b g Gold Well—Casa Queen (IRE) **Birkdale Bloodstock**
65 **MOUNT MEWS (IRE)**, 8, b g Presenting—Kneeland Lass (IRE) **Mr T. J. Hemmings**
66 **MR MCGO (IRE)**, 8, b g Touch of Land (FR)—La Principal (IRE) **Mr J. M. Glews**

MR DONALD McCAIN - Continued

67 **MR MONOCHROME**, 8, br g Indian Danehill (IRE)—Our Ethel **Mr & Mrs G Calder & Mr P M Warren**
68 **NAYATI (FR)**, 5, b g Spirit One (FR)—Smadouce (FR) **Mr N. M. Burrows**
69 **NEFYN POINT**, 5, gr g Overbury (IRE)—So Cloudy **Tim & Miranda Johnson**
70 **O'HANRAHAN BRIDGE (IRE)**, 7, b g Gold Well—Greenacre Mandalay (IRE) **Mr M. Kelly**
71 **OFCOURSEIWILL (IRE)**, 7, b g Publisher (USA)—Camden Princess (IRE) **Mr N. Hartley**
72 **ONTHEFRONTFOOT (IRE)**, 5, b g Shantou (USA)—
On The Backfoot (IRE) **Duncan, Dunnington, Nicholls & Shaw**
73 **ORMESHER**, 4, b g Sir Percy—Marakabei **Sarah & Wayne Dale**
74 4, Br g Arcadio (GER)—Oscar Show (IRE) **Don't Tell The Wife Racing Ltd**
75 **OTTONIAN**, 5, ch g Dubawi (IRE)—Evil Empire (GER) **Nigel Dunnington & David Shaw**
76 **OUR DANCING DANDY (IRE)**, 9, b g Scorpion (IRE)—Woodsia **Deva Racing Scorpion Partnership**
77 **OUR DELBOY**, 7, gr g Multiplex—Dawn's Della **Mrs E. Benson**
78 **OUR KYLIE (IRE)**, 7, b m Jeremy (USA)—Prakara (IRE) **D. McCain**
79 **PICHELOT (FR)**, 6, b g Konig Turf (GER)—Haute Chartreuse (FR) **Mr Simon Munir & Mr Isaac Souede**
80 **PINCH OF GINGER (IRE)**, 8, ch g Golden Lariat (USA)—Espiritu Santo (IRE) **That Software Company Ltd**
81 **POGUE (IRE)**, 6, gr g Stowaway—Night Palm (IRE) **Mr J. Turner**
82 **POUGNE BOBBI (FR)**, 8, b br g Protektor (GER)—Amicus **Straightline Bloodstock**
83 **PRINCE KHURRAM**, 9, b g Nayef (USA)—Saree **T. G. Leslie**
84 **PRINCESS MONONOKE (IRE)**, 8, b m Oscar (IRE)—Grande Solitaire (FR) **Donald McCain Racing Club**
85 **PROMISE OF PEACE (JPN)**, 5, ch g King Kamehameha (JPN)—Peace of World (JPN) **T. G. Leslie**
86 **QUIDS IN (IRE)**, 6, b g Pour Moi (IRE)—Quixotic **Mrs I. I. Plumb**
87 **RAINY CITY (IRE)**, 9, b g Kalanisi (IRE)—Erintante (IRE) **Birkdale Bloodstock**
88 **RAISE A SPARK**, 9, b g Multiplex—Reem Two **Mr R Pattison & Mr R Kent**
89 **ROBBING THE PREY (IRE)**, 8, b g Robin des Pres (FR)—Derravarra Lady (IRE) **The Bells Steakhouse Ltd**
90 **ROCKALZARO (FR)**, 7, gr g Balko (FR)—Royale Wheeler (FR) **First Serve Solutions Ltd**
91 **ROSE'S IN THE RAIN (IRE)**, 5, b m Yeats (IRE)—Midnight Flirt (IRE) **Mr J. M. Glews**
92 **SAME CIRCUS**, 8, b m Brian Boru—Curragh Orpen (IRE) **Penketh & Sankey Jech Racing Club 1**
93 **SECRET ESCAPE (IRE)**, 7, ch m Getaway (GER)—Portorosa (USA) **M Four Properties Partnership**
94 **SEE THE SEA (IRE)**, 5, b m Born To Sea (IRE)—Shahmina (IRE) **D. R. McCain**
95 **SHANTALUZE (IRE)**, 7, b g Shantou (USA)—Nut Touluze (IRE) **Deva Racing Cheltenham Syndicate**
96 **SHOCONA'S JOY (IRE)**, 5, b m Primary (USA)—Shocona (IRE) **Mr R. G. Thomas**
97 **SILVER CHARACTER (IRE)**, 4, gr g Camelot—Convocate (USA) **Aykroyd & Sons Limited**
98 **SNOUGAR (IRE)**, 6, b g Arakan (USA)—Thorbella **Tim & Miranda Johnson**
99 **SONIC (IRE)**, 6, b g Vinnie Roe—Bella's Bury **L. Buckley**
100 **SPIN THE COIN (IRE)**, 6, b g Witness Box (USA)—Kempinski (IRE) **Mrs S. C. Leslie**
101 **SUPER MAC (IRE)**, 7, b g Yeats (IRE)—Midnight Flirt (IRE) **Jon Glews & Brendan Richardson**
102 **SWASHBUCKLE**, 6, b g Dashing Blade—Inhibition **Mr M. J. Taylor**
103 **TAILOR TOM (IRE)**, 7, b g Fruits of Love (USA)—Anfield Lady (IRE) **The Tailor 4**
104 **TAKINGITALLIN (IRE)**, 5, b m Fame And Glory—Gilt Benefit (IRE) **Mr G. E. Fitzpatrick**
105 **TAWSEEF (IRE)**, 11, b g Monsun (GER)—Sahool **D. R. McCain**
106 **TESTIFY (IRE)**, 8, b g Witness Box (USA)—Tanya Thyne (USA) **Mr T. J. Hemmings**
107 **THE CATTLEJOBBER**, 7, b g Arvico (FR)—Stillhertoes **D. R. McCain**
108 **THE CHARACTER (IRE)**, 8, b g Bushranger (IRE)—Operissimo **Aykroyd & Sons Limited**
109 **THE CON MAN (IRE)**, 6, b g Oscar (IRE)—Phillis Hill **T. G. Leslie**
110 **THE GREAT GETAWAY (IRE)**, 7, b g Getaway (GER)—Park Mist (IRE) **Straightline Bloodstock**
111 **THE HERDS GARDEN**, 10, b g Multiplex—Eternal Legacy (IRE) **Hale Racing Limited & Mr D. McCain Jnr**
112 **THE PIERRE LARK (IRE)**, 9, b g Pierre—Kyle Lark **D. R. McCain**
113 **THE SOME DANCE KID (IRE)**, 6, b g Shantou (USA)—River Rouge (IRE) **The Blue Nuns**
114 **THOMAS DO (IRE)**, 8, b g Flemensfirth (USA)—Loughaderra (IRE) **Deva Racing Persistence Partnership**
115 **THYNE FOR GOLD (IRE)**, 8, b g Robin des Pres (FR)—My Name's Not Bin (IRE) **Livvys Racing Group**
116 **TOBOGGAN'S FIRE**, 6, b m Firebreak—Toboggan Lady **Grange Park Racing X, Mr T P & D McMahon**
117 **TWO JABS**, 9, b g Teofilo (IRE)—Red Bravo (USA) **Mr M. J. Taylor**
118 **UBALTIQUE (FR)**, 11, b g Balko (FR)—Ode Antique (FR) **T. G. Leslie**
119 **UPPERTOWN PRINCE (IRE)**, 7, b g Strategic Prince—Tarrawarra (IRE) **T. G. Leslie**
120 **UPSETTHEODDS (IRE)**, 7, b g Oscar (IRE)—Cruella de Vil **Clwydian Connections**
121 **VAL MOME (FR)**, 6, b g Turgeon (USA)—Valle Fleurie (FR) **M Four Properties Ltd**
122 **VALLEYOFMILAN (IRE)**, 12, b g Milan—Ikdam Valley (IRE) **Tim & Miranda Johnson**
123 **VISERION**, 7, ch g Tamayuz—Frivolity **Clwydian International**
124 **WAZOWSKI (IRE)**, 10, b g Overbury (IRE)—Malay **D. R. McCain**
125 **WELSH BARD (IRE)**, 10, ch g Dylan Thomas (IRE)—Delphinium (IRE) **G. E. Tobitt**
126 **WHAT HAPPENS NOW (IRE)**, 10, b g Dr Massini (IRE)—
Euro Burden (IRE) **Deva Racing Dr Massini Partnership**
127 **WHISKEY CHASER (IRE)**, 11, br g Flemensfirth (USA)—
Cregane Lass (IRE) **Deva Racing Flemensfirth Partnership**
128 **WHITEOAK FLEUR**, 6, b m Black Sam Bellamy (IRE)—Harringay **Mr B. J. Richardson**

MR DONALD MCCAIN - Continued

129 **WHITEOAK MOLLY**, 5, b m Flemensfirth (USA)—Whiteoak (IRE) **Mr B. J. Richardson**
130 **WHITEOAK STROLLER**, 6, b m Shirocco (GER)—Whiteoak (IRE) **Mr B. J. Richardson**
131 **WHITSUNDAYS (IRE)**, 10, b g Kutub (IRE)—Urdite's Vic (IRE) **Mrs L. Middleton**
132 **WILLIAM OF ORANGE**, 8, b g Duke of Marmalade (IRE)—Critical Acclaim **T W Johnson & G Maxwell**
133 **WITNESS IN COURT (IRE)**, 12, b g Witness Box (USA)—Inter Alia (IRE) **T. G. Leslie**
134 **YES NO MAYBE SO (IRE)**, 5, br g Stowaway—Godlylady (IRE) **Straightline Bloodstock**
135 **YORVIK**, 5, b g Yeats (IRE)—Overbranch **Mr & Mrs G. Calder**

THREE-YEAR-OLDS

136 **GOOBINATOR (USA)**, ch g Noble Mission—Lilac Lilly (USA) **T. G. Leslie**
137 B g Sir Percy—Maleficent **T. G. Leslie**
138 **NAVAJO PASS**, b g Nathaniel (IRE)—Navajo Charm **T. G. Leslie**
139 **OUR RODNEY (IRE)**, b g Canford Cliffs (IRE)—Sea Swell (USA) **Sarah & Wayne Dale 1**
140 **PHILYABOOTS**, b g Oasis Dream—Miracle Maid **T. G. Leslie**
141 B g Mastercraftsman (IRE)—Stroke of Six (IRE) **T. G. Leslie**

Other Owners: Mr C. Bennett, Mr S. Bland, Mr Nick Burrows, G. Calder, Mrs J. Calder, Mr J. J. Campbell, Mr J. R. Couldwell, Mr A. P Coyne, Mr K. Coyne, Mr A. D. Crombie, Mr W. R. Dale, Mrs S. J. Dale, Mr M. Dixon, Mr C. Dixon, Mr D. Duncan, Mr N. C. Dunnington, Mr W. A. Eastup, Mr M. Foster, Mr M. D. Foster, Mrs J. Foster, Richard & Katherine Gilbert, Mrs K. E. Gilbert, Mr R. P Gilbert, Grange Park Racing X, Mr R. J. Gwynne, Mr A. J. Hill, Mr T. Johnson, Mrs M. Johnson, Mr G. L. Joynson, Mrs K. F. Kent, R. Kent, Mr S. Kent, Mr W. R. Kinsey, Mr F. M. Lockwood, D. J. Lockwood, Mr G. Maxwell, Mr D. McMahon, Mr T. P McMahon, Mr P J. Mentha, Mr D. Moyes, S. E. Munir, Mr C. Nicholls, Mr T. D. Nield, Miss M. Noden, Mr E. Norris, Mr R. Pattison, Penketh & Sankey Jech Racing Club, Mr D. Rowe, Mr B. Ryan-Beswick, Mrs C. A. Shaw, Mr D. M. Shaw, Mr J. M. Smart, Mr I. Souede, Mr P.J. Spencer, Straightline Construction Ltd, Mr E. T. Surr, Mr R. A. Sutton, Mrs H. A. Thomas, Mr R. G. Thomas, Mr P. M. Warren, Mr N. Watt.

Assistant Trainer: Adrian Lane

Jockey (NH): Brian Hughes, William Kennedy. **Conditional:** Jack Dinneen, Lorcan Murtagh. **Apprentice:** Ella McCain. **Amateur:** Mr Theo Gillard, Miss Abbie McCain.

---

370 MR TIM MCCARTHY, Godstone
Postal: Nags Hall Farm, Oxted Road, Godstone, Surrey, RH9 8DB
Contacts: PHONE (01883) 740379 MOBILE (07887) 763062
E-MAIL tim@tdmccarthy.com

1 **UNDERSTORY (USA)**, 12, b g Forestry (USA)—Sha Tha (USA) **Homecroft Wealth Racing & T D McCarthy**
2 **W G GRACE (IRE)**, 4, b g Exceed And Excel (AUS)—Ownwan (USA) **Homecroft Wealth Racing & T D McCarthy**
3 **WATER THIEF (USA)**, 7, b g Bellamy Road (USA)—Sometime (IRE) **Surrey Racing Club**
4 **WHITE TOWER (IRE)**, 5, b g Cape Cross (IRE)—Star Blossom (USA) **Surrey Racing Club**

Other Owners: Homecroft Wealth Racing, T. D. McCarthy, Mrs C. V. McCarthy, Mr B. Pettis, Mr S. J. Piper.

Assistant Trainer: Mrs C.V. McCarthy

---

371 MR PHIL MCENTEE, Newmarket
Postal: Racefield Stables, Carriageway, Hamilton Road, Newmarket, Suffolk, CB8 7JQ
Contacts: PHONE (01638) 662092 FAX (01638) 662092 MOBILE (07802) 663256

1 **BERNIE'S BOY**, 6, b g Lilbourne Lad—Stoney Cove (IRE) **T. D. Johnson**
2 **BEYOND THE FRINGE (IRE)**, 4, b f Kodiac—April (IRE) **Front Runner Racing IV**
3 **CONTINGENCY FEE**, 4, b g Helmet (AUS)—Hearsay **Mr M. B. Hall**
4 **EMILY GOLDFINCH**, 6, ch m Prime Defender—Lakelands Lady (IRE) **Miss R McEntee & Mr J Paxton**
5 **GENTLEMEN**, 8, ch g Ad Valorem (USA)—Stoney Cove (IRE) **T. D. Johnson**
6 **GLOBAL MELODY**, 4, b g Hellvelyn—Dash of Lime **T. D. Johnson**
7 **MALAYSIAN BOLEH**, 9, ch g Compton Place—Orlena (USA) **Miss R. B. McEntee**
8 **MOTHER OF DRAGONS (IRE)**, 4, ch f Society Rock (IRE)—Queen O'the Desert (IRE) **Mr S. Jakes**
9 **PEARL SPECTRE (USA)**, 8, ch g Street Cry (IRE)—Dark Sky (USA) **Mr S. Jakes**
10 **RIVER CAFE (IRE)**, 4, b f High Chaparral (IRE)—Dingle View (IRE) **Miss R. B. McEntee**
11 **ROC ASTRALE (IRE)**, 5, ch g Teofilo (IRE)—Lumiere Astrale (FR) **Mr M. B. Hall**
12 **SPARE PARTS (IRE)**, 5, b g Choisir (AUS)—Grandel **Mr S. Jakes**

MR PHIL MCENTEE - Continued

13 **SWISS CROSS**, 12, b g Cape Cross (IRE)—Swiss Lake (USA) **Mr S. Jakes**
14 **TASAABOQ**, 8, b g Aqlaam—Seldemosa **Mrs R. L. Baker**
15 **THE SPECIAL ONE (IRE)**, 6, br m Cape Cross (IRE)—Capote West (USA) **Miss R. B. McEntee**

THREE-YEAR-OLDS

16 **ANGEL DUNDEE**, ch f Dunaden (FR)—Angel Cake (IRE) **Mr W. J. Sewell**
17 **MARGARET J**, gr f Bated Breath—Louverissa (IRE) **Mr S. Jakes**
18 **SPIRIT OF LUCERNE (IRE)**, br f Swiss Spirit—Fascination Street (IRE) **GG Thoroughbreds VIII**
19 **VALLEY BELLE (IRE)**, b f Slade Power (IRE)—Al Sharood **T. D. Johnson**

Other Owners: Mr G. Gill, Mr J. M. Paxton, Mr C. Pigram.

---

372 **MR MURTY MCGRATH, Maidstone**
Postal: Galway Barn, Kiln Barn Road, East Malling, Kent, ME19 6BG
Contacts: PHONE (01732) 840173 MOBILE (07818) 098073
E-MAIL mjmcgrath@hotmail.com

1 **DR JULIUS NO**, 5, b g Dick Turpin (IRE)—Royal Assent **Gallagher Bloodstock Limited**
2 4, B f Champs Elysees—Freya Tricks **Mr R. P. Gallagher**

Assistant Trainer: Heidi McGrath (07795) 178178

---

373 **MRS JEAN MCGREGOR, Milnathort**
Postal: Wester Tillyrie Steading, Milnathort, Kinross KY13 0RW
Contacts: PHONE (01577) 861792 MOBILE (07764) 464299
E-MAIL purebred68@hotmail.co.uk

1 **BURLINGTON BERT (FR)**, 8, b g Califet (FR)—Melhi Sun (FR) **The Good To Soft Firm**
2 **GIAMAS**, 6, b g Bollin Eric—Ginger Brandy **Mrs D. Thomson**
3 **GO COMPLAIN**, 7, b m Mount Nelson—Trounce **Mrs J. C. McGregor**
4 **JACKOFHEARTS**, 11, b g Beat Hollow—Boutique **Mr S. Taylor**
5 **OSCAR BLUE (IRE)**, 9, gr g Oscar (IRE)—Blossom Rose (IRE) **Mrs J. C. McGregor**

Other Owners: Mr A Birrel, Mr M Cameron, Mr G Cuthill, Mr A McDonald, Mrs Jean McGregor, Mr M O'Conner, Mrs Dorothy Thomson, Mr J Thomson.

Jockey (NH): Henry Brooke, Sean Quinlan.

---

374 **MR LUKE MCJANNET, Newmarket**
Postal: Heath View Stables, Hamilton Road, Newmarket, Suffolk, CB8 0NY
Contacts: PHONE (01638) 664505

1 **FOREIGN LEGION (IRE)**, 4, ch g Declaration of War (USA)—Solar Event **Mr I. Collier**
2 **PREMIUM PINK (IRE)**, 4, b f Camacho—Ride For Roses (IRE) **Mr N. P. Hardy**
3 **SIR HAMILTON (IRE)**, 4, b c Canford Cliffs (IRE)—Cawett (IRE) **Mr B. Syversen**
4 **TEBAY (IRE)**, 4, b g Elzaam (AUS)—Maid of Ale (IRE) **Mr B. Syversen**

THREE-YEAR-OLDS

5 B f Bated Breath—Albany Rose (IRE)
6 **FOXES FLYER (IRE)**, b c Foxwedge (AUS)—Midnight Fling **Mr M. Y. Moubarak**
7 **MAARED (IRE)**, ch g Born To Sea (IRE)—Hollow Quaill (IRE) **Mr B. Syversen**
8 **MR ZOOM ZOOM**, b g Toronado (IRE)—Gay Mirage (GER) **Mr M. E. A. Lutfallah**
9 **RED SKYE DELIGHT (IRE)**, gr f Clodovil (IRE)—Sole Bay **Miss R. Dennis**

TWO-YEAR-OLDS

10 B c 2/4 Nathaniel (IRE)—Purple Pearl (IRE) (Danehill Dancer (IRE)) (16856)
11 B c 22/4 Cable Bay (IRE)—Touching (IRE) (Kheleyf (USA)) (2000)
12 B c 11/2 Lethal Force (IRE)—Valandraud (IRE) (College Chapel)

375 MS KAREN MCLINTOCK, Newcastle-Upon-Tyne
Postal: **The Byerley Stud, Ingoe, Newcastle-Upon-Tyne, NE20 0SZ**
Contacts: **PHONE (01661) 886356 MOBILE (07966) 776710**
E-MAIL karen.mclintock@equiname.co.uk WEBSITE www.karenmclintock.co.uk

1 AVENUE OF STARS, 6, b g Makfi—Clifton Dancer **Mr D. Eddy**
2 BIG LES (IRE), 4, b g Big Bad Bob (IRE)—Love Match **Stockdale Racing**
3 BLACK FRIDAY, 4, b g Equiano (FR)—The Clan Macdonald **Mr A. C. Lamont**
4 DIODORUS (IRE), 5, b g Galileo (IRE)—Divine Proportions (USA) **Mr G. Topham**
5 DUBAWI FIFTY, 6, b g Dubawi (IRE)—Plethora **Mr & Mrs Paul & Clare Rooney**
6 EMPEROR SAKHEE, 9, ch g Sakhee (USA)—Pochard **Miss S.A Booth & Don Eddy**
7 EVERKYLLACHY (IRE), 5, br m Kyllachy—Superfonic (FR) **Ever Equine**
8 GOOD MAN (IRE), 6, ch g New Approach (IRE)—Garden City (FR) **Mr D. Eddy**
9 GREY MIST, 5, gg Mastercraftsman (IRE)—Kekova **Mr Alan Lamont & Mr Brian Chicken**
10 GURKHA FRIEND, 7, b g Showcasing—Parabola **Lease Terminated**
11 HIGH FORT (IRE), 4, b g Acclamation—Barracade (IRE) **Alan Lamont, Ian Clements & Don Eddy**
12 MIGHTY MAC (IRE), 4, b g Dragon Pulse (IRE)—Invincible Fire (IRE) **Mr & Mrs Paul & Clare Rooney**
13 PADDYPLEX, 6, b g Multiplex—Turtle Bay **G & J Park**
14 ROCKWOOD, 8, b g Rock of Gibraltar (IRE)—Hannah Frank (IRE) **Mr I. R. Clements & Dr L. G. Parry**
15 ROSE TINTED SPIRIT, 4, b g Swiss Spirit—Woolfall Rose **Mr & Mrs Paul & Clare Rooney**
16 SPRINGPLEX, 5, b m Multiplex—Turtle Bay **G & J Park**
17 TAOPIX, 7, b g Rip Van Winkle (IRE)—
Sinister Ruckus (USA) **Mr Roger Stockdale, Mr Don Eddy,Mr Alan Lamont**
18 TRINITY STAR (IRE), 8, gr g Kheleyf (USA)—Zamyila (IRE) **Trinity Racing**
19 TWIGGY, 5, b m Sixties Icon—Queen's Pudding (IRE) **Mr R. J. Sommerville**
20 WEATHER FRONT (USA), 6, ch g Stormy Atlantic (USA)—Kiswahili **Mr Ken Eales & Self Preservation Society**
21 ZABEEL STAR (IRE), 7, ch g Arcano (IRE)—Deep Winter **The Self Preservation Society**

Other Owners: Miss S. A. Booth, B. Chicken, Mr I. R. Clements, Mr W. Cockcroft, Mr R. Cockcroft, Mr J. Cockcroft, Mr S. Cockcroft, Mr K. F. Eales, Mr K. R. Elliott, Mr I. J. B. Gray, Mr G. Park, Miss J. Park, Dr L. G. Parry, Mrs C. Rooney, Mr P. A. Rooney, Mr G. R. Stockdale, Mr T. J. Whiting.

Assistant Trainer: Donald Eddy

376 MR GRAEME MCPHERSON, Stow-On-The-Wold
Postal: **Martins Hill, Bledington Road, Stow-on-the-wold, Gloucestershire, GL54 1JH**
Contacts: **PHONE (01451) 830769 MOBILE (07815) 887360**
E-MAIL info@mcphersonracing.co.uk WEBSITE www.mcphersonracing.co.uk

1 AMI DESBOIS (FR), 9, b g Dream Well (FR)—Baroya (FR) **EPDS Racing Partnership 12 & Partner**
2 ASK BEN (IRE), 6, b g Ask—Decheekymonkey (IRE) **Turf Club 2018**
3 BENTONS LAD, 8, br g Bollin Eric—Spirit of Ecstasy **Mr G. P. McPherson**
4 BOLDMERE, 6, b g Multiplex—Pugnacious Lady **W. J. Odell**
5 BUDDING ROBIN (IRE), 6, b g Robin des Pres (FR)—Another Vodka (IRE) **Mr J. Chamberlain**
6 CALUM GILHOOLEY (IRE), 5, br g Kalanisi (IRE)—Honeyed (IRE) **Mr G. P. McPherson**
7 CAPTAIN DINOSAUR (IRE), 6, b g Scorpion (IRE)—Fromrussiawithlove **The McPherson Racing Partnership**
8 CAPTAIN MCGARRY (IRE), 7, b g Oscar (IRE)—Garryduff Princess (IRE) **Captain McGarry**
9 , Ch g Salutino (GER)—Cotton Candy (IRE)
10 CRANBROOK CAUSEWAY (IRE), 7, b g Mohaajir (USA)—Kingarriff Bell (IRE) **Nino's Partnership Ii**
11 DAYDREAM AULMES (FR), 6, b g Linda's Lad—My Wish Aulmes (FR) **Ms S Howell & Partner**
12 DELIRIOUS LOVE (IRE), 7, b g Definite Article—Grangeclare Lark (IRE) **Wildcat Syndicate**
13 DERRICK D'ANJOU (FR), 8, b g Double Eclipse (IRE)—Belle d'anjou (FR) **The Odd Foxes**
14 FLANN, 4, b g Brian Boru—Lady Karinga **Mr I. M. O'Doherty**
15 FLEETING VISIT, 6, b g Manduro (GER)—Short Affair **The FV Partnership**
16 FOLLOW THE SWALLOW (IRE), 11, b g Dr Massini (IRE)—Old Chapel (IRE) **Mrs M. M. Gwillam**
17 HEY BILL (IRE), 9, b g Indian Danehill (IRE)—Grange More (IRE) **H Stephen Smith & Graeme McPherson**
18 HOLLYWOOD ALL STAR (IRE), 10, b g Kheleyf (USA)—Camassina (IRE) **EPDS Racing Partnership 24**
19 IKEJA (IRE), 5, b g Dahjee (USA)—Silly Mille (IRE) **W. J. Odell**
20 IT'S FINE WINE, 6, b g Multiplex—Reem Two **Mr & Mrs Paul & Clare Rooney**
21 JESSICA RABBIT, 5, b m Mawatheeq (USA)—Intersky High (USA) **EPDS Racing Partnership 22**
22 KAYF BLANCO, 10, b g Kayf Tara—Land of Glory **Mrs L.Day, Mr H.Burdett & Mr G.McPherson**
23 LONDONIA, 7, gr g Paco Boy (IRE)—Snowdrops **EPDS Racing 16 & Partner**
24 MISSTHECUDDLES (IRE), 5, b m Gold Well—Autumn Sky (IRE) **TyroneForSam**
25 MY CHARITY (IRE), 8, b g King's Theatre (IRE)—Benefit Ball (IRE) **Burr & Dudwell Racing**
26 NORMAN STANLEY (IRE), 7, b g Flemensfirth (USA)—Ballerina Laura (IRE) **Mr G. P. McPherson**

MR GRAEME MCPHERSON - Continued

27 **PADDYS RUNNER**, 7, gr g Sir Percy—Frosty Welcome (USA) **Paddys Runner Partnership**
28 **PASSING SHADOW**, 5, b g Passing Glance—Peel Me A Grape **Mrs E. A. Prowting**
29 **PERSHING MISSILE (IRE)**, 7, b g Milan—Banbury Cross (IRE) **Anglia & Wolves**
30 **POPERINGHE GINGER (IRE)**, 6, ch m Beneficial—Masamor (IRE) **The Reserved Judgment Partnership**
31 **RED ADMIRABLE (IRE)**, 13, b g Shantou (USA)—Eimears Pet (IRE) **The McPherson Racing Partnership**
32 **RUBY WILDE (IRE)**, 8, b m Oscar (IRE)—Hazel Grove (IRE) **Mrs L. Day**
33 **SAMMYLOU (IRE)**, 6, b g Beneficial—Carrigeen Diamond (IRE) **DI Adams, Ja Adams & G McPherson**
34 **SCOOBY (IRE)**, 8, b g Dubai Destination (USA)—Maggie Howard (IRE) **The Ladies Of Martins Hill**
35 **SERPICO (IRE)**, 8, br g Scorpion (IRE)—Call Her Again (IRE) **Anglia & Wolves**
36 **SHADY GLEN (IRE)**, 10, br g Dr Massini (IRE)—Poppins (IRE) **Mrs Jill Phillips & Graeme McPherson**
37 **SKIPTHECUDDLES (IRE)**, 8, b g Westerner—Autumn Sky (IRE) **TyroneForSam**
38 **TELSON BARLEY (IRE)**, 6, b g Scorpion (IRE)—El Monica (IRE) **Mrs L. Day**
39 **WILDE WATER (IRE)**, 5, b g Oscar (IRE)—Pay The Ferryman (IRE) **Mrs L. Day**
40 **ZULU DAWN (IRE)**, 5, b g Fame And Glory—Maslam (IRE) **The Grand Cru Partnership**

Other Owners: Mr D. L. Adams, Mrs J. A. Adams, Mr M. Ball, Mr M. Barnett, Mr H. Burdett, Mr C. G. Burr, Mr A. N. Cheyne, Mr A. N. Clark, Mr R. Cunningham, Mr S. Dudwell, EPDS Racing Partnership 12, Mr A. M. Elshout, Mr J. T. Finch, First With Mortgages Limited, Mrs A. J. Forde, Mr J. A. S. Fowke, Mr R. J. P Gilmore, Ms S. A. Howell, Col A. J. E. Malcolm, Mrs S. M. McPherson, Mr K. J. N. Meek, Mrs K. Peto, Mrs J. D. Phillips, Mr J. R. Powell, Mr G. Rodgers, Mrs C. Rooney, Mr P. A. Rooney, Miss J. E. Sherrard, Mr G. P. Sinclair, Miss T. Sloan, H. S. Smith.

Assistant Trainers: Mick Finn, Jodie Mogford

Jockey (NH): Kielan Woods. **Conditional:** Tom Humphries. **Amateur:** Miss Lily Pinchin.

---

377 | **MR TONY MCWILLIAMS**, Lancaster
Postal: 112 Dorchester Road, Garstang, Preston, Lancashire, PR3 1EE
Contacts: PHONE (01995) 606276

1 **DE LESSEPS (USA)**, 11, ch g Selkirk (USA)—Suez **J. W. Barrett**

---

378 | **MR MARTYN MEADE**, Manton
Postal: Manton Estate Office, Manton, Wiltshire, SN8 4HB
Contacts: PHONE (01672) 555000   MOBILE (07879) 891811
E-MAIL mmeade@martynmeaderacing.com   WEBSITE www.martynmeaderacing.com

1 **CASCOVA (IRE)**, 4, b c Casamento (IRE)—Sina Cova (IRE)
2 **CHILEAN (IRE)**, 4, b c Iffraaj—Childa (IRE)
3 **INFRASTRUCTURE**, 4, ch g Raven's Pass (USA)—Foundation Filly
4 **MONOXIDE**, 4, b g Galileo (IRE)—Breathe (FR)
5 **RISE HALL**, 4, b g Frankel—Forever Bond
6 **SEA ESS SEAS (IRE)**, 4, b g Swiss Spirit—Rabshih (IRE)
7 **VJ DAY (USA)**, 4, b g War Front (USA)—Sassy Image (USA)
8 **WALK IN THE SUN (USA)**, 4, b c Street Sense (USA)—Mystic Melody (USA)

THREE-YEAR-OLDS

9 Gr f Dark Angel (IRE)—Abeille (IRE)
10 **ACHIEVABLE (IRE)**, br f No Nay Never (USA)—Always A Way
11 **ADVERTISE**, b c Showcasing—Furbelow
12 **AIRWAVES**, b f Monsieur Bond (IRE)—Forever Bond
13 **ASSUMING (IRE)**, ch f Ruler of The World (IRE)—Bold Assumption
14 **BEYCHELLA (USA)**, b br f Scat Daddy (USA)—Secret Dream (IRE)
15 **CADRE DU NOIR (USA)**, b c War Front (USA)—Dynamic Feature (USA)
16 **CONFIDING**, b c Iffraaj—Entre Nous (IRE)
17 **CRACKLING (IRE)**, b c Vale of York (IRE)—Almatlaie (USA)
18 **CRAYON (IRE)**, b c Acclamation—With Colour
19 **EBURY**, ch c Iffraaj—Alabelle
20 **ENGROSSED (IRE)**, ch f Tamayuz—Last Cry (FR)
21 **FOX VARDY (USA)**, b c Frankel—Dance With Another (IRE)
22 **FRILLY**, ch f Frankel—Ladies Are Forever
23 **GLENN MILLER (IRE)**, b g Exceed And Excel (AUS)—Tupelo Honey (IRE)
24 **HEADLAND**, b c Harbour Watch (IRE)—Bazzana

MR MARTYN MEADE - Continued

25 **ISOLATE (FR),** b c Maxios—Unaided
26 **KING ADEMAR (USA),** br c Scat Daddy (USA)—Parisian Affair (USA)
27 **LOVING GLANCE,** b f Invincible Spirit (IRE)—Kissable (IRE)
28 **LYZBETH (FR),** b f Zoffany (IRE)—Arcangela
29 **MARLYN (IRE),** b f Exceed And Excel (AUS)—Myrine (IRE)
30 **MEMSIE (IRE),** b c Exceed And Excel (AUS)—Gift of Spring (USA)
31 **MONOGAMY,** br gr f Poet's Voice—White Wedding (IRE)
32 **NUMERO UNO,** br c Dubawi (IRE)—Casual Look (USA)
33 **PALLADIUM,** ch c Champs Elysees—Galicuix
34 **PEARL OF MANAMA (USA),** b br f Scat Daddy (USA)—Auction (IRE)
35 **PHOSPHOR (IRE),** b c Havana Gold (IRE)—Luminous Gold
36 **SEA STORM,** ch f Monsieur Bond (IRE)—Chez Cherie
37 B f Sea The Stars (IRE)—Silver Grey (IRE)
38 B c Toronado (IRE)—Sparkling Eyes
39 **TECHNICIAN (IRE),** gr c Mastercraftsman (IRE)—Arosa (IRE)
40 **THEOULE (FR),** b br c Le Havre (IRE)—Santa Louisia
41 **THERMAL (IRE),** b f Lawman (FR)—Rising Wind (IRE)

TWO-YEAR-OLDS

42 B f 15/4 Exceed And Excel (AUS)—Al Sharood (Shamardal (USA)) (62000)
43 Ch f 3/5 Galileo (IRE)—Aleagueoftheirown (IRE) (Danehill Dancer (IRE)) (1685629)
44 B gr f 26/1 Gutaifan (IRE)—Always Gentle (IRE) (Redback) (70000)
45 Ch f 30/1 Iffraaj—Arabian Mirage (Oasis Dream) (160000)
46 B f 15/2 Uncle Mo (USA)—As Good As Gold (IRE) (Oasis Dream) (160000)
47 Ch c 5/4 Free Eagle (IRE)—Badr Al Badoor (IRE) (Acclamation) (75853)
48 Ch c 3/3 Pastoral Pursuits—Bazzana (Zebedee)
49 B c 21/1 Slade Power (IRE)—Bonfire Heart (Exceed And Excel (AUS)) (36190)
50 B c 14/5 Hallowed Crown (AUS)—Chica Whopa (IRE) (Oasis Dream) (29498)
51 B br c 2/4 New Approach (IRE)—Clear Voice (IRE) (Cryptoclearance (USA)) (15238)
52 B c 25/4 Raven's Pass (USA)—Cry Pearl (USA) (Street Cry (IRE)) (22756)
53 B c 26/4 Born To Sea (IRE)—Dear Dream (IRE) (Montjeu (IRE)) (3371)
54 B c 10/4 Cable Bay (IRE)—Euroceleb (IRE) (Peintre Celebre (USA)) (21912)
55 B gr c 11/4 Zebedee—Fancy Feathers (IRE) (Redback) (43809)
56 Ch c 28/1 Gleneagles (IRE)—Fluvial (IRE) (Exceed And Excel (AUS)) (42140)
57 B c 24/3 Showcasing—Folly Bridge (Avonbridge) (34285)
58 B f 25/3 Exceed And Excel (AUS)—Half Truth (IRE) (Verglas (IRE))
59 B c 14/2 Hot Streak (IRE)—Lady Suesanne (IRE) (Cape Cross (IRE)) (76190)
60 B c 13/4 Siyouni (FR)—Mambo Mistress (USA) (Kingmambo (USA)) (151706)
61 B c 7/2 Clodovil (IRE)—Michael's Song (IRE) (Refuse To Bend (IRE)) (19047)
62 **OWNEY MADDEN,** b c 15/3 Oasis Dream—Terre du Vent (FR) (Kutub (IRE)) (75000)
63 B f 21/4 Kodiac—Refuse To Give Up (IRE) (Refuse To Bend (IRE)) (75000)
64 B f 2/2 Night of Thunder (IRE)—Royal Guinevere (Invincible Spirit (IRE)) (18541)
65 Ch c 19/2 Australia—San Sicharia (IRE) (Daggers Drawn (USA)) (143278)
66 B c 22/3 Kingman—Scarborough Fair (Pivotal) (100000)
67 Ch f 3/5 Dandy Man—Sheer Indulgence (FR) (Pivotal) (71428)
68 B c 23/3 Dark Angel (IRE)—Thawrah (IRE) (Green Desert (USA)) (303413)
69 B f 17/2 Pastoral Pursuits—There's Two (IRE) (Ashkalani (IRE))
70 Ch f 11/4 Australia—Timeless Call (IRE) (Sakhee (USA)) (58996)
71 Ch c 27/5 Pastoral Pursuits—Tora Bora (Grand Lodge (USA))
72 B c 22/4 Kyllachy—Trust The Wind (Dansili) (42000)
73 B f 30/4 Footstepsinthesand—Van de Cappelle (IRE) (Pivotal) (28655)
74 B f 30/3 Showcasing—Vitta's Touch (USA) (Touch Gold (USA)) (71639)
75 B f 4/2 Fountain of Youth (IRE)—Wether Girl (Major Cadeaux) (30476)

Owners: Aquis Farms, Mr J. E. M. Barnes, The Below Reserve Partnership, R. C. Bond, Nick Bradley Racing, Canning Downs, Chelsea Thoroughbreds Ltd, Mr N. de Chambure, Haras d'Etreham, Mr W. S. Farish, S. Heider, King Power Racing Co Ltd, Lordship Stud, Mrs J. E. Mackay, Mrs John Magnier, P. Makin, Manton Estate Racing, Mr F. M. Meade, Mr C. J. Murfitt, Mrs Jane Newett, Phoenix Thoroughbreds Limited, Mrs B. V. Sangster, Mrs P. Shanahan, Mr H. N. G. Sherborne, Snailwell Stud, Sun Bloodstock, Sir Peter Vela.

Assistant Trainer: Freddie Meade (Fmeade@Martynmeaderacing.Com)

379 **MR NOEL MEADE, Navan**
Postal: Tu Va, Castletown-Kilpatrick, Navan, Co. Meath, C15 F384 Ireland
Contacts: PHONE (00 353) 46 905 4197 MOBILE (00 353) 87 256 6039
E-MAIL tuvastables@gmail.com WEBSITE www.noelmeade.com

1 **ACTIVE FORCE (IRE)**, 6, br g Oscar (IRE)—Terracotta Queen (IRE)
2 4, Ch f Stowaway—Allys Bubble (IRE)
3 4, B g Well Chosen—Apache Rose (IRE)
4 **APOCALYPSE (IRE)**, 5, b g Mahler—Rachel's Choice (IRE)
5 **ARCH STANTON (IRE)**, 5, b g Jeremy (USA)—Half-Hitch (USA)
6 **ART OF AMERICA**, 4, br g American Post—Marigay's Magic
7 **ART OF SECURITY (IRE)**, 9, b g High Chaparral (IRE)—Irish Wedding (IRE)
8 **ART OF UNITY**, 4, ch g Mazameer (IRE)—Vintage Steps (IRE)
9 **ATHENEAN (IRE)**, 6, b g Westerner—Cash And New (IRE)
10 **BALLYHOT BOY (IRE)**, 4, b g Le Fou (IRE)—Esbeggi
11 **BATTLE OF MIDWAY (IRE)**, 5, b g Mahler—Womanofthemountain (IRE)
12 **BEACON EDGE (IRE)**, 5, b g Doyen (IRE)—Laurel Gift (IRE)
13 **BEHIND THE CURTAIN (IRE)**, 5, br g Curtain Time (IRE)—Veronica's Gift (IRE)
14 **BEL AMI DE SIVOLA (FR)**, 8, b g Network (GER)—Notting Hill (FR)
15 **BILL HICKOK (IRE)**, 5, ch g Tobougg (IRE)—Jungle Jewel (IRE)
16 **BRACE YOURSELF (IRE)**, 6, ch g Mahler—Angelica Garnett
17 **BRONCO BILL (IRE)**, 9, b g Kalanisi (IRE)—Mill Lady (IRE)
18 **BURGAS (FR)**, 8, b br g Protektor (GER)—Tyrolienne Bleue (FR)
19 **CALICOJACK (IRE)**, 7, b g Beneficial—Ballyoscar (IRE)
20 **CAP YORK (FR)**, 7, b g Ballingarry (IRE)—Robbe (FR)
21 4, B f Jeremy (USA)—Carrigeen Kohleria (IRE)
22 **CASK MATE (IRE)**, 6, b g Kalanisi (IRE)—Littleton Liberty
23 **CENOTICE**, 5, b g Phoenix Reach (IRE)—Kenny's Dream
24 **CHEROKEE BILL**, 8, b g Robin des Champs (FR)—Daizinni
25 **CLARA SORRENTO (FR)**, 8, gr g Maresca Sorrento (FR)—Call Me Clara (FR)
26 **COOLBAWN LAD (IRE)**, 4, b g Imperial Monarch (IRE)—Hollygrove Bonnie (IRE)
27 **COSMO'S MOON (IRE)**, 6, b g Morozov (USA)—She's A Dreamer (IRE)
28 **CURLEY BILL (IRE)**, 11, b g Heron Island (IRE)—In Excelsis (GER)
29 **DALY TIGER (FR)**, 6, b g Tiger Groom—Reine Tresor (FR)
30 **DAVY'S DILEMMA**, 5, b g Sixties Icon—Wansdyke Lass
31 **DE NAME ESCAPES ME (IRE)**, 9, ch g Vinnie Roe (IRE)—Heartlight (IRE)
32 **DEPLOYED (IRE)**, 5, b g Mahler—Brook Style (IRE)
33 **DEXTER TIGER (FR)**, 4, b g Saddex—Indian Tigress (IRE)
34 **DIOL KER (FR)**, 5, b g Martaline—Stiren Bleue (FR)
35 **DIS DONC (FR)**, 6, b g Kingsalsa (USA)—Skarina (IRE)
36 **DREAM CONTI (FR)**, 6, br g Lauro (GER)—Posterite (FR)
37 4, Ch g Getaway (GER)—Drumderry (IRE)
38 **EMPEROR OF WEST (FR)**, 5, b g Maresca Sorrento (FR)—Sin City (FR)
39 **EUROBOT**, 5, ch g Malinas (GER)—L'aventure (FR)
40 **FAUGUERNON (FR)**, 5, b g Martaline—I'm Right (USA)
41 **FIRST APPROACH (IRE)**, 6, b g Robin des Champs (FR)—Manhattan Babe (IRE)
42 5, B m Arakan (USA)—First Battle (IRE)
43 **FLAGSOFOURFATHERS (IRE)**, 5, ch g Doyen (IRE)—Dew Drop
44 **FREE RANGER (IRE)**, 5, b g Lope de Vega (IRE)—Purple Tigress
45 **FUTURE PROOF (IRE)**, 4, b g Dream Ahead (USA)—Moraga (USA)
46 **GETAWAY KID (IRE)**, 7, ch g Getaway (GER)—Bambootcha (IRE)
47 **GHURBA (IRE)**, 5, b m Aqlaam—Mahaatheer (IRE)
48 **GUIDED BY YOU (IRE)**, 6, b g Getaway (GER)—Black Ouzel (IRE)
49 **HALF THE ODDS (IRE)**, 7, b m Flemensfirth (USA)—Technohead (IRE)
50 **HARBRIO (IRE)**, 6, b g Yeats (IRE)—Raichu (IRE)
51 **HARLEY B (IRE)**, 5, ch g Arakan (USA)—Raichu (IRE)
52 **HARRY LONGABAUGH (IRE)**, 6, b g Oscar (IRE)—Ballyknock Present (IRE)
53 **HE'S NO MOLLY (IRE)**, 6, b g Beneficial—Violet Hill (IRE)
54 **HELL OR HIGH WATER (IRE)**, 6, ch g Robin des Champs (FR)—Boragh Thyme (IRE)
55 **HENRY BROWN (IRE)**, 4, b g Mahler—Blackeyedsue (IRE)
56 **HEROESANDVILLAINS (IRE)**, 6, b g Beneficial—Keys Pride (IRE)
57 **HIDDEN FIGURE (IRE)**, 4, b f Aizavoski (IRE)—Hidden Reserve (IRE)
58 **IAMASTARTOO (IRE)**, 6, ch m Well Chosen—Lobinstown Girl (IRE)
59 **IFICUDIWUD (IRE)**, 6, b g Trans Island—Manucrin
60 **IMPATIENT PARTNER (IRE)**, 6, b g Gold Well—Madmoiselle Etoile (IRE)
61 **IN YOUR SHADOW (IRE)**, 5, gr g Stowaway—Classic Lin (FR)

MR NOEL MEADE - Continued

62 **JAKOBY (IRE)**, 5, b g Frozen Fire (GER)—Morning Rise (GER)
63 **JESSICA'S BOY (IRE)**, 5, b g Court Cave (IRE)—Fathom Cross Lady (IRE)
64 **KAGNEY (IRE)**, 8, br g Kalanisi (IRE)—Clondalee (IRE)
65 **KEARNEY**, 5, ch g Medicean—Moonlight Mystery
66 **KILLER MILLER (IRE)**, 10, b g Flemensfirth (USA)—Miss Brandywell (IRE)
67 **KIRWANS LANE (IRE)**, 6, ch g Excellent Art—Sosua (IRE)
68 4, B g Flemensfirth (USA)—Lady of Appeal (IRE)
69 **LAVERTEEN (FR)**, 8, b g Laveron—Manson Teene (FR)
70 **LIEUTENANT COMMAND (FR)**, 5, gr g Kendargent (FR)—Maternelle (FR)
71 **LIGNOU (FR)**, 4, B G Rajsaman (FR)—Lady Meydan (FR)
72 **LILL SMITH (IRE)**, 6, b m Gold Well—Vivachi (IRE)
73 **LORD IN RED (GER)**, 7, ch g Noroit (GER)—Lady In Red (GER)
74 4, B g Dahjee (USA)—Lush Sister (IRE)
75 **MAD CAREW (IRE)**, 7, b g Getaway (GER)—Babygotback (IRE)
76 **MAJOR DESTINATION (IRE)**, 8, b g Dubai Destination (USA)—Clara Allen (IRE)
77 **MARY OF DE SORROWS (IRE)**, 4, br f Elusive Pimpernel (USA)—Ginger Lily (IRE)
78 **MELLY AND ME (IRE)**, 6, b g Kalanisi (IRE)—College Daisy (IRE)
79 **MILLS ON TOUR (IRE)**, 4, b f Lovelace—Headford View (IRE)
80 **MINELLA FAIR (IRE)**, 8, b g Flemensfirth (USA)—Bell Walks Run (IRE)
81 4, B g Mastercraftsman (IRE)—Minor Vamp (IRE)
82 4, B f Flemensfirth (USA)—Miss Brandywell (IRE)
83 **MOMUS (IRE)**, 6, b g Touch of Land (IRE)—Accordion To Bob (IRE)
84 **MONKSLAND (IRE)**, 12, b g Beneficial—Cush Jewel (IRE)
85 **MOYROSS**, 8, b g Kayf Tara—Dancing Dasi (IRE)
86 **NARCISSISTIC (IRE)**, 7, b g Robin des Champs (FR)—Night Therapy (IRE)
87 4, B g Carlotamix (FR)—One Edge (IRE)
88 **PAT'S PICK (IRE)**, 5, b g Shantou (USA)—Lady Lenson (IRE)
89 **PERCY B SHELLEY**, 5, ch g Archipenko (USA)—Oshiponga
90 **PIENTA (USA)**, 4, b c Liaison (USA)—Belen (USA)
91 **RAGIN CAJUN (IRE)**, 6, b g Kalanisi (IRE)—Dipp In The Dark (IRE)
92 **RATHNURE REBEL (IRE)**, 9, b g Beneficial—Euro Magic (IRE)
93 **RED JACK (IRE)**, 6, b g Mahler—Hollygrove Bonnie (IRE)
94 **RIGOUR (IRE)**, 5, ch g Getaway (GER)—Annas Theatre
95 **ROAD TO RESPECT (IRE)**, 8, ch g Gamut (IRE)—Lora Lady (IRE)
96 **ROAD WARRIOR**, 5, gr g Fair Mix (IRE)—Mimi Equal
97 **ROSENCRANTZ (IRE)**, 5, b g Flemensfirth (USA)—Miss Brandywell (IRE)
98 **ROSERIVER HAS (FR)**, 6, gr g Astarabad (USA)—Vaibuscar Has (FR)
99 **ROSGALME (IRE)**, 4, b g Mahler—Woodville Queen (IRE)
100 **RUSSIAN BILL (IRE)**, 9, b g Kalanisi (IRE)—Littleton Liberty
101 **SALLY SCULL (IRE)**, 5, b m Gold Well—Vivachi (IRE)
102 **SCHOOL BOY HOURS (IRE)**, 6, b g Presenting—Trinity Alley (IRE)
103 **SEEYOUINVINNYS (IRE)**, 5, b g Carlotamix (FR)—Deploy Or Die (IRE)
104 **SELLARBRIDGE (IRE)**, 4, b g Well Chosen—Dubai Petal (IRE)
105 **SHE'S A STAR (IRE)**, 7, br m Well Chosen—Lobinstown Girl (IRE)
106 **SHEISDIESEL**, 5, ch m Harbour Watch (IRE)—Rockme Cockney
107 **SIXSHOOTER (IRE)**, 4, ch g Well Chosen—Lobinstown Girl (IRE)
108 **SNOW FALCON (IRE)**, 9, b g Presenting—Flocon de Neige (IRE)
109 **STONEFORD (IRE)**, 8, b g Beneficial—Hester Hall (IRE)
110 **SUPER FOLLO (FR)**, 7, b g Enrique—Summer Belle (FR)
111 4, B g Arakan (USA)—Susy In The Summer (IRE)
112 **TAMLOUGH BOY**, 8, b g Central Park (IRE)—Zamyatina (IRE)
113 **THE CADDY ROSE (IRE)**, 5, br m Presenting—Las Princess (IRE)
114 **THE RED MENACE (IRE)**, 5, ch g Mountain High (IRE)—Heather Sue (IRE)
115 **TOMMY JOE (FR)**, 4, b g Turgeon (USA)—Antagua (FR)
116 **TOUT EST PERMIS (FR)**, 6, gr g Linda's Lad—Kadalbleue (FR)
117 **TRAPPIST MONK (IRE)**, 6, b g Beneficial—Cush Jewel (IRE)
118 **TWO SISTERS (IRE)**, 6, b m Scorpion (GER)—Presenting Marble (IRE)
119 **UNE LAVANDIERE (FR)**, 8, b m Laveron—Nouvelle Donne (FR)
120 **UNION GAP (IRE)**, 4, b g Canford Cliffs (IRE)—Vivachi (IRE)
121 **VALDIEU (FR)**, 6, b g Diamond Boy (FR)—Vamuna (FR)
122 **VISION D'ETAT (FR)**, 9, b g Vision d'etat (FR)—Vuelta Al Ruedo (FR)
123 **WHERE EAGLES DARE (IRE)**, 6, b g Mahler—Tariana (IRE)
124 **WINGS OF AN EAGLE (IRE)**, 5, b m Winged Love (IRE)—Like A Bolt (IRE)
125 **YOUNG TED (IRE)**, 5, b g Fame And Glory—Last of Many (IRE)
126 **ZAMBEZIR (FR)**, 4, ch g Zambezi Sun—Lanciana (IRE)

MR NOEL MEADE - Continued

THREE-YEAR-OLDS

127 **DADOOZDART,** br c Dawn Approach (IRE)—Hairpin (USA)
128 **DINARD ROSE (IRE),** b f Champs Elysees—Rose of Petra (IRE)
129 **ENCAPSULATION (IRE),** b f Zoffany (IRE)—Supercharged (IRE)
130 **HARVEST BOW (IRE),** b gr f Intikhab (USA)—Ghost of A Girl (IRE)
131 **LAURA BULLION (IRE),** b f Canford Cliffs (IRE)—Vivachi (IRE)
132 **LOTTIELOVEHEART (IRE),** ch f Es Que Love (IRE)—Dirtybirdie
133 **RED GERRY (IRE),** b c Canford Cliffs (IRE)—Hollow Talk

TWO-YEAR-OLDS

134 B c 1/4 Sayif (IRE)—Acclamare (IRE) (Acclamation) (4214)
135 B c 15/3 Hallowed Crown (AUS)—Alpine (Rail Link) (20227)
136 B c 11/3 Es Que Love (IRE)—Anazah (IRE) (Diesis) (5056)
137 B f 5/4 Tagula (IRE)—Eucharist (IRE) (Acclamation) (5478)
138 Ch c 5/3 Dawn Approach (IRE)—Jameela's Dream (Nayef (USA)) (14327)
139 B c 25/2 Epaulette (AUS)—Maoin Dor (IRE) (Manduro (GER)) (7163)
140 B c 20/3 Free Eagle (IRE)—Peace Signal (USA) (Time For A Change (USA)) (17699)
141 B c 12/3 Power—Rachevie (IRE) (Danehill Dancer (IRE)) (10113)
142 B c 18/3 Australia—Star Waves (IRE) (Sea The Stars (IRE)) (5899)
143 B c 11/3 Lawman (FR)—Xinji (IRE) (Xaar) (18541)

Assistant Trainer: Damien McGillick, **Head Man:** Paul Cullen, **Travelling Head:** Emma Connolly.

Jockey (NH): Sean Flanagan, Jonathan Moore. **Amateur:** Mr M. J. O'Hare

---

380 **MR NEIL MECHIE, Leyburn**
Postal: **55 The Springs, Middleham, Leyburn, North Yorkshire, DL8 4RB**

1 **STEEL RUN,** 7, gr g Sagamix (FR)—Safari Run (IRE) **N. Mechie**

---

381 **MR BRIAN MEEHAN, Manton**
Postal: **The Racing Office, Manton House Estate, Manton, Marlborough, Wiltshire, SN8 1PN**
Contacts: **PHONE: (01672) 517191**

1 **BACCHUS,** 5, ch g Kheleyf (USA)—Rumbled **G P M Morland, D J Erwin, John G S Woodman**
2 **BARRAQUERO (IRE),** 4, b c Zebedee—Chica Whopa (IRE) **Manton Thoroughbreds II**
3 **FOX TROTTER (IRE),** 7, br g Bushranger (IRE)—Miss Brief (IRE) **Mrs S. M. Tucker**
4 **I'VEGOTTHEPOWER (IRE),** 5, b g Power—Waterways (IRE) **Mr S. E. Sangster & Partner**
5 **PETRA'S PONY (IRE),** 4, b g Big Bad Bob—Gabriellina Klon (IRE) **The Petra Partnership**
6 **PETRUS (IRE),** 4, b g Zoffany (IRE)—Ambrosine **Mr G. P. M. Morland**
7 **SPARK PLUG (IRE),** 8, b g Dylan Thomas (IRE)—Kournikova (SAF) **Mr J. L. Day**
8 **SPIRIT OF APPIN,** 4, b f Champs Elysees—Oshiponga **Mr J. A. Stewart**
9 **TAKE THE HELM,** 6, ch g Monsieur Bond (IRE)—Oasis Breeze **Mrj.S.Threadwell/Familyamusementsltd**

THREE-YEAR-OLDS

10 **ALSAFA,** b c Dark Angel (IRE)—Jamaayel **Hamdan bin Rashid Al Maktoum**
11 **AMPLIFY (IRE),** b c Acclamation—Obsara **Manton Thoroughbreds III**
12 **ANTHEM OF PEACE (AUS),** b g Starspangledbanner (AUS)—
Easy Silence (AUS) **Mr Jonathan Harvey & Partners**
13 **AQL (IRE),** b g Exceed And Excel (AUS)—Pearl Sea (IRE) **Hamdan bin Rashid Al Maktoum**
14 **ARTHUR PENDRAGON (IRE),** b c Camelot—First of Many **ARAAM**
15 **ARTISTIC LANGUAGE,** b g Archipenko (USA)—Kiswahili **Manton Thoroughbreds III**
16 **ATHMAD (IRE),** b c Olympic Glory (IRE)—Black Mascara (IRE) **ARAAM**
17 **BARBAROSA (IRE),** br g Holy Roman Emperor (IRE)—Snow Scene (IRE) **Manton Thoroughbreds III**
18 **BELLE CHANEL (IRE),** b f Fast Company (IRE)—Raven One (IRE) **B. J. Meehan**
19 **COLONEL SLADE (IRE),** b g Dandy Man (IRE)—Sense of A Woman (IRE) **Manton Thoroughbreds III**
20 B f Rip Van Winkle (IRE)—Conveyor Belt (IRE)
21 **DARK GLORY (IRE),** b c Alhebayeb (IRE)—Glyndebourne (USA) **Biddestone Racing III**
22 **DOMINUS (IRE),** ch c Zoffany (IRE)—Gwen Lady Byron (IRE) **G P M Morland & J W Edgedale**
23 **DUBAI INSTINCT,** b c Le Havre (IRE)—Riotous Applause **ARAAM**

MR BRIAN MEEHAN - Continued

24 **HAADEF,** b g Delegator—Peace Concluded **Hamdan bin Rashid Al Maktoum**
25 **JILBAAB,** b c Havana Gold (IRE)—Sand Dancer (IRE) **Hamdan bin Rashid Al Maktoum**
26 **KAAFY (IRE),** b c Alhebayeb (IRE)—Serene Dream **Hamdan bin Rashid Al Maktoum**
27 **KALOOR,** b c Nathaniel (IRE)—Blinking **Mr J. L. Day**
28 **LAXMI (IRE),** b f War Command (USA)—Princess Patsky (USA) **Mr Siddiqui & Mr Sharma**
29 **LOLLIPOP LADY,** b gr f Garswood—Nolas Lolly (IRE) **Hot To Trot Racing - Lollipop Lady**
30 **MOKUBA (IRE),** b c Helmet (AUS)—Rocking Horse **B. J. Meehan**
31 **MUDEER (IRE),** b g Kendargent (FR)—Makisarde (FR) **B. J. Meehan**
32 **MUNAAJAAT (IRE),** ch f Tamayuz—Walayef (USA) **Hamdan bin Rashid Al Maktoum**
33 **PALAVECINO (FR),** b g Cacique (IRE)—Saltita (IRE) **ARAAM**
34 **PATRONUS,** b g Zoffany (IRE)—Miss Complex **G P M Morland & J W Edgedale**
35 **TAKEASUP,** b f Olympic Glory (IRE)—Riva Royale **Mr N. Martin**
36 **TREASURE QUEST,** b c Sepoy (AUS)—Collectable **J S Threadwell I**

TWO-YEAR-OLDS

37 B c 18/1 Equiano (FR)—Aarti (IRE) (Oasis Dream) (47619) **Centurion Thoroughbreds**
38 B c 20/2 Dark Angel (IRE)—Along Came Casey (IRE) (Oratorio (IRE)) (200000) **Hamdan bin Rashid Al Maktoum**
39 B c 5/2 Dark Angel (IRE)—Ambassadrice (Oasis Dream) (85714) **Hamdan bin Rashid Al Maktoum**
40 B c 11/1 G Force (IRE)—Beauty of The Sea (Elusive Quality (USA)) (25714) **Manton Thoroughbreds IV**
41 **CEPHEUS,** ch c 13/3 Sea The Stars (IRE)—Crimson Cheer (USA) (Van Nistelrooy (USA)) **Mr G. P. M. Morland**
42 Ch c 13/3 Slade Power (IRE)—Delira (IRE) (Namid) (32026) **Centurion Thoroughbreds**
43 B c 21/2 Sea The Stars (IRE)—Dream of The Hill (IRE) (Tiger Hill (IRE)) (75000) **Manton Thoroughbreds IV**
44 **EBONY ADAMS,** b f 27/4 Fountain of Youth (IRE)—Mortitia (Dansili) (3000) **Bearstone Stud Limited**
45 B c 28/2 Zebedee—Edwardian Era (Bering) (23809) **DJ Racing**
46 Gr f 17/5 Dark Angel (IRE)—Falsafa (Dansili) **Hamdan bin Rashid Al Maktoum**
47 B c 2/2 Zoffany (IRE)—Foolish Act (IRE) (Sadler's Wells (USA)) (62000) **Manton Thoroughbreds IV**
48 B c 31/3 Kingman—Jamaayel (Shamardal (USA)) **Hamdan bin Rashid Al Maktoum**
49 B c 15/2 Cable Bay (IRE)—Mambo Halo (USA) (Southern Halo (USA)) (57142) **Centurion Thoroughbreds**
50 B c 24/3 Baltic King—Miss Megs (IRE) (Croco Rouge (IRE)) (23809) **Mr G. P. M. Morland**
51 B c 9/4 Golden Horn—New Morning (IRE) (Sadler's Wells (USA)) **Lois Day & J L Day**
52 Ch c 14/2 Camacho—New Music (IRE) (New Approach) (19047) **Centurion Thoroughbreds**
53 B c 26/2 Nathaniel (IRE)—Rock Choir (Pivotal) (32000) **Centurion Thoroughbreds**
54 B c 10/1 Gutaifan (IRE)—Rumline (Royal Applause) (40000) **Centurion Thoroughbreds**
55 B c 30/1 Ivawood (IRE)—Spring Bouquet (IRE) (King's Best (USA)) (38000) **Manton Thoroughbreds IV**
56 Ch c 2/3 Zebedee—Tanyeli (IRE) (Mastercraftsman (IRE)) (36190) **Manton Thoroughbreds IV**
57 B c 19/4 Camacho—Tartiflette (Dr Fong (USA)) (46354) **Michael Kerr-Dineen & Martin Hughes**
58 Ch c 9/2 Dandy Man (IRE)—Tip It On The Top (War Chant (USA)) (28571) **Manton Thoroughbreds IV**
59 B c 8/4 Harbour Watch (IRE)—Zacchera (Zamindar (USA)) (37000) **Mr G. P. M. Morland**

Other Owners: T. P. Bostwick, Mrs G. P. Bostwick, Ms L. Day, Mr J. W. Edgedale, Mr D. J. Erwin, Family Amusements Ltd, Mr J. R. Harvey, Mr R. S. Hoskins, Hot To Trot Racing 1, Mr M. B. Hughes, M. Kerr-Dineen, L. Lillingston, Mrs J. F. Maitland-Jones, Mr S. E. Sangster, Mr D. K. Sharma, Mr S. Siddiqui, Mr J. S. Threadwell, Mr J. G. S. Woodman.

---

382 MR DAVID MENUISIER, Pulborough

Postal: Shinco Racing Limited, Coombelands Stables, Coombelands Lane, Pulborough, West Sussex, RH20 1BP
Contacts: MOBILE 07876 674095
E-MAIL david@dmhorseracing.com WEBSITE www.dmhorseracing.com

1 **ATALANTA'S BOY,** 4, b g Paco Boy (IRE)—Affirmatively **Mrs Monica Borton & Partner**
2 **BATTLE OF ISSUS (IRE),** 4, b g Declaration of War (USA)—Athenian Way (IRE) **Mr C. A. Washbourn**
3 **BUXLOW BELLE (FR),** 4, gr f Authorized (IRE)—Steel Woman (IRE) **Mrs A. K. Oldfield**
4 **CACOPHONOUS,** 4, b g Cacique (IRE)—Zee Zee Gee **Mr C. A. Washbourn**
5 **CHIAVE DI VOLTA,** 4, ch g Intello (GER)—Silca Chiave **Mr C. A. Washbourn**
6 **DANCETERIA (FR),** 4, b g Redoute's Choice (AUS)—Bal de La Rose (IRE) **Mr C. A. Washbourn**
7 **DRAGONS VOICE,** 5, b g Poet's Voice—China **Heart of the South Racing 106**
8 **HISTORY WRITER (IRE),** 4, b g Canford Cliffs (IRE)—Abhasana (IRE) **Clive Washbourn & Partner**
9 **MAROON BELLS,** 4, ch f Mount Nelson—Chelsea Morning **Mr Christopher Wright & Ms E L Banks**
10 **NOT AFTER HOURS (FR),** 5, b m Wiener Walzer (GER)—Nota Bene (GER) **Miss H. Loder**
11 **NUITS ST GEORGES (IRE),** 4, ch g Mount Nelson—Twelfth Night (IRE) **Boy George Partnership**
12 **PLACE DES VOSGES (IRE),** 4, b f Rip Van Winkle (IRE)—Red Blossom (USA) **Shinco Racing Limited**
13 **THUNDERING BLUE (USA),** 6, gr ro g Exchange Rate (USA)—Relampago Azul (USA) **Mr C. A. Washbourn**

ᴹR DAVID MENUISIER - Continued

THREE-YEAR-OLDS

14 **EDMOND DANTES (IRE)**, gr g Alhebayeb (IRE)—Abhasana (IRE) **Mme C. Head and Partner**
15 **LOCH LAGGAN (IRE)**, b c Sea The Stars (IRE)—Magic Sister **Mr C. A. Washbourn**
16 **MIGRATION (IRE)**, b c Alhebayeb (IRE)—Caribbean Ace (IRE) **Gail Brown Racing (ix)**
17 **MOUSQUETAIRE (FR)**, b g Anodin (IRE)—Cavaliere (FR) **One For All Racing**
18 **NYANGA (IRE)**, b f Born To Sea (IRE)—Mujadil Shadow (IRE) **Shinco Racing Limited**
19 B g Champs Elysees—Rose Ayr **Mr William Davis**
20 **SIMPLETWISTOF FATE (USA)**, b br f Quality Road (USA)—Element of Truth (USA) **Mr C. N. Wright**
21 **STAR GUIDE (GER)**, b g Maxios—Summarily (USA) **Gunter Sachs**
22 **TAC TILE (FR)**, b c Wootton Bassett—Zapiya (FR) **Mr Michael Watt**
23 **THE PASTORAL BEAR**, ch f Pastoral Pursuits—Torcella **Mrs S. Frost**

TWO-YEAR-OLDS

24 B f 13/4 Epaulette (AUS)—Abhasana (IRE) (Hawk Wing (USA)) **Mr C. A. Washbourn**
25 **GYPSY WHISPER**, b f 8/4 Helmet (AUS)—Secret Insider (USA) (Elusive Quality (USA)) **Gail Brown Racing (A)**
26 **INTO FAITH (FR)**, b c 3/4 Intello (GER)—Have Faith (IRE) (Machiavellian (USA)) (16856) **All for One Racing**
27 **LANVAL (IRE)**, b c 18/5 Camelot—Flamingo Sea (USA) (Woodman (USA)) (60000) **Gail Brown Racing (xi)**
28 B f 15/3 Poet's Voice—Lilly Junior (Cape Cross (IRE)) **Heart Of The South Racing**
29 **LUIGI VAMPA (IRE)**, b c 27/4 Elvstroem (AUS)—
Sunday Rose (Red Ransom (USA)) (20227) **Shinco Racing Limited**
30 B c 23/3 Intello (GER)—Winter Fashion (FR) (Kendor (FR)) (244416) **Mr C. A. Washbourn**
31 **WITCH HUNT (IRE)**, b c 24/3 Lawman (FR)—
Witches Brew (IRE) (Duke of Marmalade (IRE)) (40000) **Gail Brown Racing (x)**

Other Owners: Mrs E. Adamski, Mr L. Arstall, Mrs D. J. Arstall, Mr S. A. Ashley, Ms E. L. Banks, Mrs M. J. Borton, Mr S. D. Bradley, Mrs H. G. Clinch, Mr M. P. Coleman, Mr A. C. Elliott, Mrs H. J. Fitzsimons, Mr D. J. Harrison, Mr J. J. Lancaster, Mr J. R. Penny, Pollards Stables, Mr C. P. Thompkins, Mr R. J. Wright.

---

383 **MISS REBECCA MENZIES, Sedgefield**
Postal: Howe Hills Farm, Sedgefield, Stockton-On-Tees, Cleveland, TS21 2HG
Contacts: MOBILE (07843) 169217
E-MAIL rebeccaelizabeth.menzies@hotmail.co.uk
WEBSITE www.rebeccamenziesracing.com TWITTER: @Rebeccaemenzies

1 **ALL HAIL CAESAR (IRE)**, 5, b g Nathaniel (IRE)—Ragiam (ITY) **The Top Silk Syndicate**
2 **ANCHISES**, 4, b g Choisir (AUS)—Afrodita (IRE) **Premier Racing Partnerships**
3 **ANNE'S VALENTINO**, 9, b m Primo Valentino (IRE)—Annie's Gift (IRE) **The Magic Circle**
4 6, B h Malinas (GER)—Annie's Gift (IRE) **The Magic Circle**
5 **BREIZH ALKO (FR)**, 8, ch g Balko (FR)—Quisiera (FR) **Mr D. Parry**
6 **CAPTAIN MOWBRAY**, 8, ch g Shami—Some Like It Hot **Premier Racing Partnerships**
7 **CELTIC ARTISAN (IRE)**, 8, ch g Dylan Thomas (IRE)—Perfectly Clear (USA) **EPDS Racing Partnership 11**
8 **CHAMPAGNE TO GO (IRE)**, 9, b m Beneficial—Terre d'orient (FR) **Mount Racing & Kingmaker Racedays**
9 **DIGGER JOHN**, 4, b g Sulamani (IRE)—Slow Starter (IRE) **John Johnson & John Wade**
10 **DJEBEL ROME (FR)**, 6, b g Voix du Nord (FR)—Precieuze (FR) **Mr C. Buckingham**
11 **DRAGON MALL (USA)**, 6, b g Blame (USA)—Petition the Lady (USA) **Mrs K. Hall**
12 **DULCE PANEM (FR)**, 7, ch g Panis (USA)—Danissima (FR) **Tony & Pauline Weight Blacklock Simpson**
13 **EMERALD CHIEFTAN (IRE)**, 9, b g Oscar (IRE)—Its Only Gossip (IRE) **Mr C. Buckingham**
14 **FABIANSKI (IRE)**, 4, ch f Raven's Pass (USA)—Fabia (IRE) **Stoneleigh Racing**
15 **FAIR SHERIFF**, 5, gr m Fair Mix (IRE)—Sheriff's Falcon (IRE) **Gay & Peter Hartley**
16 **FEARLESS (IRE)**, 4, b g Arakan (USA)—La Spezia (IRE) **Layezy Racing Owners Club**
17 **GARDE FORESTIER (FR)**, 7, b g Forestier (FR)—Nette Rousse (FR) **J. Wade**
18 **HALCYON DAYS**, 10, b g Generous (IRE)—Indian Empress **Centaur Racing Club**
19 **IM TOO GENEROUS**, 9, ch g Generous (IRE)—Something Major (IRE) **John Dance & Partner**
20 **LANDING NIGHT (IRE)**, 7, b g Kodiac—Night Delight (IRE) **Titanium Racing Club**
21 **MONSIEUR BAGOT (IRE)**, 7, b g Robin des Pres (FR)—Hardabout (IRE) **Mr D. H. Slater**
22 **MOSSY'S LODGE**, 6, b m Royal Applause—Tee Cee **Kingmaker Racedays & Partner**
23 **MR WITMORE (IRE)**, 9, b g Whitmore's Conn (USA)—Bright Future (IRE) **Blacklock Simpson**
24 **NORTONTHORPELEGEND (IRE)**, 9, b g Midnight Legend—Tanit **Miss M. D. Myco**
25 **PAIN AU CHOCOLAT (FR)**, 8, b g Enrique—Clair Chene (FR) **Mike and Eileen Newbould**
26 **PEAK TIME**, 6, ch g Distant Peak (IRE)—Ruby Redwing **J. Wade**
27 **POKORA DU LYS (FR)**, 8, b g Saint des Saints (FR)—Shailani (FR) **Mr C. Buckingham**
28 **PORTO DU SUD (FR)**, 6, gr g Lord du Sud (FR)—Queen du Vallon (FR) **Mr S. A. Murrills**
29 **PRAIRIE IMPULSE**, 6, b m Major Cadeaux—Prairie Sun (GER) **ICM Racing and Partner**

MISS REBECCA MENZIES - Continued

30 **RETURN FLIGHT**, 8, b g Kayf Tara—Molly Flight (FR) **Mike and Eileen Newbould**
31 **RIZZLE DIZZLE**, 4, b f Foxwedge (AUS)—Greensand **Love To Race Partnership**
32 **RONN THE CONN (IRE)**, 7, ch g Whitmore's Conn (USA)—Speedy Fairy (IRE) **J. Wade**
33 **ROSSMORE'S PRIDE (IRE)**, 11, br g Heron Island (IRE)—Parsons Supreme (IRE) **Mr D. H. Slater**
34 **ROYAL MACNAB (IRE)**, 11, b g Beneficial—Tina McBride (IRE) **The Extra Time Partnership**
35 **SCOTS GAELIC (IRE)**, 12, ch g Tomba—Harmonic (USA) **Miss R. E. A. Menzies**
36 **SEARANGER (USA)**, 6, b g U S Ranger (USA)—Baby Lets Cruise (USA) **ICM Racing and Partner**
37 **SOVIET CASTLE (IRE)**, 6, b g Soviet Star (USA)—Castle Hope (IRE) **Miss M. D. Myco**
38 **STORMBAY BOMBER (IRE)**, 10, b g September Storm (GER)—Top Tottie (IRE) **Mr P R Walker & Mr R Walker**
39 **TEELAR**, 5, b m Milan—Hervey Bay **Miss R. E. A. Menzies**
40 **TETRADRACHM**, 6, b g Holy Roman Emperor (IRE)—Dahlia's Krissy (USA) **Stoneleigh Racing**
41 **THAAYER**, 4, b g Helmet (AUS)—Sakhya (IRE) **The Racing Brothers**
42 **TOI STOREY (IRE)**, 6, b g Winged Love (IRE)—Where's Herself (IRE) **Liz Dixon & Shelagh Fagen 1**
43 **TOMKEVI (FR)**, 8, b g Khalkevi (IRE)—Tamsna (FR) **Mr P J Howe & Mr R G Oliver**
44 **TRAUTMANN (IRE)**, 5, ch g Casamento (IRE)—Klang (IRE) **Mr D. H. Slater**
45 **VON BLUCHER (IRE)**, 6, ch g Zoffany (IRE)—Tropical Lady (IRE) **Mr J. E. Dance**
46 **WIDE ACCLAIM (IRE)**, 4, b f Acclamation—Riynaaz (IRE) **Where's The Line Racing**
47 **XPO UNIVERSEL (FR)**, 10, b g Poliglote—Xanadu Bliss (FR) **Club Racing Xpo Partnership**

THREE-YEAR-OLDS

48 **COOL KITTY**, b f Kodiac—Ligeia **Kingmaker Racedays & Partner**
49 **WHINNIE**, b f Garswood—Sakhya (IRE) **Saxtead Livestock Ltd**

Other Owners: Mr S. T. Avery, Mr J. R. Best, Mr I. M. Blacklock, Mr A. Brierley, Mrs E. M. Dixon, Mr A. N. Eaton, Miss S
Fagen, Mrs M. Feely, Ms D. Fields, Mr M. Gornall, Miss E. Hall, Mr I. Harle, P. A. H. Hartley, Mrs R. C. Hartley, Mr G. W
Holden, Mr P J. Howe, ICM Racing, Mr J. R. Johnson, Kingmaker Racedays Club, Mount Racing Club, P. Nelson, Mr J. M
Newbould, Mrs E. E. Newbould, Miss M. A. O Brien, Mr R. G. Oliver, Mr E. Park, Mr G. W. Peacock, Mr J. R. Powell, Mr M
Priestley, Mr S. Roberts, Mr I. Simpson, Mr P. Slater, Miss T. Sloan, Mr M. Stanley, Major P. H. K. Steveney, Mr R. E
Turner, Mr J. W. F. Veitch, Mr P. R. Walker, Mr R. Walker, Mr A. C. Weight, Dr P. M. Weight, Mrs S. Windross.

---

384 MR PHIL MIDDLETON, Aylesbury
Postal: **Dorton Place, Dorton Park Farm, Dorton, Aylesbury, Buckinghamshire, HP18 9NR**
Contacts: **PHONE (01844) 237503 FAX (01844) 237503 MOBILE (07860) 426607**

1 **DOWHATUDODOBEST (IRE)**, 6, b m City Honours (USA)—Crowning Virtue (IRE) **Mr P. W. Middleton**
2 **EXITAS (IRE)**, 11, b g Exit To Nowhere (USA)—Suntas (IRE) **P Middleton, M Lowther**
3 **GOLAN FORTUNE (IRE)**, 7, b g Golan—Ballyknock Alainn (IRE) **P Middleton, M Lowther**
4 **HOLLY BUSH HENRY (IRE)**, 8, b g Yeats (IRE)—Maslam (IRE) **P Middleton, M Lowther**

Other Owners: Mr Mark Lowther, Mr P. W. Middleton.

---

385 MR PAUL MIDGLEY, Westow
Postal: **The View, Sandfield Farm, Westow, York, North Yorkshire, YO60 7LS**
Contacts: **Office (01653) 658790 FAX (01653) 658790 MOBILE (07976) 965220**
E-MAIL ptmidgley@aol.com WEBSITE www.ptmidgley.com

1 **BUCCANEERS VAULT (IRE)**, 7, gr g Aussie Rules (USA)—Heaven's Vault (IRE) **Sheila Bradley & P. T. Midgley**
2 **CAPTAIN COLBY (USA)**, 7, b g Bernstein (USA)—Escape To Victory **Robert Bradley & P T Midgley**
3 **COASTAL DRIVE**, 4, gr g Harbour Watch (IRE)—Added Attraction (FR) **Sheila Bradley & P. T. Midgley**
4 **DESERT ACE (IRE)**, 8, ch g Kheleyf (USA)—Champion Place **M Hammond, Mad For Fun & Partner**
5 **FINAL VENTURE**, 7, b g Equiano (FR)—Sharplaw Venture **Taylor's Bloodstock Ltd**
6 **GAMESOME (FR)**, 8, b g Rock of Gibraltar (IRE)—Hot Coal (USA) **Ta & Pj Stephenson & Partner**
7 **GROUNDWORKER (IRE)**, 8, b g Tagula (IRE)—Notepad **Blackburn Family**
8 **JOHNNY CAVAGIN**, 10, b g Superior Premium—Beyond The Rainbow **A. Bell**
9 **LINE OF REASON (IRE)**, 9, br g Kheleyf (USA)—Miss Party Line (USA) **Taylor's Bloodstock Ltd**
10 **MANSHOOD (IRE)**, 6, b g Iffraaj—Thawrah (IRE) **Taylor's Bloodstock Ltd**
11 **MERRY BANTER**, 5, b m Bated Breath—Merry Diva **Mr H. Thornton & Mr P. T. Midgley**
12 **MOSSEYB (IRE)**, 4, b g Epaulette (AUS)—Allegrissimo (IRE) **Mr A. Bell & Mr P. T. Midgley**
13 **MOSTAHEL**, 5, b g Acclamation—Entente Cordiale (USA) **Mr Colin Alton & Mr P. T. Midgley**
14 **MR ORANGE**, 6, b g Paco Boy—Shirley Blake (FR) **Mr J Blackburn & Mr A Turton**
15 **MUTAFARRID (IRE)**, 4, gr g Dark Angel (IRE)—Margarita (IRE) **Mr F Brady & Mr J S Morrison**
16 **NIBRAS AGAIN**, 5, b g Kyllachy—Regina **Pee Dee Tee Syndicate & T W Midgley**

MR PAUL MIDGLEY - Continued

17 **NINJAGO,** 9, b g Mount Nelson—Fidelio's Miracle (USA) **Taylor's Bloodstock Ltd & PT Midgley**
18 **ONE BOY (IRE),** 8, ch g Captain Gerrard (IRE)—Paris Song (IRE) **Sandfield Racing & M Ezro**
19 **ORIENT CLASS,** 8, ch g Orientor—Killer Class **F Brady,A Williams,P Lindley,S Wibberley**
20 **ORVAR (IRE),** 6, b g Dandy Man (IRE)—Roskeen (IRE) **Taylor's Bloodstock Ltd**
21 **PATRICK (IRE),** 7, b g Acclamation—Red Liason (IRE) **Blackburn Family**
22 **PRESTBURY PARK (USA),** 4, br g Shamardal (USA)—Sutra (USA) **Robert Bradley & P T Midgley**
23 **RANTAN (IRE),** 6, b g Kodiac—Peace Talks **Mr P. T. Midgley**
24 **RELATED,** 5, b g Kheleyf (USA)—Balladonia **Taylor's Bloodstock Ltd**
25 **ROCK HILL (IRE),** 4, br g Rock of Gibraltar (IRE)—Pascali **Mr H. Thornton & Mr P. T. Midgley**
26 **RUSSIAN REALM,** 9, b g Dansili—Russian Rhythm (USA) **The Guys & Dolls & Partner**
27 **SALUTI (IRE),** 5, b g Acclamation—Greek Easter (IRE) **Robert Bradley & P T Midgley**
28 **START TIME (IRE),** 6, b g Invincible Spirit (IRE)—Silca's Sister **The Howarting's Partnership**
29 **TANASOQ (IRE),** 6, b g Acclamation—Alexander Youth (IRE) **Mr F Brady & Mr J S Morrison**
30 **TARBOOSH,** 6, b g Bahamian Bounty—Mullein **The Guys & Dolls & Sandfield Racing**
31 **TWENTYSVNTHLANCERS,** 6, b g Hellvelyn—Subtle Move (USA) **D Hopper & D Ellis**
32 **WAR WHISPER (IRE),** 6, b g Royal Applause—Featherweight (IRE) **The Marina Partnership**

THREE-YEAR-OLDS

33 **ALKHADRA,** b g Mawatheeq (USA)—Rainbow's Destiny **Mr M. Andrews**
34 **SAMBUCCA SPIRIT,** b g Charm Spirit (IRE)—Hokkaido **Jolly Boy's Racing Club & Partner**
35 **THE DEFIANT,** b g Morpheus—Killer Class **Mr F. Brady**

TWO-YEAR-OLDS

36 B f 5/2 Sir Prancealot (IRE)—Dispol Kylie (IRE) (Kheleyf (USA)) (761) **Mr W. B. Imison**

Other Owners: Mr C. Alton, Mr P. Bateson, Mr J. Batty, Mr A. B. Blackburn, Mr J. N. Blackburn, Mrs G. I. Blackburn, Mr R. Bradley, Mrs S. Bradley, Mr D. Chapman, Mr C. Chapman, Mr P. W. Clifton, Mr D. B. Ellis, Ms M. A. Ezro, Miss D. Gabbitas, The Guys & Dolls Syndicate, Mr M. K. Hammond, Mr G. Hardy, Mr B. E. W. Higgins, Mr D. Hopper, Jolly Boys Racing Club, Mr P. N. Lindley, Mr T. W. Midgley, Mr J S Morrison, Mrs J. Norris, Mr J. Parks, Peedeetee Syndicate, Sandfield Racing, Mr P. D. Simms, Miss S. M. Smith, R. Standring, T. A. Stephenson, Mr P. J. Stephenson, Mr H. Thornton, Mr A. Turton, Mr A. D. Ward, Mr S. Wibberley, Mr A. Williams.

Assistant Trainer: Mrs W. E. Midgley

Amateur: Mr Tom Midgley.

---

386 **MR ROD MILLMAN, Cullompton**
Postal: **The Paddocks, Dulford, Cullompton, Devon, EX15 2DX**
Contacts: **PHONE/FAX (01884) 266620 MOBILE (07885) 168447**
E-MAIL rod.millman@ic24.net

1 **ACHIANNA (USA),** 4, ch f Gemologist (USA)—Adoradancer (USA) **Mr C. Demetriou**
2 **BIOTIC,** 8, b g Aqlaam—Bramaputra (IRE) **Mrs B. Sumner & Mr B. R. Millman**
3 **CHAMPAGNE CHAMP,** 7, b g Champs Elysees—Maramba **Five Horses Ltd**
4 **CONCUR (IRE),** 6, ch g Approve (IRE)—Tradmagic (IRE) **B. R. Millman**
5 **CRYSTAL CASQUE,** 4, ch f Helmet (AUS)—Crystal Moments **The Dirham Partnership**
6 **DADDIES GIRL (IRE),** 4, b f Elzaam (AUS)—La Cuvee **Daddies Girl Partnership**
7 **HANDYTALK (IRE),** 6, b g Lilbourne Lad (IRE)—Dancing With Stars (IRE) **Cantay Racing**
8 **HAWRIDGE FLYER,** 5, b g Sir Percy—Strictly Lambada **E. J. S. Gadsden**
9 **MASTER GREY,** 4, gr g Mastercraftsman (IRE)—Market Day **David Little The Links Partnership**
10 **PUZZLE CACHE,** 5, b m Phoenix Reach—Secret Queen **Kittymore Racing**
11 **RAGSTONE VIEW,** 4, b g Requinto (IRE)—Highland Miss (USA) **Rioja Raiders 04**
12 **SINGING THE BLUES (IRE),** 4, b g Sir Prancealot (IRE)—Atishoo (IRE) **Rod Millman & Andy Smith**
13 **SIR PLATO (IRE),** 5, b g Sir Prancealot (IRE)—Dessert Flower (IRE)
14 **SIR RODERIC (IRE),** 6, b g Roderic O'Connor (IRE)—
Begin The Beguine (IRE) **David Little The Links Partnership**
15 **SPOT LITE,** 4, b g Compton Place—High Class Girl **Mr C. H. Saunders**
16 **SWEET PURSUIT,** 5, b m Pastoral Pursuits—Sugar Beet **Always Hopeful Partnership**

THREE-YEAR-OLDS

17 **ARDIMENTO (IRE),** b g Roderic O'Connor (IRE)—Begin The Beguine (IRE) **David Little The Links Partnership**
18 **BONNEVILLE (IRE),** b g Champs Elysees—Aspasi **David Little The Links Partnership**
19 **COBWEB CATCHER,** b g Swiss Spirit—Sugar Beet **Mr T. H. Chadney**
20 **DOTI,** b f Charm Spirit (IRE)—Garanciere (FR) **Seasons Holidays**

MR ROD MILLMAN - Continued

21 **GREELEY (IRE)**, b g Sir Prancealot (IRE)—Hannah Greeley (USA) **The Greeley syndicate**
22 **GREYZEE (IRE)**, gr g Zebedee—Curl (IRE) **David Little The Links Partnership**
23 **HAWRIDGE STORM (IRE)**, b g Intello (GER)—Aneedah (IRE) **E. J. S. Gadsden**
24 **JULLEY**, ch f Compton Place—Charpoy Cobra **Mr R. A. C. Toller**
25 **KEITH**, b g Rip Van Winkle—Serenity Spa **Mrs S. A. J. Kinsella**
26 **LADY WOLF**, b f Kuroshio (AUS)—Angry Bark (USA) **Howard Barton Stud**
27 **MAWDE (IRE)**, ch f Sir Prancealot (IRE)—Rise Up Lotus (IRE) **The Mawde Syndicate**
28 **PLUM DUFF**, b f Showcasing—Lady Macduff (IRE) **C. J. Harper**
29 **POWER SEEKER (IRE)**, b g Power—Eclat Royale **Five Horses Ltd**
30 **PRINCE OF HARTS**, br g Dalakhani (IRE)—Reaf **Perfect Match 2**
31 B c Motivator—Serenada (FR) **D. J. Deer**
32 **STEEVE**, ch g Lethal Force (IRE)—Club Tahiti **Mrs S. A. J. Kinsella**

TWO-YEAR-OLDS

33 Ch c 2/4 Casamento (IRE)—Angry Bark (USA) (Woodman (USA)) **Howard Barton Stud**
34 Br f 17/3 Lethal Force (IRE)—Bonnie Grey (Hellvelyn) (7619) **Howard Barton Stud**
35 **DADDIES DIVA**, b f 24/3 Coach House (IRE)—Pixey Punk (Mount Nelson) (1904) **Daddies Girl Partnership**
36 B f 22/1 Anjaal—Miss Poppy (Averti (IRE)) (2857)
37 B f 5/2 Lethal Force (IRE)—Mythical City (IRE) (Rock of Gibraltar (IRE))
38 Ch f 2/5 Es Que Love (IRE)—Pearl Power (Dutch Art) (3000)
39 Ch g 19/2 Sir Prancealot (IRE)—Porta Portese (Zamindar (USA)) (21904)
40 B g 29/4 Due Diligence (USA)—Sugar Beet (Beat Hollow) (7000)
41 B g 17/3 Hallowed Crown (AUS)—Tagula Mon (IRE) (Tagula (IRE)) (6190)
42 Ch f 2/2 Bated Breath—Under Milk Wood (Montjeu (IRE))
43 B f 21/3 Brazen Beau (AUS)—Zeyran (IRE) (Galileo (IRE)) (15238)

Other Owners: Mr R. K. Arrowsmith, Mrs J. M. R. Arrowsmith, P. Bartlam, Mr T. Bennett, Mr N. A. Clark, Mr R. W. Daly, Mrs J. A. Daly, Mr A. S. P. Drake, Mr R. T. Ferris, Mr R. D. Gamlin, Mr P. C. W. Green, Mr R. Gudge, Mr S. J. Kattau, Mrs C. Knowles, V. B. Lewer, D. A. Little, Mr D. Luscombe, Mrs H. M. Luscombe, Mr A. M. Nolan, Mrs M. O'Sullivan, Ms V. O'Sullivan, Mr S. M. Perry, Mr A. J. Smith, Mrs B. Sumner, Mr T. Tompkins.

Assistant Trainers: Louise Millman, Pat Millman

Jockey (flat): Oisin Murphy. **Apprentice:** Oliver Searle. **Amateur:** Mr Pat Millman.

---

387 MR NICK MITCHELL, Dorchester
Postal: **1 Racklands, Piddletrenthide, Dorchester, Dorset, DT2 7QP**
Contacts: **PHONE (01300) 348049 MOBILE (07770) 892085**
E-MAIL **nick.mitch@btinternet.com** WEBSITE **www.nickmitchellracing.com**

1 **BIG BOY BLUES (IRE)**, 6, ch g Resplendent Cee (IRE)—
Lovely Pride (IRE) **Mrs Robert Frosell & Mrs Andrew May**
2 4, B g Mahler—Chlolo Supreme (IRE) **Mr N. R. Mitchell**
3 **COSMIC DIAMOND**, 9, b m Multiplex—Lucy Glitters **Nick Mitchell Racing Club**
4 **DRUMLEE CITY (IRE)**, 7, b g City Honours (USA)—Alentio (IRE) **Mr H. Redknapp**
5 **OUR HENRIETTA (IRE)**, 9, b m Winged Love (IRE)—Nut Eile (IRE) **Nick Mitchell Racing Club**
6 **SHOW OF FORCE**, 4, gr f Lethal Force (IRE)—Craighall **Nick Mitchell Racing Club**
7 **SPIRIT OF ROME (IRE)**, 5, ch m Mastercraftsman (IRE)—Zagreb Flyer **Nick Mitchell Racing Club**
8 **THIS IS IT (IRE)**, 7, b g Milan—Riviera Sands (IRE) **Three Kings Partnerships**

Other Owners: Mrs S. P. B. Frosell, Mrs S. H. May, Mr E. Pritchard, Mr H. J. M. Wilson.

Jockey (NH): Daryl Jacob.

---

388 MR RICHARD MITCHELL, Dorchester
Postal: **East Hill Stables, Piddletrenthide, Dorchester, Dorset, DT2 7QY**
Contacts: **PHONE/FAX (01300) 348739 MOBILE (07775) 843136**
E-MAIL **easthillstables@tiscali.co.uk**

1 **COTTON CLUB (IRE)**, 8, b g Amadeus Wolf—Slow Jazz (USA) **J. R. Boughey**
2 **HENCHARD**, 8, b g Deltic (USA)—Kittenkat **Buck Hill**
3 **LORD WESSEX**, 8, b g Deltic (USA)—Society Night (IRE) **Mrs E. Mitchell**

MR RICHARD MITCHELL - Continued

    4 **TAGINE,** 8, b m Deltic (USA)—Panhandle **Mrs E. Mitchell**
    5 **THUNDERING HOME,** 12, gr g Storming Home—Citrine Spirit (IRE) **J. R. Boughey**

Other Owners: Mr J. R. Boughey, Mrs Andrew May, Mr N. R. Mitchell.

Assistant Trainer: Mrs E. Mitchell

---

389   **MR RICHARD MITFORD-SLADE, Norton Fitzwarren**
Postal: Pontispool Farm, Allerford, Norton Fitzwarren, Taunton, Somerset, TA4 1BG
Contacts: PHONE (01823) 461196 FAX (01823) 461508 MOBILE (07899) 994420
E-MAIL rms@pontispool.com

    1 **APPLE MACK,** 6, b g Apple Tree (FR)—Allerford Annie (IRE) **R Mitford-Slade & Lucy Johnson**
    2 **MASTER TRADESMAN (IRE),** 8, ch g Marienbard (IRE)—Tobeornotobe (IRE) **R Mitford-Slade & Lucy Johnson**
    3 **RUBY FOOL,** 9, b m Apple Tree (FR)—Westbourne (IRE) **R Mitford-Slade & Lucy Johnson**
    4 **SAMUEL JACKSON,** 7, b g Alflora (IRE)—Primitive Quest **R Mitford-Slade & Lucy Johnson**
    5 **SECOND CAPTAIN (IRE),** 7, b g Stowaway—Coolanurequeen (IRE) **R. C. Mitford-Slade**
    6 **TEDSPEED (IRE),** 9, ch g Vertical Speed (FR)—Clare Hogan (IRE) **R. C. Mitford-Slade**
    7 **WINTER SOLDIER,** 9, b g Apple Tree (FR)—Primitive Quest **R Mitford-Slade & Lucy Johnson**

Other Owners: Mrs L. Fielding-Johnson.

Assistant Trainer: Lucy Fielding-Johnson

---

390   **MR JAMES MOFFATT, Cartmel**
Postal: Pit Farm Racing Stables, Cartmel, Grange-Over-Sands, Cumbria, LA11 6PJ
Contacts: PHONE (01539) 533808 FAX (01539) 536236 MOBILE (07767) 367282
E-MAIL jamesmoffatt@hotmail.co.uk WEBSITE www.jamesmoffatt.co.uk

    1 **ALTRUISM (IRE),** 9, b g Authorized (IRE)—Bold Assumption **Mr V R Vyner-Brooks, Mr K Bowron**
    2 **BON CHIC (IRE),** 10, b m Presenting—Homebird (IRE) **Bowes Lodge Stables**
    3 **BORUMA (IRE),** 9, b g Brian Boru—Ittallendintears (IRE) **The Running In Rail Partnership**
    4 **CAPTAIN BROWN,** 11, b g Lomitas—Nicola Bella (IRE) **Mr K. Bowron**
    5 **DAGIAN (IRE),** 4, ch g Dawn Approach (IRE)—Hen Night (IRE) **Bowes Lodge Stables**
    6 **FIOSRACH (IRE),** 9, b g Bachelor Duke (USA)—Saana (IRE) **The Sheroot Partnership**
    7 **GOLDEN TOWN (IRE),** 8, b g Invincible Spirit (IRE)—Princesse Dansante (IRE) **Golden boot**
    8 **HIGHLAND LODGE (IRE),** 13, b g Flemensfirth (USA)—Supreme Von Pres (IRE) **Cheveley Park Stud Limited**
    9 **JUST A PAR (IRE),** 12, b g Island House (IRE)—Thebrownhen (IRE) **Mr M. S. Scott**
10 **LADY BOWES,** 5, b m Malinas (GER)—Blazing Bay (IRE) **Bowes Lodge Stables**
11 **LAPALALA (IRE),** 8, b m Oscar (IRE)—Lala Nova (IRE) **Dr V. M. G. Ferguson**
12 **LOUGH KENT,** 10, b g Barathea (IRE)—King's Doll (IRE) **Hadwin, Moffatt, Green, Chamberlain Bros**
13 **MEGA DOUBLE (IRE),** 5, b m Westerner—Distant Dreams (IRE) **Mr M. S. Scott**
14 **MINELLA CHARMER (IRE),** 8, b g King's Theatre (IRE)—
                                      Kim Hong (IRE) **Varlien Vyner-Brooks,Dave&Yvonne Simpson**
15 **MORNING ROYALTY (IRE),** 12, b g King's Theatre (IRE)—Portryan Native (IRE) **Mrs E. M. Milligan**
16 **NICOLAS CHAUVIN (IRE),** 11, b g Saffron Walden (FR)—Kenzie (IRE) **Ladsdoracing**
17 **NOBLE WARRIOR (IRE),** 6, b g Vertical Speed (FR)—Everdane (IRE) **Mr M. S. Scott**
18 **SHE GOT FAST (IRE),** 4, b f Fastnet Rock (AUS)—Shegotloose (USA) **The Clock Tower Partnership**
19 **START SEVEN,** 7, br g Dilum (USA)—Dancinginthenclouds (IRE) **Racing in Furness**
20 **THE STEWARD (USA),** 8, b g Street Cry (IRE)—Candlelight (USA) **Cartmel Six Pack**
21 **THINK AHEAD,** 8, b g Shamardal (USA)—Moonshadow **Mr V. R. Vyner-Brooks**

Other Owners: Mr S. B. Chamberlain, Mr K. Hadwin, Mr P. J. Higham, Mr P. A. Holt, A. R. Mills, D. J. Moffatt, Mr P. T. H. Porter, Dave & Yvonne Simpson, Mrs Y. Simpson, Mr D. J. Simpson, Mr C. Waters, Mrs J. C. Wilson, Mr S. Wilson.

Assistant Trainer: Nadine Moffatt

Jockey (NH): Henry Brooke, Brian Hughes. **Conditional:** Charlotte Jones.

391 MR ISMAIL MOHAMMED, Newmarket

Postal: **Grange House Stables, Hamilton Road, Newmarket, Suffolk, CB8 0TE**
Contacts: PHONE **(01638) 669074 MOBILE (07766) 570271 / (07747) 191606**
E-MAIL justina.stone@dubairacingclub.com

1 COMPORTA, 4, b g Iffraaj—Hot Wired **Mr Abdulla Al Mansoori**
2 COUNTER SPIRIT (IRE), 5, b m Invincible Spirit (IRE)—Counterclaim **Mr Saeed H. Altayer**
3 ITSAKINDAMAGIC, 5, b g Mount Nelson—Carsulae (IRE) **Sheikh Juma Dalmook Al Maktoum**
4 MASTER OF THE MOON, 4, b g Sea The Stars (IRE)—Crystal Mountain (USA) **Mr Abdulla Al Mansoori**
5 MY HEART, 4, b f Universal (IRE)—Mazuna (IRE) **Mr Abdulla Al Mansoori**
6 NIBRAS GALAXY (IRE), 4, b c Nathaniel (IRE)—Galaxy Dancer (USA) **Mr Saeed H. Altayer**
7 SHAWAAF AL NIJOOM (IRE), 4, b g Sea The Stars (IRE)—Kithonia (FR) **Mr Saeed H. Altayer**

THREE-YEAR-OLDS

8 B f Dark Angel (IRE)—Aertex (IRE)
9 ALLISEEISNIBRAS (IRE), b f Slade Power (IRE)—Needles And Pins (IRE) **Mr Saeed H. Altayer**
10 BITHIAH (IRE), b f Exceed And Excel (AUS)—Sharqawiyah **Mr I. Mohammed**
11 B c Australia—Blanche Dubawi (IRE) **S. Ali**
12 B f Slade Power (IRE)—Broadway Hit **Saif Ali & Saeed H. Altayer**
13 CHARMING APPROACH (IRE), b f Dawn Approach (IRE)—Superior Charm (USA) **Dr A. Ridha**
14 FANTASTIC BLUE, ch c Iffraaj—Blue Beacon **N. Mourad**
15 B c Farhh—Island Babe (USA)
16 LADY OF POWER, b f Dawn Approach (IRE)—Power of Light (IRE) **Dr A. Ridha**
17 NOW BEAT IT (IRE), b f Dream Ahead (USA)—Beat As One **Saif Ali & Saeed H. Altayer**
18 Ch c Mukhadram—Pasithea (IRE) **S. Ali**
19 B c Dawn Approach (USA)—Rainbow Desert (USA) **Saif Ali & Saeed H. Altayer**
20 SCENTASIA, b f Cape Cross (IRE)—Sweet Rose **Sheikh Juma Dalmook Al Maktoum**
21 Ch f Sepoy (AUS)—Shafaani **Mr I. Mohammed**
22 B f Nathaniel (IRE)—Synergy (FR)
23 UNWANTED BEAUTY (IRE), b f Iffraaj—Extreme Beauty (USA) **Dr A. Ridha**
24 ZHUKOVSKY (IRE), b c Zoffany (IRE)—Sea Paint (USA) **Mr I. Mohammed**

TWO-YEAR-OLDS

25 Gr f 7/4 Dark Angel (IRE)—Althea Rose (IRE) (Green Desert (USA)) (52000) **Mr Saeed H. Altayer**
26 Ch f 14/4 Night of Thunder (IRE)—Assabiya (IRE) (Cape Cross (IRE)) **Mr Abdulla Al Mansoori**
27 Gr ro f 28/4 The Factor (USA)—Crescent Moon (USA) (Seeking the Gold (USA)) (27000) **Ismail Mohammed**
28 Ch f 10/2 Exceed And Excel (AUS)—Folk Melody (IRE) (Street Cry (IRE)) (85000) **Saeed Manana**
29 Ch f 3/2 Kitten's Joy (USA)—Gotcha Good (USA) (Arch (USA)) (50000) **Saeed Manana**
30 Ch f 13/3 Pivotal—Harlequin Girl (Where Or When) (IRE) (32000) **Sheikh Juma Dalmook Al Maktoum**
31 B f 28/1 Dawn Approach (USA)—Portland River (FR) (Stormy River (FR)) **Mr Abdulla Al Mansoori**
32 B c 9/4 War Command (USA)—Queen of Skies (IRE) (Shamardal (USA)) (45000) **Mr Saeed Manana**
33 B c 26/2 Shooting To Win (AUS)—Quite Smart (IRE) (Arcano (IRE)) **Mr Abdulla Al Mansoori**
34 B f 10/4 Universal (AUS)—Ras Shaikh (USA) (Sheikh Albadou) **Mr Abdulla Al Mansoori**
35 B f 5/5 Kingman—Sweet Rose (New Approach) (IRE) (50000) **Sheikh Juma Dalmook Al Maktoum**
36 Ch c 19/3 Tamayuz—Viking Rose (IRE) (Norse Dancer (IRE)) (22000) **Mr Saeed H. Altayer**
37 B c 21/2 Sea The Stars (IRE)—Wosaita (Generous (IRE)) (44000) **Mr Abdulla Al Mansoori**

Other Owners: Mr Saif Ali.

Assistant Trainer: Mike Marshall

---

392 MRS LAURA MONGAN, Epsom

Postal: **Condover Stables, Langley Vale Road, Epsom, Surrey, KT18 6AP**
Contacts: PHONE **(01372) 271494 FAX (01372) 271494 MOBILE (07788) 122942**
E-MAIL ljmongan@hotmail.co.uk WEBSITE www.lauramongan.co.uk

1 ABLAZE, 5, ch m Arcano (IRE)—Angry Bark (USA) **Mrs P. J. Sheen**
2 ARDAMIR (FR), 7, b g Deportivo—Kiss And Cry (FR) **Mrs P. J. Sheen**
3 DALE DOBACK, 4, b g Medicean—Emulate **Mrs L. J. Mongan**
4 FIGHT FOR LOVE (FR), 6, b g Fuisse (FR)—Love Affair (FR) **Mrs P. J. Sheen**
5 GOUTEZ MOI (FR), 6, b g Dragon Dancer—Titi Jolie (FR) **Mrs P. J. Sheen**
6 IMPART, 5, b g Oasis Dream—Disclose **Charlie's Starrs & Laura Mongan**
7 MISS YEATS (IRE), 8, b m Yeats (IRE)—Mrs Wallensky (IRE) **Mrs P. J. Sheen**
8 NARJES, 5, b m Sepoy (AUS)—Dubai Sea (USA) **Mr P. R. Howell**

MRS LAURA MONGAN - Continued

9 **ORSM**, 12, b g Erhaab (USA)—Royal Roulette **Mrs P. J. Sheen**
10 **RI AN RIAN (IRE)**, 6, b g Arcadio (GER)—Live A Lot (IRE) **Mrs P. J. Sheen**
11 **SEA TIDE**, 5, b m Champs Elysees—Change Course **Mrs P. J. Sheen**
12 **SILVER TICKET (IRE)**, 8, gr g Tikkanen (USA)—Windmill View (IRE) **Mrs P. J. Sheen**
13 **SNOW MOBILE**, 4, ro f Lethal Force (IRE)—Run of The Day **Mrs L. J. Mongan**
14 **SPRING ABILITY (IRE)**, 4, b g Oasis Dream—Because (IRE) **Mrs P. J. Sheen**
15 **TANZINA**, 7, b m Equiano (FR)—Pilcomayo (IRE) **Mrs J. A. Cornwell**
16 **VOICE CONTROL (IRE)**, 7, gr g Dalakhani (IRE)—Scottish Stage (IRE) **Mrs P. J. Sheen**
17 **WITH APPROVAL (IRE)**, 7, b g Approve (IRE)—Kelsey Rose **Mrs P. J. Sheen**
18 **WOOFIE (IRE)**, 7, b g Duke of Marmalade (IRE)—Violet Ballerina (IRE) **Mrs P. J. Sheen**
19 **YOUR CHOICE**, 4, ch f Foxwedge (AUS)—Mildoura (FR) **Mrs P. J. Sheen**

THREE-YEAR-OLDS

20 **MIDOURA**, b f Delegator—Mildoura (FR) **Mrs P. J. Sheen**
21 **RED'S COMET**, b f King Raedwald (AUS)—Emperor's Hope (IRE) **Mr D. R. J. King**

Other Owners: Mr S. W. Bain, Mr A. W. Bain, Charlie's Starrs.

Assistant Trainer: Ian Mongan

Jockey (NH): Tom Cannon.

---

393 MR GARY MOORE, Horsham
Postal: Cisswood Racing Stables, Sandygate Lane, Lower Beeding, Horsham,
West Sussex, RH13 6LR
Contacts: HOME (01403) 891997 YARD (01403) 891912 MOBILE (07753) 863123
E-MAIL garyjayne.moore@cisswood.com WEBSITE www.garymoreracing.com

1 **AGAINST THE ODDS**, 6, b g Champs Elysees—Generous Diana
2 **AGE OF WISDOM (IRE)**, 6, ch g Pivotal—Learned Friend (GER) **The 1901 Partnership**
3 **AHFAD**, 4, br g Dick Turpin (IRE)—Big Moza **Mr A Watson & Mr B Malyon**
4 4, B g Mount Nelson—Aiaam Al Wafa (IRE) **Heart of the South Racing 114**
5 **AIGUILLE ROUGE (FR)**, 5, ch m Falco (USA)—Avanguardia (GER) **The Winning Hand (Robin Brown)**
6 **ALL CURRENCIES (IRE)**, 7, b m Getaway (GER)—Splendid Presence (IRE) **Mr S. N. Riley**
7 **ALTAAYIL (IRE)**, 8, br g Sea The Stars (IRE)—Alleluia **Mr P. B. Moorhead**
8 **ALTERNATE ROUTE**, 5, b g New Approach (IRE)—Almamia **Heart of the South Racing 110**
9 **ANTONY (FR)**, 9, b g Walk In The Park (IRE)—Melanie du Chenet (FR) **The Winning Hand**
10 **AR MEST (FR)**, 6, bl g Diamond Boy (FR)—Shabada (FR) **Galloping On The South Downs Partnership**
11 **ARGYLE (IRE)**, 6, gr g Lawman (FR)—All Hallows (IRE) **Mr N. J. Roach & Mr G. L. Moore**
12 **ATALANTA'S GOLD (IRE)**, 6, b m Arcadio (GER)—Sandy Desert **Dr P. Molony**
13 **AVORISK ET PERILS (FR)**, 4, b f No Risk At All (FR)—Pierre Azuree (FR) **Dedman Properties Limited**
14 **BAD BOY DU POULDU (FR)**, 8, b g Loup Solitaire (USA)—Wild Flush (USA) **Cocktail Racing Partnership**
15 **BAN SHOOF**, 6, b g Shirocco (GER)—Pasithea (IRE) **Mr Tommy Ware & Mr Bob Pettett**
16 **BARON ALCO (FR)**, 8, ch g Dom Alco (FR)—Paula (FR) **Mr J. K. Stone**
17 **BARRSBROOK**, 5, b g Doyen (IRE)—Sayrianna **G. A. Jackman**
18 **BEAT THE JUDGE (IRE)**, 4, b g Canford Cliffs—Charmingly (USA) **Mr E. P. Babington**
19 **BENATAR (IRE)**, 7, b g Beneficial—Carrigeen Lily (IRE) **Mr A. J. Head**
20 **BENEVOLENTDICTATOR**, 5, ch g Schiaparelli (GER)—Kim Fontenail (FR) **Mr B. Fry**
21 **BITOFBLINDING (IRE)**, 5, b g Jeremy (USA)—Melodique **Galloping On The South Downs Partnership**
22 **BOLISTER (FR)**, 8, b g Le Balafre (FR)—Girlish (FR) **G. L. Moore**
23 **BRIDLE LOANAN (IRE)**, 6, b g Getaway (GER)—Hanora O'brien (IRE) **Mr A. J. Head**
24 **BRITANIO BELLO (FR)**, 8, b g Irish Wells (FR)—Tchi Tchi Bang Bang (FR) **Mr A. J. Head**
25 **BULLFROG (IRE)**, 6, b m Jeremy (USA)—Tramp Stamp (IRE) **Galloping On The South Downs Partnership**
26 **CASSIVELLAUNUS (IRE)**, 7, b g Danehill Dancer (IRE)—Celtic Heroine (IRE) **Vectis Racing**
27 **CHAIN SMOKER**, 9, b g Shantou (USA)—Handmemy Moneydown (IRE) **Mr David Leon & James Devine**
28 **CHEQUE EN BLANC (FR)**, 7, b br g Bernebeau (FR)—Necossaise (FR) **Mrs E. A. Kiernan**
29 **CHIKOKO TRAIL**, 4, ch g Sixties Icon—Search Party **Mr M. L. Albon**
30 **CHIVERS (IRE)**, 8, b g Duke of Marmalade (IRE)—Thara (USA) **Mr D. R. Steele**
31 **CLAYTON**, 10, b g Peintre Celebre (USA)—Blossom **Mr A. J. Head**
32 **CLEARANCE**, 5, b g Authorized (IRE)—Four Miracles **G. L. Moore**
33 **COMPULSIVE (IRE)**, 4, ch g Lope de Vega (IRE)—Fand (USA) **L.T.D Racing**
34 **CRYSTAL LAD (FR)**, 7, ch g Kapgarde (FR)—Qrystale Mag (FR) **Mr C. E. Stedman**
35 **DANCECRAFT**, 5, b m Mastercraftsman (IRE)—Samba Chryss (IRE) **Mr R. E. Tillett**
36 **DAREBIN (GER)**, 7, ch g It's Gino (GER)—Delightful Sofie (GER) **Chris Stedman & Mark Albon**

MR GARY MOORE - Continued

37 **DEEBAJ (IRE)**, 7, br g Authorized (IRE)—Athreyaa **G. L. Moore**
38 **DELL ORO (FR)**, 6, b g Walk In The Park (IRE)—Kallistea (FR) **Galloping On The South Downs Partnership**
39 **DIAKALI (FR)**, 10, gr g Sinndar (IRE)—Diasilixa (FR) **Mr N. J. Peacock**
40 **DISTINGO (IRE)**, 6, b g Smart Strike (CAN)—Distinctive Look (IRE) **Alan Jamieson Site Services Ltd**
41 **DONNYTWOBUCKETS (IRE)**, 5, b g Jeremy (USA)—
                        Manorville (IRE) **Galloping On The South Downs Partnership**
42 **DRIFTING STAR (IRE)**, 4, b g Sea The Stars (IRE)—Drifting (IRE) **Past The Post Racing**
43 **DUCHESS OF AVON**, 4, ch f Dutch Art—Avon Lady **Caplin & Sheridan**
44 **EARLY DU LEMO (FR)**, 6, gr g Early March—Kiswa (FR) **Mr A. J. Head**
45 **EAST INDIES**, 6, b g Authorized (IRE)—Elan **Redec Ltd**
46 **EDAM DU MESTIVEL (FR)**, 5, b g Al Namix (FR)—Quidam Rochelaise (FR) **Mr A. J. Head**
47 **EDITEUR DU GITE (FR)**, 5, b g Saddex—Malaga de St Sulpice (FR) **The Preston Family, Friends & T Jacobs**
48 **EL HAGEB ROSE (FR)**, 5, b g Coastal Path—Ile Rose (FR) **Galloping On The South Downs Partnership**
49 **EPISODE (FR)**, 5, ch m Kotky Bleu (FR)—Morvandelle (FR) **Mr P. Hunt**
50 **ERAGON DE CHANAY (FR)**, 5, b g Racinger (FR)—Rose Celebre (FR) **Five Star Racing Group**
51 **ET MOI ALORS (FR)**, 5, b g Kap Rock (FR)—Qui L'eut Cru (FR) **Mr A. J. Head**
52 **FLAMINGER (FR)**, 4, gr g Racinger (FR)—Landalouse (FR) **Mrs E. H. Avery**
53 **FLASHMAN**, 10, ch g Doyen (IRE)—Si Si Si **Mr A. D. Bradmore**
54 **FURIA D'OUDAIRIES (FR)**, 4, b f Hurricane Cat (USA)—Sonate d'oudairies (FR) **Mr J. Terry**
55 **GENEROUS HELPINGS (IRE)**, 10, ch g Generous (IRE)—Saffron Pride (IRE) **Mr B. R. Tetley**
56 **GENTLEMAN'S DREAM (IRE)**, 7, b g Flemensfirth (USA)—Fair And Aisey (IRE) **Dedman Properties Limited**
57 **GLENO (IRE)**, 7, ch g Ask—Lwitikila **Crystal Racing Syndicate**
58 **GOLDSLINGER (FR)**, 7, b g Gold Away (IRE)—Singaporette (FR) **The Knights Of Pleasure**
59 **GOOD LUCK CHARM**, 10, b g Doyen (IRE)—Lucky Dice **Heart of the South Racing 101**
60 **GOSSIPING**, 7, b g Dubawi (IRE)—Gossamer **Mr G. L. Moore & Mr Ashley Carr**
61 **GRAASTEN (GER)**, 7, ch g Sholokhov (IRE)—Golden Time (GER) **Galloping On The South Downs Partnership**
62 **GUNS OF LEROS (USA)**, 6, b br g Cape Blanco (IRE)—Zappeuse (USA) **Mr P. Hunt**
63 **HERMOSA VAQUERA (IRE)**, 9, b m High Chaparral (IRE)—Sundown **Mr M. R. Baldry**
64 **HIGH UP IN THE AIR (FR)**, 5, ch g Famous Name—You Got The Love **Mr P. T. Mott**
65 **HINT OF GREY (IRE)**, 6, gr m Mastercraftsman (IRE)—Anamarka **Mrs C. Reed**
66 **HOLLYWOOD ROAD (IRE)**, 6, b g Kodiac—Rinneen (IRE) **Mrs C. Reed**
67 **HONORABLE (FR)**, 4, b g Lawman (FR)—Petite Noblesse (FR) **Mr C. E. Stedman**
68 **IBALLISTICVIN**, 6, b g Rail Link—Guntakal (IRE) **Scuderia Vita Bella**
69 **ICONIC MUDDLE**, 6, gr g Sixties Icon—Spatham Rose **Saloop**
70 **IL RE DI NESSUNO (FR)**, 4, b g Sinndar (FR)—Lady Elgar (FR) **Mr Ashley Head & Mr Garry Dreher**
71 **IMARI KID (IRE)**, 6, b g Pour Moi (IRE)—Breathe (FR) **Mr P. B. Moorhead**
72 **IMPHAL**, 5, b g Nathaniel (IRE)—Navajo Rainbow **Mr N. J. Peacock**
73 **IT'S GOT LEGS (IRE)**, 6, b g Getaway (GER)—Lady Cadia (FR) **Galloping On The South Downs Partnership**
74 4, B g Finsceal Fior (IRE)—Just Josie **Saloop**
75 **JUSTIFICATION**, 11, b g Montjeu (IRE)—Colorspin (FR) **Mrs E. A. Kiernan**
76 **KAFEEL (USA)**, 8, b g First Samurai (USA)—Ishraak (USA) **K. Johnson, K. Jessup**
77 **KALAKAWA ENKI (FR)**, 5, b g Buck's Boum (FR)—Baba San Siro (FR) **Five Star Racing Group**
78 **KAPDAD (FR)**, 5, ch g Kapgarde (FR)—Reveries (FR) **Galloping On The South Downs Partnership**
79 **KING ATHELSTAN (IRE)**, 4, b g Mayson—Ashtaroute (USA) **Caplin & Sheridan**
80 **KING COOL**, 8, b g King's Theatre (IRE)—Cool Spice **Mr P. T. Mott**
81 **KING OF THE SAND (IRE)**, 4, ch g Footstepsinthesand—Lough Mewin (IRE) **Jacobs Construction & Mr J Harley**
82 **KLOUD GATE (FR)**, 7, ch g Astronomer Royal (USA)—Talkata (IRE) **Hail Sargent Evans**
83 **KNOCKNANUSS (IRE)**, 9, b g Beneficial—Dato Vic (IRE) **Hail Sargent Evans**
84 **KOST A COAT (FR)**, 4, b g Diamond Boy (FR)—Charming Princesse (FR) **Mrs R. Arnold**
85 **L'EQUINOXE (FR)**, 5, b g Enrique—Nebuleuse (IRE) **Galloping On The South Downs Partnership**
86 **LARRY**, 6, b g Midnight Legend—Gaspaisie (FR) **Galloping On The South Downs Partnership**
87 **LE CAPRICIEUX (FR)**, 8, b g Alberto Giacometti (IRE)—Eria Flore (FR) **Mr A. Foreman & Mr G. L. Moore**
88 **LIGHT OF AIR (FR)**, 6, b g Youmzain (IRE)—Height of Vanity (IRE) **G. L. Moore**
89 **LORD CLENAGHCASTLE (IRE)**, 5, b g Big Bad Bob (IRE)—Clenaghcastle Lady (IRE) **Mr M. R. Baldry**
90 **LUNA BEAR**, 5, b m Dick Turpin (IRE)—Royal Tavira Girl (IRE) **Scuderia Vita Bella**
91 **LUXFORD (FR)**, 5, b m Mullionmileanhour (IRE)—Dolly Parton (IRE) **Bush, Mair & Summers**
92 **MASTER OF SPEED (IRE)**, 7, ch g Mastercraftsman (IRE)—
                        Mango Groove (IRE) **Mr Ashley Head & Mr Garry Dreher**
93 **MASTER POET**, 4, b g Poet's Voice—Lilli Marlane **Heart of the South Racing 113**
94 **MINMORE PRESENT (IRE)**, 8, ch g Presenting—Ballagh Dawn (IRE) **Mrs R. A. Arnold**
95 **MISTER CHOW**, 5, ch g Nathaniel (IRE)—Skimmia **G. L. Moore**
96 **MR FICKLE (IRE)**, 10, b g Jeremy (USA)—Mamara Reef **Gary Moore Racing**
97 **MUDDLE THINKING (IRE)**, 5, b g Haafhd—Just Josie **Saloop**
98 **MULTITASK**, 9, b g Multiplex—Attlongglast **Power Geneva Ltd & Mr G. L. Moore**
99 **NATURALLY HIGH (FR)**, 4, b g Camelot—Just Little (FR) **Hail Sargent Evans**

MR GARY MOORE - Continued

100 **NEEDHAMS GAP (IRE)**, 5, br g Flemensfirth (USA)—Blue Maxi (IRE) **Collins, Moorhead, Michael & O'Sullivan**
101 **NEFF (GER)**, 4, b g Pastorius (GER)—Nouvelle Fortune (IRE)
102 **NOT ANOTHER MUDDLE**, 8, b g Kayf Tara—Spatham Rose **Saloop**
103 **NOT NEVER**, 7, ch g Notnowcato—Watchoverme **Hail Sargent Evans**
104 **OLYMNIA**, 8, b m Teofilo (IRE)—Diotima **Mr M. R. Baldry**
105 **PRIDE OF ANGELS**, 6, gr m Dark Angel (IRE)—Openness **Mr M. R. Baldry**
106 **ROCCO DU BERLAIS (IRE)**, 4, gr g Shirocco (GER)—Izzy du Berlais (IRE) **The Fourth Pillar Partnership**
107 **ROCKSETTE**, 5, b m Mount Nelson—Native Nickel **Hide & Seekers**
108 **ROYAL HALL (FR)**, 7, b g Halling (USA)—Royal Fantasy (IRE) **G. L. Moore & A. Carr**
109 **RUBY YEATS**, 8, b m Yeats (IRE)—Newbay Lady **G. L. Moore**
110 **RYDAN (IRE)**, 8, ch g Intense Focus (USA)—Lough Mewin (IRE) **Jacobs Construction Ltd Partnership**
111 **SAN PEDRO DE SENAM (FR)**, 6, br g Saint des Saints (FR)—
Tetiaroa (FR) **Mrs Jane George & Mrs Helen Shelton**
112 **SCARLET COUTURE**, 6, b m Schiaparelli (GER)—Little Red Spider **Mr J. A. Jenkins**
113 **SHAMROCK EMMA (IRE)**, 4, ch f Mizzen Mast (USA)—Lisselan Diva (IRE) **Caplin & Sheridan**
114 **STORMINGIN (IRE)**, 6, gr g Clodovil (IRE)—Magadar (USA) **Mrs C. Reed**
115 **SUSSEX RANGER (USA)**, 5, b g Hat Trick (JPN)—Purple (USA) **The Tongdean Partnership**
116 **TAZKA (FR)**, 4, b f Network (GER)—Tazminya **B. Noakes & Baroness S. Noakes**
117 **TEMPLIER (IRE)**, 6, b g Mastercraftsman (IRE)—Tigertail (FR) **P. R. Chapman**
118 **THE FLYING SOFA (IRE)**, 6, b g Sholokhov (IRE)—La Julie (FR) **Galloping On The South Downs Partnership**
119 **THECHILDREN'STRUST (IRE)**, 4, br g Society Rock (IRE)—Estemaala (IRE) **Mr A. J. Head**
120 **THOUNDER (FR)**, 5, ch g Hurricane Cat (USA)—Meldown (FR) **A. Head**
121 **TOAD**, 6, b g Shirocco (GER)—One Gulp **Galloping On The South Downs Partnership**
122 **TRAFFIC FLUIDE (FR)**, 9, b g Astarabad (USA)—
Petale Rouge (FR) **Galloping On The South Downs Partnership**
123 **TWENTY TWENTY (IRE)**, 4, b g Henrythenavigator (USA)—Distinctive Look (IRE) **Mark Albon & Gary Moore**
124 **VISION CLEAR (GER)**, 4, b g Soldier Hollow—Vive Madame (GER)
125 **WAIKIKI WAVES (FR)**, 6, b g Alexandros—Lulabelle Spar (IRE) **Heart Of The South Racing**
126 **WEST DRIVE (IRE)**, 6, ch g Sea The Stars (IRE)—Fair Sailing (IRE) **B. Siddle & B. D. Haynes**
127 **WHAT A MUDDLE (IRE)**, 5, ch g Haafhd—Spatham Rose **Saloop**
128 **WINNING WILLIE (IRE)**, 10, b g Cape Cross (IRE)—Pacific Grove **Mr P. B. Moorhead**
129 **ZAMPERINI (IRE)**, 7, ch g Fast Company (USA)—Lucky Date (IRE) **Mr R. E. Tillett**
130 **ZANTE**, 7, ch g Zanzibari (USA)—Calling All Angels (FR) **Heart of the South Racing 103 & Partner**

THREE-YEAR-OLDS

131 **AIGUILLETTE**, b g Epaulette (AUS)—Lucky Dice **Heart of the South 108**
132 **CAPRICORN PRINCE**, ch c Garswood—Sakhee's Pearl **Mrs A. P. Wilkinson**
133 **CLARA PEETERS**, b f Epaulette (AUS)—Musical Key **Mr R. A. Green**
134 **DADALWAYSWANTEDONE (FR)**, ch g Creachadoir (IRE)—Peldrine (IRE) **Mr T. C. McKeever**
135 **DRUMSHANBO DESTINY (FR)**, ch g Nathaniel (IRE)—
Lacy Sunday (USA) **Chris Watkins, David Reynolds, G L Moore**
136 **GOSHEN (FR)**, b g Authorized (IRE)—Hyde (FR) **Mr S. Packham**
137 **HAITIAN SPIRIT**, b f Swiss Spirit—Haiti Dancer **Heart of the South**
138 **ILLYWHACKER (IRE)**, b c Oasis Dream—Rebecca Rolfe **Clare Salmon & Gary Moore**
139 **LADY MORPHEUS**, b f Morpheus—Tatora **Mr P. B. Moorhead**
140 **SLADE KING (IRE)**, ch g Slade Power (IRE)—Lough Mewin (IRE) **Jacobs Construction Ltd Partnership**
141 B c Kayf Tara—Sudden Light (IRE) **Mr J. Hinds**
142 **WHISTLER BOWL**, b f Mukhadram—Sablonne (USA) **Mr C. E. Stedman**

TWO-YEAR-OLDS

143 B f 10/3 Mayson—Amontillado (IRE) (Pastoral Pursuits) (6000) **Shark Bay Racing Syndicate**
144 B c 31/1 Epaulette (AUS)—
Bahamian Music (IRE) (Bahamian Bounty) (30000) **Jacobs Construction & Mr J Harley**
145 B c 31/3 Le Havre (IRE)—Fontley (Sadler's Wells) (USA) (70000) **Jacobs Construction Limited Partnership**
146 B f 25/1 Acclamation—La Grande Elisa (IRE) (Ad Valorem (USA)) (7500)
147 **POETRY AND ART**, br f 23/4 Poet's Voice—Ashford Belle (IRE) (Arakan (USA)) (80000) **Mr R. A. Green**
148 **SILVER CLIFFS (IRE)**, b c 6/4 Canford Cliffs (IRE)—Birdie Queen (Pastoral Pursuits) **The Golf Partnership**
149 **SUMMER VALLEY**, b f 24/4 Mukhadram—Pink Stone (Bigstone (IRE)) **Paul & Judy Buckfield**

Other Owners: Mrs M. Abey, Mrs E. Adamski, Mrs V. Baker, Rev L. M. Brown, R. L. Brown, Mr H. Burch, Mrs W. Bush, Mr D. Caplin, Mr J. A. Collins, Mr D. A. Cranfield, Mr David N.Reynolds & Mr Chris Watkins, J. T. Devine, Mr G. C. Dreher, Mr D. L. Evans, Mr A. J. Foreman, Mr T. Francis, G L Moore Racing, Mr M. F. Geoghegan, Mrs J. George, Mr M. Goodrum, Mr L. Graffato, Mr J. E. Hale, The Hon J. Hanham, J. E. Harley, Mr M. A. Harris, B. D. Haynes, Heart of the South Racing 103, Mr P. A. Herbert, Ms L. M. Hess, Mr M. Hess, Mr J. Hinds, Mr A. D. S. Hodges, Jacobs Construction (Holdings) Limited, Mrs L. Jenkins, Mr K. P. Jessup, Mr K. W. Johnson, Mr A. Keeley, D. Leon, Mr B. Malyon, Mr I. McMillan, Mr S. A.

MR GARY MOORE - Continued

Michael, Mr D. G. Moore, Mr G. Morley, Mrs S. L. Morley, Mrs C. S. Muddle, Baroness S. Noakes, C. B. Noakes, Mr J. Norman, Mrs M. Parker, Mr J. R. Penny, Mr R. Pettett, Power Geneva Ltd, The Preston Family & Friends Ltd, Mr G. Reeves, Mr D. N. Reynolds, Mr N. J. Roach, M. G. Rogers, Ms C. L. Salmon, Mr R. D. Sargent, Mrs P L. C. L. Sarzi-Braga, Mrs H. J. Shelton, Mr A. M. Sheridan, R. M. Siddle, Mr M. T. Titterton, Mr R. W. D. Trevelyan, Mr M. C. Waddingham, T. Ware, Mr C. D. Watkins, Mr A. Watson, Miss C. A. Webb, Mr M. K. Webb.

Assistant Trainer: David Wilson

Jockey (flat): Ryan Moore, Hector Crouch. **Jockey (NH):** Andrew Glassonbury, Jamie Moore, Joshua Moore.
Conditional: Niall Houlihan.

---

394   MR J. S. MOORE, Upper Lambourn

Postal: **Berkeley House Stables, Upper Lambourn, Hungerford, Berkshire, RG17 8QP**
Contacts: **PHONE** (01488) 73887 **FAX** (01488) 73997 **MOBILE** (07860) 811127 / (07900) 402856
E-MAIL jsmoore.racing@btopenworld.com **WEBSITE** www.stanmooreracing.co.uk

1 **BROCKAGH CAILIN**, 4, b f Helmet (AUS)—Step Softly **Gridline Racing**
2 **POETIC PRINCIPLE (IRE)**, 5, b g Royal Applause—Lady Links **Mrs F. H. Hay**
3 **POWER FROM ABOVE (IRE)**, 4, br f Power—Aspasias Tizzy (USA) **J S Moore & Mr J Carr**
4 **SHEILA'S EMPIRE (IRE)**, 4, b f Holy Roman Emperor (IRE)—Silk Mascara (IRE) **Mrs S. J. Moore**
5 **UTHER PENDRAGON (IRE)**, 4, b g Dragon Pulse (IRE)—Unreal **Mrs Wendy Jarrett & J S Moore**

THREE-YEAR-OLDS

6 **AULD BOY (USA)**, b br g Speightstown (USA)—Ilikecandy (USA) **Mr Tom Vaughan & J S Moore**
7 **CHAMPION BROGIE (IRE)**, b g Alhebayeb (IRE)—Defensive Boast (USA) **Tom Vaughan & J S Moore**
8 **COLOURFUL SKY (FR)**, ch f Dalakhani (IRE)—Sky Colours (IRE) **The Well Fleeced Partnership**
9 **DELTA BRAVO (IRE)**, b f Mastercraftsman (IRE)—Rhiannon (IRE) **Eventmasters Racing & J S Moore**
10 **EVER ROCK (IRE)**, b f Society Rock—Alhaadh (USA) **Ever Equine & J. S. Moore**
11 **MAGNETIC (IRE)**, b g Alhebayeb (IRE)—Telltime (USA) **Mrs Wendy Jarrett & J S Moore**
12 **PLEASANT GESTURE (IRE)**, ch f Dandy Man (IRE)—Validate **Mr Eoin McDonagh & J S Moore**
13 **RELATIVE EASE**, b f Sayif (IRE)—Shohrah (IRE) **Mrs F. H. Hay**
14 **RUN ASHORE (IRE)**, b g Le Havre (IRE)—Banville (IRE) **C Instone, K Badger & J S Moore**
15 **SOCIETY SWEETHEART (IRE)**, br f Society Rock (IRE)—Breakmeheart (IRE) **Eventmasters Racing & J S Moore**
16 **WARRIOR DISPLAY (IRE)**, b g Dandy Man (IRE)—Clare Glen (IRE) **Mrs Wendy O'Leary & J S Moore**
17 **WISHBONE (IRE)**, b c Footstepsinthesand—Royale Life (FR) **J. S. Moore**

TWO-YEAR-OLDS

18 B c 2/3 Anjaal—Apasiona (IRE) (Invincible Spirit (IRE)) (1263)
19 B f 15/5 Free Eagle (IRE)—Calico Moon (USA) (Seeking The Gold (USA))
20 **COLLIENE DO ROIS**, ch f 23/2 Kingston Hill—
    French Connexion (IRE) (Chineur (FR)) **Tom Yates, Evelyn Yates & J S Moore**
21 B f 12/1 Brazen Beau (AUS)—Confidente (IRE) (Awesome Again (CAN)) **J. S. Moore & Partner**
22 Ch c 10/4 Anjaal—Dancing Lauren (IRE) (Oratorio (IRE)) **Pineapple Stud & J S Moore**
23 B f 30/3 Bungle Inthejungle—Desert Alchemy (IRE) (Green Desert (USA)) (15000)
24 Gr g 25/4 Alhebayeb (IRE)—Hallbeck (Halling (USA)) **The Moore The Merrier**
25 Ch c 7/3 Society Rock—Independent Girl (IRE) (Bachelor Duke (USA)) (2949) **J S Moore & Partner**
26 Ch c 9/5 Toronado (IRE)—Let's Dance (IRE) (Danehill Dancer (USA)) (800) **Howses Stud & J S Moore**
27 Ch c 19/4 Mukhadram—Lovely Dancer (IRE) (Yeats (IRE)) (4214)
28 B f 31/3 Xtension (IRE)—Make Amends (IRE) (Indian Ridge)
29 B f 18/3 Sayif (IRE)—Peneia (USA) (Nureyev (USA))
30 B c 10/4 Requinto (IRE)—Salt Rose (Sleeping Indian) (3809) **Mrs Wendy Jarrett & J S Moore**
31 Gr f 21/1 Hallowed Crown (AUS)—She's A Minx (IRE) (Linamix (FR)) (5899) **J. S. Moore & Partner**
32 B f 10/3 Gutaifan (IRE)—The Oldladysays No (IRE) (Perugino (USA)) **Mrs S Gray, I Gray & J S Moore**
33 Br c 2/5 Gutaifan (IRE)—Treasure The Lady (IRE) (Indian Ridge) (2528) **J. S. Moore & Partner**
34 **TROUBLE**, b c 27/3 Roderic O'Connor (IRE)—Caprella (Kheleyf (USA)) **Tom Yates, Evelyn Yates & J S Moore**
35 B f 20/4 Epaulette (AUS)—Union City Blues (IRE) (Encosta de Lago (AUS))
36 B g 30/4 Alhebayeb (IRE)—Unreal (Dansili) **Mrs Wendy Jarrett & J S Moore**
37 B f 9/3 Swiss Spirit—Verge (IRE) (Acclamation) **The Petticoat Government**
38 Gr c 26/4 Elzaam (AUS)—Whitershadeofpale (IRE) (Definite Article) (10113)
39 B c 6/3 War Command (USA)—Yeah Baby (IRE) (Danehill Dancer (IRE)) (5899)

MR J. S. MOORE - Continued

Other Owners: Mr Kieron Badger, Mr J. C. Bickerton, Mrs Elisabeth Bickerton, Mrs T. Burns, Mr J. Carr, Mr A. D. Crook, Mr Kevin Elliott, Eventmasters Racing, Ever Equine, Mr Ian J. Gray, Mrs S. Gray, Mr P. J. Grimes, Howses Stud, Ms Caroline Instone, Mrs Wendy Jarrett, Mr Eoin Joseph MC Donagh, Mr Eddie McGlinchey, Mr Nigel McGlinchey, Mr J. S. Moore, The Moore The Merrier, Mrs J. A. Newell-Smyth, Mrs E. O'Leary, The Petticoat Government, Mrs Denise Sheasby, Mr E. J. N. Sheasby, Mr Thomas Gabriel Vaughan, Mr M. Winter, Mrs E. Yates, Mr T. D. S. Yates.

Assistant Trainer: Mrs S. Moore

Apprentice: Aaron McKay:

---

395 MISS KELLY MORGAN, Withcote
Postal: **Rose Cottage, Bridle Road, Withcote, Oakham, Leicestershire, LE15 8DP**
Contacts: **PHONE (01664) 454904 MOBILE (07808) 133324**
E-MAIL **kellymorgan15@hotmail.com** WEBSITE **www.prestonlodgestud.com**

1 DEISE BLESS (IRE), 6, b m Scorpion (IRE)—Nighty Bless (IRE) **Mr J. R. Weatherby**
2 EXTREME APPEAL (IRE), 7, b g Excellent Art—Silk Mascara (IRE) **Mr J. R. Weatherby**
3 RED INDIAN, 7, b g Sulamani (IRE)—Rafiya **Mr J. R. Weatherby**
4 THE WINKLER (IRE), 10, gr g Medaaly—Osirixa (FR) **Mr J. R. Weatherby**
5 TIMETOCHILL (IRE), 6, br m Scorpion (IRE)—Kilcoleman Lady (IRE) **Mr J. R. Weatherby**
6 TOP WOOD (FR), 12, ch g Kotky Bleu (FR)—Heure Bleu (FR) **Mr J. R. Weatherby**

---

396 MISS LAURA MORGAN, Waltham On The Wolds
Postal: **Foxfield Stud, Goadby Road, Waltham On The Wolds, Melton Mowbray, Leicestershire, LE14 4AG**
Contacts: **PHONE (01664) 464571 MOBILE (07817) 616622**
E-MAIL **lauramorg@hotmail.co.uk**

1 BEGGARS CROSS (IRE), 9, b g Presenting—Ballygill Heights (IRE) **Mr P. L. Read**
2 CAVALRY SCOUT (IRE), 6, b br g Mahler—Yourfinalanswer (IRE) **Giles & Pepperdine**
3 DIAMONDS A DANCING, 9, ch g Delta Dancer—Zing **Mrs S. K. McCain**
4 DJARKEVI (FR), 6, b g Khalkevi (IRE)—Onvavoir (FR) **Mrs J. A. Wakefield**
5 FENJACK (IRE), 7, b g Jimble (FR)—Katie Baby (IRE) **Mrs A. M. Williams**
6 GOLD FIELDS, 5, b g Sakhee (USA)—Realms of Gold (USA) **Mrs M. J. Pepperdine**
7 HAASAB (IRE), 6, b g Sakhee (USA)—Badweia (USA) **Roemex Ltd**
8 HEADS UP CLEMMIE, 6, b m Sulamani (IRE)—M'lady Rousseur (IRE) **The Rann Family**
9 HOLY STREET (IRE), 7, b g Presenting—Vigna Maggio (FR) **Mr S. R. W. Howlett**
10 7, B g Phoenix Reach (IRE)—Naturally Inspired (IRE) **J. W. Hardy**
11 QUIZZACLE NOMAD, 10, b m Nomadic Way (USA)—Quizzal **Laura Morgan Racing Club**
12 SKIPPING ON (IRE), 10, b g Westerner—Skipping Along (IRE) **Triumph In Mind**
13 TARAS DAY, 6, b m Kayf Tara—One of Those Days **Mrs H. M. Harvey**
14 TEMPLE GATE (IRE), 4, b f Sir Percy—Lady Rosamunde **Mrs L. G. Talbot**
15 THOMAS TODD, 9, b g Passing Glance—Miss Danbys **Burton, Copley & Todd**
16 ULIS DE VASSY (FR), 11, b g Voix du Nord (FR)—Helathou (FR) **Read & Morgan**
17 WILL O'THE WEST (IRE), 8, b g Westerner—Simply Divine (IRE) **The Racing With Will Partnership**
18 ZAKHAROVA, 5, ch m Beat Hollow—Tcherina (USA) **Mr & Mrs W. J. Williams**

Other Owners: Mr Richard Burton, Mr Martin Copley, Mr S. P. Giles, Mr Ian Guise, Miss Laura Morgan, Mrs Marian Pepperdine, Mr Philip Rann, Mrs L. E. Rann, Mr Paul L. Read, Miss Louise Todd, Mr Tim Wendels, Mr W. J. Williams, Mrs A. M. Williams, Mrs M. Williams, Mr R. Wright.

Assistant Trainer: Tom Morgan

---

397 MR MOUSE MORRIS, Fethard
Postal: **Everardsgrange, Fethard, Co. Tipperary, Ireland**
Contacts: **PHONE (00353) 52 6131474 FAX (00353) 52 6131654 MOBILE (00353) 86 8543010**
E-MAIL **mouse@eircom.net**

1 BAILY GORSE (IRE), 5, b g Milan—Lillies Bordello (IRE) **Mr R. A. Scott**
2 BAILY MOON (IRE), 8, b g Milan—Givehertime (IRE) **Mr R. A. Scott**
3 BAILY THUNDER, 5, ch g Yorgunnabelucky (USA)—Alikat (IRE) **Mr R. A. Scott**

MR MOUSE MORRIS - Continued

4 **BALAKANI (FR)**, 6, b g Khalkevi (IRE)—La Balagne (FR) **Mr R. A. Scott**
5 **BEYOND THE LAW (IRE)**, 7, b g Westerner—Thegoodwans Sister (IRE) **Exors of Alan & Anne Potts**
6 **DROMNEA (IRE)**, 12, b br g Presenting—Fifth Imp (IRE) **Mrs A. Daly**
7 **FIRST CLASS RETURN (IRE)**, 6, b g Let The Lion Roar—Chitty Bang Bang (IRE) **D. O'Donohoe & P. Nelson**
8 **FOXY JACKS (IRE)**, 5, b g Fame And Glory—Benefit Ball (IRE) **D. Desmond**
9 **LAST MAN STANDING (IRE)**, 6, ch g Flemensfirth (USA)—Tricky Present (IRE) **Mr J. Magnier**
10 **POTTSIE (IRE)**, 6, b g Robin des Champs (FR)—Present Gesture (IRE) **Exors of Alan & Anne Potts**
11 **ROMAN ROCK (IRE)**, 5, b g Presenting—Native Idea (IRE) **M. O'Flynn, J. O'Flynn**
12 **SAMS PROFILE**, 5, b g Black Sam Bellamy (IRE)—Lucylou (IRE) **M. O'Flynn, J. O'Flynn**
13 **SIZING JOSHUA (IRE)**, 6, b g Flemensfirth (USA)—Alleygrove Lass (IRE) **Exors of Alan & Anne Potts**
14 **SPRING WATCH (IRE)**, 7, b g Mahler—Taras Child (IRE) **J. P. McManus**
15 **WHATSNOTKNOW (IRE)**, 4, b g Mahler—Whos To Know (IRE) **A. R. Scott**
16 **WIGS ON THE GREEN (IRE)**, 7, b g Robin des Champs (FR)—Koko Rose (IRE) **J. P. McManus**

---

398 **MR PATRICK MORRIS, Prescot**
Postal: **Avenue House, George Hale Avenue, Knowsley Park, Prescot, Merseyside, L34 4AJ**
Contacts: **MOBILE (07545) 425235**
E-MAIL info@patmorrisracing.co.uk WEBSITE www.patmorrisracing.co.uk

1 **ANGEL GABRIAL (IRE)**, 10, b g Hurricane Run (IRE)—Causeway Song (USA) **Dr M. B. Q. S. Koukash**
2 **BAHANGO (IRE)**, 7, b g Bahamian Bounty—Last Tango (IRE) **Mr L. P. Richards**
3 **BELL HEATHER (IRE)**, 6, b m Iffraaj—Burren Rose (USA) **Dr M. B. Q. S. Koukash**
4 **BOFFO (IRE)**, 4, b g Intello (GER)—Claxon **Dr M. B. Q. S. Koukash**
5 **ENERGIA FLAVIO (BRZ)**, 9, gr g Agnes Gold (JPN)—Lira da Guanabara (BRZ) **Dr M. B. Q. S. Koukash**
6 **GABRIAL'S KAKA (IRE)**, 9, b g Jeremy (USA)—Love In May (IRE) **Dr M. B. Q. S. Koukash**
7 **GOSSIP COLUMN (IRE)**, 4, b g Arcano (IRE)—Monicalew **Dr M. B. Q. S. Koukash**
8 **HUMBLE GRATITUDE**, 4, ch g Foxwedge (AUS)—Gilt Linked **Dr M. B. Q. S. Koukash**
9 **JOCK TALK**, 5, b g Famous Name—Katdogawn **Dr S. Lane**
10 **MAGIC CIRCLE (IRE)**, 7, b g Makfi—Minkova (IRE) **Dr M. B. Q. S. Koukash**
11 **RENE MATHIS (GER)**, 9, ch g Monsieur Bond (IRE)—Remina (GER) **Dr M. B. Q. S. Koukash**
12 **RESTORER**, 9, gr g Mastercraftsman (IRE)—Moon Empress (FR) **Dr M. B. Q. S. Koukash**
13 **SHABEEB (USA)**, 6, b g Smart Strike (CAN)—Sortita (USA) **Dr M. B. Q. S. Koukash**
14 **SUEGIOO (FR)**, 10, ch g Manduro (GER)—Mantesera (IRE) **Dr M. B. Q. S. Koukash**
15 **TOP OFFER**, 10, b g Dansili—Zante **Mr M. Watkinson**

THREE-YEAR-OLDS

16 **NO MORE REGRETS (IRE)**, b f Kodiac—Shifting (IRE) **Dr M. B. Q. S. Koukash**
17 **SALAM ZAYED**, b g Exceed And Excel (AUS)—Long Face (USA) **Dr M. B. Q. S. Koukash**
18 Gr c Orpheus—Sharp And Smart (IRE)
19 B c Paco Boy (IRE)—Statua (IRE)

---

399 **MR HUGHIE MORRISON, East Ilsley**
Postal: **Summerdown, East Ilsley, Newbury, Berkshire, RG20 7LB**
Contacts: **PHONE (01635) 281678 FAX (01635) 281746 MOBILE (07836) 687799**
E-MAIL hughie@hughiemorrison.co.uk WEBSITE www.hughiemorrison.co.uk

1 **AFFAIR**, 5, b m Sakhee's Secret—Supatov (USA) **Mr & Mrs R Lloyd, Mr R Wright & Partners**
2 **APRES LE DELUGE (FR)**, 5, gr g Stormy River (FR)—Ms Cordelia (USA) **Mr Raymond Tooth**
3 **BELATED BREATH**, 4, ch f Bated Breath—Daffydowndilly **Lady Blyth**
4 **BELLA RAGAZZA**, 4, gr f Dutch Art—Sell Out **Mr Paul Brocklehurst**
5 **BUZZ (FR)**, 5, gr g Motivator—Tiysha (IRE) **Mr M Bevan, Mr A Pickford & Mr R Angliss**
6 **CANOODLE**, 7, b m Stimulation (IRE)—Flirtatious **Mrs M. D. W. Morrison**
7 4, Ch f Cityscape—Cill Rialaig **Pangfield Racing V**
8 **COMPTON MILL**, 7, b g Compton Place—
Classic Millennium **Mr M Bevan, Mrs R Luard & Mrs M D W Morrison**
9 **CORGI**, 4, b g So You Think (NZ)—Ermyn Express **Mr M Kerr-Dineen, Mr M Hughes**
10 **COUSIN KHEE**, 12, b g Sakhee (USA)—Cugina **Mrs M D W Morrison**
11 **EARLY SUMMER (IRE)**, 3, b f Sea The Stars (IRE)—Summer's Eve **Wardley Bloodstock**
12 **ESCAPE THE CITY**, 4, b f Cityscape—Jasmeno **MNC Racing**
13 **FAR CRY**, 6, b m Sakhee's Secret—Yonder **Mrs M D W Morrison**
14 **FUN MAC (GER)**, 8, ch g Shirocco (GER)—Favorite (GER) **Mrs Angela McAlpine & Partners**

MR HUGHIE MORRISON - Continued

15 **GERANIUM**, 4, ch f Sakhee's Secret—Kasumi **F Trenchard, Clare, Lady Margadale & The Hon Mary Morrison**
16 **JEDHI**, 4, b f Big Bad Bob (IRE)—
 Capriola **Mr Tony Pickford, Mr Simon Malcolm, The Hon Mary Morrison & Mr Simon de Zoete**
17 **KATABATIKA**, 5, b m Shirocco (GER)—Landinium (ITY) **Lady Blyth**
18 **MARMELO**, 6, b h Duke of Marmalade (IRE)—Capriolla **The Fairy Story Partnership & Mr Aziz Kheir**
19 **MISS AUSTEN (IRE)**, 4, b f Fame And Glory—Swap Shop (IRE) **Mr L. A. Garfield**
20 **MUSIC MAN (IRE)**, 9, b g Oratorio (IRE)—Chanter **G Crook & Sons**
21 **NEARLY CAUGHT (IRE)**, 9, b g New Approach (IRE)—Katch Me Katie **Mr A. N. Solomons**
22 **NOT SO SLEEPY**, 7, ch g Beat Hollow—Papillon de Bronze (IRE) **Lady Blyth**
23 **PAMINAH**, 4, b f Bated Breath—Starry Sky **Mrs M D W Morrison**
24 **PASTORAL PLAYER**, 12, b g Pastoral Pursuits—Copy-Cat **The Pursuits Partnership**
25 **QUICKSAND (IRE)**, 4, ch f Footstepsinthesand—Miss Bellbird (IRE) **Mrs S M Rogers & Sir Thomas Pilkington**
26 **RIPPLET**, 4, b f Rip Van Winkle (IRE)—Seradim **The Fairy Story Partnership**
27 **SOD'S LAW**, 4, b g Mayson—Lawyers Choice **Mr Raymond Tooth**
28 **STAR ROCK**, 5, b m Fastnet Rock (AUS)—Starfala **Ben & Sir Martyn Arbib**
29 4, B g Stimulation (IRE)—Supatov (USA)
30 **TEMPLE CHURCH (IRE)**, 5, b g Lawman (FR)—All Hallows (IRE) **Mr P. C. J. Dalby & Mr R. D. Schuster**
31 **THIRD WIND**, 5, b g Shirocco (GER)—Act Three **Mouse Hamilton-Fairley**

THREE-YEAR-OLDS

32 B f Mukhadram—Alkhana (IRE) **Mrs Serena Geake**
33 **ARVENSIS**, b f Sir Percy—Raindrop **Lord Margadale**
34 **ASTRAL GIRL**, ch f Intello (GER)—Celestial Girl **Helena Springfield Ltd**
35 **BORN LEADER**, ch f Nathaniel (IRE)—
 Chieftess (IRE) **Thurloe Thoroughbreds XLVII, Mr Simon De Zoete & Partners**
36 **CRASTER (IRE)**, b c Sea The Stars (IRE)—Coquet **Lord Margadale, Mr A Scott, Mr M Kerr-Dineen**
37 **DOVE DIVINE (FR)**, b f Le Havre (IRE)—Numerieus (FR) **Sir Thomas Pilkington**
38 **ENHANCED**, ch c New Approach (IRE)—Complexion **Brightwalton Bloodstock Ltd**
39 **FORBIDDEN DANCE**, ch f Dutch Art—Strictly Lambada **Sir Francis Brooke, Mr R Pilkington, Mr A Rogers**
40 **HENDRIX (IRE)**, b g War Command (USA)—Monzza **Castle Down Racing**
41 **INDIAN VICEROY**, b g Kodiac—Broadlands **Mr Simon Malcolm, Mr Harry & Mrs Julie Parkes**
42 **ITIZZIT**, ch f Mukhadram—Whatizzit **Hottotrot Racing**
43 **KORCHO**, b c Toronado (IRE)—Locharia **Mr M Kerr-Dineen, Mr M Hughes & Mr W Eason**
44 **LIEUTENANT CONDE**, b g Havana Gold (IRE)—Jasmeno **MNC Racing**
45 **MAJESTIC MAC**, b g Cape Cross (IRE)—Talent Spotter **Mr A McAlpine & Mrs M D W Morrison**
46 **MOUSEBIRD (IRE)**, b f Zoffany (IRE)—Firecrest (IRE) **Sir Thomas Pilkington**
47 **MUMS HOPE**, gr ro f Lethal Force (IRE)—Jadwiga **Marian Lyons & Patricia Zanelli**
48 **PICCOLITA**, b f Piccolo—Violet's Walk **Mr M. E. Wates**
49 **REQUITED (IRE)**, b g Requinto (IRE)—Joyfullness (USA) **Mr H. Morrison**
50 **ROBERT L'ECHELLE (IRE)**, b c Big Bad Bob (IRE)—Damhsa Le Cheile (IRE) **Mr A. N. Solomons**
51 **SANDYMAN**, ch c Footstepsinthesand—Quiz Mistress **The Fairy Story Partnership**
52 **SAY NOTHING**, b f Nathaniel (IRE)—I Say (IRE) **Mr Raymond Tooth**
53 **SEA BATTLE (FR)**, ch g Lope de Vega (IRE)—Francisca (USA) **Mrs B. V. Sangster & Mr B. V. Sangster**
54 **SPARGROVE**, b c Cacique (IRE)—Capriolla **Selwood Bloodstock & Mrs S. Read**
55 **TARTLETTE**, b f Champs Elysees—Tottie **Mr Julian Richmond-Watson**
56 **TELECASTER**, b c New Approach (IRE)—Shirocco Star **Castle Down Racing**

TWO-YEAR-OLDS

57 **AMPNEY RED**, ch f 24/2 Mukhadram—Golden Delicious (Cadeaux Genereux) **Mr Nicholas Jones**
58 B f 13/4 Raven's Pass (USA)—Belanoiva (IRE) (Motivator) **Mr Simon Malcolm**
59 B f 26/3 Kendargent (FR)—Chutney (Exceed And Excel (AUS)) (36000)
 Mrs Angela McAlpine, Mr Jeremy Gompertz & Mr Patrick Milmo
60 **ELMETTO**, b f 6/4 Helmet (AUS)—Italian Connection (Cadeaux Genereux) (27000) **Helena Springfield Ltd**
61 B f 20/1 Siyouni (FR)—Ensemble (FR) (Iron Mask (USA)) (190000) **Michael Kerr-Dineen & Martin Hughes**
62 **EXCELFILLY**, b f 13/2 Excelebration (IRE)—Respectfilly (Mark of Esteem (IRE)) **The Fairy Story Partnership**
63 B f 2/3 Kingman—Galaxy Highflyer (Galileo (IRE)) **Helena Springfield Ltd**
64 B c 27/1 Garswood—Lawyers Choice (Namid) (55000) **Mr Raymond Tooth**
65 B c 19/4 Le Havre (IRE)—Mishhar (IRE) (Authorized (IRE)) (58000) **Mr Adrian McAlpine & Partners**
66 Gr c 20/3 Gutaifan (IRE)—More Respect (Spectrum (IRE)) (71639) **Thurloe Thoroughbreds XLVIII**
67 **MR POY**, ch c 10/2 Sepoy (AUS)—Quiz Mistress (Doyen (IRE)) **The Fairy Story Partnership**
68 Ch c 7/2 Lope de Vega (IRE)—Purr Along (Mount Nelson) (125000) **Michael Kerr-Dineen & Martin Hughes**
69 **QUICKTHORN**, b c 24/3 Nathaniel (IRE)—Daffydowndilly (Oasis Dream) **Lady Blyth**
70 **ROMSEY**, b f 14/3 Mukhadram—
 Broadlands (Kheleyf (USA)) (800) **The End-R-Ways Partnership & Mr A MacDonald-Buchanan**
71 **ROYAL ASTRONOMER**, b c 18/2 Telescope (IRE)—Regal Fairy (IRE) (Desert King (IRE)) **Mr M A & Mrs J E Richards**

MR HUGHIE MORRISON - Continued

72 Gr c 22/1 War Command (USA)—
      Sixpenny Sweets (IRE) (Dalakhani (IRE)) (100000) **M Kerr-Dineen, M Hughes & W Eason**
73 **SULOCHANA (IRE),** br f 14/2 Lope de Vega (IRE)—Yakshini (IRE) (Monsun (GER)) (45000) **Mr Paul Brocklehurst**
74 B c 22/2 Stimulation (IRE)—Supatov (USA) (Johannesburg (USA))
75 B f 29/4 Champs Elysees—Tottie (Fantastic Light (USA)) **Mr Julian Richmond-Watson**
76 **TREATY OF DINGLE,** b f 23/1 Roderic O'Connor (IRE)—
      Josefa Goya (Sakhee's Secret) (6190) **The TOD Partnership**
77 **VIZA,** b c 18/3 Australia—Vizinga (FR) (Marju (IRE)) (32000) **Mrs Caroline Swire & Mrs A Scott**
78 **WHITEHAVEN (FR),** bl c 29/4 Le Havre (IRE)—
      Passion Blanche (Dutch Art) (23598) **P. C. J. Dalby & R. D. Schuster**
79 Ch c 4/2 Raven's Pass (USA)—Wonderful Desert (Green Desert (USA)) (20000)

Other Owners: Mr G Ball, Mr A Bernstein, Mrs M T Bevan, Mrs M T Bevan, Mrs G Billington, Mr T Billington, Mr T. J. Billington, Mrs P.G. Billington, Mr T M Bird, T. M. Bird, Mr I Bradbury, Mrs Ann Chapple, P.C. J. Dalby, Mrs A Dowling, E. R. Goodwin, Mr M Gregori, Mr R. W. Gregson-Williams, Mrs E. J. Gregson-Williams, Mr H Hampson, Mr T Hester, Mr A. Kheir, Mr D. S. Little, Mr D S Little, Mr R Lloyd, Mrs S Lloyd, Mr A MacDonald-Buchanan, Miss A Morrison, Miss N Morrison, Mr G Morrison, Mr D Morrison, Mrs Susan Parker, Mr J W Parker, Mr O J W Pawle, Mr R. A. Pilkington, Mr Robert Pooles, R. D. Schuster, Mr A Scott, Mrs Belinda Scott, Miss C. S. Scott-Balls, Mr Hugh Scott-Barrett, Mr C Seymour, Mr J A B Stafford, Mr K Taylor, Mr M Taylor, Viscountess Trenchard, Mrs Anne Usher, Mr G Waylen, Mr G. Waylen, Mr B Weston, Mr D Weston, Mr S Willmont, Mrs R J Wilson, Mr R Wright.

Assistant Trainer: Mr Oliver Rix

Jockey (flat): Charlie Bennett. **Amateur:** Mr Robert Pooles.

---

400 MR MOHAMED MOUBARAK, Newmarket
Postal: **3C Sunnyside, Park Lane, Newmarket, Suffolk, CB8 8AX**
E-MAIL Moubarak.mohammed17@gmail.com

1 **OUT OF THE ASHES,** 6, ch g Phoenix Reach (IRE)—Shrewd Decision **D. P. Fremel**
2 **RASHEEQ (IRE),** 6, b g Vale of York (IRE)—Limber Up (IRE) **D. P. Fremel**
3 4, B f Rail Link—Shrewd Decision **D. P. Fremel**

THREE-YEAR-OLDS

4 **ACT OF MAGIC (IRE),** b g Magician (IRE)—Davanti (IRE) **The Mojito Partnership**
5 **ASENSIO,** b c Sepoy (AUS)—Wind Surf (USA) **Mr M. Y. Moubarak**
6 **CEDAR,** ch f Sepoy (AUS)—Lilli Marlane **Mr M. Y. Moubarak**
7 **MANZONI,** b c Equiano (IRE)—Gauchita **Mr M. Y. Moubarak**
8 **SALMON FISHING (IRE),** b g Dragon Pulse (IRE)—Lake Wanaka (IRE) **D. P. Fremel**
9 **TAYLORMADE,** ch c Archipenko (USA)—Malhadinha (IRE) **Mr M. Y. Moubarak**
10 **TEXTING,** b f Charm Spirit (IRE)—Dreamily (IRE) **Mr M. Y. Moubarak**
11 **THE METER,** b f Helsinki (USA)—Lulea **Mr M. Y. Moubarak**

TWO-YEAR-OLDS

12 B c 13/4 Cable Bay (IRE)—Broughtons Flight (IRE) (Hawk Wing (USA)) (16000) **Mr N. Alhajeri**
13 B f 7/5 Poet's Voice—Deserted (Oasis Dream) (8000)
14 B f 1/2 Kodiac—Fingal Nights (IRE) (Night Shift (USA)) (22857) **Mr J. A. Alsabah**
15 B c 24/1 Sepoy (AUS)—Forbidden Love (Dubawi (IRE)) (5000)

Other Owners: Mr A. C. O Sullivan, Mrs C. E. O Sullivan.

---

401 MR WILLIAM MUIR, Lambourn
Postal: **Linkslade, Wantage Road, Lambourn, Hungerford, Berkshire, RG17 8UG**
Contacts: **OFFICE (01488) 73098 HOME (01488) 73748 FAX (01488) 73490**
MOBILE (07831) 457074
E-MAIL william@williammuir.com WEBSITE www.williammuir.com

1 **CHIEF BRODY,** 8, b g Phoenix Reach (IRE)—Cherry Plum **Lucy Sandford & Richard Phillips**
2 **CUTTIN' EDGE (IRE),** 5, b g Rip Van Winkle (IRE)—How's She Cuttin' (IRE) **Purple & Lilac Racing**
3 **DATA PROTECTION,** 4, b g Foxwedge (AUS)—Midnight Sky **Muir Racing Partnership - Santa Anita**
4 **GENERAL ZOFF,** 4, b g Zoffany (IRE)—Aunt Julia **Purple & Lilac Racing X**
5 4, B g Approve (IRE)—Heaven's Heart (IRE) **Mr J O'Mulloy & Mr K Jeffery**
6 **HOLLANDER,** 5, ch g Dutch Art—Thrill **Muir Racing Partnership - Ayr**

MR WILLIAM MUIR - Continued

   7 **JAMAICAN JILL,** 4, b f Teofilo (IRE)—Kahlua Kiss **M. J. Caddy**
   8 **JAVELIN,** 4, ch f Lethal Force (IRE)—Amitola (IRE) **G O Leach & Mrs J M Leach**
   9 **LITTLE MISS DAISY,** 5, b m Arabian Gleam—Desert Liaison **Mrs J. M. Muir**
  10 **MISS M (IRE),** 5, b m Mastercraftsman (IRE)—Tintern **Mr B. L. Willis**
  11 **PASS THE CRISTAL (IRE),** 5, b g Raven's Pass (USA)—Crystal Melody **O'Mulloy, Schwartz**
  12 **TOPS NO,** 4, b f Mount Nelson—China Beads **S. Lamb**
  13 4, B g Kyllachy—Valentina Guest (IRE) **W. R. Muir**
  14 **WHITE SHAHEEN,** 6, b g Makfi—Likeable **Mr S. P. Hussain**

THREE-YEAR-OLDS

  15 **DRUMMER JACK (IRE),** b g Toronado (IRE)—Fligaz (FR) **Perspicacious Punters Racing Club**
  16 **HAMMY END (IRE),** b g Mount Nelson—Northern Affair (IRE) **Mr J. M. O'Mulloy**
  17 **HOLD STILL (IRE),** b c Bated Breath—Effervesce (IRE) **Muir Racing Partnership - Saint Cloud**
  18 **JACK'S POINT (IRE),** b c Slade Power (IRE)—Electra Star **C. L. A. Edginton**
  19 **JUST HUBERT (IRE),** b c Dunaden (FR)—La Tulipe (FR) **Foursome Thoroughbreds**
  20 **LORNA COLE (IRE),** gr f Lethal Force (IRE)—Suedehead **Mr J. M. O'Mulloy**
  21 **MAX GUEVARA (IRE),** b g Alhebayeb (IRE)—Assumption (IRE) **Mr F Hope & Mr G Hope**
  22 **NATTY NIGHT,** b c Nathaniel (IRE)—Danehill Dreamer (USA) **O'Mulloy, Schwartz**
  23 b c Lilbourne Lad (IRE)—Ornellaia (IRE) **Mr J. M. O'Mulloy**
  24 **SO CLAIRE,** br f Kyllachy—If So **Foursome Thoroughbreds**
  25 **SUNVISOR (IRE),** ch g Helmet (AUS)—Island Sunset (IRE) **Muir Racing Partnership - Leicester**
  26 **SWEET JEMIMA (USA),** ch f More Than Ready (USA)—Sweet Nothings (USA) **C. L. A. Edginton**

TWO-YEAR-OLDS

  27 B c 30/4 Brazen Beau (AUS)—Albany Rose (IRE) (Noverre (USA)) (18000)
  28 **FINAL OPTION,** bl f 14/3 Lethal Force (IRE)—If So (Iffraaj) (40000) **Foursome Thoroughbreds**
  29 Br c 9/4 Alhebayeb (IRE)—House of Roses (New Approach (IRE)) (10113)
  30 **HOWTONSTREET HARRY (IRE),** b c 21/4 Anjaal—Kathy Sun (IRE) (Intikhab (USA)) (35000) **Mr M. P. Graham**
  31 B c 14/3 Harbour Watch (IRE)—La Pyle (FR) (Le Havre (IRE)) **Knox & Wells Limited & Mr R W Devlin**
  32 **MOLINARI (IRE),** gr c 11/2 Mastercraftsman (IRE)—
                             Moon Empress (FR) (Rainbow Quest (USA)) **C. L. A. Edginton**
  33 Gr f 30/1 Lethal Force (IRE)—Secret Era (Cape Cross (IRE)) (1000) **Carmel Stud**
  34 Ch f 11/2 Dream Ahead (USA)—
                   Sweet Secret (Singspiel (IRE)) (18000) **Carmel Stud & G.O.Leach & Mrs J.M.Leach**

Other Owners: Mr P. A. Abberley, Mr A. A. Byrne, Mr N. Clark, R. W. Devlin, Mr R. Haim, F. P. Hope, Mr Gary Hope, Mr K. Jeffery, Knox & Wells Limited, Mr J. P. Kok, Mr G. O. Leach, Mrs J. M. Leach, Mr C. Moore, P. H. Morgan, Mrs M. E. Morgan, Mr R. B. Phillips, Mr D. L. Quaintance, Mr P. D. Quaintance, Miss L. J. Sandford, Ms B. Schwartz, Mr C. A. Washbourn.

Assistant Trainer: Richard Phillips

Jockey (flat): Martin Dwyer.

---

402   **MR CLIVE MULHALL, Scarcroft**
       Postal: Trainer did not wish details of his string to appear

---

403   **MR NEIL MULHOLLAND, Limpley Stoke**
       Postal: **Conkwell Grange Stables, Conkwell, Limpley Stoke, Bath, Avon, BA2 7FD**
       Contacts: **MOBILE (07739) 258607**
       E-MAIL neil@neilmulhollandracing.com WEBSITE www.neilmulhollandracing.com

   1 **BALLYMILAN,** 4, b f Milan—Ballyhoo (IRE) **Heart Racing HR2**
   2 **BETTER NEWS,** 8, b m Fair Mix (IRE)—Welcome News **Mrs C. L. Shaw**
   3 **BISHOPS COURT,** 9, b g Helissio (FR)—Island of Memories (IRE) **Mr P. C. Tory & Mr P. S. Frampton**
   4 **BOY IN A BENTLEY (IRE),** 9, b g Kayf Tara—All Our Blessings (IRE) **Mr C. E. Weare**
   5 **CALL ME WESTIE,** 7, b g Westerner—Popsie Hall **Mrs K. Birchenhough**
   6 **CAROLE'S DESTRIER,** 11, b g Kayf Tara—Barton May **Mrs C. Skipworth**
   7 **CAROLINES CHARM (IRE),** 5, b g Masterofthehorse (IRE)—
                  Truckers Princess (IRE) **Jockey Club Ownership (SW 2018)**

MR NEIL MULHOLLAND - Continued

8 **CARRIGMOORNA MATT (IRE)**, 8, b g Westerner—Carrigmorna Flyer (IRE) **Neil Mulholland Racing Ltd**
9 **CAVICIANA**, 6, b m Court Cave (IRE)—Viciana **The Jukes Family**
10 **CESAR ET ROSALIE (FR)**, 7, ch g Network (GER)—Regle de L'art (FR) **Mrs J. M. Abbott**
11 **CINTEX (FR)**, 7, b g Assessor (IRE)—Precieuze (FR) **Miss J. A. Goddard**
12 **CODE OF LAW**, 9, ch g Papal Bull—Fyvie **The Affordable (3) Partnership**
13 **CONKWELL LEGEND**, 5, b g Midnight Legend—Gallimaufry **Mrs H. R. Cross & Mrs S. A. Keys**
14 **COR WOT AN APPLE**, 8, b g Apple Tree (FR)—Chipewyas (FR) **D. V. Stevens**
15 **CORNISH WARRIOR (IRE)**, 8, b g Oscar (IRE)—Ballylooby Moss (IRE) **Strawberry Field Catering Ltd**
16 **DALAMAN (IRE)**, 8, b g Duke of Marmalade (IRE)—Crimphill (IRE) **Diamond Racing Ltd**
17 **DANDOLO DU GITE (FR)**, 6, b g Khalkevi (IRE)—Lavande d'eproniere (FR) **Equi ex Incertis Partners**
18 **DEAD RIGHT**, 7, b g Alflora (IRE)—April Queen **Mr J. P. McManus**
19 **DELANNOY**, 5, ch g Le Havre (IRE)—Raving Monsun **Mr Ashley Carr & Mr Derek Heeney**
20 **DEPUTY JONES (IRE)**, 6, b m Milan—Hudson Hope (IRE) **A. Carr**
21 **DOING FINE (IRE)**, 11, b g Presenting—Howaya Pet (IRE) **Mr Ashley Carr & Mr Andy Smith**
22 **DREAM MACHINE (IRE)**, 5, ch g Dream Ahead (USA)—Last Cry (FR) **D. M. Bell**
23 **DUKE OF KILCORRAL (IRE)**, 6, gr g Duke of Marmalade (IRE)—Miss Shaan (FR) **Mr J. Kehoe**
24 **EXELERATOR EXPRESS (FR)**, 5, b g Poliglote—Reine de Lestrade (FR)
25 **FINGERONTHESWITCH**, 9, b g Beneficial—Houseoftherisinsun (IRE) **Cahill, Atwell & Crofts**
26 **FRAU GEORGIA (IRE)**, 5, b m Germany (USA)—Sumability (IRE) **Mr J. Henderson**
27 **FULL (FR)**, 7, b g Mr Sidney (USA)—Funny Feerie (FR) **Happy Days Racing**
28 **GLENGAR (IRE)**, 5, b g Stowaway—Accordeon Royale (IRE) **Equi ex Incertis Partners**
29 **GLENS COUNTY (IRE)**, 6, b m Court Cave (IRE)—Glendante (IRE) **The Affordable Partnership**
30 **GLOBAL RHAPSODY (IRE)**, 5, b g Presenting—Rhapsody In Blue (GER) **Dr J. Hon**
31 **GREAT FAIRY (FR)**, 6, b g Great Pretender (IRE)—Salsa Fairy (FR) **The Keith Adams Racing Partnership**
32 **GREEN OR BLACK (IRE)**, 7, gr m Zebedee—Boucheron **The Chosen Few**
33 **HADFIELD (IRE)**, 7, b g Sea The Stars (IRE)—Rezyana (AUS) **Mr T. J. Clyne**
34 **HALO MOON**, 11, br g Kayf Tara—Fragrant Rose **Level Par Racing**
35 **HARBOUR FORCE (FR)**, 5, b g Harbour Watch (IRE)—Dam Beautiful **Mr D. B. Harris**
36 **HOLLYWOOD DREAM**, 4, b f Delegator—Royal Obsession (IRE) **Neil Mulholland Racing Club**
37 **HYGROVE PERCY**, 6, ch g Sir Percy—Hygrove Welshlady (IRE) **G. P. and Miss S. J. Hayes**
38 **IMPULSIVE STAR (IRE)**, 9, b g Busy Flight—Impulsive Ita (IRE) **Robert Waley-Cohen & Men Holding**
39 **INAMINNA (IRE)**, 8, b g Oscar (IRE)—Amber Trix (IRE) **Inaminna Partnership**
40 **IRISH ODYSSEY (IRE)**, 6, gr g Yeats (IRE)—Ma Furie (FR) **Mr A. G. Bloom**
41 **JUST FOR THE CRAIC (IRE)**, 4, b g Most Improved (IRE)—Beziers (IRE) **J. J. Maguire**
42 **KALONDRA (IRE)**, 8, b g Spadoun (FR)—Mystic Vic (IRE) **Mr J. Henderson**
43 **KANSAS CITY CHIEF (IRE)**, 10, b g Westerner—Badawi Street **Mr A. G. Bloom**
44 **KRISTAL HART**, 10, b m Lucky Story (USA)—Moly (FR) **The White Hart Racing Syndicate**
45 **LA CAVSA NOSTRA (IRE)**, 7, b g Flemensfirth—Pharenna (USA) **Mr R. B. Waley-Cohen**
46 **LADY CARDUROS (IRE)**, 5, b m Byron—Saranjo (IRE) **Pray That Shes Good**
47 **LAKE BAIKAL (FR)**, 5, gr g Martaline—La Curamalal (IRE) **Mr J. P. McManus**
48 **LAST ENCHANTMENT (IRE)**, 4, b f Camelot—Illandrane (IRE) **Equi ex Incertis Partners**
49 **LEE SIDE LADY (IRE)**, 9, ch m Mountain High (IRE)—Vicante (IRE) **The Affordable (2) Partnership**
50 **LONG RIVER DANCER**, 6, b g Bollin Eric—Artist's Muse (USA) **Mrs L. E. Awdry**
51 **LOOKS FROZEN (IRE)**, 5, ch g Frozen Fire (GER)—Miss Beverley **Kevin Corcoran Aaron Pierce Chris Weare**
52 **LOUGH RYN (IRE)**, 7, br g Court Cave (IRE)—Media View (IRE) **Level Par Racing**
53 **MAGICAL THOMAS**, 7, ch g Dylan Thomas (IRE)—Magical Cliche (USA) **G. P. and Miss S. J. Hayes**
54 4, B g Universal (IRE)—Maori Legend **Mrs H. R. Cross**
55 **MASQUERADE BLING (IRE)**, 5, b m Approve—Mataji (IRE) **N Webb & P J Proudley**
56 **MASTER BURBIDGE**, 8, b g Pasternak—Silver Sequel **Dajam Ltd**
57 **MILKWOOD (IRE)**, 5, b g Dylan Thomas (IRE)—Tropical Lake (IRE) **Ms J. Bridel**
58 **MIND YOUR BACK (IRE)**, 6, b g Getaway (GER)—Local Hall (IRE) **Mr & Mrs Paul & Clare Rooney**
59 **MISS JEANNE MOON (IRE)**, 5, b m Getaway (GER)—Moon Approach (IRE) **Mrs H. R. Cross & Mrs S. A. Keys**
60 **MISS MOLLY MAE (IRE)**, 7, b m Getaway (GER)—Miss Mary Mac (IRE) **H A Marks Ltd**
61 **MOAYADD (USA)**, 7, b g Street Cry (IRE)—Aryaamm (IRE) **Mr P & Mrs K E Malcolm**
62 **MOLLIANA**, 4, b f Olden Times—The Screamer (IRE) **Dajam Ltd**
63 **MOLLY CAREW**, 7, b m Midnight Legend—Moyliscar **Mrs H. R. Cross & Mrs S. A. Keys**
64 **MOONLIGHT CAMP (GER)**, 5, br g Kamsin—Moonlight Symphony (GER) **Quantum Leap Racing I**
65 **MORNING SEQUEL**, 6, b m Revoque (IRE)—Silver Sequel **Dajam Ltd**
66 **MOVING IN STYLE (IRE)**, 8, ch g Mountain High (IRE)—Good To Travel (IRE) **B. A. Derrick**
67 **MRS BURBIDGE**, 9, b m Pasternak—Twin Time **Dajam Ltd**
68 **MY BROTHER (IRE)**, 6, b g Roderic O'Connor (IRE)—Victory Peak **BG Racing Partnership**
69 **NEACHELLS BRIDGE (IRE)**, 7, ch g Getaway (GER)—Strawberry Lane (IRE) **Mr M. C. Creed**
70 **NIBLAWI (IRE)**, 7, b g Vale of York (IRE)—Finnmark **Mr A. G. Bloom**
71 **NOVIS ADVENTUS (IRE)**, 7, b g New Approach (IRE)—Tiffed (USA) **The General Asphalte Company Ltd**
72 **OSCARS BOSS**, 9, b g Norse Dancer (IRE)—Kimmeridge Bay **Mr J. Nicholson**

MR NEIL MULHOLLAND - Continued

73 **PANIA**, 5, b m Sakhee (USA)—Maori Legend **Mrs H. R. Cross**
74 **PARWICH LEES**, 7, ch g Pasternak—Barton Dante **Mrs J. Gerard-Pearse**
75 **PASSING OCEANS**, 5, gr g Passing Glance—Sherwood Rose (IRE) **Mr B. F. Mulholland**
76 **PENNY POET (IRE)**, 6, b m Intikhab (USA)—Mneme (FR) **The Boot Inn Partnership**
77 **PERCY POPS**, 5, ch g Getaway (GER)—Popsie Hall Birchenhough, Dewilde, Dod
78 **PHYSICAL POWER (IRE)**, 4, b f Power—Street Shaana (FR) **Stephen & Gloria Seymour**
79 **PRESENTING LUCINA (IRE)**, 7, b m Presenting—Lucina (GER) **The Boot Inn Partnership**
80 **PRETTYLITTLETHING (IRE)**, 9, b m Tajraasi (USA)—Cloncunny Girl (IRE) **N Webb & P J Proudley**
81 **PRINCESS T**, 4, gr f Aussie Rules (USA)—Fairy Slipper
82 **PUTTING GREEN**, 7, ch g Selkirk (USA)—Ryella (USA) **Mr A. G. Bloom**
83 **QUEEN'S MAGIC (IRE)**, 7, b m Kalanisi (IRE)—Black Queen (IRE) **Wincanton Race Club**
84 **RAINY DAY DYLAN (IRE)**, 8, br g Spadoun (FR)—Honeyed (IRE) **Burnham Plastering & Drylining Ltd**
85 **SEVEN CLANS (IRE)**, 7, b g Cape Cross (IRE)—Cherokee Rose (IRE) **The Affordable (2) Partnership**
86 **SHANTOU VILLAGE (IRE)**, 9, b g Shantou (USA)—Village Queen (IRE) **Mrs J. Gerard-Pearse**
87 **SIMPLY SIN (IRE)**, 4, b g Footstepsinthesand—Miss Sally (IRE) **Neil Mulholland Racing Ltd**
88 **SLEEP EASY**, 7, b g Rip Van Winkle (IRE)—Strictly Lambada **Mr A. G. Bloom**
89 **SOLIGHOSTER (FR)**, 7, ch g Loup Solitaire (USA)—Miss Martine (FR) **The Colony Stable LLC & Dajam Ltd**
90 **SOUPY SOUPS (IRE)**, 8, ch g Stowaway—Near Dunleer (IRE) **Equi ex Incertis Partners**
91 **TANGO BOY (IRE)**, 6, ch g Flemensfirth (USA)—Hello Kitty (IRE) **N Webb & P J Proudley**
92 **TEST RIDE (IRE)**, 5, b g Rip Van Winkle (IRE)—Easter Fairy (USA) **The Affordable (3) Partnership**
93 **THE DETAINEE**, 6, b g Aqlaam—Jakarta Jade (IRE) **Crowd Racing Partnership**
94 **THE DRUIDS NEPHEW (IRE)**, 12, b g King's Theatre (IRE)—Gifted **The Stonehenge Druids**
95 **THE TWISLER**, 7, b g Motivator—Panna **Mrs V. J. Hodsoll**
96 **THE WAY YOU DANCE (IRE)**, 7, b g Thewayyouare (USA)—Beautiful Dancer (IRE) **BG Racing Partnership**
97 **THE WICKET CHICKEN (IRE)**, 7, b m Milan—Soniadoir (IRE) **Dajam & Colm Hearne**
98 **THE YOUNG MASTER (IRE)**, 10, b g Echo of Light—Fine Frenzy (IRE) **Mike Burbidge & The Old Masters**
99 **VANCOUVER**, 7, ch g Generous (IRE)—All Told (IRE) **J. J. Maguire**
100 **VERY EXTRAVAGANT (IRE)**, 10, ch m Touch of Land (FR)—Raveleen Rose (IRE) **B. A. Derrick**
101 **VEXILLUM (IRE)**, 10, br g Mujadil (USA)—Common Cause **Mr J. Heaney**
102 **VIKING RUBY**, 6, ch m Sulamani (USA)—Viking Torch **Ms S. M. Exell**
103 **VINNIE ROUGE (IRE)**, 5, b g Vinnie Roe (IRE)—Bewildered (IRE) **Abbott & Bunch**
104 **VIS A VIS**, 5, b g Dansili—Pretty Face **Ashley Carr, Eismark & Packham**
105 **WALT (IRE)**, 8, b g King's Theatre (IRE)—Allee Sarthoise (FR) **Mr P. M. Simmonds**
106 **WHITE LILAC (IRE)**, 8, b m Westerner—Strawberry Lane (IRE) **Mr M. C. Creed**
107 **WILLYEGOLASSIEGO**, 6, br m Kheleyf (USA)—Kryena **Mr J. Hobbs**

THREE-YEAR-OLDS

108 **WITH PRIDE**, b c Pour Moi (IRE)—Aliena (IRE) **Four Winds Racing Partnership**

Other Owners: Mr T. J. Abbott, Mr C. Adams, Mrs L. Atwell, Miss R Bailey, Mr G. J. R. Barry, Mr P. Bowden, Mr P. Boyle, Mrs S. L. Boyle, Mrs W. S. Braithwaite, Mr S. W. Broughton, Sir M. F. Broughton, Mrs P. M. Bunch, Mr M. S. Burbidge, Mr A. Butlin, Mr P. A. Cafferty, Mr M. G. Cahill, Mr B. Carter, Mr S. Clegg, Colony Stable Llc, K J. Corcoran, Mrs A. C. Crofts, Mr C. G. Dando, Mrs S. De Wilde, Mrs P. I. Dod, Mr H. G. Doubtfire, Mr F. C. Durbin, Mr M. Edwards, Mr E. Eismark, Mr P. S. Frampton, J. L. Frampton, Mr P. Gray, Mr R. T. Greenhill, Mrs H. Harding, Mr G. P. Hayes, Miss S. J. Hayes, Mr C. Hearne, Mr D. R. Heeney, M. P. Hill, R. N. Jukes, Mrs M. A. Jukes, Mrs S. A. Keys, Mr D. L. Lacey, Mrs C. Lewis, Mr M. J. Lowry, Sir I. Magee, B. D. Makepeace, Mrs K. E. Malcolm, Mr W. P. L. Malcolm, Mr C. McKenna, Mrs S. J. McKenna, Mr R. J. Mear, Mrs E. A. Mear, Mr N. P. Mulholland, R. D. Nicholas, Mr E. M. O'Connor, Mr S. Packham, Mr A. T. Pierce, Mr P. J. Proudley, Mr P. A. Rooney, Mrs C. Rooney, Mr S. G. Seymour, Mrs G. P. Seymour, Mr A. J. Smith, Mrs D. J. Symes, Mr D. Tiernan, P. C. Tory, Mrs R. A. Turner, Mr R. F. Turner, Mr G. J. Villis, N. E. Webb.

Assistant Trainer: Mark Quinlan

Conditional: Philip Donovan, Harry Reed.

404
MR LAWRENCE MULLANEY, Malton
Postal: Raikes Farm, Great Habton, Malton, North Yorkshire, YO17 6RX
Contacts: PHONE (01653) 668595 MOBILE (07899) 902565
E-MAIL nicolamullaney@yahoo.co.uk

1 **BEVERLEY BULLET**, 6, b g Makfi—Don't Tell Mary (IRE) **Mrs Jean Stapleton & Rob Wilson**
2 **FIRST SARGEANT**, 9, gr g Dutch Art—Princess Raya **B Simpson, L Taylor & Partner**
3 **GORGEOUS GENERAL**, 4, ch g Captain Gerrard (IRE)—Gorgeous Goblin (IRE) **Mr S. Humphries**
4 **HARLEQUIN DANCER (IRE)**, 4, b f Zoffany (IRE)—April Green (FR) **Mr & Mrs G. Turnbull**

MR LAWRENCE MULLANEY - Continued

5 **LORD OF THE ROCK (IRE)**, 7, b g Rock of Gibraltar (IRE)—La Sylphide **Mr & Mrs G. Turnbull**
6 4, B g Mount Nelson—Neardown Beauty (IRE) **Mr & Mrs G. Turnbull**
7 **OUR LITTLE PONY**, 4, b f Bated Breath—Cracking Lass (IRE) **Mr J. R. Swift**
8 **POLISHED ARTICLE**, 4, b f Intense Focus (USA)—File And Paint (IRE) **Mr J Blackburn, Mr A Turton & Ptr**
9 **SWEET MARMALADE (IRE)**, 4, b f Duke of Marmalade (IRE)—Lady Chaparral **Mr & Mrs G. Turnbull**
10 **TATTING**, 10, ch g Street Cry (IRE)—Needlecraft (IRE) **The Usual Suspects**
11 **URBAN SPIRIT (IRE)**, 5, b g Born To Sea (IRE)—Rose of Mooncoin (IRE) **Mr & Mrs G. Turnbull**

THREE-YEAR-OLDS

12 **KYLLACHY WARRIOR (IRE)**, gr g Kyllachy—Silver Act (IRE) **Mr & Mrs G. Turnbull**
13 **OPERA KISS (IRE)**, ch f Slade Power (IRE)—Shamardal Phantom (IRE) **21st Century Racing**
14 **ROCK PARTY (IRE)**, ch f Society Rock (IRE)—Bacchanalia (IRE) **Mr J. R. Swift**

Other Owners: Mr J. N. Blackburn, Mrs B. Catterall, A. W. Catterall, M. J. Dyas, L. A. Mullaney, Mr B. Simpson, Mrs J. Stapleton, Mr L. Taylor, Mrs S. E. Turnbull, Mr G. Turnbull, Mr A. Turton, Mr R. J. Wilson.

---

405 MR MICHAEL MULLINEAUX, Tarporley
Postal: **Southley Farm, Alpraham, Tarporley, Cheshire, CW6 9JD**
Contacts: PHONE (01829) 261440 FAX (01829) 261440 MOBILE (07753) 650263
E-MAIL southlearacing@btinternet.com WEBSITE www.southleyfarm.co.uk

1 **ANTON DOLIN (IRE)**, 11, ch g Danehill Dancer (IRE)—Ski For Gold **S. A. Pritchard**
2 **BOB'S GIRL**, 4, b f Big Bad Bob (IRE)—Linda (FR) **The City & Provincial Partnership**
3 **DODGY BOB**, 6, b g Royal Applause—Rustam **M. Mullineaux**
4 **GEORGE EDWARD**, 5, b g Jeremy (USA)—Ancone (FR) **Mrs A. J. Swadling**
5 **HES OUR ROBIN (IRE)**, 9, b g Robin des Pres (FR)—Poly Sandstorm (IRE) **The Hon Mrs S. Pakenham**
6 **INVINCIBLE PURSUIT**, 4, b f Pastoral Pursuits—Fettuccine (IRE) **We Enjoy Racing Club**
7 **JACKSONFIVE**, 7, ch g Firebreak—Fitolini **Mr O. D. Knight**
8 **KEEM BAY**, 5, b m Multiplex—Copsehill Girl (IRE) **M. Mullineaux**
9 **MINTY JONES**, 10, b g Primo Valentino (IRE)—Reveur **P. Clacher**
10 **NO FRONTIER (IRE)**, 5, ch m Sans Frontieres (IRE)—County Gate (IRE)
11 **PEACHEY CARNEHAN**, 5, ch g Foxwedge (AUS)—Zubova **Mr K. Jones**
12 **POOR DUKE (IRE)**, 9, b g Bachelor Duke (USA)—Graze On Too (IRE) **M. Mullineaux**
13 **ROCK WARBLER (IRE)**, 6, ch g Raven's Pass (USA)—Rare Tern (IRE) **Mr R. A. Royle**
14 **SECRETINTHEPARK**, 9, ch g Sakhee's Secret—Lark In The Park (IRE) **Mia Racing**
15 **SOMEWHERE SECRET**, 5, ch g Sakhee's Secret—Lark In The Park (IRE) **Mia Racing**
16 **TEEPEE TIME**, 6, b m Compton Place—Deora De **Mr G. Cornes**
17 **VERY FIRST BLADE**, 10, b g Needwood Blade—Dispol Verity **Mr G. McCarthy**
18 **YALLA HABIBTI**, 6, b m Kayf Tara—Majeeda (IRE) **Mrs A. J. Swadling**

Other Owners: Mr S. W. Barrow, S. R. Hope, Mr S. Laffan, Mrs A. Milburn, M. A. Tickle, A. Tickle, Mrs I. M. Tickle.

Assistant Trainers: Stuart Ross, Susan Mullineaux

Amateur: Miss M. J. L. Mullineaux.

---

406 MR SEAMUS MULLINS, Amesbury
Postal: **Wilsford Stables, Wilsford-Cum-Lake, Amesbury, Salisbury, Wiltshire, SP4 7BL**
Contacts: PHONE/FAX (01980) 626344 MOBILE (07702) 559634
E-MAIL info@jwmullins.co.uk WEBSITE www.seamusmullins.co.uk

1 6, B g Scorpion (IRE)—An Bothar Ard (IRE) **Andrew Cocks & Tara Johnson**
2 **ARTHINGTON**, 6, b g Haafhd—Pequenita **Mr C. J. Baldwin**
3 **BLACKDOWN HILLS**, 9, b m Presenting—Lady Prunella (IRE) **Mrs P. de W. Johnson**
4 **BONDS CONQUEST**, 10, ch g Monsieur Bond (IRE)—Another Conquest **F. G. Matthews**
5 **CAP HORNER (FR)**, 7, gr g Apsis—Rapsodie Sea (FR) **Mr M. Adams**
6 **CHESTERFIELD**, 9, ch g Pivotal—Antique (IRE) **The Rumble Racing Club**
7 **CONFEY (IRE)**, 5, b m Morozov (USA)—Barbereilla (IRE) **J. W. Mullins**
8 **EN COEUR (FR)**, 5, b g Kap Rock (FR)—Fairyleap (FR) **Woodford Valley Racing**
9 **FENLONS COURT (IRE)**, 7, b g Court Cave—Classic Note (IRE) **Mrs D. H. Potter**
10 **FURTHER NORTH (FR)**, 5, ch g Muhtathir—Shamah **Mrs A. Leftley**
11 **GIVEN NAME**, 4, b g Nathaniel (IRE)—Poly Pomona **S Mullins Racing Club**

MR SEAMUS MULLINS - Continued

12 GRANITIC (IRE), 6, b g Court Cave (IRE)—Like A Miller (IRE) **Dr & Mrs John Millar**
13 HAPPY ENDING (IRE), 4, b f Big Bad Bob (IRE)—Heroic Performer (IRE) **J. W. Mullins**
14 HARDTOROCK (IRE), 10, b g Mountain High (IRE)—Permissal (IRE) **Mr N. A. Eggleton**
15 I SEE YOU WELL (FR), 6, b g Air Chief Marshal (IRE)—Bonne Mere (FR) **A. A. Goodman**
16 INSPIREUS (IRE), 6, b g Scorpion (IRE)—Miniconjou (IRE) **Geoff Barnett & Brian Edgeley**
17 JARLATH, 8, b g Norse Dancer (IRE)—Blue Lullaby (IRE) **Phoenix Bloodstock**
18 JUBILYMPICS, 7, b m Kapgarde (FR)—Pepite de Soleil (FR) **Caloona Racing**
19 KASTANI BEACH (IRE), 13, br g Alderbrook—Atomic View (IRE) **Seamus Mullins & Philippa Downing**
20 KENTFORD HEIRESS, 9, b m Midnight Legend—Kentford Duchess **D. I. Bare**
21 KENTFORD MALLARD, 6, b m Sulamani (IRE)—Kentford Grebe **D. I. Bare**
22 LANDIN (GER), 6, b g Sir Percy—Lupita (GER) **Four Candles Partnership**
23 LYN'S SECRET (IRE), 4, ch f Sakhee's Secret—Blase Chevalier (IRE) **Mr C. Wilson**
24 MAEBH (IRE), 5, b m Doyen (IRE)—South Queen Lady (IRE) **The Up The Glens Partnership**
25 MARATT (FR), 6, gr g Martaline—Lavi (FR) **S Mullins Racing Club**
26 MICQUUS (IRE), 10, b g High Chaparral (USA)—My Potters (USA) **Mrs A. Leftley**
27 MOGESTIC (IRE), 10, b g Morozov (USA)—Crosschild (IRE) **Mrs J. C. Scorgie**
28 MORODER (IRE), 5, b g Morozov (USA)—Another Tonto (IRE) **Andrew Cocks & Tara Johnson**
29 NELSON'S TOUCH, 6, gr g Mount Nelson—Lady Friend **Mrs P de W Johnson & Mr John M Cole**
30 OBORNE LADY (IRE), 6, b m Watar (IRE)—Lady Shackleton (IRE) **Simon & Christine Prout**
31 OFFICERNISI (IRE), 6, b g Kalanisi (IRE)—Some Say (IRE) **Andrew Cocks & Tara Johnson**
32 PARDON ME, 6, ch m Tobougg (IRE)—Andromache **J. T. Brown**
33 PASSING DREAM, 6, b m Passing Glance—Violet's Walk **Kingsbere Racing**
34 PLANTAGENET, 7, b g Midnight Legend—Marsh Court **Mrs P. de W. Johnson**
35 PLAYA BLANCA (IRE), 4, b g Zoffany (IRE)—Aiming Upwards **J. W. Mullins**
36 ROMANOR, 5, b g Holy Roman Emperor (IRE)—Salinia (IRE) **The Rumble Racing Club**
37 ROYSTORY (IRE), 5, b g Thousand Words—Chase A Dream (IRE) **J. W. Mullins**
38 SHE'S GINA (GER), 6, b m It's Gino (GER)—Song of Night (GER) **Four Candles Partnership**
39 TARA NIECE, 6, b m Kayf Tara—Pepite de Soleil (FR) **Caloona Racing**
40 TARKS HILL, 5, b m Brian Boru—Risky May **J. W. Mullins**
41 THE RAVEN'S RETURN, 6, b g Scorpion (IRE)—Mimis Bonnet (FR) **The Rumble Racing Club**
42 WESTERBEE (IRE), 8, b m Westerner—Pass The Honey (IRE) **Roger & Rachel Jowett**
43 WESTERBERRY (IRE), 7, b m Westerner—Casiana (GER) **J. W. Mullins**

THREE-YEAR-OLDS

44 FYODOR, b c Dunaden (FR)—Sir Kyffin's Folly **Mrs A. Leftley**
45 MRS MEADER, b f Cityscape—Bavarica **Nj Bloodstock**
46 THE PINK'N, gr g Dunaden (FR)—Lady Friend **Mrs P. de W. Johnson**
47 UNIVERSAL SONG, ch f Universal (IRE)—Song of The Desert **D. Sutherland**

Other Owners: P. R. Attwater, Mr G. Barnett, Mr N. Child, Mr A. P. Cocks, Mr J. M. Cole, Miss P. M. Downing, B. R. Edgeley, Mr D. J. Erwin, Mr P. R. Greeves, Mr R. Hall, Mr A. K. Horsman, Miss T. Johnson, Mr N. J. Johnston, Mrs R. A. Jowett, Dr R. Jowett, Mr K. G. Kerley, Mrs J. D. Millar, Dr J. W. Millar, J. D. Oakey, Mrs C. A. Prout, Mr S. P. Prout, Mr J. C. Saunders, Mr R. J. Stammers, Miss R. Toppin.

Assistant Trainer: Paul Attwater

Jockey (NH): Kevin Jones. **Conditional:** Jeremiah McGrath. **Amateur:** Mr Daniel Sansom.

MR WILLIE MULLINS, Carlow

Postal: **Closutton, Bagenalstown, Co. Carlow, Ireland**
Contacts: **PHONE** (00353) 5997 21786 **FAX** (00353) 5997 22709 **MOBILE** (00353) 8725 64940
E-MAIL wpmullins@eircom.net **WEBSITE** www.wpmullins.com

1 ABBYSSIAL (IRE), 9, ch g Beneficial—Mega d'estruval (FR) **Mrs Violet O'Leary**
2 ACAPELLA BOURGEOIS (FR), 9, ch g Network (GER)—Jasmine (FR) **Slaneyville Syndicate**
3 AL BOUM PHOTO (FR), 7, b g Buck's Boum (FR)—Al Gane (FR) **Mrs M. Donnelly**
4 ALELCHI INOIS (FR), 11, b g Night Tango (GER)—Witness Gama (FR) **Mrs M. McMahon**
5 ALLAHO (FR), 5, b g No Risk At All (FR)—Idaho Falls (FR) **Cheveley Park Stud**
6 ALLBLAK DES PLACES (FR), 7, b br g Full of Gold (FR)—Amiraute (FR) **George Creighton**
7 ANDALUSA (FR), 4, gr f Martaline—Cadix (FR) **Lansdowne Partnership**
8 ANNAMIX (FR), 6, gr g Martaline—Tashtiyana (IRE) **Mrs S Ricci**
9 ANTEY (GER), 6, b g Lord of England (GER)—Achinora **Mrs S. Ricci**
10 AUGUSTIN (FR), 9, gr g Martaline—Lili Bleue (FR) **Luke McMahon**
11 BACARDYS (FR), 8, b br g Coastal Path—Oasice (FR) **Shanakiel Racing Syndicate**

MR WILLIE MULLINS - Continued

12 **BACHASSON (FR)**, 8, gr g Voix du Nord (FR)—Belledonne (FR) **Edward O'Connell**
13 **BALLYCASEY (IRE)**, 12, gr g Presenting—Pink Mist (IRE) **Mrs S. Ricci**
14 **BALLYWARD (IRE)**, 7, b g Flemensfirth (USA)—Ifyoucouldseemenow (IRE) **Andrea & Graham Wylie**
15 **BAMAKO MORIVIERE (FR)**, 8, b g Califet (FR)—Halladine (FR) **Mrs S. Ricci**
16 **BAPAUME (FR)**, 6, b g Turtle Bowl (FR)—Brouhaha (FR) **Mrs S. Ricci**
17 **BELLOW MOME (FR)**, 8, b g Honolulu (IRE)—Oll Mighty Fellow (FR) **Mrs Audrey Turley**
18 **BELLSHILL (IRE)**, 9, b g King's Theatre (IRE)—Fairy Native (IRE) **Andrea & Graham Wylie**
19 **BEN BUTTON (IRE)**, 9, b g Double Eclipse (IRE)—Lady Coldunell **Martin McHale**
20 **BENIE DES DIEUX (FR)**, 8, b m Great Pretender (IRE)—Cana (FR) **Mrs S. Ricci**
21 **BILLAWAY (IRE)**, 7, b g Well Chosen—Taipans Girl (IRE) **J Turner**
22 **BLACK HERCULES (IRE)**, 10, b g Heron Island (IRE)—Annalecky (IRE) **Andrea Wylie**
23 **BLACKBOW (IRE)**, 6, b g Stowaway—Rinnce Moll (IRE) **Roaringwater Syndicate**
24 **BLAZER (FR)**, 8, ch g Network (GER)—Juppelongue (FR) **J. P. McManus**
25 **BLAZING EMILY (IRE)**, 5, b m Presenting—Blazing Tempo (IRE) **Kenneth Alexander**
26 **BLEU BERRY (FR)**, 8, b g Special Kaldoun (IRE)—Somosierra (FR) **Mrs M. McMahon**
27 **BONBON AU MIEL (FR)**, 8, b g Khalkevi (IRE)—Friandise II (FR) **Andrea & Graham Wylie**
28 **BRAHMA BULL (FR)**, 8, ch g Presenting—Oligarch Society (FR) **Mrs S. Ricci**
29 **BRONAGH'S BELLE (IRE)**, 4, b f High Chaparral (IRE)—South Atlantic (USA) **Sean Sweeney**
30 **BUCK'S BILLIONAIRE (FR)**, 6, ch g Kapgarde (FR)—Buck's (FR) **Mrs J M Mullins**
31 **BUILDMEUPBUTTERCUP**, 5, ch m Sixties Icon—Eastern Paramour (IRE) **J. Turner**
32 **BUNK OFF EARLY (IRE)**, 7, ro g Zebedee—Ctesiphon (USA) **Supreme Horse Racing Club**
33 **BURROWS SAINT (FR)**, 6, b g Saint des Saints—La Bombonera (FR) **Mrs S. Ricci**
34 **C'EST JERSEY (FR)**, 7, b g Protektor (GER)—Myrtille Jersey (FR) **Simon Munir & Isaac Souede**
35 **CADMIUM (FR)**, 7, b g Early March—Mirquille (FR) **Supreme Horse Racing Club**
36 **CAMELIA DE COTTE (FR)**, 7, br m Laveron—Traviata Valtat (FR) **Mrs S. Ricci**
37 **CAREFULLY SELECTED (IRE)**, 7, b g Well Chosen—Knockamullen Girl (IRE) **Miss M. A. Masterson**
38 **CASTLE NORTH (IRE)**, 7, b g Stowaway—Fitanga (IRE) **Mrs Rose Boyd**
39 **CASTLEBAWN WEST (IRE)**, 6, b g Westerner—Cooksgrove Lady (IRE) **Mrs Rose Boyd Partnership**
40 **CHAMBORD DU LYS (FR)**, 7, b m Great Pretender (IRE)—
Pot Jolie (FR) **Supreme Horse Racing Club/Brett T.Graham**
41 **CILAOS EMERY (FR)**, 7, b g Califet (FR)—Queissa (FR) **Luke McMahon**
42 **CLITANDRE (FR)**, 7, b g Zambezi Sun—Where Is My Gold (FR) **Supreme Horse Racing Club & Kenneth Sharp**
43 **COLREEVY (IRE)**, 6, b m Flemensfirth (USA)—Poetics Girl (IRE) **Mrs N. Flynn**
44 **COME TO ME (FR)**, 7, b g Spanish Moon—Hasta Manana (FR) **Mrs M. Masterson**
45 **CONCERTISTA (FR)**, 5, ch m Nathaniel (IRE)—Zagzig **Simon Munir & Isaac Souede Partnership**
46 **CONTINGENCY (FR)**, 6, b m Champs Elysees—Cyclone Connie **Bowes Lodge Stables Partnership**
47 **COQUIN MANS (FR)**, 7, b br g Fragrant Mix (IRE)—Quissisia Mans (FR) **George Creighton**
48 **CRACK MOME (FR)**, 7, ch g Spanish Moon—Peche Mome (FR) **Andrea Wylie**
49 **CRACK TIEPY (FR)**, 7, gr m Voix du Nord (FR)—Naltiepy (FR) **Mrs S. Ricci**
50 **CUT THE MUSTARD (FR)**, 7, br m Al Namix (FR)—Tadorna (FR) **Sullivan Bloodstock Limited**
51 **DANDY MAG (FR)**, 6, b g Special Kaldoun (IRE)—Naiade Mag (FR) **G Mercer/D Mercer/Mrs Caren Walsh**
52 **DEAL D'ESTRUVAL (FR)**, 6, b g Balko (FR)—Option d'estruval (FR) **Mrs S. Ricci**
53 **DEFY DE MEE (FR)**, 6, b g Country Reel (USA)—Koeur de Mee (FR) **Mrs J. Donnelly**
54 **DENTO DES OBEAUX (FR)**, 6, gr g Balko (FR)—Quenta des Obeaux (FR) **Sullivan Bloodstock Limited**
55 **DIAMOND HILL (IRE)**, 6, b m Beat Hollow—Sixhills (FR) **Mrs A F Mee Partnership**
56 **DIONYSIS (FR)**, 6, ch g Lucarno (USA)—Oasice (FR) **Shanakiel Racing Syndicate**
57 **DOLCIANO DICI (FR)**, 6, b g Assessor (IRE)—Louve Rina (FR) **Slaneyville Syndicate**
58 **DONT HESITATE (FR)**, 6, b m Diamond Boy (FR)—Quibble (FR) **Sullivan Bloodstock Limited**
59 **DORRELLS PIERJI (FR)**, 6, br g Coastal Path—Playa Pierji (FR) **Sullivan Bloodstock Limited**
60 **DOUVAN (FR)**, 9, b g Walk In The Park (IRE)—Star Face (FR) **Mrs S. Ricci**
61 **DRACONIEN (FR)**, 6, br g Linda's Lad—Holding (FR) **Clipper Logistics Group Limited**
62 **DREAMTIDE (FR)**, 5, b m Champs Elysees—Moraine **Sullivan Bloodstock Limited**
63 **DUC DES GENIEVRES (FR)**, 6, gr g Buck's Boum (FR)—Lobelie (FR) **Sullivan Bloodstock Limited**
64 **EASY GAME (FR)**, 5, b g Barastraight—Rule of The Game (FR) **Wicklow Bloodstock (Ireland) Ltd**
65 **ECLAT DES MOTTES (FR)**, 5, b g Poliglote—Sun des Mottes (FR) **Mrs S Ricci**
66 **EGLANTINE DU SEUIL (FR)**, 5, b m Saddler Maker (IRE)—Rixia du Seuil (FR) **Sullivan Bloodstock Limited**
67 **EILEEN O (IRE)**, 7, b m Court Cave (IRE)—Downtown Train (IRE) **Supreme Horse Racing Club**
68 **EOLINE JOLIE (FR)**, 5, b m No Risk At All (FR)—Jolie Catty (FR) **Sullivan Bloodstock Limited**
69 **EPICURIS (FR)**, 7, b g Rail Link—Argumentative **Mrs S. Ricci**
70 **EPSWELL (FR)**, 5, b g Coastal Path—Prestelle (FR) **Mrs Audrey Turley**
71 **EXCHANGE RATE (GER)**, 7, b g Monsun (GER)—Erytheis (USA) **Mrs A. F. Mee**
72 **FABULOUS SAGA (FR)**, 7, b g Saint des Saints—Fabalina (FR) **Sullivan Bloodstock Limited**
73 **FACE THE FACTS (FR)**, 5, ch g Nathaniel (IRE)—Aricia (IRE) **Andrea & Graham Wylie**
74 **FARID (FR)**, 4, b g Diamond Boy (FR)—Querrana de Sivola (FR) **John P. McManus**
75 **FASOLA TIDO (IRE)**, 5, b m Flemensfirth (USA)—High Ace (IRE) **Blue Blood Racing Club**

MR WILLIE MULLINS - Continued

76 **FAST BUCK (FR)**, 5, br g Kendargent (FR)—Juvenil Delinquent (USA) **Sullivan Bloodstock Limited**
77 **FAUGHEEN (IRE)**, 11, b g Germany (USA)—Miss Pickering (IRE) **Mrs S. Ricci**
78 **FENTA DES OBEAUX (FR)**, 4, b f Denham Red (FR)—Quenta des Obeaux (FR) **Jeremy Hancock Partnership**
79 **FOOTPAD (FR)**, 7, b g Creachadoir (IRE)—Willamina (IRE) **Mr Simon Munir**
80 **FRANCIN (FR)**, 6, b g Air Chief Marshal (IRE)—Fulgence (FR) **Mrs S. Ricci**
81 **GENERAL COUNSEL (IRE)**, 6, b g Shantou (USA)—Josephine Cullen (IRE) **Clipper Logistics Group Limited**
82 **GETABIRD (IRE)**, 7, b g Getaway (GER)—Fern Bird (IRE) **Mrs S. Ricci**
83 **GETAREASON (IRE)**, 6, ch g Getaway (GER)—Simple Reason (IRE) **Sullivan Bloodstock Limited**
84 **GETAWAY GORGEOUS (IRE)**, 5, b m Getaway (GER)—Impudent (IRE) **Whitegrass Getaway Syndicate**
85 **GOLAZO (IRE)**, 6, b g Beat Hollow—Compelled (IRE) **David Manasseh**
86 **GOLDEN SPREAD**, 6, b g Duke of Marmalade (IRE)—Purely By Chance **Supreme Horse Racing Club**
87 **GOOD THYNE TARA**, 9, b br m Kayf Tara—Good Thyne Mary (IRE) **N. G. King**
88 **GREAT FIELD (FR)**, 8, b g Great Pretender (GER)—Eaton Lass (IRE) **John P. McManus**
89 **HARRIE (FR)**, 7, ch g Le Havre (IRE)—Honorable Love **Supreme Horse Racing Club Partnership**
90 **HEY LITTLE BOY (GER)**, 6, b g Adlerflug (GER)—Homing Instinct **PM Racing Syndicate**
91 **HOT BEAT (IRE)**, 7, b g Dylan Thomas (IRE)—Hungry Heart **C. V. Wentworth**
92 **IFYOUCATCHMENOW (IRE)**, 6, b m Westerner—Ifyoucouldseemenow (IRE) **Coldunell Limited**
93 **INVITATION ONLY (IRE)**, 8, b g Flemensfirth (USA)—Norabelle (FR) **Andrea Wylie**
94 **IRISH LASS (IRE)**, 6, b m Getaway (GER)—Screaming Witness (IRE) **Bowes Lodge Stables Partnership**
95 **ISLEOFHOPENDREAMS**, 12, b g Flemensfirth (USA)—Cool Island (IRE) **Sean Sweeney**
96 **JANIDIL (FR)**, 5, b g Indian Daffodil (IRE)—Janidouce (FR) **John P. McManus**
97 **KALANISI OG (IRE)**, 5, br m Kalanisi (IRE)—High Accord (IRE) **Lions Mouth Racing Club**
98 **KARL DER GROSSE (GER)**, 5, gr g Jukebox Jury (IRE)—Karsawina (GER) **Mrs S Ricci**
99 **KEMBOY (FR)**, 7, b g Voix du Nord (FR)—Vitora (FR) **Supreme Horse Racing Club**
100 **KESSELRING**, 6, ch g New Approach (IRE)—Anna Oleanda (IRE) **Mrs S Ricci**
101 **KILLULTAGH VIC (IRE)**, 10, b g Old Vic—Killultagh Dawn (IRE) **Mrs Rose Boyd**
102 **KLASSICAL DREAM (FR)**, 5, b g Dream Well (FR)—Klassical Way (FR) **Mrs Janne Coleman**
103 **KOLUMBUS (IRE)**, 8, b g Robin des Champs (FR)—Saabga (USA) **Sean Sweeney**
104 **KOSHARI (FR)**, 7, br g Walk In The Park (IRE)—Honor May (FR) **Mrs S. Ricci**
105 **LAGOSTOVEGAS (IRE)**, 7, b m Footstepsinthesand—Reine de Coeur (IRE) **Mr J. Donohue**
106 **LAURINA (FR)**, 6, b m Spanish Moon (USA)—Lamboghina (GER) **Sullivan Bloodstock Limited**
107 **LAWS OF SPIN (IRE)**, 6, b h Lawman (FR)—Spinning Well (IRE) **B. Hourihane**
108 **LEGAL SPIN (IRE)**, 4, b g Lawman (FR)—Spinning Well (IRE) **B Hourihane Partnership**
109 **LIMINI (IRE)**, 8, ch m Peintre Celebre (USA)—Her Grace (IRE) **Mrs S. Ricci**
110 **LISTEN DEAR (IRE)**, 9, b m Robin des Champs (FR)—Crescendor (FR) **Supreme Horse Racing Club**
111 **LITTLE NUGGET (IRE)**, 6, b m Daylami (IRE)—Grangeclare Gold (IRE) **Sunny Day Syndicate**
112 **LIVELOVELAUGH (IRE)**, 9, b g Beneficial—Another Evening (IRE) **Mrs S. Ricci**
113 **LOW SUN**, 6, b g Champs Elysees—Winter Solstice **Mrs S. Ricci**
114 **MAKITORIX (FR)**, 6, gr g Makfi—Goldamix (IRE) **Twenty Seven Black Partnership**
115 **MAX DYNAMITE (FR)**, 9, b h Great Journey (JPN)—Mascara (GER) **Mrs S. Ricci**
116 **MAZE RUNNER (IRE)**, 4, b g Authorized (IRE)—Alice Rose (IRE) **Mrs J. M. Mullins**
117 **MELON**, 7, ch g Medicean—Night Teeny **Mrs J. Donnelly**
118 **MIN (FR)**, 8, b g Walk In The Park (IRE)—Phemyka (FR) **Mrs S. Ricci**
119 **MINELLA BEAU (IRE)**, 8, br g King's Theatre (IRE)—Ney Will (FR) **Mrs A. F. Mee Partnership**
120 **MINELLA ENCORE (IRE)**, 7, b g King's Theatre (IRE)—Stashedaway (IRE) **David Bobbett**
121 **MISS CHEVIOUS GIRL (IRE)**, 7, br m Presenting—High Ace (IRE) **Blue Blood Racing Club**
122 **MISS SHOE CITY (FR)**, 7, b m Saddler Maker (IRE)—Miss Ecosse (FR) **Leo McArdle**
123 **MISTER BLUE SKY (IRE)**, 5, gr g Royal Applause—Mujdeya **Shanakiel Racing Syndicate**
124 **MIXMOON (FR)**, 4, gr f Al Namix (FR)—October Moon (FR) **John P. McManus**
125 **MR ADJUDICATOR**, 5, b g Camacho—Attlongglast **David Bobbett**
126 **MSASSA (FR)**, 5, b g Sholokhov (IRE)—Ramina (GER) **Sullivan Bloodstock Limited**
127 **MY SISTER SARAH (IRE)**, 5, ch m Martaline—Reste Ren Or (IRE) **Barnane Stud**
128 **NESSUN DORMA (IRE)**, 6, b g Canford Cliffs (IRE)—Idle Chatter (IRE) **N. D. Kennelly Partnership**
129 **NEXT DESTINATION (IRE)**, 7, b g Dubai Destination (USA)—Liss Alainn (IRE) **Malcolm C. Denmark**
130 **ORION D'AUBRELLE (FR)**, 6, b g Saint des Saints (FR)—Erbalunga (FR) **Multi Nationals Syndicate**
131 **PAIROFBROWNEYES (IRE)**, 10, b g Luso—Frankly Native (IRE) **Fibbage Syndicate**
132 **PANTHER SOUL (FR)**, 5, gr g Famous Name—Raheefa's Mix (IRE) **Mrs J Donnelly**
133 **PENCREEK (FR)**, 6, ch g Konig Shuffle (GER)—Couture Fleurs (FR) **Mrs G. Worcester**
134 **PENHILL**, 8, b g Mount Nelson—Serrenia (IRE) **Anthony Bloom**
135 **PLEASANT COMPANY (IRE)**, 11, b g Presenting—Katie Flame (IRE) **Malcolm C. Denmark**
136 **POKER D'AINAY (FR)**, 5, ch g No Risk At All (FR)—Guendoline d'ainay (FR) **J. R. Brennan**
137 **POLIDAM (FR)**, 10, b g Trempolino (USA)—Eladame (FR) **Mr Simon Munir/Mr Isaac Souede**
138 **POLY ROCK (FR)**, 8, b g Policy Maker (IRE)—Gastinaise (FR) **Supreme House Racing Club**
139 **PONT AVAL (FR)**, 6, b m Soldier of Fortune (IRE)—Panzella (FR) **N G King**
140 **PONT AVEN (IRE)**, 6, b g Doyen (IRE)—Behlaya (IRE) **Roderick Ryan Partnership**

MR WILLIE MULLINS - Continued

141 **PRAVALAGUNA (FR)**, 7, b m Great Pretender (IRE)—Arnette (FR) **Bruton Street IV Partnership**
142 **PRINCE D'AUBRELLE (FR)**, 9, ch g Malinas (GER)—La Star (FR) **Allan McLuckie**
143 **PYLONTHEPRESSURE (IRE)**, 9, b g Darsi (FR)—Minnie O'grady (IRE) **Mrs S. Ricci**
144 **QUEENS BOULEVARD**, 6, br m Fair Mix (IRE)—Bellino Spirit (FR) **Paul McKeon**
145 **QUICK GRABIM (IRE)**, 7, b g Oscar (IRE)—Top Her Up (IRE) **Mrs G. Worcester**
146 **RATHVINDEN (IRE)**, 11, b g Heron Island (IRE)—Peggy Cullen (IRE) **R. A. Bartlett**
147 **REAL STEEL (FR)**, 6, gr g Loup Breton (IRE)—Kalimina (FR) **Sullivan Bloodstock Limited**
148 **REBEL OG (IRE)**, 6, br m Presenting—Oscar Rebel (IRE) **Lions Mouth Racing Club**
149 **REDHOTFILLYPEPPERS (IRE)**, 7, ch m Robin des Champs (FR)—Mhuire Na Gale (IRE) **Coldunell Limited**
150 **RELEGATE (IRE)**, 6, b m Flemensfirth (USA)—Last of The Bunch **Paul McKeon**
151 **RIA D'ETEL (FR)**, 7, b m Martaline—Angesse (FR) **Simon Munir**
152 **RIO TREASURE (IRE)**, 9, b m Captain Rio—Killiney Treasure (IRE) **Luke McMahon**
153 **RIO VIVAS (FR)**, 7, b g Voix du Nord (FR)—Rio Amata (GER) **Sullivan Bloodstock Limited**
154 **RIVEN LIGHT (IRE)**, 7, b g Raven's Pass (USA)—Vivacity **Mrs S. Ricci**
155 **ROBIN DE CARLOW**, 6, br m Robin des Champs (FR)—
                                        La Reine de Riogh (IRE) **Supreme Horse Racing Club Partnership**
156 **ROBIN DES FORET (IRE)**, 9, br g Robin des Pres (FR)—Omyn Supreme (IRE) **Byerley Racing Syndicate**
157 **ROYAL ILLUSION (IRE)**, 7, b m King's Theatre (IRE)—Spirit Run (IRE) **Ballylinch Stud**
158 **ROYAL RENDEZVOUS (IRE)**, 7, b g King's Theatre (IRE)—Novacella (FR) **Dr S P Fitzgerald**
159 **SAGLAWY (FR)**, 5, b g Youmzain (IRE)—Spasha **Sullivan Bloodstock Limited**
160 **SALSARETTA (FR)**, 6, b m Kingsalsa (USA)—Kendoretta (FR) **Mrs S. Ricci**
161 **SANCTA SIMONA (FR)**, 6, b m Saddex—Desimona (GER) **John P. McManus**
162 **SAPPHIRE LADY (IRE)**, 7, b m Beneficial—Cloghoge Lady (IRE) **Anthony P. Butler**
163 **SATURNAS (FR)**, 8, b g Davidoff (GER)—Sayuri (GER) **Wicklow Bloodstock (Ireland) Ltd**
164 **SAYAR (IRE)**, 6, b g Azamour (IRE)—Seraya (FR) **Mrs Audrey Turley**
165 **SAYO**, 5, gr g Dalakhani (IRE)—Tiyi (FR) **Miss M A Masterson**
166 **SCAGLIETTI (IRE)**, 6, b m Beat Hollow—Cincuenta (IRE) **Michael F. Carroll Partnership**
167 **SCARPETA (FR)**, 6, b g Soldier of Fortune (IRE)—Sanada (IRE) **Thurloe Thoroughbreds Ireland Limited**
168 **SHANAKEY (IRE)**, 7, b m Shantou (USA)—Kaniskina (IRE) **J P M O'Connor**
169 **SHANESHILL (IRE)**, 10, b g King's Theatre (IRE)—Darabaka (IRE) **Andrea & Graham Wylie**
170 **SHANNING (FR)**, 6, b m Spanish Moon (USA)—Idaho Falls (FR) **Supreme Horse Racing Club/Brett T. Graham**
171 **SHARJAH (FR)**, 7, b g Doctor Dino (FR)—Saaryeh **Mrs S. Ricci**
172 **SHARPS CHOICE (FR)**, 6, ch g Montmartre (FR)—Behra (FR) **Supreme Horse Racing Club**
173 **SHOULDA LIED (IRE)**, 5, b g Henrythenavigator (USA)—
                                        Pray (IRE) **Supreme Horse Racing Club & Courtney L. Barr**
174 **SMALL FARM (IRE)**, 7, b g Westerner—Eastertide (IRE) **Sullivan Bloodstock Limited**
175 **SOME NECK (FR)**, 8, gr g Yeats (IRE)—Maternelle (FR) **Mrs S. Ricci**
176 **SOUTHERN NIGHTS (IRE)**, 6, b g Beat Hollow—Islandbane (IRE) **Miss M A Masterson**
177 **STAY HUMBLE (IRE)**, 6, b g Beat Hollow—Rosy de Cyborg (IRE) **Andrea & Graham Wylie**
178 **STONES AND ROSES (IRE)**, 5, b g Shantou (USA)—Compelled (IRE) **P. Reilly & C. Reilly**
179 **STORMY IRELAND (FR)**, 5, b m Motivator—Like A Storm (IRE) **Sullivan Bloodstock Limited**
180 **STRATUM**, 6, b g Dansili—Lunar Phase (IRE) **Anthony Bloom**
181 **SUINDA (IRE)**, 7, b m Mahler—Supreme Matriarch (IRE) **Luke McMahon**
182 **SWEET FLIGHT (GER)**, 6, b g Adlerflug (GER)—Sworn Pro (GER) **Supreme Horse Racing Club**
183 **THOMAS HOBSON**, 9, b g Halling (USA)—La Spezia (IRE) **Mrs S. Ricci**
184 **TORNADO FLYER (IRE)**, 6, b g Flemensfirth (USA)—Mucho Macabi (IRE) **TFP Partnership**
185 **TOTAL RECALL (IRE)**, 10, b g Westerner—Augest Weekend (IRE) **Slaneyville Syndicate**
186 **TRUE SELF (IRE)**, 6, b m Oscar (IRE)—Good Thought (IRE) **Three Mile House Partnership**
187 **TTEBBOB (IRE)**, 10, b g Milan—Our Dream (IRE) **David Bobbett**
188 **UN DE SCEAUX (FR)**, 11, b g Denham Red (FR)—Hotesse de Sceaux (FR) **E. O'Connell**
189 **UNDRESSED (FR)**, 11, b g Lost World (IRE)—Latitude (FR) **Sean Mac an Bhaird**
190 **UP FOR REVIEW (IRE)**, 10, br g Presenting—Coolsilver (IRE) **Andrea & Graham Wylie**
191 **URADEL (GER)**, 8, b g Kallisto (GER)—Unavita (GER) **Luke McMahon**
192 **URANO (FR)**, 11, b g Enrique—Neiland (FR) **Luke McMahon**
193 **VALLEY BREEZE (FR)**, 5, b g Sunday Break (JPN)—Valdemossa (FR) **Luke McMahon**
194 **VENT D'AUTOMNE (FR)**, 7, ch g Denham Red (FR)—Foret d'automne (FR) **Andrea & Graham Wylie**
195 **VOIX DES TIEP (FR)**, 7, b br g Voix du Nord (FR)—Tiepataxe (FR) **OMG II Partnership**
196 **VOIX DU REVE (FR)**, 7, br g Voix du Nord (FR)—Pommbelle (FR) **Andrea & Graham Wylie**
197 **WESTPORT LADY (FR)**, 6, b m Blue Bresil (FR)—Malandra **Cathal Hughes**
198 **WHISKEY SOUR (IRE)**, 6, b h Jeremy (USA)—Swizzle Stick (IRE) **Luke McMahon**
199 **WICKLOW BRAVE**, 10, b g Beat Hollow—Moraine **Wicklow Bloodstock Limited**
200 **YORKHILL (IRE)**, 9, ch g Presenting—Lightning Breeze (IRE) **Andrea Wylie**
201 **YUKON LIL**, 5, b m Flemensfirth (USA)—Dare To Doubt **Mrs John Magnier**

MR WILLIE MULLINS - Continued

THREE-YEAR-OLDS

202 MICRO MANAGE (IRE), ch c Rip Van Winkle (IRE)—Lillebonne (FR) **Mrs J M Mullins**

Other Owners: R. J. Brennan, Deauville Daze Partnership, Mr M. R. Dodd, Mr M. V. Hill, S. A. Kirk, Mr R. J. Whatford, Mr A. W. G. Wylie, Mrs A. Wylie.

408
MISS AMY MURPHY, Newmarket
Postal: **Southgate Stables, Hamilton Road, Newmarket, Suffolk, CB8 0WY**
Contacts: **PHONE (01638) 429033 MOBILE (07711) 992500**
E-MAIL info@amymurphyracing.com WEBSITE www.amymurphyracing.com

1 **AALIYA**, 4, b f Invincible Spirit (IRE)—Rappel **Saleh Al Homaizi & Imad Al Sagar**
2 **ANGEL'S WHISPER (IRE)**, 4, gr f Dark Angel (IRE)—Tasheyaat **Box Clever Display & Shepherd Global**
3 **APPROACHING MENACE**, 4, b f Cityscape—Candle **Gwyn & Samantha Powell**
4 **AVLOS (IRE)**, 4, b g Arcano (IRE)—Royal Blush **Charles Auld & Partner**
5 **BEAR VALLEY (IRE)**, 5, b g Manduro (GER)—Shane (GER) **Miss A. L. Murphy**
6 **BLESSED TO EMPRESS (IRE)**, 4, b f Holy Roman Emperor (IRE)—
Blessing Box **White Diamond Racing Partnership 1**
7 **CANFORD'S JOY (IRE)**, 4, b g Canford Cliffs (IRE)—Joyful (IRE) **Mr J. R. Dwyer**
8 5, B g Saint des Saints (FR)—Carole's Legacy **Mr P. Murphy**
9 **COLLATE**, 4, b f Oasis Dream—Homepage **Mr E. W. d. C. Tillett**
10 **DISCIPLE (IRE)**, 5, b g Fastnet Rock (AUS)—Gift From Heaven (IRE) **Miss A. L. Murphy**
11 **ENTERTAINING BEN**, 6, b g Equiano (FR)—Fatal Attraction **Amy Murphy Racing Club**
12 **ERISSIMUS MAXIMUS (FR)**, 5, b g Holy Roman Emperor (IRE)—Tegan (IRE) **Mr P. Venner**
13 **ESPRIT DE BAILEYS (FR)**, 7, b g Le Havre (IRE)—Lit (IRE) **G. R. Bailey Ltd (Baileys Horse Feeds)**
14 **HAWTHORN COTTAGE (IRE)**, 6, b m Gold Well—Miss Kilkeel (IRE) **Melbourne 10 Racing**
15 **JAMESSAINTPATRICK (IRE)**, 6, br g Stowaway—Cadia's Lady (IRE) **Melbourne 10 Racing**
16 **KALASHNIKOV (IRE)**, 6, br g Kalanisi (IRE)—Fairy Lane (IRE) **Mr P. Murphy**
17 **LAZARUS (IRE)**, 5, b g Zoffany (IRE)—Knysna (IRE) **Amy Murphy Racing Club**
18 **LOGAN ROCKS (IRE)**, 4, b g Yeats (IRE)—Countess Comet (IRE) **The Rann Family**
19 **MERCIAN KING (IRE)**, 8, b g Robin des Pres (FR)—Mariah Rollins (IRE) **The Thoroughbred Club II**
20 **MERCIAN PRINCE (IRE)**, 8, b g Midnight Legend—Bongo Fury (FR) **Mr P. Murphy**
21 **MOVIE STAR (GER)**, 4, b f Soldier Hollow—Mouette (GER) **Miss A. L. Murphy**
22 **NAPPING**, 6, b m Sleeping Indian—Vax Rapide **Eclipse Sports Racing Club**
23 **PEPPER STREET (IRE)**, 4, b f Born To Sea (IRE)—Mindy (IRE) **Hot Stuff Partnership**
24 **POTTERS SAPPHIRE**, 6, gr m Mayson—Privacy Order **Miss A. L. Murphy**
25 **PRIVATE MATTER**, 5, b g Mayson—Privacy Order **Miss A. L. Murphy**
26 **REALLY SUPER**, 5, b m Cacique (IRE)—Sensationally **White Diamond Racing Partnership 1**
27 **ROARING FURY (IRE)**, 5, br m Sholokhov (IRE)—Bongo Fury (FR) **Mr P. Murphy**
28 **ROCK ON BAILEYS**, 4, ch f Rock of Gibraltar (IRE)—Ring For Baileys **G. R. Bailey Ltd (Baileys Horse Feeds)**
29 **SANDKISSED (IRE)**, 4, b f Sir Prancealot (IRE)—Hapipi **Mr S. P. King**
30 **SEPRANI**, 5, b m Sepoy (AUS)—King's Guest (IRE) **Book 3 Partnership**
31 **SHES QUEEN (IRE)**, 4, b f Baltic King—Pepys Tillergirl (IRE) **Miss A. L. Murphy**
32 **TAKE IT DOWN UNDER**, 4, b g Oasis Dream—Roz
33 **THAQAFFA (IRE)**, 6, b g Kodiac—Incense **The Champagne Club**
34 **THE ACCOUNTANT**, 4, ch g Dylan Thomas (IRE)—Glorybe (GER) **The Rann Family**
35 **WELL SMITTEN**, 7, b g Gold Well—The Dark One (IRE) **Edwards & Flatt**
36 **ZAFAYAN (IRE)**, 8, b g Acclamation—Zafayra (IRE) **Ms J. A. French**

THREE-YEAR-OLDS

37 **AMOR KETHLEY**, b f Swiss Spirit—Nellie Ellis (IRE) **Miss A. L. Murphy**
38 **EUFEMIA**, ch f Dream Ahead (USA)—Shyrl **R S Hoskins & Partners**
39 **GEORGEARTHURHENRY**, b c Iffraaj—Mea Parvitas (IRE) **Glazing Refurbishment Limited**
40 **GREAT SHOUT (IRE)**, b f Kodiac—By Jupiter **Cherry and Whites**
41 **ISLAY MIST**, ch f Coach House—Amary (IRE) **Miss A. L. Murphy**
42 **JUST LATER**, b g Equiano (FR)—Lucky Legs (IRE) **Layezy Racing Owners Club**
43 **KAPONO**, b g Kuroshio (AUS)—Fair Maiden (JPN) **Mr S. M. Al Sabah**
44 **KENNOCHA (IRE)**, b f Kodiac—Of Course Darling **Dale, Knight, Darlington & Robson**
45 B c Le Havre (IRE)—Laguna Salada (IRE) **Mr J. Acheson**
46 **MINOGUE**, b f Mukhadram—Melbourne Memories **M. P. Coleman & R. J. Coleman**
47 **NEWSFLASH**, ch f Showcasing—Pivotal Bride **Nina Rajani & Partner**
48 **PHOENIX STAR (IRE)**, b c Alhebayeb (IRE)—Volcanic Lady (IRE) **Flying High Syndicate**

MISS AMY MURPHY - Continued

49 **POTTERS QUESTION,** ch g Cardinal—Scipmylo **Mrs J. May**
50 **THEGREATESTSHOWMAN,** ch g Equiano (FR)—Conversational (IRE) **Melbourne 10 Racing**
51 **UPONASTAR (IRE),** b f Zebedee—Eponastone (IRE) **Mr S. P. King**
52 **WOLF PRINCE (IRE),** b g Pour Moi (IRE)—Preach (IRE) **Mr B. Ryan-Beswick**

TWO-YEAR-OLDS

53 **BLACKBERRY JACK (IRE),** ch c 7/3 Sir Percy—Ms Grande Corniche (Pivotal) (32026) **The Twenty One Club**
54 B f 18/4 Dabirsim (FR)—Censure (FR) (Kendor (FR)) (35398) **Miss A. L. Murphy**
55 **IMPRESSION,** b f 18/2 Dutch Art—Past Forgetting (IRE) (Pivotal) **Mr S. A. Stuckey**
56 B br f 6/3 Pour Moi (IRE)—Incense (Unfuwain (USA)) (8427) **Miss A. L. Murphy**
57 B c 1/3 Hunter's Light (IRE)—Lady McKell (IRE) (Raven's Pass (USA)) (52000) **Daniel MacAuliffe & Anoj Don**
58 **LORD CHAPELFIELD,** b c 26/4 Delegator—Diamond Vanessa (IRE) (Distinctly North (USA))
59 **SMOKEY,** gr f 14/2 Outstrip—Lady Tabitha (IRE) (Tamayuz) (9000) **Saxtead Livestock Ltd**
60 **SWEET SIXTEEN (GER),** b f 1/4 Maxios—
Sugar Baby Love (GER) (Second Empire (IRE)) (12642) **Tweenhills Fillies**
61 **TEN THOUSAND STARS,** ch f 27/3 Toronado (IRE)—
Myriades d'etoiles (IRE) (Green Tune (USA)) (7000) **Saxtead Livestock Ltd**
62 **TROUSER THE CASH (IRE),** b f 3/3 Starspangledbanner (AUS)—
Bint Malyana (IRE) (Bahamian Bounty) (29498) **A & P Braithwaite**

Other Owners: Mr I. H. Al Sagar, Mr C. C. Auld, Mr I. J. Barratt, Mrs C. J. Barratt, Mr J. R. Best, Box Clever Display, Mrs P. J. Braithwaite, Mr A. W. Braithwaite, Mr S. J. Brown, Mr P. R. Burslem, Mr T. Castle, Mr R. J. Coleman, Mr M. P. Coleman, Mr A. C. Culumbarapitiyage Don, Mr C. E. Dale, Mr P. J. Darlington, Mrs K. D. Edwards, Mr D. R. Flatt, Mr I. J. Fowler, Mr M. Grant, Saleh Al Homaizi, Mr R. S. Hoskins, Mrs V. A. Knight, Mrs S. M. Langridge, Miss T. R. Lewis, Mr D. P. MacAuliffe, Mr D. Osullivan, Mrs A. Perkins, G. E. Powell, Mrs S. Powell, Miss N. K. Rajani, Mr G. P. D. Rann, Mrs L. E. Rann, Mr D. Redvers, Dr E. M. Robson, Mr J. P. Ryan, Shepherd Global Ltd, Mr M. Stanley, Mr S. Surridge, Mrs C. Wallace, White Diamond Racing Partnership.

---

409 MR MIKE MURPHY, Westoning

Postal: **Broadlands, Manor Park Stud, Westoning, Bedfordshire, MK45 5LA**
Contacts: PHONE (01525) 717305 FAX (01525) 717305 MOBILE (07770) 496103
E-MAIL mmurphy@globalnet.co.uk WEBSITE www.mikemurphyracing.com

1 **BAMO MC,** 5, gr g Hellvelyn—Soft Touch (IRE) **M&O Construction & Civil Engineering Ltd**
2 **DESERT FOX,** 5, b g Foxwedge (AUS)—Snow Moccasin (IRE) **Rogerson, Lemon, Cooper & Arlotte**
3 **JUST MAYBE,** 5, b g Mayson—Phantasmagoria **The Maysonettes**
4 **KELLINGTON KITTY (USA),** 4, b br f Kitten's Joy (USA)—
Keeping Watch (IRE) **Lemon, Papworth, Hazelwood & Sullivan**
5 **KODIAC EXPRESS (IRE),** 4, b f Kodiac—Excel Yourself (IRE) **The Kodi Bunch**
6 **LILY ASH (IRE),** 6, b m Lilbourne Lad (IRE)—Ashdali (IRE) **Ms A. D. Tibbett**
7 **MULZIM,** 5, b h Exceed And Excel (AUS)—Samaah (IRE) **Victoria Taylor & Family**
8 **OVERTRUMPED,** 4, b f Champs Elysees—Perfect Hand **Mr Borgatti & Mr Moir**
9 **RIO RONALDO (IRE),** 7, b g Footstepsinthesand—Flanders (IRE) **The Castaways**
10 **TITAN GODDESS,** 7, b m Equiano (FR)—Phoebe Woodstock (IRE) **Phoebe's Friends**
11 **WHISPERED KISS,** 6, b m Medicean—Desert Kiss **D.Ellison - B.Olkowicz - P.Speller**
12 **YAA MOUS,** 4, b f Farhh—Sweet Lilly **Ms A. D. Tibbett**
13 **YOUNG JOHN (IRE),** 6, b g Acclamation—Carpet Lady (IRE) **Murphy, Cooper & East**
14 **ZIANO,** 4, ch f Equiano (FR)—Zia (GER)

THREE-YEAR-OLDS

15 **A PLACE TO DREAM,** b g Compton Place—Phantasmagoria **Victoria Taylor & Family**
16 **DUSTY DAMSEL,** ch f Toronado (IRE)—Dusty Answer **The Calm Partnership**
17 **HAVANA SUNSET,** b g Havana Gold (IRE)—Sunset Kitty (USA) **The Sunsetters**
18 **LOUISIANA BEAT (IRE),** ch f Helmet (AUS)—Union City Blues (IRE) **Mr M. Murphy**
19 B f Rock of Gibraltar (IRE)—Samba Chryss (IRE)
20 **SUCH PROMISE,** b c Dansili—Much Promise **Rowsell, Basings & Wiltshire**

MR MIKE MURPHY - Continued

TWO-YEAR-OLDS

21 **BATTERSEA DUCHESS**, b f 10/2 Youmzain (IRE)—
    Duchessina (USA) (Henrythenavigator (USA)) (5000) **Mr Borgatti & Mr Moir**
22 B f 27/1 New Approach (IRE)—Esteemed Lady (IRE) (Mark of Esteem (IRE)) (80000)
23 B f 20/2 Cable Bay (IRE)—Excel Yourself (IRE) (Exceed And Excel (AUS)) (7619)
24 Bl f 18/4 Kyllachy—Love Your Looks (Iffraaj) (43000)
25 B c 26/1 Sea The Stars (IRE)—My Country (IRE) (Invincible Spirit (IRE)) (65000)
26 **PAISLEY'S PROMISE (IRE)**, ch f 13/3 Dandy Man (IRE)—Relinquished (Royal Applause) (9523)
27 **ROCKETEER**, b c 8/3 Equiano (FR)—Aalya (IRE) (Peintre Celebre (USA))
28 B c 13/3 Makfi—Samba Chryss (IRE) (Galileo (IRE))
29 **SILVER GRACE (IRE)**, gr f 19/3 Gutaifan (IRE)—
    Maybe Grace (IRE) (Hawk Wing (USA)) (20000) **Mr Borgatti & Mr Moir**
30 **SPACESUIT**, b c 6/5 Sea The Moon (GER)—Casaca (Medicean) (7500)

Other Owners: Basings & Wiltshire, Mr M. Borgatti, Mrs D. Ellison, Mr S. Moir, Mr B. Olkowicz, Mr B. Rogerson, J. L. Rowsell, Mrs P.S. Speller.

Assistant Trainer: Michael Keady

---

410   **MR OLLY MURPHY, Wilmcote**
Postal: **Warren Chase Stables, Wilmcote, Stratford-Upon-Avon, Warwickshire, CV37 9XG**
Contacts: **PHONE (01789) 613347**
E-MAIL office@ollymurphyracing.com WEBSITE www.ollymurphyracing.com

1 **A PERFECT GIFT (IRE)**, 5, br m Presenting—Keyras Choice (IRE) **Mr M. J. D. Lambert**
2 **ADJUTANT**, 4, b g Champs Elysees—Jubilee **Ladies In Racing**
3 **AMERICAN TOM (FR)**, 8, b g American Post—Kirkla (FR) **Mr C. J. Williams**
4 **ANGEL OF HARLEM**, 6, b m Presenting—Whoops A Daisy **Patrick & Scott Bryceland**
5 4, Gr g Kapgarde (FR)—As You Leave (FR) **Mr O. J. Murphy**
6 **BALLINSLEA BRIDGE (IRE)**, 7, b g Pierre—Feelin' Looser (IRE) **Ashley, Carr, Duncan, Ives**
7 **BANFF (IRE)**, 6, b g Papal Bull—Hugs 'n Kisses (IRE) **Mary Shalvey & Aiden Murphy**
8 **BEAU SANCY (FR)**, 7, b g Blue Bresil—Touquette (FR) **Tramore Tree**
9 **BLAZER'S MILL (IRE)**, 5, b g Westerner—Creation (IRE) **Mrs J. A. Wakefield**
10 **BON CALVADOS (FR)**, 5, b g Bonbon Rose (FR)—Lamorrese (FR) **Graeme Moore, Kate & Andrew Brooks**
11 **BREWIN'UPASTORM (IRE)**, 6, b g Milan—Daraheen Diamond (IRE) **Ms B. J. Abt**
12 **BRIGHT NEW DAWN**, 12, br g Presenting—Shuil Dorcha (IRE) **Boultbee Brooks Ltd**
13 **BUBBLES OF GOLD (IRE)**, 6, b g Gold Well—Bubble Bann (IRE) **Noel & Valerie Moran**
14 **BUCANEROS (IRE)**, 6, b g Stowaway—Silk Style **Mrs D. L. Whateley**
15 **CALIPSO COLLONGES (FR)**, 7, b g Crossharbour—Ivresse Collonges (FR) **The Black Horse Hotel Bridgnorth**
16 **CARRAIGIN AONAIR (IRE)**, 7, b m Fastnet Rock (AUS)—Omanah (USA) **Ready Steady Go**
17 **CASCAYE (IRE)**, 7, br m Merlino Mago—Castyana (IRE) **Mr M. J. D. Lambert**
18 **CELTIC TARA**, 5, b m Kayf Tara—Valdas Queen (GER) **A. P. Racing**
19 **CHARMING ZEN (FR)**, 7, gr g Youmzain (IRE)—Nioumoun (FR) **Sullivan Bloodstock Limited**
20 **CHEZ HANS (IRE)**, 5, b g Aizavoski (IRE)—Hidden Reserve (IRE) **Ms B. J. Abt**
21 **CLIFFSIDE PARK (IRE)**, 10, b g Chevalier (IRE)—Lady Toulon (IRE) **Olly Murphy Racing Club**
22 **COLLOONEY (IRE)**, 5, b g Yeats (IRE)—Amber Trix (IRE) **Mr J. P. McManus**
23 **COMPATRIOT (IRE)**, 5, b g Pour Moi (IRE)—Wooded Glade **The Brothers Grimm**
24 **CORINTO (IRE)**, 6, br g Flemensfirth (USA)—Fashion Target (IRE) **Mrs D. L. Whateley**
25 **CRAIGMOR (IRE)**, 7, b g Craigsteel—Twilight Princess (IRE) **Mr Peter. P. Elliott & Partners**
26 **DIAMOND KING (IRE)**, 11, b g King's Theatre (IRE)—Georgia On My Mind (IRE) **Mrs D. L. Whateley**
27 **DONCESAR DE PRETOT (FR)**, 6, gr g Saddler Maker (IRE)—Kobila (FR) **Sullivan Bloodstock Limited**
28 **DORETTE (FR)**, 6, b m Kingsalsa (USA)—Ombrelle (FR) **Ready Steady Go**
29 **DOVE MOUNTAIN (IRE)**, 8, b g Danehill Dancer (IRE)—Virginia Waters (USA) **Olly Murphy Racing Club**
30 **DUTCH UNCLE**, 7, b g Dutch Art—Evasive Quality (FR) **Mrs Fiona Shaw**
31 **ELENA SUE**, 6, b m Zamindar (USA)—Elasouna (FR) **Mr G. Bryan**
32 **EMMAS DILEMMA (IRE)**, 7, b m Gold Well—Emmas Island (IRE) **Olly Murphy Racing Club**
33 **ENDLESSLY (IRE)**, 4, b g Nathaniel (IRE)—What's Up Pussycat (IRE) **Mr R. Treacy**
34 **EOLIAN**, 5, b g Poet's Voice—Charlecote (IRE) **Premier Thoroughbred Racing Ltd**
35 **FIESOLE**, 7, b g Montjeu (IRE)—Forgotten Dreams (IRE) **LF Infrastructure Ltd**
36 **FIGHT COMMANDER**, 10, b g Oscar (IRE)—Creidim (IRE) **Foxtrot Racing Fight Commander**
37 **FINAWN BAWN (IRE)**, 6, b g Robin des Champs (FR)—Kayanti (IRE) **LF Infrastructure Ltd**
38 **FITZROY (IRE)**, 5, b g Fame And Glory—Forces of Destiny (IRE) **Tim Syder & Aiden Murphy**
39 **FLETCH (FR)**, 4, b g Kayf Tara—Oeuvre Vive (FR) **Ms B. J. Abt**
40 **FLYNNVINCIBLE**, 8, b g Tobougg (IRE)—Shiny Thing (USA) **Murphy's Law Partnership**

MR OLLY MURPHY - Continued

41 **FOXTROT JULIET**, 6, b m Shirocco (GER)—Miami Explorer **Foxtrot Racing: Foxtrot Juliet**
42 **FRESH NEW DAWN (IRE)**, 7, ch g Flemensfirth (USA)—Star Shuil (IRE) **Not For Friends Partnership**
43 **GARRETTSTOWN (IRE)**, 6, b g Doyen (IRE)—Azur (IRE) **The Phillies Partnership**
44 **GENERAL CUSTARD**, 6, b g Shirocco (GER)—Diamant Noir **Syder, Whateley, Murphy, Burke**
45 **GEORGIATOR (FR)**, 6, b g Simplex (FR)—Princess Demut (GER) **Kate & Andrew Brooks**
46 **HERE COMES TRUBLE (IRE)**, 4, b g Flemensfirth (USA)—Old Moon (IRE) **Ms B. J. Abt**
47 **HUNTERS CALL (IRE)**, 9, b g Medaaly—Accordiontogelica (IRE) **Holloway,Clarke,Black**
48 **I K BRUNEL**, 5, b g Midnight Legend—Somethinaboutmolly (IRE) **McNeill Family and Prodec Networks Ltd**
49 **I KNOW U TOO WELL (IRE)**, 7, b g Stowaway—Kilbricken Leader (IRE) **Mr & Mrs Paul & Clare Rooney**
50 **IMPERIAL KNIGHT (IRE)**, 8, b g Mahler—And Whatever Else (IRE) **Nicholas Piper & Claire E. Piper**
51 **IT'S O KAY**, 6, b m Shirocco (GER)—Presenting Copper (IRE) **Aiden Murphy & Alan Peterson**
53 **ITCHY FEET (FR)**, 5, b g Cima de Triomphe (IRE)—Maeva Candas (FR) **Kate & Andrew Brooks**
53 **JETAWAY JOEY (IRE)**, 4, b g Getaway (GER)—Present Your Own (IRE) **Ms B. J. Abt**
54 **JETSTREAM JACK (IRE)**, 9, b g Beneficial—Westgrove Berry (IRE) **Mrs D. L. Whateley**
55 **JONES WELL (IRE)**, 6, b g Gold Well—Mrs Jones (IRE) **H. A. Murphy**
56 **JUST MINDED (IRE)**, 8, b g Kayf Tara—Georgia On My Mind (FR) **Racing Spirit Just Minded Owners**
57 **KNOCKGRAFFON (IRE)**, 9, b g Flemensfirth (USA)—Gleaming Spire **Ms B. J. Abt**
58 **KRAZY PAVING**, 7, b g Kyllachy—Critical Path (IRE) **All The Kings Horses & Mr Aiden Murphy**
59 **LET'S GET AT IT (IRE)**, 6, b g Mustameet (USA)—Last Hope (IRE) **Kate & Andrew Brooks**
61 **LISHEEN PRINCE (IRE)**, 8, b g Oscar (IRE)—Dino's Monkey (IRE) **Mrs D. L. Whateley**
61 **MARALYSEES**, 6, b m Champs Elysees—Marathea (FR) **Mr C. D. Platel**
62 **MIGHTY MEG**, 5, b m Malinas (GER)—Harry's Bride **The Mighty Men**
63 **MILES TO MILAN (IRE)**, 9, b g Milan—Princesse Rooney (FR) **Mrs Lesley Field & Mr Jules Sigler**
64 **MIZEN MASTER (IRE)**, 6, b g Captain Rio—Nilassiba **H. A. Murphy**
65 **MON PORT (IRE)**, 7, b g Scorpion (IRE)—Sounds Charming (IRE) **J. T. Warner**
66 **MONBEG ZENA (IRE)**, 7, ch m Flemensfirth (USA)—Mandys Gold (IRE) **Sullivan Bloodstock Limited**
67 **MOTUEKA (IRE)**, 7, b g King's Theatre (IRE)—Tchouina (FR) **Mrs D. L. Whateley**
68 **NEWLANDS CROSS (IRE)**, 7, b g Stowaway—Honey Mustard (IRE) **Holloway,Clarke,Black**
69 **NICE TO SEA (IRE)**, 5, b m Born To Sea (IRE)—Campessa (IRE) **Mr H. Krebs**
70 **NICKOLSON (IRE)**, 5, b g No Risk At All (FR)—Incorrigible (FR) **Mr T. D. J. Syder**
71 **NO ALARM (IRE)**, 7, b g Getaway (GER)—Chapanga (IRE) **Touchwood Racing**
72 **OSCAR MAGUIRE (IRE)**, 6, b g Oscar (IRE)—Ballymaguirelass (IRE) **LF Infrastructure Ltd**
73 **OSKEMEN**, 4, gr g Mastercraftsman (IRE)—Ollie Olga (USA) **Knightsbridge Thoroughbreds Racing**
74 **OXFORD BLU**, 5, b g Aqlaam—Blue Zealot (IRE) **geegeez.co.uk OM**
75 **PEACHEY (IRE)**, 5, b g Robin des Champs (FR)—Zita Hall (IRE) **Mrs D. L. Whateley**
76 **PERFECT MAN (IRE)**, 8, b g Morozov (USA)—Garrisker (IRE) **Holloway,Clarke,Black**
77 **POPPY KAY**, 9, b m Kayf Tara—Double Red (IRE) **Aiden Murphy & Alan Peterson**
78 **PORT OF MARS (IRE)**, 5, b g Westerner—Sarahall (IRE) **Noel & Valerie Moran**
79 **RIO QUINTO (FR)**, 6, b g Loup Breton (IRE)—Seal of Cause (IRE) **Mrs D. L. Whateley**
80 **ROQUE IT (IRE)**, 5, b g Presenting—Roque de Cyborg (IRE) **Gordon & Su Hall**
81 **ROYAL PRACTITIONER**, 6, b m Dr Massini (IRE)—Valdas Queen **A. P. Racing**
82 **SANGHA RIVER (IRE)**, 6, br g Arcadio (GER)—Hidden Reserve (IRE) **Ms B. J. Abt**
83 **SEEMINGLY SO (IRE)**, 6, br g Dubai Destination (USA)—Jane Hall (IRE) **Emily Boultbee Brooks Racing**
84 **SKANDIBURG (FR)**, 5, b g Sageburg (IRE)—Skandia (FR) **Kate & Andrew Brooks**
85 **SMACKWATER JACK (IRE)**, 5, b g Flemensfirth (USA)—Malachy's Attic (IRE) **Par Four**
86 **SOME BOY MCCOY (FR)**, 5, b g Enrique—Khaylama (IRE) **Mr C. J. Haughey**
87 **SPIRIT OF WATERLOO**, 5, b g Malinas (GER)—Warm Front **Salmon Racing**
88 **SWAFFHAM BULBECK (IRE)**, 5, b g Jeremy (USA)—Ballygologue (IRE) **geegeez.co.uk OM**
89 **THE VERY THING (IRE)**, 5, b g Getaway (GER)—
                    Katie Quinn (IRE) **J P Magnier Mrs M V Magnier Mrs P Shanahan J Carthy**
90 **THOMAS DARBY (IRE)**, 6, b g Beneficial—Silaoce (FR) **Mrs D. L. Whateley**
91 **THREE COUNTY'S (IRE)**, 8, b br g Beneficial—Pattern Queen (IRE) **Mr M. Fitzgerald**
92 **TIME FOR ANOTHER (IRE)**, 6, ch g Shantou (USA)—Borleagh Blonde (IRE) **Mr & Mrs Paul & Clare Rooney**
93 **TODD**, 9, b g Gentlewave (IRE)—Voice **Olly Murphy Racing Club**
94 **TOUR DE FRANCE**, 5, ch g Mount Nelson—Why Nee Amy **You Betta You Betta You Bet**
95 4, b g Getaway (GER)—Ut Love (FR) **Mr O. J. Murphy**
96 **VALDAS PRINCESS**, 7, b m King's Theatre (IRE)—Valdas Queen (GER) **A. P. Racing**
97 **VAMANOS (IRE)**, 5, b g Fame And Glory—Bean Ki Moon (IRE) **Mrs D. L. Whateley**
98 **WEEBILL**, 7, b g Schiaparelli (GER)—Wee Dinns (IRE) **Mrs C. Skan**
99 **WHISKEY IN THE JAR (IRE)**, 7, b g Oscar (IRE)—Baie Barbara (IRE) **Ms B. J. Abt**
100 **WOOD PIGEON (IRE)**, 10, b g Presenting—Come In Moscow (IRE) **Touchwood Racing**
101 **WORLD OF GOOD**, 6, ch m Danehill Dancer (IRE)—Edaraat (USA) **All The Kings Horses & Mr Aiden Murphy**

MR OLLY MURPHY - Continued

THREE-YEAR-OLDS

102 ANOTHER REASON (IRE), b g Thewayyouare (USA)—Ballet School (IRE) **Ready Steady Go**
103 WHAT WILL BE (IRE), b g Thewayyouare (USA)—Gali Gal (IRE) **Ready Steady Go**

Other Owners: Mrs J. Abraham, Mr D. Abraham, All The Kings Horses, Mr S. A. Ashley, Mr N. W. Bailey, Mr S. J. Bennett, Mr M. Bisogno, Mr S. T. Black, Miss E. Boultbee-Brooks, Mr P. A. Boyle, Mr A. L. Brooks, Mrs K. L. Brooks, Mr S. Bryceland, Mr P. Bryceland, Mrs V. F. Burke, A. Carr, Mr J. Carthy, Miss E. J. Clarke, P. W. Clement, Mr W. Downs, Mr M. Duncan, Mr P. P. Elliott, Mr B. Etchells, Mrs L. H. Field, Mr R. S. Field, Mrs S. M. Gasch, Mr G. A. Hall, Mrs S. L. Hall, Mr J. R. Holloway, Mr D. L. Ives, Mr M. S. Lawson, Mr J. P. Magnier, Mrs E. Magnier, Mr P. Maloney, Mr P. McBride, McNeill Family Ltd, Mr B. H. Mellon, Mr G. Moore, Mr N. Moran, Mrs V. Moran, Mr M. Muldoon, Mrs A. L. M. Murphy, Mr P. J. O'Neill, Mr A. E. Peterson, Miss C. E. Piper, Mr N. Piper, L. M. Power, Prodec Networks Ltd, Mr P. A. Rooney, Mrs C. Rooney, Mr D. B. Salmon, Mrs Lynn Salmon, Ms M. Shalvey, Mrs L. M. Shanahan, Mr C. D. W. Sharkey, Mr J. Sigler, Mrs S. Stanley, A. J. Wall.

Assistant Trainers: Ed Telfer, Gerard Tumelty

Jockey (NH): Aidan Coleman, David England, Richard Johnson, Charlie Poste. **Conditional:** Fergus Gregory, Cillin Leonard, Callum McKinnes, Lewis Stones. **Amateur:** Mr Alex Ferguson, Mr Luke Scott.

411
MR BARRY MURTAGH, Carlisle
Postal: Hurst Farm, Ivegill, Carlisle, Cumbria, CA4 0NL
Contacts: **PHONE (01768) 484649 FAX (01768) 484744 MOBILE (07714) 026741**
E-MAIL suemurtagh7@gmail.com

1 **BAYMORE ROAD,** 5, b g Josr Algarhoud (IRE)—Animal Cracker **Hurst Farm Racing**
2 **BORDER VICTOR,** 7, b g Beat All (USA)—Sambara (IRE) **Mrs A. Stamper**
3 **CLONDAW BANKER (IRE),** 10, b g Court Cave (IRE)—Freya Alex **A. R. White**
4 **HERO'S STORY,** 9, b g Mount Nelson—Red Roses Story (FR) **I. McMath**
5 **KINGS GOLD (IRE),** 6, ch g Excellent Art—Party Feet (IRE) **Mrs S. A. Murtagh**
6 **PEAK HILL,** 6, ch g Bahamian Bounty—River Naiad **Famous Five Racing**
7 **RECOGNITION (IRE),** 6, gr g Rip Van Winkle (IRE)—Bali Breeze (IRE) **Famous Five Racing**
8 **ROBIN DE PLAN (IRE),** 8, b m Robin des Pres (FR)—Nice Resemblance (IRE) **Hurst Farm Racing**
9 **SAMTU (IRE),** 8, b g Teofilo (IRE)—Samdaniya **A. R. White**
10 **STANS BLACK FIVE,** 6, b g Multiplex—Globe Dream (IRE) **Mr E. Chapman**
11 **STARSHELL (IRE),** 5, b g Sea The Stars (IRE)—Aquarelle Bleue **Mr G Fell & Mrs Sue Murtagh**
12 **SYMBOLIC STAR (IRE),** 7, b g New Approach (IRE)—Epitome (IRE) **Murtagh, O'Rourke & Trinders**
13 **TOMMY SHELBY (FR),** 4, b g Dabirsim (FR)—Interior (USA) **Mrs S. A. Murtagh**

THREE-YEAR-OLDS

14 **GEYSER,** b g Gale Force Ten—Popocatepetl (FR) **Mrs A. Stamper**

Other Owners: Mr R. Allen, Mr G. Fell, Mr A. J. Markley, Mrs Sue Murtagh, Mr F. P. Murtagh, Mr Rory O'Rourke, Mr A. Trinder, Mrs A. Trinder, Mr Derek Wilson.

Assistant Trainer: S A Murtagh

Conditional: Lorcan Murtagh. **Apprentice:** Connor Murtagh.

412
DR JEREMY NAYLOR, Shrewton
Postal: The Cleeve Stables, Elston, Shrewton, Salisbury, Wiltshire, SP3 4HL
Contacts: **PHONE (01980) 620804 MOBILE (07771) 740126**
E-MAIL info@jeremynaylor.com WEBSITE www.jeremynaylor.com

1 **CROUCHING HARRY (IRE),** 10, b g Tiger Hill (IRE)—Catwalk Dreamer (IRE) **Mrs S. P. Elphick**
2 **FEARSOME FRED,** 10, b g Emperor Fountain—Ryewater Dream **Mrs S. P. Elphick**
3 **JUST ARCHIE (USA),** 11, b g Arch (USA)—Copper Rose (USA) **Dr J. R. J. Naylor**
4 **LADY CARDINAL (IRE),** 8, ch m Papal Bull—St Finan's Bay (IRE) **Mrs S. P. Elphick**
5 **SEERAJ,** 4, b c Fastnet Rock (AUS)—Star On High (USA) **Dr J. R. J. Naylor**
6 **WHAT LARKS (IRE),** 11, b g Pierre—Bint Rosie **Mrs H. A. Heal**

413 **MR JOHN NEEDHAM, Ludlow**
Postal: **Gorsty Farm, Mary Knoll, Ludlow, Shropshire, SY8 2HD**
Contacts: **PHONE (01584) 872112/874826 FAX (01584) 873256 MOBILE (07811) 451137**
E-MAIL johnlneedham@btconnect.com

1 BRINGEWOOD BLUE (IRE), 12, br m Blueprint (IRE)—Carramore (IRE) **Mr J. L. Needham**
2 DOWNTON FOX, 11, b g Oscar (IRE)—Leinthall Fox **Miss J. C. L. Needham**
3 MY FOXY LADY, 7, br m Sagamix (FR)—Marlbrook Fox **Miss J. C. L. Needham**
4 RIGHT ROYALS DAY, 10, b m Beneficial—Just For A Laugh **Miss J. C. L. Needham**

Assistant Trainer: J. Wall

Jockey (NH): Robbie Dunne, Richard Johnson, Jamie Moore.

414 **MRS HELEN NELMES, Dorchester**
Postal: **Warmwell Stables, 2 Church Cottages, Warmwell, Dorchester, Dorset, DT2 8HQ**
Contacts: **PHONE/FAX (01305) 852254 MOBILE (07977) 510318**
E-MAIL warmwellstud@tiscali.co.uk WEBSITE www.warmwellstables.co.uk

1 GARRYDUFF CROSS (IRE), 9, b g Stowaway—Cooleycall (IRE) **K. A. Nelmes**
2 ITSABOUTIME (IRE), 9, gr g Whitmore's Conn (USA)—Blazing Love (IRE) **K. A. Nelmes**
3 KALMBEFORETHESTORM, 11, ch g Storming Home—Miss Honeypenny (IRE) **Warmwellcome Partnership**
4 KEEPYOURHEADUP, 8, b g Sir Percy—Sweet Lemon (IRE) **Mr K. Tyre**
5 LAOCH BEAG (IRE), 8, gr g King's Theatre (IRE)—Innocentines (FR) **KA Nelmes & LJ Burden**
6 MENAPIAN (IRE), 8, b br g Touch of Land (FR)—Mannequin (IRE) **T M W Partnership**
7 MYLITTLEMOUSE (IRE), 11, b m Turtle Island (IRE)—Ballybeg Rose (IRE) **K. A. Nelmes**
8 NORSE DA, 9, b g Norse Dancer (IRE)—End of An Error **T M W Partnership**
9 SERVEONTIME (IRE), 8, b g Echo of Light—Little Lovely (IRE) **K. A. Nelmes**
10 THE FINGER POST (IRE), 12, b g Zagreb (USA)—Mystic Madam (IRE) **K. A. Nelmes**

Other Owners: Mr L. J. Burden, Miss V. O. Kardas, Ms A. M. Neville, Mr D. Price.

Assistant Trainer: K Nelmes.

415 **MR TONY NEWCOMBE, Barnstaple**
Postal: **Lower Delworthy, Yarnscombe, Barnstaple, Devon, EX31 3LT**
Contacts: **PHONE/FAX (01271) 858554 MOBILE (07785) 297210**
E-MAIL huntshawequineforest@talktalk.net

1 ANGELITO, 10, ch g Primo Valentino (IRE)—Supreme Angel **Mr A. Dunmore**
2 BUSHEL (USA), 9, b g Street Cry (IRE)—Melhor Ainda (USA) **Mr N. P. Hardy**
3 FRANGARRY (IRE), 7, b g Lawman (FR)—Divert (IRE) **Dr S. P. Hargreaves**
4 HOUSE OF FRAUDS (IRE), 11, b f Storming Home—Bogus Penny (IRE) **Joli Racing**
5 IMMINENT APPROACH, 4, b f New Approach (IRE)—Nashmiah (IRE) **Joli Racing**
6 KAY SERA, 11, b g Kayf Tara—Inflation **Mr N. P. Hardy**
7 KODIAC PEARL, 5, b m Kodiac—Valmirez (USA) **Central Racing Ltd**
8 NUZHA, 5, ch m Mayson—Always On My Mind **Central Racing Ltd**
9 SOVEREIGN STATE, 4, b g Compton Place—One Night In May (IRE) **Ss Partnership**
10 SURENESS (IRE), 9, ch m Hurricane Run (IRE)—Silk Dress (IRE) **Mr P. T. Mott**
11 WAR OF SUCCESSION, 5, b g Casamento (IRE)—Rohlindi **Dr S. P. Hargreaves**

Other Owners: Mr A. G. Craig, R. Eagle, Mr D. R. J. Freeman.

Assistant Trainer: John Lovejoy

Jockey (flat): Fergus Sweeney, Dane O'Neill.

416 **DR RICHARD NEWLAND, Claines**
Postal: **Linacres Farm, Egg Lane, Claines, Worcester, WR3 7SB**
Contacts: **PHONE (07956) 196535**
E-MAIL richard.newland1@btopenworld.com

1 **AARON LAD (IRE)**, 8, b g Daylami (IRE)—Borntobepampered **Off The Clock Partners & Dr RDP Newland**
2 **ABOLITIONIST (IRE)**, 11, b g Flemensfirth (USA)—All The Roses (IRE) **M Albon, J A Provan & C E Stedman**
3 **ARTFUL ARTIST (IRE)**, 10, b g Excellent Art—Silly Goose (IRE) **Doom Bar Beach Club**
4 **ASYLO (IRE)**, 7, b g Flemensfirth (USA)—Escrea (IRE) **Mr M. P. Tudor**
5 **BABANANGO (FR)**, 8, b g Policy Maker (IRE)—Bamileke (FR)
6 **BAND OF BLOOD (IRE)**, 11, b g King's Theatre (IRE)—Cherry Falls (IRE) **J A Provan & C E Stedman**
7 **BEAU BAY (FR)**, 8, b g Bernebeau (FR)—Slew Bay (FR) **Mr Peter Green & Dr Rdp Newland**
8 **BOLTISSIME (FR)**, 4, b g Dawn Approach (IRE)—Be Yourself (FR)
9 **BRAVE HELIOS**, 9, b g High Chaparral (IRE)—Renowned (IRE) **Dozen Dreamers Partnership**
10 **CAID DU LIN (FR)**, 7, gr g Della Francesca (USA)—Asia du Lin (FR) **Foxtrot Racing**
11 **CATAMARAN DU SEUIL (FR)**, 7, b g Network (GER)—Fleur du Tennis (FR) **Mr M. P. Tudor**
12 **CHEF DE TROUPE (FR)**, 6, b g Air Chief Marshal (IRE)—Tazminya **Mr C. E. Stedman**
13 **CLEVER AS A FOX (IRE)**, 6, b g Gold Well—Inouette (IRE) **The Leicester Lads**
14 **COMPETITION**, 7, b g Multiplex—Compolina **ValueRacingClub.co.uk**
15 **DANCING IN THE SKY (IRE)**, 6, b g Court Cave—Agasaya (IRE)
16 **DESERT SENSATION (IRE)**, 7, b g Authorized (IRE)—Awwal Malika (USA) **Doom Bar Beach Club**
17 **DOUNYAPOUR (FR)**, 6, ch g Lope de Vega (IRE)—Diamond Tango (FR)
18 **DUKE STREET (IRE)**, 7, b g Duke of Marmalade (IRE)—Act of The Pace (IRE) **Chris Stedman & Mark Albon**
19 **DUSTIN DES MOTTES (FR)**, 6, b g Kapgarde (FR)—Puszta des Mottes (FR) **Mr D. J. Smith**
20 **EVITA DU MESNIL (FR)**, 5, gr m Gris de Gris (FR)—Perle du Mesnil (FR) **Foxtrot Racing Evita Du Mesnil**
21 **EXPRESS PIERRE (IRE)**, 8, b g Pierre—Express Mail (IRE) **Dr R. D. P. Newland**
22 **GARBANZO (IRE)**, 5, gr g Mastercraftsman (IRE)—Noble Fantasy (GER) **Mr C. E. Stedman**
23 **GETTYSBURG ADDRESS (IRE)**, 8, b g Milan—Cat Burglar (IRE) **Mr M. P. Tudor**
24 **GREYED A (IRE)**, 8, gr g Daylami (IRE)—Broadcast **Plan B**
25 **INESSA (FR)**, 6, b m Samum (GER)—Isantha (GER) **Mr D. J. Smith**
26 **JIMMY RABBITTE (IRE)**, 6, b g Dubai Destination (USA)—Time To Act **P Jenkins & Partner**
27 **KATPOLI (FR)**, 4, b g Poliglote—Katkogarie (FR) **Mr C. E. Stedman**
28 **LE PATRIOTE (FR)**, 7, b g Poliglote—Sentosa (FR) **Canard Vert Racing Club**
29 **LEONCAVALLO (IRE)**, 7, br g Cape Cross (IRE)—Nafura **ValueRacingClub.co.uk**
30 **LOVATO (GER)**, 7, br g Lauro (GER)—Larella (GER) **Plan B**
31 **MAURICIO (IRE)**, 5, ch g Helmet (AUS)—Essexford (IRE) **J A Provan & Partner**
32 **MCGROARTY (IRE)**, 8, b g Brian Boru—Uffizi (IRE) **Chris Stedman & Mark Albon**
33 **NIKKI STEEL (IRE)**, 9, b g Craigsteel—Nikikita (IRE) **Foxtrot Racing: Nikki Steel**
34 **NORDICAN BLEUE (FR)**, 4, b f Anabaa Blue—Nordican Queen (FR) **Canard Vert Racing Club**
35 **PURPLE KING (IRE)**, 5, ch g Lope de Vega (IRE)—Dixie Dance (IRE) **Foxtrot Racing Purple King**
36 **RED MIX (FR)**, 6, b g Al Namix (FR)—Fidelety (FR) **Brewers Racing Club**
37 **ROCK GONE (IRE)**, 11, b g Winged Love (IRE)—Guillem (USA) **Chris Stedman & Mark Albon**
38 **ROSE SEA HAS (FR)**, 4, gr g Kapgarde (FR)—Vaibuscar Has (FR) **Mr Simon Munir/Mr Isaac Souede**
39 **SAMSON**, 8, ch g Black Sam Bellamy (IRE)—Riverine **The Cheltonians**
40 **SETTIMO MILANESE (IRE)**, 7, b g Milan—Ad Gloria (IRE) **ValueRacingClub.co.uk**
41 **SHOW AND GO (IRE)**, 10, b g Stowaway—Nooradeen (IRE)
42 **STOLE THE SHOW (IRE)**, 7, ch g Mahler—Brideview Hamshire (IRE) **Foxtrot Racing: Stole the Show**
43 **STORM RISING (IRE)**, 6, b g Canford Cliffs (IRE)—Before The Storm **M Albon & M P Tudor**
44 **SUDDEN DESTINATION (IRE)**, 7, ch g Dubai Destination (USA)—
Sudden Approach (IRE) **Foxtrot Nh Racing Syndicate**
45 **SUPREME STEEL (IRE)**, 8, b g Craigsteel—Tubber Gael Holly (IRE) **Foxtrot Racing: Supreme Steel**
46 **THEO (IRE)**, 9, b g Westerner—Jemima Jay (IRE) **P Jenkins & Partner**
47 **TRIGGER NICHOL (IRE)**, 7, b g Dubai Destination (USA)—Run For Cover (IRE) **ValueRacingClub.co.uk**
48 **URBANIST (IRE)**, 7, b g Black Sam Bellamy (IRE)—Sorcillera **Mr P. Drinkwater**
49 **VOSNE ROMANEE**, 8, ch g Arakan (USA)—Vento Del Oreno (FR) **Foxtrot NH Racing Partnership VI**
50 **WEST OF THE EDGE (IRE)**, 11, b g Westerner—Bermuda Bay (IRE) **ValueRacingClub.co.uk**
51 **WHOSHOTWHO (IRE)**, 8, br g Beneficial—Inishbeg House (IRE) **Foxtrot Racing: Whoshotwho**
52 **YCCS PORTOCERVO (FR)**, 4, gr g Martaline—Griva (FR)

Other Owners: Mr D. Abraham, Mrs J. Abraham, Mr M. L. Albon, Mr M. P. Ansell, J. E. Barnes, Mr J. R. Couldwell, Mr A. S. P. Drake, Mr J. M. O. Evans, Foxtrot Racing Management Ltd, Mr L. A. Goodfellow, Mr P. C. W. Green, Mr A. W. Hinton, Mr P. Jenkins, Mr C. R. Leech, Mr T. N. Lewis, Mr R. Mitchell, Mr L. J. Newland, Mr R. J. L. Newland, Off The Clock Partners, Mr R. T. Phillips, Mr J. A. Provan, Mrs S. L. Wood.

DR RICHARD NEWLAND - Continued

Assistant Trainer: Rod Trow

Jockey (NH): Sam Twiston-Davies. **Conditional:** Charlie Hammond.

---

417   MISS ANNA NEWTON-SMITH, Jevington
Postal: **Bull Pen Cottage, Jevington, Polegate, East Sussex, BN26 5QB**
Contacts: **PHONE (01323) 488354 MOBILE (07970) 914124**
E-MAIL annanewtonsmith@gmail.com WEBSITE www.annanewtonsmith.co.uk

1 **BEET TOPPER (IRE)**, 6, b g Beat Hollow—What A Topper (IRE) **PPS Racing**
2 **BURGESS DREAM (IRE)**, 10, b g Spadoun (FR)—Ennel Lady (IRE) **The Beano Partnership**
3 **GO GEORGE GO (IRE)**, 6, gr g Zebedee—La Bella Grande (IRE) **Mr G. E. Goring**
4 **GORING ONE (IRE)**, 14, b g Broadway Flyer (USA)—Brigette's Secret **Mr G. E. Goring**

THREE-YEAR-OLDS
5 B g Battle of Marengo (IRE)—Great Wave (IRE)

Other Owners: Mr R. Brooker, His Honour Judge A. Patience Qc, Mr Phil Worley.

Assistant Trainer: Nicola Worley

Jockey (NH): Paddy Brennan, Jeremiah McGrath, David Noonan. **Conditional:** Charlie Deutsch, Rex Dingle.

---

418   MR ADRIAN NICHOLLS, Sessay
Postal: **The Ranch, Sessay, Thirsk, North Yorkshire, YO7 3ND**
Contacts: **PHONE (01845) 597428**

1 **SFUMATO**, 5, br g Bated Breath—Modern Look **J. A. Rattigan**
2 **SIR LANCELOTT**, 7, b g Piccolo—Selkirk Rose (IRE) **The Golden Horse Racing Club**
3 **TARAAYEF (IRE)**, 4, b f Teofilo (IRE)—Shuhra (IRE) **Mr H. Sultan Saeed**
4 **VIVERNUS (USA)**, 6, b h Street Cry (IRE)—Lady Pegasus (USA) **Mr H. Sultan Saeed**

THREE-YEAR-OLDS
5 **CHEERUPMYLOVE**, b f Kyllachy—Equitissa (IRE) **Malih L. Al Basti**
6 **FAST'N FURIOUS (GER)**, b c Kendargent (FR)—Fantanella (IRE) **Mr J. Aljunaibi**
7 **GATE CITY (USA)**, b br g Animal Kingdom (USA)—Fu Cat (USA) **Mr J. Aljunaibi**
8 **HAFEET ALAIN (IRE)**, b c Elzaam (AUS)—Batuta **Mr M. R. M. E. Abdelmotaleb**
9 **MUHALLAB (IRE)**, b c War Command (USA)—Andrea Bellevica (IRE) **Mr J. Aljunaibi**
10 **XTARA (IRE)**, b c Xtension (IRE)—Brave Madam (IRE) **Mr H. Sultan Saeed**
11 **ZALMI ANGEL**, b f Swiss Spirit—Break of Dawn (USA) **Mrs N. S. Khan**

TWO-YEAR-OLDS
12 **ARMADO (IRE)**, gr ro c 9/4 Outstrip—Daring Damsel (IRE) (Van Nistelrooy (USA)) (11799) **Mr H. Sultan Saeed**
13 B f 8/3 Swiss Spirit—Berry Baby (IRE) (Rainbow Quest (USA)) (8571)
14 B c 15/4 Charm Spirit (IRE)—Chanterelle (IRE) (Trempolino (USA)) (30000) **Mr A. Bintooq**
15 **L'OPERA**, b f 19/4 Mukhadram—Al Hawa (USA) (Gulch (USA)) (3000) **Mr H. Sultan Saeed**
16 B f 20/2 Acclamation—Lafleur (IRE) (Grand Lodge (USA)) (35398)
17 B f 3/4 Bungle Inthejungle—She Mystifies (Indesatchel (IRE)) (7000) **Mr A. Bintooq**
18 **ZAKHER ALAIN**, b c 18/3 Sepoy (AUS)—
Madame Mere (IRE) (Dalakhani (IRE)) (9523) **Mr M. R. M. E. Abdelmotaleb**

Other Owners: Mr B. Tait, Mr C. J. Woods.

---

419   MR PAUL NICHOLLS, Ditcheat
Postal: **Manor Farm Stables, Ditcheat, Shepton Mallet, Somerset, BA4 6RD**
Contacts: **PHONE (01749) 860656 MOBILE (07977) 270706**
E-MAIL info@paulnichollsracing.com WEBSITE www.paulnichollsracing.com

1 **ACCOMPLICE (FR)**, 5, gr g Network (GER)—Miss Vitoria (FR) **Mrs K. A. Stuart**
2 **ADRIEN DU PONT (FR)**, 7, b g Califet (FR)—Santariyka (FR) **Mrs S. De La Hey**

MR PAUL NICHOLLS - Continued

3 **AMOUR DE NUIT (IRE)**, 7, b g Azamour (IRE)—Umthoulah (IRE) **Mr A. N. V. Williams**
4 **ART MAURESQUE (FR)**, 9, b g Policy Maker (IRE)—Modeva (FR) **Mrs S. De La Hey**
5 **AS DE MEE (FR)**, 9, b br g Kapgarde (FR)—Koeur de Mee (FR) **The Stewart Family & Judi Dench**
6 **ASHUTOR (FR)**, 5, gr g Redoute's Choice (AUS)—Ashalanda (FR) **The Roy & Stewart Families**
7 **ASK FOR GLORY (IRE)**, 5, b g Fame And Glory—Ask Helen (IRE) **Mr Colm Donlon & Mr & Mrs P. K. Barber**
8 **BATHSHEBA BAY (IRE)**, 4, b g Footstepsinthesand—Valamareha (IRE) **Mr M. F. Geoghegan**
9 **BINGE DRINKER (IRE)**, 10, b g Spadoun (FR)—Our Honey (IRE) **Corsellis & Seyfried**
10 **BIRDS OF PREY (IRE)**, 5, b g Sir Prancealot (IRE)—Cute **Mrs K. A. Stuart**
11 **BLACK CORTON (FR)**, 8, br g Laverock (IRE)—Pour Le Meilleur (FR) **The Brooks, Stewart Families & J. Kyle**
12 **BLACKJACK KENTUCKY (IRE)**, 6, b g Oscar (IRE)—My Name's Not Bin (IRE) **Owners Group 026**
13 4, B g Presenting—Bonnie Parker (IRE) **Mr C. A. Donlon**
14 **BRAQUEUR D'OR (FR)**, 8, b g Epalo (GER)—Hot d'or (FR) **Corsellis & Seyfried**
15 **BRELAN D'AS (FR)**, 8, b g Crillon (FR)—Las de La Croix (FR) **Mr J. P. McManus**
16 **BREWERS PROJECT (IRE)**, 5, b g Aizavoski (IRE)—Shaylee Wilde (IRE) **The Hon Mrs C. A. Townshend**
17 **BRIO CONTI (FR)**, 8, gr g Dom Alco (FR)—Cadouile Wood (FR) **The Gí Gí Syndicate**
18 4, B g Westerner—Brogarais (FR) **Hills of Ledbury Ltd**
19 **CAPELAND (FR)**, 7, b g Poliglote—Neiland (FR) **Mrs K. A. Stuart**
20 **CAPITAINE (FR)**, 7, gr g Montmartre (FR)—Patte de Velour (FR) **Martin Broughton & Friends 2**
21 **CAPTAIN BUCK'S (FR)**, 7, b g Buck's Boum (FR)—Ombre Jaune (FR) **Donlon & Doyle**
22 **CAPTAIN CATTISTOCK (FR)**, 6, b g Black Sam Bellamy (IRE)—Pearl Buttons **P. L. Hart**
23 **CARRY ON THE MAGIC (IRE)**, 5, b br g Jeremy (USA)—
Bisoguet (IRE) **Highclere Thoroughbred Racing - Magic**
24 **CASKO D'AIRY (FR)**, 7, b g Voix du Nord (FR)—Quaska d'airy (FR) **G.Mason & Sir A. Ferguson**
25 **CAT TIGER (FR)**, 5, b g Diamond Boy (FR)—Miss Canon (FR) **David Maxwell Racing Limited**
26 **CHAMERON (FR)**, 6, b g Laveron—Chamanka (FR) **Done, Ferguson, Fogg & Mason**
27 **CHIEF CRAFTSMAN**, 5, gr ro g Mastercraftsman (IRE)—Eurolink Raindance (IRE) **Mr & Mrs J. D. Cotton**
28 **CHOIX DES ARMES (FR)**, 7, b g Saint des Saints (FR)—Kicka **Mrs S. De La Hey**
29 **CHRISTOPHER WOOD (IRE)**, 4, b g Fast Company (IRE)—Surf The Web (IRE) **Mrs S. A. J. Kinsella**
30 **CLAN DES OBEAUX (FR)**, 7, b g Kapgarde (FR)—
Nausicaa des Obeaux (FR) **Mr&Mrs P.K.Barber,G.Mason,Sir A Ferguson**
31 **CLIFFS OF DOVER**, 6, b g Canford Cliffs (IRE)—Basanti (USA) **Mr & Mrs J. D. Cotton**
32 **COPAIN DE CLASSE (FR)**, 7, b g Enrique—Toque Rouge (FR) **Kyle, Stewart, Vogt & Wylie**
33 **COUP DE PINCEAU (FR)**, 7, b g Buck's Boum (FR)—Castagnette III (FR) **Mr C. A. Donlon**
34 **CYRNAME (FR)**, 7, b g Nickname (FR)—Narquille (FR) **Mrs S. De La Hey**
35 **DAN MCGRUE (IRE)**, 7, b g Dansant—Aahsaypasty (IRE) **Mr&Mrs P.K.Barber, D. Bennett, D. Martin**
36 **DANNY KIRWAN (IRE)**, 6, b g Scorpion (IRE)—Sainte Baronne (FR) **Mrs S. De La Hey**
37 **DANNY WHIZZBANG (IRE)**, 6, b g Getaway (GER)—Lakil Princess (IRE) **Mrs A. Tincknell**
38 **DANSE IDOL (IRE)**, 6, b m Dansant—Screen Idol (IRE) **Highclere Thoroughbred Racing-Danse Idol**
39 **DARLING MALTAIX (FR)**, 6, b g Voix du Nord (FR)—Rosalie Malta (FR) **Mrs S. De La Hey**
40 **DAYLAMI KIRK (IRE)**, 8, b g Daylami (IRE)—Uptothefrontkirk (IRE) **P. L. Hart**
41 **DEADLINE DIVA**, 4, b f Frankel—Hurry Home Hillary (USA) **Mrs S. De La Hey**
42 **DELAIZE (FR)**, 4, b f Saint des Saints (FR)—La Politique (FR) **D & M Macdonald & M & M McPherson**
43 **DENILIQUIN (IRE)**, 4, gr g Mastercraftsman (IRE)—Bernie's Moon (USA) **McNeill Family Ltd**
44 **DENSFIRTH (IRE)**, 6, b g Flemensfirth (USA)—Denwoman (IRE) **G Mason,Sir A Ferguson,Mr&Mrs P K Barber**
45 **DIAMOND GUY (FR)**, 6, b g Konig Turf (GER)—Unique Chance (FR) **Executors & Trustees of C G Roach Estate**
46 4, B g Shantou (USA)—Didinas (FR) **McNeill Family Ltd**
47 **DIEGO DU CHARMIL (FR)**, 7, b g Ballingarry (IRE)—Daramour (FR) **Mrs S. De La Hey**
48 **DIVIN BERE (FR)**, 6, b g Della Francesca (USA)—Mofa Bere (FR) **Mr C. M. Giles**
49 **DJINGLE (FR)**, 6, b g Voix du Nord (FR)—Jourie (FR) **McNeill Family Ltd**
50 **DOGON**, 4, b g Intello (GER)—Poppets Sweetlove **Middleham Park Racing LXXVIII& A&J Ryan**
51 **DOLOS (FR)**, 6, b g Kapgarde (FR)—Redowa (FR) **Mrs S. De La Hey**
52 **DR SANDERSON (IRE)**, 5, b g Jeremy (USA)—Guydus (IRE) **Million in Mind Partnership**
53 **DYNAMITE DOLLARS (FR)**, 6, b br g Buck's Boum (FR)—Macadoun (FR) **Mr M. F. Geoghegan**
54 **EASON (FR)**, 5, b g Coastal Path—Maitresse de Maison (FR) **Mr A. N. V. Williams**
55 **EASYRUN DE VASSY (FR)**, 5, b g Muhtathir—Royale The Best (FR) **The Brooks, Stewart Families & P.J. Vogt**
56 **ECCO**, 4, b g Maxios—Enjoy The Life **Mr C. A. Donlon**
57 **EGGARDON HILL (IRE)**, 5, b g Doyen (IRE)—Ma Minx (FR) **Gibson, Macdonald, Monk & Nicholls**
58 **EL BANDIT (IRE)**, 8, b br g Milan—Bonnie Parker (IRE) **Barry Fulton, Colm Donlon & Chris Giles**
59 **ELLARNA (FR)**, 5, b m Lucarno (USA)—Oeuvre d'art (FR) **Axom LXIX**
60 **EMERGING TALENT (IRE)**, 10, b g Golan (IRE)—Elviria (IRE) **Mr & Mrs Paul Barber**
61 **ENRILO (FR)**, 5, bl g Buck's Boum (FR)—Rock Treasure (FR) **Martin Broughton & Friends 4**
62 **ENVOYE SPECIAL (FR)**, 5, b g Coastal Path—Santa Bamba (FR) **Stewart, Brooks, Kyle & Mason**
63 **ERITAGE (FR)**, 5, b g Martaline—Sauves La Reine (FR) **Mrs A. Tincknell**
64 **FAVORITO BUCK'S (FR)**, 7, b g Buck's Boum (FR)—Sangrilla (FR) **Mrs S. De La Hey**
65 **FEU DU LARGE (FR)**, 4, ch g Kapgarde (FR)—Rapsodie Sea (FR) **David Maxwell Racing Limited**

MR PAUL NICHOLLS - Continued

66 **FLASH COLLONGES (FR)**, 4, b g Saddler Maker (IRE)—Prouesse Collonges (FR) **The Gi Gi Syndicate**
67 **FLEMENSTIDE (IRE)**, 4, b g Flemensfirth (USA)—Keep Face (FR) **Mr P K Barber & Mr P J Vogt**
68 **FLIC OU VOYOU (FR)**, 5, b g Kapgarde (FR)—Hillflower (FR) **Mr C. A. Donlon**
69 **FORCE TEN (FR)**, 4, b g Al Namix (FR)—Quick Siren Mae (FR) **Owners Group 029**
70 **FRIEND OR FOE (FR)**, 4, b g Walk In The Park (IRE)—Mandchou (FR) **Gordon & Su Hall**
71 **FRODON (FR)**, 7, b g Nickname (FR)—Miss Country (FR) **Mr P. J. Vogt**
72 5, B g Yeats (IRE)—Get Me Home (IRE) **M. C. Denmark**
73 **GETAWAY TRUMP (IRE)**, 6, b g Getaway (GER)—Acinorev (IRE) **Owners Group 023**
74 **GIVE ME A COPPER (IRE)**, 9, ch g Presenting—Copper Supreme (IRE) **Done, Ferguson, Kyle, Mason & Wood**
75 **GOLDEN GIFT (IRE)**, 5, b g Gold Well—Five Star Present (IRE) **Mr&Mrs P.K.Barber,G.Mason,Sir A Ferguson**
76 **GRAND SANCY (FR)**, 5, b g Diamond Boy (FR)—La Courtille (FR) **Martin Broughton Racing Partners**
77 **GREENETEEN (FR)**, 5, b g Great Pretender (FR)—Manson Teene (FR) **Mr C. M. Giles**
78 **GREAT BEYOND**, 4, b g Dansili—Solar Pursuit
79 **GREY GETAWAY (IRE)**, 5, gr g Getaway (GER)—Miss Greylands (FR) **Mr P. J. Vogt**
80 **HUGOS HORSE (FR)**, 6, gr g Turgeon (USA)—Bella Eria (FR) **The Stewart Family**
81 **HUGOS OTHER HORSE**, 5, b g Gold Well—Wicked Crack (IRE) **The Stewart Family**
82 **IBIS DU RHEU (FR)**, 8, b g Blue Bresil (FR)—Dona du Rheu (FR) **Mr J. Hales**
83 **IF YOU SAY RUN (IRE)**, 7, b m Mahler—De Lissa (IRE) **Highclere T'bred Racing If You Say Run**
84 **KAPCORSE (FR)**, 6, br g Kapgarde (FR)—Angesse (FR) **Mr J. P. McManus**
85 **KILMINGTON ROSE (IRE)**, 4, ch f Presenting—Robyn's Rose (IRE) **Mr H. T. Pelham**
86 **KINGS INN (IRE)**, 5, b g Mawatheeq (USA)—Afnoon (USA) **Owners Group 021**
87 **LE PREZIEN (FR)**, 8, br g Blue Bresil (FR)—Abu Dhabi (FR) **Mr J. P. McManus**
88 **LISA DE VASSY (FR)**, 4, b f Cokoriko (FR)—Mona Vassy (FR) **Mrs S. De La Hey**
89 **MAGIC SAINT (FR)**, 5, b g Saint des Saints (FR)—Magic Poline (FR) **Mr & Mrs J. D. Cotton**
90 **MAGOO (IRE)**, 7, gr g Martaline—Noche (IRE) **Brooks, Fulton, Stewart & Vogt**
91 **MALAYA (FR)**, 5, b m Martaline—Clarte d'or (FR) **Mrs S. De La Hey**
92 **MCFABULOUS (IRE)**, 5, b g Milan—Rossavon (IRE) **Giraffa Racing**
93 **MEAGHER'S FLAG (IRE)**, 4, b g Teofilo (IRE)—Gearanai (USA) **Mr S. White**
94 **MINELLA ROYALE**, 6, b g Shirocco (GER)—Lisa du Chenet (FR)
95 **MIRANDA**, 4, b f Camelot—Great Artist (FR) **Owners Group 034**
96 **MISTER TIMMYTUCKS**, 6, b g Kayf Tara—No Need For Alarm **A. G. Fear**
97 **MODUS**, 9, ch g Motivator—Alessandra **Mr J. P. McManus**
98 **MONT DES AVALOIRS (FR)**, 6, b g Blue Bresil (FR)—Abu Dhabi (FR) **Mrs S. De La Hey**
99 **MOVEWITHTHETIMES (IRE)**, 8, ch g Presenting—Dare To Venture (IRE) **Mr J. P. McManus**
100 **MY WAY (FR)**, 5, ch g Martaline—Royale Majesty (FR) **McNeill Family & Mr Chris Giles**
101 **NEW GUARD**, 5, b m Kayf Tara—Easibrook Jane **The Brooks, Stewart Families & J. Kyle**
102 **NINEOHTWOONEOH (IRE)**, 5, b g Fame And Glory—Oscar's Beauty (IRE) **Mr J. P. McManus**
103 **NOT A NAIL (IRE)**, 5, b g Flemensfirth (USA)—Mandys Gold (IRE) **Mr C. A. Donlon**
104 **OLD GUARD**, 8, b g Notnowcato—Dolma (FR) **The Brooks, Stewart Families & J. Kyle**
105 **OSTUNI (FR)**, 6, b g Great Pretender (FR)—Mamassita (FR) **B. N. Fulton**
106 **OVERLAND FLYER (IRE)**, 8, b g Westerner—Love Train (IRE) **Mr C. A. Donlon**
107 **PACHA DU POLDER (FR)**, 12, b g Muhtathir—Ambri Piotta (FR) **The Stewart Family**
108 **PARODY**, 5, br m Presenting—Arctic Actress **Owners Group 019**
109 **PEAK TO PEAK (IRE)**, 7, br g Authorized (IRE)—Bayourida (USA) **Mr & Mrs Mark Woodhouse**
110 **PIC D'ORHY (FR)**, 4, b g Turgeon (USA)—Rose Candy (FR)
111 **PILANSBERG**, 7, b g Rail Link—Posteritas (USA) **Martin Broughton & Friends 3**
112 **POLITOLOGUE (FR)**, 8, gr g Poliglote—Scarlet Row (FR) **Mr J. Hales**
113 **POSH TRISH (IRE)**, 6, b m Stowaway—Moscow Demon (IRE) **Highclere T'bred Racing - Posh Trish**
114 **PRESENT MAN (IRE)**, 9, b g Presenting—Glen's Gale (IRE) **Mr & Mrs Mark Woodhouse**
115 **QUEL DESTIN (FR)**, 4, ch g Muhtathir—High Destiny (FR) **Martin Broughton & Friends**
116 **RAINBOW BRIDGE**, 8, b g Exit To Nowhere (USA)—Lady of Scarvagh (IRE) **D. Downie**
117 **RED FORCE ONE**, 4, ro g Lethal Force (IRE)—Dusty Red **Done Ferguson Mason**
118 **RHYTHM IS A DANCER**, 6, b g Norse Dancer (IRE)—Fascinatin Rhythm **Mr W. A. Harrison-Allan**
119 **RIDGEWAY FLYER**, 8, b g Tobougg (IRE)—Running For Annie **A. J. Norman**
120 **RISK AND ROLL (FR)**, 5, b g No Risk At All (FR)—Rolie de Vindecy (FR) **Mrs S. De La Hey**
121 **ROMAIN DE SENAM (FR)**, 7, b g Saint des Saints (FR)—Salvatrixe (FR) **Mr Chris Giles & Mr Dan Macdonald**
122 **SABRINA (IRE)**, 4, b f Yeats (IRE)—En Vedette (FR) **Owners Group 030**
123 **SAINT DE REVE (FR)**, 5, b g Saint des Saints (FR)—Ty Mat (FR) **Mrs S. De La Hey**
124 **SAINTEMILION (FR)**, 6, b g Diamond Green (FR)—Matakana (FR) **Mrs Kathy Stuart & Mr Terry Warner**
125 **SAMETEGAL (FR)**, 10, b g Saint des Saints (FR)—Loya Lescribaa (FR) **Mr & Mrs J. D. Cotton**
126 **SAN BENEDETO (FR)**, 8, ch g Layman (USA)—Cinco Baidy (FR) **Mr P. J. Vogt**
127 **SAN SATIRO (IRE)**, 8, b g Milan—Longueville Quest (IRE) **The Manor Syndicate**
128 **SAO (FR)**, 5, b br g Great Pretender (FR)—Miss Country (FR) **Mrs S. De La Hey**
129 **SCARAMANGA (IRE)**, 4, b g Mastercraftsman (IRE)—Herboriste **M. C. Denmark**
130 **SECRET INVESTOR**, 7, b g Kayf Tara—Silver Charmer **Hills of Ledbury Ltd**

MR PAUL NICHOLLS - Continued

131 **SEELOTMOREBUSINESS (IRE)**, 4, b g Sholokhov (IRE)—Land of Pride (IRE) **The Roy & Stewart Families**
132 **SILSOL (GER)**, 10, b g Soldier Hollow—Silveria (GER) **Michelle And Dan Macdonald**
133 **SILVER FOREVER (IRE)**, 5, gr m Jeremy (USA)—Silver Prayer (IRE) **Mr C. A. Donlon**
134 **SOME MAN (IRE)**, 6, b g Beat Hollow—Miss Denman (IRE) **Grech & Parkin**
135 **SOUTHFIELD HARVEST**, 5, b g Kayf Tara—Chamoss Royale (FR) **Mrs A. B. Yeoman**
136 **SOUTHFIELD STONE**, 4, b g Fair Mix (IRE)—Laureldean Belle (IRE) **Mrs Angela Hart & Mrs Angela Yeoman**
137 **SOUTHFIELD TORR**, 6, gr ro g Fair Mix (IRE)—Chamoss Royale (FR) **Mrs Angela Hart & Mrs Angela Yeoman**
138 **SOUTHFIELD VIC (IRE)**, 10, ch g Old Vic—Chamoss Royale (FR) **Mrs A. B. Yeoman**
139 **STARSKY (IRE)**, 5, b g Shantou (USA)—Lunar Star (IRE) **Miss Rachael Evans & Mr Matt Booth**
140 **STORM ARISING (IRE)**, 5, b g Yeats (IRE)—Ceol Rua (IRE) **Mr Barry Fulton & Mr Peter Hart**
141 **STRADIVARIUS DAVIS (FR)**, 6, b g Turgeon (USA)—
                                  Trumpet Davis (FR) **D & M Macdonald & M & M McPherson**
142 **TAMAROC DU MATHAN (FR)**, 4, b g Poliglote—Thisbee du Mathan (FR) **Mrs S. De La Hey**
143 **THE DELLERCHECKOUT (IRE)**, 6, b g Getaway (GER)—Loreley (IRE) **Mr J. Hales**
144 **THE EAGLEHASLANDED (IRE)**, 9, b g Milan—Vallee Doree (FR) **Coles, Smith & McManus**
145 **TOMMY SILVER (FR)**, 7, b g Silver Cross (FR)—Sainte Mante (FR) **Done, Ferguson, Mason & Wood**
146 **TOMORROW MYSTERY**, 5, b m Nathaniel (IRE)—Retake **Mr J. P. McManus**
147 **TOPOFTHEGAME (IRE)**, 7, ch g Flemensfirth (USA)—Derry Vale (IRE) **Mr Chris Giles & Mr&mrs P K Barber**
148 **TOUCH KICK (IRE)**, 8, b g Presenting—Bay Pearl (FR) **Mr T. J. Hemmings**
149 **TREVELYN'S CORN (IRE)**, 6, b g Oscar (IRE)—Present Venture (IRE) **Mr C. M. Giles**
150 **TRUCKERS LODGE (IRE)**, 7, b g Westerner—Galeacord (IRE) **Gordon & Su Hall**
151 **UNIONISTE (FR)**, 11, gr g Dom Alco (FR)—Gleep Will (FR) **David Maxwell Racing Limited**
152 **VICENTE (FR)**, 10, b g Dom Alco (FR)—Ireland (FR) **Mr T. J. Hemmings**
153 **WARRIORS TALE**, 10, b g Midnight Legend—Samandara (FR) **Mr T. J. Hemmings**
154 **WONDERFUL CHARM (FR)**, 11, b g Poliglote—Victoria Royale (FR) **RJH Geffen, Sir J Ritblat, R Waley-Cohen**
155 **WORTHY FARM (IRE)**, 6, b g Beneficial—Muckle Flugga (IRE) **YOLO**
156 4, Br g Stowaway—Zuzka (IRE) **Mrs A. Tincknell**
157 **ZYON**, 5, gr g Martaline—Temptation (FR) **Mrs S. De La Hey**

THREE-YEAR-OLDS

158 **EIGHTEENHUNDRED (IRE)**, b g Battle of Marengo (IRE)—Kawaha (IRE) **Fogg, Nicholls, Penny & Williams**
159 **KING OF THE RING**, b g Sepoy (AUS)—Anosti **Mason, Ferguson, Bolton & Gibson**
160 **SHELLEBEAU (IRE)**, b f War Command (USA)—Attracted To You (IRE) **Macdonald, Gibson & Nicholls**

Other Owners: Mr R. J. Acock, Mr S. R. Aston, Axom Ltd, P Bamford, P.K. Barber, Mrs M. G. Barber, Mr J. Barnard, Mr D. Bennett, P.H. Betts, Mr J. F. Bolton, Mr M. Booth, Mr N. Brand, A. R. Bromley, Mr G. F. Brooks, Mr S. W. Broughton, Lady J. M. Broughton, Sir M. F. Broughton, Mr A. P. Brown, Mr D. J. Coles, Mrs J. C. Corsellis, J. D. Cotton, Mrs B. Cotton, Dame J. O. Dench, Mr J. Diver, Mr P. E. Done, Mr D. Downie, Mr A. Doyle, Mr R. G. Eddy, Miss R. Evans, Sir A. Ferguson, Mr I. J. Fogg, Mr R. J. H. Geffen, Mr A. Gibson, G. F. Goode, Mr C. M. Grech, Mrs D. M. Gregory, Miss L. J. Hales, Mr J. R. Hales, Mr R. Hales, Mr G. A. Hall, Mrs S. L. Hall, Mr P. M. P. Hammond, Mrs A. R. Hart, Highclere Nominated Partner Limited, Highclere Thoroughbred Racing Ltd, Mr A. J. Hill, Mr B. M. Hillier, Mr J. Holman, Mr J. H. Jackson, Mrs N. Jones, Mr J. Kyle, Mr W. D. Macdonald, Mrs M. Macdonald, Mr P. D. Maddocks, Mr D. J. Martin, Marwyn Asset Management SPC, g A. Mason, Mr B. J. McManus, Mr M. H. McPherson, Mr W. W. McPherson, Mr W. D. C. Minton, Mr K. Monk, Mrs M. E. Moody, P. F. Nicholls, Mrs D. C. Nicholson, T. S. Palin, Mr S. J. Parkin, R. M. Penny, M. Prince, Sir J. H. Ritblat, Mrs S. M. Roy, Mr E. J. N. Seyfried, Miss Claire Simmonds, Mr B. D. Smith, Mr D. D. Stevenson, Mr A. Stewart, Mrs J. A. Stewart, Mr C. Thompson, Mr D. J. Trembath, Mr R. B. Waley-Cohen, J. T. Warner, Mr R. J. Wood, Mrs T. A. Woodhouse, M. J. M. Woodhouse, Mrs A. Wylie, Mr A. W. G. Wylie.

Assistant Trainers: Harry Derham, Natalie Parker, Kelly O'Boyle

Jockey (NH): Harry Cobden, Sam Twiston-Davies, Sean Bowen, Bryony Frost. **Conditional:** Alex Thorne, Lorcan Williams. **Apprentice:** Megan Nicholls. **Amateur:** Mr Will Biddick, Mr Bryan Carver, Mr Matt Hampton, Miss Natalie Parker, Miss Harriet Tucker.

---

420 **MR PETER NIVEN, Malton**
Postal: **Clovafield, Barton-Le-Street, Malton, North Yorkshire, YO17 6PN**
Contacts: PHONE **(01653) 628176** FAX **(01653) 627295** MOBILE **(07860) 260999**
E-MAIL pruniven@btinternet.com WEBSITE www.peterniven.co.uk

1 **BRIAN BORANHA (IRE)**, 8, b g Brian Boru—Tapneiram (IRE) **Mrs K. J. Young**
2 **BROMANCE**, 6, b g Showcasing—Romantic Destiny **The SB Club**
3 **CLEVER COOKIE**, 11, b g Primo Valentino (IRE)—Mystic Memory **Mr P. D. Niven**
4 **HAAFAPRINCESS**, 6, b m Haafhd—Mystic Glen **Mrs J A Niven & Angus Racing Club**
5 **HARRY HUSSAR**, 9, b g Primo Valentino (IRE)—Jessie May (IRE) **Mr P. D. Niven**

MR PETER NIVEN - Continued

6 **LOVE AT DAWN (IRE)**, 6, br m Winged Love (IRE)—Presentingatdawn (IRE) **The Dawn Risers**
7 **MALYSTIC**, 5, b g Malinas (GER)—Mystic Glen **Clova Syndicate & Mrs J A Niven**
8 **PIXIEPOT**, 9, b m Alflora (IRE)—Folly Foster **The Rumpole Partnership**
9 **SIMPLY MANI**, 7, ch g Sulamani (IRE)—Simply Mystic **Mrs J A Niven & Angus Racing Club**
10 **WICKLOW WARRIOR**, 4, b g Sleeping Indian—Vale of Clara (IRE) **Mr P. D. Niven**

THREE-YEAR-OLDS

11 **AMBER**, ch f Dunaden (FR)—Secret Virtue **Keep The Faith Partnership**

Other Owners: Angus Racing Club, Mr K. Avison, S. J. Bowett, Clova Syndicate, Mr B. W. Ewart, Miss C. Foster, Mr W. E. Gill, Mr A. B. Hanna, Mr G. S. Harrison, Mr A. M. Murray, Mrs J. A. Niven, Mr M. W. G. Niven, Mrs K. M. Richardson, M A. Scaife, J. M. Swinglehurst, Mrs G. M. Swinglehurst.

---

421 MRS LUCY NORMILE, Glenfarg
Postal: Duncrievie, Glenfarg, Perthshire, PH2 9PD
Contacts: PHONE (01577) 830330 FAX (01577) 830658 MOBILE (07721) 454818
E-MAIL lucy@normileracing.co.uk WEBSITE www.normileracing.co.uk

1 **CADORE (IRE)**, 11, b g Hurricane Run (IRE)—Mansiya **Twentys Plenty**
2 **CALL ME (IRE)**, 8, b g Craigsteel—Wake Me Gently (IRE) **The Explorers**
3 **CURRAMORE (IRE)**, 5, br g Arcadio (GER)—Beale Native **Mrs F. E. Bocker**
4 **GENUINELY CROWDED (IRE)**, 4, b f Zoffany (IRE)—Genuinely (IRE) **Mrs F. E. Bocker**
5 **GLAMOROUS GOLD (IRE)**, 6, b m Gold Well—Glamorous Leader (IRE) **Mrs F. E. Bocker**
6 **GRANITE CITY DOC**, 6, b g Arabian Gleam—Hansomis (IRE) **Corsby Racing**
7 **KARINGO**, 12, ch g Karinga Bay—Wild Happening (GER) **Douglas Black & P A Carnaby**
8 4, B g Westerner—Primrose Time **Mrs F. M. Whitaker**
9 **REMEMBER ROCKY**, 10, ch g Haafhd—Flower Market **Byrne Racing**
10 **ROYAL DUCHESS**, 9, b m Dutch Art—Royal Citadel (IRE) **Mr S. W. Dick**
11 **ROYAL REGENT**, 7, b g Urgent Request (IRE)—Royal Citadel (IRE) **Mr S. W. Dick**
12 **SENSE OF URGENCY (IRE)**, 7, ch m Captain Rio—Itsallaracket (IRE) **Mrs F. E. Bocker**
13 **SILVERTON**, 12, gr m Silver Patriarch (IRE)—Gretton **Twentys Plenty**
14 **SPACE SAFARI (FR)**, 6, b g Kapgarde (FR)—Prodiga (FR) **Mrs F. E. Bocker**
15 **WOLF HEART (IRE)**, 11, b g Dalakhani (IRE)—Lisieux Orchid (IRE) **Twentys Plenty**
16 **ZAMARKHAN (FR)**, 6, b g Great Journey (JPN)—Zannkiya **Mrs F. E. Bocker**

THREE-YEAR-OLDS

17 **ROYAL COUNTESS**, b f Coach House (IRE)—Dont Tell Nan **Mr S. W. Dick**

Other Owners: Mr D. M. Black, P Byrne, Miss P. A. Carnaby, Mr G. J. D. Cocker, R. N. Ker-Ramsay, Mrs L. B. Normile, Mr A. C. Rodger, B. Thomson, J. R. Williams.

Assistant Trainer: Libby Brodie (07947) 592438

---

422 MR JOHN NORTON, Barnsley
Postal: Globe Farm, High Hoyland, Barnsley, South Yorkshire, S75 4BE
Contacts: PHONE/FAX (01226) 387633 MOBILE (07970) 212707
E-MAIL johnrnorton@hotmail.com WEBSITE www.johnrnortonracehorsetrainer.co.uk

1 **ALJUNOOD (IRE)**, 5, br g Bated Breath—Ataraxy **Jaffa Racing Syndicate**
2 **ALNEEL (IRE)**, 5, ch g New Approach (IRE)—Almass (IRE) **J. R. Norton Ltd**
3 **MAGIC SHIP (IRE)**, 4, b g Kodiac—Baltic Belle (IRE) **J. R. Norton Ltd**
4 **MUFTAKKER**, 5, gr g Tamayuz—Oertaas (IRE) **Colin Holder Racing**
5 **MUTAMAYEL (IRE)**, 5, b g Mawatheeq (USA)—Musharakaat (IRE) **J. R. Norton Ltd**
6 **NAASIK**, 6, b g Poet's Voice—Shemriyna (IRE) **J. R. Norton Ltd**
7 **ROYAL RATTLE**, 4, b g Delegator—Rattleyurjewellery **Barley Racing Club 2**
8 **SPY FI**, 5, b m Dick Turpin (IRE)—Sindarbella **J. R. Norton Ltd**
9 **THE JUNIOR MAN (IRE)**, 8, b g Darsi (FR)—Pear Tart (IRE) **Fellowship Of The Rose Partnership 2**

MR JOHN NORTON - Continued

THREE-YEAR-OLDS

10 SEDA ROSA, b f Paco Boy (IRE)—Green Silk (IRE) **J. R. Norton Ltd**

Other Owners: Barley Racing Club, Fellowship Of The Rose Partnership, Mr R. M. Firth, Mr Colin Holder, Mr P. J. Marshall, Mr P. Newman, Mr Glen Smith, Mr P. Woodcock-Jones.

423

MR JEREMY NOSEDA, Newmarket
Postal: Shalfleet, 17 Bury Road, Newmarket, Suffolk, CB8 7BX
Contacts: PHONE (01638) 664010 FAX (01638) 664100 MOBILE (07710) 294093
E-MAIL jeremy@jeremynoseda.com WEBSITE www.jeremynoseda.com

1 **ABE LINCOLN (USA)**, 6, b h Discreet Cat (USA)—Truly Blushed (USA)
2 **BETTY F**, 4, ch f Frankel—Instance
3 **CENOTAPH (USA)**, 7, b g War Front (USA)—Sanserif (IRE)
4 **DEPARTMENT OF WAR (IRE)**, 4, ch c Declaration of War (USA)—Danetime Out (IRE)
5 **JUS PIRES (USA)**, 5, br g Scat Daddy (USA)—Liza Lu (USA)
6 **LE NOTRE**, 7, b g Champs Elysees—Millistar
7 **MISSY MISCHIEF (USA)**, 4, b f Into Mischief (USA)—Ring True (USA)
8 **PERFECT HUSTLER (USA)**, 4, ch g Jimmy Creed (USA)—Jacqui's Promise (USA)

THREE-YEAR-OLDS

9 **ELLS BELLS**, b f Dansili—Instance
10 **FASHION STAKES (IRE)**, b f Dark Angel (IRE)—Warshah (IRE)
11 **GARRUS (IRE)**, b gr c Acclamation—Queen of Power (IRE)
12 **JOHNNY REB**, b c Showcasing—Specific Dream
13 **KAMIKAZE LORD (USA)**, ch c First Samurai (USA)—Le Sang Royale (USA)
14 **LADY COSETTE (FR)**, b f Wootton Bassett—Faviva (USA)
15 **LOST IN ALASKA (USA)**, b c Discreet Cat (USA)—Truly Blushed (USA)
16 **NO TROUBLE (IRE)**, b g No Nay Never—Lady Babooshka
17 **POET'S CORNER**, b g Poet's Voice—Helter Helter (USA)
18 **RIMMAL (USA)**, b f Bellamy Road (USA)—Shooting Party (USA)
19 **SAMBA SARAVAH (USA)**, b br c Union Rags (USA)—Caragh Queen (USA)
20 **TERESITA ALVAREZ (USA)**, b f Arch (USA)—Stroll By (USA)

TWO-YEAR-OLDS

21 **BOMA GREEN**, b br c 25/1 Iffraaj—Dubai Cyclone (USA) (Bernardini (USA)) (100000)
22 **BRAVE NEW WORLD (IRE)**, ch c 24/3 No Nay Never (USA)—
Dara's Girl (IRE) (Starspangledbanner (AUS)) (101137)
23 **BRING HIM HOME (FR)**, ch c 30/3 Le Havre (IRE)—Unaided (Dansili)
24 **CARMENA (IRE)**, b f 25/3 No Nay Never (USA)—Thewaytosanjose (IRE) (Fasliyev (USA)) (113780)
25 Br c 11/2 Society Rock (IRE)—Chantaleen (FR) (Falco (USA)) (100000)
26 **ETERNAL SECRET**, b f 10/4 Muhaarar—Walk On Bye (Danehill Dancer (IRE)) (125000)
27 **LA PUNTALINA (IRE)**, b f 22/3 Pivotal—Fondled (Selkirk (USA))
28 **PERSUASION (IRE)**, b c 24/2 Acclamation—Effervesce (IRE) (Galileo (IRE)) (220000)
29 **PRINCE OF TIDES (IRE)**, b c 1/3 New Approach (IRE)—Baby Houseman (Oasis Dream) (101137)
30 **ZENAIDA (IRE)**, b f 23/4 Kodiac—Constellation (Cape Cross (IRE)) (126421)

Owners: Mr Al Banwan, Lady Jocelyn Broughton, Mr Naser Buresli, Mr Charles Fox, Happy Valley Racing & Breeding, Mr N O'Sullivan, Mrs Susan Roy, Shalfleet Partnership, Mrs D A Tabor, Mr N Watts, Mr Ben Wilson.

Assistant Trainer: Dave Bradley

424

MR A. P. O'BRIEN, Ballydoyle
Postal: Ballydoyle Stables, Cashel, Co. Tipperary, Ireland
Contacts: PHONE (00353) 6262615
E-MAIL racingoffice@ballydoyle.com

1 **AMEDEO MODIGLIANI (IRE)**, 4, b c Galileo (IRE)—Gooseberry Fool
2 **CAPRI (IRE)**, 5, gr h Galileo (IRE)—Dialafara (FR)
3 4, B f Galileo (IRE)—Chintz (IRE)
4 **CYPRESS CREEK (IRE)**, 4, gr c Galileo (IRE)—Dialafara (FR)
5 **DELANO ROOSEVELT (IRE)**, 4, b c Galileo (IRE)—Again (IRE)

MR A. P. O'BRIEN - Continued

6 **FLAG OF HONOUR (IRE)**, 4, b c Galileo (IRE)—Hawala (IRE)
7 **HUNTING HORN (IRE)**, 4, b c Camelot—Mora Bai (IRE)
8 **I CAN FLY**, 4, b f Fastnet Rock (AUS)—Madonna Dell'orto
9 **IDAHO (IRE)**, 6, b h Galileo (IRE)—Hveger (AUS)
10 **KEW GARDENS (IRE)**, 4, b c Galileo (IRE)—Chelsea Rose (IRE)
11 **LE BRIVIDO (FR)**, 5, b h Siyouni (FR)—La Bugatty (IRE)
12 **LOST TREASURE (IRE)**, 4, b c War Front (USA)—Wading (IRE)
13 **MAGIC WAND (IRE)**, 4, b f Galileo (IRE)—Prudenzia (IRE)
14 **MAGICAL (IRE)**, 4, b f Galileo (IRE)—Halfway To Heaven (IRE)
15 **SOUTHERN FRANCE (IRE)**, 4, b c Galileo (IRE)—Alta Anna (FR)
16 **SQUIRE'S TALE (IRE)**, 5, b g Galileo (IRE)—Weekend Strike (USA)
17 **ST PATRICK'S DAY (USA)**, 4, b c Pioneerof the Nile (USA)—Littleprincessemma (USA)

THREE-YEAR-OLDS

18 **AFAR (IRE)**, b f Galileo (IRE)—Chanting (USA)
19 **ALBUQUERQUE (IRE)**, b c Galileo (IRE)—Looking Back (IRE)
20 **ALL THE KING'S MEN (IRE)**, b br c No Nay Never (USA)—Chaibia (IRE)
21 **ANTHONY VAN DYCK (IRE)**, b c Galileo (IRE)—Believe'n'succeed (AUS)
22 **ANTILLES (USA)**, b c War Front (USA)—Wonder of Wonders (USA)
23 **AT LAST (IRE)**, b f Galileo (IRE)—Zouzou (AUS)
24 **BARBADOS (IRE)**, b c Galileo (IRE)—Sumora (IRE)
25 **BLENHEIM PALACE (IRE)**, ch c Galileo (IRE)—Meow (IRE)
26 **BROOME (IRE)**, b c Australia—Sweepstake (IRE)
27 **CAPE OF GOOD HOPE (IRE)**, b c Galileo (IRE)—Hveger (AUS)
28 **CAPTAINOFTHEBOUNTY (USA)**, b c War Front (USA)—Drifting Cube (AUS)
29 **CAREFULLY (USA)**, b f War Front (USA)—Marvellous (IRE)
30 **CHABLIS (IRE)**, b f Galileo (IRE)—Vadawina (IRE)
31 **CIRCUS MAXIMUS (IRE)**, b c Galileo (IRE)—Duntle (IRE)
32 **CONSTANTINOPLE (IRE)**, b c Galileo (IRE)—One Moment In Time (IRE)
33 **CORAL BEACH (IRE)**, b f Zoffany (IRE)—Abbasharjah (GER)
34 **CREDENZA (IRE)**, b f Galileo (IRE)—Bye Bye Birdie (IRE)
35 **DEEP ATLANTIC (IRE)**, b c Galileo (IRE)—Wave (IRE)
36 **DELPHINIA (IRE)**, b f Galileo (IRE)—Again (IRE)
37 **DESERT ISLAND (IRE)**, b c Australia—Peeping Fawn (USA)
38 **DRESS (IRE)**, b f War Front (USA)—Silk And Scarlet
39 **DUNKIRK HARBOUR (USA)**, gr c Declaration of War (USA)—Goodness Gray (USA)
40 **EMINENCE (IRE)**, b c Sea The Stars (IRE)—Coolree Marj (IRE)
41 **EMPIRE STATE (USA)**, b c Scat Daddy (USA)—Love's Blush (USA)
42 **ENTICED (IRE)**, b f Galileo (IRE)—Dialafara (FR)
43 **FAIRY FORT (USA)**, b c War Front (USA)—Kissed (IRE)
44 **FAIRYLAND (IRE)**, b f Kodiac—Queenofthefairies
45 **FANTASY (IRE)**, b f Invincible Spirit (IRE)—Cassandra Go (IRE)
46 **FERRETTI (USA)**, b c War Front (USA)—Shell House (IRE)
47 **FIRE FLY (IRE)**, ch f Galileo (IRE)—Massarra
48 **FLEETING (IRE)**, b f Zoffany (IRE)—Azafata (SPA)
49 **FLOWERING PEACH (IRE)**, b f Galileo (IRE)—Naples Bay (USA)
50 **FLYING (IRE)**, b f Galileo (IRE)—Butterfly Cove (USA)
51 **FOUR LEAF CLOVER (IRE)**, b f Galileo (IRE)—Hawala (IRE)
52 **FRESNO (IRE)**, ch c Galileo (IRE)—Moonlight Cloud
53 **FROSTY (IRE)**, ch f Galileo (IRE)—Laddies Poker Two (IRE)
54 **GENTILE BELLINI**, b c Dubawi (IRE)—Sky Lantern (IRE)
55 **GLOBE THEATRE (USA)**, b c War Front (USA)—Was (IRE)
56 **GODDESS (USA)**, b f Camelot—Cherry Hinton
57 **GODZILLA (IRE)**, b c Galileo (IRE)—Monsoon Wedding (AUS)
58 **GOSSAMER WINGS (USA)**, b f Scat Daddy (USA)—Lavender Baby (USA)
59 **HAPPEN (USA)**, b f War Front (USA)—Alexandrova (IRE)
60 **HARPO MARX (IRE)**, b c Galileo (IRE)—Nechita (AUS)
61 **HEAVEN ON EARTH (IRE)**, b f Galileo (IRE)—Lillie Langtry (IRE)
62 **HERMOSA (IRE)**, b f Galileo (IRE)—Beauty Is Truth (IRE)
63 **I REMEMBER YOU (IRE)**, b f Australia—Remember You (IRE)
64 **IL PARADISO (USA)**, ch c Galileo (IRE)—Famous (USA)
65 **INVITATION (IRE)**, ch f Galileo (IRE)—Night Lagoon (GER)
66 **JACK YEATS (IRE)**, b c Galileo (IRE)—Fire Lily (IRE)
67 **JAPAN**, b c Galileo (IRE)—Shastye (IRE)

MR A. P. O'BRIEN - Continued

68 **JUST SO (IRE)**, ch f Galileo (IRE)—Magic Tree (UAE)
69 **JUST WONDERFUL (USA)**, b f Dansili—Wading (IRE)
70 **KANGAROO VALLEY (IRE)**, b c Australia—Dundalk Dust (USA)
71 **KING PELLINOR (IRE)**, b r c Camelot—Hitra (USA)
72 **LAKE MCKENZIE (IRE)**, b c Australia—Thai Haku (IRE)
73 **LANCASTER HOUSE (IRE)**, b c Galileo (IRE)—Quiet Oasis (IRE)
74 **MACQUARIE (IRE)**, ch c Australia—Beyond Brilliance (IRE)
75 **MAGIC FOUNTAIN (USA)**, b f War Front (USA)—Bracelet (IRE)
76 **MAGNA GRECIA (IRE)**, b c Invincible Spirit (IRE)—Cabaret (IRE)
77 **MOHAWK (IRE)**, b c Galileo (IRE)—Empowering (IRE)
78 **MONA LISA'S SMILE (USA)**, b br f War Front (USA)—Imagine (IRE)
79 **MOUNT EVEREST (IRE)**, b c Galileo (IRE)—Six Perfections (FR)
80 **NATIONAL GUARD (USA)**, b c War Front (USA)—Coin Broker (IRE)
81 **NEVER NO MORE (IRE)**, ch c No Nay Never (USA)—Law of The Jungle (IRE)
82 **NORWAY (IRE)**, ch c Galileo (IRE)—Love Me True (USA)
83 **OLD GLORY (IRE)**, b c Frankel—Belesta
84 **PACIFIC OCEAN (IRE)**, b c Galileo (IRE)—Atlantic Jewel (AUS)
85 **PEACH TREE (IRE)**, ch f Galileo (IRE)—Pikaboo
86 **PINK DOGWOOD (IRE)**, br f Camelot—Question Times
87 **QUOTE**, b f Galileo (IRE)—Sasuela (GER)
88 **SAN ANDREAS (IRE)**, b c Dark Angel (IRE)—Last Bid
89 **SECRET THOUGHTS (USA)**, b f War Front (USA)—Chicquita (IRE)
90 **SERGEI PROKOFIEV (CAN)**, b c Scat Daddy (USA)—Orchard Beach (CAN)
91 **SIMPLY BEAUTIFUL (IRE)**, gr f Galileo (IRE)—Simply Perfect
92 **SIR DRAGONET (IRE)**, b c Camelot—Sparrow (IRE)
93 **SO PERFECT (USA)**, b f Scat Daddy (USA)—Hopeoverexperience (USA)
94 **SOUTH PACIFIC**, b c Galileo (IRE)—Tonnara (IRE)
95 **SOUTH SEA PEARL (IRE)**, b f Galileo (IRE)—Cassydora
96 **SOVEREIGN (IRE)**, ch c Galileo (IRE)—Devoted To You (IRE)
97 **SYDNEY OPERA HOUSE**, ch c Australia—Sitara
98 **TEN SOVEREIGNS (IRE)**, b c No Nay Never (USA)—Seeking Solace
99 **THE IRISH ROVER (IRE)**, b c No Nay Never (USA)—Shelley Beach (IRE)
100 **THE TOOTH FAIRY (IRE)**, b f Galileo (IRE)—Red Evie (IRE)
101 **TRACING (IRE)**, b f Galileo (IRE)—Ishvana (IRE)
102 **TURNBERRY ISLE (IRE)**, b c Galileo (IRE)—Rosdhu Queen (IRE)
103 **U S S MICHIGAN (USA)**, gr ro c War Front (USA)—Photograph (USA)
104 **VAN BEETHOVEN (CAN)**, b br c Scat Daddy (USA)—My Sister Sandy (USA)
105 **WESTERN AUSTRALIA (IRE)**, ch c Australia—What A Treasure (IRE)
106 **WESTERN FRONTIER (USA)**, b c Scat Daddy (USA)—Missamerica Bertie (USA)
107 **WHITSUNDAY ISLANDS (FR)**, b c Australia—Tocqueville (FR)
108 **ZAGITOVA (IRE)**, ch f Galileo (IRE)—Penchant

TWO-YEAR-OLDS

109 B c 17/3 Galileo (IRE)—Again (IRE) (Danehill Dancer (IRE))
110 B br c 25/3 War Front (USA)—Agreeable Miss (USA) (Speightstown (USA))
111 B c 13/2 Galileo (IRE)—Airwave (Air Express (IRE))
112 B c 14/1 Galileo (IRE)—Alluring Park (IRE) (Green Desert (USA)) (1300000)
113 B f 28/3 Galileo (IRE)—Applauded (IRE) (Royal Applause)
114 B c 6/4 Galileo (IRE)—Atlantic Jewel (AUS) (Fastnet Rock (AUS))
115 B f 17/4 Galileo (IRE)—Beauty Is Truth (IRE) (Pivotal)
116 Ch f 4/3 Galileo (IRE)—Beltisaal (FR) (Belmez (USA))
117 B c 5/2 Lope de Vega (IRE)—Black Dahlia (Dansili) (758533)
118 B f 31/1 War Front (USA)—Bracelet (IRE) (Montjeu (IRE))
119 B c 1/4 Gleneagles (IRE)—Bridal Dance (IRE) (Danehill Dancer (IRE)) (240000)
120 B c 21/2 Galileo (IRE)—Butterfly Cove (USA) (Storm Cat (USA))
121 B c 28/4 American Pharoah (USA)—Canterbury Lace (USA) (Danehill (USA))
122 Gr c 25/4 Dark Angel (IRE)—Capulet Monteque (IRE) (Camacho) (425000)
123 B c 11/4 Galileo (IRE)—Chanting (USA) (Danehill (USA))
124 Ch f 15/2 Galileo (IRE)—Chelsea Rose (IRE) (Desert King (IRE)) (1200000)
125 B c 15/5 Galileo (IRE)—Christmas Kid (USA) (Lemon Drop Kid (USA))
126 B f 3/3 American Pharoah (USA)—Damson (IRE) (Entrepreneur)
127 B c 26/4 No Nay Never (USA)—Dancing Shoes (IRE) (Danehill (USA)) (380000)
128 B c 26/1 Galileo (IRE)—Danedrop (IRE) (Danehill (USA))
129 B f 26/2 Galileo (IRE)—Dialafara (FR) (Anabaa (USA)) (800000)

MR A. P. O'BRIEN - Continued

130 B c 7/2 Frankel—Dietrich (USA) (Storm Cat (USA))
131 Ch c 7/3 Galileo (IRE)—Divine Proportions (USA) (Kingmambo (USA))
132 Ch c 28/1 Zoffany (IRE)—Eirnin (IRE) (Galileo (IRE))
133 B c 28/3 Gleneagles (IRE)—Elle Woods (IRE) (Lawman (FR)) (92709)
134 B c 11/3 Galileo (IRE)—Fire Lily (IRE) (Dansili)
135 B f 29/1 War Front (USA)—Gagnoa (IRE) (Sadler's Wells (USA))
136 Ch c 20/2 American Pharoah (USA)—Global Finance (USA) (End Sweep (USA)) (211640)
137 B c 22/2 Gleneagles (IRE)—Gotlandia (FR) (Anabaa (USA)) (151706)
138 B f 29/1 Galileo (IRE)—Halfway To Heaven (IRE) (Pivotal)
139 B c 7/5 Galileo (IRE)—Hveger (AUS) (Danehill (USA))
140 B c 1/5 Invincible Spirit (IRE)—Ideal (Galileo (IRE))
141 B f 10/3 No Nay Never (USA)—Idle Chatter (IRE) (Galileo (IRE)) (200000)
142 Ch c 23/5 Galileo (IRE)—Ikat (IRE) (Pivotal)
143 B f 15/1 Galileo (IRE)—Inca Princess (IRE) (Holy Roman Emperor (IRE))
144 B c 26/2 Camelot—Inchmina (Cape Cross (IRE)) (235988)
145 B f 20/4 Dark Angel (IRE)—Kelsey Rose (Most Welcome) (325000)
146 B c 4/2 Galileo (IRE)—Kheleyf's Silver (IRE) (Kheleyf (USA))
147 B br c 16/3 War Front (USA)—Kissed (IRE) (Galileo (IRE))
148 B c 16/1 Galileo (IRE)—La Traviata (USA) (Johannesburg (USA))
149 B c 20/2 No Nay Never (USA)—Lady Ederle (USA) (English Channel (USA)) (219131)
150 B f 4/1 Galileo (IRE)—Lahinch (IRE) (Danehill Dancer (IRE))
151 B c 22/4 War Front (USA)—Lerici (USA) (Woodman (USA))
152 B c 7/5 War Front (USA)—Liscanna (IRE) (Sadler's Wells (USA))
153 B c 28/4 No Nay Never (USA)—Lumiere Noire (FR) (Dashing Blade) (140000)
154 B c 14/2 Camelot—Madeira Mist (IRE) (Grand Lodge (USA)) (219131)
155 B c 1/2 Australia—Magic Peak (IRE) (Danehill (USA))
156 B f 2/3 Galileo (IRE)—Magic Tree (UAE) (Timber Country (USA))
157 B c 29/1 War Front (USA)—Marvellous (IRE) (Galileo (IRE))
158 B f 27/4 Galileo (IRE)—Massarra (Danehill (USA))
159 Gr ro c 21/2 American Pharoah (USA)—Mekko Hokte (USA) (Holy Bull (USA)) (705467)
160 Ch c 22/3 Galileo (IRE)—Meow (IRE) (Storm Cat (USA))
161 Br gr f 26/3 Galileo (IRE)—Miarixa (FR) (Linamix (FR))
162 B br c 13/3 War Front (USA)—Misty For Me (IRE) (Galileo (IRE))
163 B c 23/3 Galileo (IRE)—Moonstone (Dalakhani (IRE))
164 B br c 14/4 Pioneerof the Nile (USA)—Mythical Bride (USA) (Street Cry (IRE)) (405643)
165 B c 8/2 War Front (USA)—Outstanding (IRE) (Galileo (IRE))
166 Ch c 5/2 Gleneagles (IRE)—Pearl Grey (Gone West (USA))
167 B f 27/1 Galileo (IRE)—Penchant (Kyllachy) (1200000)
168 Ch f 13/4 Galileo (IRE)—Pikaboo (Pivotal)
169 Ch f 17/2 American Pharoah (USA)—Pretty 'n Smart (USA) (Beau Genius (CAN)) (846560)
170 Ch c 20/3 Galileo (IRE)—Remember When (IRE) (Danehill Dancer (IRE))
171 B f 12/3 Galileo (IRE)—Saphira's Fire (IRE) (Cape Cross (IRE)) (450000)
172 B c 14/3 Zoffany (IRE)—Seatone (USA) (Mizzen Mast (USA)) (220000)
173 B f 11/5 Galileo (IRE)—Secret Garden (IRE) (Danehill (USA))
174 B f 3/4 No Nay Never (USA)—Seeking Solace (Exceed And Excel (AUS)) (600000)
175 B c 18/2 Australia—Senta's Dream (Danehill (USA))
176 B c 3/4 Galileo (IRE)—Shastye (IRE) (Danehill (USA)) (3400000)
177 B f 8/5 American Pharoah (USA)—Shawara (IRE) (Barathea (IRE)) (632111)
178 B c 14/2 War Front (USA)—Shell House (IRE) (Galileo (IRE))
179 Gr c 5/3 Kingman—Shemya (FR) (Dansili) (1050000)
180 B c 4/3 Dark Angel (IRE)—Shermeen (IRE) (Desert Style (IRE))
181 B f 10/4 Fastnet Rock (AUS)—Sleeveless (USA) (Fusaichi Pegasus (USA))
182 B f 21/3 No Nay Never (USA)—Starlet (IRE) (Sea The Stars (IRE)) (589970)
183 B br c 5/3 War Front (USA)—Streaming (USA) (Smart Strike (CAN)) (1693121)
184 B c 24/1 War Front (USA)—Sun Shower (IRE) (Indian Ridge)
185 B c 13/5 Australia—Synchronic (IRE) (Dansili)
186 B c 20/3 War Front (USA)—Tapestry (IRE) (Galileo (IRE))
187 B f 15/3 Gleneagles (IRE)—Tarbela (IRE) (Grand Lodge (USA)) (500000)
188 B c 20/1 Galileo (IRE)—Tiggy Wiggy (IRE) (Kodiac)
189 B c 11/2 War Front (USA)—Together Forever (IRE) (Galileo (IRE))
190 B c 31/3 American Pharoah (USA)—Up (IRE) (Galileo (IRE)) (529100)
191 B br c 7/2 War Front (USA)—Wading (IRE) (Montjeu (IRE))
192 B c 11/3 Authorized (IRE)—Wadyhatta (Cape Cross (IRE))
193 B c 27/1 War Front (USA)—Was (IRE) (Galileo (IRE))
194 B f 9/5 Galileo (IRE)—Wildwood Flower (USA) (Langfuhr (CAN)) (900000)

MR A. P. O'BRIEN - Continued

195 B f 22/2 War Front (USA)—Wonder of Wonders (USA) (Kingmambo (USA))
196 B f 6/1 Galileo (IRE)—Words (IRE) (Dansili)
197 Ch c 6/2 Galileo (IRE)—You'resothrilling (USA) (Storm Cat (USA))

---

425 **MR DANIEL O'BRIEN, Tonbridge**
Postal: **Knowles Bank, Capel, Tonbridge, Kent, TN11 0PU**
Contacts: **PHONE (01892) 824072**

1 BOSTIN (IRE), 11, ch g Busy Flight—Bustingoutallover (USA) **D. C. O'Brien**
2 CABERNET D'ALENE (FR), 7, b g Day Flight—Haifa du Noyer (FR) **D. C. O'Brien**
3 COUNTERACT, 4, b g Dr Massini (IRE)—Aimigayle
4 GOLD MERLION (IRE), 6, b m Alhaarth (IRE)—Sea of Time (USA) **D. C. O'Brien**

Assistant Trainer: Christopher O'Bryan

---

426 **MR FERGAL O'BRIEN, Cheltenham**
Postal: **Upper Yard, Grange Hill Farm, Naunton, Cheltenham, Gloucestershire, GL54 3AY**
Contacts: **PHONE (01451) 850538 MOBILE (07771) 702829**
E-MAIL admin@fergalobrienracing.com

1 A BOOK OF INTRIGUE, 6, b g Alflora (IRE)—Kahlua Cove **Mr Oscar Singh & Miss Priya Purewal**
2 AGENT VALDEZ, 6, b m Arvico (FR)—Soleil Sauvage **The FOB Racing Partnership 6**
3 ASK DILLON (IRE), 6, b g Ask—Mum's Miracle (IRE) **4 The Fun Partnership**
4 AYE AYE CHARLIE, 7, b g Midnight Legend—Trial Trip **All Four One**
5 BALLYHOME (IRE), 8, b g Westerner—Nostra (FR) **A & K Ecofilm Ltd**
6 BARNEY DWAN (IRE), 9, b g Vinnie Roe (IRE)—Kapricia Speed (FR) **Mr & Mrs Paul & Clare Rooney**
7 BELLE AMIS, 6, ch m Black Sam Bellamy (IRE)—Amaretto Rose **Peter Hockenhull & Paul Rich**
8 BELLS 'N' BANJOS (IRE), 9, b g Indian River (FR)—Beechill Dancer (IRE) **The Maple Hurst Partnership**
9 BENNY'S BRIDGE (IRE), 6, b g Beneficial—Wattle Bridge (IRE) **Biddestone Racing I**
10 BLUE MONDAY (IRE), 6, b g Beneficial—Bradbury Baby (IRE) **The FOB Racing Partnership 5**
11 BORN TO SIZE (GER), 7, b g Sholokhov (IRE)—Beyonce (GER) **Millington, Harvey & Jenkins**
12 CALL ME VIC (IRE), 12, b g Old Vic—Call Me Dara (IRE) **Mrs R. J. Tufnell**
13 CAP SOLEIL (FR), 6, b m Kapgarde (FR)—Move Again (GER) **Mrs S. A. Noott**
14 CARROLLS MILAN (IRE), 6, b m Milan—Native Crystal (IRE) **The Gud Times Partnership**
15 CHAMPAGNE WELL (IRE), 6, b g Gold Well—Perkanod (IRE) **The Bolly Champagne Crew**
16 CHASE THE SPUD, 11, b g Alflora (IRE)—Trial Trip **Mrs C. J. Banks**
17 CHILLI ROMANCE (IRE), 8, b m Flemensfirth (USA)—Blue Romance (IRE) **Mr I. Slatter**
18 COOLANLY (IRE), 7, b g Flemensfirth (USA)—La Fisarmonica (IRE) **Five Go Racing**
19 CROSSGALESFAMEGAME (IRE), 5, b m Mahler—Fame Forever (IRE) **Walid Marzouk & Richard Rowland**
20 CUDDLES MCGRAW (IRE), 6, b g Court Cave (IRE)—Stefphonic (IRE) **Graham & Alison Jelley**
21 DAN GUN (IRE), 5, b g Intikhab (USA)—Lady Magdalena (IRE) **Mr F. M. O'Brien**
22 DE NAME EVADES ME (IRE), 7, b g Vinnie Roe (IRE)—
Sound of The Crowd (IRE) **Brown Campbell James Foylan**
23 DIAMOND FORT (IRE), 7, ch g Gamut (IRE)—Ellie Forte **D. J. Shorey**
24 GOLDEN TAIPAN (IRE), 5, b g Golden Lariat (USA)—Rose of Taipan (IRE) **Double Barrels Of Courage**
25 GOOD AND HARDY (IRE), 6, b g Westerner—Kilganey Maid (IRE) **Mr P. E. Smith**
26 GRAGEELAGH GIRL (IRE), 8, b m Craigsteel—Smiths Lady (IRE) **The Yes No Wait Sorries**
27 HUNNY MOON, 5, ch m Flemensfirth (USA)—No More Money **C. B. Brookes**
28 I'M WISER NOW (IRE), 5, b g Presenting—Reine Angevine (FR) **Mr & Mrs Paul & Clare Rooney**
29 IMPERIAL ALCAZAR (IRE), 5, b g Vinnie Roe (IRE)—
Maddy's Supreme (IRE) **Imperial Racing Partnership 2016**
30 IMPERIAL ELIXIR (IRE), 6, b g Doyen (IRE)—Blond's Addition (IRE) **Imperial Racing Partnership 2016**
31 IMPERIAL ELYSIAN (IRE), 5, br g Kalanisi (IRE)—Diva Antonia (IRE) **Imperial Racing Partnership**
32 JARVEYS PLATE (IRE), 6, ch g Getaway (GER)—She's Got To Go (IRE) **The Yes No Wait Sorries**
33 JENNYS SURPRISE (IRE), 11, b m Hawk Wing (USA)—Winning Jenny (IRE) **Foxtrot Nh Racing Syndicate**
34 LILY OF LEYSBOURNE (IRE), 8, b m Shirocco (GER)—Alegralil **C. B. Brookes**
35 LIOSDUIN BHEARNA (IRE), 6, b g Beneficial—Cloth Fair (IRE) **The FOB Racing Partnership 4**
36 LOVELY JOB (IRE), 9, ch g Touch of Land (FR)—Wyckoff Queen (IRE) **Mr & Mrs Paul & Clare Rooney**
37 LUNGARNO PALACE (USA), 8, b g Henrythenavigator (USA)—
Good Time Sally (USA) **Caveat Emptor Partnership**
38 MASTER DEE (IRE), 10, b g King's Theatre (IRE)—Miss Lauren Dee (IRE) **Mr & Mrs Paul & Clare Rooney**

MR FERGAL O'BRIEN - Continued

39 MERCY MERCY ME, 7, b g Shirocco (GER)—Monsignorita (IRE) **M. C. Denmark**
40 MIGHTY LEADER (IRE), 11, b g Milan—Madam Leader (IRE) **Mr Oscar Singh & Miss Priya Purewal**
41 MRS HYDE (IRE), 6, b m Flemensfirth (USA)—Funny Times **Mr M. K. Warren**
42 OCEAN COVE (IRE), 7, ch g Ask—Sand Eel (IRE) **The FOB Racing Partnership**
43 OSCAR ROSE (IRE), 7, b m Oscar (IRE)—Ben Roseler (IRE) **Mrs K. Exall / The General Asphalte Company Ltd**
44 PAINT THE DREAM, 5, b g Brian Boru—Vineuil (FR) **D. Brace**
45 PARISH HILL (IRE), 7, b g Marienbard (IRE)—Lunar Star (IRE) **The B Lucky Partnership**
46 PERFECT CANDIDATE (IRE), 12, b g Winged Love (IRE)—Dansana (IRE) **ISL Recruitment**
47 PHOENICIAN STAR (IRE), 4, ch g Mastercraftsman (IRE)—Place de L'etoile (IRE) **The FOB Racing Partnership 2**
48 POETIC RHYTHM (IRE), 8, ch g Flemensfirth (USA)—Sommer Sonnet (IRE) **The Yes No Wait Sorries**
49 PRIDE OF LECALE, 8, b g Multiplex—Rock Gossip (IRE) **Mr & Mrs Paul & Clare Rooney**
50 QUANTUM OF SOLACE, 9, b m Kayf Tara—Fashion House **007 Partnership**
51 RED HOT CHILLY (IRE), 6, ch g Frozen Power (IRE)—She's Got The Look **Mr & Mrs A. J. Mutch**
52 RISKY GOLD (IRE), 6, b g Gold Well—Ask Me Sister (IRE) **The Yes No Wait Sorries**
53 RIVER OF INTRIGUE (IRE), 9, b g Indian River (FR)—

               Molly Hussey (IRE) **Mr Oscar Singh & Miss Priya Purewal**
54 ROBYNDZONE (IRE), 5, br g Frammassone (IRE)—Rebecca Susan **East India Racing**
55 SATURDAYNIGHTFEVER, 7, b g King's Theatre (IRE)—Get Me Home (IRE) **M. C. Denmark**
56 SHARPE'S RIFLES, 5, b g Arabian Gleam—High Meadow Jo (IRE) **Mrs L. C. Donovan**
57 SHOW'S OVER (IRE), 8, b g Curtain Time (IRE)—Sailors Run (IRE) **Mr B Jones & Son**
58 SOCKSY (IRE), 8, ch m Flemensfirth (USA)—Bachello (IRE) **C. B. Brookes**
59 SOLDIER OF LOVE, 6, b g Yeats (IRE)—Monsignorita (IRE) **M. C. Denmark**
60 STRONG GLANCE, 6, bl g Passing Glance—Strong Westerner (IRE) **Welfordgolf syndicate**
61 4, Gr g Black Sam Bellamy (IRE)—Sylvan Wings **Biddestone Racing Club**
62 TASHUNKA (IRE), 6, b m Flemensfirth (USA)—Las Palmlas (IRE) **The FOB Racing Partnership 3**
63 TIME TO MOVE ON (IRE), 6, ch g Flemensfirth (USA)—Kapricia Speed (FR) **Mr & Mrs Paul & Clare Rooney**
64 TROIKA STEPPES, 11, b g Pasternak—Killerton Clover **Mr W. Williamson**
65 TROUBLED SOUL (IRE), 10, ch m Definite Article—Dorrha Lass (IRE) **Mr F. M. O'Brien**

Other Owners: Mr D. Abraham, Mr Marc Blackford, Mrs Gill Bostwick, Mr Tim Bostwick, Mr S. W. Bowers, Mr J. R. Brown, Mr Chris Coley, Mr M. R. Costello, Mr S. Crabb, Mr Mark Craze, Mr Simon Devereux, Mrs Judy England, Mr Duncan England, Mrs K. Exall, Foxtrot Racing Management Ltd, Mr Bill Foylan, The General Asphalte Company Ltd, Mr Mark Goodall, Mr J. N. Greenley, Mr Martin Higgs, Mr S. Hind, Mr P. D. Hockenhull, Mrs Alison Jelley, Mr Graham Jelley, Mr Brian Jones, Mr Wayne Jones, Mr Geoffrey Keeys, Mrs Donna Keeys, Mr John B. Lawson, Mr Walid Marzouk, Mr Bryan Mathieson, Mr A. J. Mutch, Mrs S. Mutch, Mr P. Nurden, Mr Fergal O'Brien, Mr Chris Plumb, Miss D. Porter, Miss Priya Purewal, Mr R. J. Rainbow, Mr P. M. Rich, Mr Ian A. Robinson, Miss Michelle Robinson, Mr P. A. Rooney, Mrs C. Rooney, Dr Richard Rowland, Mr William Rucker, Mrs A. Rucker, Mr Richard Shorting, Mr Autar Singh, Mrs S. Spencer-Jones, Mr S. Spencer-Jones, Mr Neville Statham, Mr Graham Stone, Miss Michelle Taylor, Mr M. Warren, Mr Richard Williams.

Assistant Trainer: Sally Randell

Jockey (NH): Paddy Brennan. **Conditional:** Connor Brace.

---

427 | **MR JEDD O'KEEFFE, Leyburn**
Postal: Highbeck, Brecongill, Coverham, Leyburn, North Yorkshire, DL8 4TJ
Contacts: PHONE (01969) 640330 MOBILE (07710) 476705
E-MAIL jedd@jeddokeefferacing.co.uk WEBSITE www.jeddokeefferacing.co.uk

1 AIR RAID, 4, b g Raven's Pass (USA)—Siren Sound **Caron & Paul Chapman**
2 BREANSKI, 5, b g Delegator—Jubilee **Quantum**
3 CHARLIE THE SQUID, 5, b g Rainbow High—Bar Blu (IRE) **Miss J. M. Burke**
4 DESERT RULER, 6, b g Kheleyf (USA)—Desert Royalty (IRE) **Highbeck Racing 4**
5 ECHO (IRE), 4, b g Zoffany (IRE)—Aweebounce (IRE) **Miss S.E. Hall & Mr C. Platts**
6 EMMA LAMB, 5, b m Passing Glance—Lucinda Lamb **Miss S. E. Hall**
7 GROVEMAN, 4, b g Holy Roman Emperor (IRE)—Raving Monsun **Quantum**
8 HARBOUR BAY, 4, b c Harbour Watch (IRE)—Three Secrets (IRE) **Norcroft Park Stud**
9 INSTANT ATTRACTION (IRE), 8, b g Tagula (IRE)—Coup de Coeur (IRE) **United We Stand**
10 JACK LAMB, 4, b g Sulamani (IRE)—Charlotte Lamb **Miss S. E. Hall**
11 JAZEEL (IRE), 4, b g Roderic O'Connor (IRE)—Simla Bibi **Quantum**
12 LORD YEATS, 6, b g Yeats (IRE)—Bogside Theatre (IRE) **Mr & Mrs G. Turnbull**
13 MR SCRUMPY, 5, b g Passing Glance—Apple Days **Mr H. M. Posner**
14 NATIVE FIGHTER (IRE), 5, b g Lawman (FR)—Night of Magic (IRE) **Quantum**
15 ONLY SPOOFING (IRE), 5, b g Approve (IRE)—Golden Anthem (USA) **Mrs H. Mannion**
16 ORBURSTOCK (IRE), 4, b g Millenary—Auction Girl (IRE) **The Ordnary Folk**

MR JEDD O'KEEFFE - Continued

17 **RARE GROOVE (IRE)**, 4, ch c Lope de Vega (IRE)—Ascot Lady (IRE) **Mr J. E. Dance**
18 **REBEL STATE (IRE)**, 6, b g Zoffany (IRE)—Stately Princess **J. E. D. O'Keeffe**
19 **REMEMBER THE DAYS (IRE)**, 5, b g Kyllachy—Pointed Arch (IRE) **Ingham Racing Syndicate**
20 **SAISONS D'OR (IRE)**, 4, ro g Havana Gold (IRE)—Deux Saisons **The Fatalists**
21 **SAM SPINNER**, 7, b g Black Sam Bellamy (IRE)—Dawn Spinner **Caron & Paul Chapman**
22 **SEEK THE MOON (USA)**, 4, b f Giant's Causeway (USA)—Crescent Moon (USA) **Mr & Mrs G. Turnbull**
23 4, B f Malinas (GER)—Silver Gypsy (IRE) **Caron & Paul Chapman**
24 **STARCASTER**, 4, b g Dansili—Shirocco Star **Quantum**
25 4, Ch g Black Sam Bellamy (IRE)—Still Runs Deep **Caron & Paul Chapman**

THREE-YEAR-OLDS

26 **ANNA BUNINA (FR)**, b f Poet's Voice—Russian Society **Highbeck Racing 3**
27 **ARCHAEOLOGY**, b g Charm Spirit (IRE)—Shuttle Mission **Quantum**
28 **CONUNDRUM**, ch g Sir Percy—Famusa **Highbeck Racing 2**
29 **DEVIL'S ANGEL**, gr c Dark Angel (IRE)—Rocking The Boat (IRE) **Mr J. E. Dance**
30 **EVIE SPEED (IRE)**, br f Dawn Approach (IRE)—French Bid (AUS) **Caron & Paul Chapman**
31 **FREQUENCY CODE (FR)**, ch c Le Havre (IRE)—Stylish **Mr J. E. Dance**
32 **KODELIGHT**, b f Kodiac—Night Delight (IRE) **Mr J. E. Dance**
33 **LEWIS SLACK**, b g Coach House (IRE)—Pelican Key (IRE) **Caron & Paul Chapman**
34 **PRESERVATION**, b f Kyllachy—Protectress **Mr J. E. Dance**
35 **RIPON SPA**, b g Rock of Gibraltar (IRE)—Lady Lahar **Mr T. S. Ingham & Mrs Liz Ingham**
36 **SCHNAPPS**, b f Swiss Spirit—Where's Broughton **Highbeck Racing 1**
37 **THEATRO (IRE)**, b f Camelot—Bogside Theatre (IRE) **Mr & Mrs G. Turnbull**

TWO-YEAR-OLDS

38 Ch c 8/3 Teofilo (IRE)—Craic Agus Spraoi (IRE) (Intense Focus (USA)) **Elwick Stud**
39 B gr f 21/3 Most Improved (IRE)—Dansili Dutch (IRE) (Dutch Art) **Elwick Stud**
40 Ch f 3/3 Sepoy (AUS)—Different (Bahamian Bounty) (22000) **W A Tunstall & Son**
41 B f 20/2 Free Eagle (IRE)—Heart of Hearts (Oasis Dream) **Highbeck Racing**
42 Ch c 30/3 Mukhadram—Incarnation (IRE) (Samum (GER)) (21000) **Highbeck Racing**
43 B f 22/4 War Command (USA)—Lady Chaparral (High Chaparral (IRE)) **Elwick Stud**
44 B f 1/5 Equiano (FR)—Onlyyouknowme (IRE) (Martino Alonso) **Highbeck Racing**
45 B c 5/4 Acclamation—Out of Context (IRE) (Intikhab (USA)) (26666) **Elwick Stud**
46 Ch c 20/2 Dream Ahead (USA)—Shamsalmaidan (IRE) (Fantastic Light (USA)) (7500) **The Fatalists**

Other Owners: Mr R. Butler, P. Chapman, Mrs C. A. Chapman, Mr D. G. Colledge, Mr A. J. Hollis, Mr D. M. Hollis, Mr T. S. Ingham, Mrs M. E. Ingham, Mr R. P. Ord, Mr M. D. Parker, Colin Platts, Mr J. Ramsden, Mr G. Turnbull, Mrs S. E. Turnbull, A. Walker.

Assistant Trainers: Mr Tim Hogg, Miss Leanne Kershaw

Amateur: Miss Alana Cawley.

---

428 **MR DAVID O'MEARA, Upper Helmsley**
Postal: Willow Farm, Upper Helmsley, York, Yorkshire, YO41 1JX
Contacts: PHONE (01759) 372427 MOBILE (07747) 825418
E-MAIL info@davidomeara.co.uk WEBSITE www.davidomeara.co.uk

1 **ADDIS ABABA (IRE)**, 4, ch g Declaration of War (USA)—Song of My Heart (IRE) **Sir Robert Ogden**
2 **AGINCOURT (IRE)**, 4, b f Declaration of War (USA)—El Diamante (FR) **Sir Robert Ogden**
3 **AL QAHWA (IRE)**, 6, b g Fast Company (IRE)—Cappuccino (IRE) **Gallop Racing & Partner**
4 **ALSVINDER**, 6, b h Footstepsinthesand—Notting Hill (BRZ) **Mr F. Gillespie**
5 **ANYTHINGTODAY (IRE)**, 5, b g Zoffany (IRE)—Corking (IRE) **Woodhurst Construction Ltd**
6 **ARECIBO (FR)**, 4, b c Invincible Spirit (IRE)—Oceanique (USA) **Mr George Turner & Clipper Logistics**
7 **AREEN HEART (FR)**, 5, b g Exceed And Excel (AUS)—Reine Zao (FR) **Sheikh A. H. F. M. A. Al Sabah**
8 **AUTRETOT (FR)**, 4, b g Youmzain (IRE)—Great Queen (FR) **Mr C. J. Miller**
9 **BALLARD DOWN (IRE)**, 6, b g Canford Cliffs (IRE)—Mackenzie's Friend **Thoroughbred British Racing**
10 **BILLY DYLAN (IRE)**, 4, b g Excelebration (IRE)—It's True (IRE) **Gallop Racing**
11 **BLACK ISLE BOY (IRE)**, 5, b g Elzaam (AUS)—Shadow Mountain **Mr E. M. Sutherland**
12 **BRAVERY (IRE)**, 6, b g Galileo (IRE)—Lady Icarus **Thoroughbred British Racing**
13 **COLD START (IRE)**, 4, b g Intense Focus (USA)—Ziria (IRE) **Middleham Park Racing XC**
14 **COURTSIDE (FR)**, 4, ch g Siyouni (FR)—Memoire (FR) **Mr E. M. Sutherland**
15 **CUSTOM CUT (IRE)**, 10, b g Notnowcato—Polished Gem (IRE) **Frank Gillespie & Pat Breslin**
16 **ESCOBAR (IRE)**, 5, b g Famous Name—Saying Grace (IRE) **Withernsea Thoroughbred Limited**

MR DAVID O'MEARA - Continued

17 **FAYEZ (IRE)**, 5, b g Zoffany (IRE)—Gems **Northern Lads & Nawton Racing**
18 **FIRMAMENT**, 7, b g Cape Cross (IRE)—Heaven Sent **Gallop Racing**
19 **FRANKUUS (IRE)**, 5, gr h Frankel—Dookus (IRE) **Mr H. A. Lootah**
20 **GULLIVER**, 5, b g Sayif (IRE)—Sweet Coincidence **Withernsea Thoroughbred Limited**
21 **HAJJAM**, 5, b g Paco Boy (IRE)—Amanda Carter **Sheikh A. H. F. M. A. Al Sabah**
22 **HIGHLAND ACCLAIM (IRE)**, 8, b g Acclamation—Emma's Star (ITY) **Mr E. M. Sutherland**
23 **HIGHLAND BOBBY**, 4, b g Big Bad Bob (IRE)—Eolith **Mr E. M. Sutherland**
24 **HORTZADAR**, 4, b g Sepoy (AUS)—Clouds of Magellan (USA) **Akela Construction Ltd**
25 **HUMBERT (IRE)**, 5, b g Kodiac—Fee Eria (FR) **Woodhurst Construction Ltd**
26 **INGLEBY HOLLOW**, 7, ch g Beat Hollow—Mistress Twister **Dave Scott & The Fallen Angels**
27 **INTISAAB**, 8, b g Elnadim (USA)—Katoom (IRE) **Mr S. M. Graham**
28 **ISIDOR BONHEUR YES (FR)**, 5, b g Sageburg (IRE)—Isarnixe (GER) **Akela Construction Ltd**
29 **KHARBETATION (IRE)**, 6, b g Dream Ahead (USA)—Anna's Rock (IRE) **Mr H. R. Bin Ghedayer**
30 **KINGDOM BRUNEL**, 4, gr c Mastercraftsman (IRE)—Messias da Silva (USA) **Sir Robert Ogden**
31 **LAMLOOM (IRE)**, 5, b g Cape Cross (IRE)—Lulua (USA) **Mr H. R. Bin Ghedayer**
32 **LAUBALI**, 4, ch g Kyllachy—Different **Mrs F. Denniff**
33 **LIAMBA**, 4, b f Equiano (IRE)—Hisaronu (IRE) **Diamond Racing Ltd**
34 **LORD GLITTERS (FR)**, 6, gr g Whipper (USA)—Lady Glitters (FR) **Mr & Mrs G. Turnbull**
35 **MAKAWEE (IRE)**, 4, b f Farhh—Storming Sioux **Mr & Mrs G. Turnbull**
36 **MARKAZI (FR)**, 5, gr g Dark Angel (IRE)—Marasima (IRE) **Thoroughbred British Racing**
37 **MUJASSAM**, 7, ch g Kyllachy—Naizak **Thoroughbred British Racing**
38 **MUSCIKA**, 5, b g Kyllachy—Miss Villefranche **Gallop Racing & Dynast Racing**
39 **MYTHICAL MADNESS**, 8, b g Dubawi (IRE)—Miss Delila (USA) **Mr C. G. J. Chua**
40 **PERFECTION**, 4, ch f Dutch Art—Cantal **Cheveley Park Stud Limited**
41 **PRIMERO (FR)**, 6, b g Cape Cross (IRE)—Flamenba (USA) **Sheikh A. H. F. M. A. Al Sabah**
42 **REMARKABLE**, 6, b g Pivotal—Irresistible **Hambleton Racing Ltd XXVII**
43 **SALATEEN**, 7, ch h Dutch Art—Amanda Carter **Sheikh A. H. F. M. A. Al Sabah**
44 **SARYSHAGANN (FR)**, 6, gr g Iffraaj—Serasana **Middleham Park Racing IV**
45 **SO BELOVED**, 9, b g Dansili—Valencia **Thoroughbred British Racing**
46 **SPIORAD (IRE)**, 4, b c Invincible Spirit (IRE)—Gift From Heaven (IRE) **Hambleton Racing Ltd XXXVII**
47 **STAR SHIELD**, 4, ch g Helmet (AUS)—Perfect Star **Middleham Park Racing XXIX**
48 **STEEL TRAIN (FR)**, 8, b g Zafeen (FR)—Silent Sunday (IRE) **Rasio Cymru I & Dutch Rose Partnerhsip**
49 **STONIFIC (IRE)**, 6, b g Sea The Stars (IRE)—Sapphire Pendant (IRE) **Rasio Cymru 1 & Hurn Racing Club**
50 **SUEDOIS (FR)**, 8, b g Le Havre (IRE)—Cup Cake (IRE) **Mr George Turner & Clipper Logistics**
51 **SUMMERGHAND (IRE)**, 5, b g Lope de Vega (IRE)—Kate The Great **Mr H. R. Bin Ghedayer**
52 **SUNRISE (IRE)**, 5, b g Azamour (IRE)—Valmari (IRE) **Leonard Jay Ltd - Stanley Cohen**
53 **TAMLEEK (USA)**, 5, b br g Hard Spun (USA)—Tafaneen (USA) **Godolphin Management Company Ltd**
54 **THREE SAINTS BAY (IRE)**, 4, b g Kodiac—Fiuise (IRE) **Mr G. J. Douglas**
55 **THREE WEEKS (USA)**, 4, gr g Tapit (USA)—Midnight Thoughts (USA) **Apple Tree Stud**
56 **TIME'S ARROW (IRE)**, 5, b h Redoute's Choice (AUS)—Gilt Edge Girl **Mr George Turner & Clipper Logistics**
57 **VENTURA ROYAL (IRE)**, 4, ch f Teofilo (IRE)—Ermine And Velvet **Middleham Park Racing CXVII**
58 **WAARIF (IRE)**, 6, b g Arcano (IRE)—Indian Belle (IRE) **Middleham Park Racing XLIX**
59 **WATCHABLE**, 9, ch g Pivotal—Irresistible **Hambleton XXXIX P Bamford Roses Partners**
60 **ZORAWAR (FR)**, 5, b g Shamardal (USA)—Zerkeriya (IRE) **Mr E. M. Sutherland**

THREE-YEAR-OLDS

61 **ALEEKA (USA)**, b f Distorted Humor (USA)—Vapour **Nick Bradley Racing 7 & Partner 2**
62 **AMLIBA**, b f Mayson—Hisaronu (IRE) **Diamond Racing Ltd**
63 **ASTROLOGER**, ch f Intello (GER)—Starscope **Cheveley Park Stud Limited**
64 **BERYL THE PETAL (IRE)**, b f Dandy Man (IRE)—
Pinewoods Lily (IRE) **N D Crummack Ltd & A Rhodes & Partner**
65 **BLUE GARDENIA (IRE)**, b f Mastercraftsman (IRE)—Alegra **Sir Robert Ogden**
66 B g Dawn Approach (IRE)—Camlet **Mr & Mrs G. Turnbull**
67 **CHILLON CASTLE**, b f Swiss Spirit—Positivity **Mrs F. Denniff**
68 **CONSTANT**, ch g Dutch Art—West of The Moon **Gallop Racing**
69 **DABOUK (IRE)**, b c Kyllachy—Amanda Carter **Sheikh A. H. F. M. A. Al Sabah**
70 **DANCING RAVE**, b f Coach House (IRE)—Right Rave (IRE) **David Lumley & Partner**
71 **EMILANDRA (IRE)**, b f Slade Power—Soul Mountain (IRE) **Mr G. J. Douglas**
72 **FASTMAN (IRE)**, br c Elzaam (AUS)—Manalisa (IRE) **Mr C. J. Miller**
73 **GYLO (IRE)**, b g Tamayuz—She's A Character **Gallop Racing**
74 **HARD SOLUTION**, ch g Showcasing—Copy-Cat **Sheikh A. H. F. M. A. Al Sabah**
75 **HARTLEPOOL (IRE)**, b g Le Havre (IRE)—Hestia (FR) **Nfh Corner & Lord Ronaldshay**
76 **HIKAYAH (IRE)**, b f Bated Breath—Aubrietia **Sheikh A. H. F. M. A. Al Sabah**
77 **INGENIUM (IRE)**, ch f Exceed And Excel (AUS)—Lady Docker (IRE) **Apple Tree Stud**
78 **KUWAIT STATION (IRE)**, br g Swiss Spirit—Summer Spice (IRE) **Sheikh A. H. F. M. A. Al Sabah**

MR DAVID O'MEARA - Continued

79 **LEODIS DREAM (IRE)**, b g Dandy Man (IRE)—Paddy Again (IRE) **Andrew Kendall-jones I**
80 **LINCOLN SPIRIT**, gr f Piccolo—Lincolnrose (IRE) **G.P.S. Heart of Racing (Bloodstock) Ltd**
81 **LINCOLN TALE (IRE)**, b f Intello (GER)—Pine Chip (USA) **PC Coaches of Lincoln Ltd**
82 **LOVIN (USA)**, ch f Orb (USA)—Innocent Love (USA) **Nick Bradley Racing 26 & Partners**
83 **MACHO LADY (IRE)**, br f Camacho—Jouel (FR) **Northern Lads Racing & Beadle Bloodstock**
84 **MORNING DUEL (IRE)**, ch g Dawn Approach (IRE)—Days of Summer (IRE) **Clipper Group Holdings Ltd**
85 **MURQAAB**, b g Showcasing—Ahwahnee **Sheikh A. H. F. M. A. Al Sabah**
86 **MYKLACHI (FR)**, b g Style Vendome (FR)—Perle Noire (FR) **Middleham Park Racing XCVII**
87 **OLLIVANDER (IRE)**, b g Heeraat (IRE)—Coy (IRE) **York Thoroughbred Racing**
88 **OXYGENIC**, b f Showcasing—Viola d'amour (IRE) **Nawton Racing Partnership**
89 **PORTOFINO (IRE)**, ch g Australia—Song of My Heart (IRE) **Sir R. Ogden C.B.E., LLD**
90 **RAKSHA (IRE)**, b f Dandy Man (IRE)—Violet Lashes (USA) **Akela Construction Ltd & Partner**
91 **SCARLETT O'HALO**, b f Garswood—Red Halo (IRE) **Dreaming Victory**
92 **SPIRITUAL BOY (IRE)**, b g Paco Boy (IRE)—Spiritual Air **M Eves & Partner**
93 B f Dalakhani (IRE)—Valmari (IRE)
94 **VERY DAINTY (IRE)**, b f Equiano (FR)—Daintily Done **Malih L. Al Basti**

TWO-YEAR-OLDS

95 B c 16/2 Kingman—Ashley Hall (USA) (Maria's Mon (USA)) (115000) **Sheikh A. H. F. M. A. Al Sabah**
96 B f 20/4 Dragon Pulse (IRE)—Asterism (Motivator) (10956)
97 B c 7/5 Teofilo (IRE)—Bawaakeer (USA) (Kingmambo (USA)) (20000)
98 B c 26/4 Swiss Spirit—Bibury (Royal Applause) (14327)
99 **BUBBLY SPLASH (IRE)**, b c 2/3 Lawman (FR)—
Brunch Bellini (FR) (Peintre Celebre (USA)) (6500) **Mrs M. C. Hancock**
100 Ch f 4/2 Dandy Man (IRE)—Dame Hester (IRE) (Diktat) (28571)
101 **DAZZLING DES (IRE)**, b c 5/2 Brazen Beau (AUS)—
Secret Liaison (IRE) (Dandy Man (IRE)) (27812) **Mr E. M. Sutherland**
102 B c 30/3 Dandy Man (IRE)—Eolith (Pastoral Pursuits) (16856) **York Thoroughbred Racing**
103 B f 13/4 War Command (USA)—Fikrah (Medicean)
104 Ch f 19/1 Night of Thunder (IRE)—
Giveupyeraulsins (IRE) (Mark of Esteem (IRE)) (19384) **Mr Stuart Graham & Partner**
105 **INFINITE GRACE**, ch f 1/2 Sepoy (AUS)—Pepper Lane (Exceed And Excel (AUS)) **Mr K. Nicholson**
106 B c 4/2 Sepoy (AUS)—Intrusion (Indesatchel (IRE)) (18000)
107 **KUMASI**, ch c 4/4 New Approach (IRE)—Ghanaian (FR) (Shamardal (USA)) **Cheveley Park Stud Limited**
108 **MERRY MILLER (IRE)**, b c 29/3 Camacho—Tender Surprise (Doyen (IRE)) (20952) **Mr G. J. Douglas**
109 B br c 14/3 Slade Power (IRE)—Miss Cape (IRE) (Cape Cross (IRE)) (30000)
110 Ch f 26/3 Monsieur Bond (IRE)—Moonwood (Three Valleys (USA)) **Gallop Racing**
111 B f 20/1 Swiss Spirit—Noble Cause (Showcasing) (11428)
112 **NORTHERN HOPE**, b c 21/4 Equiano (FR)—Heading North (Teofilo (IRE)) (15000)
113 B f 17/2 Swiss Spirit—Nurse Gladys (Dr Fong (USA)) (13000)
114 B c 4/4 Dandy Man (IRE)—Nutshell (Dubai Destination (USA)) (9270)
115 **OSO RAPIDO (IRE)**, b c 13/3 Kodiac—
Burke's Rock (Cape Cross (IRE)) (90000) **Mr Kevin Bailey & Mr Gabriel Chrysanthou**
116 **PAYNES BAY (IRE)**, ch c 22/2 Raven's Pass (USA)—
Wildsplash (USA) (Deputy Minister (CAN)) (29498) **Mr G. J. Douglas**
117 B c 24/4 Due Diligence (USA)—Red Mischief (IRE) (Red Clubs (IRE)) (28571)
118 B f 8/3 Mayson—Regal Salute (Medicean) **Cheveley Park Stud Limited**
119 B f 19/2 Slade Power (IRE)—Sharaasa (IRE) (Approve (IRE))
120 B g 15/5 Elusive Pimpernel (USA)—Spiritville (IRE) (Invincible Spirit (IRE)) (4214) **N D Crummack Ltd**
121 B g 13/3 Roderic O'Connor (IRE)—Sugar Free (IRE) (Oasis Dream) (5714)
122 B g 20/4 Born To Sea (IRE)—Valmari (IRE) (Kalanisi (IRE))
123 **WAR KITTEN**, b f 4/4 Due Diligence (USA)—Kip (Rip Van Winkle (IRE)) **Mr C. Napthine**

Other Owners: Mr K. B. Bailey, Mr P. I. Baker, P. Bamford, Beadle Bloodstock Limited, Mr J. M. Binns, Mr N. Bradley, Mr P. Breslin, Mr P. A. Burgess, Mr S. E. Chappell, Mr G. Chrysanthou, Mr S. J. Cohen, Mr N. F. H. Corner, Mr J. Cox, Mr C. Cox, Mr J. W. Cox, P. J. Dunkley, Mrs D. Dunkley, Mr M. Dunn, Dutch Rose Partnership, Dynast Racing, Mr A. W. Ellis, Mr M. Eves, The Fallen Angels, Ms J. C. Finucane, Hambleton Racing Ltd, Hambleton Racing Ltd XXXIX, Mr P. Hancock, Miss S. Holden, Hurn Racing Club, Mrs I. M. Jessop, Mr J. Kelly, Mr A. Kendall-Jones, J. A. Knight, Leonard Jay Ltd, Mr David John Lumley, Mrs S. Magnier, Mr A. J. McLaren, Nick Bradley Racing 26, Nick Bradley Racing 7, Northern Lads Racing, Mr D. B. O'Meara, T. S. Palin, Mr J. D. Pierce, M. Prince, Rasio Cymru Racing 1, Hugh T. Redhead, A. Rhodes, Mrs C. B. Rogers, The Earl of R. L. Ronaldshay, The Roses Partnership, Mr D. Scott, Star Bloodstock Partnership, Mr S. M. Taylor, Mr A. S. Trott, Mrs S. E. Turnbull, Mr G. Turnbull, Mr G. D. Turner, Mr S. R. H. Turner, Mr R. Walker, Miss A. M. Walker.

Assistant Trainer: Jason Kelly

Jockey (flat): Daniel Tudhope. **Apprentice:** Conor McGovern.

429 MISS DANIELLE O'NEILL, North Fawley
Postal: **The Old Granary, North Fawley, Wantage, Oxfordshire, OX12 9NJ**
Contacts: **PHONE (01488) 639350 MOBILE (07931) 193790**
E-MAIL danni@fawleyhousestud.com

1 **BARDD (IRE)**, 7, b g Dylan Thomas (IRE)—Zarawa (IRE) **Fawley House Stud**
2 **BISHOPSLOUGH (IRE)**, 11, b g Fruits of Love (USA)—Maid In Blue (IRE) **Fawley House Stud**
3 **CAUTORILLO**, 7, ch m Black Sam Bellamy (IRE)—Cent Prime **Fawley House Stud**
4 **FINGERS CROSSED (IRE)**, 9, b g Bach (IRE)—Awesome Miracle (IRE) **Fawley House Stud**

Other Owners: Mrs S. McGrath, Mr R. McGrath.

Assistant Trainer: Stephen O'Neill

430 MR JOHN O'NEILL, Bicester
Postal: **Hall Farm, Stratton Audley, Nr Bicester, Oxfordshire, OX27 9BT**
Contacts: **PHONE (01869) 277202 MOBILE (07785) 394128**
E-MAIL jgoneill4@gmail.com

1 **BOLLYWOOD BOY**, 8, b g Indian Danehill (IRE)—Little Miss Prim **Ms D. Keane**
2 **CAPPARATTIN**, 4, b g Universal (IRE)—Little Miss Prim **J. G. O'Neill**
3 **ONURBIKE**, 11, b g Exit To Nowhere (USA)—Lay It Off (IRE) **J. G. O'Neill**
4 **PHOENIX SONG**, 6, b g Phoenix Reach (IRE)—Temple Heather **J. G. O'Neill**
5 **SLEPTWITHMEBOOTSON**, 4, b f Universal (IRE)—Temple Heather **Ms D. Keane**
6 **W S GILBERT**, 5, b g Librettist (USA)—Little Miss Prim **Ms D. Keane**

431 MR JONJO O'NEILL, Cheltenham
Postal: **Jackdaws Castle, Temple Guiting, Cheltenham, Gloucestershire, GL54 5XU**
Contacts: **PHONE (01386) 584209**
E-MAIL reception@jonjooneillracing.com WEBSITE www.jonjooneillracing.com

1 **ABOVE BOARD (IRE)**, 8, b g Mahler—Blackwater Babe (IRE) **Mr J. P. McManus**
2 4, B g Fame And Glory—Accordian Lady (IRE)
3 **ALLELU ALLELUIA (GER)**, 8, b g Doyen (IRE)—Anna Spectra (IRE) **Mr J. P. McManus**
4 **ANNIE MC (IRE)**, 5, b m Mahler—Classic Mari (IRE) **Coral Champions Club**
5 **AQUARIAN (IRE)**, 5, b g Rock of Gibraltar (IRE)—Inchina **Mr J. P. McManus**
6 **ARRIVEDERCI (FR)**, 4, gr g Martaline—Etoile d'ainay (FR) **Martin Broughton & Friends 1**
7 **ASPEN COLORADO (IRE)**, 7, b g Galileo (IRE)—St Roch **Mr J. P. McManus**
8 **BAHAMA MOON (IRE)**, 7, b g Lope de Vega (IRE)—Bahama Bay (GER) **Eric Chapman & Douglas Pryde**
9 **BHUTAN (IRE)**, 6, gr g Galileo (IRE)—Ecology (USA) **Mr J. P. McManus**
10 **BIG PENNY (IRE)**, 7, b m Oscar (IRE)—Lady Marnay (IRE) **Mrs D. Carr**
11 **BLACKSTAIRS LAD (IRE)**, 5, b g Flemensfirth (USA)—Blarney Kestrel (IRE)
12 **BOX OFFICE (IRE)**, 8, b g Great Pretender (IRE)—Quelle Mome (FR) **Mr J. P. McManus**
13 **CAKE DE L'ISLE (FR)**, 7, b g Fragrant Mix (IRE)—Taiga De L'isle (FR) **Mr T. J. Hemmings**
14 **CALL TO ORDER**, 9, b g Presenting—Theatre Girl **Mr R. J. Stanton-Gleaves**
15 **CARYS' COMMODITY**, 4, b g Fame And Glory—Native Sunrise (IRE) **Mrs F. H. Hay**
16 **CHAMPAGNE AT TARA**, 10, gr g Kayf Tara—Champagne Lil **Mr J. P. McManus**
17 **CHEAP AND CHEERFUL**, 6, b g Shirocco (GER)—Shayaza **Mr J. P. McManus**
18 **CLOTH CAP (IRE)**, 7, b g Beneficial—Cloth Fair (IRE) **Mr T. J. Hemmings**
19 **COBOLOBO (FR)**, 7, br g Maresca Sorrento (FR)—Nanou des Brosses (FR) **Anne, Harriet & Lucinda Bond**
20 **DARSI IN THE PARK (IRE)**, 6, b g Darsi (FR)—Rock In The Park (IRE) **Mrs G. K. Smith**
21 **DEMON D'AUNOU (FR)**, 6, b g Martaline—Jimagine II (FR) **Mr J. P. McManus**
22 **DESERT CROSS**, 6, b g Arcano (IRE)—Secret Happiness **Mr P. Hickey**
23 **DHOWIN (IRE)**, 5, b g Yeats (IRE)—On The Way Home (IRE) **Mr T. J. Hemmings**
24 **DJANGO DJANGO (FR)**, 6, gr g Voix du Nord (FR)—Lady Jannina **Martin Broughton & Friends 8**
25 **DOESYOURDOGBITE (IRE)**, 7, b g Notnowcato—Gilah (IRE) **DYDB Marketing & Friends Of Jackdaws**
26 **DONTBITEDABAIT (IRE)**, 6, b g Oscar (IRE)—Newcastlebeauty (IRE) **Mr J. P. McManus**
27 **DREAMSOFTHEATRE (IRE)**, 11, gr g King's Theatre (IRE)—Caroline Fontenail (IRE) **Mr J. P. McManus**
28 **EASTLAKE (IRE)**, 13, b g Beneficial—Guigone (FR) **Mr J. P. McManus**
29 **EASY STREET (IRE)**, 9, b g High Chaparral (IRE)—Victorine (IRE) **Mr J. P. McManus**
30 **ECLAT DE STAR (FR)**, 5, b g Special Kaldoun (FR)—Rose Star (FR) **Mr J. P. McManus**
31 **EY UP ROCKY**, 6, b g Dylan Thomas (IRE)—Polo **Martyn & Elaine Booth**
32 **FANACKAPAN (FR)**, 4, b f Martaline—Beni Abbes (FR) **Mr C. Johnston**

MR JONJO O'NEILL - Continued

33 **FLEMINPORT (IRE)**, 6, b g Flemensfirth (USA)—Geek Chic (IRE) **Mr J. P. McManus**
34 **FLIGHT DECK (IRE)**, 5, b g Getaway (GER)—Rate of Knots (IRE) **Mr J. P. McManus**
35 **FOLKS ON THE HILL**, 4, b g Black Sam Bellamy (IRE)—Any Pearl **Mr R. J. Stanton-Gleaves**
36 **FORZA MILAN (IRE)**, 7, b g Milan—Nonnetia (FR) **Deep Sea Partnership**
37 **FOUNDATION MAN (IRE)**, 12, b g Presenting—Function Dream (IRE) **Mr P. Hickey**
38 4, Ch g Shantou (USA)—Galshan (IRE)
39 **GENERATION GAP (IRE)**, 5, b g Olden Times—Kerso (IRE) **The Hon Mrs E. J. Wills**
40 **GEORGE HILL**, 5, b g Bollin Eric—Salybia Bay **Atwell Martin Holdings & Angela Crofts**
41 **GLOBAL ANCHOR (IRE)**, 5, b g Stowaway—Loreley (IRE) **Dr J. Hon**
42 **HALLMARK (IRE)**, 7, b g Montjeu (IRE)—Starlight Night (USA) **Mr J. P. McManus**
43 **HANG TOUGH**, 5, b g Geordieland (FR)—Allerford Lily
44 **HEAD LAD (FR)**, 6, b br g Linda's Lad—Orabelle (FR) **Mrs J. S. T. O'Neill**
45 **HIS DREAM (IRE)**, 6, b g Yeats (IRE)—Rosa Muscosa (USA) **Local Parking Security Limited**
46 **I'DLIKETHEOPTION (IRE)**, 8, b g Presenting—Supreme Dreamer (IRE) **Mr J. P. McManus**
47 4, B g Oscar (IRE)—Jordrell (IRE) **J. C. & S. R. Hitchins**
48 **KITIKAT (IRE)**, 5, b g Fame And Glory—Felinious **Mrs G. K. Smith**
49 **KNIGHT DESTROYER (IRE)**, 5, b g Dark Angel (IRE)—Do The Deal (IRE) **Mrs D. Carr**
50 **LAD OF LUCK (FR)**, 6, b g Soldier of Fortune (IRE)—Baraka du Berlais (FR) **Mrs S. Hoffmann**
51 **LITHIC (IRE)**, 8, b g Westerner—Acoola (IRE) **Jon & Julia Aisbitt**
52 **LOCK'S CORNER (IRE)**, 5, b g Gold Well—Last Century (IRE) **Mr J. P. McManus**
53 **LOVE THE DREAM (IRE)**, 4, b g Mahler—Norah's Quay (IRE) **The Number One Dream Team**
54 4, B g Shirocco (GER)—Lughnasa (IRE) **Mrs S. McAuley**
55 **LUNAR BABY (IRE)**, 4, b f Fame And Glory—Fiddlededee (IRE) **Mrs A. F. Bond**
56 **MAD JACK MYTTON (IRE)**, 9, b g Arcadio—Gilt Ridden (IRE) **J. C. & S. R. Hitchins**
57 **MARCH IS ON (IRE)**, 6, b g Gold Well—Shannon Tiara (IRE) **Steve Killalea & Richard & Maralyn Seed**
58 **MAYPOLE CLASS (IRE)**, 5, b g Gold Well—
Maypole Queen (IRE) **Delancey Real Estate Asset Management Limited**
59 **MINELLA ROCCO (IRE)**, 9, b g Shirocco (GER)—Petralona (USA) **Mr J. P. McManus**
60 **MONBEG GOLD (IRE)**, 9, b g Gold Well—Little Hand (IRE) **Martin Broughton Racing Partners 2**
61 **MONT ROYALE**, 11, b g Hurricane Run (IRE)—Wild Academy (IRE) **Phil Tufnell Racing**
62 **MONTALBANO**, 7, ch g Monsieur Bond (IRE)—Alpen Glen **London Design Group Limited**
63 **MUSTMEETALADY (IRE)**, 9, b g Mustameet (USA)—Ladymcgrath (IRE) **Mrs D. Carr**
64 **OAKLEY HALL (IRE)**, 7, b g Milan—Rockwell College (IRE) **Mr P. Hickey**
65 **ORRISDALE (IRE)**, 5, b g Oscar (IRE)—Back To Loughadera (IRE) **Mr T. J. Hemmings**
66 **PAGERO (FR)**, 4, b g Nathaniel (IRE)—Pagera (FR) **Mr J. P. McManus**
67 **PHOENIX ROCK (IRE)**, 7, br m Winged Love (IRE)—Guillaume Rock (IRE) **Successio**
68 **PIGGY WINKLE (IRE)**, 5, b g Fame And Glory—Ar Muin Na Muice (IRE) **Mrs G. K. Smith**
69 **POP ROCKSTAR (IRE)**, 7, b br g Flemensfirth (USA)—Special Ballot (IRE) **Mrs L. Day**
70 **POTTLEREAGHEXPRESS (IRE)**, 6, b m Beneficial—Needle Doll (IRE) **Dalziel Family & Partners**
71 **PRESENT CHIEF (IRE)**, 5, b g Presenting—Daizinni **Mr P. Hickey**
72 **QUARENTA (FR)**, 7, b br g Voix du Nord (FR)—Negresse de Cuta (FR) **Martin, Jocelyn & Steve Broughton**
73 4, B g Mount Nelson—Queen Soraya
74 **READY AND ABLE (IRE)**, 6, b g Flemensfirth (USA)—
Gypsy Mo Chara (IRE) **Mr D Smith, Mrs J Magnier & Mr M Tabor**
75 4, Br f Presenting—Saddleeruppat (IRE) **Mr D Smith, Mrs J Magnier & Mr M Tabor**
76 **SANTIAGO DE CUBA (IRE)**, 6, b g Pour Moi (IRE)—Marjalina (IRE) **Mr J. P. McManus**
77 **SCOTTSHILL (IRE)**, 7, ch g Flemensfirth (USA)—Loch Lomond (IRE) **The Scottshill Partnership**
78 **SEATON CAREW (IRE)**, 5, b m Getaway (GER)—Millys Gesture (IRE) **Jon & Julia Aisbitt**
79 **SERMANDO (FR)**, 5, ch g Fuisse (FR)—Josephjuliusjodie (IRE) **Mrs J. S. T. O'Neill**
80 **SKY PIRATE**, 6, b g Midnight Legend—Dancingwithbubbles (IRE) **Lady Bamford & Alice Bamford**
81 **SOARING GLORY (IRE)**, 4, b g Fame And Glory—Hapeney (IRE) **Mr P. Hickey**
82 **SPIRITUAL MAN (IRE)**, 7, b g Lawman (FR)—Vee Gita (IRE) **The Breakfast Club**
83 **STONY STREAM (IRE)**, 5, b g Watar (IRE)—Chiminee Lamp (IRE) **Kate & Andrew Brooks**
84 4, B f Jeremy (USA)—Sun Disc (IRE) **Jackdaws Racing**
85 **TEDHAM**, 5, b g Shirocco (GER)—Alegralil **Mr M. J. Tedham**
86 **TEGEREK (FR)**, 5, b g Mount Nelson—Takaniya (IRE) **Local Parking Security Limited**
87 **TERRY THE FISH (IRE)**, 7, b g Milan—Have More **Terry The Fishers**
88 **THE CRAFTY TOUCH (IRE)**, 6, ch m Touch of Land (FR)—Dicharachera **Ten Belles Partnership**
89 **THE MAJOR GENERAL (IRE)**, 6, b g Galileo (IRE)—Scribonia (IRE) **Mr J. P. McManus**
90 **THE MANUSCRIPT (IRE)**, 6, b g Mahler—Limavady (IRE) **The Valentine Partnership**
91 **TIDAL WATCH (IRE)**, 5, b g Harbour Watch (IRE)—Najmati **Mrs D. Carr**
92 **TOUT POUR TOI (FR)**, 5, b g Fuisse (FR)—Malandra **Mr M. J. Tedham**
93 **TRANSPENNINE STAR**, 6, ch g Mount Nelson—Brave Mave **Transpennine Partnership**
94 **TRAVERTINE (IRE)**, 9, b g Danehill Dancer (IRE)—Mer de Corail (IRE) **Mr J. P. McManus**

MR JONJO O'NEILL - Continued

95 **WASDELL**, 5, b m Black Sam Bellamy (IRE)—Lady Hight (FR) **Mr M. J. Tedham**
96 **WESTERLY WIND (IRE)**, 5, b g Westerner—Milanella (IRE) **Mr C Taylor & Mr A Bound**
97 **YOUNG WOLF (IRE)**, 6, b g Vinnie Roe (IRE)—Missy O'brien (IRE) **Mrs G. K. Smith**
98 **ZIGGY ROSE (IRE)**, 5, b m Fame And Glory—Koko Rose (IRE) **Elaine Chivers Racing**

THREE-YEAR-OLDS

99 **EXTREME FORCE (IRE)**, ch c Exceed And Excel (AUS)—Great Hope (IRE) **Mrs G. K. Smith**
100 **POP THE CORK**, b c Harbour Watch (IRE)—Gospel Music **Martyn & Elaine Booth**

TWO-YEAR-OLDS

101 B c 17/2 War Command (USA)—Acts Out Loud (USA) (Mr Greeley (USA)) (67424)
102 Ch c 20/3 Ivawood (IRE)—Jawlaat (IRE) (Shamardal (USA)) (60000) **Roll the Dice Racing**

Other Owners: J. R. Aisbitt, Mrs J. M. Aisbitt, Atwell Martin (Holdings) Limited, Miss A. C. Bamford, Lady Bamford, Mr N. J. Bate, Mr K. J. Bell, Mrs N. D. Blakemore, Miss H. Bond, Miss L. Bond, Mrs E. Booth, Mr M. Booth, Mr A. Bound, Mr K. Bradbury, Mr N. Brand, Mr L. H. Brewin, Mr A. Brookes, Mr A. L. Brooks, Mrs K. L. Brooks, Sir M. F. Broughton, Mr S. W. Broughton, Lady J. M. Broughton, Mr E. Chapman, Miss C. I. Chivers, Ms E. C. Chivers, Ms L. D. Chivers, Mr S. Clare, Mr J. Cockcroft, Mr D. J. Coles, Mr G. Cook, Countess R. Coventry, Mrs A. C. Crofts, DYDB Marketing Limited, Mr R. S. Dalziel, Mr J. J. Elliot, Mrs E. J. Elliot, Friends Of Jackdaws, Ms C. M. Gilder, Mr T. C. B. Hale, Mrs S. Hall-Tinker, Mr M. P. Hammond, Mr T. Hanrahan, Ms L. C. Hewett, Mr S. R. Hitchins, Mr J. C. Hitchins, Mr M. J. Holman, Mr T. Jackson, Mr C. S. P. Johnson, Mr S. J. Killalea, W. S. D. Lamb, Mrs S. Magnier, Mr R. Marks, Mr K. R. Norton, Mr P. T. Norton, Mr J. O'Neill, Oi Digital Limited, Mr S. L. A. Perry, D. G. Pryde, Mrs M. L. Seed, Mr R. Seed, Ms R. J. Slater, D. Smith, Mr M. Smith, Mr M. A. Stone, M. Tabor, Mr C. Taylor, Mr J. Williams.

Jockeys (NH): Aidan Coleman, Richie McLernon. **Conditional:** Jonjo O'Neill.

---

432 **MR JOHN O'SHEA**, Newnham-on-Severn
Postal: **The Stables, Bell House, Lumbars Lane, Newnham, Gloucestershire, GL14 1LH**
Contacts: **(01452) 760835 FAX (01452) 760233 MOBILE (07917) 124717**
WEBSITE www.johnoshearacing.co.uk

1 **AGENT GIBBS**, 7, ch g Bertolini (USA)—Armada Grove **Mr P. G. Hart**
2 **ARISTOCRACY**, 8, b g Royal Applause—Pure Speculation **Mr R. S. Parker**
3 **CAPE DIGNITY (IRE)**, 6, b g Teofilo (IRE)—Eclaircie (IRE) **K. W. Bell**
4 **CELER ET AUDAX**, 7, b m Kayf Tara—Wannaplantatree **Mr N. G. H. Ayliffe**
5 **CLEMENT (IRE)**, 9, b g Clodovil (IRE)—Winnifred **K. W. Bell**
6 **COUGAR KID (IRE)**, 8, b g Yeats (IRE)—Western Skylark (IRE) **The Cross Racing Club**
7 **DALNESS EXPRESS**, 6, b g Firebreak—Under My Spell **Mr P. Smith**
8 **DIMMESDALE**, 4, b g Nathaniel (IRE)—Diara Angel (IRE) **The Cross Racing Club**
9 **FRIDAY FEELING**, 5, b m Schiaparelli (GER)—Lac Marmot (FR) **S. P. Bloodstock**
10 **FROZEN LAKE (USA)**, 7, b g Elusive Quality (USA)—
 Creative Design **N G Ayliffe & The Cross Racing Club**
11 **GENERAL BROOK (IRE)**, 9, b g Westerner—Danse Grecque (IRE) **K. W. Bell**
12 **GET UP THEM STEPS**, 5, b g Excelebration (IRE)—Flag Day **Quantum Equus I**
13 **JIMMY BELL**, 8, b g Tiger Hill (IRE)—Armada Grove **K. W. Bell**
14 **KINGLAMI**, 10, b g Kingsalsa (USA)—Red Japonica **Pete Smith & Phil Hart Racing**
15 **KNIGHT CRUSADER**, 7, b g Sir Percy—Lac Marmot (FR) **S. P. Bloodstock**
16 **MAJOR VALENTINE**, 7, b g Major Cadeaux—Under My Spell **Mr P. Smith**
17 **ONE LINER**, 5, b g Delegator—Quip **A Cooke,R Martin & the Cross Racing Club**
18 **OUTRAGEOUS ROMANA (IRE)**, 8, b m Mahler—South West Nine (IRE) **Ms S. A. Howell**
19 **RIVER OF INTRIGUE (IRE)**, 9, b g Indian River (FR)—
 Molly Hussey (IRE) **Mr Oscar Singh & Miss Priya Purewal**
20 **SWENDAB (IRE)**, 11, b g Trans Island—Lavish Spirit (USA) **E&G Racing: Swendab**
21 **WAROFINDEPENDENCE (USA)**, 7, b br g War Front (USA)—
 My Dear Annie (USA) **Keith Davies & The Cross Racing Club**

THREE-YEAR-OLDS

22 **DARK FRUIT**, ch c Dunaden (FR)—Radmores Surprise **Miss S. F. Willis**
23 **REDEMPTRESS (IRE)**, b f Zebedee—Sina Cova (IRE) **Mr M. G. Wooldridge**
24 **SHOW ME THE BUBBLY**, b f Showcasing—Folly Bridge **A. Cooke & the Cross Racing Club**

R JOHN O'SHEA - Continued

er Owners: Mr D. Abraham, Mr A. D. Cooke, Mr K. Davies, Mr R. D. J. East, Mr J. M. Gibbs, Mrs S. Guest, Mr A. G. nter, Mr R. Martin, Mr S. P. Price, Miss P. Purewal, Mr A. Singh, Mr S. T. Wallace, Mrs P. S. Wallace.

key (flat): Robert Havlin, Luke Morris, Fergus Sweeney.

---

433 **MR HENRY OLIVER, Abberley**
Postal: **Stable End, Worsley Racing Stables, Bank Lane, Abberley, Worcester, Worcestershire, WR6 6BQ**
Contacts: **PHONE (01299) 890143 MOBILE (07701) 068759**
E-MAIL henryoliverracing@hotmail.co.uk WEBSITE www.henryoliverracing.co.uk

1 AMERICAN CRAFTSMAN (IRE), 5, gr g Mastercraftsman (IRE)—Quiet Mouse (USA) **Mr M. P. Dunphy**
2 ANOTHER THEATRE (IRE), 6, b m Shantou (USA)—Whats Another One (IRE) **Catch Twenty Two**
3 ARTHUR MAC (IRE), 6, ch g Getaway (GER)—Orchardstown Moss (IRE) **The Vacuum Pouch Company Limited**
4 AVANTGARDIST (GER), 5, ch g Campanologist (USA)—Avocette (GER) **Mr D. M. J. Lloyd**
5 BURRENBRIDGE HOTEL, 8, b g Ivan Denisovich (IRE)—Hearthstead Dancer (USA) **Mr H. J. Oliver**
6 CALTEX (FR), 7, bl g Network (GER)—Qomposita (FR) **Mr M. P. Dunphy**
7 CASUAL CAVALIER (IRE), 11, br g Presenting—Asklynn **martingrayracing**
8 CHASE END CHARLIE (IRE), 8, b g Scorpion (IRE)—Artist's Muse (IRE) **Mr N T Griffith & H M Haddock**
9 DARLYN, 6, b m Authorized (IRE)—Darariyna (IRE) **Best Foot Forward**
10 DIAMOND ROCK, 8, b g Kayf Tara—Crystal Princess (IRE) **R. G. Whitehead**
11 DOC CARVER (IRE), 8, ch g Lakeshore Road (USA)—Tuney Tulip (IRE) **WKD Four**
12 DR DES (IRE), 8, b g Double Eclipse (IRE)—Dans Belle (IRE) **R. G. Whitehead**
13 DR OAKLEY (IRE), 5, ch g Le Fou (IRE)—Two Choices (IRE) **R. G. Whitehead**
14 ENVOL DE LA COUR (FR), 5, b g Maresca Sorrento (FR)—Reveuse de La Cour (FR) **Mr M. P. Dunphy**
15 GENEROUS DAY (IRE), 7, b g Daylami (IRE)—Our Pride **R. G. Whitehead**
16 HARD TO FORGET (IRE), 6, b g Gold Well—Raheen Na Hoon (IRE) **Inspire Racing Club Ltd**
17 HIJRAN (IRE), 6, ch m Mastercraftsman (IRE)—Sunny Slope **Catch Twenty Two, Andyfreight Holdings Ltd**
18 LITTLE RORY MAC (IRE), 5, b g Yeats (IRE)—Solar Quest (IRE) **The Vacuum Pouch Company Limited**
19 LOUIS' VAC POUCH (IRE), 7, b g Oscar (IRE)—Coming Home (FR) **The Vacuum Pouch Company Limited**
20 LOVE LANE (IRE), 6, b m Stowaway—Inquisitive Look **D Pain & Sons**
21 MAJOR HINDRANCE (IRE), 9, ch g Kris Kin (USA)—
                                          Ten Dollar Bill (IRE) **Catch Twenty Two, Andyfreight Holdings Ltd**
22 ROLLERCOSTER (IRE), 7, br m Helissio (FR)—Full Deck (IRE) **Mr M. P. Dunphy**
23 SALLY CAN'T WAIT, 6, b m Sulamani (IRE)—Kate Hill Dancer (IRE) **Ms S. A. Howell**
24 SPARKLING RIVER (IRE), 9, gr m Indian River (FR)—Full Deck (IRE) **Mr M. P. Dunphy**
25 STEPS AND STAIRS (IRE), 9, b g Robin des Pres (FR)—Be Mine Tonight (IRE) **Mr M. P. Dunphy**
26 TALKINGPICTURESTV, 6, b m Flying Legend (USA)—Banoo (IRE) **Talking Pictures TV Limited**
27 THE CRAZED MOON (IRE), 7, b m Yeats (IRE)—Rose Gallery (FR) **Mr M. P. Dunphy**
28 THE DAWN MAN (IRE), 8, b g Milan—Calling Classy (IRE) **Mr M. P. Dunphy**
29 YORGONNAHEARMEROAR (IRE), 8, b g Scorpion (IRE)—Etoile Margot (FR) **Mr M. P. Dunphy**

er Owners: Andyfreight Holdings Limited, Catch Twenty Two, Mr Mark Dunphy, Mr I. M. Gray, Mrs G. Gray, Mr N. ffith, Heather Haddock, Mr George Hibbert, Mr Tino Mastoras, Mrs Heather Oliver, Mr H. J. Oliver, Mr P. Pain, Mr Alan n, Mrs S. Pain, Mrs P. Pain, Mr A. Taylor.

sistant Trainer: Heather Oliver.

nditional: Jay Dixon.

---

434 **MR JAMIE OSBORNE, Upper Lambourn**
Postal: **The Old Malthouse, Upper Lambourn, Hungerford, Berkshire, RG17 8RG**
Contacts: **PHONE (01488) 73139 FAX (01488) 73084 MOBILE (07860) 533422**
E-MAIL info@jamieosborne.com WEBSITE www.jamieosborne.com

1 BATTALION (IRE), 9, b g Authorized (IRE)—Zigarra **Melbourne 10 Racing**
2 BORN TO FINISH (IRE), 6, b g Dark Angel (IRE)—Music Pearl (IRE) **Crowd Racing Partnership**
3 CLIFFS OF CAPRI, 5, b g Canford Cliffs (IRE)—Shannon Spree **Melbourne 10 Racing**
4 DREAM TODAY (IRE), 4, b g Dream Ahead (USA)—Macheera (IRE) **Melbourne 10 Racing**
5 FARAASAH (IRE), 4, br g Arcano (IRE)—Falsafa **Mr J. A. Osborne**
6 FLORENCIO, 6, b g Equiano (FR)—Mary Pekan (IRE) **Melbourne 10 Racing**
7 GATES PASS, 4, b g Showcasing—Molly Mello (GER) **Mr Michael H. Watt**
8 HATHAL (USA), 7, ch h Speightstown (USA)—Sleepytime (IRE) **Dr A Sedrati & Partner**

MR JAMIE OSBORNE - Continued

9 **HIDDEN DEPTHS (IRE)**, 4, b g Dark Angel (IRE)—Liber Nauticus (IRE) **Livock, Sexton, Lewis & O'Grady**
10 **HUNGARIAN RHAPSODY**, 5, b g Exceed And Excel (AUS)—Sharp Terms **M. A. C. Buckley**
11 **JUKEBOX JIVE (FR)**, 5, b g Jukebox Jury (IRE)—Sweetheart **Melbourne 10 Racing**
12 **LUSH LIFE (IRE)**, 4, gr f Mastercraftsman (IRE)—
Break of Day (USA) **Mr Michael Buckley & Mrs Paul Shanaha**
13 **MANS NOT TROT (IRE)**, 4, b g Kodiac—Turuqaat **Mr J. A. Osborne**
14 **MONUMENTAL MAN**, 10, b g Vital Equine (IRE)—Spark Up **Melbourne 10 Racing**
15 **MURAAHIN**, 4, ch g Teofilo (IRE)—Fatanah (IRE) **Melbourne 10 Racing**
16 4, B g Zoffany (IRE)—Myrtle Beach (IRE)
17 **RAISING SAND**, 7, b g Oasis Dream—Balalaika **Nick Bradley Racing 22 & Partner**
18 **RIPPLING WATERS (FR)**, 5, b m Areion (GER)—Pepples Beach (GER) **Melbourne 10 Racing**
19 **SARASOTA (IRE)**, 4, b f Zoffany (IRE)—Saldenaera (GER)
20 **SKYDIVING**, 4, b g Al Kazeem—How High The Sky (IRE) **Melbourne 10 Racing**
21 **SUNSHINE COAST**, 4, b g Kyllachy—Sunseek **Mr J. A. Osborne**
22 **TOAST OF NEW YORK (IRE)**, 8, b g Thewayyouare (USA)—Claire Soleil (USA) **Al Shaqab Racing UK Limit**
23 **TURN OF LUCK (IRE)**, 4, b c Pivotal—Side of Paradise (USA) **Merriebelle Irish Farm Limited**
24 **VEGAS BOY (IRE)**, 4, ch g Society Rock—Consensus (IRE) **N Bashir, N Dearman & R Ridout**
25 **YOUR BAND**, 4, b g Helmet (AUS)—Kampai **Mr F. McGrath**

THREE-YEAR-OLDS

26 **AGNES GRAND**, ch f Footstepsinthesand—Noble Penny **Five Grand Fillies**
27 **AUDACITY**, ch g Pivotal—Carlanda (FR) **M. A. C. Buckley**
28 **BRAINS (IRE)**, b g Dandy Man (IRE)—Pure Jazz (IRE) **The Judges & Partner**
29 B g Mayson—Capacious **Recycled Products Ltd**
30 **CAPOFARO**, b g Kyllachy—Pious **M. A. C. Buckley**
31 **DOTTY GRAND**, b f Dream Ahead (USA)—Dartrix **Five Grand Fillies**
32 **DUISBURG (FR)**, gr c Kendargent (FR)—Desca (GER) **I Barratt, A Signy & B Spiers**
33 **DUKE DEBONAIR (IRE)**, b g Dream Ahead (USA)—Nurture (IRE) **Mrs H Allanson & Partner**
34 **HEN (IRE)**, b f Camelot—Lily of Kenmare (IRE)
35 Ch g Mastercraftsman (IRE)—High Praise (USA) **Mrs T Hyde**
36 B f War Command (USA)—Highindi
37 **INDEPENDENCE (USA)**, b c More Than Ready (USA)—Frivolous Alex (USA)
38 **JERSEY WONDER (IRE)**, ch c Zoffany (IRE)—Magena (USA) **Mr A. Taylor**
39 **LE BOULEVARDIER**, b g Champs Elysees—Daffydowndilly **Lady Blyth**
40 **MATILDA BAY (IRE)**, b f Australia—Teddy Bears Picnic **Mrs H Allanson & Partners**
41 **MEMENTO (IRE)**, b c Sea The Stars (IRE)—Wizz Kid (IRE) **Mr Michael Buckley & Ballylinch Stud**
42 **MOLOTOV (IRE)**, ch g No Nay Never (USA)—Brigids Cross (IRE) **M. A. C. Buckley**
43 **NATSOVIA**, ch f Nathaniel (IRE)—So Belle **Mr H. J. Shipton**
44 **ORION'S SHORE (IRE)**, ch c Sea The Stars (IRE)—Bright Snow (USA) **Mr R Kinch & Partner**
45 **RICOCHET (IRE)**, b g Lope de Vega (IRE)—Sound of Guns **M. A. C. Buckley**
46 **RIVIERA CLAIRE**, b f Showcasing—Seldemosa **Mr & Mrs I. Barratt**
47 **RUSPER DREAMS (IRE)**, b g Dream Ahead (USA)—Daganya (IRE) **B Spiers, I Barratt & A Signy**
48 **RUSPER'S GIFT (IRE)**, b c Requinto (IRE)—Cadescia (IRE) **B Spiers, I Barratt & A Signy**
49 Ch f No Nay Never (USA)—Sliabh Na Mban (IRE) **Mrs P Shanahan**
50 **SYBIL GRAND**, b f Canford Cliffs (IRE)—Life Is Golden (USA) **Five Grand Fillies**
51 **THE NUMISMATIST (IRE)**, b c Sir Prancealot (IRE)—Friendly Heart (CAN) **One More Coin Racing**
52 B g Iffraaj—Titian's Pride (USA) **Nick Bradley Racing 46 & Partners**
53 **USANECOLT (IRE)**, b g Olympic Glory (IRE)—Never Busy (USA) **Homecroft Wealth Racing VIII**
54 **WATERPROOF**, b g Pour Moi (IRE)—Laughing Water (FR) **R. C. Tooth**

TWO-YEAR-OLDS

55 Gr c 21/2 Leroidesanimaux (BRZ)—Albaraka (Selkirk (USA)) (52000) **The Q Party**
56 B c 19/3 Mukhadram—Anbella (FR) (Common Grounds) (16000) **The 10 for 10 Partnership**
57 Gr c 30/3 Gutaifan (IRE)—Arabian Pearl (IRE) (Refuse To Bend (IRE)) (225000) **Al Shaqab Racing**
58 B f 12/3 Dandy Man (IRE)—Belgique (IRE) (Compton Place) (16856) **The 10 for 10 Partnership**
59 Gr c 27/2 Gutaifan (IRE)—Carallia (IRE) (Common Grounds) (50000) **The Q Party**
60 B c 31/1 Harbour Watch (IRE)—Chincoteague (IRE) (Daylami (IRE)) (7000) **The 10 for 10 Partnership**
61 **CONSTANZIA**, b f 26/1 Dandy Man (IRE)—Mara Grey (IRE) (Azamour (IRE)) (13000) **The Judges**
62 **COQUETA (IRE)**, b f 11/4 Teofilo (IRE)—Atamana (IRE) (Lahib (USA)) (117993) **M. A. C. Buckley**
63 Gr c 23/4 Lope de Vega (IRE)—Dazzle Dancer (IRE) (Montjeu (IRE)) (54782) **Ballylinch Stud and Partner**
64 B c 20/3 Camacho—Deira Dubai (Green Desert (USA)) (8428) **The 10 for 10 Partnership**
65 Gr f 26/3 Gutaifan (IRE)—Ellasha (Shamardal (USA)) (30000) **The 10 for 10 Partnership**
66 B br f 20/4 Invincible Spirit (IRE)—Fidelite (IRE) (In The Wings) (60000) **The Joy of Six Partnership**
67 B f 25/3 Dragon Pulse (IRE)—Fillothewisp (Teofilo (IRE)) (40000) **Clipper Logistics**
68 B c 27/4 Toronado (IRE)—Frigid (Indian Ridge) (11000) **The Joy of Six Partnership**

R JAMIE OSBORNE - Continued

9 B f 19/3 Acclamation—Golden Shadow (IRE) (Selkirk (USA)) (26970) **The Joy of Six Partnership**
0 **HASHTAGMETOO,** b f 24/3 Declaration of War (USA)—
    Caribbean Princess (USA) (Henrythenavigator (USA)) (25283) **The Other Club**
1 B f 6/4 New Approach (IRE)—Illandrane (IRE) (Cape Cross (IRE)) (20000) **The Q Party**
2 B f 19/2 Hallowed Crown (AUS)—Indian Angel (Indian Ridge) (13333) **The 10 for 10 Partnership**
3 **JERSEY MASTER (IRE),** ch c 10/3 Mastercraftsman (IRE)—Banquise (IRE) (Last Tycoon) (54782) **Mr A. Taylor**
4 Ch f 1/4 Zoffany (IRE)—Kirinda (IRE) (Tiger Hill (IRE)) (55000) **Mrs P Shanahan**
5 B c 2/2 Australia—Kitty Matcham (IRE) (Rock of Gibraltar (IRE)) (130636) **M. A. C. Buckley & Barronstown Stud**
6 B c 2/3 Gregorian (IRE)—Lady Bee (IRE) (Lawman (FR)) (5238) **The 10 for 10 Partnership**
7 B c 26/3 Iffraaj—Libys Dream (IRE) (Invincible Spirit (IRE)) (25000) **The Joy of Six Partnership**
8 **LOVE MY LIFE (IRE),** ch f 18/4 Ivawood (IRE)—
    Cradle Brief (IRE) (Brief Truce (USA)) (32000) **Bashir, Dearman and Ridout & Partner**
9 Gr f 21/4 Gutaifan (IRE)—Lovely Thought (Dubai Destination (USA)) (8000) **The Q Party**
0 B f 22/2 Bungle Inthejungle—Lucky Leigh (Piccolo) (34285) **Melbourne 10 Racing**
1 Gr c 25/3 Dark Angel (IRE)—Masaya (Dansili) (32000) **The Joy of Six Partnership**
2 B br f 1/4 Gleneagles (IRE)—Miss Lacey (IRE) (Diktat) (30000) **The 10 for 10 Partnership**
3 B f 22/2 Holy Roman Emperor (IRE)—Modern Art (New Approach (IRE)) (42857) **Mrs P Shanahan**
4 **MR BEAU BLUE,** br c 21/2 Brazen Beau (AUS)—
    Precious Secret (USA) (Fusaichi Pegasus (USA)) (76190) **Mr & Mrs I. H. Bendelow**
5 **MYSTIC RIVER (IRE),** b c 9/2 Animal Kingdom (USA)—
    Harriet Tubman (USA) (Medaglia d'oro (USA)) (63210) **M. A. C. Buckley**
6 B c 14/3 Bated Breath—Parisi (Rahy (USA)) (20000) **The 10 for 10 Partnership**
7 B c 7/3 Kingman—Ravissante (IRE) (Galileo (IRE)) **Mrs S. Rogers**
8 B c 17/4 Kodiac—Sanaya (IRE) (Barathea (IRE)) (57310) **The Joy of Six Partnership**
9 Ch f 6/4 Showcasing—Sharp Relief (IRE) (Galileo (IRE)) (38095) **The 10 for 10 Partnership**
0 B c 29/4 Make Believe—Sound of Guns (Acclamation) (35000) **Ballylinch Stud and Partner**
1 **ST PETERSBURG (FR),** b c 11/3 Wootton Bassett—Sagariya (FR) (Shamardal (USA)) (105351) **M. A. C. Buckley**
2 **VALENTINE BLUES (IRE),** gr f 14/2 Clodovil (IRE)—
    Grecian Artisan (IRE) (Mastercraftsman (IRE)) **Mr and Mrs I. H. Bendelow**
3 **WEBUYANYHORSE,** br gr c 19/3 Gutaifan (IRE)—
    Hairicin (IRE) (Hurricane Run (IRE)) (33712) **Bashir, Dearman, Ridout & Ennistown Stud**

sistant Trainer: Jimmy McCarthy

ckey (flat): Dougie Costello, Adam McNamara, Rossa Ryan. **Apprentice:** Nicola Currie. **Amateur:** Miss Alexandra
il.

---

135   MISS EMMA OWEN, Nether Winchendon
Postal: Muskhill Farm, Nether Winchendon, Aylesbury, Buckinghamshire, HP18 0EB
Contacts: PHONE (01844) 290282 MOBILE (07718) 984799
E-MAIL emma.l.owen@hotmail.com

1 **BAHAMIAN HEIGHTS,** 8, b g Bahamian Bounty—Tahirah **Miss E. L. Owen**
2 **BLACK WIDOW,** 8, b m Bertolini (USA)—Malvadilla (IRE) **Miss E. L. Owen**
3 **BORU'S BROOK (IRE),** 11, b g Brian Boru—Collybrook Lady (IRE) **Miss E. L. Owen**
4 **DIVINE MESSENGER,** 5, b g Firebreak—Resentful Angel **Miss E. L. Owen**
5 **DUTIFUL SON (IRE),** 9, b g Invincible Spirit (IRE)—Grecian Dancer **Miss E. L. Owen**
6 **ERTIDAAD (IRE),** 7, b g Kodiac—Little Scotland **Miss E. L. Owen**
7 **FIREGUARD,** 6, b g Firebreak—Leaping Flame (USA) **Miss E. L. Owen**
8 **GUNNER MOYNE,** 7, b g Excellent Art—Maramkova (IRE) **H. G. Owen**
9 **HIGHER COURT (USA),** 11, b g Shamardal (USA)—Nawaiet (USA) **Miss E. L. Owen**
0 **HIGHPLAINS DRIFTER (IRE),** 8, b g High Chaparral (IRE)—Qhazeenah **Miss E. L. Owen**
1 **JOSHLEE (IRE),** 5, b m Dark Angel (IRE)—Kay Es Jay (FR) **Miss E. L. Owen**
2 **LEGAL MIND,** 6, ch h Firebreak—La Sorrela (IRE) **Miss E. L. Owen**
3 **RED HANRAHAN (IRE),** 8, b g Yeats (IRE)—Monty's Sister (USA) **Miss E. L. Owen**
4 **REIGNITE,** 4, b c Firebreak—Resentful Angel **Miss E. L. Owen**
5 **SEA THE WAVES,** 6, b g Canford Cliffs (IRE)—April (IRE) **Mr L. F. Daly**
6 **THE ARISTOCAT (IRE),** 4, b f Kitten's Joy (USA)—Letters (FR) **Miss E. L. Owen**

HREE-YEAR-OLDS

7 **MILLDEAN BILLY (IRE),** b g Dandy Man (IRE)—Strawberriesncream (IRE) **Miss E. L. Owen**
8 **PEDDERY,** b c Pastoral Pursuits—Resentful Angel **Miss E. L. Owen**
9 **VERETA (IRE),** b f Dick Turpin (IRE)—Vera Lou (IRE) **Mr L. F. Daly**

436 **MR HUGO PALMER, Newmarket**
Postal: **Kremlin Cottage Stables, Snailwell Road, Newmarket, Suffolk, CB8 7DP**
Contacts: **PHONE (01638) 669880 FAX (01638) 666383 MOBILE (07824) 887886**
E-MAIL info@hugopalmer.com WEBSITE www.hugopalmer.com

1 **ARBALET (IRE)**, 4, gr c Dark Angel (IRE)—Miss Beatrix (IRE) **Mr V. I. Araci**
2 **ARCHITECTURE (IRE)**, 6, b m Zoffany (IRE)—Brigayev (ITY) **Lael Stable**
3 **ATLAAL**, 4, b f Dansili—Igugu (AUS) **Sheikh M. B. K. Al Maktoum**
4 **BREAKING RECORDS (IRE)**, 4, b g Kodiac—Querulous (USA) **Dr A. Ridha**
5 **COLLIDE**, 4, b c Frankel—Scuffle **K. Abdullah**
6 **CONFEDERATE**, 4, b g Teofilo (IRE)—Merry Jaunt (USA) **Highclere T'bred Racing-Kelly Holmes**
7 **DAWN DELIGHT**, 4, b f Dawn Approach (IRE)—Al Mahmeyah **Mr H. R. Bin Ghedayer**
8 **DUBAI EYE**, 4, ch f Pivotal—Jumeirah Palm Star **Mr H. R. Bin Ghedayer**
9 **DUKHAN**, 4, br g Teofilo (IRE)—Vedela (FR) **Al Shaqab Racing UK Limited**
10 **EL GHAZWANI (IRE)**, 4, b c Cape Cross (IRE)—Almansoora (USA) **Mr H. R. Bin Ghedayer**
11 **ENCRYPTED**, 4, b g Showcasing—Disclose **K. Abdullah**
12 **FAJJAJ (IRE)**, 4, ch c Dawn Approach (IRE)—Pleasantry **Al Shaqab Racing UK Limited**
13 **FORMULA ONE (IRE)**, 4, b g Frankel—Wizz Kid (IRE) **Mrs Fiona Carmichael / Ballylinch Stud**
14 **GHAITH**, 4, b g Invincible Spirit (IRE)—Wild Mimosa (IRE) **Al Shaqab Racing UK Limited**
15 **GIFTED MASTER (IRE)**, 6, b g Kodiac—Shobobb **Dr A. Ridha**
16 **HEAVENLY HOLLY (IRE)**, 4, b f Shamardal (USA)—Happy Holly (IRE) **Hunscote Stud**
17 **KARAKAMA (IRE)**, 4, b f Redoute's Choice (AUS)—Karasiyra (IRE)
18 **LABREGA**, 4, b f Cacique (IRE)—Postale **Al Shaqab Racing UK Limited**
19 **LOVELY APPROACH**, 4, ch g New Approach (IRE)—Lovely Pass (IRE) **Dr A. Ridha**
20 **MAZYOUN**, 5, br g Mayson—Hypnotize **Al Shaqab Racing UK Limited**
21 **MOOTASADIR**, 4, b c Dansili—Mahbooba (AUS) **Sheikh M. B. K. Al Maktoum**
22 **NEVER BACK DOWN (IRE)**, 4, b g Kodiac—Steer By The Stars (IRE) **M M Stables**
23 **PATHS OF GLORY**, 4, b g Mastercraftsman (IRE)—Pacific Rim (IRE) **China Horse Club International Limit**
24 **RASHDAN (FR)**, 4, b g Big Bad Bob (IRE)—On Fair Stage (USA) **Al Shaqab Racing UK Limited**
25 **REFEREE**, 4, b g Dansili—Zulema **K. Abdullah**
26 **STAGE NAME**, 5, ch m Famous Name—Striking Choice (USA) **Mrs V. Palmer**
27 **SUDONA**, 4, b f Zoffany (IRE)—Vickers Vimy **D. Hulse S. Saunders & Lady Cobham**
28 **TO BE WILD (IRE)**, 6, br g Big Bad Bob (IRE)—Fire Up **Mrs F. J. Carmichael**
29 **VOICE OF DUBAI**, 4, b g Poet's Voice—Pencarrow **Rabbah Racing**
30 **WHITE MOCHA (USA)**, 4, ch g Lope de Vega (IRE)—Lastroseofsummer (IRE) **Dr A. Ridha**

THREE-YEAR-OLDS

31 **ABR AL HUDOOD (JPN)**, b f Deep Impact (JPN)—Amanee (AUS) **Sheikh M. B. K. Al Maktoum**
32 **ALMUFTI**, c Toronado (ITY)—Green Tern (ITY) **Al Shaqab Racing UK Limited**
33 **AMORE BELLO (IRE)**, ch f Bated Breath—I'm In Love (USA) **Lady Mimi Manton & Partners**
34 **ARTOIS**, gr c Mizzen Mast (USA)—Intercontinental **K. Abdullah**
35 **ASSEMBLED**, gr c Iffraaj—Bezique **Mr V I Araci & Partners**
36 **BEAUTY OF DEIRA (IRE)**, ch f Pivotal—Phillipina **Dr A. Ridha**
37 **BIRDCAGE WALK**, b f Sea The Moon (GER)—Baisse **Mr G. Schoeningh**
38 **BIZ MARKEE (IRE)**, b g Slade Power (IRE)—Heart's Desire (IRE) **Nick Bradley Racing 23 & Sohi & Partne**
39 **BLONDE WARRIOR (IRE)**, ch c Zoffany (IRE)—Dame Blanche (IRE) **Mrs F. J. Carmichael**
40 **CARAVAN OF HOPE (IRE)**, b c Nathaniel (IRE)—Caravan of Dreams (IRE) **Dr A. Ridha**
41 **CROCHET (USA)**, b f First Defence (USA)—Magic Motif (USA) **K. Abdullah**
42 **DAHAWI**, b c Heeraat (IRE)—Piranha (IRE) **M M Stables**
43 **DEBBONAIR (IRE)**, b g Slade Power (IRE)—Bryanstown Girl (IRE) **Commission Air Limited**
44 **DEIRA SURPRISE**, ch f Slade Power (IRE)—Beautiful Filly **Dr A. Ridha**
45 **DESERT WAR (USA)**, gr c Oasis Dream—Gracie Square (USA) **Mr Martin Hughes & Lord de La Warr**
46 **DIANTHA (IRE)**, b f Dansili—Souviens Toi **Nick Bradley Racing 24 & Sohi & Partner**
47 **DJIBOUTI (IRE)**, gr f Dark Angel (IRE)—Late Night Movie (IRE) **Mr E. D. Tynan**
48 **DRAGON KUZA**, b g Dragon Pulse (IRE)—Mylaporyours (IRE) **Mr K. Kurt**
49 **ENGRAVE**, b f Dark Angel (IRE)—Hot Wired **K. Abdullah**
50 **EVERYMANANEMPROR**, br g Gregorian (IRE)—Winterbourne **Mr G. M. Richardson**
51 **FENJAL (IRE)**, gr g Kodiac—Spinamix **Al Shaqab Racing UK Limited**
52 **GEORGE FORMBY (IRE)**, br g Mayson—Supa Sal **Chelsea Thoroughbreds-ukulele & Partner**
53 **GOLD FLEECE**, b f Nathaniel (IRE)—Conquete (FR) **Lady Mary Manton**
54 **HAPPY FACE (IRE)**, b f Kingman—Intense Pink **Dr A. Ridha**
55 **HOT TEAM (IRE)**, b g Zoffany (IRE)—Ahd (USA) **Mr L. L. Lee**
56 **IRONCLAD**, br c Dubawi (IRE)—Heat Haze **K. Abdullah**
57 **JAMES STREET (IRE)**, b c Gale Force Ten—Paris Glory (USA) **M M Stables**

MR HUGO PALMER - Continued

58 **KAHINA (IRE)**, b f Camelot—Close Regards (IRE) **Mph Close Regards**
59 **MINA VAGANTE**, b f Exceed And Excel (AUS)—Unity (IRE) **Mr V. I. Araci**
60 **MORE SERENITY**, b f Dark Angel (IRE)—Vasilia **Mr V. I. Araci**
61 **ON THE LINE (IRE)**, gr c Dark Angel (IRE)—Crimson Cheer (USA) **Mr V. I. Araci**
62 **OURS PUISSANT (IRE)**, b c Kodiac—Lady Emly (IRE) **Mr Kevin Bailey & Mr Gabriel Chrysanthou**
63 **PERSEPONE**, b f Dubawi (IRE)—Filia Regina **The Earl Of Derby**
64 **PILSLEY**, ch f Lope de Vega (IRE)—Request **The Duke of Devonshire**
65 **POWER OF STATES (IRE)**, b c Lope de Vega (IRE)—Allegation (FR) **Dr A. Ridha**
66 **RACHEL ZANE (IRE)**, b f Sea The Moon (GER)—Mark of An Angel (IRE) **FOMO Syndicate**
67 **RED OCTOBER (IRE)**, ch c Dawn Approach (IRE)—Mamonta **Mrs Clodagh McStay & Partner**
68 **SET PIECE**, b c Dansili—Portodora (USA) **K. Abdullah**
69 **SIGLO SIX**, ch c Havana Gold—Yensi **Mr J. W. Livock**
70 **TAKE FRIGHT**, br f Bated Breath—Tipping Over (IRE) **Lady Mimi Manton & Partner**
71 **WALL OF SAPPHIRE (IRE)**, b f Lawman (FR)—Bright Sapphire (IRE) **Mr A. Kheir**
72 **WILLIAM MCKINLEY**, b g Exceed And Excel (AUS)—Pure Song **W. J. and T. C. O. Gredley**
73 **WOJOOD**, b g Dansili—Endless **Sheikh M. B. K. Al Maktoum**
74 **ZOFELLE (IRE)**, b f Zoffany (IRE)—Height of Elegance (IRE) **Lady Mary Manton**

TWO-YEAR-OLDS

75 B c 11/4 Lawman (FR)—Abunai (Pivotal) (35000)
76 B f 7/4 Mastercraftsman (IRE)—Arosa (Sadler's Wells (USA)) (42140)
77 B c 27/3 Zoffany (IRE)—Awohaam (IRE) (Iffraaj) (76190)
78 Ch c 2/5 Sepoy (AUS)—Beautiful Filly (Beauty Dream) (70000) **Dr A. Ridha**
79 B c 30/1 Oasis Dream—Bella Nostalgia (IRE) (Raven's Pass (USA)) **Mr V. I. Araci**
80 B c 8/2 Night of Thunder (IRE)—Blameless (IRE) (Authorized (IRE)) (50568)
81 B c 19/3 Due Diligence (USA)—Brick Tops (Danehill Dancer (IRE)) (25283)
82 B c 29/4 Gleneagles (IRE)—Caphene (Sakhee (USA)) **Qatar Racing Limited**
83 B f 16/1 Dansili—Chigun (Oasis Dream) **Mr V. I. Araci**
84 **DOUBLING DICE**, br c 13/5 Teofilo (IRE)—Garanciere (FR) (Anabaa (USA)) (80000) **Mr V. I. Araci**
85 Ch f 27/2 Toronado (IRE)—Ego (Green Desert (USA)) **Highclere Thoroughbred Racing Ltd**
86 **EMISSARY**, b c 1/5 Kingman—Soviet Moon (IRE) (Sadler's Wells (USA)) **K. Abdullah**
87 B c 16/4 Helmet (AUS)—Empress Ella (IRE) (Holy Roman Emperor (IRE)) (40455) **Mr L. L. Lee**
88 **EVENTFUL**, b f 4/3 Oasis Dream—Spectacle (Dalakhani (IRE)) **K. Abdullah**
89 B c 7/4 Invincible Spirit (IRE)—Filia Regina (Galileo (IRE)) (120000) **The Earl Of Derby**
90 Ch c 22/3 Showcasing—Katalea (Mr Greeley (USA)) (202275)
91 **KOSSUTH**, b c 17/2 Dansili—Ultrasonic (USA) (Mizzen Mast (USA)) **K. Abdullah**
92 B c 7/2 Camelot—Logjam (IRE) (Royal Academy (USA)) (75853) **Mr J. W. Livock**
93 B f 19/1 Golden Horn—Lovely Pass (IRE) (Raven's Pass (USA)) (150000) **Dr A. Ridha**
94 Ch c 26/4 Anjaal—Nijah (IRE) (Pivotal) (28000)
95 **OASIS JOY**, b f 20/3 Oasis Dream—Pure Joy (Zamindar (USA)) **K. Abdullah**
96 B f 9/3 Iffraaj—Power of Light (IRE) (Echo of Light) (50000) **Dr A. Ridha**
97 B c 14/3 Havana Gold (IRE)—Prospera (IRE) (Cape Cross (IRE)) (80952) **Mrs F. J. Carmichael**
98 **RACHMANINOV (USA)**, b c 28/3 Mizzen Mast (USA)—Solo Piano (USA) (Empire Maker (USA)) **K. Abdullah**
99 B c 18/3 Havana Gold (IRE)—Royal Warranty (Sir Percy) (11000)
100 B f 13/4 Siyouni (FR)—Ruby Rocket (IRE) (Indian Rocket) (160000) **Al Shaqab Racing UK Limited**
101 **RUSHCUTTERS BAY**, b c 14/1 Cable Bay (IRE)—Kicker Rock (Fastnet Rock (AUS)) (9523)
102 B c 5/4 Toronado (IRE)—Saskia's Dream (Oasis Dream) (63210) **H Moorhead, C Fahy & J Collins**
103 B c 21/3 Camacho—Savida (IRE) (King's Best (USA)) (54782) **East 11 Limited**
104 B c 9/3 Zoffany (IRE)—Sharnberry (Shamardal (USA)) (28000) **Mr L. L. Lee**
105 B c 4/2 Kingman—She's Mine (IRE) (Sea The Stars (IRE)) **Mr V. I. Araci**
106 B f 23/1 Zoffany (IRE)—Silent Thoughts (IRE) (Galileo (IRE)) (109565) **Dr A. Ridha**
107 Ch c 24/2 Dubawi (IRE)—Splashdown (Falbrav (IRE)) (105000) **Mr V. I. Araci**
108 B c 9/2 Rock of Gibraltar (IRE)—Strawberry Vodka (Azamour (IRE)) (26970) **FOMO (Rock) Syndicate**
109 Ch f 20/2 Hot Streak (IRE)—Stroll Patrol (Mount Nelson) (84280) **Dr A. Ridha**
110 B c 7/4 Australia—Tessa Reef (IRE) (Mark of Esteem (IRE)) (134850) **Mr J. W. Livock**
111 B c 20/1 Iffraaj—The Madding Crowd (Dansili) (190000) **Al Shaqab Racing UK Limited**
112 B f 15/4 Zoffany (IRE)—Unity (IRE) (Sadler's Wells (USA)) (80000) **Lady Mary Manton**
113 Gr f 28/1 Dark Angel (IRE)—Ventura Mist (Pastoral Pursuits) (120000) **Dr A. Ridha**
114 **VINTAGE POLLY (IRE)**, br f 25/4 Gutaifan (IRE)—Payphone (Anabaa (USA)) (45000) **Mr R. W. Hill-Smith**
115 Ch g 14/2 Zoffany (IRE)—Wandering Spirit (GER) (Dashing Blade) (40455)

MR HUGO PALMER - Continued

Other Owners: S. Ali, Mr M. Almutairi, Mr M. Almutairi, Aston House Stud, Mr K. B. Bailey, Ballylinch Stud, Mr N. Bradley, Chelsea Thoroughbreds - Ukulele, Chelsea Thoroughbreds Ltd, Mr G. Chrysanthou, Lady N. F. Cobham, Mr J. A. Collins, Lord De La Warr, Mr C. J. Fahy, T. C. O. Gredley, W. J. Gredley, Highclere Nominated Partner Limited, Highclere Thoroughbred Racing Ltd, Mr M. P Hills, Miss S. Holden, W. M. B. Hughes, The Hon Mrs D Hulse, Mrs G. S. Jackson, Mr R. Jackson, Mrs E. Magnier, Mr M. J. McStay, Mrs C. McStay, Nick Bradley Racing 23, Nick Bradley Racing 24, Mr T. O'Connor, Mr H. Palmer, Mr T. J. Ramsden, Mrs S. Saunders, Mrs L. M. Shanahan, Mrs L. A. Smith, Mr S. Smith.

Jockey (flat): Josephine Gordon

---

437 MR MARK PATTINSON, Epsom
Postal: Flat 3, White House Stables, Tattenham Corner Road, Epsom, Surrey, KT18 5PP
Contacts: **PHONE (01737) 913469**

1 **ALMANACK**, 9, b g Haatef (USA)—Openness **M I Pattinson Racing**
2 **BRECQHOU ISLAND**, 4, b g Pastoral Pursuits—Lihou Island **Mrs F A Veasey & G. B. Partnership**
3 **GOLCONDA PRINCE (IRE)**, 5, b g Arcano (IRE)—Mujarah (IRE) **M I Pattinson Racing**
4 **OUR OYSTERCATCHER**, 5, br g Pastoral Pursuits—The Dark Eider **Mrs F A Veasey & G. B. Partnership**
5 **PERFECT SYMPHONY (IRE)**, 5, br g Dandy Man (IRE)—Fields of Joy (GER) **Lynne Stanbrook & Julian Power**
6 **TOBACCO ROAD (IRE)**, 9, b g Westerner—Virginias Best **M I Pattinson Racing**

THREE-YEAR-OLDS

7 B c Nayef (USA)—The Lady Lapwing **M I Pattinson Racing**

TWO-YEAR-OLDS

8 B f 12/2 Medicean—Copper Penny (Dansili) (3000) **Mrs F. A. Veasey**

Other Owners: M. G. H. Heald, Mr A. M. H. Heald, Mr C. R. Pattinson, Mr M. Pattinson, Mr J. Power, Mrs L. C. Stanbrook.

---

438 MR BEN PAULING, Bourton-on-the-Water
Postal: Bourton Hill Farm, Bourton Hill, Bourton-On-The-Water, Cheltenham, Gloucestershire, GL54 2LF
Contacts: **PHONE (01451) 821252 MOBILE (07825) 232888**
E-MAIL ben@benpaulingracing.com **WEBSITE** www.benpaulingracing.com

1 **A HARE BREATH (IRE)**, 11, b g Alkaadhem—Lady Willmurt (IRE) **Mrs S. N. J. Embiricos**
2 **AMETHEA (IRE)**, 5, b m Yeats (IRE)—Moricana (GER) **Pump&Plant ServicesLtd&TheLateMrMartinHolder**
3 **ANIGHTINLAMBOURN (IRE)**, 5, b m Gold Well—Madgehil (IRE) **Mr & Mrs Paul & Clare Rooney**
4 **APPLE ROCK (IRE)**, 5, b g Royal Anthem (USA)—Wayward Cove **Presumption in Favour Partnership**
5 4, Ch g Stowaway—Babyshan (IRE)
6 **BANANA JOE (IRE)**, 5, b g Getaway (GER)—Rosetiepy (FR) **Slater Stockwood Nicholson Partnership**
7 **BARLEY HILL (IRE)**, 6, ch g Stowaway—Saysi (IRE) **The Buckshees**
8 **BATTYS DILEMMA (IRE)**, 7, b g Darsi (FR)—Rosetiepy (FR) **Mrs S. Pauling**
9 **BERBORU (IRE)**, 7, b m Brian Boru—Relic Hunter (IRE) **Mrs L. Osborne**
10 **BIG DIFFERENCE (IRE)**, 6, b g Presenting—Roque de Cyborg (IRE) **Mr M. Waters**
11 **BOLD REASON (GER)**, 4, b g Invincible Spirit (IRE)—Bufera (IRE) **Mrs C. J. Djivanovic**
12 **BRAVE DANCING**, 5, b g Mount Nelson—Purring (USA) **Bruton Street**
13 **BRIGHT FORECAST (IRE)**, 5, b g Arcadio (GER)—Check The Forecast (IRE) **The Aldaniti Partnership**
14 **CANGODEMAYO**, 7, b m Lucarno (USA)—Cadoutene (FR) **The Swing Along Partnership**
15 **CARLOS DU FRUITIER (FR)**, 7, b g Diableneyev (USA)—Odyssee Madrik (FR) **The Sandbaggers Club**
16 **CAVERNOUS (IRE)**, 6, br g Court Cave (IRE)—Willoughby Sue (IRE) **Mr C. A. Washbourn**
17 **CAVOK (IRE)**, 7, b m Kayf Tara—Timon's Present **Mrs C. J. Zetter-Wells**
18 **CHESS PLAYER (IRE)**, 4, ch g No Risk At All (FR)—Merci Jandrer (FR) **Mrs Rachel Brodie & Mr John Brodie**
19 **CHUFFY CHUFFNELL (IRE)**, 5, b g Flemensfirth (USA)—Cathy Doun (IRE) **The Megsons**
20 **CITY STAR**, 7, b m Black Sam Bellamy (IRE)—Danarama **J & A Young (Leicester) Ltd**
21 **COEUR PENSIF (FR)**, 7, br g Laveron—Lady Easter (FR) **Lost In 1936 Partnership**
22 **CREEP DESBOIS (FR)**, 7, b g Great Pretender (IRE)—Brigade Mondaine (FR) **Slater Stockwood Nicholson Partnership**
23 **DELIRE D'ESTRUVAL (FR)**, 6, b g Youmzain (IRE)—Question d'estruval (FR) **Mr Simon Munir & Mr Isaac Souede**
24 **EARL BIFFY BIFFEN (FR)**, 5, bl g Day Flight—Similaresisoldofa (FR) **The Megsons**

MR BEN PAULING - Continued

25 **EAU TOP (FR)**, 5, b g Barastraight—Monepopee (FR) **Mr O. Troup**
26 **EQUUS SECRETUS (IRE)**, 7, b g Brian Boru—Bodega Bay (IRE) **The Bourtoneers**
27 **ESPOIR DE LOIRE (FR)**, 5, b g Anabaa Blue—Grischa (FR) **Merriebelle Irish Farm Limited**
28 **FAWSLEY SPIRIT (IRE)**, 6, b g Stowaway—Apple Trix (IRE) **Mrs Rachel Brodie & Mr Clive Bush**
29 **FIFTH SYMPHONY (IRE)**, 5, b g Mahler—Nicolemma (IRE) **Clive Washbourn & David Howard**
30 **FOR LUCK (FR)**, 4, ch g Coastal Path—Isis de Sormain (FR) **The Bourtoneers**
31 **GLOBAL CITIZEN (IRE)**, 7, b g Alkaadhem—Lady Willmurt (IRE) **The Megsons**
32 **GOWITHTHEFLOW (IRE)**, 6, b g Westerner—Mariyver (IRE) **Bruton Street**
33 **GRANNY'S SECRET (IRE)**, 5, b m Stowaway—Ask My Granny (IRE)
34 **HIDDEN GLEN (IRE)**, 6, ch g Stowaway—Gleanntan (IRE) **J Petit,C Skinner,R Sanders & J Tuttiett**
35 **IFYOUCANSEEMENOW (IRE)**, 5, br g Stowaway—Sandrinechoix (FR) **Mr & Mrs Paul & Clare Rooney**
36 4, B g Califet (FR)—Iktitafs Sister (IRE) **Mrs S. Pauling**
37 **IMPERIAL BAY (IRE)**, 7, br g Flemensfirth (USA)—Nun Better (IRE) **The Urban Partnership**
38 **KARABUNGA DUDE**, 5, b g Black Sam Bellamy (IRE)—Danarama **J & A Young (Leicester) Ltd**
39 **KENNACK BAY (FR)**, 4, b g Balko (FR)—Nuance Tartare (FR) **The Kennack Bay Partnership**
40 **KERRY'S BOY (IRE)**, 6, b g Oscar (IRE)—Kerry's Girl (IRE) **Mr M. P. Ardley**
41 **KILDISART (IRE)**, 7, b g Dubai Destination (USA)—Princess Mairead (IRE) **Mr Simon Munir & Mr Isaac Souede**
42 **LADY CHUFFNELL (IRE)**, 5, b m Jeremy (USA)—Taraval (USA) **The Megsons**
43 **LE BREUIL (FR)**, 7, ch g Anzillero (GER)—Slew Dancer **Mrs E. A. Palmer**
44 **LEGAL EYES (IRE)**, 6, br g Court Cave (IRE)—Grass Tips (IRE) **OAP Syndicate**
45 **MALACHYS GIRL (IRE)**, 6, b m Darsi (FR)—Borleagh Princess (IRE) **Mrs S. J. Lanz**
46 **MARKOV (IRE)**, 9, b g Morozov (USA)—Willoughby Sue (IRE) **Mr A. R. W. Marsh**
47 **MARTEN (FR)**, 7, b g Martaline—Commande Blue (FR) **Lord Vestey**
48 **MONK'S VIEW**, 6, bl g Multiplex—Evelith Abbey (IRE) **The High T Party**
49 **MY TURGEON (FR)**, 6, gr g Turgeon (USA)—My Belle (FR) **Peel Racing Club**
50 **MYSTIC COURT (IRE)**, 6, b g Court Cave (IRE)—My Mystic Rose (IRE) **Mystic Band of Brothers**
51 **NADAITAK**, 5, b g Teofilo (IRE)—Tanfidh **The Megsons**
52 **NESTOR PARK (FR)**, 6, b g Walk In The Park (IRE)—Cila (FR) **Mrs S. P. Davis**
53 **NORTHERN BOUND (IRE)**, 5, b g Fruits of Love (USA)—Noble Choice **Mrs E. L. Kendall**
54 **NOT AT PRESENT (IRE)**, 4, b g Presenting—Anna Magdalena (IRE) **Mrs Rachel Brodie & Mr John Brodie**
55 **NOW IS THE WINTER (IRE)**, 5, b g Fame And Glory—Supreme Melody (IRE) **Mrs S. Pauling**
56 **OISTRAKH LE NOIR (FR)**, 5, b g Kentucky Dynamite (USA)—
                                      Linares Noire (FR) **Mr Simon Munir & Mr Isaac Souede**
57 **PERFECT PIRATE**, 7, b g Black Sam Bellamy (IRE)—Supreme Gem (IRE) **The Ben Pauling Racing Club**
58 **PLUS ONE (IRE)**, 7, b g Winged Love (IRE)—Balwaney (FR) **The Megsons**
59 **POWERFUL SYMBOL**, 9, b g Robin des Champs (FR)—Be My Rainbow (IRE) **The Megsons**
60 4, B g Presenting—Princess Gaia (IRE) **McNeill Family and Prodec Networks Ltd**
61 **RAISE YOUR SHADES (IRE)**, 5, b g Morozov (USA)—
                                      Couleurs de Barra (IRE) **Foxtrot Racing Raise Your Shades**
62 **RAVEN'S TOWER (USA)**, 9, b g Raven's Pass (USA)—Tizdubai (USA) **Faithful Friends**
63 **RINTULLA (IRE)**, 5, ch g Tobougg (IRE)—The Millers Tale (IRE) **McNeill Family Ltd**
64 4, B g Flemensfirth (USA)—Rose Island **Mr & Mrs J Tuttiett**
65 **RUBY RING**, 6, b m Sulamani (IRE)—Royal Bride **Mrs S. N. J. Embiricos**
66 **SAVANNA ROAR (IRE)**, 6, b g Let The Lion Roar—Addie's Choice (IRE) **The Jp Girls**
67 **SHAKEM UP'ARRY (IRE)**, 5, b g Flemensfirth (USA)—Nun Better (IRE) **Mr H. Redknapp**
68 **SHANROE TIC TEC (IRE)**, 7, b g Flemensfirth (USA)—Bonny Hall (IRE) **Easy Going Racing**
69 **SKIDOOSH**, 6, b g Midnight Legend—Southern Exit **Mr L. J. Strangman**
70 **STAGE SUMMIT (IRE)**, 6, gr g Tikkanen (USA)—Summittotalkabout (IRE) **Fortnum Racing**
71 **SUPREME SOVIET (IRE)**, 5, b g Sholokhov (IRE)—Bay Pearl (FR) **El Vino Did Flow Syndicate**
72 **TEL'ART (FR)**, 5, b g Montmartre (FR)—Textuelle (FR) **Mr & Mrs J Tuttiett**
73 **TENNEWROW (IRE)**, 7, b m Stowaway—Silent Supreme (IRE) **Mr Andrew Bickmore & Mr Peter Bickmore**
74 **THE CAPTAINS INN (IRE)**, 5, b g Flemensfirth (USA)—Killeen (IRE) **The Megsons**
75 **THE COB (IRE)**, 5, b g Let The Lion Roar—Millenium Love (IRE) **Mrs S. Pauling**
76 4, B g Dubai Destination (USA)—The Legislator (IRE) **The Aldaniti Partnership**
77 **THE MACON LUGNATIC**, 5, b g Shirocco (GER)—Didbrook **Genesis Racing Partnership II**
78 4, B g Court Cave (IRE)—The Millers Tale (IRE)
79 **TIP TOP CAT (IRE)**, 4, b g Milan—Pilgara (IRE)
80 **TOWARDS THE DAWN**, 5, b g Midnight Legend—Wakeful **Mrs S. L. Lloyd-Baker**
81 **TREATY GIRL (IRE)**, 8, b m Milan—Back To Cloghoge (IRE) **The Bourtoneers**
82 **WAY BACK THEN (IRE)**, 8, b g Robin des Champs (FR)—Ashwell Lady (IRE) **Nicholas Piper & Claire E. Piper**
83 **WHIN PARK**, 7, b g Great Pretender (IRE)—Pocahontas (FR) **Mrs S. P. Davis**
84 4, B g Mahler—Wild Fuchsia (IRE)
85 **WORLD PREMIER (FR)**, 6, gr g Montmartre (FR)—Kelbelange (FR) **Mr J. P. McManus**

MR BEN PAULING - Continued

Other Owners: Mr D. Abraham, Mr R. V. Alberto, Mr J. A. C. Ayton, Mr P. C. Bickmore, Mr A. R. Bickmore, Mr M. Booth, Mr J. W. Brodie, Mrs R. A. Brodie, Mr C. P. E. Brooks, Mr C. Bush, Mrs P. L. Capper, Mr Charles E. Noell Esq, Mrs G. Collier, Mrs P. M. Colson, Mr J. Deacon, Mr M. G. Donnellan, Mrs M. S. Drummond, Exors of the Late Mr S. N. Embiricos, Ms A. E. Embiricos, Mr C. Fenwick, Mr R. Foxon, Mr D. E. Greenway, Mr M. D. Hankin, Mrs C. S. Heber-Percy, Mr B. L. Hiskey, Exors of the Late M. J. Holder, The Hon David F. Howard, J H & N J Foxon Ltd, Mr W. R. Kinsey, Mr P. McGrath, Mrs J. Megson, Mr A. P. Megson, Mr J. M. Melvin, S. E. Munir, J. M. Nicholson, Mr B. P. Pauling, Mrs J. Pauling, Mr J. W. Petit, Mr N. Piper, Miss C. E. Piper, Prodec Networks Ltd, Pump & Plant Services Ltd, Mrs C. Rooney, Mr P. A. Rooney, Mr R. D. Sanders, Mr T. A. Simmons, Mr C. A. L. Skinner, Mr I. Souede, Mr J. Stockwood, Mrs M. T. Stopford-Sackville, Mr D. F. Sumpter, Mr P. Taylor, Mrs A. J. Tuttiett, Mr J. E. Tuttiett, The Hon A. G. Vestey, Mrs C. A. Waters, Mr W. R. B. Webb, Mr R. W. P. Weeks, Mr B. H. Wilson.

Assistant Trainer: Thomas David

Jockey (NH): David Bass, Daryl Jacob, Nico De Boinville. **Amateur:** Mr A. Rid.

---

439 **MR RAY PEACOCK, Tenbury Wells**
Postal: Elliott House Farm, Vine Lane, Kyre, Tenbury Wells, Worcestershire, WR15 8RL
Contacts: **PHONE (01885) 410772 MOBILE (07748) 565574/ 07881440135**

1 INTERCHOICE STAR, 14, b g Josr Algarhoud (IRE)—Blakeshall Girl **Mr J. P. Evitt**
2 LES GAR GAN (IRE), 8, b m Iffraaj—Story **Mr J. P. Evitt**
3 MUNAAWIB, 11, b g Haafhd—Mouwadh (USA) **R. E. Peacock**
4 PORTRUSH STORM, 14, ch m Observatory (USA)—Overcast (IRE) **R. E. Peacock**
5 RICH HARVEST (USA), 14, b br g High Yield (USA)—Mangano (USA) **R. E. Peacock**

Assistant Trainer: Mrs C Peacock

Jockey (flat): David Probert. **Amateur:** Miss S. Peacock.

---

440 **MRS LYDIA PEARCE, Newmarket**
Postal: Wroughton House, 37 Old Station Road, Newmarket, Suffolk, CB8 8DT
Contacts: **PHONE (01638) 664669 MOBILE (07787) 517864**
E-MAIL lsp_8@live.co.uk

1 BARTHOLOMEW J (IRE), 5, ch g Fast Company (IRE)—Mana (IRE) **Jay Three Racing & Partners**
2 CAMARADORIE (IRE), 5, ch m Camacho—Lady Duxyana **Mr R. G. Thurston Partnership**
3 CONQUERESS (IRE), 5, ch m Dandy Man (IRE)—Sesmen **Game Of Chance**
4 DYAGILEV, 4, ch c Kheleyf (USA)—Dancemetothemoon **Killarney Glen & Lydia Pearce**
5 FULL INTENTION, 5, b g Showcasing—My Delirium **Killarney Glen & Lydia Pearce**
6 GENERAL PATTON, 5, b g Intense Focus (USA)—Blandish (USA) **Miss Audrey Lanham and Partners**
7 LUNA MAGIC, 5, b m Mayson—Dayia (IRE) **Lady J. Green**
8 MILLIE KHEE, 7, b m Sakhee (USA)—Cugina **Jay Three Racing 1**
9 MYTHOLOGICAL, 4, gr c Galileo (IRE)—Pembina (IRE) **Mr W. J. S. Prosser**
10 NOBLE PEACE, 6, b g Kyllachy—Peace Concluded **Killarney Glen**
11 SEXY SECRET, 8, b g Sakhee's Secret—Orange Walk (IRE) **Personal Racehorse Owners 1**

THREE-YEAR-OLDS

12 ANNAKONDA (IRE), b f Morpheus—Royal Esteem **Mr W. J. S. Prosser**
13 CLARION LADY, b f Epaulette (AUS)—Tanwir **Clarion Racing**
14 LYNCHPIN (IRE), b c Camacho—River Bounty **Mr W. J. S. Prosser**
15 MISS COMMUNICATE, b f Gregorian (IRE)—Love Quest **Mr W. J. S. Prosser**
16 MITIGATOR, b c Delegator—Snake Skin **Mr W. J. S. Prosser**
17 REFORMED CHARACTER (IRE), b c Zoffany—Sallysaysso (IRE) **Mr W. J. S. Prosser**
18 TWO FACED, b f Coach House (IRE)—Blushing (IRE) **Mr W. J. S. Prosser**

Other Owners: S. Andrews, Mr S. J. Bush, Mr H. Crothers, Mr G. Fox, N. M. Hanger, J. Harrison, Mr C. S. Heaps, Jay Three Racing, Mr E. Jones, Miss A. Lanham, Mrs L. Matthews, Mrs L. S. Pearce, A. B. Puddick, R. G. Thurston.

Assistant Trainers: Jeff Pearce, Simon Pearce

441 MR OLLIE PEARS, Malton

Postal: **The Office, Old Farmhouse, Beverley Road, Norton, Malton, North Yorkshire, YO17 9PJ**
Contacts: PHONE **(01653) 690746** MOBILE **(07760) 197103**
E-MAIL **info@olliepearsracing.co.uk** WEBSITE **www.olliepearsracing.co.uk**

1 **AMITY ISLAND**, 4, ch g Harbour Watch (IRE)—Mylington Light **Ollie Pears & Ownaracehorse Ltd**
2 **CARRY ON DERYCK**, 7, b g Halling (USA)—Mullein **NP Racing Syndicate**
3 **CHRISTMAS NIGHT**, 4, ch g Compton Place—Night Haven **Ownaracehorse Ltd & Mr Ollie Pears**
4 **DANDY HIGHWAYMAN (IRE)**, 5, ch g Dandy Man (IRE)—Paradise Blue (IRE) **Ontoawinner & Ollie Pears**
5 **JENNIES GEM**, 6, b g Mount Nelson—Kaspirit (IRE) **Mr R. S. Marshall**
6 **KROY**, 5, b g Sleeping Indian—Valley of The Moon (IRE) **Mrs S. A. Elsey**
7 **LEAN ON PETE (IRE)**, 10, b g Oasis Dream—Superfonic (FR) **Keith West & Ollie Pears Racing Club**
8 **MONT ROYAL (FR)**, 5, gr g Naaqoos—Take Blood (FR) **T. Elsey**
9 **MR C (IRE)**, 5, b g Fast Company (IRE)—Vanitycase (IRE) **Mr A. Caygill**
10 **PLACEBO EFFECT (IRE)**, 4, b g Lilbourne Lad (IRE)—
Hawaiian Dream (IRE) **Timothy O'Gram, Keith West & Ollie Pears**
11 **ROARING RORY**, 6, ch g Sakhee's Secret—Barbieri (IRE) **Ownaracehorse Ltd & Mr Ollie Pears**
12 **STRAIGHT ASH (IRE)**, 4, gr g Zebedee—Blackangelheart (IRE) **NP Racing Syndicate**

THREE-YEAR-OLDS

13 **LETHAL GUEST**, gr g Lethal Force (IRE)—Holberg Suite **NP Racing Syndicate**
14 **LEXIKON**, b f Mayson—Fairy Steps **Mrs S. D. Pearson**
15 **NORTHERN FOOTSTEPS**, b f Footstepsinthesand—Raktina **NP Racing Syndicate**
16 **SAPPHIRE JUBILEE**, b f Lethal Force (IRE)—Queens Jubilee **Mrs S. D. Pearson**
17 **SMASHING LASS (IRE)**, ch f Sir Prancealot (IRE)—Gilded Truffle (IRE) **Ownaracehorse Ltd & Mr Ollie Pears**
18 **SUPREME DREAM**, b f Captain Gerrard (IRE)—Sweet Lily Pea (USA) **Supreme Bloodstock**
19 **SWERVED (IRE)**, b f Excelebration (IRE)—Manoeuvre (IRE) **Ownaracehorse Ltd & Mr Ollie Pears**

TWO-YEAR-OLDS

20 B g 8/5 Sleeping Indian—Anushka Noo Noo (Makfi) **Mr A. Caygill**
21 **BELLA FIGLIA**, bl f 18/3 Brazen Beau (AUS)—
Powerfulstorm (Bertolini (USA)) (6500) **Mr T O'Gram, Mrs P Moll & Mr R Marshall**
22 **BLITZLE**, gr f 21/1 Toronado (IRE)—Kept Under Wraps (IRE) (Clodovil (IRE)) **Np Racing Syndicate & Ollie Pears**
23 B f 3/3 Coach House (IRE)—Charlevoix (IRE) (King Charlemagne (USA)) (1904) **Mr A. Caygill**
24 **CHRISTMAS DIAMOND**, ch f 31/3 Bated Breath—
Velma Kelly (Vettori (IRE)) **Ownaracehorse Ltd & Mr Ollie Pears**
25 **CLASSY LADY**, b f 16/3 Garswood—Classic Vision (Classic Cliche (IRE)) (3000) **Ollie Pears Racing Club**
26 **HARRY LOVE (IRE)**, b g 15/4 Lawman (FR)—
Gimmick (IRE) (Siyouni (FR)) (4213) **Ownaracehorse Ltd & Mr Ollie Pears**
27 **INVER SILVER**, ch f 24/3 Fast Company (IRE)—
My Best Bet (Best of The Bests (IRE)) (1904) **Ownaracehorse Ltd & Mr Ollie Pears**
28 **PIVOTAL ART (IRE)**, br g 25/4 Dutch Art—Up Tempo (Pivotal) (5714) **Mary Carter, Stuart Carter & Ollie Pears**
29 **WRIGHTIA (IRE)**, gr f 9/4 Mastercraftsman (IRE)—Gerika (FR) (Galileo (IRE)) (25000) **T. Elsey**
30 **YOUTHFILLY**, b f 30/1 Fountain of Youth (IRE)—
Quiet Elegance (Fantastic Light (USA)) (800) **Ollie Pears Racing Club**

Other Owners: Mrs M. E. Carter, Mr S. J. Carter, Mr C. Harris, Mr W. Hobson, Mrs P. E. Moll, Mr N. J. O'Brien, T. J. O'Gram, Ownaracehorse Ltd, O. J. Pears, Mrs N. Watson, K. C. West.

Assistant Trainer: Vicky Pears

Jockey (NH): Brian Hughes.

442 MISS LINDA PERRATT, East Kilbride

Postal: **North Allerton Farm, East Kilbride, Glasgow, Lanarkshire, G75 8RR**
Contacts: PHONE **(01355) 303425** MOBILE **(07931) 306147**
E-MAIL **linda.perratt@btinternet.com**

1 **BAREED (USA)**, 4, ch g Kitten's Joy (USA)—Sweet Harp (USA) **Jackton Racing Club**
2 **DARK CRYSTAL**, 8, b m Multiplex—Glitz (IRE) **Nil Sine Labore Partnership**
3 **DAWOODI**, 5, ch g Exceed And Excel (AUS)—Anna Amalia (IRE) **Mr J. Murphy**
4 **DUTCH DREAM**, 6, ch m Dutch Art—Starry Sky **Mr B. A. Jordan**

MISS LINDA PERRATT - Continued

5 **INDIE GROOVE (IRE)**, 4, b g Intikhab (USA)—Cristal Groove (IRE) **Jackton Racing Club**
6 **LET RIGHT BE DONE**, 7, gr g Lawman (FR)—Cheerfully **Linda Perratt Racing Club**
7 **LUCKY VIOLET (IRE)**, 7, b m Dandy Man (IRE)—Rashida **Nil Sine Labore Partnership**
8 **PALAVICINI RUN (IRE)**, 6, ch m Palavicini (USA)—Dawn's Sharp Shot (IRE) **Ayr Racecourse Club**
9 **RETIREMENT BECKONS**, 4, b g Epaulette (AUS)—Mystical Ayr (IRE) **Nil Sine Labore Partnership**
10 **SCHMOOZE (IRE)**, 10, b m One Cool Cat (USA)—If Dubai (USA) **Miss L. A. Perratt**
11 **STARDRIFTER**, 7, b g Rock of Gibraltar (IRE)—Alchemilla **Jackton Racing Club**
12 **WAHWEI SPIRIT (IRE)**, 4, b g Mustameet (USA)—La Belle de Serk (IRE) **Mr Peter Tsim & Miss Linda Perratt**

THREE-YEAR-OLDS

13 **INDIARO**, b g Sleeping Indian—Cafe Express (IRE) **The Hon Miss H. Galbraith**
14 **JORDAN ELECTRICS**, b g Dandy Man (IRE)—Ruby Slippers **Mr Brian Jordan,B.Jordan &stephen Jordan**
15 **JORDAN'S CHRIS (IRE)**, ch f Society Rock (IRE)—Crimson Sunrise (IRE) **Mr Brian Jordan & Mr B Jordan**
16 **LAOISE (USA)**, b f Noble Mission—Lilbourne Eliza (IRE) **Miss L. A. Perratt**
17 **POPPING CORKS (IRE)**, b f Camacho—Shamardyh (IRE) **Miss L. A. Perratt**
18 **PRINCE MAZMEER**, ch g Mazameer (IRE)—Big Mystery (IRE)

Other Owners: Mr B. Atkins, Mr T. Hughes, Mr S. Jordan, Mr B. Jordan, Exors of the Late Mrs H. F. Perratt, Mr J. J. Sheridan, P. Tsim, Western Meeting Club Ltd.

Apprentice: Leanne Ferguson.

---

443   **MRS AMANDA PERRETT, Pulborough**
Postal: **Coombelands Racing Stables, Pulborough, West Sussex, RH20 1BP**
Contacts: **OFFICE (01798) 873011 HOME (01798) 874894 FAX (01798) 875163**
MOBILE (07803) 088713
E-MAIL aperrett@coombelands-stables.com WEBSITE www.amandaperrett.com

1 **ANNIE ANGEL (IRE)**, 8, b m King's Theatre (IRE)—Lady Rene (IRE) **G. D. P. Materna**
2 **ASTROMACHIA**, 4, b g Sea The Stars (IRE)—Fontley **John Connolly & Odile Griffith**
3 **BIRTHDAY GIRL (IRE)**, 4, b f Excelebration (IRE)—Street Style (IRE) **Mrs A. M. Lewis**
4 **COGITAL**, 4, b g Invincible Spirit (IRE)—Galaxy Highflyer **John Connolly & Odile Griffith**
5 **COUNT OTTO (IRE)**, 4, b g Sir Prancealot (IRE)—Dessert Flower (IRE) **Count Otto Partnership**
6 **DOUBLE LEGEND (IRE)**, 4, b g Finsceal Fior (IRE)—Damask Rose (IRE) **Dean Angell & Partner**
7 **FLIRTARE (IRE)**, 4, b f Oasis Dream—Federation **Mr & Mrs F Cotton,Mr & Mrs P Conway**
8 **FRONTISPIECE**, 5, b g Shamardal (USA)—Free Verse **The Frontispiece Partnership**
9 **HAWRIDGE GLORY (IRE)**, 5, b g Royal Applause—Saint Lucia (IRE) **Hawridge Glory Partnership**
10 **LIGHTNING CHARLIE**, 7, b g Myboycharlie (IRE)—Lighted Way **Lightning Charlie Partnership**
11 **MAZZURI (IRE)**, 4, ch f Raven's Pass (USA)—Essexford (IRE) **Mrs S. M. Conway**
12 **OPEN WIDE (USA)**, 5, b br g Invincible Spirit (IRE)—Nunavik (IRE) **George Materna & John McInerney**
13 **PLATITUDE**, 6, b g Dansili—Modesta (IRE) **Mrs S. M. Conway**
14 **SENSIBLE FRIEND (GR)**, 6, b g Reel Buddy (USA)—
                                          Senseansensibility (USA) **Winterfields Farm, Hancock & Pope**
15 **SPIRIT RIDGE**, 4, b g Nathaniel (IRE)—Tates Creek (USA) **K. Abdullah**
16 **THRESHOLDOFADREAM (IRE)**, 4, b f Camelot—Signella **Mr D M James & Woodcote Stud**
17 **YOU'RE HIRED**, 6, b g Dalakhani (IRE)—Heaven Sent **G. D. P. Materna**
18 **ZHUI FENG (IRE)**, 6, b g Invincible Spirit (IRE)—Es Que **John Connolly & Odile Griffith**
19 **ZZORO (IRE)**, 6, br g Manduro (GER)—Krynica (USA) **Mr & Mrs F Cotton,Mr & Mrs P Conway**

THREE-YEAR-OLDS

20 **ABANICA**, b f Iffraaj—Abated **K. Abdullah**
21 **AEGEUS (USA)**, b g First Defence (USA)—Supposition **K. Abdullah**
22 **AZETS**, b g Dubawi (IRE)—Nashmiah (IRE) **John Connolly & Odile Griffith**
23 **BARRENJOEY**, ch c Australia—Heavenly Dawn **Mr M Quigley & Mr D M James**
24 **DEFERENCE**, b g Showcasing—Quiet **K. Abdullah**
25 **DUTCH STORY**, ch g Dutch Art—Shamandar (FR) **Mr & Mrs R Scott & Mr & Mrs D Bevan**
26 **IF AT SEA**, b f Pour Moi (IRE)—Ebble **Mrs A. J. Chandris**
27 **INHALE**, b f Bated Breath—Innocent Air **K. Abdullah**
28 **LAVENDER'S BLUE (IRE)**, b f Sea The Stars (IRE)—Beatrice Aurore **B. Andersson**
29 **MANUCCI (IRE)**, b c Nathaniel (IRE)—American Spirit (IRE) **John Connolly & Odile Griffith**
30 **MAYKIR**, b g Mayson—Kiruna **Maykir Partnership**
31 **PASEO**, b g Champs Elysees—Posteritas (USA) **K. Abdullah**

MRS AMANDA PERRETT - Continued

32 **SASH,** b c Oasis Dream—Surcingle (USA) **K. Abdullah**
33 **SEEING RED (IRE),** b f Sea The Stars (IRE)—Red Fantasy (IRE) **Mr & Mrs F Cotton,Mr & Mrs P Conway**
34 **SPEED SKATER,** b f Olympic Glory (IRE)—My Love Thomas (IRE) **Mr Alan Spence**
35 **TINTO,** b g Compton Place—Amirah (IRE) **D James, S Jenkins & M Quigley**
36 **ZUBA,** b c Dubawi (IRE)—Purr Along **John Connolly & Odile Griffith**

TWO-YEAR-OLDS

37 **ART FOR ART'S SAKE (IRE),** ch c 31/3 Dutch Art—Anayid (A P Indy) (USA) (15000) **Mr R. J. B. Cheadle**
38 Ch c 17/3 Australia—Beatrice Aurore (IRE) (Danehill Dancer (IRE)) **B. Andersson**
39 **BEST ADDRESS (USA),** b l 8/3 City Zip (USA)—Preferential (Dansili) **K. Abdullah**
40 **COZONE,** b c 27/1 Pour Moi (IRE)—Bella Nouf (Dansili) (200000) **John Connolly & Odile Griffith**
41 **GIFT OF YOUTH,** b c 3/2 Fountain of Youth (IRE)—
Margrets Gift (Major Cadeaux) (40000) **Gift Of Youth Partnership**
42 **PENNY DIAMOND,** b f 23/4 War Command (USA)—
Penny Sixpence (FR) (Kheleyf) (13000) **Penny Diamond Partnership**
43 B f 10/5 Holy Roman Emperor (IRE)—Rougette (Red Ransom (USA)) (3809) **Mr D. M. James**
44 **ROVERA (IRE),** ch f 6/4 No Nay Never (USA)—
Minnie Hazel (IRE) (Excellent Art) (40000) **The The Rovera Partnership**
45 B f 19/2 Cable Bay (IRE)—Royal Confidence (Royal Applause) (1142) **Mr D. M. James**
46 **SAUCY ENCORE,** b f 13/2 Showcasing—
Saucy Minx (IRE) (Dylan Thomas (IRE)) **Mr & Mrs F Cotton,Mr & Mrs P Conway**
47 **SIR CHANCEALOT (IRE),** b g 30/4 Sir Prancealot (IRE)—
Hypocrisy (Bertolini) (USA)) (15170) **Coombelands Racing Syndicate**
48 **SUNS UP GUNS UP,** ch c 19/4 Lope de Vega (IRE)—Strictly Silca (Danehill Dancer (IRE)) (55000) **G. C. Stevens**
49 **ZELLERATE (IRE),** b c 27/2 Gutaifan (IRE)—
Ride For Roses (IRE) (Barathea (IRE)) (31428) **Mr John E. Bodie & Partners**

Other Owners: Mr D. P. Angell, J. P. Connolly, Mr F. G. Cotton, Mrs S. H. Cotton, Mr P. Cuttill, Mrs R. J. Doel, Ms O. L. Griffith, Guy Harwood, Mr S. J. Jenkins, Mrs B. A. Karn-Smith, Dr J. P. McInerney, Mrs A. J. Perrett, Mr M. F. Quigley, Mr R. J. Steele, Winterfields Farm Ltd, Woodcote Stud Ltd.

Assistant Trainer: Mark Perrett

---

444 MR PAT PHELAN, Epsom
Postal: **Ermyn Lodge, Shepherds Walk, Epsom, Surrey, KT18 6DF**
Contacts: PHONE **(01372) 229014** FAX **(01372) 229001** MOBILE **(07917) 762781**
E-MAIL **pat.phelan@ermynlodge.com** WEBSITE **www.ermynlodge.com**

1 **CHAMPS INBLUE,** 4, ch g Champs Elysees—Ellablue **Mr P. Cox**
2 **DOLYDAYDREAM,** 4, b f Equiano (FR)—Ellie In The Pink (IRE) **A. B. Pope**
3 **ERMYN'S EMERALD,** 7, b br g Alflora (IRE)—Emerald Project (IRE) **Ermyn Lodge Stud Limited**
4 **GRANGE WALK (IRE),** 4, ch g Thewayyouare (USA)—A Woman In Love **Mr E. Gleeson**
5 **HACKBRIDGE,** 4, br g Archipenko (USA)—Famcred **Sutton Business Centre**
6 **HATSAWAY (IRE),** 8, b g Dubawi (IRE)—Scotch Bonnet (IRE) **P. P. Mclaughlin**
7 **LEGEND OF FRANCE,** 6, ch m Flying Legend (USA)—Bonne Anniversaire **Ermyn Lodge Stud Limited**
8 **MAYTHEORSEBEWITHU (IRE),** 4, b f Shirocco (GER)—Amoya (GER) **Mr A. Smith**
9 **MAZALTO (IRE),** 6, b m Teofilo (IRE)—Mazaaya (USA) **Maginn Hasan**
10 **PIVOTAL FLAME (IRE),** 6, b m Pivotal—Saadiah (IRE) **Mr J. F. Lang**
11 **PRESENCE PROCESS,** 5, b g Dansili—Loulwa (IRE) **Mr P. Bocking**
12 **REECELTIC,** 4, b g Champs Elysees—Sense of Pride **Celtic Contractors Limited**
13 **SINGER IN THE SAND (IRE),** 4, b f Footstepsinthesand—Village Singer (USA) **I. W. Harfitt**
14 **THE CELTIC MACHINE,** 4, b g Rip Van Winkle (IRE)—Lyra's Daemon **Celtic Contractors Limited**
15 **THE PREMIER CELTIC,** 6, b g Black Sam Bellamy (IRE)—Maria Antonia (IRE) **Celtic Contractors Limited**
16 **WITCHES GLEN (IRE),** 7, b m Helissio (FR)—Native Cheer (IRE) **Ermyn Lodge Stud Limited**

THREE-YEAR-OLDS

17 **EDE'S,** b g Sir Percy—My Amalie (IRE) **Ede's (UK) Ltd**
18 **KEEP IT COUNTRY TV,** ch g Archipenko (USA)—Monda (USA) **Keep It Country**
19 **LAGUNA SPIRIT,** ro f Swiss Spirit—Laguna Belle **Mr P. Bocking**
20 **TIME TRIALIST,** b g Footstepsinthesand—Les Verguettes (IRE) **Mr D. M. J. Gilbert**
21 **WE ARE ALL DOTTIE,** b f Mayson—Young Dottie **Mr A. Smith**

Other Owners: Mr N. M. Hasan, Mr G. Maginn.

Conditional: Sean Houlihan. **Apprentice:** Paddy Bradley, Sophie Ralston.

445 MR ALAN PHILLIPS, Callow End

Postal: **Jennet Tree Farm, Kents Green, Callow End, Worcestershire, WR2 4UA**
Contacts: **PHONE** (01905) 831774 **MOBILE** (07870) 112235
E-MAIL alan@alanphillipsracing.com **WEBSITE** www.alanphillipsracing.com

1 **BOHER LAD (IRE)**, 12, b g Gold Well—Shindeesharnick (IRE) **Miss R. L. Edwards**
2 **MR STANDFAST**, 6, b g Mullionmileanhour (IRE)—Phantom Ridge (IRE) **Miss R. L. Edwards**
3 **TARRONA**, 10, b g Kayf Tara—Lisrona (IRE) **Mr D. G. Redfern**
4 **THE MODEL COUNTY (IRE)**, 9, b m Robin des Champs (FR)—Ware It Vic (IRE) **Mr D. G. Redfern**
5 **WHY LIE (IRE)**, 8, b g Zagreb (USA)—Persian Avenue (IRE) **Miss R. L. Edwards**

446 MR RICHARD PHILLIPS, Moreton-in-Marsh

Postal: **Adlestrop Stables, Adlestrop, Moreton-in-Marsh, Gloucestershire, GL56 0YN**
Contacts: **PHONE** (01608) 658710 **FAX** (01608) 658713 **MOBILE** (07774) 832715
E-MAIL info@richardphillipsracing.com **WEBSITE** www.richardphillipsracing.com

1 **ARCTIC CHIEF**, 9, b g Sleeping Indian—Neiges Eternelles (FR) **Too Many Chiefs**
2 **BEAUTIFUL PEOPLE (FR)**, 8, b br m Early March—Night Fever (FR) **Beautiful People**
3 **BELLA'S VISION (FR)**, 6, ch m Vision d'etat (FR)—Dalina (FR) **Mr R. T. Phillips**
4 **BIG FIDDLE**, 6, b m Kayf Tara—Fiddling Again **Mrs E. C. Roberts**
5 **FERMAIN BAY**, 5, b g Major Cadeaux—Fisher Island (IRE) **The Dreamers**
6 6, B m Kayf Tara—Giovanna **Mr R. T. Phillips**
7 **GOLDEN DEAL (IRE)**, 4, b f Havana Gold (IRE)—Lady Rockfield (IRE) **Mr T. F. Parrett**
8 **IRON HORSE**, 8, b g Kayf Tara—What A Vintage (IRE) **The Someday's Here Racing Partnership**
9 **JUAN HORSEPOWER**, 5, b g Foxwedge (AUS)—Elysee (IRE) **Chuckle Brothers Racing Ltd**
10 **LADY OF AUTHORITY**, 4, b f Kheleyf (USA)—Miss Authority **Mr R. T. Phillips**
11 **MADAME RITZ (IRE)**, 4, b f Canford Cliffs (IRE)—Sky Red **The Firebirds**
12 **MASTER VINTAGE**, 11, b g Kayf Tara—What A Vintage (IRE) **The Adlestrop Club**
13 **MIGHTY ELSA**, 6, b m Schiaparelli (GER)—Tiger Moss **Mr S. Smith**
14 **MINELLA WHISPER**, 8, b g Kayf Tara—Celtic Native (IRE) **Mrs E. A. Prowting**
15 **MRS BARNES (IRE)**, 6, b m Ask—Jills Oscar (IRE) **Mr & Mrs R. Scott**
16 **MUTHABIR (IRE)**, 9, b g Nayef (USA)—Northern Melody (IRE) **The Adlestrop Experience**
17 **ORGANDI (FR)**, 7, br m Early March—Creme Pralinee (FR) **Beautiful People**
18 **OVER STATED (IRE)**, 7, b g Shantou (USA)—Mrs Gordi **Mr E. J. Ware**
19 **PICANHA**, 5, br g Malinas (GER)—Royal Bride **Mrs E. A. Prowting**
20 **PRESENT FROM DUBAI (IRE)**, 6, b g Dubai Destination (USA)—Inch Promise (IRE) **Hopeful Travellers**
21 **ROUNDHEAD**, 4, ch g Helmet (AUS)—Blue Mistral (IRE) **Mr E. J. Ware**
22 **SHADOW WALKER (IRE)**, 5, b g Stowaway—Ilikeyou (IRE) **Mr C. Pocock**
23 **STONEY CROSS**, 7, b m Sulamani (IRE)—Stoney Path **Mrs S. C. Welch**
24 **TIMETOBENEFIT (IRE)**, 8, b m Beneficial—Shokalocka Baby (IRE) **Mrs H. M. Nixseaman**
25 **TOTTERDOWN**, 8, b g Pasternak—Yeldham Lady **Fairford Goes Racing**
26 **TULANE (IRE)**, 4, br g Arcano (IRE)—Jeunesse Doree (IRE) **The Tulanes**
27 **VIVA RAFA (IRE)**, 9, b g Scorpion (IRE)—Back To Stay (IRE) **Mr R. T. Phillips**
28 **WESTERN STORM (IRE)**, 7, b g Westerner—Torduff Storm (IRE) **Ware & Fish**

THREE-YEAR-OLDS

29 Ch f Helmet (AUS)—Cintsa Sun (IRE) **W. D. S. Murdoch**
30 **DANDY LASS (IRE)**, b f Dandy Man (IRE)—El Mirage (IRE) **The Aspirationals**
31 **J GAYE (IRE)**, b f Canford Cliffs (IRE)—Ice Pie **S. F. Benton**
32 **TWOKANDATOUPEE (IRE)**, b f Clodovil (IRE)—Puca (IRE) **Chuckle Brothers Racing Ltd**

Other Owners: Mrs J. Abraham, Ms K. M. Anderson, Mr M. R. Barnes, Mr J. E. S. Colling, Mr J. A. Cover, B. J. Duckett, Mr T. B. N. Farazmand, Mr D. T. Fish, Mr O. S. Harris, Mrs S. H. Jones, Mr L. Olley, M. T. Phillips, Mr R. B. Rowe, Mrs P. M. Scott, R. Scott, Dr E. D. Theodore, Mr M. A. W. Thompson.

Conditional: Daniel Hiskett.

447 **MR TIM PINFIELD, Upper Lambourn**
Postal: Flemington Stables, Upper Lambourn, Hungerford, Berkshire, RG17 8QH
Contacts: MOBILE: (07980) 104309 E-MAIL timpinfieldracing@hotmail.com

1 BAMBAJEE (FR), 6, b m Rock of Gibraltar (IRE)—Heaven's Dream (IRE) **Mrs G. A. Pinfield**
2 FLAKA, 7, ch m Lucarno (USA)—A Fistful of Euros **Mrs G. A. Pinfield**
3 FOREVER WORDS, 7, b m Multiplex—Silver Gyre (IRE) **Arion Equine Limited**
4 FREEDOM FIGHTER (IRE), 9, b g Danehill Dancer (IRE)—Rose of Petra (IRE) **Mr K. M. Pinfield**
5 GALE FORCE OSCAR (IRE), 14, br g Oscar (IRE)—Distant Gale (IRE) **Ladies who Lunch Syndicate**
6 KAVASS, 5, b g Kheleyf (USA)—Purely By Chance **Arion Equine Limited**
7 8, B m Royal Applause—Lone Spirit (IRE) **Arion Equine Limited**
8 MAXIMUM POWER (FR), 4, b g Power—Keisha (FR) **Bigmores Racing Partnership**
9 5, B g Mayson—Milkie Way **Arion Equine Limited**
10 ONEOVDEM, 5, ch g Yorgunnabelucky (USA)—Noor El Houdah (IRE) **Arion Equine Limited**
11 SIR THOMAS GRESHAM (IRE), 4, b c Dutch Art—Loquacity **Happy Get Lucky Syndicate**
12 ZAYDANIDES (FR), 7, bl g American Post—Ouarzazate (IRE) **Ladies who Lunch Syndicate**

THREE-YEAR-OLDS

13 MERAKI, b g Heeraat (IRE)—Sound of Life (IRE) **Mr A. Davis**
14 TALK LIKE THIS (USA), ch c More Than Ready (USA)—Will Prevail (USA) **Arion Equine Limited**

▌**Other Owners:** Mr J. Davies, Mr A. C. Nettleship.

448 **MR DAVID PIPE, Wellington**
Postal: Pond House, Nicholashayne, Wellington, Somerset, TA21 9QY
Contacts: PHONE (01884) 840715 FAX (01884) 841343
E-MAIL david@davidpipe.com WEBSITE www.davidpipe.com

1 AIRTON, 6, b g Champs Elysees—Fly In Style **D. E. Pipe**
2 AURILLAC (FR), 9, gr g Martaline—Ombrelle (FR) **D Mossop, P John & R White**
3 BIDOUREY (FR), 8, b br g Voix du Nord (FR)—Love Wisky (FR) **Brocade Racing**
4 BUSTER EDWARDS (IRE), 6, b g Kalanisi (IRE)—Hot Oscar (IRE) **Mr Jonathan Williams & Partner**
5 CATCH THE SWALLOWS (IRE), 5, b g Masterofthehorse (IRE)—Nafrah (USA) **Mr T. J. Hemmings**
6 CELESTIAL PATH (IRE), 7, br g Footstepsinthesand—Miss Kittyhawk (IRE) **Prof C. Tisdall**
7 CHAMPERS ON ICE (IRE), 9, gr g Robin des Champs (FR)—
      Miss Nova **Professor Caroline Tisdall & Bryan Drew**
8 CRAWFORDS MILL (IRE), 7, b m Getaway—Lough Cuan (IRE) **N. Shutts**
9 DAKLONDIKE (IRE), 7, b g Gold Well—Strong Irish (IRE) **Prof C. Tisdall**
10 DAUPHINE EREINE (FR), 7, b m Saint des Saints (FR)—Bellissima de Mai (FR) **John White & Anne Underhill**
11 DELFACE (FR), 6, b g Della Francesca (USA)—Septieme Face (USA) **Pipe's Prospectors**
12 DELL' ARCA (IRE), 10, b g Sholokhov (IRE)—Daisy Belle (GER) **Prof C. Tisdall**
13 DRAMA KING (IRE), 8, b g King's Theatre (IRE)—Miss Artea (IRE) **Mr M. D. Poland**
14 DREAM FREE, 6, b g Oasis Dream—Freedonia **D. E. Pipe**
15 DROMINEER (IRE), 6, br g Oscar (IRE)—Aileen Supreme (IRE) **Mr William Frewen & Partner**
16 DRUIDE PREMIER (FR), 6, gr g Martaline—Bellissima de Mai (FR) **The Arthur White Partnership**
17 DUC DE BEAUCHENE (FR), 6, b g Saddler Maker (IRE)—Quatia d'angron (FR) **Mr J. P. McManus**
18 DUSKY HERCULES (IRE), 5, b g Shantou (USA)—Annalecky (IRE) **Prof C. Tisdall**
19 EAMON AN CNOIC (IRE), 8, b g Westerner—Nutmeg Tune (IRE) **The Angove Family**
20 EASTER ERIC, 5, b g Martaline—Easter Comet **Mr & Mrs S. C. Willes**
21 EDEN DU HOUX (FR), 5, b g Irish Wells (FR)—Maralypha (FR) **Prof C. Tisdall**
22 EKAYBURG (FR), 5, b g Sageburg (IRE)—Kayseri (FR) **Cheveley Park Stud Limited**
23 EUR GONE WEST (IRE), 6, b g Westerner—Floating Euro (IRE) **Mrs J. Gerard-Pearse**
24 EXTRA MAG (FR), 5, b g Kapgarde (FR)—Qrystale Mag (FR) **The Angove Family**
25 FIRST LORD DE CUET (FR), 5, gr g Lord du Sud (FR)—Alyce (FR) **D. E. Pipe**
26 FRIDAY NIGHT LIGHT (FR), 6, b g Air Chief Marshal (IRE)—
      Peninsula **Prof. Caroline Tisdall & William Frewen**
27 GLEN VINE, 5, ch g Robin des Champs (FR)—Gaspara (FR) **Mr T. J. Hemmings**
28 GREAT TEMPO (FR), 6, b g Great Pretender (IRE)—Prima Note (FR) **D. E. Pipe**
29 HONEYMOON COCKTAIL (FR), 8, gr g Martaline—Caipirinia (FR) **M. C. Pipe**
30 HUCCABY, 4, b g Arvico (FR)—Burrator **Somerset Racing**
31 INDUNO (IRE), 5, b g Flemensfirth (USA)—Vast Consumption (IRE) **R. A. Bartlett**
32 IRISH PRINCE (IRE), 6, b g Presenting—Court Leader (IRE) **Professor Caroline Tisdall & Alan Kaplan**
33 IT'S OBVIOUS, 7, gr g Tobougg (IRE)—Hiho Silver Lining **Prof C. Tisdall**
34 JACBEQUICK, 8, b g Calcutta—Toking N' Joken (IRE) **Mrs L. Webb**

MR DAVID PIPE - Continued

35 JASMIN DES BORDES (FR), 5, b g Great Pretender (IRE)—
      Queen des Bordes (FR) **John White & Anne Underhill**
36 KEATING (IRE), 7, b g King's Theatre (IRE)—Tus Nua (IRE) **Pond House Classics**
37 KING'S SOCKS (FR), 7, b g King's Best (USA)—Alexandrina (GER) **Mr B. J. C. Drew**
38 KNOW THE SCORE (IRE), 6, b g Flemensfirth (USA)—Prairie Bell (IRE) **The Angove Family**
39 LEGAL HISTORY (IRE), 4, b g Lawman (FR)—Nina Celebre (IRE) **Middleham Park Racing XXXII & Partner 2**
40 LITTLE RED LION (IRE), 5, b g Sans Frontieres (IRE)—Rever Up (IRE) **Prof C. Tisdall**
41 MAIN FACT (USA), 6, b g Blame (USA)—Reflections **The Blue Ball Syndicate**
42 MALANGEN (IRE), 4, b g Born To Sea (IRE)—Lady's Locket (IRE) **Teddington CC Racing**
43 MARTABOT (FR), 8, gr g Martaline—Reine de Sabot (FR) **Mrs S. J. Ling**
44 MAX DO BRAZIL (FR), 7, b g Blue Bresil (FR)—Lili Valley (FR) **Professor Caroline Tisdall & Bryan Drew**
45 MIDNIGHT MAGIC, 7, b g Midnight Legend—Arctic Magic (IRE) **Midd Shire Racing**
46 MIRO (IRE), 7, b g Rock of Gibraltar (IRE)—Mission Secrete (IRE) **The Blue Ball Syndicate**
47 MISS TYNTE (IRE), 7, b m Mahler—Top Quality **N. Shutts**
48 MOON RACER (IRE), 10, b g Saffron Walden (FR)—Angel's Folly **Professor Caroline Tisdall & Bryan Drew**
49 MR BIG SHOT (IRE), 8, br g Flemensfirth (USA)—Une Etoile (IRE) **Prof C. Tisdall**
50 MR CLARKSON (IRE), 7, b g Jeremy (USA)—Wynsleydale (USA) **Pipe's Prospectors**
51 MRS MIGGINS (IRE), 6, b m Presenting—Carrigeen Lunaria (IRE) **Mr Barry Wright & Mrs Rosemary White**
52 MUTANAQEL, 4, b g Havana Gold (IRE)—Audaz **J. T. Ennis**
53 NEW AGE DAWNING (IRE), 5, ch g Stowaway—Captain Supreme (IRE) **Brocade Racing**
54 NORDIC COMBINED (IRE), 5, b g Haafhd—Chilly Filly (IRE) **Chris & David Stam**
55 ORCHARD THIEVES (IRE), 7, b g Ask—Ballycleary (IRE) **Brocade Racing**
56 OURMULLION, 5, br g Sir Percy—Star of Gibraltar (IRE) **David & Elaine Long**
57 PERCY STREET, 6, br g Zoffany (IRE)—Sisceal **The Blue Ball Syndicate**
58 PICTURE PAINTER (IRE), 6, gr g Zoffany (IRE)—Sisceal **The Blue Ball Syndicate**
59 POKER PLAY (FR), 6, ch g Martaline—Becquarette (FR) **The Angove Family**
60 QUEENS CAVE (IRE), 6, b m Court Cave—Shuilan (IRE) **Mr K. Alexander**
61 RAMSES DE TEILLEE (FR), 7, gr g Martaline—Princesse d'orton (FR) **John White & Anne Underhill**
62 RATHLIN ROSE (IRE), 11, b g Bonbon Rose (FR)—A Plus Ma Puce (FR) **Mr F. G. Wilson**
63 REMASTERED, 6, ch g Network (GER)—Cathodine Cayras (FR) **Brocade Racing**
64 SHAAMA GRISE (FR), 7, gr m Montmartre (FR)—Shaama Rose (FR) **The Angove Family**
65 STORY OF FRIENDS (FR), 5, b g Kingsalsa (USA)—Royale Malinelle (FR) **Brocade Racing**
66 STREAM LADY (IRE), 6, b m Curtain Time (IRE)—Victory Queen (IRE) **Mr K. Alexander**
67 TAKE THE HIGH ROAD, 5, b g Kyllachy—China Tea (USA) **D. E. Pipe**
68 TEASER, 4, b g Dansili—Tottie **The Willpower Partnership**
69 THREE STAR GENERAL, 6, b g Montjeu (IRE)—Honorlina (FR) **Mr Stuart & Simon Mercer & D E Pipe**
70 TIGGER TWO (IRE), 7, b g Getaway (GER)—Anne Hathaway (IRE) **Prof C. Tisdall**
71 TIMEFORBEN (IRE), 7, ch m Beneficial—Shokalocka Baby (IRE) **The Bravo Partnership**
72 UMBRIGADO (IRE), 5, br g Stowaway—Dame O'neill (IRE) **John White & Anne Underhill**
73 UN TEMPS POUR TOUT (IRE), 10, b g Robin des Champs (FR)—
      Rougedespoir (FR) **Professor Caroline Tisdall & Mr John Gent**
74 VIEUX LION ROUGE (FR), 10, ch g Sabiango (GER)—Indecise (FR) **Prof Caroline Tisdall & Mr John Gent**
75 WARTHOG (FR), 7, gr g Martaline—Shekira (FR) **Professor Caroline Tisdall & Bryan Drew**
76 WHAT A MOMENT (IRE), 9, b g Milan—Cuiloge Lady (IRE) **Bryan Drew & Steve Roper**
77 WHITLEY NEILL (IRE), 7, b g Shantou (USA)—Maidrin Rua (IRE) **JMH Racing Limited**
78 YOU SAY WHAT (IRE), 9, b g Milan—Wave Back (IRE) **Turner Webb**

Other Owners: Mr S. J. Angove, Mr D. B. Angove, Mrs A. E. M. Broom, Mr G. R. Broom, J. S. Dale, Mr P. A. Deal, Mrs L. A. Farquhar, W. F. Frewen, J. A. Gent, Mr P George, Mr P. J. Green, S. R. Harman, Mr P. D. H. John, Mr S. D. Johnson, Mrs D. A. Johnson, Alan Kaplan, Mrs E. Long, Mr D. J. Long, Mr S. M. Mercer, Mr S. S. Mercer, Middleham Park Racing XXXII, B. G. Middleton, D. Mossop, Mr J. S. Nutley, Mr C. G. Paletta, T. S. Palin, Mr G. L. Phippen, M. Prince, D. J. Reid, Mr S. R. Roper, A. J. Shire, Mr D. B. Stam, Dr C. Stam, Mrs S. M. Teague, Mr P. Turner, Mrs A. Underhill, J. B. Webb, Mr A. J. White, Mrs R. E. White, Mr R. C. Wilkin, Mr S. C. Willes, Mrs M. Willes, Mr J. C. Williams, Mr B. Wright.

Assistant Trainer: Mr M. C. Pipe C.B.E.

Jockey (NH): David Noonan, Tom Scudamore. **Conditional:** Rex Dingle, Michael Heard. **Amateur:** Mr Fergus Gillard

---

449 **MR CHARLES POGSON**, Newark
Postal: Allamoor Farm, Mansfield Road, Farnsfield, Nottinghamshire, NG22 8HZ
Contacts: PHONE (01623) 882275 MOBILE (07977) 016155

1 ALLAMOOR BOY, 4, b g Kayf Tara—Candello **P & P Wordingham, J Allott, C Pogson**
2 BRIDEY'S LETTUCE (IRE), 7, b g Iffraaj—Its On The Air (IRE) **Pete & Pauline Wordingham & Partner**
3 BUSY LILLY, 10, b m Bollin Eric—Princess Derry **Pete & Pauline Wordingham & Partner**

MR CHARLES POGSON - Continued

4 **CUSHEEN BRIDGE (IRE)**, 11, b g Oscar (IRE)—One Hell Ofa Woman (IRE) **Pete & Pauline Wordingham**
5 **MOIDORE**, 10, b g Galileo (IRE)—Flash of Gold **C. T. Pogson**
6 **MONDO CANE (IRE)**, 12, b g Beneficial—La Vita E Bella (FR) **C. T. Pogson**
7 **OVERTOUJAY**, 9, b b g Overbury (IRE)—Ouh Jay **Pete & Pauline Wordingham & Partner**
8 **PINGLEY LAD**, 6, b g Jamaican Flight (USA)—Worlaby Rose **Mrs J. Woodward**
9 **QUASHA**, 6, b m Black Sam Bellamy (IRE)—Gloriana **Pete & Pauline Wordingham & Partner**
10 **REAL KING**, 7, b g Multiplex—Gertrude Webb **C. T. Pogson**
11 **REAL WARRIOR (IRE)**, 8, b g Tikkanen—Muffin Top (IRE) **Charles Pogson John Allott**
12 **ROLLERBALL ROCCO (IRE)**, 7, b g Ask—Jamica Ginger (IRE) **C. T. Pogson**
13 **SHADY OAKS (IRE)**, 6, b g Getaway (GER)—Naked Poser (IRE) **C. T. Pogson**
14 **SHARP REPLY (IRE)**, 5, b g Holy Roman Emperor (IRE)—Sabindra **Caroline Lawson & Jennifer Woodward**
15 **UNZING (FR)**, 11, b g Voix du Nord (FR)—Magik (FR) **Pete & Pauline Wordingham & Partner**
16 **WEST TO CROSSGALES (IRE)**, 8, b g Westerner—
Mooreshill Bay (IRE) **Pete & Pauline Wordingham & Partner**

Other Owners: Mr J. Allott, Sotby Farming Company Limited, P. L. Wordingham, Mrs P. A. Wordingham.

Assistant Trainer: Adam Pogson.

---

450 **MR JONATHAN PORTMAN, Upper Lambourn**
Postal: Whitcombe House Stables, Upper Lambourn, Hungerford, Berkshire, RG17 8RA
Contacts: **PHONE** (01488) 73894 **MOBILE** (07798) 824513
E-MAIL jonathan@jonathanportmanracing.com WEBSITE www.jonathanportmanracing.com

1 **ASHAZURI**, 5, b m Dick Turpin (IRE)—Shesha Bear **RWH Partnership**
2 **BALMORAL CASTLE**, 10, b g Royal Applause—Mimiteh (USA) **J. G. B. Portman**
3 **BROAD APPEAL**, 5, ch g Medicean—Shy Appeal (IRE) **Jaliza Partnership**
4 **GAINSAY**, 4, b f Sayif (IRE)—Pesse (IRE) **J. G. B. Portman**
5 **GOODNIGHT GIRL (IRE)**, 4, gr f Clodovil (IRE)—Leenavesta (USA) **Alex Chesterman**
6 4, B f Poet's Voice—Inaminute (IRE) **Ray Bailey**
7 **INDISCRETION (IRE)**, 4, b f Big Bad Bob (IRE)—Fleeting Affair (USA) **Fillies First**
8 **MANCINI**, 5, ch g Nathaniel (IRE)—Muscovado (USA) **Laurence Bellman**
9 **MANDALAYAN (IRE)**, 4, b g Arakan (USA)—Danza Nera (IRE) **Simon Skinner & Partners**
10 **MY FOOTSTEPS**, 4, b c Footstepsinthesand—Luminous Gold **Mrs B Cuthbert**
11 **ORIN SWIFT (IRE)**, 5, b g Dragon Pulse (IRE)—Hollow Green (IRE) **Laurence Bellman**
12 **QUICK BREATH**, 4, b g Bated Breath—Shy Appeal (IRE) **Wood Street Syndicate**
13 **WALK ON WALTER (IRE)**, 4, b g Footstepsinthesand—Hajmah (IRE) **Philip Simpson**

THREE-YEAR-OLDS

14 **ADENA STAR (IRE)**, b f Big Bad Bob (IRE)—Silicon Star (FR) **Fillies First**
15 **CARRIAGEWAY**, b f Coach House (IRE)—Emma Peel **Mrs D Barker**
16 **CHARMED SPIRIT**, b g Charm Spirit (IRE)—Arch of Colours **Mr A. Chesterman**
17 **EVEN KEEL (IRE)**, ch g Born To Sea (IRE)—Dew (IRE) **Berkeley Racing**
18 **FLORENCE ROSE**, b f Medicean—Masque Rose **Turf Club 2016 & Partner**
19 **FLYING MOON (GER)**, b g Sea The Moon (GER)—Finity (USA) **Crimbourne Racing Partnership**
20 **INVINCIBELLA**, b f Kodiac—Sahath (USA) **Hot To Trot 1**
21 **JOLYON**, ch g Raven's Pass (USA)—Fleurissimo **Normandie Stud**
22 **LONDON PRIDE**, ch f Cityscape—Heartsease **British Racing Club**
23 **MONETA**, b f Kodiac—Money Note **W. Clifford**
24 **MRS WORTHINGTON (IRE)**, b f Dark Angel (IRE)—Mirror Effect (IRE) **Mrs A Plummer / Tony Wechsler**
25 **ONEDOWNUNDER**, b g Aussie Rules (USA)—Saffron Fox **M J Vandenberghe**
26 **POET'S MAGIC**, b f Poet's Voice—Magic Destiny **Ray Bailey**
27 **SPRING RUN**, ch f Nathaniel (IRE)—May Fox **British Racing Club**
28 B f Dutch Art—Station House (IRE) **Mascalls Stud**
29 **SWISS CHEER (FR)**, b g Swiss Spirit—Happy Clapper **Whitcombe Park Racing**
30 **TOYBOX**, ch f Paco Boy (IRE)—Play Street **Anthony Boswood / Mrs R Pease**

TWO-YEAR-OLDS

31 B f 27/4 Requinto (IRE)—Afnoon (USA) (Street Cry (IRE)) (17142) **Berkeley Racing**
32 B f 3/5 Sir Percy—Alice's Dancer (IRE) (Clodovil (IRE)) (22000) **Portlee Bloodstock**
33 **BITING**, b f 6/1 Lope de Vega (IRE)—Nibbling (IRE) (Invincible Spirit (IRE)) **Mrs J Wigan**
34 Ch c 12/3 Camacho—Coming Back (Fantastic Light (USA)) (40000) **Kangyu International Racing**
35 **CULOTTE (IRE)**, b f 17/1 Camelot—Aertex (IRE) (Exceed And Excel (AUS)) (16000) **Mrs J. Wigan**
36 Ch f 12/3 Camacho—Dew (IRE) (Whipper (USA)) (8427) **Unregistered partnership**

MR JONATHAN PORTMAN - Continued

37 B f 24/3 Cable Bay (IRE)—Divine Power (Kyllachy)
38 **JUNGLE BOOK (GER),** ch c 2/3 Sea The Moon (GER)—
Josefine (GER) (Kallisto (GER)) (5478) **Crimbourne Racing Partnership**
39 **KING OF THE NORTH,** b c 16/3 Kodiac—
Scotch Bonnet (IRE) (Montjeu (IRE)) (255000) **Tony Wechsler & Ann Plummer**
40 **LETHAL TALENT,** gr f 24/3 Lethal Force (IRE)—
Talent Spotter (Exceed And Excel (AUS)) (4761) **Whitcoombe Park Racing**
41 B f 18/4 Brazen Beau (AUS)—Lovellian (Machiavellian (USA)) **Mrs S Clifford**
42 B f 7/5 Requinto (IRE)—Mirror Effect (IRE) (Shamardal (USA)) (1000)
43 Ch f 25/4 Ivawood (IRE)—Much Faster (IRE) (Fasliyev (USA)) (7619) **Berkeley Racing**
44 Ch f 18/3 Mayson—Pavonine (High Chaparral (IRE)) (761)
45 Ch f 13/4 Casamento (IRE)—Play Street (Tobougg (IRE)) **Anthony Boswood**
46 **PRETTY PACKET (FR),** b f 19/5 Style Vendome (FR)—Costa Packet (IRE) (Hussonet (USA)) (6742)
47 B f 26/3 Epaulette (AUS)—Ragtime Dancer (Medicean) (761) **M A & C E Burton**
48 **ROCKMORE,** b c 25/3 Mukhadram—Double Star (Elusive City (USA)) (10000) **The Hon Mrs D Joly**
49 **RUSSIAN RUMOUR (IRE),** b f 4/5 Make Believe—Russian Rave (Danehill Dancer (IRE)) (4000) **Fillies First**
50 Ch f 18/4 Australia—Sky Boat (IRE) (Dansili) (761) **Mrs J Wigan**
51 B f 22/3 Muhaarar—Station House (IRE) (Galileo (IRE)) (55000) **Mascalls Stud**
52 B c 10/3 Kingston Hill—Sweetly Does It (Shirocco (GER)) (10000) **Laurence Bellman**

Other Owners: Mr P Afia, Mr D Brocklehurst, Mr Jeremy Brownlee, Ms J Challen, Mr N Cheyne, Mr G. F. Clark, Mrs P Cooper, Miss M Davin, Mr Steve Dawes, Mr S Dibb, Mr R Dollar, Mr P Edwards, Mr A Edwards, Mr M. I. Forbes, Mr R Fowler, Mr C Hawkins, Mr S Hearn, Mr J Hobson, Mr Jonathan Homan, Mr S Hope, Mr R. S. Hoskins, Mr C. R. Lambourne, Mr K Lau, Mr D. R. Losse, Mrs L. J. Losse, Mr P Martin, Mr C Nash, Mr C Parker, Mr D Powell, Mr R Pritchard, Mrs L Pritchard, Mr J Repard, Mrs A Tearne, Mrs S Von Shilcher, Mr R White, Mr G. C. Wickens, Mr H Wigan, Mr S Williams.

Amateur: Mr J. Harding.

---

451 ## MR BRENDAN POWELL, Upper Lambourn
Postal: **Frenchmans Lodge Stables, Upper Lambourn, Hungerford, Berkshire, RG17 8QW**
Contacts: **PHONE (01488) 73650 FAX (01488) 73650 MOBILE (07785) 390737**
E-MAIL brendan.powell@btconnect.com WEBSITE www.powell-racing.com

1 **BIG 'N BETTER,** 7, b g Revoque (IRE)—Donastrela (IRE) **W. M. Smith**
2 **CHORAL CLAN (IRE),** 8, b g Oratorio (IRE)—Campbellite (IRE) **Bob Harris & Patricia Mitchell**
3 **DE BRUYNE HORSE,** 4, b c Showcasing—Right Rave (IRE) **B. G. Powell**
4 **GANNICUS,** 8, b g Phoenix Reach (IRE)—Rasmani **BP Racing Club (The Dublin Flyers)**
5 **GARTH ROCKETT,** 5, b g Delegator—Leelu **P. Banfield**
6 **GINGER LACEY,** 4, b g Showcasing—Flying Hi **Mr & Mrs Nigel Bailey & Paddy Durnin**
7 **IN THE PIPELINE (IRE),** 6, b g Oscar (IRE)—Kerriemuir Lass (IRE) **Mr J. P. McManus**
8 **KASPERENKO,** 5, b g Archipenko (USA)—Jardin **Mr C. F. Harrington**
9 **MERE IRONMONGER,** 7, ch g Galileo (IRE)—Kindling **The Arkle Bar Partnership**
10 **MR ANDROS,** 6, b g Phoenix Reach (IRE)—Chocolada **BP Racing Club (The Dublin Flyers)**
11 **MY DESTINY (IRE),** 6, ch g Flemensfirth (USA)—Gaye Melody (IRE) **B. G. Powell**
12 **OLDTOWN POLLY (IRE),** 7, b m Publisher (USA)—Oldtown Gill **B. G. Powell**
13 **PHOENIX DAWN,** 5, b g Phoenix Reach (IRE)—Comtesse Noire (CAN) **Winterbeck Manor Stud Ltd**
14 **THOMAS CROMWELL,** 6, b g Sixties Icon—Salim Toto **J. H. Widdows**
15 **ZARRAR (IRE),** 4, b g Thewayyouare (USA)—Featherlight **Mr W. A. A. Qayyum**

THREE-YEAR-OLDS

16 B c Gregorian (IRE)—Flying Hi **Mrs S. Bailey**
17 **FREEDOM AND WHEAT (IRE),** b c Fast Company (IRE)—Rustam **I. S. Smith**
18 **POET PETE (IRE),** ch c Poet's Voice—My Body Is A Cage (IRE) **Mr R. C. Penney**
19 **THE GREAT PHOENIX,** ch g Phoenix Reach (IRE)—Comtesse Noire (CAN) **Winterbeck Manor Stud Ltd**
20 **ZALMI FORCE (IRE),** b g Gale Force Ten—Arabela (IRE) **Mrs N. S. Khan**

Other Owners: Mr N. Bailey, Mr P. Durnin, G. M. Flood, Mr G. R. Harris, D. Leon, Mrs P. A. Mitchell, Miss K. Thacker.

Jockey (NH): Brendan Powell.

452 **SIR MARK PRESCOTT BT, Newmarket**
Postal: Heath House, Moulton Road, Newmarket, Suffolk, CB8 0DZ
Contacts: PHONE (01638) 662117 FAX (01638) 666572
E-MAIL sirmark@heathhousestables.com WEBSITE www.heathhousestables.com
Twitter: @HeathHouseNkt

1 **ALABASTER**, 5, gr g Archipenko (USA)—Alvarita **Charles C. Walker - Osborne House**
2 **ALTRA VITA**, 4, b f Animal Kingdom (USA)—Alma Mater **Miss K. Rausing**
3 **DISTANT CHIMES (GER)**, 4, b g Campanologist (USA)—Dyveke (GER) **Phil Fry - Osborne House**
4 **DONE DEAL (IRE)**, 4, b g Azamour (IRE)—Dundel's Spirit (IRE) **Baxter, Gregson, Jenkins & Warman**
5 **ELYSEES PALACE**, 5, b g Champs Elysees—Ventura Highway **J. Fishpool - Osborne House**
6 **FINAL ROCK**, 4, b g Rock of Gibraltar (IRE)—Up At Last **Mr G. C. Woodall**
7 **GREY SPIRIT (IRE)**, 4, gr g Dark Angel (IRE)—Buttonhole **Philip Bamford - Osborne House**
8 **MASTER DIVER**, 4, gr g Mastercraftsman (IRE)—Lottie Dod (IRE) **Lee,Mrs Baxter,Bouverie,Chisholm,Howard**
9 **MATCHMAKING (GER)**, 4, ch g Mastercraftsman (IRE)—Monami **W. E. Sturt - Osborne House II**
10 **PIEDITA (IRE)**, 5, b m Authorized (IRE)—Archina (IRE) **Mrs Carmen Frubeck & Denford Stud**
11 **TIMOSHENKO**, 4, ch g Archipenko (USA)—Nezhenka **Middleham Park Racing XXXVI**
12 **TROUBLE AND STRIFE (IRE)**, 4, b f Declaration of War (USA)—Rare Tern (IRE) **Lady O'Reilly**
13 **TRUE NORTH (IRE)**, 4, b g Henrythenavigator (USA)—Cosmic Fire (FR) **Owners Group 018**

THREE-YEAR-OLDS

14 **ALBANITA**, gr f Sea The Moon (GER)—Alba Stella **Miss K. Rausing**
15 **ALL POINTS WEST**, b g Speightstown (USA)—Albamara **Tim Bunting - Osborne House II**
16 **ALMA LINDA**, gr f Invincible Spirit (IRE)—Alvarita **Miss K. Rausing**
17 **AUTONOMY**, b g Dansili—Funsie (FR) **Tim Bunting - Osborne House**
18 **BATTLE OF PARADISE (USA)**, b c Declaration of War (USA)—
                              Garden of Eden (USA) **Charles C. Walker - Osborne House III**
19 **BLAME IT ON SALLY (IRE)**, b g Canford Cliffs (IRE)—Sliding Scale **Mr & Mrs John Kelsey-Fry**
20 **BRASSICA (IRE)**, b f Australia—Lasilia (IRE) **Denford Stud**
21 **BUCKMAN TAVERN (FR)**, b g Pastorius (GER)—Breezy Hawk (GER) **Middleham Park Racing (VII)**
22 **CALLING THE WIND (IRE)**, b g Authorized (IRE)—Al Jasrah (IRE) **Sheikh Juma Dalmook Al Maktoum**
23 **CHANCER**, b g Lope de Vega (IRE)—Misk (FR) **Denford Stud**
24 **FESTINA**, gr f Lethal Force (IRE)—Quite A Thing **Lady Fairhaven & The Hon Melanie Broughton**
25 **HEATWAVE (IRE)**, b g Leroidesanimaux (BRZ)—Here To Eternity (USA) **Miss K. Rausing**
26 **HYDROPLANE (IRE)**, b g Pour Moi (IRE)—Walk On Water **Axom LXXIII**
27 **INFALLIBILITY (USA)**, gr g Oasis Dream—Infamous (IRE) **Mt. Brilliant Farm & Ranch, LLC**
28 **LAND OF OZ**, ch c Australia—Madame Defarge (IRE) **Mr John Brown & Mrs Megan Dennis**
29 **MILLERS CREEK**, b g Aussie Rules (USA)—Miss Katmandu (IRE) **John Pearce Racing Ltd**
30 **MIRABAI**, ch f Poet's Voice—Classical Flair **Hot To Trot Racing & Paddy Barrett**
31 **MISS CELESTIAL (IRE)**, b f Exceed And Excel (AUS)—Liber Nauticus (IRE) **John Pearce Racing Ltd**
32 **MON FRERE**, b g Pour Moi (IRE)—Sistine **Elite Racing Club**
33 **PERCY'S PRINCE**, b g Sir Percy—Attainable **W. F. Charnley, Helen Jones & Chris Jenkins**
34 **RAMATUELLE**, ch f Champs Elysees—Florentia **Mr Neil Greig**
35 **ROAD TO PARIS (IRE)**, b g Champs Elysees—Alchemilla **Jones, Julian, Lee, Royle & Wicks**
36 **SCHEME**, b f Pivotal—Between Us **Cheveley Park Stud**
37 **SHINING SEA (IRE)**, b f Sea The Stars (IRE)—Shamwari Lodge (IRE) **Elite Racing Club**
38 **STARTER**, b g Sea The Stars (IRE)—Froglet **Mr B. Haggas**
39 **THE GAME IS ON**, b g Garswood—Paqueretza (FR) **Mr Timothy J. Rooney**
40 **VOLCANIQUE (IRE)**, b f Galileo (IRE)—Pink Symphony **Mrs Fitri Hay**
41 **YVETTE**, b f Le Havre (FR)—Macleya (GER) **Cheveley Park Stud**

TWO-YEAR-OLDS

42 B c 22/4 Oasis Dream—Albamara (Galileo (IRE)) (58996) **Middleham Park Racing LIX**
43 **ALPHABETICAL**, gr c 9/3 Archipenko (USA)—Albanova (Alzao (USA)) (85000) **Tim Bunting - Osborne House III**
44 **ALPINISTA**, gr f 16/2 Frankel—Alwilda (Hernando (FR)) **Miss K. Rausing**
45 **ANIMAL INSTINCT**, ch c 1/2 Leroidesanimaux (BRZ)—
                     Alea Iacta (Invincible Spirit (IRE)) (55000) **G. Moore - Osborne House**
46 **ANNO LUCIS (IRE)**, gr c 1/4 Mastercraftsman (IRE)—
                     Summer's Eve (Singspiel (IRE)) (44000) **Attenborough,Casterton,Harenstam,JonesCG**
47 **BELLE ROUSSE**, ch f 3/2 Archipenko (USA)—Jolie Blonde (Sir Percy) **Miss K. Rausing**
48 B c 23/4 Camelot—Blue Zealot (IRE) (Galileo (IRE)) **Mrs Olivia Hoare & Mr J. M. Castle**
49 **BODYLINE (IRE)**, b c 1/5 Australia—Eurirs (FR) (Indian Ridge) (92000) **Tim Bunting - Osborne House IV**
50 **CAPLA CUBISTE**, b f 9/4 Archipenko (USA)—Eurolink Artemis (Common Grounds) **Strawberry Fields Stud**
51 **CARIBENO**, ch c 9/2 Archipenko (USA)—
                     Cubanita (Selkirk (USA)) (90000) **Charles C Walker - Osborne House IV**

SIR MARK PRESCOTT BT - Continued

52 **CLIFF WIND**, gr f 4/4 Invincible Spirit (IRE)—Fork Lightning (USA) (Storm Cat (USA)) **Denford Stud**
53 **ESCALADE (IRE)**, b f 25/2 Canford Cliffs (IRE)—Sliding Scale (Sadler's Wells (USA)) **Mr & Mrs John Kelsey-Fry**
54 B c 19/5 Union Rags (USA)—
                Garden of Eden (USA) (Curlin (USA)) (63492) **Charles C. Walker - Osborne House II**
55 **GLEN FORCE (IRE)**, b c 9/4 Gleneagles (IRE)—
                Lethal Quality (USA) (Elusive Quality (USA)) (134849) **Mr G. C. Woodall & Partners**
56 **KITOS**, b f 16/5 Showcasing—
                Cool Question (Polar Falcon (USA)) **Lady Fairhaven & The Hon Melanie Broughton**
57 **LADY ANGELA (IRE)**, b f 24/4 Dark Angel (IRE)—Marlinka (Marju (IRE)) **Elite Racing Club**
58 **LISMORE (IRE)**, b f 21/4 Zoffany (IRE)—Tecla (IRE) (Whipper (USA)) **Mrs Sonia Rogers & Anthony Rogers**
59 **MISS FRANGIPANI**, ch f 31/3 Frankel—Miss Cap Estel (Hernando (FR)) **John Pearce Racing**
60 **NIKOLAYEVA**, b f 19/4 Archipenko (USA)—Nezhenka (With Approval (CAN)) **Miss K. Rausing**
61 **ORDER OF MERRITT (IRE)**, b c 5/3 Kyllachy—
                Merritt Island (Exceed And Excel (AUS)) **Mr & Mrs John Kelsey-Fry**
62 B c 19/2 Intrinsic—Paint The Star (IRE) (Acclamation) **Mr Malih Al Basti**
63 **PRIVATE TREATY**, b f 19/2 Pivotal—Between Us (Galileo (IRE)) **Cheveley Park Stud**
64 **REVOLVER (IRE)**, b c 10/4 Slade Power (IRE)—
                Swizzle Stick (IRE) (Sadler's Wells (USA)) (53940) **Ne'er Do Wells VI**
65 B c 9/4 Pivotal—Sunrise Star (Shamardal (USA)) **Mr Malih Al Basti**
66 **TAIMA**, b f 4/2 Make Believe—Highest (Dynaformer (USA)) **Denford Stud**
67 **TELL ME ALL**, b c 16/4 Lope de Vega (IRE)—Confidential Lady (Singspiel (IRE)) **Cheveley Park Stud**

Other Owners: Mr N Attenborough, Mr P Bamford, Mrs M Baxter, Mrs J Budd, Mr B D Burnet, Mr D Casterton, Mr D Ellis, Mr C Fipke, Mr J Fishpool, Mr Phil Fry, The Hon Mrs G Greenwood, Mr R Greenwood, Mrs Caroline Gregson, Mrs B Harenstam, Mr David Howard, Mrs H Jones, Mr C Jones, Mr M Julian, Mr P Lee, Mrs P Mailer, Mr I Mailer, Mr P J McSwiney, Mr G Moore, Mr T S Palin, The Hon Pleydell-Bouverie, Mr M Prince, Dr J Royle, Mr Mike Rudd, Mr W E Sturt, Mr Mark Tracey, The Hon Lady Troubridge, Sir T Troubridge, Mr G Warman, Mrs E Wicks, Mr E J Williams.

Assistant Trainer: William Butler (William@Heathhousestables.Com), **Pupil Assistant:** Tommy Lyon-Smith

Jockey (flat): Luke Morris, Ryan Tate. **Apprentice:** Gavin Ashton.

---

453 MISS KATY PRICE, Llanigon
Postal: Willow Croft, Llanigon, Hay-On-Wye, Herefordshire, HR3 5PN
Contacts: PHONE (07976) 820819
E-MAIL katyprice2005@aol.com WEBSITE www.facebook.com/katypriceracing

1 **A TAIL OF INTRIGUE (IRE)**, 11, b g Tillerman—
                Princess Commanche (IRE) **Mr Oscar Singh & Miss Priya Purewal**
2 **BEECHER (IRE)**, 4, ch g Shirocco (GER)—Roli Flight (IRE) **Mr N. Elliott**
3 **CLONDAW RIGGER (IRE)**, 7, b g Stowaway—Daytona Lily (IRE) **Katy Price Racing Club**
4 **DEFINITE WINNER (IRE)**, 8, b m Definite Article—Sindabezi (IRE) **Mr N. Sander**
5 **FARM THE ROCK (IRE)**, 8, b g Yeats (IRE)—Shades of Lavender (IRE) **Mr N. Elliott**
6 **FRIARY GOLD (IRE)**, 7, b g Mountain High (IRE)—Platinium Ambition (IRE) **Peers Pleasure**
7 **GOLDRAPPER (IRE)**, 6, b g Gold Well—Mrs Bukay (IRE) **Katy Price Racing Club**
8 **ITSAMANSLIFE (IRE)**, 6, b g Mahler—Medieval Banquet (IRE) **McLeish & Elliott**
9 **JOHNNY YUMA (IRE)**, 6, b g Alfred Nobel (IRE)—Rossbridge Lass (IRE) **Alastair & Pippa McLeish**
10 **KILMOGANNY (IRE)**, 7, b g Stowaway—Gowayourdat (IRE) **Clive Price & Katy Price**
11 **LUCCA LADY (IRE)**, 8, b m Milan—Trail Storm (IRE) **Making Hay**
12 **MINELLACELEBRATION (IRE)**, 9, b g King's Theatre (IRE)—Knocktartan (IRE) **Mr N. Elliott**
13 **ORCHARD LANE (IRE)**, 7, b g Gamut (IRE)—Me No Puppet **Katy Price Racing Club**
14 **OUT FOR JUSTICE (IRE)**, 6, b g Beneficial—Dustys Delight (IRE) **Alastair & Pippa McLeish**
15 **PALAWAN (IRE)**, 6, b g Mount Nelson—Apple Sauce **Out Of Bounds & Mike Harris Racing Club**
16 **ROSEISAROSEISAROSE (IRE)**, 5, gr m Jeremy (USA)—Roses And Wine (IRE) **Mr A. D. McLeish**
17 **SEA TEA DEA**, 5, b m Archipenko (USA)—Half Sister (IRE) **Katy Price Racing Club**
18 **WOODFIELD ROBIN (IRE)**, 8, ch m Robin des Champs (FR)—Ticket To Mars (IRE) **Alastair & Pippa McLeish**

Other Owners: Mr M. E. Harris, A. D. I. Harris, Mr M. D. Kilsby, Mrs P. J. McLeish, Out Of Bounds Racing Club, Miss K. J. Price, C. G. Price, Miss P. Purewal, Mr A. Singh.

454 MR RICHARD PRICE, Hereford
Postal: **Criftage Farm, Ullingswick, Hereford, Herefordshire, HR1 3JG**
Contacts: **PHONE (01432) 820263 MOBILE (07929) 200598**

1 **BELLEVARDE (IRE)**, 5, b m Kodiac—Pearl Mountain (IRE) **B. Veasey**
2 **BONJOUR STEVE**, 8, b g Bahamian Bounty—Anthea **B. Veasey**
3 **BRISTOL MISSILE (USA)**, 5, b br g Kitten's Joy (USA)—Dearest Girl (IRE) **Mrs K. E. Oseman**
4 **CAPTAIN JACK**, 6, b g Mount Nelson—Court Princess **Mr & Mrs D. C. Holder**
5 **CHAMPAGNE BOB**, 7, gr g Big Bad Bob (IRE)—Exclusive Approval (USA) **Mr M. F. Oseman**
6 **DAVERON (IRE)**, 11, b g Winged Love (IRE)—Double Doc (IRE) **Mr N. A. Holder**
7 **DISTANT HIGH**, 8, b m High Chaparral (IRE)—Distant Dreamer (USA) **My Left Foot Racing Syndicate**
8 **EASTERN LADY (IND)**, 6, ch m Dancing Forever (USA)—Oriental Lady (IRE) **K. Reece**
9 **FLIGHT TO NOWHERE**, 7, ch m Aeroplane—River Beauty **Mrs V. J. Morse**
10 **HELLOFAGAME**, 4, b g Hellvelyn—Gracie's Games **Mr D. Prosser & Mr K. Warrington**
11 **OCEAN GALE**, 6, b m Shirocco (GER)—Ocean Transit (IRE) **The Super Fruit Partnership**
12 **OLLIE VAAR**, 7, b g Sulamani (IRE)—It's A Discovery (IRE) **Kevin & Anne Glastonbury**
13 **OUR MAN IN HAVANA**, 4, b g Havana Gold (IRE)—Auntie Kathryn (IRE) **D. J. Oseman**
14 **SAMSON'S REACH**, 6, b g Phoenix Reach (IRE)—Court Wing (IRE) **Court Reclamation & Salvage Ltd**

THREE-YEAR-OLDS

15 **OCEAN REACH**, b f Phoenix Reach (IRE)—Ocean Transit (IRE) **Mr G E Amey & Mr D M Boddy**

Other Owners: Mr G. E. Amey, Mr D. Boddy, Mr S. J. Fletcher, Mr K. J. Glastonbury, Mrs A. J. Glastonbury, Mr P. J. Hoare, Mrs C. R. Holder, D. C. Holder, D. J. Prosser, K. A. Warrington.

Assistant Trainer: Jane Price

455 MR PETER PRITCHARD, Shipston-on-Stour
Postal: **Upper Farm Lodge, Upper Farm, Whatcote, Shipston-On-Stour, Warwickshire, CV36 5EF**
Contacts: **MOBILE (07376) 500499**
E-MAIL pennypritch55@hotmail.co.uk

1 **EARCOMESALI**, 6, b m Passing Glance—Earcomesannie (IRE) **Mrs Alison Pritchard & Mr R W Stowe**
2 4, Ch g Yorgunnabelucky (USA)—Earcomesannie (IRE) **Mrs Alison Pritchard & Mr R W Stowe**
3 **FRANZ KLAMMER**, 7, b g Midnight Legend—Ski **Mr M. J. Miller**

Other Owners: Mrs A. D. Pritchard, Mr R. W. Stowe, Woodlands (Worcestershire) Ltd.

Assistant Trainer: Mrs. E. Gardner

Jockey (NH): Tom Bellamy. **Conditional:** Charlie Hammond.

456 MR DENIS QUINN, Newmarket
Postal: **Stockbridge Stables, 192 High Street, Newmarket, Suffolk, CB8 9AP**
Contacts: **MOBILE (07435) 340008**

1 **ARSENIO LUPIN**, 5, b h Delegator—Tenebrae (IRE) **Mr A. Dal Pos**
2 **DUNSTALL DREAMER**, 4, b c Swiss Spirit—Nordic Theatre (IRE) **Mr D. P. Quinn**
3 **RELIGHT THE FIRE**, 8, ch g Firebreak—Alula **Mr D. P. Quinn**
4 **ROCKIES SPIRIT**, 4, br c Swiss Spirit—Red Mischief (IRE) **J Mangan & D Quinn**
5 **SPECTACULIS**, 4, b g Champs Elysees—Merry Diva **Mr S. J. Bryan**
6 **STONECOLDSOBA**, 6, b g Aqlaam—Aswaaq (IRE) **Mr J. T. Mangan**
7 **WIRRAL GIRL (IRE)**, 4, b f Kodiac—Ursula (IRE) **Mr D. P. Quinn**

THREE-YEAR-OLDS

8 **ADASHELBY (IRE)**, gr f Zebedee—Abby Cadabby (IRE)
9 **BOSMANN**, b c Mastercraftsman (IRE)—Flavian **Mr B. T. Nygard**
10 **LITTLE LADY LUCK**, ch f Yorgunnabelucky (USA)—Dockside Strike
11 **THE GALLA GIRL (IRE)**, b f Footstepsinthesand—Headborough Lass (IRE) **Mr D. P. Quinn**

TWO-YEAR-OLDS

12 B c 24/4 Morpheus—Beau Petite (Kyllachy)

457 **MR JOHN QUINN, Malton**
Postal: Bellwood Cottage Stables, Settrington, Malton, North Yorkshire, YO17 8NR
Contacts: **PHONE (01944) 768370 MOBILE (07899) 873304**
E-MAIL info@johnquinnracing.co.uk WEBSITE www.johnquinnracing.co.uk

1 **AL KHERB**, 4, b g Al Kazeem—Perfect Spirit (IRE) **Blackburn, Balfe & Partner**
2 **ALEXANDERTHEGREAT (FR)**, 4, b g Redoute's Choice (AUS)—Garota da Ipanema (FR) **The Top Silk Syndicate**
3 **ALEXIS CARRINGTON (IRE)**, 4, b f Mastercraftsman (IRE)—Cozzene's Angel (USA) **Rathordan Partnership**
4 **ASCOT WEEK (USA)**, 5, br g Lonhro (AUS)—Millenia **JJ Quinn Racing Ltd**
5 **ASHINGTON**, 4, b g Canford Cliffs (IRE)—Kadoma **Mr T. Alderson**
6 **BENJAMIN THOMAS (IRE)**, 5, b g Mayson—Strudel (IRE) **Hart Inn I**
7 **BODACIOUS NAME (IRE)**, 5, b g Famous Name—Nice Wee Girl (IRE) **Excelsior Racing Ltd**
8 **BURNIEBOOZLE (IRE)**, 4, b g Frozen Power (IRE)—Tea Chest (IRE) **Excelsior Racing Ltd**
9 **CAPTAIN JAMESON (IRE)**, 4, b g Camacho—Cross Section (USA) **The JAM Partnership**
10 **CHEBSEY BEAU**, 9, b g Multiplex—Chebsey Belle (IRE) **Kent, Greaves, Dawson**
11 **CLEMENTO (IRE)**, 5, b g Canford Cliffs (IRE)—Street Style (IRE) **Blackburn, Balfe, Houlton**
12 **DUSTY'S CHOICE (IRE)**, 4, gr g Elusive Pimpernel (USA)—Raheefa's Mix (IRE) **Mr & Mrs Paul & Clare Rooney**
13 **EL ASTRONAUTE (IRE)**, 6, ch g Approve (IRE)—Drumcliffe Dancer (IRE) **Mr Ross Harmon**
14 **GEMINI**, 4, b f Makfi—Gaze **Fulbeck Horse Syndicate**
15 **INDIAN PURSUIT (IRE)**, 6, b g Compton Place—Church Melody **Mr M. Walker**
16 **INDY (IRE)**, 8, b g Indian Haven—Maddie's Pearl (IRE) **White Rose Racing**
17 **JE SUIS CHARLIE**, 5, b g High Chaparral (IRE)—Fin **The JAM Partnership**
18 **LOOK MY WAY**, 5, b g Pour Moi (IRE)—Casual Glance **Drew & Ailsa Russell**
19 **LORD RIDDIFORD**, 4, gr g Zebedee—Beacon of Hope (IRE) **The JAM Partnership**
20 **MASTER OF IRONY (IRE)**, 7, b g Makfi—Mother of Pearl (IRE) **Highfield Racing 6**
21 **MILITARY MADAME (IRE)**, 4, b f Epaulette (AUS)—Sweet Kristeen (USA) **The Jam Partnership & Partner**
22 **MISTIROC**, 8, br g Rocamadour—Mistinguett (IRE) **Drew & Ailsa Russell**
23 **MOONLIGHTNAVIGATOR (USA)**, 7, br g Henrythenavigator (USA)—Victorica (USA) **Mr Malcolm Walker**
24 **MR WAGYU (IRE)**, 4, ch g Choisir (AUS)—Lake Louise (IRE) **The New Century Partnership**
25 **PROJECT BLUEBOOK (FR)**, 6, bl g Sinndar (IRE)—Apperella **Mr J. P. McManus**
26 **REPUTATION (IRE)**, 6, b g Royal Applause—Semaphore **Fulbeck Horse Syndicate**
27 **SAFE VOYAGE (IRE)**, 6, b g Fast Company (IRE)—Shishangaan (IRE) **Mr Ross Harmon**
28 **SPIRIT OF ZEBEDEE (IRE)**, 6, gr g Zebedee—Sampers (IRE) **Mr M. Walker**

THREE-YEAR-OLDS

29 **AL SUIL EILE (FR)**, gr c Alhebayeb (IRE)—Visual Element (USA) **Harmon, Bruton & Partner**
30 **BALANCE OF POWER**, b g Slade Power—Classic Falcon (IRE) **JJ Quinn Racing Ltd**
31 **BUGLER BOB (IRE)**, ch g Dandy Man (IRE)—Callanish **Mr Robert Houlton**
32 **CAREY STREET (IRE)**, b g Bungle Inthejungle—Undulant Way **Mr P. G. Shorrock**
33 **COUNTESS WELLS (IRE)**, b f So You Think (NZ)—Alzaroof (USA) **Excelsior Racing Ltd**
34 **CRYSTAL CAROLE**, b f Canford Cliffs (IRE)—Crystal Gale (IRE) **Mrs V. J. Williams**
35 **DIVIED (USA)**, b g Lope de Vega (IRE)—Vied (USA) **Mrs S. Quinn**
36 **ENCORE MAM'SELLE (IRE)**, b f Dark Angel (IRE)—Encore View **Lowther Racing & Partners**
37 **GRAZEON ROY**, ch c Archipenko (USA)—Graze On And On **Mr J. Rowbottom**
38 **HERE'S ROCCO (IRE)**, b g Charm Spirit (IRE)—Aqraan **Mr R. Kaye**
39 **KICKHAM STREET**, ch g Olympic Glory (IRE)—Alzanti (USA) **Mr Ross Harmon & Partner**
40 **MOONLIGHT ESCAPADE**, ch c Cityscape—Marmalade Moon **Lord D. G. Crawshaw**
41 **MY UKULELE (IRE)**, ch f Power—Island Music (IRE) **Alan Wight & Andrew W Robson**
42 **PANDORA STAR**, b f Epaulette (AUS)—Gracefully **Ryedale Racing**
43 **PRINCESS PALLISER (IRE)**, b f Slade Power (IRE)—Piccola Sissi (IRE) **The JAM Partnership**
44 **RUM LAD**, b g Heeraat (IRE)—Madam Mojito (USA) **Dalwhinnie Bloodstock Limited**
45 **SARASOTA BAY**, ch f Coach House (IRE)—Bird Key **JJ Quinn Racing Ltd**
46 **SECRET PICNIC (FR)**, b g Penny's Picnic (IRE)—Secret Marks (FR) **Mr Ross Harmon & Partner**
47 **SENORITA GRANDE (IRE)**, b f Garswood—Spring Green **Zen Racing**
48 **SIGNORA CABELLO (IRE)**, b f Camacho—Journalist (IRE) **Phoenix Thoroughbred Limited**
49 **SKEETAH**, b f Heeraat (IRE)—Skylla **The JAM Partnership**
50 **TEASE MAID**, b f Heeraat (IRE)—Flirtinaskirt **Mr Philip Wilkins**
51 **TEASING GEORGIA (IRE)**, b f New Approach (IRE)—Hallowed Park (IRE) **Mr David Ward**
52 **THE SINGING HILLS**, b f Nathaniel (IRE)—Glen Rosie (IRE) **Mr David Ward**

TWO-YEAR-OLDS

53 B c 29/3 Kodiac—Annie The Doc (Nayef (USA)) (126422) **Phoenix Thoroughbred Limited**
54 B f 17/4 Kodiac—Bonnie Lesley (IRE) (Iffraaj) (18000) **The Odd One Out Partnership**

MR JOHN QUINN - Continued

55 B f 8/2 Camacho—Cross Section (USA) (Cape Cross (IRE)) (19047) **The JAM Partnership**
56 Br f 11/3 Kodiac—Duchess of Foxland (IRE) (Medecis) (45511)
57 B g 20/4 Elzaam (AUS)—Greatest Dancer (IRE) (Iffraaj) (12642)
58 **IL MAESTRO (IRE),** b c 8/2 Camacho—Dance On (Caerleon (USA)) (27812) **Zen Racing**
59 Ch f 8/4 Exceed And Excel (AUS)—Imperialistic Diva (IRE) (Haafhd) (66666) **Phoenix Thoroughbred Limited**
60 Ch c 21/3 Starspangledbanner (AUS)—Jamesbo's Girl (Refuse To Bend (IRE))
61 B f 15/4 Frankel—L'ancresse (IRE) (Darshaan) (404551) **Phoenix Thoroughbred Limited**
62 B f 16/4 Night of Thunder (IRE)—Look Busy (IRE) (Danetime (IRE)) (34000)
63 B c 19/4 Camacho—Night Sphere (IRE) (Night Shift (USA)) (119047) **Phoenix Thoroughbred Limited**
64 **REBEL REDEMPTION,** b c 17/2 Lethal Force (IRE)—Tempting (Pivotal) (32000) **The JAM Partnership**
65 B gr c 15/3 Gutaifan (IRE)—She's A Character (Invincible Spirit (IRE)) (22756)
66 B g 7/3 Heeraat (IRE)—Skylla (Kyllachy) (34285) **Fact's & Figures & Partner**
67 B c 29/3 Gleneagles (IRE)—Sweet Coincidence (Mujahid (USA)) (72000)
68 Gr c 11/3 Gregorian (IRE)—Trentini (IRE) (Singspiel (IRE)) (22756)
69 B f 15/4 Swiss Spirit—Valiantly (Anabaa (USA)) (10000) **Ryedale Racing**
70 B c 20/4 Outstrip—Wings of Fame (IRE) (Namid) (11799) **Mr Thompson Mrs Allen Adams & Cranston**

Other Owners: Mr J. M. Adams, Mr Steve Avery, Mr D. E. Balfe, Mr J. N. Blackburn, Mr R. Blades, Mr J. Bloom, Mr J. Bruton, Mrs Pam Dawson, Mr Andrew Derry, Mr J. I. Derry, Mr C. J. Edwards, Miss Mary A. Greaves, Miss Liz Hall, Mr M. Heffernan, Mr R. Kent, The Countess of Lonsdale, Mr G. Oxtoby, Mr S. A. T. Quinn, Mr Martin Rapley, Mr Andrew W. Robson, Mrs J. Rolls, Mr P. Rolls, Mr P. A. Rooney, Mrs C. Rooney, Mr Drew Russell, Mrs Ailsa Russell, Mr R. A. Sankey, M. A. Scaife, Mr A. J. Scaife, Mr Nick Simpson, Mr Patrick Stakelum, Mr Robert Turner, Alan Wight, Mrs S. M. Wood.

Assistant Trainer: Sean Quinn

Jockey (flat): Jason Hart.

---

458 **MR MICK QUINN, Newmarket**
Postal: **50 Edinburgh Road, Newmarket, Suffolk, CB8 0QF**
Contacts: **PHONE (01638) 660017 FAX (01638) 660017 MOBILE (07973) 260054**
E-MAIL mickquinn2562@gmail.com

1 **COLONEL FRANK,** 5, b g Dutch Art—Loquacity **Mr K. F. C. Bruce**
2 **GREAT HALL,** 9, b g Halling (USA)—L'affaire Monique **Mr M. Quinn**
3 **NO MORE COMMISERY (IRE),** 4, b f Dandy Man (IRE)—Lady Bracknell (IRE) **Mr K. F. C. Bruce**
4 **PRINCESS HARLEY (IRE),** 4, gr f Dark Angel (IRE)—Tonle Sap (IRE) **Mr K. F. C. Bruce**
5 **PRINCESS KEIRA (IRE),** 4, b f Acclamation—La Reine de Pearls (IRE) **Mr K. F. C. Bruce**
6 **PURPLE DRAGON,** 4, b f Captain Gerrard (IRE)—Dragon Flyer (IRE) **Mr Kenny Bruce & Mr M Quinn**
7 **TAWAAFOQ,** 5, b g Showcasing—Gilt Linked **Mr K. F. C. Bruce**
8 **THE NIGHT KING,** 4, b g Arcano (IRE)—Semplicita (IRE) **Andy Viner, John Quorn, Mick Quinn**

THREE-YEAR-OLDS

9 **ELUSIVE EXCEL (IRE),** b f Exceed And Excel (AUS)—Elusive Girl (IRE) **Mr K. F. C. Bruce**
10 **GEORGE THOMAS,** b g Heeraat (IRE)—Lexington Rose **Mr K. F. C. Bruce**
11 **GREEK KODIAC (IRE),** b c Kodiac—Greek Easter (IRE) **Mr K. F. C. Bruce**
12 **INVINCIBLE LARNE (IRE),** b c Invincible Spirit (IRE)—Caphene **Mr K. F. C. Bruce**
13 **MRS DISCOMBE,** b f Garswood—Dora's Sister (IRE) **Mr K. F. C. Bruce**

Other Owners: J. E. Quorn, Mr A. Viner.

Assistant Trainer: Miss Karen Davies

---

459 **MR ALASTAIR RALPH, Bridgnorth**
Postal: **Bynd Farm, Bynd Lane, Billingsley, Bridgnorth, Shropshire, WV16 6PQ**
Contacts: **PHONE (07912) 184217**
E-MAIL alistair_ralph1@hotmail.com WEBSITE www.alastairralphracing.co.uk

1 **A BOLD MOVE (IRE),** 9, b g Shantou (USA)—Sprint For Gold (USA) **Rowlestuffinjonespool**
2 **BATTLE DUST (IRE),** 10, b g Portrait Gallery (IRE)—Katie O'toole (IRE) **Mr & Mrs Mark Laws**
3 **BEAN IN TROUBLE (IRE),** 5, gr g Sulamani (IRE)—Bouncing Bean **Bundle Pickard Racing Club**
4 **BILLINGSLEY (IRE),** 7, b g Millenary—Retain That Magic **Walters Plant Hire & James & Jean Potter**
5 **BLUE SKIMMER (IRE),** 7, b g Arcano (IRE)—Cattiva Generosa **B. Hawkins**
6 **BOB FORD (IRE),** 12, b g Vinnie Roe (IRE)—Polar Lamb (IRE) **Bundle Pickard Racing Club**

MR ALASTAIR RALPH - Continued

7 **BROUGHTONS ADMIRAL**, 5, b g Born To Sea (IRE)—Chanter **ValueRacingClub.co.uk**
8 4, B g Mahler—Castle Lake (IRE) **Bill Hawkins**
9 **CHAMPAGNE MIST (IRE)**, 7, b g Stowaway—Valentines Misty (IRE) **Mrs D J Ralph & Mr R D Ralph**
10 **COMBER MILL (FR)**, 7, ch g Le Fou (IRE)—Kalistina (FR) **Rrrs Partnership**
11 **DAARIO NAHARIS (IRE)**, 6, b g Winged Love (IRE)—Luck's A Lady (IRE) **Mr A. Walker**
12 **DESERT GREY (IRE)**, 5, b ro g Mastercraftsman (IRE)—Endure (IRE) **Mrs H. Hawkins**
13 **DILYS THOMAS (IRE)**, 4, ch f Dylan Thomas (IRE)—South Queen Lady (IRE) **Bind Racing Club**
14 **MICK MONA (IRE)**, 5, ro m Blue Bresil (FR)—Mick Toscane (FR) **The Burling Family Ltd**
15 **MIX OF CLOVER**, 5, b g Fair Mix (IRE)—Allforclover (IRE) **Miss S. Troughton**
16 **MOVE ABOVE (IRE)**, 5, br g Dubai Destination (USA)—
From Above (IRE) **Walters Plant Hire & Spiers & Hartwell**
17 4, B g Getaway (GER)—Native Diva (IRE)
18 **SEYMOUR SOX**, 5, b g Multiplex—Seymour Chance **Mrs C J Black & Mrs Sue Briscoe**
19 **SEYMOUR STAR**, 11, b g Alflora (IRE)—Seymour Chance **Mrs C J Black & Mrs Sue Briscoe**
20 **SHARP ROCK**, 4, b g Kheleyf (USA)—Fair View (GER) **Mr B. R. Marsden**
21 4, B g Yeats (IRE)—She's On The Case (IRE)
22 **STUNG FOR CASH (IRE)**, 6, b g Scorpion (IRE)—Cash A Lawn (IRE) **ValueRacingClub.co.uk**
23 **TEMPURAN**, 10, b g Unbridled's Song (USA)—Tenderly (IRE) **Rrrs Partnership**
24 **THE GREEN OGRE**, 9, b g Dubai Destination (USA)—Takegawa **ValueRacingClub.co.uk**

Other Owners: Mrs C. J. Black, Mrs Sue Briscoe, Mr James Couldwell, James and Jean Potter, Mr P. A. Jones, Mrs Melinda Laws, Mr Mark Laws, B. R. Marsden, Mrs Kate Maxwell, Miss I. H. Pickard, Mr Richard Pool, Mr J. E. Potter, Mrs J. E. Potter, Mr R. D. Ralph, Mrs D. J. Ralph, Mr Glenn Rowles, Mr Richard John Simpson, Spiers & Hartwell Ltd, Mr W. Tuffin, Walters Plant Hire Ltd, Mrs Margaret J. Wilson.

Jockey (flat): Rob Hornby. **Jockey (NH):** Lee Edwards, Richard Johnson, Andrew Tinkler.
Conditional: Charlie Hammond. **Amateur:** Mr Huw Edwards, Mr Alex Edwards.

---

460 **MR TIM REED, Hexham**
Postal: Moss Kennels, Haydon Bridge, Hexham, Northumberland, NE47 6NL
Contacts: **PHONE (01434) 344016 MOBILE (07703) 270408**
E-MAIL timreedracing@gmail.com

1 **BAY WATCH (IRE)**, 5, b g Harbour Watch (IRE)—Karuga **Mr G. B. Davidson**
2 **BORDER BREAKER (IRE)**, 10, br g Indian Danehill (IRE)—Flying Answer (IRE) **Mr W. T. Reed**
3 **CARLINGFORD PRINCE (IRE)**, 10, ch g Definite Article—Castle Hope (IRE) **Mr W. T. Reed**
4 **FAIR HOUXTY**, 7, bl m Fair Mix (IRE)—Border Mist (IRE) **Mr W. M. Aitchison**
5 **FIVE DEAR BRIAN (IRE)**, 5, br g Elusive Pimpernel (USA)—Vayenga (FR) **Mr B. Ryan-Beswick**
6 **INDIAN TEMPLE (IRE)**, 10, b g Indian River (FR)—Ballycraggan (IRE) **Mr J. K. Huddleston**
7 **LEVEROCK LASS (IRE)**, 6, b m Olden Times—Hazelhall Princess (IRE) **Mr B. Ryan-Beswick**
8 **NAUGHTY NANCIE**, 4, b f Bahri (USA)—Oh So Perky (IRE) **Mrs C. J. Todd**
9 **TERMINAL ONE (IRE)**, 5, b m Stowaway—Kalyfa Royale (IRE) **Mr J. K. Huddleston**
10 **WEAVE SOME MAGIC**, 4, b g Cityscape—Didbrook **Mr B. Ryan-Beswick**
11 4, B f Stowaway—Youngborogal (IRE) **Mr B. Ryan-Beswick**

Assistant Trainer: Mrs E. J. Reed (07889) 111885

Conditional: Harry Reed.

---

461 **MR DAVID REES, Haverfordwest**
Postal: The Grove Yard, Clarbeston Road, Haverfordwest, Pembrokeshire, SA63 4SP
Contacts: **PHONE (01437) 731308 FAX (01437) 731551 MOBILE (07775) 662463**
E-MAIL davidreesfencing@lineone.net

1 **BACKOFTHEROCK**, 10, b g Scorpion (IRE)—Oscars Vision (IRE) **Mr D Rees & Mr P Evans**
2 **BUCK BRAVO (IRE)**, 7, b g Mahler—Damoiselle **D. A. Rees**
3 **CAWDOR HOUSE BERT**, 12, b g Kayf Tara—Lady Shanan **A. J. & Dai Rees**
4 **CONTROL ME (IRE)**, 5, b m Yeats (IRE)—Cullian **D. A. Rees**
5 **DREAM BOLT (IRE)**, 11, ch g Urban Ocean (FR)—Riviera Dream (IRE) **Mr D A Rees & Mr N Adams**
6 **GARDINERS HILL (IRE)**, 9, br g Stowaway—Mysterious Lass (IRE) **Mr D A Rees & Mr N Adams**
7 **GONE PLATINUM (IRE)**, 10, b g Mountain High—Miss Platinum (IRE) **D. A. Rees**
8 **MAY'S MILAN (IRE)**, 8, b g Milan—Opera Mask (IRE) **Mr R. J. C. Lewis**
9 **MISTY MAI (IRE)**, 9, b m Westerner—Arcanum (IRE) **Eddie & Dai**

MR DAVID REES - Continued

10 PERSISTANTPRINCESS (IRE), 7, b m Scorpion (IRE)—Classy Conflict (IRE) **D. A. Rees**
11 ROBIN OF SHERWOOD (IRE), 6, b br g Robin des Pres (FR)—Galleta **D. A. Rees**
12 STEEL NATIVE (IRE), 8, b g Craigsteel—Princess Gloria (IRE) **Mr R. J. C. Lewis**

Other Owners: Mr N. Adams, Mr P. Evans, Mr E. W. Morris, Mr D. Rees, Mr A. J. Rees.

---

462 **MR SEAN REGAN, Middleham**
Postal: **Low Beck, Coverham, Middleham, Leyburn, North Yorkshire, DL8 4TJ**
Contacts: **MOBILE (07866) 437476**
E-MAIL sean@seanreganracing.com WEBSITE www.seanreganracing.com

1 MOONSHINE DANCER, 5, b m Dark Angel (IRE)—Raggle Taggle (IRE) **Mrs C. D. Taylor**
2 PROSECUTE (FR), 6, b g Lawman (FR)—Dissitation (IRE) **Mrs C. D. Taylor**
3 SHE'S A PRIMADIVA, 7, b m Primitive Academy—Petrovka (IRE) **S. Regan**
4 SOUTHVIEW LADY, 7, b m Misu Bond (IRE)—Salalah **S. Regan**
5 TOM'S ANNA (IRE), 9, b m Antonius Pius (USA)—Vanilla Delight (IRE) **Mrs C. D. Taylor**

---

463 **MRS JACKIE RETTER, Cullompton**
Postal: **7 Manor Close, Kentisbeare, Cullompton, Devon, EX15 2BG**
Contacts: **PHONE/FAX (01884) 266078 MOBILE (07912) 889655**

1 ALYASAN (IRE), 8, ch g Sea The Stars (IRE)—Alaya (IRE) **Mrs J. G. Retter**
2 ON THE RAZ, 12, b m Rakaposhi King—Trillow **Mrs J. G. Retter**

---

464 **MRS LYDIA RICHARDS, Chichester**
Postal: **Lynch Farm, Hares Lane, Funtington, Chichester, West Sussex, PO18 9LW**
Contacts: **PHONE (01243) 574882 MOBILE (07803) 199061**
E-MAIL lydia.richards@sky.com

1 DEMONS AND WIZARDS (IRE), 4, b g Elnadim (USA)—Crystal Theatre (IRE) **Mrs L. Richards**
2 FAHEEM, 8, b g Halling (USA)—White Star (IRE) **Mrs E. F. J. Seal**
3 GOLD DECREE (IRE), 7, b g Golan (IRE)—De Verdict (IRE) **Mrs L. Richards**
4 GOOD NEWS, 7, b g Midnight Legend—Venetian Lass **The Good News Partnership**
5 MONSIEUR FOX, 4, b g Foxwedge (AUS)—Demoiselle Bond **The Demoiselle Bond Partnership**
6 MURHIB (IRE), 7, b g Sea The Stars (IRE)—Mood Swings (IRE) **The Murhib Partnership**
7 ROYAL GOLDIE (IRE), 4, b f Havana Gold (IRE)—Dream Maker (IRE) **Mrs E. F. J. Seal**
8 SOUTHERN STATES, 6, b g Medaglia d'oro (USA)—Little Belle (USA) **The Beep Partnership**
9 5, Ch g Midnight Legend—Venetian Lass **Mrs L. Richards**

Other Owners: Mr Hamish Kinmond, Mr Bryan Mathieson, Mr Graeme Musker, Mrs Lydia Richards, Mrs Judy Seal.

---

465 **MR NICKY RICHARDS, Greystoke**
Postal: **Rectory Farm, Greystoke, Penrith, Cumbria, CA11 0UJ**
Contacts: **OFFICE (01768) 483392 HOME (01768) 483160 FAX (01768) 483933**
MOBILE (07771) 906609
E-MAIL office@nickyrichardsracing.com WEBSITE www.nickyrichardsracing.com

1 AMBEROSE, 6, ch m Sulamani (IRE)—Miss Nellie (IRE) **Langdale Bloodstock**
2 BALLYCRYSTAL COURT (IRE), 7, b g Court Cave (IRE)—Monavale (IRE) **PMPro31 Ltd**
3 BAYWING (IRE), 10, br g Winged Love (IRE)—Cerise de Totes (FR) **David & Nicky Robinson**
4 BERNARDELLI (IRE), 11, b g Golan (IRE)—Beautiful Blue (IRE) **Henriques & Lloyd-Bakers**
5 BETTER GETALONG (IRE), 8, b g Gold Well—Arequipa (IRE) **Mr David Wesley-Yates**
6 BIG BAD BEAR (IRE), 5, br g Jeremy (USA)—Our Polly (IRE) **Tor Side Racing**
7 BLAKERIGG (IRE), 8, b g Presenting—Azalea (IRE) **David & Nicky Robinson**
8 BOOYAKASHA (IRE), 7, b g Presenting—Land of Honour **Celtic Shamrock Racing**
9 CAIUS MARCIUS (IRE), 8, b g King's Theatre (IRE)—Ain't Misbehavin (IRE) **C. P. Norbury**
10 CARRY ON ARCADIO (IRE), 7, b g Arcadio (GER)—Carryonharriet (IRE) **Paul & Clare Rooney**
11 CATHAL'S STAR, 6, ch g Malinas (GER)—Hand Inn Glove **Charlie Doocey / Cathal Doocey**

MR NICKY RICHARDS - Continued

12 **CHIDSWELL (IRE)**, 10, b g Gold Well—Manacured (IRE) **David & Nicky Robinson**
13 **COURT DREAMING (IRE)**, 6, b g Court Cave (IRE)—Louis's Teffia (IRE) **Dark Horse Racing Ltd**
14 **CULTRAM ABBEY**, 12, br g Fair Mix (IRE)—Kansas City (FR) **Tarzan Bloodstock**
15 **DERRIANA SPIRIT (IRE)**, 6, b m Flemensfirth (USA)—Distillery Lane (IRE) **The Spirit Partnership**
16 **DUKE OF NAVAN (IRE)**, 11, b br g Presenting—Greenfieldflyer (IRE) **David & Nicky Robinson**
17 **EASTER FIRTH**, 5, b m Flemensfirth (USA)—Easter Vic **Mr R. H. Goldie**
18 **ECHO EXPRESS (IRE)**, 7, b g Echo of Light—If Dubai (USA) **Henriques, Lloyd-Baker, Westoll, Wrigley**
19 **ELIOS D'OR (FR)**, 5, b g Puit d'or (IRE)—Naker Mome (FR) **Langdale Bloodstock**
20 **GLENDUFF (IRE)**, 5, b g Gold Well—Last of The Bunch **Mr Trevor Hemmings**
21 **GLINGER FLAME (IRE)**, 7, ro g Daylami (IRE)—Titian Flame (IRE) **Mr James Westoll**
22 **GLITTERING LOVE (IRE)**, 7, b g Winged Love (IRE)—Glittering Image (IRE) **Paul & Clare Rooney**
23 **GUITAR PETE (IRE)**, 9, gr g Dark Angel (IRE)—Innishmore (IRE) **Mrs Pat Sloan**
24 **HOLME ABBEY**, 6, b g Fair Mix (IRE)—Brockwell Abbey **The Roper Family**
25 **IMADA (IRE)**, 9, br g Arcadio (GER)—Anck Su Namun (IRE) **Kenny & Laura Haughey**
26 **INNISFREE SPIRIT (IRE)**, 5, br m Yeats (IRE)—Mrs Dempsey (IRE) **The Spirit II Partnership**
27 **ISAACSTOWN LAD (IRE)**, 12, b g Milan—Friends of Friends (IRE) **Multiple Sclerosis Borders Racing Club 1**
28 **KARAMOKO (IRE)**, 7, b g Manduro (GER)—Virevolle (FR) **Tarzan Bloodstock & Mr Oliver Brownlee**
29 **KILCOOLEY (IRE)**, 10, b g Stowaway—Bealaha Essie (IRE) **J. H. & S. M. Wall**
30 **KITTY HALL (IRE)**, 5, b m Fame And Glory—Set In Her Ways (IRE) **Langdale Bloodstock**
31 **LOOKING WELL (IRE)**, 10, b g Gold Well—Different Level (IRE) **Mr David Wesley-Yates**
32 **MAROWN (IRE)**, 5, b g Milan—Rosie Suspect (IRE) **Mr Trevor Hemmings**
33 **MY OLD GOLD (IRE)**, 9, b m Gold Well—Tenbo (IRE) **Tor Side Racing**
34 **ONE FOR HARRY (IRE)**, 11, b g Generous (IRE)—Strawberry Fool (FR) **The Fife Boys**
35 **PETERS COUSIN (IRE)**, 6, b m Presenting—Sunwake (GER) **Mr K. Alexander**
36 **PETITE GANACHE (IRE)**, 7, ch g Presenting—Ain't Misbehavin (IRE) **Golden Dragon Racing**
37 **PROGRESS DRIVE (IRE)**, 8, b g Stowaway—Dolphins View (IRE) **Straightline Bloodstock**
38 **REIVERS LAD**, 8, b g Afflora (IRE)—Reivers Moon **Mr J. M. Stenhouse**
39 **RIBBLE VALLEY (IRE)**, 6, b g Westerner—Miss Greinton (GER) **Mr David Wesley-Yates**
40 **RUBYTWO**, 7, b m Sulamani (IRE)—Miss Nellie (IRE) **Langdale Bloodstock**
41 **SIMPLY NED (IRE)**, 12, ch g Fruits of Love (USA)—Bishops Lass (IRE) **David & Nicky Robinson**
42 **SKIDDAW VALLEYS**, 7, ch g Three Valleys (USA)—Skiddaw Wolf **J. R. Wills**
43 **TAKINGRISKS (IRE)**, 10, b g Golden Tornado (IRE)—Downtown Rosie (IRE) **Mr F. Bird**
44 **TEDDY TEE (IRE)**, 10, b g Mountain High (IRE)—Knocksouna Lady (IRE) **David & Nicky Robinson**
45 **TOP BILLING (IRE)**, 10, br g Monsun (GER)—La Gandilie (FR) **Tarzan Bloodstock & Stewart Tate**
46 **UNCLE ALASTAIR**, 7, b g Midnight Legend—Cyd Charisse **Paul & Clare Rooney**
47 **WESTERN RULES (IRE)**, 9, b g Westerner—Ryehill Lady (IRE) **Bob Bennett & Jimmy Dudgeon**
48 **WILHELM VONVENSTER (FR)**, 5, b g Apsis—Princesse Gaelle **Mrs S. Ricci**
49 **WOT A SHOT (IRE)**, 10, b g Refuse To Bend (IRE)—Ashdali (IRE) **Multiple Sclerosis Borders Racing Club 1**

Other Owners: Mr & Mrs S. Alderson, Mr A. Cartledge, Mrs R. L. Elliot, Mr R. P. Gilbert, Mr M. Henriques, Mr Guy Henriques, Miss Rhonda Hill, Mrs E. M. Lloyd, Mrs Charles Lloyd-Baker, Mr H. M. A. Lloyd-Baker, Mr W. J. Peacock, Mrs Elinor M. Roper, Mr Ken Roper, Mrs Caren Walsh, Mrs Nicholas Wrigley.

Assistant Trainers: Miss Joey Richards, Mr Harry Haynes

Jockey (NH): Ryan Day, Brian Hughes, Craig Nichol. **Conditional:** Danny McMenamin. **Amateur:** Mr Lyall Hodgins.

---

466 MR JOHN DAVID RICHES, Pilling
Postal: Moss Side Farm, Off Lancaster Road, Scronkey, Pilling, Lancashire, PR3 6SR
Contacts: PHONE (01253) 799190
E-MAIL jrracing@btinternet.com

1 **ANGEL EYES**, 4, b f Piccolo—Miacarla **J R Racing**
2 **PICKS PINTA**, 8, b g Piccolo—Past 'n' Present **J R Racing**
3 **SPOKEN WORDS**, 10, b m Fruits of Love (USA)—Jerre Jo Glanville (USA) **J R Racing**
4 **TRULOVE**, 6, b m Piccolo—Snow Dancer (IRE) **J R Racing**

TWO-YEAR-OLDS

5 **MR GAMBINO**, b c 18/4 Music Master—Snow Dancer (IRE) (Desert Style (IRE)) **J R Racing**
6 **STORM MASTER**, b c 1/5 Music Master—Miacarla (Forzano) **J R Racing**

Other Owners: J. D. Riches, Mrs L. Wohlers.

467 **MR MARK RIMELL, Witney**
Postal: **Fairspear Equestrian Centre, Fairspear Road, Leafield, Witney, Oxfordshire, OX29 9NT**
Contacts: **PHONE (01993) 878551 MOBILE (07778) 648303/(07973) 627054**
E-MAIL rimell@rimellracing.com WEBSITE www.rimellracing.com

1 BUACHAILL BEAG, 8, gr g And Beyond (IRE)—Bon Enfant (IRE) **Mrs P. Duncan**
2 I'M A STARMAN, 6, ch g Schiaparelli (GER)—Strathtay **Mrs M. R. T. Rimell**
3 MAGIC MIRROR, 6, b m Dutch Art—Balatoma (IRE) **Mr W. J. Wood**
4 WILD EVE, 5, b m Sulamani (IRE)—Vin Rose **Mr J. R. Henley**

Assistant Trainer: Anne Rimell

468 **MR DAVE ROBERTS, Kenley**
Postal: **Leasowes Farm, Kenley, Shrewsbury, Shropshire, SY5 6NY**
Contacts: **PHONE (01746) 785255**

1 G'DAY AUSSIE, 6, b g Aussie Rules (USA)—Moi Aussi (USA) **Mr D. Bradbury**
2 MILAN OF CRYSTAL (IRE), 10, b m Milan—Native Crystal (IRE) **D. B. Roberts**
3 RACING SPIRIT, 7, ch g Sir Percy—Suertuda **D. B. Roberts**
4 SACKFULLOFDREAMS (IRE), 6, b g Rock of Gibraltar (IRE)—Nymphaea Alba (IRE) **D. B. Roberts**
5 SPECIAL PRINCESS (IRE), 9, br m Cloudings (IRE)—Cockpit Rose (IRE) **Mr R Morgan Evans & Mrs C Lockett**
6 VIF ARGENT (FR), 10, b g Dom Alco (FR)—Formosa (FR) **B. Hawkins**

Other Owners: Mr R. M. Evans, Mrs C. M. Lockett.

Jockey (NH): Lee Edwards.

469 **MR MIKE ROBERTS, Hailsham**
Postal: **Summertree Farm, Bodle Street Green, Hailsham, East Sussex, BN27 4QT**
Contacts: **PHONE (01435) 830231 MOBILE (07774) 208040**
E-MAIL mike@summertree-racing.com

1 ANDAPA (FR), 5, br m Kapgarde (FR)—Daniety (FR) **M. J. Roberts**
2 CONCHITA (GER), 4, b f Zoffany (IRE)—Cross Check (IRE) **M. J. Roberts**
3 DJARKALIN (FR), 7, b g Martaline—Djarissime (FR) **M. J. Roberts**
4 DREAM BAIE (FR), 6, b g Crillon (FR)—Montaraza (FR) **M. J. Roberts**
5 KING MURO, 9, b g Halling (USA)—Ushindi (IRE) **M. J. Roberts**
6 PERFECT MOMENT (IRE), 6, b m Milan—Faucon M. A. **M. J. Roberts**
7 RISKS EMERY (FR), 4, ch g Vision d'etat (FR)—Take Emery (FR) **M. J. Roberts**
8 SNIPPETYDOODAH, 11, b m King's Theatre (IRE)—Kimpour (FR) **M. J. Roberts**

Assistant Trainer: Marie Martin

470 **MISS SARAH ROBINSON, Bridgwater**
Postal: **Newnham Farm, Shurton, Stogursey, Bridgwater, Somerset, TA5 1QG**
Contacts: **PHONE (01278) 732357 FAX (01278) 732357 MOBILE (07866) 435197 / (07518) 785291**
E-MAIL info@sarahrobinsonracing.co.uk WEBSITE www.sarahrobinsonracing.co.uk

1 DONT CALL ME DORIS, 9, b m Franklins Gardens—Grove Dancer **Mr M. L. J. Fooks**
2 MARTHA'S DREAM, 5, ch m Captain Gerrard (IRE)—Rose Bounty **Mr B. Robinson**
3 MONTOCHINE, 6, ch m Volochine (IRE)—Miss Montgomery (IRE) **Mrs S. M. Farr**
4 MONTY MASSINI, 8, b g Dr Massini (IRE)—Miss Montgomery (IRE) **Mrs S. M. Farr**
5 SPANISH OPTIMIST (IRE), 13, b g Indian Danehill (IRE)—La Traviata **Mr R. J. Bailey**

Assistant Trainers: Mr B. Robinson, Mr R. J. Bailey

471 MISS PAULINE ROBSON, Capheaton
Postal: **Kidlaw Farm, Capheaton, Newcastle Upon Tyne, NE19 2AW**
Contacts: **PHONE (01830) 530241 MOBILE (07721) 887489 or (07814) 708725 (David)**
E-MAIL **pauline@prracing.co.uk**

1 CASTLETOWN (FR), 7, gr g Poliglote—Message Personnel (FR) **Mr & Mrs Raymond Anderson Green**
2 DIVINE PORT (USA), 9, b g Arch (USA)—Out of Reach **J. Wade**
3 KATGARY (FR), 9, b g Ballingarry (IRE)—Kotkira (FR) **D&D Armstrong Limited**
4 MARTILA (FR), 7, b m Martaline—Paola Pierji (FR) **Mr & Mrs Raymond Anderson Green**
5 MARTILOO (FR), 9, b m Martaline—Paola Pierji (FR) **Mr & Mrs Raymond Anderson Green**
6 SPECIAL PREP (IRE), 7, b g Brian Boru—Schindler's Dame (IRE) **Mr E. A. Elliott**
7 UPSILON BLEU (FR), 11, b g Panoramic—Glycine Bleue (FR) **Mr & Mrs Raymond Anderson Green**

Other Owners: Mrs A. Green, R. A. Green.

Assistant Trainer: David Parker

Jockey (NH): Brian Hughes, Craig Nichol.

472 MR WILLIAM M. ROPER, The Curragh
Postal: **French Furze, Maddenstown, The Curragh, Co. Kildare, Ireland**
Contacts: **PHONE (00353) 45 441821 MOBILE (00353) 86 823 4279**
E-MAIL **markroper1@eircom.net**

1 4, B g Elusive Pimpernel (USA)—Larsen Bee (IRE) **Mr W. M. Roper**
2 PLAY THE PART (IRE), 8, b g Kutub (IRE)—Pretty Contender (IRE) **P. E. I. Newell**
3 ROONEY O'MARA, 5, ch m Dragon Pulse (IRE)—Date Mate (USA) **M. H. Keogh**
4 SAMMYJADE (IRE), 5, b m Zoffany (IRE)—Dama'a (IRE) **Barry & Alfie Partnership**

THREE-YEAR-OLDS

5 AMAREDDY, b f Red Jazz (USA)—Amatara (IRE) **M. H. Keogh**
6 B g Red Jazz (USA)—Barbsiz (IRE) **M. H. Keogh**

Assistant Trainer: Barry Heffernan

Amateur: Mr Archie Macauley.

473 MR RUSSELL ROSS, Consett
Postal: **Rock Cottage Farm, 79 Iveston Lane, Consett, County Durham, DH8 7TB**

1 MR KIT CAT, 9, ch g Lucarno (USA)—Makeabreak (IRE) **R. A. Ross**
2 STORNAWAY (IRE), 7, b br g Stowaway—Lucy Cooper (IRE) **R. A. Ross**

474 MR BRIAN ROTHWELL, Helmsley
Postal: **Old Post Office, Oswaldkirk, York, North Yorkshire, YO62 5XT**
Contacts: **PHONE (01439) 788859 MOBILE (07969) 968241**
E-MAIL **brian.rothwell1@googlemail.com**

1 ROSE MARMARA, 6, ch m Exceed And Excel (AUS)—Show Rainbow **Mrs G. Sparks**
2 SIRIUS STAR, 10, b g Beat All (USA)—Miss Sirius **B. S. Rothwell**
3 TIGER TWENTY TWO, 8, b g Authorized (IRE)—Collette's Choice **B. S. Rothwell**

THREE-YEAR-OLDS

4 B f Kuroshio (AUS)—Artistic Dawn (IRE) **B. S. Rothwell**
5 PARKER'S PRIDE, b g Burwaaz—Lady Norlela **The Sirius Racing Partnership**
6 THORNTON KATIE, b f Kuroshio (AUS)—Byton **S. P. Hudson**
7 YASMIN FROM YORK, b f Sixties Icon—Bonnie Burnett (IRE) **Mrs G. Sparks**

MR BRIAN ROTHWELL - Continued

TWO-YEAR-OLDS

8 **AETHON,** b f 4/5 Multiplex—Bonnie Burnett (IRE) (Hawk Wing (USA)) **Mr A. J. Sparks**
9 B f 7/4 Heeraat (IRE)—Srimenanti (Diktat) **B. S. Rothwell**

---

475 MR RICHARD ROWE, Pulborough
Postal: **Ashleigh House Stables, Sullington Lane, Storrington, Pulborough, West Sussex, RH20 4AE**
Contacts: PHONE **(01903) 742871** MOBILE **(07831) 345636**
E-MAIL **r.rowe.racing@virgin.net** WEBSITE **www.richardrowe-racing.co.uk**

1 **BATTLE ANTHEM (IRE),** 8, b g Royal Anthem (USA)—Chika Boom (IRE) **The Battle Anthem Partnership**
2 **CELMA DES BOIS (FR),** 7, b g Ballingarry (IRE)—Palafixe (FR) **Encore Partnership V**
3 **COLONEL KEATING (IRE),** 7, b g Yeats (IRE)—Jabroot (IRE) **Capt Adrian Pratt & Friends**
4 **DARK FLAME (IRE),** 10, b g Gold Well—Glorys Flame (IRE) **The Encore Partnership III**
5 **FLASHDANZA,** 4, ch g Sepoy (AUS)—Photo Flash (IRE) **B. H. Page**
6 **GOTHIC EMPIRE (IRE),** 7, b g Dark Angel (IRE)—Box of Frogs (IRE) **R. Rowe**
7 **IDIDITFORYOOOO (IRE),** 5, b g Fast Company (IRE)—Ann's Annie (IRE)
8 **OVER THE ARCH (IRE),** 7, br g Presenting—On The Outside (IRE) **Encore Partnership VI**
9 **REMEMBER FOREVER (IRE),** 9, b g Indian River (FR)—Running Wild (IRE) **The Forever Partnership**
10 **REMEMBER ME WELL (IRE),** 6, b m Doyen (IRE)—Creidim (IRE) **Pink Birds**
11 **SOARLIKEANEAGLE (IRE),** 7, b g Scorpion (IRE)—Wayward Cove **Capt A Pratt,Lord Clinton,P Anwyl-harris**
12 **SUNDAY AT AUGUSTA (IRE),** 6, b g Arakan (USA)—Alla Marcia (IRE) **Scott Parnell Limited**
13 **SWEET'N'CHIC (IRE),** 9, b m Midnight Legend—Sweetbitter (FR) **Richard Rowe Racing Partnership**
14 **TRUCKERS TIME (IRE),** 7, b g Curtain Time (IRE)—Truckers Lady (FR) **Mr J. L. J. Butcher**
15 **TZAR DE L'ELFE (FR),** 9, b g Satri (IRE)—Rue Tournefort (FR) **Lord Clinton & Captain Adrian Pratt**
16 **WE'LLCWHATHAPPENS (IRE),** 6, b m Court Cave (IRE)—Lost Prairie (IRE) **Mr D. Scott**

Other Owners: Mr P. D. Anwyl-Harris, Mr D. M. Bradshaw, Mrs H. C. G. Butcher, Mr N. S. Campbell, Mrs J. Case, Lord Clinton, Mr C. S. Coombe-Tennant, Mrs S. K. Coombe-Tennant, Mrs J. E. Debenham, Capt A. Pratt, Mrs J. D. M. Sadler, T. W. Wellard, Mr P. D. West, Mr P. R. Wilby, Winterfields Farm Ltd.

---

476 MISS MANDY ROWLAND, Lower Blidworth
Postal: **Kirkfields, Calverton Road, Lower Blidworth, Nottingham, Nottinghamshire, NG21 0NW**
Contacts: PHONE **(01623) 794831** MOBILE **(07768) 224666**
E-MAIL **kirkfieldsriding@hotmail.co.uk**

1 **CHINA EXCELS,** 12, b g Exceed And Excel (AUS)—China Beauty **Miss M. E. Rowland**
2 **JAZZ LEGEND (USA),** 6, b g Scat Daddy (USA)—Champion Ride (USA) **Miss M. E. Rowland**
3 **LET'S BE HAPPY (IRE),** 5, gr m Mastercraftsman (IRE)—Corrozal (GER) **Miss M. E. Rowland**
4 **MABAADY,** 5, b g Bated Breath—Fifty (IRE) **Miss M. E. Rowland**
5 **MISS ME NOW (IRE),** 9, b m Presenting—Miss Toulon (IRE) **Miss M. E. Rowland**
6 **RICHARDS REJECT,** 6, b m Dutch Art—Focal

THREE-YEAR-OLDS

7 **GO ANNIE GO,** b f Es Que Love (IRE)—Make It Snappy **Miss M. E. Rowland**

Assistant Trainer: Sarah Thomas

Jockey (flat): Rob Hornby. **Apprentice:** William Cox.

---

477 MR ALAIN DE ROYER-DUPRE, Chantilly
Postal: **3 Chemin des Aigles, 60500 Chantilly, France**
Contacts: PHONE **(00 33) 3 44580303** MOBILE **(00 33) 6 70232901**
E-MAIL **de-royer-dupre@wanadoo.fr**

1 **ASHTIYR (USA),** 4, b br c Lonhro (AUS)—Ashiyla (FR) **S.A. Aga Khan**
2 **DALVINI (FR),** 4, b c Lawman (FR)—Daltama (IRE) **Antoine Fontaine**
3 **JIZELLITA (FR),** 4, b f Muhtathir—Jacira (FR) **Mme Magalen Bryant**
4 **MONTY (FR),** 4, b c Motivator—Antebellum (FR) **Duke of Bedford**
5 **QUEMADA (IRE),** 4, b f Teofilo (IRE)—Quanzhou (FR) **Haras De La Perelle**
6 **RECOVER ME (FR),** 4, gr f Fastnet Rock (AUS)—Marie Rossa **Suc. De Moratalla**

MR ALAIN DE ROYER-DUPRE - Continued

   7 SHAHNAZA (FR), 4, b f Azamour (IRE)—Shanndiyra (IRE) **S.A. Aga Khan**
   8 SHAMDOR (FR), 4, b c Kendargent (FR)—Shamiyra (FR) **Pierre-Yves Lefevre**
   9 SHANAKEE (FR), 6, b g Dalakhani (IRE)—Bocanegra (IRE) **Alain de Royer Dupre**
10 SHENDELIYA (FR), 4, b f Pivotal—Shemiyla (FR) **S.A. Aga Khan**
11 VADAVAR (FR), 4, b c Redoute's Choice (AUS)—Vadapolina (FR)
12 VAZIRABAD (FR), 7, b g Manduro (GER)—Visorama (IRE) **H.H. Aga Khan**
13 ZABADANI (FR), 4, b c Myboycharlie (IRE)—Zayanida (IRE) **S.A. Aga Khan**

THREE-YEAR-OLDS

14 ASHAMYA (FR), b f Nathaniel (IRE)—Asharna (IRE) **S.A. Aga Khan**
15 ASHTARA (USA), b f Gio Ponti (USA)—Ashiyla (FR) **S.A. Aga Khan**
16 AVAITRESS (IRE), gr f Shamardal (USA)—Manerbe (USA) **LNJ Foxwoods SC**
17 BALKA (FR), gr f Mastercraftsman (IRE)—Balankiyla (FR) **S.A. Aga Khan**
18 BELSANNDI (FR), b c Sinndar (IRE)—Starboard Beam (IRE) **S.A. Aga Khan**
19 CANNDANA (IRE), ch f Motivator—Candara (FR) **H.H. Aga Khan**
20 CREALA (GER), b f Sea The Stars (IRE)—Celenza (FR) **Haras De La Perelle**
21 DALIGAR (FR), b c Invincible Spirit (IRE)—Dalkala (USA) **S.A. Aga Khan**
22 DALKEYA (FR), gr f Exceed And Excel (AUS)—Daltama (IRE) **S.A. Aga Khan**
23 DARENDA (FR), b f Siyouni (FR)—Darenjana (FR) **Princess Zahra Aga Khan**
24 DARIYMA (FR), b f City Zip (USA)—Darma (FR) **S.A. Aga Khan**
25 DARIYZA (FR), ch f Dawn Approach (IRE)—Daryakana (FR) **S.A. Aga Khan**
26 EDISA (USA), ch f Kitten's Joy (USA)—Ebiyza (IRE) **S.A. Aga Khan**
27 GOLDEN BOX (USA), ch f Kitten's Joy (USA)—Gold Round (IRE) **LNJ Foxwoods SC**
28 GRACE SPIRIT, b f Invincible Spirit (IRE)—Gracefully (IRE) **Haras De La Perelle**
29 KOTAYA (FR), gr f Mastercraftsman (IRE)—Kozaka (FR) **S.A. Aga Khan**
30 LOPEVEGAS (FR), ch c Lope de Vega (IRE)—Elle Same **Rashit Shaykhutdinov**
31 MANDANI (FR), ch c Pivotal—Mandesha (FR) **Princess Zahra Aga Khan**
32 MIRANN (FR), b c Motivator—Mila (FR) **H.H. Aga Khan**
33 MYTHIC (FR), b f Camelot—Gyrella (IRE) **Ecurie des Charmes**
34 NIRMALI (FR), b c Invincible Spirit (IRE)—Narniyn (FR) **S.A. Aga Khan**
35 RAYAPOUR (FR), b c Mastercraftsman (IRE)—Radiyya (IRE) **H.H. Aga Khan**
36 REGNANTE, b f Iffraaj—Reggane **Haras De La Perelle**
37 RESTLESS (FR), b f Le Havre (IRE)—Reine Zao (FR) **Haras De La Perelle**
38 RIAZANA (FR), gr f Sinndar (IRE)—Rosawa (FR) **H.H. Aga Khan**
39 ROSEYA (FR), b f Invincible Spirit (IRE)—Rosanara (FR) **H.H. Aga Khan**
40 SAMEER (FR), b c Nathaniel (IRE)—Sanabyra (FR) **S.A. Aga Khan**
41 SANARY, gr c Invincible Spirit (IRE)—Sagawara **H.H. Aga Khan**
42 SARTAJ (USA), b br c Giant's Causeway (USA)—Sarkiyla (FR) **S.A. Aga Khan**
43 SHAMIYLA (FR), b f Kingman—Shamakiya (IRE) **S.A. Aga Khan**
44 SHANNDOURA (FR), b f Oasis Dream—Shamanova (FR) **S.A. Aga Khan**
45 SHANNKIYR (USA), b c Elusive Quality (USA)—Shankardeh (IRE) **S.A. Aga Khan**
46 SHARGHANN (FR), b c Sea The Stars (IRE)—Shareta (FR) **H.H. Aga Khan**
47 SHIRDIYA (FR), b f Siyouni (FR)—Shivana (FR) **S.A. Aga Khan**
48 SIYARAFINA (FR), b f Pivotal—Siyenica (FR) **H.H. Aga Khan**
49 SULTANPOUR (FR), b c Pivotal—Soriya (FR) **H.H. Aga Khan**
50 VALEYA (FR), gr f Mastercraftsman (IRE)—Valdiyana (FR) **S.A. Aga Khan**
51 VANANNDI (FR), ch c Siyouni (FR)—Vadapolina (FR) **H.H. Aga Khan**
52 VARIYANN (FR), b c Shamardal (USA)—Vazira (FR) **H.H. Aga Khan**
53 VERIMLI (FR), b g Born To Sea (IRE)—Verriya (FR) **S.A. Aga Khan**
54 VORASHANN (FR), b g Sinndar (IRE)—Visorama (IRE) **H.H. Aga Khan**
55 ZARKALLANI (FR), b c Invincible Spirit (IRE)—Zarkava (IRE) **S.A. Aga Khan**
56 ZERKOUR (FR), gr c Oasis Dream—Zerkaza (IRE) **S.A. Aga Khan**

TWO-YEAR-OLDS

57 B f 9/2 Le Havre (IRE)—Afsheen (FR) (Invincible Spirit (IRE)) **S.A. Aga Khan**
58 B f 21/4 Dawn Approach (IRE)—Candara (FR) (Barathea (IRE)) **H.H. Aga Khan**
59 B f 24/3 American Pharoah (USA)—Dalayna (FR) (Anabaa (USA)) **S.A. Aga Khan**
60 B f 29/1 Le Havre (IRE)—Daradiyna (FR) (Sea The Stars (IRE)) **S.A. Aga Khan**
61 B f 12/5 Golden Horn—Daryakana (FR) (Selkirk (USA)) **S.A. Aga Khan**
62 B c 3/2 Dubawi (IRE)—Dolniya (FR) (Azamour (IRE)) **S.A. Aga Khan**
63 B f 26/2 Distorted Humor (USA)—Ebiyza (IRE) (Rock of Gibraltar (IRE)) **S.A. Aga Khan**
64 B c 30/3 Siyouni (FR)—Kasatana (IRE) (Hernando (FR)) **S.A. Aga Khan**
65 B f 9/3 Reliable Man—Kastelliya (FR) (Elusive City (USA)) **S.A. Aga Khan**

MR ALAIN DE ROYER-DUPRE - Continued

66 B c 8/4 Siyouni (FR)—Kataniya (IRE) (Raven's Pass (USA)) **S.A. Aga Khan**
67 B f 9/4 Siyouni (FR)—Mandesha (FR) (Desert Style (IRE)) **Princess Zahra Aga Khan**
68 B c 15/3 Exceed And Excel (AUS)—Mila (FR) (Cape Cross (IRE)) **H.H. Aga Khan**
69 B f 7/3 Iffraaj (FR)—Minya (IRE) (Sinndar (IRE)) **H.H. Aga Khan**
70 B f 25/4 Dawn Approach (IRE)—Radiyya (FR) (Sinndar (IRE)) **H.H. Aga Khan**
71 B c 29/1 Speightstown (USA)—Sarkiyla (FR) (Oasis Dream) **S.A. Aga Khan**
72 B f 28/2 Dawn Approach (IRE)—Shamakiya (IRE) (Intikhab (USA)) **S.A. Aga Khan**
73 B c 29/1 Mastercraftsman (IRE)—Shanndiyra (IRE) (King's Best (USA)) **S.A. Aga Khan**
74 B c 24/2 Sea The Stars (IRE)—Shemiyla (IRE) (Dalakhani (IRE)) **S.A. Aga Khan**
75 B f 28/4 Invincible Spirit (IRE)—Siyenica (FR) (Azamour (IRE)) **H.H. Aga Khan**
76 B f 2/4 Invincible Spirit (IRE)—Soriya (FR) (Azamour (IRE)) **H.H. Aga Khan**
77 B f 2/2 Pivotal—Varana (FR) (Sea The Stars (IRE)) **H.H. Aga Khan**
78 B c 31/3 Dansili—Vazira (FR) (Sea The Stars (IRE)) **H.H. Aga Khan**
79 B f 19/4 Sea The Stars (IRE)—Veda (FR) (Dansili) **H.H. Aga Khan**
80 B c 19/2 Mastercraftsman (IRE)—Verriya (FR) (Zamindar (USA)) **S.A. Aga Khan**
81 B c 7/2 Mastercraftsman (IRE)—Visinova (FR) (Anabaa (USA)) **H.H. Aga Khan**
82 B c 4/4 Charm Spirit (IRE)—Visorama (IRE) (Linamix (FR)) **H.H. Aga Khan**
83 B c 7/4 Born To Sea (IRE)—Zaidiyna (IRE) (Azamour (IRE)) **S.A. Aga Khan**
84 **ZAYKAVA (FR),** b f 21/3 Siyouni (FR)—Zarkava (IRE) (Zamindar (USA)) **S.A. Aga Khan**
85 B c 22/4 Sea The Stars (IRE)—Zerkaza (IRE) (Dalakhani (IRE)) **S.A. Aga Khan**

---

478 | **MS LUCINDA RUSSELL, Kinross**
Postal: **Arlary House Stables, Milnathort, Kinross, Tayside, KY13 9SJ**
Contacts: **PHONE** (01577) 865512 **FAX** (01577) 861171 **MOBILE** (07970) 645261
E-MAIL lucindarussellracing@outlook.com **WEBSITE** www.lucindarussell.com

1 **AIN'T MY FAULT (IRE),** 6, b g Beneficial—Coolnasneachta (IRE) **Foresight Racing**
2 **ALIZEE DE JANEIRO (FR),** 9, b m Network (GER)—Katana (GER) **Ms D. Thomson**
3 **ARIZONA BOUND (IRE),** 7, b g Presenting—Loyal Gesture (IRE) **Kelso Lowflyers & Mr PJS Russell**
4 **ASK THE TYCOON (IRE),** 6, b g Ask—Mountainviewqueen (IRE) **Mrs S Russell & A M Russell**
5 **AURORA THUNDER,** 5, b m Malinas (GER)—Ninna Nanna (FR) **Allson Sparkle Ltd**
6 **BEHINDTHELINES (IRE),** 7, b g Milan—Sunset Leader (IRE) **London Scots for Doddie**
7 **BIALCO (FR),** 8, gr g Dom Alco (FR)—Lacanale (FR) **Mr M. Buskop**
8 **BIG RIVER (IRE),** 9, b g Milan—Call Kate (IRE) **Two Black Labs**
9 **BLAYDON (IRE),** 6, b g Milan—Pretty Impressive (IRE) **Mrs S Russell & A M Russell**
10 **BLOORIEDOTCOM (IRE),** 4, b g Holy Roman Emperor (IRE)—Peaceful Kingdom (USA) **Mr P. J. S. Russell**
11 **BOLLINGERANDKRUG (IRE),** 4, b g Getaway (GER)—Out Performer (IRE) **Ms D. Thomson**
12 **BOY'S ON TOUR (IRE),** 7, b g Beneficial—Galant Tour (IRE) **Foresight Racing**
13 **BUDDHA SCHEME (IRE),** 5, b g Milan—Benefit Scheme (IRE) **Mr G. R. McGladery**
14 **CATCHTHEMOONLIGHT,** 11, b m Generous (IRE)—Moon Catcher (IRE) **Dig In Racing**
15 **CELTIC FLAMES (IRE),** 9, gr g Celtic Swing—Don't Forget Shoka (IRE) **Mr W. T. Scott**
16 **CHANCEITON (IRE),** 8, b g Vinnie Roe (IRE)—Lissnabrucka (IRE) **Mr P. J. S. Russell**
17 **CHARMIX (FR),** 9, br g Laveron—Open Up (FR) **Mr J. Fyffe**
18 **COCKLE BAY (IRE),** 7, b g Milan—Theredandthegreen (IRE) **The Kestrel Partnership**
19 **CRUMBS,** 5, gr g Fair Mix (IRE)—Granary House **The Crumpets**
20 **DEEPSAND (IRE),** 10, br g Footstepsinthesand—Sinamay (USA) **Mrs B. V. Evans**
21 **DEVITO'SGOLDENGIRL (IRE),** 8, b m Gold Well—Caracool (FR) **County Set Five & Peter J S Russell**
22 **DR HOOVES (IRE),** 6, b g Yeats (IRE)—Sejour (IRE) **Mr G. R. McGladery**
23 **DRAGONHOV (FR),** 6, b g Dragon Dancer—Kalistina (FR) **Miss A. Bramall**
24 **EFFET SPECIAL (FR),** 5, b g Network (GER)—Tisane (FR) **Brahms & Liszt**
25 **ELMONO (FR),** 8, ch g Epalo (GER)—Monareva (FR) **Gerry And The Pacemakers**
26 **EMIRAT DE CATANA (FR),** 5, b g Linda's Lad—Kolada (FR) **British Racing Club**
27 **EMISSAIRE (FR),** 5, b g Kap Rock (FR)—Jacee (FR) **A Nicol & L S Russell**
28 **EXIT TO WHERE (FR),** 5, b g Kapgarde (FR)—Rapsodie Sea (FR) **Mr & Mrs Raymond Anderson Green**
29 **FINAL ASSAULT (IRE),** 10, b br g Beneficial—Last Campaign (IRE) **Mrs S Russell & A M Russell**
30 **FLUTTER DOWN (FR),** 4, b g Rob Roy (USA)—Florifere (FR) **Peter & Suzy Brown & Tony Evans**
31 **FOREST DES AIGLES (FR),** 8, b g Balko (FR)—Rose des Aigles (FR) **Mr & Mrs Raymond Anderson Green**
32 **GARS BAR DINE (FR),** 8, b g Martaline—Treekle Toffee (FR) **Miss A. Bramall**
33 **GLENPARK (FR),** 4, b g Enrique—Sweet Jaune (FR) **Patrick & Scott Bryceland**
34 **GRAND MORNING,** 7, b g Midnight Legend—Valentines Lady (IRE) **Mr J. P. McManus**
35 **GRIPPER,** 4, b g Thewayyouare (USA)—Hold On Tight (IRE) **Mr P. J. S. Russell**
36 **HIGHLAND HUNTER (IRE),** 6, gr g Subtle Power (IRE)—Loughine Sparkle (IRE) **T. Barr**
37 **ISLAND HEIGHTS (IRE),** 10, b g Heron Island (IRE)—La Reina (IRE) **Mr G. R. McGladery**

MS LUCINDA RUSSELL - Continued

38 **IZZY'S CHAMPION (IRE)**, 5, b g Gold Well—Native Crystal (IRE) **Mr & Mrs T. P. Winnell**
39 **KATALYSTIC (IRE)**, 8, br g Kalanisi (IRE)—Beltane Queen (IRE) **Mr R. B. H. Young**
40 **KELPIES MYTH**, 6, b g Dutch Art—Miss Respect **Bolton, McGladery, Duncan & Buchanan**
41 **KILBREE CHIEF (IRE)**, 11, b g Dr Massini (IRE)—Lame Excuse (IRE) **Mr J. R. Adam**
42 **LE FRANK (IRE)**, 7, b g King's Theatre (IRE)—Dream Lass (IRE) **Mr S. Smith**
43 **LOOKS LIKE MURT (IRE)**, 6, b g Well Chosen—Ninetypenceapound (IRE) **Mr J. R. Adam**
44 **LOST FREQUENCY (IRE)**, 7, b g Yeats (IRE)—Lauderdale (GER) **The County Set Three**
45 **MAKE IT HAPPEN (IRE)**, 10, b g Saffron Walden (FR)—Kelpie (IRE) **Wright Mitchell**
46 **MANNOCHMORE**, 4, b g Dylan Thomas (IRE)—Loch Dhu (IRE) **Distillery Racing Club**
47 **MARAWEH (IRE)**, 9, b g Muhtathir—Itqaan (USA) **Mr P. J. S. Russell**
48 **MAX LIEBERMANN (IRE)**, 5, b g Galileo (IRE)—Anna Karenina (IRE) **Mr G. R. McGladery**
49 **METHODTOTHEMADNESS (IRE)**, 5, b m Gold Well—Odeeka (IRE) **Mrs S Russell & A M Russell**
50 **MIGHTY THUNDER**, 6, b g Malinas (GER)—Cool Island (IRE) **Allson Sparkle Ltd**
51 **MINT GOLD (IRE)**, 5, b g Gold Well—Lady Flyer (IRE) **Mrs S Russell & A M Russell**
52 **MISFITS (IRE)**, 8, b g Beneficial—Park Rose (IRE) **County Set Four & Keith Hunter**
53 **MISS BATTEN (IRE)**, 5, b m Vinnie Roe (IRE)—Awesome Miracle (IRE) **Mr K. Alexander**
54 **MON AMI (IRE)**, 8, ch g Schiaparelli (GER)—Maid of Perth **R. F. Gibbons**
55 **MORITO DU BERLAIS (FR)**, 10, b g Turgeon (USA)—Chica du Berlais (FR) **British Racing Club**
56 **MR GRUMPY**, 6, b g Sir Percy—Panna **County Set & Kendall Stewart Johnston**
57 **MR TOASTIE**, 4, b g Brian Boru—Granary House **Major A. R. Trotter**
58 **MUMGOS DEBUT (IRE)**, 11, b g Royal Anthem (USA)—Black Queen (IRE) **Mrs Suzy Brown & Mr Peter R Brown**
59 **ONE FOR ARTHUR (IRE)**, 10, b g Milan—Nonnetia (FR) **Two Golf Widows**
60 **ORIONINVERNESS (IRE)**, 8, b g Brian Boru—Woodville Leader (IRE) **Tay Valley Chasers Racing Club**
61 **OTELLO MOOR (IRE)**, 4, b g Milan—Founding Daughter (IRE) **Mrs R. A. Stobart**
62 **PARKER (IRE)**, 5, b g Cape Cross (IRE)—Mount Elbrus **Champagne Charlies Club**
63 **PINSPOT**, 5, ch g Presenting—Amber Cloud **Mr Michael & Lady Jane Kaplan**
64 **PRESENT FLIGHT (IRE)**, 10, ch g Presenting—Grangeclare Flight (IRE) **Mr G. R. McGladery**
65 **PRINCE DUNDEE (IRE)**, 6, b g Stowaway—Miss Dundee (IRE) **Jw McNeill & County Set Three**
66 **REVOCATION**, 11, b g Revoque (IRE)—Fenella **Mr Michael & Lady Jane Kaplan**
67 **RISING MARIENBARD (IRE)**, 7, b g Marienbard (IRE)—Dromkeen Wood **Mrs R. A. Stobart**
68 **RIVABODIVA (IRE)**, 9, ch m Flemensfirth (USA)—Sheebadiva (IRE) **Mrs S Russell & A M Russell**
69 **ROSSAMILAN (IRE)**, 8, b g Milan—Beautiful Blue (IRE) **Mr D. W. Ross**
70 **ROYAL RESERVE**, 6, b g Duke of Marmalade (IRE)—Lady Hawkfield (IRE) **London Scots for Doddie**
71 **RUN ROCKY RUN (IRE)**, 6, b g Vertical Speed (FR)—Marlatara (IRE) **County Set & Kendall Stewart Johnston**
72 **RYALEX (IRE)**, 8, b g Arcadio (GER)—Lady Ramona (IRE) **County Set Five & Keith Hunter**
73 **SAINT FREULE (FR)**, 6, br g Saint des Saints (FR)—Topsy Blue (FR) **Mr K. Alexander**
74 **SAMMY B**, 9, br g Overbury (IRE)—This Thyne **G. S. Brown**
75 **SEVEN DEVILS (IRE)**, 9, b g Definite Article—Top Lot (IRE) **Mrs S Russell & A M Russell**
76 **SHANROE STREET (IRE)**, 9, b g Mustameet (USA)—Zaffran Lady (IRE) **Netherfield House Stud**
77 **SKY KHAN**, 10, b g Cape Cross (IRE)—Starlit Sky **The Ormello Way**
78 **SLAINTE MHOR (IRE)**, 5, b g Milan—Founding Daughter (IRE) **Mr P. J. S. Russell**
79 **SPEAK OF THE DEVIL (IRE)**, 6, ch g Mahler—A Fine Romance (IRE) **Mr P. J. S. Russell**
80 **SUTTON MANOR (IRE)**, 8, b g Gold Well—Nighty Bless (IRE) **Mr P. J. S. Russell**
81 **TANTAMOUNT**, 10, b g Observatory (USA)—Cantanta **Mutual Friends**
82 **TARSET HINNY (IRE)**, 4, ch f Presenting—Avondhu Lady (IRE) **Mr & Mrs J. Morrison-Bell**
83 **THE BANASTOIR (IRE)**, 10, b br g Presenting—Kimouna (FR) **Mr P. J. S. Russell**
84 **THE COMPELLER (IRE)**, 7, b g Lawman (FR)—Mark Too (IRE) **W M D Racing**
85 **THE ROAD HOME (IRE)**, 7, b g Oscar (IRE)—In Fact (IRE) **Mrs S Russell & A M Russell**
86 **THEPENSIONFUND (IRE)**, 7, b g Big Bad Bob (IRE)—Whizz **Gerry & the Jocks**
87 **THORPE (IRE)**, 9, b g Danehill Dancer (IRE)—Minkova (IRE) **Mr Michael & Lady Jane Kaplan**
88 **TIMESAWAITING (IRE)**, 6, b g Arakan (USA)—Princess Nicole (IRE) **Goodtimes**
89 **TOUCHEDBYANANGEL (IRE)**, 7, gr g Beneficial—Gray's Anatomy (IRE) **Tay Valley Chasers Racing Club**
90 **URBAN KODE (IRE)**, 11, b g Kodiac—Urbanize (USA) **Suzy Brown, John Baird, Tony Evans**
91 **VENGEUR DE GUYE (FR)**, 10, b g Dom Alco (FR)—Mascotte de Guye (FR) **Brahms & Liszt**
92 **VOIX D'EAU (FR)**, 9, b g Voix du Nord (FR)—Eau de Chesne (FR) **Mr J Fyffe & Mr Gerry McGladery**
93 **WELL ABOVE PAR (IRE)**, 7, b g Gold Well—Glynn Glory (IRE) **The Eagle Partnership**
94 **WHERE'S PHOENIX**, 5, b g Phoenix Reach—Ceiriog Valley **Mr P. J. S. Russell**

THREE-YEAR-OLDS

95 **DIAMOND STATE (FR)**, b g Vision d'etat (FR)—Wonderful Diamond (GER) **Mr P. J. S. Russell**
96 **FONTCOMBEAU (FR)**, ch g Kapgarde (FR)—La Ville Aux Dames (FR) **Mr P. J. S. Russell**
97 **SPARK OF MADNESS (FR)**, b g Walk In The Park (IRE)—Prosopopee (FR) **Mrs S Russell & A M Russell**
98 B c Dylan Thomas (IRE)—Zarata (IRE) **Mr P. J. S. Russell**

MS LUCINDA RUSSELL - Continued

Other Owners: Mr W. Agnew, Mr W. M. Allan, Mr J. B. Baird, Mrs S. Brown, Mr P. R. Brown, Mr G. R. Brown, C. Bryce, Mr S. Bryceland, Mr P. Bryceland, A. Cadger, The County Set, The County Set (Five), County Set Four, Mr N. A. Crofts, Mr A. B. Cuthill, Mr H. J. Davies, Mr C. Dempster, Mr E. W. Dempster, Mr R. Doak, Mr A. S. Duncan, Mr A. Evans, Mr R. J. Fowler, Mrs B. S. Fowler, Mr A. T. Galloway, Gilbert McClung (Kelso) Ltd, G. Godsman, E. Graham, Mrs I. M. Grant, Mrs A. Green, R. A. Green, E. D. Haggart, Mr C. D. Harrison, K. L. Hunter, Mr D. R. James, Mrs P. James, Mr J. A. Johnston, Kelso Members Lowflyers Club, Mr T. S. Kendall, Mr A. Kerr, Mrs C. J. Lamb, Mr R. M. Landale, Mrs Y. M. V. Learmonth, Mr J. S. Lessells, M. W. Lightbody, Mrs J. Lightbody, Ms A. M. MacInnes, Mr J. W. McNeill, Mr M. G. Mellor, Mr J. Mitchell, Mrs K. A. Morrison-Bell, Mr J. Morrison-Bell, Mr A. G. Nicol, Racing Club Ltd, R. Robinson, Mr A. M. Russell, Ms L. V. Russell, Mrs S. C. Russell, Mr L. S. Russell, A. W. Sinclair, Ms P. Spours, T Kendall VM Stewart J Johnston, Mr P. A. Taylor, Mr N. J. Turnbull, Mr T. P. Winnell, Mrs M. Winnell, Mr D. J. Gordon Wright.

Assistant Trainers: Peter Scudamore, Jamie Turnbull, Jaimie Duff

Jockey (NH): Derek Fox. **Conditional:** Blair Campbell, Stephen Mulqueen, Thomas Willmott.
Amateur: Mr Patrick Wadge, Mr Cameron Wadge.

---

479   MR JOHN RYAN, Newmarket
Postal: **Cadland Stables, Moulton Road, Newmarket, Suffolk, CB8 8DU**
Contacts: PHONE **(01638) 664172** MOBILE **(07739) 801235**
E-MAIL **john.ryan@jryanracing.com** WEBSITE **www.jryanracing.com** Twitter: **@JohnRyanRacing**

1 AIRCRAFT CARRIER (IRE), 4, b c Declaration of War (USA)—Strategy **Mr J. F. Stocker**
2 BATTLE OF MARATHON (USA), 7, b g War Front (USA)—Sayedah (IRE) **Mrs E. Ryan**
3 BOOK OF INVASIONS (IRE), 4, ch g Declaration of War (USA)—Cedar Sea (IRE) **Mr G. R. McGladery**
4 CAPTIVATING LIGHT, 4, b f Harbour Watch (IRE)—Enthralled **Mr J. B. Ryan**
5 DON'T THINK SO (IRE), 4, b g So You Think (NZ)—Lady Sefton **Mr G. R. McGladery**
6 GREY BRITAIN, 5, gr g Arcano (IRE)—Reaching Ahead (USA) **Mr G. F. Smith-Bernal**
7 LADY FREYJA, 5, b m Mayson—Third Party **Mr J. A. Thompson**
8 MERHOOB (IRE), 7, b g Cape Cross (IRE)—Lady Slippers (IRE) **Mr G. R. McGladery**
9 MIDNIGHT WILDE, 4, gr g Poet's Voice—Si Belle (IRE) **Mr J. A. Thompson**
10 MUTABARREJA (IRE), 4, b f Sea The Stars (IRE)—Directa Princess (GER)
11 NEEDS TO BE SEEN (FR), 4, b g Motivator—Morning Line (FR) **Mr J Fyffe & Mr Gerry McGladery**
12 NORMAL NORMAN, 5, ch g Shamardal (USA)—Ambria (GER) **Mr G. R. McGladery**
13 PLUCKY DIP, 8, b g Nayef (USA)—Plucky Me **Mr J. B. Ryan**
14 QUEEN ADELAIDE, 4, b f Helmet (AUS)—Spunger **BB Bloodstock**
15 SEVENNA STAR (IRE), 4, b c Redoute's Choice (AUS)—Sevenna (FR) **Mr G. F. Smith-Bernal**
16 SPENNY'S LASS, 4, br f Bated Breath—Midnight Hush (FR) **Mr M. Firth**
17 TENOR (IRE), 9, b g Oratorio (IRE)—Cedar Sea (IRE) **Mr G. R. McGladery**
18 THUNDERHOOVES, 4, ro g Raven's Pass (USA)—Regrette Rien (USA) **Mr G. R. McGladery**

THREE-YEAR-OLDS

19 BATTLE OF WATERLOO (IRE), b g Big Bad Bob (IRE)—Anything (IRE) **Mr G. R. McGladery**
20 BELLA BELUGA, br f Nathaniel (IRE)—Move **Mr G. F. Smith-Bernal**
21 CATCH MY BREATH, ch g Bated Breath—Likeable **The Out of Puff Partnership**
22 FACETHEPUCKOUT (IRE), b c Excelebration (IRE)—Taarkod (IRE) **Mr J. F. Stocker**
23 HIROSHIMA, b c Nathaniel (IRE)—Lisiere (IRE) **Mr G. F. Smith-Bernal**
24 JASMINE B (IRE), ch f Exceed And Excel (AUS)—Fashionable **John Ryan Racing Partnership**
25 LITTLE TIPPLE, b f Gregorian (IRE)—Back On Baileys **Emma Ryan & Partner**
26 PRINCESS FLORENCE (IRE), b f Zebedee—Villa Nova (IRE) **BB Bloodstock**
27 SANDRIDGE LAD (IRE), b g Equiano (FR)—Quixada (GER) **Mr J. F. Stocker**
28 SHINING ARMOR, b g Morpheus—Kenyan Cat **Mr G. R. McGladery**

TWO-YEAR-OLDS

29 FLUTTERSHY, ch f 2/3 Roderic O'Connor (IRE)—
    Twilight Sparkle (IRE) (Rock of Gibraltar (IRE)) **Mr G. R. McGladery**
30 HOMEGROWNALLIGATOR, b c 14/5 Poet's Voice—Samar Qand (Selkirk (USA)) (1000) **Mr J. A. Thompson**
31 SEA OF COOL (IRE), b c 22/1 Sea The Stars (IRE)—
    Magh Meall (Monsieur Bond (IRE)) (35000) **Mr G. F. Smith-Bernal**

Other Owners: DAS Racing Limited, Mr J. Fyffe, Mrs L. M. Lambert, Mr S. D. Russell, Mrs J. Williams.

Apprentice: Laura Pearson. **Amateur:** Mr Thomas Miles.

480 MR KEVIN RYAN, Hambleton

Postal: Hambleton Lodge, Hambleton, Thirsk, North Yorkshire, YO7 2HA
Contacts: PHONE Office (01845) 597010 / (01845) 597622 FAX (01845) 597622
MOBILE (07768) 016930
E-MAIL kevin.hambleton@virgin.net WEBSITE www.kevinryanracing.com

1 ALKHAWANEEJ BOY (IRE), 4, b c Elzaam (AUS)—Kaplinsky (IRE) Ahmad Al Shaikh
2 AYUTTHAYA (IRE), 4, ch g Lope de Vega (IRE)—Pivotal Role JCG Chua & CK Ong 1
3 BEYOND THE CLOUDS, 6, ch g Peintre Celebre (USA)—Evening Guy Reed Racing
4 BIELSA (IRE), 4, b c Invincible Spirit (IRE)—Bourbon Ball (USA) Highbank Stud
5 BILLY RUSKIN, 4, b g Bahamian Bounty—Fluffy K&J Bloodstock Ltd
6 BIN MAKFI, 4, b g Makfi—Sayyedati Storm (USA) Miss E J Butterworth & Partner
7 BRANDO, 7, ch g Pivotal—Argent du Bois Mrs Angie Bailey
8 BRILLIANT VANGUARD (IRE), 6, b g Fast Company (IRE)—Alyska (IRE) JCG Chua & CK Ong
9 COMMANDER HAN (FR), 4, ch g Siyouni (FR)—Acentela (IRE) Mr T. A. Rahman
10 DANDY'S BEANO (IRE), 4, ch f Dandy Man (IRE)—Hear My Cry (USA) Hambleton Racing Ltd XLVII
11 ERIK THE RED (FR), 7, b g Kendargent (FR)—Norwegian Princess (IRE) Mr F. Gillespie
12 EVERYTHING FOR YOU (IRE), 5, b g Pivotal—Miss Delila (USA) Mr T. A. Rahman
13 FOXY LADY, 4, b f Foxwedge—Catherine Palace K&J Bloodstock Ltd
14 GOLD STONE, 4, b f Havana Gold (IRE)—Slatey Hen (IRE) Mrs J. Ryan
15 HEY JONESY (IRE), 4, b g Excelebration (IRE)—Fikrah Pallister Racing
16 KAJAKI (IRE), 6, gr g Mastercraftsman (IRE)—No Quest (IRE) Mr F. Gillespie
17 KNIGHTED (IRE), 4, b g Sir Prancealot (IRE)—Olympia Theatre Highclere T'bred Racing- Nick Skelton
18 KODICAT (IRE), 5, b m Kodiac—Mimiteh (USA) Reilly JDM Holdings Ltd
19 LUALIWA, 5, b g Foxwedge (AUS)—Sunpearl Mrs Rosie Richer
20 MAJOR JUMBO, 5, gr g Zebedee—Gone Sailing Mr T. A. Rahman
21 MONT KINABALU (IRE), 4, b g Society Rock (IRE)—Startori JCG Chua & CK Ong 1
22 MORNING WONDER (IRE), 4, ch g Dawn Approach (IRE)—Mount Elbrus Mr Sultan Ali
23 MOUNT TAHAN (IRE), 7, b g Lope de Vega (IRE)—Sorpresa (USA) Mr T. A. Rahman
24 NAADIRR (IRE), 8, b g Oasis Dream—Beach Bunny (IRE) Middleham Park Racing XXX
25 ORIENTATE, 4, b f Equiano (FR)—Classic Vision Hambleton Racing XXV & Manor Farm Stud
26 PENNSYLVANIA DUTCH, 5, b g Dutch Art—Map of Heaven K&J Bloodstock Ltd
27 QUEEN'S SARGENT (FR), 4, gr g Kendargent (FR)—Queen's Conquer Mr Dave Stone
28 SAVALAS (IRE), 4, gr g Zebedee—Tap The Dot (IRE) Mrs Angie Bailey
29 SCRUTINY, 8, b g Aqlaam—Aunty Mary Miss E. J. Butterworth
30 STORMBRINGER, 4, b g Dutch Art—Riva Royale Mr Charles Wentworth
31 TAGUR (IRE), 5, ch g Tagula (IRE)—Westcote (USA) Andy Turton & John Blackburn
32 TOMMY TAYLOR (USA), 5, b g Mizzen Mast (USA)—Sharp Apple (USA) Mrs Angie Bailey

THREE-YEAR-OLDS

33 AGHAST, b f Bated Breath—Classic Vision Manor Farm Stud & Mr John E. Rose
34 ALOYSIUS LILIUS (IRE), b g Gregorian (IRE)—Nafa (IRE) K&J Bloodstock Ltd
35 AROGO, b g Iffraaj—Chocolate Hills (FR) Mrs Angie Bailey
36 BALDWIN (IRE), b g Moohaajim (IRE)—Cheherazad (IRE) Mrs Angie Bailey & Partner
37 BATTLE OF YARMOUK (IRE), ch c Lope de Vega (IRE)—Spesialta Mr T. A. Rahman
38 CAMBELEZA (IRE), b g Camacho—Blessed Beauty (IRE) Hambleton Racing Ltd XXIX
39 CAPTAIN COMBAT (FR), ch c French Fifteen (FR)—Lasdramad (FR) Mr T. A. Rahman
40 CELEBRITY DANCER (IRE), ch g Excelebration (IRE)—Dance Hall Girl (IRE) Hambleton Racing Ltd XXII
41 CONGA, ch f Footstepsinthesand—Palais Glide Guy Reed Racing
42 EAST, ch f Frankel—Vital Statistics East Partners
43 EMARAATY ANA, b c Shamardal (USA)—Spirit of Dubai (IRE) Sheikh Mohammed Obaid Al Maktoum
44 EVANGELINE SAMOS, b f Foxwedge (AUS)—Vive Les Rouges K&J Bloodstock Ltd
45 GEORGE MALLORY, b g Kingman—Rose Et Noire (IRE) Mr F. Gillespie
46 GIACOMO CASANOVA (IRE), b c Es Que Love (IRE)—Off Stage (IRE) Giacomo Casanova Partners
47 GLASS SLIPPERS, b f Dream Ahead (USA)—Night Gypsy Bearstone Stud Limited
48 HELLO YOUMZAIN (IRE), b c Kodiac—Spasha Mr Jaber Abdullah
49 HURRICANE SPEED (IRE), ch g Gale Force Ten—Ma Nikitia (IRE) Hambleton Racing Ltd XXXI & Partner
50 JOEY BOY (IRE), b g Zebedee—Lady Day Royale Racing Syndicate & Partner
51 LAST EMPIRE, b f Pivotal—Final Dynasty Clipper Logistics
52 LAULLOIR (IRE), ch f More Than Ready (USA)—Legs Lawlor (USA) K&J Bloodstock Ltd
53 LAURIER (USA), b br f Scat Daddy (USA)—Abundantly Blessed (USA) Laurier Partners
54 LILLE, b f Equiano (FR)—Interlace Lille Partners
55 MAGICAL SPIRIT (IRE), ch g Zebedee—La Dame de Fer (IRE) Hambleton Racing Ltd XXXII
56 MO EMMAD ALI (IRE), b g No Nay Never (USA)—Special Assignment (USA) Mr T. A. Rahman

MR KEVIN RYAN - Continued

57 **PRINCES DES SABLES**, ch f Monsieur Bond (IRE)—Hopes N Dreams (IRE) **JCG Chua & CK Ong**
58 **QUEEN JO JO**, br f Gregorian (IRE)—River Song (USA) **Mr Roger Peel**
59 **RATHBONE**, b g Foxwedge (AUS)—Frequent **Mrs Angie Bailey**
60 **ROULSTON SCAR (IRE)**, b g Lope de Vega (IRE)—Pussycat Lips (IRE) **K&J Bloodstock Ltd**
61 **SECRET VENTURE**, b c Kyllachy—Resort **Clipper Logistics**
62 **SENSE OF BELONGING (FR)**, ch g Dutch Art—Bertie's Best **KRS Partnership**
63 **SHAQWAR**, ch f Sea The Moon (GER)—Majestic Roi (USA) **Mr Jaber Abdullah**
64 **SWINGING EDDIE**, b c Swiss Spirit—Bling Bling (IRE) **Mr T. A. Rahman**
65 **THE GREAT HEIR (FR)**, b c Pedro The Great (USA)—Lady McKell (IRE) **Mr Dave Stone**
66 **THREE CARD TRICK**, ch c Piccolo—Card Games **Guy Reed Racing**
67 **VOICEOFTHEEMIRATES**, b c Showcasing—Makaaseb (USA) **Ahmad Al Shaikh**
68 **VRAI (IRE)**, b f Dark Angel (IRE)—Sogno Verde (IRE) **Mrs R. G. Hillen**
69 **WILD HOPE**, b g Kingman—Wild Mimosa (USA) **Hambleton Racing Ltd XLIV**
70 **YOUSINI**, b g Siyouni (FR)—War Effort (USA) **Middleham Park Racing XXI**

TWO-YEAR-OLDS

71 B f 2/2 Hot Streak (IRE)—Acid (Clodovil (IRE)) (40000) **Mrs Angie Bailey**
72 Br f 26/2 Free Eagle (IRE)—Acquifer (Oasis Dream) (16000) **Mr John M. Troy**
73 **ALYOUM EMARAATY (IRE)**, b c 6/2 Bated Breath—Roseraie (IRE) (Lawman (FR)) (46354) **Ahmad Al Shaikh**
74 B g 25/2 Poet's Voice—Angel Song (Dansili) (10000)
75 **ARABIAN MAIDEN**, b f 9/5 New Approach (IRE)—
          Spirit of Dubai (IRE) (Cape Cross (IRE)) (165000) **Sheikh Mohammed Obaid Al Maktoum**
76 **ARROW OF GOLD (IRE)**, ch c 28/2 Galileo (IRE)—
          Fleche d'or (Dubai Destination (USA)) (450000) **Sheikh Mohammed Obaid Al Maktoum**
77 **BALTIC STATE (IRE)**, b c 21/3 Dandy Man (IRE)—Estonia (Exceed And Excel (AUS)) (37142) **Mr J. C. Fretwell**
78 **BLACK CASPIAN (IRE)**, b c 11/5 Dark Angel (IRE)—
          Catch The Sea (IRE) (Barathea (IRE)) (200000) **Sheikh Mohammed Obaid Al Maktoum**
79 Gr f 25/4 Hot Streak (IRE)—Blue Moon (Trade Fair)
80 **BORN TO GLORY**, b c 16/2 Muhaarar—Dulcet (IRE) (Halling (USA)) (110000) **Ahmad Al Shaikh**
81 **CHARDONEIGH**, b f 23/4 Fountain of Youth (IRE)—
          Razzle (IRE) (Green Desert (USA)) (8571) **Bearstone Stud Limited**
82 B c 10/2 Fountain of Youth (IRE)—Choisette (Choisir (AUS)) (33333) **Middleham Park Racing CVII**
83 **CLEVER TRICK**, b c 22/3 Pivotal—Trick Or Treat (Lomitas) **Mr Peter Onslow**
84 **COAST OF DUBAI (IRE)**, b c 7/4 Elzaam (AUS)—
          Instant Memories (Ad Valorem (USA)) (27619) **Ahmad Al Shaikh**
85 **COAST OFALFUJAIRAH (IRE)**, b c 7/4 Brazen Beau (AUS)—Khameela (Equiano (FR)) (24761) **Ahmad Al Shaikh**
86 Ch f 14/2 Casamento (IRE)—Danega (Galileo (IRE)) **Mr Jaber Abdullah**
87 B c 27/2 Bated Breath—Danlepordamsterdam (IRE) (War Front (USA)) (17699) **Middleham Park Racing XLVI**
88 **DIVINA GLORIA (FR)**, b f 3/4 Dabirsim (FR)—
          Amouage (GER) (Tiger Hill (IRE)) (230000) **Sheikh Mohammed Obaid Al Maktoum**
89 **EVEEAAJ (IRE)**, b f 20/1 Iffraaj—Albaraari (Green Desert (USA)) (25284) **Mr J. Matthews**
90 **GALADRIEL**, b f 28/1 Dutch Art—Handbell (Acclamation) **Sheikh Mohammed Obaid Al Maktoum**
91 **HISTORICAL**, b f 25/3 New Approach (IRE)—
          Joys of Spring (IRE) (Invincible Spirit (USA)) **Sheikh Mohammed Obaid Al Maktoum**
92 **JUAN ELCANO**, ch c 4/4 Frankel—Whatami (Daylami (IRE)) (360000) **Sheikh Mohammed Obaid Al Maktoum**
93 **LADY ERIMUS**, b f 3/3 Due Diligence (USA)—Orapids (Oratorio (IRE)) **Riverside Racing Syndicate**
94 B c 13/2 Dabirsim (FR)—Lady Family (FR) (Sinndar (IRE)) (37926) **Mr Dave Stone**
95 B c 10/2 Shamardal (USA)—Lady of The Desert (USA) (Rahy (USA)) **Mr Jaber Abdullah**
96 B c 15/2 Muhaarar—Lauren Louise (Tagula (IRE)) (140000)
97 B c 8/4 Kodiac—Lututi (IRE) (Kheleyf (USA)) (42857)
98 **MAGICAL MOMENT (FR)**, b f 20/3 Dubawi (IRE)—Maka (IRE) (Slickly (FR)) (170000)
99 B c 28/1 Zoffany (IRE)—Miss Delila (USA) (Malibu Moon (USA)) **Highbank Stud**
100 **OAKENSHIELD (IRE)**, b c 5/3 Invincible Spirit (IRE)—
          War Effort (USA) (War Front (USA)) (200000) **Sheikh Mohammed Obaid Al Maktoum**
101 B f 3/2 Starspangledbanner (AUS)—On The Dark Side (IRE) (Kheleyf (USA)) (40000)
102 **OUT OF HERE (IRE)**, ch c 5/1 G Force (IRE)—Wee Jean (Captain Gerrard (IRE)) (33333) **Mr J. C. Fretwell**
103 B c 6/2 Starspangledbanner (AUS)—Peig (Refuse To Bend (IRE)) (35000) **Hambleton Racing Ltd XXV**
104 B c 10/3 Sir Percy—Princess Aurora (USA) (Mr Greeley (USA)) (35000)
105 B f 9/4 Kyllachy—Readyandaway (USA) (More Than Ready (USA)) (1000) **Highbank Stud**
106 **REPARTEE (IRE)**, br c 4/2 Invincible Spirit (IRE)—
          Pleasantry (Johannesburg (USA)) (310000) **Sheikh Mohammed Obaid Al Maktoum**
107 **RHEA**, ch f 19/4 Siyouni (FR)—
          Titian's Pride (USA) (Giant's Causeway (USA)) (130000) **Sheikh Mohammed Obaid Al Maktoum**
108 B f 12/4 No Nay Never (USA)—Rocking (Oasis Dream) (29498) **Hambleton Racing Ltd XVIII**

MR KEVIN RYAN - Continued

109 B c 16/2 Hot Streak (IRE)—Rohesia (High Chaparral (IRE)) (15238)
110 Ch f 31/3 Mayson—Special Queen (IRE) (Clodovil (IRE)) **Mr Jaber Abdullah**
111 **SWITCHMAN (IRE),** b c 11/5 Lawman (FR)—
            Faraday Light (IRE) (Rainbow Quest (USA)) (290000) **Sheikh Mohammed Obaid Al Maktoum**
112 B f 15/2 Night of Thunder (IRE)—Thames Pageant (Dansili) (14327) **Hambleton Racing Ltd XXXVIII**
113 **VEGA MAGIC (IRE),** b c 23/2 Lope de Vega (IRE)—
            Oriental Magic (GER) (Doyen (IRE)) (140000) **Sheikh Mohammed Obaid Al Maktoum**
114 **YORKSHIRE GOLD,** b c 4/3 Muhaarar—
            Swift Campaign (IRE) (Intikhab (USA)) (160000) **Sheikh Mohammed Obaid Al Maktoum**
115 **ZABEEL KING (IRE),** b c 24/2 Frankel—
            Vital Statistics (Indian Ridge) (337125) **Sheikh Mohammed Obaid Al Maktoum**
116 **ZANY,** ch c 12/3 Zoffany (IRE)—Frivolity (Pivotal) (64761) **Mr J. C. Fretwell**

Other Owners: Mr J. N. Blackburn, Mr C. G. J. Chua, Mr A. Fellowes, Mr G. B. Frankland, Hambleton Racing Ltd, Hambleton Racing Ltd XXXI, Highclere Nominated Partner Limited, Highclere Thoroughbred Racing Ltd, B. E. Holland, Mrs S. Kelly, Manor Farm Stud (Rutland), Mr F. Ong, T. S. Palin, Mrs A. H. Pallister, Mr J. G. Pallister, Mrs J. E. Pallister, M. Prince, J. E. Rose, Royale Racing Syndicate, Mrs L. M. Shanahan, Mr D. M. Standring, Mr S. R. H. Turner, Mr A. Turton, Mr M. A. Wainwright, Mrs I. M. Wainwright, Mr E. Wilson.

Assistant Trainer: Adam Ryan

Jockey (flat): Tom Eaves, Shane Gray, Kevin Stott. **Amateur:** Miss Harriet Lees.

---

481 **MR AYTACH SADIK, Kidderminster**
Postal: **Wolverley Court Coach House, Wolverley, Kidderminster, Worcestershire, DY10 3RP**
Contacts: **PHONE (01562) 852362 MOBILE (07803) 040344**

1 **BURNING SANDS (IRE),** 6, ch g Approve (IRE)—Innishmore (IRE) **A. M. Sadik**
2 **LOPE DE LOOP (IRE),** 4, b f Lope de Vega (IRE)—Patroller (USA) **A. M. Sadik**
3 **SPORTY YANKEE (USA),** 6, gr g Paddy O'prado (USA)—I Insist (USA) **A. M. Sadik**
4 **SUSSEX ROAD (IRE),** 9, b g Mahler—Rose Island **A. M. Sadik**

---

482 **MR MATTHEW SALAMAN, Porth**
Postal: **Ty-Yr-Heol Farm, Tonyrefail, Porth, Mid Glamorgan, CF39 8HX**
Contacts: **MOBILE (07912) 039015**
E-MAIL matthewsalaman@hotmail.com

1 4, B f Mazameer (IRE)—American Statement (USA) **Mrs D. J. Hughes**
2 4, Ch f Sir Percy—Bhima **Mrs D. J. Hughes**
3 **BIRIKYNO,** 8, b g Piccolo—Alvarinho Lady **Mrs D. J. Hughes**
4 **BORN TO FROLIC (IRE),** 4, b g Born To Sea (IRE)—Desert Frolic (IRE) **Mrs D. J. Hughes**
5 **CALL HIM ANYTHING,** 5, b g Mount Nelson—Focosa (ITY) **Mrs D. J. Hughes**
6 6, B m Mount Nelson—Focosa (ITY) **Mrs D. J. Hughes**
7 **IGNIGHT,** 8, ch g Compton Place—Time Clash **Mrs D. J. Hughes**
8 7, B m Piccolo—In Some Style (IRE)
9 **INSPIRE,** 7, gr m Hellvelyn—Time Clash **Mrs D. J. Hughes**
10 4, Ch f Mazameer (IRE)—Jinks And Co **Mrs D. J. Hughes**
11 **LESS OF THAT (IRE),** 5, b m Canford Cliffs (IRE)—Night Glimmer (IRE) **Mrs D. J. Hughes**
12 **LOCOMMOTION,** 7, gr g Proclamation (IRE)—Miss Madame (IRE) **Susannah Green, Debbie Hughes**
13 **LOVELY ACCLAMATION (IRE),** 5, b m Acclamation—Titova **Mrs D. J. Hughes**
14 **NATTY DRESSER (IRE),** 4, b g Dandy Man (IRE)—Parlour **Mrs D. J. Hughes**
15 **PICC AND GO,** 6, b m Piccolo—Just Down The Road (IRE) **Mrs D. J. Hughes**
16 **STOP N START,** 7, ch m Piccolo—Dim Ots **Mrs D. J. Hughes**
17 4, Ch c Indian Haven—Time Clash **Mrs D. J. Hughes**

THREE-YEAR-OLDS

18 B f Piccolo—Bhima **Mrs D. J. Hughes**
19 B f Captain Gerrard (IRE)—Focosa (ITY) **Mrs D. J. Hughes**

MR MATTHEW SALAMAN - Continued

TWO-YEAR-OLDS

20 B f 11/2 Ivawood (IRE)—Annacurra (IRE) (Verglas (IRE)) **Mrs D. J. Hughes**

Other Owners: Ms S. Green.

Assistant Trainer: Debbie Hughes

---

483 **MR GARY SANDERSON, Sheriff Hutton**
Postal: **Lilling Hall Farm, Sheriff Hutton, York, North Yorkshire, YO60 6RL**
Contacts: **(01904) 468200 MOBILE (07950) 622402**
E-MAIL garysanderson.lhf@gmail.com
WEBSITE http://lillinghallracing.wix.com/lilling-hall-racing

1 BEAUTY DRAGON (IRE), 7, b g Rip Van Winkle (IRE)—Turning Light (GER) **Miss S. J. Perry**
2 DAWLISH, 8, b g Rail Link—Pnyka (IRE) **Lilling Hall Racing**
3 5, B m Champs Elysees—Leah's Pride
4 MISS GISELLE, 10, b m Desideratum—Pride of The Oaks **Lilling Hall Racing**
5 MISS REBERO, 9, b m Cockney Rebel (IRE)—One Zero (USA) **Lilling Hall Racing**
6 5, B g Native Ruler—Pride of The Oaks
7 WHIGWHAM, 5, ch m Sleeping Indian—Normandy Maid **Lilling Hall Racing**

THREE-YEAR-OLDS

8 B c Passing Glance—Clipper Line (USA)
9 MY BOY MONTY, b c Passing Glance—Sudden Impulse **Lilling Hall Racing**

TWO-YEAR-OLDS

10 B f 7/5 Passing Glance—Audley (Averti (IRE))
11 Ch f 18/5 Burwaaz—Balinka (Bahamian Bounty) **Lilling Hall Racing**

Other Owners: Peter Dodsworth, Dermot Fallon, Neil Francis, Mark Holdsworth, Richard Mansfield, Steven Nellis, Teresa Nellis, Sarah Perry, John Seymour Reed, G. Sanderson, Colin Smith, David Woods, Stuart Woods, Mr N. Woods, Sallie Wrath.

Assistant Trainer: Lynne Sanderson

Jockey (flat): Cam Hardie. **Conditional:** Aiden Blakemore.

---

484 **MR JOSE SANTOS, Hungerford**
Postal: **Glebe House Stables, School Lane, East Garston, Hungerford, Berkshire, RG17 7HR**
Contacts: **MOBILE (07789) 906694**

1 FORMIGA (IRE), 4, b f Worthadd (IRE)—Hymn of Love (IRE) **Jose Santos Racing Ltd**
2 GALTEE MOUNTAIN (IRE), 4, br g Mountain High (IRE)—Kings Queen (IRE) **P. G. Murphy**
3 JABAROUT (USA), 4, b c Uncle Mo (USA)—Tell Me Twice (CAN) **Mr A. Alqallaf**
4 NESSFIELD BLUE, 5, b g Kayf Tara—Bella Medici **Murphy & Chantler**
5 POETA BRASILEIRO (IRE), 4, b c Poet's Voice—Top Act (FR) **Mr P. Moyles**

THREE-YEAR-OLDS

6 FRENCHMANS CREEK (IRE), b c Most Improved (IRE)—Reveuse de Jour (IRE) **Miss V. Griffith**

Other Owners: Mrs B. I. Chantler.

---

485 **MR MALCOLM SAUNDERS, Wells**
Postal: **Blue Mountain Farm, Wells Hill Bottom, Haydon, Wells, Somerset, BA5 3EZ**
Contacts: **OFFICE/FAX (01749) 841011 MOBILE (07771) 601035**
E-MAIL malcolm@malcolmsaunders.co.uk WEBSITE www.malcolmsaunders.co.uk

1 AMBERINE, 5, b m Equiano (FR)—Crimson Fern (IRE) **M. S. Saunders**
2 BABYFACT, 8, b m Piccolo—Pennyspider (IRE) **Mrs Ginny Nicholas & Mr M. S. Saunders**
3 CORONATION COTTAGE, 5, b m Pastoral Pursuits—Avrilo **Pat Hancock & Eric Jones**
4 LUCKY CLOVER, 8, ch m Lucky Story (USA)—Willisa **Paul Nicholas / M S Saunders**

MR MALCOLM SAUNDERS - Continued

5 **PASTFACT**, 5, br g Pastoral Pursuits—Matterofact (IRE) **Premier Conservatory Roofs**
6 **SCARLET RED**, 4, b f Equiano (FR)—Crimson Fern (IRE) **M. S. Saunders**
7 **SECRETFACT**, 6, br g Sakhee's Secret—Matterofact (IRE) **Premier Conservatory Roofs**

THREE-YEAR-OLDS

8 **BLUEBELL TIME (IRE)**, br f Coach House (IRE)—Matterofact (IRE) **M. S. Saunders**

Other Owners: D. J. Collier, Mr P. K. Hancock, Mr E. W. Jones, Mrs V. L. Nicholas, Mr P. S. G. Nicholas.

---

486 MRS DIANNE SAYER, Penrith
Postal: **Town End Farm, Hackthorpe, Penrith, Cumbria, CA10 2HX**
Contacts: PHONE **(01931) 712245** MOBILE **(07980) 295316**

1 **BAILEYS ARTIST**, 4, ch g Zoffany (IRE)—Marasima (IRE) **Mr G. H. Bell**
2 **BEENO (IRE)**, 10, b g Exit To Nowhere (USA)—Kay Theatre (IRE) **Mrs Margaret Coppola & Mr Arthur Slack**
3 **BRADDAN HEAD**, 6, br g Recharge (IRE)—Solid Land (FR) **J. A. Sayer**
4 **DA DOU RON RON (FR)**, 6, b m Early March—I Am Free (FR) **A. R. White**
5 **FRIGHTENED RABBIT (USA)**, 7, b g Hard Spun (USA)—Champagne Ending (USA) **Mr R. A. Harrison**
6 **HOT GOSSIP (IRE)**, 5, b m Fast Company (IRE)—
On The Make (IRE) **Mr Dennis J. Coppola & Mrs Dianne Sayer**
7 **I'LL RUN WITH YOU (IRE)**, 6, b m Darsi (FR)—Suzy Q (IRE) **Mr Dennis J. Coppola & Mrs Dianne Sayer**
8 **IOLANI (GER)**, 7, b g Sholokhov (IRE)—Imogen (GER) **SJD Racing & Dianne Sayer**
9 **JACKHAMMER (IRE)**, 5, b g Thewayyouare (USA)—Ask Annie (IRE) **Mrs H. D. Sayer**
10 **MILLIE THE MINX (IRE)**, 5, b m Medicean—Popocatepetl (FR) **A. R. White**
11 **MY SHIROCCO**, 4, ch f Shirocco (GER)—Auberge (GER) **Mrs D. E. Slack**
12 **MY VALENTINO (IRE)**, 6, ch g Duke of Marmalade (IRE)—
Nadwah (USA) **Mr Dennis J. Coppola & Mrs Dianne Sayer**
13 **REDARNA**, 5, ch g Aqlaam—Curtains **Graham Lund & Dianne Sayer**
14 **RODRIGO (IRE)**, 5, b g Roderic O'Connor (IRE)—Dixie Fine (USA) **Margaret Coppola & Dianne Sayer**
15 **SIXTIES GLENARK**, 6, b g Sixties Icon—Cashback Rose (IRE) **Mrs M. R. Lewis**
16 **THE NAVIGATOR**, 4, gr g Mastercraftsman (IRE)—Blessing (USA) **Mr G. H. Bell**
17 **ZARIB (IRE)**, 8, b g Azamour (IRE)—Zariziyna (IRE) **Mrs Margaret Coppola & Mrs Dianne Sayer**

THREE-YEAR-OLDS

18 **SIMUL AMICIS**, b f Hurricane Run (IRE)—Xaphania **Graham Lund & Dianne Sayer**
19 **VITA VIVET**, ch f Bated Breath—Cresta Gold **Graham Lund & Dianne Sayer**

Other Owners: Mr I. T. Conroy, Mr D. J. Coppola, Mrs M. Coppola, Mr G. Lund, Mr S. Nicholson, S J D Racing, A. Slack.

Assistant Trainer: Miss Joanna Sayer

Amateur: Miss Emma Sayer.

---

487 DR JON SCARGILL, Newmarket
Postal: **Red House Stables, Hamilton Road, Newmarket, Suffolk, CB8 0TE**
Contacts: PHONE **(01638) 667767** MOBILE **(07785) 350705**
E-MAIL jdscargill@gmail.com WEBSITE www.jonscargill.co.uk

1 **BILLIE BEANE**, 4, b f Sir Percy—Torver **Silent Partners**
2 **CHERBOURG (FR)**, 7, b g Dunkerque (FR)—Seduisante (FR) **S J Howard & Partner**
3 5, B g Fair Mix (IRE)—Itssmokinggun (IRE) **Peter Wales**
4 **MILITRY DECORATION (IRE)**, 4, b g Epaulette (AUS)—Funcheon Vale (IRE) **GB Horseracing**
5 **MISSISSIPPI MISS**, 5, ch m Equiano (FR)—Junket **Silent Partners**
6 5, B g Showcasing—Torver **Mrs Susan Scargill**

THREE-YEAR-OLDS

7 **INDIAN SEA**, b f Born To Sea (IRE)—Indian Dumaani **Dr E. M. Robson**
8 **MISS FIRECRACKER (IRE)**, ch f Dragon Pulse (IRE)—Miss Otis **Theme Tune Partnership**

DR JON SCARGILL - Continued

TWO-YEAR-OLDS

9 B f 18/3 Camelot—Dansable (IRE) (Dansili) (10000) **Sirka Bloodstock**
10 DISARMING (IRE), b f 24/4 War Command (USA)—
Gloved Hand (Royal Applause) (12000) **Dr E M Robson & Partner**
11 HAVANA PRINCESS, b f 14/3 Havana Gold (IRE)—
Yat Ding Yau (FR) (Air Chief Marshal (IRE)) (10000) **JPT Partnership**

Other Owners: Mr Mohammed Ali, Alan Beardsall, R A Dalton, Paul Dancer, Peter Darlington, John Dutton, P J Edwards, Anna Frahm, Mr S. J. Howard, Peter Lewsey, Mr D. J. Meilton, Chris O'Dowd, Mr P J. Scargill, Pauline Thorp, D Tunmore, R Warner, B Watson, R Watson.

---

488 MR DERRICK SCOTT, Minehead
Postal: **East Lynch, Minehead, Somerset, TA24 8SS**
Contacts: **PHONE (01643) 702430 FAX (01643) 702430**

1 ACTONETAKETWO, 9, b m Act One—Temple Dancer **Mrs R. Scott**
2 ROYBUOY, 12, b g Royal Applause—Wavy Up (IRE) **Mrs R. Scott**

Jockey (NH): James Best.

---

489 MR GEORGE SCOTT, Newmarket
Postal: **Saffron Stables, Hamilton Road, Newmarket, Suffolk, CB8 0NY**
Contacts: **MOBILE (07833) 461294**
E-MAIL george@georgescottracing.com WEBSITE www.georgescottracing.com

1 CRASH HELMET, 4, b g Helmet (AUS)—Hot Secret **Ontoawinner & Saffron Racing II**
2 FOUZ, 4, b f Iffraaj—Bronwen (IRE) **Mr A. S. Belhab**
3 GILGAMESH, 5, b g Foxwedge (AUS)—Flaming Cliffs (USA) **Niarchos Family**
4 JAARIH (IRE), 7, ch g Starspangledbanner (AUS)—Bridge Note (USA) **Mr G. O. Scott**
5 JACK THE TRUTH (IRE), 5, ch g Dandy Man (IRE)—Friendly Heart (CAN) **Mr J. Stephenson**
6 STORM OVER (IRE), 5, b g Elnadim (USA)—Stormy View (USA) **Mr A. Al Mansoori**

THREE-YEAR-OLDS

7 AQUARIUS MIRACLE, ch g Iffraaj—Aquatinta (GER) **Mr A. Al Mansoori**
8 CONCIERGE (IRE), br g Society Rock (IRE)—Warm Welcome **Bartram,Kilburn & Ware**
9 CRANTOCK BAY, b c Havana Gold (IRE)—Orton Park (IRE) **Mr K. J. Breen**
10 DUBAI METRO, ch g Shamardal (USA)—Fragrancy (IRE) **M. Al Nabouda**
11 EARTH AND SKY (USA), b f Noble Mission—Youre So Sweet (USA) **Flaxman Stables Ireland Ltd**
12 FILLES DE FLEUR, gr ro f Gregorian (IRE)—Big Moza (IRE) **Mr A Watson & Mr B Malyon**
13 HOLD ON NOW (IRE), ch f Farhh—First Embrace (IRE) **Mr A. S. Belhab**
14 ILLUSIVE APPEAL, b f Universal (IRE)—Eluding **A. Saeed**
15 LAHESSAR, b c Exceed And Excel (AUS)—Burlesque Star (IRE) **Al Rabban Racing**
16 LEO DAVINCI (USA), b c Artie Schiller (USA)—Sweet Temper (USA) **Excel Racing**
17 LIBERATA BELLA, b f Iffraaj—Namaadhej (USA) **Biddestone Racing Club**
18 MOLL DAVIS (IRE), b f Kingman—Stupendous Miss (USA) **Sonia M. Rogers & Anthony Rogers**
19 MY EXCELSA (IRE), b f Exceed And Excel (AUS)—Emirates Joy (USA) **Mr A Boyd Rochfort & Mr S Leslie**
20 NARAK, ch f Dubawi (IRE)—Chachamaidee (IRE) **Mr R. A. H. Evans**
21 RELOADED (IRE), b c Excelebration (IRE)—Wooded Glade **Excel Racing & Keith Breen Ii**
22 SO I'M TOLD (IRE), b g Lope de Vega (IRE)—Satopanth **Niarchos Family**
23 STRAWBERRY JACK, b g Foxwedge (AUS)—Strawberry Leaf **Mr J. Stephenson**
24 THE GREAT STORY, b g Sea The Moon (GER)—Lovina (ITY) **A. Al Shaikh**
25 USAIN BOAT (IRE), b g Casamento (IRE)—Emerald Peace (IRE) **Blue StaRR Racing**

TWO-YEAR-OLDS

26 AMAZING NEWS, ch c 4/3 Toronado (IRE)—Angelic Air (Oasis Dream) **W. J. and T. C. O. Gredley**
27 Ch c 22/3 Harbour Watch (IRE)—Blue Maiden (Medicean) (26970) **The Black Dragon**
28 CHARLES STREET, ch c 22/4 Helmet (AUS)—Fleur de Lis (Nayef (USA)) **W. J. and T. C. O. Gredley**
29 CHATTANOOGA BOY (IRE), b c 12/1 Acclamation—
Sign From Heaven (IRE) (Raven's Pass (USA)) (32000) **W. J. and T. C. O. Gredley**

MR GEORGE SCOTT - Continued

30 B c 6/3 War Command (USA)—Court Circular (Pivotal) (12642)
31 DAKOTA J (IRE), b f 12/2 Dandy Man (IRE)—
　　Florida City (IRE) (Pennekamp (USA)) (14285) **The Harnage Partnership II**
32 DRAGON COMMAND, b c 18/2 War Command (USA)—Zari (Azamour (IRE)) (26127) **The Black Dragon**
33 DRAGON FLIGHT (IRE), b f 20/3 No Nay Never (USA)—
　　Real Charm (IRE) (Duke of Marmalade (IRE)) (24761) **The Black Dragon**
34 B c 10/3 Requinto (IRE)—Edrea (FR) (American Post) (23598) **Blue StaRR Racing**
35 EMARATY HERO, b c 24/2 Lope de Vega (IRE)—Valtina (IRE) (Teofilo (IRE)) (55000) **A. Al Shaikh**
36 B c 9/4 Holy Roman Emperor (IRE)—Fine If (IRE) (Iffraaj) (82000) **Mr A. Al Mansoori**
37 FLASH HENRY, b c 6/2 Cable Bay (IRE)—
　　Angels Wings (IRE) (Dark Angel (IRE)) (21000) **W. J. and T. C. O. Gredley**
38 LUCKY LESLIE (IRE), b c 11/3 Camacho—Somewhere (IRE) (Dalakhani (IRE)) (25000) **Simon Leslie & Partner**
39 B c 21/4 Zoffany (IRE)—March (Dutch Art) (16856) **Al Asayl Bloodstock Ltd**
40 B c 9/3 Dandy Man (IRE)—Nancy Astor (Shamardal (USA)) (80952) **Bartram, Kilburn & Ware Ii**
41 NOTION OF TIME (USA), b f 1/5 Into Mischief (USA)—
　　Sea of Showers (USA) (Seattle Slew (USA)) **Flaxman Stables Ireland Ltd**
42 PUFFTHEMAGICDRAGON, b c 21/3 Brazen Beau (AUS)—Marmot Bay (IRE) (Kodiac) (18095) **The Black Dragon**
43 QUEEN SALAMAH (IRE), b f 14/4 No Nay Never (USA)—
　　Cape Jasmine (IRE) (Danehill (USA)) (16856) **A. Al Shaikh**
44 B c 8/5 Dandy Man (IRE)—Raspberry Beret (IRE) (Danehill Dancer (IRE)) (20952) **The Black Dragon**
45 B c 4/5 Elzaam (AUS)—Reehan (USA) (Bernardini) (6741) **Mr M. S. Al Shahi**
46 SARVAN, gr c 11/3 Lope de Vega (IRE)—Tequila Sunrise (Dansili) (50000) **Mr K Breen & Mr C Wright**
47 B c 7/4 Kodiac—Soft Power (IRE) (Balmont (USA)) (54782) **Mr A. Al Mansoori**
48 TEACH (USA), ch f 20/1 Karakontie (JPN)—Twinkler (USA) (Benny the Dip (USA)) **Flaxman Stables Ireland Ltd**

Other Owners: Mr C. Austin, Mr M. Bartram, Mrs G. P. Bostwick, T. P. Bostwick, J. R. Boughey, Mr A. R. Boyd-Rochfort, Mr A. C. Elliott, Mr P. Fisher, T. C. O. Gredley, W. J. Gredley, Mr W. A. Jackson-Stops, D. Kilburn, Mr S. Leslie, Mr M. J. Lilley, Mr B. Malyon, Mr N. J. O'Brien, A. P. Rogers, Mrs S. M. Rogers, Saffron Racing Ii, Mr G. O. Scott, Mrs J. A. Scott, Mr E. J. Ware, Mr A. Watson, Mr C. N. Wright.

490　MR JEREMY SCOTT, Dulverton

Postal: Higher Holworthy Farm, Brompton Regis, Dulverton, Somerset, TA22 9NY
Contacts: **PHONE** (01398) 371414 **MOBILE** (07709) 279483
E-MAIL holworthyfarm@yahoo.com

1 BALLYBOUGH NORA (IRE), 6, b m Oscar (IRE)—Perspex Queen (IRE) **Pillhead House Partners**
2 BANG ON (IRE), 6, ch g Fracas (IRE)—Carramanagh Lady (IRE) **Cash For Honours**
3 BLUE APRIL (FR), 8, b g Blue Bresil (FR)—Royale Little (FR) **Mr J P Carrington & Partner**
4 BONZA GIRL, 6, b m Midnight Legend—Purple Patch **Mr G. T. Lever**
5 BUSTER MOON (IRE), 7, b g Darsi (FR)—Orinocco Blue (IRE) **The The Buster Moon Partnership**
6 CHAMPAGNE COURT (IRE), 6, b g Court Cave—Lady Taipan (IRE) **Mr I F Gosden & Mr Dj Coles**
7 CHANCE IT (IRE), 9, b g Tajraasi (USA)—Lafanta (IRE) **Mr D. O. Winzer**
8 COLMERS HILL, 9, b g Crosspeace (IRE)—My Dancing Kin **Gale Force Four**
9 DASHEL DRASHER, 6, b g Passing Glance—So Long **Mrs B Tully & Mr R Lock**
10 DAY OF ROSES (IRE), 10, b g Acambaro (GER)—Dan's Choice (IRE) **Derek Coles & John H W Finch**
11 DEMON FOU (FR), 6, b g Le Fou (IRE)—Nevka (FR) **Friends From Insurance**
12 ESPALION (FR), 5, b g Khalkevi (IRE)—Somosierra (FR) **Mr J. H. Frost**
13 GARRANE (IRE), 7, b g Tikkanen (USA)—Ballooley (IRE) **Friends From Insurance**
14 GONNABEGOOD (IRE), 8, b g Kutub (IRE)—Angels Flame (IRE) **The Free Spirits Partnership**
15 GREENVIEW PARADISE (IRE), 5, gr m Exchange Rate (USA)—Senza Rete (IRE) **Friends From Insurance**
16 GUERRILLA TACTICS (IRE), 9, b g Presenting—Karens Flight (IRE) **The Exmoor Partners**
17 HEY BUD, 6, b g Fair Mix (IRE)—Aizone **Mr M. P. P. Brend**
18 KELTUS (IRE), 9, gr g Keltos (FR)—Regina d'orthe (FR)
19 KILCARA (IRE), 6, b m Court Cave (IRE)—Easter Day (IRE) **London Erratics Racing Club**
20 KISSESFORKATIE (IRE), 5, b m Jeremy (USA)—Now Were Broke (IRE) **Derek Coles & Ian Gosden**
21 LADY LONGSHOT (IRE), 8, b m Needle Gun (IRE)—So Long **Mr R Lock, Mrs B Tully & Mrs C Scott**
22 MISS KATNISS, 5, br m Kayf Tara—Kate Hill Dancer (IRE) **Bet the Farm & Greenlands Racing**
23 MOORLANDS GEORGE, 11, b g Grape Tree Road—Sandford Springs (USA) **Mr C. H. Vicary**
24 MOORLANDS JACK, 14, b g Cloudings (IRE)—Sandford Springs (USA) **Mr C. H. Vicary**
25 NATIVE ROBIN (IRE), 9, br g Robin des Pres (FR)—Homebird (IRE) **The Punchestown Syndicate**
26 NIFTY AT FIFTY (IRE), 6, b g Gold Well—Tropical Sunset (IRE) **Mrs H. L. Stoneman**
27 ORCHARDSTOWN CROSS (IRE), 8, b g Westerner—Shang A Lang (IRE) **Mr J. H. Frost**
28 OUR DOT'S BABY (IRE), 7, b m Helissio (FR)—Our Dot (IRE) **Mr A. P. Maddox**
29 PELORIC, 4, ch g Intello (GER)—New Orchid (USA) **Wot No Coz**

MR JEREMY SCOTT - Continued

30 **PULLING POWER,** 9, br m Erhaab (USA)—Pulling Strings (IRE) **The Real Partnership**
31 **PURPLE JAZZ (IRE),** 4, b g Red Jazz (USA)—Breakmeheart (IRE) **The Barmy Men 3**
32 **RESCUED GLORY (IRE),** 10, b g Milan—Stand Girl (IRE) **Mrs A. E. Baker**
33 **STORMY FLIGHT (IRE),** 5, gr g Cloudings (IRE)—Help Yourself (IRE) **Mr Ian Murray & Mrs Camilla Scott**
34 **SUPER SNIPE,** 8, b g Kayf Tara—Sea Snipe **Mrs L. J. C. Tylor**
35 **TIKKINTHEBOX (IRE),** 7, b g Tikkanen (USA)—Surfing France (FR) **On A Mission**
36 **TRENCH BOX (IRE),** 5, b g Scorpion (IRE)—Sonne Cinq (IRE) **Derek Coles & Darren Langley**
37 **UNISON (IRE),** 9, b g Jeremy (USA)—Easter Song (USA) **Mr J. P. Carrington**
38 **URTHEONETHATIWANT (IRE),** 6, ch g Shantou (USA)—Roberta Supreme (IRE) **The Barmy Men 4**

Other Owners: Mr M. P. Ansell, Mr J. F. C. Atkins, Mr J. Bagwell-Purefoy, Bet The Farm Partners, Mr M. Bower-Dyke, Mr A. P. Brown, Mr P. R. Cartwright, Mrs K. Casini, Mr C. Cole, Mr A. Coles, Mr D. J. Coles, Miss Alison Delve, Mr J. M. O. Evans, Mr J. H. W. Finch, Mr R. J. L. Flood, Mr A. P. Gale, Mr S. G. D. Giles, Mr I. F. Gosden, Mr P. Govier, Mr P. F. Govier, Greenlands Racing Syndicate, Mr M. J. Holman, Mr J. L. T. Illingworth, Mr C. L. Keey, Mr D. E. Langley, Mr R. J. Lock, Mr C. J. Lyles, Mr B. J. McManus, Mr P. D. Moore, I. R. Murray, Mrs S. M. Ragg, Mr A. M. Rennison, Mrs C. C. Scott, Mr B. D. Smith, Dr J. M. Steer-Fowler, Mrs S. J. Steer-Fowler, Mr M. J. Swallow, Mrs B. J. Tully, Mr P. J. Upton, Mr G. J. Wilson.

Assistant Trainer: Camilla Scott

Jockey (NH): Matt Griffiths, Nick Scholfield. **Amateur:** Mr Rob Hawker.

491

MISS KATIE SCOTT, Galashiels
Postal: **Stables Cottage, Millhaugh, Lindean, Galashiels, Scottish Borders**
Contacts: **MOBILE (07826) 344577**

1 **ALL ABOUT THE PACE,** 5, ch m Sixties Icon—Phoebe Woodstock (IRE) **Miss K. Scott**
2 4, B f Imperial Monarch (IRE)—Caoba **Miss K. Scott**
3 **CHAIN OF BEACONS,** 10, b g Midnight Legend—Millennium Girl **Simon & Angela Gillie**
4 **GETAWAY GERRY,** 5, b g Getaway (GER)—Loch Dhu (IRE) **Edward Cassie, Mark Hay & Murray Scott**
5 **KNOCKLAYDE (IRE),** 7, b g Mountain High (IRE)—Foret Noire (IRE) **The Jackson Partnership**
6 **NAPLES BAY,** 5, b g Kodiac—Trombe (FR) **Miss K. Scott**
7 **NEWSTART (IRE),** 8, br g Stowaway—Joes Annie (IRE) **The Bandits**
8 **ROBBEN RAINBOW,** 5, b g Delegator—Sally Can Wait **Edward Cassie & Katie Scott**
9 **ROCKLEY POINT,** 6, b g Canford Cliffs (IRE)—Statua (IRE) **The Vintage Flyers**
10 **RORY'S VALENTINE (IRE),** 8, br m Windsor Knot (IRE)—Housekeeping (IRE) **Mrs S. Scott**
11 **STONEY ROVER,** 6, b g Scorpion (IRE)—Consultation (IRE) **Mr K. J. Telfer**
12 **WESTERN LASS (IRE),** 6, br m Westerner—Lady Roania (IRE) **Edward Cassie & Katie Scott**
13 **WESTERN SUPERNOVA,** 5, b m Westerner—Supreme Nova **Edward Cassie & Katie Scott**

Other Owners: Mr E. Cassie, Mrs A. Gillie, Mr S. P. Gillie, Mr M. W. Hay, Dr D. E. McGuiness, Mr W. M. Scott.

492

MR MICHAEL SCUDAMORE, Bromsash
Postal: **Eccleswall Court, Bromsash, Nr. Ross-on-Wye, Herefordshire, HR9 7PP**
Contacts: **PHONE (01989) 750844 FAX (01989) 750281 MOBILE (07901) 853520**
E-MAIL michael.scu@btconnect.com WEBSITE www.michaelscudamoreracing.co.uk

1 **AMARANTH (IRE),** 6, b g New Approach (IRE)—Kitty Kiernan **Mr C. G. J. Chua**
2 **ASK HIMSELF (IRE),** 5, ch g Ask—Wintry Day (IRE) **Mrs L. Maclennan**
3 **BALACH MOR (IRE),** 7, b g Robin des Champs (FR)—
 Silver Skirt (IRE) **Mr John J Murray & Mrs Lynne MacLennan**
4 **BEE CROSSING,** 8, b m Mac Fhir Mix (IRE)—Indeed To Goodness (IRE) **Mr M. Scudamore**
5 **BELMONT JEWEL,** 7, b m Westerner—
 Maddy's Supreme **Having A Mare Mr WJ Fenn Mr DI Alexander**
6 **CADEYRN (IRE),** 7, b g Flemensfirth (USA)—Kapricia Speed (FR) **Mr John J Murray & Mrs Lynne MacLennan**
7 **COPPER COIN,** 6, ch g Sulamani (IRE)—Silken Pearls **Mr P. E. Truscott**
8 **CORNER CREEK (IRE),** 9, b g Presenting—No Moore Bills **Mr M. R. Blandford**
9 **COURT MASTER (IRE),** 6, b g Court Cave—Lusos Wonder (IRE) **Mrs L. Maclennan**
10 **CZECH HER OUT (IRE),** 5, b m Fame And Glory—Molly Hussey (IRE) **Gabby Gajova and Friends**
11 **DAN EMMETT (USA),** 9, ch g Flower Alley (USA)—Singing Dixie (USA) **Mrs L. Maclennan**
12 **DANCING HEARTS,** 6, b m Makfi—Danceabout **Mr Mark Savidge Mr Richard Green**
13 **DAWNIERIVER (IRE),** 9, br m Indian River (FR)—In Sin (IRE) **Having A Mare I**
14 **DINSDALE,** 6, b g Cape Cross (IRE)—Emmy Award (IRE) **Mr M. Jones**
15 **FANCY SHAPES (IRE),** 5, ch m Golden Lariat (USA)—Panglao Island (IRE) **Mrs L. Maclennan**

MR MICHAEL SCUDAMORE - Continued

16 **HURRICANE MINNIE**, 6, b m Authorized (IRE)—Hurricane Milly (IRE) **John J. Murray & Niall Farrell**
17 **ISAAC WONDER (IRE)**, 4, b g Born To Sea (IRE)—Najaaba (USA) **Mrs L. Maclennan**
18 **JUPITER CUSTOS (FR)**, 7, b g Le Havre (IRE)—Angel Rose (IRE) **Mr C. G. J. Chua**
19 **JUSTICE KNIGHT (IRE)**, 7, b g Raven's Pass (USA)—New Story (USA) **Mark Savidge & Michael Scudamore**
20 **KINGSWELL THEATRE**, 10, b g King's Theatre (IRE)—Cresswell Native (IRE) **Mr J. J. Murray**
21 **LADY MARWAH (IRE)**, 6, b br Iffraaj—Eyrecourt (IRE) **W J Fenn Mrs Lesley Sluman & D Lee**
22 **LAWMAKING**, 6, b g Zamindar (USA)—Canada Water **Marchwood Aggregates**
23 **MALINELLO (IRE)**, 4, b g Malinas (GER)—Wyldello **Mr M. Jones**
24 **MISS FLYING FOX**, 4, b br f Kayf Tara—Nile Cristale (FR) **Mr M. Jones**
25 **MONBEG AQUADUDE (IRE)**, 8, b g Flemensfirth (USA)—Mite Dash (IRE) **Mr M. R. Blandford**
26 **MYSTEREE (IRE)**, 11, b g Gold Well—Hillside Native (IRE) **Mrs L. Maclennan**
27 **NEWTOWN LAD (IRE)**, 9, b g Craigsteel—Rocher Lady (IRE) **Mr John J Murray & Mrs Lynne MacLennan**
28 **NORTHERN BEAU (IRE)**, 6, b m Canford Cliffs (IRE)—View (IRE) **Lynne & Angus Maclennan**
29 **ONE TOUCH (IRE)**, 5, b g Court Cave (IRE)—Star Bui (IRE) **Mr M. Jones**
30 **PLENTY OF BUTTY (IRE)**, 6, b g Germany (USA)—Jump For Joy (IRE) **Mr M. R. Blandford**
31 **ROSIE AND MILLIE (IRE)**, 6, ch m Flemensfirth (USA)—Madgehill (IRE) **Mrs L. Maclennan**
32 **SATURN 'N SILK**, 4, b f Universal (IRE)—Manaphy (FR) **Mr P. E. Truscott**
33 **SHE'S BLORENGE**, 4, ch f Arvico (FR)—Lefty's Dollbaby (USA) **Mr & Mrs M. Frieze**
34 **SHENEEDEDTHERUN (IRE)**, 9, b m Kayf Tara—Lady Moon (FR) **Mr M. Jones**
35 **SKINT**, 13, b g King's Theatre (IRE)—No More Money **Mrs B. V. Evans**
36 **SMITHS CROSS**, 7, b br g Westerner—Blue Supreme (IRE) **Mrs L. Maclennan**
37 **SNATCHITBACK**, 8, b g Overbury (IRE)—Talk The Talk **Mr & Mrs M. Frieze**
38 **SOME CHAOS (IRE)**, 8, b g Brian Boru—Iruna Iris (IRE) **Mason Scudamore Racing**
39 **SPEEDY BUCK (IRE)**, 6, b g Beat Hollow—Attymon Lill (IRE) **Marchwood Aggregates**
40 **STATE SOVEREIGNTY**, 7, b m Authorized (IRE)—Sovereign's Honour (USA) **Mr C. G. J. Chua**
41 **SUMELIA**, 4, ch f Sulamani (IRE)—Aimela (IRE) **Mr P. E. Truscott & Mr M. Scudamore**
42 **SUNDAY SESSION (IRE)**, 5, b g Scorpion (IRE)—Casiana (GER) **Mr M. Scudamore**
43 **THOR DE CERISY (FR)**, 5, b g Enrique—Midalisy (FR) **Mrs L. Maclennan**
44 **TIGER'S LEGACY**, 5, b g So You Think (NZ)—Tiger Moss **Mr S. Smith**
45 **TURBOTIM (IRE)**, 6, b g Arakan (USA)—Katy McKay (IRE) **Gempro**
46 **TWO SMOKIN BARRELS**, 10, b m Kayf Tara—Coldabri (IRE) **Mr M. Jones**
47 **VOILA ERIC**, 7, b g Bollin Eric—Et Voila **Wink N' A Drink**
48 **ZAYFIRE ARAMIS**, 10, ch g Zafeen (FR)—Kaylifa Aramis **Aramis Racing**

Other Owners: Mr D. I. Alexander, Mr C. Breeze, Mr D. E. Coltman, Mr N. Farrell, Mr W. J. Fenn, Mr M. A. Frieze, Mrs J. Frieze, Mr R. R. Green, Having A Mare, Mr T. S. Hopkins, Mr D. J. Lee, Mr A. Maclennan, Mr A. Mason, Mr N. McGawley, Mrs J. M. Murray, Ms I. Phipps Coltman, Mr S. Robson, Mr M. G. Savidge, Mrs M. L. Scudamore, Mrs L. J. Sluman.

Assistant Trainer: Mrs Marilyn Scudamore

Jockey (NH): Tom Scudamore, Ben Poste, Brendan Powell.

---

493 MR DEREK SHAW, Sproxton
Postal: **The Sidings, Saltby Road, Sproxton, Melton Mowbray, Leicestershire, LE14 4RA**
Contacts: **PHONE** (01476) 860578 **FAX** (01476) 860578 **MOBILE** (07721) 039645
E-MAIL mail@derekshawracing.com WEBSITE www.derekshawracing.com

1 **ALWAYS AMAZING**, 5, ch g Kyllachy—Amazed **Mr N. Andersen**
2 **AMAZING AMAYA**, 4, b f New Approach (IRE)—Faslen (USA) **P. E. Barrett**
3 **ATYAAF**, 4, b g Invincible Spirit (IRE)—Eshaadeh (USA) **GB Civil Engineering (Leicester) LTD**
4 **BOMAD**, 4, b g Kheleyf (USA)—Fenella Fudge **Mr B. Johnson**
5 **CRIKEYITSWHYKIE**, 4, b g Piccolo—Kitty Kitty Cancan **Mrs L. J. Shaw**
6 **DUBAI ELEGANCE**, 5, ch m Sepoy (AUS)—Some Sunny Day **Shawthing Racing Partnership**
7 **DYNAMO WALT (IRE)**, 8, b g Acclamation—Cambara **The Whiteman Partnership**
8 **ELLIOT THE DRAGON (IRE)**, 4, b g Raven's Pass—Somerset Falls (UAE) **Mr D. Shaw**
9 **EMIGRATED (IRE)**, 6, b g Fastnet Rock (AUS)—Ecoutila (USA) **Mr D. Shaw**
10 **EURATO (FR)**, 9, ch g Medicean—Double Green (IRE) **Mr L. Martell**
11 **HAMMER GUN (USA)**, 6, b g Smart Strike (CAN)—Caraboss **Mr A. Flint**
12 **HARBOUR VISION**, 4, gr g Harbour Watch—Holy Nola (USA) **New Vision Bloodstock**
13 **LE MANEGE ENCHANTE (IRE)**, 6, gr g Zebedee—Beth **Mr N. P. Franklin**
14 **LOYALTY**, 12, b g Medicean—Ecoutila (USA) **The Whiteman Partnership**
15 **NARALSAIF (IRE)**, 5, b m Arcano (IRE)—Mejala (IRE) **Shawthing Racing Partnership (d Shaw)**
16 **POLARBROOK (IRE)**, 12, gr g Alderbrook—Frozen Cello (IRE) **Mr J. R. Saville**
17 **POLITICAL SLOT**, 4, ch f Helmet (AUS)—Lady Elalmadol (IRE) **Mr B. Johnson**
18 **ROCK ON BERTIE (IRE)**, 4, b g Rock of Gibraltar (IRE)—Princess Banu **Mr J. R. Saville**

MR DEREK SHAW - Continued

19 **SAMPHIRE COAST**, 6, b g Fastnet Rock (AUS)—Faslen (USA) **P. E. Barrett**
20 **TOP BOY**, 9, b g Exceed And Excel (AUS)—Injaaz **BGC Racing**
21 **WELLIESINTHEWATER (IRE)**, 9, b g Footstepsinthesand—
Shadow Ash (IRE) **Shawthing Racing Partnership (whiteman)**

THREE-YEAR-OLDS

22 **COOL WALK**, br f Poet's Voice—Lady Elalmadol (IRE) **Mr B. Johnson**
23 **EAGRE**, b g Dutch Art—Tahlia Ree (IRE) **P. E. Barrett**
24 **FOUR WHEEL DRIVE**, b g Doncaster Rover (USA)—Lawless Bridget
25 **HURRICANE HEIDI**, gr f Kyllachy—The Manx Touch (IRE) **Mrs L. J. Shaw**
26 **PRINCE MAMILLIUS**, ch c Coach House (USA)—Queen Hermione (IRE) **Dr D. Chapman-Jones**
27 **PURELY PROSECCO**, b f Poet's Voice—Nabat Sultan **Shawthing Racing Partnership & L Shaw**
28 **REMISSION**, b g Epaulette (AUS)—Fenella Fudge **Mr B. Johnson**
29 **SING BERTIE (IRE)**, b g Zebedee—Emirates Challenge (IRE) **Mr J. R. Saville**

Other Owners: Mr N. Blencowe, Mr Graham Felston, Mr M. Lenton, Mr Derek Shaw, Mrs Lyndsey Shaw, Shawthing Racing Partnership, Mr Richard Ward, Mr S. A. Whiteman, The Whiteman Partnership.

Yard Sponsor: Grosvenor Contracts Leasing Ltd

---

494 **MRS FIONA SHAW, Dorchester**
Postal: **Skippet Cottage, Bradford Peverell, Dorchester, Dorset, DT2 9SE**
Contacts: **PHONE (01305) 889821 MOBILE (07970) 370444**
E-MAIL fiona.shaw05@gmail.com

1 **BIG BAMBOO**, 7, ch g Kier Park (IRE)—Waheeba **Starting Gate Racing**
2 **BOUND HILL**, 10, b g Kayf Tara—Ardent Bride **John & Heather Snook**
3 **DARWINS THEORY (IRE)**, 11, b g Montjeu (IRE)—Thrift (IRE) **Mrs F. M. Shaw**
4 5, Ch g Eastern Anthem—Duchcov **Miss H. Pease**
5 **HIGHDAWN (IRE)**, 6, b m Alflora (IRE)—Wychnor Dawn (IRE) **John & Heather Snook**
6 **HOLLYWOOD KEN (IRE)**, 6, b g Arcano (IRE)—Third Dimension (FR) **Mr J. R. Dodington**
7 **HYMN AND A PRAYER**, 6, br g Eastern Anthem (IRE)—Kryssa **Mrs F. M. Shaw**
8 **KIWI MYTH**, 7, b m Midnight Legend—Kiwi Katie **John & Heather Snook**
9 **NIGHTHAWKER**, 6, b g Bollin Eric—Bird Without Wings (IRE) **John & Heather Snook**
10 **THE MIGHTY ASH (IRE)**, 9, b g Arcadio (GER)—She's Got To Go (IRE) **Mrs A. Hollier**

Other Owners: Mr David Bond, J. W. Snook, Mrs H. A. Snook.

---

495 **MR MARK SHEARS, Newton Abbot**
Postal: **Lower Nattadon, Chagford, Newton Abbot, Devon, TQ13 8ER**
Contacts: **PHONE (01647) 432356 FAX (01647) 432356 MOBILE (07881) 745314**
E-MAIL markshearsracing@gmail.com

1 **HOW'S VIENNA (IRE)**, 9, b g Westerner—Plant A Smacker (IRE) **Mr M. B. Shears**
2 **NICE THOUGHTS (IRE)**, 7, b g Shamardal (USA)—Zacheta **Mr M. B. Shears**

Assistant Trainer: Miss K. Reynolds

---

496 **MR MATT SHEPPARD, Ledbury**
Postal: **Home Farm Cottage, Eastnor, Ledbury, Herefordshire, HR8 1RD**
Contacts: **FAX (01531) 634846 MOBILE (07770) 625061**
E-MAIL matthew.sheppard@cmail.co.uk

1 **ALL GOOD THINGS (IRE)**, 7, b g Dahjee (USA)—Material Lady (IRE) **Exors of the Late Mr S. J. D. Gegg**
2 **BALLYDARSI (IRE)**, 9, br m Darsi (FR)—Ballyday June (IRE) **Mrs N. Sheppard**
3 **KAYF TIGER**, 10, b g Kayf Tara—La Marette **Miss N. A. Jameson**
4 **KESTREL VALLEY**, 5, b m Dr Massini (IRE)—Lady Karinga **Mrs J. M. Johnson**
5 **METATRONS CUBE (IRE)**, 4, b g Artie Schiller (USA)—Quiet Down (USA) **Michael & Lesley Wilkes**
6 **MICRAS**, 8, b m Medicean—Purple Heather (USA) **G. A. Moore**
7 **MODELIGO (IRE)**, 10, b g Indian Danehill (IRE)—Glens Lady (IRE) **Exors of the Late Mr S. J. D. Gegg**
8 **ROCK ON ROCKY**, 11, b g Overbury (IRE)—Tachometer (IRE) **Jan Johnson & Terry Harman**

MR MATT SHEPPARD - Continued

   9 RULE THE OCEAN (IRE), 9, gr m Stowaway—Page Ten (IRE) **Lost In The Summer Wine**
  10 THE BAY BIRCH (IRE), 8, b m Beneficial—Tournant Vic (IRE) **Mr A. J. Scrivin**
Other Owners: Mr T. A. Harman, R. A. Kujawa, Mr P. R. W. Smith, Mrs L. Wilkes, Mr M. H. A. Wilkes.
Conditional: Stan Sheppard.

---

497   MR OLIVER SHERWOOD, Upper Lambourn
Postal: Rhonehurst House, Upper Lambourn, Hungerford, Berkshire, RG17 8RG
Contacts: PHONE (01488) 71411 FAX (01488) 72786 MOBILE (07979) 591867
E-MAIL oliver.sherwood@virgin.net WEBSITE www.oliversherwood.co.uk

  1 BLAMEITALONMYROOTS (IRE), 9, b m Turtle Island (IRE)—Makingyourmindup (IRE) **Mr T. D. J. Syder**
  2 BOOK OF GOLD (IRE), 7, b g Flemensfirth (USA)—Ballerina Queen (IRE) **Mr A Lousada & Mr A Kaplan**
  3 BRIERY BUNNY, 7, b m Lucarno (USA)—Blackbriery Thyne (IRE) **Mrs H. Plumbly**
  4 BROUGHTONS RHYTHM, 10, b g Araafa (IRE)—Broughton Singer (IRE) **Broughton Thermal Insulations**
  5 BRUMMIE BOYS (IRE), 4, b g Flemensfirth (USA)—Bobs Article (IRE) **Mr Andrew Cohen & Mr Alan Kaplan**
  6 CAPTAIN PEACOCK, 6, b g Champs Elysees—Blast Furnace (IRE) **Apiafi & Black**
  7 CERVARO MIX (FR), 5, gr g Al Namix (FR)—Semiramiss (FR) **Kate & Andrew Brooks**
  8 CHEEKY RASCAL (IRE), 4, b g Most Improved (IRE)—Bessie Lou (IRE) **Mr Charlie Rosier & Mrs Julia Rosier**
  9 CILAOS GLACE (FR), 6, br g Voix du Nord (FR)—Miss Glacee (FR) **Heart Of The South Racing**
 10 DOMINATOR (IRE), 6, b g Desir d'un Soir (FR)—Sourya d'airy (FR) **Kate & Andrew Brooks**
 11 DONLADD (IRE), 5, b g Cloudings—Kentford Serotina **Mr T. J. Hemmings**
 12 ENJOY RESPONSIBLY (IRE), 10, b g Flemensfirth (USA)—Spice Patrol (IRE) **Mr J. Beswick**
 13 FELIX D'AUTRY (FR), 5, b g Khalkevi (IRE)—Hassaya (FR) **Mr O. M. C. Sherwood**
 14 GEORDIELAD, 5, ch g Geordieland (FR)—Adees Dancer **Mr A. Taylor**
 15 GOT AWAY (FR), 6, b m American Post—Hideaway Girl **B McDonald & B Mellon**
 16 JERSEY BEAN (IRE), 6, b g Court Cave (IRE)—Jennifers Diary (IRE) **Mr A. Taylor**
 17 JURBY, 9, b g Motivator—Darariyna (IRE) **Mr T. J. Hemmings**
 18 LADY IN HIDING (IRE), 5, br m Stowaway—Crackin' Liss (IRE) **A F Lousada & Mark Burton**
 19 LAURIE COME ON (IRE), 5, b g Robin des Champs (FR)—Seekayclaire (IRE) **Mr P. Mellett**
 20 MAKETY, 5, ch m Black Sam Bellamy (IRE)—Mi Money **Mrs S. A. White**
 21 MANNING ESTATE (IRE), 5, b g Stowaway—Specifiedrisk (IRE) **Mr & Mrs Norman**
 22 MANOLLO, 5, b g Milan—Wyldello **Mr T. D. J. Syder**
 23 MILLARVILLE (IRE), 6, b m Court Cave (IRE)—Portavoe (IRE) **Million in Mind Partnership**
 24 MINELLA ON LINE (IRE), 10, b g King's Theatre (IRE)—Bally Bolshoi (IRE) **AHB Racing Partnership**
 25 MONKEY PUZZLE, 7, ch g Sulamani (IRE)—Hunca Munca (IRE) **Melbourne 10 Racing**
 26 MR DORRELL SAGE (FR), 6, b g Sageburg (IRE)—Miss Breezy (FR) **The Three Fields**
 27 NO NO JOLIE (FR), 7, gr m Martaline—Virgata (FR) **R. Jenner & J. Green**
 28 NO NO JULIET (IRE), 6, br m Scorpion (IRE)—Full Imperatrice (FR) **Don Sebastiao Partnership**
 29 4, B g Kayf Tara—Noun de La Thinte (FR) **Mr E. J. Ware**
 30 PAPAGANA, 6, b m Martaline—New Destiny **Mr D. J. Burke**
 31 PEUR DE RIEN (FR), 6, b g Kapgarde (FR)—Tango Princess (FR) **British Racing Club**
 32 PINK ROCK (IRE), 5, b m Westerner—Eliane di Rupette **Mr A. L. Brooks**
 33 PITON PETE (IRE), 8, b g Westerner—Glenair Lucy (IRE) **Mr P. Mellett**
 34 QUERRY HORSE (FR), 7, b g Equerry (USA)—La Richelandiere (FR) **Luksonwood Partnership**
 35 RAYVIN BLACK, 10, b g Halling (USA)—Optimistic **Mr R. White & Mr V. J. Walsh**
 36 ROBINESSE (IRE), 8, ch m Robin des Champs (FR)—Jennifers Diary (IRE) **Mr A. Taylor**
 37 ROUGE ET BLANC (FR), 14, ch g Mansonnien (FR)—Fidelety (FR) **Mr O. M. C. Sherwood**
 38 SAMMY BILL, 6, b g Black Sam Bellamy (IRE)—Samrana (FR) **Mr T. J. Hemmings**
 39 SEASTON SPIRIT, 6, b g Kayf Tara—Aphrodisias (FR) **Mr M. Fiddy**
 40 SEVARANO (IRE), 6, b g Shantou (USA)—Eva La Diva (IRE) **Mr T. D. J. Syder**
 41 SHAUGHNESSY, 6, b g Shantou (USA)—Sudden Beat **Mr T. D. J. Syder**
 42 SOTOMAYOR, 4, b c Havana Gold (IRE)—No Frills (IRE) **Blunt, Ensor, Palmer-brown & Partner**
 43 SOUTHERN SAM, 5, b g Black Sam Bellamy (IRE)—Pougatcheva (FR) **Mr T. D. J. Syder**
 44 TARADA, 6, br g Kayf Tara—Kerada (FR) **Mr T. J. Hemmings**
 45 THE GROOVY HOOVY, 7, b g Sulamani (IRE)—Kingennie **The Groovy Hoovy Partnership**
 46 VALJAN, 5, b m Shirocco (GER)—Miracle **David Bellamy & Dominic Burke**
 47 VENTURA DRAGON (IRE), 4, ch g Dragon Pulse (IRE)—Dancing Duchess (IRE) **B. T. McDonald**
 48 VERSIFIER (FR), 7, b m Yeats (IRE)—Daprika (FR) **Personal Racehorse Owners 4**
 49 VINNIE THE HODDIE (IRE), 5, b g Vinnie Roe (IRE)—Blackwater Babe (IRE) **Five Guys & A Striker Syndicate**
 50 WESTSTREET (IRE), 9, b g Westerner—Klipperstreet (IRE) **Weststreet Partnership**
 51 WHAT'S OCCURRING (IRE), 6, b g Rail Link—Lovely Orígny (FR) **Mr Andrew Cohen & Mr Alan Kaplan**
 52 WORKING CLASS, 5, b g Bahri (USA)—Louise d'arzens **Mr B. Ryan-Beswick**

MR OLIVER SHERWOOD - Continued

Other Owners: Mrs E. Adamski, Mr J. Allison, Mr J. Apiafi, Mrs C. J. Barratt, Mr I. J. Barratt, D. Bellamy, A. W. Black, Mr R. J. Blunt, A. R. Bromley, Mrs K. L. Brooks, Mr M. A. Burton, Mr A. L. Cohen, Mr H. W. Cox, Mrs S. Ensor, Mrs B. S. Fowler, Mr R. J. Fowler, G. F. Goode, Mrs A. J. Green, R. Hannon, Mr C. S. Heaps, Mr J. C. I. Heilbron, Ms R. A. Jenner, Alan Kaplan, Mrs A. T. Lambert, G. J. Larby, Mr A. F. Lousada, Mrs J. K. Lukas, Mr B. H. Mellon, Mr W. D. C. Minton, Mrs D. C. Nicholson, Mrs S. D. Norman, Mr R. R. Norman, Mr J. Palmer-Brown, Mr J. R. Penny, Racing Club Ltd, Mrs J. E. Rosier, Mr C. F. J. Rosier, The Hon Mrs L. J. Sherwood, Mr M. A. Sherwood, Mr P. J. Smith, Lady Thompson, V. J. Walsh, Mr R. White, Winterfields Farm Ltd.

Assistant Trainer: Andy Llewellyn **Head Lad:** Stefan Namesansky **Secretary:** Emma Chugg

Jockey (NH): Leighton Aspell, Thomas Garner. **Conditional:** Harrison Beswick.

498

MISS LYNN SIDDALL, Tadcaster
Postal: Stonebridge Farm, Colton, Tadcaster, North Yorkshire, LS24 8EP
Contacts: **PHONE (01904) 744291 FAX (01904) 744291 MOBILE (07778) 216692/4**

1 **ASTROPHYSICS**, 7, ch g Paco Boy (IRE)—Jodrell Bank (IRE) **Mr J. A. Kay**
2 **BEVSBOY (IRE)**, 5, b g Elzaam (AUS)—Eurolink Sundance **Mr A. Longden**
3 **CADGERS HOLE**, 12, b g Helissio (FR)—Not So Prim **Jan Slater & Partners**
4 **ENCODED (IRE)**, 6, ch m Sakhee's Secret—Confidentiality (IRE) **Mr J. A. Kay**
5 **FIRST OF NEVER (IRE)**, 13, b g Systematic—Never Promise (FR) **Lynn Siddall Racing II**
6 **IN VINO VERITAS (IRE)**, 8, b g Art Connoisseur (IRE)—Robin **Mr J. A. Kay**
7 **JAZZ MAGIC (IRE)**, 4, ch g Red Jazz (USA)—Caerella (IRE) **Mr J. A. Kay**
8 **LA HAVRESE (FR)**, 8, ch m Le Havre (IRE)—La Buena (FR) **Mr J. A. Kay**
9 **LITTLE MISS LOLA**, 5, ch m Dandy Man (IRE)—Purepleasureseeker (IRE) **Lynn Siddall Racing II**
10 **MR CONUNDRUM**, 6, b g Paco Boy (IRE)—Folly Drove **Lynn Siddall Racing II**
11 **PADDY'S ROCK (IRE)**, 8, b g Whipper (USA)—Hedera (USA) **Mr J. A. Kay**
12 **SERVO (IRE)**, 5, b g Power—Parade Scene (USA) **Mr J. A. Kay**
13 **YORKSHIREMAN (IRE)**, 9, b g Red Clubs (IRE)—Ossiana (IRE) **Jan Slater & Partners**

THREE-YEAR-OLDS

14 **ALLSFINEANDANDY (IRE)**, b c Dandy Man (IRE)—Swish Dancer (IRE) **Mr G. Kennington**
15 **KYLLACHY CASTLE**, ch c Kyllachy—Amicable Terms **Mr G. Kennington**

Other Owners: Miss L. C. Siddall, Miss J. M. Slater.

Assistant Trainer: Stephen Hackney

499

MR DAVID SIMCOCK, Newmarket
Postal: The Office, Trillium Place, Birdcage Walk, Newmarket, Suffolk, CB8 0NE
Contacts: **PHONE (01638) 662968 FAX (01638) 663888**
MOBILE (07808) 954109 (David) (07702) 851561 (Jennie)
E-MAIL david@davidsimcock.co.uk WEBSITE www.davidsimcock.co.uk

1 **ALACRITAS**, 4, gr f Leroidesanimaux (BRZ)—Albaraka
2 **ALGOMETER**, 6, gr h Archipenko (USA)—Albanova
3 **APPEARED**, 7, b g Dubawi (IRE)—Appearance
4 **AROD (IRE)**, 8, b h Teofilo (IRE)—My Personal Space (USA)
5 **BIRCH GROVE (IRE)**, 4, b f Galileo (IRE)—Danehurst
6 **BLESS HIM (IRE)**, 5, b g Sea The Stars (IRE)—Happy Land (IRE)
7 **BRETON ROCK (IRE)**, 9, b g Bahamian Bounty—Anna's Rock (IRE)
8 **CALLING OUT (FR)**, 8, b br g Martaline—Exit The Straight (IRE)
9 **COME ON TIER (FR)**, 4, b c Kendargent (FR)—Milwaukee (FR)
10 **DESERT ENCOUNTER (IRE)**, 7, b g Halling (USA)—La Chicana (IRE)
11 **DUBAWI MEEZNAH (IRE)**, 4, b f Dubawi (IRE)—Meeznah (USA)
12 **ENCRYPTION (IRE)**, 4, br g High Chaparral (IRE)—Challow Hills (USA)
13 **GLORY AWAITS (IRE)**, 9, ch g Choisir (AUS)—Sandbox Two (IRE)
14 **HIGHBROW**, 4, b g Intello (GER)—Wild Gardenia
15 **HIGHLAND SKY (IRE)**, 4, br g Camelot—Healing Music (FR)
16 **IMPERIAL COURT (IRE)**, 4, b g Zoffany (FR)—La Vita Bella
17 **KWANZA**, 4, b f Exchange Rate (USA)—Kiswahili
18 **LADY OF SHALOTT**, 4, b f Camelot—Silent Act (USA)
19 **MISS LATIN (IRE)**, 4, b f Galileo (IRE)—Breeze Hill (IRE)

MR DAVID SIMCOCK - Continued

20 **MRS SIPPY (USA)**, 4, b f Blame (USA)—Qushchi
21 **MUGATOO (IRE)**, 4, b g Henrythenavigator (USA)—Elopa (GER)
22 **NONIOS (IRE)**, 7, b g Oasis Dream—Young and Daring (USA)
23 **POLYBIUS**, 8, b g Oasis Dream—Freedonia
24 **WEST COAST FLYER**, 6, b g Cape Cross (IRE)—La Felicita
25 **WHITE CHOCOLATE (IRE)**, 5, br m Mastercraftsman (IRE)—Coco Demure (IRE)

THREE-YEAR-OLDS

26 **ALEMAGNA**, b f Sea The Moon (GER)—Alta Moda
27 **ANGUS (IRE)**, gr g Dark Angel (IRE)—Secret Key (IRE)
28 **ANNECY**, b f Swiss Spirit—Atheera (IRE)
29 **APPROACH BY SEA (IRE)**, ch f Dawn Approach (IRE)—Galley
30 **BATTLE OF PEMBROKE (USA)**, b c Declaration of War (USA)—Beauty O' Gwaun (IRE)
31 Ch g Helmet (AUS)—Bint Doyen
32 B f Farhh—Bronwen (IRE)
33 **BUBBELAH (IRE)**, b g Zoffany (IRE)—Sanadaat
34 **CLAP YOUR HANDS**, b g Universal (IRE)—Woop Woop (IRE)
35 **DELACHANCE (FR)**, b c Linngari (IRE)—Three French Hens (IRE)
36 **DESERT LAND (IRE)**, b c Kodiac—La Chicana (IRE)
37 **DR JEKYLL (IRE)**, b c Scat Daddy (USA)—Similu
38 **DURSTON**, ch c Sea The Moon (GER)—Caribana
39 B c Universal (IRE)—Fly Free
40 **FURIOUS**, b f Oasis Dream—Noyelles (IRE)
41 B g Intello (GER)—Galipette
42 **GARRISON LAW**, b g Garswood—Cushat Law (IRE)
43 Ch f Iffraaj—Go Angellica (IRE)
44 **J'OUVERT (IRE)**, b f Dawn Approach (IRE)—Areyaam (USA)
45 B c Siyouni (FR)—Late Night (GER)
46 **LEOPARDINA (IRE)**, b f Lawman (FR)—Leopard Creek
47 **LIBERTY ISLAND**, b f Shamardal (USA)—Lady Liberty (IRE)
48 **MOMENT OF HOPE (IRE)**, b f Casamento (IRE)—Hikayati (USA)
49 **OMNIVEGA (FR)**, b c Siyouni (FR)—Vermentina (IRE)
50 **ONLY GAME IN TOWN (USA)**, b g Speightstown—Love Me Only (IRE)
51 **PERSUER**, ch f Intello (GER)—Chase The Lady (USA)
52 **POETIC ERA**, b f Poet's Voice—Secret Era
53 **PREJUDICE**, ch c Dubawi (IRE)—Ever Rigg
54 Br f Speightstown (USA)—Qushchi
55 **RAAKIB ALHAWA (IRE)**, b c Kingman—Starlet (IRE)
56 **RANGALI ISLAND (IRE)**, b c Camacho—Tender Surprise
57 **REVAMP (USA)**, br g Tapizar (USA)—Lady Siphonica (USA)
58 **SHAMAMEYA (IRE)**, ch f New Approach (IRE)—Alasha (IRE)
59 **SHINOBI (IRE)**, ch c Iffraaj—Ninja Lady
60 **SIBYLLINE**, ch f Leroidesanimaux (BRZ)—Selenography
61 **SPANISH MISSION (USA)**, br c Noble Mission—Limonar (IRE)
62 **STARCZEWSKI (USA)**, b g Magician (IRE)—Lucifer's Stone (USA)
63 **UNIVERSAL ORDER**, ch c Universal (IRE)—My Order
64 **VEXED**, b g Charm Spirit (IRE)—Kite Mark
65 **VICTORY AHEAD (IRE)**, b c Dream Ahead (USA)—Rush
66 **WIRETAP (FR)**, b g Charm Spirit (IRE)—Ysper (FR)
67 **WOVEN**, ch c Dutch Art—Regal Silk

TWO-YEAR-OLDS

68 **ALCHIMISTA**, b f 28/2 Archipenko (USA)—Alta Moda (Sadler's Wells (USA))
69 B f 24/3 Sea The Moon (GER)—Brigitta (IRE) (Sadler's Wells (USA)) (35000)
70 B c 8/2 Dark Angel (IRE)—Brown Eyed Honey (Elusive City (USA))
71 B c 23/5 Free Eagle (IRE)—Bryanstown (IRE) (Galileo (IRE)) (72000)
72 B c 11/3 Brazen Beau (AUS)—Celestial Empire (USA) (Empire Maker (USA)) (55000)
73 B f 21/2 Iffraaj—Counterclaim (Pivotal) (90000)
74 B c 15/3 Dutch Art—Crying Lightening (IRE) (Holy Roman Emperor (IRE)) (50000)
75 Ch f 17/2 Raven's Pass (USA)—Fibou (USA) (Seeking The Gold (USA)) (38000)
76 B f 17/3 Golden Horn—Folk Opera (IRE) (Singspiel (IRE))
77 Br f 18/2 Ivawood (IRE)—Foreplay (IRE) (Lujain (USA)) (35398)

MR DAVID SIMCOCK - Continued

78 B f 1/5 Nathaniel (IRE)—Honorine (IRE) (Mark of Esteem (IRE))
79 B c 17/3 Oasis Dream—I'm A Dreamer (IRE) (Noverre (USA)) (101137)
80 B c 3/4 Sea The Stars (IRE)—Interim Payment (USA) (Red Ransom (USA)) (60000)
81 B f 20/2 Intello (GER)—Kamarinskaya (USA) (Storm Cat (USA))
82 **LADY TATI (IRE)**, b f 28/2 Charm Spirit (IRE)—Melodique (FR) (Falco (USA)) (100000)
83 B c 3/3 Oasis Dream—Landmark (USA) (Arch (USA)) (320000)
84 B f 25/3 Kingman—Marine Bleue (IRE) (Desert Prince (IRE))
85 **MICROSCOPIC (IRE)**, br f 21/4 Intense Focus (USA)—Royal Esteem (Mark of Esteem (IRE)) (13333)
86 B f 10/2 Kitten's Joy (USA)—Mistaken Love (USA) (Bernardini (USA)) (75000)
87 B f 4/4 Invincible Spirit (IRE)—Moment In Time (IRE) (Tiger Hill (IRE)) (140000)
88 B f 16/4 Dark Angel (IRE)—Momentus (IRE) (Montjeu (IRE)) (110000)
89 **ORIENTAL MYSTIQUE**, b f 25/2 Kingman—Madame Chiang (Archipenko (USA))
90 **PAX BRITANNICA (IRE)**, b f 14/4 Zoffany (IRE)—Athreyaa (Singspiel (IRE)) (80000)
91 Ch c 13/4 Outstrip—Pink Flames (IRE) (Redback) (50000)
92 **PRINCE ALEX**, b c 16/2 Excelebration (IRE)—Interchange (IRE) (Montjeu (IRE)) (220000)
93 B f 6/3 Blame (USA)—Qushchi (Encosta de Lago (AUS))
94 B c 25/4 Intrinsic—Red Kyte (Hawk Wing (USA))
95 Ch f 27/2 Sepoy (AUS)—Self Centred (Medicean) (48000)
96 B f 26/4 Camelot—Similu (Danehill Dancer (IRE)) (70000)
97 Ch f 19/3 Bated Breath—Sky Crystal (GER) (Galileo (IRE))
98 B f 20/3 Cable Bay (IRE)—Spotlight (Dr Fong (USA))
99 B c 28/3 Zoffany (IRE)—Susan Stroman (Monsun (GER)) (16856)
100 Ch c 6/4 Dragon Pulse (IRE)—Taalluf (USA) (Hansel (USA)) (18000)
101 Ch f 21/3 Dutch Art—Tahirah (Green Desert (USA)) (25000)
102 Br c 23/2 Iffraaj—Terentia (Diktat) (55000)
103 Br c 6/5 City Zip (USA)—Traffic Sister (USA) (More Than Ready (USA))
104 B f 19/4 Muhaarar—Up In Time (Noverre (USA)) (70000)
105 B f 17/5 Galileo (IRE)—Walklikeanegyptian (IRE) (Danehill (USA))

Owners: Abdullah Al Mansoori, Malih Al Basti, Sheikh Juma Dalmook Al Maktoum, Abdullah Saeed Al Nabooda, Mohammed Al Nabooda, Saeed Al Qassimi, Saeed Al Tayer, Amo Racing Ltd, Andrew Whitlock Racing Ltd, Abdullah Belhab, Marcella Burns, Chola Dynasty, John Cook, The Crepello Partnership, Khalifa Dasmal, Dunchurch Lodge Stud Co, El Catorce Partnership, Equine Racing Ltd, Mr & Mrs M Franklin, Steven Furniss & Ryan Maddocks, Genting Casinos Ltd, Mrs Fitri Hay, Highclere Thoroughbreds, Hot To Trot, Ahmed Jaber, Saeed Jaber, Lordship Stud, Lynch Bages, The Honourable Earle Mack & Team Valor LLC, Millingbrooke Racing, Colin Murfitt, Never Say Die Partnership, Tony Perkins, Daniel Pittack, Qatar Racing Ltd, Qatar Racing Ltd & Mister Kin Hung Kei, Kirsten Rausing, Jos & Jane Rodosthenous, Rumble Racing Club, Ali Saeed, St Albans Bloodstock, Sun International Group, Talentschmiede Racing, Tick Tock Partnership, Tweenhills Fillies Syndicate, Two Towers Partnership, Walters Plant Hire.

Assistant Trainers: Sam Goldsmith, Jack Jones

Jockey (flat): Jamie Spencer. **Apprentice:** George Bass, Dylan Hogan.

---

500 MR DAN SKELTON, Alcester
Postal: **Lodge Hill, Shelfield Green, Shelfield, Alcester, Warwickshire, B49 6JR**
Contacts: **PHONE (01789) 336339**
E-MAIL office@danskeltonracing.com WEBSITE www.danskeltonracing.com

1 **ACCORDINGTOGINO (IRE)**, 6, ch g Perugino (USA)—Accordintomags (IRE) **Mrs Gill Duckworth & Mrs Pat Dry**
2 **AGGY WITH IT (IRE)**, 5, b m Presenting—Agathe du Berlais (FR) **Andy & Sharon Measham**
3 **AHEADFULLOFDREAMS (IRE)**, 6, b g Sandmason—Aphra Benn (IRE) **WPL Group Holdings Limited**
4 **AINTREE MY DREAM (FR)**, 9, b br g Saint des Saints (FR)—Pretty Melodie (FR) **Mr M. Olden**
5 **AL SHAHIR (IRE)**, 7, b g Robin des Champs (FR)—Sarah Massini (IRE) **N. W. Lake**
6 **ALCOCK AND BROWN (IRE)**, 7, b g Oasis Dream—Heart Stopping (USA) **Mr M. Olden**
7 **ALLONOK**, 6, b g Kalanisi (IRE)—Isabello (IRE) **The Can't Say No Partnership**
8 **ALNADAM (FR)**, 6, b g Poliglote—Rosadame (FR) **Mr B. J. C. Drew**
9 **ANGE DES MALBERAUX (FR)**, 9, b g Michel Georges—Petite Baie (FR) **Hools & Forces Partnership**
10 **ANGEL OF THE NORTH (IRE)**, 4, gr f Dark Angel (IRE)—Kay Es Jay (FR) **Mr K. Wetton**
11 **ANTUNES**, 5, b g Nathaniel (IRE)—Aigrette Garzette (IRE) **Mr M. Adams**
12 **ANYTIME WILL DO (IRE)**, 6, b g Scorpion (IRE)—Pellerossa (IRE) **Surrey Racing (at)**
13 **ARDERA CROSS (IRE)**, 8, ch g Shantou (USA)—Fair Maid Marion (IRE) **Hools & Forces Partnership**
14 **ARDLETHEN (IRE)**, 6, ch g Arakan (USA)—Itsafamilyaffair (IRE) **Mike and Eileen Newbould**
15 **AUX PTITS SOINS (FR)**, 9, gr g Saint des Saints (FR)—Reflexion Faite (FR) **Mr J. Hales**
16 **AZZURI**, 7, b g Azamour (IRE)—Folly Lodge **The Blind Squirrels**

MR DAN SKELTON - Continued

17 **BANDSMAN**, 8, b g Bandmaster (USA)—Soleil Sauvage **Mrs S. J. Faulks**
18 **BBOLD (IRE)**, 5, b g Aizavoski (IRE)—Molly Be **BAA Management Ltd**
19 **BEAKSTOWN (IRE)**, 6, b g Stowaway—Midnight Reel (IRE) **Mr B. J. C. Drew**
20 **BENNYS KING (IRE)**, 8, b g Beneficial—Hellofafaithful (IRE) **Mezzone Family**
21 **BERGAMOT (IRE)**, 4, b f Azamour (IRE)—Behrama (IRE) **Chris Humber & Dan Skelton**
22 **BETAMECHE (FR)**, 8, gr g Kapgarde (FR)—Kaldona (FR) **Miss J. Craymer**
23 **BEYONDAPPROACH (IRE)**, 5, b m Jeremy (USA)—Gonebeyondajoke (IRE) **Mr M. Olden**
24 **BIG G**, 4, b g Cityscape—Crazy (GER) **BAA Management Ltd**
25 **BONBONNIERE**, 5, br m Martaline—La Bombonera (FR) **Mrs S. J. Faulks**
26 **BORN SURVIVOR (IRE)**, 8, b g King's Theatre (IRE)—
    Bob's Flame (IRE) **Mrs G. Widdowson & Mrs R. Kelvin-Hughes**
27 **BOSTON HEATHER (IRE)**, 11, b m Elusive City (USA)—Colour's Red (IRE) **Mr D. N. Skelton**
28 **BOURBON BORDERLINE (IRE)**, 5, b g Milan—Daraheen Diamond (IRE) **Mike and Eileen Newbould**
29 **CALL ME CHRIS**, 5, b m Kayf Tara—I'm Delilah **Mr C. S. Johnston**
30 **CAPTAIN CHAOS (IRE)**, 8, ch g Golan (IRE)—Times Have Changed (IRE) **Mike and Eileen Newbould**
31 **CH'TIBELLO (FR)**, 8, b g Sageburg (IRE)—Neicha (FR) **The Can't Say No Partnership**
32 **CHARMING DREAM (FR)**, 5, b g Dream Well (FR)—Changing Times (FR) **Mr & Mrs J. D. Cotton**
33 **CLONDAW ANCHOR (IRE)**, 6, gr g Stowaway—Masiana (IRE) **Highclere Thoroughbred Racing - Anchor**
34 **COBRA DE MAI (FR)**, 7, b g Great Pretender (IRE)—Miria Galanda (FR) **Norman Lake & Susan Carsberg**
35 **COCK A DOODLE DOO (FR)**, 7, b m Della Francesca (USA)—Jiletta (FR) **Rio Gold Racing Club**
36 **COMRADE CONRAD (IRE)**, 5, br g Canford Cliffs (IRE)—View (IRE) **Mr J. Lane**
37 **CRUCIAL ROLE**, 7, b g Westerner—The Lyme Volunteer (IRE) **Mr D. W. Fox**
38 **DENMEAD**, 6, b g Champs Elysees—Glorious Dreams (USA) **John O'Donnell & Noel Kelly**
39 **DESIRABLE COURT (IRE)**, 6, b m Court Cave (IRE)—Desirable Rhythm (IRE) **Mr C. Buckingham**
40 **DESTRIER (FR)**, 6, b g Voix du Nord (FR)—Razia (FR) **Three Celts**
41 **DIOMEDE DES MOTTES (FR)**, 6, ch g Kapgarde (FR)—Nellyssa Bleu (FR) **Belbroughton Racing Club**
42 **DOG OF WAR (FR)**, 5, b g Soldier of Fortune (IRE)—Zainzana (FR) **Mr C. A. Donlon**
43 **DURL ROCK (IRE)**, 4, b g Milan—Greenfieldflyer (IRE) **Simon & Lisa Hobson**
44 **ECLAIR D'AINAY (FR)**, 5, b br g Network (GER)—Etoile d'ainay (FR) **Mr J. Hales**
45 **ELTON DES MOTTES (FR)**, 5, b g Maresca Sorrento (FR)—
    Ouhetu des Mottes (FR) **Horne, Hudson, Nolan & Ryans**
46 **EMBOLE (FR)**, 5, b g Buck's Boum (FR)—Urielle Collonges (FR) **Mr C. A. Donlon**
47 **EMMAS JOY (IRE)**, 6, b m Gold Well—Emma Jane (IRE) **Julian Howl & Ian Tyrrell**
48 **ETAMINE DU COCHET (FR)**, 5, gr m Martaline—Nuance du Cochet (FR) **Mrs S. L. Edwards**
49 **EVER SO COOL (IRE)**, 4, b f Shantou (USA)—Cool Cool (FR) **Bullen-smith & Faulks**
50 **EYREN (IRE)**, 4, b f Rip Van Winkle (IRE)—Ella Ransom (GER) **Yorton Racing & Dan Skelton**
51 **FALCON SUN (FR)**, 5, b g Falco (USA)—Pray For Sun (IRE) **Mezzone Family**
52 **FERROBIN (IRE)**, 5, br g Robin des Champs (FR)—Fedaia (IRE) **Three Celts**
53 **FLASH THE STEEL (IRE)**, 7, b br g Craigsteel—Anna's Melody (IRE) **Mr J. J. Reilly**
54 **FLEGMATIK (FR)**, 4, ch g Fuisse (FR)—Crack d'emble (FR) **N. W. Lake**
55 **FLOKI**, 5, b g Kalanisi (IRE)—La Dame Brune (FR) **Mr D. N. Skelton**
56 **FRANKIE RAPPER (IRE)**, 7, b g Milan—Parkdota (IRE) **Miss J. Craymer**
57 **GET ON THE YAGER**, 9, b g Tamure (IRE)—Florentino **Dick and Mandy Higgins**
58 **GETARIVER (IRE)**, 6, br m Getaway (GER)—Watson River (IRE) **Mr & Mrs Gordon Pink**
59 **GLOBAL HARMONY (IRE)**, 4, b f Flemensfirth (USA)—Violin Davis (FR) **Mrs S. Carsberg**
60 **GLOBAL RULER**, 7, b g Kalanisi (IRE)—Queen's Leader **Mrs S. Carsberg**
61 **GOLD CHAIN (IRE)**, 9, b m Authorized (IRE)—Mountain Chain (USA) **Mr D. N. Skelton**
62 **GOLDEN VISION (FR)**, 7, bl m Vision d'etat (FR)—My Gold du Fanil (FR) **Mr C. Buckingham**
63 **GOODTHYNEAWAY (IRE)**, 6, b g Stowaway—Calling Classy (IRE) **Rio Gold Racing Club**
64 **GORTROE JOE (IRE)**, 7, b g Beneficial—Rowlands Star (IRE) **J. T. Warner**
65 **GRAND SLAMMER (IRE)**, 4, b g Milan—Ballyknock Present (IRE) **Mr D. N. Skelton**
66 **GRANDE WALTZ (GER)**, 4, b g Wiener Walzer (GER)—Giralda (IRE) **Foxtrot Racing: Grande Waltz**
67 **HALA PRINCESS (IRE)**, 4, b f Bernebeau (FR)—Aroka (FR) **Mr C. Buckingham**
68 **HATCHER (IRE)**, 6, b g Doyen (IRE)—African Keys (IRE) **P. H. Betts**
69 **HEAR NO EVIL (IRE)**, 7, b g Getaway—Listening (IRE) **Mrs S. Magnier**
70 **HIGH SECRET (IRE)**, 8, b g High Chaparral (IRE)—Secret Question (USA) **Hools & Forces Partnership**
71 **HOLRYALE (IRE)**, 7, b g Trans Island—Lady Ramona (IRE) **The Holryale Partnership**
72 **HUMBLE HERO (IRE)**, 5, b g High Chaparral (IRE)—Alamouna (IRE) **Notalotterry**
73 **I'D BETTER GO NOW (IRE)**, 6, b g Alkaadhem—Pohutakawa (FR) **Mr & Mrs Paul & Clare Rooney**
74 **IDEE DE GARDE (FR)**, 6, b g Kapgarde (FR)—Idee Recue (FR) **Mr B. G. Acheson**
75 **INCH RISE (IRE)**, 10, br g Heron Island (IRE)—Rosetown Girl (IRE) **Hools & Forces Partnership**
76 **ISTIMRAAR (IRE)**, 8, b g Dansili—Manayer (IRE) **Rio Gold Racing Club Ltd**
77 **JANE LAMB**, 6, b m Haafhd—Lucinda Lamb **Foxtrot Racing: Jane Lamb**
78 **KASAKH NOIR (FR)**, 7, ch g Redback—Vale of Honor (FR) **Mr T. P. Radford**

MR DAN SKELTON - Continued

79 KEREMAN (IRE), 5, b g Azamour (IRE)—Kerania (IRE) **Rio Gold Racing Club Ltd**
80 KING D'ARGENT (FR), 4, ch g Kendargent (FR)—Ephigenie (IRE) **Andrew Dick & John Stevenson**
81 KNIGHT IN DUBAI (IRE), 6, b g Dubai Destination (USA)—Bobbies Storm (IRE) **Mr & Mrs Ben Houghton**
82 KONIGIN ARA (GER), 4, br f Kamsin (GER)—Konigin Arte (GER) **Yorton Racing**
83 LADY MALEFICENT, 5, b m Malinas (GER)—Lush Lady (FR) **Lodge Hill Syndicate**
84 LADY RIDGEMERE (IRE), 5, b m Milan—Sorcillera **Mr N. Skelton**
85 LEX ELEVEN (IRE), 4, b f Getaway (GER)—Sixofone (IRE) **Mr D. N. Skelton**
86 LYFORD (IRE), 4, ch g Intense Focus (USA)—Nurture (IRE) **Mr D. N. Skelton**
87 MABELA, 5, b m Oscar (IRE)—Histoire de Moeurs (FR) **S Smith & S Campion**
88 MAIRE BANRIGH, 5, b m King's Theatre (IRE)—La Marianne **Mr J Hales & Mr J Diver**
89 MARLEY FIRTH (IRE), 7, b g Flemensfirth (USA)—Merrill Gaye (IRE) **Surrey Racing (mf)**
90 MARRACUDJA (FR), 8, b g Martaline—Memorial (FR) **Hools & Forces Partnership**
91 MASSINI'S LADY, 8, b m Dr Massini (IRE)—Lady du Bost (FR) **Hools & Forces Partnership**
92 MENTAL MICKY (IRE), 4, b g Darsi (FR)—Kyle Hill (IRE) **Mr N. Skelton**
93 MERCER'S TROOP (IRE), 4, b g Canford Cliffs (IRE)—Meek Appeal (USA) **Mr B. H. Turner**
94 MIDNIGHT RIVER, 4, ch g Midnight Legend—Well Connected **Mr D. N. Skelton**
95 MISTER UNIVERSUM (GER), 7, b g Cape Cross (IRE)—Miss Europa (IRE) **Notalotterry**
96 MOHAAYED, 7, b g Intikhab (USA)—Reyaada **Mrs J. A. Watts**
97 MOLLY OLLYS WISHES, 5, b m Black Sam Bellamy (IRE)—September Moon **West Mercia Fork Trucks Ltd**
98 MOLLY THE DOLLY (IRE), 8, b m Flemensfirth (USA)—Pistol Flash (IRE) **Mr D. Hanafin**
99 MONSIEUR D'ARQUE (IRE), 5, b g Muhtathir—Nervous Breakdown (FR) **WPL Group Holdings Limited**
100 MONTEGO GREY (FR), 5, gr g Montmartre (FR)—Anna Kalinka (GER) **Dick and Mandy Higgins**
101 MOONLIGHT DANCER, 6, gr m Kayf Tara—Dissolve **Mrs J. A. Watts**
102 NEW QUAY (IRE), 6, b g Mahler—Beg La Eile (IRE) **Norman Lake & Susan Carsberg**
103 NIMBY (IRE), 5, ch g Doyen (IRE)—Ain't Misbehavin (IRE) **Mr & Mrs Paul & Clare Rooney**
104 NO GETAWAY (IRE), 6, ch g Getaway (GER)—Nonnetia (FR) **Dick, Keenan, Sawer, Stevenson**
105 NO HASSLE HOFF (IRE), 7, b br g Craigsteel—Endless Patience (IRE) **Mr Simon Munir & Mr Isaac Souede**
106 NORTHOFTHEWALL (IRE), 5, b g Mahler—Sherchanceit (IRE) **Winter Gold Racing**
107 NOT THAT FUISSE (FR), 6, b g Fuisse (FR)—Edelmira (FR) **Mr C. A. Donlon**
108 NOTNOW SEAMUS, 8, b g Notnowcato—Special Beat **Bgc Racing Six Pack**
109 NOTWHATIAM (IRE), 9, b g Morozov (USA)—Riverfort (IRE) **Hools & Forces Partnership**
110 NUBE NEGRA (SPA), 5, b g Dink (FR)—Manly Dream (FR) **Mr T. Spraggett**
111 OLDGRANGEWOOD, 8, b g Central Park (IRE)—Top of The Class (IRE) **Chris Giles & Sandra Giles**
112 OLLY THE BRAVE, 6, b g Black Sam Bellamy (IRE)—September Moon **West Mercia Fork Trucks Ltd**
113 PEPPAY LE PUGH (IRE), 8, b g Arakan (USA)—Pinaflore (FR) **Hools & Forces Partnership**
114 PERCY'S WORD, 5, b g Sir Percy—Laverre (IRE) **Mezzone Family**
115 PETER THE MAYO MAN (IRE), 9, ch g Dylan Thomas (IRE)—Mommkin **Mr C. Buckingham**
116 POINT TAKEN (IRE), 5, b g Papal Bull—Grand Isla **Mr D. W. Fox**
117 POTTERS APPROACH (IRE), 8, b g Scorpion (IRE)—Moon Approach (IRE) **Surrey Racing (PA)**
118 PRESENT RANGER (IRE), 6, b g Presenting—Papoose (IRE) **Dick and Mandy Higgins**
119 PROTEKTORAT (FR), 4, b g Saint des Saints (FR)—Protektion (FR) **Sir A Ferguson G Mason J Hales & L Hales**
120 PRUSSIA WITH LOVE, 5, b m Presenting—Ruby Royale **Mr N. Skelton**
121 QUIET FLOW, 4, b g Sholokhov (IRE)—Sardagna (FR) **Mr C. A. Donlon**
122 RATOUTE YUTTY, 6, b m Midnight Legend—Easibrook Jane **The Yes We Named Her Syndicate**
123 REALMS OF FIRE, 6, ch g Malinas (GER)—Realms of Gold (USA) **Mrs S. C. Welch**
124 RED RISING (IRE), 8, ch g Flemensfirth (USA)—Fugal Maid (FR) **Mr & Mrs Paul & Clare Rooney**
125 REDZOR (IRE), 6, b g Shantou (USA)—Knockara One (IRE) **Bryan Drew & Steve Roper**
126 4, Gr g Martaline—Reform Act (USA) **Mr D. N. Skelton**
127 RENE'S GIRL (IRE), 9, b m Presenting—Brogella (IRE) **Andy & Sharon Measham**
128 RENWICK (IRE), 6, b g Milan—Come In Moscow (IRE) **Mrs D. L. Whateley**
129 ROBIN WATERS (FR), 6, b g Irish Wells (FR)—Skandia (FR) **Mr C. A. Donlon**
130 ROCKU, 9, b g Great Palm (USA)—Suetsu (IRE) **Stirrups Racing**
131 RODEO DODO (IRE), 9, b g Milan—Laney Mary (IRE) **Hools & Forces Partnership**
132 ROKSANA (IRE), 7, b m Dubai Destination (USA)—Talktothetail (IRE) **Mrs S. J. Faulks**
133 ROSER MOTER (IRE), 4, b f Motivator—Rosia Bay **Rio Gold Racing Club**
134 ROYAL BEEKEEPER, 6, ch g Champs Elysees—Lasso **Rio Gold Racing Club Ltd**
135 SAM RED (IRE), 8, b g Denham Red (FR)—Call Me Nana (FR) **Bgc Racing & Rob Pitcher**
136 SAVELLO (IRE), 13, ch g Anshan—Fontaine Frances (IRE) **S Smith & S Campion**
137 SEA OF MYSTERY (IRE), 6, b g Sea The Stars (IRE)—Sassenach (IRE) **Mr Frank McAleavy & Mr Ian McAleavy**
138 SENSE OF ADVENTURE, 5, ch g Getaway (GER)—Lady Jurado (IRE) **Mr B. G. Acheson**
139 SERRALUNGA, 6, b g Robin des Champs (FR)—Milan Athlete (IRE) **Mr C. A. Donlon**
140 SET LIST (IRE), 10, b g Heron Island (IRE)—Copper Magic (IRE) **Rio Gold Racing Club**
141 SGROPPINO (IRE), 7, b g Getaway (GER)—Boadicea **Mr D. N. Skelton**
142 SHAN BLUE (IRE), 5, b g Shantou (USA)—Lady Roberta (IRE) **Mr C. A. Donlon**

MR DAN SKELTON - Continued

143 **SHANNON BRIDGE (IRE)**, 6, ch g Flemensfirth (USA)—
                    Bridgequarter Lady (IRE) **M Boothright G Lovett P Deffains**
144 **SHELFIELD**, 4, b c Kayf Tara—Isabello (IRE) **Mr N. Skelton**
145 **SIGNIFICANT OTHER (IRE)**, 5, b m Fame And Glory—Etoile Margot (FR) **Mr N. Skelton**
146 **SIMPLY LOVELEH**, 6, b m Beneficial—Pippedatthepost **Mr J. J. Reilly**
147 **SIR MANGAN (IRE)**, 11, b g Darsi (FR)—Lady Pep (IRE) **Mr Frank McAleavy & Mr Ian McAleavy**
148 **SO LONELY (IRE)**, 5, b m So You Think (NZ)—Via Aurelia (IRE) **The Can't Say No Partnership**
149 **SOFIA'S ROCK (FR)**, 5, b g Rock of Gibraltar (IRE)—Princess Sofia (UAE) **Mezzone Family 1**
150 **SOLO SAXOPHONE (IRE)**, 5, b g Frankel—Society Hostess (USA) **BGC Racing**
151 **SOLOMON GREY (FR)**, 7, gr g Sulamani (IRE)—Sardagna (FR) **Mrs S. J. Faulks**
152 **SOYOUTHINKSOAGAIN (IRE)**, 4, b g So You Think (NZ)—Al Saqiya (USA) **WPL Group Holdings Limited**
153 **SPIRITOFTHEGAMES (IRE)**, 7, b g Darsi (FR)—Lucy Walters (IRE) **N. W. Lake**
154 **STOWAWAY MAGIC (IRE)**, 8, b g Stowaway—Irish Mystics (IRE) **Grech & Parkin**
155 **STYLISH DANCER**, 5, b m Nathaniel (IRE)—Hazy Dancer **John J Reilly & Dan Skelton**
156 **SUPREMELY LUCKY (IRE)**, 7, b g Milan—Lucky Supreme (IRE) **Mr M. Olden**
157 **SYMPHONY OF ANGELS**, 7, b g Sulamani (IRE)—Flying Lion **Good Evans Racing Partnership**
158 **THE RAVEN MASTER**, 5, b g Raven's Pass (USA)—
                    Rainbow Desert (USA) **M Boothright G Lovett P Deffains**
159 **THE ROSARY FLYER (IRE)**, 4, b g Robin des Champs (FR)—Present Gesture (IRE) **Mr D. N. Skelton**
160 **THEATREBAR**, 11, b g King's Theatre (IRE)—Ardenbar **Mrs C. A. Wyatt**
161 **THREE MUSKETEERS (IRE)**, 9, b g Flemensfirth (USA)—
                    Friendly Craic (IRE) **Mr Frank McAleavy & Mr Ian McAleavy**
162 **TIGERALLEY**, 10, b m Revoque (IRE)—Run Tiger (IRE) **Rio Gold Racing Club Ltd**
163 **TOKAY DOKEY (IRE)**, 5, b g Gold Well—Charming Present (IRE) **Mr C. A. Donlon**
164 **TOMMY RAPPER (IRE)**, 8, b g Milan—Supreme Evening (IRE) **Judy Craymer & Nick Skelton**
165 **TOO MANY DIAMONDS (IRE)**, 8, br g Diamond Green (FR)—Too Much Color (USA) **Mr D. N. Skelton**
166 4, Ch g Planteur (IRE)—Turtledove (FR) **Mr & Mrs Paul & Clare Rooney**
167 **UP THE DRIVE (IRE)**, 6, b g Olden Times—Black Magic Baby (IRE) **Rio Gold Racing Club**
168 **VALUE AT RISK**, 10, b g Kayf Tara—Miss Orchestra (IRE) **Mr M. Adams**
169 **WELCOME POLLY**, 7, br m Milan—Culmore Lady (IRE) **Hools & Forces Partnership**
170 **WEST CORK**, 5, b g Midnight Legend—Calamintha **Mike and Eileen Newbould**
171 **WEST TO THE BRIDGE (IRE)**, 6, b g Flemensfirth (USA)—Godlylady (IRE) **Mr P. J. Tierney**
172 **WESTERN BREEZE (IRE)**, 10, b m Westerner—Winsome Breeze (IRE) **Mr D. N. Skelton**
173 **WHATDUHAVTOGET (IRE)**, 7, b m Presenting—
                    Smooching (IRE) **Highclere Thoroughbred Racing - Presenting**
174 **WHITE WALKER**, 4, gr g Dream Eater (IRE)—Soleil Sauvage **Winter Gold Racing**
175 **WHOCALLEDMESPEEDY (IRE)**, 4, b f Rip Van Winkle (IRE)—Fig Tree Drive (USA) **Mr C. Buckingham**
176 **WILDE ABOUT OSCAR (IRE)**, 6, b g Oscar (IRE)—Baie Barbara (IRE) **Mike and Eileen Newbould**
177 **WISHFUL TINKER (IRE)**, 6, b g Milan—Third Wish (IRE) **Pending Approval Partners**
178 **YORKIST (IRE)**, 11, ch g Urban Ocean (FR)—Kilbarry Demon (IRE) **Mike and Eileen Newbould**
179 **ZAMPARELLI (IRE)**, 7, b g Mahler—Goulburn Bridge (IRE) **Mrs S. C. Welch**
180 **ZEPHYROS BLEU (IRE)**, 9, b g Westerner—Quel Bleu (IRE) **Rio Gold Racing Club**

Other Owners: Mr D. Abraham, Mr A. C. Allan, Mr D. Balchin, M. Boothright, Mr M. J. Brown, Mr N. J. Brown, Mr P. P. J. Bullen-Smith, Ms J. S. Campion, Mr J. C. Cleary, J. D. Cotton, Mrs B. Cotton, Mr P. Deffains, Mr A. D. Dixi, Mr J. Diver, Mrs P. Dry, Mrs C. M. Du Pon, Mrs G. Duckworth, Mr C. J. Edwards, Mr M. Evans, Mrs L. Fellows, Sir A. Ferguson, Foxtrot Racing Management Ltd, Mr D. Futter, Mrs A. E. Giles, Mr C. M. Giles, Mr J. B. Gilruth, Mr C. M. Grech, Mr S. Grubb, Mr C. R. Hadingham, Mr J. R. Hales, Miss L. J. Hales, Mr R. S. Higgins, Mrs A. J. Higgins, Highclere Nominated Partner Limited, Highclere Thoroughbred Racing Ltd, Mr S. E. Hobson, Mrs L. C. Hobson, Mr P. B. R. Houghton, Mrs V. K. Houghton, Mr J. Howl, Mr C. M. Humber, Johnston Racing Ltd, Mr K. D. Jones, Mr W. E. N Kelly, R. G. Kelvin-Hughes, Mrs E. A. Kelvin-Hughes, Mr G. P. A. Lovett, Mr I. Marmion, G. A. Mason, Mr I. McAleavy, Mr F. McAleavy, Mrs S. M. Measham, Mr A. R. Measham, Mrs S. M. Mezzone, Mr M. L. Mezzone, Mr G. G. Mezzone, Mrs K. J. Morgan, S. E. Munir, Mr J. Murphy, Mrs E. E. Newbould, Mr J. M. Newbould, T. H. Northwood, Mr J. O'Donnell, Mr S. J. Parkin, Mrs K. M. Pink, Mr G. K. G. Pink, Mr R. Pitcher, Mr K. Place, Mr A. Randle, Mr D. Richardson, Mrs C. Rooney, Mr P. A. Rooney, Mr S. R. Roper, Mr P. Ryan, Mr D. M. Scott, Mrs S. Smith, Mr I. Souede, Mr J. M. Stevenson, Surrey Racing Limited, Mr I. Tyrrell, Mr R. Ward, Mrs B. A. Widdowson.

Assistant Trainer: Tom Messenger

Jockey (NH): Harry Skelton, Bridget Andrews. **Conditional:** William Marshall. **Amateur:** Mr Tristan Durrell.

501 **MR KEN SLACK, Appleby**
Postal: Heather Bank, Brackenber, Appleby-In-Westmorland, Cumbria, CA16 6LP
Contacts: **PHONE** (01768) 351354 **MOBILE** (07931) 137413

1 **CALLIOPE,** 6, b m Poet's Voice—Costa Brava (IRE) **Mr E. G. Tunstall**
2 **FAST AND FRIENDLY (IRE),** 5, b g September Storm (GER)—Merewood Lodge (IRE) **Ar White Racing**
3 **JOKERS AND ROGUES (IRE),** 11, b g Beneficial—Ashfield Girl (IRE) **A. Slack**
4 **LEGALIZED,** 5, br m Authorized (IRE)—Laurena (GER) **Boom Racing**
5 **ONWITHTHEPARTY,** 10, b g Sir Harry Lewis (USA)—Kentford Fern **Boom Racing**
6 **PORT SOIF,** 5, b m Foxwedge (AUS)—Positivity **A. Slack**
7 **SUMMER LIGHTENING,** 5, gr m Fair Mix (IRE)—Kristineau **Messrs A & R Lyle**
8 **TONTO'S SPIRIT,** 7, b g Authorized (IRE)—Desert Royalty (IRE) **A. Slack**

Other Owners: Mr K. Buckle, Mr T. Ewbank, Mr James Lyle, Mr R. Lyle, Mrs Avril Lyle, Mr A. Slack, Mr Anthony White.

502 **MRS PAM SLY, Peterborough**
Postal: Singlecote, Thorney, Peterborough, Cambridgeshire, PE6 0PB
Contacts: **PHONE** (01733) 270212 **MOBILE** (07850) 511267
E-MAIL pamslyracing@btconnect.com

1 **ALL MY LOVE (IRE),** 7, b m Lord Shanakill (USA)—Afilla **D. L. Bayliss**
2 **DARK SPEC,** 4, b c Dark Angel (IRE)—Speciosa (IRE) **M. H. Sly, Dr T. Davies & Mrs P. Sly**
3 **ESKENDASH (USA),** 6, ch g Eskendereya (USA)—Daffaash (USA) **Boyle Racing**
4 **FRANSHAM,** 5, b g Sulamani (IRE)—Circus Rose **Mrs P. M. Sly**
5 **GAYTON,** 5, ch m Haafhd—Wistow **Mrs P. M. Sly**
6 **HAAFAPIECE,** 6, ch g Haafhd—Bonnet's Pieces **Mrs I. A. Coles**
7 **HEAVENLY SHADES,** 4, ch f Haafhd—Kaloni (IRE) **Mrs P. M. Sly**
8 **KEEPUP KEVIN,** 5, b g Haafhd—Black Salix (USA) **Mrs P. M. Sly**
9 **PACIFIC SALT (IRE),** 6, gr g Zebedee—Villa Nova (IRE) **D.L. Bayliss & G.A. Libson**
10 **RAINYDAY WOMAN,** 4, b f Kayf Tara—Wistow **Mrs P. M. Sly**
11 **SPINART,** 6, ch g Dutch Art—Spinneret **Mr D. J. Bourne**
12 **TAKEIT EASY,** 4, b g Malinas (GER)—Circus Rose **Mrs P. M. Sly**
13 **WALSINGHAM GRANGE (USA),** 6, b g Paddy O'prado (USA)—Mambo Queen (USA) **Pam's People**
14 **WELLAND,** 6, ch g Beat Hollow—Circus Rose **Mrs P. M. Sly**
15 **WITHAM,** 6, b m Beat Hollow—Wistow **G Libson & P M Sly**
16 **XCITATIONS,** 4, b g Universal (IRE)—Bonnet's Pieces **Mrs P. M. Sly**
17 **ZAFARANAH (USA),** 5, ch m Raven's Pass (USA)—Jiwen (CAN) **Pam's People**

THREE-YEAR-OLDS

18 **DAZZLING DAN (IRE),** b g Dandy Man (IRE)—Scrumptious **Thorney Racing Partners**
19 **DRUMMOND WARRIOR (IRE),** b g Zoffany (IRE)—Ulanova (IRE) **Mr G. A. Libson & Mrs P. M. Sly**
20 **JOHN CLARE (IRE),** b c Poet's Voice—Specialty (IRE) **Michael H. Sly & Mrs Pam Sly**
21 **LIAM'S LASS (IRE),** b f Dandy Man (IRE)—Rupa (IRE) **Mrs P. M. Sly**
22 **LIQUIDISER,** b g Monsieur Bond (IRE)—Kaloni (IRE) **Mrs P. M. Sly**
23 **SILKSTONE (IRE),** b c Alhebayeb—Fine Silk (USA) **Pam's People**

TWO-YEAR-OLDS

24 B f 1/3 War Command (USA)—Asteroidea (Sea The Stars (IRE)) **M. H. Sly & Mrs P. M. Sly**
25 **EILEENDOVER,** b f 16/3 Canford Cliffs (IRE)—Specialty (IRE) (Oasis Dream) **M. H. Sly & Mrs P. M. Sly**
26 B c 1/5 Kyllachy—Speciosa (IRE) (Danehill Dancer (IRE)) **M. H. Sly, Dr T. Davies & Mrs P. M. Sly**

Other Owners: Mr David L. Bayliss, Mr S. Boyle, Mr P. J. J. Boyle, Dr T. J. W. Davies, Mr S.R.T. Jones, Mr G. A. Libson, Mrs P. M. Sly, Mr Michael H. Sly.

Assistant Trainer: Chris Scudder

Jockey (NH): Kielan Woods. **Amateur:** Miss Gina Andrews.

503 **MR DAVID SMAGA, Lamorlaye**
Postal: **17 Voie de la Grange des Pres, 60260 Lamorlaye, France**
Contacts: **PHONE (0033) 3442 15005 FAX (0033) 3442 15356 MOBILE (0033) 6078 37287**
E-MAIL david-smaga@wanadoo.fr

1 **DON TOMMASINO (IRE)**, 6, b h Fastnet Rock (AUS)—M'oubliez Pas (USA) **Mr A. M. Haddad**
2 **DUQUE**, 4, b c Elusive City (USA)—Dariena (FR) **Mr M. Lagasse**
3 **EL MANIFICO**, 4, b c High Chaparral (IRE)—Envoutement (FR) **Mr A. Louis-Dreyfus**
4 **FIVE ICE CUBES**, 4, ch c Rip Van Winkle (IRE)—Victoria College (FR) **Mr A. M. Haddad**
5 **FLYING DESIRE**, 6, b g Rail Link—Arrow of Desire **Mr David Smaga**
6 **GAETANO DONIZETTI (IRE)**, 6, b h Makfi—Galipette (FR) **Mr M. Lagasse**
7 **GALOUSKA (FR)**, 4, b f Kentucky Dynamite (USA)—Calia (FR) **Mr A. Louis-Dreyfus**
8 **JEITOSO BAYER (BRZ)**, 7, b h Peintre Celebre (USA)—Kyanite (BRZ) **Benjamin Steinbruch**
9 **KIT KAT JET (BRZ)**, 6, gr h T H Approval (USA)—Yiddish Mama (ARG) **Benjamin Steinbruch**
10 **KIWI GREEN SUITE (BRZ)**, 6, b h T H Approval (USA)—Hypnose (BRZ) **Benjamin Steinbruch**
11 **LA POUTANESCA (IRE)**, 5, ch m Falco (USA)—Victoria College (FR) **Mr A. M. Haddad**
12 **LUMINOSA (FR)**, 4, b f Makfi—Katchagua (FR) **Mr A. Louis-Dreyfus**
13 **MAKTAVA (FR)**, 4, b c Makfi—Poltava (FR) **Ecurie Haras du Cadran**
14 **MILLFIELD (FR)**, 6, b h Whipper (USA)—Victoria College (FR) **Mr A. M. Haddad**
15 **PRIMUS INCITATUS (IRE)**, 8, ch h Mastercraftsman (IRE)—Chaibia (IRE) **Mr A. M. Haddad**
16 **SAPHIRSIDE (IRE)**, 10, b g Elusive City (USA)—Silirisa (FR) **Mr G. Augustin-Normand**
17 **VICTORIOUS CHAMP (FR)**, 8, b g New Approach (IRE)—Sasanuma (USA) **Mr David Smaga**
18 **VILARO (FR)**, 6, b h Whipper (USA)—Envoutement (FR) **Mr A. Louis-Dreyfus**
19 **WESTFIELD**, 4, b c Nathaniel (IRE)—Ossun (FR) **Mr J. E. Dubois**

THREE-YEAR-OLDS

20 **ABOLISH**, b c Sepoy (AUS)—Striking Choice (USA) **Prince Khalid Abdullah**
21 **AGUANA (FR)**, b f Motivator—Katchagua (FR) **Alain Louis-Dreyfus**
22 **DUKESSA (FR)**, gr f Makfi—Dariena (FR) **Mr Maurice Lagasse, Haras d'Etreham, Riviera Equine**
23 **FOFO (FR)**, ch c Kendargent (FR)—Envoutement (FR) **A. Louis-Dreyfus, D. Smaga**
24 **HOLD TRUE**, ch f Bated Breath—Honest Quality (USA) **Prince Khalid Abdullah**
25 **KERDASSA (IRE)**, ch f Mastercraftsman (IRE)—Renowned **John Kalmanson**
26 **MISSION ORANGE (USA)**, b c Noble Mission—Orangery (USA) **Prince Khalid Abdullah**
27 **NAVETTE (FR)**, b f Lemon Drop Kid (USA)—Winsili **Prince Khalid Abdullah**
28 **NELITA (FR)**, b f Makfi—Calia (FR) **A. Louis-Dreyfus**
29 **PIKES PEAK (FR)**, b f Sepoy (AUS)—Pietra Santa (FR) **Aleyrion Bloodstock Ltd, David Smaga**
30 **REDESIGN (IRE)**, ch f Champs Elysees—Intricate Design **John Kalmanson**
31 **SWINGY (FR)**, b c Anodin (IRE)—La Fee de Breizh (FR) **A. Louis-Dreyfus**
32 **WILPENA (IRE)**, ch f Makfi—Loutka (FR) **Malcolm Parish, D. Smaga**

TWO-YEAR-OLDS

33 **CHUBASCO (FR)**, ch c 19/3 Anodin (IRE)—Strelkita (FR) (Dr Fong (USA)) **Mr A. Louis-Dreyfus**
34 **EL MESIO (FR)**, b c 20/2 Le Havre (IRE)—Victoria College (FR) (Rock of Gibraltar (IRE)) **Mr A. M. Haddad**
35 **FUGAZ (FR)**, b c 22/4 Anodin (IRE)—Calia (FR) (Orpen (USA)) **Mr A. Louis-Dreyfus**
36 **HAVENVOUS (FR)**, ch c 27/2 Le Havre (IRE)—Envoutement (FR) (Vettori (IRE)) **A. Louis-Dreyfus, D. Smaga**
37 **MACHITO (FR)**, ch c 8/1 Makfi—Miss Derna (FR) (Air Chief Marshal (IRE)) **Mr A. Louis-Dreyfus**
38 **MEGUSTAS (FR)**, b c 24/4 Wootton Bassett—Katchagua (FR) (Anabaa (USA)) **Mr A. Louis-Dreyfus**
39 Ch f 21/4 Le Havre (IRE)—Mezzo Mezzo (FR) (Mount Nelson) **Mr A. M. Haddad**
40 **STAR LAD (FR)**, b c 2/3 Planteur (IRE)—La Fee de Breizh (FR) (Verglas (IRE)) **Mr A. Louis-Dreyfus**
41 **SUMMER DRIVE (USA)**, b f 15/4 Hard Spun (USA)—
                July Jasmine (USA) (Empire Maker (USA)) **Prince Khalid Abdullah**

504 **MR BRYAN SMART, Hambleton**
Postal: **Hambleton House, Sutton Bank, Thirsk, North Yorkshire, YO7 2HA**
Contacts: **PHONE (01845) 597481 FAX (01845) 597480 MOBILE (07748) 634797**
E-MAIL office@bryansmart.plus.com WEBSITE www.bryansmart-racing.com

1 **ALFA MCGUIRE (IRE)**, 4, b g Lord Shanakill (USA)—Watsdaplan (IRE) **Ms D. Aldridge**
2 **ALPHA DELPHINI**, 8, b g Captain Gerrard (IRE)—Easy To Imagine (USA) **The Alpha Delphini Partnership**
3 **BLACK HAMBLETON**, 6, b g Dick Turpin (IRE)—Duena **The Smart Duena Partnership**
4 **BONANZA BOWLS**, 4, b g Zebedee—Twilight Belle (IRE) **Mr J A Milburn & Partner**
5 **COMPTON RIVER**, 7, b g Compton Place—Inagh River **The Smart Inagh River Partnership**

MR BRYAN SMART - Continued

6 **FAIRY FALCON**, 4, ch f Sepoy (AUS)—Easy To Imagine (USA) **Clipper Group Holdings Ltd**
7 **FENDALE**, 7, b g Exceed And Excel (AUS)—Adorn **Mr S. Chappell & Partner**
8 **GAMESTERS ICON**, 4, b f Sixties Icon—Gamesters Dana **Gamesters Partnership**
9 **HELOVAPLAN (IRE)**, 5, b g Helmet (AUS)—Watsdaplan (IRE) **The Smart Set**
10 **KENTUCKYCONNECTION (USA)**, 6, b g Include (USA)—Youcanringmybell (USA) **Woodcock Electrical Limited**
11 **MYTHMAKER**, 7, b g Major Cadeaux—Mythicism **Crossfields Racing**
12 **PEPYS**, 5, b g Aqlaam—Generously Gifted **Mr G. Lowe & Mr P. Darling**
13 **RED PIKE (IRE)**, 8, ch g Kheleyf (USA)—Fancy Feathers (IRE) **Eyre, Watson & Styles**
14 **SHE'S ROYAL**, 4, b f Delegator—Sukuma (IRE) **Davis, Moody, Hogan,**
15 **SIRIUS MOVE**, 6, b g Monsieur Bond (IRE)—Lady Paris (IRE)
16 **SIYAHAMBA (IRE)**, 5, ch g Helmet (AUS)—Kalabunga (IRE) **Mr B. Smart**
17 **STRAIGHTOTHEPOINT**, 7, b g Kyllachy—Choisette **Crossfields Racing**
18 **TREVITHICK**, 4, b g Champs Elysees—New Choice (IRE) **Mrs P. A. Clark**
19 **WRENTHORPE**, 4, b g Hellvelyn—Milly-M **Mr Dan Maltby & Mr B. Smart**

THREE-YEAR-OLDS

20 **ALFA DAWN (IRE)**, b f No Nay Never (USA)—Aitch (IRE) **SYPS (UK) Ltd**
21 **ANTAGONIZE**, b c Epaulette (AUS)—Hakuraa (IRE) **Crossfields Racing**
22 Ch f Garswood—Ardessie
23 **FARRDHANA**, ch f Farhh—Dhan Dhana (IRE) **D Aldridge, D Town & N Derbyshire**
24 **FLINT SAID NO**, gr g Harbour Watch (IRE)—Rock Ace (IRE) **Middleham Park Racing (viii) & Partner**
25 **LEGAL TENDER (IRE)**, b g Camacho—A Childs Dream (IRE) **Mr M. Barber Racing**
26 **MIDNIGHT IN HAVANA**, b g Havana Gold (IRE)—Eleventh Hour **The Smart Set**
27 **MIXED UP MISS (IRE)**, b f Kodiac—Kerfuffle (IRE) **The Smart Kerfuffle Partnership**
28 **NEIGH DRAMAS**, ch g Equiano (FR)—Silvee **Mr B. Smart**
29 **NORTHERNPOWERHOUSE**, b c Harbour Watch (IRE)—Mortitia **Mr Michael Moses & Mr Terry Moses**
30 **PALAZZO**, b g Morpheus—Sweet Power **Syps (uk) Ltd & Partner**
31 **STRONSAY (IRE)**, b g Gale Force Ten—Perfect Blossom **The Unscrupulous Judges**
32 **SWISS CONNECTION**, b g Swiss Spirit—Sofonisba **Woodcock Electrical Ltd & Ms D Aldridge**
33 **TICK TOCK CROC (IRE)**, b g Requinto (IRE)—Quinine **Ceffyl Racing**

TWO-YEAR-OLDS

34 **ASTROZONE**, ch f 22/1 Fast Company (IRE)—Rhal (IRE) (Rahy (USA)) (20952) **Crossfields Racing**
35 B f 19/2 Swiss Spirit—Ayasha (Indesatchel (IRE)) (2857) **Crossfields Racing**
36 **AZTECA**, b f 3/5 Fountain of Youth (IRE)—Irrational (Kyllachy) (5714) **Crossfields Racing**
37 **CHOCOHOLIC**, b c 25/4 Due Diligence (USA)—Unwrapit (USA) (Tapit (USA)) (9523) **Ontoawinner 1 & Partner**
38 **HURAA**, b f 14/2 Brazen Beau (AUS)—Hakuraa (IRE) (Elnadim (USA)) (12000) **Crossfields Racing**
39 B c 18/2 Fountain of Youth (IRE)—Ice Mayden (Major Cadeaux) (17142) **Mr J. Ball & Bearstone Stud Ltd**
40 **JAKODOBRO**, b c 13/2 Fountain of Youth (IRE)—Equinox (Medicean) (761) **Crossfields Racing**
41 Ch c 6/3 Casamento (IRE)—Katabatik Katie (Sir Percy) (8000)
42 **KISKADEE**, b f 10/4 Mukhadram—Generously Gifted (Sakhee (USA)) (3000) **Mr G. Lowe & Mr P. Darling**
43 B c 26/3 Due Diligence (USA)—Malelane (IRE) (Prince Sabo) (19047)
44 B c 31/3 Sepoy (AUS)—Mythician (Oasis Dream) (29000) **Crossfields Racing**
45 B c 1/3 Brazen Beau (AUS)—Olivia Grace (Pivotal) (34000) **Mr Michael Moses & Mr Terry Moses**
46 B c 30/3 Footstepsinthesand—Omanome (IRE) (Acclamation) (9523)
47 **SLINGSHOT**, b f 29/1 Due Diligence (USA)—Nizhoni (USA) (Mineshaft (USA)) (9523) **Crossfields Racing**
48 B f 7/4 Fountain of Youth (IRE)—So Discreet (Tragic Role (USA)) (3809)
49 B c 20/2 Moohaajim (IRE)—Spacecraft (USA) (Distant View (USA)) (20000)
50 **ZIVJELI**, b f 29/4 Fountain of Youth (IRE)—Virtuality (USA) (Elusive Quality (USA)) (4761) **Crossfields Racing**

Other Owners: Mr M. Barber, Mr David Blake, Mr Simon Bridge, Mr M. G. Bullock, Mrs Tina Bullock, Mr S. Chappell, Mr Paul Darling, Mr I. F. Davis, Mr N. V. Derbyshire, Mr Charlie Dinsdale, Mr Dave Elders, Mr K. Harle, Mr K. Hogan, Mrs A. C. Hudson, Mr T. D. Jones, Exors of the Late Mr G. A. Lowe, Mr D. L. Maltby, Mrs B. A. Matthews, Middleham Park Racing VIII, Mr John Allan Milburn, Mrs Freda Moody, Mr M. Moses, Mr T. J. Moses, Mr N. J. O'Brien, Ontoawinner, R. A. Page, Mr T. S. Palin, Mr M. Prince, Mr B. Smart, Mrs V. R. Smart, Mr E. Styles, Mr D. Town, Mr A. Welch, Mr D. V. Williams.

Assistant Trainers: Mrs V. R. Smart, Mr K. Edmunds **Pupil Assistant:** Miss Beth Smart

Jockey (flat): Graham Lee. **Apprentice:** Harry Russell.

505 **MR CHARLES SMITH, Temple Bruer**
Postal: **6-7 Thompsons Bottom, Temple Bruer, Lincoln, Lincolnshire, LN5 0DE**
Contacts: **PHONE/FAX (01526) 833245 MOBILE (07778) 149188**

1 ALPHA TAURI (USA), 13, b g Aldebaran (USA)—Seven Moons (JPN) **Mr J. R. Theaker**
2 EJABAH (IRE), 5, b m Iffraaj—Relinquished **Mr N. J. Baines**
3 ROBBIAN, 8, b g Bertolini (USA)—Crathes **R. J. Lewin**

THREE-YEAR-OLDS
4 ATWAAR, b f Slade Power (IRE)—Musharakaat (IRE) **Mr M. J. Smeed**

506 **MR JULIAN SMITH, Tirley**
Postal: **Tirley Court, Tirley, Gloucester**
Contacts: **PHONE (01452) 780461 FAX (01452) 780461 MOBILE (07748) 901175**
E-MAIL nicola.smith9156@o2.co.uk

1 CARO DES FLOS (FR), 7, b g Tiger Groom—Royale Marie (FR) **Mrs J.A. Benson & Miss S.N. Benson**
2 DIAMOND ROSE, 7, b m Sagamix (FR)—Swiss Rose **Grand Jury Partnership**
3 EMERALD ROSE, 12, b m Sir Harry Lewis (USA)—Swiss Rose **Grand Jury Partnership**
4 IONA DAYS (IRE), 14, br g Epistolaire (IRE)—Miss Best (FR) **Mrs J.A. Benson & Miss S.N. Benson**
5 MIDNIGHT SENSATION, 7, gr m Proclamation (IRE)—Midnight Ocean **Exors of the Late Mr D. E. S. Smith**
6 PENNIES AND POUNDS, 12, b m Sir Harry Lewis (USA)—Sense of Value **Exors of the Late Mr D. E. S. Smith**
7 THE RORY STORY (IRE), 8, b g Flemensfirth (USA)—Phardester (IRE) **Exors of the Late Mr D. E. S. Smith**

Other Owners: Mrs J. A. Benson, Miss S. N. Benson, Mr A. W. Brookes, R. Brookes.

Assistant Trainer: Mrs Nicky Smith

Jockey (NH): Mark Grant, Sam Twiston-Davies. **Amateur:** Mr J. M. Ridley.

507 **MR MARTIN SMITH, Newmarket**
Postal: **Stable Cottage, Calder Park, Hamilton Road, Newmarket, Suffolk, CB8 0NY**
Contacts: **MOBILE (07712) 493589**
WEBSITE www.martinsmithracing.com

1 AFFLUENCE (IRE), 4, b g Thewayyouare (USA)—Castalian Spring (IRE) **The Affluence Partnership**
2 ARCH MY BOY, 5, b g Archipenko (USA)—Fairy Slipper **Mr Robert P Clarke & Mr Martin Smith**
3 FRANK'S LEGACY, 5, ch g Aqlaam—Quite A Thing **Miss C. McPhillips-Witt**
4 HAWATIF (IRE), 6, b m Royal Applause—Excellerator (IRE) **W. F. H. Carson**
5 IFWECAN, 8, b g Exceed And Excel (AUS)—Kirk **Henry & Jade Syndicate**
6 IN THE RED (IRE), 6, b g Elusive Pimpernel (USA)—Roses From Ridey (IRE) **Sunville Rail Limited**
7 LISNAMOYLE LADY (IRE), 4, ch f Roderic O'Connor (IRE)—Allegheny Dawn (IRE) **Mrs S. B. Nundram**
8 MISTER TICKLE (IRE), 5, b g Morozov (USA)—Tatiana (IRE) **Sunville Rail Limited**
9 MORE HARRY, 4, b g Aussie Rules (USA)—Native Ring (IRE) **Four Winds Racing Partnership**
10 ROMAN RIVER, 4, b c Holy Roman Emperor (IRE)—Inagh River **M B S Racing**
11 THE EMPEROR WITHIN (FR), 4, b c Holy Roman Emperor (IRE)—Watchful (IRE) **M B S Racing**

THREE-YEAR-OLDS
12 ALEATORIC (IRE), b c Dylan Thomas (IRE)—Castalian Spring (IRE) **Mr Martin Smith & Mr Philip Brooks**
13 BREAK THE RULES, br f Aussie Rules (USA)—Fairy Slipper **Mr Robert P Clarke & Partners**
14 THREEFEETFROMGOLD (IRE), ch c Helmet (AUS)—Lady Pitrizza (IRE) **Mr M. P. B. Smith**

Other Owners: H.H. Sheikh S. B. M. Al Khalifa, Sheikh Mohammed Bin Isa Al Khalifa, Mr J. Bridger, Mr P. Brooks, Mr R. P. Clarke, Mr R. J. Mear, Mrs E. A. Mear, Mrs R. T. Rennie, Mrs M. E. Smith, Mrs M. Smyth.

Apprentice: Jay Clark. **Amateur:** Mr Alex Teasdale.

508 MR R. MIKE SMITH, Galston
Postal: **West Loudoun Farm, Galston, Ayrshire, KA4 8PB**
Contacts: **PHONE** (01563) 822062 **MOBILE** (07711) 692122
E-MAIL mike@mikesmithracing.co.uk **WEBSITE** www.mikesmithracing.co.uk

1 **AKAMANTO (IRE),** 5, b g Cape Cross (IRE)—Allofus (IRE) **Reid Ross Smith**
2 **ALPHABETICAL ORDER,** 11, b g Afflora (IRE)—Lady Turk (FR) **Great Northern Partnership**
3 **AN FEAR CIUIN (IRE),** 8, b g Galileo (IRE)—Potion **P. Tsim**
4 **ASTUTE BOY (IRE),** 5, b g Arcano (IRE)—Spa **Mr R. M. Smith**
5 **BEAU ET SUBLIME (FR),** 9, b g Saddler Maker (IRE)—Jolie Jouvencelle (FR) **Mr R. M. Smith**
6 **CAN CAN SIXTY TWO,** 4, b f Sixties Icon—Natalie Jay **Cityhopper**
7 **DIOCESE (FR),** 6, b g Linda's Lad—Sempiternelle (FR) **Spittal Family**
8 **FOUR KINGDOMS (IRE),** 5, b g Lord Shanakill (USA)—Four Poorer (IRE) **Smith & Stewart**
9 **FOURTH OF JULY (IRE),** 4, b g Salutino (GER)—Akasha (IRE) **Quigley & Smith**
10 **GLASSES UP (USA),** 4, ch g English Channel (USA)—Hurricane Hallie (USA) **The Jolly Beggars**
11 **GLINGERSIDE (IRE),** 8, b g Milan—Kettle 'n Cran (IRE) **West Loudoun Racing Club**
12 **GO GUARANTOR,** 5, b g Medicean—Furbelow **Mr D. Orr**
13 **GWORN,** 9, b g Aussie Rules (USA)—Crochet (IRE) **Mr R. Gibson**
14 **HAYMARKET,** 10, b g Singspiel (IRE)—Quickstyx **Mr A. M. Ross**
15 **JUDITH GARDENIER,** 7, b m Rip Van Winkle (IRE)—Millagros (IRE) **J. A. Cringan**
16 **LAS TUNAS (FR),** 7, b br g Country Reel (USA)—Grey Winner (FR) **Spittal Family**
17 **NAKADAM (FR),** 9, b g Nickname (FR)—Cadoudame (FR) **Smith & Spittal**
18 **NO NO MAC (IRE),** 10, b g Oscar (IRE)—Whatdoyouthinkmac (IRE) **B H McFadzean & A L Gregg**
19 **ORIENTAL TIGER,** 8, b g Tiger Hill (IRE)—Cal Norma's Lady (IRE) **Mr A. Barclay**
20 **PUDDING CHARE (IRE),** 5, b g Arcano (IRE)—Rosy Dudley (IRE) **Ayr Racecourse Club**
21 **ROSEMARY (IRE),** 5, b m Mayson—Maine Rose **Dal Riata - A Barclay**
22 **TOM AND TONY H (IRE),** 4, b br g Masterofthehorse (IRE)—Then Came Bronson (IRE) **Mr J. C. Higgins**
23 **URIAH HEEP (FR),** 10, b g Danehill Dancer (IRE)—Canasita **Mrs P. McLeish**
24 **WEST COAST LASS (IRE),** 6, br m Westerner—Afairs (IRE) **West Loudoun Racing Club**

THREE-YEAR-OLDS

25 **BE PROUD (IRE),** b g Roderic O'Connor (IRE)—Agnista (IRE) **Gregg & O Shea**
26 **CALEDONIA LASS,** b f Firebreak—Golden Nun **Mr R. M. Kean**
27 **MILABELLA,** b f Bated Breath—Miss Noble **Mr R. M. Smith**

Other Owners: Mr G. W. B. Bryson, Miss H. A. Cross, Dal Riata, Mr A. L. Frew, Mr A. L. Gregg, Mr B. McFadzean, Mr G. P. O'Shea, Mr R. Quigley, Mr G. Reid, Mr A. H. Spittal, Miss B. Spittal, Mr I. Stewart, Mrs S. Stienlet, Mr H. S. Watson, Western Meeting Club Ltd.

509 MR RALPH J. SMITH, Chipstead
Postal: **25A Rosebery Road, Epsom, Surrey, KT18 6AF**
Contacts: **PHONE** (01372) 273870 **FAX** (01737) 201693 **MOBILE** (07795) 327003
E-MAIL rjsmith.racing@hotmail.com **WEBSITE** www.rjsmithracing.com

1 **ANOTHER GO (IRE),** 6, gr g Strategic Prince—Golden Rose (GER) **Richard Penney & Hoolabaloo Racing**
2 **DUHR (IRE),** 5, b g Mawatheeq (USA)—Dijlah **Mrs J. C. Smith**
3 **FULL SUIT,** 5, gr m Dalakhani (IRE)—Perfect Hand **Clear Racing & Jayne Smith**
4 **LONDON GRAMMAR (IRE),** 5, b m Sir Prancealot (IRE)—Emmas Princess (IRE) **Mr K. Old**
5 **VICTOR'S BET (SPA),** 10, b g Leadership—Marmaria (SPA) **Homecroft Wealth Racing & Mr Kevin Old**

Other Owners: Clear Racing, Mrs M. M. Greening, Mr B. J. Greening, Homecroft Wealth Racing, Mr R. C. Penney, Mr B. Pettis, Mr S. J. Piper.

Assistant Trainer: Jayne Smith

510 MRS SUE SMITH, Bingley
Postal: **Craiglands Farm, High Eldwick, Bingley, West Yorkshire, BD16 3BE**
Contacts: **PHONE** (01274) 564930 **FAX** (01274) 560626
E-MAIL craiglandsracing@yahoo.co.uk

1 **ABSOLUTELY DYLAN (IRE),** 6, b g Scorpion (IRE)—Cash Customer (IRE) **Mr T. J. Hemmings**
2 **ALFIBOY,** 9, b g Afflora (IRE)—Cloudy Pearl **Mrs S. J. Smith**

MRS SUE SMITH - Continued

3 4, B g Lucarno (USA)—Arctic Ring **Mrs S. J. Smith**
4 BEA MY STAR (FR), 5, b g Sea's Legacy (IRE)—Lillibits (USA) **Mrs A. Clarke**
5 BEAR THAT N MIND (IRE), 7, b g Mahler—Gibboghstown (IRE) **Mrs S. J. Smith**
6 BLACK ART, 7, ch g Black Sam Bellamy (IRE)—Art Series **Jacqueline & John Conroy**
7 BLAKEMOUNT (IRE), 11, br g Presenting—Smashing Leader (IRE) **Mrs J. Conroy**
8 BLOTTOS (IRE), 7, b g Westerner—Autumn Beauty (IRE) **Mr T. J. Hemmings**
9 BOBNDAVE (IRE), 7, b g Brian Boru—Sidblack (IRE) **Mrs S. J. Smith**
10 8, Gr g Tikkanen (USA)—Bonnie Rock (IRE) **Mrs S. J. Smith**
11 5, B g Schiaparelli (GER)—Bonnie Rock (IRE) **Mrs S. J. Smith**
12 4, B g Schiaparelli (GER)—Bonnie Rock (IRE) **Mrs S. J. Smith**
13 CAPTAIN MOIRETTE (FR), 7, gr g Kap Rock (FR)—Rahana Moirette (FR) **Mrs S. J. Smith**
14 CRACKING FIND (IRE), 8, b g Robin des Pres (FR)—Crack The Kicker (IRE) **Mrs A. Ellis**
15 DARSI'S JEWEL (IRE), 6, b g Darsi (FR)—Bettys Daughter (IRE) **Mrs S. J. Smith**
16 DARTFORD WARBLER (IRE), 12, b g Overbury (IRE)—Stony View (IRE) **The Cartmel Syndicate**
17 DE VOUS A MOI (FR), 11, b g Sinndar (IRE)—Dzinigane (FR) **Mrs J. Morgan**
18 DICK DARSIE (IRE), 9, br g Darsi (FR)—Hurricane Jane (IRE) **Mrs S. J. Smith**
19 GETAWAY BAY (IRE), 7, b g Getaway (GER)—Wayward Star (IRE) **Mrs S. J. Smith**
20 HILL SIXTEEN, 6, b g Court Cave—Chasers Chic **Mr T. J. Hemmings**
21 I JUST KNOW (IRE), 9, b g Robin des Pres (FR)—Desperado Queen (IRE) **Mrs M. B. Scholey**
22 INFORMATEUR (FR), 6, b g Maresca Sorrento (FR)—Isarella (GER) **Mrs J M Gray & Mr G R Orchard**
23 ISKABEG LANE (IRE), 8, b g Westerner—Nosey Oscar (IRE) **Mrs S. J. Smith**
24 IT'S BUSTER (IRE), 8, b g Stowaway—Late Guest (IRE) **Mrs S. J. Smith**
25 JOKE DANCER, 6, ch g Authorized (IRE)—Missy Dancer **Mrs A. Clarke**
26 JUST GEORGIE, 9, b g Kayf Tara—Just Kate **Mrs M. B. Scholey**
27 LADRONNE (FR), 5, b g Linda's Lad—Worldeta (FR) **Mrs V. J. Walker**
28 LE DRAPEAU (FR), 7, ch g Satri (IRE)—La Bandera **A. D. Hollinrake**
29 LOUGH DERG FARMER (IRE), 7, b g Presenting—Maryiver (IRE) **Mrs S. J. Smith**
30 LOUGH LEGEND (IRE), 5, b g Watar (IRE)—Gibboghstown (IRE) **Broadway Racing Club 15**
31 LUCKY LUCARNO (IRE), 7, b g Lucarno (USA)—Sari Rose (FR) **Mrs S. J. Smith**
32 MACS GIFT (IRE), 7, b g Scorpion (IRE)—Gift Wrapped (IRE) **Mrs S. J. Smith**
33 MAXED OUT KING (IRE), 11, ch g Desert King (IRE)—Lady Max (IRE) **Mrs S. J. Smith**
34 MIDNIGHT SHADOW, 6, b g Midnight Legend—Holy Smoke **Mrs A. Clarke**
35 MINELLA FIVEO (IRE), 11, b g Westerner—Autumn Sky (IRE) **Mrs S. J. Smith**
36 MUTAWAASEL, 7, b g Teofilo (IRE)—Muwakleh **Mrs S. J. Smith**
37 NEVER UP (GER), 8, b g Danehill Dancer (IRE)—Never Green (IRE) **Mrs S. J. Smith**
38 4, B g Yeats (IRE)—Nolans Legacy (IRE) **Mrs S. J. Smith**
39 NOTONEBUTTWO (IRE), 12, b g Dushyantor (USA)—Daiquiri (IRE) **Mr N. Taylor**
40 OSCAR WILDE (IRE), 5, b g Oscar (IRE)—Deep Supreme (IRE) **Formulated Polymer Products Ltd**
41 PUDSEY, 5, b g Multiplex—Midsummer Legend **Mrs S. J. Smith**
42 RARE CLOUDS, 5, b g Cloudings (IRE)—Rare Vintage (IRE) **Mr T. J. Hemmings**
43 RED DANAHER (IRE), 12, ch g Shantou (USA)—Red Rover (USA) **Mrs S. J. Smith**
44 4, Br g Dylan Thomas (IRE)—Retain That Magic (IRE) **Mrs S. J. Smith**
45 4, B g Yeats (IRE)—Santia **Mrs S. J. Smith**
46 SCORCHIN, 5, b g Multiplex—Lemon Queen (IRE) **Mrs S. J. Smith**
47 4, Ch g Schiaparelli (GER)—Shankhouse Wells (IRE) **Mrs S. J. Smith**
48 SHARP RESPONSE (IRE), 8, b g Oscar (IRE)—Lambourne Lace (IRE) **Formulated Polymer Products Ltd**
49 SILVA ECLIPSE, 6, gr g Multiplex—Linen Line **Mrs S. J. Smith**
50 SMALL PRESENT (IRE), 4, b g Presenting—Serpentaria **Mrs A. Clarke**
51 STRAIDNAHANNA (IRE), 10, gr g Medaaly—Sue's Song **Mrs M. B. Scholey**
52 THE PADDY PIE (IRE), 6, b g Beneficial—Salsita (FR) **J. Wade**
53 THELONGWAYAROUND (IRE), 6, b g Fruits of Love (USA)—Brass Neck (IRE) **Mrs J. Morgan**
54 TRESHNISH (FR), 6, ch g Gold Away (IRE)—Didn't I Tell You (IRE) **D G Pryde & D Van Der Hoeven**
55 TROOBLUE, 7, gr m Great Palm (USA)—Touch of Ivory (IRE) **Mrs S. J. Smith**
56 VALENCE D'AUMONT (FR), 5, b g Sinndar (IRE)—Ice Ti (ITY) **Mrs J. Morgan**
57 VENDOR (FR), 11, gr g Kendor (FR)—Village Rainbow (FR) **Mrs S. J. Smith**
58 VINTAGE CLOUDS (IRE), 9, gr g Cloudings (IRE)—Rare Vintage (IRE) **Mr T. J. Hemmings**
59 WAKANDA (IRE), 10, b g Westerner—Chanson Indienne (FR) **Mrs M. B. Scholey**
60 WHAT'S THE SCOOP (IRE), 9, ch g Presenting—Dame d'harvard (USA) **Mrs S. J. Smith**
61 WOLF RUN (IRE), 4, b br g Presenting—Our Pride **Mr G. R. Orchard & Mrs J. M. Gray**

Other Owners: J. Conroy, Mrs J. M. Gray, Mr C. C. S. MacMillan, D. Musgrave, G. R. Orchard, D. G. Pryde, Mrs J. B. Pye, Mr D. P. van der Hoeven.

Assistant Trainer: Ryan Clavin

Jockey (NH): Danny Cook, Sean Quinlan. **Conditional:** Sam Coltherd, Kane Yeoman.

511 MISS SUZY SMITH, Lewes

Postal: County Stables, The Old Racecourse, Lewes, East Sussex, BN7 1UR
Contacts: PHONE (01273) 477173 FAX (01273) 477173 MOBILE (07970) 550828
E-MAIL suzy@suzysmithracing.co.uk WEBSITE www.suzysmithracing.co.uk

1 CLONDAW BISTO (IRE), 8, b g September Storm (GER)—
Solo Venture (IRE) Mr J.Gordon-watson & Suzy Smith
2 CRACKER JAK (IRE), 5, b g September Storm (GER)—Princess Jaffa (IRE) Mrs V. Palmer
3 DEBESTYMAN (IRE), 6, b g Mahler—Deise All Star (IRE) The Plumpton Party
4 GETAWAY SUZY (IRE), 6, b m Getaway (GER)—Ashanti Dancer (IRE) Miss S. Smith
5 HOOK LANE ROOBEE, 6, b g Spendent—Sharp Action Hook Lane Syndicate
6 ILLTELLMEMA (IRE), 7, gr m Milan—Cullenstown Lady (IRE) Miss S. L. Parker
7 INVICTA LAKE (IRE), 12, b g Dr Massini (IRE)—Classic Material The Invicta Partnership
8 LITTLE BOY BORU (IRE), 11, b g Brian Boru—How Is Things (IRE) J Logan, D Harrison, T Loftus & S Smith
9 MADAME VOGUE, 6, b m Multiplex—Roslin Mr & Mrs R. Allsop
10 MIGHTY VIC (IRE), 11, b g Old Vic—Mighty Marble (IRE) Miss S. Smith
11 MOODY MAGGIE (IRE), 6, b m Milan—Golden Bay Mrs S. A. Addington-Smith
12 RED DEVIL STAR, 9, b g Beneficial—Gortbofearna (IRE) Mrs V. Palmer
13 ROSY WORLD, 6, b m Shirocco (GER)—Material World Kate Allisat & Hilary Ames
14 SISANIA (IRE), 6, gr ro m Mastercraftsman (IRE)—Avril Rose (IRE) Heart of the South Racing 111
15 STORM PATROL, 8, b m Shirocco (GER)—Material World Miss S. Smith
16 STRIKE THE FLINT, 5, b m Shirocco (GER)—Material World Table For Six
17 VUE CAVALIERE (FR), 5, b m Spirit One (FR)—Grande Cavale (FR)

TWO-YEAR-OLDS

18 THE BLUE BOWER (IRE), b f 21/4 Morpheus—Blue Holly (IRE) (Blues Traveller (IRE)) (7000) Mr A. I. F. Sim

Other Owners: Mrs E. Adamski, Mrs K. H. Allisat, Mr W. Allisat, Mr R. Allsop, Mrs Y. E. Allsop, Mrs H. J. Ames, Mr J. M. F. Gordon-Watson, Mr D. J. Harrison, Mr T. H. Loftus, J. A. A. S. Logan, Mr J. R. Penny, Mrs J. Reece, Mr J. Rimmer, Mrs C. A. Smith, Mrs H. M. T. Woods.

Assistant Trainer: Mr S E Gordon-Watson

Jockey (flat): Luke Morris. Jockey (NH): Micheal Nolan, Tom O'Brien, Gavin Sheehan.

512 MR GILES SMYLY, Broadway

Postal: Garden Cottage, Wormington Grange, Broadway, Worcestershire, WR12 7NJ
Contacts: PHONE (01386) 584085 FAX (01386) 584085 MOBILE (07747) 035169
E-MAIL gilessmiler@aol.com WEBSITE www.smylyracing.co.uk

1 BIG BANG DE LOIRE (FR), 8, b g Califet (FR)—Grischa (FR) D. Maxwell
2 BRICE CANYON (FR), 8, b g Kapgarde (FR)—Fille Formidable (USA) David Maxwell Racing Limited
3 DESCARO (USA), 13, gr g Dr Fong (USA)—Miarixa (FR) Miss N. L. Slack
4 EDABEAN (IRE), 5, b m Arcadio (GER)—Victorian Lady A. C. Ward-Thomas
5 GALICE DU CIEL, 8, br g Septieme Ciel (USA)—Galice Du Soleil (FR) Ms Gillian Metherell
6 MAYBE PLENTY, 10, b m Overbury (IRE)—Mays Delight (IRE) N. R. A. Sutton
7 MINERFORTYNINER (IRE), 10, br g Catcher In The Rye (IRE)—Hungry Eyes (IRE) A. C. Ward-Thomas

Assistant Trainer: Kim Smyly

513 MR JAMIE SNOWDEN, Lambourn

Postal: Folly House, Upper Lambourn Road, Lambourn, Hungerford, Berkshire, RG17 8QG
Contacts: PHONE (01488) 72800 (office) MOBILE (07779) 497563
E-MAIL info@jamiesnowdenracing.co.uk WEBSITE www.jamiesnowdenracing.co.uk
Twitter: @jamiesnowden

1 ADRRASTOS (IRE), 7, b g Areion (GER)—Laren (GER) Karen Gunn
2 ALRIGHTJACK (IRE), 5, b g Stowaway—Brogella (IRE) The GD Partnership
3 AMORLETTE, 5, b m Fair Mix (IRE)—Amaretto Rose Foxtrot Racing: Amorlette
4 , B, g Westerner—Ariesanne (IRE)
5 ASK ROBIN (IRE), 7, b g Robin des Champs (FR)—Ask June (IRE) The Galloping Grannies
6 BETWEEN THE WATERS (IRE), 8, ch g Indian River (FR)—Catch Ball The Folly Partnership
7 BLUE BULLET (FR), 8, b g Le Fou (IRE)—Jiletta (FR) Racegoers Club & Me Myself & I

MR JAMIE SNOWDEN - Continued

  8 **CARNTOP**, 6, b g Dansili—Milford Sound **Foxtrot Racing**
  9 **CAUTORILLO**, 7, ch m Black Sam Bellamy (IRE)—Cent Prime **Fawley House Stud**
10 **CHAPMANSHYPE (IRE)**, 5, b g Aizavoski (IRE)—Call Her Something (IRE) **The GD Partnership**
11 **CLOUD HOPPER (IRE)**, 5, gr g Dubai Destination (USA)—Drain Hopper **Mr & Mrs R. H. F. Fuller**
12 **COOLE WELL (IRE)**, 6, b g Gold Well—Bobs Lass (IRE) **Mrs C. Kendrick**
13 **COURT OUT (IRE)**, 6, b g Court Cave (IRE)—Madame Martine (IRE) **Mr A Signy & Mr P Jacobs**
14 **CROWN THEATRE (IRE)**, 10, b g King's Theatre (IRE)—Palesa's Legacy (IRE) **Jamie Snowden Racing Club**
15 **DANS LE VENT (FR)**, 6, b g Skins Game—Boreade (FR) **Marek Gumienny & Adam Signy**
16 **DOUBLE TREASURE**, 8, b g King's Theatre (IRE)—Double Red (IRE) **Mrs C. Kendrick**
17 **EARLY MORNING RAIN (FR)**, 5, gr m Martaline—Rosewater (GER) **Mrs J A Thomas & Heart Racing**
18 **ETAT MAJOR AULMES (FR)**, 6, b g Della Francesca (USA)—River Gold Aulmes (FR) **Mr A. Signy**
19 **FACT OF THE MATTER (IRE)**, 9, b g Brian Boru—Womanofthemountain (IRE) **The Sandylini Racing Partnership**
20 **FATIMA BLUSH**, 6, b m Black Sam Bellamy (IRE)—Samar Qand **Fawley House Stud**
21 **FILEMON**, 7, gr g Kayf Tara—L'ultima (FR) **E. Penser**
22 **FLORAL BOUQUET**, 6, b l m Fair Mix (FR)—Florarossa **The Picnic Party**
23 **FOOTLOOSE**, 5, b g Sulamani (IRE)—Altesse de Sou (FR) **Wiggin Robinson Wainwright Hill Davison**
24 **GRANGE RANGER (IRE)**, 7, b g Kalanisi (IRE)—Grangeclare Flight (IRE) **Wiggin Robinson Wainwright Hill Davison**
25 **HOGAN'S HEIGHT (IRE)**, 8, b g Indian River (FR)—Electre du Berlais (FR) **Foxtrot Racing: Hogan's Height**
26 **KALAHARI QUEEN**, 6, br m Kalanisi (IRE)—Queen's Leader **The Cherry Pickers**
27 4, Ch g Norse Dancer (IRE)—Katmai (IRE) **The Radleian Society Racing Syndicate**
28 **KILTEALY BRIGGS (IRE)**, 5, b g Fame And Glory—Baby Briggs (IRE) **McNeill Family Ltd**
29 **KING VINCE**, 6, gr g Mawatheeq (USA)—Tussah **P Fox, S Beccle, D Scott Et Al**
30 **LEGENDS RYDE**, 4, ch f Midnight Legend—Ryde Back **AWTP Racing Partnership**
31 **LIKELY AS NOT (IRE)**, 4, b f Oscar (IRE)—My Native (IRE) **H Pinniger & Peter Cook**
32 **LOSTNFOUND**, 6, b m Midnight Legend—La Cerisaie **Turf Club, Mayoh & Callan**
33 **MANOFTHEMOUNTAIN (IRE)**, 6, b g Mahler—Womanofthemountain (IRE) **Mr A Signy & Mr P Jacobs**
34 **MARLOW MOSS (IRE)**, 5, b m Fame And Glory—Moss Artiste (IRE) **Duckworth Jordan Wright & Chalke Valley**
35 **MIDNIGHT CHILL**, 7, b g Midnight Legend—Chilla Cilla **League Of Nations**
36 **MINELLA BEAT (IRE)**, 6, b g Beat Hollow—Tear Drops (IRE) **Sir Chips Keswick**
37 **MONBEG THEATRE (IRE)**, 10, b g King's Theatre (IRE)—Amberina (IRE) **Tim Dykes & Lynda Lovell**
38 **OSCAR STAR (IRE)**, 6, b m Oscar (IRE)—Tucacas (FR) **Lambourne, Forbes, Losse, Beese & Fiddes**
39 **OUR REWARD (IRE)**, 9, b g Morozov (USA)—Paddyeoin (IRE) **EPDS Racing Partnership 17**
40 **OUR THREE SONS (IRE)**, 8, b g Shantou (USA)—Ballyquinn (IRE) **Mr A. J. & Mrs J. Ward**
41 **PACIFY**, 7, b g Paco Boy (IRE)—Supereva (IRE) **The Duchess Of Cornwall & Sir Chips Keswick**
42 **REDBRIDGE GOLD (IRE)**, 6, b m Gold Well—Marikala (IRE) **O'Connor, Coomes, Scholefield, Allen**
43 **RICHIE VALENTINE**, 5, b g Native Ruler—Karmest **Mr R. Davies**
44 **SCORPION SID (IRE)**, 7, b g Scorpion (IRE)—Gaye Lady (IRE) **Apache Star Racing**
45 **SHANTEWE (IRE)**, 5, b m Shantou (USA)—Step On My Soul (IRE) **Sheep As A Lamb Syndicate**
46 **SOME DAY SOON (IRE)**, 6, b g Robin des Champs (FR)—
                              Creative Approach (IRE) **Ogilvy, Shaw, Morley&the Racegoers Club**
47 **THEBANNERKINGREBEL (IRE)**, 6, b g Arakan (USA)—One Love (IRE) **Sir Chippendale Keswick**
48 **THISTLE DO NICELY (IRE)**, 5, b g Arcadio (GER)—April Thistle (IRE) **Appletree Stud, M Gumienny & A Signy**
49 **THOMAS MACDONAGH**, 5, b g Black Sam Bellamy (IRE)—
                                Taqreem (IRE) **Sperling, Coomes, Davies, Hague, Collins**
50 **THREE WAYS**, 8, b g Flemensfirth (USA)—Serenique **Mr D. E. Brownlow**
51 **TIMCODA (IRE)**, 6, b g Milan—Sorelia (FR) **Mr P O'Leary & Mr P Mcginley**
52 **VIEUX LILLE (IRE)**, 9, b g Robin des Champs (FR)—Park Athlete (IRE) **Arwel Richards, Chas Dellar & Friends**
53 **WINTER HOLIDAY**, 5, b m Dubai Destination (USA)—Tamara King (IRE) **Mr & Mrs R. H. F. Fuller**

Other Owners: Duchess of Cornwall, Mr D. Abraham, Mrs J. Abraham, Miss Barbara Allen, Apple Tree Stud, Miss R. Bailey, Mr Tony Bath, Mr S. Beccle, Mr J. Beese, Mr Ian Callan, Chalke Valley Racing Partnership, Mr A. N. Cheyne, Mr Peter Cook, Mr Spencer Coomes, Mrs Robert Cooper, Mr A. Courtine, Mr Chris Craig-Wood, Miss C. Davies, Mr G. B. Davison, Mrs Rollo Duckworth, Duckworth, Jordan, Wright, Mr P.J. Dunkley, Mrs Denise Dunkley, Mr Tim Dykes, Mr S. J. Fiddes, Col P. Flach, Mrs Camilla Flach, Mr M. I. Forbes, Mr Philip Fox, Foxtrot Racing Management Ltd, Mr N. S. Freeland, Mrs R. Fuller, Mr R. H. F. Fuller, Mr H. M. Glyn-Davies, Mrs Jane Glyn-Davies, Mr Marek Gumienny, Heart Racing, Mr Michael D. Hill, Mr Paul G. Jacobs, Mr R. J. Kilford, Mr C. R. Lambourne, Mr D. R. Losse, Mrs L. J. Losse, Mrs L. R. Lovell, Mrs I. M. J. Matthews, Mr J. T. S. Matthews, Dr Bryan Mayoh, Mr Peter McGinley, Mrs S. McGrath, Mr R. McGrath, Me, Myself & I, Ms P Mohabir, Mr A. Morley, Mr D O'Connor, Mr P O'Leary, Dr M. M. Ogilvy, Mr W. Palk, Mr A. Palk, Ms H. N. Pinniger, Mr John Powell, Mr M. M. J. Pryce, Racegoers Club Owners Group, Mr Alex Rice, Mr Nick R. Robinson, S Beccle D Scott et al, Mr A. Scholefield, Mr D. Scott, Mr W. G. Shaw, Mr Adam Signy, Miss T. Sloan, Mr J. E. Snowden, Mrs L. Snowden, Mrs J. A. Thomas, Mr Graham P. Triefus, Turf Club 2018, Mr Michael Wainwright, Mr William Wallace, Mr A. J. Ward, Mrs J. Ward, Mr David Wiggin, Mr Jordan Wylie.

Assistant Trainer: Oliver Signy **Head Girl:** Kate Robinson

Jockey (NH): Tom O'Brien, Gavin Sheehan, Sam Twiston Davies. **Conditional:** Page Fuller.

514 MR MIKE SOWERSBY, York
Postal: **Southwold Farm, Goodmanham Wold, Market Weighton, York, East Yorkshire, YO43 3NA**
Contacts: **PHONE (01430) 810534 MOBILE (07855) 551056**

1 AGENT LOUISE, 11, b m Alflora (IRE)—Oso Special **Mr M.E. Sowersby/Mrs Carrie Zetter-Wells**
2 ARBORETUM, 11, b g Kayf Tara—Step Lively **A. Lyons**
3 BEAUTIFUL BEAR (IRE), 9, b g Beneficial—Almnadia (IRE) **A. Lyons**
4 HARMONIC LADY, 9, ch m Trade Fair—First Harmony **M. E. Sowersby**
5 HESSLE ROAD (IRE), 5, b m September Storm (GER)—Antinomy (IRE) **Mr G. Parkinson**
6 KIWAYU, 10, b g Medicean—Kibara **Mounted Games Assoc Syndicate**
7 LARKHALL, 12, b g Saddlers' Hall (IRE)—Larkbarrow **T. J. Stubbins**
8 MAMOO, 6, ch g Sir Percy—Meredith **M. E. Sowersby**
9 NO CEILING (IRE), 9, b g Turtle Island (IRE)—Pyrexie (FR) **Mrs Janet Cooper & Mr M. E. Sowersby**
10 RED SEEKER, 4, ch g Red Jazz (USA)—Purepleasureseeker (IRE) **Mr B. Valentine**
11 RIDGEWAY PEARL, 6, b m Malinas (GER)—Sparkling Jewel **R. D. Seldon**
12 RIP VAN GO, 5, b g Rip Van Winkle (IRE)—Thousandkissesdeep (IRE) **M. E. Sowersby**
13 SIMPLY LUCKY (IRE), 10, b g Flemensfirth (USA)—Derrygowna Court (IRE) **The Southwold Set**
14 THAT MAN OF MINE (IRE), 7, ch g Thewayyouare (USA)—
Do The Deal (IRE) **Mr Brian Valentine & Mr M. E. Sowersby**
15 TIR DUBH (IRE), 10, br m Sandmason—Turbine Hill (IRE) **Miss E. C. Forman**
16 TURTLE CASK (IRE), 10, b g Turtle Island (IRE)—Sayce (IRE) **T. J. Stubbins**

Other Owners: Mr P. W. Clifton, Mrs J. H. Cooper, Mr J. E. Scott, Mrs C. J. Zetter-Wells.

Assistant Trainer: Mary Sowersby

Conditional: Ryan Day.

515 MR JOHN SPEARING, Kinnersley
Postal: **Kinnersley Racing Limited, Kinnersley Racing Stables, Kinnersley, Severn Stoke, Worcestershire, WR8 9JR**
Contacts: **PHONE (01905) 371054 FAX (01905) 371054 MOBILE (07801) 552922**
E-MAIL jlspearing@aol.com

1 A SURE WELCOME, 5, b g Pastoral Pursuits—Croeso Bach **Kinnersley Partnership 3**
2 CAPTAIN SEDGWICK (IRE), 5, b m Approve (IRE)—Alinda (IRE) **Personal Racehorse Owners 3**
3 CLEAR SPRING (IRE), 11, b g Chineur (FR)—Holly Springs **Mr H. James**
4 COOL STRUTTER (IRE), 7, b g Kodiac—Cassava (IRE) **Mr J. L. Spearing**
5 IT'S HOW WE ROLL (IRE), 5, b g Fastnet Rock (AUS)—Clodora (FR) **Kinnersley Partnership**
6 KEY TO THE WEST (IRE), 12, b g Westerner—Monte Solaro (IRE) **Miss R S Newell & Mr T P Morrissey**
7 LADY GWHINNYVERE (IRE), 5, b m Sir Prancealot (IRE)—Johar Jamal (IRE) **Mr J. L. Spearing**
8 LOST HISTORY (IRE), 6, b g Strategic Prince—Prelude **Mr J. J. Reilly**
9 4, B f Shirocco (GER)—Miss Conduct **Miss C. J. Ive**
10 PEARLS LEGEND, 12, b g Midnight Legend—Pearl's Choice (IRE) **The Corsairs**
11 SHUTTHEGATE (IRE), 5, b g Milan—Miss Conduct **Miss C. J. Ive**

Other Owners: Mr C. S. Heaps, Mrs S. R. Keable, Mr T. P. Morrissey, Miss R. S. Newell, Mr H. C. M. Porter, Mrs C. J. Welch.

Assistant Trainer: Miss C. Ive

516 MR RICHARD SPENCER, Newmarket
Postal: **The Flat, Albert House Stables, Moulton Road, Newmarket, Suffolk, CB8 8DU**
Contacts: **PHONE (01638) 675780**

1 APTLY PUT (IRE), 7, b br g Yeats (IRE)—Versatile Approach (IRE) **Mr G. M. Spencer**
2 BERNARDO O'REILLY, 5, b g Intikhab (USA)—Baldovina **Rebel Racing (2)**
3 CLUB TROPICANA, 4, ch f Helmet (AUS)—Twenty Seven **Rebel Racing**
4 FINK HILL (USA), 4, b g The Factor (USA)—Matroshka (IRE) **Morecool & Cool Racing 2**
5 GUSTAVO FRING (IRE), 5, b g Kodiac—Maleha (IRE) **Rebel Racing (2)**
6 HANDSOME SAMSON, 4, b g Nathaniel (IRE)—Factice (USA) **Rebel Racing**
7 INVISIBLE SHADOW, 4, b g Oasis Dream—Tavy **Equinox Racing**
8 ITS'AFREEBEE (IRE), 9, br g Danroad (AUS)—Aphra Benn (IRE) **Rebel Jumping**
9 KEYSER SOZE (IRE), 5, ch g Arcano (IRE)—Causeway Queen (IRE) **Rebel Racing (2)**

MR RICHARD SPENCER - Continued

10 **MOVIE SET (USA)**, 7, b br g Dubawi (IRE)—Short Skirt **Fathers & Sons**
11 **PHILAMUNDO (IRE)**, 4, b g Sir Prancealot (IRE)—Rublevka Star (USA) **Rebel Racing**
12 **REBEL SURGE (IRE)**, 6, b m Kodiac—Face The Storm (IRE) **Mr P. M. Cunningham**
13 **SEA OF FLAMES**, 6, ch g Aqlaam—Hidden Fire **Rebel Racing**—
14 **SIR JACK YEATS (IRE)**, 8, b g Yeats (IRE)—Quadrennial (IRE) **Gowing's Eleven**
15 **STRATEGIC HEIGHTS (IRE)**, 10, b g Strategic Prince—
                                     Shot of Redemption **Mr Phil Cunningham & Mr Richard Spencer**
16 **THISTIMENEXTYEAR**, 5, gr g New Approach (IRE)—Scarlet Empire (IRE) **Rebel Racing (2)**

THREE-YEAR-OLDS

17 **ALFIE SOLOMONS (IRE)**, b g Acclamation—Vastitas (IRE) **Rebel Racing Premier**
18 **CALIFORNIA LOVE**, ch f Power—La Pantera **Mr A. Cunningham**
19 **COOKUPASTORM (IRE)**, b f Camacho—No Clubs (IRE) **Balasuriya,Cook Cunningham,Gowing,Spencer**
20 **JEAN VALJEAN**, b g Bated Breath—Waitingonacloud **Six Amigos**
21 **LE FREAK (IRE)**, b f Born To Sea (IRE)—Bunditten (IRE) **Balasuriya,CookCunningham,Gowing,Spencer**
22 **LOUIS TREIZE (IRE)**, ch c Slade Power (IRE)—Black Rodded **Rebel Racing Premier**
23 **MATERIAL GIRL**, b f Pivotal—Apace (IRE) **Miss L. Cunningham**
24 **NERVOUS NERYS (IRE)**, b f Kodiac—Sassy (FR) **Equinox Racing**
25 **NOSTROVIA (IRE)**, gr f Alhebayeb (IRE)—Na Zdorovie **Bland, Cunningham, Hall, Cliff Stud.**
26 **RED ARCHANGEL (IRE)**, b f Dark Angel (IRE)—Illuminating Dream (IRE) **Mr P. M. Cunningham**
27 **REVICH (IRE)**, b g Requinto (IRE)—Kathleen Rafferty (IRE) **Middleham Park Lxvii & Phil Cunningham**
28 **RUMBLE INTHEJUNGLE (IRE)**, ch c Bungle Inthejungle—
                                     Guana (IRE) **Rebel Racing Premier & Cheveley Park Stud**
29 **SPENCERS SON (IRE)**, b g Arcano (IRE)—Zalama (FR) **Balasuriya,CookCunningham,Gowing,Spencer**
30 **STALLONE (IRE)**, b g Dandy Man (IRE)—Titian Queen **Rebel Racing Premier**
31 **STAY CLASSY (IRE)**, ch f Camacho—Hollow Green (IRE) **Balasuriya,CookCunningham,Gowing,Spencer**
32 **SUSSUDIO**, b f Compton Place—Glen Molly (IRE) **Balasuriya,CookCunningham,Gowing,Spencer**
33 **THRILLA IN MANILA**, b c Iffraaj—Tesary **Rebel Racing Premier**
34 **WHITE IVERSON (IRE)**, ch g Tale of The Cat (USA)—
                                     Illaunglass (IRE) **Balasuriya,CookCunningham,Gowing,Spencer**
35 **YOU NEVER CAN TELL (IRE)**, b c Elzaam (AUS)—Zanida (IRE) **Six Amigos**

TWO-YEAR-OLDS

36 B c 29/4 Elzaam (AUS)—Abandon (USA) (Rahy (USA)) (33333)
37 B c 3/4 Dandy Man (IRE)—Caramel Sundae (Oratorio (IRE)) (25283) **Rebel Racing III**
38 **CATECHISM**, b f 23/2 Dutch Art—Postulant (Kyllachy) **Cheveley Park Stud Limited**
39 Ch c 6/3 Coach House (IRE)—Clara Schumann (Medicean) **Mr P. M. Cunningham**
40 **DUTUGAMUNU (IRE)**, ch c 3/5 Ivawood (IRE)—
                                     Bunditten (IRE) (Soviet Star (USA)) **Balasuriya, Cook Cunningham, Gowing, Spencer**
41 B c 2/3 Camacho—Flawless Pink (More Than Ready (USA)) (42857)
42 **GRACE PLUNKETT**, b f 24/2 Brazen Beau (AUS)—Goodnightsuzy (IRE) (Azamour (IRE)) **Mr P. M. Cunningham**
43 **HOLLABACK GIRL**, ch f 16/4 Camacho—Jimmy's Girl (IRE) (Equiano (FR)) **Miss L. Cunningham**
44 **JOANIE STUBBS**, b f 11/3 Garswood—Cherry Malotte (Pivotal) **Mr P. M. Cunningham**
45 B f 15/2 Camacho—Laheen (IRE) (Bluebird (USA)) (14327) **Rebel Racing III**
46 B f 5/2 Camacho—Luanas Pearl (IRE) (Bahri (IRE)) (8428) **Rebel Racing III**
47 B f 18/4 Kodiac—Miss Corinne (Mark of Esteem (IRE)) (75853)
48 **ODYSSEY GIRL (IRE)**, gr f 6/4 Gutaifan (IRE)—Lady Marita (IRE) (Dandy Man (IRE)) (10113)
49 **PARADE**, b gr f 13/4 Lethal Force (IRE)—Catwalk (IRE) (Pivotal) **Cheveley Park Stud Limited**
50 B c 13/2 Camacho—Sahah (USA) (Rock Hard Ten (USA)) (38095)
51 **SEFTON WARRIOR**, b c 23/3 Frankel—
                                     Maid To Master (IRE) (Danehill Dancer (IRE)) (75000) **Rebel Racing Premier II**
52 B c 7/3 Bungle Inthejungle—Starfleet (Inchinor) (13484) **Rebel Racing III**
53 **THE CITY'S PHANTOM**, b c 2/4 Free Eagle (IRE)—Meet Marhaba (IRE) (Marju (IRE)) (8000) **A. Al Shaikh**
54 Ch c 16/4 Iffraaj—Za Za Zoom (IRE) (Le Vie Dei Colori) **Balasuriya,CookCunningham,Gowing,Spencer**

Other Owners: Mr C. Bennett, Mr S. Bland, Mr P Cunningham, Mr M.R Gowing, Middleham Park Racing LXVII, Mr T. D. Nield, T. S. Palin, M. Prince, Mr R. G. R. Spencer, Mr M. Sykes.

517 MR SEB SPENCER, Malton

Postal: **79 Harvest Drive, Malton, North Yorkshire, YO17 7BF**
Contacts: **MOBILE (07790) 060050**
E-MAIL sebspencerracing@gmail.com

1 ADIATOR, 11, b m Needwood Blade—Retaliator **Jetset Racing Club**
2 DON'T BE SURPRISED, 4, ch g Monsieur Bond (IRE)—Julie's Gift **N Bycroft & Partners**
3 DONNCHA (IRE), 8, br g Captain Marvelous (IRE)—Seasonal Style (IRE) **Mr D. Bannon**
4 GENEVA TRUMPET, 8, b g Virtual—Quotation **Mr G. R. Oldroyd**
5 JET SET GO, 4, ch f Equiano (FR)—Golden Valley **Jetset Racing Club**
6 ORSINO (IRE), 5, b g Galileo (IRE)—Birmanie (USA) **David Bannon & Partner**

Other Owners: Mr D. R. Bainbridge, N. Bycroft, Mr R. Kaye, Mr R. Postlethwaite.

Assistant Trainer: Geoff Oldroyd

---

518 MR HENRY SPILLER, Newmarket

Postal: **Henry Spiller Racing, Sackville House Stables, Sackville Street, Newmarket, Suffolk, CB8 8DX**
Contacts: **PHONE (01638) 662899 MOBILE (07786) 263997**
E-MAIL office@henryspillerracing.com WEBSITE www.henryspillerracing.com

1 AERODROME, 4, b f Nathaniel (IRE)—Westerly Air (USA) **pcracing.co.uk**
2 ARGANTE (FR), 10, b br g Singspiel (IRE)—Abyaan (IRE) **Dethrone Racing**
3 ARNOUL OF METZ, 4, b g Kyllachy—Appointee (IRE) **Mr R. P. A. Spiller**
4 COLOURFIELD (IRE), 4, b f Makfi—Rainbow Desert (USA) **GG Thoroughbreds II**
5 FOLIE DOUZE, 4, b g Foxwedge (AUS)—Chicklade **Dethrone Racing**
6 GOOD BUSINESS (IRE), 5, ch m Dutch Art—Parakopi (IRE) **Front Runner Racing II**
7 HERRINGSWELL (FR), 4, b f Pour Moi (IRE)—Sovereign's Honour (USA) **Mr B. Boyle**
8 INTREPIDLY (USA), 5, b g Medaglia d'oro (USA)—Trepidation (USA) **C Pigram, T Hind, GG Thoroughbreds**
9 IRISH TIMES, 4, b g Swiss Spirit—Amouage Royale (IRE) **Mr D. M. Forrester**
10 KAMRA (USA), 5, b g Stay Thirsty (USA)—Milliondollarbill (USA) **Iredale Racing & GG Thoroughbreds I**
11 KING OF ROOKS, 6, b g Acclamation—Slap Shot (IRE) **Dethrone Racing**
12 KYOTO STAR (FR), 5, b g Oasis Dream—Hanami **G. B. Partnership**
13 LEADER WRITER (FR), 7, b h Pivotal—Miss Emma May (IRE) **G. B. Partnership**
14 MOUNT WELLINGTON (IRE), 4, b g Invincible Spirit (IRE)—Marvada (IRE) **GG Thoroughbreds IX**
15 NATALIE EXPRESS (FR), 5, b m Excelebration (IRE)—Miss Emma May (IRE) **G. B. Partnership**
16 ROTHERHITHE, 4, b f Finjaan—Reeling N' Rocking (IRE) **Franconson Partners**
17 ROYAL MEZYAN (IRE), 8, b g Royal Applause—Rice Mother (IRE) **Muttley Management**
18 THE THIRD MAN, 8, gr g Dalakhani (IRE)—Spinning Queen **Mrs D. Spiller**
19 THEYDON BOXER, 4, b g Piccolo—Angel of Fashion (IRE) **Eamonn O'Riordan Peter Charalambous**
20 THEYDON SPIRIT, 4, ch g Piccolo—Ela Gorrie Mou **Eamonn O'Riordan Peter Charalambous**
21 TRULEE SCRUMPTIOUS, 10, b m Strategic Prince—Morning Rise (GER) **pcracing.co.uk**
22 VAN DIEST, 7, b g Hurricane Run (IRE)—Miracle **Mr R. P. A. Spiller**

THREE-YEAR-OLDS

23 BAROSSA BAL (IRE), b f Delegator—Anamarka
24 CHAKRII (IRE), b c Mukhadram—Chalet Girl **Mr B. Boyle**
25 DAPHINIA, b f Kuroshio (AUS)—Phantom Spirit **The Hightailers**
26 EXOUSIA, b c Epaulette (AUS)—Lady McGonagall (USA) **Muttley Management**
27 LAST TO BID (FR), ch c Makfi—Last Song **Mr R. P. A. Spiller**
28 MYSUSY (IRE), b f Dawn Approach (IRE)—Gold Lace (IRE) **GG Thoroughbreds IV**
29 PARKNACILLA (IRE), b f Mukhadram—Patuca **Charles & Fiona Spiller**
30 PICTURE POET (IRE), b g Camacho—Cockney Rhyme **The Select Racing Club Limited**
31 SEPAHI, ch f Sepoy (AUS)—Katevan (IRE) **Mr F. Nass**
32 Ch c Makfi—Soho Rocks **Dethrone Racing**
33 TEODULA (IRE), ch f Tagula—Lady Kildare (IRE) **The Select Racing Club Limited**

TWO-YEAR-OLDS

34 B c 11/2 Helmet (AUS)—Critical Path (IRE) (Noverre (USA)) (841) **The Champagne Poppers**

Other Owners: P. Charalambous, Mrs C. Cummings, Mr D. Curran, Mrs D. Curran, GG Thoroughbreds I, Mr G. Gill, Miss J. S. Gill, M. G. H. Heald, Mr A. M. H. Heald, Mr A. A. F. Iredale, Mr K. Lines, Mr K. W. Marks, Mr E. O'Riordan, Mr C. Pigram, Mr C. R. G. Spiller, Mrs F. J. D. Spiller, Mr H. C. Spiller, Miss T. L. Tideswell, Mrs H. M. Worboys, J. R. Worboys.

519 **MR FOZZY STACK, Cashel**
Postal: **Thomastown Castle Stud, Golden, Cashel, Co. Tipperary, Ireland**
Contacts: **PHONE (00353) 62 54129**
E-MAIL contact@stackracing.ie WEBSITE www.stackracing.ie

1 **CARLO BIRAGHI (IRE)**, 4, ch c Galileo (IRE)—Kirinda (IRE)
2 **DREAM ASCOT (IRE)**, 4, b f Oasis Dream—World Class
3 **HAND ON HEART (IRE)**, 4, ch f Mastercraftsman (IRE)—Insight (FR)
4 **HARVESTFORTHEWORLD (IRE)**, 4, b br f So You Think (NZ)—Israar
5 **IIEX EXCELSA (IRE)**, 4, ch f Excelebration (IRE)—Holly Blue
6 **PEACE PROCESS (IRE)**, 4, b f Declaration of War (USA)—Front House (IRE)
7 **SHIFTED STRATEGY (IRE)**, 4, b c Choisir (AUS)—Pure Greed (IRE)
8 **SON OF REST**, 5, b h Pivotal—Hightime Heroine (IRE)
9 **ZIHBA (IRE)**, 4, b c Choisir (AUS)—Fancy Vivid (IRE)

THREE-YEAR-OLDS

10 **ANY OTHER NEWS (IRE)**, ch f Zoffany (IRE)—Umniya (IRE)
11 **AUSTRALIAN WALTZ (USA)**, b f Australia—Waltzing Matilda (IRE)
12 B c No Nay Never (USA)—Bright Bank (IRE)
13 **DESERT VIPER (IRE)**, b br c Footstepsinthesand—Neds Bypass (IRE)
14 **DRUMQUINA (IRE)**, b f Holy Roman Emperor (IRE)—Tarascon (IRE)
15 **ECLIPSE STORM**, ch c Dream Ahead (USA)—Gentle Breeze (IRE)
16 **EMPIRE LINE (IRE)**, b c Holy Roman Emperor (IRE)—Many Hearts (USA)
17 B f Camelot—Flamingo Sea (USA)
18 **GATSBY CAP (IRE)**, b c Gale Force Ten—Blue Dahlia (IRE)
19 Ch c Ruler of The World (IRE)—Lady Miletrian (IRE)
20 **LADY WANNABE (IRE)**, b f Camelot—Wannabe Better (IRE)
21 B f Holy Roman Emperor (IRE)—Mango Groove (IRE)
22 **MARLONEBUNDO**, b c Kodiac—Pearl City (IRE)
23 B f War Command (USA)—Medican Star (IRE)
24 **MODRED (IRE)**, b c Camelot—Israar
25 **NEVER RAINS (IRE)**, b f No Nay Never (USA)—Falling Rain (IRE)
26 **NEVEREVERSAYNEVER (IRE)**, b f No Nay Never (USA)—Dowager
27 **NICARO (IRE)**, b c No Nay Never (USA)—Mironica (IRE)
28 B c Canford Cliffs (IRE)—Pivotalia (IRE)
29 **SEMILLON (IRE)**, ch f Australia—Silver Rain (FR)
30 **TRIPLE NICKLE (IRE)**, b f So You Think (NZ)—Secret Shine (IRE)
31 **WARGRAVE (IRE)**, b c Galileo (IRE)—Scream Blue Murder (IRE)
32 **WOODY CREEK**, b f Zoffany (IRE)—Belle Isle

TWO-YEAR-OLDS

33 Ch c 7/4 Pivotal—Adore (Oasis Dream) (38000)
34 B c 20/3 Power—Aine (IRE) (Danehill Dancer (IRE))
35 B c 6/4 Muhaarar—Alasha (IRE) (Barathea (IRE)) (67424)
36 Ch f 5/4 Declaration of War (USA)—Alegendinmyownmind (Cape Cross (IRE)) (246913)
37 Ch f 31/1 Starspangledbanner (AUS)—Big Boned (IRE) (Street Sense (USA)) (88495)
38 B f 15/3 No Nay Never (USA)—Danehill's Dream (IRE) (Danehill (USA)) (110000)
39 B c 21/4 Holy Roman Emperor (IRE)—Dark Orchid (Shamardal (USA)) (33712)
40 B f 22/4 Holy Roman Emperor (IRE)—Double Fantasy (GER) (Indian Ridge) (42857)
41 B f 3/2 Dark Angel (IRE)—Dutch Diamond (Dutch Art) (30000)
42 B f 5/5 Holy Roman Emperor (IRE)—Emirate Jewel (USA) (Pivotal)
43 B f 30/1 No Nay Never (USA)—Falling Rain (IRE) (Danehill Dancer (IRE)) (47619)
44 Ch c 25/1 Anjaal—Fancy Vivid (IRE) (Galileo (IRE)) (15170)
45 Ch f 2/2 Starspangledbanner (AUS)—Fataawy (IRE) (Invincible Spirit (IRE)) (71428)
46 B br c 24/3 Warrior's Reward (USA)—Fly Again (USA) (Fusaichi Pegasus (USA)) (35273)
47 B f 3/2 Cable Bay (IRE)—Gentle Breeze (IRE) (Dubawi (IRE))
48 B c 26/1 No Nay Never (USA)—High Savannah (IRE) (High Chaparral (IRE)) (202275)
49 Ch f 16/2 No Nay Never (USA)—Hula Angel (USA) (Woodman (USA))
50 B c 24/3 Power—Love Rosie (USA) (Zebedee)
51 B f 25/3 No Nay Never (USA)—Mala Mala (IRE) (Brief Truce (USA))
52 B f 22/4 War Command (USA)—Medican Star (IRE) (Galileo (IRE))
53 B f 12/2 Lawman (FR)—Miracolia (IRE) (Montjeu (IRE)) (85000)
54 Ch c 11/4 Australia—Mohican Princess (Shirley Heights) (84280)
55 Ch f 25/2 Gale Force Ten—Muizenberg Nights (IRE) (Shamardal (USA))
56 B f 18/1 Zoffany (IRE)—Private Paradise (IRE) (Galileo (IRE)) (33712)

MR FOZZY STACK - Continued

57 B c 11/2 No Nay Never (USA)—Queen of Lyons (USA) (Dubai Destination (USA)) (78095)
58 B f 28/3 Gleneagles (IRE)—Scream Blue Murder (IRE) (Oratorio (IRE))
59 B f 27/3 Starspangledbanner (AUS)—Show Me Off (Showcasing) (49725)
60 B c 22/4 Gleneagles (IRE)—Snowfields (IRE) (Raven's Pass (USA)) (95238)
61 STALINGRAD, b c 16/4 War Front (USA)—I Am Beautiful (IRE) (Rip Van Winkle (IRE)) (220000)
62 B f 28/2 Dark Angel (IRE)—Taraeff (IRE) (Cape Cross (IRE)) (134849)

Owners: Mr Rick Barnes, Mr Michael Begley, Craig Bernick, Peter Chiu, Iman Hartono, Mr T. Hyde Jnr, Mr D. Keoghan, Mrs J. Magnier, Mr Casey McLiney, The New Pension Fund Syndicate, Mr B. Parker, The Pension Fund II Syndicate, Mr P. Piller, Mrs Jane Rowlinson, G. A. Rupert, Mary Slack, Mr M L Slevin, Mr Michael Tabor, Sir Peter Vela, Mr Neil Werrett.

Jockey (flat): Chris Hayes, W. J. Lee. **Apprentice:** Killian K. Hennessy, Michael J. O'Connor.

520
MR EUGENE STANFORD, Newmarket
Postal: **2 Rous Memorial Cottages, Old Station Road, Newmarket, Suffolk, CB8 8DP**
Contacts: **PHONE (01638) 665507 MOBILE (07761) 223096**
E-MAIL **e.stanford077@btinternet.com** WEBSITE **www.eugenestanfordracing.com**

1 AMNA, 5, b m Sayif (IRE)—Island Dreams (USA) **Mr E. V. Stanford**
2 BELLA BLUR, 7, ch m Showcasing—Ellablue **Miss C. R. Williams**
3 ISLAND AUTHORITY, 4, b m Authorized—Island Odyssey **Mr E. V. Stanford**
4 OCEAN SPRAY, 4, ch f Showcasing—Gibraltar Lass (USA) **Mr M. W. Goodridge**
5 Q CEE, 6, b g Denounce—Gibraltar Lass (USA) **Mr M. W. Goodridge**
6 SHOW THE MONEY, 4, ch g Showcasing—Rio Belle (IRE) **Mr M. W. Goodridge**
7 UNTIL MIDNIGHT (IRE), 9, b g Moss Vale (IRE)—Emma's Star (ITY) **Newmarketracingclub.co.uk**

THREE-YEAR-OLDS

8 TINKERBIRD, br c Gregorian (IRE)—Swan Queen **Sir Thomas Pilkington**

Other Owners: New Sports Media Ltd, C. Woof.

521
MRS JACKIE STEPHEN, Inverurie
Postal: **Conglass Farmhouse, Inverurie, Aberdeenshire, AB51 5DN**
Contacts: **PHONE (01467) 621267 FAX (01467) 620511 MOBILE (07980) 785924**
E-MAIL **jackiestephen123@hotmail.com** WEBSITE **www.jackiestephenracing.com**

1 AMILLIONTIMES (IRE), 11, b g Olden Times—Miss Million (IRE) **Mr P. G. Stephen**
2 BERMONDSEY BELLE (IRE), 5, b m Sir Percy—Bermondsey Girl **Mrs J. S. Stephen**
3 BRIDANE HIGH (IRE), 6, b g Mountain High—Maylee (IRE) **Truscott & Stephen**
4 BRIGHT PROSPECT (IRE), 10, b g Kutub (IRE)—Bright Future (IRE) **Lessells, Pirie, Ritchie & Stephen**
5 CAPTAIN KURT, 5, b g Distant Peak (IRE)—Choral Singer **Mr P. G. Stephen**
6 HIGHLAND PEAK, 7, b g Distant Peak (IRE)—Flower Appeal **Northern Lights Racing**
7 LADYVIE (FR), 12, b m Vic Toto (FR)—Ladykish (FR) **Mrs J. S. Stephen**
8 LOVELY SCHTUFF (IRE), 7, b g Court Cave (IRE)—The Long Bill (IRE) **High Country Racing**
9 MIDNIGHT KATE (IRE), 5, gr m Midnight Legend—Primrose Time **Mr C. T. Reid**
10 SCHIEHALLION RIDGE (IRE), 4, b g Mountain High—Upton Lodge (IRE) **Mrs J. S. Stephen**
11 STAROZOV (IRE), 6, b g Morozov (USA)—Star of Arcady (IRE) **Jackie Stephen Racing Club**
12 WELCOME BEN (IRE), 10, b g High Roller (IRE)—Bramble Cottage (IRE) **Northern Lights Racing**

Other Owners: Mr M. C. Barron, Mr J. A. Dickson, Mr J. S. Lessells, Mr N. Patience, Mr A. C. Pirie, Mr G. G. Ritchie, Mr G. Truscott.

Assistant Trainer: Patrick Stephen

522
MR ROBERT STEPHENS, Caldicot
Postal: **The Knoll, St. Brides Netherwent, Caldicot, Gwent, NP26 3AT**
Contacts: **MOBILE (07717) 477177**
E-MAIL **robertdavidstephens@btinternet.com** WEBSITE **www.robertstephensracing.com**

1 AWAYWITHTHEBLUES (IRE), 7, ch g Stowaway—Rhythm 'n' Blues (IRE) **Mrs B Ayres, Mr E & Mrs K Neville**
2 BALKINSTOWN (IRE), 9, b g Westerner—Graffogue (IRE) **Mrs C. Ford-Ellis**

MR ROBERT STEPHENS - Continued

3 **BELTOR**, 8, b g Authorized (IRE)—Carahill (AUS) **A. J. Mossop**
4 **BROPHIES DOLL (IRE)**, 7, ch m Gamut (IRE)—Crossbar Lady (IRE)
5 **BUMBLE BAY**, 9, b g Trade Fair—Amica **A Mossop & H Scale**
6 **CASTLELYONS (IRE)**, 7, br g Papal Bull—Summercove (IRE) **Robert Stephens Racing Club**
7 **CLIFF FACE (IRE)**, 6, b m Canford Cliffs (IRE)—Kotdiji **Threes Company**
8 **COMEONTHEBULL (IRE)**, 7, ch g Papal Bull—Maratanas Gift (IRE) **M Duthie & T Moynihan**
9 **DIAMOND BENNY (IRE)**, 7, b g Milan—Ben's Pride **Paul Duffy Diamond Partnership**
10 **ESPRESSO FREDDO (IRE)**, 5, b g Fast Company (IRE)—Spring Bouquet (IRE) **Threes Company**
11 **FIRST DESTINATION**, 7, b m Rail Link—Hollow Quaill (IRE) **A. J. Mossop**
12 **LEADER OF THE LAND (IRE)**, 12, ch g Halling (USA)—Cheerleader **Mark Duthie & Partners**
13 **MERE ANARCHY (IRE)**, 8, b g Yeats (IRE)—Maracana (IRE) **Les Oxley & R Stephens**
14 **MILE HOUSE (IRE)**, 11, b g Close Conflict (USA)—Clogheen Lass (IRE) **Castle Farm Racing**
15 **MISKIN**, 10, b g Motivator—Castellina (USA) **Mrs C. Ford-Ellis**
16 **MUSKETEER**, 7, ch g Schiaparelli (GER)—Suave Shot **Mr R. D. Stephens**
17 **POWER SURGE (IRE)**, 5, ch g Power—Silver Skates (IRE) **Mr R. D. Stephens**
18 **PUSH THE TEMPO**, 6, b g Gold Well—Fairpark (IRE) **Castle Farm Racing**
19 **QUINNSBOROTEMPTRES (IRE)**, 7, ch m Gamut (IRE)—Quinnsboro Native (IRE) **Mr R. D. Stephens**
20 **SECONDO (FR)**, 9, b g Sakhee's Secret—Royal Jade **Robert Stephens Racing Club**
21 **THREE COLOURS RED (IRE)**, 7, b g Camacho—Colour's Red (IRE) **The Red Partnership**
22 **TOSHIMA (IRE)**, 4, b g Sea The Stars (IRE)—Sabreon **Threes Company**
23 **TUDORS TREASURE**, 8, b g Dr Massini (IRE)—Rude Health **Four Seasons Partnership**

Other Owners: Mrs B. M. Ayres, Mr I. J. K. Croker, Mr D. P. Duffy, Mr M. Duthie, Mr T. J. Moynihan, Mrs K. A. Neville, Mr E. J. Neville, Mr E. M. O'Connor, Mr L. T. Oxley, Mr W. B. H. Scale, Mrs J. E. Scale, D. T. Shorthouse, Mr K. Slade, Mr D. O. Stephens, Mr G. M. Winstone.

Assistant Trainer: Rosie Stephens

Jockey (NH): Tom O'Brien. **Conditional:** Ciaran Gethings. **Amateur:** Mr Craig Dowson, Mr Morgan Winstone.

---

523 MR WILLIAM STONE, West Wickham
Postal: **The Meadow, Streetly End, West Wickham, Cambridge, Cambridgeshire, CB21 4RP**
Contacts: **MOBILE (07788) 971094**
E-MAIL williamstone1@hotmail.co.uk

1 **DIAMOND LADY**, 8, b m Multiplex—Ellen Mooney **Miss C. M. Scott**
2 **EAST COAST LADY (IRE)**, 7, b m Kodiac—Alexander Anapolis (IRE) **Miss C. M. Scott**
3 **EVENING ATTIRE**, 8, b g Pastoral Pursuits—Markova's Dance **Miss C. M. Scott**
4 **INVISIBLE STORM**, 4, gr f Multiplex—Dawn Lightning **Mr A Wittering & Dr C Scott**
5 **MISTRESS NELLIE**, 4, ch f Mount Nelson—Watchoverme **Mrs Denis Haynes & Dr Caroline Scott**
6 **RED SNAPPER**, 4, b f Kheleyf (USA)—Amistress **Miss C. M. Scott**
7 **THE JEAN GENIE**, 5, b br m Lawman (FR)—Miracle Seeker **Miss C. M. Scott**
8 **TIGERFISH (IRE)**, 5, b m Lilbourne Lad (IRE)—Nisriyna (IRE) **Miss C. M. Scott**

THREE-YEAR-OLDS

9 **JEANETTE MAY**, b f Dick Turpin (IRE)—Clock Opera (IRE) **Mr Shane Fairweather & Dr C Scott**

TWO-YEAR-OLDS

10 B c 2/5 Casamento (IRE)—Clock Opera (IRE) (Excellent Art)
11 Ch c 29/3 Equiano (FR)—Smile For Me (IRE) (Elnadim (USA))

Other Owners: Mr S. A. Fairweather, Mrs E. A. P. Haynes, Mr A. J. Wittering.

---

524 MR WILF STOREY, Consett
Postal: **Grange Farm & Stud, Muggleswick, Consett, County Durham, DH8 9DW**
Contacts: **PHONE (01207) 255259 MOBILE (07860) 510441**
E-MAIL wlstorey@metronet.co.uk WEBSITE www.wilfstorey.com

1 **BETTY GRABLE (IRE)**, 5, b m Delegator—Danella (IRE) **Mr W. L. Storey**
2 **CARD HIGH (IRE)**, 9, b g Red Clubs (IRE)—Think (FR) **Gremlin Racing**
3 **CIRCUIT**, 5, br m Foxwedge (AUS)—Lady Circe (USA) **Mr W. L. Storey**
4 **CLIMAX**, 5, b m Acclamation—Blue Rocket (IRE) **Mr W. L. Storey**
5 **HIGHWAY ROBBER**, 6, b g Dick Turpin (IRE)—Lawyers Choice **Gremlin Racing**

MR WILF STOREY - Continued

  6 **NEARLY THERE**, 6, b g Virtual—Nicoise (IRE) **Geegeez.co.uk 1**
  7 **TARNHELM**, 4, b f Helmet (AUS)—Anosti **Mr W. L. Storey**

THREE-YEAR-OLDS
  8 **SOMEWHAT SISYPHEAN**, b g Mount Nelson—Nine Red **Geegeez.co.uk 1**

Other Owners: Mr M. Bisogno, M. Burton, J. Cannon, Mr D. D. Gillies, P. McVey, A. Rugg, Mr W. Storey, I. Wallis, P. Williams.

Assistant Trainer: Miss S. Storey (07711) 091275

Amateur: Miss S. M. Doolan.

---

525   **SIR MICHAEL STOUTE, Newmarket**
Postal: **Freemason Lodge, Bury Road, Newmarket, Suffolk, CB8 7BY**
Contacts: **PHONE (01638) 663801 FAX (01638) 667276**

  1 **CRYSTAL KING**, 4, ch g Frankel—Crystal Star
  2 **CRYSTAL MOONLIGHT**, 4, ch f New Approach (IRE)—Crystal Capella
  3 **CRYSTAL OCEAN**, 5, b h Sea The Stars (IRE)—Crystal Star
  4 **DESERT SON**, 4, ch c Dubawi (IRE)—Russelliana
  5 **DREAM OF DREAMS (IRE)**, 5, ch h Dream Ahead (USA)—Vasilia
  6 **ELECTOR**, 4, b g Dansili—Enticement
  7 **EQTIDAAR (IRE)**, 4, b c Invincible Spirit (IRE)—Madany (IRE)
  8 **HAMLUL (FR)**, 4, gr c Frankel—Alix Road (FR)
  9 **IHTITHAR (IRE)**, 4, b c Lope de Vega (IRE)—Kapria (FR)
10 **KHAIRAAT (IRE)**, 6, b g Shamardal (USA)—Mumayeza
11 **LEDHAM (IRE)**, 4, b c Shamardal (USA)—Pioneer Bride (USA)
12 **MEKONG**, 4, b g Frankel—Ship's Biscuit
13 **MELTING DEW**, 5, b g Cacique (IRE)—Winter Sunrise
14 **MIRAGE DANCER**, 5, b h Frankel—Heat Haze
15 **MUSTASHRY**, 6, b br g Tamayuz—Safwa (IRE)
16 **QAROUN**, 4, b c Dark Angel (IRE)—Exotic Isle
17 **RAWDAA**, 4, b f Teofilo (IRE)—Lady Lahar
18 **REGAL REALITY**, 4, b c Intello (GER)—Regal Realm
19 **SEXTANT**, 4, b g Sea The Stars (IRE)—Hypoteneuse (IRE)
20 **SHAREEF STAR**, 4, b c Sea The Stars (IRE)—Gotlandia (FR)
21 **SUN MAIDEN**, 4, b f Frankel—Midsummer
22 **TAHREEK**, 4, b g Dansili—Rifqah (USA)
23 **VERACIOUS**, 4, b f Frankel—Infallible
24 **ZAAKI**, 4, b g Leroidesanimaux (BRZ)—Kesara

THREE-YEAR-OLDS
25 **ACCOMMODATE (IRE)**, b f Acclamation—Malaspina (IRE)
26 **ACCOMPLISHED FACT (IRE)**, b c Acclamation—Ellen (IRE)
27 **ALBANDERI**, b f Kingman—Hazel Lavery (IRE)
28 **ALHAAZM**, b c Cape Cross (IRE)—Asheerah
29 **ALIGNAK**, gr c Sea The Moon (GER)—Albanova
30 **ALIGNED (IRE)**, b c Dubawi (IRE)—Ikat (IRE)
31 **ALKARAAMA (USA)**, b c War Front (USA)—Agreeable Miss (USA)
32 **ALMANIA (IRE)**, b c Australia—Sent From Heaven (IRE)
33 **ALNASHERAT**, b c Kingman—Split Trois (FR)
34 **ANNA OF LORRAINE**, b f Dutch Art—Ladyship
35 **ARCTIC OCEAN (IRE)**, b f Camelot—Hurricane Emma (USA)
36 **BUTTERFLY KISS (USA)**, b f Medaglia d'oro (USA)—Laughing Lashes (USA)
37 **CALCULATION**, br g Dubawi (IRE)—Estimate (IRE)
38 **CAPE SHAMA (IRE)**, b c Cape Cross (IRE)—Shama's Song (IRE)
39 **CLARION**, b f Dubawi (IRE)—Caraboss
40 **CLERISY**, b f Kingman—Exemplify
41 **CRYSTAL DREAM**, b f Oasis Dream—Crystal Etoile
42 **CUTTING SWORD**, b f Intello (GER)—Ventura Highway
43 **DANTE'S VIEW (IRE)**, ch c Galileo (IRE)—Daivika (USA)
44 **DAVYDENKO**, ch c Intello (GER)—Safina
45 **DEAL A DOLLAR**, b c Frankel—Cape Dollar (IRE)

SIR MICHAEL STOUTE - Continued

46 **DEREVO**, b c Dansili—Pavlosk (USA)
47 **DETECTIVE**, b c Kingman—Promising Lead
48 **DILMUN DYNASTY (IRE)**, b c Sea The Stars (IRE)—Elegant Shadow (GER)
49 **DUBIOUS AFFAIR (IRE)**, b f Frankel—Dubian To (IRE)
50 **DUCHESS OF PARMA**, b f Cape Cross (IRE)—Maria Letizia
51 **EL PICADOR (IRE)**, b c Dansili—West of Venus (USA)
52 **EPIC (IRE)**, b g Australia—Rock Kristal (IRE)
53 **FALLEN FROM HEAVEN**, b c Kingman—Fallen Star
54 **FELIX**, ch c Lope de Vega (IRE)—Luminance (IRE)
55 **FIERY MISSION (USA)**, b c Noble Mission—Quickfire
56 **GHADBBAAN**, ch c Intello (GER)—Rock Choir
57 **GIVE ME BREATH**, b f Bated Breath—Watchoverme
58 **GRACEFULLY DONE (IRE)**, ch f Australia—Sense of Style (USA)
59 **HAWTHORN ROSE**, ch f Nathaniel (IRE)—Russelliana
60 **HAZARANDA**, b f Dansili—Hazariya (IRE)
61 **HEAVENLY BLISS**, ch f Intello (GER)—Heaven Sent
62 **HONFLEUR (IRE)**, ch f Le Havre (IRE)—Galistic (IRE)
63 **INVICTUS SPIRIT**, b c Frankel—Daring Aim
64 **JEWELLER**, ch c Mastercraftsman (IRE)—Allegretto (IRE)
65 **JOYFUL MISSION (USA)**, b c Noble Mission—Hint of Joy (USA)
66 **JUBILOSO**, b f Shamardal (USA)—Joyeuse
67 **JUNOOH (IRE)**, b c Le Havre (IRE)—Mumayeza
68 **JUSOOR (IRE)**, b f Intello (GER)—Bristol Fashion
69 **KARNAVAAL (IRE)**, b br c Dubawi (IRE)—Qareenah (USA)
70 **KING'S GIRL**, b f Kingman—Damaniyat Girl (USA)
71 **LAAFY (USA)**, b c Noble Mission—Miner's Secret (USA)
72 **LAYALEENA (IRE)**, b f Sea The Stars (IRE)—Nectar de Rose (FR)
73 **LONDON EYE (USA)**, ch c Australia—Circle of Life (USA)
74 **LOOLWAH (IRE)**, gr f Pivotal—Yanabeeaa (USA)
75 **MADEEH**, b c Oasis Dream—Ashaaqah (IRE)
76 **MOKAMMAL**, b c Mukhadram—My Inspiration (IRE)
77 **MUBAKKER (USA)**, gr c Speightstown (USA)—Ready to Act (USA)
78 **MULAN (IRE)**, b f Kingman—Platonic
79 **NANTUCKET (IRE)**, b f Sea The Stars (IRE)—Lucy Cavendish (USA)
80 **NASHY (FR)**, b c Frankel—This Time (FR)
81 **NEFERTITI (IRE)**, b f Galileo (IRE)—Divine Proportions (USA)
82 **NEON SEA (FR)**, b f Siyouni (FR)—Carnoustie (FR)
83 **PRODIGIOUS**, ch f Intello (GER)—Spacious
84 **QUEEN POWER (IRE)**, ch f Shamardal (USA)—Princess Serena (USA)
85 **QUEEN'S SCEPTRE**, b f Pivotal—Queen's Best
86 **ROMOLA**, b f Pivotal—Dianora
87 **SANGARIUS**, b c Kingman—Trojan Queen (USA)
88 B br f Declaration of War (USA)—Shawara (IRE)
89 **SOLID STONE (IRE)**, br c Shamardal (USA)—Landmark (USA)
90 **SONG WITHOUT END (IRE)**, b c Pour Moi (IRE)—Amathusia
91 **SOVEREIGN GRANT**, b c Kingman—Momentary
92 **THE VERY MOON**, ch f Teofilo (IRE)—Carisolo
93 **TOP TOP (IRE)**, b c Frankel—Jira
94 **VIVIONN**, ch f Dubawi (IRE)—Giants Play (USA)
95 **WAVE OF WAVES**, b c Acclamation—Missisipi Star (IRE)
96 **WEMYSS WARE (IRE)**, b c Dubawi (IRE)—White Moonstone (USA)

TWO-YEAR-OLDS

97 **A LA VOILE**, b f 29/1 Invincible Spirit (IRE)—All At Sea (Sea The Stars (IRE))
98 **APPROXIMATE**, br f 6/2 Dubawi (IRE)—Estimate (IRE) (Monsun (GER))
99 B f 9/5 Kingman—Ashaaqah (IRE) (Dansili)
100 B c 2/3 Kingman—Astroglia (USA) (Montjeu (IRE)) (375000)
101 B c 4/4 Galileo (IRE)—Best Terms (Exceed And Excel (AUS)) (525000)
102 B c 16/2 Siyouni (FR)—Blue Chip (Galileo (IRE)) (100000)
103 B c 12/3 Frankel—Cape Dollar (IRE) (Cape Cross (IRE))
104 **CHICHESTER**, b c 26/4 Dansili—Havant (Halling (USA))
105 **CLINICIAN**, b f 22/2 Kingman—Clinical (Motivator)
106 **CRYSTAL PEGASUS**, ch c 2/5 Australia—Crystal Etoile (Dansili)
107 B f 16/3 Galileo (IRE)—Dawning (USA) (War Chant (USA))
108 **DESERT WAVE**, b c 11/2 Kingman—Waila (Notnowcato)

SIR MICHAEL STOUTE - Continued

109 B c 20/4 Shamardal (USA)—Dreaming Beauty (Oasis Dream)
110 B c 3/4 Siyouni (FR)—Dreamlike (Oasis Dream) (100000)
111 B c 4/5 Deep Impact (JPN)—Dubawi Heights (Dubawi (IRE))
112 FIRST RECEIVER, b c 29/1 New Approach (IRE)—Touchline (Exceed And Excel (AUS))
113 FOX NEVER QUIT, br c 5/3 Dark Angel (IRE)—Minwah (IRE) (Oasis Dream) (420000)
114 GALATA BRIDGE, b c 9/4 Golden Horn—Infallible (Pivotal)
115 B c 8/2 Fastnet Rock (AUS)—Galileano (IRE) (Galileo (IRE))
116 GLITTERING GIFT, ch c 4/2 Dubawi (IRE)—Golden Stream (IRE) (Sadler's Wells (USA))
117 B f 22/1 Golden Horn—Handana (IRE) (Desert Style (IRE))
118 HEAVEN FORFEND, b c 16/3 Frankel—Heaven Sent (Pivotal)
119 HIGHEST GROUND (IRE), b c 13/5 Frankel—Celestial Lagoon (JPN) (Sunday Silence (USA))
120 INHERENT, b c 18/3 Dubawi (IRE)—Integral (Dalakhani (IRE))
121 JEAN BAPTISTE (IRE), b c 22/4 Invincible Spirit (IRE)—Pioneer Bride (USA) (Gone West (USA))
122 JOVIAL, b f 16/2 Dubawi (IRE)—Joyeuse (Oasis Dream)
123 KESARINA, b f 3/4 Medicean—Kesara (Sadler's Wells (USA))
124 B c 4/4 Frankel—La Vinchina (GER) (Oasis Dream) (375000)
125 B c 1/2 Muhaarar—Lady Francesca (Montjeu (IRE)) (114285)
126 LAW OF ONE (IRE), ch c 6/5 Galileo (IRE)—Strawberry Fledge (USA) (Kingmambo (USA))
127 LIGHTS ON, ch f 15/3 Siyouni (FR)—In The Light (Inchinor)
128 B c 10/5 Muhaarar—Maakra (Dubai Destination (USA))
129 MARS LANDING (IRE), b c 13/1 Dark Angel (IRE)—Psychometry (FR) (Danehill Dancer (IRE))
130 MELNIKOVA, ch f 26/3 Frankel—Safina (Pivotal)
131 B c 4/4 Poet's Voice—Milady Eileen (IRE) (Footstepsinthesand) (140000)
132 MY POEM, ch f 5/4 Poet's Voice—Watchoverme (Haafhd)
133 B c 16/3 Frankel—My Special J's (USA) (Harlan's Holiday (USA)) (380000)
134 OSLO, b c 30/3 Gleneagles (IRE)—Intercontinental (Danehill (USA))
135 Ch c 14/4 Australia—Pivotalia (IRE) (Pivotal) (20000)
136 Ch c 17/2 Shamardal (USA)—Prime Run (Dansili)
137 PROPRIETY (IRE), b f 25/3 Galileo (IRE)—Wannabe Better (IRE) (Duke of Marmalade (IRE)) (1200000)
138 B f 22/1 Le Havre (IRE)—Queen Margherita (Montjeu (IRE)) (180000)
139 QUEEN'S FAVOUR, b f 1/5 Muhaarar—Queen's Best (King's Best (USA))
140 QUICK WALTZ, b f 9/2 Australia—Momentary (Nayef (USA))
141 RANSOM, b c 25/3 Kingman—Arizona Jewel (Dansili)
142 RUBY DREAM, b c 8/2 Oasis Dream—Russelliana (Medicean)
143 Br f 21/5 Shamardal (USA)—Safwa (IRE) (Green Desert (USA))
144 B c 27/2 Australia—Sannkala (FR) (Medicean) (200000)
145 Ch c 3/3 Frankel—Shama's Crown (IRE) (New Approach (IRE))
146 B c 5/3 Golden Horn—Snow Pine (Dalakhani (IRE)) (280000)
147 SOFFIKA (IRE), b f 9/4 Zoffany (IRE)—Rosika (Sakhee (USA))
148 B f 29/4 Sea The Stars (IRE)—Solar Moon (Pivotal) (475000)
149 B f 5/3 Iffraaj—Spiritual Air (Royal Applause) (200000)
150 B c 17/3 Le Havre (IRE)—Stella Bellissima (IRE) (Sea The Stars (IRE)) (150000)
151 TANITA, b f 14/3 Frankel—Shoal (Oasis Dream)
152 TOUTATIS (USA), b c 19/3 Karakontie (JPN)—Afleet Lass (USA) (Northern Afleet (USA)) (91710)
153 VASARI (USA), b c 30/1 Muhaarar—Honest Quality (USA) (Elusive Quality (USA))
154 B c 25/2 Camelot—Venus de Milo (IRE) (Duke of Marmalade (IRE)) (337126)
155 VINDICATE, ch c 20/3 Lope de Vega (IRE)—Aurore (IRE) (Fasliyev (USA))
156 B c 18/2 Siyouni (FR)—Wannabe Posh (IRE) (Grand Lodge (USA)) (700000)
157 B c 21/1 Frankel—Where (IRE) (Danehill Dancer (IRE)) (700000)
158 B f 9/3 Pivotal—Zibeling (IRE) (Cape Cross (IRE))

Owners: Her Majesty The Queen, Mr K. Abdullah, Mr Hamdan al Maktoum, Mr Abdullah Saeed Al Naboodah, Al Rabban Racing, Al Shaqab Racing, Mr Ahmad Alotaibi, Mr Andrew Bengough, Mr Danny Boorer, Mr Phil Booth, Cheveley Park Stud, Mr Athos Christodoulou, Sir Evelyn de Rothschild, Fittocks Stud, Flaxman Stables Ireland Ltd, Mrs Denis Haynes, Highclere Thoroughbred Racing, Mr Kin Hung Kei, King Power Racing Co Limited, Mrs John Magnier, Newsells Park Stud, Mr Philip Newton, Mr Robert Ng, Niarchos Family, Normandie Stud Limited, Mr Mohamed Obaida, Mr Salem Bel Obaida, Orchard Bloodstock Limited, Phoenix Thoroughbred Limited, Qatar Racing Limited, Miss K Rausing, Satomi Horse Company Ltd, Mr Paul Silver, Mrs Mary Slack, Mr Derrick Smith, Mr Gary Steed, Mr George Strawbridge, Mr Saeed Suhail, Mr Michael Tabor, Mr James Wigan.

Jockey (flat): Ryan Moore.

526 MRS ALI STRONGE, Eastbury

Postal: **Castle Piece Racing Stables, Eastbury, Hungerford, Berkshire, RG17 7JR**
Contacts: **PHONE (01488) 72818 FAX (01488) 670378 MOBILE (07779) 285205**
E-MAIL office@castlepiecestables.com WEBSITE www.castlepiecestables.com

1 **AMANTO (GER)**, 9, b g Medicean—Amore (GER) **Shaw Racing Partnership 2**
2 **ARDMAYLE (IRE)**, 7, ch g Whitmore's Conn (USA)—Welsh Connection (IRE) **The Wishful Thinkers**
3 **BLU CAVALIER**, 9, b g Kayf Tara—Blue Ride (IRE) **The Select Racing Club Limited**
4 **CAMAKASI (IRE)**, 8, b g Camacho—Innocence **Friends Of Castle Piece**
5 **CHEZ CASTEL MAIL (FR)**, 7, ch g My Risk (FR)—Queenly Mail (FR) **The One and Only Partnership**
6 **DON'T CRY ABOUT IT (IRE)**, 4, ch g Casamento (IRE)—Back At de Front (IRE) **Pms Oxford & Mrs Ali Stronge**
7 **DREWMAIN LEGEND**, 7, b m Midnight Legend—Ryders Hill **Hot To Trot Jumping & Mrs Jane Andrews**
8 **GOOD IMPRESSION**, 4, b g Showcasing—Daintily Done **Mrs Margaret Kidger & Mr Geoffrey Bishop**
9 **GORHAM'S CAVE**, 5, b g Rock of Gibraltar (IRE)—Moiava (FR) **Mrs A. L. Lofts**
10 **HATTERS RIVER (IRE)**, 12, b g Milan—Curzon Ridge (IRE) **Mrs A. J. Stronge**
11 **HE'S OUR STAR (IRE)**, 4, b g Lord Shanakill (USA)—Afilla **Mrs Jayne French & Mrs Jacqueline Pilling**
12 **HEPBURN**, 6, b m Sixties Icon—Mighty Splash **ROA Racing Partnership V**
13 **HERESMYNUMBER (IRE)**, 9, b g Kalanisi (IRE)—Broken Rein (IRE) **Pieces Of Eight Racing**
14 **JALINGO (IRE)**, 8, b g Cape Cross (IRE)—Just Special **Paul Whitehead & Clare Spencer-Herbert**
15 **MEETINGS MAN (IRE)**, 12, gr g Footstepsinthesand—Missella (IRE) **Mrs B. V. Evans**
16 **NAVAJO WAR DANCE**, 6, b g Makfi—Navajo Rainbow **Mrs Bernice Stronge**
17 **PROUD TIMES (USA)**, 13, b br g Proud Citizen (USA)—Laura's Pistolette (USA) **Mrs A. J. Stronge**
18 **SCORPION HAZE (IRE)**, 6, b g Scorpion (IRE)—Sea Maiden (IRE) **Shaw Racing Partnership 2**
19 **SHIROCCO SUNFLOWER**, 4, ch f Shirocco (GER)—Fleur de Nikos (FR) **Wellington Thoroughbred Racing 1**
20 **STAR OF ATHENA**, 4, b f Champs Elysees—Aswaaq (IRE) **Tim Dykes & Hugh Doubtfire**
21 **STORM MELODY**, 6, b g Royal Applause—Plume **Shaw Racing Partnership 2**
22 **SUM FUN NOW (IRE)**, 5, b g Jeremy (USA)—Blond's Addition (USA) **Mrs M. Kidger**
23 **ZOFFANY BAY (IRE)**, 5, b g Zoffany (IRE)—Trois Graces (USA) **Mrs Margaret Kidger & Mr Geoffrey Bishop**

THREE-YEAR-OLDS

24 **BOOROWA**, b f Dunaden (FR)—Sleep Dance **Mrs J Redvers & Mr N Burton Taylor**
25 **ESTRELA STAR (IRE)**, ch g Casamento (IRE)—Reem Star **Mr James Burley & Mrs Ali Stronge**
26 **GRANDAD'S LEGACY**, ch g Harbour Watch (IRE)—Vodka Shot (USA) **Ms J. Powell**
27 **IP DIP (USA)**, gr ro f Exchange Rate (USA)—Wendy Wow **Four Desperate Housewives**
28 **RENARDEAU**, b g Foxwedge (AUS)—La Cucina (IRE) **Mr L. A. Bellman**
29 **SIR CANFORD (IRE)**, b g Canford Cliffs (IRE)—Alexander Divine **The Select Racing Club Limited**

TWO-YEAR-OLDS

30 B f 3/4 Swiss Spirit—Amary (IRE) (Acclamation)
31 Ch f 25/4 Nathaniel—Bravia (Shamardal (USA)) (8000) **Mrs A. J. Stronge**
32 B c 30/1 Famous Name—Gilah (Saddlers' Hall (IRE)) (25283)
33 Ch c 19/4 Al Kazeem—Greenery (IRE) (Green Desert (USA)) (10000) **Larkhills & Shaw Racing 2**
34 B c 2/2 Born To Sea (IRE)—Pearl Bell (IRE) (Camacho) (10113) **Mr J. R. Corsan**

Other Owners: Mrs J. Andrews, Mr G. S. Bishop, Mr J. Burley, Mr N. Burton Taylor, Mr H. G. Doubtfire, Mr T. J. Dykes, Mrs S. Evans, Mrs J. French, R. Frisby, Mr R. S. Hoskins, Hot To Trot Jumping, Mr I. Kidger, Larkhills Racing Partnership, Mr I. P. Mason, Mr R. B. Merriman, Mrs J. M. Pilling, G. C. Pratt, Project Management Services Oxford Ltd, Mrs M. U. B. Redvers, Ms A. M. Simmons, Ms C. L. Spencer-Herbert, Mr P. Whitehead, Mr T. Williams.

Assistant Trainer: Sam Stronge

527 MR ROB SUMMERS, Solihull

Postal: **Summerhill Cottage, Danzey Green, Tanworth-in-Arden, Solihull**
Contacts: **PHONE (01564) 742667 MOBILE (07775) 898327**

1 **ATLANTIC STORM (IRE)**, 7, b g September Storm (GER)—Double Dream (IRE) **Mr A. R. Price**
2 **EPSOM DAY (IRE)**, 6, b g Teofilo (IRE)—Dubai Flower **Mrs G. M. Summers**
3 **SECRET BERI**, 5, ch m Schiaparelli (GER)—Secret Whisper **Mrs G. M. Summers**
4 **ST MERRYN (IRE)**, 8, b g Oscar (IRE)—Kigali (IRE) **Mrs G. M. Summers**

Assistant Trainer: Mrs G. M. Summers

528 **MR ALEX SWINSWOOD, Lambourn**
Postal: **4 Walkers Lane, Lambourn, Hungerford, Berkshire, RG17 8YE**

1 **FIFTY PEACH WAY,** 7, b m Black Sam Bellamy (IRE)—Aphrodisia **Mr M. Swinswood**

---

529 **MR TOM SYMONDS, Hentland**
Postal: **Dason Cottage, Hentland, Ross-On-Wye, Herefordshire, HR9 6LW**
Contacts: **PHONE** (01989) 730869 **MOBILE** (07823) 324649
E-MAIL dasoncourt@gmail.com **WEBSITE** www.thomassymonds.co.uk

1 **ASK CATKIN (IRE),** 7, b m Ask—Simple Reason (IRE) **Mrs C. M. Antcliff**
2 **BOBO MAC (IRE),** 8, gr g Whitmore's Conn (USA)—Blazing Love (IRE) **C & M Baker, K Ibberson, H Pearman**
3 **COBRA COMMANDER (IRE),** 5, b g Beneficial—Run For Help (IRE) **Dean, Willetts & Vernon**
4 **DR TIME (IRE),** 7, b g Dubai Destination (USA)—Long Time (IRE) **Mr T. R. Symonds**
5 **DRAMATIC PAUSE (IRE),** 6, b g Oscar (IRE)—Night Heron (IRE) **The Dramatic Partners**
6 **EATON MILLER (IRE),** 7, b g Milan—Four Fields (IRE) **Mr K. J. Price**
7 **EST ILLIC (IRE),** 5, b br g Court Cave (IRE)—Ten Friends **Mr F Green & Mr J Chinn**
8 **EVERYTHING NOW (IRE),** 5, b g Gold Well—Givehertime (IRE) **Mr T. R. Symonds**
9 **FALCONS FALL (IRE),** 8, ch g Vertical Speed (FR)—Ellie Park (IRE) **The Eventful Partnership**
10 **FISCAL SPACE (IRE),** 7, b g Court Cave (IRE)—Honeyed (IRE) **Celia & Michael Baker**
11 **FRANKLY SPEAKING,** 9, ch g Flemensfirth (USA)—No More Money **David Jenks & Celia & Michael Baker**
12 **GOLDEN IMAGE,** 4, b f Havana Gold (IRE)—Photographie (USA) **Mr S. Davies**
13 **HOLLYWOODIEN (FR),** 8, gr g Martaline—Incorrigible (FR) **Sir Peter & Lady Gibbings**
14 **LLANTARA,** 8, b m Kayf Tara—Lady Llancillo (IRE) **Bailey-Carvill Equine**
15 **LOUD AS LIONS (IRE),** 6, b g Flemensfirth (USA)—Misspublican (IRE) **C & M Baker, K Ibberson, H Pearman**
16 **LUGG RIVER,** 5, b m Kayf Tara—Supreme Gem (IRE) **Frank Green & Mike Roberts**
17 **MAGNETIZE (IRE),** 6, b m Gold Well—Ersa (IRE) **Magnetize Partnership**
18 **METEORITE,** 5, b g Bollin Eric—Running Hotter **Mr M. L. Engel**
19 **MIRZAM (IRE),** 5, gr m Mastercraftsman (IRE)—Luxie (IRE) **Mr S. Davies**
20 **PLANSINA,** 4, b f Planteur (IRE)—Sina (GER) **Simon Davies & Tom Symonds**
21 **POLITICAL QUIZ,** 9, b g Lucarno (USA)—Quiz Night **I. A. Low**
22 **RIVER ARROW,** 8, b m Kayf Tara—Supreme Gem (IRE) **Frank Green & Mike Roberts**
23 **ROYAL CLARET,** 7, b m Yeats (IRE)—Kerada (FR) **The Nigel Jones & Roy Ovel Syndicate**
24 **SAINT DE VASSY (FR),** 6, br g Saint des Saints (FR)—
                                       Mona Vassy (FR) **Jakeman,Booth,Lanchbury,Mason,Hewlett**
25 **SANTANI (GER),** 4, b g Jukebox Jury (IRE)—Sun Society (GER)
26 **SONG FOR SOMEONE (GER),** 4, ch g Medicean—Sweni Hill (IRE) **Sir Peter & Lady Gibbings**

Other Owners: Mrs P. Andrews, R. F. Bailey, Mr M. J. Baker, Mrs C. A. M. Baker, Dr M. Booth, Mrs P. J. Buckler, R. K. Carvill, Mr W. J. Chinn, Mr T. Dean, The Hon Lady Gibbings, Sir Peter Gibbings, F. M. Green, Miss K. J. Ibberson, Mr L. J. Jakeman, M. D. C. Jenks, Mr N. A. Jones, Mr R. M. Ovel, Mr H. J. Pearman, Mr M. B. Roberts, Mrs A. Symonds, Mr T R Symonds & Mrs A Symonds, Miss S. J. Vernon, Mr P. J. Willetts.

---

530 **MR JAMES TATE, Newmarket**
Postal: **Jamesfield Place, Hamilton Road, Newmarket, Suffolk, CB8 7JQ**
Contacts: **PHONE** (01638) 669861 **FAX** (01638) 676634 **MOBILE** (07703) 601283
E-MAIL james@jamestateracing.com **WEBSITE** www.jamestateracing.com

1 **ASTONISHED (IRE),** 4, ch f Sea The Stars (IRE)—An Saincheann (IRE) **S. Manana**
2 **FORESEEABLE FUTURE (FR),** 4, b c Harbour Watch (IRE)—Russian Spirit **S. Manana**
3 **HEY GAMAN,** 4, b c New Approach (IRE)—Arsaadi (FR) **Sultan Ali**
4 **INVINCIBLE ARMY (IRE),** 4, b c Invincible Spirit (IRE)—Rajeem **S. Manana**
5 **KYLLANG ROCK (IRE),** 5, b g Kyllachy—Megec Blis (IRE) **Sheikh Juma Dalmook Al Maktoum**
6 **NEW GRADUATE (IRE),** 4, ch c New Approach (IRE)—Srda (USA) **S. Manana**
7 **ROYAL RESIDENCE,** 4, b c Epaulette (AUS)—Jubilant Queen **S. Manana**
8 **TRIBAL WARRIOR,** 4, b c New Approach (IRE)—Lunda (IRE) **S. Manana**

MR JAMES TATE - Continued

THREE-YEAR-OLDS

9 **ACROSS THE SEA**, b f Dubawi (IRE)—Alsindi (IRE) **S. Manana**
10 **ANOTHER OPINION (IRE)**, b f Morpheus—Your Opinion (IRE) **S. Manana**
11 **ATTAINMENT**, ch c Exceed And Excel (AUS)—Wahylah (IRE) **S. Manana**
12 **BATTLE OF WILLS (IRE)**, b c Lawman (FR)—Maidin Maith (IRE) **S. Manana**
13 **CAMELOT RAKTI (IRE)**, b f Camelot—Carioca (IRE) **Saif Ali**
14 **CAPE VICTORY (IRE)**, b c Dawn Approach (IRE)—Cape Alex **S. Manana**
15 **COASTLINE (IRE)**, br f Cape Cross (IRE)—Without Precedent (FR) **Sheikh Juma Dalmook Al Maktoum**
16 **COLONY QUEEN**, b f Gregorian (IRE)—Queen Margrethe **S. Manana**
17 **COURT ORDER**, b c Lawman (FR)—Polygon (USA) **S. Manana**
18 B f Kingman—Deveron (USA) **S. Ali**
19 **DISTANT MIRAGE**, b f Toronado (IRE)—Oasis Jade **S. Manana**
20 C f Farhh—Dorraar (IRE) **Sheikh Rashid Dalmook Al Maktoum**
21 **EARLY RISER (IRE)**, b f Dawn Approach (IRE)—Cape Good Hope **S. Manana**
22 **EVOLUTIONARY (IRE)**, b f Morpheus—Lilium **S. Manana**
23 B f New Approach (IRE)—Excel's Beauty **Sheikh Juma Dalmook Al Maktoum**
24 **FIELDS OF ATHENRY (USA)**, b c Candy Ride (ARG)—Purple (IRE) **S. Manana**
25 **FUTURISTIC (IRE)**, b c Shamardal (USA)—Aqlaam Vision **S. Manana**
26 **HARBOUR CITY (USA)**, b f Australia—Who Is Camille (USA) **S. Manana**
27 **INTUITIVE (IRE)**, b c Haatef (USA)—Majraa (FR) **Sheikh Hamad Dalmook Al Maktoum**
28 **LOCAL HISTORY**, b f Sepoy (AUS)—Local Fancy **S. Manana**
29 **MULTINATIONAL (IRE)**, b c Poet's Voice—International Love (IRE) **S. Manana**
30 **NAME THE WIND**, b c Toronado (IRE)—Trust The Wind **Sheikh Rashid Dalmook Al Maktoum**
31 **NEW ARRANGEMENT**, b g New Approach (IRE)—Sooraah **S. Manana**
32 **NOBLE LINEAGE (IRE)**, ch c Iffraaj—Regal Hawk **S. Manana**
33 **PERCY ALEXANDER**, ch c Sir Percy—Rosy Alexander **S. Manana**
34 **PLATINUM COAST (USA)**, ch c Speightstown (USA)—Aerocat (USA) **S. Ali**
35 **PROMOTE (IRE)**, b f Dandy Man (IRE)—Park Haven (IRE) **S. Manana**
36 **REWRITE THE STARS (IRE)**, ch f Sea The Stars (IRE)—Table Bay (IRE) **S. Manana**
37 **RIVER SANDS**, b f Kingman—The Miniver Rose (IRE) **S. Manana**
38 **SAMEEM (IRE)**, b c New Approach (IRE)—Ahla Wasahl **Sultan Ali**
39 **SHIMMERING DAWN (IRE)**, b f Morpheus—Subtle Shimmer **Sheikh Juma Dalmook Al Maktoum**
40 **SOCIAL CALENDAR**, b br c Gregorian (IRE)—Beautiful Lady (IRE) **S. Manana**
41 **SOCIAL NETWORK (IRE)**, ch f Australia—Mona Lisa **S. Manana**
42 **SOLAR HEIGHTS (IRE)**, b f Cape Cross (IRE)—Solar Moon **S. Manana**
43 **SOLAR PARK (IRE)**, ch c Kendargent (FR)—Solandia (IRE) **S. Manana**
44 **SOUL SEARCHING**, ch f Iffraaj—Remember **S. Manana**
45 **SUBCONSCIOUS**, b c Sea The Moon (GER)—Angeleno (IRE) **Sheikh Hamad Dalmook Al Maktoum**
46 **THE MET**, b c Gregorian (IRE)—Kasalla (IRE) **S. Manana**
47 **TOP RANK (IRE)**, gr c Dark Angel (IRE)—Countess Ferrama **S. Manana**
48 **UNDER THE STORM**, ch f Toronado (IRE)—Under The Rainbow **S. Manana**
49 **WATER'S EDGE (IRE)**, b c Footstepsinthesand—Sommer Queen (IRE) **S. Manana**
50 **WITH CAUTION (IRE)**, ch f Dandy Man (IRE)—Kitty Softpaws (IRE) **S. Manana**
51 **ZMHAR (IRE)**, ch c Shamardal (USA)—Guarantia **S. Manana**

TWO-YEAR-OLDS

52 B f 15/2 Muhaarar—Al Fareej (IRE) (Iffraaj) (70000) **Saif Ali**
53 Ch f 17/3 Night of Thunder (IRE)—Aljaazya (USA) (Speightstown (USA)) (57142) **S. Manana**
54 B f 9/2 Muhaarar—Bright Approach (IRE) (New Approach (IRE)) (72000) **S. Manana**
55 B c 22/3 New Approach (IRE)—Cadenza (FR) (Dansili) (50000) **S. Manana**
56 B f 9/2 New Approach (IRE)—Cape of Night (IRE) (Cape Cross (IRE)) (20000) **Sultan Ali**
57 B f 12/2 Zoffany (IRE)—Caster Sugar (USA) (Cozzene (USA)) (101137) **S. Manana**
58 B f 26/4 Camacho—Certainly Brave (Indian Ridge) (13000) **S. Manana**
59 **CLAUDIUS SECUNDUS (IRE)**, br c 6/3 Holy Roman Emperor (IRE)—
     Tasha's Dream (USA) (Woodman (USA)) (54782) **S. Manana**
60 B c 26/3 Dansili—Cloud Castle (In The Wings) (50000) **S. Manana**
61 Ch f 10/4 Pivotal—Crinoline (USA) (Street Cry (IRE)) (45000) **S. Manana**
62 Ch c 8/4 Night of Thunder (IRE)—Doors To Manual (USA) (Royal Academy (USA)) (40000) **S. Manana**
63 Gr f 13/3 Gutaifan (IRE)—Doula (USA) (Gone West (USA)) (4500) **S. Manana**
64 B f 15/4 Le Havre (IRE)—Downhill Dancer (USA) (Montjeu (USA)) (33000) **S. Manana**
65 B f 11/4 Kingman—El Manati (IRE) (Iffraaj) **Sheikh Rashid Dalmook Al Maktoum**
66 B f 12/3 Invincible Spirit (IRE)—Fann (USA) (Diesis) (40000) **S. Manana**
67 B c 27/4 Coach House (IRE)—Gospel Music (Beat Hollow) (10000) **S. Manana**
68 B c 23/2 Golden Horn—Gwael (USA) (A P Indy (USA)) (200000) **S. Manana**

MR JAMES TATE - Continued

69 Ch c 10/5 Hot Streak (IRE)—Hanella (IRE) (Galileo (IRE)) (24000) **S. Manana**
70 B c 1/2 Sir Percy—Hanzada (USA) (Arch (USA)) (7000) **S. Manana**
71 B f 28/4 Dark Angel (IRE)—Impressible (Oasis Dream) (12000) **S. Manana**
72 B c 16/2 Shooting To Win (AUS)—Jillanar (IRE) (Lawman (FR)) (7000) **S. Manana**
73 B c 29/4 Dandy Man (IRE)—Journey's End (IRE) (In The Wings) (42000) **S. Manana**
74 B f 24/2 Night of Thunder (IRE)—Jumeirah Palm Star (Invincible Spirit (IRE)) (6000) **S. Manana**
75 B c 4/4 Siyouni (FR)—Kahira (IRE) (King's Best (USA)) (18000) **S. Manana**
76 B c 15/3 Clodovil (IRE)—Lady Spangles (IRE) (Starspangledbanner (AUS)) (20000) **S. Manana**
77 Ch c 5/3 Sir Percy—Lady Sylvia (Haafhd) (10000) **S. Manana**
78 B f 27/4 Iffraaj—Lalectra (King Charlemagne (USA)) (55000) **S. Manana**
79 B f 17/4 Zoffany (IRE)—Mary's Daughter (Royal Applause) (30000) **S. Manana**
80 B f 15/3 Night of Thunder (IRE)—Mathanora (IRE) (Anabaa (USA)) (20000) **S. Manana**
81 B f 7/2 Showcasing—Minnaloushe (IRE) (Lawman (FR)) (9000) **S. Manana**
82 B c 20/2 Dream Ahead (USA)—Miss Buckshot (IRE) (Tamayuz) (12000) **S. Manana**
83 B c 27/1 Dubawi (IRE)—Nashmiah (IRE) (Elusive City (USA)) (260000) **S. Manana**
84 Ch c 30/4 Night of Thunder (IRE)—Permission Slip (Authorized (IRE)) (54782) **S. Manana**
85 B c 27/2 Clodovil (IRE)—Queen Zain (IRE) (Lawman (FR)) (23809) **S. Manana**
86 B f 25/4 Camacho—Quickstyx (Night Shift (USA)) (52254) **S. Manana**
87 B c 9/4 Zoffany (IRE)—Raggety Ann (IRE) (Galileo (IRE)) (104761) **S. Manana**
88 B c 27/5 Muhaarar—Rainbow Desert (USA) (Dynaformer (USA)) (42000) **Saif Ali**
89 B c 1/3 Night of Thunder (IRE)—Raskutani (Dansili) (38000) **S. Manana**
90 B c 7/5 Shamardal (USA)—Saltanat (IRE) (Duke of Marmalade (IRE)) (45000) **S. Manana**
91 Ch f 24/4 Night of Thunder (IRE)—Varsity (Lomitas) (109565) **S. Manana**
92 B f 1/3 No Nay Never (USA)—Virginia Celeste (IRE) (Galileo (IRE)) (98000) **S. Manana**

Other Owners: S. H. Altayer.

Assistant Trainer: Mrs Lucinda Tate

531

MR TOM TATE, Tadcaster
Postal: **Castle Farm, Hazelwood, Tadcaster, North Yorkshire, LS24 9NJ**
Contacts: **PHONE (01937) 836036 MOBILE (07970) 122818**
E-MAIL tomtate@zen.co.uk WEBSITE www.tomtate.co.uk

1 **AWAKE MY SOUL (IRE),** 10, ch g Teofilo (IRE)—Field of Hope (IRE) **T T Racing**
2 **DESTROYER,** 6, b g Royal Applause—Good Girl (IRE) **T T Racing**
3 **EMPRESS ALI (IRE),** 8, b m Holy Roman Emperor—Almansa (IRE) **T T Racing**
4 **EQUIANO SPRINGS,** 5, b g Equiano (FR)—Spring Clean (FR) **T T Racing**
5 **FIRST DANCE (IRE),** 5, b m Cape Cross (IRE)—Happy Wedding (IRE) **T T Racing**
6 **GLACIER FOX,** 4, ch g Foxwedge (AUS)—Beat Seven **T T Racing**
7 **GROUPIE,** 5, b m Requinto (IRE)—Amour Fou (IRE) **T T Racing**
8 **LUCY'S LAW (IRE),** 5, b m Lawman (FR)—Lucy Limelites **Ms Fionnuala Cassidy & Mr T. P. Tate**
9 **RIVER GLADES,** 4, b g Cape Cross (IRE)—Everglades **The Ivy Syndicate**
10 **WAITING FOR RICHIE,** 6, b g Rail Link—Heart of Hearts **The Ivy Syndicate**
11 **YOUNG TIGER,** 6, b g Captain Gerrard (IRE)—Blades Princess **T T Racing**

THREE-YEAR-OLDS

12 **BAYRAAT,** b g Heeraat—Baymist **T T Racing**
13 **FAIR ALIBI,** b g Paco Boy (IRE)—Alybgood (CAN) **T T Racing**

TWO-YEAR-OLDS

14 B g 14/5 Night of Thunder (IRE)—Regal Hawk (Singspiel (IRE)) **T T Racing**
15 B g 20/3 Heeraat (IRE)—Ringtail (USA) (Street Cry (IRE)) (4000) **T T Racing**

Other Owners: Ms Fionnuala Cassidy, Mrs S. Hodgkiss, Mr D. M. W. Hodgkiss, Mrs Hazel Tate, Mr T. P. Tate.

Assistant Trainer: Hazel Tate

Jockey (flat): Andrew Mullen, James Sullivan.

532 MR COLIN TEAGUE, Wingate

Postal: **Bridgefield Farm, Trimdon Lane, Station Town, Wingate, County Durham, TS28 5NE**
Contacts: **PHONE (01429) 837087 MOBILE (07967) 330929**
E-MAIL colin.teague@btopenworld.com

1 **GRANDAD CHUNK (IRE)**, 8, gr g Acclamation—Silverdreammachine (IRE) **Arc Racing Yorkshire Xv**
2 **INGLEBY ANGEL (IRE)**, 10, br g Dark Angel (IRE)—Mistress Twister **Arc Racing Yorkshire Xx**
3 **INGLEBY GEORGE**, 5, b h Rail Link—Ingleby Princess **Ingleby Bloodstock Limited**
4 **LEES ANTHEM**, 12, b g Mujahid (USA)—Lady Rock **Collins Chauffeur Driven Executive Cars**
5 **ON THE HIGH TOPS (IRE)**, 11, b g Kheleyf (USA)—Diplomats Daughter **Arc Racing Yorkshire Xv**
6 **ORSAY**, 4, b f Champs Elysees—Umlilo **Mr G. Singh**
7 **SULAFAAT (IRE)**, 4, ch f Haatef (USA)—Elraabeya (CAN) **Mr J. A. Lister**
8 **THORNABY PRINCESS**, 8, b m Camacho—Ingleby Princess **Mr D. Scott**
9 **YORKSHIRE ROVER**, 5, b g Doncaster Rover (USA)—Mother Jones **Mr A. Rice**

Other Owners: Mr M. Marsh.

533 MR ROGER TEAL, Hungerford

Postal: **Shefford Valley Stables, East Shefford Farm, Hungerford, Berkshire, RG17 7EF**
Contacts: **PHONE (01488) 649869 MOBILE (07710) 325521**
E-MAIL info@rogertealracing.com WEBSITE www.rogertealracing.co.uk

1 **AGINCOURT REEF (IRE)**, 10, b g Gold Well—Hillside Native (IRE) **Mrs S. M. Teal**
2 **BLISTERING BOB**, 4, b g Big Bad Bob (IRE)—Kristalette (IRE) **Bex Design & Print Ltd**
3 **HIGH ACCLAIM (IRE)**, 5, b g Elusive Quality (USA)—La Reine Lionne (USA) **Excel Racing**
4 **JACK BEAR**, 8, b g Joe Bear (IRE)—Colins Lady (FR) **Joe Bear Racing**
5 **JACK OF DIAMONDS (IRE)**, 10, b g Red Clubs (IRE)—Sakkara Star (IRE) **Great Shefford Racing**
6 **JONNIGRAIG (IRE)**, 6, b g Masterofthehorse (IRE)—Vanudski (IRE) **Mr Austin Whelan**
7 **KYLLACHYS TALE (IRE)**, 5, b m Kyllachy—Betray **Barry Kitcherside & Darren Waterer**
8 **LANGLEY VALE**, 10, b g Piccolo—Running Glimpse (IRE) **Mrs Muriel Forward & Dr G C Forward**
9 **LOOK SURPRISED**, 6, ch m Kier Park (IRE)—Cloridja **Starting Gate Racing**
10 **LUCKY LOUIE**, 6, ch g Dutch Art—Ardessie **Great Shefford Racing**
11 4, Gr g Indian Haven—Non Disclosure (IRE) **Withyslade**
12 **ROSIE ROYALE (IRE)**, 7, gr m Verglas (IRE)—Fearn Royal (IRE) **The Idle B'S**
13 **SHAKE ME HANDY**, 4, gr c Eastern Anthem (IRE)—Cloridja **Mr B. M. Parish**
14 **STONEMADFORSPEED (IRE)**, 11, b g Fruits of Love (USA)—Diamond Forever **Mr R. A. Teal**
15 **SWOT**, 7, b g Exceed And Excel (AUS)—House Point **The Big Cat Partnership**
16 **TAUREAN DANCER (IRE)**, 4, b g Intello (GER)—Traou Mad (IRE) **C. B. Goodyear**
17 **TIP TWO WIN**, 4, gr c Dark Angel (IRE)—Freddie's Girl (USA) **Mrs A. Cowley**
18 4, B g Thewayyouare (USA)—Titian's Pride (USA)

THREE-YEAR-OLDS

19 **DUKE OF DUNABAR**, b c Dunaden (FR)—Litewska (IRE) **Excel Racing**
20 **FITWOOD STAR**, b c Archipenko (USA)—Sasheen **Calne Engineering Ltd**
21 **OXTED**, b g Mayson—Charlotte Rosina **Homecroft Wealth & Partners**
22 **SPIRIT OF MAY**, ch c Coach House (IRE)—Bengers Lass (USA) **Mrs C. A. Borras**
23 **WHELANS WAY (IRE)**, b c Requinto (IRE)—Lupine (IRE) **Mr Austin Whelan**

TWO-YEAR-OLDS

24 **GERT LUSH (IRE)**, b f 12/3 Bated Breath—
 Agent Allison (Dutch Art) (25000) **Mrs Muriel Forward & Dr G C Forward**
25 **MARION'S BOY (IRE)**, ch c 2/5 Mastercraftsman (IRE)—
 Freddie's Girl (USA) (More Than Ready (USA)) **Mrs Anne Cowley**

Other Owners: Mr Charlie Austin, Mr David Bond, Mr A. Chambers, Mrs Emma Curley, Mr David Fish, Mr P. Fisher, Dr G. C. Forward, Mrs Muriel Forward, Mr Tony Hirschfeld, Homecroft Wealth Racing, Mr Barry Kitcherside, Mr R. Kolien, Miss Helen Pease, Mr Bob Pettis, Mr S. J. Piper, Mrs R. Pott, Mr M. A. Ransom, Mr S. M. Ransom, Mrs Sue Teal, Mr Darren Waterer, Mr Martin Wynn.

Conditional: Harry Teal.

534 MR HENRY TETT, Lambourn
Postal: **Delamere Cottage Stables, Folly Road, Lambourn, Berkshire, RG17 8QE**
Contacts: **MOBILE (07796) 098220**
WEBSITE www.henrytettracing.co.uk

1 **ALANJOU (FR)**, 9, b g Maresca Sorrento (FR)—Partie Time (FR) **The Cap All Partnership**
2 **LIGHT GUNNER (IRE)**, 5, b g Lawman (FR)—Neve Lieve (IRE) **Mr C. C. Tett**
3 **MR RED CLUBS (IRE)**, 10, b g Red Clubs (IRE)—Queen Cobra (IRE) **Mrs Victoria Tett**
4 **SHAMROCK ROVER (FR)**, 5, gr g No Risk At All (FR)—Lady Scarlet (FR) **Mrs Victoria Tett**

Other Owners: Mr A. Crichton, Mr P. D. Hensher.

Amateur: Mr F. Tett.

535 MR SAM THOMAS, Cardiff
Postal: **Crossways, St Mellons Road, Lisvane, Cardiff, South Glamorgan, CF14 0SH**
Contacts: **PHONE (07929) 101751**
E-MAIL samthomasracing@outlook.com / emma@samthomasracing.com
WEBSITE www.samthomasracing.com

1 **COAL STOCK (IRE)**, 4, ch g Red Jazz (USA)—Scar Tissue **Walters Plant Hire Ltd Egan Waste Ltd**
2 **DANCING DOUG (IRE)**, 6, br g Kalanisi (IRE)—Drumcay Polly (IRE) **Mr W. Ryan-Beswick**
3 **DARLING ALKO (FR)**, 6, b g Al Namix (FR)—Padalko Tatou (FR) **Walters Plant Hire & James & Jean Potter**
4 **DOCTE DINA (FR)**, 5, ch m Doctor Dino (FR)—Artofmen (FR)
5 **DON'T SHOUT (IRE)**, 5, b g Oscar (IRE)—Asta Belle (FR) **Walters Plant Hire & James & Jean Potter**
6 **FALBERTO (FR)**, 4, b g Alberto Giacometti (IRE)—Valrina (FR) **Walters Plant Hire Ltd**
7 **GALILEO SILVER (IRE)**, 4, gr g Galileo (IRE)—Famous (IRE) **Walters Plant Hire & James & Jean Potter**
8 **GLENTROOL (IRE)**, 6, b g Passing Glance—Killala Bay (IRE) **Mr S. C. Appelbee**
9 **IVY'S SHADOW (IRE)**, 4, b f Jammaal—Red Chili (IRE) **Mr W. D. Morris**
10 **IWILLDOIT (IRE)**, 6, b g Flying Legend (USA)—Lyricist's Dream **Diamond Racing Ltd**
11 **JUST GOT TO GET ON (IRE)**, 5, ch g Malinas (GER)—Just Cliquot **Mrs C. Swarbrick**
12 **LA REINE POUTINE (FR)**, 4, b f Kapgarde (FR)—Miss Poutine (FR) **Walters Plant Hire & James & Jean Potter**
13 **LOVELY TOUCH (IRE)**, 10, b g Humbel (USA)—My Touch (IRE) **Third Match Officials**
14 **MARIO DE PAIL (FR)**, 4, gr g Blue Bresil (FR)—Sauveterre (FR) **Walters Plant Hire & James & Jean Potter**
15 **MEGA MIND (IRE)**, 6, ch g Captain Rio—Final Leave (IRE) **Mr S. J. Thomas**
16 **NOT A ROLE MODEL (IRE)**, 7, b g Helissio (FR)—Mille Et Une Nuits (FR) **St Mamadasado**
17 **OCEAN BOY (FR)**, 4, b g Diamond Boy (FR)—Line Salsa (FR) **Walters Plant Hire & James & Jean Potter**
18 **OUR BOY (IRE)**, 5, ch g Raven's Pass (USA)—Burren Rose (USA) **Walters Plant Hire & Spiers & Hartwell**
19 **ROCK AND BEL (FR)**, 6, b g Laverock (IRE)—Belmiesque (FR) **Mr B. Ryan-Beswick**
20 **ROYAL MAGIC (IRE)**, 7, b g Whitmore's Conn (USA)—Room To Room Magic (IRE) **Luke Harvey Racing Club**
21 **SIR VALENTINE (IRE)**, 6, b g Cacique (IRE)—Singuna (GER) **Walters Plant Hire & James & Jean Potter**
22 **SMOKEY LANE (IRE)**, 5, ch g Zebedee—Masela (IRE) **Walters Plant Hire P T Civil Engineering**
23 **SPONTHUS (FR)**, 4, b g Alianthus (GER)—Pavane du Kalon (FR) **Walters Plant Hire Ltd**
24 **STOLEN SILVER (FR)**, 4, gr g Lord du Sud (FR)—
Change Partner (FR) **Walters Plant Hire & James & Jean Potter**
25 **SWEDISHHORSEMAFIA (IRE)**, 4, b g Shantou (USA)—Carrigmoorna Style (IRE) **Mr S. J. Thomas**
26 **THE CANNISTER MAN (IRE)**, 7, b g Arakan (USA)—Ladyrosaro (IRE) **Keith Ali & Eamon Murchan**
27 **THE ENCHANTER (FR)**, 5, gr g Martaline—Fille Formidable (USA)
28 **TORHOUSEMUIR (FR)**, 8, b g Sagamix (FR)—Royal Musical **Honourable Scoundrels**
29 **WHISPER (FR)**, 11, b g Astarabad (USA)—Belle Yepa (FR) **Walters Plant Hire Ltd**

THREE-YEAR-OLDS

30 **AGENT SAONOIS (FR)**, gr g Saonois (FR)—Agosta (FR)
31 **DOBRYN (FR)**, b g No Risk At All (FR)—Brava (FR)
32 **FANTOMAS (FR)**, b g Sinndar (IRE)—Trudente (FR)
33 **FONTANA ELLISSI (FR)**, b g Sinndar (IRE)—Leni Riefenstahl (IRE)
34 **GOOD RISK AT ALL (FR)**, ch g No Risk At All (FR)—Sissi Land (FR)
35 **JAZZ KING (FR)**, gr g Kapgarde (FR)—Jaragua (FR)
36 **JUST NO RISK (FR)**, ch g No Risk At All (FR)—Just Divine (FR)
37 **MARVELLOUS MARVEL (FR)**, b br g Masked Marvel—Miss Rodeo (FR)
38 **MONT SAINT VINCENT (FR)**, gr g Montmartre (FR)—Chamanka (FR)
39 **SKYTASTIC (FR)**, b g Way of Light (USA)—Verzasca (IRE)

MR SAM THOMAS - Continued

Other Owners: Mr K. Ali, Egan Waste Services Ltd, Mrs S. C. Fillery, Mr T. G. Fillery, Mr L. J. Harvey, Mr C. Haslam, Mr S. Howell, James & Jean Potter, Mr E. Murchan, P T Civil Engineering Ltd, Mr J. E. Potter, Mrs M. J. Potter, Mr M. Saunders, Spiers & Hartwell Ltd, Mr J. Trolan.

Jockey (NH): James Davies, Charlie Deutsch. **Conditional:** Harry Beswick, Richard Patrick.

---

536 | MRS JOANNE THOMASON-MURPHY, Chelmsford
Postal: **Oakview, Leighams Road, Bicknacre, Chelmsford, Essex, CM3 4HF**

1 **DELIVERINGPROMISES (IRE)**, 7, b g Oscar (IRE)—Monanore Music (IRE) **Mrs J. Thomason-Murphy**
2 **FOXY'S SPIRIT**, 4, b f Foxwedge (AUS)—Jessie's Spirit (IRE) **Mrs J. Thomason-Murphy**
3 **KERRY'S LORD (IRE)**, 10, br g Lend A Hand—Tesses Express (IRE) **Mrs J. Thomason-Murphy**

---

537 | MR DAVID THOMPSON, Darlington
Postal: **South View Racing, Ashley Cottage, South View, Bolam, Darlington, County Durham, DL2 2UP**
Contacts: **PHONE (01388) 835806 (01388) 832658 FAX (01325) 835806 MOBILE (07795) 161657**
E-MAIL dwthompson61@hotmail.co.uk WEBSITE www.dwthompson.co.uk

1 **CAPTAIN MURTEK (IRE)**, 5, gr g Zebedee—Absolutely Cool (IRE) **Mr S. Murray**
2 **CONHALT**, 7, b g Rainbow High—Girl of Pleasure (IRE) **J. A. Moore**
3 **DIRCHILL (IRE)**, 5, b g Power—Bawaakeer (USA) **Mr S. Murray**
4 **GLAN Y GORS (IRE)**, 7, b br g High Chaparral (IRE)—Trading Places **Mr B. Lapham & J Souster**
5 **HIGHWAYMAN**, 6, b g Dick Turpin (IRE)—Right Rave (IRE) **Mr N. Park**
6 **LITTLE POEM**, 4, b f Holy Roman Emperor (IRE)—Gerika (FR) **Mr B. Lapham & J Souster**
7 **LORD ROB**, 5, b g Rob Roy (USA)—First Grey **A. Suddes**
8 **LUKOUTOLDMAKEZEBAK**, 6, b g Arabian Gleam—Angelofthenorth **Mr P. J. McMahon**
9 **MAZZA ROCKS (IRE)**, 4, b f Red Rocks (IRE)—Sun City **Mr B. Lapham**
10 **RAJAPUR**, 6, gr ro g Dalakhani (IRE)—A Beautiful Mind (GER) **Mr B. Lapham**
11 **RED CARAVEL (IRE)**, 5, b g Henrythenavigator (USA)—Red Fantasy (IRE) **Mr T. J. A. Thompson**
12 **ROMAN COIN**, 8, b g I Was Framed (USA)—Classic Quartet **J. A. Moore**
13 **ROMAN NUMERAL (IRE)**, 11, b g King's Best (USA)—Trespass **Mr S. Murray**
14 **SHAIYZAR (IRE)**, 10, b g Azamour (IRE)—Shaiyzima (IRE) **J. A. Moore**
15 **SOMEONE EXCITING**, 6, b m Notnowcato—Quite Something **Mr W. Fleming**
16 **SPLASH OF VERVE (IRE)**, 7, b g Fast Company (IRE)—Ellistown Lady (IRE) **HorsingAround**
17 **UNIQUE COMPANY (IRE)**, 4, ch g Fast Company (IRE)—Unique Blanche (IRE) **Mr W. Fleming**
18 **VISITANT**, 6, ch g Pivotal—Invitee **Mr N. Park**

THREE-YEAR-OLDS

19 **NOCIVILJUSTICEHERE**, b f Lilbourne Lad (IRE)—Cameo Tiara (IRE) **Mrs A. Kenny**

Other Owners: Mr S. P French, Mr N. Saint, Mr J. Souster.

Assistant Trainer: J. A. Moore

Jockey (flat): Tony Hamilton.

---

538 | MR RONALD THOMPSON, Doncaster
Postal: **No 2 Bungalow, Haggswood Racing Stable, Stainforth, Doncaster, South Yorkshire, DN7 5PS**
Contacts: **PHONE (01302) 845904 FAX (01302) 845904 MOBILE (07713) 251141**
E-MAIL ronracing@gmail.com

1 **CLAUDIA RANIERI (IRE)**, 4, b br f Most Improved (IRE)—Holly Hill (IRE) **Mr N. D. Rawcliffe**
2 **DEBBI'S DREAM**, 4, b f Foxwedge (AUS)—Let's Dance (IRE) **Ronald Thompson**
3 **FAZAMOUR (FR)**, 4, b f Legolas (JPN)—Salina d'airy (FR) **Mr N D Rawcliffe & Mr R Thompson**
4 **FURNI FACTORS**, 4, b g Captain Gerrard (IRE)—Calgary **B. Bruce & R. Thompson**
5 **ISE LODGE BABE**, 4, b f Libranno—Scented Garden **Mr N D Rawcliffe & Mr R Thompson**

MR RONALD THOMPSON - Continued

6 **MAJESTIC MAN (IRE)**, 6, b g Majestic Missile (IRE)—Windomen (IRE) **R Thompson & W A Robinson**
7 **MAJOR CRISPIES**, 8, b g Pastoral Pursuits—Nellie Melba **Mrs A. Harrison**
8 **MALLY COLLIER**, 6, ch g Flying Legend (USA)—Isaflo **Ronald Thompson**
9 **MR STRUTTER (IRE)**, 5, ch g Sir Prancealot (IRE)—Khajool (IRE) **Mrs A. Harrison**
10 **WESTFIELD WONDER**, 4, b g Captain Gerrard (IRE)—Flying Highest **R Thompson & W A Robinson**

THREE-YEAR-OLDS

11 B g Burwaat—Cara's Delight (AUS) **Ronald Thompson**
12 **CHEAP JACK**, b g Coach House (IRE)—Ice Mayden **Ronald Thompson**
13 **DOTHRAKI (IRE)**, b g Bungle Inthejungle—Ellistown Lady (IRE) **R Thompson & W A Robinson**
14 **HAGGSWOOD BOY**, ch g Coach House (IRE)—Bustling Darcey **Ronald Thompson**
15 **OLIVIA ON GREEN**, ch f Assertive—Dimashq **Alan Bell & Ronald Thompson**
16 **STAINFORTH SWAGGER**, b g Havana Gold (IRE)—Ferayha (IRE) **Mr N. D. Rawcliffe**

TWO-YEAR-OLDS

17 B f 9/5 Music Master—Beyond The Rainbow (Mind Games) (761) **Mr A. Bell**
18 B f 21/4 Music Master—Dimashq (Mtoto) (761) **Mr A Bell & Ronald Thompson**

Other Owners: Mr B. Bruce, Mr N.D.Rawcliffe, Mr W. A. Robinson, Mr Ronald Thompson.

---

539 | **MR VICTOR THOMPSON, Alnwick**
Postal: Link House Farm, Newton By The Sea, Embleton, Alnwick, Northumberland, NE66 3ED
Contacts: **PHONE (01665) 576272 MOBILE (07739) 626248**

1 **BOW STREET RUNNER**, 4, b g Sixties Icon—Lakaam **V. Thompson**
2 **CHANCEOFA LIFETIME (IRE)**, 12, ch g Beneficial—Bounty Queen (IRE) **V. Thompson**
3 **COURT PAINTER (IRE)**, 9, b g Court Cave (IRE)—Comings (IRE) **V. Thompson**
4 **DOLLY'S DOT (IRE)**, 8, b m Vertical Speed (FR)—Our Dot (IRE) **V. Thompson**
5 **DUBA PLAINS**, 4, b g Sixties Icon—Selinda **V. Thompson**
6 **DUHALLOWCOUNTRY (IRE)**, 13, b g Beneficial—Milltown Lass (IRE) **V. Thompson**
7 **GIN COBBLER**, 13, b g Beneficial—Cassia **V. Thompson**
8 **MILLROSE BELL (IRE)**, 7, b m Flemensfirth (USA)—Laboc **V. Thompson**
9 **PC DIXON**, 6, ch g Sixties Icon—Lakaam **V. Thompson**
10 **RAPID FRITZ (IRE)**, 10, ch g Kutub (IRE)—Another Pet (IRE) **V. Thompson**
11 **SCORPO (IRE)**, 8, b g Scorpion (IRE)—Maltesse (IRE) **V. Thompson**
12 **TRUST ME I'M A DR (IRE)**, 10, b g Dr Massini (IRE)—Friendly Flick (IRE) **V. Thompson**

Assistant Trainer: M Thompson

---

540 | **MR SANDY THOMSON, Greenlaw**
Postal: Lambden, Greenlaw, Duns, Berwickshire, TD10 6UN
Contacts: **PHONE (01361) 810211 MOBILE (07876) 142787**
E-MAIL sandy@lambdenfarm.co.uk WEBSITE www.sandythomsonracing.co.uk

1 **ARTHURS SECRET**, 9, ch g Sakhee's Secret—Angry Bark (USA) **Mr J. K. McGarrity**
2 **BARACALU (FR)**, 8, gr g Califet (FR)—Myragentry (FR) **SprayClad UK**
3 **BLUE KASCADE (IRE)**, 12, ch g Kaieteur (USA)—Lydia Blue (IRE) **Mr J. K. McGarrity**
4 **BUCKLED**, 9, b g Midnight Legend—Mulberry Wine **Miss S. McQueen**
5 **CAVENTARA**, 7, b g Kayf Tara—L'aventure (FR) **Mr C. J. Harriman**
6 **DIMPLE (FR)**, 8, gr g Montmartre (FR)—Dynella (FR) **D&D Armstrong Limited**
7 **DONNA'S DELIGHT (IRE)**, 8, b g Portrait Gallery (IRE)—Hot Lips (IRE) **D&D Armstrong Limited**
8 **DUC DE GRISSAY (FR)**, 6, b g Denham Red (FR)—Rhea de Grissay (FR) **Mrs Q. R. Thomson**
9 **ELF DE RE (FR)**, 5, ch g Anabaa Blue—Ninon de Re (FR) **Mrs Q. R. Thomson**
10 **FAIR MINX**, 5, gr m Fair Mix (IRE)—Blazing Diva (IRE) **Mrs Q. R. Thomson**
11 **FULLY BOOKED**, 6, b g Beat Hollow—Friendly Craic (IRE) **Black Bull Hotel (Borders) Ltd**
12 **GERONIMO**, 8, ch g Kadastrof (FR)—Triggers Ginger **Mr J. K. McGarrity**
13 **GLENLORA**, 6, ch m Supreme Sound—Rainha **Mr A. M. Thomson**
14 **HARRY THE VIKING**, 14, ch g Sir Harry Lewis (USA)—Viking Flame **Jim Beaumont & Quona Thomson**
15 **JOHN WILLIAMS (IRE)**, 10, b g Presenting—Duhallow Park (IRE) **Mrs C. S. Stephenson**
16 **KING'S WHARF (IRE)**, 10, gr g Clodovil—Global Tour (USA) **Ken McGarrity & the Western Chasers**
17 **MCGOWAN'S PASS**, 8, b g Central Park (IRE)—Function Dreamer **Mrs A. E. Lee**
18 **MILVALE (IRE)**, 5, b g Ask—House-of-Hearts (IRE) **Mrs Q. R. Thomson**

MR SANDY THOMSON - Continued

19 MYMILAN (IRE), 6, b g Milan—Jill's Girl (IRE) **Mrs Q. R. Thomson**
20 NENDRUM (IRE), 10, br g Westerner—Westgrove Berry (IRE) **Mrs M. Coppola**
21 ROBINTHEAULAD (IRE), 8, b g Robin des Champs (FR)—Brotenstown (IRE) **Quona Thomson & Ken McGarrity**
22 SAINT LEO (FR), 6, b g Maresca Sorrento (FR)—Sainte Lea (FR) **Mr & Mrs Raymond Anderson Green**
23 SEEMORELIGHTS (IRE), 7, b g Echo of Light—Star Lodge **Watson & Lawrence**
24 SEEYOUATMIDNIGHT, 11, b g Midnight Legend—Morsky Baloo **Mrs P. Thompson**
25 SHADES OF MIDNIGHT, 9, b g Midnight Legend—Hannah Park (IRE) **The Potassium Partnership**
26 SIRWILLIAMWALLACE (IRE), 6, b g Getaway (GER)—Mars Milan (IRE) **Mr J. K. McGarrity**
27 SOPHIE FATALE, 7, b m Robin des Champs (FR)—Buffy **Midnight Racing Club**
28 UNITE THE CLANS (IRE), 5, b g Danehill Dancer (IRE)—Janna's Jewel (IRE) **Tweed Valley Racing Club**

Other Owners: Mr Nick Bannerman, Mr Jim Beaumont, Mr Neil Boyle, Mr L. Ellison, Mr Raymond Anderson Green, Mrs Anita Anderson Green, Mr David Lawrence, Mr Duncan Lawrence, Mr D. R. A. McCreath, Mr Ken McGarrity, Mr Derek McIntyre, The Western Chasers, Mrs A. M. Thomson, Mr A. M. Thomson.

Assistant Trainer: Mrs A. M. Thomson

Conditional: Rachael McDonald.

---

541 | **MR NIGEL TINKLER, Malton**
Postal: Trainer did not wish details of his string to appear

---

542 | **MR COLIN TIZZARD, Sherborne**
Postal: Venn Farm, Milborne Port, Sherborne, Dorset, DT9 5RA
Contacts: **PHONE** (01963) 250598 **FAX** (01963) 250598 **MOBILE** (07976) 778656
E-MAIL info@colintizzard.co.uk **WEBSITE** www.colintizzard.co.uk

1 AINCHEA (IRE), 6, b g Flemensfirth (USA)—Lady Petit (IRE) **Ann & Alan Potts Limited**
2 AMBION HILL (IRE), 4, b br g Getaway (GER)—Vertality (IRE) **Mr O. C. R. Wynne & Mrs S. J. Wynne**
3 ANNIVERSARY GIFT, 6, b g Sulamani (IRE)—Methodical **Miss Juliet E Reed & Mr Michael Truan**
4 BALLY LONGFORD (IRE), 11, b g Gold Well—Stay On Line (IRE) **Ann & Alan Potts Limited**
5 BATTLE OF IDEAS (IRE), 6, ch g Fracas (IRE)—Haven't A Notion **Coral Champions Club**
6 BEARS RAILS, 9, b g Flemensfirth (USA)—Clandestine **Mr P. M. Warren**
7 BEAUFORT WEST (IRE), 5, b g Getaway (GER)—Blessingindisguise (IRE) **Taylor & O'Dwyer**
8 BLACK CENTAUR (IRE), 6, b g Oscar (IRE)—Arcanum (IRE) **Davies King Selway Wavish**
9 BOLD CONDUCT (IRE), 5, b g Stowaway—Vics Miller (IRE)
10 BOY NAMED SIOUX, 8, b g Indian Danehill—Annie's Gift (IRE) **The Corse Lawners**
11 BRAMBLE BROOK, 9, b g Kayf Tara—Briery Ann **Brocade Racing**
12 BRYNMAWR, 9, b g Double Trigger (IRE)—Little Feat **Mr G. Nicholas**
13 BUCKHORN TIMOTHY, 10, b g Tamure (IRE)—Waimea Bay **The Buckhorn Racing Team**
14 BURN VALLEY, 6, ch m With The Flow (USA)—Countess Point **Mr D. S. Purdie**
15 CARRICK ROADS (IRE), 5, ch g Robin des Champs (FR)—Jay Lo (IRE) **Brocade Racing**
16 CHRISTMAS IN APRIL (FR), 7, b g Crillon (FR)—Similaresisoldofa (FR) **Swallowfield Racing**
17 COASTAL DRIFT, 5, b g Black Sam Bellamy (IRE)—Absalom's Girl **Brocade Racing**
18 COPPERHEAD, 5, ch g Sulamani (IRE)—How's Business **Mrs G. C. Pritchard**
19 CUCKLINGTON, 8, b g Kayf Tara—Ardrom **Mrs C. M. Hinks**
20 CYRUS DARIUS, 10, b g Overbury (IRE)—Barton Belle **Mr & Mrs G Calder & Mr P M Warren**
21 DARLAC (FR), 6, b br g Lucarno (USA)—Pail Mel (FR) **Mrs G. C. Pritchard**
22 DINOS BENEFIT (IRE), 7, ch m Mr Dinos (IRE)—Beneficial Lady (IRE) **Mr A Maddox & Mr S Langdon**
23 DRINKS INTERVAL, 7, b m King's Theatre (IRE)—Dame Fonteyn **The Land Value Partnership**
24 DUC KAUTO (FR), 6, b g Ballingarry (IRE)—Kauto Lorette (FR) **Ann & Alan Potts Limited**
25 EARL OF WISDOM, 4, ch g Flemensfirth (USA)—Golden Sunbird (IRE) **The Wychwood Partnership**
26 ELDORADO ALLEN (FR), 5, gr g Khalkevi (IRE)—Hesmeralda (FR) **J P Romans & Terry Warner**
27 ELEGANT ESCAPE (IRE), 7, b g Dubai Destination (USA)—Graineuaile (IRE) **Mr J. P. Romans**
28 ELIXIR DE NUTZ (FR), 5, gr g Al Namix (FR)—Nutz (FR) **J. T. Warner**
29 EMPREINTE RECONCE (FR), 5, b m Voix du Nord (FR)—Petite Fille (FR) **Mr J. P. McManus**
30 EXXARO (IRE), 9, b g Presenting—Mandys Gold (IRE) **Ann & Alan Potts Limited**
31 FAUSTINOVICK, 5, b g Black Sam Bellamy (IRE)—Cormorant Cove
32 FLEMENCO TEMPO (IRE), 5, ch g Flemensfirth (USA)—Tap The Beat (IRE) **Wendy & Malcolm Hezel**
33 FLO'SBOY SAM, 6, b g Tobougg (IRE)—Madam Flora **Wendy Pope & Tim Swaffield**

MR COLIN TIZZARD - Continued

34 **FLY TO MARS**, 5, b g Schiaparelli (GER)—Patsie Magern **Brocade Racing**
35 **FOX NORTON (FR)**, 9, b g Lando (GER)—Natt Musik (FR) **Ann & Alan Potts Limited**
36 **GENTLEMAN JON**, 11, b g Beat All (USA)—Sudden Spirit **Mr J. P. Romans**
37 **GOLDEN ETOILE (FR)**, 5, b m Muhtathir—Golden Firebird (IRE) **Mr M. J. P. Fordham**
38 **GOLDEN PAPILLON (FR)**, 4, b f Turgeon (USA)—Golden Electra (IRE) **Mr M. J. P. Fordham**
39 **GOLDEN SUNRISE (IRE)**, 6, ch g Stowaway—Fairy Dawn (IRE) **Brocade Racing**
40 **GRAND VISION (IRE)**, 13, gr g Old Vic—West Hill Rose (IRE) **J K Farms**
41 **HARRY SENIOR (IRE)**, 5, b g Oscar (IRE)—Surf Like A Lady (IRE) **Brocade Racing**
42 **HELFORD RIVER**, 5, b g Presenting—Lovely Origny (FR) **Brocade Racing**
43 **HIGHEST SUN (FR)**, 5, b g Sunday Break (JPN)—Highest Price (FR) **Mr A. J. Head**
44 **JAYTRACK PARKHOMES**, 5, b g Multiplex—Sudden Beat **DT Hoyland JS Hoyland JP Romans**
45 **KALARIKA (IRE)**, 6, br m Kalanisi (IRE)—Katariya (IRE) **Gale Force Three**
46 **KATAHDIN (IRE)**, 6, b g Kayf Tara—Keyaza (IRE) **Jay Three Racing**
47 **KAUTO THE KING (FR)**, 5, b g Ballingarry (IRE)—Kauto Luisa (FR) **Jenny Perry & Celia Goaman**
48 **KILBRICKEN STORM (IRE)**, 8, b g Oscar (IRE)—Kilbricken Leader (IRE) **A Selway & P Wavish**
49 **KINGS LAD (IRE)**, 12, b g King's Theatre (IRE)—Festival Leader (IRE) **G. F. Gingell**
50 **KINGS WALK (IRE)**, 8, b g King's Theatre (IRE)—Shuil Sionnach (IRE) **Mrs J. R. Bishop**
51 **LAMANVER PIPPIN**, 6, b g Apple Tree (FR)—Lamanver Homerun **Dr D. Christensen**
52 **LILLINGTON (IRE)**, 7, br g Westerner—Kind Word (IRE) **The Colin Tizzard Racing Club**
53 **LIST ONE**, 7, b m Tobougg (IRE)—Minibelle **Robert & Lucy Dickinson**
54 **LITTLE VERN (IRE)**, 5, b g Oscar (IRE)—Silver Valley (IRE) **Nightingale Syndicate**
55 **LIZZIE LANGTON**, 8, b m Kayf Tara—Madam Flora **Wendy Pope & Tim Swaffield**
56 **LOSTINTRANSLATION (IRE)**, 7, b g Flemensfirth (USA)—Falika (FR) **Taylor & O'Dwyer**
57 **LOUGH DERG DIAMOND (IRE)**, 6, b g Flemensfirth (USA)—
                Ballerina Laura (IRE) **James Messenger Jean-Marie Buob-Aldorf**
58 **LOVERBOY (FR)**, 8, b g Winged Love (IRE)—Tartan Belle **C. L. Tizzard**
59 **MASTER DEBONAIR**, 5, br g Yeats (IRE)—Swincombe Flame **SprayClad UK**
60 **MICK THONIC**, 9, gr g Maresca Sorrento (FR)—Mick Madona (FR) **Ann & Alan Potts Limited**
61 **MISTER MALARKY**, 6, ch g Malinas (GER)—Priscilla **Wendy & Malcolm Hezel**
62 **MOLINEAUX (IRE)**, 8, b g King's Theatre (IRE)—Steel Grey Lady (IRE) **John & Heather Snook**
63 **MOUNT RUSHMOORE (IRE)**, 7, b g Shantou (USA)—Knock On The Door (IRE) **Jenny Perry & Celia Goaman**
64 **MY LADY GREY**, 5, gr m Presenting—Wassailing Queen **The Alyasan Partnership**
65 **NATIVE RIVER (IRE)**, 9, ch g Indian River (FR)—Native Mo (IRE) **Brocade Racing**
66 **NATIVEGETAWAY (IRE)**, 6, b g Getaway (GER)—Clonsingle Native (IRE) **Orchard Racing**
67 **NEVER LEARN (IRE)**, 8, b g King's Theatre (IRE)—
                Hamari Gold (IRE) **Brocade Racing J P Romans Terry Warner**
68 **NEW TO THIS TOWN (IRE)**, 8, b g Milan—Jade River (FR) **Ann & Alan Potts Limited**
69 **NORSE LEGEND**, 8, b g Norse Dancer (IRE)—Methodical **Woodhaven Racing Syndicate**
70 **OSCARS MOONSHINE (IRE)**, 4, b g Oscar (IRE)—Scrapper Jack (IRE) **Mrs E. Lane**
71 **PADLEYOUROWNCANOE**, 5, b g Nayef (USA)—
                Pooka's Daughter (IRE) **Kevin Corcoran Aaron Pierce Chris Weare**
72 **PINGSHOU (IRE)**, 9, b g Definite Article—Quest of Passion (FR) **Ann & Alan Potts Limited**
73 **PRINCESS MIDNIGHT**, 4, ch m Midnight Legend—Setter's Princess **The Gardens Entertainments Ltd**
74 **QUEEN OF THE WIND**, 6, b m Shirocco (GER)—Kaydee Queen (IRE) **Chasing Gold Limited**
75 **QUITE BY CHANCE**, 10, b g Midnight Legend—Hop Fair **T Hamlin,J M Dare,J W Snook,J T Warner**
76 **QUIZ MASTER (IRE)**, 7, b g Ask—Good Bye Dolly (IRE) **Brocade Racing**
77 **RESERVE TANK (IRE)**, 5, b g Jeremy (USA)—Lady Bellamy (IRE) **The Reserve Tankers**
78 **ROBINSFIRTH (IRE)**, 10, b g Flemensfirth (USA)—Phardester (IRE) **Christine Knowles & Wendy Carter**
79 **ROCKPOINT**, 6, b g Shirocco (GER)—Tinagoodnight (IRE) **John & Heather Snook**
80 **ROYAL VACATION (IRE)**, 8, b g King's Theatre (IRE)—Summer Break (IRE) **Mrs J. R. Bishop**
81 **RUBY RUSSET**, 7, b m Apple Tree (FR)—Fair Coppelia **Mrs G. C. Pritchard**
82 **RUFFLING FEATHERS (IRE)**, 5, b g Presenting—Oilily (IRE) **Mr & Mrs R. Tizzard**
83 **RUSSIAN HAWK**, 5, b g Malinas (GER)—Sparron Hawk (FR) **The Gosden Mob**
84 **SANDY BEACH**, 9, b g Notnowcato—Picacho (IRE) **Brocade Racing**
85 **SARTORIAL ELEGANCE**, 8, b g Kayf Tara—Blue Ride (IRE) **R. G. Tizzard**
86 **SHANAHAN'S TURN (IRE)**, 11, b g Indian Danehill (USA)—Chanson Indienne (FR) **Ann & Alan Potts Limited**
87 **SHILLINGSWORTH (IRE)**, 6, b g Presenting—Miss Bobs Worth (IRE) **J. M. Dare, T. Hamlin, J. W. Snook**
88 **SHOAL BAY (IRE)**, 6, b g Gold Well—Ring Hill **Mrs C. Skan**
89 **SILVERHOW (IRE)**, 8, br g Yeats (IRE)—Monte Solaro (IRE) **Swallowfield Racing**
90 **SIZING AT MIDNIGHT (IRE)**, 7, br g Midnight Legend—Issaquah (USA) **Ann & Alan Potts Limited**
91 **SIZING BRISBANE**, 11, b g Nayef (USA)—Elaine Tully (IRE) **J K Farms**
92 **SIZING CODELCO (IRE)**, 10, b g Flemensfirth (USA)—La Zingarella (IRE) **Ann & Alan Potts Limited**
93 **SIZING CUSIMANO (IRE)**, 6, b g Midnight Legend—Combe Florey **Ann & Alan Potts Limited**
94 **SIZING GRANITE (IRE)**, 11, br g Milan—Hazel's Tisrara (IRE) **Ann & Alan Potts Limited**
95 **SIZING PLATINUM (IRE)**, 11, b g Definite Article—Quest of Passion (FR) **Ann & Alan Potts Limited**

MR COLIN TIZZARD - Continued

96 SIZING SCORPION (IRE), 10, b g Scorpion (IRE)—Fair Present (IRE) **Ann & Alan Potts Limited**
97 SIZING TARA, 6, b g Kayf Tara—As Was **Ann & Alan Potts Limited**
98 SIZING TENNESSEE (IRE), 11, ch g Robin des Champs (FR)—Jolivia (FR) **Ann & Alan Potts Limited**
99 SLATE HOUSE (IRE), 7, b g Presenting—Bay Pearl (FR) **Eric Jones, Geoff Nicholas, John Romans**
100 STORM HOME (IRE), 7, br g King's Theatre (IRE)—Miss Mayberry (IRE) **Mr J. P. Romans**
101 SWINCOMBE WIZ, 4, b f Westerner—Lady Everywhere **Mrs K. D. Yeo**
102 THE BROTHERS (IRE), 6, b g Flemensfirth (USA)—Laboc **DT Hoyland JS Hoyland JP Romans**
103 THE DUTCHMAN (IRE), 9, b g King's Theatre (IRE)—Shivermetimber (IRE) **SprayClad UK**
104 THE RUSSIAN DOYEN (IRE), 6, b g Doyen (IRE)—Namloc (IRE) **The Gosden Mob**
105 THEATRE GUIDE (IRE), 12, b g King's Theatre (IRE)—Erintante (IRE) **Mrs J. R. Bishop**
106 THISTLECRACK, 11, b g Kayf Tara—Ardstown **John & Heather Snook**
107 TIKKAPICK (IRE), 9, b g Tikkanen (USA)—Takeanotherpick (IRE) **The Con Club**
108 ULTRAGOLD (FR), 11, b br g Kapgarde (FR)—Hot d'or (FR) **Brocade Racing J P Romans Terry Warner**
109 UNSAFE CONDUCT, 6, ch g Pasternak—Symbiosis **The Alyasan Partnership**
110 VALHALLA (IRE), 9, b g Scorpion (IRE)—Fox Theatre (IRE) **J P Romans & Terry Warner**
111 VICONTE DU NOYER (FR), 10, gr g Martaline—Zouk Wood (USA) **Ann & Alan Potts Limited**
112 VISION DES FLOS (FR), 6, b g Balko (FR)—Marie Royale (FR) **Ann & Alan Potts Limited**
113 WAR LORD (GER), 4, gr c Jukebox Jury (IRE)—Westalin (GER) **The Wychwood Partnership**
114 WATERLOO WARRIOR (IRE), 7, b g Kalanisi (IRE)—Vindonissa (IRE) **Brocade Racing**
115 WEE SAXON, 10, b g Kayf Tara—Countess Point **Mr D. S. Purdie**
116 WEST APPROACH, 9, b g Westerner—Ardstown **John & Heather Snook**
117 WHITE MOON (GER), 7, gr g Sholokhov (IRE)—Westalin (GER) **Brocade Racing**
118 WHO SHOT JR (IRE), 5, b g Scorpion (IRE)—Ariesanne (IRE) **Wednesday Night Syndicate**
119 WIZARDS BRIDGE, 10, b g Alflora (IRE)—Island Hopper **The Butterwick Syndicate**

THREE-YEAR-OLDS

120 CATCH THE CUBAN, b g Havana Gold (IRE)—Reyamour **Castro's Army**

Other Owners: Mr G. S. Bennet, Mr J. G. Bennet, Mrs A. E. M. Broom, Mr G. R. Broom, Mr J. P. R. Buob-Aldorf, Mrs J. Calder, G. Calder, Mrs W. Carter, S. J. Clare, Mrs S. S. Cole, K. J. Corcoran, Mr J. M. Dare, Mrs C. E. Davies, Mrs R. L. J. Dickinson, Mr R. R. Dickinson, Mrs P. E. Dolan-Abrahams, Mr E. J. Dolan-Abrahams, Mr A. L. Ellison, Mr A. P. Gale, Mr K. P. Gibbs, Mrs S. Gillett, Mrs C. J. Goaman, Mr L. F. Gosden, T. Hamlin, N. M. Hanger, Mr T. Hanrahan, Mr M. W. Hezel, Mrs W. M. Hezel, Mr K. F. Honeybun, Mrs J. Honeybun, M. M. Hooker, Mr M. J. Hoskins, Mr D. T. Hoyland, Mr J. S. Hoyland, Mr D. R. Jeanes, Mr R. Jones, Mr E. Jones, Mrs L. M. King, Mrs C. Knowles, Mr S. R. Langdon, Mr G. J. Le Prevost, C. A. Leafe, Mr A. P. Maddox, Mr D. A. Makins, Mrs S. A. Mayes, Mr D. A. Mayes, Mr D. R. Mayes, J. M. Messenger, Mr R. O'Dwyer, Mrs J. M. Perry, Mr A. T. Pierce, Mrs W. M. Pope, Miss J. E. Reed, Mr D. J. Rushbrook, A. G. Selway, Mr M. L. Sharp, Mrs H. A. Snook, J. W. Snook, Mr T. J. Swaffield, Mr R. L. Tappin, Mr P. A. Taylor, Mrs S. L. Tizzard, Mr M. R. Truan, Mr E. R. Vickery, Mr J. A. Waterworth, Mr P. T. J. Wavish, Mr C. E. Weare, Mrs S. J. Wynne, O. C. R. Wynne.

Assistant Trainers: Mrs Kim Gingell, Joe Tizzard

Jockey (NH): Paddy Brennan, Harry Cobden, Tom O'Brien, Robbie Power, Tom Scudamore.
Conditional: A. Cheleda, B. Godfrey, H. Kimber.

---

543 MR MARTIN TODHUNTER, Penrith
Postal: **The Park, Orton, Penrith, Cumbria, CA10 3SD**
Contacts: PHONE (01539) 624314 FAX (01539) 624314 MOBILE (07976) 440082
WEBSITE www.martintodhunter.co.uk

1 ASKING FOR ANSWERS (IRE), 6, ch g Ask—Equation (IRE) **Mrs Matthews & Mrs G Hazeldean**
2 BOCASIEN DESBOIS (FR), 8, gr g Smadoun (FR)—Quocasienne (FR) **J. D. Gordon**
3 BULLS HEAD (IRE), 7, b g Darsi (FR)—Mrs Jenks **Murphy's Law Partnership**
4 CHOCOLAT NOIR (IRE), 6, b m Yeats (IRE)—Valrhona (IRE) **Javas Charvers**
5 DARRY DESBOIS (FR), 6, ch g Ballingarry (IRE)—Tiwa (FR) **Mr & Mrs Ian Hall**
6 JOIE DE VIVRE (IRE), 4, gr f Mastercraftsman (IRE)—Fragonard **Leeds Plywood & Doors Ltd**
7 MONBEG RIVER (IRE), 10, br g Indian River (FR)—So Pretty (IRE) **Bill Hazeldean & V Vyner-brookes**
8 OLDTIMER (IRE), 8, br g Olden Times—Supreme Surprise (IRE) **Park Farms Racing Syndicate 1**
9 PLAN OF ESCAPE (IRE), 6, ch g Presenting—Pilgara (IRE)
10 PRETTY MISS MAHLER (IRE), 8, b m Mahler—So Pretty (IRE) **Murphy's Law Partnership**
11 PRETTY PASSE, 5, b m Exceed And Excel (AUS)—Passe Passe (USA) **J. D. Gordon**
12 QUESTION OF FAITH, 8, b m Yeats (IRE)—Anastasia Storm **Mr K. Fitzsimons & Mr G. Fell**
13 RINGARINGAROSIE (IRE), 6, ch m Stowaway—Megan's Magic **Mr G Fell & Mr P G Airey**
14 SOPHIE OLIVIA (IRE), 7, gr m Ask—Gill's Honey (IRE) **Mr A. Bell**
15 SOUTHEAST ROSE (IRE), 6, b m Beat Hollow—Sunny South East (IRE) **The Surf & Turf Partnership**

MR MARTIN TODHUNTER - Continued

16 **TALKOFGOLD (IRE)**, 7, gr m Gold Well—Talk of Rain (FR) **Leeds Plywood & Doors Ltd**
17 **WESTERN AUSSIE (IRE)**, 6, b g Westerner—Squeekaussie (IRE) **Mr & Mrs Ian Hall**

Other Owners: Mr P. G. Airey, P. W. Clement, Mr P. M. Croan, Mr W. Downs, Mr G. Fell, K. Fitzsimons, Mr J. W. Fryer-Spedding, Mrs G. M. Hazeldean, J. W. Hazeldean, Mrs S. J. Matthews, Mr C. G. Snoddy, Mr J. I. A. Spedding, Mr D. M. Todhunter, Mr V. R. Vyner-Brooks.

---

544 **MR MARK TOMPKINS, Newmarket**
Postal: **Frankland Lodge, Hamilton Road, Newmarket, Suffolk, CB8 7JQ**
Contacts: **PHONE (01638) 661434 FAX (01638) 668107 MOBILE (07799) 663339**
E-MAIL mht@marktompkins.co.uk WEBSITE www.marktompkins.co.uk

1 **ASTROBREEZE**, 4, b f Lawman (FR)—Astromagick **Mystic Meg Limited**
2 **ASTROJEWEL**, 4, b f Havana Gold (IRE)—Astrolibra **Mystic Meg Limited**
3 **BABOCHOFF**, 7, b g Babodana—Charm Offensive **Mr & Mrs D D Scott**
4 **NESS OF BRODGAR**, 4, b f Harbour Watch (IRE)—Missouri **Tompkins, Harvey, King & Tompkins**
5 **ROOF GARDEN**, 4, ch g Cityscape—Celebrity **Sarabex**
6 **TRUE CALLING**, 4, ch f Pastoral Pursuits—Trew Class **Raceworld**
7 **VELVET VISION**, 4, b f Nathaniel (IRE)—Battery Power **Sarabex**
8 **VELVET VOICE**, 5, b m Azamour (IRE)—Battery Power **Sarabex**

THREE-YEAR-OLDS

9 **ASTROMERRY**, br f Farhh—Astrodonna **Mystic Meg Limited**
10 **ASTROSPARKLE**, b f Dunaden (FR)—Astrodiva **Mystic Meg Limited & Mr M. H. Tompkins**
11 **BELLE BAYEUX**, b f Epaulette (AUS)—Trew Class **Aedos & Tompkins**
12 B f Royal Applause—Callisto Light **Mrs J. Degnan**
13 **GARREL GLEN**, ch f Mount Nelson—Azure Mist **Mr David P. Noblett & Mr M. H. Tompkins**
14 **ISAAC MURPHY (USA)**, b g Medaglia d'oro (USA)—Marietta (USA) **Sarabex**
15 **PAGEANT MASTER (IRE)**, ch g Casamento (IRE)—Skiphall **Aedos & Tompkins**
16 **QUANAH (IRE)**, ch g Dandy Man (IRE)—Boucheron **Killarney Glen & Sarabex**
17 **ROSIE SCOT (IRE)**, b f Holy Roman Emperor (IRE)—Nisriyna (IRE)
18 **VELVET VISTA**, b f Sea The Moon (GER)—Battery Power **Sarabex**

TWO-YEAR-OLDS

19 **AMSBY**, b c 8/5 Sir Percy—Astrodiva (Where Or When (IRE))
20 B f 1/2 Equiano (FR)—Astromancer (USA) (Silver Hawk (USA)) **Mystic Meg Limited**
21 **BREAK COVER**, ch c 12/2 Casamento (IRE)—Brushing (Medicean) **Sarabex**
22 **HALF PAST EIGHT**, b c 18/3 Mount Nelson—Tenpence (Bob Back (USA)) **Dullingham Park**
23 B c 10/3 Casamento (IRE)—Lady Bellatrix (Singspiel (IRE))
24 B c 16/3 Garswood—Mega (IRE) (Petardia) **Mystic Meg Limited**
25 B f 19/2 Equiano (FR)—Missouri (Charnwood Forest (IRE)) **Dullingham Park**
26 B f 12/2 Mount Nelson—Seasonal Blossom (IRE) (Fairy King (USA)) **Dullingham Park**
27 **TOPANTICIPATION**, b f 2/5 Mount Nelson—Topatoo (Bahamian Bounty) **Mr M. P. Bowring & Partner**

Other Owners: S. Andrews, M. P. Bowring, N. M. Hanger, Mr M. D. Harvey, Mr E. Jones, Killarney Glen, Mr G. R. King, Mr O. P. C. Magnus, Mr R. D. E. Marriott, Mrs W. L. Marriott, Mr D. P. Noblett, Mr D. D. Scott, Mrs R. Scott, Mr M. H. Tompkins, D. G. Tompkins, Mrs A. M. Tompkins.

Assistant Trainer: Tim Bryce

---

545 **MR MARCUS TREGONING, Whitsbury**
Postal: **Whitsbury Manor Racing Stables, Whitsbury, Fordingbridge, Hampshire, SP6 3QQ**
Contacts: **PHONE (01725) 518889 FAX (01725) 518042 MOBILE (07767) 888100**
E-MAIL info@marcustregoningracing.co.uk WEBSITE www.marcustregoningracing.co.uk

1 **CLOVELLY BAY (IRE)**, 8, b g Bushranger (IRE)—Crystalline Stream (FR) **Mr M. P. Tregoning**
2 **DIVA STAR**, 4, ch f Siyouni (FR)—Kissin Sign **FTP Equine Holdings Ltd**
3 **EXCEEDINGLY DIVA**, 4, b f Exceed And Excel (AUS)—Anqooda (USA) **FTP Equine Holdings Ltd**
4 **FIELDEN FROLIC**, 4, br f Pastoral Pursuits—Full Flight (USA) **Boanas, Raw & Tregoning**
5 **FRECKLES**, 4, ch f Arakan (USA)—Tarneem (USA) **John & Heather Raw**
6 **HONOURBOUND (IRE)**, 4, b g Thewayyouare (USA)—Lavender List (IRE) **Park Walk Racing**
7 **LANDUE**, 4, b c Champs Elysees—Time of Gold (USA) **Mr M. P. Tregoning**

MR MARCUS TREGONING - Continued

8 **MARQUISETTE**, 4, b f Archipenko (USA)—Maria di Scozia **Miss E. K. E. Rausing**
9 **MISS BLONDELL**, 6, ch m Compton Place—Where's Broughton **Miss S. M. Sharp**
10 **POWER OF DARKNESS**, 4, b g Power—Summers Lease **R. C. C. Villers**
11 **SEAFARER (IRE)**, 5, b g Henrythenavigator (USA)—Rose of Petra (IRE) **Green, Hoare, Raw & Tregoning**
12 **SIR TITAN**, 5, b g Aqlaam—Femme de Fer **Wedgewood Estates**
13 **SMILES A LOT**, 4, b g Motivator—Azariane (FR) **Mrs M. E. Wates**
14 **STRATHSPEY STRETTO (IRE)**, 4, ch f Kyllachy—
  Rhythm And Rhyme (IRE) **Owenstown Stud & Mr M. P. N. Tregoning**
15 **WAQT (IRE)**, 5, b g Acclamation—Needles And Pins (IRE) **FTP Equine Holdings Ltd**

THREE-YEAR-OLDS

16 **ALAMINTA**, b f Archipenko (USA)—Almamia **Miss E. K. E. Rausing**
17 **ATALANTA BREEZE**, b f Champs Elysees—Craighall **Miss S. M. Sharp**
18 **BARON SLICK (IRE)**, b g Raven's Pass (USA)—Namely (IRE) **Mr M. P. Tregoning**
19 **DENIS THE DIVA**, b c Aussie Rules (USA)—Lunarian **FTP Equine Holdings Ltd**
20 **MISS SWIFT**, b f Sir Percy—Lady Hestia (USA) **The FOPS**
21 **MOGHRAM (IRE)**, b c Sir Percy—Red Blossom (USA) **Hamdan bin Rashid Al Maktoum**
22 **MOHAATHER**, b c Showcasing—Roodeye **Hamdan bin Rashid Al Maktoum**
23 **MOHTARRIF (IRE)**, b c Cape Cross (IRE)—Sharedah (IRE) **Hamdan bin Rashid Al Maktoum**
24 **MONAAFASAH (IRE)**, b br f Cape Cross (IRE)—Salhooda (IRE) **Hamdan bin Rashid Al Maktoum**
25 **MOQAARANA**, b f Mukhadram—Sulaalah (IRE) **Hamdan bin Rashid Al Maktoum**
26 **SADLERS BEACH (IRE)**, b f Pour Moi (IRE)—Dusty Boots (IRE) **Mr R. E. Kingston**
27 **SPIRIT OF ANGEL (IRE)**, b g Dark Angel (IRE)—Spirit of Cuba (IRE) **Owenstown Stud & Mr M. P. N. Tregoning**
28 **STRINDBERG**, b c Sea The Moon (GER)—Summer Night **Mr M. P. Tregoning**
29 **SUMMER SKIES**, b f Leroidesanimaux (BRZ)—Sunset Shore **Miss E. K. E. Rausing**
30 **TELL WILLIAM**, b g Invincible Spirit (USA)—Swiss Kiss **R. C. C. Villers**
31 **TRELINNEY (IRE)**, b f Dandy Man (IRE)—Silvertine (IRE) **Mr M. P. Tregoning**

Trainer did not supply details of his two-year-olds.

Other Owners: Mrs Ann Boanas, Mr R. F. U. Gaskell, Mr A. E. Pakenham, Mrs Victoria Pakenham, Mrs H. Raw, Mr John Raw, Lady Tennant, Mr M. P. N. Tregoning, Mr J. Tuthill, Mr J. R. Wallis.

Assistant Trainer: Angie Kennedy

Jockey (flat): Martin Dwyer, Hayley Turner. **Apprentice:** Tyler Saunders.

---

546 | **MR GRANT TUER, Northallerton**
Postal: Home Farm, Great Smeaton, Northallerton, North Yorkshire, DL6 2EP
Contacts: **PHONE (01609) 881094 FAX (01609) 881094 MOBILE (07879) 698869**
E-MAIL grant_tuer@btinternet.com

1 **ARABIC CULTURE (USA)**, 5, b g Lonhro (AUS)—Kydd Gloves (USA) **Mr G. F. Tuer**
2 **CHAMPARISI**, 4, b f Champs Elysees—Parisi **Allerton Racing & G Tuer**
3 **ESCAPE CLAUSE (IRE)**, 5, b g Lawman (FR)—Discophilia **Mr G. F. Tuer**
4 **ETIKAAL**, 5, ch g Sepoy (AUS)—Hezmah **Moment Of Madness**
5 **FINAL GO**, 4, b g Equiano (FR)—Ipsa Loquitur **Mr J. A. Swinbank**
6 **FYRECRACKER**, 8, ch g Kheleyf (USA)—Spirit of Hope (IRE) **Allerton Racing**
7 **HIPPEIA (IRE)**, 4, b f Lilbourne Lad (IRE)—Majestic Oasis **Mr & Mrs G. Turnbull**
8 **IBERICA ROAD (USA)**, 6, b br g Quality Road (USA)—Field of Clover (CAN) **Mr G. F. Tuer**
9 **LADY ISLE**, 4, b f Monsieur Bond—Ailsa Craig (IRE) **Mr G. F. Tuer**
10 **MYWAYISTHEONLYWAY (IRE)**, 6, b g Tamayuz—Soul Custody (CAN) **ARC Racing Yorkshire X**
11 **SO MACHO (IRE)**, 4, ch g Camacho—Turban Heights (IRE) **Mr J. A. Swinbank**

THREE-YEAR-OLDS

12 B f Helmet (AUS)—Cry Pearl (USA) **Mr G. F. Tuer**
13 **CUSTARD**, ch g Monsieur Bond (IRE)—Ailsa Craig (IRE) **Mr G. F. Tuer**
14 **KEMMERIDGE BAY**, b f Coach House (IRE)—Bookiesindexdotnet **D. R. Tucker**
15 **KERMOUSTER**, b f Garswood—Rise **D. R. Tucker**
16 B c Epaulette (AUS)—Point Perfect **Hornby Hornets**
17 **TERMONATOR**, ch c Monsieur Bond (IRE)—Easy Terms **E. Tuer**

MR GRANT TUER - Continued

TWO-YEAR-OLDS

18 B f 9/2 Fountain of Youth (IRE)—Citron (Reel Buddy (USA)) (10000) **Mr G. F. Tuer**
19 B f 18/5 Champs Elysees—Easy Terms (Trade Fair) (1000) **E. Tuer**
20 Ch f 4/4 Anjaal—Generous Heart (Sakhee's Secret) (6000) **Mr G. F. Tuer**
21 B c 26/2 Due Diligence (USA)—M'selle (IRE) (Elnadim (USA)) (2857) **D. R. Tucker**
22 B c Gutaifan (IRE)—Suite (IRE) (Invincible Spirit (IRE)) (21069) **Mr G. F. Tuer**
23 B c 12/2 Magician—Thewandaofu (IRE) (Clodovil (IRE)) (15238) **Mr G. F. Tuer**
24 B f 3/3 Gutaifan (IRE)—Worthington (IRE) (Kodiac) (28571) **Miss M. A. Thompson**

Other Owners: Mr J. Black, Mr A. G. Leggott, Mr M. Marsh, Mrs V. Thompson, Mrs S. E. Turnbull, Mr G. Turnbull.

---

547 ### MR JOSEPH TUITE, Lambourn
Postal: **Felstead Stables, Folly Road, Lambourn, Hungerford, Berkshire, RG17 8QE**
Contacts: **MOBILE (07769) 977351**
E-MAIL joe.tuite@tuiteracing.com WEBSITE www.tuiteracing.co.uk

1 AVON GREEN, 4, b f Avonbridge—Greenery (IRE) **I & K Prince**
2 BLACK KALANISI (IRE), 6, b g Kalanisi (IRE)—Blackthorne Winter (IRE) **The Harefield Racing Club**
3 CONKERING HERO (IRE), 5, ch g Arakan (USA)—Brioney (IRE) **C.R. Lambourne, M. Forbes, D. Losse**
4 FAST DANCER, 7, b g Fast Company (IRE)—Tereed Elhawa **Alan & Christine Bright**
5 FORTUNE AND GLORY (USA), 6, b g War Front (USA)—Spain (USA) **Mr R. J. Gurr**
6 INTERMODAL, 5, b g Rail Link—Rule of Nature **Mr R. J. Gurr**
7 JUNGLE ROOM (USA), 4, b g Violence (USA)—Raised Right (USA) **Matt & Lauren Morgan**
8 KIMIFIVE (IRE), 4, ch g Born To Sea (IRE)—Appletreemagic (IRE) **Mr R. J. Gurr**
9 LARCHMONT LAD (IRE), 5, b h Footstepsinthesand—Fotini (IRE) **Mr M. F. Geoghegan**
10 MACHINE LEARNER, 6, b g Sir Percy—My First Romance **Mr M. F. Geoghegan**
11 PENWOOD (FR), 4, b f Orpen (USA)—In The Woods **Mr A. R. Pittman**
12 REBEL WOODS (FR), 6, br g Cockney Rebel (IRE)—In The Woods **Mr A. R. Pittman**
13 REDGRAVE (IRE), 5, b g Lope de Vega (IRE)—Olympic Medal **Jon Beard & Partner**
14 SPARKLEANDSHINE (IRE), 6, b g Olden Times—Little Flower (IRE) **Mr R. J. Gurr**
15 SURREY BLAZE (IRE), 4, b g Thewayyouare (USA)—Catadalya (IRE) **Surrey Racing (sb)**
16 SURREY HOPE (USA), 5, b g Lemon Drop Kid (USA)—She Be Classy (USA) **Surrey Racing (SH)**
17 TOPOLOGY, 6, br g Passing Glance—Bold Byzantium **The Singleton Park Partnership 2**
18 WHO TOLD JO JO (IRE), 5, b g Bushranger (IRE)—Shenkara (IRE) **Felstead Court Flyers**
19 ZIPEDEEDODAH (IRE), 7, gr g Zebedee—Beverley Macca **D.M Synergy & Mark Wellbelove**

THREE-YEAR-OLDS

20 ANGEL MEAD, b f Archipenko (USA)—Red Sovereign **Mr D. A. Klein**
21 COCKNEY HILL, b g Bated Breath—Espagnolette **Mr D. A. Klein**
22 HELDTORANSOM, br f Dick Turpin (IRE)—Wassendale **Penny/Adrian Burton, Bob/Angela Lampard**
23 HIGHEST MOUNTAIN (FR), b g Siyouni (FR)—Chanson Celeste **M. Morgan**
24 OLD RED EYES (USA), ch g Speightstown (USA)—Grand Mere (USA) **Matt & Lauren Morgan**
25 SHAFFIRE, b f Clodovil (IRE)—Wigan Lane **Mr R. J. Gurr**
26 SKATING AWAY (IRE), b f Bungle Inthejungle—She Runs (FR) **Wintle, Wilson & Partner**
27 SOPHOSC (IRE), ch g Society Rock (IRE)—Ichiuma (USA) **The Harefield Racing Club**
28 SURREY THUNDER (FR), b c Le Havre (IRE)—Zakania (IRE) **Surrey Racing (TH)**
29 SYLVIA'S MOTHER, b f Foxwedge (AUS)—Majestic Song **Morgan, Beard & Wellbelove**
30 THE GREY DANCER (IRE), gr g Alhebayeb (IRE)—Key Girl (IRE) **Alan & Christine Bright**
31 TRAIN TO GEORGIA, b br g Scat Daddy (USA)—Ghost Galaxy (USA) **Matt & Lauren Morgan**

TWO-YEAR-OLDS

32 DARK NIGHTMARE (IRE), br gr f 2/1 Gutaifan (IRE)—Yet Again (Oasis Dream) (16856) **Mr W. Evans**
33 B f 15/4 Baltic King—Hapipi (Bertolini (USA)) (4761) **A. F. Walls**
34 B f 13/4 Evasive—Hypatia (IRE) (Holy Roman Emperor) (4213)
35 Ch g 7/4 Zebedee—Ichiuma (USA) (Mizzen Mast (USA)) (13062)
36 B c 28/2 Rock of Gibraltar (IRE)—Little Miss Gracie (Efisio) **Mr & Mrs A. J. Mutch**
37 MACSTREAK, ch c 23/3 Hot Streak (IRE)—No Song (Zamindar (USA)) (571) **Mr R. J. Gurr**
38 TIGERTEN, b c 24/1 Born To Sea (IRE)—Morning Bride (IRE) (Danehill Dancer (IRE)) (11428) **Mr R. J. Gurr**

MR JOSEPH TUITE - Continued

Other Owners: Mr D. Barrett, Mrs D. M. Barrett, Mr J. Beard, Mr G. Bennett, Mr A. D. Bright, Mrs C. Bright, Mrs P. C. Burton, Mr M. Chesney, M. I. Forbes, Mr S. Grubb, Mr C. R. Hadingham, Mrs R. G. Hillen, Mr C. R. Lambourne, Mr R. J. Lampard, Mrs L. J. Losse, Mr D. R. Losse, Mr D. Marsh, Mrs L. K. Morgan, Mr A. J. Mutch, Mrs S. Mutch, Mrs K. Prince, Mr I. D. Prince, Mr T. Robinson-Gamby, Surrey Racing Limited, Mr J. M. Tuite, Mr M. J. Wellbelove, Mr E. Wilson, Mr J. D. Wintle.

---

548 MR BILL TURNER, Sherborne

Postal: **Sigwells Farm, Sigwells, Corton Denham, Sherborne, Dorset, DT9 4LN**
Contacts: **PHONE (01963) 220523 FAX (01963) 220046 MOBILE (07932) 100173**
E-MAIL billturnerracing@gmail.com

1 **BORN AT MIDNIGHT,** 4, b g Midnight Legend—Wavet **Mr B. J. Goldsmith**
2 **BORN TO BOOGIE,** 5, b m Bahri (USA)—Turtle Dove **C. J. White**
3 **BUNCH OF THYME (IRE),** 4, b g Elzaam (AUS)—Goodie Goodie **Mrs P. A. Turner**
4 **DEVIL OR ANGEL,** 4, ch f Assertive—Level Pegging (IRE) **Tracy Turner**
5 **HOLDENHURST,** 4, gr g Hellvelyn—Michelle Shift **Ansells Of Watford**
6 **LITTLE BOY BLUE,** 4, gr g Hellvelyn—Dusty Dazzler (IRE) **Tracy Turner**
7 **MARETTIMO (IRE),** 5, b g Harbour Watch (IRE)—Renowned (IRE) **R. A. Bracken**
8 **REBEL HEART,** 5, b m Kyllachy—Just Like A Woman **Mascalls Stud**
9 **SPRINGCOMBE JOE,** 7, b g Kayf Tara—Dissolve **D. Coombes**
10 **YORKSHIRE STAR (IRE),** 5, ch g Fast Company (IRE)—March Star (IRE) **Mrs P. A. Turner**
11 **YOUVEBROKENMYDREAM,** 4, b f Geordieland (FR)—Mollycarrs Gambul

THREE-YEAR-OLDS

12 **JOHN BETJEMAN,** b g Poet's Voice—A Great Beauty **Ronald Rivers**
13 Ch f Coach House (IRE)—Lisa Jane **Mrs P. A. Turner**
14 **WHAT A DAZZLER,** ch f Coach House (IRE)—Dusty Dazzler (IRE) **Mrs P. A. Turner**

TWO-YEAR-OLDS

15 B f 27/2 Casamento (IRE)—Constant Craving (Pastoral Pursuits) **Mascalls Stud**
16 Ch f 23/2 Equiano (FR)—Halfwaytoparadise (Observatory (USA)) **Mascalls Stud**
17 **HELL OF A JOKER,** br c 30/4 Hellvelyn—Oceanico Dot Com (IRE) (Hernando (FR)) (4761) **Tracy Turner**
18 Ch f 23/2 Hot Streak (IRE)—Liberty Lady (IRE) (Statue of Liberty) (18095) **Tracy Turner**
19 **LITTLE DEVIL,** ch f 8/4 Hot Streak (IRE)—Sunburnt (Haafhd) (1904) **Tracy Turner**
20 Br f 10/4 Coach House (IRE)—Piste (Falbrav (IRE)) **Tracy Turner**
21 **QUEENS ROAD (IRE),** b f 9/1 Make Believe—Okba (USA) (Diesis) (5238) **Ansells Of Watford**
22 **SHOW ME HEAVEN,** br f 10/3 Stimulation (IRE)—Hot Pursuits (Pastoral Pursuits) **Mrs I. Eavis**
23 B c 6/3 Delegator—Up And Running (Compton Place) (3809) **Tracy Turner**

Other Owners: Mr B. C. Ansell, Mrs B. C. Ansell, Mrs Susan Hearn, Mr Barry Hearn.

Amateur: Mr Ryan Withey.

---

549 MRS KAREN TUTTY, Northallerton

Postal: **Trenholme House Farm, Osmotherley, Northallerton, North Yorkshire, DL6 3QA**
Contacts: **PHONE (01609) 883624 FAX 01609 883624 MOBILE (07967) 837406**
E-MAIL karentutty@btinternet.com WEBSITE www.karentuttyracing.co.uk

1 **DASHEEN,** 6, b g Bahamian Bounty—Caribbean Dancer (USA) **Thoroughbred Homes Ltd**
2 **IDEAL CANDY (IRE),** 4, b f Canford Cliffs (IRE)—Forever More (IRE) **Mr D. A. Robinson**
3 **IDEAL SPIRIT,** 4, b f Swiss Spirit—Silver Sail **Mr D. A. Robinson**
4 **JORVIK PRINCE,** 5, br g Kheleyf (USA)—Wotatomboy **Thoroughbred Homes Ltd**
5 **KINGOFMERROWS (IRE),** 5, br g Kodiac—
     Tamara Gervasoni (IRE) **Max Europe Ltd & Thoroughbred Homes Ltd**
6 **NOVABRIDGE,** 11, ch g Avonbridge—Petrovna (IRE) **Thoroughbred Homes Ltd**
7 **SEARCHING (IRE),** 7, ro g Mastercraftsman (IRE)—Miracolia (USA) **Thoroughbred Homes Ltd**
8 **TWIN APPEAL,** 8, b g Oratorio (IRE)—
     Velvet Appeal (IRE) **Mrs Mary Winetroube & Thoroughbred Homes**

THREE-YEAR-OLDS

9 **IDEAL DESTINY,** b f Dawn Approach (IRE)—Early Morning Rain (IRE) **Mr D. A. Robinson**

RS KAREN TUTTY - Continued

ther Owners: Max Europe Limited, Mrs M. T. Winetroube.

pprentice: Gemma Tutty.

---

550 **MR NIGEL TWISTON-DAVIES, Cheltenham**
Postal: **Grange Hill Farm Limited, Grange Hill Farm, Naunton, Cheltenham, Gloucestershire, GL54 3AY**
Contacts: **PHONE (01451) 850278 MOBILE (07836) 664440**
E-MAIL nigel@nigeltwistondavies.co.uk WEBSITE www.nigeltwistondavies.co.uk

1 **AL DANCER (FR)**, 6, gr g Al Namix (FR)—Steel Dancer (FR) **Walters Plant Hire Ltd**
2 **ANGELS ANTICS**, 6, b m Schiaparelli (GER)—Safari Run (IRE) **Walters Plant Hire & Spiers & Hartwell**
3 **ANOTHER FRONTIER (IRE)**, 8, b g Darsi (FR)—Scent With Love (IRE) **Jump For Fun Racing**
4 **ARCTIC GOLD (IRE)**, 8, b g Gold Well—Arctic Warrior (IRE) **Geoffrey & Donna Keeys**
5 **ARTHUR'S GIFT (IRE)**, 8, b g Presenting—Uncertain Affair (IRE) **Arthur's Gift Partnership**
6 **ASTRACAD (FR)**, 13, br g Cadoudal (FR)—Astre Eria (FR) **Mr M. Barlow**
7 **BABY TED**, 6, ch g Pasternak—Dd's Glenalla (IRE) **Mr N. A. Twiston-Davies**
8 **BALLYANDY**, 8, b g Kayf Tara—Megalex **Options O Syndicate**
9 **BALLYART (IRE)**, 6, b g Scorpion (IRE)—Candle Massini (IRE) **Mr N. A. Twiston-Davies**
10 **BALLYARTHUR (IRE)**, 9, b g Kayf Tara—Ariels Serenade (IRE) **Graham & Alison Jelley**
11 **BALLYBLAKE (IRE)**, 5, b g Arakan (USA)—Nonnetia (FR) **Mr N. A. Twiston-Davies**
12 **BALLYBOLLEY (IRE)**, 10, b g Kayf Tara—Gales Hill (IRE) **Mr Simon Munir & Mr Isaac Souede**
13 **BALLYCROSS**, 8, b g King's Theatre (IRE)—Ninna Nanna (FR) **The Autism Rockers**
14 **BALLYELLIS (IRE)**, 6, b g Shantou (USA)—Chalice Wells (IRE) **Mr N. A. Twiston-Davies**
15 **BALLYHILL (IRE)**, 8, b br g Al Namix (FR)—Laly Light (FR) **S Such & CG Paletta**
16 **BALLYKAN**, 9, b g Presenting—La Marianne **Mr Simon Munir & Mr Isaac Souede**
17 **BALLYMALIN (IRE)**, 9, b g Presenting—Murrurundi (IRE) **Mills & Mason Partnership**
18 **BALLYMOY (IRE)**, 6, b g Flemensfirth (USA)—John's Eliza (IRE) **Mr Simon Munir & Mr Isaac Souede**
19 **BALLYOPTIC (IRE)**, 9, b g Old Vic—Lambourne Lace (IRE) **Mills & Mason Partnership**
20 **BELMOUNT (IRE)**, 10, b g Westerner—Artist's Jewel **Mrs S. Jones**
21 **BIGBADJOHN (IRE)**, 10, b g Vinnie Roe (IRE)—Celtic Serenade (IRE) **Mr N. D. Morris**
22 **BISHOPSWOOD FLYER (IRE)**, 5, b g Arcadio (GER)—
                                    Catch The Class (IRE) **Walters Plant Hire Ltd & Geoff Bruce**
23 **BLAKLION**, 10, b g Kayf Tara—Franciscaine (FR) **S Such & CG Paletta**
24 **BLUE FLIGHT (FR)**, 6, b g Blue Bresil (FR)—Lover Flight (FR) **Mr J. Fyffe**
25 **BOMBER'S MOON**, 8, b g Erhaab (USA)—Flaviola (IRE) **Charlie Walker & Jim Old**
26 **BRING BACK CHARLIE**, 9, b g Green Card (USA)—Nafertiti (IRE) **Mr D. D. Genner**
27 **BRISTOL DE MAI (FR)**, 8, gr g Saddler Maker (IRE)—La Bole Night (FR) **Mr Simon Munir & Mr Isaac Souede**
28 **BROOKEVALE (IRE)**, 5, b g Kalanisi (IRE)—Railway House (IRE) **Mr N. A. Twiston-Davies**
29 **BROWNDODD (IRE)**, 5, gr g Arcadio (GER)—Lady Greydoun (IRE) **Mr N. A. Twiston-Davies**
30 **CALETT MAD (FR)**, 7, b br g Axxos (GER)—Omelia (FR) **Mr Simon Munir & Mr Isaac Souede**
31 **CHANCE A TUNE (FR)**, 4, b g My Risk (FR)—Lyric Melody (FR) **Mr C. S. Hinchy**
32 **CHINENSIS (IRE)**, 6, b g Well Chosen—Emily Vard (IRE) **Mr T. J. Hemmings**
33 **COGRY**, 10, b g King's Theatre (IRE)—Wyldello **Graham & Alison Jelley**
34 **COSTANTE VIA (IRE)**, 8, b m Milan—Spirit Rock (IRE) **Miss K. J. Holland**
35 **COUNT MERIBEL**, 7, ch g Three Valleys (USA)—Bakhtawar (IRE) **C.C. Walker**
36 **CRIEVEHILL (IRE)**, 7, b g Arcadio (GER)—Ma Douce (IRE) **Highclere T'Bred Racing- Crievehill**
37 **CYDERCOURT (IRE)**, 6, b g Court Cave (IRE)—Lavender Track (IRE) **Mr N. A. Twiston-Davies**
38 **DOUBLE COURT (IRE)**, 8, b g Court Cave (IRE)—Miss Top (IRE) **Synergy Racing**
39 **DOUBLE ROSS (IRE)**, 13, ch g Double Eclipse (IRE)—Kinross **Options O Syndicate**
40 **EARLOFTHECOTSWOLDS (FR)**, 5, bl g Axxos (GER)—Sissi Land (FR) **Twiston-Davies, Mason, Greer & Kiely**
41 **EL TERREMOTO (FR)**, 7, b g Spirit One (FR)—By Decree (USA) **Mr Simon Munir & Mr Isaac Souede**
42 **EQUUS MILLAR (IRE)**, 6, b g Masterofthehorse (IRE)—Lets Get Busy (IRE) **James & Jean Potter**
43 **EYRESHILL (IRE)**, 6, ch g Beneficial—Eyres And Graces (IRE) **Mr N. A. Twiston-Davies**
44 **FAMILY MAN (IRE)**, 6, b g Gold Well—Greenacre Mandalay (IRE) **Mr N. A. Twiston-Davies**
45 **FIER ECHEZEAUX (FR)**, 4, b g Network (GER)—Montre En Main (FR) **Ged Mason & Jim McGoff**
46 **FLORRIE BOY (IRE)**, 8, b g Milan—Second Best (IRE) **Options O Syndicate**
47 **FLYING ANGEL (IRE)**, 8, gr g Arcadio (GER)—Gypsy Kelly (IRE) **Mr R. J. Rexton**
48 **FOXTAIL HILL (IRE)**, 10, b g Dr Massini (IRE)—Flynn's Girl (IRE) **Options O Syndicate**
49 **GINGE DE SOPHIA (FR)**, 6, b m Presenting—Me Grannys Endoors (IRE) **Mr J. Neild**
50 **GO CONQUER (IRE)**, 10, b g Arcadio (GER)—Ballinamona Wish (IRE) **Mr & Mrs Paul & Clare Rooney**
51 **GOOD BOY BOBBY (IRE)**, 6, b g Flemensfirth (USA)—Princess Gaia (IRE) **Mr & Mrs Paul & Clare Rooney**
52 **GOODBYE DANCER (FR)**, 8, b g Dragon Dancer—Maribia Bella (FR) **The Yes No Wait Sorries**
53 **GUY (IRE)**, 4, ch g Getaway (GER)—Sept Verites (FR)

MR NIGEL TWISTON-DAVIES - Continued

54 **HILLARY C**, 7, b m Kayf Tara—Dd's Glenalla (IRE) **Mr N. A. Twiston-Davies**
55 **IMPERIAL ACOLYTE**, 5, b g Kalanisi (IRE)—Isabello (IRE) **Imperial Racing Partnership**
56 **IMPERIAL NEMESIS (IRE)**, 6, b g Stowaway—Liss Alainn (IRE) **Imperial Racing Partnership 2016**
57 **JABULANI (FR)**, 6, gr g Martaline—Incorrigible (FR) **Walters Plant Hire Ltd**
58 **JELSKI (GER)**, 5, b g Kallisto (GER)—Just Zoud **Mr T. J. Hemmings**
59 **JUGE ET PARTI (FR)**, 8, gr g Martaline—Nakota Rag (FR) **Walters Plant Hire Ltd**
60 **KAPGARRY (FR)**, 6, b g Ballingarry (IRE)—Kaprissima (FR) **Options O Syndicate**
61 **KERISPER (FR)**, 10, b g Robin des Champs (FR)—Tina Rederie (FR) **The Autism Rockers**
62 **KINGOFTHECOTSWOLDS (IRE)**, 5, b g Arcadio (GER)—Damoiselle **Mr N. A. Twiston-Davies**
63 **KINGSPLACE (IRE)**, 7, b g Ask—Winsome Breeze (IRE) **Mr R. J. Rexton**
64 **LARCH HILL (IRE)**, 6, ch g Presenting—Misty Move (IRE) **Mr N. A. Twiston-Davies**
65 **LIGHT BREAKS (IRE)**, 7, b g Dylan Thomas (IRE)—Anywaysmile (IRE) **Mr N. A. Twiston-Davies**
66 **LITTLE JON**, 11, b g Pasternak—Jowoody **Mr R. N. Frosell**
67 **LITTLE POP**, 11, b g Pasternak—Flagship Daisy May (IRE) **S Such & CG Paletta**
68 **LOCKER ROOM TALK (IRE)**, 6, b g Beneficial—Whistling Gypse (IRE) **Mr C. S. Hinchy**
69 **LUCKOFTHEDRAW (FR)**, 6, gr g Martaline—La Perspective (FR) **Walters Plant Hire Ltd**
70 **MARIA FRANCESCA (IRE)**, 4, b f Califet (FR)—Miss Kettlewell (IRE) **Gingearmy Two**
71 **MAYOHILL (IRE)**, 6, b g Beneficial—Deara Mayo (IRE) **Mr N. A. Twiston-Davies**
72 **MILANSTORM (IRE)**, 6, b g Milan—Deise Rose (IRE) **S Such & CG Paletta**
73 **MR ANTOLINI (IRE)**, 9, b g Catcher In The Rye (IRE)—Victory Run (IRE) **Alan & Sally Coney**
74 **MUCKLE ROE (IRE)**, 10, b g Westerner—Island Crest **Mrs V. J. Lane**
75 **MURATELLO (FR)**, 5, b g Blue Bresil (FR)—Nesle de La Roque (FR) **Mr Simon Munir & Mr Isaac Souede**
76 **NYE BEVAN (IRE)**, 4, b g Arcadio (GER)—Emma Jane (IRE) **Mr J. Neild**
77 **OH MICHELLE**, 8, br m Kayf Tara—Grenfell (IRE) **The True Acre Partnership**
78 **ONE FOR ROSIE**, 6, gr g Getaway—Whisky Rose (IRE) **Mr & Mrs Paul & Clare Rooney**
79 **ONE FORTY SEVEN (IRE)**, 7, b g Beneficial—Still Bubbly (IRE) **Graham & Alison Jelley**
80 **PINK GIN**, 11, ch g Alflora (IRE)—Miss Mailmit **Mrs J Fowler & Mr C Jenkins**
81 **RAVENSDALE (IRE)**, 7, ch g Flemensfirth (USA)—Thunder Belle (IRE) **Mr Simon Munir & Mr Isaac Souede**
82 **RIZZARDO**, 7, gr g Tikkanen (USA)—Last Spruce (USA) **Mr N. A. Twiston-Davies**
83 **ROBINSHILL (IRE)**, 8, ch g Robin des Champs (FR)—I Remember It Well (IRE) **Mr R. J. Rexton**
84 **ROCCO (IRE)**, 6, b g Shantou (USA)—Navaro (IRE) **Mr & Mrs P Carter**
85 **ROOTLESS TREE (IRE)**, 4, b g Jeremy (USA)—Miss Compliance (IRE) **Mr C. S. Hinchy**
86 **SCARLETT OF TARA**, 6, b m Kayf Tara—Late For Class (IRE) **Mr N. A. Twiston-Davies**
87 **SCOTCHTOWN (IRE)**, 7, ch g Beneficial—Always Present (IRE) **Valda Burke & Bryan Burrough**
88 **SIR GEORGE SOMERS (USA)**, 6, ch g Cape Blanco (IRE)—Sense of Class (USA) **Mr N. A. Twiston-Davies**
89 **SOUTHERLY BUSTER**, 7, b g Shirocco (GER)—Appleby **Partnership Terminated**
90 **SPLASH OF GINGE**, 11, b g Oscar (IRE)—Land of Honour **Mr J. Neild**
91 **SUMMIT LIKE HERBIE**, 7, ch g Sulamani (IRE)—Colline de Fleurs **Friends Of Herbie**
92 **SUPAKALANISTIC (IRE)**, 6, b g Kalanisi (IRE)—Keys Hope (IRE) **Jump For Fun Racing**
93 **TARA MUCK**, 12, br m Kayf Tara—Madam Muck **Mr N. A. Twiston-Davies**
94 **TEMPLEHILLS (IRE)**, 8, b br g Kalanisi (IRE)—Sissinghurst Storm (IRE) **Oi Digital Limited**
95 **THE HOLLOW GINGE (IRE)**, 6, b g Oscar (IRE)—Some Gem (IRE) **The Ginge Army**
96 **TINTERN THEATRE (IRE)**, 8, b g King's Theatre (IRE)—Rith Ar Aghaidh (IRE) **Jimmy & Susie Wenman**
97 **TOPOFTHECOTSWOLDS (IRE)**, 5, b g Arcadio (GER)—Bambootcha (IRE) **Mr N. A. Twiston-Davies**
98 **TORN AND FRAYED (IRE)**, 5, b g Califet (FR)—Chic Et Zen (FR) **Mr C. S. Hinchy**
99 **TORPILLO (FR)**, 4, ch g Alanadi (FR)—Astherate (FR) **Mr Simon Munir & Mr Isaac Souede**
100 **TOWER VIEW (IRE)**, 5, b g Oscar (IRE)—Atomic Betty (IRE) **Mr C. S. Hinchy**
101 **TOWNSHEND (GER)**, 8, b g Lord of England (GER)—Trikolore (GER) **Million in Mind Partnership**
102 **TURNING GOLD**, 5, ch g Pivotal—Illusion **Turning Gold**
103 **UNBLINKING**, 6, b g Cacique (IRE)—Deliberate **R. Bevis**
104 **VOLCANO (FR)**, 5, gr g Martaline—Lyli Rose (FR) **Walters Plant Hire Ltd**
105 **WHOLESTONE (IRE)**, 8, br g Craigsteel—Last Theatre (IRE) **Mr Simon Munir & Mr Isaac Souede**
106 **WICKED WILLY (IRE)**, 8, br g Arcadio (GER)—How Provincial **Mr C. Roberts**
107 **YANMARE (IRE)**, 9, b g Soapy Danger—Bell Walks Caroll (IRE) **Bryan & Philippa Burrough**

Other Owners: A. R. Bromley, Mr C. G. W. Bruce, Mrs V. F. Burke, B. R. H. Burrough, Mrs P. J. Burrough, Mrs J. Carter Mr P. A. Carter, C. S. J. Coley, Mrs S. Coney, Mr A. R. Coney, Mr C. G. Dando, Mr H. G. Doubtfire, Mr J. Flannery, Mrs J A. Fowler, G. F. Goode, Mr T. M. Hailstone, Mr P. R. Henderson, Highclere Nominated Partner Limited, Highclere Thoroughbred Racing Ltd, Mrs A. D. Jelley, G. S. Jelley, Mr C. J. Jenkins, Mr J. Jessemey, Mrs C. M. Keeys, G. F. Keeys Mr H. J. Kelly, Mr P Marray, G. A. Mason, Mr D. M. Mason, Mr J. M. McGoff, Mrs L. Merson, W. R. Mills, F. J. Mills, Mr W. D. C. Minton, S. E. Munir, Mrs D. C. Nicholson, J. A. B. Old, Mr D. E. Owens, Mr C. G. Paletta, Mr N. L. Payne, Mr J. E Potter, Mrs M. J. Potter, Mr P. Preston, Miss M. R. Robinson, Mr I. Robinson, Mr P. A. Rooney, Mrs C. Rooney, Mr S. Shah Mr I. Souede, Spiers & Hartwell Ltd, Mr M. A. Stratford, Mrs S. E. Such, Miss M. L. Taylor, Mr W. Twiston-Davies, Mrs S Wenman, J. Wenman, Mr S. G. Wignall.

Jockey (NH): Sam Twiston-Davies. **Conditional:** Jamie Bargary.

551 **MR JAMES UNETT, Wolverhampton**
Postal: **1 Dunstall Mews, Gorsebrook Road, Wolverhampton, West Midlands, WV6 0PE**
Contacts: PHONE **(01691) 610001** FAX **(01691) 610001** MOBILE **(07887) 534753**
E-MAIL **jamesunett1327@yahoo.co.uk** WEBSITE **www.jamesunettracing.com**

1 BOUCLIER (IRE), 9, ch g Zamindar (USA)—Bastet (IRE) **Mr M. Chung**
2 CITTA D'ORO, 4, b g Cityscape—Corsa All Oro (USA) **P. S. Burke**
3 EBQAA (IRE), 5, b m Cape Cross (IRE)—Estedaama (USA) **J. W. Unett**
4 KING OSWALD (USA), 6, b g Street Cry (IRE)—Northern Melody (IRE) **M. Watkinson & Mr P. Steadman**
5 NONEEDTOTELLME (IRE), 6, gr m Fast Company (IRE)—Gemma's Delight (IRE) **J. W. Unett**
6 NUTINI (IRE), 6, b g Lope de Vega (IRE)—My Eurydice **Mrs L. F. Wei**
7 QUIXOTE (GER), 9, b h Pivotal—Quebrada (IRE) **Lease Terminated**

THREE-YEAR-OLDS

8 LOVEATFIRSTLIGHT (IRE), b f Es Que Love (IRE)—Spark Up **J. W. Unett**
9 SYMPHONY (IRE), gr f Gregorian (IRE)—Anazah (USA) **Paul Steadman & Partner**

Other Owners: Mr D. P. Steadman, Mr M. Watkinson.

Assistant Trainer: Miss C. H. Jones

552 **MR MARK USHER, Upper Lambourn**
Postal: **Rowdown House Stables, Upper Lambourn, Hungerford, Berkshire, RG17 8QP**
Contacts: PHONE **(01488) 72598** (01488) 73630 MOBILE **(07831) 873531**
E-MAIL **markusher.racing@btconnect.com** WEBSITE **www.markusherracing.co.uk**

1 ARLECCHINO'S ARC (IRE), 4, ch g Arcano (IRE)—Sir Cecil's Girl (IRE) **Mr K. Senior**
2 BAYSTON HILL, 5, br g Big Bad Bob (IRE)—Jessica Ennis (USA) **High Five Racing and Partners**
3 BIRD FOR LIFE, 5, b m Delegator—Birdolini **The Mark Usher Racing Club**
4 BLACK TRUFFLE (FR), 9, b g Kyllachy—Some Diva **The Mark Usher Racing Club**
5 BORN TO PLEASE, 5, b m Stimulation (IRE)—Heart Felt **The Mark Usher Racing Club**
6 DREAMBOAT ANNIE, 4, b f Piccolo—Bold Rose **Ushers Court**
7 DYLAN'S SEA SONG, 5, b m Dylan Thomas (IRE)—Mary Sea (FR) **Ushers Court**
8 MARSHALL AID (IRE), 6, b g Lawman (FR)—Dievotchkina (IRE) **Mr B. C. Rogan**
9 MEZMAAR, 10, b g Teofilo (IRE)—Bay Tree (IRE) **Roemex Ltd**
10 MIRACLE OF MEDINAH, 8, ch g Milk It Mick—Smart Ass (IRE) **The Mark Usher Racing Club**
11 MISTRY, 6, b m Mullionmileanhour (IRE)—Smart Ass (IRE) **Ushers Court**
12 MISU PETE, 7, b g Misu Bond (IRE)—Smart Ass (IRE) **The Mark Usher Racing Club**
13 POINT IN TIME (IRE), 4, b f Champs Elysees—Creme Anglaise **GAF Racing**
14 ROODEPARIS, 4, ch g Champs Elysees—Roodeye **Rowdown Racing Partnership**
15 SHUFOOG, 6, b m Mawatheeq (USA)—Hamloola **Champagne And Shambles**
16 THREEDIAMONDRINGS, 6, ch g Geordieland (FR)—Five Gold Rings (IRE) **Miss L. A. Harbord**
17 TIN FANDANGO, 4, b g Steele Tango (USA)—Littlemoor Lass **Mr M. A. Humphreys**
18 WAQAAS, 5, b g Showcasing—Red Mischief (IRE) **Goodracing Partnership**

THREE-YEAR-OLDS

19 CALA SVEVA (IRE), b f Footstepsinthesand—Sveva (IRE) **The Ridgeway Partnership**
20 PADURA BRAVE, b f Havana Gold (IRE)—Audaz **Twenty Four Carrot Racing**

Other Owners: Mr R. H. Brookes, Mrs T. J. Channing-Williams, Mr D. P. Duffy, Paul Duffy, David Semmens, Viv Williams, High Five Racing, Mr P. Hobbs, Ms D. M. Ray, Mr D. M. Semmens, Mr J. A. Stansfield, Mr M. D. I. Usher.

Assistant Trainer: Michael Usher

Jockey (flat): Liam Keniry.

553 **MR ROGER VARIAN, Newmarket**
Postal: **Carlburg Stables, 49 Bury Road, Newmarket, Suffolk, CB8 7BY**
Contacts: PHONE **(01638) 661702** FAX **(01638) 667018**
E-MAIL **office@varianstable.com** WEBSITE **www.varianstable.com**

1 BARSANTI (IRE), 7, b g Champs Elysees—Silver Star **Sheikh Mohammed Obaid Al Maktoum**
2 BOWERMAN, 5, b h Dutch Art—Jamboretta (IRE) **Mr Paul Smith**
3 CANVASSED (IRE), 4, b g Shamardal (USA)—Painter's Pride (FR) **Sheikh Mohammed Obaid Al Maktoum**

MR ROGER VARIAN - Continued

4 **CAPE BYRON**, 5, ch g Shamardal (USA)—Reem Three **Sheikh Mohammed Obaid Al Maktoum**
5 **CONTRIVE (IRE)**, 4, gr f Mastercraftsman (IRE)—Sixpenny Sweets (IRE) **Miss Yvonne Jacques**
6 **DEFOE (IRE)**, 5, gr g Dalakhani (IRE)—Dulkashe (IRE) **Sheikh Mohammed Obaid Al Maktoum**
7 **FUJAIRA PRINCE (IRE)**, 5, gr ro g Pivotal—Zam Zoom (IRE) **Sheikh Mohammed Obaid Al Maktoum**
8 **GAME PLAYER (IRE)**, 4, gr g Dark Angel (IRE)—Lucky Clio (IRE) **Sheikh Mohammed Obaid Al Maktoum**
9 **GIBBS HILL (GER)**, 6, gr g Mastercraftsman (IRE)—Gold Charm (GER) **Mr Paul Smith**
10 **HERMOSITA**, 4, b f Exceed And Excel (AUS)—Honorlina (FR) **Newsells Park Stud**
11 **HOWMAN (IRE)**, 4, b g Sea The Stars (IRE)—Hoity Toity **Sheikh Mohammed Obaid Al Maktoum**
12 **IBRAZ**, 4, b c Farhh—Wadaa (USA) **Mr Hamdan Al Maktoum**
13 **LAUGH A MINUTE**, 4, b g Mayson—Funny Enough **Sheikh Mohammed Obaid Al Maktoum**
14 **MONTEJA**, 4, b f Shamardal (USA)—Ferdoos **Sheikh Ahmed Al Maktoum**
15 **MOUNTAIN ANGEL (IRE)**, 5, b g Dark Angel (IRE)—Fanciful Dancer **Mr Ziad A. Galadari**
16 **MUBHIJ (IRE)**, 4, b c Dark Angel (IRE)—Diva (GER) **Mr Hamdan Al Maktoum**
17 **NARYNKOL**, 4, ch g Declaration of War (USA)—Nazym (IRE) **Mr Nurlan Bizakov**
18 **PILASTER**, 4, b f Nathaniel (IRE)—Portal **Cheveley Park Stud**
19 **QAZYNA (IRE)**, 4, b f Frankel—First **Mr Nurlan Bizakov**
20 **QUEEN OF DESIRE (IRE)**, 4, b f Dubawi (IRE)—Beyond Desire **Clipper Logistics**
21 **RASIMA**, 4, gr f Iffraaj—Raushan (FR) **Mr Nurlan Bizakov**
22 **SHARJA BRIDGE**, 5, b h Oasis Dream—Quetena (GER) **Sheikh Mohammed Obaid Al Maktoum**
23 **SHARJA SILK**, 4, b g Dubawi (IRE)—So Silk **Sheikh Mohammed Obaid Al Maktoum**
24 **SHENANIGANS (IRE)**, 5, b m Arcano (IRE)—Ladylishandra (IRE) **Ann Black, M Al Qatami & K M Al Mudha⬦**
25 **SPANISH CITY**, 6, ch g Exceed And Excel (AUS)—Annabelle's Charm (IRE) **Merry Fox Stud Ltd**
26 **SPARKLING SURF**, 4, ch f Frankel—Shimmering Surf (IRE) **Mr Peter Winkworth**
27 **TA ALLAK**, 4, ch c New Approach (IRE)—Nahrain **Sheikh Ahmed Al Maktoum**
28 **UAE KING**, 5, b h Frankel—Zomaradah **Sheikh Mohammed Obaid Al Maktoum**
29 **UAE PRINCE (IRE)**, 6, b g Sea The Stars (IRE)—By Request **Sheikh Mohammed Obaid Al Maktoum**
30 **WILLIE JOHN**, 4, b c Dansili—Izzi Top **Sheikh Mohammed Obaid Al Maktoum**
31 **ZABEEL PRINCE (IRE)**, 6, ch g Lope de Vega (IRE)—
Princess Serena (USA) **Sheikh Mohammed Obaid Al Maktoum**

THREE-YEAR-OLDS

32 **A HUNDRED ECHOES**, b c Kyllachy—Kapsiliat (IRE) **Mr Rashed Al Kamda**
33 **AKTAU**, b g Teofilo (IRE)—Rare Ransom **Mr Nurlan Bizakov**
34 **ALAPAT**, ch c Teofilo (IRE)—Albanka (USA) **Mr Nurlan Bizakov**
35 **APPARATE**, b c Dubawi (IRE)—Appearance **Sheikh Mohammed Obaid Al Maktoum**
36 **AUSTRALIS (IRE)**, b c Australia—Quiet Down (USA) **Biddestone Racing Stud**
37 **BACKSTREET GIRL (IRE)**, b f Shamardal (USA)—Beyond Desire **Clipper Logistics**
38 **BARDO CONTIGUO (IRE)**, b c Lope de Vega (IRE)—Jillnextdoor (IRE) **Sheikh Mohammed Obaid Al Maktoum**
39 **BAYROOT (IRE)**, b c Exceed And Excel (AUS)—Alwarga (USA) **Sheikh Ahmed Al Maktoum**
40 **DALAKINA (IRE)**, ch f Mastercraftsman (IRE)—White Cay **Sheikh Juma Dalmook Al Maktoum**
41 **DARING VENTURE (IRE)**, b f Dabirsim (FR)—Glorious Adventure (IRE) **Sheikh Juma Dalmook Al Maktoum**
42 **DASHED**, b f Pivotal—Shatter (IRE) **Cheveley Park Stud**
43 **DESIRE FOR FREEDOM (USA)**, b f Fed Biz (USA)—Leinster Lady (USA) **Mr Rashed Al Kamda**
44 **DUBRAVA**, b f Dansili—Rose Diamond (IRE) **Sheikh Mohammed Obaid Al Maktoum**
45 **EDARAAT**, b c Exceed And Excel (AUS)—Deglet Noor **Mr Hamdan Al Maktoum**
46 **EJTILAAB (IRE)**, b c Slade Power—Miranda Frost (IRE) **Mr Hamdan Al Maktoum**
47 **ELA KATRINA**, gr f Kendargent (FR)—Ela Athena **Newsells Park Stud**
48 **ELAMIRR (IRE)**, b c Exceed And Excel (AUS)—Ameerat **Sheikh Ahmed Al Maktoum**
49 **EMIRATES KNIGHT (IRE)**, b c Dark Angel (IRE)—Interim Payment (USA) **Mr Ziad A. Galadari**
50 **ENOUGH ALREADY**, b g Coach House (IRE)—Funny Enough **Sheikh Mohammed Obaid Al Maktoum**
51 **FARNHAM**, b f Farhh—Purple Tiger (IRE) **Clipper Logistics**
52 **FARZEEN**, ch f Zee Zee Gee **Helena Springfield Ltd**
53 **FEARLESSLY (IRE)**, gr f Dalakhani (IRE)—Mid Mon Lady (IRE) **Mr Saif Ali**
54 **FIFTH POSITION (IRE)**, b g Dark Angel (IRE)—Ballet Move **Sheikh Mohammed Obaid Al Maktoum**
55 **FUJAIRA KING (USA)**, b c Kitten's Joy (USA)—Cat On A Tin Roof (USA) **Sheikh Mohammed Obaid Al Maktoum**
56 **GENEVA SPUR (USA)**, b f Distorted Humor (USA)—My Dark Rosaleen **Merry Fox Stud Ltd**
57 **GLEEFUL**, b f Pivotal—Merletta **Cheveley Park Stud**
58 **GOING PLACES**, ch c Frankel—Khor Sheed **Sheikh Mohammed Obaid Al Maktoum**
59 **HEALING POWER**, b c Kodiac—Loch Ma Naire (IRE) **Sheikh Mohammed Obaid Al Maktoum**
60 **IDEOLOGICAL (IRE)**, b f Dawn Approach (IRE)—Micaela's Moon (USA) **Tactful Finance**
61 **IMPULSION (IRE)**, b f Footstepsinthesand—Danidh Dubai (IRE) **Miss Yvonne Jacques**
62 **INVINCIBLE KNIGHT**, b c Invincible Spirit (IRE)—Nancy O (IRE) **Mr Ziad A. Galadari**
63 **INVITATIONAL**, ch f Poet's Voice—Platinum Pearl **Mr Ziad A. Galadari**
64 **JALEEL**, b g Iffraaj—Precariously Good **Mr Abdullatif Al Abdulrazzaq**
65 **JUST MY TYPE**, ch f Iffraaj—Sweet Cecily (IRE) **Sheikh Mohammed Obaid Al Maktoum**

MR ROGER VARIAN - Continued

66 **KAHALA QUEEN (IRE)**, b f Shamardal (USA)—Whazzis **Sheikh Mohammed Obaid Al Maktoum**
67 **KHABEERAH**, b f Dubawi (IRE)—Hadaatha (IRE) **Mr Hamdan Al Maktoum**
68 **KHUZAAM (USA)**, ch c Kitten's Joy (USA)—Afraah (USA) **Mr Hamdan Al Maktoum**
69 **KINGDOM OF DUBAI (FR)**, b c Iffraaj—Caprarola (USA) **Mr Rashed Al Kamda**
70 **LAST SOLDIER (FR)**, b c Intello (GER)—Dream Girl **Sheikh Mohammed Obaid Al Maktoum**
71 **LASTOCHKA**, ch f Australia—Lashyn (USA) **Mr Nurlan Bizakov**
72 **LEGEND OF DUBAI (IRE)**, ch c Dubawi (IRE)—Finsceal Beo (IRE) **Sheikh Mohammed Obaid Al Maktoum**
73 **LEHOOGG**, ch c Bated Breath—Button Moon (IRE) **Sheikh Ahmed Al Maktoum**
74 **LILLIGRAM**, ch f Leroidesanimaux (BRZ)—Millistar **Helena Springfield Ltd**
75 **LOOK CLOSELY**, b c Sea The Stars (IRE)—Lady Heidi **Sheikh Mohammed Obaid Al Maktoum**
76 **LUFRICIA**, br f Kodiac—Lucrece **Sheikh Mohammed Obaid Al Maktoum**
77 **MACKAAR (IRE)**, b c Cape Cross (IRE)—Albemarle **Sheikh Ahmed Al Maktoum**
78 **MANORAH (IRE)**, b f The Factor (USA)—Fifth Avenue Doll (USA) **Mr Abdullatif Al Abdulrazzaq**
79 **MAWAKIB**, b c Havana Gold—Keladora (USA) **Sheikh Ahmed Al Maktoum**
80 **MILITARY MOVE**, ch c Dubawi (IRE)—Rainbow Dancing **Sheikh Mohammed Obaid Al Maktoum**
81 **MOJMAL (IRE)**, ch g Raven's Pass (USA)—Almashooqa (USA) **Mr Hamdan Al Maktoum**
82 **MONSIEUR NOIR**, b c Shamardal (USA)—Night Frolic **Sheikh Mohammed Obaid Al Maktoum**
83 **MOQTARREB**, b c Kingman—Elshaadin **Mr Hamdan Al Maktoum**
84 **MORAAWED**, b g Swiss Spirit—Hot Secret **Mr Hamdan Al Maktoum**
85 **MOSAKHAR**, b c Dawn Approach (IRE)—Min Banat Alreeh (IRE) **Mr Hamdan Al Maktoum**
86 **MOT JUSTE (USA)**, b f Distorted Humor (USA)—Time On **Mr Robert Barnett**
87 **MOTALAQQY (IRE)**, b c Kingman—Pontenuovo (FR) **Mr Hamdan Al Maktoum**
88 **MOTAWAJ**, b c Dubawi (IRE)—Tantshi **Sheikh Ahmed Al Maktoum**
89 **MUNAAZIL (IRE)**, br g Dubawi (IRE)—Aljaaziah **Mr Hamdan Al Maktoum**
90 **MUSHAAGEB (IRE)**, b g War Command—Divisme (USA) **Mr Majed Almarzooqi**
91 **MUTAMAASIK**, ch c Dubawi (IRE)—Muhawalah (IRE) **Mr Hamdan Al Maktoum**
92 **MUTASAAMY (IRE)**, b c Oasis Dream—Eswarah **Mr Hamdan Al Maktoum**
93 **NABBEYL (IRE)**, b c New Approach (IRE)—Sajjhaa **Sheikh Ahmed Al Maktoum**
94 **NABEYLA**, b br f New Approach (IRE)—Feedyah (USA) **Sheikh Ahmed Al Maktoum**
95 **NAUSHA**, b f Kingman—Nazym (IRE) **Mr Nurlan Bizakov**
96 **NEAROOZ**, b f New Approach (IRE)—Modeyra **Sheikh Ahmed Al Maktoum**
97 **NESPOLA**, b f New Approach (IRE)—Nargys (IRE) **Sheikh Mohammed Obaid Al Maktoum**
98 **PREFONTAINE (IRE)**, gr g Mastercraftsman (IRE)—Cochabamba (IRE) **Mr Paul Smith**
99 **PRINCE EIJI**, ch c Dubawi (IRE)—Izzi Top **Sheikh Mohammed Obaid Al Maktoum**
100 **QABALA**, b f Scat Daddy (USA)—Entwine (USA) **H.H. Sheikh Mohammed bin Khalifa Al Thani**
101 **QAMKA**, b f Mastercraftsman (IRE)—First **Mr Nurlan Bizakov**
102 **REGAL BANNER**, ch f Lope de Vega (IRE)—Regal Riband **Cheveley Park Stud**
103 **REVAIN (FR)**, b c Oasis Dream—Cast In Gold (USA) **Sheikh Rashid bin Ahmed Al Nuaimi**
104 **REVOLUTIONISE (IRE)**, gr c Lope de Vega (IRE)—Modeeroch (IRE) **Mr A D Spence**
105 **ROSEMAN (IRE)**, b c Kingman—Go Lovely Rose (IRE) **Sheikh Mohammed Obaid Al Maktoum**
106 **SAN DONATO (IRE)**, b c Lope de Vega (IRE)—Boston Rocker (IRE) **Sheikh Mohammed Obaid Al Maktoum**
107 **SEZIM**, b g Dansili—Serres (IRE) **Mr Nurlan Bizakov**
108 **SHAGALLA**, b f Lawman (FR)—Shabyt **Mr Nurlan Bizakov**
109 **SMART NADA (IRE)**, ch f Lope de Vega (IRE)—Solar Event **Sheikh Mohammed Obaid Al Maktoum**
110 **SPECIALISE**, gr f Mastercraftsman (IRE)—My Special J's (USA) **Mr Saif Ali**
111 **SUBAANA (IRE)**, b f Cape Cross (IRE)—Suba (USA) **Sheikh Mohammed Obaid Al Maktoum**
112 **SURFMAN**, b c Kingman—Shimmering Surf (IRE) **Mr Peter Winkworth**
113 **TAKUMI (IRE)**, b c Mastercraftsman (IRE)—Nebraas **China Horse Club**
114 **TAMMOOZ**, b c Lawman—La Concorde (FR) **Sheikh Ahmed Al Maktoum**
115 **TAUTEKE**, b f Sea The Stars (IRE)—Tamarind (IRE) **Mr Nurlan Bizakov**
116 **THREE COMETS (GER)**, b c Sea The Moon (GER)—Tickle Me Pink **Sheikh Mohammed Obaid Al Maktoum**
117 **TURJOMAAN (USA)**, b br c War Front (USA)—Almoutezah (USA) **Mr Hamdan Al Maktoum**
118 **UAE JEWEL**, b c Dubawi (IRE)—Gemstone (IRE) **Sheikh Mohammed Obaid Al Maktoum**
119 **VAST**, b f Intello (GER)—Portal **Cheveley Park Stud**
120 **WORLDLY APPROACH (IRE)**, b f Dawn Approach (IRE)—Mundana (IRE) **Sheikh Mohammed Obaid Al Maktoum**
121 **YOURTIMEISNOW**, b f Charm Spirit (IRE)—Maid For Winning (USA) **Sheikh Mohammed Obaid Al Maktoum**

TWO-YEAR-OLDS

122 **A DAY AT THE RACES (IRE)**, b f 3/3 Gutaifan (IRE)—
Al Andalyya (Kingmambo (USA)) (50000) **James Barnett & Tactful Finance**
123 B f 19/4 Candy Ride (ARG)—Afraah (USA) (Hard Spun (USA)) **Mr Hamdan Al Maktoum**
124 **ALASH ORDA**, b f 25/2 Kodiac—Albanka (USA) (Giant's Causeway (USA)) **Mr Nurlan Bizakov**
125 **ALETTA DE FREY**, ch f 3/3 Dutch Art—
Rosaline (IRE) (New Approach (IRE)) **Sheikh Mohammed Obaid Al Maktoum**
126 Br f 12/5 Dawn Approach (IRE)—Aljaaziah (Medaglia d'oro (USA)) **Mr Hamdan Al Maktoum**

MR ROGER VARIAN - Continued

127 B c 23/3 Kyllachy—Allegro Viva (USA) (Distant View (USA)) (45000) **Biddestone Racing Club**
128 B c 7/4 Distorted Humor (USA)—Almoutezah (USA) (Storm Cat (USA)) **Mr Hamdan Al Maktoum**
129 B f 26/4 Invincible Spirit (IRE)—Alwarga (USA) (Street Sense (USA)) **Sheikh Ahmed Al Maktoum**
130 ASCENSION, b c 18/1 Dark Angel (IRE)—
      Making Eyes (IRE) (Dansili) (135000) **Highclere Thoroughbred Racing - Benedict Allen**
131 BLAZING BEAU (IRE), b c 21/3 War Front (USA)—My Dark Rosaleen (Sadler's Wells) **Merry Fox Stud Ltd**
132 B f 11/2 Lope de Vega (IRE)—Burning Rules (Aussie Rules) (150000) **King Power Racing**
133 CABALETTA, ch gr f 31/3 Mastercraftsman (IRE)—Allegretto (Galileo (IRE)) **Cheveley Park Stud**
134 Ch c 9/4 Night of Thunder (IRE)—Cantal (Pivotal) (160000) **Mr Hamdan Al Maktoum**
135 CHARMING SPIRIT (IRE), b f 4/2 Invincible Spirit (IRE)—
      Willow View (USA) (Lemon Drop Kid (USA)) **Merry Fox Stud Ltd**
136 CINDY BEAR (IRE), b f 25/1 Kodiac—My Twinkle (IRE) (Sea The Stars (IRE)) **Cheveley Park Stud**
137 CLAN ROYALE, b c 14/4 Siyouni (FR)—
      Ascot Family (IRE) (Desert Style (IRE)) (200000) **Sheikh Mohammed Obaid Al Maktoum**
138 B f 7/3 Acclamation—Debutantin (Big Shuffle (USA)) (350000) **King Power Racing**
139 DESERT EMPEROR, b c 17/3 Camelot—
      Praia (GER) (Big Shuffle (USA)) (280000) **Sheikh Mohammed Obaid Al Maktoum**
140 B c 27/2 Gutaifan (IRE)—Dominatrix (Whipper (USA)) (95238) **Mr Hamdan Al Maktoum**
141 ELBEGEI, b f 6/2 Dark Angel (IRE)—Elik (IRE) (Dalakhani (IRE)) **Mr Nurlan Bizakov**
142 Gr c 23/3 Dubawi (IRE)—Elshaadin (Dalakhani (IRE)) **Mr Hamdan Al Maktoum**
143 ESPRIT ROSE (IRE), b f 23/3 Invincible Spirit (IRE)—
      Intense Pink (Pivotal) (200000) **Sheikh Mohammed Obaid Al Maktoum**
144 B c 1/2 Invincible Spirit (IRE)—Freezy (Dalakhani (IRE)) (150000) **Sheikh Ahmed Al Maktoum**
145 B c 2/3 Bated Breath—Golden Legacy (IRE) (Rossini (USA)) (160000) **Mr Hamdan Al Maktoum**
146 GOOD HUMOR, b c 22/4 Distorted Humor (USA)—Time On (Sadler's Wells (USA)) **Mr Robert Barnett**
147 B f 25/3 Dansili—Hadaatha (IRE) (Sea The Stars (IRE)) **Mr Hamdan Al Maktoum**
148 IKEBANA, b f 17/3 Pivotal—Sea The Bloom (Sea The Stars (IRE)) **Cheveley Park Stud**
149 B br f 8/3 Shamardal (USA)—Jiwen (CAN) (Singspiel (IRE)) **Mr Hamdan Al Maktoum**
150 Ch f 1/2 Pivotal—Khatiba (IRE) (Kheleyf (USA)) **Sheikh Ahmed Al Maktoum**
151 B c 21/3 Lope de Vega (IRE)—Lamps of Heaven (Invincible Spirit (IRE)) (325000) **Mr Hamdan Al Maktoum**
152 Ch c 2/4 Dubawi (IRE)—Lanansaak (IRE) (Zamindar (USA)) **Mr Hamdan Al Maktoum**
153 B c 10/4 Distorted Humor (USA)—Liffey Dancer (Sadler's Wells (USA)) (140000) **Merry Fox Stud Ltd**
154 LIGERA, b f 8/3 Showcasing—Lashyn (USA) (Mr Greeley (USA)) **Mr Nurlan Bizakov**
155 B f 29/3 Mastercraftsman (IRE)—Lisanor (Raven's Pass (USA)) (92709) **King Power Racing**
156 LORD CAMPARI (IRE), b c 20/3 Kingman—
      Blanche Dubawi (IRE) (Dubawi (IRE)) (350000) **Sheikh Mohammed Obaid Al Maktoum**
157 MAGNETISED, b c 25/3 Shamardal (USA)—
      Princess Nada (Baratheon) **Sheikh Mohammed Obaid Al Maktoum**
158 Ch c 30/4 Pivotal—Maid For Winning (Gone West (USA)) (160000) **Sheikh Ahmed Al Maktoum**
159 MILLVINA, b f 9/2 Dutch Art—Molly Brown (Rudimentary (USA)) (450000) **Cheveley Park Stud**
160 B c 16/3 Mukhadram—Min Banat Alreeh (IRE) (Oasis Dream) **Mr Hamdan Al Maktoum**
161 MOUNT MAYON (IRE), b c 18/4 Kodiac—Nisriyna (IRE) (Intikhab (USA)) **Cheveley Park Stud**
162 Ch f 5/4 Nathaniel (IRE)—Muhawalah (IRE) (Nayef (USA)) **Mr Hamdan Al Maktoum**
163 Ch f 6/2 Intello (GER)—Murahana (IRE) (Invincible Spirit (IRE)) **Mr Hamdan Al Maktoum**
164 B f 14/3 Dubawi (IRE)—Nahrain (Selkirk (USA)) **Sheikh Ahmed Al Maktoum**
165 NAIZAGAI, b c 12/3 Dark Angel (IRE)—Nazym (IRE) (Galileo (IRE)) **Mr Nurlan Bizakov**
166 Ch c 11/2 Hot Streak (IRE)—Never In (IRE) (Elusive City (USA)) (200000) **Sheikh Ahmed Al Maktoum**
167 Ch c 25/2 Siyouni (FR)—Pelerin (IRE) (Shamardal (USA)) (300000) **King Power Racing**
168 B c 10/3 Ivawood (IRE)—Perfect Blossom (One Cool Cat (USA)) (33712) **Varian Racing I**
169 PIERRE LAPIN (IRE), b c 22/1 Cappella Sansevero—
      Beatrix Potter (IRE) (Cadeaux Genereux) (140000) **Sheikh Mohammed Obaid Al Maktoum**
170 POLARIS BOUND, ch c 26/2 Intello (GER)—Starbound (IRE) (Captain Rio) (68000) **Cheveley Park Stud**
171 POSTILEO (IRE), b c 8/5 Galileo (IRE)—
      Posterity (IRE) (Indian Ridge) (500000) **Sheikh Mohammed Obaid Al Maktoum**
172 PROGRESSIVE, b f 13/3 Nathaniel (IRE)—Graduation (Lomitas) **Cheveley Park Stud**
173 B c 27/3 Farhh—Radhaadh (IRE) (Nayef (USA)) (72000) **Mr Hussain Lootah**
174 RAINFORD, ch c 23/2 Sea The Moon (GER)—Cushat Law (IRE) (Montjeu (IRE)) **Mr Nurlan Bizakov**
175 RASTAMA, b f 26/2 Le Havre (FR)—Raushan (IRE) (Dalakhani (IRE)) **Mr Nurlan Bizakov**
176 B f 17/2 Golden Horn—Rekdhat (IRE) (Shamardal (USA)) **Sheikh Ahmed Al Maktoum**
177 RETROSPECT (IRE), b c 10/3 Frankel—
      Looking Back (IRE) (Stravinsky (USA)) (850000) **Sheikh Mohammed Obaid Al Maktoum**
178 B f 1/2 Galileo (IRE)—Royal Delta (Empire Maker (USA)) **Mr Benjamin Leon**
179 Ch c 23/3 Night of Thunder (IRE)—
      Semayyel (IRE) (Green Desert (USA)) (70476) **Mr Jon Collins, Mr Chris Fahy & Mrs Heather Moorhead**
180 SEMSER, b c 11/3 Siyouni (FR)—Serres (IRE) (Daylami (IRE)) **Mr Nurlan Bizakov**

MR ROGER VARIAN - Continued

81 **SHANDOZ**, b c 15/3 Golden Horn—Shabyt (Sadler's Wells (USA)) **Mr Nurlan Bizakov**
82 B c 28/1 Free Eagle (IRE)—Shauna's Princess (IRE) (Soviet Star (USA)) (50000) **Sheikh Ahmed Al Maktoum**
83 B f 6/3 Muhaarar—Shimah (USA) (Storm Cat (USA)) **Mr Hamdan Al Maktoum**
84 B f 15/2 Golden Horn—Shimmering Surf (IRE) (Danehill Dancer (IRE)) **Mr Peter Winkworth**
85 **SOLAR SCREEN (IRE)**, gr c 22/4 Golden Horn—
                     Screen Star (IRE) (Tobougg (IRE)) (210000) **Sheikh Mohammed Obaid Al Maktoum**
86 **SPREADSHEET (IRE)**, b c 23/4 Exceed And Excel (AUS)—
                     Mundana (IRE) (King's Best (USA)) **Sheikh Mohammed Obaid Al Maktoum**
87 **STYLISTIQUE**, b f 27/2 Dansili—Sleek (Oasis Dream) **Miss Yvonne Jacques**
88 **SUBELLA (IRE)**, b f 7/5 Teofilo (IRE)—
                     Suba (USA) (Seeking The Gold (USA)) **Sheikh Mohammed Obaid Al Maktoum**
89 **SWAN RIVER (IRE)**, b f 2/3 Australia—Theann (Rock of Gibraltar (IRE)) (176990) **Cheveley Park Stud**
90 B c 11/2 Nathaniel (IRE)—Ta Ammol (Halling (USA)) **Sheikh Ahmed Al Maktoum**
91 **TALAP**, b c 13/3 Kingman—Tamarind (IRE) (Sadler's Wells (USA)) **Mr Nurlan Bizakov**
92 B f 13/3 New Approach (IRE)—Tantshi (IRE) (Invincible Spirit (IRE)) **Sheikh Ahmed Al Maktoum**
93 B f 30/4 Make Believe—Topka (FR) (Kahyasi) (55000) **North Hills Co. Ltd**
94 **TROLL PENINSULA (USA)**, b c 22/3 Karakontie (JPN)—Perfect Step (IRE) (Iffraaj) **Niarchos Family**
95 **TURKESTAN**, b c 8/4 New Approach (IRE)—Totally Devoted (USA) (Seeking The Gold (USA)) **Mr Nurlan Bizakov**
96 B c 22/5 Frankel—Vodka (JPN) (Tanino Gimlet (JPN)) **Mr Yuzo Tanimizu**
97 B c 26/3 Free Eagle (IRE)—Weekend Lady (IRE) (Bahamian Bounty) (50568) **Varian Racing I**
98 **WINTER THORN (IRE)**, gr c 28/3 Muhaarar—
                     Rose of Summer (USA) (El Prado (IRE)) (375000) **Sheikh Mohammed Obaid Al Maktoum**
99 **ZEEBAND (IRE)**, b c 15/4 Sea The Stars (IRE)—
                     Zeeba (IRE) (Barathea (IRE)) **Sheikh Mohammed Obaid Al Maktoum**
200 **ZEGALOO (IRE)**, b c 5/4 Zoffany (IRE)—Mzyoon (IRE) (Galileo (IRE)) **Mr Hussain Lootah**

Other Owners: K. M. Al-Mudhaf, Mohammed Jasem Al-Qatami, Mr Imad Al-Sagar, Mr K. Allen, Mr J. Barnett, Mrs A. C. Black, Mrs Gill Bostwick, Mr Tim Bostwick, Mr J. A. Collins, Mr Chris Fahy, Mrs Sheila Grassick, Highclere Thoroughbred Racing Ltd, Mr Saleh Al Homaizi, Mr Stuart J. Marchant, Mr R. P. Marchant, Mr Gerald Moss, Mr S. Roden, Mr J. Shack, Mrs H. Varian.

Assistant Trainer: John O'Donoghue

Jockey (flat): Andrea Atzeni, David Egan, Jack Mitchell.

---

554 **MR ED VAUGHAN, Newmarket**
Postal: Machell Place Cottage, Old Station Road, Newmarket, Suffolk, CB8 8DW
Contacts: PHONE (01638) 667411 FAX (01638) 667452 MOBILE (07799) 144901
E-MAIL ed@efvaughan.com WEBSITE www.efvaughan.com

1 **BLAZED (IRE)**, 5, gr g Dark Angel (IRE)—Sudden Blaze (IRE)
2 **CHOCO BOX**, 4, b f Harbour Watch (IRE)—Bible Box (IRE)
3 **DANCING BRAVE BEAR (USA)**, 4, b f Street Cry (IRE)—Baghdaria (USA)
4 **DESERT WIND (IRE)**, 4, b c Worthadd (IRE)—Matula (IRE)
5 **NASEE**, 4, b c Intello (GER)—Mischief Making (USA)
6 **TRAILBOSS (IRE)**, 4, b g High Chaparral (IRE)—Seeking Solace

THREE-YEAR-OLDS

7 **AL BATTAR (IRE)**, b c Dubawi (IRE)—Giofra
8 **ARDIENTE**, b f Australia—Hoyam
9 **ATTORNEY GENERAL**, b g Dream Ahead (USA)—Avodale (IRE)
10 **DAME MALLIOT**, b f Champs Elysees—Stars In Your Eyes
11 **DEBONAIR DON JUAN (IRE)**, b c Lope de Vega (IRE)—Dolled Up (IRE)
12 **DUBAI DOMINION**, b c Pivotal—Hoodna (IRE)
13 **LOVE EXPLODES**, b f Champs Elysees—Acquainted
14 **MAGIC J (USA)**, ch c Scat Daddy (USA)—Miss Lamour (USA)
15 **MAGICAL MOVEMENT**, b c Alpha (USA)—Palestrina (USA)
16 **ROCK THE CRADLE (IRE)**, ch g Ruler of The World (IRE)—Independent Girl (IRE)
17 **THE DANCING POET**, ch c Poet's Voice—Caldy Dancer (IRE)

TWO-YEAR-OLDS

18 B c 1/2 Bated Breath—Al Joudha (FR) (Green Desert (USA))
19 **BURNISTON ROCKS**, ch c 28/2 Monsieur Bond (IRE)—Miss Fridaythorpe (Pastoral Pursuits)
20 Ch c 16/4 Dragon Pulse (IRE)—Contenance (IRE) (Dansant) (25000)

MR ED VAUGHAN - Continued

21 B f 6/3 Gleneagles (IRE)—Rive Gauche (Fastnet Rock (AUS)) (55000)
22 **SCARBOROUGH CASTLE**, b c 22/5 Fastnet Rock (AUS)—Charlotte O Fraise (IRE) (Beat Hollow) (10000)
23 B f 18/4 Hallowed Crown (AUS)—Snowdrops (Gulch (USA)) (30000)
24 **WHITBY HARBOUR**, b c 19/4 No Nay Never (USA)—Secrets Away (IRE) (Refuse To Bend (IRE)) (15000)

Owners: Sheikh Juma Dalmook Al Maktoum, Sheikh Hamed Dalmook Al Maktoum, Mr Saeed Bin Mohammed Al Qassim, Ballymore Sterling Syndicate, Bloomsbury Stud, Mr K A Dasmal, Mr M J C Hawkes, Mr E W Lee, Mr P A Moroney, Mr C Murfitt, Mr A E Oppenheimer, Phoenix Thoroughbred Limited, Mr A M Pickering, Mr M Rashid, Mr S Rashid, Mr S Russell, Mr G Seavall-Green, Mr G Sharp, Mr J Sims, Mr M Sinclair, Mr J Singh, Mr Saeed Suhail, Mr G Van Ameyden, Mr E Ware

---

555 | MR TIM VAUGHAN, Cowbridge
Postal: **Pant Wilkin Stables, Aberthin, Cowbridge, CF71 7GX**
Contacts: **PHONE** (01446) 771626 **FAX** (01446) 774371 **MOBILE** (07841) 800081
E-MAIL tim@timvaughanracing.com **WEBSITE** www.timvaughanracing.com

1 **ADHERENCE**, 6, b g Sir Percy—Straight Laced **T. E. Vaughan**
2 **AKKAPENKO (FR)**, 5, b g Archipenko (USA)—Akka **The Bill & Ben Partnership**
3 **ALLTIMEGOLD (IRE)**, 6, b g Gold Well—Carryonharriet **Mrs B. N. Ead**
4 **AN LAOCH (IRE)**, 7, b g Flemensfirth (USA)—Petite Ballerina **Mr O. S. Harris**
5 4, B g Scorpion (IRE)—April Thistle **R. M. Kirkland**
6 **BARRIER REEF (IRE)**, 4, b g Galileo (IRE)—Honour Bright (IRE) **T. E. Vaughan**
7 **BASSARABAD (FR)**, 8, b g Astarabad (USA)—Grivette (FR) **Pearn's Pharmacies Ltd**
8 **BELIZE**, 8, b g Rail Link—Costa Rica (IRE) **Mr D. R. Passant**
9 **BELLS OF AILSWORTH (IRE)**, 9, b g Kayf Tara—Volverta (FR) **Mr S. Grys & Mr M. O'Boyle**
10 **BELLS OF WANSFORD (IRE)**, 5, b g Multiplex—Et Voila **Mr S. Grys & Mr M. O'Boyle**
11 **BLEU ET NOIR**, 8, b g Enrique—Gastina (FR) **The Rydon Pynes Partnership**
12 **BOBMAHLEY (IRE)**, 4, b g Mahler—Supreme Von Pres (IRE) **Mrs B. N. Ead**
13 **BOETHIUS**, 6, b g Manduro (GER)—Perfect Note **David & Susan Luke**
14 **BOLTON BOY (IRE)**, 5, b g Arcadio (GER)—Peggy Maddock (IRE) **JRFB Ltd**
15 **BRIAC (FR)**, 8, b g Kapgarde (FR)—Jarwin Do (FR) **Mr O. S. Harris**
16 **C'EST DU GATEAU (FR)**, 7, b g Laveron—Programmee (FR) **Pearn's Pharmacies Ltd**
17 **CALARULES**, 6, gr g Aussie Rules (USA)—Ailincala (IRE) **Oceans Racing**
18 **CANTON PRINCE (IRE)**, 8, b g Shantou (USA)—Hasainm (IRE) **Tertia Racing**
19 **CAP ST VINCENT (FR)**, 6, b g Muhtathir—Criquetot (FR) **Mr B Jones & Son**
20 **CAPE HIDEAWAY**, 7, b g Mount Nelson—Amiata **Kings Head Duffield Racing Partnership**
21 **CAPPIELOW PARK**, 10, b g Exceed And Excel (AUS)—Barakat **Mr O. S. Harris**
22 **CHAMPAGNE CHASER**, 9, b g Tobougg (IRE)—Champagne Lil **Mrs M. A. O'Sullivan**
23 **CHAMPIONS CLUB (IRE)**, 5, b g Jeremy (USA)—Mrs Masters (IRE) **Coral Champions Club**
24 **CHIMES OF DYLAN (IRE)**, 6, b g Court Cave (IRE)—What A Princess (IRE) **Oceans Racing**
25 **CHOZEN (IRE)**, 7, b g Well Chosen—Kneeland Lass (IRE) **Pearn's Pharmacies Ltd**
26 **CLONDAW ACE (IRE)**, 6, b g Flemensfirth (USA)—Peace Time Beauty (IRE) **Paul & Louise Bowtell**
27 **CONCEALED AMBITION (IRE)**, 7, br g Stowaway—Clairefontaine **The Pant Wilkin Partnership**
28 **COPPER GONE WEST (IRE)**, 6, b m Westerner—Copper Dusht (IRE) **Paul & Louise Bowtell**
29 **DADSINLUCK**, 6, b g Presenting—Gemini Lucy (IRE) **Paul & Louise Bowtell**
30 **DADSINTROUBLE (IRE)**, 9, b g Presenting—Gemini Lucy (IRE) **Mr J. P. M. Bowtell**
31 **DANBORU (IRE)**, 8, b g Brian Boru—Dandouce
32 **DE FORGOTTEN ONE**, 5, b g Malinas (GER)—As Was **Mr D. W. Fox**
33 **DEBECE**, 8, b g Kayf Tara—Dalamine **R. M. Kirkland**
34 **DOVILS DATE**, 10, gr g Clodovil (IRE)—Lucky Date (IRE) **Itsfuninit**
35 **ERIC THE THIRD (IRE)**, 10, b g Mountain High (IRE)—Commanche Princess (IRE) **T. E. Vaughan**
36 4, B g Mahler—Escrea (IRE) **R. M. Kirkland**
37 **EVA'S OSKAR (IRE)**, 5, gr g Shirocco (GER)—Sardagna (FR) **Mrs Sally & Richard Prince**
38 **FORT DENISON**, 5, b g Galileo (IRE)—Honour Bright (IRE) **T. E. Vaughan**
39 **GAELIC POET (IRE)**, 5, b g Yeats (IRE)—Hasainm (IRE) **G & L Handley & M & C Hardcastle**
40 **GLIMPSE OF GOLD**, 8, b g Passing Glance—Tizzy Blue (IRE) **The Craftsmen**
41 **HAZM (IRE)**, 4, br g Shamardal (USA)—Hikari (IRE) **Mr P. A. Syson**
42 **IUSETALUVHERONCE (IRE)**, 7, b g Golan (IRE)—Mollys Present (IRE) **T. E. Vaughan**
43 **JAUNTY FLYER**, 7, b g Sulamani (IRE)—Jaunty June **Mr D. W. Fox**
44 **JEFFERSON DAVIS (IRE)**, 6, b g Duke of Marmalade (IRE)—Samorra (IRE) **Syson & Vaughan**
45 **JEMBUG DRUMMER (IRE)**, 5, b g Jeremy (USA)—Drumbug (IRE) **Paul & Louise Bowtell**
46 **JOSEPH HOBSON (IRE)**, 4, b g Dubawi (IRE)—Profound Beauty (IRE) **The Wheatsheafs**
47 **KENMARE RIVER**, 4, gr g Kendargent (FR)—Isabella Glyn (IRE) **The Select Racing Club Limited**

MR TIM VAUGHAN - Continued

48 **KOVERA (FR)**, 7, b g Antarctique (IRE)—Kesakao (FR) **Oceans Racing**
49 **LANDSMAN (IRE)**, 6, b g Canford Cliffs (IRE)—Mowaadah (IRE) **T. E. Vaughan**
50 **LAUBERHORN ROCKET (GER)**, 4, b g Maxios—La Hermana **T. E. Vaughan**
51 **LAUGHARNE**, 8, b g Authorized (IRE)—Corsican Sunset (USA) **Oceans Racing**
52 **LE MILOS**, 4, b g Shirocco (GER)—Banjaxed Girl **Bovian Racing**
53 **LEN BRENNAN (IRE)**, 6, b g Westerner—Letthedancebegin (IRE) **The Oxymorons**
54 **LIVE FOR TODAY (IRE)**, 8, b g Afflora (IRE)—Uppermost **Phillips & Codell**
55 **LOOKSNOWTLIKEBRIAN (IRE)**, 8, b g Brian Boru—Sheebadiva (IRE) **SC Botham & RG Botham**
56 **MARONETTE**, 6, b m Milan—Wyldello **Pearn's Pharmacies Ltd**
57 **MASTER DANCER**, 8, gr g Mastercraftsman (IRE)—Isabella Glyn (IRE) **select-racing-club.co.uk & Mr C Davies**
58 **MIDNIGHT QUEEN**, 9, b m Rainbow High—Questionit **Mr B Jones & Son**
59 **MODERN WARFAIR (IRE)**, 5, b g Well Chosen—Brooklyn Brook (IRE) **Brian Ead & Martin Moore**
60 **MONSIEUR ARKADIN (FR)**, 8, b g Dream Well (FR)—Quenta des Bordes (FR) **Passant & Butt**
61 **MRSROBIN (IRE)**, 9, b m Robin des Pres (FR)—Regents Dancer (IRE) **Mr M. J. D. Matthews**
62 **NATHANS PRIDE (IRE)**, 11, ch g Definite Article—Tricias Pride (IRE) **Oceans Racing**
63 **NORWEGIAN WOODS (IRE)**, 6, b g Arcadio (GER)—Water Ore (IRE) **S J Kiss & the Lucky Strats**
64 **ONE LEADER (IRE)**, 8, b g Oscar (IRE)—Be My Leader (IRE) **Tertia Racing**
65 **ORIENTAL CROSS (IRE)**, 6, b m Cape Cross (IRE)—Orion Girl (GER) **Mr J Durston & Mr N Harris**
66 **OSKAR'S EVA (IRE)**, 9, gr m Black Sam Bellamy (IRE)—Sardagna (FR) **Mrs Sally & Richard Prince**
67 **PANIS ANGELICUS (FR)**, 10, b g Panis (USA)—Pyu (GER) **Oceans Racing**
68 **PLENEY**, 5, b g Martaline—Knock Down (IRE) **Pearn's Pharmacies Ltd**
69 **POINT OF PRINCIPLE (IRE)**, 6, b g Rip Van Winkle (IRE)—L'ancresse (IRE) **Oceans Racing**
70 **PRINCE CHARMIN' (IRE)**, 6, b g High Chaparral (IRE)—Dream Club **select-racing-club.co.uk & Mr C Davies**
71 **ROYALE DJANGO (IRE)**, 10, b g Kayf Tara—Royale Boja (FR) **Mr J Durston & Mr N Harris**
72 **RUACANA**, 10, b g Cape Cross (IRE)—Farrfesheena (USA) **The 600 Club**
73 4, B g Fame And Glory—Ryehill Lady (IRE) **R. M. Kirkland**
74 **SAD EYED DYLAN**, 6, br g Multiplex—Congressional (IRE) **S. Clarke & and the Late Mr M. S. Clarke**
75 **SCRUTINISE**, 7, b g Intense Focus (USA)—Tetravella (IRE) **Paul & Louise Bowtell**
76 **SERGIO (IRE)**, 7, b g Flemensfirth (USA)—Aventia (IRE) **Mr J. P. M. Bowtell**
77 **SHAMAN DU BERLAIS (FR)**, 6, b g Saint des Saints (FR)—Shinca (FR) **Mrs C. M. Marles**
78 **SPECTATOR**, 8, b g Passing Glance—Averami **Pearn's Pharmacies Ltd**
79 **STAUNTON**, 8, b m Kayf Tara—Aranga (IRE) **T. E. Vaughan**
80 4, B g Robin des Champs (FR)—Sweet Poli (IRE) **R. M. Kirkland**
81 **TAKE EM OUT (IRE)**, 7, b g Amadeus Wolf—Toorah Laura La (USA) **The Bill & Ben Partnership**
82 **TANACANDO (FR)**, 7, b g Ballingarry (IRE)—Tamaziya (IRE) **Flat Out Shinton Racing**
83 **TANIT RIVER (IRE)**, 9, br g Indian River (FR)—Tanit Lady (IRE) **Brian Ead & Martin Moore**
84 **TARA MAC**, 10, b m Kayf Tara—Macklette (IRE) **Mr B Jones & Son**
85 **THELIGNY (FR)**, 8, gr g Martaline—Romilly (FR) **Pearn's Pharmacies Ltd**
86 **THIS LOVELY LADY (IRE)**, 6, b m Getaway (GER)—
    Princesse Rooney (FR) **Kings Head Duffield Racing Partnership**
87 **TIGHT CALL (IRE)**, 5, ch g Mahler—Victory Anthem **ER Newnham & JD Shinton**
88 **TIMELY GIFT (IRE)**, 6, b g Presenting—Give It Time **Carl, JJ, Chris, Mike, John & Hugh**
89 **TIPPINGITUPTONANCY (IRE)**, 5, ch m Stowaway—Dyrick Daybreak (IRE) **Paul & Louise Bowtell**
90 **TRIXSTER (IRE)**, 6, b g Beneficial—Our Trick (IRE) **The Pant Wilkin Partnership**
91 **WAX AND WANE**, 4, br g Maxios—Moonavvara (IRE) **ER Newnham & JD Shinton**
92 **WILLIAM B (IRE)**, 8, b br g Yeats (IRE)—Gallic Approach (IRE) **Optimumracing.Co.Uk & Alex Percy**
93 **WITHOUTDEFAVOURITE (IRE)**, 11, b g Oscar (IRE)—Camden Confusion (IRE) **Kendari Racing**

Other Owners: Mr P. G. Amos, Mr R. G. Botham, S. C. Botham, Mr A. Bott, Mrs L. Bowtell, Mr T. G. Brooks, Mr G. W. T. Butt, S. J. Clare, Exors of the Late Mr M. S. Clarke, Mr S. A. Clarke, Mr J. Codell, Mr J. L. Coombs, Mr C. Davies, Mr H. G. Doubtfire, Mr J. Durston, Mr B. Ead, Mr P. C. Etty, Mr S. Grys, Mr G. Handley, Mr T. Hanrahan, Mr M. J. Hardcastle, Mr N. Harris, Mr D. L. Hill, Mrs K. E. Hollingworth, Mr B. Jagger, Mr D. M. Jenkins, Mr W. Jones, Mr B. M. Jones, Mr T. E. Kerfoot, Mr S. J. Kiss, Mrs D. J. Lowrie, A. D. Lowrie, The Lucky Strats, Mr D. A. Luke, Mrs S. Luke, Dr C. H. Mason, Mr M. E. Moore, Mr J. M. Mordecai, Mr E. R. Newnham, Mr M. O'Boyle, Mr K. A. Percy, Miss D. E. Pettle, Mr J. T. Phillips, Mr D. Phillips, Mr R. G. Price, R. J. Prince, Mrs S. Prince, Mr N. S. C. Proctor, A. Robinson, Mr J. D. Shinton, Mr D. A. Shinton, Mr A. Smallman, Mr A. Spencer, Mr M. A. Stratford, Mr P. J. Sumner, Mr N. D. Whitham, Mrs C. S. Wilson, optimumracing.co.uk.

Assistant Trainer: Robbie Llewelyn

Jockey (flat): David Probert. **Jockey (NH):** Richard Johnson, Alan Johns. **Conditional:** Charlie Price.
Amateur: Mr Morgan Winstone.

556 MR CHRISTIAN VON DER RECKE, Weilerswist

Postal: **Rennstall Recke GmbH, Hovener Hof 1, D-53919, Weilerswist, Germany**
Contacts: **PHONE (0049) 2254 84 53 14 FAX (0049) 2254 845315 MOBILE (0049) 171 542 50 50**
E-MAIL recke@t-online.de WEBSITE www.rennstall-recke.de

1 ABBAFRIDA (IRE), 4, b f Most Improved (IRE)—Abbasharjah (GER) **M-B-A Racing**
2 ALLONGE (IRE), 4, ch f Dansant—Paix Royale **BMK Racing**
3 BASILLUS, 4, ch c Kendargent (FR)—Bambara **Cabkhat s.r.o.**
4 BENTELE (IRE), 4, b f Rock of Gibraltar (IRE)—Divisme (USA) **Rennstall Recke GmbH**
5 CADMIUM, 8, b m Major Cadeaux—Miss Mirasol **Stall Walcheren**
6 CUMBRIANO (GER), 6, b h Wiener Walzer (GER)—Carrie Anne **Dieter Brand**
7 DAULYS ANTHEM (IRE), 11, br g Royal Anthem (USA)—Over Dubai **Bernd Robert Gossens**
8 DICKTATION, 4, b g Dick Turpin (IRE)—Curly Come Home **Rennstall Recke**
9 DIVISIONIST, 6, b h Oasis Dream—Exemplify **von Hodenberg Marquardt**
10 DREAM OF FUTURE (IRE), 4, b c Dream Ahead (USA)—Deportment **Stall Schildhorst**
11 FISHERMAN'S BLUES (IRE), 6, b g Zebedee—Southern Barfly (USA) **Stall esto87**
12 FIT FOR THE JOB (IRE), 7, b g Lawman (FR)—Spesialta **Stall Chevalex**
13 FLAMINGO LOVE (GER), 4, b f Areion (GER)—Flamingo Island (GER) **Stall Nizza**
14 FOUR ON EIGHT, 6, gr g Lawman (FR)—Pocket Watch **Stall Wollin**
15 FUMAROLE, 4, b g Maxios—Solar Midnight (USA) **Stall Wollin**
16 GET READY FREDDY, 9, b g Sixties Icon—Summer Shades **Rennstall Recke**
17 GOOD GRACE (GER), 4, b f Reliable Man—Good Hope (GER) **Gestut Romerhof**
18 HAKAM (USA), 7, b br g War Front (USA)—Lauren Byrd (USA) **A. Krauliger**
19 INTERIOR MINISTER, 9, b g Nayef (USA)—Sister Maria (USA) **Sonja Darostewski**
20 ISANDRO (FR), 7, b h Muhtathir—Isantha (GER) **B.-R. Gossens**
21 KOLONEL KIRKUP, 9, b g Dr Fong (USA)—Strawberry Lolly **Stall Rettstadt**
22 LIPS LEGEND (IRE), 4, b g Azamour (IRE)—Lone Ascent (IRE) **Stall Lintec**
23 MARRACASH (GER), 4, gr c Reliable Man—Magic Love (GER) **M-B-A Racing**
24 PALMETTO BAY, 4, b f Champs Elysees—Palmette **Stall Karlshorst**
25 PARADISE LAKE (IRE), 5, b g Siyouni (FR)—Kalandara (IRE) **Rennstall Recke**
26 PEARL DRAGON (FR), 8, b g Nicobar—La Marlia (FR) **Rennstall Recke**
27 POMME DE TERRE (IRE), 7, ch g Sakhee's Secret—Suzie Quw **Rennstall Recke**
28 ROSINANTE (IRE), 4, b f Maxios—Russian Samba (IRE) **Gestut IDEE GmbH & Co. KG**
29 RUSSIAN FLAMENCO (GER), 6, b h Tertullian (USA)—Russian Samba (IRE) **Gestut IDEE GmbH & Co. KG**
30 SCALERO (USA), 4, b g Lemon Drop Kid (USA)—Scolara (USA) **E.-A. Wahler**
31 SEPTIMER (IRE), 4, br g Maxios—Freedonia **Frau U. u.H. Alck**
32 SHOJA (GER), 6, ch m Dylan Thomas (IRE)—Serenata (GER) **Stall Burg Muggenhausen**
33 SHRUBLAND, 6, b g High Chaparral (IRE)—Ratukidul (FR) **St. Ahrens u.a.**
34 THEODOSIA (IRE), 5, b h Teofilo (IRE)—Tiz The Whiz (USA) **M-B-A Racing**
35 TOGETHERNESS (IRE), 6, b g Pour Moi (IRE)—Madeira Mist (IRE) **Rennstall Recke**

THREE-YEAR-OLDS

36 ALFONSO (GER), b c Maxios—Artemisia (IRE) **Stall Nizza**
37 ALHAMMER (GER), ch g Martillo (GER)—All I Want **E.-A. Wahler**
38 B f Makfi—Bambara **Cabkhat s.r.o.**
39 CANTERBURY (GER), b c Mamool—Carrie Anne **Dieter Brand**
40 CHEZ HANS (GER), b c Mamool—Chandos Rose (IRE) **D A Brand**
41 DR SMOLDER (IRE), b c Bungle Inthejungle—Chimay **M. E. Veeck**
42 DYNAMITE GOLD (GER), b f Lord of England (GER)—Dynamite Cat (GER) **Rennstall Saarbrucken e.V.**
43 JASON, b c Lawman (FR)—Jardina (GER) **Stall Nizza**
44 RICHELIEU (GER), b c Lilbourne Lad (IRE)—Right Key (IRE) **Stall Nizza**
45 Br g Most Improved (IRE)—Sacre Fleur (GER) **Stall Sternental**
46 SO KNIGHTY (GER), b f So You Think (NZ)—Knightsbridge (BRZ) **Cabkhat s.r.o.**

TWO-YEAR-OLDS

47 DYNAMITE STAR (GER), b gr f 25/2 Jukebox Jury (IRE)—
Dynamite Cat (GER) (One Cool Cat (USA)) **Stall Schmeer**
48 JESSICA (GER), b f 28/4 Nutan (IRE)—Jardina (GER) (Shirocco (GER)) **Stall Nizza**
49 JULIETTE (GER), ch f 29/3 Amarillo (GER)—Juvena (GER) (Platini (GER)) **Stall Nizza**
50 SERGEANT (GER), b c 14/4 Nutan (IRE)—Stella Marina (IRE) (Dylan Thomas (IRE)) **Stall Nizza**
51 WINSOME BELLE (GER), b f 3/2 Thewayyouare (USA)—Wild Blossom (GER) (Areion (GER)) **M-B-A Racing**

Other Owners: Mr L. A. Bellman, Mr P. R. Chamings, Mr M. Dixon, Mr C. Dixon, T. F. Harris, Mrs E. A. Harris, Mr P. Jenkins, Mr K. Place, Mr M. Sinclair, Mr M. J. Taylor, Mr R. M. Whitaker.

Assistant Trainer: Anika Seiler

MR CHRISTIAN VON DER RECKE - Continued

Jockey (flat): Liubov Grigorieva. **Jockey (NH):** Sonja Daroszewski, Paul Johnson. **Conditional:** Amin Hajbabay.
Apprentice: Saado Alsyd. **Amateur:** Miss Laura Giesgen.

---

557 **MRS LUCY WADHAM, Newmarket**
Postal: **The Trainer's House, Moulton Paddocks, Newmarket, Suffolk, CB8 7PJ**
Contacts: **PHONE (01638) 662411 MOBILE (07980) 545776**
E-MAIL lucy@wadhamracing.com WEBSITE www.lucywadhamracing.co.uk

1 ADMIRAL BARRATRY (FR), 6, b g Soldier of Fortune (IRE)—Haskilclara (FR) **Forster, Pepper & Summers**
2 ANNA JAMMEELA, 4, b f Big Bad Bob (IRE)—All Annalena (IRE) **Mr & Mrs A. E. Pakenham**
3 4, B g Jeremy (USA)—Ballynarry (IRE) **Mr J. D. Abell**
4 CONNIE WILDE (IRE), 4, b f Oscar (IRE)—Mandys Native (IRE) **The Sanguiners**
5 DANCE TO PARIS, 4, b f Champs Elysees—Riabouchinska **The Calculated Speculators**
6 EASTER GOLD (FR), 5, b m Kapgarde (FR)—Une Dame d'or (FR) **Mr J. Summers**
7 ECLAIR DE GUYE (FR), 5, gr g Lord du Sud (FR)—
Jouvence de Guye (FR) **E R Wakelin, R W Hayward & J J W Wadham**
8 GALMARLEY, 4, b f Sir Percy—Crystal Gal (IRE) **Chasemore Farm LLP**
9 GREGARIOUS (IRE), 6, gr g Big Bad Bob (IRE)—Sense of Greeting (IRE) **Mr J. Summers**
10 HARBOUR BREEZE (IRE), 4, b c Le Havre (IRE)—Retiens La Nuit (USA) **Mr B. J. Painter**
11 ICONIC SKY, 6, gr m Sixties Icon—Kentucky Sky **Mr Tim Wood**
12 LE REVE (IRE), 11, br g Milan—Open Cry (IRE) **P. H. Betts**
13 MOVIE LEGEND, 9, b g Midnight Legend—Cyd Charisse **The Movie Legend Partnership**
14 MR LOVE (IRE), 7, b g Winged Love (IRE)—Bonny Rathlin (IRE) **Ms E. L. Banks**
15 MYSTIC SKY, 8, b m Midnight Legend—Kentucky Sky **Mr T. R. Wood**
16 NORTHERN PRINCESS, 5, b m Authorized (IRE)—Julatten (IRE) **Mr J. D. Abell**
17 PEACEFUL VALLEY (FR), 5, b m No Risk At All (FR)—
Si Parfaite (FR) **Suiter Developments Ltd & JJW Wadham**
18 POTTERS HEDGER, 7, b g Midnight Legend—Loose Morals (IRE) **Mrs J. May**
19 POTTERS LADY JANE, 7, b m Sir Percy—Arabescato (UAE) **Mrs J. May**
20 POTTERS MIDNIGHT, 9, b m Midnight Legend—Craughwell Suas (IRE) **Mrs J. May**
21 REGARDING RUTH (IRE), 5, b m Flemensfirth (USA)—
May's June (IRE) **Suiter Developments Ltd & JJW Wadham**
22 4, B f Getaway (GER)—Second Best (IRE) **J. J. W. Wadham**
23 SHAMBRA (IRE), 5, b m Clodovil (IRE)—Shambodia (IRE) **Pali Pali Syndicate**
24 SHANROE SANTOS (IRE), 10, b g Definite Article—Jane Hall (IRE) **Mr J. Summers**
25 SHANTUNG (IRE), 6, ch m Shantou (USA)—Sarah's Cottage (IRE) **P A Philipps & Mrs G J Redman**
26 SHOCK TACTICS, 5, b g Schiaparelli (GER)—Fashionable Gal (IRE) **Dr & Mrs Clive Layton**
27 SOMEKINDOFSTAR (IRE), 6, ch g Getaway (GER)—Katty Barry (IRE) **G. Pascoe & S. Brewer**
28 SORBET, 4, b f Passing Glance—Fireburst **Mrs P. J. Toye**
29 TENSION TIME (IRE), 5, b g Dubai Destination (USA)—Leader's Hall (IRE) **Suiter Developments Limited**
30 THE QUIET DON (IRE), 4, b g Sholokhov (IRE)—Ailincala (IRE) **Mr J. Summers**
31 THE WHITE MOUSE (IRE), 5, br m Stowaway—Maxwells Demon **Ms E. L. Banks**
32 TRINCOMALEE, 6, b g Malinas (GER)—Royal Tango **Hot to Trot Jumping & Mrs E Gordon Lennox**
33 STING (IRE), 4, br g Scorpion (IRE)—Undecided Hall (IRE) **The Cyclones**

THREE-YEAR-OLDS

34 SCARLET SILK, ch f Sir Percy—Tussah **The FOPS**
35 SKY PATROL, b g Camacho—Patroller (USA) **Mr T. R. Wood**
36 THEBAN AIR, b f Bated Breath—Temple of Thebes (IRE) **Mr & Mrs A. E. Pakenham**
37 WATERFALL, b f Mukhadram—Jump Ship **M. H. Dixon**

TWO-YEAR-OLDS

38 B f 18/2 Camelot—Ape Attack (Nayef (USA)) **Chasemore Farm LLP**
39 B f 13/3 Sir Percy—Atwix (Sakhee (USA)) **The Calculated Speculators**
40 B f 11/2 Youmzain (IRE)—Bermondsey Girl (Bertolini) (1142) **Mr & Mrs A. E. Pakenham**
41 B c 10/3 Sir Percy—Cartoon (Danehill Dancer (IRE)) (45000) **Mr & Mrs A. E. Pakenham**
42 B f 12/3 Make Believe—Famusa (Medicean) (571) **Mr & Mrs A. E. Pakenham**

Other Owners: The A. T. Partnership, Mrs J. E. Black, A. W. Black, Mrs E. C. Gordon Lennox, Mr S. J. High, D. J. Hing, Mr R. S. Hoskins, Hot To Trot Jumping, Miss N. J. Langstaff, Dr C. A. Layton, Mrs H. M. Layton, Mr K. Little, Mr A. E. Pakenham, Mrs Victoria Pakenham, Mr Martin Pendlebury, Exors of the Late Mr P. A. Philipps, Mrs G. J. Redman, Suiter Developments Limited, Mrs L. A. M. Wadham, J. J. W. Wadham, Mr E. R. Wakelin.

Jockey (NH): Leighton Aspell, Maxime Tissier.

558 **MISS TRACY WAGGOTT, Spennymoor**
Postal: **Awakening Stables, Merrington Road, Spennymoor, County Durham, DL16 7HD**
Contacts: PHONE **(01388) 819012** MOBILE **(07979) 434498**
E-MAIL **tracywaggott@hotmail.com**

1 BILLY WEDGE, 4, b g Arabian Gleam—Misu Billy **Mr D. Tate**
2 DEEDS NOT WORDS (IRE), 8, b g Royal Applause—Wars (IRE) **Mr D. Tate**
3 HADLEY, 6, b g Royal Applause—Brush Strokes **Mr D. Tate**
4 HENLEY, 7, b g Royal Applause—Making Waves (IRE) **Mr D. Tate**
5 LAST GLANCE (IRE), 4, b g Shamardal (USA)—Linda Radlett (USA) **Mr D. Tate**
6 LITTLE KINGDOM (IRE), 5, b m Royal Applause—Hadba (IRE) **Miss T. Waggott**
7 PAPARAZZI, 4, b g Iffraaj—Columella **Gordon Allan Elsa Crankshaw**
8 PATHWAY TO FREEDOM, 5, b g Cape Cross (IRE)—Emancipation **David Tate & Tracy Waggott**
9 PROCEEDING, 4, b g Acclamation—Map of Heaven **Mr D. Tate**
10 RASELASAD (IRE), 5, b g Acclamation—Wajaha (IRE) **Mr D. Tate**
11 SPECIAL YOU, 5, b m Arabian Gleam—Mighty Flyer (IRE) **Mr D. Tate**
12 SUPREME POWER (IRE), 5, b g Power—Supreme Spirit (IRE) **Mr D. Tate**
13 WINDFORPOWER (IRE), 9, b g Red Clubs (IRE)—Dubai Princess (IRE) **Mr D. Tate**

THREE-YEAR-OLDS

14 ALFRED THE GREY (IRE), gr g Alhebayeb (IRE)—Roseska (USA) **Elsa Crankshaw Gordon Allan**
15 CURFEWED (IRE), br g Most Improved (IRE)—Evening Sunset (GER) **Tracy Waggott & Sally Booth**
16 GHATHANFAR (IRE), br g Invincible Spirit (IRE)—Cuis Ghaire (IRE) **Mr W. J. Laws**

TWO-YEAR-OLDS

17 B c 22/3 Casamento (IRE)—Saru (Iffraaj) (4761) **Elsa Crankshaw Gordon Allan**

Other Owners: Mr G. Allan, Miss S. A. Booth, Miss E. Crankshaw.

559 **MR JOHN WAINWRIGHT, Malton**
Postal: **Granary House, Beverley Road, Norton, Malton, North Yorkshire, YO17 9PJ**
Contacts: PHONE **(01653) 692993** MOBILE **(07798) 778070**
E-MAIL **jswainwright@googlemail.com**

1 ANGIE B (IRE), 4, b f Acclamation—Musical Peace (IRE) **Mr W Bavill & Mr D. Bavill**
2 CLAYTON HALL (IRE), 6, b g Lilbourne Lad (IRE)—Hawk Dance (IRE) **I. J. Barran**
3 DALLAS COWBOY (IRE), 9, b g Beneficial—Watson River (IRE) **Mr D. J. Sturdy**
4 HENRIETTA'S DREAM, 5, b m Henrythenavigator (USA)—Timeless Dream **Chatterbox Racing Partnership**
5 JUST HEATHER (IRE), 5, gr m Zebedee—Miss Sundance (IRE) **Mr T. G. Davies**
6 LOTS OV (IRE), 5, b m Rock of Gibraltar (IRE)—Bright Enough **I. J. Barran**
7 MR WING (IRE), 4, b br g Dandy Man (IRE)—Siesta Time **Gareth Davis & John Wainwright**
8 PRINCE CONSORT (IRE), 4, b g Most Improved (IRE)—Fame And Fortune (IRE) **Caballo Racing**
9 TICKS THE BOXES (IRE), 7, ch g Fast Company (IRE)—Swan Sea (USA) **Caballo Racing**
10 ZARKAVON, 5, b m Avonbridge—Zarkavean **J. S. Wainwright & Peter Clarke**

THREE-YEAR-OLDS

11 DILLY DILLY (IRE), b f Moohaajim (IRE)—Scarlet Rosefinch **Mr W. C. Bavill**

Other Owners: Mr D. Bavill, Mr P. R. Clarke, J. S. Wainwright, Mr B. J. P. Walker.

Assistant Trainer: Mrs Fiona Wainwright

560 **MR MARK WALFORD, Sheriff Hutton**
Postal: **Cornborough Manor, Cornborough Road, Sheriff Hutton, York, North Yorkshire, YO60 6QN**
Contacts: PHONE: **(01347) 878382**

1 ANOTHER DAY DONE (IRE), 8, b g Davorin (JPN)—Perfect Memory (IRE) **Mr J. N. Readman**
2 BIT OF A QUIRKE, 6, ch g Monsieur Bond (IRE)—Silk (IRE) **Mr A. Quirke & Mrs G. B. Walford**
3 BRAVANTINA, 4, b f Trans Island—Falbrina (IRE) **Nunstainton Racing Club & Partner**
4 CARLOVIAN, 6, b g Acclamation—Mimisel **Profit Pony Racing**
5 CASH TO ASH (IRE), 6, b g Westerner—Knocklayde Rose (IRE) **8 Amigos,E Holmes, S Morrell & M Johnson**
6 CORNBOROUGH, 8, ch g Sir Percy—Emirates First (IRE) **Cornborough Racing Club**

MR MARK WALFORD - Continued

7 **CRUSHED (IRE)**, 5, b g Beat Hollow—Sel **Wright, Jervis & Whitestonecliff Racing**
8 **EVENT OF SIVOLA (FR)**, 5, ch g Noroit (GER)—Surprise de Sivola (FR) **Cw Racing Club & Ursa Major Racing**
9 **GABRIEL'S OBOE (IRE)**, 4, b g Rip Van Winkle (IRE)—
　　　　　　　　　　　　　　　　　　　　　　　　Tinaar (USA) **Cambridge People, Colclough & the Amigos**
10 **MISS AMELIA**, 5, b m Midnight Legend—Miss Pross **Cambridge People & Mr John Craggs**
11 **MR DAVIES**, 5, ch g Shirocco (GER)—Pasithea (IRE) **Lady Legard**
12 **OLIVER'S GOLD**, 11, b g Danehill Dancer (IRE)—Gemini Gold (IRE) **Cw Racing Club & Partner**
13 **ORKAN**, 5, b g Shirocco (GER)—Zefooha (FR) **Mr C J Grindal & Mr J Scarrow**
14 **PARIS PROTOCOL**, 6, b g Champs Elysees—Island Vista **Mrs G. B. Walford**
15 **PASSIONATE LOVE (IRE)**, 4, b f Bated Breath—Magic Nymph (IRE) **Let's Get Racing Ltd**
16 **PELICAN PIE**, 5, ch m Salutino (GER)—Pelican Point **Mrs E. Holmes**
17 **QUEST FOR LIFE**, 7, b g Dapper—Lewesdon Duchess **Little & Large Racing Partnership**
18 **RICKYROADBOY**, 4, b g Mazameer (IRE)—Black Baccara **Pims Funding Solutions & the 8 Amigos**
19 **ROCK ISLAND LINE**, 5, b g Haafhd—Diablo Dancer **Miss J. L. Gittus**
20 **ROCKMAN (FR)**, 4, b g Kap Rock (FR)—All Berry (FR) **Mr C. N. Herman**
21 **SIZE MATTERS**, 5, b g Captain Gerrard—Icky Woo **Cambridge People,Mr M Eddery & 8 Amigos**
22 **ST QUINTIN**, 9, b g Act One—Gloriana **Lady Legard & G B Walford**
23 **TAKE A BREAK (FR)**, 8, b br g Sunday Break (JPN)—Popee (FR) **URSA Major Racing**
24 **UNO VALOROSO (FR)**, 11, b g Voix du Nord (FR)—Danse d'avril (FR) **Mr C. N. Herman**
25 **WOODY BAY**, 9, b g New Approach (IRE)—Dublino (USA) **Mr P. C. Thompson & Mrs G. B. Walford**

THREE-YEAR-OLDS

26 **HALF BOLLY**, ch g Haafhd—Zefooha (FR) **Mr Bolingbroke & Mrs G B Walford**
27 **HAMMERTIME (IRE)**, b c Tough As Nails (IRE)—Berenica (IRE) **Cambridge People & Mrs G B Walford**
28 B c Albaasil (IRE)—Littlemoor Lass
29 **POLARIS ANGEL**, gr ro f Lethal Force (IRE)—Grand Slam Maria (FR) **URSA Major Racing**
30 **SPRING TO FREEDOM (IRE)**, b c Zebedee—Liberty Grace (IRE) **Mrs G. B. Walford**
31 B g Garswood—Tessie
32 **VINTAGE ROSE**, ch f Cityscape—Jozafeen

TWO-YEAR-OLDS

33 B g 16/4 Westerner—Annimation (IRE) (Accordion)
34 B g 18/3 Getaway (GER)—Bright Cloud (IRE) (Cloudings (IRE)) **Mrs M. Cooper**
35 **CLIFFTOP HEAVEN**, b g 28/4 Canford Cliffs (IRE)—Heaven's Sake (Cape Cross (IRE)) (7500)
36 B g 19/2 Music Master—Front Page News (Assertive) (9523)
37 B f 15/3 Elzaam (AUS)—Spavento (GER) (Verglas (IRE)) (6320)
38 Ro f 16/2 Lethal Force (IRE)—Sunbula (USA) (Singspiel (IRE)) (3370)
39 Ch f 8/4 Dawn Approach (IRE)—Tetard (IRE) (Lawman (FR)) (2949)
40 Gr g 19/4 Coach House (IRE)—Vellena (Lucky Story (USA)) (6000) **Mrs G. B. Walford**

Other Owners: The 8 Amigos, Mr L. A. Bolingbroke, Mr D. Burrell, CW Racing Club, Cambridge People, Cambridge Racing Limited, Mr P. A. P. Clays, Mr R. Colclough, Mr J. Craggs, Mr C. T. Dawson, D. J. Dickson, Mr A. R. Douglas, Mr M. D. Eddery, Mr J. Frew, C. J. Grindal, P. Hampshire, Mr S. R. Henry, Mr P. Jervis, Mr M. Johnson, Mrs S. E. Morrell, Nunstainton Racing Club, Mr D. Percival, Mr A. K. Quirke, Mr J. A. Scarrow, Mr C. Talbot, Mr P. C. Thompson, Mr P. L. Welsby, Whitestoncliffe Racing Partnership, J. Wright.

561	**MR ROBERT WALFORD, Blandford Forum**

Postal: **Heart of Oak Stables, Okeford Fitzpane, Blandford, Dorset, DT11 0LW**
Contacts: MOBILE (07815) 116209
E-MAIL robertwalford1@gmail.com

1 **ACARO (FR)**, 5, b g Sinndar (IRE)—Accusation (IRE) **Alvin Trowbridge & Christine Hinks**
2 **BACT TO BLACK**, 7, b g Black Sam Bellamy (IRE)—Linagram **Cole, Gale, Levy & Mortimer**
3 **CHLOE'S COURT (IRE)**, 6, br m Court Cave (IRE)—Howaya Pet (IRE) **Cole, Gale, Levy & Mortimer**
4 **DUSKY LARK**, 9, b g Nayef (USA)—Snow Goose **Mrs Sara Biggins & Mrs Celia Djivanovic**
5 **EASTERN PROMISES**, 6, gr m Eastern Anthem (IRE)—Chilli Rose **David McNeill & Withyslade**
6 **ESCRIME D'ART (FR)**, 5, b g Spider Flight (FR)—Quiss Mi (FR) **Ksb, Mike Doughty & C Djivanovic**
7 **FRESNO EMERY (FR)**, 4, b g Vision d'etat (FR)—Urfie Star (FR) **Mr E Eames, Mr A Ham & Mr R Trevor**
8 **HOT SMOKED**, 6, br m Eastern Anthem (IRE)—Waheeba **Mrs M. M. Rayner**
9 **LE BOIZELO (FR)**, 8, b g Irish Wells (FR)—Bois Tendre (FR) **Dr & Mrs John Millar**
10 **MANVERS HOUSE**, 6, b g Schiaparelli (GER)—Freydis (FR) **K S B, Mr M Doughty & Mrs Sarah Tizzard**
11 **MR MEDIC**, 8, b g Dr Massini (IRE)—Danse Slave (FR) **The White Hart Company**
12 **OUR MERLIN**, 7, b g Pasternak—Lornette **A. J. M. Trowbridge**

MR ROBERT WALFORD - Continued

13 SKELLIG ROCKS (FR), 8, b g Poliglote—Skellig Mist (FR) **DT Hoyland JS Hoyland JP Romans**
14 SMAOINEAMH ALAINN (IRE), 7, b m Shantou (USA)—Dathuil (IRE) **Yeo Racing Partnership**
15 SPRING WOLF, 11, br g Loup Sauvage (USA)—Spring Grass **B. J. M. Ryall**
16 SYDNEY DE BAUNE (FR), 8, b g Califet (FR)—Perle De Baune (FR) **Mrs S. De Wilde**
17 TIKKEN AWAY (IRE), 8, gr g Tikkanen (USA)—Lady Goldilocks (IRE) **The Keightley Lambert Partnership**
18 VAZIANI (FR), 5, b g Sinndar (IRE)—Visinova (FR) **Chris Pugsley & Acorn Builders Dorset**
19 WALK IN THE MILL (FR), 9, b g Walk In The Park (IRE)—Libre Amour (FR) **Baroness D. M. Harding**
20 WINTER SOLDIER (FR), 6, b g Soldier Hollow—Wintersonne (GER) **A. J. M. Trowbridge**

Other Owners: Acorn Builders Dorset Ltd, Mrs S. J. Biggins, Mr David Bond, Mr C. Cole, Mrs C. J. Djivanovic, Mr M. Doughty, Mr E. R. D. Eames, Mr A. P. Gale, Mr A. G. Ham, Mrs C. M. Hinks, Mr J. S. Hoyland, Mr D. T. Hoyland, K S B Bloodstock, Mrs C. Keightley, Mr T P Lambert, Mr A. R. Levy, Mr D. E. T. McNeill, Dr J. W. Millar, Mrs J. D. Millar, Mr B. Mortimer, K. B. W. Parkhouse, Miss H. Pease, C. C. Pugsley, Mr J. P. Romans, Mrs S. L. Tizzard, Mr R. Trevor, Mr E. W. White, Withyslade, Mrs K. D. Yeo.

Jockey (NH): James Best.

---

562   **MR ED WALKER, Upper Lambourn**
Postal: **Kingsdown Stables, Upper Lambourn, Hungerford, Berkshire, RG17 8QX**
Contacts: **PHONE (01488) 674148 MOBILE (07787) 534145**
E-MAIL ed@edwalkerracing.com WEBSITE www.edwalkerracing.com

1   AGROTERA (IRE), 4, ch f Mastercraftsman (IRE)—Lombatina (FR) **B. E. Nielsen**
2   BIG BAD LOL (IRE), 5, b g Big Bad Bob (IRE)—Indienne (IRE) **Mr L. A. Bellman**
3   BLACKHEATH, 4, b g Excelebration (IRE)—Da's Wish (IRE) **Mr M. J. Cottis**
4   BRIGHAM YOUNG, 4, br g Street Cry (IRE)—Bible Belt (IRE) **B. E. Nielsen**
5   CAPRIOLETTE (IRE), 4, b f Most Improved (IRE)—Greta d'Argent (IRE) **Mr & Mrs Andrew Blaxland**
6   CARADOC (IRE), 4, b g Camelot—Applause (IRE) **Mr P. K. Siu**
7   DESERT DOCTOR (IRE), 4, ch g Society Rock (IRE)—Dorn Hill **Mrs F. H. Hay**
8   EASY MONEY (IRE), 4, b g Iffraaj—Ezalli (IRE) **B. E. Nielsen**
9   FARL (IRE), 4, b f Cape Cross (IRE)—Oatcake **L. Lillingston**
10 FILLE DE REVE, 4, b f Iffraaj—Danehill Dreamer (USA) **Mr Bjorn Nielsen & Lord Lloyd Webber**
11 HE'S AMAZING (IRE), 4, b g Fastnet Rock (AUS)—Kahyasi Moll (IRE) **Eight Investment Holdings Ltd**
12 ICONIC KNIGHT (IRE), 4, b g Sir Prancealot (IRE)—Teutonic (IRE) **J Nicholls, J Moorhouse & J Kinning**
13 INDIAN BLESSING, 5, ch m Sepoy (AUS)—Alpen Glen **Mr P. K. Siu**
14 MAYGOLD, 4, b f Mayson—Spanish Gold **Farleigh Racing**
15 MIRACLE WORKS, 4, gr g Kyllachy—Eastern Destiny **Mr P. K. Siu**
16 MOLLS MEMORY, 4, ch f Helmet (AUS)—Bright Moll **Mr A. R. F. Buxton**
17 MOOD FOR MISCHIEF, 4, b g Nathaniel (IRE)—Tina's Spirit (IRE) **Miss Alison Jones**
18 MOUNTAIN PEAK, 4, b g Swiss Spirit—Nolas Lolly (IRE) **Ebury Racing**
19 SINGING SHERIFF, 4, b g Lawman (FR)—La Felicita **Mr R. Ng**
20 SKY EAGLE (IRE), 5, ch h Lope de Vega (IRE)—Penelope Star (GER) **Mr M. Betamar**
21 SMILEY BAGEL (IRE), 6, b g Kyllachy—Epistoliere (IRE) **Mr L. A. Bellman**
22 STORMY ANTARCTIC, 6, ch g Stormy Atlantic (USA)—Bea Remembered **Mr P. K. Siu**
23 WAR NO MORE (USA), 4, br f War Front (USA)—Moth (IRE) **H.H. Sheikh Mohammed bin Khalifa Al-Thani**

THREE-YEAR-OLDS

24 AL DAIHA, ch f Olympic Glory (IRE)—Alpen Glen **Al Shaqab Racing UK Limited**
25 ASSIMILATION (IRE), b c Xtension (IRE)—Park Glen (IRE) **Mr S. F. Hui**
26 BABA GHANOUJ (IRE), b f Sea The Stars (IRE)—Lombatina (FR) **B. E. Nielsen**
27 BARYSHNIKOV, ch g Mastercraftsman (IRE)—Tara Moon **Mr Bjorn Nielsen & Eastwind Racing Ltd**
28 BEESWAX (IRE), gr c Exceleration (IRE)—Alfa **Quantum Leap Racing V**
29 BEGUILING CHARM (IRE), b f Charm Spirit (IRE)—Bryanstown (IRE) **Mr M. J. Cottis**
30 CAME FROM THE DARK (IRE), gr c Dark Angel (IRE)—Silver Shoon (IRE) **Mr P. K. Siu**
31 CAP FRANCAIS, b c Frankel—Miss Cap Ferrat **John Pearce Racing Limited**
32 CLOSER THAN CLOSE, b g Lope de Vega (IRE)—Close At Hand **Normandie Stud Ltd**
33 DIZZIER, b c Dansili—Spinning Queen **Exors of the Late Lady Rothschild**
34 DREAMWEAVER (IRE), b g Mastercraftsman (IRE)—Livia's Dream **Mrs O. Hoare**
35 DUCKETT'S GROVE (USA), ch c Point of Entry (USA)—Xylonia (USA) **Mr P. K. Siu**
36 GALLIC, b f Kodiac—Gallipot **Exors of the Late Lady Rothschild**
37 GINISTRELLI (IRE), b c Frankel—Guaranda **Mr Bjorn Nielsen & Eastwind Racing Ltd**
38 GLORIOUS CHARMER, b g Charm Spirit (IRE)—Fantacise **Kangyu International Racing (HK) Limited**

MR ED WALKER - Continued

39 **GLORIOUS GALAXY**, b g Garswood—Celeste **Kangyu International Racing (HK) Limited**
40 **HIDDEN PEARL**, ch f Dunaden (FR)—Volkovkha **Mr R. A. Pegum**
41 **HOTSY TOTSY (IRE)**, b f Casamento (IRE)—Siphon Melody (USA) **Mr D. Ward**
42 **IMMORAL (IRE)**, b g Helmet (AUS)—Loose Julie (IRE) **Highclere Thoroughbred Racing -SyonHouse**
43 **KIMBRIKI**, b c Dansili—Cascata (IRE) **Mr S. A. Stuckey**
44 **KYBOSH (IRE)**, b g Dansili—Super Sleuth (IRE) **Mr L. A. Bellman**
45 **LEGEND ISLAND (FR)**, b g Dabirsim (FR)—Carolla Bay (IRE) **Mr P. K. Siu**
46 **LEP**, b c Nathaniel (IRE)—Liel **Exors of the Late Lady Rothschild**
47 **MIDAS SPIRIT**, b c Charm Spirit (IRE)—Pearlofthequarter **A. Maclean-Perryment**
48 **MY LADY CLAIRE**, ch f Cityscape—Lady Sylvia **The DJK Racing Club**
49 **NARYSHKINA**, ch f Leroidesanimaux (BRZ)—Nadeszhda **Miss K. Rausing**
50 **ON THE STAGE**, b f Swiss Spirit—Spotlight **Lordship Stud**
51 **PADMAVATI**, b f New Approach (IRE)—Padmini **Turf 2018 & Partner**
52 **QUICKSILVER**, b f Coach House (IRE)—Poulaine Bleue **Mr B Greenwood & Mr Hatter**
53 **RANSOMED DREAMS (USA)**, b br g Arch (USA)—Dark Sky (USA) **East Wind Racing Ltd**
54 **RETICENT (IRE)**, br f New Approach (IRE)—Hoity Toity **B. E. Nielsen**
55 **ROYAL INTERVENTION (IRE)**, ch f Exceed And Excel (AUS)—
    Exciting Times (FR) **Lord Lloyd Webber & Mr W S Farish**
56 **SHERPA TRAIL (USA)**, gr ro g Gio Ponti (USA)—Vapour Musing **Mrs G. Walker**
57 **SHUG**, b g Slade Power (IRE)—Midnight Fantasy **B O'Rourke Bloodstock Ltd & Rory Maher**
58 **STATE OF AFFAIR (IRE)**, ch c Giant's Causeway (USA)—Circumstances (IRE) **Mrs F. H. Hay**
59 **STORMBOMBER (CAN)**, ch c Stormy Atlantic (USA)—Swanky Bubbles (CAN) **Mr P. K. Siu**
60 **SUNDAY STAR**, b f Kodiac—Northern Star (IRE) **Mr D. Ward**
61 **SWINDLER**, b g Invincible Spirit (IRE)—Priceless Jewel **B. E. Nielsen**
62 B f Dabirsim (FR)—Takara Girl (FR) **A. Maclean-Perryment**
63 **TRIGGERED (IRE)**, b c Dandy Man (IRE)—Triggers Broom (IRE) **Mr P. K. Siu**
64 **TURN TO ROCK (IRE)**, ch g Slade Power (IRE)—Pivotal's Princess (IRE) **Mr P. K. Siu**
65 **VERIFY**, b c Dansili—Victoire Finale **Mr S. A. Stuckey**

TWO-YEAR-OLDS

66 Ch c 12/3 Sir Percy—Amanjena (Beat Hollow) (52000) **Kangyu International Racing (HK) Limited**
67 Gr c 2/2 Mastercraftsman (IRE)—Ange Bleu (USA) (Alleged (USA)) **B. E. Nielsen**
68 B c 16/2 Kyllachy—Belle Josephine (Dubawi (IRE)) (75000) **Kangyu Int. Racing (HK) Ltd & Mr F Ma**
69 Ch f 13/3 Speightstown—Bold Lass (IRE) (Sea The Stars (IRE)) **B. E. Nielsen**
70 B c 23/4 Siyouni (FR)—Cascata (IRE) (Montjeu (IRE)) (250000) **Mr S. A. Stuckey**
71 Ch f 14/2 Iffraaj—Cradle of Life (IRE) (Notnowcato) **Chasemore Farm LLP**
72 **CRITIQUE (IRE)**, b c 30/1 Cacique (IRE)—Noble Fantasy (GER) (Big Shuffle (USA)) (18000) **Ebury Racing 4**
73 B c 6/3 Declaration of War (USA)—Easton Arch (USA) (Arch (USA)) (62000) **Mr C. U. F. Ma**
74 B c 30/4 Holy Roman Emperor (IRE)—
    Electric Feel (Firebreak) (80000) **Kangyu International Racing (HK) Limited**
75 B f 4/2 Camelot—Emirates Joy (USA) (Street Cry (IRE)) (84280) **Mr D. Ward**
76 Ch c 10/3 Gleneagles (IRE)—Euphrasia (IRE) (Windsor Knot (IRE)) (185419) **Mr P. K. Siu**
77 **FIRST CHARGE (IRE)**, b c 31/3 Dansili—Melodramatic (IRE) (Sadler's Wells (USA)) (80000) **Mr L. A. Bellman**
78 Ch c 2/4 New Approach (IRE)—Indignant (Gold Away (IRE)) **Mr P. K. Siu**
79 **JUAN LES PINS**, b c 24/3 Invincible Spirit (IRE)—Miss Cap Ferrat (Darshaan) **John Pearce Racing Limited**
80 B c 21/4 Fastnet Rock (AUS)—La Salina (GER) (Singspiel (IRE)) (80067) **O.T.I Racing & Partner**
81 B f 22/2 Make Believe—Lady Pimpernel (Sir Percy) (151706) **Mr P. K. Siu**
82 B f 4/5 Free Eagle (IRE)—Malaspina (IRE) (Whipper (USA)) (250000) **Lord Lloyd Webber & Mr A Rosen**
83 B c 15/2 Lope de Vega (IRE)—Miss You Too (Montjeu (IRE)) (220275) **Mr Bjorn Nielsen & Eastwind Racing Ltd**
84 **NYAH**, b f 4/3 Assertive—Dyanita (Singspiel (IRE)) **Mrs L. M. Alexander**
85 Ch c 18/4 Sea The Stars (IRE)—Pine Chip (USA) (Nureyev (USA)) (46000) **B. E. Nielsen**
86 Ch c 9/3 Zoffany (IRE)—Pink Diva (IRE) (Giant's Causeway (USA)) **Mrs F. H. Hay**
87 B c 11/4 Camelot—Platonic (Zafonic (USA)) (176991) **B. E. Nielsen**
88 C 3/3 Brazen Beau (AUS)—Samasana (IRE) (Redback) (78000) **Kangyu International Racing (HK) Limited**
89 Ch f 14/3 Helmet (AUS)—Show Aya (IRE) (Showcasing) **S. Al Ansari**
90 B c 28/3 Dark Angel (IRE)—Silver Shoon (IRE) (Fasliyev (USA)) (202275) **Mr P. K. Siu**
91 **STARMAN**, b c 31/3 Dutch Art—Northern Star (IRE) (Montjeu (IRE)) **Mr D. Ward**
92 B c 14/2 Siyouni (FR)—Sweet Dream (Oasis Dream) (63210) **Dubai Thoroughbred Racing**
93 B c 8/3 Exceed And Excel (AUS)—
    Swiss Dream (Oasis Dream) (120000) **Kangyu Int. Racing (HK) Ltd & Mr F Ma**
94 B f 4/2 Kodiac—Table Bay (IRE) (Nayef (USA)) (67000) **Mr L. A. Bellman**
95 B c 18/4 Lawman (FR)—True Crystal (IRE) (Sadler's Wells (USA)) (40000) **Mr R. A. Pegum**

MR ED WALKER - Continued

Other Owners: Mr P Afia, Mr A. M. Basing, A. W. Black, Mrs J. E. Black, Mrs T. J. Blaxland, A. Blaxland, Brian O'Rourke Bloodstock Ltd, Mr J. J. Brummitt, Mr A. N. Cheyne, Mr A. Donald, Mr W. S. Farish, B. J. R. Greenwood, T. F. Harris, Mrs E. A. Harris, Mr R. M. Hatter, Mr T. Henderson, Highclere Thoroughbred Racing Ltd, Lady A. Hobhouse, Sir C. J. S. Hobhouse, Mr J. Hobson, John Nicholls (Trading) Ltd, Mr D. J. Keast, Mr J. Kinning, Lord A. Lloyd Webber, Mr R. Maher, Col A. J. E. Malcolm, Mr J. H. Moorhouse, Mr E. M. O'Connor, Mr S. O'Donnell, O.T.I. Racing, Mr R. Pritchard, Mr A. Rosen, Turf Club 2018, Mr I. R. Twigden, Mr E. C. D. Walker.

Assistant Trainer: Jack Steels

563

MR CHRIS WALL, Newmarket
Postal: **Induna Stables, Fordham Road, Newmarket, Suffolk, CB8 7AQ**
Contacts: **OFFICE (01638) 661999 HOME (01638) 668896 FAX (01638) 667279**
MOBILE (07764) 940255
E-MAIL christianwall@btconnect.com WEBSITE www.chriswallracing.co.uk

1 **BLACK LOTUS**, 4, b f Declaration of War (USA)—Ravensburg **Ms A. Fustoq**
2 **DELILAH PARK**, 5, b m Delegator—Sarah Park (IRE) **Mr & Mrs DE & J Cash and Mr P Turner**
3 **FIRST SITTING**, 8, b g Dansili—Aspiring Diva (USA) **Bringloe & Clarke**
4 **FOLLOW INTELLO (IRE)**, 4, b g Intello (GER)—Sauvage (FR) **Ms A. Fustoq**
5 **HAN SOLO BERGER (IRE)**, 4, b g Lord Shanakill (USA)—Dreamaway (IRE) **Mrs B. J. Berresford**
6 **HI HO SILVER**, 5, gr g Camacho—Silver Spell **Mrs P. J. Toye**
7 **ICE LORD (IRE)**, 7, gr g Verglas (IRE)—Special Lady (FR) **Hintlesham Racing Ltd**
8 **JUMPING CATS**, 4, ch g Champs Elysees—Pivotal Drive (IRE) **Mr Des Thurlby**
9 **OH IT'S SAUCEPOT**, 5, b m Sir Percy—Oh So Saucy **The Eight of Diamonds**
10 **THE FIDDLER**, 4, b g Big Bad Bob (IRE)—Strings **The Equema Partnership**
11 **TRADE TALKS**, 4, b g Cacique (IRE)—Esteemed Lady (IRE) **Mr Des Thurlby & Mrs Doreen M Swinburn**
12 **ZEYZOUN (FR)**, 5, b g Excelebration (IRE)—Zayanida (IRE) **Mr M. J. Bringloe**

THREE-YEAR-OLDS

13 **CAPLA HUNTRESS**, gr f Sir Percy—Great White Hope (IRE) **Strawberry Fields Stud**
14 **CARLEEN**, ch f Sepoy (AUS)—Generous Lady **Ms A. Fustoq**
15 **LUCKY CHARM**, b f Charm Spirit (IRE)—Drift And Dream **Lady Juliet Tadgell**
16 **PURGATORY**, b g Dark Angel (IRE)—Meet Me Halfway **Mr Des Thurlby**
17 **SMART SAMBA (IRE)**, b g Intello (GER)—Brazilian Bride **Induna Racing**
18 **SOLFEGGIO (IRE)**, br f Bated Breath—Superfonic (FR) **Hughes & Scott**
19 **SPIRITUALLY**, b f Charm Spirit (IRE)—Lalectra **Mrs P. J. Green**
20 **THE CORPORAL (IRE)**, b g Dansili—Ideal **Bringloe & Clarke**
21 **TSARMINA (IRE)**, b f Ruler of The World (IRE)—Caelis **Belinda Rose**
22 **WALK IT TALK IT**, b f Nathaniel (IRE)—Windy Britain **Scuderia Giocri Ltd**

TWO-YEAR-OLDS

23 **CHEESE AND WINE**, b f 26/2 Nathaniel (IRE)—Meet Me Halfway (Exceed And Excel (AUS) **Mr Des Thurlby**
24 **DOUBLE OR BUBBLE (IRE)**, b f 2/5 Exceed And Excel (AUS)—Mango Lady (Dalakhani (IRE)) **Ms A. Fustoq**
25 **FRONT OF LINE**, b f 28/4 Cable Bay (IRE)—Pivotal Drive (IRE) (Pivotal) (8000) **Mr Des Thurlby**
26 **GLEN ESK**, b g 18/2 Kyllachy—Ski Slope (Three Valleys (USA)) (10000) **Botham & Partner**
27 **GOLDIE HAWK**, b f 9/2 Golden Horn—Always Remembered (IRE) (Galileo (IRE)) **Ms A. Fustoq**
28 **GREEK OASIS**, b f 10/2 Oasis Dream—Greek Goddess (IRE) (Galileo (IRE)) **Ms A. Fustoq**
29 **MOLLY SHAW**, b f 19/4 Helmet (AUS)—Paradise Isle (Bahamian Bounty) (11000) **Mr Des Thurlby**
30 **PENKELLA**, b f 10/3 Archipenko (USA)—Ermyn Express (Selkirk (USA)) (25000) **The Leap Year Partnership**
31 **SI J** b f 9/5 Bated Breath—Sewards Folly (Rudimentary (USA)) (10000) **Dahab Racing**
32 **SMOKE SHADOW (IRE)**, b c 12/2 Mayson—Ravensdale (Raven's Pass (USA)) **Ms A. Fustoq**
33 Ch c 16/2 Starspangledbanner (AUS)—Snow Scene (IRE) (Singspiel (IRE)) (37926) **Hintlesham Racing**

Other Owners: P. J. W. Botham, Mr D. E. Cash, Mrs J. Cash, Mrs R. A. Clarke, Mrs S V Durcan, Mr T. Durcan, Mr R. Fraiser, Mr C. J. A. Hughes, Mr Roger Nash, Mr Kieran D. Scott, Mrs Jill Smith, Mrs Doreen M. Swinburn, Lady Juliet Tadgell, Mr Des Thurlby, Mr M. Tilbrook, Mr P. J. Turner, Mrs C. J. Walker, Mrs C. A. Wall, Mr R. J. Wayman.

Assistant Trainer: Hayley Burton

Jockey (flat): Ted Durcan.

564 **MR TREVOR WALL, Ludlow**
Postal: **Gorsty Farm Flat, Whitcliffe, Ludlow, Shropshire, SY8 2HD**
Contacts: **PHONE (01588) 660219 MOBILE (07972) 732080**
E-MAIL trevorwall56@outlook.com

1 **ARAGON KNIGHT**, 6, b g Kheleyf (USA)—Midnight Allure **Mark Goggin & Dave White**
2 **HOT MADRAS (IRE)**, 11, b m Milan—Hot Fudge (IRE) **Lease Terminated**
3 **I THINK SO (IRE)**, 4, b f So You Think (NZ)—Nawaashi **A. H. Bennett**
4 **LONGVILLE LILLY**, 4, b f Mawatheeq (USA)—Curtains **A. H. Bennett**
5 **MAY MIST**, 7, b m Nayef (USA)—Midnight Mist (IRE) **A. H. Bennett**

Other Owners: Mr M. J. Goggin, Mr D. White.

Assistant Trainer: Mrs J. A. Wall

Conditional: Josh Wall.

---

565 **MR CHARLIE WALLIS, Ardleigh**
Postal: **Benson Stud, Harts Lane, Ardleigh, Colchester, Essex, CO7 7QE**
Contacts: **PHONE (01206) 230779 MOBILE (07725) 059355**
E-MAIL cwallis86@hotmail.com

1 **AGUEROOO (IRE)**, 6, b g Monsieur Bond (IRE)—Vision of Peace (IRE) **P. E. Axon**
2 **ARZAAK (IRE)**, 5, br g Casamento (IRE)—Dixieland Kiss (USA) **Mr M. M. Foulger**
3 **BILLYOAKES (IRE)**, 7, b g Kodiac—Reality Check (IRE) **Roalco Ltd**
4 **CAPPANANTY CON**, 5, gr g Zebedee—Fairmont (IRE) **Mr J. Biggane**
5 **DARK SIDE DREAM**, 7, b g Equiano (FR)—Dream Day **Mr M. M. Foulger & Mrs Shelley Dwyer**
6 **DIVINE CALL**, 12, b g Pivotal—Pious **Roalco Ltd**
7 **EIGHTSIXSIX**, 5, b m Fair Mix (IRE)—Quiz Night **I. A. Low**
8 **FAREEQ**, 5, gr g Dark Angel (IRE)—Spate (IRE) **P. E. Axon**
9 **GEORGE DRYDEN (IRE)**, 7, gr g Zebedee—Key To Fortune (GER) **Dab Hand Racing**
10 **KESTREL DOT COM**, 7, br g Oasis Dream—Tanfidh **Mr F. Nass**
11 **KING ROBERT**, 6, b g Royal Applause—Generously Gifted **Dab Hand Racing**
12 **KYLLUKEY**, 6, b g Kyllachy—Money Note **Mr L. Howe**
13 **LA FORTUNA**, 6, b m Zamindar (USA)—Hyperspace **P. E. Axon**
14 **LADY YORK (IRE)**, 4, b f Vale of York (IRE)—Brave Truth (IRE) **Queens Head Racing Syndicate**
15 **PRECIOUS PLUM**, 5, b m Equiano (FR)—Miss Polly Plum **Mrs J. V. Hughes**
16 **RESTIVE SPIRIT**, 4, b g Intello (GER)—Hooray **The Restive Spirit Partnership**
17 **ROSE BERRY**, 5, b m Archipenko (USA)—Desert Berry **Strawberry Fields Stud**
18 **SHARP OPERATOR**, 6, ch g Medicean—Helen Sharp **Mr L. Brooks**
19 **SIR HECTOR (IRE)**, 4, ch g Sir Prancealot (IRE)—Awwal Malika (USA) **Roalco Ltd**
20 **STORM TROOPER**, 8, b g Acclamation—Maid To Order (IRE) **Mrs H. Wallis**
21 **TARSEEKH**, 6, b g Kyllachy—Constitute (USA) **P. E. Axon**
22 **TIME TO REASON (IRE)**, 6, b g Kyllachy—Danehurst **J.E.Titley & J.Goddard**
23 **ZAC BROWN (IRE)**, 8, b g Kodiac—Mildmay (USA) **Porterhouse Ltd. J Goddard**

THREE-YEAR-OLDS

24 **AWAKE IN ASIA**, ch g Dragon Pulse (IRE)—Gladiatrix **Mr Simon Munir & Mr Isaac Souede**
25 **TEMPLE OF WONDER (IRE)**, b g Clodovil (IRE)—Noble Fantasy (GER) **Mr Simon Munir & Mr Isaac Souede**

TWO-YEAR-OLDS

26 **DARK SIDE PRINCE**, b c 21/3 Equiano (FR)—Dark Side Princess (Strategic Prince)
27 B c 20/3 Mukhadram—Tadpole (Sir Percy)
28 Ch f 30/1 Casamento (IRE)—Violet (IRE) (Mukaddamah (USA))

Other Owners: Mrs S. Dwyer, Mr J. W. Goddard, Mr B. Kantor, S. E. Munir, D. Pearson, A. D. Pirie, Porterhouse Building Services Ltd, G. F. L. Robinson, Somerville Lodge Limited, Mr I. Souede, J. E. Titley.

Assistant Trainer: Hayley Wallis

566 MRS JANE WALTON, Otterburn
Postal: **Dunns Houses, Otterburn, Newcastle Upon Tyne, Tyne and Wear, NE19 1LB**
Contacts: **PHONE (01830) 520677 FAX (01830) 520677 MOBILE (07808) 592701**
E-MAIL dunnshouses@hotmail.com WEBSITE www.janewaltonhorseracing.co.uk

1 CHAUVET CAVE (IRE), 7, b g Court Cave (IRE)—Kindle Ball (FR) **Mrs J. M. Walton**
2 EVEQUE (FR), 5, ch g Kotky Bleu (FR)—Gloria IV (FR) **Mrs J. M. Walton**
3 REAL ARMANI, 7, ch g Sulamani (IRE)—Reel Charmer **Jane Walton & George Charlton Partner**
4 REVERSE THE CHARGE (IRE), 12, b g Bishop of Cashel—Academy Jane (IRE) **Mrs J. M. Walton**
5 UPTOWN HARRY (IRE), 5, b br g Morozov (USA)—Tudor Glyn (IRE) **Fresh Start Partnership**
6 WESTEND THEATRE (IRE), 10, b g Darsi (FR)—Ballyvelig Lady (IRE) **Mrs J. M. Walton**

Other Owners: Mr George A. Charlton, Mrs M. R. Ridley, Mrs J. M. Walton.

Assistant Trainer: Mrs Patricia Robson (07947) 152350

567 MR JASON WALTON, Morpeth
Postal: **Flotterton Hall, Thropton, Morpeth, Northumberland, NE65 7LF**
Contacts: **PHONE (01669) 640253 FAX (01669) 640288 MOBILE (07808) 592701**

1 CATCHAMAT, 10, b m Overbury (IRE)—More Flair **Messrs F. T. Walton**
2 CUDGEL, 6, b g Sulamani (IRE)—Posh Stick **Messrs F. T. Walton**
3 DUN FAW GOOD, 12, br g Grape Tree Road—Dun Rose **Messrs F. T. Walton**
4 FRANKIES FIRE, 6, b m Flying Legend (USA)—Watch The Wind **Messrs F. T. Walton**
5 FRENCH TICKET, 8, b g Bollin Eric—Merry Tina **Messrs F. T. Walton**
6 MATTHEW MAN, 8, b g Bollin Eric—Garden Feature **Messrs F. T. Walton**
7 PLAY PRACTICE, 9, b m Josr Algarhoud (IRE)—More Flair **Messrs F. T. Walton**
8 RIPSTICK, 8, b g Lucarno (USA)—Posh Stick **Messrs F. T. Walton**
9 ROLL OF THUNDER, 10, b g Antonius Pius (USA)—Ischia **Messrs F. T. Walton**

Other Owners: F. A. Walton, J. B. Walton.

568 MRS SHEENA WALTON, Hexham
Postal: **Linacres, Wark, Hexham, Northumberland, NE48 3DP**
Contacts: **PHONE (01434) 230656 MOBILE (07752) 755184**
E-MAIL linacres@btconnect.com

1 NATIVE OPTIMIST (IRE), 12, b g Broadway Flyer (USA)—Native Orchid (IRE) **R. H. & S. C. Walton**
2 SAILING AWAY (IRE), 6, ch m Stowaway—Drama Chick **R. H. & S. C. Walton**
3 THE CONN (IRE), 9, b g Milan—Grandy Invader (IRE) **R. H. & S. C. Walton**

Other Owners: R. H. Walton, Mrs S. Walton.

Assistant Trainer: Mr R. H. Walton

Amateur: Miss C. Walton.

569 MR JASON WARD, Thirsk
Postal: **Tall Trees, Sessay, Thirsk, North Yorkshire, YO7 3ND**
Contacts: **MOBILE (07967) 357595**
E-MAIL info@jasonwardracing.co.uk WEBSITE www.jasonwardracing.co.uk

1 AISLABIE (FR), 6, gr g Soldier of Fortune (IRE)—Someries (FR) **Lamont Racing**
2 DARK RULER (IRE), 10, b g Dark Angel (IRE)—Gino Lady (IRE) **Mr K. Walters**
3 HIGH PRIEST, 4, b g High Chaparral (IRE)—Princess Aurora (USA) **Mr P. Ward**
4 INGLEBY GEORGE, 5, b h Rail Link—Ingleby Princess **Mr D. Scott**
5 INGLEBY MOLLY (IRE), 4, ch f Choisir (AUS)—Mistress Twister **Ingleby Bloodstock Ltd**
6 4, B g Swiss Spirit—Ingleby Princess **Mr D. Scott**
7 KING'S PAVILION (IRE), 6, b g King's Best (USA)—Embassy **Mr P. Ward**
8 SWEETNESSANDLIGHT, 10, b m Aussie Rules (USA)—Taschlynn (IRE) **Mrs J. Ward**
9 THORNABY NASH, 8, b g Kheleyf (USA)—Mistress Twister **Mr D. Scott**
10 THORNABY PRINCESS, 8, b m Camacho—Ingleby Princess **Mr D. Scott**

MR JASON WARD - Continued

THREE-YEAR-OLDS

11 **ANNE NEVILLE (FR)**, gr f Toronado (IRE)—Alabastrine **Mr O. A. G. Ortmans**
12 **ELISABETH GREY (FR)**, b f Hurricane Run (IRE)—Driven Snow (FR) **Mr O. A. G. Ortmans**
13 B g Requinto (IRE)—Ingleby Princess **Mr D. Scott**
14 **OSMOSIS**, gr f Tamayuz—Spectacle **Mr P. Ward**

TWO-YEAR-OLDS

15 B f 26/2 Dawn Approach (IRE)—Alfaayza (IRE) (Dansili) (6666) **Mr O. A. G. Ortmans**
16 **BASRAH (IRE)**, b g 7/4 Free Eagle (IRE)—Crimphill (IRE) (Sadler's Wells (USA)) (6320) **Lamont Racing**
17 B f 10/1 Rajsaman (FR)—Clutter (Three Valleys (USA)) (1500) **Da Costa Family**
18 B f 1/3 Intrinsic—Dutch Girl (Dutch Art) (1200) **Dante Racing Club**
19 **GWEEDORE**, b c 15/2 Epaulette (AUS)—Ares Choix (Choisir (AUS)) (10476) **Lamont Racing Club**
20 B f 9/4 Bated Breath—Heronetta (Halling (USA)) (11904) **Mr O. A. G. Ortmans**
21 B f 15/4 Charm Spirit (IRE)—Holy Moly (USA) (Rock of Gibraltar (IRE)) (9047) **Mr O. A. G. Ortmans**
22 Ch f 15/2 Rock of Gibraltar (IRE)—Ingleby Exceed (IRE) (Exceed And Excel (AUS)) **Mr D. Scott**
23 B c 19/3 War Command (USA)—Mistress Twister (Pivotal) **Mr D. Scott**
24 **PLUSDARGENT (FR)**, b br f 15/2 Kendargent (FR)—
                              Moricandor (IRE) (King's Best (USA)) (14327) **Lamont Racing**
25 **PUSSYCAT RIOT (IRE)**, b f 24/2 Dragon Pulse (IRE)—
                              Texas Ruby (USA) (Henrythenavigator (USA)) (5056) **Lamont Racing**
26 Gr f 15/2 Outstrip—Rancho Montoya (Shamardal (USA)) (10476) **Mr O. A. G. Ortmans**
27 B f 4/3 Intrinsic—Spring Goddess (IRE) (Daggers Drawn (USA)) (1000) **Dante Racing Club**
28 B f 4/2 Casamento (IRE)—Sweetnessandlight (Aussie Rules (USA)) **Dante Racing Club**
29 **TAMOSHANTER KID**, b f 6/3 Helmet (AUS)—The City Kid (IRE) (Danetime (IRE)) **Mr G. Lampard**

Other Owners: Mrs E. McClymont, Mr C. McClymont, Mr D. McClymont.

570	**MISS TRACEY WATKINS, Kington** Postal: Rose Villa, Holmes Marsh, Lyonshall, Kington, Herefordshire, HR5 3JS Contacts: **MOBILE (07812) 804758** E-MAIL traceyswatkins@googlemail.com

1 **BIG WATER (IRE)**, 11, ch g Saffron Walden (FR)—Magic Feeling (IRE) **Tracey Watkins**
2 **GOAL (IRE)**, 11, b g Mujadil (USA)—Classic Lin (FR) **K. M. Parry**
3 **ONE COOL BOY (IRE)**, 10, b br g One Cool Cat (USA)—Pipewell (IRE) **K. M. Parry**

Assistant Trainer: Kevin Parry

Jockey (NH): Ben Poste. **Amateur:** Miss Brodie Hampson, Miss Natalie Parker.

571	**MR ARCHIE WATSON, Upper Lambourn** Postal: Saxon Gate, Upper Lambourn, Hungerford, Berkshire, RG17 8QH Contacts: **PHONE (01488) 491247** E-MAIL office@archiewatsonracing.com WEBSITE www.archiewatsonracing.com

1 **ATTAIN**, 10, b g Dansili—Achieve **Boadicea Bloodstock**
2 **CAPTAIN LARS (SAF)**, 10, b g Captain Al (SAF)—Polar Charge **Greenfield Racing**
3 **CHEVALLIER**, 7, b g Invincible Spirit (IRE)—Magical Romance (IRE) **The Chevallier Partnership II**
4 **CHOICE ENCOUNTER**, 4, ch g Choisir (AUS)—Gimme Some Lovin (IRE) **Greenfield Racing**
5 **CORINTHIA KNIGHT (IRE)**, 4, ch g Society Rock (IRE)—Victoria Lodge (IRE) **Ontoawinner & Partner**
6 **DOTTED SWISS (IRE)**, 4, b f Swiss Spirit—Luxuria (IRE) **Saxon Thoroughbreds**
7 **FAVORI ROYAL (FR)**, 4, b g Wootton Bassett—Matin de Tempete (FR) **Qatar Racing Ltd & Mr Kin Hung Kei**
8 **GORGEOUS NOORA (IRE)**, 5, b m Raven's Pass (USA)—Aneedah (IRE) **Mr David Howden & Mr David Redvers**
9 **IT'S ALL A JOKE (IRE)**, 4, ch g Dandy Man (IRE)—Jesting **Greenfield Racing**
10 **LAFILIA (GER)**, 4, b f Teofilo (IRE)—Labrice **Mr A. M. B. Watson**
11 **LETMESTOPYOUTHERE (IRE)**, 5, ro g Sir Prancealot (IRE)—Romanylei (IRE) **Boadicea Bloodstock**
12 **MANGO TANGO (FR)**, 6, b m Siyouni (FR)—Alexandrina (GER) **Mojave Thoroughbred Partners**
13 **NATIONAL GLORY (IRE)**, 4, b g Invincible Spirit (IRE)—Ponty Acclaim (IRE) **Boadicea Bloodstock**
14 **PEAK PRINCESS (IRE)**, 5, b m Foxwedge (AUS)—Foot of Pride (IRE) **Clipper Group Holdings Ltd**
15 **PROCEED (IRE)**, 4, ch f Mastercraftsman (IRE)—Roanne (USA) **Mr R. Treacy**

MR ARCHIE WATSON - Continued

16 **RARE (IRE)**, 4, b f Galileo (IRE)—Miarixa (FR) **Qatar Racing Limited**
17 **SHEBERGHAN (IRE)**, 4, b br g Sea The Stars (IRE)—Shebella (IRE) **Mrs E. Capon**
18 **SILVER QUARTZ**, 4, gr g Frankel—Rosamixa (FR) **Al Asayl Bloodstock Ltd**
19 **ULSTER (IRE)**, 4, gr ro g Intello (GER)—Ronaldsay **J Allison, S Barrow & Partner**
20 **VIVIANITE (IRE)**, 4, b f Teofilo (IRE)—Crystany (IRE) **Mojave Thoroughbred Partners**
21 **YABASS (IRE)**, 4, ch g Lope de Vega (IRE)—Fresh Mint (IRE) **The Ride The Lightning Partnership**

THREE-YEAR-OLDS

22 **ALPASU (IRE)**, gr g Dalakhani (IRE)—St Roch (IRE) **The Ride The Lightning Partnership**
23 **BARYS**, b c Kodiac—Balatoma (IRE) **N. Bizakov**
24 **BELEAGUERMENT (IRE)**, b br g Kodiac—Blockade (IRE) **Mr A. M. B. Watson**
25 **BREAKFAST TIME**, b f Nathaniel (IRE)—Eventfull Meet (IRE) **The Breakfast Time Syndicate**
26 **BUDANOVA**, b f Epaulette (AUS)—Generously Gifted **Mr A. M. B. Watson**
27 **CONCELLO (IRE)**, b f Society Rock—Daneville (IRE) **Ontoawinner & Partner**
28 **END OVER END**, b f Intello (GER)—Overturned **P. D. Player**
29 **HARVEY DENT**, ch g Mayson—Accede **Saxon Thoroughbreds**
30 **IN TRUTINA**, ch f Firebreak—Yearbook **Mrs S. E. A. Sloan**
31 **ISAAN QUEEN (IRE)**, b f War Command (USA)—Dundel's Spirit (IRE) **Mr C. R. Hirst**
32 **ITS NICE TOBE NICE**, b f Dalakhani (IRE)—Bright Halo (IRE) **It's Nice Tobe Nice**
33 **IZVESTIA (IRE)**, b f Battle of Marengo (IRE)—Westcote (USA) **Saxon Thoroughbreds**
35 **KASHAGAN**, b c New Approach (IRE)—Card Shop (USA) **N. Bizakov**
35 **KINGI COMPTON**, b g Compton Place—Missprint **Wood Family & Partner**
36 **MEDAL WINNER (FR)**, gr c Olympic Glory (IRE)—Pax Mina (FR) **Qatar Racing Limited**
37 **NATE THE GREAT**, b c Nathaniel (IRE)—Theladyinquestion **Mildmay Racing & D. H. Caslon**
38 **PERFECT GRACE**, b f Bated Breath—Bassinet (USA) **Dr Bridget Drew & Partners**
39 **PROBABILITY (IRE)**, b f Moohaajim (IRE)—Fine Prospect (IRE) **Mrs Catherine Cashman**
40 **QUIET ENDEAVOUR (IRE)**, b g Society Rock (IRE)—My Eurydice **Ontoawinner & Partners**
41 **ROANOKE (IRE)**, b f Sea The Stars (IRE)—Roanne (USA) **Al Asayl Bloodstock Ltd**
42 **SADLER'S SOUL (USA)**, b f Revolutionary (USA)—Sadler's Secretary (IRE) **Mr C. R. Hirst**
43 **SECRET ACE**, ch f Compton Place—Secret Romance **Mr C. Brammer**
44 **SHUMOOKHI (IRE)**, ch f Society Rock (IRE)—Three Knots (IRE) **Mr S. B. M. Al Qassimi**
45 **SOLDIER'S CALL**, b br c Showcasing—Dijarvo **Clipper Group Holdings Ltd**
46 **SURREY BREEZE (IRE)**, b c Footstepsinthesand—Breezeway (IRE) **Surrey Racing (SZ)**
47 **SURREY WARRIOR (USA)**, b g Data Link (USA)—Spring Heather (IRE) **Surrey Racing (wa)**
48 **TADASANA**, b f Battle of Marengo (IRE)—Letters (FR) **Al Asayl Bloodstock Ltd**
49 **THAI TERRIER (USA)**, b c Kitten's Joy (USA)—Perfect Agility (USA) **Mr C. R. Hirst**
50 **THE GREATEST SHOW (IRE)**, b g Mukhadram—Kayd Kodaun (IRE)
51 **TIMES PAST (IRE)**, b c Dandy Man (IRE)—Cant Hurry Love **Clipper Group Holdings Ltd**
52 **TOFFEE GALORE**, b f Lope de Vega (IRE)—Poppets Sweetlove **Jim Mellon & Partner**
53 **VICTORIANO (IRE)**, b g Teofilo (IRE)—Victorian Beauty (USA) **Ebury Racing 3**
54 **WHISPER ALOUD**, b f Swiss Spirit—Lulla **Clipper Group Holdings Ltd**
55 **YDRA**, b c Mayson—Camelopardalis **Star Partnership**
56 **ZAULA**, gr f Dark Angel (IRE)—Zimira (IRE) **N. Bizakov**
57 **ZORRO'S GIRL**, b f Toronado (IRE)—Broughtons Charm (IRE) **Apple Tree Stud**

Trainer did not supply details of his two-year-olds.

Other Owners: Mr P. Afia, Mr J. Allison, Mr S. W. Barrow, Mr T. E. Biggs, Mr S. Bridge, D. H. Caslon, Mr S. A. Cawkwell, Mr G. Charles, The Chevallier Partnership, Mr J. F. P. Cork, Mrs F. H. B. Cork, Mr L. J. Dowley, Miss P. B. Drew, N. R. R. Drew, Dr S. B. Drew, P. J. Dunkley, Mrs D. Dunkley, Miss D. F. Fleming, Mr S. Grubb, Mr C. R. Hadingham, Mr S. Hill, Mr J. Hobson, Mr D. Howden, J Allison and S Barrow, Mr K. H. Kei, Mr J. Mellon, Mrs S. Mercer, Mildmay Racing, WJA Nash & E Readett-Bayley, Mr N. J. O'Brien, Mr R. O'Callaghan, Mrs A. Oakshott, Ontoawinner, M Pescod, Ms E. Readett-Bayley, Mr D. Redvers, Mr G. E. C. Sloan, Surrey Racing Limited, Mrs M. F. Taylor, Mr C. G. Wood.

Assistant Trainers: Steph Joannides, Chris Grassick.

Jockey (flat): Hollie Doyle, Edward Greatrex, Oisin Murphy. **Apprentice:** Thomas Greatrex, Pierre-Louis Jamin.

---

572 **MR FREDERICK WATSON, Sedgefield**
Postal: Beacon Hill, Sedgefield, Stockton-On-Tees, Cleveland, TS21 3HN
Contacts: PHONE (01740) 620582 MOBILE (07773) 321472
E-MAIL fredwatson@talktalk.net

1 **DESTINATION AIM**, 12, b g Dubai Destination (USA)—Tessa Reef (IRE) **F. Watson**
2 **GLEAMING ARCH**, 5, b g Arabian Gleam—Mrs Quince **F. Watson**

MR FREDERICK WATSON - Continued

3 **HOP MADDOCKS (IRE)**, 4, b g Roderic O'Connor (IRE)—Yurituni **Mr M. Marsh**
4 **JOYFUL STAR**, 9, b g Teofilo (IRE)—Extreme Beauty (USA) **F. Watson**
5 **LUCYHILUCYLOW**, 7, b m Josr Algarhoud (IRE)—Shardda **Mr M. Marsh**
6 **NEWSPEAK (IRE)**, 7, b g New Approach (IRE)—Horatia (IRE) **F. Watson**
7 **ROYAL LEGEND**, 5, ch g New Approach (IRE)—Villarrica (USA) **F Watson**
8 **STAR CITIZEN**, 7, b g New Approach (IRE)—Faslen (USA) **F. Watson**

THREE-YEAR-OLDS

9 B f Arabian Gleam—Mrs Quince **F. Watson**

TWO-YEAR-OLDS

10 B f 16/3 Paco Boy (IRE)—Female Spring (Mujahid (USA)) (761) **F. Watson**
11 **LADY VALLETTA (IRE)**, ch f 13/4 Ivawood (IRE)—Cesca (IRE) (Fastnet Rock (AUS)) **Mr M. Marsh**
12 B c 11/5 Monsieur Bond (IRE)—Mad Jazz (Sir Percy) (2000) **F. Watson**

573
MRS SHARON WATT, Richmond
Postal: Rosey Hill Farm, Scorton Road, Brompton on Swale, Richmond, North Yorkshire, DL10 7EQ
Contacts: PHONE (01748) 812064 FAX (01748) 812064 MOBILE (07970) 826046
E-MAIL wattfences@aol.com

1 **ARCTIC VODKA**, 7, gr g Black Sam Bellamy (IRE)—Auntie Kathleen **Rosey Hill Partnership**
2 **CHAMPAGNE RULES**, 8, gr g Aussie Rules (USA)—Garabelle (IRE) **Rosey Hill Partnership**
3 **MOON RUA (IRE)**, 6, b g Sandmason—Dusky Palm (IRE)
4 **MYSTERIAL**, 9, b g Invincible Spirit (IRE)—Diamond Dilemma (IRE) **Major E. J. Watt**
5 **SHAKIAH (IRE)**, 4, b f Farhh—Dubai Sea (USA) **Mr D H & E Montgomerie**
6 **TOO MANY CHIEFS (IRE)**, 8, br g Indian River (FR)—Wahiba Hall (IRE) **Major E. J. Watt**

Other Owners: D. H. Montgomerie, Mrs E. Montgomerie, F. C. Previtali.

574
MR SIMON WAUGH, Morpeth
Postal: A G Waugh & Sons Limited, Molesden House, Molesden, Morpeth,
Northumberland, NE61 3QF
Contacts: MOBILE (07860) 561445
E-MAIL swaugh@dircon.co.uk

1 **BORIC**, 11, b g Grape Tree Road—Petrea **Mrs S. A. York**
2 **DARK AND DANGEROUS (IRE)**, 11, b g Cacique (IRE)—Gilah (IRE) **Yacht London Racing Ltd**
3 **IMPERIAL FOCUS (IRE)**, 6, b g Intense Focus (USA)—Mrs Cee (IRE) **Yacht London Racing Ltd**
4 **KARAT OF GOLD**, 8, ch m Lucarno (USA)—Coole Presence (IRE) **S. G. Waugh**
5 **MAYBE MICKEY**, 6, b g Multiplex—Mays Delight (IRE) **S. G. Waugh**
6 **MAYBE MOSTLEY**, 8, b m Multiplex—Mays Delight (IRE) **S. G. Waugh**
7 **MY ESCAPADE (IRE)**, 8, ch m Tamayuz—Highly Respected (IRE) **Northumberland Racing Club**
8 **NO BOUNDARIES (IRE)**, 7, ch g Spadoun (FR)—Dawn Princess (IRE) **Northumberland Racing Club**
9 **RASHEE (IRE)**, 7, gr m Daylami (IRE)—Celtic Angel (IRE) **Mrs S. A. York**
10 **ROYAL FLUSH**, 8, b g Multiplex—Mystical Feelings (BEL) **S. G. Waugh**
11 **SINGLE ESTATE**, 5, b g Tamayuz—Duo de Choc (IRE) **Northumberland Racing Club**
12 **SKYE CHIEF**, 7, b g Sulamani (IRE)—Isle of Skye **Mrs S. A. Sutton**
13 **SKYE VIEW**, 5, ch g Malinas (GER)—Isle of Skye **Mrs S. A. Sutton**
14 **TOTAL ASSETS**, 11, b m Alflora—Maid Equal **Northumberland Racing Club**

575
MR PAUL WEBBER, Banbury
Postal: Cropredy Lawn, Mollington, Banbury, Oxfordshire, OX17 1DR
Contacts: PHONE (01295) 750226 FAX (01295) 758482 MOBILE (07836) 232465
E-MAIL paul@paulwebberracing.com WEBSITE www.paulwebberracing.com

1 **ALL CHANGE**, 6, b m Motivator—Polly Flinders **R Jago & A Perry**
2 **BIG DATA (IRE)**, 5, br g Oscar (IRE)—Nolagh Supreme (IRE) **Mrs L. M. Shanahan**
3 **BOUGHTBEFORELUNCH (IRE)**, 6, b g Dubai Destination (USA)—Anie (IRE) **The Let's Do Lunch Partnership**

MR PAUL WEBBER - Continued

4 COPPERFACEJACK (IRE), 9, b g Robin des Pres (FR)—Leone Des Pres (FR) **R. W. Barnett**
5 DENIS, 4, b g Universal (IRE)—Exchanging Glances **Big Bucks Racing**
6 DON'T FENCE ME IN (IRE), 4, b f Fame And Glory—Great Idea (IRE) **R. C. Moody**
7 DREYFUS (IRE), 8, ch g Notnowcato—Trauquebise (FR) **Fawley House Stud**
8 ELITE GARDE (FR), 5, b g Kapgarde (FR)—Queyrann (FR) **R. P. Rocher**
9 EURKASH (IRE), 5, b g Irish Wells (FR)—Meralda (FR) **Paul Webber & Partner**
10 FORGET YOU NOT (FR), 4, ch g Smadoun (FR)—Baby Sitter (FR) **Richard Dodson & Partners**
11 FRIPPON DE VAIGE (FR), 4, b g Apsis—Ratina de Vaige (FR) **Mrs Michael Banks**
12 GO AS YOU PLEASE (IRE), 6, b g Jeremy (USA)—Aweebounce (IRE) **Mr J. P. McManus**
13 GWAFA (IRE), 8, gr g Tamayuz—Atalina (FR) **P. R. Webber**
14 HOUSE ISLAND (IRE), 5, ch g Casamento (IRE)—Fuaigh Mor (IRE) **Economic Security Partnership**
15 INDEFATIGABLE (IRE), 6, b m Schiaparelli (GER)—
Spin The Wheel (IRE) **Mr Philip Rocher & Mr John B. O'Connor**
16 KERRERA, 6, ch m Champs Elysees—Questa Nova **Mrs G. Thomas**
17 4, B g Winged Love (IRE)—Kiss Jolie (FR) **R. P. Rocher**
18 LORD MARMADUKE, 6, ch g Duke of Marmalade (IRE)—Maid To Treasure (IRE) **The Good Lord Partnership**
19 MAXI JAZZ (FR), 4, gr g Enrique—Andria (FR) **Mr B. Bailey**
20 MISS TONGABEZI, 10, b m Overbury (IRE)—Shiwa **Mrs D. J. Webber**
21 NEW AGENDA, 7, b g New Approach (IRE)—Prove **P. R. Webber**
22 PHOENIX RIVER, 5, b g Phoenix Reach (IRE)—Griselina (IRE) **Big Bucks Racing**
23 ROBIN DEUZ POIS (IRE), 7, ch m Robin des Champs (FR)—Native Wood (IRE) **Equi ex Incertis Partners**
24 SEE FOREVER (IRE), 5, gr m Stowaway—Flaming Poncho (IRE) **Mrs C. Kendrick**
25 SPARKY STOWAWAY (IRE), 7, b g Stowaway—Torose (IRE) **John Nicholls (Trading) Ltd**
26 SPECIAL ACCEPTANCE, 6, b g Malinas (GER)—Doubly Guest **The Syndicators 2**
27 STARJAC (FR), 5, gr g Linda's Lad—Star's Mixa (FR) **The Starjac Partnership**
28 THE CITY COBBLER, 4, b f Mount Nelson—Galante (FR) **Sir W. J. A. Timpson**
29 VERY LIVE (FR), 10, b g Secret Singer—Iona Will (FR) **Miss Sheena Pilkington & Partner**
30 VOLT FACE (FR), 10, ch g Kapgarde (FR)—Jourenuit (FR) **Big Bucks Racing**
31 YOUKNOWELL (IRE), 6, b m Gold Well—Islands Sister (IRE) **Mr J. P. McManus**

THREE-YEAR-OLDS

32 BRASS (FR), b f Linngari (IRE)—Silver Pivotal (IRE) **Mr M. B. Hughes**
33 DOCTOR ZEN (FR), gr g Doctor Dino (FR)—Zenitude (FR) **P. R. Webber**
34 POURMORECHAMPAGNE, b g Pour Moi (IRE)—Aqua Aura (USA) **The Pour More Syndicate**
35 TULIPE ANGELIQUE (FR), b f Planteur (IRE)—Belle Chasse **The Bailey Stokes Partnership**
36 YOUR THOUGHTS (FR), b f So You Think (NZ)—Moraga (FR) **P. R. Rocher & Partners**

Other Owners: Mr Bill Bailey, Mr Peter Bell, Mr Nigel Birch, Mr P. Bowden, Mr D. G. Carrington, Mr Peter Charter, Mr D. W. Higgins, Higgy Mette & Friends, Mr R. S. Jago, Sir I. Magee, Mrs S. D. McGrath, Mr R. H. McGrath, Mr J. Neville, Mr John Bernard. O Connor, Mr J. G. O'Neill, Mr Martin Pepper, Miss S. Pilkington, Mr Philip Rocher, Mr Paul Webber.

Jockey (NH): Richie McLernon.

---

576 **MR DERMOT K. WELD, The Curragh**
Postal: Rosewell House, Curragh, Curragh, Co. Kildare, Ireland
Contacts: **PHONE (00353) 4544 1273 FAX (00353) 4544 1119**
E-MAIL dkweld@rosewellracing.ie

1 BETSEY TROTTER (IRE), 4, b f Camacho—Inourthoughts (IRE) **Mr Frank Gillespie**
2 BROAD STREET, 4, b c Sea The Stars (IRE)—Bracing Breeze **Mr K. Abdullah**
3 CENTROID, 4, b c Dansili—Concentric **Mr K. Abdullah**
4 FALCON EIGHT (IRE), 4, b c Galileo (IRE)—Polished Gem (IRE) **Moyglare Stud Farm**
5 HASANABAD (IRE), 4, b c Nathaniel (IRE)—Hasanka (IRE) **H. H. Aga Khan**
6 HAZAPOUR (IRE), 4, ch c Shamardal (USA)—Hazarafa (IRE) **H. H. Aga Khan**
7 HAZEL BAY (IRE), 4, b f Iffraaj—Sadima (IRE) **Moyglare Stud Farm**
8 IMAGING, 4, b c Oasis Dream—Mirror Lake **Mr K. Abdullah**
9 JAEGA (IRE), 4, b f Fastnet Rock (AUS)—Farranjordan **Newtown Anner Stud**
10 JASSAAR, 4, b c Dansili—Rasmeyaa (IRE) **Sheikh Hamdan Al Maktoum**
11 JEWEL MAKER (IRE), 4, b c Invincible Spirit (IRE)—Sapphire (IRE) **Moyglare Stud Farm**
12 MAKE THE SWITCH (IRE), 4, b c Dansili—Switch (USA) **Moyglare Stud Farm**
13 MAKING LIGHT (IRE), 5, b m Tamayuz—Instant Sparkle **Moyglare Stud Farm**
14 MUJID (IRE), 4, b c Frankel—Bethrah (IRE) **Sheikh Hamdan Al Maktoum**
15 NEPTUNE (IRE), 5, ch h Galileo (IRE)—Caumshinaun (IRE) **Dr Ronan Lambe**

MR DERMOT K. WELD - Continued

16 **SMILE AHEAD (IRE)**, 4, b f Dream Ahead (USA)—Instant Sparkle (IRE) **Moyglare Stud Farm**
17 **YULONG GOLD FAIRY (IRE)**, 4, b f Mount Nelson—Quite A Thing **Mr Y. Zhang**

THREE-YEAR-OLDS

18 **ACAPELLA BLU (IRE)**, b f Dubawi (IRE)—Galvaun (IRE) **Moyglare Stud Farm**
19 **ACCOMPANIED (USA)**, b g Distorted Humor (USA)—Unaccompanied (IRE) **Moyglare Stud Farm**
20 **ALEZIA (IRE)**, b f Dansili—Alanza (IRE) **H. H. Aga Khan**
21 **ALL OUR TOMORROWS (IRE)**, b f Kingman—Justlookdontouch (IRE) **Moyglare Stud Farm**
22 **ANYA YLINA (IRE)**, b f Oasis Dream—Es Que **Moyglare Stud Farm**
23 **ASDAA (IRE)**, b g Dutch Art—Danseuse de Reve (IRE) **Sheikh Hamdan Al Maktoum**
24 **AZWAH (IRE)**, b f Invincible Spirit (IRE)—Bethrah (IRE) **Sheikh Hamdan Al Maktoum**
25 **BALADIYA (IRE)**, ch f Pivotal—Balansiya (IRE) **H. H. Aga Khan**
26 **BROGUE (IRE)**, b c Frankel—Bracing Breeze **Mr K. Abdullah**
27 **COEUR D'OR (IRE)**, b c Dubawi (IRE)—Irresistible Jewel (IRE) **Moyglare Stud Farm**
28 **DAWRY (IRE)**, b g Showcasing—May Day Queen (IRE) **Sheikh Hamdan Al Maktoum**
29 **EGRECIO (IRE)**, br c Intello (GER)—Aspiring Diva (USA) **Mr K. Abdullah**
30 **ESTRELLA (IRE)**, b f Zoffany (IRE)—Nightime (IRE) **Mrs C. C. Regalado Gonzalez**
31 **FEATHER STEP (IRE)**, ch f Tamayuz—Majestic Dancer (IRE) **Ballylinch Stud**
32 **FIREY FLOWER (IRE)**, ch f Lemon Drop Kid (USA)—Firey Red (IRE) **Moyglare Stud Farm**
33 **FROSTY BEACH (IRE)**, ch f Footstepsinthesand—Sharp Crisp Air (IRE) **Moyglare Stud Farm**
34 **GEORGEVILLE**, b c Dawn Approach (IRE)—Big Break **Mr K. Abdullah**
35 **GREY HILL (IRE)**, b c Grey Swallow (IRE)—Scarlet O'hara (IRE) **Mr G. Davies**
36 **HASANKEY (IRE)**, gr c Mastercraftsman (IRE)—Haziyna (IRE) **H. H. Aga Khan**
37 **HAZAKIYRA (IRE)**, b f Camelot—Hazarafa (IRE) **H. H. Aga Khan**
38 **HIGHTIMEYOUWON (IRE)**, b c Garswood—Hightime Heroine (IRE) **Newtown Anner Stud**
39 **INSAAN (IRE)**, b c Cape Cross (IRE)—Khulood (USA) **Sheikh Hamdan Al Maktoum**
40 **KARASHALA (IRE)**, b f Siyouni (FR)—Karamaya (IRE) **H. H. Aga Khan**
41 **KARASHENI (IRE)**, ch c Poet's Voice—Karasiyra (IRE) **H. H. Aga Khan**
42 **KASTASA (IRE)**, b f Rock of Gibraltar (IRE)—Kasanka (IRE) **H. H. Aga Khan**
43 B f Ruler of The World (IRE)—Katch Me Katie **The Irish National Stud**
44 **KATTANI (IRE)**, b c Tamayuz—Katiola (IRE) **H. H. Aga Khan**
45 **KISS FOR A JEWEL (IRE)**, b f Kingman—Sapphire (IRE) **Moyglare Stud Farm**
46 **LAND GIRL (USA)**, b f War Front (USA)—Principal Role (USA) **Mr K. Abdullah**
47 **LEO DE FURY (IRE)**, ch c Australia—Attire (IRE) **Mr Y. Zhang**
48 **LIGHTNING AMBER (IRE)**, ch f Dutch Art—Amber Romance (IRE) **Moyglare Stud Farm**
49 **LUXURIANT**, b f Kingman—Sense of Joy **Mr K. Abdullah**
50 **MANQOOSH (IRE)**, b c Dubawi (IRE)—Qaadira (USA) **Sheikh Hamdan Al Maktoum**
51 **MARIA CHRISTINA (IRE)**, b f Kodiac—Suitably Discreet (USA) **Moyglare Stud Farm**
52 **MARWARI (IRE)**, b c Exceed And Excel (AUS)—Miss Polaris **Newtown Anner Stud**
53 **MASAFF (IRE)**, ch c Raven's Pass (USA)—Masiyma (IRE) **H. H. Aga Khan**
54 **MIA MARIA (IRE)**, gr f Dansili—Majestic Silver (IRE) **Moyglare Stud Farm**
55 **MIDNIGHT SUNSHINE (USA)**, b f Medaglia d'oro (USA)—Princess Highway (USA) **Moyglare Stud Farm**
56 **MOURIYANI (USA)**, b c City Zip (USA)—Mouraniya (IRE) **H. H. Aga Khan**
57 **MUFARREJ (IRE)**, ch c Dubawi (IRE)—Rasmeyaa (IRE) **Sheikh Hamdan Al Maktoum**
58 **MUNEES GEMINI (IRE)**, b f Australia—Muneefa (USA) **Mr Y. Zhang**
59 **MUSALSAL (IRE)**, b c Shamardal (USA)—Sundus (USA) **Sheikh Hamdan Al Maktoum**
60 **NOSTRA CASA (IRE)**, b c Dubawi (IRE)—Utterly Heaven (IRE) **Moyglare Stud Farm**
61 **PROXY**, b f Frankel—Vote Often **Mr K. Abdullah**
62 **QUEEN MIA (IRE)**, ch f Famous Name—Agnetha (GER) **Mr J. Higgins**
63 **RACINE**, b f Kingman—Proportional **Mr K. Abdullah**
64 **RAKAN (IRE)**, b c Sea The Stars (IRE)—Tarfasha (IRE) **Sheikh Hamdan Al Maktoum**
65 **SEARCH FOR A SONG (IRE)**, ch f Galileo (IRE)—Polished Gem (IRE) **Moyglare Stud Farm**
66 **SHELIR (IRE)**, gr c Dark Angel (IRE)—Shelina (IRE) **H. H. Aga Khan**
67 **SHERKALI (IRE)**, b c Siyouni (FR)—Sharleez (IRE) **H. H. Aga Khan**
68 **SWITCH AROUND (IRE)**, b f Galileo (IRE)—Switch (USA) **Moyglare Stud Farm**
69 **TALIYNA (IRE)**, ch f Dawn Approach (IRE)—Tanoura (IRE) **H. H. Aga Khan**
70 **TANKERVILLE (USA)**, b c Kitten's Joy—Starformer (USA) **Mr K. Abdullah**
71 **TARNAWA (IRE)**, ch f Shamardal (USA)—Tarana (IRE) **H. H. Aga Khan**
72 **TAURAN SHAMAN (IRE)**, br c Shamardal (USA)—Danelissima (IRE) **Mr Y. Zhang**
73 **THIRD WORLD (IRE)**, b c Dansili—Sense of Purpose (IRE) **Moyglare Stud Farm**
74 **TIME CAPSULE (IRE)**, b c Kingman—All Time **Mr K. Abdullah**
75 **TIME TUNNEL (IRE)**, b f Invincible Spirit (IRE)—Timepiece **Mr K. Abdullah**
76 **TINANDALI (IRE)**, b c Oasis Dream—Timarwa (IRE) **H. H. Aga Khan**
77 **TITANIUM SKY (IRE)**, gr f Dark Angel (IRE)—She's Our Mark **Moyglare Stud Farm**
78 **TRANCHEE (IRE)**, b c War Front (USA)—Terrific (IRE) **Moyglare Stud Farm**

MR DERMOT K. WELD - Continued

79 **ZARAFSHAN (IRE),** b c Shamardal (USA)—Zarshana (IRE) **H. H. Aga Khan**
80 **ZARANDI (IRE),** b c Scat Daddy (USA)—Zaralanta (IRE) **H. H. Aga Khan**
81 **ZUENOON (IRE),** gr c Havana Gold (IRE)—Zindana (IRE) **H. H. Aga Khan**

TWO-YEAR-OLDS

82 Ch f 18/2 Siyouni (FR)—Afternoon Sunlight (IRE) (Sea The Stars (IRE)) **Moyglare Stud Farm**
83 Ch f 4/5 Lethal Force (IRE)—Amber Romance (IRE) (Bahamian Bounty) **Moyglare Stud Farm**
84 B br c 4/2 No Nay Never (USA)—Antique Platinum (IRE) (Holy Roman Emperor (IRE)) **Moyglare Stud Farm**
85 B c 20/1 Sea The Stars (IRE)—Askeria (IRE) (Sadler's Wells (USA)) **H. H. Aga Khan**
86 B f 27/3 Dark Angel (IRE)—Azama (IRE) (Sea The Stars (IRE)) **H. H. Aga Khan**
87 **CALDWELL,** b c 7/5 Dansili—Milford Sound (Barathea (IRE)) **Mr K. Abdullah**
88 **CANNOLI,** br b f 24/1 Oasis Dream—Caponata (USA) (Selkirk (USA)) **Mr K. Abdullah**
89 B f 8/5 Fastnet Rock (AUS)—Chatifa (IRE) (Titus Livius (FR) (26126) **Mr Y. Zhang**
90 **CLASSIFY,** b c 23/3 Nayef (USA)—Winter Silence (Dansili) **Mr K. Abdullah**
91 B c 1/4 Fastnet Rock (USA)—Cochabamba (IRE) (Hurricane Run (IRE)) (65739) **Mr Y. Zhang**
92 B f 18/3 Galileo (IRE)—Discreet Marq (USA) (Discreet Cat (USA)) **Moyglare Stud Farm**
93 **EBENDI (IRE),** ch c 6/4 Le Havre (IRE)—Ebalista (IRE) (Selkirk (USA)) **H. H. Aga Khan**
94 B c 11/5 Invincible Spirit (IRE)—Edelmira (IRE) (Peintre Celebre (USA)) **H. H. Aga Khan**
95 **EIGER (USA),** b c 13/4 Noble Mission—Quickfire (Dubai Millennium) **Mr K. Abdullah**
96 Gr f 23/1 Dark Angel (IRE)—Eshera (IRE) (Oratorio (IRE)) **H. H. Aga Khan**
97 B f 24/3 No Nay Never (USA)—Eva's Time (IRE) (Monsun (GER)) **Moyglare Stud Farm**
98 B f 16/3 Kitten's Joy (USA)—Freedom Reigns (IRE) (Jeremy (USA)) **Mr Kenneth Ramsey**
99 B f 17/3 Free Eagle (IRE)—I'm Yours (Invincible Spirit (IRE)) **Moyglare Stud Farm**
100 B c 25/3 Dubawi (IRE)—Irresistible Jewel (IRE) (Danehill (USA)) **Moyglare Stud Farm**
101 Ch f 4/5 Free Eagle (IRE)—Kapera (FR) (Linamix (FR)) **Moyglare Stud Farm**
102 B c 27/2 Bated Breath—Lifting Me Higher (IRE) (Sea The Stars (IRE)) (175000) **Sheikh Hamdan Al Maktoum**
103 B c 2/3 Oasis Dream—Mad About You (IRE) (Indian Ridge) **Moyglare Stud Farm**
104 B gr c 14/4 Sea The Stars (IRE)—Majestic Silver (IRE) (Linamix (FR)) **Moyglare Stud Farm**
105 B f 16/2 Fastnet Rock (AUS)—Marie Celeste (IRE) (Galileo (IRE)) (130636) **Mr Y. Zhang**
106 B f 1/1 Toronado (IRE)—Middle Persia (Dalakhani (IRE)) **Lady Chryss O'Reilly**
107 B c 15/5 Declaration of War (USA)—Mouraniya (IRE) (Azamour (IRE)) **H. H. Aga Khan**
108 Ch f 29/4 Teofilo (IRE)—Moving Heart (IRE) (Anabaa (USA)) **Moyglare Stud Farm**
109 Ch f 15/3 Kitten's Joy (USA)—Mumtaazah (USA) (Tapit (USA)) **Sheikh Hamdan Al Maktoum**
110 Ch c 9/4 Kitten's Joy (USA)—Oak Trees Dancing (USA) (Forestry (USA)) **Mr Kenneth Ramsey**
111 B f 9/2 Fastnet Rock (AUS)—Oui Say Oui (IRE) (Royal Applause) **Mr Y. Zhang**
112 B f 13/4 Galileo (IRE)—Polished Gem (IRE) (Danehill (USA)) **Moyglare Stud Farm**
113 B c 13/4 Exceed And Excel (AUS)—Princess Icicle (Iceman) **Newtown Anner Stud**
114 **RADETSKY (USA),** b c 27/2 Speightstown (USA)—Brooch (USA) (Empire Maker (USA)) **Mr K. Abdullah**
115 B c 4/4 Free Eagle (IRE)—Reclamation (IRE) (Red Ransom (USA)) **Moyglare Stud Farm**
116 **REFERENDA,** b f 3/3 Frankel—Vote Often (Beat Hollow) **Mr K. Abdullah**
117 B c 8/2 Muhaarar—Rifqah (USA) (Elusive Quality (USA)) **Sheikh Hamdan Al Maktoum**
118 B c 2/3 Brazen Beau (AUS)—Rose Kazan (IRE) (Teofilo (IRE)) (100000) **Sheikh Hamdan Al Maktoum**
119 B f 8/3 Galileo (IRE)—Sapphire (IRE) (Medicean) **Moyglare Stud Farm**
120 B f 10/1 Sea The Stars (IRE)—Shamooda (IRE) (Azamour (IRE)) **H. H. Aga Khan**
121 B f 6/2 Raven's Pass (USA)—Sharleez (IRE) (Marju (IRE)) **H. H. Aga Khan**
122 B c 29/3 Free Eagle (IRE)—She's Our Mark (Ishiguru (USA)) **Moyglare Stud Farm**
123 Ch c 20/4 Zoffany (IRE)—Shelina (IRE) (Dalakhani (IRE)) **H. H. Aga Khan**
124 **SILIQUA,** br f 8/3 Dubawi (IRE)—Emulous (Dansili) **Mr K. Abdullah**
125 **SKYE (IRE),** b f 26/1 Golden Horn—Caumshinaun (IRE) (Indian Ridge) **Springbank Way Stud**
126 B c 30/3 Kodiac—Society Hostess (USA) (Seeking The Gold (USA)) **Moyglare Stud Farm**
127 B f 27/3 Pour Moi (IRE)—Sparkling View (IRE) (Danehill Dancer (IRE)) **Moyglare Stud Farm**
128 B c 23/4 Dandy Man (IRE)—Suitably Discreet (USA) (Mr Prospector (USA)) **Moyglare Stud Farm**
129 B f 7/4 Pivotal—Supernovae (IRE) (Dalakhani (IRE)) **Moyglare Stud Farm**
130 B c 25/2 Dansili—Tanoura (IRE) (Dalakhani (IRE)) **H. H. Aga Khan**
131 B f 3/3 Dansili—Tarfasha (IRE) (Teofilo (IRE)) **Sheikh Hamdan Al Maktoum**
132 B br f 30/4 Dansili—Terrific (IRE) (Galileo (IRE)) **Moyglare Stud Farm**
133 B f 18/4 Camelot—Thoughtless Moment (IRE) (Pivotal) **Moyglare Stud Farm**
134 B br c 9/3 Elusive Quality (USA)—Unaccompanied (IRE) (Danehill Dancer (IRE)) **Moyglare Stud Farm**
135 B c 26/3 Born To Sea (IRE)—Zaralanta (IRE) (Danehill Dancer (IRE)) **H. H. Aga Khan**
136 B c 21/4 Le Havre (IRE)—Zvarkhova (FR) (Makfi) **Springbank Way Stud**

577   MR ADAM WEST, Epsom
Postal: **Flat 2, Lorretta Lodge, Tilley Lane, Headley, Epsom, Surrey, KT18 6EP**
Contacts: **MOBILE (07939) 030046**
E-MAIL westtraining@outlook.com

1 **BAMBINO LOLA**, 4, b f Helmet (AUS)—Lifetime Romance (IRE) **Mrs J. M. West**
2 **CLAUDIO MONTEVERDI (IRE)**, 6, b g Galileo (IRE)—Dance For Fun
3 **COULDN'T COULD SHE**, 4, b f Sixties Icon—Emperatriz **Ross Deacon & Partners**
4 4, b g Arakan (USA)—Dancing Jest (IRE) **Mr P. O'Neill**
5 **FINAL CHOICE**, 6, b g Makfi—Anasazi (IRE) **Mr A. J. Morton**
6 4, B f Kayf Tara—Gold Reef **West Racing Partnership**
7 **INTREPID (IRE)**, 9, b g Invincible Spirit (IRE)—Imiloa (USA) **Mr D. Phelan**
8 **LORD DIGBY**, 4, b g Dick Turpin (IRE)—Chrissycross (IRE) **Mr A. J. Morton**
9 **MIRROR MIRROR (IRE)**, 4, ch f Intello (GER)—Nouvelle Lune **Flash Harries**
10 **ONE HANDSOME DUDE (IRE)**, 4, b g Canford Cliffs (IRE)—Allegrina (IRE) **Steve & Jolene de'Lemos**
11 5, B g Oscar (IRE)—Presenting Tara (IRE)
12 **RAINBOW JAZZ (IRE)**, 4, b g Red Jazz (USA)—Let's Pretend **Mr S. W. Lang**
13 **REGULAR INCOME (IRE)**, 4, b g Fast Company (IRE)—Max Almabrouka (USA) **Partnership Terminated**
14 **TORNEQUETA MAY**, 4, b f Style Vendome (FR)—Alabastrine **Mrs Neila Wohanka & Mrs Janice West**
15 **ULYSSES OF TROY**, 7, ch g Rock of Gibraltar (IRE)—Takegawa **Mr Peter Hagger & Mrs Roseanne Hagger**

THREE-YEAR-OLDS
16 **AND YET SHE MOVES (IRE)**, ch f Roderic O'Connor (IRE)—Ms Cromby (IRE) **Nick Pike & John Morton**
17 **CAPALA (IRE)**, b c Swiss Spirit—Jezebel **Ross Deacon & Oliver Blatchford**
18 **COMEONFEELTHEFORCE (IRE)**, b f Slade Power (IRE)—Balladiene **Kestonracingclub**
19 B f Thewayyouare (USA)—Dubaianswer
20 **DUKE OF YORKIE (IRE)**, b g Morpheus—Fingal Nights (IRE) **Mrs J. M. West**
21 **GET US ON (IRE)**, b f Approve (IRE)—Marju Lass (IRE) **Mr S. W. Lang**
22 **GINGE N TONIC**, ch g Sixties Icon—Romantic Retreat **Steve & Jolene de'Lemos**
23 **HEERCOMESHARRIE**, b c Heeraat (IRE)—Aunt Minnie **Flash Harries**
24 **ILLEGITIMATE GAINS**, b f Zebedee—Jillolini **Mr S. W. Lang**
25 **JANE CAMILLE**, b f Harbour Watch (IRE)—Emulate **Hever Stud Farm Ltd**
26 **LOVE YOUR WORK (IRE)**, ch c Helmet (AUS)—Little Italy (USA) **Mrs J. M. West**
27 B f Maxios—Purely By Chance
28 **QUARTO CAVALLO**, b f Epaulette (AUS)—Oriental Romance (IRE) **S &j De'lemos K Allen T Goodwin L Eggar**
29 **TATTENHAMS**, b f Epaulette (AUS)—Tattling **Mr Peter Hagger & Mrs Roseanne Hagger**
30 **THEDEVILINNEVILLE**, b g Paco Boy (IRE)—Ribbon Royale **Flash Harries & Keston Rc**

TWO-YEAR-OLDS
31 B f 14/4 Heeraat (IRE)—Aquasulis (IRE) (Titus Livius (FR)) (9523) **Hever Stud Farm Ltd**
32 **AUSTIN TAETIOUS**, b c 5/5 Archipenko (USA)—Akdarena (Hernando (FR)) (2000) **Ownaracehorse Ltd**
33 B c 9/1 Epaulette (AUS)—Azamoura (Azamour (IRE))
34 B c 28/4 Helmet (AUS)—Daheeya (Daylami (IRE)) (3000) **Hever Stud Farm Ltd**
35 B f 29/1 Harbour Watch (IRE)—B Berry Brandy (USA) (Event of The Year (USA)) (3333) **Mr A. J. Morton**
36 B f 2/5 Elzaam (AUS)—Irina Princess (Selkirk (USA)) (5714) **West Racing Partnership**
37 B c 20/4 Harbour Watch (IRE)—Kodiac Island (Kodiac (IRE)) (4761) **Mr S. Wingrove**
38 **KOMOREBI**, ch f 3/4 Ivawood (IRE)—Spangle (Galileo (IRE)) (8571) **Ownaracehorse & Partners**
39 B c 2/4 Shooting To Win (AUS)—Marju Lass (IRE) (Marju (IRE))
40 B g 11/2 Fast Company (IRE)—Mestizo (Oratorio (IRE)) (571) **Mr P. Sills**
41 Ch f 3/4 Mukhadram—Pompeia (Singspiel (IRE)) **Hever Stud Farm Ltd**
42 Gr f 2/3 Outstrip—Strasbourg Place (Compton Place) (9047)
43 B c 1/2 Sepoy (AUS)—Time Crystal (IRE) (Sadler's Wells (USA)) **Hever Stud Farm Ltd**
44 B f 18/3 Dandy Man (IRE)—
        Tomintoul Magic (IRE) (Holy Roman Emperor (IRE)) (18952) **Raj Matharu & Suresh Sivagnanam**
45 B f 22/3 Nayef (USA)—Zaaneh (IRE) (Aqlaam) **Mr Stuart McPhee**

Other Owners: Miss K. Allen, Mr O. Blatchford-Potten, Mr D. R. Botterill, Mr E. Boumans, Mrs J. De'Lemos, Mr S. De'Lemos-Pratt, Mr R. C. P. Deacon, Mr L. Eggar, Mr S. K. Francis, Mr T. J. Goodwin, Mr A. Gorman, Mrs R. Hagger, Mr R. S. Matharu, Mr N. B. Pike, Mr S. Sivagnanam, Mr J. Webb, Mrs N. Wohanka.

578 **MISS SHEENA WEST, Lewes**
Postal: **5 Balmer Farm Cottages, Brighton Road, Lewes, East Sussex, BN7 3JN**
Contacts: **PHONE (01273) 621303 FAX (01273) 622189 MOBILE (07748) 181804**
E-MAIL sheenawest11@aol.com WEBSITE www.sheenawest.com

1 DING DING, 8, ch m Winker Watson—Five Bells (IRE) **Mr I. E. Poysden**
2 FADING ICON, 4, b f Sixties Icon—Fading Away **Quench Racing Partnership**
3 GOLDEN CANNON, 8, b m Winker Watson—Kalmina (USA) **M. J. Hills**
4 HARMONISE, 5, b m Sakhee's Secret—Composing (IRE) **Mr I. E. Poysden**
5 JUSTANOTHER MUDDLE, 10, gr g Kayf Tara—Spatham Rose **Saloop**
6 KENNY GEORGE, 4, b g Mawatheeq (USA)—One For Philip **Miss S. West**
7 SIXTIES IDOL, 6, b m Sixties Icon—Fading Away **Mr M. Moriarty**
8 SIXTIES SECRET, 4, b f Sixties Icon—Jollyhockeysticks **Mr M. Moriarty**

THREE-YEAR-OLDS

9 ABENAKI, gr g Gregorian (IRE)—Blakeshall Rose **Miss S. West**
10 B c Sixties Icon—Hi Note

Other Owners: Mr B. Downard, Mrs C. S. Muddle, Mr M. Preedy, Mrs P. L. C. L. Sarzi-Braga.

Jockey (NH): M. Goldstein.

579 **MR SIMON WEST, Middleham**
Postal: **14A St Alkeldas Road, Middleham, Leyburn, North Yorkshire, DL8 4PW**
Contacts: **MOBILE (07855) 924529**
E-MAIL simonwest21@hotmail.co.uk WEBSITE www.mkmracing.co.uk

1 AMOOD (IRE), 8, ch g Elnadim (USA)—Amanah (USA) **Mr S. G. West**
2 BANDOL (IRE), 11, b g Zagreb (USA)—Formal Affair **Mr P. Hothersall**
3 CAPTAIN CLAYTON (IRE), 12, b g Subtle Power (IRE)—Dont Hurry (IRE) **Wild West Racing**
4 CRANK EM UP (IRE), 8, b g Royal Anthem (USA)—Carrawaystick (IRE) **Mr P. Hothersall**
5 6, B g Tikkanen (USA)—Dusty Road (IRE) **Mr S. G. West**
6 ELLA NUTRAGILE (FR), 5, gr m Kapgarde (FR)—Odile de Neulliac (FR) **Mr P. Hothersall**
7 ERUDIT (FR), 5, b g Maresca Sorrento (FR)—Miss d'anjou (FR) **Mr P. Hothersall**
8 JESSE JUDE (IRE), 6, ch g Doyen (IRE)—La Belle Bleu (IRE) **J. D. Gordon**
9 JIMINY CRICKET (IRE), 8, ch g Golden Lariat (USA)—Lady Smurfette (IRE) **J. D. Gordon**
10 MAXIMISER (IRE), 11, gr g Helissio (FR)—Clydeside (IRE) **J. D. Gordon**
11 NELLIE DEEN (IRE), 6, b m Dream Ahead (USA)—Dorothy Dene **Mr S. G. West**
12 NEWS FOR PASCAL (IRE), 11, b g Kutub (IRE)—Direction **Mr P. Hothersall**
13 OVERTHEEDGE (IRE), 10, b g Morozov (USA)—Ballyroe Hill (IRE) **Mr P. Hothersall**
14 SHORT HEAD (GER), 4, b f Fastnet Rock (AUS)—Slight Advantage (IRE) **Wild West Racing**
15 SLIPPER SATIN (IRE), 9, m Excellent Art—In The Ribbons **Mrs J. M. L. Milligan**
16 SO YOU THOUGHT (USA), 5, b br h So You Think (NZ)—Lady of Akita (USA) **J. D. Gordon**

Other Owners: Mrs B. Hothersall, Mr D. Howarth.

580 **MR DAVID WESTON, West Overton**
Postal: **c/o Flintstone Stud, West Overton, Marlborough, Wiltshire, SN8 4ER**
Contacts: **MOBILE (07966) 641001**
E-MAIL flintstone007@icloud.com

1 ADMIRAL'S SUNSET, 6, b m Mount Nelson—Early Evening **Miss E. Tanner**
2 AT FIRST LIGHT, 10, b m Echo of Light—Bisaat (USA) **Miss E. Tanner**
3 BEDROCK FRED, 13, ch g Monsieur Bond (IRE)—Sea Mist (IRE) **Miss E. Tanner**
4 SOLSTALLA, 7, b m Halling (USA)—Solstice **Miss E. Tanner**
5 THE LION QUEEN, 4, b f Helmet (AUS)—Bisaat (USA) **Miss E. Tanner**

581 **MR TOM WESTON, Hindlip**
Postal: Offerton Farm, Offerton Lane, Hindlip, Worcester, Worcestershire, WR3 8SX
Contacts: **MOBILE (07752) 313698**

1 COOPERS SQUARE (IRE), 8, b g Mahler—Jessaway (IRE) **Mr T. H. Weston**
2 DINA MAKER (FR), 6, b m Policy Maker (IRE)—Kalinca de Thaix (FR) **Mr T. H. Weston**
3 SUNDAY CENTRAL, 8, ch g Central Park (IRE)—Sunday News'n'echo (USA) **Int-Ex Contracting Limited**
4 WESTERN CLIMATE (IRE), 10, b g Westerner—Jo Peeks (IRE) **Mr D. M. J. Lloyd**

582 **MR JOHN WEYMES, Sedgefield**
Postal: Trainer did not wish details of his string to appear

583 **MR ALISTAIR WHILLANS, Hawick**
Postal: Hilltop House, Newmill on Slitrig, Hawick, Roxburghshire, TD9 9UQ
Contacts: **PHONE (01450) 376642 FAX (01450) 376082 MOBILE (07771) 550555**
E-MAIL acwracing@hotmail.com

1 AJMAN PRINCE (IRE), 6, b g Manduro (GER)—Jumaireyah **Mr J. D. Wright & Mrs S. Wright**
2 ALEXANDRAKOLLONTAI (IRE), 9, b m Amadeus Wolf—Story **Chris Spark & William Orr**
3 ANNIE BROWN, 4, b f And Beyond (IRE)—Nevsky Bridge **Mr J. R. L. Wilson**
4 BRACKENMOSS RORY, 7, b g Overbury (IRE)—Thorterdykes Lass (IRE) **John & Liz Elliot**
5 CLARY, 9, b m Clodovil (IRE)—Kibarague **Mrs L. M. Whillans**
6 CORKED (IRE), 6, b m Mastercraftsman (IRE)—Dama'a (IRE) **Shmelt For Gold**
7 CORRIEBEN REIVER, 5, ch g Malinas (GER)—Wild Child Lucy **John & Liz Elliot**
8 COURT BALOO (IRE), 8, b g Court Cave (IRE)—Tremplin (IRE) **A. C. Whillans**
9 DONNACHIES GIRL (IRE), 6, b m Manduro (GER)—Russian Society **Mrs K. Spark**
10 FERLOCH, 4, b g Rail Link—Modesta (IRE) **Mrs E. B. Ferguson**
11 FIELDS OF FIRE, 5, b g Aqlaam—Blazing Field **Chris Spark & William Orr**
12 FLY VINNIE (IRE), 10, b g Vinnie Roe (IRE)—Great Days (IRE) **Simon & Angela Gillie**
13 GALILEE CHAPEL (IRE), 10, b g Baltic King—Triple Zero (IRE) **A. C. Whillans**
14 GUN CASE, 7, b g Showcasing—Bassinet (USA) **A. C. Whillans**
15 HELLAVASHOCK, 6, gr g Hellvelyn—Surprise Statement **Mrs H. Greggan**
16 KAIZER, 4, ch g Nathaniel—Perse **Mrs E. B. Ferguson**
17 KALAHARRY (IRE), 7, b g Kalanisi (IRE)—Full Imperatrice (FR) **Big Teeree Racing & Partner**
18 KILLONE (IRE), 10, gr g Flemensfirth (USA)—Ceol Tire (IRE) **Mr A. Turnbull**
19 LADY GRIGIO (IRE), 4, gr f Casamento (IRE)—Park Approach (IRE) **Big Teeree Racing**
20 LEOSTAR, 5, ch g Nathaniel—Gaditana **Mrs E. B. Ferguson**
21 NEARLY MAN (FR), 6, b g Turgeon (USA)—La Loute (FR) **Mr & Mrs Paul & Clare Rooney**
22 NEW RHYTHM, 4, b f Monsieur Bond (IRE)—Social Rhythm **J. D. Wright**
23 4, B g Court Cave (IRE)—Poncho Murray (IRE)
24 PUT THE LAW ON YOU (IRE), 4, b g Declaration of War (USA)—
Spirit of Tara (IRE) **Mr J D Wright & Mrs S Wright**
25 ROOM AT THE TOP (IRE), 4, b g New Approach (IRE)—Baila Me (GER) **Mrs E. B. Ferguson**
26 ROYAL SHAHEEN (FR), 6, b g Myboycharlie (IRE)—Viola Royale (IRE) **Mr F. Lowe**
27 SAMSTOWN, 12, b g Kingsalsa (USA)—Red Peony **Mrs E. B. Ferguson**
28 SHTAN ON (IRE), 8, b g Generous (USA)—Lady Oakwell (USA) **Simon & Angela Gillie**
29 SIENNA DREAM, 4, b f Swiss Spirit—Angry Bark (USA) **A. C. Whillans**
30 THE BRORA POBBLES, 4, b f Helmet (AUS)—Snow Blossom **Mrs L. M. Whillans**
31 TRY IT YOU (IRE), 6, b m Scorpion (IRE)—Tabita (IRE) **Charlie Baxter Bloodstock**
32 WISE COCO, 6, b m Shirocco (GER)—Sensible **Mclafferty & Pacheco**
33 ZEALOUS (IRE), 6, br g Intense Focus (USA)—Velvet Kiss (IRE) **Mr W J E Scott & Mrs M A Scott**

THREE-YEAR-OLDS

34 DARWINA, gr f Dark Angel (IRE)—Anadolu (IRE) **K & L Fitzsimons**
35 FIRSTEEN, b f Requinto (IRE)—Teide Mistress (USA) **Star Racing**
36 LIZZIE LOCH, br f Maxios—Quenched **Mrs E. B. Ferguson**

MR ALISTAIR WHILLANS - Continued

Other Owners: J. D. Baxter, Mrs E. J. Elliot, Mr J. J. Elliot, K. Fitzsimons, Mrs L. Fitzsimons, Mr S. P. Gillie, Mrs A. Gillie, Mr S. W. Hogg, Mr M. McLafferty, Mr W. J. Muir, Mr W. Orr, Mr J. Parkes, Mrs A. M. Rhind, Mr P. A. Rooney, Mrs C. Rooney, W. J. E. Scott, Mrs M. A. Scott, Mr C. Spark, Mr S. A. Taylor, Mrs S. L. Wright.

584
MR DONALD WHILLANS, Hawick
Postal: **Dodlands Steading, Hawick, Roxburghshire, TD9 8LG**
Contacts: **PHONE (01450) 379810 FAX (01450) 376082 MOBILE (07565) 609007**
E-MAIL helenwhillans24@gmail.com WEBSITE www.donaldwhillansracing.com

1 **BABY TICKER**, 10, ch m Endoli (USA)—Baby Gee **C. N. Whillans**
2 **BIG BAD DREAM (IRE)**, 7, b g Mountain High (IRE)—Stay At Home (IRE) **D. W. Whillans**
3 7, B g Spadoun (FR)—Blue Dragon (IRE)
4 **BUSHMILL BOY**, 5, b g Malinas (GER)—Miss Holly **J. R. Bewley**
5 **DALI MAIL (FR)**, 6, gr g Satri (IRE)—Queenly Mail (FR) **The Zidane Partnership**
6 **DANCED EVERY DANCE (IRE)**, 6, b m Oscar (IRE)—Kinnegads Pride (IRE) **D. W. Whillans**
7 **ETERNALLY YOURS**, 6, b m Sulamani (IRE)—Well Disguised (IRE) **Mr A. J. M. Duncan**
8 **HONDA FIFTY (IRE)**, 5, b g Arakan (USA)—Shuil Le Vic (IRE) **D. W. Whillans**
9 **KEYBOARD GANGSTER (IRE)**, 8, b g Gamut (IRE)—Vic O'tully (IRE) **The Buyers Club**
10 **LUCARNO DANCER**, 9, b m Lucarno (USA)—Sing And Dance **R. Shiels**
11 **NIGHT COMES IN (IRE)**, 7, b g Definite Article—Couture Daisy (IRE)
12 **ONECALLAWAY (IRE)**, 5, b m Getaway (GER)—Pocket Call (IRE) **The Brave Lads Partnership**
13 **PAPER PROMISE (IRE)**, 7, ch m Gamut (IRE)—Rose Vic (IRE) **Mrs E. Smith**
14 **PAPER ROSES (IRE)**, 8, b m Gamut (IRE)—Rose Vic (IRE) **Mrs E. Smith**
15 **PRINCESS APOLLO**, 5, b m Mullionmileanhour (IRE)—Speedy Senorita (IRE) **Mr S. B. Chamberlain**
16 **SIDE OF THE ROAD (IRE)**, 7, b m Beneficial—Roses And Wine (IRE) **Mr A. J. M. Duncan**
17 **STAINSBY GIRL**, 5, ch m Shirocco (GER)—Charmaine Wood **Mr A. J. M. Duncan**
18 **THE BOO BOX (IRE)**, 6, b g Scorpion (IRE)—High Court Action (IRE) **Denholm Park Racing**

THREE-YEAR-OLDS

19 **SEE MY BABY JIVE**, ch f Coach House (IRE)—Lady Fiona **Mrs H. M. Whillans**

Other Owners: Mr C. Murphy.

Assistant Trainer: Callum Whillans

Jockey (NH): Callum Whillans.

585
MR RICHARD WHITAKER, Scarcroft
Postal: **Hellwood Racing Stables, Hellwood Lane, Scarcroft, Leeds, West Yorkshire, LS14 3BP**
Contacts: **PHONE (01132) 892265 MOBILE (07831) 870454**
E-MAIL rmwhitaker@btconnect.com WEBSITE www.richardwhitaker.org

1 **DAWN BREAKING**, 4, b g Firebreak—Jubilee Dawn **D Gration, G Sutcliffe, N Farman, Jeaton**
2 **PENNY POT LANE**, 6, b m Misu Bond (IRE)—Velvet Band **Mr A. Melville**
3 **PONTECARLO BOY**, 5, ch g Piccolo—Dahshah **Mr A. Lumb**
4 **ROUND THE ISLAND**, 6, b g Royal Applause—Luanshya **Nice Day Out Partnership**
5 **SILK MILL BLUE**, 5, b g Piccolo—Marysienka **Lease Terminated**
6 **STONEY LANE**, 4, b g Mayson—Spin A Wish **Mr R. M. Whitaker**
7 **TOTALLY MAGIC (IRE)**, 7, b m Captain Rio—Hypocrisy **Mr James Marshall & Mr Chris Marshall**
8 4, Ch g Equiano (FR)—Wotatomboy

THREE-YEAR-OLDS

9 **HAWK IN THE SKY**, ch g Coach House (IRE)—Cocabana **Mr M. Hawkins**
10 **JILL ROSE**, ch f Coach House (IRE)—Wotatomboy **J.W.'s Wotafun Club**
11 **MOONLIGHT STAR**, b f Dick Turpin (IRE)—Cosmic Song
12 B g Harbour Watch (IRE)—Pigeon Pie

TWO-YEAR-OLDS

13 **THRILLER'S MOON**, ch c 22/3 Mayson—
Rio's Rosanna (IRE) (Captain Rio) **Mr James Marshall & Mr Chris Marshall**
14 Gr f 1/2 Coach House (IRE)—Velvet Band (Verglas (IRE)) (8500)
15 Ch c 22/4 Roderic O'Connor (IRE)—Wotatomboy (Captain Rio)

MR RICHARD WHITAKER - Continued

Other Owners: Mr N. Farman, Mr D. Gration, Jeaton Ltd, J. R. Marshall, Mr C. R. Marshall, Mr G. Sutcliffe, Mrs R. M. Whitaker.

Assistant Trainer: Simon R Whitaker (07771) 821955

---

586 | **MR ARTHUR WHITEHEAD, Craven Arms**
Postal: **Lawn Farm, Beambridge, Aston on Clun, Craven Arms, Shropshire, SY7 0HA**
Contacts: PHONE **(01588) 660424**
E-MAIL ajwhitehead@farming.co.uk

1 **DELLA SUN (FR)**, 13, b g Della Francesca (USA)—Algarve Sunrise (IRE) **A. J. Whitehead**
2 **MARLAIS**, 7, b g Dylan Thomas (IRE)—Super Motiva **A. J. Whitehead**
3 **ZALIAPOUR (FR)**, 13, b g Daliapour (IRE)—Spleen (FR) **A. J. Whitehead**

---

587 | **MR ARTHUR WHITING, Dursley**
Postal: **38 Barrs Lane, North Nibley, Dursley, Gloucestershire, GL11 6DT**
Contacts: PHONE **(01453) 546375** MOBILE **(07786) 152539**

1 **DECK OF CARDS (IRE)**, 7, br g Daylami (IRE)—Miss Edgehill (IRE) **A. J. Whiting**
2 **MASSINIS ADVENTURE (IRE)**, 11, b g Dr Massini (IRE)—Deirdre Eile (IRE) **A. J. Whiting**

---

588 | **MR HARRY WHITTINGTON, Sparsholt**
Postal: **Harry Whittington Racing Ltd, Hill Barn, Sparsholt, Wantage, Oxfordshire, OX12 9XB**
Contacts: PHONE **(01235) 751869** MOBILE **(07734) 388357**
E-MAIL info@harrywhittington.co.uk WEBSITE www.harrywhittington.co.uk

1 **ANEMOI (FR)**, 5, b g Manduro (GER)—Recambe (IRE) **Kate & Andrew Brooks**
2 **ARCADIAN SPRING (IRE)**, 5, b g Arcadio (GER)—Chloes Choice (IRE) **Holt,Macnabb,Robinson,Taylor,Tucker**
3 **BIGMARTRE (FR)**, 8, b g Montmartre (FR)—Oh La Miss (FR) **Mr P. J. Dixon**
4 **BRANDY JAMES (GER)**, 4, b g Motivator—Bold Classic (USA) **Incitatus**
5 **CAROLE'S VIGILANTE (IRE)**, 8, ch g Flemensfirth (USA)—Gotta Goa (IRE) **Mrs C. Skipworth**
6 **CATELINE (FR)**, 4, b f Martaline—Kitara (GER) **The Atkin Family**
7 **CHARLEMAR (FR)**, 7, b g Ballingarry (IRE)—Passemare (FR) **The Hennessy Six**
8 **COLD MARCH (FR)**, 9, b br g Early March—Tumultueuse (FR) **Kate & Andrew Brooks**
9 **COURT LIABILITY (IRE)**, 6, b g Court Cave (IRE)—
Whataliability (IRE) **Nashwebbpavervandenberghe&10percenters**
10 **DARA'S PRESENT (IRE)**, 8, b g Presenting—Ginandit (IRE) **Holt Robinson Atkin Macnabb Tucker Webb**
11 4, B g Well Chosen—Dizzy Rascal **Harry Whittington & Partners**
12 **DJIN CONTI (FR)**, 6, b g Lucarno (USA)—Regina Conti (FR) **Kate & Andrew Brooks**
13 **GENIUS**, 3, b g Beat Hollow—Natsuke (FR) **Mrs V. F. Burke**
14 **HENRIETTA BELL (IRE)**, 6, b m Shantou (USA)—Close To Shore (IRE) **The Racing Demon Partnership**
15 4, B f Flemensfirth (USA)—Hollygrove Rumba (IRE)
16 **HONOURMISSION (FR)**, 5, b g Linda's Lad—Orabelle (FR) **Kate & Andrew Brooks**
17 **JAMMY GEORGE**, 6, b g Multiplex—Dantes Mile (IRE) **Kate & Andrew Brooks**
18 **JUMBO DAVIS (IRE)**, 6, b m Doyen (IRE)—Banjo Davis (IRE) **J. H. Henderson**
19 **KHAGE (IRE)**, 6, b g Stowaway—Made Easy (IRE) **Kate & Andrew Brooks**
20 **KLEOS (IRE)**, 5, b m Fame And Glory—Ginandit (IRE) **Holt,Atkin,Macnabb,O'Connor, Milton**
21 **LANTIERN (IRE)**, 5, ch g Salutino (GER)—Luas Luso (IRE) **Holt, Robinson, Macnabb, Clark, Weedon**
22 **MASTER SNOOPY (IRE)**, 5, b g Milan—Senora Snoopy (IRE) **Nash, Bannister & Gardiner**
23 **MISTER COFFEY (FR)**, 4, b g Authorized (IRE)—Mamitador **Harry Whittington & Partners**
24 **PARKIN**, 5, b g Passing Glance—Patacake **The Parkin Lot**
25 **PAT KELLY**, 4, ch g Makfi—Speech **Mrs J. A. Fowler**
26 **PERFECT MYTH**, 5, b m Midnight Legend—Perfect Silence **Richard Vines & David Nott**
27 **POLLYAMOROUS (IRE)**, 4, b f Califet (FR)—Our Polly (FR) **British Racing Club**
28 **ROUGE VIF (FR)**, 5, b g Sageburg (IRE)—Rouge Amour (FR) **Kate & Andrew Brooks**
29 **SAINT CALVADOS (FR)**, 6, b g Saint des Saints (FR)—Lamorrese (FR) **Kate & Andrew Brooks**
30 **SALTO CHISCO (IRE)**, 11, b g Presenting—Dato Fairy (IRE) **British Racing Club**
31 **SHANTOU VOW (IRE)**, 4, b g Shantou (USA)—Holy Vow (IRE) **Holt, Carpenter, Peters, Macnabb, Webb**
32 **SHORE SHANTY (IRE)**, 4, b f Shantou (USA)—Close To Shore (IRE) **A Holt J Robinson I Macnabb & C Clark**
33 **SIMPLY THE BETTS (IRE)**, 6, b g Arcadio (GER)—Crimson Flower (IRE) **Kate & Andrew Brooks**

MR HARRY WHITTINGTON - Continued

34 **SPEEDY CARGO (IRE)**, 6, b g Stowaway—Vics Miller (IRE) **N.W.A. Bannister & M.J.R. Bannister**
35 **STICK WITH BILL**, 5, b g Oscar (IRE)—Made In Kk (IRE) **Kate & Andrew Brooks**
36 **THE DUBAI WAY (IRE)**, 7, b g Dubai Destination (USA)—Britway Lady (IRE) **A. Carr**
37 **THE GO TOU MAN (IRE)**, 6, b g Shantou (USA)—Golan Lady (IRE) **A Lady & The Tramps Partnership**
38 **THE KINGS BABY (IRE)**, 8, b br m King's Theatre (IRE)—Assidua (IRE) **Harry Whittington Racing Club**
39 **VINNIE LEWIS (IRE)**, 8, b g Vinnie Roe (IRE)—Ballyann Lewis (IRE) **The Racing Demon Partnership**
40 **WEAPONS OUT (FR)**, 5, b g Brave Mansonnien (FR)—Scenaria (IRE) **Kate & Andrew Brooks**
41 **YOUNG BULL (IRE)**, 5, b g Dubai Destination (USA)—Jane Hall (IRE) **Nash & Webb**
42 **ZANZI WIN (FR)**, 4, b g Zanzibari (USA)—Go To Win (FR) **Kate & Andrew Brooks**

Other Owners: 10 Percenters, Mrs Catherine Atkin, Mr O. Atkin, Mr N. W. A. Bannister, Mr M. J. R. Bannister, Mrs Kate Brooks, Mr A. Brooks, Mr Brian Carpenter, Mr Chris N. Clark, Mr P. D. Dennis, Mr P. J. Dixon, Mr D. Ellis, Mrs A. Fitzgerald-O'Connor, Mr Rupert Fowler, Mrs Belinda Fowler, Mrs Mary Gardiner, Mr Andrew Harding, Sir N. Hare Bt., Mr D. W. R. Harrington, Mr A. Holt, Mr Ian Macnabb, Mr C. Milton, Mr Chris Nash, Mr D. F. Nott, Mr G. J. Paver, Mr Alan David Penfold, Mr D. G. Peters, Racing Club Ltd, Mrs Sandra Robinson, Mr Peter James Robinson, Mr J. Robinson, Mrs Julia Scott, Miss E. Scott, Mr A. Taylor, Mr A. Tucker, Mr M. J. Vandenberghe, Mr R. J. Vines, Exors of the Late Mr H. J. M. Webb, Mrs Isobel Webb, Mr John Weedon, Mr H. Whittington, Mr E. J. Williams.

Assistant Trainer: Joe Quintin

Jockey (NH): Harry Bannister.

589

MR MICHAEL WIGHAM, Newmarket
Postal: Hamilton Stables, Hamilton Road, Newmarket, Suffolk, CB8 7JQ
Contacts: **PHONE** (01638) 668806 **MOBILE** (07831) 456426
E-MAIL michaelwigham@hotmail.co.uk **WEBSITE** www.michaelwighamracing.co.uk

1 **AL NAFOORAH**, 5, b m Bated Breath—Cat O' Nine Tails
2 **AWSAAF**, 4, b g Swiss Spirit—Atheera (IRE)
3 **CHARLESTON BELLE**, 5, b m Danehill Dancer (IRE)—Blanche Dubawi (IRE)
4 **CLEAR WATER (IRE)**, 6, b m Hard Spun (USA)—Storm Lily (USA)
5 **EXECUTIVE FORCE**, 5, b g Sepoy (AUS)—Mazuna (IRE)
6 **FOXY FOREVER (IRE)**, 5, b g Kodiac—Northern Tara (IRE)
7 **GIN AND TONIC**, 9, ch g Phoenix Reach (IRE)—Arctic Queen
8 **GLENAMOY LAD**, 5, b g Royal Applause—Suzy Alexander
9 **JAI HANUMAN (IRE)**, 5, b g Requinto (IRE)—Almost Blue (USA)
10 **JESSIES CHOICE**, 5, b m Malinas (GER)—Cool Spice
11 **MY TARGET (IRE)**, 8, b g Cape Cross (IRE)—Chercheuse (USA)
12 **NICK VEDDER**, 5, b g Rip Van Winkle (IRE)—Devotion (IRE)
13 **PALERMO (IRE)**, 5, b g Intikhab (USA)—La Spezia (IRE)
14 **SANAADH**, 6, ch g Exceed And Excel (AUS)—Queen's Logic (IRE)
15 **SILVER ASSET (IRE)**, 5, gr ro g Zebedee—Tipperary Boutique (IRE)
16 **VERNE CASTLE**, 6, ch g Sakhee's Secret—Lochangel

THREE-YEAR-OLDS

17 **ANYCITY (IRE)**, b g Zoffany (IRE)—Loquacity
18 **DREAMING OF LOVE (IRE)**, b f Requinto (IRE)—Hawaiian Dream (IRE)
19 **ELYSIAN LADY**, b f Champs Elysees—King's Guest (IRE)
20 B g Sepoy (AUS)—Impetious
21 **SILK ISLAND (IRE)**, b f Tagula (IRE)—Silk Affair (IRE)
22 **WHERE'S PERLE**, b f Kyllachy—Highland Jewel (IRE)

Owners: Mr C. T. Appleton, Mr W. R. Asquith, J. Cullinan, Mr A. Dearden, M. H. Dixon, Mr P. J. Edwards, D. Hassan, S. Hassiakos, L. Lillington, G. D. J. Linder, Palatinate Thoroughbred Racing Limited, Miss M. A. Quinlan, Mrs C. G. Scott, Mr D. T. Spratt, Mr J. B. Williams.

Assistant Trainer: Sharon Kenyon

590 MR MARTIN WILESMITH, Dymock
Postal: **Bellamys Farm, Dymock, Gloucestershire, GL18 2DX**
Contacts: **PHONE (01531) 890410 (01684) 561238 FAX (01684) 893428 MOBILE (07970) 411638**
E-MAIL martin@mswilesmith.co.uk

1 BELLAMYS BELLE, 9, b m Black Sam Bellamy (IRE)—Mrs White (IRE) **M. S. Wilesmith**
2 BELLAMYS BOY, 5, b g Black Sam Bellamy (IRE)—Mrs White (IRE) **M. S. Wilesmith**
3 FAIR ALICE, 10, gr m Fair Mix (IRE)—Mrs White (IRE) **M. S. Wilesmith**
4 LOOKSLIKERAINTED (IRE), 12, b g Milan—Kilcrea Gale (IRE) **M. S. Wilesmith**
5 MIDNIGHT FRENSI, 10, b g Midnight Legend—Flame O'frensi **M. S. Wilesmith**

Assistant Trainer: Ms E. C. Wilesmith (07976 926906)

591 MR CHRISTIAN WILLIAMS, Bridgend
Postal: **The Hollies, Heol Yr Ysgol, Coity, Bridgend, Mid Glamorgan, CF35 6BL**
Contacts: **MOBILE (07702) 896759**

1 BIG CHIP AND PIN, 7, b g Generous (IRE)—Supreme Cove **Smerdon Tree Services Ltd**
2 CAP DU NORD (FR), 6, br g Voix du Nord (FR)—Qualite Controlee (FR) **The Unnamed Favourites**
3 CONAS TAOI (IRE), 10, b g Exit To Nowhere (USA)—Zudika (IRE) **Mr C. R. P. Williams**
4 COTTONVALE (IRE), 8, b g Touch of Land (FR)—Shuil Le Vic (IRE) **Chiefs and a Dragon**
5 COURT FRONTIER (IRE), 11, b g Court Cave (IRE)—Dame En Rouge (IRE) **The Unnamed Favourites**
6 DONTCASHTHECHEQUE (IRE), 4, b g Mastercraftsman (IRE)—La Zona (IRE) **The Can't Say No Partnership**
7 FEARNIE LOU (IRE), 5, b m Mahler—Wet And Dry (IRE) **Mr C. R. P. Williams**
8 FEU ARDENT (FR), 4, ch g Secret Singer (FR)—Vierge Sainte (FR) **Christian Williams Racing Club**
9 FIFTY SHADES (IRE), 6, gr g Tajraasi (USA)—Baylough Mist (IRE) **Hugh Downs & Partner**
10 JUST FOR TARA, 6, b m Malinas (GER)—Just For Jean (IRE) **Mr C. R. P. Williams**
11 LITTLE CHARLOTTE (FR), 4, b f Diogenes (IRE)—Neicha (FR) **The Can't Say No Partnership**
12 POTTERS CORNER (IRE), 9, b g Indian Danehill (IRE)—
Woodford Beauty (IRE) **All Stars Sports Racing & J Davies**
13 PRIMAL FOCUS (IRE), 5, b g Intense Focus (USA)—
Churn Dat Butter (USA) **John & Paul Stanaway & Nicola Reed**
14 SIDEWAYS (IRE), 8, b g Gamut (IRE)—Daras Mayo (IRE) **Christian Williams Racing Club**
15 STRICTLYADANCER (IRE), 5, b g Yeats (IRE)—Feale Dancer (IRE) **Christian Williams Racing Club**
16 THE BOOM IS BACK (IRE), 7, b g Publisher (USA)—Wild Coast (IRE) **Burnham Plastering & Drylining Ltd**
17 UNO MAS, 5, b g Morozov (USA)—Broomhill Lady **Christian Williams Racing Club**
18 WHERE NOW (IRE), 8, b g Where Or When (IRE)—Exciting Prospect (IRE) **All Stars Sports Racing**
19 WIN MY WINGS (IRE), 6, b m Gold Well—Telstar (IRE) **Ms S. Howell & Partner 1**
20 YOUNGOCONNOR (IRE), 6, b m Kalanisi (IRE)—Strike Three (IRE) **All Stars Sports Racing**

THREE-YEAR-OLDS
21 B c Nathaniel (IRE)—Daraiyna (FR)
22 B c Vocalised (USA)—Gilded Butterfly (USA)

Other Owners: Mr J. J. V. Davies, Mr B. H. Downs, Ms S. A. Howell, Mr A. James, Mr I. Marmion, Mr G. C. Maule, Mr A. Randle, Mr J. Stanaway.

Assistant Trainer: Nicky Williams

592 MR DAI WILLIAMS, Broad Hinton
Postal: **Flat Ashley House, Hodson, Swindon, Wiltshire, SN4 0QG**
Contacts: **HOME (01488) 638636 FAX (01488) 638121 MOBILE (07879) 403160 (07879) 403595**

1 ANGELICAL EVE (IRE), 5, gr m Dark Angel (IRE)—First Lady (IRE) **Mr A. M. Rennison**
2 BABYTAGGLE (IRE), 8, b g Brian Boru—Ardnataggle (IRE) **Mr F. Michael**
3 BEAN LIATH (IRE), 8, gr m Portrait Gallery (IRE)—Coolnasmear (IRE) **Hewitt & Michael Partnership**
4 BENNYS GIRL (IRE), 11, b m Beneficial—Be My Flower (IRE) **We Must Be Barmy**
5 BOBONYX, 9, b g Phoenix Reach (IRE)—Twist The Facts (USA) **Caldona Racing Club**
6 COLD FUSION (IRE), 6, b m Frozen Power (IRE)—Tuscania (USA) **Mr A. M. Rennison**
7 HAVE A GO HERO (IRE), 11, b g Flemensfirth (USA)—Blue Bank (IRE) **We Must Be Barmy**
8 LINGUINE (IRE), 9, ch g Linngari (IRE)—Amerissage (USA) **Mr A. M. Rennison**
9 NORUKI (IRE), 9, b g Flemensfirth (USA)—Classic Material **Mr F. Michael**
10 OMEGA SPRINGS (IRE), 11, b g Great Exhibition (USA)—Leefield Rose (IRE) **Hewitt & Michael Partnership**

MR DAI WILLIAMS - Continued

11 **PETIT ECUYER (FR)**, 13, b g Equerry (USA)—Petite Majeste (FR) **Mr G. C. Farr**
12 **POSITIVE TOUCH (IRE)**, 8, b g Misternando—Independant Flora **Mr S. R. Williams**
13 **STOLBERG (IRE)**, 11, br g Vinnie Roe (IRE)—Giveherthewhistle (IRE) **Mr A. M. Rennison**

Other Owners: Mr G. Bell, R. J. Hewitt.

Assistant Trainer: Miss Lucy Horner

Amateur: Miss L. Horner.

---

593 **MR EVAN WILLIAMS, Llancarfan**
Postal: Fingerpost Farm, Llancarfan, Nr Barry, Vale of Glamorgan, CF62 3AE
Contacts: PHONE (01446) 754069 FAX (01446) 754069 MOBILE (07950) 381227
E-MAIL cath@evanwilliams.co.uk WEBSITE www.evanwilliamsracing.co.uk

1 **ABBEYGREY (IRE)**, 10, b g Generous (IRE)—Garw Valley **R. E. R. Williams**
2 **AGENT WESTY (IRE)**, 5, b g Fame And Glory—Isis Du Berlais (FR) **R. E. R. Williams**
3 **ANNIE BONNY**, 6, b m Black Sam Bellamy (IRE)—Queenoz (IRE) **Mrs C. A. Williams**
4 **ANNSAM**, 4, b g Black Sam Bellamy (IRE)—Bathwick Annie **H. M. W. Clifford**
5 **ARCADE ATTRACTION (IRE)**, 5, b g Arcadio (GER)—Tobetall **R. E. R. Williams**
6 **ASTRA VIA**, 4, b f Multiplex—Wou Oodd **Mrs J. Davies**
7 **BALLYBREEN (IRE)**, 6, b g Gold Well—Miss Colclough (IRE) **R. E. R. Williams**
8 **BILLY BRONCO**, 8, ch g Central Park—Nan **Mr & Mrs William Rucker**
9 **BISCAY BAY**, 4, ch c Champs Elysees—Cinnamon Bay **John Swinnerton & Partner**
10 **BOLD PLAN (IRE)**, 5, b g Jeremy (USA)—Kings Orchid (IRE) **Mr & Mrs William Rucker**
11 **BURN BABY BYRNE**, 6, b m Malinas (GER)—Top of The Dee **R. E. R. Williams**
12 **BUYWISE (IRE)**, 12, b g Tikkanen (USA)—Greenogue Princess (IRE) **Mr T. Hywel Jones**
13 **CAROUSE (IRE)**, 4, b g Excelebration (IRE)—Terre du Vent (FR) **Richard Abbott & Mario Stavrou**
14 **CASWELL BAY**, 4, b g Fame And Glory—Lauderdale (GER) **Mr David M. Williams**
15 **CESAR COLLONGES (FR)**, 7, ch g Fragrant Mix (IRE)—Prouesse Collonges (FR) **Mr & Mrs William Rucker**
16 **CLYNE**, 9, b g Hernando (FR)—Lauderdale (GER) **Mr D. M. Williams**
17 **COTTON JENNY (IRE)**, 8, br m Craigsteel—Rose N Alice (IRE) **Mr W. P. Bates**
18 **COURT DANCER (IRE)**, 4, b g Court Cave (IRE)—Windsor Dancer (IRE) **Mrs J. Davies**
19 **COURT ROYALE (IRE)**, 6, b g Court Cave (IRE)—Windsor Dancer (IRE) **Mrs Janet Davies**
20 **CRACKLE LYN ROSIE**, 5, b m Kayf Tara—Native Sunrise (IRE) **R. E. R. Williams**
21 **DARK INVADER (FR)**, 7, b g Saint des Saints (FR)—Minirose (FR) **Mrs C. A. Williams**
22 4, B g Sholokhov (IRE)—Elphis (IRE)
23 **ESPRIT DU LARGE (FR)**, 5, b g No Risk At All (FR)—Tuffslolyloly (FR) **Mr & Mrs William Rucker**
24 **FILLE DES CHAMPS (IRE)**, 8, b m Robin des Champs (FR)—South Queen Lady (IRE) **Mrs Janet Davies**
25 **FIREBIRD FLYER (IRE)**, 12, b g Winged Love (IRE)—Kiora Lady (IRE) **R. E. R. Williams**
26 **FLIGHT TO MILAN (IRE)**, 6, b g Milan—Kigali (IRE) **R. E. R. Williams**
27 **GO LONG (IRE)**, 9, b g Hurricane Run (IRE)—Monumental Gesture **Mr & Mrs William Rucker**
28 **GOLDEN WHISKY (IRE)**, 6, ch g Flemensfirth (USA)—Derry Vale (IRE) **Mr & Mrs William Rucker**
29 **GRANIA O'MALLEY (IRE)**, 6, ch m Beat Hollow—Oh Susannah (FR) **Ms S. Howell**
30 **GWALIA (IRE)**, 6, b g Beat Hollow—Payphone **Mr D. M. Williams**
31 **HANDS OF STONE (IRE)**, 7, b g Shantou (USA)—Hayabusa **Morse, Footman & Williams**
32 **HOLDBACKTHERIVER (IRE)**, 7, b g Presenting—Fairy Lane (IRE) **W J Evans Racing**
33 **INCH LALA (IRE)**, 7, ch m Mahler—Aboo Lala (IRE) **Clifford, Gosden & House**
34 **JOHN CONSTABLE (IRE)**, 8, b g Montjeu (IRE)—Dance Parade (USA) **Walters Plant Hire Ltd**
35 **JONAGOLD**, 8, b g Apple Tree (FR)—Single Handed **Mr W. J. Evans**
36 **JOUR A LA PLAGE (FR)**, 4, gr g Coastal Path—Juntina (FR) **R. E. R. Williams**
37 **KEEPING FAITH (IRE)**, 5, br m Sholokhov (IRE)—Elphis (IRE) **Mr & Mrs William Rucker**
38 **KHANISARI (IRE)**, 5, gr g Dark Angel (IRE)—Kadayna (IRE) **Pos Partnership 2**
39 **KING'S ODYSSEY (IRE)**, 10, b g King's Theatre (IRE)—Ma Furie (FR) **Mr & Mrs William Rucker**
40 **MAC BELLA**, 7, ch m Black Sam Bellamy (IRE)—Macnance (IRE) **Keith & Sue Lowry**
41 **MACK THE MAN (IRE)**, 5, b g Flemensfirth (USA)—Nifty Nuala (IRE) **Mr & Mrs William Rucker**
42 **MARBLE MOON (IRE)**, 7, b g Millenary—Royal Marble (IRE) **Mr Emrys Jones & Partner**
43 **MARKET ROAD (IRE)**, 9, gr g Tikkanen (USA)—Clydeside (IRE) **W J Evans Racing**
44 **MOUSEINTHEHOUSE (IRE)**, 5, b g Milan—Mandysue (IRE) **R. E. R. Williams**
45 **NEWQUAY CARDS (IRE)**, 7, gr g Tikkanen (USA)—Sanadja (IRE) **Mr T. Hywel Jones**
46 **NO REMATCH (IRE)**, 5, b g Westerner—Loadsofability (IRE) **Mr & Mrs William Rucker**
47 **ON THE QUIET (FR)**, 4, b br f Ballingarry (IRE)—Royale Sulawesie (FR) **Mrs C. A. Williams**
48 **ON THE ROAD (IRE)**, 9, b g Stowaway—B Greenhill **Mrs C. A. Williams**
49 **ON THE ROX (IRE)**, 6, b g Fastnet Rock (AUS)—Dance Parade (USA) **R. E. R. Williams**
50 **ON TOUR (IRE)**, 11, b g Croco Rouge (IRE)—Galant Tour (IRE) **Mr T. Hywel Jones**

MR EVAN WILLIAMS - Continued

51 **OXWICH BAY (IRE)**, 7, b g Westerner—Rose de Beaufai (FR) **Mr David M. Williams**
52 **PAXMAN (IRE)**, 5, b g Jeremy (USA)—Dreamy Lagoon (IRE) **Mr & Mrs William Rucker**
53 **PETERBOROUGH (FR)**, 6, b g Fuisse (FR)—Peony Girl (FR) **Norwester Racing Club & Partner**
54 **POBBLES BAY (IRE)**, 9, b g Oscar (IRE)—Rose de Beaufai (FR) **Mr D. M. Williams**
55 **PRESENT TIMES (IRE)**, 8, b g Kalanisi (IRE)—Beguiling (IRE) **Mrs C. A. Waters**
56 **PRESENT VALUE (IRE)**, 5, b g Gold Well—Presenting Shares (IRE) **Mr & Mrs William Rucker**
57 **PRIME VENTURE (IRE)**, 8, br g Primary (USA)—Next Venture (IRE) **Mrs Janet Davies**
58 **QUOI DE NEUF (FR)**, 5, b g Anzillero (GER)—Qualite Controlee (FR) **Mr & Mrs William Rucker**
59 **RADICAL ARCHIE**, 8, ch g Prince Arch (USA)—Radical Gunner **Mrs Janet Davies**
60 **RAILROAD JUNKIE (IRE)**, 6, b g Thousand Words—Eckbeag (USA) **Mrs J. Davies**
61 **SECRET REPRIEVE (IRE)**, 5, b g Flemensfirth (USA)—Oscar's Reprieve (IRE) **Mr & Mrs William Rucker**
62 **SHREWD TACTICS (IRE)**, 8, ch g Broadway Flyer (USA)—Taking My Time (IRE) **W. J. Evans**
63 **SIGN OF WAR (IRE)**, 5, b g Oscar (IRE)—Irish Wedding (IRE) **R. E. R. Williams**
64 **SILVER STREAK (IRE)**, 6, gr g Dark Angel (IRE)—Happy Talk (IRE) **Mr T. L. Fell**
65 **SKEWIFF (IRE)**, 7, b m Doyen (IRE)—Skew **Mrs Janet Davies**
66 4, Br g Arcadio (GER)—Spangle Island
67 **ST JOHN'S**, 6, b g Aqlaam—Diam Queen (GER) **Simone & Yasmin Cuddy**
68 **STILL BELIEVING (IRE)**, 11, ch m Blueprint (IRE)—Im A Believer (IRE) **R. E. R. Williams**
69 **SUTTER'S MILL (IRE)**, 8, b g Gold Well—Shamriyna (IRE) **R. E. R. Williams**
70 **THE GIPPER (IRE)**, 9, b g King's Theatre (IRE)—Merrill Gaye (IRE) **POS Partnership**
71 **THE LAST DAY (IRE)**, 7, b g Oscar (IRE)—The Last Bank (IRE) **Mr & Mrs William Rucker**
72 **TREASURE DILLON (IRE)**, 5, b g Sans Frontieres (IRE)—Treasure Trix (IRE) **Mr R Abbott & Mr M Stavrou**
73 **VIRGINIA CHICK (FR)**, 7, b g Nickname (FR)—Sweet Jaune (FR) **Mrs C. A. Williams**
74 **VOODOO DOLL (IRE)**, 6, b g Getaway (GER)—Voodoo Magic (GER) **R. E. R. Williams**

Other Owners: R. J. Abbott, Mrs S. Cuddy, Miss Y. Cuddy, M. V. Dawson, Mr D. C. Footman, Mr I. F. Gosden, Mr R. House, Ms S. A. Howell, Mr E. C. Jones, Mr T. H. Jones, Mr D. G. Long, K. R. Lowry, Mrs S. B. Lowry, W. J. G. Morse, Norwester Racing Club, Mrs A. Rucker, W. J. Rucker, M. Stavrou, W. J. Swinnerton, Mr C. Trigg.

Assistant Trainer: Cath Williams

Jockey (NH): Adam Wedge. **Conditional:** Conor Ring. **Amateur:** Miss Isabel Williams.

594

MR IAN WILLIAMS, Alvechurch
Postal: **Dominion Racing Stables, Seafield Lane, Alvechurch, Birmingham, B48 7HL**
Contacts: **PHONE** (01564) 822392 **FAX** (01564) 829475 **MOBILE** (07976) 645384
E-MAIL info@ianwilliamsracing.com **WEBSITE** www.ianwilliamsracing.com

1 **ACES (IRE)**, 7, b g Dark Angel (IRE)—Cute Ass (IRE) **The Tuesday Syndicate and Michael Watt**
2 **ADMAN SAM (IRE)**, 8, b g Black Sam Bellamy (IRE)—Koral Bay (FR) **Mr P. A. Downing**
3 **ALLBARONE (IRE)**, 5, b g September Storm (GER)—Tippeenan Lass (IRE) **R. S. Brookhouse**
4 4, B g Winged Love (IRE)—Ally Rose (IRE)
5 **ALMOST GOLD (IRE)**, 6, b g Gold Well—Shining Lights (IRE) **Mr S. Cox**
6 **ALWAYS RESOLUTE**, 8, b g Refuse To Bend (IRE)—Mad Annie (USA) **Ne-Chance**
7 **AMBER GAMBLER (GER)**, 9, b g Doyen (IRE)—Auenglocke (GER) **P. Kelly**
8 **BAMAKO DU CHATELET (FR)**, 8, gr g Voix du Nord (FR)—Royale du Chatelet (FR) **Macable Partnership**
9 **BANDITRY (IRE)**, 7, b g Iffraaj—Badalona **Buxted Partnership**
10 **BARON DU PLESSIS (FR)**, 8, b g Network (GER)—Larme A L'oeil (FR) **I. P. Williams**
11 **BAYDAR**, 6, b g Rock of Gibraltar (IRE)—Splashdown **Mr K. Sohi**
12 **BELLE BELLA (IRE)**, 7, b m Kalanisi (IRE)—Reseda (GER) **I. P. Williams**
13 **BLUE RAMBLER**, 9, b g Monsun (GER)—La Nuit Rose (FR) **Mr P. A. Downing**
14 **BOL D'AIR (FR)**, 8, b g Blue Bresil (FR)—Holding (FR) **Mr P. Hernon**
15 **BOY IN THE BAR**, 8, ch g Dutch Art—Lipsia (IRE) **Allwins Stables**
16 **BREATH CAUGHT**, 4, b g Bated Breath—Double Crossed **Amo Racing Limited**
17 **BUXTED DREAM (USA)**, 5, gr g Dream Ahead (USA)—America Nova (FR) **Buxted Partnership**
18 **BYRON FLYER**, 8, b g Byron—Nursling (USA) **Anchor Men**
19 **CAPTAIN SUE (IRE)**, 5, ch m Tamayuz—Correct **I. P. Williams**
20 **CARLITA MORIVIERE (FR)**, 7, b m Balko (FR)—Halladine (FR) **Mr C. S. Hinchy**
21 **CAUSE TOUJOURS (FR)**, 7, b g Khalkevi (FR)—Viana (FR) **Mr C. S. Hinchy**
22 **CENTRAL CITY (IRE)**, 4, b g Kodiac—She Basic (IRE) **Mr S. Coomes**
23 4, Ch g Sholokhov (IRE)—Chiltern Hills (IRE)
24 **COOL SKY**, 10, b g Milkom—Intersky High (USA) **Norte Sur Partnership**
25 **CRACKING DESTINY (IRE)**, 6, b g Dubai Destination (USA)—Cracking Gale (IRE) **Grech & Parkin**
26 4, B g Mustameet (USA)—Crescendor (IRE)
27 **DADS LEGACY**, 4, ch g Schiaparelli (GER)—Our Jess (IRE)

MR IAN WILLIAMS - Continued

28 DARKSIDEOFTARNSIDE (IRE), 5, b g Intense Focus (USA)—Beautiful Dancer (IRE) **Mr L. G. Horsfield**
29 DESERT TRIP (FR), 4, b g Fuisse (FR)—Sea Life (FR) **Mr S. Coomes**
30 DIAKTOROS (IRE), 9, b g Red Clubs (IRE)—Rinneen (IRE) **Mr S. Coomes**
31 DON'T ACT UP, 8, gr g Act One—Lucky Arrow **Ian Williams Racing Club**
32 DORY (IRE), 6, br m Westerner—Papal Princess (IRE) **Mr C. S. Hinchy**
33 DOUBLE UP, 8, b g Exceed And Excel (AUS)—My Love Thomas (IRE) **Mr & Mrs H. Parmar**
34 DR DORO (IRE), 6, b m Holy Roman Emperor (IRE)—Stellarina (IRE) **Allwins Stables**
35 EAT MY DIRT (IRE), 7, b g Mahler—Aos Dana (IRE) **I. P. Williams**
36 EGYPT MILL DUKE, 4, b g Intikhab (USA)—Questama **Mr S. R. Webb**
37 FAITHFUL MOUNT, 10, b g Shirocco (GER)—Lady Lindsay (IRE) **Macable Partnership**
38 FALDO (IRE), 4, gr g Jukebox Jury (IRE)—Fusca (GER) **M. H. Watt**
39 FIRE AHEAD (IRE), 6, b g Yeats (IRE)—Ring of Fire (USA) **P. Kelly**
40 FIRST ASSIGNMENT (IRE), 6, b g Vinnie Roe (IRE)—Rebel Dream (IRE) **The DTTW Partnership**
41 FIRST CALL (FR), 4, ch g Shamardal (USA)—Reponds Moi (USA) **Dr M. B. Q. S. Koukash**
42 FOLAU, 4, br c Aussie Rules (USA)—Sky High Diver (IRE)
43 FREEBE ROCKS (IRE), 4, ch g Camacho—Shamardyh (IRE) **S. Hassiakos**
44 GAS LINE BOY (IRE), 13, b g Blueprint (IRE)—Jervia **The Three Graces**
45 GETAWAY MISSION (IRE), 5, b g Getaway (IRE)—Emeranna (IRE) **Andrew Dick & Steve Roberts**
46 GOING GOLD (IRE), 7, b g Gold Well—Wednesday Girl (IRE) **Mr C. S. Hinchy**
47 GRAND INQUISITOR, 7, b g Dansili—Dusty Answer **Macable Partnership & Mr S Hassiakos**
48 HARLOW, 5, b g Harlan's Holiday (USA)—Glowing (USA) **S. Ross**
49 HEART OF SOUL (IRE), 4, b g Makfi—Hadrian's Waltz (USA) **Dr M. B. Q. S. Koukash**
50 HERESTHETHING (IRE), 6, b g Milan—The Mighty Matron (IRE) **John Nicholls (Trading) Ltd**
51 IDILICO (FR), 4, b g Lawman (FR)—Ydillique (IRE) **Mr A. D. Dick**
52 JAM SESSION (IRE), 7, ch g Duke of Marmalade (IRE)—Night Dhu **Mr A. L. R. Morton**
53 JAWSHAN (USA), 4, b g Denman (AUS)—Diamond Baby (USA) **I. P. Williams**
54 JAYTEE, 4, ch g Schiaparelli (GER)—Archway Copse **J. Tredwell**
55 JUMPSUIT, 6, b g Tobougg (IRE)—Charmaine Wood **The Ferandlin Peaches**
56 KAPSTADT (FR), 9, b br g Country Reel (USA)—King's Parody (IRE) **Anchor Men**
57 KING OF REALMS (IRE), 7, b g King's Theatre (IRE)—Sunny South East (IRE) **Chandler Ferguson Hanafin Kelly**
58 LERICHI BELLE (IRE), 8, b m King's Theatre (IRE)—Lerichi (IRE) **The Transporters**
59 LOLLYS DREAM (IRE), 4, b f Declaration of War (USA)—Bunood (IRE) **Amo Racing Limited**
60 LUCKY RESET, 4, ch f Yorgunnabelucky (USA)—Reset City **I. P. Williams**
61 LUCKY'S DREAM, 4, ch g Yorgunnabelucky (USA)—Dream Esteem **R. S. Brookhouse**
62 MACHIATO (IRE), 8, b g Milan—Wychnor Dawn (IRE) **Inspire Racing Club & Partner**
63 MAGICAL MISS (IRE), 6, ch m Beat Hollow—Sorivera **Equinox Racing**
64 MANDARIN (GER), 5, ch g Lope de Vega (IRE)—Margarita (GER) **Sohi & Sohi**
65 MANJAAM (IRE), 6, ch g Tamayuz—Priory Rock (IRE) **Sohi & Sohi**
66 MATEWAN (IRE), 4, b g Epaulette (AUS)—Cochin (USA) **J. Tredwell**
67 MEXICAN DAVE, 4, b g Sakhee (USA)—Artic Bliss **First Chance Racing**
68 MICHAEL'S MOUNT, 9, ch g Mount Nelson—Dumnoni **Andrew Dick & Mark Dennis**
69 MIRACLE GARDEN, 7, ch g Exceed And Excel (AUS)—Sharp Terms **Mr M. A. Geobey**
70 MISS MUMTAZ (IRE), 4, ch f Lope de Vega (IRE)—Ispanka **Sohi & Sohi**
71 MISTY BIRNAM (SAF), 6, gr g Toreador (IRE)—In The Mist (SAF) **Mr P. E. Wildes**
72 MOKAATIL, 4, br g Lethal Force (IRE)—Moonlit Garden (IRE) **Midtech**
73 MONJENI, 6, b g Montjeu (IRE)—Polly's Mark (IRE) **Corinthian Racing Club**
74 MOUNTAIN ROCK (IRE), 7, b g Mountain High (USA)—Ajo Green (IRE) **Mr M. Fitzgerald**
75 NIGH OR NEVER (IRE), 5, b g Excelebration (IRE)—Nigh (IRE) **P. Kelly**
76 NOBLE BEHEST, 5, b g Sir Percy—Lady Hestia (USA) **Mr A. C. Elliott**
77 NORTH HILL (IRE), 8, b g Westerner—Hill Fairy **Ms S. A. Howell**
78 OI THE CLUBB OI'S, 4, gr g Champs Elysees—Red Boots (USA) **The Albatross Club**
79 ONE FLEW OVER (IRE), 4, b g Jeremy—Coill Cri (IRE) **I. P. Williams**
80 ONE MORE FLEURIE (IRE), 5, b g Mustameet (USA)—Auburn Cherry (IRE)
81 OSCAR HOOF (IRE), 11, b g Oscar (IRE)—New Legislation (IRE) **A Chandler Racing**
82 OUR IDIC BOY (IRE), 5, b g Royal Anthem (USA)—Next Best Thing (IRE) **Mr K. McKenna**
83 PADDY A (IRE), 5, b g Holy Roman Emperor (IRE)—Lilting (IRE) **DBAC Syndicate**
84 PADDY THE CHEF (IRE), 4, b g Dandy Man (IRE)—The Reek **Mr & Mrs H. Parmar**
85 PERFECT SUMMER, 9, b m High Chaparral (IRE)—Power of Future (GER) **The Ferandlin Peaches**
86 POKER SCHOOL (IRE), 9, b g Gold Well—Broken Pockets (IRE) **Mr A Aniol, Mr S Turner, Mr A Chandler**
87 PORTWAY FLYER (IRE), 11, br g King's Theatre (IRE)—Next Best Thing (IRE) **P. Kelly**
88 POUR JOIE (IRE), 4, b g Pour Moi (IRE)—Lupa Montana (USA) **Helen Jameson Racing Partnership**
89 PREVENT, 4, br g Poet's Voice—Emergency **Sohi & Sohi**
90 PSYCHEDELIC ROCK, 8, b g Yeats (IRE)—Gemini Lucy (IRE) **John Nicholls (Trading) Ltd**
91 PURE AFFECTION (IRE), 8, b m Beneficial—Regents Dancer (IRE) **Ian Williams Racing Club**
92 PURE SHORES, 5, b m Dubawi (IRE)—Polly's Mark (IRE) **Fergus Anstock**

MR IAN WILLIAMS - Continued

93 READER'S CHOICE, 5, b g Redoute's Choice (AUS)—Forever Times **Mr A. Belshaw**
94 RED INFANTRY (IRE), 9, ch g Indian River (FR)—Red Rover **Mr R. Little**
95 RESHOUN (FR), 5, b g Shamardal (USA)—Radiyya (IRE) **Michael Watt & Roy David**
96 RICHIE MCCAW, 6, b g Zamindar (USA)—Cochin (USA) **Michael Watt & Billy Slater (aus)**
97 ROCKNROLLRAMBO (IRE), 12, b g Winged Love (IRE)—Lady Padivor (IRE) **Ian Williams Racing Club**
98 5, B m Arvico (FR)—Sainte Kadette (FR) **The Ferandlin Peaches**
99 SECRET LEGACY (IRE), 8, b g Flemensfirth (USA)—Wingfield Lady (IRE) **Andrew Dick & Mike Askew**
00 SEVEN DE BAUNE (FR), 6, ch g Tiger Groom—Venus de Baune (FR) **R. S. Brookhouse**
01 SHADY MCCOY (USA), 9, b g English Channel (USA)—Raw Gold (USA) **Moukey**
02 SHIP OF THE FEN, 4, b g Champs Elysees—Ruffled **M. H. Watt**
03 SIR MAXIMILIAN (IRE), 10, b g Royal Applause—Nebraska Lady (IRE) **Mr P. E. Wildes**
04 SLIDING DOORS (IRE), 6, b g Ask—Reseda (GER) **The Three Graces**
05 SOLAR IMPULSE (IRE), 9, b g Westerner—Moon Glow (FR) **Andy Bell & Fergus Lyons**
06 SOME OPERATOR (IRE), 5, b g September Storm (GER)—Emilies Pearl (IRE) **A. Stennett**
07 SOMETIMES ALWAYS (IRE), 4, b g Presenting—Noras Fancy (IRE) **Mr S. Cox**
08 SPEED COMPANY (IRE), 6, b g Fast Company (IRE)—Trentini (USA) **A. Stennett**
09 SPEEDO BOY (FR), 5, ch g Vision d'etat (FR)—Shamardanse (FR) **Mr P. R. Williams**
11 SQUATS (IRE), 7, b g Dandy Man (IRE)—Light Sea (IRE) **M. H. Watt**
11 STELLARISTA (IRE), 5, b m Mastercraftsman (IRE)—Stellarina (IRE) **Allwins Stables**
12 SUNNYTAHLIATEIGAN (IRE), 7, b g Robin des Pres (IRE)—Wavering Bee (IRE) **Mr P. Hernon**
13 SWORDBILL, 4, ch g Champs Elysees—Dream Wild **Sohi & Sohi**
14 TAKING A CHANCE (IRE), 6, b m Flemensfirth (USA)—Northern Mill (IRE) **Ian Williams Racing Club**
16 THEHOSSBEHIND (IRE), 8, ch g Mahler—Bayloughbess (IRE) **The Piranha Partnership**
17 TIDE TIMES (IRE), 5, gr g Vinnie Roe (IRE)—Lady Wagtail (IRE) **The DTTW Partnership**
18 TIKK TOCK BOOM (IRE), 7, gr m Tikkanen (USA)—Henrietta (IRE) **The Ferandlin Peaches**
19 TIME TO STUDY (FR), 5, ch g Motivator—Dissertation (FR) **Mr K. Sohi**
20 WAR BRIGADE (IRE), 5, b g Manduro (GER)—Adjudicate **The DTTW Partnership**
21 WATT BRODERICK (IRE), 10, ch g Hawk Wing (USA)—Kingsridge (IRE) **P. Kelly**
22 WESTERN DUKE (IRE), 5, b g High Chaparral (IRE)—Witch of Fife (USA) **London City Bloodstock**
23 WHISPERING AFFAIR, 8, b m Black Sam Bellamy (IRE)—City of Angels **R. S. Brookhouse**
24 WOLFCATCHER (IRE), 7, b g King's Best (USA)—Miss Particular (IRE) **Buxted Partnership**
25 YORBELUCKY, 4, b g Yorgunnabelucky (USA)—Circle of Angels **R. S. Brookhouse**
26 ZERACHIEL (IRE), 9, b g Winged Love (IRE)—At Dawn (IRE) **John Nicholls (Trading) Ltd**
27 ZUBAYR (IRE), 7, b g Authorized (IRE)—Zaziyra (IRE) **Mr P. J. Vogt**

THREE-YEAR-OLDS

28 Ch f Piccolo—Basle **Mr M. A. Geobey**
29 CANOODLING, b f Nathaniel (IRE)—Tequila Sunrise **Mr C. N. Wright**
30 CARDANO (USA), b g Oasis Dream—Astorgs Galaxy **Sohi & Sohi**
31 CHAMPAGNE MARENGO (IRE), b c Battle of Marengo (IRE)—Sidney Girl **Champagne Charlies Racing Club**
32 FAST ENDEAVOUR, b f Pastoral Pursuits—Scented Garden **Middleham Park Racing Cii & Partner 2**
33 GABRIAL THE GIANT (IRE), b g Battle of Marengo (IRE)—Compassion **Dr M. B. Q. S. Koukash**
34 GINGER FOX, b g Iffraaj—Rimth **Denford Stud Limited**
35 GOD HAS GIVEN, b g Nathaniel (IRE)—Langs Lash (IRE) **Sohi & Sohi**
36 GOLDEN GRENADE (FR), b g Zanzibari (USA)—King's Parody **Mr R. Little**
37 PUNJAB MAIL, b g Charm Spirit (IRE)—Harryana **Sohi & Sohi**
38 SHAMRAD (FR), b g Casamento (IRE)—Shamsa (FR) **Midtech 2**
39 TRIBAL COMMANDER, gr g Intikhab (USA)—Jessica Ennis (USA) **Lease Terminated**

Other Owners: Mr S. M. P. Adcock, Mr G. Anderson, Mr M. Aniol, Mr M. R. Askew, Mr A. J. Bell, Mr M. L. W. Bell, Mrs T. Bell, Mr C. Bennett, Blythe Stables LLP, Mr T. J. Boniface, Mr D. E. Carolan, Mr A. Chandler, Mr A. Cocum, Mr K. A. Cosby, Mr R. David, Mr M. N. Dennis, Dr P. A. I. Doro, Sir A. Ferguson, Mr N. D. Ford, Mrs M. Forsyth, J. A. Gent, Mr C. M. Grech, Mr D. Hanafin, J. P. Hanifin, Ms R. J. Harris, T. Hart, Mr M. Hilton, Miss D. Hitchins, Mrs D. Hopkins, Inspire Racing Club Ltd, Mrs H. Jameson, Mr D. P. G. Jones, Mr N. N. Kane, Mrs B. J. Keighley, Mr P. J. Legros, Mrs C. Lyons, Fergus & Caroline Lyons, Mr F. Lyons, Mr S. Mackintosh, Mr F. W. Mackintosh, Mr C. R. Mander, Mr G. Marshall, Mr C. McHale, Middleham Park Racing CII, Mr A. Miles, Mr F. Mooney, Mr A. J. R. Moseley, Palatinate Thoroughbred Racing Limited, T. S. Palin, Mr S. J. Parkin, Mrs K. Parmar, Mr H. Parmar, M. Prince, Mr P Ratcliffe, Mr A. M. Reason, Mr J. A. Reynard, Mrs S. Roberts, J. L. Rowsell, Mr S. Rudolf, Mrs J. Ruthven, Mr M. J. Savage, Seven Barrows Limited, Mr W. N. Slater, Mr J. Sohi, Mr P. Southall, Mr P. Thwaites, Mr S. W. Turner.

Assistant Trainer: Ben Brookhouse

Jockey (NH): Tom O'Brien. **Conditional:** Edward Austin. **Apprentice:** Luke Catton.

595 MRS JANE WILLIAMS, South Molton
Postal: **Culverhill Farm, George Nympton, South Molton, Devon, EX36 4JE**

1 **AUBUSSON (FR)**, 10, b g Ballingarry (IRE)—Katioucha (FR) **Mrs J. R. Williams**
2 **DAIM PIERJI (FR)**, 6, b g Coastal Path—Keensland (FR) **Mrs J. R. Williams**
3 **DIABLE DE SIVOLA (FR)**, 6, b g Noroit (GER)—Grande Route (IRE) **Mr R. Forster**
4 **ERICK LE ROUGE (FR)**, 5, ch g Gentlewave (IRE)—Imperia II (FR) **The Culverhill Racing Club**
5 **ESPRIT DE SOMOZA (FR)**, 5, b g Irish Wells (FR)—Topaze de Somoza (FR) **Mr R. Forster**
6 **FOLLY GATE (FR)**, 4, b g Montmartre—Cate Bleue (FR) **Mrs Jane Williams & Mr R Stark**
7 **FOX PRO (FR)**, 4, b g Coastal Path—Devise II (FR) **Mrs J. R. Williams**
8 **GAMAIN (IRE)**, 10, b g Gamut (IRE)—Glass Curtain (IRE) **Mrs J. R. Williams**
9 **IN REM (FR)**, 4, b g Kapgarde (FR)—Etoile des Iles (FR) **Mr R. Forster**
10 **JEU DE MOTS (FR)**, 6, b g Saint des Saints (FR)—Nanouska (GER) **Mrs J. R. Williams**
11 **MONSIEUR LECOQ (FR)**, 5, b g Diamond Boy (FR)—Draga (FR) **Mrs J. R. Williams**
12 **MONTESTREL (FR)**, 4, b g Montmartre (FR)—La Estrella (GER) **Mrs J. R. Williams**
13 **MOONLIGHTER**, 6, b g Midnight Legend—Countess Camilla **Mrs Jane Williams, Huw & Richard Davies**
14 **PERUVIEN BLEU (FR)**, 7, b br g Fuisse (FR)—Edelmira (FR) **Mrs J. R. Williams**
15 **ROCOCO RIVER**, 5, b g Shirocco (GER)—Noun de La Thinte (FR) **Mrs Jane Williams & Mr R Stark**
16 **ROMEO BROWN**, 5, br g Yeats (IRE)—Santia **Mrs J. R. Williams**
17 **SPARKY VALENTINE (FR)**, 4, b f Kapgarde (FR)—Qualite Controlee (FR) **Mrs J. R. Williams**
18 **TEA FOR TWO**, 10, b g Kayf Tara—One For Me **Mrs Jane Williams & Mr Len Jakeman**
19 **WILLOW MAY**, 5, b m Sakhee (USA)—Cerise Bleue (FR) **Mrs J. R. Williams**

THREE-YEAR-OLDS

20 **GLADIATEUR ALLEN (FR)**, b g Saint des Saints (FR)—Une Epoque (FR) **Mrs J. R. Williams**
21 B f Fame And Glory—Laetitia (IRE) **Mrs J. R. Williams**
22 **LE CRUNCH (FR)**, b g Cokoriko (FR)—Line Divine (FR) **Mrs J. R. Williams**

TWO-YEAR-OLDS

23 **HAMILTON DICI (FR)**, b g 23/5 Coastal Path—Umbria Dici (FR) (Assessor (IRE)) (15170) **Mrs J. R. William**

Other Owners: Dr Martin Booth, Mr Huw Davies, Mr R. L. Davies, Mr Len Jakeman, Mr R. Stark.

Conditional: Lizzie Kelly, Chester Williams.

596 MR NICK WILLIAMS, South Molton
Postal: **Culverhill Farm, George Nympton, South Molton, Devon, EX36 4JE**
Contacts: **PHONE (01769) 574174 MOBILE (07855) 450379**
E-MAIL nandjwilliams@live.co.uk

1 **AGRAPART (FR)**, 8, b br g Martaline—Afragha (IRE) **Gascoigne, Brookes & Barker**
2 **AIMEE DE SIVOLA (FR)**, 5, ch m Network (GER)—Neva de Sivola (FR) **Larkhills Racing Partnership**
3 **COO STAR SIVOLA (FR)**, 7, b g Assessor (IRE)—Santorine (FR) **Babbit Racing**
4 **CULTURE DE SIVOLA (FR)**, 7, b m Assessor (IRE)—Neva de Sivola (FR) **Larkhills Racing Partnership II**
5 **DENTLEY DE MEE (FR)**, 6, b g Lauro (GER)—Natty Twigy (FR) **Babbit Racing**
6 **DILSON (IRE)**, 4, b g Sholokhov (IRE)—Diligent **Chasing Gold Limited**
7 **FAIRE PART SIVOLA (FR)**, 4, b g Noroit (GER)—Lettre d'estruval (FR) **K Alexander/ R Watts**
8 **FAVORI DE SIVOLA (FR)**, 4, b g Noroit (GER)—Suave de Sivola (FR) **John White & Anne Underhill**
9 **FLYING TIGER (IRE)**, 6, bl g Soldier of Fortune (IRE)—Ma Preference (FR) **The Macaroni Beach Society**
10 **HORATIO HORNBLOWER (IRE)**, 11, b br g Presenting—Countess Camilla **Chasing Gold Limited**
11 **LE CAMELEON**, 4, b br g Great Pretender (IRE)—Countess Camilla **The Pretenders**
12 **LE ROCHER (FR)**, 5, b g Saint des Saints (FR)—Belle du Roi (FR) **John White & Anne Underhill**
13 **MERCENAIRE (FR)**, 5, gr g Soldier of Fortune (IRE)—Southwold (FR) **K Alexander/ R Watts**
14 **NIGHT OF SIN (FR)**, 6, gr g Sinndar (IRE)—Natt Musik (FR) **Simon Brown & Ron Watts**
15 **ONE FOR THE TEAM**, 5, b g Shirocco (GER)—Forty Winks **Forty Winks Syndicate 2**
16 **ONE OF US**, 7, b g Presenting—One Gulp **Forty Winks Syndicate**
17 **PRUDHOMME (FR)**, 4, ch g Martaline—Panzella (FR) **Gascoigne, Brookes & Barker**
18 **SIRUH DU LAC (FR)**, 6, b g Turgeon (USA)—Margerie (FR) **John White & Anne Underhill**

THREE-YEAR-OLDS

19 **BORO BABE (FR)**, ch f Sea The Stars (IRE)—Lockup (IRE) **Miss Eliisa Morgan Joseph**
20 **CHOCKS AWAY (FR)**, b g Le Havre (IRE)—Salvation **The Macaroni Beach Society**
21 **COLONEL MANDERSON (FR)**, b g Kapgarde (FR)—Playact (IRE) **Babbit Racing**

1R NICK WILLIAMS - Continued

22 **GALAHAD QUEST (FR)**, b g American Post—Atacames (FR) **Holt, Macnabb, Robinson & Jeffrey**
23 **GALICE MACALO (FR)**, b f Saddler Maker (IRE)—Victoire de Forme (FR) **Culverhill Racing Club**
24 **GINGEMBRE MENTHE (FR)**, ch g Barastraight—Jolie Menthe (FR) **French Gold**
25 **LE GRAND ROCHER (FR)**, b g Saint des Saints (FR)—Belle du Roi (FR) **John White & Anne Underhill**
26 **MOON TIGER (FR)**, b g Le Havre (IRE)—Lune Orientale (IRE) **The Macaroni Beach Society**

WO-YEAR-OLDS

27 **ALBERIC (FR)**, b g 23/3 Poliglote—Khayance (FR) (Kahyasi) **Corrina Ltd**
28 **FIGHTING TIGER (FR)**, b g 16/4 Elvstroem (AUS)—
                    Ma Preference (FR) (American Post) (33712) **My Racing Manager Friends**
29 **HECTOR DE SIVOLA (FR)**, b g 11/3 Noroit (GER)—
                    Little Memories (IRE) (Montjeu (IRE)) **Larkhills Racing Partnership**
30 **HELIOS ALLEN (FR)**, b g 19/3 Coastal Path—Silane (FR) (Dom Alco (FR)) **French Gold**
31 **HURRICANE SIVOLA (FR)**, b g 9/4 Noroit (GER)—Surprise de Sivola (FR) (Discover d'auteuil (FR)) **N S L Williams**

her Owners: Mr K. Alexander, Mr Kerry Barker, Mr N. Brookes, Mr Simon Brown, Mr Kevin Conlan, Mr Graham Devlin,
r Robert Forster, Mr Marcus Freer, Mr C. Garner, Mr S. D. Garner, Mr D. A. Gascoigne, Mr A. Holt, Mr Joe Lawrence, Mr
avid Morgan, Mrs Eliisa Morgan Joseph, Mr Ian Paye, Mr Martin Pepper, Mr G. C. Pratt, Mr J. Robinson, Mrs Karen
alters, Miss Alice Simmons, Mr James Summers, Mrs A. Underhill, Mr Ron Watts, Mr A. J. White, Mr N. S. L. Williams.

onditional: Lizzie Kelly, Chester Williams.

597	**MR NOEL WILLIAMS, Blewbury**

Postal: **Churn Stables, Churn Estate, Blewbury, Didcot, Oxfordshire, OX11 9HG**
Contacts: PHONE **(01235) 850806** MOBILE **(07887) 718678**
E-MAIL info@noelwilliamsracing.co.uk WEBSITE www.noelwilliamsracing.co.uk

1 **ANOTHER CRICK**, 6, b g Arcadio (GER)—Suetsu (IRE) **Mr D. J. S. Sewell**
2 **ANOTHER DRAMA (IRE)**, 7, b g Gamut (IRE)—Rachrush (IRE) **Mr N. Williams**
3 **AUTHORIZED TOO**, 8, b g Authorized (IRE)—Audaz **Stonepoint Racing Club**
4 **BALLI MARTINE (FR)**, 6, b g Ballingarry (IRE)—Miss Martine (FR) **Alma Vale Racing**
5 **BREAKING WAVES (IRE)**, 5, b g Yeats (IRE)—Acoola (IRE) **Colin Peake & Julie Slater**
6 **BRIERY EXPRESS**, 6, b m Rail Link—Blackbriery Thyne (IRE) **Helen Plumbly & Kathryn Leadbeater**
7 **CECILATOR**, 5, b m Delegator—Cecily Parsley **EPDS Racing**
8 4, B g Winged Love (IRE)—Courting Whitney (IRE) **Mr J. Allison & Mr A. Allison**
9 **DIVA DU MAQUIS (FR)**, 6, b m Buck's Boum (FR)—
                    Qualine du Maquis (FR) **Mr Stuart Campbell & Non League Racing**
10 **DRIFT**, 6, b m With The Flow (USA)—Lady Exe **Mr N. Williams**
11 **DRUNKEN PIRATE**, 6, b g Black Sam Bellamy (IRE)—Peel Me A Grape **Mrs E. A. Prowting**
12 **EASKEY LAD (IRE)**, 4, b g Most Improved (IRE)—Lilakiya (IRE) **D. MacAuliffe & Anoj Don Partnership**
13 **EDWARD BLUE (IRE)**, 4, b br g Vinnie Roe (IRE)—Gold Shot **Mr R. Skillen**
14 **KALINIHTA (IRE)**, 5, b g Kalanisi (IRE)—Valamareha (IRE) **Mr J. Allison & Mr A. Allison**
15 **PERCY PROSECCO**, 4, b g Sir Percy—Grapes Hill **Didnt Partnership**
16 **PURE COUNTRY**, 4, b c Frankel—Plante Rare (IRE) **Williams Racing & Partners**
17 **SAMSON THE MAN**, 6, b g Black Sam Bellamy (IRE)—Princess Cara **Ms S. Flook**
18 **SAUCHIEHALL STREET (IRE)**, 4, b g Mastercraftsman (IRE)—Top Trail (USA) **Noel Williams Racing Club**
19 **SENSULANO (IRE)**, 6, b m Milan—Espresso Lady (IRE) **Allison, Allison, Williams**
20 4, B f Kayf Tara—Shilpa (IRE) **EPDS Racing**
21 **TWIN STAR (IRE)**, 5, ch g Tagula (IRE)—Chronicle **Happy Star Partnership**

HREE-YEAR-OLDS

22 **GINO WOTIMEAN (USA)**, b br g Gio Ponti (USA)—Promulgation (USA) **Mr D. J. S. Sewell**

her Owners: Mr Austin Allison, Mr Jonny Allison, Miss L. Barry, Mr David Bellamy, Mr Stuart Campbell, Mr N. Clyne,
r M. Coleman, Mrs Kathryn Leadbeater, Mr L. Martin, Non League Racing, Mr Colin Peake, Mrs Helen Plumbly, Mr J. R.
owell, Mrs Julie Slater, Miss T. Sloan, Mr G. Spurway.

ssistant Trainer: Jeremy Mahot

ockey (NH): Thomas Garner, Wayne Hutchinson. **Conditional:** Harry Teal.

598 MR OLLY WILLIAMS, Market Rasen
Postal: **Stone Cottage, Nettleton Top, Market Rasen, Lincolnshire, LN7 6SY**
Contacts: **MOBILE (07793) 111600**
E-MAIL williams.olly@yahoo.co.uk WEBSITE www.ollywilliamsracing.co.uk

1 ESSENTIAL, 5, b g Pivotal—Something Blue **Mr D. Milthorp**
2 GOING NATIVE, ch f Speightstown—Latin Love (IRE) **D. L. Bayliss**
3 THA'IR (IRE), 9, b g New Approach (IRE)—Flashing Green **Mr D. Milthorp**
4 TRICKY DICKY, 6, b g Holy Roman Emperor (IRE)—Tricky Situation **Eight Gents & A Lady**
5 VIKING WAY (IRE), 4, ch g Society Rock (IRE)—Patrimony **Folk From The Shire**

THREE-YEAR-OLDS
6 BATTLE COMMANDER, b g Avonbridge—Antica Medusa **Mr O. R. Williams**
7 Br f Sayif (IRE)—Can Can Dancer **I. Robinson**
8 KOSTANTINA, b f Oasis Dream—Missy O' Gwaun (IRE) **Mr David L. Bayliss**
9 LINCOLN RED, ch g Monsieur Bond (IRE)—Roxy Hart **Top of the Wolds Racing**
10 RASPBERRY, b f Avonbridge—Spennymoor (IRE) **Mr O. R. Williams**

Other Owners: Mr Danny Ablott, Mr N. Baker, Mr T. A. Pocklington, Mr Ralph Roberts, Mr Trevor Smithson, Mr Ma~~rk~~ Spincer, Mr Evan Williams, Mr Olly Williams.

Assistant Trainer: Lynsey Williams

599 MR STUART WILLIAMS, Newmarket
Postal: **Diomed Stables, Hamilton Road, Newmarket, Suffolk, CB8 0PD**
Contacts: **STABLES/OFFICE (01638) 663984 HOME (01638) 560143 MOBILE (07730) 314102**
E-MAIL stuart@stuartwilliamsracing.co.uk
WEBSITE www.stuartwilliamsracing.co.uk Twitter:@Williamsstuart

1 ABLE JACK, 6, b g Iffraaj—Solva **Happy Valley Racing & Breeding Limited**
2 ALAADEL, 6, ch g Dubawi (IRE)—Infallible **Mr T. W. Morley**
3 ALEMARATALYOUM (IRE), 5, ch g Lope de Vega (IRE)—Heart of Ice (IRE) **Mrs J. Morley**
4 ALLEGIANT (USA), 4, b g City Zip (USA)—Preferential **Mr T W Morley & Partner**
5 BREATHTAKING LOOK, 4, b f Bated Breath—Love Your Looks **J. W. Parry**
6 BROUGHTON EXCELS, 4, b f Kyllachy—Excello **Broughton Thermal Insulations**
7 BURGUILLOS, 6, ch g Lope de Vega (IRE)—Hazy Dancer **Mr S Chappell and Partners**
8 CAPE CYCLONE (IRE), 4, b f Cape Cross (IRE)—Dubai Cyclone (USA) **Mr A. A. Lyons**
9 COMPAS SCOOBIE, 6, br g Kheleyf (USA)—Fantastic Santanyi **Mrs M. J. Morley**
10 DASCHAS, 5, b g Oasis Dream—Canada Water **Mr T. W. Morley**
11 DEPARTMENT OF WAR (IRE), 4, ch c Declaration of War (USA)—
Danetree Out (IRE) **Happy Valley Racing & Breeding Limited**
12 ENTHAAR, 4, ch g Sepoy (AUS)—Caledonia Princess **Mr B Piper & Mr D Cobill**
13 EQUITATION, 5, b g Equiano (FR)—Sakhee's Song (IRE) **Mr A Lyons & Mr T W Morley**
14 EXCELLENT GEORGE, 7, b g Exceed And Excel (AUS)—Princess Georgina **Mr Stuart Williams & Mr J W Parry**
15 FIELD GUN (USA), 4, b g More Than Ready (USA)—D'wild Beach (USA) **Mr T. W. Morley**
16 GHAYADH, 4, b g Kyllachy—Safe House (IRE) **Mr T. W. Morley**
17 GLENN COCO, 5, gr g Aussie Rules (USA)—Las Hilanderas (USA) **Miss Emily Stevens Partnership**
18 HART STOPPER, 5, b g Compton Place—Angel Song **Mr T. W. Morley**
19 HUMAN NATURE (IRE), 6, b g Kodiac—Sundown **Enticknap, Reynolds & Watkins**
20 INDIAN RAJ, 5, b g Iffraaj—Princess Georgina **Mr J W Parry & Partner**
21 JUANITO CHICO (IRE), 5, br g Pour Moi (IRE)—Miss Kittyhawk (IRE) **Mr A. N. Verrier**
22 KEYSTROKE, 7, b h Pivotal—Fondled **Front Runner Racing III**
23 LALANIA, 4, br f Kheleyf (USA)—George's Gift **Mrs M. Shone**
24 LETHAL ANGEL, 4, gr f Lethal Force (IRE)—Heliograph **The Secretly Hopeful Partnership**
25 LUNAR DEITY, 10, b g Medicean—Luminda (IRE) **Mr W E Enticknap & Partner**
26 MARATHA (IRE), 5, gr g Cape Cross (IRE)—Middle Persia **Happy Valley Racing & Breeding Limited**
27 ME TOO NAGASAKI (IRE), 5, b g Iffraaj—Distinguish (IRE) **Mrs M. J. Morley**
28 MY BOY SEPOY, 4, ch g Sepoy (AUS)—Emily Carr (IRE) **Mr & Mrs George Bhatti**
29 PACTOLUS (IRE), 8, b g Footstepsinthesand—Gold Mane (IRE) **T W Morley & Mrs J Morley**
30 PINNATA (IRE), 5, b g Shamardal (USA)—Lavande Violet (GER) **Mr David N Reynolds & Mr C D Watkins**
31 RESTLESS ROSE, 4, ch f Power—Albany Rose (IRE) **Happy Valley Racing & Breeding Limited**
32 ROYAL BIRTH, 8, b g Exceed And Excel (AUS)—Princess Georgina **The Morley Family**
33 SHAMSHON (IRE), 8, b g Invincible Spirit (IRE)—Greenisland (IRE) **T W Morley & Regents Racing**
34 SWIFT APPROVAL (IRE), 7, ch g Approve (IRE)—Tiitili (IRE) **JLM Racing**

MR STUART WILLIAMS - Continued

35 **TAWNY PORT**, 5, ch g Arcano (IRE)—Tawaasul **Mrs J. Morley**
36 **VIA VIA (IRE)**, 7, b h Lope de Vega (IRE)—Atalina (FR) **Mrs M. J. Morley**
37 **WIFF WAFF**, 4, b g Poet's Voice—Eraadaat (IRE) **Mr J W Parry & Partner**

THREE-YEAR-OLDS

38 **ANTONIA CLARA**, b f Lope de Vega (IRE)—Anna Sophia (USA) **J. W. Parry**
39 **BROUGHTONS BEAR (IRE)**, b g Kodiac—Though (IRE) **Broughton Thermal Insulations**
40 **CAN I KICK IT (IRE)**, b f Acclamation—Church Melody **Mr & Mrs George Bhatti**
41 **CINZENTO (IRE)**, gr g Lawman (FR)—Silver Samba **Mr & Mrs G. Bhatti**
42 **DANCE TO FREEDOM**, b c Equiano (FR)—Posy Fossil (USA) **J. W. Parry**
43 **DIAMOND CARA**, ch f Equiano (FR)—Tychy **Mr & Mrs George Bhatti**
44 **DON ARMADO (IRE)**, b c Camacho—Bella Ophelia (IRE) **Mr T. W. Morley**
45 **HANAKOTOBA (USA)**, b f Can The Man (USA)—Dalis On Stage (USA) **Mrs M. J. Morley**
46 B g Aussie Rules (USA)—Lady Guinevere **J. W. Parry**
47 **MARRONNIER (IRE)**, ch g Lope de Vega (IRE)—Beach Bunny (IRE) **GG Thoroughbreds III**
48 **NO TROUBLE (IRE)**, b g No Nay Never (USA)—Lady Babooshka **Happy Valley Racing & Breeding Limited**
49 **RHYTHMIC INTENT (IRE)**, ch c Lope de Vega (IRE)—Kerry Gal (IRE) **Happy Valley Racing & Breeding Limited**
50 **SARSAPARILLA KIT**, b f Footstepsinthesand—Cincinnati Kit **Mr J W Parry & Partner**
51 **STREET PARADE**, b g Swiss Spirit—Jollification (USA) **Mr T. W. Morley**
52 **THE GILL BROTHERS**, gr g Mukhadram—Si Belle (IRE) **The Gill Brothers**
53 **TONE THE BARONE**, ch g Lope de Vega (IRE)—A Huge Dream (IRE) **Mr B Piper & Partner**
54 **VIN D'HONNEUR (IRE)**, ch f Le Havre (IRE)—Happy Wedding (IRE) **J. W. Parry**
55 **WATCHMYEVERYMOVE (IRE)**, b g War Command (USA)—Glympse (IRE) **Mr T. W. Morley**

TWO-YEAR-OLDS

56 B c 10/2 Equiano (FR)—Holley Shiftwell (Bahamian Bounty) (32000) **Mr J W Parry**
57 Ch f 11/2 Sir Percy—Lady Guinevere (Pivotal) **Mr J. W. Parry**
58 B c 21/2 Lope de Vega (IRE)—Lunar Spirit (Invincible Spirit (IRE)) (10000) **GG Thoroughbreds**
59 Ch f 9/2 Sepoy (AUS)—Pivotting (Pivotal) (45000) **Mr J W Parry**
60 B c 21/4 Lethal Force (IRE)—Semaphore (Zamindar (USA)) (57000) **Patrick B Doyle (Construction) Ltd**
61 B f 21/4 Dawn Approach (IRE)—Viletta (GER) (Doyen (IRE)) **Essex Racing Club**

Other Owners: Mrs C. J. Bhatti, Mr G. Bhatti, Mr S. E. Chappell, Mr D. L. Cobill, W. E. Enticknap, Mr G. Gill, Mr G. M. C. Johnson, Mrs H. J. Lewis, Mr C. Pigram, Mr B. V. Piper, Mr G. R. Pooley, Regents Racing, Mr D. N. Reynolds, Mrs C. I. Shekells, Ms L. Siggins, P. W. Stevens, Miss E. V. Stevens, Mr C. D. Watkins, Mr S. C. Williams.

Assistant Trainer: Mr J W Parry

---

600 **MISS VENETIA WILLIAMS, Hereford**
Postal: **Aramstone, Kings Caple, Hereford, Herefordshire, HR1 4TU**
Contacts: **PHONE (01432) 840646 MOBILE (07770) 627108**
E-MAIL office@venetiawilliams.com WEBSITE www.venetiawilliams.com

1 **ACHILLE (FR)**, 9, gr g Dom Alco (FR)—Hase (FR) **Mrs Vida Bingham**
2 **AIR DE ROCK (FR)**, 7, b g High Rock (IRE)—Onciale (FR) **Lady Bolton**
3 **ARQALINA (IRE)**, 7, b m Arcano (IRE)—Pride Celebre (IRE) **The Hon Lady Heber-Percy & V Williams**
4 **ASO (FR)**, 9, b br g Goldneyev (USA)—Odyssee du Cellier (FR) **The Bellamy Partnership**
5 **BELAMI DES PICTONS (FR)**, 8, b g Khalkevi (FR)—Nina des Pictons (FR) **Hills of Ledbury (AGA)**
6 **BONNE QUESTION (FR)**, 10, gr g Tagula (IRE)—Amonita (GER) **Falcon's Line Ltd**
7 **BRIANSTORM (IRE)**, 7, b g Brian Boru—Coco Moon (IRE) **David & Carol Shaw**
8 **BURROWS PARK (FR)**, 7, b g Astarabad (USA)—La Vie de Boitron (FR) **Venetia Williams Racehorse Syndicate III**
9 **CALIPTO (FR)**, 9, b g Califet (FR)—Peutiot (FR) **Lady Bolton**
10 **CEPAGE (FR)**, 7, b g Saddler Maker (IRE)—Sience Fiction (FR) **The Bellamy Partnership**
11 **CHAMBARD (FR)**, 7, b g Gris de Gris (IRE)—Regina Park (FR) **David & Carol Shaw**
12 **CLOUDY GLEN (IRE)**, 6, b g Cloudings (IRE)—Ribble (IRE) **Mr Trevor Hemmings**
13 **COLD AS ICE (FR)**, 7, gr g Montmartre (FR)—Turiama (FR) **Miss V. M. Williams**
14 **COMMIS D'OFFICE (FR)**, 7, b g Califet (FR)—Pas de Bal (FR) **Julian Blackwell & Mrs Angus Maclay**
15 **COMMODORE (FR)**, 7, gr g Fragrant Mix (IRE)—Morvandelle (FR) **Mrs C Watson & Mrs S Graham**
16 **CUBAN PETE (IRE)**, 7, b g Flemensfirth (USA)—Gee Whizz (FR) **Mrs J. Jones**
17 **CUP OF COFFEE (FR)**, 5, b m Dragon Dancer—Danser Sur La Lune (FR) **Mr David A. Hunt**
18 **DESTINEE ROYALE (FR)**, 6, b m Balko (FR)—Viana (FR) **Boultbee Brooks Ltd**
19 **DIDERO VALLIS (FR)**, 6, b g Poliglote—Oreade Vallis (FR) **Lady Bolton**
20 **DON HERBAGER (FR)**, 5, b g Saddler Maker (IRE)—Marie d'altoria (FR) **M Willcocks & V Williams**
21 **DU SOLEIL (FR)**, 7, ch g Zambezi Sun—Cykapri (FR) **Kate & Andrew Brooks**

MISS VENETIA WILLIAMS - Continued

22 **ECEPARTI (FR)**, 5, b g Enrique—La Pommeraie (FR) **Mrs Sandra Champ**
23 **ELEANOR BOB**, 4, b f Midnight Legend—Red And White (IRE) **Mr Francis Mahon**
24 **ELIXIR DU GOUET (FR)**, 5, ch g Vision d'etat (FR)—My Asadore (FR) **Charles & Mary Rose Barlow**
25 **EMINENT POET**, 8, b g Montjeu (IRE)—Contare **B. C. Dice**
26 **ENOLA GAY (FR)**, 6, b g Fuisse (FR)—Enolaland (FR) **Calvados Racing**
27 **ESPOIR DE GUYE (FR)**, 5, b g Khalkevi (FR)—Penelope de Guye (FR) **Mrs J. Hitchings**
28 **EXCUSE ME (FR)**, 5, b g Saddler Maker (IRE)—Mexcala (FR) **Boultbee Brooks Ltd**
29 **FARRANTS WAY (IRE)**, 5, b g Shantou (USA)—Shuil A Hocht (IRE) **Mr Trevor Hemmings**
30 **FIONN MAC CUL (IRE)**, 8, b g Oscar (IRE)—No Moore Bills **Mr Trevor Hemmings**
31 **FIRST FIGARO GARE**, 9, ch g Silvano (GER)—Felina (GER) **The Bellamy Partnership**
32 **FREDDIE FLIP FLOP (IRE)**, 4, b g Imperial Monarch (IRE)—Moon Over Thefirth (IRE) **Sir John Timpson**
33 **FRENCHY DU LARGE (FR)**, 4, gr g Al Namix (FR)—Quadence de Sivola (FR) **Mr Andrew Wiles**
34 **GARDEFORT (FR)**, 10, b br g Agent Bleu (FR)—La Fresnaie (FR) **Kate & Andrew Brooks**
35 **GENERAL PROBUS**, 5, b br g Geordieland (FR)—Drop The Hammer **E G M Beard & R A Scott**
36 **GEORDIE B**, 6, gr g Geordieland (FR)—Sari Rose (FR) **Boultbee Brooks Ltd**
37 **HOUBLON DES OBEAUX (FR)**, 12, b g Panoramic—Harkosa (FR) **Julian Blackwell & Mrs Angus Maclay**
38 **JURYS OUT (IRE)**, 6, b g Witness Box (USA)—
　　　　　　　　　　　　　　No Complaints But (IRE) **Venetia Williams Racehorse Syndicate III**
39 **KAPGA DE LILY (FR)**, 6, ch m Kapgarde (FR)—Louvisy (FR) **Miss V. M. Williams**
40 **KHAIRAGASH (FR)**, 6, b g Sinndar (IRE)—Khazina (FR) **David & Carol Shaw**
41 **KING UTHER**, 9, b g Master Blade—Cadbury Castle **Charles Nugent & Lady Eliza Mays-Smith**
42 **LADY CHARTREUSE (FR)**, 6, ch m Flemensfirth (USA)—Verde Goodwood **Old Carthusian Racing Society (I)**
43 **LITTLE GINGE (FR)**, 6, ch g Kapgarde (FR)—Aconit (FR) **Boultbee Brooks Ltd**
44 **LONGHOUSESIGNORA (IRE)**, 7, b m Milan—Moscow Madame (IRE) **Nora's Playmates**
45 **MIDNIGHT SONATA (IRE)**, 5, b g Big Bad Bob (IRE)—Symphonique (FR) **Mrs Patricia Pink**
46 **MIXCHIEVOUS (IRE)**, 8, gr g Fair Mix (IRE)—Cheeky Mare **Tolostley Partnership**
47 **MOUNTAIN LEOPARD**, 4, b br g Shantou (USA)—Laurel Gift (IRE) **The Shantou Partnership**
48 **NESTERENKO (GER)**, 10, b g Doyen (IRE)—Nordwahl (GER) **Mrs Vida Bingham**
49 **ONE STYLE (FR)**, 9, b g Desert Style (IRE)—Arieta (FR) **Miss V. M. Williams**
50 **OTAGO TRAIL (IRE)**, 11, b g Heron Island (IRE)—Cool Chic (IRE) **Mrs Marie Shone**
51 **PENNY MALLOW (FR)**, 5, b br m Kapgarde (FR)—Louvisy (FR) **Kate & Andrew Brooks**
52 **PINK LEGEND**, 5, b m Midnight Legend—Red And White (IRE) **Mr Francis Mahon**
53 **PONIENTE**, 5, br m Shirocco (GER)—Tazzarine (FR) **R. F. Bailey**
54 **PRESSURIZE (IRE)**, 13, b g Witness Box (USA)—Cockpit Rose (IRE) **Mrs Sarah Williams**
55 **QUICK WAVE (FR)**, 6, b m Gentlewave (IRE)—Magicaldoun (FR) **Ms Sharon Kinsella**
56 **ROYAL PALLADIUM (FR)**, 11, gr g King's Theatre (IRE)—Dent Sucree (FR) **Sir John Timpson**
57 **ROYAL TARA (IRE)**, 10, b g Kayf Tara—The Irish Whip **Boultbee Brooks Ltd**
58 **SHALAKAR (IRE)**, 6, b g Cape Cross (IRE)—Shalanaya (IRE) **Sheila Schwartz & Lady Eliza Mays-Smith**
59 **SHIVERMETIMBERS (IRE)**, 7, br g Black Sam Bellamy (IRE)—Kimoura (FR) **Old Carthusian Racing Society**
60 **SNUFF BOX (IRE)**, 8, b g Witness Box (USA)—Dara Supreme (IRE) **Mr & Mrs Peter Nathan & Mrs Julia Young**
61 **STORM WIZARD (IRE)**, 7, b g Milan—Tempest Belle (IRE) **Taylor,Coe,Vaughan & Lambert**
62 **SUBCONTINENT (IRE)**, 7, b g Dubawi (IRE)—Saree **Shire Birds**
63 **SUPERVISOR (IRE)**, 5, b g Flemensfirth (USA)—Coolamaine Star (IRE) **Lady Bolton**
64 **TARA CHIEFTAIN**, 4, b g Kayf Tara—Molly Flight (FR) **The Winter Partnership**
65 **TARA FLOW**, 9, b m Kayf Tara—Poppet **Falcon's Line Ltd**
66 **TENOR NIVERNAIS (FR)**, 12, b g Shaanmer (IRE)—Hosanna II (FR) **Boultbee Brooks Ltd**
67 **THE CROONER (FR)**, 4, gr g Martaline—Viva Maria (FR) **The Crooner Partnership**
68 **TOP AND DROP**, 8, b m Kayf Tara—Ismene (FR) **Lady Judith Price & Mrs Carol Shaw**
69 **UHLAN BUTE (FR)**, 11, ch g Brier Creek (USA)—Jonquiere (FR) **The Autumn Partnership**
70 **UN PROPHETE (FR)**, 8, gr g Carlotamix (FR)—Pollita (FR) **Sir John Timpson**
71 **VIVACCIO (FR)**, 10, b g Antarctique (IRE)—Cybelle (FR) **Boultbee Brooks Ltd**
72 **WYE AYE**, 4, b g Shirocco (GER)—A Media Luz (IRE) **Mr & Mrs R Kelvin-Hughes**
73 **YALA ENKI (FR)**, 9, b br g Nickname (FR)—Cadiane (FR) **Hills of Ledbury (AGA)**
74 **YALLTARI**, 8, gr g Kayf Tara—Lily Grey (FR) **Venetia Williams Racehorse Syndicates II**
75 **ZAMDY MAN**, 10, b g Authorized (IRE)—Lauderdale (GER) **Mr John P. McManus**

Other Owners: Mr Simon Batcheler, Mr E. G. M. Beard, Mr Edward Beckley, Mr Julian Blackwell, Mrs C. Boultbee-Brooks, Mrs Kate Brazier, Mr A. Brooks, Mrs Kate Brooks, Mr D. Cliff, Lady Coe, Mr Michael J. Davies, Mr P. Davies, Mr G. P. Ford, Mr R. Gaskins, Mrs Douglas Graham, The Hon Lady Heber-Percy, Mrs H Herdman, Mrs Michael Lambert, Mr B. H. Lenaghan, The Hon Mrs Angus Maclay, Lady Eliza Mays-Smith, Mr P. G. Nathan, Mrs Peter Nathan, Mr C. R. Nugent, Mr Nigel Peace, Lady Judith Price, Mrs Sheila Schwartz, Mr Jeremy Schwartz, Mr R. A. Scott, Mr David Shaw, Mrs Carol Shaw, Mr Ian Stirling Tagg, Mr Julian Taylor, Mr James Richard Terry, Mr Julian Tolhurst, Mr Phil Turner, Mr Charlie Vaughan, Venetia Williams Ltd, Mrs Robert Watson, Mrs Marion Willcocks, Miss V. M. Williams, Ms C. F. Wilson, Mrs J. Young.

Jockey (NH): Charlie Deutsch. **Conditional:** Hugh Nugent. **Amateur:** Miss Lucy Turner.

601 MRS LISA WILLIAMSON, Tarporley
Postal: **Kelsall Hill Equestrian Centre, Middlewich Road, Tarporley, Cheshire, CW6 0SR**
Contacts: **PHONE (07970) 437679**
E-MAIL **info@lisawilliamson.co.uk** WEBSITE **www.lisawilliamson.co.uk**

1 BRANDY STATION (IRE), 4, b g Fast Company (IRE)—Kardyls Hope (IRE) **A V Wilding (Chester) Ltd**
2 CALEDONIAN GOLD, 6, b m Acclamation—Moonlight Rhapsody (IRE) **Heath House Racing**
3 CELERITY (IRE), 5, ch m Casamento (IRE)—Shinko Dancer (IRE) **Heath House Racing**
4 GO CHARLIE, 8, b g Myboycharlie (IRE)—Branston Gem **Miss H. J. Roberts**
5 ISABELLA RUBY, 4, b f Power—Scarlet Rocks (IRE) **Mr D. Woods**
6 LAMBRINI LEGACY, 5, b m Captain Gerrard (IRE)—Lambrini Lace (IRE) **JMH Racing Limited**
7 LAMBRINI LULLABY, 4, b f Captain Gerrard (IRE)—Lambrini Lace (IRE) **JMH Racing Limited**
8 MATILDA GRACE (IRE), 4, gr f Lilbourne Lad (IRE)—New Deal **Mr D. Woods**
9 PICCOLO RAMOSCELLO, 6, b m Malinas (GER)—Dusky Dancer **Mr P. R. D'Amato**
10 RED STRIPES (USA), 7, b g Leroidesanimaux (BRZ)—Kaleidoscopic (USA) **E. H. Jones (Paints) Ltd**
11 SAYESSE, 5, b g Sayif (IRE)—Pesse (IRE) **Mr P. Drinkwater**
12 SECRET ASSET (IRE), 14, gr g Clodovil (IRE)—Skerray **Simon & Mrs Jeanette Pierpoint**
13 SHESTHEDREAM (IRE), 6, b m Dream Ahead (USA)—Tatiana Romanova (USA) **The Cheshire Taverners**

THREE-YEAR-OLDS

14 AMBER LILY, ch f Captain Gerrard (IRE)—Lily Jicaro (IRE) **Miss H. J. Roberts**
15 ANDIES ARMIES, b g Piccolo—Shaymee's Girl **Pritchard & Woodward**
16 HILBRE LAKE (USA), b br c Revolutionary (USA)—Countess Clare (USA) **E. H. Jones (Paints) Ltd**
17 KINGS WAY, ch g Leroidesanimaux (BRZ)—Apparatchika **E. H. Jones (Paints) Ltd**
18 PICCOPIN, b g Piccolo—Pinball (IRE) **The Cheshire Taverners**

TWO-YEAR-OLDS

19 B f 18/3 Zebedee—Art Critic (USA) (Fusaichi Pegasus (USA)) (10476)
20 B f 21/3 Finjaan—Fancy Rose (USA) (Joyeux Danseur (USA))
21 LA CHICA LOBO, b f 29/3 Captain Gerrard (IRE)—Senora Lobo (IRE) (Amadeus Wolf)
22 B f 20/4 Heeraat (IRE)—Lily Jicaro (IRE) (Choisir (AUS))
23 B f 22/4 Finjaan—Riabouchinska (Fantastic Light (USA))

Other Owners: Exors of the Late Mr M. S. Heath, Miss C. Howard, Mr S. W. Pierpoint, Mrs Jeanette Pierpoint, Mr Andrew Pritchard, Mrs Lisa Williamson, Mr Jeremy Woodward.

602 MR ANDREW WILSON, Greystoke
Postal: **Silver Howe, Orton, Penrith, Cumbria, CA10 3RQ**
Contacts: **PHONE (01539) 624071 MOBILE (07813) 846768**
E-MAIL **andywilsonorton@gmail.com**

1 CULLY MAC (IRE), 8, b g Coroner (IRE)—Catch Those Kisses **Mr A. C. Wilson**
2 FRIENDS IN HEAVEN (IRE), 7, br g Asian Heights—Native Bev (IRE) **Mr A. C. Wilson**
3 KINGS ECLIPSE (IRE), 9, b g Double Eclipse (IRE)—Good Times Ahead (IRE) **Mr A. C. Wilson**
4 SENDIYM (FR), 12, b g Rainbow Quest (USA)—Seraya (FR) **Mr A. C. Wilson**

603 MR NOEL WILSON, Barnard Castle
Postal: **Mount Pleasant, Coal Road, Marwood, Barnard Castle, Co. Durham, DL12 8RP**
Contacts: **MOBILE (07939) 905477**
E-MAIL **nlwilson69@live.com**

1 ARGON, 4, b g Kyllachy—Cool Question **Marwood Racing Limited**
2 BARNEY BULLET (IRE), 4, b g Havana Gold (IRE)—Lalinde **Marwood Racing Limited**
3 DESAI, 5, br g Dansili—Arabesque **Matt Morgan & The Harrington Arms**
4 DISCREET HERO (IRE), 6, ch g Siyouni (FR)—Alfaguara (USA) **Slaters Arms Racing Club**
5 HAYWARD FIELD (IRE), 6, b g Cape Blanco (IRE)—Keepers Hill (IRE) **Marwood Racing Limited**
6 KINLOCH PRIDE, 7, ch m Kyllachy—Pride of Kinloch **Mr G. J. Paver**
7 LONGROOM, 7, br g Oasis Dream—Phantom Wind (USA) **Marwood Racing Limited**
8 MAJDOOL (IRE), 6, b g Acclamation—Maany (USA) **Marwood Racing Limited**
9 OUR PLACE IN LOULE, 6, ch g Compton Place—Show Off **Mr G. J. Paver**
10 PAVERS PRIDE, 5, ch g Bahamian Bounty—Pride of Kinloch **Mr G. J. Paver**

MR NOEL WILSON - Continued

11 THE MEKON, 4, ch g Red Jazz (USA)—Date Mate (USA) **Marwood Racing & Trevor Alderson**
12 UPSTAGING, 7, b g Mount Nelson—Corndavon (USA) **Argrain**

THREE-YEAR-OLDS

13 SLIEVE DONARD, b g Hellvelyn—Bladewood Girl **The Slaters Arms**
14 THE BIG HOUSE (IRE), b g Coach House (IRE)—Tekhania (IRE) **Mr D. Stone**
15 TORQUE OF THE TOWN (IRE), gr g Zebedee—Elaysa **The Slaters Arms**

TWO-YEAR-OLDS

16 Ch f 29/1 Hot Streak (IRE)—Maid In Heaven (IRE) (Clodovil (IRE)) (13485) **Mr D Stone**
17 Gr c 28/4 Gutaifan (IRE)—Peace Talks (Pivotal) (16856) **Marwood Racing**

Other Owners: Mr T. Alderson, Mr M. R. Baker, Mr J. M. Barker, The Harrington Arms, Matt Morgan.

Assistant Trainer: Miss Alex Porritt

Jockey (flat): Connor Beasley, Phil Dennis, Graham Lee.

---

604 **MR KEN WINGROVE, Bridgnorth**
Postal: **6 Netherton Farm Barns, Netherton Lane, Highley, Bridgnorth, Shropshire, WV16 6NJ**
Contacts: **HOME (01746) 861534 MOBILE (07974) 411267**
E-MAIL kenwingrove@btinternet.com

1 BIG AMIGO (IRE), 6, b g Bahamian Bounty—Goldamour (IRE) **Mr D. G. Wingrove**
2 EDE'S THE BUSINESS, 8, ch m Halling (USA)—My Amalie (IRE) **Mr D. G. Wingrove**
3 EGG LANE, 6, b g Multiplex—Sunisa (IRE) **Mr D. G. Wingrove**
4 6, B h Mount Nelson—Ellcon (IRE) **Mr D. G. Wingrove**
5 FALLING LEAF (IRE), 9, ch m Sandmason—Turbine Hill (IRE) **Mr D. G. Wingrove**
6 HEAVEN SCENT, 6, ch m Phoenix Reach (IRE)—Hel's Angel (IRE) **Mr D. G. Wingrove**
7 LYME PARK, 8, gr m Multiplex—So Cloudy (IRE) **Mr D. G. Wingrove**
8 MIDTECH VALENTINE, 8, b m Act One—Eveon (IRE) **Mr D. G. Wingrove**
9 PIVOTAL DREAM (IRE), 6, br m Excellent Art—Oasis Fire (IRE) **Mr D. G. Wingrove**
10 PLAY WITH ME, 5, ch m Captain Gerrard (IRE)—Plead (FR) **Mr D. G. Wingrove**
11 TRENDY NURSE (IRE), 11, b m Gold Well—Rotoruasprings (IRE) **Mr D. G. Wingrove**
12 WILLIE'S ANNE (IRE), 5, b m Lilbourne Lad (IRE)—Cape Sydney (IRE) **Mr D. G. Wingrove**

THREE-YEAR-OLDS

13 HOLY MACARONI, b f Heeraat (IRE)—Sopran Cross (ITY) **Mr D. G. Wingrove**

Assistant Trainer: Isobel Willer

---

605 **MR PETER WINKS, Barnsley**
Postal: **Homefield, Rotherham Road, Little Houghton, Barnsley, South Yorkshire, S72 0HA**
Contacts: **MOBILE (07846) 899993**
E-MAIL pwracing@outlook.com

1 AGENTLEMAN (IRE), 9, b g Trans Island—Silvine (IRE) **Mr R. H. Lee**
2 BACK TO BALLOO (IRE), 13, gr g Jimble (FR)—Fleur Du Chenet (FR) **Mr P. Winks**
3 BALLYFARSOON (IRE), 8, ch g Medicean—Amzara (IRE) **Barnsley Burglars**
4 CAVALRY, 4, b c Exceed And Excel (AUS)—Queen's Best **Mr R. Taberner**
5 GROW NASA GROW (IRE), 8, ch g Mahler—Dereenavurrig (IRE) **Nature and Science Agriculture Limited**
6 HARTSIDE (GER), 10, b g Montjeu (IRE)—Helvellyn (USA) **Mr P. Winks**
7 HEDIDDODINTHE (IRE), 5, gr g Kendargent (FR)—Damoiselle (USA) **Severnwinks**
8 MODULUS, 10, b g Motivator—Wild Academy (USA) **Mr P. Winks**
9 PRESENTING STREAK (IRE), 10, b g Presenting—Kuwalla (IRE) **Dennis Manterfield & Bill Baggaley**
10 SOLSTICE DAWN, 11, b m Lyphento (USA)—Ryders Hill **Mr P. Winks**
11 WEST CLASS (IRE), 8, b g Westerner—Catch The Class (IRE) **Mr P. Winks**

Other Owners: Mr W. Baggaley, Mr D. Manterfield, Mr P. W. O'Mara, Mr P. Rowbottom.

Assistant Trainer: Ryan Winks

Amateur: Mr Ryan Winks.

606 MR ADRIAN WINTLE, Westbury-On-Severn
Postal: **Yew Tree Stables, Rodley, Westbury-On-Severn, Gloucestershire, GL14 1QZ**
Contacts: **MOBILE (07767) 351144**

1 **ALEX THE LION (IRE)**, 6, b g Let The Lion Roar—Belle Dame (IRE) **Mr A. J. Rhead**
2 **AMLOVI (IRE)**, 6, b m Court Cave (IRE)—Portanob (IRE) **Mr S. R. Whistance**
3 **BOYCIE**, 6, b g Paco Boy (IRE)—Eve **A. A. Wintle**
4 5, B m Dr Massini (IRE)—Brackets (IRE)
5 **DE BENE ESSE (IRE)**, 9, br g Scorpion (IRE)—Benedicta Rose (IRE) **Amroth Racing Club**
6 **DUBAI MISSION (IRE)**, 6, b g New Approach (IRE)—Al Joza **G. Byard**
7 **EXOTIC FRIEND (IRE)**, 11, ch g Croco Rouge (IRE)—Prima Nox **Mr S. R. Whistance**
8 **FREIGHT TRAIN (IRE)**, 7, b g Manduro (GER)—Sigonella (IRE) **A. A. Wintle**
9 **IS LOVE ALIVE**, 10, ch g Presenting—Lovely Origny (FR) **Mr S. R. Whistance**
10 **KENSTONE (FR)**, 6, gr g Kendargent (FR)—Little Stone (FR) **G. Byard**
11 **RIVER RULE**, 4, b f Bated Breath—Ocean Countess (IRE) **Terry Warren & Adrian Wintle**
12 **ROCKET RONNIE (IRE)**, 9, b g Antonius Pius (USA)—Ctesiphon (USA) **Inspire Racing Club Ltd**
13 **SEAFORTH (IRE)**, 7, b g Acclamation—Hendrina (IRE) **A. A. Wintle**
14 **SECRET GLANCE**, 7, b g Sakhee's Secret—Look Here's Dee **A. A. Wintle**
15 **SUNNY GIRL (IRE)**, 5, b m Arcadio (GER)—Vincenta (IRE) **Mr S. R. Whistance**
16 **THREE C'S (IRE)**, 5, b g Kodiac—Ms Mary C (IRE) **A. A. Wintle**
17 **TWISTSANDTURNS (IRE)**, 8, b g Acclamation—Shesthebiscuit **A. A. Wintle**

Other Owners: Mr C. Beecher, Mr T. G. Warren, Mr C. J. Williams.

607 MISS REBECCA WOODMAN, Chichester
Postal: **Souters Cottage, 21 East Lavant, Chichester, West Sussex, PO18 0AG**
Contacts: **PHONE (01243) 527260 MOBILE (07821) 603063**
E-MAIL rebeccawoodman@msn.com

1 **BIT SPICY (IRE)**, 8, gr m Tikkanen (USA)—Like A Bolt (IRE) **Miss R. Woodman**
2 **HIGHLY LIKELY (IRE)**, 10, b g Elnadim (USA)—Height of Fantasy (IRE) **Miss R. Woodman**
3 **HONEY P (IRE)**, 8, b m Winged Love (IRE)—Luck's A Lady (IRE) **Miss R. Woodman**
4 **SWEEP OF DIAMONDS**, 6, br g Mawatheeq (USA)—Apple Blossom (IRE) **Miss R. Woodman**

608 MR STEVE WOODMAN, Chichester
Postal: **Parkers Barn Stables, Pook Lane, East Lavant, Chichester, West Sussex, PO18 0AU**
Contacts: **OFFICE (01243) 527136 FAX (01243) 527136 MOBILE (07889) 188519**
E-MAIL stevewoodman83@msn.com

1 **BLACK LACE**, 4, b f Showcasing—Ivory Lace **The Lacemakers**
2 **LORD ALDERVALE (IRE)**, 12, br g Alderbrook—Monavale (IRE) **Mr D. N. Boxall**
3 **SOLVEIG'S SONG**, 7, b m Norse Dancer (IRE)—Ivory Lace **Sally Woodman & D. Mortimer**

Other Owners: Mrs P. A. Miles, Mr David Mortimer, Mrs Trish Tyler, Mrs Sally Woodman.

609 MRS KAYLEY WOOLLACOTT, South Molton
Postal: **Big Brook Park, Rose Ash, South Molton, Devon, EX36 4RQ**
Contacts: **PHONE (01769) 550483**
E-MAIL info@richardwoollacottracing.co.uk WEBSITE www.richardwoollacottracing.co.uk

1 **CASPERS COURT (IRE)**, 5, gr g Court Cave (IRE)—Kindle Ball (FR) **Mr D Stevens & Mrs S Stevens**
2 **CLONDAW'S ANSWER (IRE)**, 6, b g Ask—Monabricka Lady (IRE) **D. G. Staddon**
3 **DIABLERETS (FR)**, 6, ch g Vendangeur (IRE)—Lavande (FR) **West Country Partners**
4 **DORRANA (IRE)**, 5, br m Darsi (FR)—Arts Theater (IRE) **Gale Force Five**
5 **FLORESCO (GER)**, 9, ch g Santiago (GER)—Fiori (GER) **D. G. Staddon**
6 **GOODGIRLTERESA (IRE)**, 9, b m Stowaway—Decheekymonkey (IRE) **Kayley Woollacott Racing Club**
7 **LALOR (GER)**, 9, b g It's Gino (GER)—Laviola (GER) **D. G. Staddon**
8 **MILLANISI BOY**, 10, b g Kalanisi (FR)—Millennium Rose (IRE) **Mr D Stevens & Mrs S Stevens**
9 **NICKELSONTHEDIME (IRE)**, 5, b g Shantou (USA)—Penny Fiction (IRE) **Layezy Racing Owners Club**
10 **SHELCOMEONFORDRUN (IRE)**, 6, b m Flemensfirth (USA)—Hazel Sylph (IRE) **Mr D. J. Stevens**

MRS KAYLEY WOOLLACOTT - Continued

11 **THE KINGS WRIT (IRE),** 8, b g Brian Boru—Letterwoman (IRE) **Mr D Stevens & Mrs S Stevens**
12 **THE MAJOR,** 6, b g Major Cadeaux—Ballerina Suprema (IRE) **Mr D Stevens & Mrs S Stevens**

Other Owners: Mr J. R. Best, Mrs A. G. Gale, Mr A. P. Gale, Mr J. Heal, Mr M. N. Higgs, Mr M. R. Rhoades, Mr M. Stanley, Mrs S. E. Stevens, Mrs K. Woollacott.

---

610 MR PHILLIP YORK, Leatherhead
Postal: **Mornhill Farm, Banks Lane, Effingham, Leatherhead, Surrey, KT24 5JB**
Contacts: **PHONE (01372) 457102**

1 **AMBANADORA,** 10, b g Amber Life—La Ganadora **Mrs K. H. York**
2 **BROUGHTONS BANDIT,** 12, b g Kyllachy—Broughton Bounty **P. York**
3 **CARRIED AWAY,** 7, b m Trans Island—Carry Me (IRE) **Mrs K. H. York**
4 **GEE PEE,** 7, b m Dr Massini (IRE)—Woodford Consult **P. York**
5 **GERSJOEYCASEY (IRE),** 10, b m Milan—Derrigra Sublime (IRE) **P. York**
6 **INTERCOOLER TURBO (IRE),** 10, gr g Dr Massini (IRE)—Moigh Endeavour (IRE) **Mrs K. H. York**
7 **MAKIN IT,** 4, b f North Light (IRE)—Saltpetre (IRE) **Mrs K. H. York**
8 **OVERSHOT,** 7, b m Overbury (IRE)—Aya **P. York**
9 **RENDEZVOUS PEAK,** 10, b g High-Rise (IRE)—Jurado Park (IRE) **Mrs K. H. York**
10 **SPENDABLE,** 7, ch m Spendent—Eastern Point **Mrs K. H. York**
11 **SPIRITOFCHARTWELL,** 11, ch g Clerkenwell (USA)—Rollin Rock **Mrs K. H. York**

---

611 MRS LAURA YOUNG, Bridgwater
Postal: **Rooks Castle Stables, Broomfield, Bridgwater, Somerset, TA5 2EW**
Contacts: **PHONE (01278) 664595 FAX (01278) 661555 MOBILE (07766) 514414**
E-MAIL ljyracing@hotmail.com WEBSITE www.laurayoungracing.com

1 **AUENWIRBEL (GER),** 8, b g Sholokhov (IRE)—Auentime (GER) **Mr T. J. Moynihan**
2 **AUMIT HILL,** 6, b g Authorized (IRE)—Eurolinka (IRE) **The Isle Of Frogs Partnership**
3 **BUCKBORU (IRE),** 11, b m Brian Boru—Buckland Filleigh (IRE) **Mrs L. J. Young**
4 **EGGESFORD,** 5, b g Foxwedge (AUS)—Elegant Pride **Mrs L. J. Young**
5 **HITCHHIKER (IRE),** 8, b g Milan—No Easy Way (IRE) **Mrs L. J. Young**
6 **JIGSAW FINANCIAL (IRE),** 13, b g Brian Boru—Ardcolm Cailin (IRE) **Mrs L. J. Young**
7 **MEGAUDAIS SPEED (FR),** 7, b g Puit d'or (IRE)—La Rouadiere (FR) **The Isle Of Frogs Partnership**
8 **MY DIAMOND (IRE),** 8, b g Brian Boru—Our Idol (IRE) **The Isle Of Frogs Partnership**
9 **PATENT,** 6, b g Paco Boy (IRE)—Film Script **Mrs L. J. Young**
10 **THE GREENVET (IRE),** 9, b g Acrobat (IRE)—Glacial Air (IRE) **The Isle Of Frogs Partnership**
11 **TRUE THOUGHTS (IRE),** 4, b g So You Think (NZ)—True Joy (IRE) **Soul Galore**
12 **VALSHAN TIME (IRE),** 7, b br g Atraf—Valshan (IRE) **Mrs L. J. Young**
13 **WHITE NILE (IRE),** 10, b h Galileo (IRE)—Super Gift (IRE) **Mrs L. J. Young**

Other Owners: Mr M. J. Rees, Mr G. C. Vining, Mr C. V. Vining.

Assistant Trainer: James Young

Jockey (NH): Robert Dunne.

---

612 MR WILLIAM YOUNG, Carluke
Postal: **Watchknowe Lodge, Crossford, Carluke, Lanarkshire, ML8 5QT**
Contacts: **PHONE (01555) 860856 (01555) 860226 FAX (01555) 860137 MOBILE (07900) 408210**
E-MAIL watchknowe@talktalk.net

1 **COOL VALLEY (IRE),** 10, b g Zerpour (IRE)—Jilly Jaffa Cake (IRE) **W. G. Young**
2 **FORMIDABLEOPPONENT (IRE),** 12, b g Arakan (USA)—Sliding **W. G. Young**
3 **GALAHILL,** 6, gr m Ferrule (IRE)—Gala Queen **W. G. Young**
4 **HERE COMES LOVE (IRE),** 9, b g Winged Love (IRE)—Heres McGoogan (IRE) **W. G. Young**
5 **KICKS BEFORE SIX (IRE),** 7, b g Scorpion (IRE)—Square Up (IRE) **W. G. Young**
6 **MILANS WELL (IRE),** 13, b g Milan—Panoora Queen (IRE) **W. G. Young**
7 **SPECIALIST (IRE),** 5, b g Mastercraftsman (IRE)—My Lass **W. G. Young**

Assistant Trainer: William G Young Snr

INDEX TO HORSES

The Figure before the name of the horse refers to the number of the team in which it appears and
The Figure after the horse supplies a ready reference to each animal. Horses are indexed strictly
alphabetically, e.g. THE CATTLEJOBBER appears in the T's, MR NICE GUY in the MR's, ST PATRICK'S DAY in the ST'S etc.

507 **AFFLUENCE** (IRE) 1
316 **AFLORALDANCE** (GB) 1
450 **AFNOON** (USA) F 31
109 **AFRA KADABRA** (IRE) 31
553 **AFRAAH** (USA) F 123
35 **AFRICAN BLESSING** (GB) 1
206 **AFRICAN FRIEND** (IRE) 1
5 **AFRICAN JAZZ** (IRE) 1
124 **AFRICAN RIDE** (GB) 1
225 **AFRICAN SHOWGIRL** (GB) 1
278 **AFRO** (GB) F 11
263 **AFRO BLUE** (IRE) 110
477 **AFSHEEN** (FR) F 57
100 **AFTER JOHN** (GB) 34
576 **AFTERNOON SUNLIGHT** (IRE) F 82
424 **AGAIN** (GB) C 109
319 **AGAINN DUL AGHAIDH** (GB) 2
393 **AGAINST THE ODDS** (GB) 1
232 **AGAMEMNON** (IRE) 2
175 **AGAR'S PLOUGH** (GB) 1
263 **AGE OF CHIVALRY** (IRE) C 111
85 **AGE OF GLORY** (GB) 1
393 **AGE OF WISDOM** (IRE) 2
16 **AGENT BASTERFIELD** (IRE) 49
432 **AGENT GIBBS** (GB) 1
514 **AGENT LOUISE** (GB) 1
14 **AGENT MEMPHIS** (IRE) 3
171 **AGENT OF FORTUNE** (GB) 1
535 **AGENT SAONOIS** (FR) 30
79 **AGENT SMITH** (IRE) 2
426 **AGENT VALDEZ** (GB) 2
593 **AGENT WESTY** (IRE) 2
605 **AGENTLEMAN** (IRE) 2
500 **AGGY WITH IT** (IRE) 2
82 **AGHAREED** (USA) C 53
480 **AGHAST** (GB) 33
428 **AGINCOURT** (IRE) 2
533 **AGINCOURT REEF** (IRE) 1
6 **AGITARE** (IRE) 64
434 **AGNES GRAND** (GB) 26
119 **AGONY AND ECSTASY** (GB) C 58
596 **AGRAPART** (FR) 1
176 **AGRAVAIN** (GB) 90
424 **AGREEABLE MISS** (USA) C 110
193 **AGREEMENT** (IRE) 1
562 **AGROTERA** (IRE) 1
503 **AGUANA** (FR) 21
565 **AGUEROOO** (IRE) 1
148 **AGUIDA** (FR) F 2
227 **AH WELL** (IRE) 1
65 **AHDAAF** (USA) C 36
168 **AHDAB** (IRE) 57
199 **AHEAD OF THE GAME** (IRE) 1
500 **AHEADFULLOFDREAMS** (IRE) 3
393 **AHFAD** (GB) 2
257 **AHLAN BIL ZAIN** (FR) 1
168 **AHLAN SAYIDATY** (GB) 58
185 **AHORSEWITHNONAME** (GB) 1
393 **AIAAM AL WAFA** (IRE) G 4
20 **AIAAM AL WAFA** (IRE) F 26
186 **AIDE MEMOIRE** (IRE) 12
272 **AIDEN'S DELIGHT** (IRE) 32
120 **AIGIARNE** (IRE) 27
41 **AIGUE MARINE** (GB) F 45
393 **AIGUILLE ROUGE** (IRE) 3
393 **AIGUILLETTE** (GB) 132
245 **AILETTE** (GB) G 1
263 **AIM POWER** (IRE) 24

596 **AIMEE DE SIVOLA** (FR) 2
478 **AIN'T MY FAULT** (IRE) 1
542 **AINCHEA** (IRE) 1
519 **AINE** (IRE) C 34
125 **AINMISFEARR** (IRE) 3
330 **AINNE** (IRE) 3
500 **AINTREE MY DREAM** (FR) 4
263 **AIR BENDER** (GB) 25
600 **AIR DE ROCK** (FR) 2
100 **AIR FORCE AMY** (GB) 35
114 **AIR GLIDER** (IRE) 2
223 **AIR HORSE ONE** (GB) 2
232 **AIR NAVIGATOR** (GB) 3
208 **AIR OF YORK** (IRE) 1
29 **AIR PILOT** (GB) 1
427 **AIR RAID** (GB) 1
479 **AIRCRAFT CARRIER** (IRE) 1
175 **AIRGLOW** (IRE) 2
203 **AIRLINE HOSTESS** (IRE) F 50
176 **AIRPLANE** (IRE) 3
6 **AIRSHOW** (IRE) 3
448 **AIRTON** (GB) 1
424 **AIRWAVE** (GB) C 111
378 **AIRWAVES** (GB) 11
50 **AISEIRIGH** (IRE) 65
569 **AISLABIE** (FR) 1
50 **AISLING GHEAR** (IRE) 17
176 **AIYA** (IRE) 4
263 **AJA** (IRE) C 112
100 **AJIG DANCER** (GB) F 79
583 **AJMAN PRINCE** (IRE) 1
508 **AKAMANTO** (IRE) 1
327 **AKARITA LIGHTS** (IRE) 1
146 **AKAVIT** (IRE) 1
246 **AKILAYA** (IRE) 3
555 **AKKAPENKO** (FR) 2
553 **AKTAU** (GB) 1
29 **AKVAVERA** (GB) 2
124 **AKWAAN** (IRE) 21
133 **AL AMLAH** (USA) G 72
105 **AL ANAAB** (FR) 5
103 **AL ARESH** (FR) 14
53 **AL ASEF** (GB) 1
29 **AL BAIDAA** (GB) F 89
263 **AL BARG** (IRE) 1
554 **AL BATTAR** (IRE) 1
407 **AL BOUM PHOTO** (FR) 3
562 **AL DAIHA** (GB) 24
550 **AL DANCER** (FR) 1
176 **AL ERAYG** (IRE) 5
530 **AL FAREEJ** (IRE) F 52
263 **AL HAAMY** (IRE) 113
255 **AL HADEER** (USA) 32
53 **AL HAMDANY** (IRE) 2
5 **AL HILALEE** (GB) 46
120 **AL JELLABY** (GB) 1
554 **AL JOUDHA** (IRE) F C 18
457 **AL KHERB** (GB) 1
357 **AL KOUT** (GB) 1
103 **AL MALHOUF** (GB) 1
100 **AL MANAAL** (GB) F 80
103 **AL MARROUNA** (GB) 15
263 **AL MESSIAH** (GB) 26
41 **AL MIKDAM** (USA) 40
255 **AL MUFFRIH** (GB) 1
41 **AL MUREIB** (IRE) 41
589 **AL NAFOORAH** (GB) 1
263 **AL NAMIR** (IRE) 114

202 **AL OZZDI** (GB) 3
428 **AL QAHWA** (IRE) 3
6 **AL REEF** (IRE) 4
53 **AL REEH** (IRE) 3
500 **AL SHAHIR** (IRE) 5
457 **AL SUIL EILE** (IRE) 29
255 **AL TARMAAH** (IRE) 116
318 **AL THOORAYAH** (USA) 38
599 **ALAADEL** (GB) 2
255 **ALAATA** (USA) F 117
133 **ALABANZA** (GB) 1
452 **ALABASTER** (GB) 1
499 **ALACRITAS** (GB) 1
291 **ALADDIN SANE** (IRE) 1
257 **ALAKAHAN** (IRE) 13
168 **ALAMEERY** (GB) 20
545 **ALAMINTA** (GB) 16
284 **ALANDALOS** (GB) 29
534 **ALANJOU** (FR) 1
553 **ALAPAT** (GB) 34
553 **ALASH ORDA** (GB) 124
519 **ALASHA** (IRE) C 35
350 **ALASKA RANGE** (FR) 2
252 **ALASKAN BAY** (FR) 1
297 **ALATIA** (IRE) 16
318 **ALAVA** (GB) F C 132
119 **ALB** (USA) F 59
225 **ALBA DEL SOLE** (IRE) 2
103 **ALBA POWER** (IRE) 2
29 **ALBAFLORA** (GB) 90
452 **ALBAMARA** (GB) C 42
178 **ALBAN'S DREAM** (GB) 8
525 **ALBANDERI** (GB) 27
452 **ALBANITA** (GB) 14
401 **ALBANY ROSE** (IRE) C 27
374 **ALBANY ROSE** (IRE) F 5
434 **ALBARAKA** (GB) C 55
5 **ALBASHARAH** (USA) F 89
255 **ALBAWAADY** (USA) 33
596 **ALBERIC** (FR) 27
152 **ALBERT BOY** (IRE) 1
140 **ALBERT GEORGE** (GB) 2
175 **ALBERT'S BACK** (GB) 3
334 **ALBERTO'S DREAM** (GB) 1
266 **ALBIGNA** (IRE) 122
158 **ALBISHR** (IRE) 1
424 **ALBUQUERQUE** (IRE) 19
8 **ALBURN** (GB) 1
95 **ALCANAR** (USA) 3
499 **ALCHIMISTA** (GB) 69
500 **ALCOCK AND BROWN** (IRE) 6
124 **ALDANA** (GB) 22
16 **ALDENTE** (GB) 50
261 **ALDERBROOK LAD** (IRE) 1
175 **ALDRETH** (GB) 4
507 **ALEATORIC** (IRE) 1
428 **ALEEKA** (USA) 61
519 **ALEGENDINMYOWNMIND** (GB) C 36
407 **ALELCHI INOIS** (FR) 4
499 **ALEMAGNA** (GB) 26
599 **ALEMARATALYOUM** (IRE) 3
5 **ALESSANDRIA** (GB) C 90
297 **ALESSANDRO ALLORI** (IRE) 1
553 **ALETTA DE FREY** (GB) 125
606 **ALEX THE LION** (IRE) 1
255 **ALEXANA** (GB) 4
67 **ALEXANDER DUCHESS** (IRE) F 1
82 **ALEXANDER GOLDRUN** (IRE) C 54

354 **ART ECHO** (GB) 2
443 **ART FOR ART'S SAKE** (IRE) 37
419 **ART MAURESQUE** (FR) 4
379 **ART OF AMERICA** (GB) 6
318 **ART OF GOLD** (GB) C 138
223 **ART OF PAYROLL** (GER) 8
379 **ART OF SECURITY** (IRE) 7
261 **ART OF SUPREMACY** (IRE) 2
97 **ART OF SWING** (IRE) 1
379 **ART OF UNITY** (GB) 8
176 **ART POWER** (IRE) 138
5 **ART SONG** (USA) 49
30 **ARTAIR** (IRE) 14
30 **ARTARMON** (IRE) 2
416 **ARTFUL ARTIST** (IRE) 3
406 **ARTHINGTON** (GB) 2
137 **ARTHUR KITT** (GB) 18
433 **ARTHUR MAC** (IRE) 3
381 **ARTHUR PENDRAGON** (IRE) 14
248 **ARTHUR SHELBY** (IRE) 15
550 **ARTHUR'S GIFT** (IRE) 5
244 **ARTHUR'S QUEEN** (IRE) 1
89 **ARTHUR'S REUBEN** (GB) 4
14 **ARTHUR'S SIXPENCE** (GB) 7
540 **ARTHURS SECRET** (GB) 1
1 **ARTIC MANN** (GB) 4
34 **ARTIC QUEST** (IRE) 4
369 **ARTICHOKE HEART** (GB) 3
245 **ARTICLE FIFTY** (IRE) 3
2 **ARTICLE OF WAR** (IRE) 1
33 **ARTISTIC BELLE** (IRE) G 2
474 **ARTISTIC DAWN** (IRE) F 4
381 **ARTISTIC LANGUAGE** (GB) 15
310 **ARTISTIC LIASON** (GB) F 3
310 **ARTISTIC LIASON** (GB) F 34
284 **ARTISTIC RIFLES** (IRE) 31
137 **ARTISTIC STREAK** (GB) 19
436 **ARTOIS** (GB) 34
351 **ARTSCAPE** (GB) 1
279 **ARTURUS** (IRE) 8
346 **ARTY CAMPBELL** (IRE) 1
399 **ARVENSIS** (GB) 33
140 **ARVICO'S LIGHT** (GB) 3
82 **ARWAAH** (IRE) C 58
565 **ARZAAK** (IRE) 2
419 **AS DE MEE** (FR) 5
223 **AS I SEE IT** (GB) 9
410 **AS YOU LEAVE** (FR) G 5
239 **ASAATIER** (USA) 34
255 **ASCENDED** (IRE) 36
553 **ASCENSION** (IRE) 130
346 **ASCOT DAY** (FR) 2
194 **ASCOT DE BRUYERE** (FR) 4
74 **ASCOT DREAMER** (GB) 2
29 **ASCOT LADY** (IRE) F 93
457 **ASCOT WEEK** (USA) 4
576 **ASDAA** (IRE) 23
400 **ASENSIO** (GB) 5
113 **ASH PARK** (IRE) 2
525 **ASHAAQAH** (IRE) F 99
477 **ASHAMYA** (FR) 14
36 **ASHAREDMOMENT** (GB) 2
450 **ASHAZURI** (GB) 1
266 **ASHDALE BOB** (IRE) 5
69 **ASHES CORNER** (IRE) 1
457 **ASHINGTON** (GB) 5
428 **ASHLEY HALL** (USA) C 95
161 **ASHPAN SAM** (GB) 1

477 **ASHTARA** (USA) 15
477 **ASHTIYR** (USA) 1
419 **ASHUTOR** (FR) 6
310 **ASHWELL ROSE** (GB) F 31
318 **ASIAN ANGEL** (FR) 44
376 **ASK BEN** (IRE) 2
241 **ASK CAITLIN** (IRE) 5
529 **ASK CATKIN** (IRE) 1
426 **ASK DILLON** (IRE) 3
419 **ASK FOR GLORY** (IRE) 7
492 **ASK HIMSELF** (IRE) 2
259 **ASK JD** (IRE) 1
52 **ASK JILLY** (GB) 1
261 **ASK PADDINGTON** (IRE) 3
188 **ASK PADDY** (IRE) 1
513 **ASK ROBIN** (IRE) 5
88 **ASK SHANROE** (IRE) 1
10 **ASK THE GURU** (GB) 1
478 **ASK THE TYCOON** (IRE) 4
19 **ASK THE WEATHERMAN** (GB) 2
183 **ASKARI** (GB) 10
576 **ASKERIA** (IRE) C 85
138 **ASKGARMOR** (IRE) 2
543 **ASKING FOR ANSWERS** (IRE) 1
246 **ASKING QUESTIONS** (IRE) 5
241 **ASKMEWHY** (IRE) 1
340 **ASKNOTWHAT** (IRE) 3
600 **ASO** (FR) 4
41 **ASOOF** (GB) 1
5 **ASPEN** (AUS) F 94
431 **ASPEN COLORADO** (IRE) 7
106 **ASPETAR** (FR) 1
106 **ASPIRE** (GB) C 66
237 **ASPIRE TOWER** (IRE) 11
100 **ASPIRING DIVA** (GB) 37
391 **ASSABIYYA** (FR) F 26
318 **ASSAULT ON ROME** (GB) C 139
436 **ASSEMBLED** (GB) 35
562 **ASSIMILATION** (IRE) 25
378 **ASSUMING** (IRE) 12
50 **ASSURANCE** (IRE) 69
428 **ASTERISM** (GB) F 96
502 **ASTEROIDEA** (GB) F 24
70 **ASTIGOS** (FR) 1
95 **ASTONE MAN** (FR) 6
530 **ASTONISHED** (IRE) 1
266 **ASTONISHING** (IRE) C 126
593 **ASTRA VIA** (GB) 6
550 **ASTRACAD** (FR) 6
175 **ASTRAEA** (GB) 6
399 **ASTRAL GIRL** (GB) 34
176 **ASTRAL WEEKS** (GB) F 139
79 **ASTRO JAKK** (IRE) 3
544 **ASTROBREEZE** (GB) 1
525 **ASTROGLIA** (USA) C 100
544 **ASTROJEWEL** (GB) 3
428 **ASTROLOGER** (GB) 63
443 **ASTROMACHIA** (GB) 2
544 **ASTROMANCER** (USA) F 20
544 **ASTROMERRY** (GB) 9
498 **ASTROPHYSICS** (GB) 1
544 **ASTROSPARKLE** (GB) 10
198 **ASTROSPEED** (IRE) 1
504 **ASTROZONE** (GB) 34
508 **ASTUTE BOY** (IRE) 4
329 **ASUM** (GB) 6
416 **ASYLO** (IRE) 4
580 **AT FIRST LIGHT** (GB) 2

286 **AT ITS OWN EXPENSE** (IRE) 1
424 **AT LAST** (IRE) 23
108 **AT PEACE** (IRE) 10
296 **AT YOUR SERVICE** (GB) 2
284 **ATAB** (IRE) C 85
229 **ATAGUISEAMIX** (FR) 1
545 **ATALANTA BREEZE** (GB) 17
67 **ATALANTA QUEEN** (GB) 3
382 **ATALANTA'S BOY** (GB) 1
393 **ATALANTA'S GOLD** (IRE) 12
169 **ATARFE** (IRE) C 23
82 **ATAYEB** (USA) F 59
190 **ATHASSEL** (GB) 3
379 **ATHENEAN** (IRE) 9
381 **ATHMAD** (IRE) 16
286 **ATIRELARIGO** (FR) 4
307 **ATKINSON GRIMSHAW** (FR) 4
436 **ATLAAL** (GB) 3
114 **ATLANTIC BREAKER** (IRE) 3
330 **ATLANTIC CITY** (IRE) 11
111 **ATLANTIC CROSSING** (IRE) 26
220 **ATLANTIC GREY** (IRE) 1
424 **ATLANTIC JEWEL** (AUS) C 114
527 **ATLANTIC STORM** (IRE) 1
193 **ATLANTIC SUNSHINE** (GB) 6
190 **ATLETICO** (IRE) 4
120 **ATMOSPHERIC** (GB) 80
15 **ATOMIC JACK** (GB) 1
72 **ATOMIC RUMBLE** (IRE) 2
72 **ATRAFAN** (IRE) 1
266 **ATTACHEE DE PRESSE** (IRE) F 127
571 **ATTAIN** (GB) 1
530 **ATTAINMENT** (GB) 11
263 **ATTENDOLO** (IRE) 121
154 **ATTENTION PLEASE** (IRE) 4
176 **ATTENTION SEEKER** (GB) 8
245 **ATTEST** (GB) 4
318 **ATTIMA** (GB) C 45
356 **ATTLONGGLAST** (GB) F 14
554 **ATTORNEY GENERAL** (GB) 9
364 **ATTY'S EDGE** (GB) 3
505 **ATWAAR** (GB) 4
557 **ATWIX** (GB) F 39
493 **ATYAAF** (GB) 3
148 **AUBIS PARK** (IRE) 3
263 **AUBRETIA** (IRE) 30
595 **AUBUSSON** (FR) 1
434 **AUDACITY** (GB) 27
198 **AUDARYA** (FR) 31
263 **AUDIO** (GB) 122
483 **AUDLEY** (GB) F 10
295 **AUDORA** (GB) 3
611 **AUENWIRBEL** (GER) 1
125 **AUGAR** (GB) 31
407 **AUGUSTIN** (FR) 2
394 **AULD BOY** (USA) 6
60 **AULD SOD** (IRE) 2
50 **AUMA** (IRE) 70
353 **AUMERLE** (GB) 1
611 **AUMIT HILL** (GB) 2
320 **AUNT HARRIET** (GB) G 2
79 **AUNT NICOLA** (GB) F 79
231 **AUNTIE NEILA** (GB) 1
245 **AURELLO** (GB) 5
448 **AURILLAC** (FR) 2
478 **AURORA THUNDER** (GB) 5
5 **AURUM** (IRE) 3
318 **AUSSIE VIEW** (IRE) 46

407 **BALLYCASEY** (IRE) 13
550 **BALLYCROSS** (IRE) 13
185 **BALLYCRYSTAL** (IRE) 5
465 **BALLYCRYSTAL COURT** (IRE) 2
496 **BALLYDARSI** (IRE) 2
350 **BALLYDINE** (IRE) 3
77 **BALLYEGAN** (IRE) 2
550 **BALLYELLIS** (IRE) 14
605 **BALLYFARSOON** (IRE) 3
286 **BALLYGOWN BAY** (IRE) 5
166 **BALLYHACKAMORE** (GB) 4
238 **BALLYHEIGUE BAY** (IRE) 4
550 **BALLYHILL** (FR) 15
426 **BALLYHOME** (IRE) 5
379 **BALLYHOT BOY** (IRE) 10
550 **BALLYKAN** (GB) 16
19 **BALLYKNOCK CLOUD** (IRE) 3
298 **BALLYLEMON** (IRE) 19
273 **BALLYMAGROARTY BOY** (IRE) 2
550 **BALLYMALIN** (IRE) 17
403 **BALLYMILAN** (GB) 1
255 **BALLYMORE CÉLÈBRE** (IRE) F 124
137 **BALLYMORE CELEBRE** (IRE) F 20
175 **BALLYMOUNT** (GB) 7
320 **BALLYMOUNTAIN BOY** (IRE) 4
550 **BALLYMOY** (IRE) 18
1 **BALLYNANTY** (IRE) 5
557 **BALLYNARRY** (IRE) G 3
550 **BALLYOPTIC** (IRE) 19
16 **BALLYQUIN** (IRE) 3
185 **BALLYVIC BORU** (IRE) 6
407 **BALLYWARD** (IRE) 14
327 **BALLYWOOD** (FR) 6
450 **BALMORAL CASTLE** (GB) 2
236 **BALMUICK** (IRE) 36
104 **BALTIC MOON** (GB) 13
95 **BALTIC PRINCE** (IRE) 7
480 **BALTIC STATE** (IRE) 7
594 **BAMAKO DU CHATELET** (FR) 8
407 **BAMAKO MORIVIERE** (FR) 15
447 **BAMBAJEE** (FR) 1
556 **BAMBARA** (GB) F 38
114 **BAMBI DU NOYER** (FR) 4
577 **BAMBINO LOLA** (GB) 1
409 **BAMO MC** (GB) 1
393 **BAN SHOOF** (GB) 15
438 **BANANA JOE** (IRE) 6
416 **BAND OF BLOOD** (IRE) 6
594 **BANDITRY** (IRE) 9
50 **BANDIUC EILE** (IRE) 21
579 **BANDOL** (IRE) 2
14 **BANDON ROC** (GB) 9
500 **BANDSMAN** (GB) 17
410 **BANFF** (IRE) 7
55 **BANG BANG ROSIE** (IRE) 4
490 **BANG ON** (IRE) 2
363 **BANG ON FRANKIE** (IRE) 2
16 **BANGKOK** (IRE) 51
232 **BANISH** (USA) 9
67 **BANK ON BLACK** (IRE) C 30
100 **BANKSY'S ART** (GB) 1
35 **BANTA BAY** (GB) 2
407 **BAPAUME** (FR) 16
266 **BAR ROOM BORE** (IRE) 83
82 **BARAAJEEL** (GB) 26
540 **BARACALU** (FR) 2
79 **BARACCA ROCKS** (GB) 80
284 **BARAKA** (IRE) F 32

26 **BARAKATLE** (GB) 47
79 **BARASTI DANCER** (IRE) 27
188 **BARATINEUR** (FR) 2
424 **BARBADOS** (IRE) 2
279 **BARBADOS BLUE** (IRE) 10
190 **BARBARA VILLIERS** (GB) 5
381 **BARBAROSA** (IRE) 17
100 **BARBILL** (IRE) 40
286 **BARBROOK STAR** (IRE) 6
472 **BARBSIZ** (G 6
100 **BARD OF BRITTANY** (GB) 2
429 **BARDD** (IRE) 1
553 **BARDO CONTIGUO** (IRE) 38
353 **BARE NECESSITIES** (IRE) 2
442 **BAREED** (USA) 1
241 **BARFLY** (GB) 4
214 **BARISTA** (IRE) 1
438 **BARLEY HILL** (IRE) 7
369 **BARNABY BROOK** (CAN) 5
15 **BARNADY FREDERICK** (FR) 25
182 **BARNAY** (GB) 3
603 **BARNEY BULLET** (IRE) 2
381 **BARNEY DWAN** (IRE) 6
22 **BARNEY'S CAULKER** (GB) 3
293 **BARNSDALE** (GB) 2
393 **BARON ALCO** (FR) 16
111 **BARON BOLT** (GB) 2
185 **BARON DE MIDLETON** (IRE) 7
594 **BARON DU PLESSIS** (FR) 10
79 **BARON RUN** (GB) 2
545 **BARON SLICK** (IRE) 18
196 **BARONIAL PRIDE** (IRE) 73
518 **BAROSSA BAL** (IRE) 23
16 **BAROSSA RED** (IRE) 52
176 **BARQEYYA** (IRE) F 140
183 **BARRA** (FR) 17
381 **BARRAQUERO** (IRE) 2
443 **BARRENJOEY** (GB) 23
555 **BARRIER REEF** (IRE) 6
6 **BARRINGTON** (IRE) 6
137 **BARRISTAN THE BOLD** (GB) 21
15 **BARRITUS** (GB) 2
393 **BARRSBROOK** (GB) 17
185 **BARRYS JACK** (IRE) 8
553 **BARSANTI** (IRE) 1
284 **BARTHOLOMEU DIAS** (GB) 4
440 **BARTHOLOMEW J** (IRE) 1
110 **BARTIMAEUS** (IRE) 16
354 **BARTON KNOLL** (GB) 3
175 **BARTON MILLS** (GB) 8
358 **BARWICK** (GB) 2
571 **BARYS** (GB) 23
562 **BARYSHNIKOV** (GB) 27
41 **BASIC BEAUTY** (IRE) 112
185 **BASILDON** (GB) 9
106 **BASILISK** (USA) 17
556 **BASILLUS** 3
594 **BASLE** (GB) F 128
569 **BASRAH** (IRE) 16
555 **BASSARABAD** (FR) 7
18 **BASTANTE** (FR) 1
5 **BASTET** (IRE) F 95
327 **BASTIEN** (FR) 7
196 **BATAAR** (IRE) 74
419 **BATHSHEBA BAY** (IRE) 8
199 **BATHWICK BRAVE** (IRE) 5
284 **BATTAASH** (IRE) 2
434 **BATTALION** (IRE) 1

29 **BATTERED** (GB) 4
409 **BATTERSEA DUCHESS** (GB) 21
475 **BATTLE ANTHEM** (IRE) 1
598 **BATTLE COMMANDER** (GB) 6
459 **BATTLE DUST** (IRE) 2
239 **BATTLE FOR GLORY** (USA) 36
54 **BATTLE HARD** (IRE) 1
542 **BATTLE OF IDEAS** (IRE) 5
382 **BATTLE OF ISSUS** (IRE) 2
479 **BATTLE OF MARATHON** (USA) 2
379 **BATTLE OF MIDWAY** (IRE) 11
452 **BATTLE OF PARADISE** (USA) 18
499 **BATTLE OF PEMBROKE** (GB) 30
232 **BATTLE OF SHILOH** (IRE) 10
479 **BATTLE OF WATERLOO** (IRE) 19
530 **BATTLE OF WILLS** (IRE) 12
480 **BATTLE OF YARMOUK** (IRE) 37
251 **BATTLEBRAVE** (IRE) 1
76 **BATTLEOFTHESOMME** (IRE) 1
183 **BATTLEOVERDOYEN** (IRE) 18
438 **BATTYS DILEMMA** (IRE) 8
318 **BAVARDAGES** (IRE) 141
168 **BAWAADER** (IRE) 4
428 **BAWAAKEER** (USA) C 97
248 **BAWTRY LADY** (GB) 16
156 **BAY FILLY ROLLA** (GB) 46
318 **BAY OF NAPLES** (IRE) 48
460 **BAY WATCH** (IRE) 1
198 **BAY WATCHING** (GB) 60
282 **BAYAANAAT** (GB) 10
594 **BAYDAR** (GB) 11
411 **BAYMORE ROAD** (IRE) 1
531 **BAYRAAT** (GB) 12
553 **BAYROOT** (IRE) 39
552 **BAYSTON HILL** (GB) 2
465 **BAYWING** (IRE) 3
208 **BAZ'S BOY** (GB) 5
209 **BAZOOKA** (IRE) 1
500 **BBOLD** (IRE) 18
27 **BE BOLD** (GB) 2
238 **BE DARING** (FR) 5
30 **BE IN VERSE** (GB) 58
185 **BE KOOL** (IRE) 10
53 **BE LIKE ME** (IRE) 20
175 **BE LUCKY** (GB) C 87
16 **BE MORE** (GB) 53
327 **BE MY GRANNY** (GB) G 8
95 **BE MY SEA** (IRE) 8
93 **BE PERFECT** (USA) 3
508 **BE PROUD** (IRE) 25
284 **BE TOGETHER** (GB) 33
510 **BEA MY STAR** (FR) 4
94 **BEA RYAN** (IRE) 2
369 **BEACH BREAK** (GB) 6
379 **BEACON EDGE** (IRE) 12
332 **BEACON LADY** (GB) C 27
202 **BEADLAM** (IRE) 4
500 **BEAKSTOWN** (IRE) 19
200 **BEALLANDENDALL** (IRE) 2
282 **BEAMING** (GB) 2
459 **BEAN IN TROUBLE** (GB) 3
592 **BEAN LIATH** (IRE) 3
510 **BEAR THAT N MIND** (IRE) 5
408 **BEAR VALLEY** (IRE) 5
169 **BEARLITA** (GER) F 24
542 **BEARS RAILS** (GB) 6
133 **BEAST OF BELSTANE** (IRE) 4
263 **BEAT LE BON** (FR) 32

411 **BORDER VICTOR** (GB) 2
90 **BORDER WARRIOR** (GB) 27
5 **BORDER ZONE** (IRE) 51
15 **BORDERFORCE** (FR) 3
237 **BOREAGH LASS** (IRE) 1
175 **BOREAS DUKE** (GB) 61
338 **BOREHAM BILL** (IRE) 2
26 **BORGIA GOLD** (IRE) C 48
574 **BORIC** (GB) 1
183 **BORICE** (FR) 24
255 **BORN A KING** (GB) 130
548 **BORN AT MIDNIGHT** (GB) 1
225 **BORN IN THORNE** (GB) 7
399 **BORN LEADER** (FR) 35
318 **BORN POOR** (IRE) 51
500 **BORN SURVIVOR** (IRE) 26
79 **BORN TO BE ALIVE** (IRE) 3
548 **BORN TO BOOGIE** (GB) 2
434 **BORN TO FINISH** (IRE) 2
482 **BORN TO FROLIC** (IRE) 4
480 **BORN TO GLORY** (GB) 80
552 **BORN TO PLEASE** (GB) 5
221 **BORN TO REASON** (IRE) 4
426 **BORN TO SIZE** (GER) 11
232 **BORN TO STING** (IRE) 15
596 **BORO BABE** (FR) 19
435 **BORU'S BROOK** (IRE) 3
390 **BORUMA** (IRE) 3
175 **BOSHAM** (GB) 9
456 **BOSMANN** (GB) 9
291 **BOSS DES MOTTES** (FR) 3
246 **BOSSINEY BAY** (IRE) 7
176 **BOSSIPOP** (GB) 13
425 **BOSTIN** (IRE) 1
266 **BOSTON BRUIN** (IRE) 87
133 **BOSTON GEORGE** (IRE) 75
500 **BOSTON HEATHER** (IRE) 27
98 **BOSTON T PARTY** (GB) 1
353 **BOSTONIAN** (GB) 3
125 **BOTTOMLESS PIT** (IRE) 7
315 **BOUCHERON** (GB) C 58
551 **BOUCLIER** (IRE) 1
4 **BOUDICA BAY** (IRE) 2
83 **BOUDRY** (FR) 3
80 **BOUGGIETOPIECES** (GB) 1
575 **BOUGHTBEFORELUNCH** (IRE) 3
494 **BOUND HILL** (GB) 2
351 **BOUNDERBY** (GB) 3
196 **BOUNDSY** (IRE) 5
47 **BOUNTY PURSUIT** (GB) 3
500 **BOURBON BORDERLINE** (IRE) 28
120 **BOURBON EDITION** (USA) 29
267 **BOUTAN** (GB) 1
16 **BOUTONNIERE** (USA) 56
272 **BOUVREUIL** (FR) 2
175 **BOW BRIDGE** (GB) F 89
539 **BOW STREET RUNNER** (GB) 1
553 **BOWERMAN** (GB) 2
325 **BOWIE** (IRE) 2
358 **BOWL IMPERIOR** (GB) 3
175 **BOWSON FRED** (GB) 10
324 **BOX AND COX** (GB) 4
431 **BOX OFFICE** (FR) 12
201 **BOXATRICKS** (IRE) 1
70 **BOXER BEAT** (IRE) 2
403 **BOY IN A BENTLEY** (IRE) 4
594 **BOY IN THE BAR** (GB) 15
542 **BOY NAMED SIOUX** (GB) 10

478 **BOY'S ON TOUR** (IRE) 12
606 **BOYCIE** (GB) 3
232 **BOYHOOD** (IRE) 16
5 **BOYNTON** (USA) 7
188 **BRAAVOS** (GB) 3
358 **BRAC JAG** (FR) 4
379 **BRACE YOURSELF** (IRE) 16
424 **BRACELET** (IRE) F 118
59 **BRACHO** (GB) 1
583 **BRACKENMOSS RORY** (GB) 4
606 **BRACKETS** (IRE) F 4
137 **BRAD THE BRIEF** (GB) 50
486 **BRADDAN HEAD** (GB) 3
286 **BRADFORD BRIDGE** (IRE) 8
363 **BRADLEY BROOK** (IRE) 4
407 **BRAHMA BULL** (IRE) 28
133 **BRAHMA KAMAL** (GB) 76
5 **BRAIDED** (USA) C 99
279 **BRAIN POWER** (IRE) 17
108 **BRAINEY BAXTER** (USA) 12
434 **BRAINS** (IRE) 28
542 **BRAMBLE BROOK** (GB) 11
186 **BRANCASTER** (IRE) 1
480 **BRANDO** (GB) 7
53 **BRANDON** (FR) 23
328 **BRANDON CASTLE** (GB) 2
232 **BRANDON HILL** (IRE) 17
143 **BRANDY CROSS** (IRE) 1
588 **BRANDY JAMES** (GER) 4
175 **BRANDY SPIRIT** (GB) 62
601 **BRANDY STATION** (IRE) 1
419 **BRAQUEUR D'OR** (FR) 14
29 **BRASCA** (GB) 27
575 **BRASS** (FR) 32
452 **BRASSICA** (IRE) 20
560 **BRAVANTINA** (GB) 3
438 **BRAVE DANCING** (GB) 3
279 **BRAVE EAGLE** (IRE) 18
416 **BRAVE HELIOS** (GB) 9
423 **BRAVE NEW WORLD** (IRE) 22
49 **BRAVE SPARTACUS** (IRE) 1
232 **BRAVENTARA** (GB) 18
428 **BRAVERY** (IRE) 12
526 **BRAVIA** (GB) F 31
284 **BRAWNY** (GB) 34
357 **BRAZEN ORANGE** (GB) 21
30 **BRAZEN SAFA** (GB) 61
137 **BRAZILIAN BRIDE** (IRE) C 14
165 **BRAZILIAN SPIRIT** (IRE) C 15
50 **BREACA AN LAE** (GB) 74
544 **BREAK COVER** (GB) 21
255 **BREAK OF DAY** (GB) 42
507 **BREAK THE RULES** (GB) 13
152 **BREAK THE SILENCE** (GB) 5
369 **BREAKFAST** (IRE) 10
571 **BREAKFAST TIME** (GB) 25
50 **BREAKING NEWS** (GB) 75
436 **BREAKING RECORDS** (IRE) 4
597 **BREAKING WAVES** (IRE) 5
427 **BREANSKI** (GB) 2
594 **BREATH CAUGHT** (GB) 16
284 **BREATH OF AIR** (GB) 35
53 **BREATH OF SPRING** (IRE) 24
176 **BREATHABLE** (GB) 14
106 **BREATHLESS TIMES** (GB) 4
253 **BREATHOFFRESHAIR** (GB) 2
599 **BREATHTAKING LOOK** (GB) 5
184 **BREATHTAKING VIEW** (GB) 7

299 **BRECON HILL** (IRE) 6
437 **BRECQHOU ISLAND** (GB) 2
313 **BREDEN** (IRE) 1
229 **BREDON HILL LAD** (GB) 2
229 **BREDON HILL LEO** (GB) 3
266 **BREEDJ** (IRE) F 128
330 **BREEZING** (GB) 13
383 **BREIZH ALKO** (FR) 5
183 **BRELADE** (GB) 25
419 **BRELAN D'AS** (FR) 15
158 **BRENBAR** (USA) 20
236 **BRENDAN** (IRE) 3
265 **BRERETON** (IRE) 1
499 **BRETON ROCK** (IRE) 7
419 **BREWERS PROJECT** (IRE) 16
410 **BREWIN'UPASTORM** (IRE) 11
125 **BREX DRAGO** (ITY) 8
263 **BREXITMEANSBREXIT** (GB) 3
555 **BRIAC** (FR) 15
420 **BRIAN BORANHA** (IRE) 1
263 **BRIAN EPSTEIN** (IRE) 37
196 **BRIAN THE SNAIL** (IRE) 6
600 **BRIANSTORM** (IRE) 7
512 **BRICE CANYON** (FR) 2
266 **BRICK BY BRICK** (IRE) 9
436 **BRICK TOPS** (GB) C 81
252 **BRICKLEBRIT** (GB) 14
424 **BRIDAL DANCE** (IRE) C 119
354 **BRIDAL MARCH** (GB) 5
521 **BRIDANE HIGH** (IRE) 3
449 **BRIDEY'S LETTUCE** (IRE) 2
142 **BRIDGE OF SIGHS** (GB) 1
293 **BRIDGE OF SIGHS** (GB) 5
100 **BRIDIE FFRENCH** (GB) F 85
393 **BRIDLE LOANAN** (IRE) 23
497 **BRIERY BUNNY** (GB) 3
597 **BRIERY EXPRESS** (GB) 6
327 **BRIGADE OF GUARDS** (IRE) 13
119 **BRIGADIER** (GB) 33
340 **BRIGADIER BOB** (IRE) 5
6 **BRIGADOON** (GB) 11
131 **BRIGAND** (GB) 1
562 **BRIGHAM YOUNG** (GB) 4
530 **BRIGHT APPROACH** (IRE) F 54
519 **BRIGHT BANK** (IRE) C 12
5 **BRIGHT BEACON** (GB) C 100
560 **BRIGHT CLOUD** (IRE) G 34
438 **BRIGHT FORECAST** (IRE) 13
82 **BRIGHT GLOW** (FR) 61
410 **BRIGHT NEW DAWN** (IRE) 12
521 **BRIGHT PROSPECT** (IRE) 4
287 **BRIGHT SAFFRON** (GB) 1
369 **BRIGHT SIDE OFLIFE** (IRE) 11
245 **BRIGHT TOMORROW** (IRE) 12
124 **BRIGHT VIEW** (GB) 75
325 **BRIGHTS PARK** (IRE) 3
499 **BRIGITTA** (IRE) F 70
320 **BRILLARE MOMENTO** (IRE) 10
41 **BRILLIANT LIGHT** (GB) 117
110 **BRILLIANT RIPOSTE** (GB) 1
480 **BRILLIANT VANGUARD** (IRE) 8
42 **BRINESTINE** (USA) 3
550 **BRING BACK CHARLIE** (GB) 26
423 **BRING HIM HOME** (FR) 23
284 **BRING HIM HOME** (GB) 90
413 **BRINGEWOOD BLUE** (IRE) 1
290 **BRINGTHEHOUSEDOWN** (IRE) 1
231 **BRINKLEYS KATIE** (GB) 15

23 **CLONDAW WHISPER** (IRE) 8
609 **CLONDAW'S ANSWER** (IRE) 2
50 **CLONGOWES** (IRE) 3
313 **CLONUSKER** (IRE) 3
14 **CLOONE LADY** (IRE) 15
266 **CLOSE SHAVE** (GB) 12
330 **CLOSE TO THE EDGE** (IRE) C 26
50 **CLOSER NOW** (GB) 24
562 **CLOSER THAN CLOSE** (GB) 32
338 **CLOSING CEREMONY** (IRE) 12
431 **CLOTH CAP** (IRE) 18
530 **CLOUD CASTLE** (GB) C 60
30 **CLOUD DRIFT** (GB) 65
513 **CLOUD HOPPER** (IRE) 11
357 **CLOUD ILLUSIONS** (USA) G 11
357 **CLOUD ILLUSIONS** (USA) C 22
95 **CLOUD NINE** (IRE) 16
369 **CLOUDY DREAM** (IRE) 18
600 **CLOUDY GLEN** (IRE) 12
41 **CLOUDY WATERS** (GB) 118
63 **CLOVELLY** (GB) 1
545 **CLOVELLY BAY** (IRE) 1
98 **CLOVER GREEN** (IRE) F 33
516 **CLUB TROPICANA** (GB) 3
202 **CLUB WEXFORD** (IRE) 7
569 **CLUTTER** (GB) F 17
593 **CLYNE** (GB) 16
307 **CMONBABYLITEMYFIRE** (IRE) F 59
71 **CNOC SION** (IRE) 1
171 **COACH MONTANA** (IRE) 5
146 **COACHELLA** (IRE) 6
535 **COAL STOCK** (IRE) 1
480 **COAST OF DUBAI** (IRE) 84
480 **COAST OFALFUJAIRAH** (IRE) 85
169 **COASTAL CYCLONE** (GB) 1
542 **COASTAL DRIFT** (GB) 17
385 **COASTAL DRIVE** (GB) 3
298 **COASTGUARD WATCH** (FR) 23
530 **COASTLINE** (IRE) 15
198 **COBNUT** (IRE) 63
431 **COBOLOBO** (FR) 19
529 **COBRA COMMANDER** (IRE) 3
500 **COBRA DE MAI** (FR) 34
386 **COBWEB CATCHER** (IRE) 19
229 **COBY NINE** (GB) 4
319 **COCARDIER** (FR) 18
576 **COCHABAMBA** (IRE) C 91
256 **COCHISE** (GB) 22
194 **COCHISE** (GB) 14
500 **COCK A DOODLE DOO** (FR) 35
202 **COCKALORUM** (IRE) 8
46 **COCKER** (GB) 1
478 **COCKLE BAY** (IRE) 18
6 **COCKNEY BOY** (GB) 19
547 **COCKNEY HILL** (GB) 21
313 **COCKNEY SEAGULL** (IRE) 4
186 **COCKTAIL QUEEN** (IRE) C 28
156 **COCO MOTION** (IRE) 28
30 **COCONUT KREEK** (GB) C 66
119 **COCONUT SUGAR** (IRE) 82
140 **CODDINGTON BANKS** (GB) 6
106 **CODE OF CONDUCT** (GB) 72
403 **CODE OF LAW** (GB) 12
98 **CODED MESSAGE** (GB) 2
55 **CODESHARE** (GB) 8
360 **CODY WYOMING** (GB) 4
229 **COEUR BLIMEY** (IRE) 5
576 **COEUR D'OR** (IRE) 27

183 **COEUR DE BEAUCHENE** (FR) 35
327 **COEUR DE LION** (GB) 19
438 **COEUR PENSIF** (FR) 21
183 **COEUR SUBLIME** (IRE) 36
327 **COGBURN** (GB) 20
443 **COGITAL** (GB) 4
550 **COGRY** (GB) 33
255 **COIN A PHRASE** (GB) C 134
246 **COISA BLANCO** (IRE) 9
152 **COISTE BODHAR** (IRE) 8
61 **COJACK** (IRE) 2
600 **COLD AS ICE** (IRE) 13
67 **COLD FIRE** (IRE) 5
592 **COLD FUSION** (IRE) 6
67 **COLD HARBOUR** (GB) 6
588 **COLD MARCH** (FR) 8
308 **COLD SNAP** (IRE) 3
428 **COLD STARE** (IRE) 13
327 **COLDITZ CASTLE** (IRE) 21
408 **COLLATE** (GB) 9
79 **COLLECT CALL** (IRE) 30
171 **COLLEGE KING** (GB) 6
436 **COLLIDE** (GB) 5
394 **COLLIENE DO ROIS** (GB) 20
157 **COLLODI** (GER) 1
410 **COLLOONEY** (IRE) 22
490 **COLMERS HILL** (GB) 8
363 **COLONEL CUSTARD** (IRE) 6
458 **COLONEL FRANK** (GB) 1
475 **COLONEL KEATING** (IRE) 3
596 **COLONEL MANDERSON** (FR) 21
106 **COLONEL MORDAUNT** (FR) 73
381 **COLONEL SLADE** (IRE) 19
279 **COLONIAL DREAMS** (IRE) 34
108 **COLONIALISTE** (IRE) F 51
530 **COLONY QUEEN** (GB) 16
59 **COLORADO DOC** (GB) 3
54 **COLORADO GOLD** (GB) 3
5 **COLOUR** (AUS) F 103
307 **COLOUR CONTRAST** (IRE) C 5
41 **COLOUR IMAGE** (FR) 119
518 **COLOURFIELD** (IRE) 4
394 **COLOURFUL SKY** (FR) 8
407 **COLREEVY** (IRE) 43
183 **COLUMN OF FIRE** (IRE) 37
178 **COLWOOD** (GB) 1
328 **COMANCHE CHIEFTAIN** (CAN) 4
459 **COMBER MILL** (IRE) 10
81 **COMBUSTIBLE GIRL** (IRE) 2
50 **COME AT DAWN** (IRE) 4
108 **COME BACK TO ME** (IRE) 16
286 **COME ON CHARLIE** (FR) 15
120 **COME ON COME ON** (IRE) 3
131 **COME ON DAVE** (IRE) 2
263 **COME ON LEICESTER** (FR) 40
232 **COME ON TEDDY** (IRE) 25
499 **COME ON TIER** (FR) 9
407 **COME TO ME** (FR) 44
577 **COMEONFEELTHEFORCE** (IRE) 18
522 **COMEONTHEBULL** (IRE) 8
450 **COMING BACK** (GB) C 34
59 **COMMANCHE CHEIF** (GB) 3
238 **COMMANCHE RED** (IRE) 7
480 **COMMANDER HAN** (FR) 9
266 **COMMANDER LADY** (IRE) 13
279 **COMMANDER MILLER** (GB) 35
183 **COMMANDER OF FLEET** (IRE) 38
183 **COMMENTARIOLUS** (IRE) 39

600 **COMMIS D'OFFICE** (FR) 14
332 **COMMIT NO NUISANCE** (IRE) 28
600 **COMMODORE** (FR) 15
14 **COMMODORE BARRY** (IRE) 16
318 **COMMUNICATE** (IRE) 7
65 **COMOTION** (FR) 5
191 **COMPADRE** (IRE) 2
120 **COMPANY MINX** 83
599 **COMPASS SCOOBIE** (GB) 9
16 **COMPASS** (GB) 61
297 **COMPASS HILL** (USA) 8
67 **COMPASS POINT** (GB) 7
315 **COMPASSIONATE** (GB) 21
410 **COMPATRIOT** (IRE) 23
16 **COMPENSATE** (GB) 146
207 **COMPETENT** (GB) 1
416 **COMPETITION** (GB) 14
103 **COMPIEGNE** (FR) 22
391 **COMPORTA** (GB) 1
170 **COMPTON ABBEY** (GB) 9
310 **COMPTON BRAVE** (GB) 9
399 **COMPTON MILL** (GB) 8
60 **COMPTON PRINCE** (GB) 4
504 **COMPTON RIVER** (GB) 5
393 **COMPULSIVE** (IRE) 34
176 **COMPUTABLE** (GB) 16
500 **COMRADE CONRAD** (IRE) 36
38 **CONAGLEN** (GB) 11
591 **CONAS TAOI** (IRE) 3
555 **CONCEALED AMBITION** (IRE) 27
571 **CONCELLO** (IRE) 27
407 **CONCERTISTA** (FR) 45
469 **CONCHITA** (GER) 2
489 **CONCIERGE** (IRE) 8
318 **CONCORDIA** (GB) C 152
386 **CONCUR** (FR) 4
61 **CONEYGREE** (GB) 3
15 **CONFAB** (USA) 26
436 **CONFEDERATE** (GB) 6
108 **CONFETTI** (FR) 17
406 **CONFEY** (FR) 7
239 **CONFIDE** (GB) 44
394 **CONFIDENTE** (IRE) F 21
378 **CONFIDING** (GB) 15
15 **CONFILS** (FR) 27
15 **CONFRERIE** (IRE) 4
203 **CONFUSING** (GB) F 53
480 **CONGA** (GB) 41
6 **CONGRESS PLACE** (IRE) 81
537 **CONHALT** (GB) 2
334 **CONINGSBY** (GB) 3
547 **CONKERING HERO** (IRE) 3
403 **CONKWELL LEGEND** (GB) 13
199 **CONNA CROSS** (IRE) 9
232 **CONNECT FOUR** (GB) 26
261 **CONNECTIVE** (IRE) 13
83 **CONNEMARA QUEEN** (GB) 5
191 **CONNETABLE** (FR) 3
557 **CONNIE WILDE** (IRE) 4
137 **CONNIPTION** (IRE) F 54
440 **CONQUERESS** (GB) 3
266 **CONRON** (IRE) 14
326 **CONS AMIGO** (IRE) 1
106 **CONSCIOUS** (GB) 74
284 **CONSPIRITOR** (GB) 38
369 **CONSTANCIO** (IRE) 19
428 **CONSTANT** (GB) 68
548 **CONSTANT CRAVING** (GB) F 15

535 **DOBRYN** (FR) 31
433 **DOC CARVER** (IRE) 10
221 **DOC PENFRO** (GB) 9
95 **DOC SPORTELLO** (IRE) 19
225 **DOCKSIDE STRIKE** (GB) F 59
232 **DOCTOR DEX** (IRE) 30
14 **DOCTOR HAZE** (GB) 22
347 **DOCTOR PARKES** (GB) 2
183 **DOCTOR PHOENIX** (IRE) 55
137 **DOCTOR SARDONICUS** (GB) 6
102 **DOCTOR THEA** (GB) 3
221 **DOCTOR WONDERFUL** (GB) 10
575 **DOCTOR ZEN** (IRE) 33
221 **DOCUMENTING** (GB) 11
21 **DODDINGTON DI** (GB) 1
405 **DODGY BOB** (GB) 3
431 **DOESYOURDOGBITE** (IRE) 25
500 **DOG OF WAR** (FR) 42
419 **DOGON** (GB) 50
403 **DOING FINE** (IRE) 21
280 **DOITFORTHEVILLAGE** (IRE) 5
154 **DOKTOR GLAZ** (FR) 12
407 **DOLCIANO DICI** (FR) 57
119 **DOLLAR VALUE** (USA) 5
338 **DOLLNAMIX** (FR) 15
106 **DOLLY COLMAN** (IRE) F 78
298 **DOLLY DAYDREAMER** (GB) F 65
131 **DOLLY DUPREE** (GB) 17
539 **DOLLY'S DOT** (IRE) 4
310 **DOLLYWAGGON PIKE** (GB) 12
477 **DOLNIYA** (FR) C 62
419 **DOLOS** (FR) 51
270 **DOLPHIN VILLAGE** (IRE) 4
29 **DOLPHIN VISTA** (IRE) 12
444 **DOLYDAYDREAM** (GB) 2
227 **DOM GARO CATELINE** (FR) 4
53 **DOMAGNANO** (IRE) 8
89 **DOMESTIC DIVA** (IRE) 10
24 **DOMINANNIE** (IRE) 1
497 **DOMINATEUR** (IRE) 10
369 **DOMINATING** (GER) 31
553 **DOMINATRIX** (GB) C 140
381 **DOMINUS** (IRE) 22
202 **DOMMERSEN** (IRE) 13
599 **DON ARMADO** (IRE) 44
245 **DON DES FOSSES** (FR) 18
333 **DON DIEGO VEGA** (GB) 13
600 **DON HERBAGER** (FR) 20
53 **DON JUPP** (USA) 28
183 **DON POLI** (IRE) 56
503 **DON TOMMASINO** (IRE) 1
594 **DON'T ACT UP** (GB) 31
245 **DON'T ASK** (IRE) 19
517 **DON'T BE SURPRISED** (GB) 2
526 **DON'T CRY ABOUT IT** (IRE) 6
6 **DON'T DO IT** (IRE) 28
575 **DON'T FENCE ME IN** (IRE) 6
303 **DON'T LOOK DOWN** (GB) 5
535 **DON'T SHOUT** (IRE) 5
53 **DON'T STOP TO SHOP** (USA) C 72
238 **DON'T TELL GEORGE** (FR) 10
479 **DON'T THINK SO** (IRE) 5
148 **DONATELLO MAIL** (FR) 11
53 **DONATIA** (GB) F 73
225 **DONCASTER STAR** (GB) 11
410 **DONCESAR DE PRETOT** (FR) 27
452 **DONE DEAL** (IRE) 4

16 **DONJUAN TRIUMPHANT** (IRE) 14
497 **DONLADD** (IRE) 11
100 **DONNA RAY** (GB) 91
540 **DONNA'S DELIGHT** (IRE) 7
241 **DONNA'S DIAMOND** (IRE) 8
583 **DONNACHIES GIRL** (IRE) 9
241 **DONNAS DREAM** (IRE) 9
517 **DONNCHA** (IRE) 3
27 **DONNELLY'S RAINBOW** (IRE) 5
393 **DONNYTWOBUCKETS** (IRE) 42
53 **DONO** (GB) 74
356 **DONO DI DIO** (GB) 2
213 **DONT BE ROBIN** (IRE) 1
470 **DONT CALL ME DORIS** (GB) 1
407 **DONT HESITATE** (FR) 58
13 **DONT TELL THE WIFE** (GB) 4
431 **DONTBITEDABAIT** (IRE) 26
263 **DONTCALLMEJUNIOR** (FR) 144
591 **DONTCASHTHECHEQUE** (IRE) 6
148 **DONTCOUNTURCHIKENS** (IRE) 12
261 **DONTDELAY** (IRE) 2
137 **DONTHOLDYOURBREATH** (IRE) 23
150 **DONTMINDDBOYS** (IRE) 7
236 **DOON STAR** (GB) 7
530 **DOORS TO MANUAL** (USA) C 62
303 **DOR'S DIAMOND** (GB) 40
303 **DOR'S LAW** (GB) 6
331 **DORA'S FIELD** (FR) 4
14 **DORABELLE** (FR) F 23
98 **DORADO DOLLAR** (IRE) 5
53 **DORCHESTER** (GB) 29
410 **DORETTE** (FR) 28
103 **DORIANA GRAY** (FR) 24
152 **DORIES DELIGHT** (IRE) 11
196 **DORIS BLEASEDALE** (IRE) 87
334 **DORKING BOY** (GB) 4
334 **DORKING COCK** (IRE) 5
276 **DOROTHY'S FLAME** (GB) 4
530 **DORRAAR** (IRE) C 20
609 **DORRANA** (IRE) 4
407 **DORRELLS PIERJI** (FR) 59
183 **DORTMUND PARK** (FR) 57
594 **DORY** (IRE) 32
196 **DOSE** (GB) 11
335 **DOSILA** (GB) 8
286 **DOSTAL PHIL** (FR) 24
538 **DOTHRAKI** (IRE) 13
241 **DOTHRAKI PRINCE** (GB) 10
341 **DOTHRAKI RAIDER** (FR) 7
386 **DOTI** (GB) 20
571 **DOTTED SWISS** (IRE) 6
55 **DOTTIES DILEMA** (IRE) 11
434 **DOTTY GRAND** (GB) 31
108 **DOUALA** (GB) F 52
282 **DOUBLE COFFEE** (GB) 11
550 **DOUBLE COURT** (IRE) 38
315 **DOUBLE ESPRIT** (GB) 24
519 **DOUBLE FANTASY** (GER) F 40
38 **DOUBLE HONOUR** (GB) 12
142 **DOUBLE KODIAC** (IRE) 34
443 **DOUBLE LEGEND** (IRE) 6
563 **DOUBLE OR BUBBLE** (IRE) 7
79 **DOUBLE REFLECTION** (GB) 5
550 **DOUBLE ROSS** (IRE) 39
232 **DOUBLE SHUFFLE** (IRE) 31
513 **DOUBLE TREASURE** (GB) 16
594 **DOUBLE UP** (GB) 33
309 **DOUBLE W'S** (IRE) 6

307 **DOUBLE WHAMMY** (GB) 8
436 **DOUBLING DICE** (GB) 84
106 **DOUBLY BEAUTIFUL** (IRE) 25
47 **DOUBLY CLEVER** (IRE) 8
184 **DOUGAL BUG** (GB) 8
263 **DOUGHAN ALB** (GB) 46
318 **DOUGLAS FIR** (IRE) 159
530 **DOULA** (USA) F 63
16 **DOUNE CASTLE** (GB) 65
183 **DOUNIKOS** (FR) 58
416 **DOUNYAPOUR** (FR) 17
99 **DOURADO** (IRE) 2
407 **DOUVAN** (FR) 60
279 **DOUX PRETENDER** (FR) 45
399 **DOVE DIVINE** (FR) 37
410 **DOVE MOUNTAIN** (IRE) 29
303 **DOVER LIGHT** (GB) 52
555 **DOVILS DATE** (GB) 34
384 **DOWHATUDOBEST** (IRE) 1
338 **DOWN THE HIGHWAY** (IRE) 16
61 **DOWN TO THE SEA** (FR) 4
250 **DOWNE MILKING LANE** (GB) 5
530 **DOWNHILL DANCER** (IRE) F 64
65 **DOWNLOADTHEAPP** (IRE) 8
413 **DOWNTON FOX** (GB) 2
279 **DOWNTOWN GETAWAY** (IRE) 46
19 **DOYANNIE** (IRE) 5
100 **DOZEN** (FR) C 92
263 **DR AVERY** (GB) 145
433 **DR DES** (IRE) 11
594 **DR DORO** (IRE) 34
55 **DR DUNRAVEN** (GB) 12
478 **DR HOOVES** (IRE) 22
499 **DR JEKYLL** (IRE) 37
372 **DR JULIUS NO** (GB) 1
114 **DR MOLONEY** (IRE) 5
433 **DR OAKLEY** (IRE) 12
318 **DR RICHARD KIMBLE** (IRE) 9
55 **DR ROBIN** (IRE) 13
419 **DR SANDERSON** (IRE) 52
556 **DR SMOLDER** (IRE) 41
529 **DR TIME** (IRE) 4
127 **DRACARYS** (GB) 4
407 **DRACONIEN** (FR) 61
6 **DRAGON BEAT** (IRE) 82
489 **DRAGON COMMAND** (GB) 32
279 **DRAGON D'ESTRUVAL** (FR) 47
489 **DRAGON FLIGHT** (GB) 33
71 **DRAGON GIRL** (IRE) 4
230 **DRAGON KHAN** (IRE) 3
436 **DRAGON KUZA** (GB) 48
383 **DRAGON MALL** (USA) 11
133 **DRAGON MOUNTAIN** (IRE) 15
266 **DRAGON ROLL** (IRE) 96
263 **DRAGON SUN** (GB) 47
313 **DRAGON TATTOO** (GB) 7
181 **DRAGONFLI** (GB) 4
478 **DRAGONHOV** (FR) 23
185 **DRAGONS HEART** (GB) 53
137 **DRAGONS TAIL** (IRE) 7
382 **DRAGONS VOICE** (GB) 7
261 **DRAGONS WILL RISE** (IRE) 79
263 **DRAKEFELL** (IRE) 3
448 **DRAMA KING** (IRE) 13
138 **DRAMATIC MOMENT** (GB) 5
529 **DRAMATIC PAUSE** (IRE) 5
255 **DRAMATIC QUEEN** (USA) 11
519 **DREAM ASCOT** (GB) 2

440 DYAGILEV (GB) 4
15 DYAMI (FR) 34
552 DYLAN'S SEA SONG (GB) 7
143 DYLANSEOGHAN (IRE) 5
13 DYLIEV (FR) 6
419 DYNAMITE DOLLARS (FR) 53
556 DYNAMITE GOLD (GER) 42
556 DYNAMITE STAR (GER) 47
493 DYNAMO WALT (IRE) 7
261 EAGER TO KNOW (IRE) 23
16 EAGLE QUEEN (GB) 68
1 EAGLE RIDGE (IRE) 5
38 EAGLE'S FOOT (GB) 22
30 EAGLES BY DAY (IRE) 21
109 EAGLESGLEN (GB) 34
493 EAGRE (GB) 2
448 EAMON AN CNOIC (IRE) 19
179 EARCOMESALI (GB) 1
455 EARCOMESANNIE (IRE) G 2
438 EARL BIFFY BIFFEN (FR) 24
266 EARL OF DESMOND (GB) 17
100 EARL OF HARROW (GB) 52
542 EARL OF WISDOM (GB) 9
550 EARLOFTHECOTSWOLDS (FR) 40
179 EARLSHILL (IRE) 5
126 EARLY BOY (FR) 5
393 EARLY DU LEMO (FR) 45
14 EARLY LEARNER (GB) 24
513 EARLY MORNING RAIN (FR) 17
13 EARLY RETIREMENT (FR) 7
530 EARLY RISER (IRE) 21
399 EARLY SUMMER (IRE) 11
165 EARLY VOICE (FR) 9
489 EARTH AND SKY (USA) 11
19 EARTH SPIRIT (GB) 6
346 EARTHLY (USA) 3
100 EASEE ON (IRE) F 53
597 EASKEY LAD (IRE) 12
419 EASON (FR) 54
480 EAST (GB) 42
523 EAST COAST LADY (IRE) 2
393 EAST INDIES (GB) 46
176 EAST STREET REVUE (GB) 22
186 EASTER DIVA (IRE) F 30
448 EASTER ERIC (GB) 20
465 EASTER FIRTH (GB) 17
557 EASTER GOLD (FR) 6
5 EASTERN JOY (GB) C 108
454 EASTERN LADY (IND) 8
561 EASTERN PROMISES (GB) 5
431 EASTLAKE (GB) 28
562 EASTON ARCH (USA) C 73
55 EASY BUCKS (GB) 15
407 EASY GAME (FR) 64
562 EASY MONEY (IRE) 8
431 EASY STREET (IRE) 29
546 EASY TERMS (GB) F 19
232 EASY WOOD (FR) 34
313 EASYONTHEEYE (IRE) 8
419 EASYRUN DE VASSY (FR) 55
594 EAT MY DIRT (GER) 35
340 EATON COLLINA (IRE) 9
340 EATON HILL (IRE) 10
529 EATON MILLER (GB) 6
438 EAU TOP (FR) 25
354 EBBISHAM (IRE) 9
124 EBBRAAM (GB) 36
208 EBEN DUBAI (IRE) 12

576 EBENDI (IRE) 93
152 EBITDA (GB) 12
477 EBIYZA (FR) F 63
381 EBONY ADAMS (GB) 44
286 EBONY GALE (GB) 26
115 EBONY ROSE (GB) 4
551 EBQAA (IRE) 3
263 EBTISAMA (USA) F 149
378 EBURY (GB) 7
419 ECCO (GB) 56
600 ECEPARTI (FR) 22
103 ECHELLE DU LEVANT (IRE) 26
427 ECHO (IRE) 5
36 ECHO BRAVA (GB) 4
465 ECHO EXPRESS (IRE) 18
266 ECHO PARK (IRE) 18
288 ECHO WATT (FR) 5
500 ECLAIR D'AINAY (FR) 44
557 ECLAIR DE GUYE (FR) 7
168 ECLAIRCIE (IRE) C 63
431 ECLAT DE STAR (FR) 30
407 ECLAT DES MOTTES (FR) 35
519 ECLIPSE STORM (GB) 15
53 ECLITTICA (IRE) 30
335 ECOLO (FR) 9
32 ECONOMIC CRISIS (IRE) 2
335 ECRIVAIN (FR) 41
252 ECSTASEA (IRE) 17
245 ECTOR (FR) 21
286 ECU DE LA NOVERIE (FR) 27
82 EDAARAH (GB) 31
512 EDABEAN (IRE) 4
393 EDAM DU MESTIVEL (FR) 47
553 EDARAAT (GB) 45
263 EDDIE COCHRAN (IRE) 48
208 EDDIEMAURICE (IRE) 13
214 EDDIES PEARL (IRE) 3
229 EDDY (GB) 6
35 EDDYSTONE ROCK (IRE) 5
444 EDE'S (GB) 17
604 EDE'S THE BUSINESS (GB) 2
576 EDELMIRA (IRE) C 94
448 EDEN DU HOUX (FR) 21
124 EDEN GARDENS (FR) 37
298 EDEN PACE (IRE) 66
100 EDEN ROSE (GB) 9
183 EDENE D'ARC (FR) 60
65 EDGAR (GER) 9
27 EDGAR ALLAN POE (IRE) 6
346 EDGE (FR) 4
364 EDGED OUT (GB) 1
38 EDGEWOOD (GB) 13
16 EDINBURGH CASTLE (GB) 69
477 EDISA (GB) 26
393 EDITEUR DU GITE (FR) 48
382 EDMOND DANTES (IRE) 14
82 EDRAAK (IRE) 32
489 EDREA (FR) C 34
597 EDWARD BLUE (IRE) 13
381 EDWARDIAN ERA (GB) C 45
327 EDWARDSTONE (GB) 30
53 EESHA MY FLOWER (USA) 31
95 EESHA SAYS (IRE) 20
225 EESHA'S SMILE (IRE) 39
178 EEVILYNN DREW (GB) 13
478 EFFET SPECIAL (FR) 24
100 EFFIE B (GB) F 93
604 EGG LANE (GB) 3

419 EGGARDON HILL (IRE) 57
611 EGGESFORD (GB) 4
61 EGLANTIER (FR) 5
407 EGLANTINE DU SEUIL (FR) 66
436 EGO (GB) F 85
576 EGRECIO (GB) 29
594 EGYPT MILL DUKE (GB) 36
41 EGYPTIAN KING (GB) 130
104 EHMAJ (JPN) 5
82 EHTIRAAS (GB) 9
576 EIGER (USA) 95
419 EIGHTEENHUNDRED (IRE) 158
565 EIGHTSIXSIX (GB) 7
30 EIGHTSOME REEL (GB) 22
407 EILEEN O (IRE) 67
502 EILEENDOVER (GB) 25
303 EIRENE (GB) 7
424 EIRNIN (IRE) C 132
82 EITHAAR (GB) 33
505 EJABAH (IRE) 2
82 EJADAH (IRE) C 65
125 EJAYTEEKAY (GB) 17
553 EJTILAAB (IRE) 46
448 EKAYBURG (FR) 42
32 EKHRAAJ (USA) F 14
457 EL ASTRONAUTE (IRE) 13
419 EL BANDIT (GB) 58
158 EL BORRACHO (IRE) 7
100 EL CHE (GB) F 94
436 EL GHAZWANI (IRE) 10
124 EL GUMRYAH (IRE) 38
393 EL HAGEB ROSE (FR) 49
133 EL HOMBRE (GB) 16
279 EL KALDOUN (FR) 51
530 EL MANATI (IRE) F 65
503 EL MANIFICO 3
503 EL MESIO (FR) 34
239 EL MISK (GB) 51
175 EL MOLINO BLANCO (GB) F 93
525 EL PICADOR (IRE) 51
14 EL PRESENTE (GB) 25
251 EL SCORPIO (IRE) 3
550 EL TERREMOTO (FR) 41
349 ELA D'ARGENT (IRE) G 4
553 ELA KATRINA (GB) 47
553 ELAMIRR (IRE) 48
318 ELARQAM (GB) 10
553 ELBEGEI (GB) 141
542 ELDORADO ALLEN (FR) 26
103 ELEA CHOPE (FR) 78
600 ELEANOR BOB (GB) 23
67 ELEANOR ELOISE (USA) F 8
223 ELEANOROFAQUITAINE (IRE) 23
525 ELECTOR (GB) 6
562 ELECTRIC FEEL (GB) C 74
110 ELECTRIC LANDLADY (IRE) 3
263 ELEGANT ERIN (GB) 150
542 ELEGANT ESCAPE (FR) 27
190 ELEGANT LOVE (GB) 28
298 ELEGANT PEACE (IRE) F 67
5 ELEGANT SHADOW (GER) C 109
318 ELEGIAC (GB) 11
284 ELENA (GB) 42
410 ELENA SUE (GB) 31
53 ELENORA DELIGHT (GB) 9
27 ELERFAAN (IRE) 7
540 ELF DE RE (FR) 9
327 ELGIN (GB) 31

358 FOURNI (IRE) 8
327 FOURSHOES (GB) 40
508 FOURTH OF JULY (IRE) 9
489 FOUZ (GB) 2
338 FOX APPEAL (IRE) 24
16 FOX CHAIRMAN (GB) 74
263 FOX CHAMPION (IRE) 55
16 FOX DUTY FREE (IRE) 153
79 FOX FEARLESS (GB) 36
263 FOX HAPPY (IRE) 56
4 FOX HILL (GB) 13
263 FOX KASPER (IRE) 57
16 FOX LEICESTER (GB) 75
16 FOX MAFIA (IRE) 18
16 FOX MORGAN (GB) 76
525 FOX NEVER QUIT (GB) 113
542 FOX NORTON (FR) 35
263 FOX POWER (IRE) 58
16 FOX PREMIER (FR) 77
595 FOX PRO (FR) 7
16 FOX SHINJI (GB) 78
381 FOX TAL (GB) 79
50 FOX TERRIER (IRE) 88
381 FOX TROTTER (IRE) 3
378 FOX VARDY (USA) 20
16 FOX WIN WIN (IRE) 80
374 FOXES FLYER (IRE) 6
194 FOXEY (GB) 22
253 FOXRUSH TAKE TIME (FR) 4
550 FOXTAIL HILL (IRE) 48
410 FOXTROT JULIET (GB) 41
93 FOXTROT KNIGHT (GB) 13
16 FOXTROT LADY (GB) 19
279 FOXWORTHY (GB) 59
159 FOXY ACT (GB) 7
27 FOXY BOY (GB) 8
226 FOXY FEMME (GB) 13
589 FOXY FOREVER (IRE) 6
397 FOXY JACKS (IRE) 8
480 FOXY LADY (GB) 13
170 FOXY LASS (GB) 17
93 FOXY REBEL (GB) 14
536 FOXY'S SPIRIT (GB) 2
17 FOYLESIDEVIEW (IRE) 2
29 FRAGRANT BELLE (GB) 41
284 FRAGRANT DAWN (GB) 44
50 FRAME (IRE) 89
307 FRAME RATE (GB) 13
407 FRANCIN (FR) 80
221 FRANCIS XAVIER (IRE) 12
146 FRANCISCO BAY (GB) 28
55 FRANCKY DU BERLAIS (FR) 18
278 FRANCO'S SECRET (GB) 3
318 FRANCOPHILIA (GB) 13
415 FRANGARRY (IRE) 3
9 FRANK COOL (GB) 24
315 FRANK ROGERS (GB) 3
261 FRANK THE SLINK (GB) 27
133 FRANK'S LAW (GB) 85
507 FRANK'S LEGACY (GB) 3
137 FRANKADORE (IRE) 27
255 FRANKELLINA (GB) 60
216 FRANKIE BALLOU (IRE) 4
500 FRANKIE RAPPER (IRE) 57
567 FRANKIES FIRE (GB) 4
529 FRANKLY SPEAKING (GB) 11
261 FRANKSTER (FR) 28
428 FRANKUUS (IRE) 19

502 FRANSHAM (GB) 4
95 FRANTICAL (GB) 25
239 FRANZ KAFKA (IRE) 64
455 FRANZ KLAMMER (GB) 3
50 FRAOCHAN (IRE) 90
318 FRASER ISLAND (IRE) 70
50 FRATERCULUS (IRE) 91
403 FRAU GEORGIA (GB) 26
186 FRAULEIN (GB) C 31
169 FREA (GB) 14
545 FRECKLES (GB) 5
318 FRED (GB) 170
600 FREDDIE FLIP FLOP (IRE) 32
331 FREDDY FANATAPAN (GB) 7
310 FREDDY WITH A Y (IRE) 15
295 FREE (FR) 8
33 FREE BIRD (GB) 7
182 FREE BOUNTY (GB) 5
95 FREE GIFT (GB) 74
6 FREE LOVE (GB) 84
20 FREE RANGE (IRE) 6
379 FREE RANGER (GB) 44
318 FREE REIN (GB) F 171
266 FREE SOLO (IRE) 134
10 FREE TALKIN (GB) 5
98 FREE TRAVEL (IRE) 7
594 FREEBE ROCKS (IRE) 43
451 FREEDOM AND WHEAT (IRE) 17
230 FREEDOM CHIMES (GB) 4
447 FREEDOM FIGHTER (IRE) 4
576 FREEDOM REIGNS (IRE) F 98
338 FREEDOM RUN (GB) 25
6 FREEDOM'S BREATH (GB) 85
95 FREEDREAMS (GB) 75
203 FREEROLLING (GB) 9
333 FREESIA GOLD (GB) 14
553 FREEZY (IRE) C 144
606 FREIGHT TRAIN (IRE) 8
68 FRENCH (GB) 5
35 FRENCH ACCENT (GB) C 33
279 FRENCH CRUSADER (FR) 60
191 FRENCH DE GUYE (FR) 5
30 FRENCH FERN (GB) C 74
16 FRENCH FLIRT (GB) C 154
27 FRENCH FLYER (IRE) 9
94 FRENCH HEROINE (GB) 5
95 FRENCH KISS (IRE) 9
170 FRENCH MIX (USA) 18
65 FRENCH PIECE (GB) 12
29 FRENCH RIVIERA (FR) 13
266 FRENCH STEPS (GB) 25
567 FRENCH TICKET (GB) 5
318 FRENCH TWIST (GB) 71
484 FRENCHMANS CREEK (IRE) 6
600 FRENCHY DU LARGE (GB) 33
427 FREQUENCY CODE (FR) 31
156 FREQUENT (GB) C 50
410 FRESH NEW DAWN (FR) 42
41 FRESH SNOW (GB) 135
424 FRESNO (IRE) 52
561 FRESNO EMERY (FR) 7
327 FRET D'ESTRUVAL (FR) 41
372 FREYA TRICKS (GB) F 2
453 FRIARY GOLD (IRE) 6
96 FRICKA (GB) 13
432 FRIDAY FEELING (GB) 9
448 FRIDAY NIGHT LIGHT (FR) 26
419 FRIEND OR FOE (FR) 70

133 FRIENDLY ADVICE (IRE) 86
182 FRIENDS DON'T ASK (GB) 6
602 FRIENDS IN HEAVEN (IRE) 2
191 FRIENDSHIP BAY (GB) 6
486 FRIGHTENED RABBIT (USA) 5
434 FRIGID (GB) C 68
103 FRILLY BOLERO (FR) 81
575 FRIPPON DE VAIGE (FR) 11
239 FRISELLA (GB) 65
176 FRITTA MISTA (IRE) C 149
419 FRODON (FR) 71
255 FROGLET (GB) C 139
286 FROM THE HEART (IRE) 34
333 FRONSAC (GB) 3
369 FRONT AT THE LAST (IRE) 38
563 FRONT OF LINE (GB) 25
560 FRONT PAGE NEWS (GB) G 36
50 FRONT PAGING (IRE) 92
443 FRONTISPIECE (GB) 8
79 FRONTLINE PHANTOM (IRE) 6
23 FROSTED GRAPE (IRE) F 27
25 FROSTED LASS (GB) 25
424 FROSTY (IRE) 53
576 FROSTY BEACH (IRE) 33
147 FROSTY TERN (GB) 11
432 FROZEN LAKE (USA) 10
350 FROZEN MOTION (GB) 16
263 FROZEN WATERS (IRE) 155
279 FRUCTINE (FR) 61
30 FRYERNS (GB) 75
14 FUBAR (IRE) 28
93 FUEL INJECTION (GB) 15
133 FUENTE (GB) 37
503 FUGAZ (FR) 35
279 FUGITIVES DRIFT (IRE) 62
553 FUJAIRA KING (USA) 55
553 FUJAIRA PRINCE (IRE) 7
65 FUKUTO (FR) 13
403 FULL (FR) 27
279 FULL BORE (IRE) 63
327 FULL GLASS (FR) 42
440 FULL INTENTION (GB) 5
338 FULL IRISH (GB) 26
284 FULL MOON FEVER (IRE) C 97
341 FULL SHIFT (FR) 9
103 FULL SNOW MOON (USA) C 82
509 FULL SUIT (GB) 3
14 FULL TILT (GB) 29
129 FULL TIME PARTY (IRE) 8
284 FULLAAH (IRE) C 98
261 FULLMOON LUNA LADY (FR) 29
540 FULLY BOOKED (GB) 4
50 FULVIO (USA) 30
556 FUMAROLE (GB) 15
27 FUMBO JUMBO (IRE) 10
26 FUN LEGEND (GB) 13
399 FUN MAC (GER) 14
255 FUNDTANK (GB) 140
272 FUNKADELIC (GB) 13
79 FUNNY BAY (USA) C 93
393 FURIA D'OUDAIRIES (FR) 55
499 FURIOUS (GB) 41
78 FURIOUSLY FAST (IRE) 6
538 FURNI FACTORS (GB) 4
82 FURQAAN (IRE) 34
26 FURTHER MEASURE (USA) 52
406 FURTHER NORTH (FR) 10
308 FURY AND FIRE (GB) 9

576 **GEORGEVILLE** (GB) 34
339 **GEORGIAN FIREBIRD** (GB) 3
410 **GEORGIATOR** (FR) 45
241 **GEORGIE BEAR** (GB) 13
214 **GEORGIEZAR** (GB) 4
183 **GER'S LAD** (IRE) 81
399 **GERANIUM** (GB) 15
257 **GERASH** (FR) C 55
38 **GERASH** (FR) F 14
540 **GERONIMO** (GB) 12
97 **GERRY THE GLOVER** (IRE) 2
610 **GERSJOEYCASEY** (IRE) 5
533 **GERT LUSH** (IRE) 24
55 **GET AN OSCAR** (IRE) 21
120 **GET BACK GET BACK** (IRE) 5
297 **GET EVEN** (GB) 11
113 **GET HELP** (IRE) 10
223 **GET IN THE QUEUE** (GB) 26
6 **GET IT READY** (GB) 86
156 **GET KNOTTED** (IRE) 8
419 **GET ME HOME** (IRE) G 72
500 **GET ON THE YAGER** (GB) 58
236 **GET OUT THE GATE** (IRE) 10
556 **GET READY FREDDY** (GB) 16
232 **GET RHYTHM** (IRE) 43
196 **GET THE RHYTHM** (GB) 95
432 **GET UP THEM STEPS** (GB) 12
577 **GET US ON** (IRE) 21
136 **GET WISHING** (IRE) 7
407 **GETABIRD** (IRE) 82
125 **GETAFLYER** (IRE) 19
407 **GETAREASON** (IRE) 83
500 **GETARIVER** (IRE) 59
510 **GETAWAY BAY** (IRE) 19
491 **GETAWAY GERRY** (GB) 4
407 **GETAWAY GORGEOUS** (IRE) 84
148 **GETAWAY HONEY** (IRE) 15
183 **GETAWAY JOHN** (IRE) 82
379 **GETAWAY KID** (IRE) 46
594 **GETAWAY MISSION** (IRE) 45
179 **GETAWAY MIXIE** (IRE) 8
511 **GETAWAY SUZY** (IRE) 4
419 **GETAWAY TRUMP** (IRE) 73
298 **GETBACK IN PARIS** (IRE) 5
120 **GETCHAGETCHAGETCHA** (GB) 37
416 **GETTYSBURG ADDRESS** (IRE) 23
411 **GEYSER** (GB) 14
525 **GHADBBAAN** (GB) 56
436 **GHAITH** (GB) 14
5 **GHAIYYATH** (IRE) 19
27 **GHALIB** (IRE) 11
41 **GHALY** (GB) 63
41 **GHASABAH** (GB) F 136
558 **GHATHANFAR** (IRE) 16
599 **GHAYADH** (GB) 16
176 **GHAYYAR** (IRE) 29
221 **GHAZAN** (IRE) 13
255 **GHAZIYAH** (GB) 61
99 **GHEPARDO** (GB) 4
331 **GHERKIN** (GB) 25
225 **GHOST BUY** (IRE) 43
341 **GHOST SERGE** (IRE) 12
5 **GHOSTWATCH** (IRE) 20
379 **GHURBA** (IRE) 47
480 **GIACOMO CASANOVA** (IRE) 46
373 **GIAMAS** (GB) 2
5 **GIANTS PLAY** (USA) F 118
77 **GIBB HILL** (GB) 5

553 **GIBBS HILL** (GER) 9
6 **GIBENO** (IRE) 28
203 **GIBRALTARIAN** (IRE) 23
266 **GIBSON DESERT** (GB) 135
222 **GIFT FROM GOD** (GB) 1
112 **GIFT IN TIME** (IRE) 2
186 **GIFT OF MUSIC** (IRE) C 32
443 **GIFT OF YOUTH** (GB) 41
436 **GIFTED MASTER** (IRE) 15
25 **GIFTED ZEBEDEE** (IRE) 26
41 **GIFTS OF GOLD** (IRE) 12
526 **GILAH** (IRE) C 32
591 **GILDED BUTTERFLY** (USA) C 22
190 **GILDED VERSE** (GB) F 42
489 **GILGAMESH** (GB) 3
238 **GILL HALL LADY** (GB) F 11
220 **GILLY GRACE** (GB) 4
324 **GILMER** (IRE) 7
364 **GILT EDGE** (GB) 6
589 **GIN AND TONIC** (GB) 7
539 **GIN COBBLER** (GB) 7
79 **GIN GEMBRE** (FR) 94
196 **GIN IN THE INN** (IRE) 27
315 **GIN PALACE** (GB) 29
550 **GINGE DE SOPHIA** (IRE) 49
577 **GINGE N TONIC** (GB) 22
596 **GINGEMBRE MENTHE** (FR) 24
594 **GINGER FOX** (GB) 134
451 **GINGER LACEY** (GB) 6
196 **GINGER MAX** (GB) 96
199 **GINGILI** (GB) 13
562 **GINISTRELLI** (IRE) 37
340 **GINO TRAIL** (GB) 12
597 **GINO WOTIMEAN** (USA) 22
235 **GINVINCIBLE** (GB) 12
255 **GIOFRA** (GB) C 141
345 **GIOGIOBBO** (GB) 6
446 **GIOVANNA** (GB) F 6
210 **GIRL POWRE** (GB) 3
183 **GIRLEY TALK** (IRE) 83
50 **GIROLAMO** (IRE) 32
190 **GIVE EM A CLUMP** (IRE) 10
233 **GIVE HIM TIME** (GB) 15
176 **GIVE IT SOME TEDDY** (GB) 30
419 **GIVE ME A COPPER** (IRE) 74
525 **GIVE ME BREATH** (GB) 57
171 **GIVE US A BELLE** (GB) 8
327 **GIVEAWAY GLANCE** (GB) 45
406 **GIVEN NAME** (GB) 11
110 **GIVEPEACEACHANCE** (GB) 4
428 **GIVEUPYERAULSINS** (IRE) F 104
327 **GIVING BACK** (GB) 46
327 **GIVING GLANCES** (GB) 47
315 **GIVINITSUM** (SAF) 4
304 **GLACEON** (IRE) 1
26 **GLACIATE** (GB) 15
531 **GLACIER FOX** (GB) 6
97 **GLADDEN** (IRE) 3
595 **GLADIATEUR ALLEN** (FR) 20
119 **GLADIATRIX** (GB) C 63
269 **GLAM'SELLE** (GB) 12
364 **GLAMOROUS ANNA** (GB) 8
269 **GLAMOROUS DREAM** (IRE) 13
421 **GLAMOROUS GOLD** (IRE) 5
269 **GLAMOROUS ROCKET** (IRE) 14
537 **GLAN Y GORS** (IRE) 4
29 **GLANCE** (GB) 43
42 **GLANCE BACK** (GB) 5

122 **GLASGON** (GB) 5
327 **GLASHA'S PEAK** (GB) 48
480 **GLASS SLIPPERS** (GB) 47
148 **GLASSBOY** (IRE) 16
508 **GLASSES UP** (USA) 10
41 **GLASSY WATERS** (USA) 13
572 **GLEAMING ARCH** (GB) 2
553 **GLEEFUL** (GB) 57
563 **GLEN ESK** (GB) 55
452 **GLEN FORCE** (IRE) 55
100 **GLEN FORSA** (IRE) 12
137 **GLEN GINNIE** (IRE) C 60
176 **GLEN MOOAR** (IRE) 31
233 **GLEN ROCCO** (GB) 16
362 **GLEN ROE** (IRE) 1
448 **GLEN VINE** (GB) 27
319 **GLENAIR LUCY** (IRE) G 5
589 **GLENAMOY LAD** (GB) 8
176 **GLENCADAM GLORY** (GB) 32
298 **GLENDEVON** (USA) 6
465 **GLENDUFF** (IRE) 20
189 **GLENDUN** (USA) 7
44 **GLENFINN HALL** (GB) 3
14 **GLENFORDE** (IRE) 31
403 **GLENGAR** (IRE) 28
133 **GLENGARRY** (GB) 23
236 **GLENLINI** (GB) G 39
183 **GLENLOE** (IRE) 84
540 **GLENLORA** (GB) 13
599 **GLENN COCO** (GB) 17
378 **GLENN MILLER** (IRE) 21
393 **GLENO** (IRE) 58
478 **GLENPARK** (GB) 33
403 **GLENS COUNTY** (IRE) 29
535 **GLENTROOL** (GB) 8
35 **GLENYS THE MENACE** (FR) 7
555 **GLIMPSE OF GOLD** (GB) 49
465 **GLINGER FLAME** (IRE) 21
508 **GLINGERSIDE** (IRE) 11
525 **GLITTERING GIFT** (GB) 116
465 **GLITTERING LOVE** (IRE) 22
323 **GLOBAL ACADEMY** (IRE) 4
168 **GLOBAL ACCLAMATION** (GB) 24
431 **GLOBAL ANCHOR** (IRE) 41
119 **GLOBAL APPLAUSE** (GB) 8
168 **GLOBAL ART** (GB) 8
13 **GLOBAL BONUS** (GB) 9
323 **GLOBAL CHALLENGER** (IRE) 20
438 **GLOBAL CITIZEN** (IRE) 5
168 **GLOBAL COMMAND** (IRE) 25
124 **GLOBAL CONQUEROR** (GB) 5
50 **GLOBAL CROSSING** (IRE) 95
168 **GLOBAL DESTINATION** (IRE) 26
13 **GLOBAL DOMINATION** (GB) 10
13 **GLOBAL DREAM** (GB) 9
119 **GLOBAL EXCEED** (GB) 9
168 **GLOBAL EXPRESS** (GB) 27
284 **GLOBAL FALCON** (GB) 9
424 **GLOBAL FINANCE** (USA) C 136
168 **GLOBAL FREEDOM** (GB) 28
168 **GLOBAL GIANT** (GB) 9
168 **GLOBAL GIFT** (FR) 29
323 **GLOBAL GODDESS** (IRE) 21
500 **GLOBAL HARMONY** (IRE) 60
41 **GLOBAL HEAT** (GB) 64
323 **GLOBAL HOPE** (IRE) 5
168 **GLOBAL HUMOR** (USA) 10
41 **GLOBAL HUNTER** (IRE) 65

164 **GORSE** (IRE) 8
232 **GORSKY ISLAND** (GB) 46
500 **GORTROE JOE** (IRE) 65
90 **GOSCOTE** (GB) 5
393 **GOSHEN** (FR) 137
286 **GOSHEVEN** (IRE) 38
100 **GOSPEL** (GB) 57
530 **GOSPEL MUSIC** (GB) C 67
424 **GOSSAMER WINGS** (USA) 58
398 **GOSSIP COLUMN** (IRE) 7
393 **GOSSIPING** (GB) 61
497 **GOT AWAY** (FR) 15
266 **GOT TRUMPED** (GB) 27
391 **GOTCHA GOOD** (USA) F 29
475 **GOTHIC EMPIRE** (IRE) 6
424 **GOTLANDIA** (FR) C 137
168 **GOTTARDO** (IRE) 11
257 **GOUGANE BARRA** (USA) 4
392 **GOUTEZ MOI** (FR) 5
115 **GOWANBUSTER** (GB) 3
226 **GOWER GOLD** (GB) 3
438 **GOWITHTHEFLOW** (IRE) 32
393 **GRAASTEN** (GB) 62
16 **GRACE AND DANGER** (IRE) 84
516 **GRACE PLUNKETT** (GB) 42
477 **GRACE SPIRIT** (GB) 28
24 **GRACEFUL ACT** (GB) 3
217 **GRACEFUL JAMES** (IRE) 5
178 **GRACEFUL LADY** (IRE) 4
98 **GRACEFUL LEGEND** (GB) 8
315 **GRACEFUL MAGIC** (GB) 66
525 **GRACEFULLY DONE** (IRE) 58
369 **GRACELAND** (FR) 43
198 **GRACIE** (GB) 39
95 **GRACIE STANSFIELD** (GB) 28
217 **GRACIOUS GEORGE** (IRE) 6
190 **GRACIOUS JOHN** (IRE) 11
426 **GRAGEELAGH GIRL** (IRE) 26
29 **GRAIN OF SENSE** (IRE) 105
183 **GRAINEYHILL** (IRE) 86
267 **GRAMS AND OUNCES** (GB) 4
339 **GRAND COUREUR** (FR) 4
263 **GRAND DEPART** (GB) F 159
291 **GRAND ENTERPRISE** (GB) 4
594 **GRAND INQUISITOR** (GB) 47
478 **GRAND MORNING** (GB) 34
419 **GRAND SANCY** (FR) 76
500 **GRAND SLAMMER** (IRE) 66
542 **GRAND VISION** (IRE) 40
532 **GRANDAD CHUNK** (IRE) 1
526 **GRANDAD'S LEGACY** (GB) 6
500 **GRANDE WALTZ** (GER) 67
297 **GRANDEE DAISY** (GB) 20
119 **GRANDFATHER TOM** (GB) 10
185 **GRANDMA** (GB) 61
293 **GRANDMA TILLY** (GB) 8
109 **GRANDMAS DREAM** (GB) F 35
168 **GRANDSCAPE** (GB) 12
513 **GRANGE RANGER** (IRE) 24
444 **GRANGE WALK** (IRE) 4
238 **GRANGECLARE RHYTHM** (IRE) F 44
36 **GRANGEROSIE** (IRE) 6
593 **GRANIA O'MALLEY** (IRE) 30
421 **GRANITE CITY DOC** (IRE) 6
406 **GRANITIC** (IRE) 12
347 **GRANNY ANNE** (IRE) 4
351 **GRANNY FRANKHAM** (GB) 12
122 **GRANNY ROZ** (GB) 6

255 **GRANNY'S ECLIPSE** (IRE) 142
438 **GRANNY'S SECRET** (IRE) 33
89 **GRANVILLE ISLAND** (IRE) 13
284 **GRAPEVINE** (IRE) 10
29 **GRAPHIC GUEST** (GB) C 106
120 **GRAPHITE STORM** (GB) 6
12 **GRASMERE** (IRE) 7
357 **GRATOT** (FR) 5
318 **GRAVISTAS** (GB) 72
79 **GRAVITY FORCE** (GB) 96
330 **GRAVITY WAVE** (IRE) 4
369 **GRAY DAY** (IRE) 44
74 **GRAYBOY** (GB) 4
250 **GRAYHAWK** (IRE) 4
113 **GRAYSTOWN** (IRE) 11
457 **GRAZEON ROY** (GB) 37
103 **GRAZZIA** (FR) 31
419 **GREANETEEN** (FR) 77
106 **GREAT BEAR** (GB) 29
419 **GREAT BEYOND** (GB) 78
49 **GREAT COLACI** (GB) 5
5 **GREAT ESTEEM** (IRE) 61
41 **GREAT EXAMPLE** (GB) 66
403 **GREAT FAIRY** (FR) 31
407 **GREAT FIELD** (FR) 88
458 **GREAT HALL** (IRE) 2
41 **GREAT IMAGE** (IRE) 139
90 **GREAT MIDGE** (GB) 2
41 **GREAT ORDER** (USA) 14
196 **GREAT PROSPECTOR** (IRE) 28
245 **GREAT RETURN** (GB) 28
137 **GREAT SCOT** (GB) 28
408 **GREAT SHOUT** (IRE) 40
308 **GREAT SUSPENSE** (GB) 10
448 **GREAT TEMPO** (IRE) 28
5 **GREAT VIRTUES** (IRE) F 121
183 **GREAT VIZIER** (GB) 87
417 **GREAT WAVE** (GB) G 5
457 **GREATEST DANCER** (IRE) G 57
6 **GREATEST JOURNEY** (IRE) 36
241 **GREEBA** (GB) 14
458 **GREEK KODIAC** (IRE) 11
563 **GREEK OASIS** (GB) 28
386 **GREELEY** (IRE) 21
266 **GREEN CASTLE** (IRE) F 136
223 **GREEN DOLPHIN** (IRE) 30
119 **GREEN DOOR** (IRE) 11
327 **GREEN ETOILE** (GB) 158
103 **GREEN MEDIA** (FR) F 84
403 **GREEN OR BLACK** (IRE) 32
293 **GREEN POPPY** (GB) F 15
226 **GREEN POWER** (GB) 4
51 **GREEN SIREN** (FR) 8
51 **GREEN SPIRIT** (FR) 17
271 **GREEN ZONE** (IRE) 1
526 **GREENERY** (IRE) C 33
26 **GREENLAND** (USA) 53
90 **GREENSIDE** (GB) 7
490 **GREENVIEW PARADISE** (IRE) 15
557 **GREGARIOUS** (IRE) 9
303 **GREGORIAN GIRL** (GB) 42
293 **GREGORY THE GREAT** (GB) 16
176 **GREMOBOY** (GB) 105
318 **GRENADIER GUARD** (IRE) 73
176 **GREY BERRY** (IRE) 106
479 **GREY BRITAIN** (GB) 6
68 **GREY DESTINY** (GB) 6
327 **GREY DIAMOND** (FR) 50

235 **GREY EMINENCE** (GB) 26
183 **GREY EXCHANGE** (GB) 88
120 **GREY GALLEON** (USA) 7
419 **GREY GETAWAY** (IRE) 79
340 **GREY GOLD** (IRE) 13
576 **GREY HILL** (IRE) 35
375 **GREY MIST** (GB) 9
187 **GREY MONK** (IRE) 3
452 **GREY SPIRIT** (IRE) 7
273 **GREYBOUGG** (GB) 8
345 **GREYBYCHOICE** (IRE) 15
198 **GREYCOAT** (GB) 72
416 **GREYED A** (FR) 24
25 **GREYFIRE** (GB) 47
386 **GREYZEE** (IRE) 22
196 **GRIGGY** (IRE) 97
79 **GRIMBOLD** (GB) 97
176 **GRIMSDYKE** (GB) 107
106 **GRIMSTHORPE CASTLE** (GB) 83
304 **GRIMTHORPE** (GB) 2
263 **GRINLING** (IRE) 160
156 **GRINTY** (IRE) 9
478 **GRIPPER** (GB) 35
291 **GRIS DE PRON** (FR) 5
196 **GRISE LIGHTNING** (FR) 29
120 **GRISONS** (FR) 41
137 **GRIV GIRL** (IRE) 63
266 **GRIZZLY** (IRE) 137
100 **GROTTA DEL FAUNO** (IRE) C 104
194 **GROUND CONTROL** (FR) 23
245 **GROUNDUNDERREPAIR** (IRE) 29
385 **GROUNDWORKER** (IRE) 7
16 **GROUP ONE POWER** (IRE) 5
327 **GROUP STAGE** (GER) 159
531 **GROUPIE** (GB) 7
16 **GROVE FERRY** (IRE) 159
89 **GROVE SILVER** (IRE) 14
427 **GROVEMAN** (GB) 7
605 **GROW NASA GROW** (IRE) 5
196 **GROWL** (GB) 30
257 **GRUFALO** (IRE) 22
137 **GUANDI** (USA) 29
170 **GUARACHA** (GB) 22
50 **GUARANTEED** (IRE) 33
202 **GUARDIA SVIZZERA** (IRE) 18
273 **GUARDIA TOP** (FR) 38
346 **GUARDIOLA** (USA) 8
490 **GUERRILLA TACTICS** (IRE) 16
379 **GUIDED BY YOU** (IRE) 48
120 **GUIDING SPIRIT** (IRE) 42
29 **GUILDHALL** (GB) 44
79 **GUIPURE** (GB) 98
465 **GUITAR PETE** (IRE) 23
175 **GULF OF POETS** (GB) 23
96 **GULLAND ROCK** (GB) 5
176 **GULLANE ONE** (IRE) 35
428 **GULLIVER** (GB) 20
19 **GULSHANIGANS** (GB) 7
286 **GUMBALL** (FR) 39
583 **GUN CASE** (GB) 14
183 **GUN DIGGER** (IRE) 89
200 **GUN SHY** (IRE) 5
338 **GUNFLEET** (IRE) 27
93 **GUNMAKER** (IRE) 16
25 **GUNMETAL** (IRE) 9
307 **GUNNABEDUN** (IRE) 52
435 **GUNNER MOYNE** (GB) 8
279 **GUNNERY** (FR) 68

279 **HAUL AWAY** (IRE) 70
304 **HAVANA BAY** (GB) 16
108 **HAVANA BOUND** (GB) 53
185 **HAVANA BROWN** (GB) 62
133 **HAVANA GO** (GB) 28
179 **HAVANA HERMANO** (IRE) 10
326 **HAVANA JACK** (IRE) 2
16 **HAVANA JANE** (GB) 21
79 **HAVANA OOH NA NA** (GB) 40
487 **HAVANA PRINCESS** (GB) 11
16 **HAVANA ROCKET** (IRE) 87
409 **HAVANA SUNSET** (GB) 17
592 **HAVE A GO HERO** (IRE) 7
162 **HAVE THIS FOR NOW** (IRE) 7
503 **HAVENVOUS** (FR) 36
83 **HAVEONEYERSELF** (IRE) 9
284 **HAVIN' A GOOD TIME** (IRE) F 100
106 **HAWA BLADI** (IRE) 31
41 **HAWAAFEZ** (GB) C 141
176 **HAWAAJIB** (FR) C 151
202 **HAWAAM** (IRE) 20
41 **HAWAFEZ** (GB) 67
507 **HAWATIF** (IRE) 4
297 **HAWK CLIFF** (FR) 21
176 **HAWK HIGH** (GB) 37
585 **HAWK IN THE SKY** (GB) 9
338 **HAWK'S WELL** (GB) 28
233 **HAWKERLAND** (IRE) 17
255 **HAWRAA** (GB) F 144
386 **HAWRIDGE FLYER** (GB) 8
443 **HAWRIDGE GLORY** (IRE) 5
386 **HAWRIDGE STORM** (IRE) 23
408 **HAWTHORN COTTAGE** (IRE) 14
525 **HAWTHORN ROSE** (GB) 59
27 **HAYADH** (GB) 14
61 **HAYLEY BELLE** (IRE) 7
508 **HAYMARKET** (GB) 14
603 **HAYWARD FIELD** (IRE) 5
58 **HAYYEL** (IRE) 2
576 **HAZAKIYRA** (IRE) 37
341 **HAZAMAR** (IRE) 13
576 **HAZAPOUR** (IRE) 6
257 **HAZARABA** (FR) C 57
525 **HAZARANDA** (GB) 60
100 **HAZARDOUS** (GB) G 106
111 **HAZE** (GB) 11
576 **HAZEL BAY** (IRE) 7
555 **HAZM** (IRE) 41
274 **HAZRAN** (IRE) 24
334 **HAZZAAR** (GB) 12
176 **HE LOVES ME MORE** (USA) C 152
334 **HE'S A GOER** (IRE) 13
562 **HE'S AMAZING** (IRE) 11
207 **HE'S MAGIC** (GB) 2
379 **HE'S NO MOLLY** (IRE) 53
526 **HE'S OUR STAR** (IRE) 11
263 **HE'ZANARAB** (IRE) 63
431 **HEAD LAD** (FR) 45
158 **HEADLEY GEORGE** (IRE) 28
106 **HEADMAN** (GB) 32
396 **HEADS UP CLEMMIE** (GB) 8
553 **HEALING POWER** (GB) 59
284 **HEAR MY CRY** (USA) C 101
500 **HEAR NO EVIL** (GB) 70
270 **HEAR THE CHIMES** (GB) 6
427 **HEART OF HEARTS** (GB) F 41
273 **HEART OF KERNOW** (IRE) 10
594 **HEART OF SOUL** (IRE) 49

115 **HEARTASIA** (IRE) 9
30 **HEARTBREAK HOTEL** (IRE) 26
41 **HEARTOFTHEEMPIRE** (IRE) 142
164 **HEARTSTRING** (IRE) 18
120 **HEARTWARMING** (GB) 43
154 **HEATHER BURNING** (IRE) 17
350 **HEATHER SONG** (GB) 18
30 **HEATHERDOWN** (IRE) 27
279 **HEATSTROKE** (IRE) 71
452 **HEATWAVE** (GB) 25
525 **HEAVEN FORFEND** (GB) 118
424 **HEAVEN ON EARTH** (IRE) 61
604 **HEAVEN SCENT** (GB) 6
401 **HEAVEN'S HEART** (GB) G 5
525 **HEAVENLY BLISS** (GB) 61
436 **HEAVENLY HOLLY** (IRE) 16
251 **HEAVENLY PROMISE** (IRE) 5
79 **HEAVENLY RIVER** (IRE) F 99
502 **HEAVENLY SHADES** (GB) 7
29 **HEAVENLY TALE** (IRE) 45
337 **HEAVENS ALIGN** (IRE) 2
596 **HECTOR DE SIVOLA** (FR) 29
158 **HECTOR LOZA** (GB) 29
168 **HECTOR'S GIRL** (GB) C 66
225 **HECTOR'S HERE** (GB) 44
315 **HEDGING** (IRE) 6
605 **HEDIDDOIDINTHE** (GB) 7
313 **HEER ME** (GB) 23
577 **HEERCOMESHARRIE** (GB) 23
53 **HEEYAAM** (GB) 11
203 **HEIGHT OF VANITY** (IRE) C 57
339 **HELAMIS** (GB) 5
547 **HELDTORANSOM** (GB) 22
79 **HELEN SHERBET** (GB) 9
246 **HELF** (IRE) 13
52 **HELFIRE** (GB) 6
542 **HELFORD RIVER** (GB) 42
168 **HELIAN** (FR) 33
266 **HELIERS BAY** (IRE) 28
263 **HELIOCENTRIC** (FR) C 161
94 **HELIOGRAPH** (GB) C 29
596 **HELIOS ALLEN** (FR) 30
103 **HELIOS DES SOURCES** (FR) 85
548 **HELL OF A JOKER** (GB) 17
199 **HELL OF A LADY** (GB) 14
379 **HELL OR HIGH WATER** (FR) 54
223 **HELL'S KITCHEN** (GB) 31
583 **HELLAVASHOCK** (GB) 15
147 **HELLEBERRY** (GB) 2
309 **HELLO BERTIE** (GB) 8
38 **HELLO BOB** (GB) 3
303 **HELLO GIRL** (GB) 12
480 **HELLO YOUMZAIN** (FR) 48
454 **HELLOFAGAME** (GB) 10
298 **HELLOVAQUEEN** (GB) 9
309 **HELMSLEY LAD** (GB) 9
504 **HELOVAPLAN** (GB) 9
136 **HELUVAGOOD** (GB) 9
100 **HELVETIAN** (GB) 15
50 **HEMINA** (IRE) 98
434 **HEN** (IRE) 34
388 **HENCHARD** (GB) 2
399 **HENDRIX** (IRE) 40
558 **HENLEY** (GB) 4
55 **HENLLAN HARRI** (IRE) 22
340 **HENRI LE BON** (IRE) 15
588 **HENRIETTA BELL** (IRE) 14
559 **HENRIETTA'S DREAM** (GB) 4

379 **HENRY BROWN** (IRE) 55
95 **HENRY CROFT** (GB) 30
369 **HENRY'S JOY** (IRE) 46
55 **HENRYVILLE** (GB) 23
526 **HEPBURN** (GB) 12
179 **HEPJEU** (FR) 11
106 **HERCULEAN** (GB) 8
29 **HERE AND NOW** (GB) 14
612 **HERE COMES LOVE** (IRE) 4
21 **HERE COMES MOLLY** (IRE) 3
108 **HERE COMES SUMMER** (FR) 22
410 **HERE COMES TRUBLE** (IRE) 46
16 **HERE COMES WHEN** (IRE) 22
250 **HERE I AM** (IRE) 5
229 **HERE'S HERBIE** (GB) 8
457 **HERE'S ROCCO** (IRE) 38
29 **HEREBY** (IRE) 6
140 **HEREFORDSHIRE** (GB) 9
526 **HERESMYNUMBER** (IRE) 13
594 **HERESTHETHING** (IRE) 50
327 **HEREWEGO HEREWEGO** (IRE) 52
120 **HERITAGE** (GB) 44
190 **HERM** (IRE) 12
263 **HERMANO BELLO** (FR) 162
324 **HERMANUS** (IRE) 9
263 **HERMOCRATES** (FR) 64
424 **HERMOSA** (IRE) 62
393 **HERMOSA VAQUERA** (IRE) 64
553 **HERMOSITA** (GB) 10
16 **HERO HERO** (IRE) 88
411 **HERO'S STORY** (GB) 4
379 **HEROESANDVILLAINS** (GB) 56
284 **HEROIC** (GB) 48
314 **HERON** (USA) 3
569 **HERONETTA** (GB) F 20
294 **HERRING BAY** (GB) 10
518 **HERRINGSWELL** (FR) 7
14 **HES NO TROUBLE** (GB) 33
405 **HES OUR ROBIN** (IRE) 5
514 **HESSLE ROAD** (IRE) 5
38 **HESSLEWOOD** (IRE) 15
337 **HESSSA** (GB) 27
106 **HEXAGON** (GB) 87
376 **HEY BILL** (IRE) 17
241 **HEY BOB** (IRE) 16
490 **HEY BUD** (GB) 17
530 **HEY GAMAN** (GB) 3
120 **HEY HO LET'S GO** (GB) 45
126 **HEY JAZZY LADY** (IRE) 17
480 **HEY JONESY** (IRE) 15
407 **HEY LITTLE BOY** (GER) 90
100 **HEYDOUR** (IRE) 16
79 **HFLAH** (IRE) C 100
563 **HI HO SILVER** (GB) 6
578 **HI NOTE** (GB) C 10
100 **HI NOTE** (GB) F 107
356 **HI THERE SILVER** (IRE) 5
318 **HIBERNICUS** (IRE) 15
352 **HIC BIBI** (GB) 12
434 **HIDDEN DEPTHS** (IRE) 9
171 **HIDDEN DREAM** (IRE) 11
379 **HIDDEN FIGURE** (IRE) 57
438 **HIDDEN GLEN** (IRE) 34
5 **HIDDEN GOLD** (IRE) C 123
26 **HIDDEN LAND** (USA) 54
255 **HIDDEN MESSAGE** (USA) 64
299 **HIDDEN PASSAGE** (IRE) 8
562 **HIDDEN PEARL** (GB) 40

518 INTREPIDLY (USA) 8
239 INTRICATE (GB) 78
428 INTRUSION (GB) C 106
530 INTUITIVE (IRE) 27
441 INVER SILVER (GB) 27
43 INVERARITY (GB) 6
511 INVICTA LAKE (IRE) 7
525 INVICTUS SPIRIT (GB) 63
450 INVINCIBELLA (GB) 20
530 INVINCIBLE ARMY (IRE) 4
266 INVINCIBLE CARA (IRE) G 141
183 INVINCIBLE CAVE (IRE) 91
266 INVINCIBLE DIVA (IRE) 142
553 INVINCIBLE KNIGHT (GB) 62
458 INVINCIBLE LARNE (IRE) 12
330 INVINCIBLE ONE (IRE) 16
405 INVINCIBLE PURSUIT (GB) 6
313 INVINCIBLE SEA (IRE) 21
196 INVIOLABLE SPIRIT (IRE) 33
245 INVISIBLE CLOUDS (IRE) 33
516 INVISIBLE SHADOW (IRE) 7
523 INVISIBLE STORM (GB) 4
424 INVITATION (IRE) 65
407 INVITATION ONLY (IRE) 93
553 INVITATIONAL (GB) 63
333 INVOLVED (GB) 4
5 INVOLVED (USA) C 127
235 INYORDREAMS (GB) F 27
486 IOLANI (GER) 8
506 IONA DAYS (IRE) 4
11 IONA ISLAND (GB) 2
23 IOWEU (GB) 10
526 IP DIP (USA) 27
152 IPCRESS FILE (GB) 13
330 IRENE MAY (IRE) 17
30 IRIDESCENCE (GB) G 80
329 IRIDESCENT RESDEV (IRE) 7
577 IRINA PRINCESS (GB) F 36
95 IRIS'S SPIRIT (GB) 71
337 IRISH ART (IRE) 13
225 IRISH CHARM (FR) 20
407 IRISH LASS (IRE) 94
266 IRISH MASTER (IRE) 143
230 IRISH OCTAVE (IRE) 5
403 IRISH ODYSSEY (IRE) 40
448 IRISH PRINCE (IRE) 32
338 IRISH PROPHECY (IRE) 31
9 IRISH ROE (IRE) 1
111 IRISH SONG (FR) C 28
337 IRISH STEPS 14
518 IRISH TIMES (GB) 9
328 IROLIN JACK (GB) 10
124 IRON DOVE (IRE) 8
446 IRON HORSE (GB) 8
133 IRON MIKE (GB) 91
436 IRONCLAD (GB) 56
576 IRRESISTIBLE JEWEL (IRE) C 100
196 IRREVERENT (GB) 101
261 IRV (GB) 81
314 IRVING'S GIRL (GB) 4
232 IS A REAL CHAMP (IRE) 47
128 IS IT OFF (IRE) 3
606 IS LOVE ALIVE (GB) 9
16 ISAAC MURPHY (FR) 160
544 ISAAC MURPHY (USA) 14
492 ISAAC WONDER (IRE) 17
465 ISAACSTOWN LAD (IRE) 27
571 ISAAN QUEEN (IRE) 31

29 ISABELLA BRANT (FR) 48
190 ISABELLA RED (IRE) 29
601 ISABELLA RUBY (GB) 5
556 ISANDRO (FR) 20
203 ISANGO (GB) G 3
538 ISE LODGE BABE (GB) 5
223 ISHKHARA LADY (GB) 34
168 ISHRAAK (USA) C 67
428 ISIDOR BONHEUR YES (FR) 28
510 ISKABEG LANE (IRE) 23
520 ISLAND AUTHORITY (GB) 3
391 ISLAND BABE (USA) C 15
357 ISLAND BRAVE (IRE) 6
190 ISLAND ESCAPE (USA) C 30
41 ISLAND FALCON (GB) 144
195 ISLAND FLAME (IRE) 9
357 ISLAND GLEN (USA) 13
196 ISLAND GREETING (IRE) 102
478 ISLAND HEIGHTS (IRE) 37
255 ISLAND OF LIFE (USA) 12
357 ISLAND REEL (IRE) 14
368 ISLAND RHAPSODY (GB) F 15
284 ISLAND SUNSET (IRE) C 105
408 ISLAY MIST (GB) 41
183 ISLE OF DESTINY (IRE) 92
57 ISLE OF WOLVES (IRE) 15
407 ISLEOFHOPENDREAMS (GB) 95
253 ISNTSHESOMETHING (GB) 5
242 ISOBEL BLEU (IRE) 1
124 ISOCRATES (USA) 40
79 ISOLA VERDE (GB) C 105
378 ISOLATE (FR) 22
16 ISOMER (USA) 25
257 ISOSCELES (IRE) 25
1 ISPOLINI (GB) 23
136 ISTANBUL PASHA (IRE) 11
500 ISTIMRAAR (IRE) 77
255 IT HAD TO BE YOU (GB) 68
125 IT HAS TO BE (IRE) 21
6 IT MUST BE FAITH (GB) 38
196 IT'LLCOMEIN (FR) 103
295 IT'S A LILY (GB) 12
571 IT'S ALL A JOKE (IRE) 9
261 IT'S ALL ABOUT ME (IRE) 32
175 IT'S ALL GUCCI (GB) 70
510 IT'S BUSTER (IRE) 24
194 IT'S ENOUGH (GB) 45
376 IT'S FINE WINE (GB) 20
141 IT'S FOR ALAN (GB) 3
393 IT'S GOT LEGS (IRE) 74
515 IT'S HOW WE ROLL (IRE) 5
106 IT'S MY TIME (GB) F 89
194 IT'S NEVER ENOUGH (GB) 27
410 IT'S O KAY (GB) 51
448 IT'S OBVIOUS (GB) 33
77 ITALIAN RIVER (GB) 7
279 ITALIAN SUMMER (GB) 76
410 ITCHY FEET (FR) 52
399 ITIZZIT (GB) 42
175 ITLAAQ (GB) 27
351 ITMAKESYOUTHINK (GB) 14
313 ITOLDYOU (IRE) 10
106 ITS A GIVEN (GB) 90
369 ITS ALL A LARK (IRE) 51
183 ITS ALL GUESSWORK (IRE) 93
571 ITS NICE TOBE NICE (GB) 32
516 ITS'AFREEBEE (IRE) 8
414 ITSABOUTIME (IRE) 2

391 ITSAKINDAMAGIC (GB) 3
453 ITSAMANSLIFE (IRE) 8
22 ITSNOTYOUITSME (GB) 11
238 ITSONLYROCKNROLL (IRE) 17
487 ITSSMOKINGGUN (IRE) G 3
107 ITSUPFORGRABSNOW (IRE) 3
555 IUSETALUVHERONCE (IRE) 42
106 IVADREAM (GB) 91
48 IVANHOE (GB) 5
360 IVILNOBLE (IRE) 8
263 IVOR (GB) 168
187 IVOR THE FOX (GB) 4
304 IVORS INVOLVEMENT (IRE) 3
196 IVORY CHARM (GB) 104
175 IVORY COMMAND (IRE) 100
303 IVORY STAR (GB) 43
50 IVY AVENUE (IRE) 103
535 IVY'S SHADOW (IRE) 9
176 IWASTHEFUTUREONCE (IRE) 40
535 IWILLDOIT (GB) 10
571 IZVESTIA (IRE) 33
478 IZZY'S CHAMPION (IRE) 38
446 J GAYE (IRE) 31
5 J WONDER (USA) C 128
98 J'AI FROID (IRE) 12
499 J'OUVERT (IRE) 45
489 JAARIH (IRE) 4
168 JABALALY (IRE) 36
484 JABAROUT (USA) 3
307 JABBAAR (GB) 18
4 JABBAROCKIE (GB) 5
327 JABOTICABA (FR) 58
550 JABULANI (FR) 57
258 JAC BROWN (GB) 1
268 JACAMAR (GER) 5
448 JACBEQUICK (GB) 34
533 JACK BEAR (GB) 4
203 JACK BERRY HOUSE (GB) 27
154 JACK DEVINE (IRE) 20
266 JACK FIASCO (GB) 32
427 JACK LAMB (GB) 10
303 JACK LOUIE (GB) 44
533 JACK OF DIAMONDS (IRE) 5
263 JACK RUBY (IRE) 169
279 JACK SHARP (IRE) 77
298 JACK TAYLOR (IRE) 10
489 JACK THE TRUTH (IRE) 5
424 JACK YEATS (IRE) 66
401 JACK'S POINT (GB) 18
94 JACKAMUNDO (FR) 21
169 JACKFINBAR (FR) 3
486 JACKHAMMER (IRE) 9
331 JACKLINE (GB) C 26
306 JACKMAN (GB) 3
373 JACKOFHEARTS (GB) 4
245 JACKSON HILL (IRE) 34
405 JACKSONFIRE (GB) 7
29 JACKSONIAN (IRE) 113
137 JACKSTAR (IRE) 31
133 JACOB BLACK (GB) 34
532 JACOB CATS (GB) 5
27 JACOB'S PILLOW (GB) 18
239 JADEERAH (GB) 79
263 JADELLA WILLFIN (FR) 68
576 JAEGA (IRE) 9
152 JAFFAR (GB) 14
126 JAGERBOND (GB) 18
239 JAHAFIL (GB) 80

424 **LISCANNA** (IRE) C 152
350 **LISDOONVARNA LAD** (IRE) 29
279 **LISHEEN CASTLE** (IRE) 90
410 **LISHEEN PRINCE** (IRE) 60
452 **LISMORE** (IRE) 72
124 **LISMORE** (USA) F 88
129 **LISNAGAR OSCAR** (IRE) 15
507 **LISNAMOYLE LADY** (IRE) 7
327 **LISP** (IRE) 70
215 **LISSEN TO THE LADY** (IRE) 6
16 **LISSITZKY** (IRE) 26
343 **LISSYCASEY** (IRE) 2
542 **LIST ONE** (GB) 53
407 **LISTEN DEAR** (IRE) 110
255 **LISTEN TO THE WIND** (IRE) 73
154 **LISTENING** (IRE) G 24
431 **LITHIC** (IRE) 52
239 **LITIGIOUS** (GB) 87
299 **LITTLE ANNIE** (GB) G 20
30 **LITTLE AUDIO** (IRE) F 31
263 **LITTLE AUDIO** (IRE) C 180
260 **LITTLE BAVINGTON** (GB) 1
263 **LITTLE BIRD** (IRE) 181
548 **LITTLE BOY BLUE** (GB) 6
511 **LITTLE BOY BORU** (IRE) 8
329 **LITTLE BRUCE** (IRE) 30
225 **LITTLE BUSTARD** (IRE) 46
591 **LITTLE CHARLOTTE** (FR) 11
56 **LITTLE CHOOSEY** (GB) 8
548 **LITTLE DEVIL** (GB) 19
205 **LITTLE DOTTY** (GB) 2
193 **LITTLE FOLKE** (GB) 13
103 **LITTLE FOLLY** (FR) 38
600 **LITTLE GINGE** (FR) 43
79 **LITTLE INDIA** (FR) 48
310 **LITTLE INDIAN** (GB) 18
245 **LITTLE JACK** (GB) 40
247 **LITTLE JIMMY** (GB) 9
185 **LITTLE JO** (GB) 23
550 **LITTLE JON** (GB) 66
79 **LITTLE KIM** (GB) 49
558 **LITTLE KINGDOM** (IRE) 6
456 **LITTLE LADY LUCK** (GB) 10
185 **LITTLE LEGS** (GB) 56
328 **LITTLE MILLIE** (IRE) 13
401 **LITTLE MISS DAISY** (GB) 6
360 **LITTLE MISS DARSI** (IRE) 11
547 **LITTLE MISS GRACIE** (GB) C 36
351 **LITTLE MISS KODI** (IRE) 18
120 **LITTLE MISS LILLY** (GB) 14
498 **LITTLE MISS LOLA** (GB) 9
286 **LITTLE MISS POET** (GB) 52
407 **LITTLE NUGGET** (IRE) 111
120 **LITTLE PALAVER** (GB) 15
121 **LITTLE PIPPIN** (GB) 3
537 **LITTLE POEM** (GB) 5
550 **LITTLE POP** (GB) 67
448 **LITTLE RED LION** (IRE) 40
65 **LITTLE RICH** (IRE) 16
301 **LITTLE ROBIN** (IRE) 3
298 **LITTLE ROCK** (IRE) 33
433 **LITTLE RORY MAC** (IRE) 17
20 **LITTLE STEVIE** (GB) 9
20 **LITTLE THORNTON** (GB) 24
479 **LITTLE TIPPLE** (GB) 25
542 **LITTLE VERN** (GB) 54
328 **LITTLE WINDMILL** (IRE) 14
156 **LITTLEBITOFMAGIC** (GB) 36

120 **LITTLEMISSSUNSHINE** (IRE) F 93
190 **LITTLEMISSTUTTI** (IRE) F 46
560 **LITTLEMOOR LASS** (GB) C 28
369 **LIVA** (IRE) 57
64 **LIVE DANGEROUSLY** (GB) 10
555 **LIVE FOR TODAY** (IRE) 54
243 **LIVE SHOW** (IRE) 11
41 **LIVE YOUR DREAM** (IRE) 149
407 **LIVELOVELAUGH** (IRE) 112
315 **LIVELY LYDIA** (GB) 34
318 **LIVING LEGEND** (IRE) 83
284 **LIVVYS DREAM** (IRE) 13
16 **LIXIROVA** (FR) F 166
67 **LIZ'S DREAM** (GB) 12
542 **LIZZIE LANGTON** (GB) 55
583 **LIZZIE LOCH** (GB) 36
529 **LLANTARA** (GB) 14
124 **LOCAL AFFAIR** (GB) 44
50 **LOCAL FOCUS** (IRE) 108
530 **LOCAL HISTORY** (GB) 28
299 **LOCAL SHOW** (IRE) 12
262 **LOCH GARMAN ARIS** (IRE) 6
29 **LOCH LADY** (GB) 53
382 **LOCH LAGGAN** (IRE) 15
49 **LOCH LINNHE** (GB) 9
263 **LOCH MA NAIRE** (IRE) C 182
6 **LOCH NESS MONSTER** (IRE) 89
350 **LOCHINVER** (FR) 30
16 **LOCHRIDGE** (GB) C 167
203 **LOCK SEVENTEEN** (USA) 31
431 **LOCK'S CORNER** (IRE) 53
550 **LOCKER ROOM TALK** (IRE) 68
332 **LOCO AMOR** (IRE) 20
482 **LOCOMMOTION** (GB) 12
369 **LOFGREN** (GB) 16
25 **LOFTY** (GB) 29
154 **LOG ON** (IRE) 25
408 **LOGAN ROCKS** (IRE) 18
106 **LOGAN'S CHOICE** (GB) 9
27 **LOGI** (IRE) 21
239 **LOGICIAN** (GB) 88
30 **LOGIE BAIRD** (IRE) 32
436 **LOGJAM** (IRE) C 92
137 **LOLA'S THEME** (GB) 35
315 **LOLITA PULIDO** (IRE) 35
381 **LOLLIPOP LADY** (GB) 29
594 **LOLLYS DREAM** (IRE) 59
279 **LOMACHENKO** (IRE) 91
30 **LOMAPAMAR** (GB) C 83
133 **LOMU** (IRE) 36
169 **LONDON CALLING** (ITY) 32
525 **LONDON EYE** (USA) 73
36 **LONDON GLORY** (GB) 7
509 **LONDON GRAMMAR** (IRE) 4
450 **LONDON PRIDE** (GB) 22
354 **LONDON PROTOCOL** (FR) 14
376 **LONDONIA** (GB) 23
447 **LONE SPIRIT** (IRE) F 7
95 **LONE VOICE** (IRE) 36
120 **LONELY AHEAD** (USA) F 94
239 **LONG BEACH** (GB) 89
95 **LONG CALL** (GB) 37
5 **LONG LASHES** (USA) F 139
266 **LONG MARCH** (IRE) 42
403 **LONG RIVER DANCER** (GB) 50
327 **LONG SOCKS** (GB) 71
41 **LONG TRADITION** (IRE) 150
600 **LONGHOUSESIGNORA** (IRE) 44

603 **LONGROOM** (GB) 7
189 **LONGSIDE** (GB) 9
564 **LONGVILLE LILLY** (GB) 4
90 **LONICERA** (GB) 34
6 **LONIMOSS BARELIERE** (FR) 90
16 **LOOK AROUND** (GB) 98
5 **LOOK AT ME** (IRE) F 140
457 **LOOK BUSY** (IRE) F 62
553 **LOOK CLOSELY** (GB) 75
457 **LOOK MY WAY** (GB) 18
194 **LOOK NOW** (GB) 30
176 **LOOK OUT LOUIS** (GB) 113
533 **LOOK SURPRISED** (GB) 9
292 **LOOKFORARAINBOW** (GB) 7
169 **LOOKING FOR CARL** (GB) 6
465 **LOOKING WELL** (IRE) 31
403 **LOOKS FROZEN** (IRE) 51
478 **LOOKS LIKE MURT** (IRE) 43
258 **LOOKS LIKE POWER** (IRE) 3
590 **LOOKSLIKERAINTED** (IRE) 4
555 **LOOKSNOWTLIKEBRIAN** (IRE) 55
525 **LOOLWAH** (IRE) 74
225 **LOOSE CHIPPINGS** (IRE) 23
350 **LOOSE CHIPS** (GB) 31
481 **LOPE DE LOOP** (IRE) 2
29 **LOPE SCHOLAR** (IRE) 54
37 **LOPES DANCER** (IRE) 1
477 **LOPEVEGAS** (FR) 30
223 **LOQUACIOUS LADY** (IRE) 43
608 **LORD ALDERVALE** (IRE) 2
14 **LORD APPARELLI** (GB) 41
273 **LORD BALLIM** (FR) 16
55 **LORD BRYAN** (IRE) 30
553 **LORD CAMPARI** (IRE) 156
272 **LORD CAPRIO** (IRE) 15
408 **LORD CHAPELFIELD** (GB) 58
393 **LORD CLENAGHCASTLE** (IRE) 90
206 **LORD COOPER** (GB) 8
246 **LORD COUNTY** (FR) 17
10 **LORD DEL BOY** (GB) 10
577 **LORD DIGBY** (GB) 8
288 **LORD DU MESNIL** (FR) 28
286 **LORD DUVEEN** (IRE) 53
249 **LORD EDWARD** (IRE) 2
126 **LORD FRANKLIN** (GB) 12
198 **LORD GEORGE** (IRE) 15
191 **LORD GETAWAY** (IRE) 7
428 **LORD GLITTERS** (FR) 34
203 **LORD HALIFAX** (IRE) 32
100 **LORD HOWARD** (IRE) 65
379 **LORD IN RED** (GER) 73
318 **LORD LAMINGTON** (GB) 84
575 **LORD MARMADUKE** (GB) 18
351 **LORD MURPHY** (IRE) 19
55 **LORD NAPIER** (IRE) 31
239 **LORD NORTH** (IRE) 90
79 **LORD OBERON** (GB) 12
236 **LORD OF THE GLEN** (GB) 14
404 **LORD OF THE ROCK** (IRE) 5
457 **LORD RIDDIFORD** (IRE) 19
537 **LORD ROB** (GB) 7
329 **LORD ROCCOCO** (FR) 31
183 **LORD SCOUNDREL** (IRE) 103
369 **LORD SPRINGFIELD** (IRE) 59
239 **LORD TENNYSON** (GB) 91
327 **LORD WALSINGHAM** (GB) 72
30 **LORD WARBURTON** (IRE) 84
388 **LORD WESSEX** (GB) 3

238 **MOROMAC** (IRE) 27
266 **MOROSINI** (FR) 52
266 **MORPHO BLUE** (IRE) 106
369 **MORRAMAN** (IRE) 64
274 **MORTENS LEAM** (GB) 3
133 **MORTICIA** (GB) 44
252 **MORZINE** (GB) F 25
225 **MOSA MINE** (GB) F 61
553 **MOSAKHAR** (GB) 85
106 **MOSEY** (IRE) 93
16 **MOSQUERAS ROMANCE** (GB) C 172
38 **MOSS GILL** (IRE) 16
232 **MOSS ON THE MILL** (GB) 55
385 **MOSSEYB** (IRE) 12
191 **MOSSING** (GB) 9
35 **MOSSKETEER** (GB) 10
383 **MOSSY'S LODGE** (GB) 22
119 **MOST TEMPTING** (GB) F 69
385 **MOSTAHEL** (GB) 13
60 **MOSTASHREQAH** (GB) 8
357 **MOSTAWAA** (GB) 17
553 **MOT JUSTE** (USA) 86
263 **MOTAFAAWIT** (IRE) 80
284 **MOTAGALLY** (GB) 53
94 **MOTAHASSEN** (IRE) 10
298 **MOTAJAASID** (IRE) 13
553 **MOTALAQQY** (IRE) 87
82 **MOTARAABET** (GB) 12
553 **MOTAWAJ** (GB) 88
82 **MOTFAEL** (IRE) 39
371 **MOTHER OF DRAGONS** (IRE) 8
50 **MOTHER VINCENT** (IRE) 41
318 **MOTION** (GB) 204
159 **MOTTS CROSS** (IRE) 13
410 **MOTUEKA** (IRE) 67
47 **MOUCHEE** (IRE) 12
228 **MOUDALLAL** (GB) 6
5 **MOULIN DE MOUGIN** (USA) C 147
257 **MOUNEERA** (IRE) 34
79 **MOUNT ARARAT** (IRE) 16
131 **MOUNT CLESHAR** (GB) 7
203 **MOUNT CRYSTAL** (GB) C 61
424 **MOUNT EVEREST** (IRE) 79
553 **MOUNT MAYON** (IRE) 65
369 **MOUNT MEWS** (IRE) 65
26 **MOUNT POPA** (IRE) 5
328 **MOUNT RADHWA** (GB) G 18
542 **MOUNT RUSHMOORE** (IRE) 63
480 **MOUNT TAHAN** (IRE) 23
280 **MOUNT VESUVIUS** (IRE) 15
518 **MOUNT WELLINGTON** (IRE) 14
553 **MOUNTAIN ANGEL** (IRE) 15
252 **MOUNTAIN DOG** (GB) 20
190 **MOUNTAIN GLOW** (GB) C 50
176 **MOUNTAIN HAWK** (IRE) 50
41 **MOUNTAIN HUNTER** (USA) 21
67 **MOUNTAIN LAW** (USA) F 14
600 **MOUNTAIN LEOPARD** 47
45 **MOUNTAIN OF MOURNE** (IRE) 5
218 **MOUNTAIN OF STARS** (IRE) 4
562 **MOUNTAIN PEAK** (GB) 18
256 **MOUNTAIN RANGER** (IRE) 19
88 **MOUNTAIN RAPID** (IRE) 6
10 **MOUNTAIN RESCUE** (IRE) 12
594 **MOUNTAIN ROCK** (IRE) 74
318 **MOUNTAIN RULER** (GB) 93
227 **MOUNTAIN SO HIGH** (IRE) 7
576 **MOURANIYA** (IRE) C 107

576 **MOURIYANI** (USA) 56
399 **MOUSEBIRD** (IRE) 46
593 **MOUSEINTHEHOUSE** (IRE) 45
239 **MOUSER** (USA) 103
382 **MOUSQUETAIRE** (FR) 17
459 **MOVE ABOVE** (IRE) 16
284 **MOVEMENTNEVERLIES** (GB) C 111
323 **MOVEONUP** (IRE) 24
419 **MOVEWITHTHETIMES** (IRE) 99
557 **MOVIE LEGEND** (GB) 13
516 **MOVIE SET** (USA) 10
408 **MOVIE STAR** (GER) 21
19 **MOVIE THEATRE** (GB) 16
50 **MOVING** (GB) 112
576 **MOVING HEART** (IRE) F 108
403 **MOVING IN STYLE** (IRE) 67
41 **MOVING LIGHT** (IRE) 152
351 **MOXY MARES** (GB) 21
67 **MOYNSHA LADY** (IRE) F 37
379 **MOYROSS** (GB) 85
68 **MOZAYADA** (USA) G 23
320 **MOZZARO** (IRE) 27
407 **MR ADJUDICATOR** (GB) 125
451 **MR ANDROS** (GB) 10
550 **MR ANTOLINI** (IRE) 73
434 **MR BEAU BLUE** (GB) 84
448 **MR BIG SHOT** (IRE) 49
196 **MR BUTTONS** (GB) 115
441 **MR C** (IRE) 9
329 **MR CARBONATOR** (GB) 38
337 **MR CARPENTER** (GB) 18
448 **MR CLARKSON** (IRE) 50
25 **MR COCO BEAN** (USA) 15
498 **MR CONUNDRUM** (GB) 10
139 **MR COOL CASH** (GB) 9
560 **MR DAVIES** (GB) 11
155 **MR DEALER** (IRE) 1
196 **MR DIAMOND** (IRE) 116
497 **MR DORRELL SAGE** (FR) 26
338 **MR FENTON** (IRE) 41
393 **MR FICKLE** (IRE) 97
141 **MR FITZROY** (IRE) 9
71 **MR FRANKIE** (GB) 9
466 **MR GAMBINO** (GB) 5
168 **MR GENT** (IRE) 14
176 **MR GREENLIGHT** (GB) 51
14 **MR GREY SKY** (IRE) 48
478 **MR GRUMPY** (GB) 56
227 **MR HARP** (IRE) 8
313 **MR JACK** (IRE) 15
30 **MR KIKI** (GB) 87
473 **MR KIT CAT** (GB) 1
115 **MR KITE** (GB) 15
199 **MR LANDO** (GB) 21
183 **MR LINGO** (IRE) 119
557 **MR LOVE** (IRE) 14
196 **MR LUPTON** (IRE) 40
278 **MR MAC** (GB) 5
320 **MR MAFIA** (IRE) 28
80 **MR MAGILL** (FR) 8
176 **MR MAXX** (IRE) 52
369 **MR MCGO** (GB) 66
230 **MR MCGUINESS** (IRE) 7
561 **MR MEDIC** (GB) 11
298 **MR MINERALS** (GB) 14
369 **MR MONOCHROME** (GB) 67
280 **MR MULLINER** (IRE) 16
330 **MR NICE GUY** (IRE) 19

332 **MR NUTHERPUTT** (IRE) 31
385 **MR ORANGE** (IRE) 14
150 **MR PALMTREE** (IRE) 12
253 **MR POTTER** (GB) 9
399 **MR POY** (GB) 7
327 **MR PUMBLECHOOK** (GB) 86
227 **MR RAJ** (IRE) 9
534 **MR RED CLUBS** (IRE) 3
280 **MR SCAFF** (IRE) 17
158 **MR SCARAMANGA** (GB) 11
427 **MR SCRUMPY** (GB) 13
266 **MR SECRETARY** (IRE) 107
445 **MR STANDFAST** (GB) 2
538 **MR STRUTTER** (IRE) 9
280 **MR STUBBS** (IRE) 18
478 **MR TOASTIE** (GB) 57
190 **MR TOP HAT** (GB) 18
263 **MR TYRRELL** (IRE) 9
457 **MR WAGYU** (IRE) 24
148 **MR WASHINGTON** (IRE) 26
279 **MR WHIPPED** (IRE) 107
304 **MR WIGGINS** (GB) 10
559 **MR WING** (IRE) 7
383 **MR WITMORE** (IRE) 23
279 **MR WOODY** (IRE) 108
328 **MR WOOLLEY** (GB) 9
246 **MR YOUNG** (FR) 21
374 **MR ZOOM ZOOM** (GB) 8
446 **MRS BARNES** (IRE) 15
6 **MRS BELLAMY** (GB) 44
48 **MRS BENSON** (IRE) 6
238 **MRS BUKAY** (GB) G 28
403 **MRS BURBIDGE** (GB) 68
133 **MRS DAVIES** (IRE) 45
458 **MRS DISCOMBE** (GB) 13
196 **MRS HOO** (IRE) 117
426 **MRS HYDE** (IRE) 41
29 **MRS IVY** (GB) 59
313 **MRS JACK** (IRE) 16
48 **MRS LANE** (IRE) 19
183 **MRS LOVETT** (IRE) 120
406 **MRS MEADER** (GB) 45
448 **MRS MIGGINS** (IRE) 51
572 **MRS QUINCE** (GB) F 9
499 **MRS SIPPY** (USA) 20
95 **MRS TODD** (GB) 42
113 **MRS VONN** (IRE) 13
450 **MRS WORTHINGTON** (IRE) 24
555 **MRSROBIN** (IRE) 61
295 **MS PARFOIS** (IRE) 22
407 **MSASSA** (FR) 126
202 **MUATADEL** (GB) 23
525 **MUBAKKER** (USA) 77
106 **MUBARIZ** (GB) 44
553 **MUBHIJ** (IRE) 16
450 **MUCH FASTER** (IRE) F 43
239 **MUCHLY** (GB) 104
16 **MUCHO TALENTO** (GB) 102
550 **MUCKLE ROE** (IRE) 74
82 **MUDAARAAH** (GB) F 74
119 **MUDAMMER** (IRE) C 70
82 **MUDAWANAH** (GB) C 75
38 **MUDAWWAN** (IRE) 6
393 **MUDDLE THINKING** (IRE) 98
381 **MUDEER** (IRE) 31
576 **MUFARREJ** (GB) 57
422 **MUFTAKKER** (GB) 4
499 **MUGATOO** (IRE) 21

533 **OXTED** (GB) 21
593 **OXWICH BAY** (IRE) 52
428 **OXYGENIC** (GB) 88
335 **OYAMBRE** (GB) 21
29 **OYDIS** (GB) 64
6 **OYSTER CARD** (GB) 48
77 **OYSTER PERCH** (GB) 10
89 **OZARK** (GB) 35
286 **OZZIE THE OSCAR** (IRE) 66
255 **PABLO ESCOBARR** (IRE) 86
12 **PABLOW** (GB) 9
100 **PACCHES** (IRE) F 126
419 **PACHA DU POLDER** (FR) 107
303 **PACHANGA** (GB) C 55
279 **PACIFIC DE BAUNE** (FR) 116
424 **PACIFIC OCEAN** (IRE) 84
502 **PACIFIC SALT** (IRE) 9
158 **PACIFICADORA** (USA) 22
513 **PACIFY** (GB) 41
196 **PACINO** (GB) 120
120 **PACKED HOUSE** (GB) F 101
262 **PACKETTOTHERAFTERS** (IRE) 10
95 **PACO DAWN** (GB) 46
87 **PACO ESCOSTAR** (GB) 13
193 **PACO FILLY** (GB) 16
345 **PACO'S PRINCE** (GB) 7
208 **PACOFILHA** (GB) 25
599 **PACTOLUS** (IRE) 29
261 **PADDLING** (FR) 52
182 **PADDOCKS LOUNGE** (IRE) 8
594 **PADDY A** (IRE) 83
137 **PADDY AGAIN** (IRE) F 75
327 **PADDY BOSS** (IRE) 96
196 **PADDY POWER** (IRE) 43
594 **PADDY THE CHEF** (IRE) 84
267 **PADDY THE OSCAR** (IRE) 10
54 **PADDY THE PANDA** (IRE) 6
233 **PADDY'S POEM** (GB) 22
351 **PADDY'S PURSUIT** (IRE) 36
498 **PADDY'S ROCK** (IRE) 11
375 **PADDYPLEX** (GB) 13
376 **PADDYS RUNNER** (GB) 27
542 **PADLEYOUROWNCANOE** (GB) 71
562 **PADMAVATI** (IRE) 5
108 **PADMINI** (GB) F 61
5 **PADS** (IRE) 7
552 **PADURA BRAVE** (GB) 20
544 **PAGEANT MASTER** (IRE) 15
431 **PAGERO** (FR) 67
159 **PAHASKA** (GER) 14
257 **PAIMPOLAISE** (IRE) F 65
383 **PAIN AU CHOCOLAT** (FR) 25
426 **PAINT THE DREAM** (GB) 44
452 **PAINT THE STAR** (IRE) C 62
201 **PAINTBALL WIZARD** (IRE) 24
361 **PAINTED DREAM** (GB) 6
259 **PAINTERS LAD** (IRE) 5
407 **PAIROFBROWNEYES** (IRE) 131
338 **PAISLEY PARK** (IRE) 45
459 **PAISLEY'S PROMISE** (IRE) 26
50 **PAISTIUL** (IRE) 47
10 **PALACE MOON** (GB) 17
381 **PALAVECINO** (FR) 33
442 **PALAVICINI RUN** (IRE) 8
453 **PALAWAN** (GB) 15
504 **PALAZZO** (GB) 30
589 **PALERMO** (IRE) 13
279 **PALIXANDRE** (FR) 117

378 **PALLADIUM** (GB) 28
183 **PALLASATOR** (GB) 127
556 **PALMETTO BAY** (GB) 24
89 **PALOMA ROSA** (GB) 16
335 **PALOMBA** (IRE) 22
399 **PAMINAH** (GB) 23
236 **PAMMI** (GB) 20
198 **PAMPER** (GB) 47
457 **PANDORA STAR** (GB) 42
403 **PANIA** (GB) 74
555 **PANIS ANGELICUS** (FR) 67
256 **PANKO** (IRE) 20
26 **PANNOTIA** (GB) 66
231 **PANOPTIC** (GB) G 23
407 **PANTHER SOUL** (IRE) 132
318 **PANZANO** (GB) 100
497 **PAPAGANA** (GB) 30
266 **PAPAL PEARL** (IRE) 55
558 **PAPARAZZI** (GB) 7
584 **PAPER PROMISE** (IRE) 13
172 **PAPER ROSES** (IRE) 14
172 **PARA MIO** (IRE) 6
357 **PARA QUEEN** (IRE) 18
284 **PARABOLA** (GB) F 114
516 **PARADE** (GB) 49
16 **PARADISE BOY** (FR) 106
556 **PARADISE LAKE** (IRE) 25
25 **PARADISE PAPERS** (GB) 33
79 **PARALLEL WORLD** (IRE) 56
29 **PARAPHERNALIA** (IRE) C 126
406 **PARDON ME** (GB) 32
87 **PARIS DIXIE** (GB) 14
560 **PARIS PROTOCOL** (IRE) 14
315 **PARISEAN ARTISTE** (IRE) 44
111 **PARISH POET** (IRE) 18
434 **PARISI** (GB) C 86
328 **PARISIAN AFFAIR** (GB) 23
137 **PARISIAN AFFAIR** (USA) F 76
122 **PARK HOUSE** (GB) 7
353 **PARK PADDOCKS** (IRE) 8
23 **PARKALITY** (IRE) F 17
478 **PARKER** (IRE) 62
474 **PARKER'S PRIDE** (GB) 5
588 **PARKIN** (GB) 24
284 **PARKMILL** (GB) 18
518 **PARKNACILLA** (IRE) 29
275 **PARLOUR MAID** (GB) 3
419 **PARODY** (GB) 108
176 **PAROLE** (IRE) 62
299 **PARSONAL** (IRE) 13
124 **PARTITA** (GB) C 96
203 **PARTLY SUNNY** (GB) C 65
263 **PARTRIDGE** (IRE) 212
16 **PARTY** (IRE) C 177
137 **PARTY FEET** (IRE) C 77
14 **PARTY FUZZ** (GB) 50
233 **PARTY ROYAL** (GB) 23
403 **PARWICH LEES** (GB) 75
176 **PARYS MOUNTAIN** (IRE) 63
23 **PAS DE BLANC** (IRE) 18
443 **PASEO** (GB) 31
315 **PASHION** (IRE) F 72
391 **PASITHEA** (IRE) C 18
50 **PASO DOBLE** (IRE) 117
401 **PASS THE CRISTAL** (IRE) 11
16 **PASS THE GIN** (GB) 107
173 **PASSAM** (GB) 8
51 **PASSEFONTAINE** (FR) 18

327 **PASSERINA** (GB) 163
327 **PASSING CALL** (GB) 97
10 **PASSING CLOUDS** (GB) 18
406 **PASSING DREAM** (GB) 33
403 **PASSING OCEANS** (GB) 76
376 **PASSING SHADOW** (GB) 28
560 **PASSIONATE LOVE** (IRE) 15
90 **PAST MASTER** (GB) 16
208 **PASTAMAKESUFASTER** (GB) 26
485 **PASTFACT** (GB) 5
323 **PASTIME** (GB) 9
399 **PASTORAL PLAYER** (GB) 24
588 **PAT KELLY** (GB) 25
183 **PAT'S OSCAR** (IRE) 128
379 **PAT'S PICK** (IRE) 88
100 **PATCHOULI** (GB) 67
611 **PATENT** (GB) 9
119 **PATH OF PEACE** (GB) F 72
50 **PATH TO FAME** (IRE) 118
436 **PATHS OF GLORY** (GB) 23
558 **PATHWAY TO FREEDOM** (GB) 8
67 **PATIENCE ALEXANDER** (IRE) F 38
181 **PATIENCE TONY** (IRE) 12
171 **PATIENCEISAVIRTUE** (GB) 15
385 **PATRICK** (IRE) 21
5 **PATRONESS** (GB) C 152
381 **PATRONUS** (GB) 34
59 **PATSIO** (IRE) 8
16 **PATTAYA** (GB) 108
100 **PATTIE** (GB) 23
426 **PAULS HILL** (IRE) 45
603 **PAVERS PRIDE** (GB) 10
450 **PAVONINE** (GB) F 44
338 **PAWN STAR** (IRE) 46
16 **PAX AETERNA** (USA) C 178
499 **PAX BRITANNICA** (IRE) 91
593 **PAXMAN** (IRE) 53
255 **PAY COURT** (GB) 87
428 **PAYNES BAY** (IRE) 116
539 **PC DIXON** (GB) 9
185 **PEA SHOOTER** (GB) 30
119 **PEACE DREAMER** (IRE) 20
57 **PEACE PREVAILS** (GB) 11
519 **PEACE PROCESS** (IRE) 6
269 **PEACE SEEKER** (GB) 22
379 **PEACE SIGNAL** (USA) C 140
603 **PEACE TALKS** (GB) C 17
23 **PEACEFUL SOUL** (USA) G 28
557 **PEACEFUL VALLEY** (FR) 17
164 **PEACH PAVLOVA** (IRE) 13
424 **PEACH TREE** (GB) 85
410 **PEACHEY** (IRE) 75
405 **PEACHEY CARNEHAN** (GB) 11
411 **PEAK HILL** (GB) 6
1 **PEAK OF BEAUTY** (IRE) 35
571 **PEAK PRINCESS** (GB) 14
383 **PEAK TIME** (GB) 26
419 **PEAK TO PEAK** (IRE) 109
248 **PEARL ACCLAIM** (GB) 9
526 **PEARL BELL** (GB) C 34
165 **PEARL BLUE** (IRE) F 17
556 **PEARL DRAGON** (FR) 26
424 **PEARL GREY** (GB) C 166
255 **PEARL JAM** (GB) 88
152 **PEARL NOIR** (GB) 22
5 **PEARL OF FREEDOM** (GB) 74
378 **PEARL OF MANAMA** (USA) 29
185 **PEARL OF QATAR** (GB) 57

318 PICO DUARTE (USA) F 211
41 PICTURE FRAME (GB) 159
448 PICTURE PAINTER (IRE) 58
518 PICTURE POET (IRE) 30
181 PICTURE YOUR DREAM (GB) 13
241 PIECEOFTHEACTION (IRE) 22
452 PIEDITA (IRE) 90
379 PIENTA (USA) 90
553 PIERRE LAPIN (IRE) 169
585 PIGEON PIE (GB) G 12
431 PIGGY WINKLE (IRE) 69
424 PIKABOO (GB) F 168
146 PIKE CORNER CROSS (IRE) 13
503 PIKES PEAK (FR) 29
419 PILANSBERG (GB) 111
553 PILASTER (GB) 18
255 PILATES (IRE) F 169
340 PILGRIM SOUL (GB) 25
29 PILITA (IRE) 121
148 PILOT WINGS (IRE) 32
436 PILSLEY (GB) 64
257 PIMPERNEL (IRE) F 67
255 PIN UP (IRE) C 170
272 PINARELLA (FR) 29
35 PINATAR (IRE) 34
369 PINCH OF GINGER (IRE) 80
83 PINCHPOINT (IRE) 14
64 PINCTADA (GB) 18
94 PINDARIC (GB) 13
284 PINDROP (GB) F 116
562 PINE CHIP (USA) C 85
179 PINE WARBLER (GB) 22
286 PINEAPPLE RUSH (GB) 68
449 PINGLEY LAD (GB) 8
542 PINGSHOU (IRE) 72
111 PINK DAMSEL (IRE) F 31
562 PINK DIVA (IRE) C 86
424 PINK DOGWOOD (IRE) 86
59 PINK EYED PEDRO (GB) 9
499 PINK FLAMES (IRE) C 92
318 PINK FLAMINGO (GB) 102
550 PINK GIN (GB) 80
298 PINK ICEBURG (IRE) 38
600 PINK LEGEND (GB) 52
337 PINK MOON (IRE) C 32
497 PINK ROCK (IRE) 32
5 PINK ROSE (GB) C 154
111 PINK SYMPHONY (GB) C 32
318 PINK TEQUILA (GB) C 212
126 PINKIE PIE (GB) 20
320 PINNACLE PEAK (GB) 30
599 PINNATA (GB) 30
478 PINSPOT (GB) 63
202 PIONEERING (IRE) 28
16 PIPER ARROW (GB) 110
93 PIPERS NOTE (GB) 36
172 PIPES OF PEACE (IRE) 7
279 PIPESMOKER (FR) 120
235 PIPOCA (GB) 17
169 PIRATE KING (GB) 7
320 PIRATE LOOK (IRE) 31
65 PIRATE SAM (GB) 22
103 PISANELLO (IRE) 98
548 PISTE (GB) F 20
151 PISTOL (IRE) 3
185 PISTOL PARK (FR) 32
363 PISTOL SHOOT (IRE) 11
279 PISTOL WHIPPED (IRE) 121

497 PITON PETE (IRE) 33
109 PIVELLO (GB) 10
16 PIVOINE (IRE) 38
103 PIVOINE ROSE (FR) 47
441 PIVOTAL ART (IRE) 28
604 PIVOTAL DREAM (IRE) 9
124 PIVOTAL ERA (GB) F 97
444 PIVOTAL FLAME (IRE) 10
519 PIVOTALIA (IRE) C 28
525 PIVOTALIA (GB) C 135
599 PIVOTTING (GB) F 59
145 PIXELATIT (GB) 4
420 PIXIEPOT (GB) 8
103 PIZZICATO (ITY) 48
382 PLACE DES VOSGES (IRE) 12
108 PLACE PASDELOUP (FR) 33
120 PLACE THAT FACE (GB) C 103
441 PLACEBO EFFECT (IRE) 10
22 PLACEDELA CONCORDE (GB) 19
30 PLAIT (GB) 9
543 PLAN OF ESCAPE (IRE) 9
154 PLANET NINE (IRE) 29
266 PLANET VENUS (IRE) 108
36 PLANETOID (IRE) 14
529 PLANSINA (GB) 20
35 PLANTADREAM (GB) 13
406 PLANTAGENET (GB) 34
32 PLASTIKI (GB) 9
335 PLATANE (GB) 23
30 PLATFORM NINETEEN (IRE) 38
530 PLATINUM COAST (USA) 34
41 PLATINUM STAR (IRE) 160
443 PLATITUDE (GB) 13
562 PLATONIC (GB) C 87
307 PLAY IT BY EAR (IRE) 55
195 PLAY IT COOL (IRE) 12
567 PLAY PRACTICE (GB) 7
450 PLAY STREET (GB) F 45
55 PLAY THE ACE (IRE) 39
472 PLAY THE PART (IRE) 2
604 PLAY WITH ME (GB) 10
406 PLAYA BLANCA (IRE) 35
257 PLAYA DEL PUENTE (IRE) 36
407 PLEASANT COMPANY (IRE) 135
394 PLEASANT GESTURE (IRE) 12
50 PLEASANT SLANEY (IRE) 122
266 PLEASURABLE (IRE) 109
555 PLENEY (GB) 68
146 PLENTY IN THE TANK (IRE) 14
492 PLENTY OF BUTTY (GB) 30
345 PLETTENBERG GREY (GB) 8
109 PLISSKEN (GB) 26
332 PLOVER (GB) C 32
318 PLUCKY (GB) F 213
479 PLUCKY DIP (GB) 13
386 PLUM DUFF (GB) 28
196 PLUMETTE (GB) 122
111 PLUNGER (GB) 4
168 PLUNKETT (GB) 73
307 PLUS JAMAIS (FR) 32
438 PLUS ONE (IRE) 58
569 PLUSDARGENT (FR) 24
284 PLUTONIAN (IRE) 19
593 POBBLES BAY (FR) 55
119 POCKET DYNAMO (USA) 46
106 POCKET SQUARE (GB) 96
266 POCOTALIGO (GB) 110
451 POET PETE (IRE) 18

423 POET'S CORNER (GB) 17
176 POET'S DAWN (GB) 64
450 POET'S MAGIC (GB) 5
25 POET'S PRIDE (GB) 16
45 POET'S REFLECTION (IRE) 6
484 POETA BRASILEIRO (IRE) 5
5 POETIC CHARM (GB) 33
120 POETIC DANCER (GB) C 104
108 POETIC DIVA (FR) 34
499 POETIC ERA (GB) 53
95 POETIC FORCE (IRE) 47
57 POETIC MOTION (GB) 16
394 POETIC PRINCIPLE (IRE) 2
426 POETIC RHYTHM (IRE) 48
175 POETIC VERSE (GB) F 105
30 POETRY (GB) 39
393 POETRY AND ART (GB) 148
284 POGO (IRE) 61
223 POGO I AM (GB) 58
369 POGUE (IRE) 81
260 POINT BREAK (IRE) 3
552 POINT IN TIME (IRE) 13
273 POINT N SHOOT (IRE) 24
55 POINT OF DEPARTURE (IRE) 40
93 POINT OF HONOUR (IRE) 37
555 POINT OF PRINCIPLE (IRE) 69
304 POINT OF WOODS (GB) 10
546 POINT PERFECT (GB) C 16
500 POINT TAKEN (IRE) 117
6 POINT ZERO (IRE) 49
286 POINTED AND SHARP (IRE) 69
363 POISON ARROW (IRE) 12
319 POKARI (FR) 11
407 POKER D'AINAY (FR) 136
368 POKER MASTER (IRE) 16
448 POKER PLAY (FR) 59
594 POKER SCHOOL (IRE) 86
383 POKORA DU LYS (FR) 7
273 POLA CHANCE (FR) 41
280 POLAR LIGHT (GB) 19
493 POLARBROOK (IRE) 16
560 POLARIS ANGEL (GB) 29
553 POLARIS BOUND (IRE) 170
183 POLI ROI (FR) 130
5 POLICORO (IRE) F 155
407 POLIDAM (FR) 137
106 POLISH (GB) 11
404 POLISHED ARTICLE (GB) 8
576 POLISHED GEM (IRE) F 112
199 POLISHED ROCK (IRE) 23
266 POLISHED STEEL (GB) 58
316 POLITELYSED (GB) 6
125 POLITICAL POLICY (IRE) 26
529 POLITICAL QUIZ (GB) 21
493 POLITICAL SLOT (GB) 17
255 POLITICISE (IRE) 89
419 POLITOLOGUE (FR) 112
193 POLKADOT PRINCESS (IRE) 17
231 POLLY'S GOLD (FR) 8
588 POLLYAMOROUS (IRE) 27
99 POLLYISSIMO (GB) 10
170 POLO THE MUMM (FR) 28
407 POLY ROCK (FR) 138
499 POLYBIUS (GB) 23
334 POLYDORA (IRE) 22
200 POLYMATH (GB) 7
354 POLYPHONY (IRE) 19
556 POMME DE TERRE (IRE) 27

257 **RAYDARA** (IRE) F 69
79 **RAYDIANCE** (GB) 17
263 **RAYMOND TUSK** (IRE) 14
329 **RAYNA'S WORLD** (IRE) 48
203 **RAYON ROUGE** (IRE) C 67
257 **RAYOUNPOUR** (IRE) 37
94 **RAYPETEAFTERME** (GB) 24
497 **RAYVIN BLACK** (GB) 35
125 **RAZ DE MAREE** (FR) 29
1 **RAZIN' HELL** (GB) 5
168 **REACHING AHEAD** (USA) F 74
41 **REACTION TIME** (GB) 4
235 **REACTIVE** (GB) 6
368 **READ FEDERICA** (GB) F 17
594 **READER'S CHOICE** (GB) 93
431 **READY AND ABLE** (IRE) 75
480 **READYANDAWAY** (USA) F 105
566 **REAL ARMANI** (GB) 3
10 **REAL ESTATE** (IRE) 19
449 **REAL KING** (GB) 10
279 **REAL PAPOOSE** (IRE) F 127
263 **REAL SMOOTH** (GB) 87
407 **REAL STEEL** (FR) 147
449 **REAL WARRIOR** (IRE) 11
41 **REAL WORLD** (IRE) 165
223 **REALITY BITES** (GB) 19
103 **REALITYHACKING** (FR) 51
133 **REALLY LOVELY** (IRE) C 106
408 **REALLY SUPER** (GB) 26
238 **REALLYRADICAL** (IRE) 33
500 **REALMS OF FIRE** (GB) 124
204 **REALT OR** (IRE) 10
241 **REAPLEE** (GB) 23
189 **REASONED** (IRE) 18
176 **REASSURANCE** (GB) 68
90 **REBECCA ROCKS** (GB) 19
16 **REBECCA ROMERO** (GB) G 185
120 **REBECKE** (GB) 61
294 **REBEL CAUSE** (IRE) 5
19 **REBEL COMMANDER** (IRE) 19
548 **REBEL HEART** (GB) 8
407 **REBEL OG** (IRE) 148
457 **REBEL REDEMPTION** (GB) 64
427 **REBEL STATE** (IRE) 18
516 **REBEL SURGE** (IRE) 12
547 **REBEL WOODS** (FR) 12
266 **RECALL THE SHOW** (GB) 152
114 **RECIPROCITY** (GB) 9
13 **RECKLESS BEHAVIOR** (IRE) 16
25 **RECKLESS ENDEAVOUR** (IRE) 17
576 **RECLAMATION** (GB) C 115
411 **RECOGNITION** (IRE) 7
95 **RECON MISSION** (IRE) 77
29 **RECONDITE** (IRE) 67
109 **RECONNAISSANCE** (GB) 28
477 **RECOVER ME** (FR) 6
16 **RECTORY ROAD** (IRE) 116
158 **RECUERDAME** (USA) 24
376 **RED ADMIRABLE** (IRE) 31
95 **RED ALERT** (GB) 52
516 **RED ARCHANGEL** (IRE) 26
120 **RED ARMADA** (IRE) 62
255 **RED BLOOM** (GB) C 175
133 **RED BOND** (IRE) 97
53 **RED BOOTS** (IRE) F 88
284 **RED BRAVO** (GB) 63
537 **RED CARAVEL** (IRE) 11
168 **RED CELEBRE** (IRE) 75

36 **RED CHARMER** (IRE) 15
308 **RED CHOIS** (IRE) 6
303 **RED COSSACK** (CAN) 23
248 **RED CYMBAL** (GB) 10
510 **RED DANAHER** (IRE) 43
142 **RED DEVIL LADS** (IRE) 4
511 **RED DEVIL STAR** (IRE) 12
152 **RED DOUGLAS** (GB) 24
137 **RED DRAGONESS** (IRE) 40
124 **RED DUNE** (IRE) F 100
343 **RED EMPEROR** (IRE) 3
120 **RED FEDORA** (GB) 63
168 **RED FOR ALL** (GB) 76
419 **RED FORCE ONE** (GB) 11
130 **RED FOREVER** (GB) 1
41 **RED GALILEO** (GB) 26
379 **RED GERRY** (IRE) 133
89 **RED GIANT** (GB) 18
351 **RED GUNNER** (GB) 26
30 **RED HALO** (IRE) C 91
196 **RED HOT** (FR) 125
426 **RED HOT CHILLY** (IRE) 51
32 **RED HOT FUSION** (IRE) 11
106 **RED IMPRESSION** (GB) 50
395 **RED INDIAN** (GB) 3
594 **RED INFANTRY** (GB) 94
131 **RED INVADER** (IRE) 10
379 **RED JACK** (IRE) 93
499 **RED KYTE** (GB) C 95
235 **RED MAHARANI** (GB) 30
428 **RED MISCHIEF** (IRE) C 117
124 **RED MIST** (GB) 16
416 **RED MIX** (FR) 36
241 **RED OCHRE** (GB) 24
436 **RED OCTOBER** (IRE) C 67
36 **RED ORATOR** (GB) 16
318 **RED PHOENIX** (GB) 105
504 **RED PIKE** (IRE) 13
241 **RED REMINDER** (GB) 25
500 **RED RISING** (GB) 125
14 **RED RIVER** (IRE) 54
120 **RED ROMANCE** (GB) 64
179 **RED ROYALIST** (GB) 25
168 **RED SECRET** (CAN) 43
514 **RED SEEKER** (GB) 10
25 **RED SHAREEF** (GB) F 35
186 **RED SHELLEY** (GB) 35
221 **RED SKY IN SPAIN** (GB) 32
374 **RED SKYE DELIGHT** (IRE) 9
523 **RED SNAPPER** (GB) 6
263 **RED STARLIGHT** (GB) 15
601 **RED STRIPES** (USA) 10
197 **RED TORNADO** (FR) 4
6 **RED TOUCH** (USA) 56
127 **RED TYCOON** (IRE) 8
168 **RED VERDON** (USA) 16
392 **RED'S COMET** (GB) 21
486 **REDARNA** (GB) 13
513 **REDBRIDGE GOLD** (IRE) 42
168 **REDDIAC** (GB) 44
221 **REDEMPTION SONG** (IRE) 21
186 **REDEMPTIVE** (GB) 21
432 **REDEMPTRESS** (IRE) 23
503 **REDESIGN** (IRE) 30
547 **REDGRAVE** (IRE) 13
407 **REDHOTFILLYPEPPERS** (IRE) 149
327 **REDICEAN** (GB) 105

19 **REDMOND** (IRE) 20
4 **REDROSEZORRO** (GB) 9
500 **REDZOR** (IRE) 126
444 **REECELTIC** (GB) 12
67 **REEDWAY** (IRE) 18
489 **REEHAN** (USA) C 45
221 **REEL COOL** (GB) C 35
338 **REELINGINTHEYEARS** (IRE) 50
119 **REEVES** (GB) 48
436 **REFEREE** (GB) 25
576 **REFERENDA** (GB) 116
79 **REFLECTED** (IRE) 59
137 **REFLEKTOR** (IRE) 14
500 **REFORM ACT** (USA) G 127
440 **REFORMED CHARACTER** (IRE) 17
352 **REFUSETOLISTEN** (IRE) F 47
120 **REGAL AMBITION** (GB) 65
553 **REGAL BANNER** (GB) 102
124 **REGAL DIRECTOR** (IRE) 17
295 **REGAL ENCORE** (IRE) 26
77 **REGAL FLOW** (GB) 11
275 **REGAL FLUTE** (GB) 5
158 **REGAL GAIT** (IRE) 13
531 **REGAL HAWK** (GB) G 14
67 **REGAL KISS** (GB) C 39
176 **REGAL MIRAGE** (IRE) 69
99 **REGAL MISS** (GB) 11
525 **REGAL REALITY** (GB) 18
79 **REGAL RIBAND** (GB) C 123
428 **REGAL SALUTE** (GB) F 118
263 **REGALLINE** (IRE) C 216
22 **REGARDE MOI** (GB) 21
557 **REGARDING RUTH** (IRE) 21
103 **REGINA MUNDI** (IRE) C 101
477 **REGNANTE** (GB) 36
30 **REGULAR** (GB) 45
577 **REGULAR INCOME** (IRE) 13
328 **REGULATION** (IRE) 27
170 **REGULATOR** (IRE) 31
318 **REHN'S NEST** (IRE) C 218
39 **REIGN BACK DANCER** (IRE) 16
120 **REIGNING ICE** (GB) 66
279 **REIGNING SUPREME** (IRE) 128
435 **REIGNITE** (GB) 14
286 **REIKERS ISLAND** (IRE) 72
255 **REIMS** (GB) 91
185 **REINA DE LUZ** (IRE) C 67
108 **REINE DE VITESSE** (FR) 36
198 **REINE MAGNIFIQUE** (FR) 50
465 **REIVERS LAD** (GB) 38
115 **REIVERS LODGE** (IRE) 17
553 **REKDHAT** (IRE) F 176
385 **RELATED** (GB) 24
394 **RELATIVE EASE** (GB) 13
358 **RELAXED BOY** (FR) 14
50 **RELAXING MODE** (IRE) 125
407 **RELEGATE** (IRE) 150
129 **RELENTLESS DREAMER** (IRE) 18
108 **RELIABLE SON** (FR) 37
176 **RELIGHT MY FIRE** (GB) 70
456 **RELIGHT THE FIRE** (GB) 3
176 **RELKADAM** (FR) 71
54 **RELKWOOD** (IRE) 8
489 **RELOADED** (FR) 21
428 **REMARKABLE** (GB) 42
448 **REMASTERED** (GB) 63
475 **REMEMBER FOREVER** (IRE) 9
475 **REMEMBER ME WELL** (IRE) 10

428 **SALATEEN** (GB) 43
140 **SALAZAR** (IRE) 15
272 **SALDENAERA** (GER) F 36
51 **SALINAS GRANDE** (FR) 19
142 **SALLA** (GB) 5
433 **SALLY CAN'T WAIT** (GB) 22
226 **SALLY HOPE** (GB) 16
379 **SALLY SCULL** (IRE) 101
327 **SALMANAZAR** (GB) 111
400 **SALMON FISHING** (IRE) 8
103 **SALMON PLEASE** (FR) 54
298 **SALOME** (FR) F 83
53 **SALONA** (GER) F 89
330 **SALOUEN** (IRE) 6
252 **SALSA BRAVA** (IRE) F 22
146 **SALSA VERDE** (IRE) 17
5 **SALSABEEL** (IRE) 34
407 **SALSARETTA** (FR) 160
394 **SALT ROSE** (GB) C 30
252 **SALT WHISTLE BAY** (IRE) 10
530 **SALTANAT** (IRE) C 90
25 **SALTIE GIRL** (GB) 37
588 **SALTO CHISCO** (IRE) 30
120 **SALUTE THE SOLDIER** (GER) 20
385 **SALUTI** (IRE) 27
31 **SALVE DEL RIO** (IRE) 14
90 **SALVE ETOILES** (IRE) 38
241 **SALVEN** (GB) 26
156 **SALYDORA** (FR) C 55
295 **SAM BROWN** (GB) 28
140 **SAM CHISOLM** (IRE) 16
29 **SAM COOKE** (GB) 72
223 **SAM I** (FR) 64
500 **SAM RED** (FR) 136
427 **SAM SPINNER** (GB) 21
185 **SAM'S ADVENTURE** (GB) 36
15 **SAM'S GUNNER** (GB) 46
19 **SAMANDARA** (FR) F 21
223 **SAMARQUAND** (GB) 65
562 **SAMASANA** (IRE) C 88
409 **SAMBA CHRYSS** (IRE) C 28
409 **SAMBA CHRYSS** (IRE) F 19
423 **SAMBA SARAVAH** (USA) 19
39 **SAMBA TIME** (GB) 19
20 **SAMBARINA** (IRE) F 30
139 **SAMBARINA** (IRE) F 9
385 **SAMBUCCA SPIRIT** (GB) 34
286 **SAMBURU SHUJAA** (FR) 75
183 **SAMCRO** (IRE) 142
263 **SAMDANIYA** (GB) C 218
369 **SAME CIRCUS** (IRE) 37
530 **SAMEEM** (IRE) 38
477 **SAMEER** (FR) 40
176 **SAMEROUS** (FR) C 165
419 **SAMETEGAL** (FR) 125
478 **SAMMY B** (GB) 74
497 **SAMMY BILL** (GB) 38
472 **SAMMYJADE** (IRE) 4
376 **SAMMYLOU** (IRE) 33
152 **SAMOVAR** (GB) 25
493 **SAMPHIRE COAST** (GB) 19
397 **SAMS PROFILE** (GB) 12
335 **SAMSKARA** (IRE) 27
416 **SAMSON** (GB) 39
378 **SAMSON THE MAN** (GB) 17
454 **SAMSON'S REACH** (GB) 14
318 **SAMSTAR** (GB) 110
583 **SAMSTOWN** (GB) 27

411 **SAMTU** (IRE) 9
389 **SAMUEL JACKSON** (GB) 4
315 **SAMYA** (GB) C 77
424 **SAN ANDREAS** (IRE) 88
419 **SAN BENEDETO** (FR) 126
321 **SAN CARLOS** (GB) 16
168 **SAN DIACO** (IRE) 47
553 **SAN DONATO** (IRE) 106
103 **SAN HUBERTO** (IRE) 55
393 **SAN PEDRO DE SENAM** (FR) 112
158 **SAN QUIRICO** (GB) 33
327 **SAN RUMOLDO** (GB) 112
419 **SAN SATIRO** (IRE) 127
179 **SAN SEB** (GB) 26
168 **SAN SEBASTIAN** (IRE) 48
589 **SANAADH** (GB) 14
120 **SANADAAT** (GB) F 105
477 **SANARY** (GB) 41
434 **SANAYA** (IRE) C 88
407 **SANCTA SIMONA** (FR) 161
176 **SAND AND DELIVER** (GB) F 124
29 **SAND SHARE** (GB) 73
332 **SANDBOX TWO** (IRE) 12
199 **SANDFORD CASTLE** (IRE) 26
123 **SANDFRANKSKIPSGO** (IRE) 1
245 **SANDHURST LAD** (IRE) 63
408 **SANDKISSED** (IRE) 29
195 **SANDRA'S SECRET** (IRE) 15
272 **SANDRET** (IRE) 31
479 **SANDRIDGE LAD** (IRE) 27
170 **SANDRO BOTTICELLI** (IRE) 33
152 **SANDS CHORUS** (GB) 26
191 **SANDS COVE** (IRE) 14
196 **SANDS OF MALI** (FR) 50
542 **SANDY BEACH** (GB) 84
286 **SANDY BOY** (IRE) 76
266 **SANDY CAY** (USA) C 155
103 **SANDY LIGHT** (IRE) F 105
399 **SANDYMAN** (GB) 51
232 **SANDYMOUNT** (IRE) 63
266 **SANDYMOUNT DUKE** (IRE) 64
248 **SANDYTOWN** (IRE) 11
525 **SANGARIUS** (GB) 87
410 **SANGHA RIVER** (IRE) 82
525 **SANNKALA** (FR) C 144
152 **SANS SOUCI BAY** (GB) 27
87 **SANTAFIORA** (GB) 18
183 **SANTANA PLESSIS** (FR) 143
235 **SANTANA SLEW** (GB) 20
529 **SANTANI** (GB) 25
510 **SANTINA** (GB) G 45
431 **SANTIAGO DE CUBA** (IRE) 77
279 **SANTINI** (GB) 132
419 **SAO** (IRE) 128
194 **SAO MAXENCE** (FR) 37
112 **SAOIRSE ROSE** (GB) 4
318 **SAPA INCA** (IRE) 111
108 **SAPFO** (FR) C 63
424 **SAPHIRA'S FIRE** (IRE) F 171
503 **SAPHIRSIDE** (IRE) 16
576 **SAPPHIRE** (IRE) F 119
441 **SAPPHIRE JUBILEE** (IRE) 16
407 **SAPPHIRE LADY** (IRE) 162
273 **SAPPHIRE NOIRE** (IRE) 25
65 **SAQUEBOUTE** (FR) 38
106 **SARACENE** (IRE) 13
345 **SARAH BERRY** (GB) C 16
255 **SARAHA** (GB) C 179

1 **SARAHALL** (IRE) G 39
164 **SARALEA** (FR) C 28
226 **SARAS HOPE** (GB) 22
434 **SARASOTA** (IRE) 19
457 **SARASOTA** (GB) 45
320 **SARASOTA STAR** (IRE) 39
266 **SARAWATI** (IRE) F 156
158 **SARGENTO** (GB) 15
110 **SARI MAREIS** (GB) 18
245 **SARIM** (GB) 64
30 **SARITA** (GB) C 92
190 **SARK** (IRE) 19
477 **SARKIYLA** (FR) C 71
124 **SAROOG** (GB) 18
142 **SARPECH** (IRE) 6
599 **SARSAPARILLA KIT** (GB) 50
477 **SARTAJ** (USA) 42
26 **SARTILLY** (FR) 68
542 **SARTORIAL ELEGANCE** (GB) 85
558 **SARU** (GB) C 17
489 **SARVAN** (GB) 46
103 **SARVANA** (FR) C 106
236 **SARVI** (GB) 25
428 **SARYSHAGANN** (FR) 44
443 **SASH** (GB) 32
436 **SASKIA'S DREAM** (GB) C 102
330 **SASSIE** (GB) 7
111 **SASSOON** (GB) 22
50 **SASTA** (IRE) 129
190 **SATCHVILLE FLYER** (GB) 47
257 **SATIN SLIPPER** (IRE) 70
26 **SATIRISTE** (GB) C 69
115 **SATIS HOUSE** (GB) 20
298 **SATISFYING** (IRE) 44
426 **SATURDAYNIGHTFEVER** (GB) 55
492 **SATURN 'N SILK** (GB) 32
407 **SATURNAS** (FR) 163
337 **SATWA PEARL** (GB) F 34
597 **SAUCHIEHALL STREET** (IRE) 18
443 **SAUCY ENCORE** (GB) 16
261 **SAUCY SALLY** (IRE) 57
62 **SAUCYSIOUX** (GB) 5
110 **SAUMUR** (GB) 10
106 **SAVAANAH** (IRE) 14
480 **SAVALAS** (IRE) 28
438 **SAVANNA ROAR** (IRE) 66
5 **SAVANNAH BELLE** (GB) C 161
183 **SAVANNAH STORM** (GB) 144
29 **SAVE ME THE WALTZ** (FR) C 130
91 **SAVE THE PENNIES** (GB) 8
500 **SAVELLO** (IRE) 137
436 **SAVIDA** (IRE) C 103
270 **SAVLAD** (GB) 10
169 **SAVOIE** (FR) C 37
10 **SAVOY BROWN** (GB) 29
39 **SAVOY COURT** (IRE) 20
50 **SAVVY RULER** (USA) 130
16 **SAWASDEE** (IRE) 119
82 **SAWWAAH** (GB) 15
341 **SAXO JACK** (FR) 21
196 **SAXONROAD BOY** (USA) 51
337 **SAY NO NOW** (IRE) F 35
399 **SAY NOTHING** (GB) 52
124 **SAY THE WORD** (GB) 55
407 **SAYAR** (IRE) 164
83 **SAYEDAATI SAADATI** (IRE) 15
601 **SAYESSE** (GB) 11
407 **SAYO** (GB) 165

SWIFT APPROVAL (IRE) 34 599
SWIFT CRUSADOR (GB) 39 170
SWIFT EMPEROR (IRE) 18 25
SWIFT INTRIGUE (IRE) 21 164
SWIFT JUSTICE (GB) 43 351
SWIFT ROSE (IRE) 103 41
SWIFT WING (GB) 129 239
SWILLY SUNSET (GB) 5 342
SWINCOMBE SCORCHIO (GB) 9 254
SWINCOMBE WIZ (GB) 101 542
SWINDLER (GB) 61 562
SWINGBRIDGE (IRE) 155 183
SWINGING EDDIE (GB) 64 480
SWINGING JEAN (GB) 74 100
SWINGY (FR) 31 503
SWINLEY (IRE) 88 298
SWINTON DIAMOND (IRE) 65 261
SWISH (GER) C 78 257
SWISS AIR (GB) 106 255
SWISS CHEER (FR) 29 450
SWISS CHIME (GB) 48 303
SWISS CONNECTION (GB) 32 504
SWISS CROSS (GB) 13 371
SWISS DREAM (GB) C 93 562
SWISS LADY (GB) 14 121
SWISS MISS (GB) 17 226
SWISS PEAK (GB) 49 30
SWISS PHILLY (GB) 75 100
SWISS PRIDE (IRE) 48 298
SWISS STORM (GB) 10 30
SWISS VALLEY (IRE) 176 41
SWISSAL (IRE) 38 148
SWITCH AROUND (IRE) 68 576
SWITCHMAN (IRE) 111 480
SWORD BEACH (IRE) 80 315
SWORD EXCEED (GER) 34 225
SWORD OF FATE (IRE) 4 326
SWORDBILL (GB) 113 594
SWOT (GB) 15 533
SYBIL GRAND (IRE) 50 434
SYDNEY DE BAUNE (FR) 16 561
SYDNEY OPERA HOUSE (GB) 97 424
SYKES (IRE) 16 363
SYLVAN WINGS (GB) G 61 426
SYLVIA'S MOTHER (GB) 29 547
SYLVIACLIFFS (FR) 72 79
SYMBOLIC STAR (IRE) 12 411
SYMBOLINE (GB) F 144 100
SYMBOLIZATION (IRE) 40 5
SYMPHONY (IRE) 9 551
SYMPHONY OF ANGELS (GB) 158 500
SYMPOSIA (GB) F 91 53
SYNCHRONIC (IRE) C 185 424
SYNERGY (FR) F 107 120
SYNERGY (FR) F 22 391
SYNOPSIS (GB) 156 183
TA ALLAK (GB) 27 553
TA AMMOL (GB) C 190 553
TAALLUF (USA) C 101 499
TABASSOR (IRE) 75 284
TABDEED (GB) 17 82
TABLA (GB) 8 97
TABLE BAY (IRE) F 94 562
TABOU BEACH BOY (GB) 83 175
TABRINA (GB) C 174 176
TAC TILE (FR) 22 382
TACENDA (IRE) 35 295
TACITLY (GB) 105 106

TACITURN (GB) 130 239
TACTICAL MANOEUVRE (IRE) 40 170
TADAABEER (GB) 76 284
TADAANY (IRE) 45 93
TADAAWOL (GB) 31 202
TADASANA (GB) 48 571
TADPOLE (GB) C 27 565
TAFISH (IRE) 89 298
TAGINE (GB) 4 388
TAGLE (IRE) 35 225
TAGULA MON (IRE) G 41 386
TAGUR (IRE) 31 480
TAHIRAH (GB) F 102 499
TAHNEED (IRE) 131 239
TAHREEK (GB) 22 525
TAHRIR (IRE) C 130 284
TAILOR TOM (IRE) 103 369
TAILS I WIN (CAN) 46 202
TAIMA (GB) 66 452
TAJAWOZ (USA) 47 82
TAKARA GIRL (FR) F 62 562
TAKARNA (IRE) C 26 67
TAKBEER (IRE) 20 193
TAKE A BREAK (IRE) F 23 560
TAKE EM OUT (IRE) 81 555
TAKE FIVE (IRE) 10 34
TAKE FRIGHT (GB) 70 436
TAKE IT AWAY (IRE) 148 279
TAKE IT DOWN UNDER (GB) 32 408
TAKE IT THUNDER (IRE) 76 119
TAKE SILK (IRE) 48 257
TAKE THE HELM (GB) 9 381
TAKE THE HIGH ROAD (GB) 67 448
TAKE TWO (GB) 30 256
TAKEASUP (GB) 35 381
TAKEIT EASY (GB) 12 502
TAKEITTOTHELIMITS (IRE) 157 183
TAKEMEOUT FREDDIE (IRE) 28 98
TAKEONEFORTHETEAM (GB) 30 351
TAKIAH (GB) 7 282
TAKING A CHANCE (IRE) 114 594
TAKING AIM (GB) 3 241
TAKINGITALLIN (IRE) 104 369
TAKINGRISKS (IRE) 43 465
TAKUMI (GB) 113 553
TALAP (GB) 191 553
TALENT TO AMUSE (IRE) 55 338
TALITHA KUM (IRE) C 79 257
TALIYNA (IRE) 69 576
TALK LIKE THIS (USA) 14 447
TALK OF FAME (GB) 67 14
TALK OF THE SOUTH (IRE) 27 280
TALKINGPICTURESTV (GB) 25 433
TALKISCHEAP (IRE) 127 327
TALKOFGOLD (IRE) 16 543
TALKTOMENOW (GB) 66 245
TALLULAH'S QUEST (IRE) 15 201
TALLY'S SONG (GB) 11 267
TAMACHAN (GB) 56 106
TAMALAIN (USA) C 16 139
TAMARA BAY (GB) C 17 139
TAMARA MOON (GB) F 25 110
TAMARILLO GROVE (IRE) 25 341
TAMARISK (GER) C 100 30
TAMAROC DU MATHAN (FR) 142 419
TAMBOURINE SAM (GB) 10 345
TAMERLANE (IRE) 25 120
TAMLEEK (USA) 53 428

TAMLOUGH BOY (GB) 112 379
TAMMOOZ (GB) 114 553
TAMOK (IRE) 50 304
TAMOSHANTER KID (GB) 29 569
TAMREER (GB) 32 202
TAN (GB) 68 6
TAN ARABIQ (GB) 69 6
TANAAWOL (GB) 121 318
TANACANDO (FR) 82 555
TANARPINO (GB) 28 89
TANASOQ (IRE) 29 385
TANGLED (IRE) 20 263
TANGO BOY (IRE) 92 403
TANGRAMM (GB) 30 303
TANIT RIVER (IRE) 83 555
TANITA (GB) 151 525
TANKERVILLE (USA) 70 576
TANOJIN (IRE) F 145 100
TANOURA (IRE) C 130 576
TANQEEB (GB) 48 82
TANRUDY (IRE) 34 273
TANTAMOUNT (GB) 81 478
TANYELI (IRE) C 56 381
TANZERIN (IRE) 46 203
TANZINA (GB) 13 392
TAOPIX (GB) 17 375
TAPENADE (IRE) 158 183
TAPESTRY (IRE) C 186 424
TAPIS LIBRE (GB) 5 118
TAPISSERIE (GB) 107 255
TAPPITY TAP (GB) 8 333
TARA BRIDGE (GB) 38 238
TARA CHIEFTAIN (GB) 64 600
TARA FLOW (GB) 65 600
TARA FORCE (GB) 86 176
TARA MAC (GB) 84 555
TARA MUCK (GB) 93 550
TARA NIECE (GB) 39 406
TARA TIARA (GB) 10 122
TARA TOO (IRE) C 190 255
TARA VIEW (GB) 128 327
TARA WELL (IRE) 18 150
TARA WEST (GB) 36 295
TARAAYEF (IRE) 3 418
TARADA (GB) 44 497
TARAEFF (IRE) F 62 519
TARAKONA (IRE) 27 201
TARAS DAY (GB) 13 396
TARBELA (IRE) F 187 424
TARBEYAH (IRE) 28 221
TARBOOSH (GB) 30 385
TARFASHA (IRE) F 131 576
TARGET ZONE (GB) 23 186
TARKS HILL (GB) 40 406
TARNAWA (IRE) 71 576
TARNEEM (USA) F 15 121
TARNHELM (GB) 7 524
TARRONA (GB) 3 445
TARRZAN (IRE) 18 226
TARSEEKH (GB) 21 565
TARSET HINNY (IRE) 82 478
TARTARIA (GB) 16 35
TARTIFLETTE (GB) C 57 381
TARTLETTE (GB) 55 399
TASAABOQ (GB) 14 371
TASHUNKA (IRE) 62 426
TATHMEEN (IRE) 16 68

331 **TOBOUGGALOO** (GB) 16
245 **TOBY MAGUIRE** (IRE) 69
263 **TOCOPILLA** (FR) C 238
30 **TOCQUEVILLE** (FR) C 102
263 **TODAY POWER** (IRE) 239
176 **TODAY'S THE DAY** (GB) C 175
410 **TODD** (GB) 93
258 **TOE TO TOE** (IRE) 7
53 **TOFAN** (GB) 16
571 **TOFFEE GALORE** (GB) 52
424 **TOGETHER FOREVER** (GB) C 189
556 **TOGETHERNESS** (IRE) 35
5 **TOHAZIE** (GB) 82
383 **TOI STOREY** (IRE) 42
307 **TOKARAMORE** (GB) 42
500 **TOKAY DOKEY** (IRE) 164
508 **TOM AND TONY H** (IRE) 22
198 **TOM HART** (GB) 83
462 **TOM'S ANNA** (GB) 5
226 **TOMAHAWK RIDGE** (IRE) 19
183 **TOMBSTONE** (IRE) 165
29 **TOMFRE** (GB) 138
263 **TOMILY** (IRE) 21
577 **TOMINTOUL MAGIC** (IRE) F 44
383 **TOMKEVI** (IRE) 43
284 **TOMMY DE VITO** (GB) 132
133 **TOMMY DOCC** (IRE) 64
236 **TOMMY G** (GB) 35
206 **TOMMY HALLINAN** (IRE) 16
379 **TOMMY JOE** (FR) 115
500 **TOMMY RAPPER** (IRE) 165
411 **TOMMY SHELBY** (IRE) 13
419 **TOMMY SILVER** (FR) 145
480 **TOMMY TAYLOR** (USA) 32
89 **TOMMY THE RASCAL** (GB) 30
115 **TOMMYCOLE** (GB) 23
356 **TOMMYS GEAL** (GB) 9
419 **TOMORROW MYSTERY** (GB) 146
307 **TOMORROW'S ANGEL** (GB) 43
69 **TOMORROW'S LEGEND** (GB) 9
41 **TOMOUH** (IRE) 178
41 **TOMOUH DUBAI** (GB) 179
119 **TOMSHALFBROTHER** (GB) 54
599 **TONE THE BARONE** (GB) 53
95 **TONI'S A STAR** (GB) 65
133 **TONICNGIN** (FR) 65
501 **TONTO'S SPIRIT** (GB) 9
239 **TOO DARN HOT** (GB) 135
335 **TOO LOUD** (USA) 33
573 **TOO MANY CHIEFS** (IRE) 6
500 **TOO MANY DIAMONDS** (GB) 166
35 **TOO MANY SHOTS** (GB) 17
223 **TOODLEPIP** (IRE) 76
83 **TOOFI** (FR) 20
23 **TOOLATETODELEGATE** (GB) 21
266 **TOORA LOORA** (GB) 160
600 **TOP AND DROP** (GB) 68
197 **TOP ATTRACTION** (GB) 10
234 **TOP BEAK** (IRE) 14
465 **TOP BILLING** (GB) 45
493 **TOP BOY** (GB) 20
298 **TOP BREEZE** (IRE) 49
22 **TOP CAT DJ** (IRE) 25
263 **TOP CLASS ANGEL** (IRE) 240
269 **TOP COP** (GB) 31
162 **TOP DECISION** (IRE) 17
186 **TOP FOX** (GB) 24
340 **TOP GAMBLE** (IRE) 33

227 **TOP MAN TIM** (IRE) 10
279 **TOP NOTCH** (FR) 154
245 **TOP OF THE CHARTS** (FR) 70
398 **TOP OFFER** (GB) 15
16 **TOP POWER** (FR) 128
530 **TOP RANK** (IRE) 47
245 **TOP ROCK TALULA** (IRE) 71
41 **TOP SCORE** (GB) 33
335 **TOP SPACE** (USA) 34
525 **TOP TOP** (IRE) 93
327 **TOP TUG** (IRE) 139
329 **TOP VILLE BEN** (IRE) 65
395 **TOP WOOD** (FR) 6
544 **TOPANTICIPATION** (GB) 27
221 **TOPFLIGHT PRINCESS** (GB) C 36
263 **TOPICAL** (GB) 97
553 **TOPKA** (FR) F 193
323 **TOPMEUP** (GB) 14
550 **TOPOFTHECOTSWOLDS** (IRE) 97
419 **TOPOFTHEGAME** (IRE) 147
547 **TOPOLOGY** (IRE) 17
256 **TOPPER THORNTON** (IRE) 34
401 **TOPS NO** (GB) 12
307 **TOR** (GB) 44
35 **TORBELLINO** (GB) 28
120 **TORENTOSA** (FR) C 110
535 **TORHOUSEMUIR** (GB) 28
345 **TORIANO** (GB) 11
550 **TORN AND FRAYED** (FR) 98
407 **TORNADO FLYER** (IRE) 184
577 **TORNEQUETA MAY** (GB) 14
168 **TORO DORADO** (GB) 52
35 **TOROCHICA** (GB) 29
298 **TOROLIGHT** (GB) 50
221 **TORONTO SOUND** (GB) 30
100 **TOROSAY CASTLE** (GB) 27
550 **TORPILLO** (FR) 99
603 **TORQUE OF THE TOWN** (IRE) 15
266 **TORREADOR** (GB) 118
116 **TORRENT DES MOTTES** (FR) 3
175 **TORRID** (GB) 53
194 **TORTUGA BAY** (GB) 40
487 **TORVER** (GB) G 6
119 **TOSCA** (GER) F 55
522 **TOSHIMA** (IRE) 22
574 **TOTAL ASSETS** (GB) 14
106 **TOTAL COMMITMENT** (IRE) 60
263 **TOTAL PERFECTION** (GB) 241
407 **TOTAL RECALL** (IRE) 185
257 **TOTAL RECHARGE** (IRE) 50
50 **TOTAL RETHINK** (IRE) 147
585 **TOTALLY MAGIC** (IRE) 7
446 **TOTTERDOWN** (GB) 25
399 **TOTTIE** (GB) F 75
183 **TOUCH BASE** (IRE) 166
419 **TOUCH KICK** (IRE) 148
234 **TOUCH SCREEN** (IRE) 15
478 **TOUCHEDBYANANGEL** (IRE) 89
374 **TOUCHING** (IRE) C 11
141 **TOUCHY SUBJECT** (IRE) 13
133 **TOUGH REMEDY** (IRE) 66
410 **TOUR DE FORCE** (GB) 94
327 **TOUR DE PARIS** (IRE) 140
318 **TOURNER** (USA) F 236
379 **TOUT EST PERMIS** (FR) 116
431 **TOUT POUR TOI** (FR) 93
525 **TOUTATIS** (USA) 152
438 **TOWARDS THE DAWN** (GB) 80

256 **TOWER OF ALLEN** (IRE) 35
550 **TOWER VIEW** (IRE) 100
259 **TOWERBURN** (IRE) 10
175 **TOWN HEAD** (GB) 54
340 **TOWN PARKS** (IRE) 34
550 **TOWNSHEND** (GER) 101
6 **TOY THEATRE** (GB) 72
450 **TOYBOX** (GB) 30
223 **TRABREGA BAY** (IRE) G 77
124 **TRACHELIUM** (GB) 106
424 **TRACING** (IRE) 101
50 **TRACKER SAGA** (IRE) 55
76 **TRACTOR FRED** (IRE) 3
563 **TRADE TALKS** (GB) 11
263 **TRADING PLACES** (GB) F 242
50 **TRADING UP** (IRE) 148
307 **TRADITIONAL DANCER** (IRE) 45
176 **TRADITIONELLE** (GB) F 176
393 **TRAFFIC FLUIDE** (IRE) 123
499 **TRAFFIC SISTER** (USA) C 104
554 **TRAILBOSS** (IRE) 6
547 **TRAIN TO GEORGIA** (USA) 31
278 **TRALEE HILLS** (GB) 8
576 **TRANCHEE** (IRE) 78
329 **TRANS DES OBEAUX** (GB) 66
229 **TRANS EXPRESS** (IRE) 14
156 **TRANSPENNINE GOLD** (GB) 43
431 **TRANSPENNINE STAR** (GB) 94
124 **TRAPEZE** (GB) G 61
324 **TRAPPER PEAK** (IRE) 16
379 **TRAPPIST MONK** (IRE) 117
26 **TRAPPIST ONE** (IRE) 40
383 **TRAUTMANN** (IRE) 44
176 **TRAVEL LIGHTLY** (GB) 87
239 **TRAVEL ON** (GB) 136
352 **TRAVEL PLANS** (USA) G 34
68 **TRAVELLER** (FR) 18
95 **TRAVELLERS JOY** (GB) 66
431 **TRAVERTINE** (IRE) 95
208 **TRAVIS BICKLE** (IRE) 27
108 **TRAWANGANE** (FR) 6
146 **TREACHEROUS** (GB) 22
350 **TREACKLE TART** (IRE) 56
280 **TREACY HOTELS BOY** (IRE) 29
593 **TREASURE DILLON** (IRE) 73
203 **TREASURE ME** (GB) 16
381 **TREASURE QUEST** (GB) 36
394 **TREASURE THE LADY** (IRE) C 3
253 **TREASURED COMPANY** (IRE) 1
438 **TREATY GIRL** (IRE) 81
399 **TREATY OF DINGLE** (GB) 76
97 **TREBLE CLEF** (GB) 10
335 **TREBUJENA** (IRE) 35
340 **TREE OF LIBERTY** (IRE) 35
29 **TREFOIL** (GB) 139
545 **TRELINNEY** (FR) 31
490 **TRENCH BOX** (IRE) 36
604 **TRENDY NURSE** (IRE) 11
457 **TRENTINI** (IRE) C 68
120 **TREORCHY** (GB) 73
510 **TRESHNISH** (FR) 54
266 **TRETHIAS** (IRE) 119
419 **TREVELYN'S CORN** (IRE) 149
504 **TREVITHICK** (GB) 18
133 **TRIANGLE ROCK** (IRE) 67
594 **TRIBAL COMMANDER** (GB) 139
16 **TRIBAL CRAFT** (GB) 129
530 **TRIBAL WARRIOR** (GB) 8

53 **UNDERCOLOURS** (IRE) 65
17 **UNDERCOVER BROTHER** (GB) 8
370 **UNDERSTORY** (USA) 1
194 **UNDISPUTED** (FR) 42
255 **UNDRESS** (IRE) F 192
407 **UNDRESSED** (FR) 189
379 **UNE LAVANDIERE** (FR) 119
131 **UNFORGIVING MINUTE** (GB) 14
298 **UNFORTUNATE** (GB) F 92
156 **UNIFIER** (GB) 62
394 **UNION CITY BLUES** (IRE) F 35
379 **UNION GAP** (IRE) 120
269 **UNION ROSE** (GB) 33
419 **UNIONISTE** (FR) 151
537 **UNIQUE COMPANY** (IRE) 17
490 **UNISON** (FR) 37
332 **UNIT OF ASSESSMENT** (IRE) 15
540 **UNITE THE CLANS** (IRE) 28
436 **UNITY** (IRE) F 112
30 **UNIVERSAL CIRCUS** (GB) C 103
337 **UNIVERSAL EFFECT** (GB) 22
133 **UNIVERSAL GLEAM** (GB) 68
499 **UNIVERSAL ORDER** (GB) 64
406 **UNIVERSAL SONG** (IRE) 47
266 **UNKNOWN PLEASURES** (IRE) 161
591 **UNO MAS** (GB) 17
560 **UNO VALOROSO** (FR) 24
43 **UNONOTHINJONSNOW** (GB) 3
223 **UNOWHATIMEANHARRY** (GB) 78
16 **UNPLUGGED** (IRE) 131
394 **UNREAL** (GB) G 36
119 **UNRESTRAINED** (GB) 78
542 **UNSAFE CONDUCT** (GB) 109
60 **UNSUSPECTED GIRL** (IRE) 14
520 **UNTIL MIDNIGHT** (IRE) 7
391 **UNWANTED BEAUTY** (IRE) 23
77 **UNWIN VC** (GB) 13
449 **UNZING** (FR) 15
424 **UP** (IRE) C 190
548 **UP AND RUNNING** (GB) C 23
407 **UP FOR REVIEW** (IRE) 190
1 **UP HELLY AA KING** (GB) 45
499 **UP IN TIME** (GB) F 105
175 **UP TEN DOWN TWO** (IRE) 56
500 **UP THE DRIVE** (IRE) 168
50 **UP WITH THE PLAY** (IRE) 149
266 **UP'N'OVER** (IRE) 75
9 **UPAVON** (GB) 67
263 **UPDATED** (FR) F 243
76 **UPHAM RUNNING** (IRE) 4
408 **UPONASTAR** (IRE) 51
369 **UPPERTOWN PRINCE** (IRE) 119
369 **UPSETTHEODDS** (IRE) 120
23 **UPSIDE** (GB) 25
471 **UPSILON BLEU** (FR) 7
603 **UPSTAGING** (GB) 12
133 **UPTOWN FUNK** (IRE) 69
566 **UPTOWN HARRY** (IRE) 5
407 **URADEL** (GB) 191
407 **URANO** (FR) 17
65 **URANUS DES BORDES** (FR) 35
266 **URBAN DAYDREAM** (IRE) F 162
95 **URBAN HIGHWAY** (IRE) 80
263 **URBAN ICON** (GB) 99
478 **URBAN KODE** (IRE) 90
203 **URBAN SCENE** (GB) 49
404 **URBAN SPIRIT** (IRE) 11
416 **URBANIST** (IRE) 48

295 **URCA DE LIMA** (GB) 38
508 **URIAH HEEP** (FR) 23
82 **UROOBAH** (USA) C 85
108 **URSUS ARCTOS** (IRE) 42
490 **URTHEONETHATIWANT** (IRE) 38
489 **USAIN BOAT** (IRE) 25
434 **USANECOLT** (IRE) 53
100 **USHINDI** (IRE) C 147
82 **USTATH** (GB) 50
410 **UT LOVE** (FR) G 95
136 **UT MAJEUR AULMES** (FR) 18
394 **UTHER PENDRAGON** (FR) 5
65 **UTILITY** (GB) 26
318 **UTRECHT** (GB) C 238
268 **VA'VITE** (IRE) C 17
268 **VA'VITE** (IRE) G 16
477 **VADAVAR** (FR) 11
334 **VADO FORTE** (FR) 32
26 **VADROUILLEUR** (FR) 41
318 **VAGUELY FAMILIAR** (USA) C 239
103 **VAIANA** (USA) 64
100 **VAILLANCE** (GB) 29
327 **VAIN GIRL** (GB) 141
16 **VAKILITA** (IRE) 132
369 **VAL MOME** (FR) 121
288 **VALADOM** (FR) 14
5 **VALAIS GIRL** (GB) F 176
379 **VALANDRAUD** (IRE) C 12
410 **VALDAS PRINCESS** (GB) 96
327 **VALDEZ** (GB) 142
379 **VALDIEU** (FR) 121
318 **VALE OF KENT** (IRE) 33
168 **VALENCE** (GB) 54
510 **VALENCE D'AUMONT** (FR) 56
401 **VALENTINA GUEST** (IRE) G 13
434 **VALENTINE BLUES** (IRE) 92
242 **VALENTINE MIST** (IRE) 4
239 **VALENTINE'S DAY** (IRE) 138
37 **VALENTINO BOY** (IRE) 7
100 **VALENTINO SUNRISE** (GB) 77
477 **VALEYA** (FR) 50
261 **VALGOR DU RONCERAY** (FR) 71
542 **VALHALLA** (IRE) 110
457 **VALIANTLY** (GB) F 69
497 **VALJAN** (GB) 46
133 **VALKENBURG** (GB) 70
255 **VALLADO** (IRE) F 193
93 **VALLARTA** (IRE) 46
201 **VALLETTA SUNSET** (GB) 32
371 **VALLEY BELLE** (IRE) 19
407 **VALLEY BREEZE** (FR) 193
41 **VALLEY MIST** (GB) 180
195 **VALLEY OF FIRE** (GB) 1
369 **VALLEYOFMILAN** (IRE) 122
428 **VALMARI** (IRE) F 93
428 **VALMARI** (GB) G 122
199 **VALSE AU TAILLONS** (IRE) 31
232 **VALSEUR DU GRANVAL** (FR) 78
611 **VALSHAN TIME** (FR) 12
279 **VALTOR** (FR) 158
500 **VALUE AT RISK** (IRE) 169
165 **VALUE CHAIN** (GB) 11
410 **VAMANOS** (GB) 97
368 **VAMPISH** (GB) 3
424 **VAN BEETHOVEN** (CAN) 104
518 **VAN DIEST** (GB) 22
195 **VAN GERWEN** (GB) 18
477 **VANANNDI** (GB) 51

284 **VANBRUGH** (USA) 25
403 **VANCOUVER** (GB) 100
239 **VANDELLA** (IRE) 139
234 **VANDERBILT** (IRE) 16
286 **VANGO DE VAIGE** (FR) 96
270 **VANILLA BREEZE** (GB) 11
108 **VANILLA GOLD** (IRE) 43
124 **VANISHING GREY** (IRE) C 109
318 **VANITY RULES** (GB) C 240
5 **VANITY RULES** (GB) C 83
110 **VANITY VANITY** (USA) 15
120 **VANITY'S GIRL** (IRE) C 111
243 **VANITYCASE** (IRE) C 20
29 **VAPE** (GB) 140
477 **VARANA** (FR) F 77
19 **VARDS** (GB) 25
315 **VARIOUS** (IRE) 81
477 **VARIYANN** (FR) 52
137 **VARNAY** (GB) C 89
530 **VARSITY** (GB) F 91
243 **VARTANO** (IRE) 4
525 **VASARI** (USA) 153
69 **VASCO D'YCY** (FR) 11
120 **VASILIEV** (GB) 75
263 **VASSARIA** (IRE) C 244
553 **VAST** (GB) 119
255 **VASTITAS** (IRE) C 194
328 **VAXALCO** (FR) 34
561 **VAZIANI** (FR) 18
477 **VAZIRA** (FR) C 78
477 **VAZIRABAD** (FR) 12
470 **VEDA** (FR) F 79
225 **VEE MAN TEN** (GB) 56
480 **VEGA MAGIC** (IRE) 113
255 **VEGA'S ANGEL** (GB) 195
279 **VEGAS BLUE** (IRE) 159
434 **VEGAS BOY** (IRE) 24
5 **VEIL OF SILENCE** (IRE) F 177
148 **VEILED SECRET** (IRE) 39
183 **VEINARD** (FR) 169
120 **VELETA** (GB) 112
560 **VELLENA** (GB) G 40
197 **VELMA** (GB) 11
110 **VELMA KELLY** (GB) G 22
5 **VELORUM** (GB) 84
585 **VELVET BAND** (GB) F 14
332 **VELVET MORN** (GB) 16
544 **VELVET VISION** (GB) 7
544 **VELVET VISTA** (GB) 18
297 **VELVET VIXEN** (GB) 26
544 **VELVET VOICE** (GB) 8
303 **VENA D'AMORE** (IRE) 49
510 **VENDOR** (FR) 57
338 **VENDREDI TROIS** (FR) 61
168 **VENEDEGAR** (IRE) 55
464 **VENETIAN LASS** (GB) G 9
143 **VENETIAN PROPOSAL** (IRE) 19
478 **VENGEUR DE GUYE** (FR) 91
407 **VENT D'AUTOMNE** (FR) 194
181 **VENT DE FORCE** (FR) 16
26 **VENT MARIN** (FR) 42
158 **VENTRILOQUIST** (GB) 18
196 **VENTURA BAY** (FR) 136
170 **VENTURA BLUES** (IRE) 45
497 **VENTURA DRAGON** (IRE) 47
263 **VENTURA GLORY** (GB) 100
196 **VENTURA GOLD** (IRE) 62
263 **VENTURA ISLAND** (FR) 101

LATE ENTRIES

MR ARTHUR MOORE, Naas

Postal: **Dereens, Naas, Co. Kildare, Ireland**
Contacts: PHONE **(00353) 4587 6292** MOBILE **(00353) 8725 52535**
E-MAIL arthurlmoore@eircom.net

   1 **AT YOUR EASE (IRE)**, 6, b g Scorpion (IRE)—Victoria Bridge (IRE) **Mr J. P. McManus**
   2 **CONNARD (IRE)**, 6, b g Shantou (USA)—Sparkling Sword **R. Bartlett**
   3 **CROSSED MY MIND (IRE)**, 7, b g Beneficial—Coolvane (IRE) **Mr J. P. McManus**
   4 4, B g Arcadio (GER)—Dancerfromthedance (IRE) **Mrs A. L. T. Moore**
   5 **FAG AN BEALACH (IRE)**, 5, b m Stowaway—Market Niche (IRE) **Mrs A. L. T. Moore**
   6 **GENTLEMAN DUKE (IRE)**, 11, b g Bachelor Duke (USA)—Housekeeping **Mr J. P. McManus**
   7 **JAIL BOREEN (IRE)**, 5, ch g Presenting—Pop Princess **Mr J. P. McManus**
   8 **KING CON (FR)**, 4, ch g Rio de La Plata (USA)—Ionia (IRE) **Mrs A. L. T. Moore**
   9 **MIDLAND MILLIE (IRE)**, 5, b m Kalanisi (IRE)—Cave Woman (IRE) **A. Trappe**
  10 4, B g Milan—No Time For Tears (IRE) **Mrs A. L. T. Moore**
  11 **ORGANISED SOLUTION (FR)**, 5, b g Azamour (IRE)—Phille Phuong (USA) **Mrs A. L. T. Moore**
  12 **STAY ONBOARD (IRE)**, 4, br g Jeremy (USA)—Keep The Grip (IRE) **Mrs M. Ryan**
  13 **THE PRIESTS LEAP (IRE)**, 5, ch g Flemensfirth (USA)—Castlekelly Girl (IRE) **D. Ducken**
  14 **WHATS THE PLOT (IRE)**, 7, b g Alfred Nobel (IRE)—Hazarama (IRE) **D. Jones**

THREE-YEAR-OLDS

  15 B g Makfi—Sanaya (IRE) **Mrs A. L. T. Moore**
  16 B g Sea The Moon (GER)—Swarm (IRE) **J. D. Moore**

TWO-YEAR-OLDS

  17 B c 23/2 French Navy—Hannah's Magic (IRE) (Lomitas) (6741) **Mrs A. L. T. Moore**

Assistant Trainer: J. D. Moore

Jockey (NH): N. P. Madden, D. Meyler.

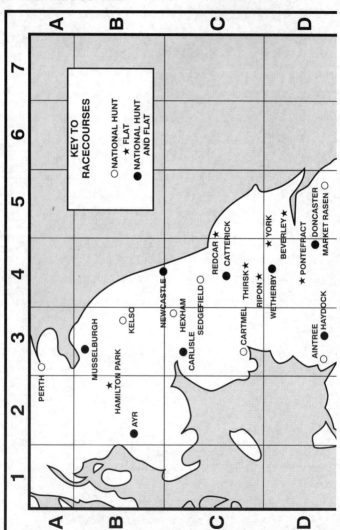

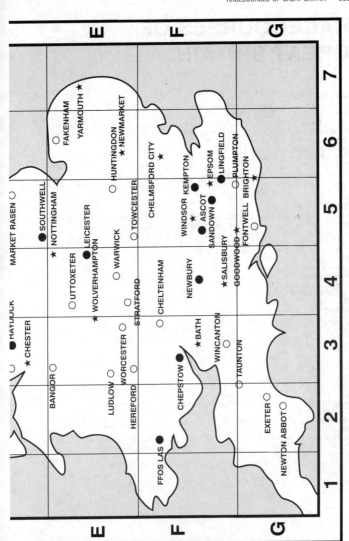

RACECOURSES OF GREAT BRITAIN

AINTREE (L.H)

Grand National Course: Triangular, 2m2f (16 fences) 494y run-in with elbow. Perfectly flat. A severe test for both horse and rider, putting a premium on jumping ability, fitness and courage.
Mildmay Course: Rectangular, 1m4f (8) 260y run-in. A very fast, flat course with sharp bends.
Address: Aintree Racecourse, Ormskirk Road, Aintree, Liverpool, L9 5AS Tel: 0151 523 2600
Website: www.aintree.co.uk
Managing Director: John Baker
Clerk of the Course: Andrew Tulloch 07831 315104
By Road: North of the City, near the junction of the M57 and M58 with the A59 (Preston).
By Rail: Aintree Station is adjacent to the Stands, from Liverpool Central.
By Air: Liverpool (John Lennon) Airport is 10 miles. Helicopter landing facility by prior arrangement.

ASCOT (R.H)

Flat: Right-handed triangular track just under 1m6f in length. The Round course descends from the 1m4f start into Swinley Bottom, the lowest part of the track. It then turns right-handed and joins the Old Mile Course, which starts on a separate chute. The course then rises to the right-handed home turn over an underpass to join the straight mile course. The run-in is about 3f, rising slightly to the winning post. The whole course is of a galloping nature with easy turns.
N.H. Triangular, 1m6f (10), 240y run-in mostly uphill. A galloping course with an uphill finish, Ascot provides a real test of stamina. The fences are stiff and sound jumping is essential, especially for novices.
Address: Ascot Racecourse, Ascot, Berkshire SL5 7JX Tel: 08707 271234
Website: www.ascot.co.uk
Clerk of the Course: Chris Stickels 01344 878502 / 07970 621440
Chief Executive: Guy Henderson
By Road: West of the town on the A329. Easy access from the M3 (Junction 3) and the M4 (Junction 6). Car parking adjoining the course and Ascot Heath.
By Rail: Regular service from Waterloo to Ascot (500y from the racecourse).
By Air: Helicopter landing facility at the course. London (Heathrow) Airport 15 miles, White Waltham Airfield 12 miles (01427) 718800.

AYR (L.H)

Flat: A left-handed, galloping, flat oval track of 1m4f with a 4f run-in. The straight 6f is essentially flat.
N.H. Oval, 1m4f (9), 210y run-in. Relatively flat and one of the fastest tracks in Great Britain. It is a well-drained course and the ground rarely becomes testing. The track suits the long-striding galloper.
Address: Ayr Racecourse, Whitletts Road, Ayr, KA8 0JE Tel: 01292 264179
Website: www.ayr-racecourse.co.uk
Clerk of the Course: Graeme Anderson
Managing Director: David Brown
By Road: East of the town on the A758. Free parking for buses and cars.
By Rail: Ayr Station (trains on the half hour from Glasgow Central). Journey time 55 minutes. Buses and taxis also to the course.
By Air: Prestwick International Airport (10 minutes), Glasgow Airport (1 hour).

BANGOR-ON-DEE (L.H)

N.H. Circular, 1m4f (9), 325y run-in. Apart from some 'ridge and furrow', this is a flat course notable for three sharp bends, especially the paddock turn. Suits handy, speedy sorts.
Address: Bangor-On-Dee Racecourse, Overton Road, Bangor-On-Dee, Wrexham, LL13 0DA
Tel: 01978 782081
Website: www.bangorondeeraces.co.uk
Racecourse Manager and Clerk of the Course and Racing Manager: Andrew Morris
Chief Executive: Richard Thomas
General Manager: Jeannie Chantler
By Road: 5 miles south-east of Wrexham, off the B5069.
By Rail: Wrexham Station (bus or taxi to the course).
By Air: Helicopters may land by prior arrangement with Clerk of the Course.

BATH (L.H)

Flat: Galloping, left-handed, level oval of 1m4f, with long, stiff run-in of about 4f which bends to the left. An extended chute provides for sprint races.
Address: The Racecourse, Lansdown, Bath, BA1 9BU Tel: 01225 424609
Website: www.bath-racecourse.co.uk
Clerk of the Course: Katie Stephens
Executive Director: Jo Hall
By Road: 2 miles northwest of the City (M4 Junction 18) at Lansdown. Unlimited free car and coach parking immediately behind the stands. Special bus services operate from Bath to the racecourse.
By Rail: Bath Station (from Paddington).
By Air: Bristol or Colerne Airports. Helicopter landing facilities available by prior arrangement.

BEVERLEY (R.H)

Flat: A right-handed oval of 1m3f, generally galloping, with an uphill run-in of two and a half furlongs. The 5f course is very stiff.
Address: Beverley Race Co. Ltd., York Road, Beverley, Yorkshire HU17 9QZ Tel: 01482 867488 / 882645
Website: www.beverley-racecourse.co.uk
Chief Executive and Clerk of the Course: Sally Iggulden 07850 458605
By Road: 7 miles from the M62 (Junction 38) off the A1035. Free car parking opposite the course. Owners and trainers use a separate enclosure.
By Rail: Beverley Station (Hull-Scarborough line). Occasional bus service to the course (1 mile).

BRIGHTON (L.H)

Flat: Left-handed, 1m4f horseshoe with easy turns and a run-in of three and a half furlongs. Undulating and sharp, the track suits handy types.
Address: Brighton Racecourse, Brighton, East Sussex BN2 2XZ Tel: 01273 603580
Website: www.brighton-racecourse.co.uk
Clerk of the Course: Philip Hide
Executive Director: Paul Ellison
By Road: East of the city on the A27 (Lewes Road). Car park adjoins the course.
By Rail: Brighton Station (from Victoria on the hour, London Bridge or Portsmouth). Special bus service to the course from the station (approx 2 miles).
By Air: Helicopters may land by prior arrangement.

CARLISLE (R.H)

Flat: Right-handed, 1m4f pear-shaped track. Galloping and undulating with easy turns and a stiff uphill run-in of three and a half furlongs. The 6f course begins on an extended chute.
N.H. Pear-shaped, 1m5f (9), 300y run-in uphill. Undulating and a stiff test of stamina, ideally suited to the long-striding thorough stayer.
Address: Carlisle Racecourse, Durdar Road, Carlisle CA2 4TS Tel: 01228 554700
Website: www.carlisle-races.co.uk
Regional Director: Dickon White
Clerk of the Course: Andrew Tulloch
General Manager: Molly Dingwald
By Road: 2 miles south of the city (Durdar Road). Easy access from the M6 (Junction 42). The car park is free (adjacent to the course).
By Rail: Carlisle Station (2 miles from the course).
By Air: Helicopter landing facility by prior arrangement.

CARTMEL (L.H)

N.H. Oval, 1m1f (6), 800y run-in. Almost perfectly flat but very sharp, with the longest run-in in the country, approximately half a mile. The fences are stiff but fair.
Address: Cartmel Racecourse, Cartmel, nr Grange-Over-Sands, Cumbria LA11 6QF Tel: 01539 536340
Out of season: 01539 533335
Website: www.cartmel-racecourse.co.uk
Managing Director: Stephen Cooper
Clerk of the Course: Anthea Morshead 07837 559861
By Road: 1 mile west of the town, 2 miles off the B5277 (Grange-Haverthwaite road). M6 (Junction 36).
By Rail: Cark-in-Cartmel Station (2 miles) (Carnforth-Barrow line). Raceday bus service.
By Air: Light aircraft facilities available at Cark Airport (4 miles from the course). Helicopter landing facility at the course, by prior arrangement only.

CATTERICK (L.H)

Flat: A sharp, left-handed, undulating oval of 1m180y with a downhill run-in of 3f.
N.H. Oval, 1m1f (9), 240y run-in. Undulating, sharp track that favours the handy, front-running sort, rather than the long-striding galloper.
Address: The Racecourse, Catterick Bridge, Richmond, North Yorkshire DL10 7PE Tel: 01748 811478
Website: www.catterickbridge.co.uk
General Manager and Clerk of the Course: Fiona Needham 07831 688625
By Road: The course is adjacent to the A1, 1 mile northwest of the town on the A6136. There is a free car park.
By Rail: Darlington Station (special buses to course - 14-mile journey).
By Air: Helicopters can land by prior arrangement. Fixed wing planes contact RAF Leeming
Tel: 01677 423041

CHELMSFORD CITY (L.H)

Flat: A left-handed, floodlit Polytrack oval of 1m with sweeping bends and a 2f home straight. Races over 7f and 1m start from separate chutes.
Address: Chelmsford City Racecourse, Great Leighs, Essex, CM3 1QP Tel: 01245 362412
Website: www.chelmsfordcityracecourse.com
Manager: Fraser Garrity
Clerk of the Course: Andy Waitt
By Road: At Great Leighs, five miles north of Chelmsford on the A31
By Rail: Chelmsford station (from Liverpool Street)
By Air: Stansted Airport (17 miles)

CHELTENHAM (L.H)

Old Course: Oval, 1m4f, (9) 350y run-in. A testing, undulating track with stiff fences. The ability to stay is essential.

New Course: Oval, 1m5f (10), 220y run-in. Undulating, stiff fences, testing course, uphill for the final half-mile.

Address: Cheltenham Racecourse, Prestbury Park, Cheltenham, Gloucestershire GL50 4SH

Tel: 01242 513014

Website: www.cheltenham.co.uk

Regional Director: Ian Renton

Regional Head of Racing and Clerk of the Course: Simon Claisse 07785 293966

By Road: 1.5 miles north of the town on the A435. M5 (Junction 10 or 11).

By Rail: Cheltenham Spa Station. Buses and taxis to course.

By Air: Helicopter landing site to the northeast of the stands.

CHEPSTOW (L.H)

Flat: A left-handed, undulating oval of about 2m, with easy turns, and a straight run-in of 5f. There is a straight track of 1m14y.

N.H. Oval, 2m (11), 240y run-in. Many changing gradients, five fences in the home straight. Favours the long-striding front-runner, but stamina is important.

Address: Chepstow Racecourse, Chepstow, Monmouthshire NP16 6BE Tel: 01291 622260

Website: www.chepstow-racecourse.co.uk

General Manager: Caroline Williams

Clerk of the Course: Libby O'Flaherty 07970 831987

Executive Director: Phil Bell

By Road: 1 mile north-west of the town on the A466. (1 mile from Junction 22 of the M4 (Severn Bridge) or M48 Junction 2. There is a free public car park opposite the entrance.

By Rail: Chepstow Station (from Paddington, change at Gloucester or Newport). The course is a mile from the station.

By Air: Helicopter landing facility in the centre of the course.

CHESTER (L.H)

Flat: A level, sharp, left-handed, circular course of 1m73y, with a short run-in of 230y. Chester is a specialists' track which generally suits the sharp-actioned horse.

Address: The Racecourse, Chester CH1 2LY Tel: 01244 304600

Website: www.chester-races.co.uk

Racecourse Manager and Clerk of the Course: Andrew Morris

Chief Executive: Richard Thomas

By Road: The course is near the centre of the city on the A548 (Queensferry Road). The Owners' and Trainers' car park is adjacent to the Leverhulme Stand. There is a public car park in the centre of the course.

By Rail: Chester Station (¾ mile from the course). Services from Euston, Paddington and Northgate.

By Air: Hawarden Airport (2 miles). Helicopters are allowed to land on the racecourse by prior arrangement only.

DONCASTER (L.H)

Flat: A left-handed, flat, galloping course of 1m7f 110y, with a long run-in which extends to a straight mile.

N.H. Conical, 2m (11), 247y run-in. A very fair, flat track ideally suited to the long-striding galloper.

Address: Doncaster Racecourse, Leger Way, Doncaster, DN2 6BB Tel: 01302 304200

Website: www.doncaster-racecourse.co.uk

Clerk of the Course: Roderick Duncan 07772 958685

Executive Director: Russell Smith

By Road: East of the town, off the A638 (M18 Junctions 3 and 4). Club members' car park reserved. Large public car park free and adjacent to the course.

By Rail: Doncaster Central Station (from King's Cross). Special bus service from the station (1 mile).

By Air: Helicopter landing facility by prior arrangement only. Doncaster Robin Hood Airport is 15 minutes from the racecourse.

EPSOM (L.H)

Flat: Left-handed and undulating with easy turns, and a run-in of just under 4f. The straight 5f course is also undulating and downhill all the way, making it the fastest 5f in the world.
Address: The Racecourse, Epsom Downs, Surrey KT18 5LQ Tel: 01372 726311
Website: www.epsomderby.co.uk
Regional Director: Phil White
Clerk of the Course: Andrew Cooper Tel: 01372 726311 Mobile: 07774 230850
General Manager: Simon Durrant
By Road: Two miles south of the town on the B290 (M25 Junctions 8 and 9). For full car park particulars apply to: The Club Secretary, Epsom Grandstand, Epsom Downs, Surrey KT18 5LQ. Tel: 01372 726311
By Rail: Epsom, Epsom Downs or Tattenham Corner Stations (trains from London Bridge, Waterloo, Victoria). Regular bus services run to the course from Epsom and Morden Underground Station.
By Air: London (Heathrow) and London (Gatwick) are both within 30 miles of the course.
Heliport (Derby Meeting only) - apply to Hascombe Aviation. Tel: 01279 680291.

EXETER (R.H)

N.H. Oval, 2m (11), 300y run-in uphill. Undulating with a home straight of half a mile. A good test of stamina, suiting the handy, well-balanced sort.
Address: Exeter Racecourse, Kennford, Exeter, Devon EX6 7XS Tel: 01392 832599
Website: www.exeter-racecourse.co.uk
Regional Director: Ian Renton
Clerk of the Course: Barry Johnson 07976 791578
General Manager: Jack Parkinson
By Road: The course is at Haldon, 5 miles south-west of Exeter on the A38 (Plymouth) road, 2 miles east of Chudleigh.
By Rail: Exeter (St Davids) Station. Free bus service to course.
By Air: Helicopters can land by prior arrangement.

FAKENHAM (L.H)

N.H. Square, 1m (6), 200y run-in. On the turn almost throughout and undulating, suiting the handy front-runner. The going rarely becomes heavy.
Address: The Racecourse, Fakenham, Norfolk NR21 7NY Tel: 01328 862388
Website: www.fakenhamracecourse.co.uk
Clerk of the Course and Chief Executive: David Hunter Tel: 01328 862388 Mobile: 07767 802206
By Road: A mile south of the town on the B1146 (East Dereham) road.
By Rail: Norwich Station (26 miles) (Liverpool Street line), King's Lynn (22 miles)
(Liverpool Street/Kings Cross).
By Air: Helicopter landing facility in the centre of the course by prior arrangement only.

FFOS LAS (L.H)

Flat The track is a 60m wide, basically flat, 1m4f oval with sweeping bends. Races over 5f and 6f start on a chute.
N.H. A flat, 1m4f oval (9). The going is often testing which places the emphasis on stamina.
Address: Ffos Las Racecourse, Trimsaran, Carmarthenshire SA17 4DE Tel: 01554 811092
Website: www.ffoslasracecourse.com
Executive Director: Phil Bell
General Manager: Simon Rowlands
Clerk of the Course: Tim Long
By Road: From the east take J48 from the M4 and join the A4138 to Llanelli, then follow the brown tourist signs to the racecourse. From the west take the A48 to Carmarthen then the A484 to Kidwelly before following the brown signs.
By Air: The course has the facilities to land helicopters on race days.

FONTWELL PARK (Fig. 8)

N.H. 2m (7), 230y run-in with left-hand bend close home. The figure-of-eight chase course suits handy types and is something of a specialists' track. The left-handed hurdle course is oval and one mile round. The bottom bend, which is shared, has been converted to Fibresand.

Address: Fontwell Park Racecourse, nr Arundel, West Sussex BN18 0SX Tel: 01243 543335
Website: www.fontwellpark.co.uk
Clerk of the Course: Philip Hide
Executive Director and General Manager: Jonathan Acott
By Road: South of village at the junction of the A29 (Bognor) and A27 (Brighton-Chichester) roads.
By Rail: Barnham Station (2 miles). Brighton-Portsmouth line (access via London Victoria).
By Air: Helicopter landing facility by prior arrangement with the Clerk of the Course.

GOODWOOD (R.H)

Flat: A sharp, undulating, essentially right-handed track with a long run-in. There is also a straight 6f course.

Address: Goodwood Racecourse Ltd., Goodwood, Chichester, West Sussex PO18 0PX Tel: 01243 755022
Website: www.goodwood.co.uk
Managing Director: Adam Waterworth
General Manager: Alex Eade
Clerk of the Course: Ed Arkell
By Road: 6 miles north of Chichester between the A286 and A285. There is a car park adjacent to the course. Ample free car and coach parking.
By Rail: Chichester Station (from Victoria or London Bridge). Regular bus service to the course (6 miles).
By Air: Helicopter landing facility by prior arrangement 01243 755030. Goodwood Airport 2 miles (taxi to the course).

HAMILTON PARK (R.H)

Flat: A sharp, undulating, right-handed course of 1m5f with a five and a half-furlong, uphill run-in. There is a straight track of 6f.

Address: Hamilton Park Racecourse, Bothwell Road, Hamilton, Lanarkshire ML3 0DW Tel: 01698 283806
Website: www.hamilton-park.co.uk
Racing Manager and Clerk of the Course: Sulekha Varma
Chief Executive: Vivien Currie 01698 283806
By Road: Off the A72 on the B7071 (Hamilton-Bothwell road). (M74 Junction 5). Free parking for cars and buses.
By Rail: Hamilton West Station (1 mile).
By Air: Glasgow Airport (20 miles).

HAYDOCK PARK (L.H)

Flat: A galloping, almost flat, oval track, 1m5f round, with a run-in of four and a half furlongs and a straight six-furlong course.
N.H. Oval, 1m5f (10), 440y run-in. A flat, galloping chase course using portable fences. The hurdles track, which is sharp, is inside the chase course and has some tight bends.

Address: Haydock Park Racecourse, Newton-le-Willows, Merseyside WA12 0HQ Tel: 01942 402609
Website: www.haydock-park.co.uk
Regional Director: Dickon White
Regional Head of Racing and Clerk of the Course: Kirkland Tellwright 01942 725963 or 07748 181595
By Road: The course is on the A49 near Junction 23 of the M6.
By Rail: Newton-le-Willows Station (Manchester-Liverpool line) is 2.5 miles from the course. Earlstown 3 miles from the course. Warrington Bank Quay and Wigan are on the London to Carlisle/Glasgow line.
By Air: Landing facilities in the centre of the course for helicopters and planes not exceeding 10,000lbs laden weight.

HEREFORD (R.H)

N.H. Square, 1m4f (9), 300y run-in. The turns, apart from the final one that is on falling ground, are easily negotiated, placing the emphasis on speed rather than stamina. A handy position round the home turn is vital, as winners rarely come from behind. The hurdle track is on the outside of the chase course.
Address: Hereford Racecourse, Roman Road, Holmer, Hereford, HR4 9QU Tel: (01432) 273560
Website: www.hereford-racecourse.co.uk
Executive Director: Rebecca Davies
Clerk of the Course: Tim Long
By Road: 1 mile north-west of the city centre off the A49 (Leominster) road.
By Rail: Hereford Station (1 mile from the course).

HEXHAM (L.H)

N.H. Oval, 1m4f (10), 220y run-in. An undulating course that becomes very testing when the ground is soft; it has easy fences and a stiff climb to the finishing straight, which is on a separate spur.
Address: Hexham Racecourse, The Riding, Hexham, Northumberland NE46 2JP Tel: 01434 606881
Racedays: 01434 603738
Website: www.hexham-racecourse.co.uk
Chief Executive: Robert Whitelock
Clerk of the Course: James Armstrong 01434 606881 or 07801 166820
By Road: 1.5 miles south-west of the town off the B6305.
By Rail: Hexham Station (Newcastle-Carlisle line). Free bus to the course.
By Air: Helicopter landing facility in centre of course (by special arrangement only).

HUNTINGDON (R.H)

N.H. Oval, 1m4f (9), 200y run-in. A perfectly flat, galloping track with a tricky open ditch in front of the stands. The two fences in the home straight can cause problems for novice chasers. Suits front-runners.
Address: The Racecourse, Brampton, Huntingdon, Cambridgeshire PE28 4NL Tel: 01480 453373
Website: www.huntingdon-racecourse.co.uk
Regional Director: Amy Starkey
Clerk of the Course: Jack Pryor
General Manager: Liam Johnson
By Road: The course is situated at Brampton, 2 miles west of Huntingdon on the A14. Easy access from the A1 (½ mile from the course).
By Rail: Huntingdon Station. Buses and taxis to course.
By Air: Helicopter landing facility by prior arrangement.

KELSO (L.H)

N.H. Oval, 1m1f (8), uphill run-in of just over a furlong. Rather undulating with two downhill fences opposite the stands, it suits the nippy, front-running sort, though the uphill finish helps the true stayer. The hurdle course is smaller and very sharp with a tight turn away from the stands.
Address: Kelso Racecourse, Kelso, Roxburghshire TD5 7SX Tel: 01668 280800
Website: www.kelso-races.co.uk
Clerk of the Course: Anthea Morshead
Managing Director: Jonathan Garratt
By Road: 1 mile north of the town, off the B6461.
By Rail: Berwick-upon-Tweed Station. 23-mile bus journey to Kelso.
By Air: Helicopters can land at course by arrangement, fixed wing aircraft at Winfield, regular aircraft at Edinburgh.

KEMPTON PARK (R.H)

Flat: A floodlit Polytrack circuit. A 1m2f outer track accommodates races over 6f, 7f, 1m, 1m3f, 1m4f and 2m. The 1m inner track caters for races over 5f and 1m2f.

N.H. Triangular, 1m5f (10), 175y run-in. A practically flat, sharp course where the long run between the last obstacle on the far side and the first in the home straight switches the emphasis from jumping to speed. The hurdles track is on the outside of the chase track. The course crosses the Polytrack at two points on each circuit.

Address: Kempton Park Racecourse, Sunbury-on-Thames, Middlesex TW16 5AQ Tel: 01932 782292

Website: www.kempton.co.uk

Regional Director: Phil White

Clerk of the Course and Director of Racing: Brian Clifford 07880 784484

Assistant Clerk of the Course: Sarah Dunster

General Manager: Steve Parlett

By Road: On the A308 near Junction 1 of the M3.

By Rail: Kempton Park Station (from Waterloo).

By Air: London (Heathrow) Airport 6 miles.

LEICESTER (R.H)

Flat: A stiff, galloping, right-handed oval of 1m5f, with a 5f run-in. There is a straight course of seven furlongs.

N.H. Rectangular, 1m6f (10), 175y run-in uphill. An undulating course with an elbow 150y from the finish, it can demand a high degree of stamina, as the going can become extremely testing and the last three furlongs are uphill.

Address: Leicester Racecourse, Oadby, Leicester, LE2 4AL Tel: 01162 716515

Website: www.leicester-racecourse.co.uk

Clerk of the Course: Jimmy Stevenson 01162 712115 or 07774 497281

General Manager: Rob Bracken

By Road: The course is 2.5 miles south-east of the city on the A6 (M1, Junction 21). The car park is free.

By Rail: Leicester Station (from St Pancras) is 2.5 miles.

By Air: Helicopter landing facility in the centre of the course.

LINGFIELD PARK (L.H)

Flat, Turf: A sharp, undulating left-handed circuit, with a 7f 140y straight course.

Flat, Polytrack: The left-handed Polytrack is 1m2f round, with an extended chute to provide a 1m5f start. It is a sharp, level track with a short run-in.

N.H. Conical, 1m5f (10), 200y run-in. Severely undulating with a tight downhill turn into the straight, the chase course suits front-runners.

Address: Lingfield Park Racecourse, Lingfield, Surrey RH7 6PQ Tel: 01342 834800

Website: www.lingfield-racecourse.co.uk

Clerk of the Course: George Hill

Executive Director: Kieran Gallagher

By Road: South-east of the town off the A22; M25 (Junction 6). Ample free parking.

By Rail: Lingfield Station (regular services from London Bridge and Victoria). Half-mile walk to the course.

By Air: London (Gatwick) Airport 10 miles. Helicopter landing facility south of wind-sock.

LUDLOW (R.H)

N.H. Oval, 1m4f (9), 185y run-in. The chase course is flat and has quite sharp bends into and out of the home straight, although long-striding horses never seem to have any difficulties. The hurdle course is on the outside of the chase track and is not so sharp.

Address: Ludlow Race Club Ltd, The Racecourse, Bromfield, Ludlow, Shropshire SY8 2BT

Tel: 01584 856221 (Racedays) or see below.

Website: www.ludlowracecourse.co.uk

General Manager and Clerk of the Course: Simon Sherwood

By Road: The course is situated at Bromfield, 2 miles north of Ludlow on the A49.

By Rail: Ludlow Station (Hereford-Shrewsbury line) 2 miles.

By Air: Helicopter landing facility in the centre of the course by arrangement with the Clerk of the Course .

MARKET RASEN (R.H)

N.H. Oval, 1m2f (8), 250y run-in. A sharp, undulating course with a long run to the straight, it favours the handy, front-running type.

Address: Market Rasen Racecourse, Legsby Road, Market Rasen, Lincolnshire LN8 3EA

Tel: 01673 843434

Website: www.marketrasenraces.co.uk

Regional Director: Amy Starkey

Clerk of the Course: Jack Pryor

General Manager: Nadia Powell

By Road: The town is just off the A46, and the racecourse is one mile east of the town on the A631. Free car parks.

By Rail: Market Rasen Station 1 mile (King's Cross - Cleethorpes line).

By Air: Helicopter landing facility by prior arrangement only.

MUSSELBURGH (R.H)

Flat: A sharp, level, right-handed oval of 1m2f, with a run-in of 4f. There is an additional 5f straight course. **N.H.** Rectangular, 1m3f (8), 150y run-in (variable). A virtually flat track with sharp turns, suiting the handy, front-running sort. It drains well. There is a section of Polytrack going away from the stands.

Address: Musselburgh Racecourse, Linkfield Road, Musselburgh, East Lothian EH21 7RG

Tel: 01316 652859

Website: www.musselburgh-racecourse.co.uk

Clerk of the Course: Harriet Graham 07843 380401

General Manager: Bill Farnsworth 07710 536134

By Road: The course is situated at Musselburgh, 5 miles east of Edinburgh on the A1. Car park, adjoining course, free for buses and cars.

By Rail: Waverley Station (Edinburgh). Local Rail service to Musselburgh.

By Air: Edinburgh (Turnhouse) Airport 30 minutes.

NEWBURY (L.H)

Flat: Left-handed, oval track of about 1m7f, with a slightly undulating straight mile. The round course is level and galloping with a four and a half-furlong straight. Races over the round mile start on the adjoining chute. **N.H.** Oval, 1m6f (11), 255y run-in. Slightly undulating, wide and galloping in nature. The fences are stiff and sound jumping is essential. One of the fairest tracks in the country.

Address: Newbury Racecourse, Newbury, Berkshire RG14 7NZ Tel: 01635 40015

Website: www.newbury-racecourse.co.uk

Chief Executive: Julian Thick

Clerk of the Course: Keith Ottesen 07813 043453

By Road: East of the town off the A34 (M4, Junction 12 or 13). Car park, adjoining enclosures, free.

By Rail: Newbury Racecourse Station adjoins the course.

By Air: Light Aircraft landing strip East/West. 830 metres by 30 metres wide. Helicopter landing facilities.

NEWCASTLE (L.H)

Flat: A 1m6f Tapeta track outside the jumps course. The straight mile is floodlit.
N.H. Oval, 1m6f (11), 220y run-in. A gradually rising home straight of four furlongs makes this galloping track a true test of stamina, especially as the ground can become very heavy.
Address: High Gosforth Park, Newcastle-Upon-Tyne, NE3 5HP Tel: 01912 362020
Website: www.newcastle-racecourse.co.uk
Clerk of the Course: James Armstrong 07801 166820
Executive Director: David Williamson
By Road: 4 miles north of the city on the A6125 (near the A1). Car and coach park free.
By Rail: Newcastle Central Station (from King's Cross). A free bus service operates from South Gosforth and Regent Centre Metro Station.
By Air: Helicopter landing facility by prior arrangement. The Airport is 4 miles from the course.

NEWMARKET (R.H)

Rowley Mile Course: There is a straight ten-furlong course, which is wide and galloping. Races over 1m4f or more are right-handed. The Rowley Mile course has a long run-in and a stiff finish.
July Course: Races up to a mile are run on the Bunbury course, which is straight. Races over 1m2f or more are right-handed, with a bend. Like the Rowley Mile course, the July Course track is stiff.
Address: Newmarket Racecourse, Westfield House, The Links, Newmarket, Suffolk CB8 0TG
Tel: 01638 663482 (Main Office) 01638 663762 (Rowley Mile) 01638 675416 (July) .
Website: www.newmarketracecourses.co.uk
Clerk of the Course: Michael Prosser 01638 675504 or 07802 844578
Regional Director: Amy Starkey
By Road: South-west of the town on the A1304 London Road (M11 Junction 9). Free car parking at the rear of the enclosure. Annual Badge Holders' car park free all days. Courtesy bus service from Newmarket Station, Bus Station and High Street. , commencing 90 minutes prior to the first race.
By Rail: Infrequent rail service to Newmarket Station from Cambridge (Liverpool Street) or direct bus service from Cambridge (13-mile journey).
By Air: Landing facilities for light aircraft and helicopters on racedays at both racecourses. See Flight Guide. Cambridge Airport 11 miles.

NEWTON ABBOT (L.H)

N.H. Oval, 1m2f (7), 300y run-in. Flat with two tight bends. The nippy, agile sort is favoured. The run-in can be very short on the hurdle course.
Address: Newton Abbot Races Ltd., Kingsteignton Road, Newton Abbot, Devon TQ12 3AF
Tel: 01626 353235
Website: www.newtonabbotracing.com
Clerk of the Course: Jason Loosemore 07766 228109
Managing Director: Pat Masterson Tel: 01626 353235 Mobile: 07917 830144
By Road: North of the town on the A380. Torquay 6 miles, Exeter 17 miles.
By Rail: Newton Abbot Station (from Paddington) ¾ mile. Buses and taxis operate to and from the course.
By Air: Helicopter landing pad in the centre of the course.

NOTTINGHAM (L.H)

Flat: Left-handed, galloping, oval of about 1m4f, and a straight of four and a half furlongs. Flat with easy turns.
Address: Nottingham Racecourse, Colwick Park, Nottingham, NG2 4BE Tel: 0870 8507634
Website: www.nottinghamracecourse.co.uk
Regional Director: Amy Starkey
Managing Director: James Knox
Clerk of the Course: Jane Hedley
By Road: 2 miles east of the city centre on the B686.
By Rail: Nottingham (Midland) Station. Regular bus service to course (2 miles).
By Air: Helicopter landing facility in the centre of the course.

PERTH (R.H)

N.H. Rectangular, 1m2f (8), 283y run-in. A flat, easy track with sweeping turns. Not a course for the long-striding galloper.
Address: Perth Racecourse, Scone Palace Park, Perth, PH2 6BB Tel: 01738 551597
Website: www.perth-races.co.uk
Clerk of the Course: Harriet Graham 07843 380401
General Manager: Hazel Peplinski
By Road: 4 miles north of the town off the A93.
By Rail: Perth Station (from Dundee) 4 miles. There are buses to the course.
By Air: Scone Airport (3.75 miles). Edinburgh Airport 45 minutes.

PLUMPTON (L.H)

N.H. Oval, 1m1f (7), 200y run-in uphill. A tight, undulating circuit with an uphill finish, Plumpton favours the handy, fast jumper. The ground often gets heavy, as the course is based on clay soil.
Address: Plumpton Racecourse, Plumpton, East Sussex BN7 3AL Tel: 01273 890383
Website: www.plumptonracecourse.co.uk
Clerk of the Course: Mark Cornford 07759 151617
Chief Executive: Daniel Thompson
By Road: 2 miles north of the village off the B2116.
By Rail: Plumpton Station (from Victoria) adjoins course.
By Air: Helicopter landing facility by prior arrangement with the Clerk of the Course.

PONTEFRACT (L.H)

Flat: Left-handed oval, undulating course of 2m133y, with a short run-in of 2f. It is a particularly stiff track with the last 3f uphill.
Address: Pontefract Park Race Co. Ltd., The Park, Pontefract, West Yorkshire Tel: 01977 781307
Website: www.pontefract-races.co.uk
Managing Director: Norman Gundill 01977 781307
Assistant Manager and Clerk of the Course: Richard Hamill
Assistant Clerk of the Course: George Chaloner
By Road: 1 mile north of the town on the A639. Junction 32 of M62. Free car park adjacent to the course.
By Rail: Pontefract Station (Tanshelf, every hour to Wakefield), 1½ miles from the course. Regular bus service from Leeds.
By Air: Helicopters by arrangement only. (Nearest Airfields: Robin Hood (Doncaster), Sherburn-in-Elmet, Yeadon (Leeds Bradford).

REDCAR (L.H)

Flat: Left-handed, level, galloping, oval course of 1m6f with a straight run-in of 5f. There is also a straight mile.
Address: Redcar Racecourse, Redcar, Cleveland TS10 2BY Tel: 01642 484068
Website: www.redcarracing.com
Clerk of the Course: Jonjo Sanderson Tel: 01642 484068 Mobile: 07766 022893
General Manager: Amy Fair
By Road: In the town off the A1085. Free parking adjoining the course for buses and cars.
By Rail: Redcar Station (¼ mile from the course).
By Air: Landing facilities at Turners Arms Farm (600yds runway) Yearby, Cleveland. Two miles south of the racecourse - transport available. Durham Tees Valley airport (18 miles west of Redcar).

RIPON (R.H)

Flat: A sharp, undulating, right-handed oval of 1m5f, with a 5f run-in. There is also a 6f straight course.
Address: Ripon Racecourse, Boroughbridge Road, Ripon, North Yorkshire HG4 1UG Tel: 01765 530530
Website: www.ripon-races.co.uk
Clerk of the Course and Managing Director: James Hutchinson 07860 679904
By Road: The course is situated 2 miles south-east of the city, on the B6265. There is ample free parking for cars and coaches.
By Rail: Harrogate Station (11 miles) or Thirsk (15 miles). Bus services to Ripon.
By Air: Helicopters only on the course. Otherwise Leeds/Bradford airport.

SALISBURY (R.H)

Flat: Right-handed and level, with a run-in of 4f. There is a straight mile track. The last half-mile is uphill, providing a stiff test of stamina.
Address: Salisbury Racecourse, Netherhampton, Salisbury, Wiltshire SP2 8PN Tel: 01722 326461
Website: www.salisburyracecourse.co.uk
Clerk of the Course and General Manager: Jeremy Martin 07880 744999
By Road: 3 miles south-west of the city on the A3094 at Netherhampton. Free car park adjoins the course.
By Rail: Salisbury Station is 3.5 miles (from London Waterloo). Bus service to the course.
By Air: Helicopter landing facility near the 1m2f start.

SANDOWN PARK (R.H)

Flat: An easy right-handed oval course of 1m5f with a stiff, straight uphill run-in of 4f. Separate straight 5f track is also uphill. Galloping.
N.H. Oval, 1m5f (11), 220y run-in uphill. Features seven fences on the back straight; the last three (the Railway Fences) are very close together and can often decide the outcome of races. The stiff climb to the finish puts the emphasis very much on stamina, but accurate-jumping, free-running sorts are also favoured. Hurdle races are run on the Flat course.
Address: Sandown Park Racecourse, Esher, Surrey KT10 9AJ Tel: 01372 464348
Website: www.sandown.co.uk
Regional Director: Phil White
Clerk of the Course: Andrew Cooper: 01372 461213 Mobile: 07774 230850
By Road: Four miles south-west of Kingston-on-Thames, on the A307 (M25 Junction 10).
By Rail: Esher Station (from Waterloo) adjoins the course.
By Air: London (Heathrow) Airport 12 miles.

SEDGEFIELD (L.H)

N.H. Oval, 1m2f (8), 200y run-in. Undulating with fairly tight turns, it doesn't suit big, long-striding horses.
Address: Sedgefield Racecourse, Sedgefield, Stockton-on-Tees, Cleveland TS21 2HW Tel: 01740 621925
Website: www.sedgefield-racecourse.co.uk
Clerk of the Course: Paul Barker
General Manager: Emma White
By Road: ¾ mile south-west of the town, near the junction of the A689 (Bishop Auckland) and the A177 (Durham) roads. The car park is free.
By Rail: Darlington Station (9 miles). Durham Station (12 miles).
By Air: Helicopter landing facility in car park area by prior arrangement only.

SOUTHWELL (L.H)

Flat, Fibresand: Left-handed oval, Fibresand course of 1m2f with a 3f run-in. There is a straight 5f. Track floodlit from 2019.Sharp and level, Southwell suits front-runners.
N.H. Oval, 1m 1f (7), 220y run-in. A tight, flat track with a short run-in, it suits front-runners.
Address: Southwell Racecourse, Rolleston, Newark, Nottinghamshire NG25 0TS Tel: 01636 814481
Website: www.southwell-racecourse.co.uk
Executive Director: Mark Clayton
Clerk of the Course: Roderick Duncan 07772 958685
By Road: The course is situated at Rolleston, 3 miles south of Southwell, 5 miles from Newark.
By Rail: Rolleston Station (Nottingham-Newark line) adjoins the course.
By Air: Helicopters can land by prior arrangement.

STRATFORD-ON-AVON (L.H)

N.H. Triangular, 1m2f (8), 200y run-in. Virtually flat with two tight bends, and quite a short home straight A sharp and turning course, it suits the well-balanced, handy sort.
Address: Stratford Racecourse, Luddington Road, Stratford-upon-Avon, Warwickshire CV37 9SE
Tel: 01789 267949
Website: www.stratfordracecourse.net
Managing Director: Ilona Barnett
Clerk of the Course: Nessie Chanter
By Road: A mile from the town centre, off the A429 (Evesham road).
By Rail: Stratford-on-Avon Station (from Birmingham New Street or Leamington Spa) 1 mile.
By Air: Helicopter landing facility by prior arrangement.

TAUNTON (R.H)

N.H. Elongated oval, 1m2f (8), 150y run-in uphill. Sharp turns, especially after the winning post, with a steady climb from the home bend. Suits the handy sort.
Address: Taunton Racecourse, Orchard Portman, Taunton, Somerset TA3 7BL Tel: 01823 337172
Website: www.tauntonracecourse.co.uk
Clerk of the Course: Jason Loosemore
Chief Executive: Bob Young
By Road: Two miles south of the town on the B3170 (Honiton) road (M5 Junction 25).
By Rail: Taunton Station 2 miles. There are buses and taxis to course.
By Air: Helicopter landing facility by prior arrangement.

THIRSK (L.H)

Flat: Left-handed oval of 1m2f with sharp turns and an undulating run-in of 4f. There is a straight 6f track.
Address: The Racecourse, Station Road, Thirsk, North Yorkshire YO7 1QL Tel: 01845 522276
Website: www.thirskracecourse.net
Clerk of the Course and Managing Director: James Sanderson
By Road: West of the town on the A61. Free car park adjacent to the course for buses and cars.
By Rail: Thirsk Station (from King's Cross), ½ mile from the course.
By Air: Helicopters can land by prior arrangement. Tel: Racecourse 01845 522276. Fixed wing aircraft can land at RAF Leeming. Tel: 01677 423041. Light aircraft at Bagby. Tel: 01845 597385 or 01845 537555.

TOWCESTER (R.H)

N.H. Square, 1m6f (10), 200y run-in uphill. The final six furlongs are uphill. One of the most testing tracks in the country with the emphasis purely on stamina.
Address: The Racecourse, London Road, Towcester, Northants NN12 6LB Tel: 01327 353414
Website: www.towcester-racecourse.co.uk
Clerk of the Course: Robert Bellamy 07836 241458
General Manager: Kevin Ackerman
By Road: 1 mile south-east of the town on the A5 (Milton Keynes road). M1 (Junction 15a).
By Rail: Northampton Station (Euston) 9 miles, buses to Towcester; or Milton Keynes (Euston) 12 miles, taxis available.
By Air: Helicopters can land by prior arrangement with the Racecourse Manager.

UTTOXETER (L.H)

N.H. Oval, 1m2f (8), 170y run-in. A few undulations, easy bends and fences and a flat home straight of over half a mile. Suits front-runners, especially on the 2m hurdle course.
Address: The Racecourse, Wood Lane, Uttoxeter, Staffordshire ST14 8BD Tel: 01889 562561
Website: www.uttoxeter-racecourse.co.uk
Clerk of the Course: Eloise Quayle
General Manager: David MacDonald
By Road: South-east of the town off the B5017 (Marchington Road).
By Rail: Uttoxeter Station (Crewe-Derby line) adjoins the course.
By Air: Helicopters can land by prior arrangement with the raceday office.

WARWICK (L.H)

N.H. Circular, 1m6f (10), 240y run-in. Undulating with tight bends, five quick fences in the back straight and a short home straight, Warwick favours handiness and speed rather than stamina.
Address: Warwick Racecourse, Hampton Street, Warwick, CV34 6HN Tel: 01926 491553
Website: www.warwickracecourse.co.uk
Regional Director: Ian Renton
Clerk of the Course: Jane Hedley
Managing Director: Andre Klein
By Road: West of the town on the B4095 adjacent to Junction 15 of the M40.
By Rail: Warwick or Warwick Parkway Stations.
By Air: Helicopters can land by prior arrangement with the Clerk of the Course.

WETHERBY (L.H)

Flat: First used in 2015, the Flat course is left-handed with a 1m4f circuit.
N.H. Oval, 1m4f (9), 200y run-in slightly uphill. A flat, very fair course which suits the long-striding galloper.
Address: The Racecourse, York Road, Wetherby, LS22 5EJ Tel: 01937 582035
Website: www.wetherbyracing.co.uk
Clerk of the Course and Chief Executive: Jonjo Sanderson 07831 437453
By Road: East of the town off the B1224 (York Road). Adjacent to the A1. Excellent bus and coach facilities. Car park free.
By Rail: Leeds Station 12 miles. Buses to Wetherby.
By Air: Helicopters can land by prior arrangement

WINCANTON (R.H)

N.H. Rectangular, 1m3f (9), 200y run-in. Good galloping course where the going rarely becomes heavy The home straight is mainly downhill.
Address: Wincanton Racecourse, Wincanton, Somerset BA9 8BJ Tel: 01963 435840
Website: www.wincantonracecourse.co.uk
Regional Director: Ian Renton
Clerk of the Course: Barry Johnson 07976 791578
General Manager: Huw Williams
By Road: 1 mile north of the town on the B3081.
By Rail: Gillingham Station (from Waterloo) or Castle Cary Station (from Paddington). Buses and taxis to the course.
By Air: Helicopter landing area is situated in the centre of the course.

WINDSOR (Fig. 8)

Flat: Figure of eight track of 1m4f 110y. The course is level and sharp with a long run-in. The 6f course is essentially straight.
Address: Royal Windsor Racecourse, Maidenhead Road, Windsor, Berkshire SL4 5JJ Tel: 01753 498400
Website: www.windsor-racecourse.co.uk
Clerk of the Course: To be announced
Executive Director: Simon Williams
By Road: North of the town on the A308 (M4 Junction 6).
By Rail: Windsor Central Station (from Paddington) or Windsor and Eton Riverside Station (from Waterloo)
By Air: London (Heathrow) Airport 15 minutes. Also White Waltham Airport (West London Aero Club) 15 minutes.
River Bus: Seven minutes from Barry Avenue promenade at Windsor.

WOLVERHAMPTON (L.H)

Flat: Left-handed, floodlit, oval Tapeta track of 1m, with a run-in of 380y. A level track with sharp bends.
Address: Wolverhampton Racecourse, Dunstall Park, Gorsebrook Road, Wolverhampton, WV6 0PE Tel: 01902 390000
Website: www.wolverhampton-racecourse.co.uk
Clerk of the Course: Fergus Cameron 07971 531162
General Manager: Dave Roberts
By Road: 1 mile north of the city centre on the A449 (M54 Junction 2 or M6 Junction 12). Car parking free.
By Rail: Wolverhampton Station (from Euston) 1 mile.
By Air: Halfpenny Green Airport 8 miles.

WORCESTER (L.H)

N.H. Elongated oval, 1m5f (9), 220y run-in. Flat with easy turns, it is a very fair, galloping track.
Address: Worcester Racecourse, Pitchcroft, Worcester, WR1 3EJ Tel: 01905 25364
Website: www.worcester-racecourse.co.uk
Clerk of the Course: To be announced
Executive Director: Jenny Cheshire
By Road: West of the city centre off the A449 (Kidderminster road) (M5 Junction 8).
By Rail: Foregate Street Station, Worcester (from Paddington) ¾ mile.
By Air: Helicopter landing facility in the centre of the course, by prior arrangement only.

YARMOUTH (L.H)

Flat: Left-handed, level circuit of 1m4f, with a run-in of 5f. The straight course is 1m long.
Address: The Racecourse, Jellicoe Road, Great Yarmouth, Norfolk NR30 4AU Tel: 01493 842527
Website: www.greatyarmouth-racecourse.co.uk
Clerk of the Course: Richard Aldous 07738 507643
Executive Director: Glenn Tubby
By Road: 1 mile east of town centre (well signposted from A47 and A12).
By Rail: Great Yarmouth Station (1 mile). Bus service to the course.
By Air: Helicopter landing available by prior arrangement with Racecourse Office

YORK (L.H)

Flat: Left-handed, level, galloping track, with a straight 6f. There is also an adjoining chute for races over 7f.
Address: The Racecourse, York, YO23 1EX Tel: 01904 683932
Website: www.yorkracecourse.co.uk
Clerk of the Course and Chief Executive: William Derby 07812 961176
Assistant Clerk of the Course: Anthea Morshead
By Road: 1 mile south-east of the city on the A1036.
By Rail: 1½ miles York Station (from King's Cross). Special bus service from station to the course.
By Air: Light aircraft and helicopter landing facilities available at Rufforth aerodrome (5,000ft tarmac runway). Leeds Bradford airport (25 miles).

THE INVESTEC DERBY STAKES (GROUP 1)
EPSOM DOWNS ON SATURDAY 1ST JUNE 2019

SECOND ENTRIES BY NOON APRIL 2ND; SUPPLEMENTARY ENTRIES BY NOON MAY 25TH.

HORSE	TRAINER	HORSE	TRAINER
ACHAEUS (GER)	ED DUNLOP	DILMUN DYNASTY (IRE)	SIR MICHAEL STOUTE
ADONIJAH	HENRY CANDY	DISRUPTIVE (IRE)	M. DELZANGLES
ALBUQUERQUE (IRE)	AIDAN O'BRIEN	DREADNOUGHTUS	MICHAEL APPLEBY
ALFAATIK	JOHN GOSDEN	DUBAI WARRIOR	JOHN GOSDEN
ALHAAZM	SIR MICHAEL STOUTE	EAGLE HUNTER	FRANCIS-HENRI GRAFFARD
ALIGNAK	SIR MICHAEL STOUTE	EAGLES BY DAY (IRE)	MICHAEL BELL
ALIGNED (IRE)	SIR MICHAEL STOUTE	EDESSANN (IRE)	
ALKHAWANEEJ EMPIRE (FR)		EL MISK	JOHN GOSDEN
ALLMANKIND	MICHAEL BELL	EL PICADOR (IRE)	SIR MICHAEL STOUTE
ANTHONY VAN DYCK (IRE)	AIDAN O'BRIEN	EMARAATY ANA	KEVIN RYAN
APPARATE	ROGER VARIAN	EMINENCE (IRE)	AIDAN O'BRIEN
ARCTIC SNOW		EMINENT AUTHORITY (IRE)	JOSEPH PATRICK O'BRIEN
ARUMAMA (JPN)	YOSHIHIRO HATAKEYAMA	EMIRATES EMPIRE (IRE)	MICHAEL BELL
ARZU	FRANCIS-HENRI GRAFFARD	ENDEAVOURING (IRE)	DAVID ELSWORTH
ASAD (IRE)		ESCAPE THE RAIN (CAN)	CHARLES HILLS
AZETS	AMANDA PERRETT	FABRIANO (GER)	
BALLYLEMON (IRE)	RICHARD HUGHES	FAYLAQ	WILLIAM HAGGAS
BALTIC SONG (IRE)	JOHN GOSDEN	FEARLESS WARRIOR (FR)	RALPH BECKETT
BANGKOK (IRE)	ANDREW BALDING	FERID	M. DELZANGLES
BARBADOS (IRE)	AIDAN O'BRIEN	FIERY MISSION (USA)	SIR MICHAEL STOUTE
BARDO (IRE)		FINTAS	RICHARD HUGHES
BARREG	A. FABRE	FIRST IN LINE	JOHN GOSDEN
BARRENJOEY	AMANDA PERRETT	FLAMMARION (GER)	JOHN GOSDEN
BATTLE OF PARADISE (USA)	SIR MARK PRESCOTT BT	FOX CHAIRMAN (IRE)	ANDREW BALDING
BLADESMITH (IRE)	JOHN GOSDEN	FOX FEARLESS	K. R. BURKE
BLENHEIM PALACE (IRE)	AIDAN O'BRIEN	FOX PREMIER (IRE)	ANDREW BALDING
BOARDMAN	P. BARY	FOX TAL	ANDREW BALDING
BOREAS (IRE)	A. FABRE	FOX VARDY (USA)	MARTYN MEADE
BROGUE	D. K. WELD	FRANKADORE (IRE)	TOM DASCOMBE
BROOME (IRE)	AIDAN O'BRIEN	FRESNO (IRE)	AIDAN O'BRIEN
BUCKHURST (IRE)	JOSEPH PATRICK O'BRIEN	FRONTMAN	
BUFFALO RIVER (USA)		GANTIER	JOHN GOSDEN
CADRE DU NOIR (USA)	MARTYN MEADE	GEORGEVILLE	D. K. WELD
CALCULATION	SIR MICHAEL STOUTE	GHADBBAAN	SIR MICHAEL STOUTE
CAPE OF GOOD HOPE (IRE)	AIDAN O'BRIEN	GINISTRELLI (IRE)	ED WALKER
CARPIO	FRANCIS-HENRI GRAFFARD	GLOBAL EXPRESS	ED DUNLOP
CARTES	JOSEPH PATRICK O'BRIEN	GLOBAL FALCON	CHARLES HILLS
CASANOVA	JOHN GOSDEN	GLOBAL FREEDOM	ED DUNLOP
CERBERUS	JOSEPH PATRICK O'BRIEN	GLOBAL ROCK (FR)	ED DUNLOP
CIRCUS MAXIMUS (IRE)	AIDAN O'BRIEN	GODZILLA (IRE)	AIDAN O'BRIEN
CLARENDON	JOSEPH PATRICK O'BRIEN	GOING PLACES	ROGER VARIAN
COEUR D'OR (IRE)	D. K. WELD	GREAT BEAR	ROGER CHARLTON
CONSTANTINOPLE (IRE)	AIDAN O'BRIEN	GRENADIER GUARD (IRE)	MARK JOHNSTON
COSMO REMIX (JPN)	TSUYOSHI TANAKA	GUANDI (USA)	TOM DASCOMBE
CRASTER (IRE)	HUGHIE MORRISON	HARPO MARX (IRE)	AIDAN O'BRIEN
CRETE (IRE)	FRANCIS-HENRI GRAFFARD	HASANKEY (IRE)	D. K. WELD
CROCKFORD (IRE)	JOSEPH PATRICK O'BRIEN	HAWA BLADI (IRE)	ROGER CHARLTON
CURRENT OPTION (IRE)	WILLIAM HAGGAS	HAZRAN (IRE)	M. HALFORD
DAIJOOR		HELIAN (IRE)	ED DUNLOP
DAL HORRISGLE	WILLIAM HAGGAS	HENDRIX (IRE)	HUGHIE MORRISON
DAMLAJ	OWEN BURROWS	HESSDALEN	FRANCIS-HENRI GRAFFARD
DANTE'S VIEW (IRE)	SIR MICHAEL STOUTE	HE WILL CALL (FR)	F. VERMEULEN
DAWAAM (USA)	OWEN BURROWS	HIGH CHIEF (IRE)	AIDAN O'BRIEN
DEACON	F. HEAD	HIROSHIMA	JOHN RYAN
DEBONAIR DON JUAN (IRE)	ED VAUGHAN	HOLY KINGDOM (IRE)	TOM CLOVER
DEHRADUN		HOMER (IRE)	A. FABRE
DELAWARE	A. FABRE	HTILOMINLO	SYLVESTER KIRK
DELGANY (IRE)	JOSEPH PATRICK O'BRIEN	HUMANITARIAN (USA)	JOHN GOSDEN
DESERT ISLAND (IRE)	AIDAN O'BRIEN	IL PARADISO (USA)	AIDAN O'BRIEN

HORSE	TRAINER
UAE JEWEL	ROGER VARIAN
UP HELLY AA (IRE)	W. MCCREERY
VALENCE	ED DUNLOP
VARIYANN (FR)	A. DE ROYER DUPRE
VAST KINGDOM	
VAYENI (FR)	JEAN CLAUDE ROUGET
VERIMLI (FR)	A. DE ROYER DUPRE
VORASHANN (FR)	A. DE ROYER DUPRE
WALDSTERN	JOHN GOSDEN
WAR EAGLE (IRE)	JOHN GOSDEN
WARGRAVE (IRE)	J. A. STACK
WELD ALDAR	A. AL RAYHI
WEMYSS WARE (IRE)	SIR MICHAEL STOUTE
WESTERN AUSTRALIA (IRE)	AIDAN O'BRIEN
WHITSUNDAY ISLANDS (FR)	AIDAN O'BRIEN
WILL OF IRON	JOHN GOSDEN
WIRRAWAY (USA)	JOHN GOSDEN
YURI GAGARIN	JOHN GOSDEN
ZARAFSHAN (IRE)	D. K. WELD
ZARKALLANI (FR)	A. DE ROYER DUPRE
ZEYDABAD (IRE)	M. HALFORD
ZUBA	AMANDA PERRETT
ZUENOON (IRE)	D. K. WELD
EX LADY MILETRIAN (IRE)	J. A. STACK
EX MONTBRETIA	

THE bet365
EUROPEAN FREE HANDICAP STAKES
NEWMARKET CRAVEN MEETING 2019
(ON THE ROWLEY MILE COURSE)
TUESDAY APRIL 16TH

The bet365 European Free Handicap Stakes (Class 1) (Listed race) with total prize fund of £50,000 for three-year-olds only (Two-year-olds of 2018 which are included in the European 2-y-o Thoroughbred Rankings or which, in 2018, either ran in Great Britain or ran for a trainer who at the time was licensed by the British Horseracing Authority, and are Rated 100 or above); lowest weight 8st; highest weight 9st 7lb.

Penalty for a winner after December 31st 2018 to be at the discretion of the BHA Handicapper. Seven furlongs.

Rating		st	lb	Rating		st	lb
126	TOO DARN HOT (GB)	9	7	109	VINTAGE BRUT (GB)	8	4
121	QUORTO (IRE)	9	2	108	CHELSEA CLOISTERS (USA)	8	3
120	TEN SOVEREIGNS (IRE)	9	1	108	CHRISTMAS (IRE)	8	3
119	ADVERTISE (GB)	9	0	108	MARIE'S DIAMOND (IRE)	8	3
118	ANTHONY VAN DYCK (IRE)	8	13	108	MOHAATHER (GB)	8	3
118	JASH (IRE)	8	13	108	STAR TERMS (GB)	8	3
116	PRETTY POLLYANNA (GB)	8	11	108	VANGE (GB)	8	3
115	CALYX (GB)	8	10	107	BEYOND REASON (IRE)	8	2
115	MADHMOON (IRE)	8	10	107	BOITRON (FR)	8	2
115	ROYAL MEETING (IRE)	8	10	107	BYE BYE HONG KONG (USA)	8	2
114	HELLO YOUMZAIN (FR)	8	9	107	EAST (GB)	8	2
114	LINE OF DUTY (IRE)	8	9	107	MAIN EDITION (IRE)	8	2
114	PERSIAN KING (IRE)	8	9	107	VAN BEETHOVEN (CAN)	8	2
114	SIGNORA CABELLO (IRE)	8	9	107	WELL DONE FOX (GB)	8	2
114	SKITTER SCATTER (USA)	8	9	106	CAPE OF GOOD HOPE (IRE)	8	1
114	SOLDIER'S CALL (GB)	8	9	106	CARDINI (USA)	8	1
113	IRIDESSA (IRE)	8	8	106	DUNKERRON (GB)	8	1
113	MAGNA GRECIA (IRE)	8	8	106	FLEETING (IRE)	8	1
113	ROYAL MARINE (IRE)	8	8	106	GOSSAMER WINGS (USA)	8	1
112	BROOME (IRE)	8	7	106	LA PELOSA (IRE)	8	1
112	FAIRYLAND (IRE)	8	7	106	POCKET DYNAMO (USA)	8	1
112	GRAIGNES (FR)	8	7	106	SANGARIUS (GB)	8	1
112	KESSAAR (IRE)	8	7	106	SHINE SO BRIGHT (GB)	8	1
112	MOHAWK (IRE)	8	7	106	SPORTING CHANCE (GB)	8	1
112	PHOENIX OF SPAIN (IRE)	8	7	106	TRUE MASON (GB)	8	1
111	ANODOR (FR)	8	6	106	ZAGITOVA (IRE)	8	1
111	DARK VISION (IRE)	8	6	105	ANGEL'S HIDEAWAY (IRE)	8	0
111	JAPAN (GB)	8	6	105	DANDHU (GB)	8	0
111	JUST WONDERFUL (USA)	8	6	105	DUKE OF HAZZARD (FR)	8	0
111	SERGEI PROKOFIEV (CAN)	8	6	105	INDIGO BALANCE (IRE)	8	0
111	THE MACKEM BULLET (IRE)	8	6	105	KHAADEM (IRE)	8	0
110	ARCTIC SOUND (GB)	8	5	105	KICK ON (GB)	8	0
110	CIRCUS MAXIMUS (IRE)	8	5	105	KUWAIT CURRENCY (USA)	8	0
110	EMARAATY ANA (GB)	8	5	105	LEGENDS OF WAR (USA)	8	0
110	GREAT SCOT (GB)	8	5	105	QUEEN OF BERMUDA (IRE)	8	0
110	HERMOSA (IRE)	8	5	105	SAN DONATO (IRE)	8	0
110	LAND FORCE (IRE)	8	5	105	THE IRISH ROVER (IRE)	8	0
110	MOUNT EVEREST (IRE)	8	5	105	WATAN (GB)	8	0
110	NOBLE MOON (GB)	8	5	104	AZANO (GB)	7	13
110	RUMBLE INTHEJUNGLE (IRE)	8	5	104	DUBAI BEAUTY (IRE)	7	13
110	SO PERFECT (USA)	8	5	104	KONCHEK (GB)	7	13
110	SYDNEY OPERA HOUSE (GB)	8	5	104	NEVERLAND ROCK (GB)	7	13
110	WESTERN AUSTRALIA (IRE)	8	5	104	NO NEEDS NEVER (IRE)	7	13
109	ARTHUR KITT (GB)	8	4	104	NORWAY (IRE)	7	13
109	FOX TAL (GB)	8	4	104	PEACH TREE (IRE)	7	13

Rating		st	lb
104	**PRINCE EIJI** (GB)	7	13
104	**SABRE** (GB)	7	13
104	**SHANG SHANG SHANG** (USA)	7	13
103	**BARBILL** (IRE)	7	12
103	**CERTAIN LAD** (GB)	7	12
103	**CHARMING KID** (GB)	7	12
103	**CONFIDING** (GB)	7	12
103	**MOT JUSTE** (USA)	7	12
103	**VICTORY COMMAND** (IRE)	7	12
102	**AL HILALEE** (GB)	7	11
102	**CERATONIA** (GB)	7	11
102	**COMEDY** (IRE)	7	11
102	**COURT POET** (GB)	7	11
102	**FLOATING ARTIST** (GB)	7	11
102	**HOT TEAM** (IRE)	7	11
102	**PERSIAN MOON** (IRE)	7	11
102	**SPACE TRAVELLER** (GB)	7	11
102	**TURGENEV** (GB)	7	11
102	**YOURTIMEISNOW** (GB)	7	11
101	**ART DU VAL** (GB)	7	10

Rating		st	lb
101	**CONCIERGE** (IRE)	7	10
101	**ICONIC CHOICE** (GB)	7	10
101	**LIFE OF RILEY** (GB)	7	10
101	**NATE THE GREAT** (GB)	7	10
101	**SAND SHARE** (GB)	7	10
101	**SHUMOOKHI** (IRE)	7	10
100	**DARK JEDI** (IRE)	7	9
100	**DUBAI DOMINION** (GB)	7	9
100	**GETCHAGETCHAGETCHA** (GB)	7	9
100	**HAPPY ODYSSEY** (IRE)	7	9
100	**JUNIUS BRUTUS** (FR)	7	9
100	**LADY ARIA** (GB)	7	9
100	**LETHAL PROMISE** (IRE)	7	9
100	**MAGNETIC CHARM** (GB)	7	9
100	**NATALIE'S JOY** (GB)	7	9
100	**POETRY** (GB)	7	9
100	**SHADES OF BLUE** (IRE)	7	9
100	**SHAMBOLIC** (IRE)	7	9
100	**SUNDAY STAR** (GB)	7	9
100	**SWISSTERIOUS** (GB)	7	9

LONGINES WORLD'S BEST RACEHORSE RANKINGS AND EUROPEAN THOROUGHBRED RANKINGS 2018

three-year-olds rated 115 or greater by the IFHA World's Best Racehorse Rankings Conference. orses rated 114-110 by the European Thoroughbred Rankings Conference do not constitute a part of e World's Best Racehorse Rankings. Those ratings were compiled on behalf of the European Pattern mmittee.

Rating	Trained	Rating	Trained
127 ROARING LION (USA)	GB	116 KNIGHT TO BEHOLD (IRE)	GB
125 JUSTIFY (USA)	USA	116 ONE WORLD (SAF)	SAF
124 ALMOND EYE (JPN)	JPN	116 VINO ROSSO (USA)	USA
124 ALPHA CENTAURI (IRE)	IRE	116 WILD ILLUSION (GB)	GB
122 BLAST ONEPIECE (JPN)	JPN	116 WISSAHICKON (USA)	GB
122 CATHOLIC BOY (USA)	USA	116 WITHOUT PAROLE (GB)	GB
122 MAGICAL (IRE)	IRE	116 WORLD OF TROUBLE (USA)	USA
122 SEA OF CLASS (IRE)	GB	116 YOUNG RASCAL (FR)	GB
122 GOOD MAGIC (USA)	USA	116 ZOUSAIN (AUS)	AUS
121 MASAR (IRE)	GB	115 AMERICAN TATTOO (ARG)	ARG
121 SAXON WARRIOR (JPN)	IRE	115 ANCIENT SPIRIT (GER)	GER
120 AUDIBLE (USA)	USA	115 BILLESDON BROOK (GB)	GB
120 KEW GARDENS (IRE)	IRE	115 BRAVAZO (USA)	USA
120 THE AUTUMN SUN (AUS)	AUS	115 BRUNDTLAND (IRE)	GB
119 EXPERT EYE (GB)	GB	115 CASCADIAN (FR)	FR
119 MENDELSSOHN (USA)	IRE	115 CHIMICHURI RUN (SAF)	SAF
119 U S NAVY FLAG (USA)	IRE	115 DREAM TREE (USA)	USA
119 WAGNERIAN (JPN)	JPN	115 EL PICARO (CHI)	CHI
118 DEE EX BEE (GB)	GB	115 ESKIMO KISSES (USA)	USA
118 EPOCA D'ORO (JPN)	JPN	115 EXTRA BRUT (AUS)	AUS
118 LE VENT SE LEVE (JPN)	JPN	115 FIRENZE FIRE (USA)	USA
118 MONOMOY GIRL (USA)	USA	115 GUSTAV KLIMT (IRE)	IRE
118 OLD PERSIAN (GB)	GB	115 HAPPILY (IRE)	IRE
118 SANDS OF MALI (FR)	GB	115 HOFBURG (USA)	USA
118 STELVIO (JPN)	JPN	115 LATROBE (IRE)	IRE
118 WIND CHIMES (GB)	FR	115 MADISON COUNTY (NZ)	NZ
117 ANALYZE IT (USA)	USA	115 MIDNIGHT BISOU (USA)	USA
117 BOLT D'ORO (USA)	USA	115 NATIONAL PARK (SAF)	SAF
117 CROSS COUNTER (GB)	GB	115 NELSON (IRE)	IRE
117 DANON PREMIUM (JPN)	JPN	115 OMEGA PERFUME (JPN)	JPN
117 FIEREMENT (JPN)	JPN	115 OSTILIO (GB)	GB
117 FLAG OF HONOUR (IRE)	IRE	115 RED RUBY (USA)	USA
117 GRONKOWSKI (USA)	USA	115 RUSHING FALL (USA)	USA
117 INSTILLED REGARD (USA)	USA	115 STUDY OF MAN (IRE)	FR
117 JAMES GARFIELD (IRE)	GB	115 TENFOLD (USA)	USA
117 LAURENS (FR)	GB	115 TIP TWO WIN (GB)	GB
117 MAGNUM MOON (USA)	USA	115 WELTSTAR (GER)	GER
117 MCKINZIE (USA)	USA	115 WITH YOU (FR)	FR
117 POLYDREAM (IRE)	FR	115 WRITTEN BY (AUS)	AUS
117 PROMISES FULFILLED (USA)	USA	114 ATHENA (IRE)	IRE
117 ROMANISED (IRE)	IRE	114 DESTINO (GER)	GER
117 SOQRAT (AUS)	SAF	114 ELARQAM (GB)	GB
116 ARCADIA QUEEN (AUS)	AUS	114 GHAIYYATH (IRE)	GB
116 CARIBLANCO (CHI)	CHI	114 HOMERIQUE (USA)	FR
116 COSMIC FORCE (JPN)	JPN	114 HUNTING HORN (IRE)	IRE
116 ETARIO (JPN)	JPN	114 LAH TI DAR (GB)	GB
116 FOREVER TOGETHER (IRE)	IRE	114 MAGIC WAND (IRE)	IRE
116 I CAN FLY (GB)	IRE	114 OLMEDO (FR)	FR
116 IL MERCATO (ARG)	ARG	113 DICE ROLL (FR)	FR
116 INTELLOGENT (IRE)	FR	113 EFAADAH (IRE)	FR

Rating	Trained
113 HAVANA GREY (GB)	GB
113 HEY GAMAN (GB)	GB
113 LOUIS D'OR (IRE)	FR
113 MR SATCHMO (FR)	FR
113 MUSIS AMICA (IRE)	FR
113 NEUFBOSC (FR)	FR
113 PATASCOY (FR)	FR
113 ROSTROPOVICH (IRE)	IRE
113 SHEIKHA REIKA (FR)	GB
113 TANTHEEM (GB)	FR
113 WOOTTON (FR)	FR
112 ALTYN ORDA (IRE)	GB
112 CLEMMIE (IRE)	IRE
112 EQTIDAAR (IRE)	GB
112 FLEET REVIEW (USA)	IRE
112 INVINCIBLE ARMY (IRE)	GB
112 LOST TREASURE (IRE)	IRE
112 LOXLEY (IRE)	GB
112 ROYAL YOUMZAIN (FR)	GER
112 VINTAGER (GB)	GB
112 WADILSAFA (GB)	GB
112 WELLS FARHH GO (IRE)	GB

Rating	Trained
111 COULD IT BE LOVE (USA)	IF
111 EMARAATY (GB)	G
111 LUMINATE (IRE)	F
111 MARY TUDOR (IRE)	IF
111 MISSION IMPASSIBLE (IRE)	F
111 RAYMOND TUSK (IRE)	G
111 SIOUX NATION (USA)	IF
111 SOUTHERN FRANCE (IRE)	IF
111 SPEAK IN COLOURS (GB)	IF
111 SUMMER FESTIVAL (GB)	T
111 WUSOOL (USA)	F
111 ZARKAMIYA (FR)	F
110 CARDSHARP (GB)	G
110 HAZAPOUR (IRE)	IF
110 NOT MINE (GER)	F
110 SALVE DEL RIO (IRE)	GE
110 SIR EREC (IRE)	IF
110 SNAZZY JAZZY (IRE)	G
110 TEPPAL (FR)	G
110 THREADING (IRE)	G
110 VERACIOUS (GB)	G
110 YAFTA (GB)	G

OLDER HORSES 2018

or **four-year-olds and up** rated 115 or greater by the IFHA World's Best Racehorse Rankings Conference. Horses rated 114-110 by the European Thoroughbred Rankings Conference do not constitute a part of the World's Best Racehorse Rankings. Those ratings were compiled on behalf of the European Pattern Committee.

Rating	Age	Trained	Rating	Age	Trained
30 CRACKSMAN (GB)	4	GB	119 WERTHER (NZ)	7	HK
30 WINX (AUS)	7	AUS	118 ABEL TASMAN (USA)	4	USA
28 ACCELERATE (USA)	5	USA	118 ACE HIGH (AUS)	4	AUS
27 BEAUTY GENERATION (NZ)	6	HK	118 AL AIN (JPN)	4	JPN
27 GUN RUNNER (USA)	5	USA	118 BEAT THE CLOCK (AUS)	5	HK
26 POET'S WORD (IRE)	5	GB	118 BRAVE SMASH (JPN)	5	AUS
25 CRYSTAL OCEAN (GB)	4	GB	118 CAPRI (IRE)	4	IRE
25 ENABLE (GB)	4	GB	118 CATALINA CRUISER (USA)	4	USA
24 ROY H (USA)	6	USA	118 COMIN' THROUGH (AUS)	5	AUS
23 BATTAASH (IRE)	4	GB	118 CORAL FEVER (SAF)	6	SAF
23 BENBATL (GB)	4	UAE/GB	118 DESERT ENCOUNTER (IRE)	6	GB
23 CLOTH OF STARS (IRE)	5	FR	118 DO IT AGAIN (SAF)	4	SAF
23 HAPPY CLAPPER (AUS)	8	AUS	118 DSCHINGIS SECRET (GER)	5	GER
23 REY DE ORO (JPN)	4	JPN	118 ERTIJAAL (IRE)	7	UAE
23 TRAPEZE ARTIST (AUS)	4	AUS	118 HELENE PARAGON (FR)	6	HK
22 HARRY ANGEL (IRE)	4	GB	118 HUMIDOR (NZ)	6	AUS
22 KISEKI (JPN)	4	JPN	118 IQUITOS (GER)	6	GER
22 REDZEL (AUS)	6	AUS	118 HOT KING PRAWN (AUS)	4	HK
22 SANTA ANA LANE (AUS)	6	AUS	118 JUNGLE CAT (IRE)	6	GB
22 THUNDER SNOW (IRE)	4	UAE	118 LANCASTER BOMBER (USA)	4	IRE
22 WALDGEIST (GB)	4	FR	118 LEGAL EAGLE (SAF)	7	SAF
22 WEST COAST (USA)	4	USA	118 MARINARESCO (SAF)	6	SAF
21 BEST SOLUTION (IRE)	4	GB	118 MERCHANT NAVY (AUS)	4	IRE
21 GUNNEVERA (USA)	4	USA	118 MONARCHS GLEN (GB)	4	GB
21 HARTNELL (GB)	7	AUS	118 MOZU ASCOT (USA)	4	JPN
21 IVICTORY (AUS)	5	HK	118 NORTH AMERICA (GB)	6	UAE
21 MR STUNNING (AUS)	6	HK	118 OSBORNE BULLS (AUS)	5	AUS
21 RECOLETOS (FR)	4	FR	118 RAINBOW LINE (JPN)	5	JPN
21 REDKIRK WARRIOR (GB)	7	AUS	118 SEASONS BLOOM (AUS)	6	HK
21 SUAVE RICHARD (JPN)	4	JPN	118 THEWIZARDOFOZ (AUS)	7	HK
120 BLUE POINT (IRE)	4	GB	118 THUNDERING BLUE (USA)	5	GB
120 CITY OF LIGHT (USA)	4	USA	118 TORCEDOR (IRE)	6	IRE
120 DIVERSIFY (USA)	5	USA	118 VAZIRABAD (FR)	6	FR
120 GAILO CHOP (FR)	7	AUS	117 ADDEYBB (IRE)	4	GB
120 GRUNT (NZ)	4	AUS	117 ALMANDIN (GER)	8	AUS
120 HAWKBILL (USA)	5	UAE	117 AMAZING KIDS (NZ)	7	HK
120 IMPERIAL HINT (USA)	5	USA	117 BEAUTY ONLY (IRE)	7	HK
120 MIND YOUR BISCUITS (USA)	5	USA	117 BEE JERSEY (USA)	4	USA
120 PAKISTAN STAR (GER)	5	HK	117 CAPTAIN AMERICA (SAF)	8	SAF
120 PUERTO ESCONDIDO (ARG)	5	ARG	117 WESTERN EXPRESS (AUS)	6	HK
120 STRADIVARIUS (IRE)	4	GB	117 CATAPULT (USA)	5	USA
120 SUNGRAZER (JPN)	4	JPN	117 CITY LIGHT (FR)	4	FR
120 TIME WARP (GB)	5	HK	117 CLIFFS OF MOHER (IRE)	4	IRE
120 YOSHIDA (JPN)	4	USA	117 DEFOE (IRE)	4	GB
119 ARMY MULE (USA)	4	USA	117 ELATE (USA)	4	USA
119 CHEVAL GRAND (JPN)	6	JPN	117 GOLD DREAM (JPN)	5	JPN
119 D B PIN (NZ)	6	HK	117 HEART TO HEART (CAN)	7	USA
119 EXULTANT (IRE)	4	HK	117 MARMELO (GB)	5	GB
119 GLORIOUS FOREVER (GB)	4	HK	117 MONKS HOOD (SAF)	4	SAF
119 IMPENDING (AUS)	5	AUS	117 OSCAR PERFORMANCE (USA)	4	USA
119 KEMENTARI (AUS)	4	AUS	117 PLUMATIC (GB)	4	FR
119 LAST WINTER (SAF)	4	SAF	117 RHODODENDRON (IRE)	4	IRE
119 LE ROMAIN (AUS)	6	AUS	117 RUSSIAN REVOLUTION (AUS)	5	AUS
119 LEVENDI (AUS)	4	AUS	117 SADLER'S JOY (USA)	5	USA
119 LIGHTNING SPEAR (GB)	7	GB	117 SALOUEN (IRE)	4	GB
119 MIKKI ROCKET (JPN)	5	JPN	117 SATONO DIAMOND (JPN)	5	JPN
119 PERSIAN KNIGHT (JPN)	4	JPN	117 SISTERCHARLIE (IRE)	4	USA
119 VEGA MAGIC (AUS)	6	AUS	117 STORMY LIBERAL (USA)	6	USA

Rating	Age	Trained
117 **TE AKAU SHARK (NZ)**	4	NZ
117 **THE TIN MAN (GB)**	6	GB
117 **UNDERCOVER AGENT (SAF)**	4	SAF
117 **WUHEIDA (GB)**	4	GB
116 **ACCIDENTAL AGENT (GB)**	4	GB
116 **AFRICAN NIGHT SKY (SAF)**	5	SAF
116 **ALIZEE (AUS)**	4	AUS
116 **BEACH PATROL (USA)**	5	USA
116 **BEAT THE BANK (GB)**	4	GB
116 **LITTLE GIANT (NZ)**	6	HK
116 **BLAIR HOUSE (IRE)**	5	UAE/GB
116 **BOUND FOR NOWHERE (USA)**	4	USA
116 **BRANDO (GB)**	6	GB
116 **CENTURY DREAM (IRE)**	4	GB
116 **CHANNEL MAKER (CAN)**	4	USA
116 **CLINCHER (JPN)**	5	JPN
116 **D'ARGENTO (AUS)**	4	AUS
116 **DISCO PARTNER (USA)**	6	USA
116 **DIVISIDERO (USA)**	6	USA
116 **EYES WIDE OPEN (SAF)**	4	SAF
116 **FINE NEEDLE (JPN)**	5	JPN
116 **FRONTIERSMAN (GB)**	5	GB
116 **GANDHI DI JOB (BRZ)**	5	URU
116 **HELLBENT (AUS)**	6	AUS
116 **HOMESMAN (USA)**	4	AUS
116 **IN HER TIME (AUS)**	6	AUS
116 **K T BRAVE (JPN)**	5	JPN
116 **LEOFRIC (USA)**	5	USA
116 **MAGIC CIRCLE (IRE)**	6	GB
116 **MIRAGE DANCER (GB)**	4	GB
116 **NONKONO YUME (JPN)**	6	JPN
116 **ORDER OF ST GEORGE (IRE)**	6	IRE
116 **PIERATA (AUS)**	4	AUS
116 **REAL STEEL (JPN)**	6	JPN
116 **ROBERT BRUCE (CHI)**	4	USA
116 **ROMAN ROSSO (ARG)**	4	ARG
116 **SHOALS (AUS)**	4	AUS
116 **SIR DANCEALOT (IRE)**	4	GB
116 **SOUTHERN LEGEND (AUS)**	6	HK
116 **FIFTY FIFTY (NZ)**	6	HK
116 **TOSEN STARDOM (JPN)**	7	AUS
116 **UNIQUE BELLA (USA)**	4	USA
116 **WHITMORE (USA)**	5	USA
116 **WORLD APPROVAL (USA)**	6	USA
116 **YUCATAN (IRE)**	4	IRE
115 **A RAVING BEAUTY (GER)**	4	USA
115 **ABASHIRI (SAF)**	6	SAF
115 **ALPHA DELPHINI (GB)**	7	GB
115 **AMBITIOUS (JPN)**	6	AUS
115 **AMERICAN GAL (USA)**	4	USA
115 **ANDA MUCHACHO (IRE)**	4	ITY
115 **ARROCHA (BRZ)**	4	BRZ
115 **AVILIUS (GB)**	4	AUS
115 **BARBON (PER)**	5	PER
115 **BOLD RESPECT (SAF)**	4	SAF
115 **BOWIES HERO (USA)**	4	USA
115 **CALL THE WIND (GB)**	4	FR
115 **COPPER FORCE (SAF)**	5	SAF
115 **CORONET (GB)**	4	GB
115 **DADDYS LIL DARLING (USA)**	4	USA
115 **DANZDANZDANCE (AUS)**	4	NZ
115 **DARK DREAM (AUS)**	4	AUS
115 **DEAUVILLE (IRE)**	5	IRE
115 **DISCREET LOVER (USA)**	5	USA
115 **EAGLE WAY (AUS)**	6	HK
115 **ECUADOR (NZ)**	9	AUS

Rating	Age	Trained
115 **EMOTIONLESS (IRE)**	5	GB
115 **ENGLISH (AUS)**	6	AUS
115 **EQUAL MILLER (ARG)**	4	ARG
115 **FAME GAME (JPN)**	8	JPN
115 **FAULT (USA)**	4	USA
115 **GLORIOUS EMPIRE (IRE)**	7	USA
115 **GOLDEN LEAF (ARG)**	4	PER
115 **HARLEM (GB)**	4	AU
115 **HEAD HONCHO (SAF)**	5	SAF
115 **HI HAPPY (ARG)**	6	USA
115 **HOLDTHASIGREEN (FR)**	6	FR
115 **HOPPERTUNITY (USA)**	7	USA
115 **HUNT (IRE)**	6	USA
115 **IDAHO (IRE)**	5	IRE
115 **ITSINTHEPOST (FR)**	6	USA
115 **KAWI (NZ)**	8	NZ
115 **KINGS WILL DREAM (IRE)**	4	AUS
115 **KITESURF (GB)**	4	FR
115 **LORD GLITTERS (FR)**	5	GB
115 **LUCKY BUBBLES (AUS)**	7	HK
115 **MAKAHIKI (JPN)**	5	JPN
115 **MUNTAHAA (IRE)**	5	GB
115 **MUSTASHRY (GB)**	5	GB
115 **NATURE STRIP (AUS)**	4	AUS
115 **NEXT SHARES (USA)**	5	USA
115 **NOT LISTENIN'TOME (AUS)**	8	HK
115 **OH SUSANNA (AUS)**	4	SAF
115 **PAVEL (USA)**	4	USA
115 **PEACEFUL STATE (AUS)**	4	AUS
115 **PROCTOR'S LEDGE (USA)**	4	USA
115 **QUARTETO DE CORDAS (BRZ)**	4	BRZ
115 **RANSOM THE MOON (CAN)**	6	USA
115 **SAIL SOUTH (SAF)**	8	SAF
115 **SAVVY COUP (NZ)**	4	NZ
115 **SELCOURT (USA)**	4	USA
115 **SERGEANT HARDY (SAF)**	5	SAF
115 **SHOWTIME (AUS)**	4	AUS
115 **SINGAPORE SLING (SAF)**	5	HK
115 **SIXTIES SONG (ARG)**	5	ARG
115 **SPIRIT OF VALOR (USA)**	4	IRE
115 **STORM RODRIGO (CHI)**	4	CH
115 **SUEDOIS (FR)**	7	GB
115 **SURCHARGE (SAF)**	4	SAF
115 **TALISMANIC (GB)**	5	FR
115 **PING HAI STAR (NZ)**	5	HK
115 **TOSEN BASIL (JPN)**	6	AUS
115 **TRAP FOR FOOLS (AUS)**	5	AUS
115 **UNFORGOTTEN (AUS)**	4	AUS
115 **UNI (GB)**	6	USA
115 **VA BANK (IRE)**	6	GER
115 **VALE DORI (ARG)**	4	AUS
115 **VIDDORA (AUS)**	6	AUS
115 **VIN DE DANCE (NZ)**	4	NZ
115 **VOODOO LAD (AUS)**	7	AUS
115 **WHO SHOT THEBARMAN (NZ)**	10	AUS
115 **WIN BRIGHT (JPN)**	4	JPN
115 **WOW CAT (CHI)**	4	USA
115 **WREN'S DAY (GB)**	4	FR
115 **X Y JET (USA)**	6	USA
115 **YAMAKATSU ACE (JPN)**	6	JPN
115 **YOUNGSTAR (AUS)**	4	AUS
114 **AIR PILOT (GB)**	9	GB
114 **ALJAZZI (GB)**	6	GB
114 **BATEEL (IRE)**	6	FR
114 **CALLED TO THE BAR (IRE)**	4	FR
114 **CASPIAN PRINCE (IRE)**	9	GB

Rating	Age	Trained
114 COUNT OCTAVE (GB)	4	GB
114 DURETTO (GB)	6	GB
114 GOLD VIBE (IRE)	5	FR
114 INNS OF COURT (IRE)	4	FR
114 KHAN (GER)	4	GER
114 RARE RHYTHM (GB)	6	UAE/GB
114 SHEIKHZAYEDROAD (GB)	9	GB
114 STORMY ANTARCTIC (GB)	5	GB
114 WAY TO PARIS (GB)	5	FR
114 WEEKENDER (GB)	4	GB
113 BRETON ROCK (GB)	8	GB
113 DEGAS (GER)	5	GER
113 DUTCH CONNECTION (GB)	6	GB
113 FOREST RANGER (IRE)	4	GB
113 JIMMY TWO TIMES (FR)	5	FR
113 LIMATO (IRE)	6	GB
113 MORANDO (FR)	5	GB
113 NONZA (FR)	4	FR
113 ONE MASTER (GB)	4	GB
113 RED VERDON (USA)	5	GB
113 ROYAL JULIUS (IRE)	5	FR
113 SOUND CHECK (GER)	5	GER
113 TIBERIAN (FR)	6	FR
113 URBAN FOX (GB)	4	GB
113 WINDSTOSS (GER)	4	GER
113 WONNEMOND (GER)	5	GER
112 ALGOMETER (GB)	5	GB
112 ALMODOVAR (IRE)	6	GB
112 COLOMANO (GB)	4	GER
112 DANEHILL KODIAC (GB)	5	GB
112 DESERT SKYLINE (IRE)	4	GB
112 DONJUAN TRIUMPHANT (IRE)	5	GB
112 FABRICATE (GB)	6	GB
112 GIFTED MASTER (IRE)	5	GB
112 GUIGNOL (GER)	6	GER
112 ICE BREEZE (GB)	4	FR
112 LARAAIB (IRE)	4	GB
112 LESHLAA (USA)	4	UAE/GB
112 MABS CROSS (GB)	4	GB
112 NOOR AL HAWA (FR)	5	FR
112 ORIENTAL EAGLE (GER)	4	GER
112 PRESLEY (ITY)	5	ITY
112 RIVEN LIGHT (IRE)	6	IRE
112 SUBWAY DANCER (IRE)	6	CHR
112 THOMAS HOBSON (GB)	8	IRE
112 WHISKY BARON (AUS)	6	GB
111 ABOVE THE REST (IRE)	7	GB
111 BARSANTI (IRE)	6	GB
111 D'BAI (IRE)	4	UAE/GB
111 DAL HARRAILD (GB)	5	GB
111 DEVASTAR (GER)	6	GER
111 EZIYRA (IRE)	4	IRE
111 FINCHE (GB)	4	FR
111 FINSBURY SQUARE (IRE)	6	FR
111 GOLDEN LEGEND (FR)	4	FR
111 HAMADA (GB)	4	GB
111 KACHY (GB)	5	GB
111 MAKING LIGHT (IRE)	4	IRE
111 MILLE ET MILLE (GB)	8	FR
111 MORGAN LE FAYE (GB)	4	FR
111 MUSTAJEER (GB)	5	IRE
111 NIGHT MUSIC (GER)	5	GB
111 OH THIS IS US (IRE)	5	GB
111 PRINCE OF ARRAN (GB)	5	GB
111 PROJECTION (GB)	5	GB
111 ROYAL LINE (GB)	4	GB
111 SO BELOVED (GB)	8	GB
111 SON CESIO (FR)	7	FR
111 SON OF REST (GB)	4	IRE
111 TRUE SELF (IRE)	5	IRE
111 WAI KEY STAR (GER)	5	GER
111 WASHINGTON DC (IRE)	5	IRE
111 ZABEEL PRINCE (IRE)	5	GB
110 ALIGNEMENT (GB)	5	FR
110 CALL TO MIND (GB)	4	GB
110 CHAIN OF DAISIES (GB)	6	GB
110 CHASEDOWN (IRE)	4	ITY
110 CROWNED EAGLE (GB)	4	GB
110 DIPLOMAT (GER)	7	GER
110 DOLPHIN VISTA (IRE)	5	GB
110 DREAMFIELD (GB)	4	GB
110 EUGINIO (IRE)	4	GB
110 GAME STARTER (IRE)	4	GB
110 GARLINGARI (FR)	7	GB
110 GENIALE (JPN)	4	JPN
110 GOD GIVEN (GB)	4	GB
110 GRAPHITE (FR)	4	FR
110 HIT THE BID (GB)	4	IRE
110 HORSEPLAY (GB)	4	GB
110 I KIRK (SWE)	4	SWE
110 KARAR (GB)	6	FR
110 LARCHMONT LAD (IRE)	4	GB
110 MAX DYNAMITE (FR)	8	IRE
110 MR LUPTON (IRE)	5	GB
110 NEARLY CAUGHT (IRE)	8	GB
110 OPAL TIARA (IRE)	5	GB
110 PINCHECK (IRE)	4	IRE
110 PSYCHEDELIC FUNK (IRE)	4	IRE
110 SECOND STEP (IRE)	7	GB
110 SHARJA BRIDGE (GB)	4	GB
110 TAAREEF (USA)	5	FR
110 TEODORO (IRE)	4	GB
110 TOAST OF NEW YORK (USA)	7	GB
110 TWILIGHT PAYMENT (IRE)	5	IRE
110 UNFORGETABLE FILLY (IRE)	4	GB
110 WALSINGHAM (GER)	4	GER
110 ZONDERLAND (GB)	5	GB

RACEFORM CHAMPIONS 2018

ONLY HORSES WHICH HAVE RUN IN EUROPE ARE INCLUDED

FOUR-YEAR-OLDS AND UP

CRACKSMAN 131	HARRY ANGEL 127
BATTAASH 129	ENABLE 126
POET'S WORD 128	BENBATL 124
CRYSTAL OCEAN 127	CLOTH OF STARS 123

THREE-YEAR-OLD COLT

ROARING LION 127	U S NAVY FLAG 122
MASAR 122	KEW GARDENS 121
SAXON WARRIOR 122	EXPERT EYE 120

THREE-YEAR-OLD FILLY

ALPHA CENTAURI 124	POLYDREAM 119
MAGICAL 121	LAURENS 117
SEA OF CLASS 121	WIND CHIMES 117

SPRINTER

BATTAASH 129	MERCHANT NAVY 122
HARRY ANGEL 127	U S NAVY FLAG 122
BLUE POINT 123	

STAYER

KEW GARDENS 121	TORCEDOR 119
STRADIVARIUS 121	VAZIRABAD 119
ORDER OF ST GEORGE 119	

TWO-YEAR-OLD COLT

TOO DARN HOT 126	JASH 119
QUORTO 121	ADVERTISE 118
TEN SOVEREIGNS 120	ANTHONY VAN DYCK 118

TWO-YEAR-OLD FILLY

PRETTY POLLYANNA 115	FAIRYLAND 112
IRIDESSA 114	SKITTER SCATTER 112
SIGNORA CABELLO 113	

MEDIAN TIMES 2019

The following Raceform median times are used in the calculation of the Split Second speed figures. They represent a true average time for the distance, which has been arrived at after looking at the winning times for all races over each distance within the past five years, except for those restricted to two or three-year-olds.

Some current race distances have been omitted as they have not yet had a sufficient number of races run over them to produce a reliable average time.

ASCOT

5f 1m 0.70	1m Straight 1m 41.40	1m 7f 209y 3m 33.30
6f 1m 13.70	1m 1f 212y 2m 7.70	2m 3f 210y 4m 22.00
7f 1m 27.50	1m 3f 211y 2m 32.60	2m 5f 143y 4m 43.60
7f 213y Round 1m 40.60	1m 6f 34y 3m 4.30	

AYR

5f 58.40	1m 1m 42.80	2m 5f 26y 2m 58.40
5f 110y 1m 6.50	1m 1f 20y 2m 0.20	1m 7f 3m 27.00
6f 1m 13.10	1m 2f 2m 12.40	2m 1f 105y 4m 1.50
7f 50y 1m 32.50		

BATH

5f 10y 1m 2.00	1m 2f 37y 2m 11.10	1m 6f 3m 6.10
5f 160y 1m 11.10	1m 3f 137y 2m 30.80	2m 1f 24y 3m 51.40
1m 1m 41.70	1m 5f 11y 2m 52.80	

BEVERLEY

5f 1m 2.90	1m 100y 1m 46.40	1m 4f 23y 2m 38.80
7f 96y 1m 32.60	1m 1f 207y 2m 5.70	2m 32y 3m 37.90

BRIGHTON

5f 60y 1m 3.00	6f 210y 1m 23.80	1m 1f 207y 2m 5.00
5f 215y 1m 11.10	7f 211y 1m 36.90	1m 3f 198y 2m 36.00

CARLISLE

5f 1m 2.10	7f 173y 1m 40.00	1m 6f 32y 3m 11.60
5f 193y 1m 14.60	1m 1f 1m 59.00	2m 1f 47y 3m 54.30
6f 195y 1m 28.00	1m 3f 39y 2m 29.70	

CATTERICK

5f 1m 0.50	7f 6y 1m 27.40	1m 5f 192y 3m 7.60
5f 212y 1m 13.60	1m 4f 13y 2m 40.60	1m 7f 189y 3m 36.00

CHELMSFORD (A.W)

5f 1m 0.20	1m 1m 39.90	1m 6f 3m 3.20
6f 1m 13.70	1m 2f 2m 8.60	2m 3m 30.00
7f 1m 27.20	1m 5f 66y 2m 53.60	

CHEPSTOW

5f 16y 59.40	1m 14y 1m 36.00	2m 3m 42.10
6f 16y 1m 11.50	1m 2f 2m 12.80	2m 2f 4m 9.90
7f 16y 1m 23.90	1m 4f 2m 40.30	

CHESTER

5f 15y 1m 2.10	7f 127y 1m 35.70	1m 5f 84y 2m 56.60
5f 110y 1m 9.00	1m 2f 70y 2m 14.30	1m 6f 87y 3m 9.80
6f 17y 1m 15.50	1m 3f 75y 2m 27.40	1m 7f 196y 3m 31.90
7f 1y 1m 27.50	1m 4f 63y 2m 42.20	2m 2f 140y 4m 4.60

DONCASTER

5f 3y.................................. 59.60	7f 6y.................................1m 26.40	1m 3f 197y....................2m 36.60
5f 143y.............................1m 8.10	7f 213y Round....................1m 40.80	1m 6f 115y....................3m 11.60
6f 2y..............................1m 12.70	1m Straight........................1m 40.20	2m 109y........................3m 40.40
6f 111y...........................1m 19.60	1m 2f 43y..........................2m 12.30	2m 1f 197y....................3m 55.00

EPSOM

5f.. 55.30	7f 3y	1m 2f 17y......................2m 10.00
6f 3y................................1m 9.90	1m 113y............................1m 46.40	1m 4f 6y........................2m 40.80

FFOS LAS

5f.. 59.00	1m....................................1m 42.90	1m 6f..............................3m 8.60
6f....................................1m 10.90	1m 2f................................2m 12.70	2m..................................3m 36.70
7f 80y.............................1m 33.10	1m 3f 209y........................2m 40.20	

GOODWOOD

5f.. 58.10	1m 1f 11y..........................1m 57.40	1m 6f..............................3m 3.70
6f....................................1m 12.10	1m 1f 197y........................2m 8.90	2m..................................3m 30.90
7f....................................1m 26.70	1m 3f 44y..........................2m 28.30	2m 4f 134y....................4m 31.80
1m...................................1m 39.20	1m 3f 218y........................2m 39.60	

HAMILTON

5f 7y................................1m 0.40	1m 1f 35y..........................1m 59.00	1m 4f 15y......................2m 38.60
6f 6y...............................1m 12.70	1m 3f 15y..........................2m 25.50	1m 5f 16y......................2m 54.70
1m 68y.............................1m 48.40		

HAYDOCK

5f....................................1m 0.40	7f 212y Inner.....................1m 42.70	1m 3f 175y....................2m 33.30
5f Inner............................1m 0.40	1m 37y..............................1m 44.90	1m 6f Inner.....................3m 4.60
6f....................................1m 13.90	1m 2f 42y Inner.................2m 10.80	1m 6f..............................3m 4.60
6f Inner...........................1m 13.90	1m 2f 100y........................2m 16.60	2m 45y Inner.................3m 36.70
6f 212y Inner...................1m 29.30	1m 3f 140y Inner...............2m 33.30	2m 45y..........................3m 36.70
7f 37y.............................1m 31.40		

KEMPTON (A.W)

5f....................................1m 0.50	1m....................................1m 39.80	1m 3f 219y....................2m 34.50
6f....................................1m 13.10	1m 1f 219y........................2m 8.00	1m 7f 218y....................3m 10.10
7f....................................1m 26.00	1m 2f 219y........................2m 21.90	

LEICESTER

5f....................................1m 1.80	7f....................................1m 25.70	1m 2f..............................2m 9.20
6f....................................1m 12.10	1m 53y..............................1m 46.30	1m 3f 179y....................2m 35.00

LINGFIELD

4f 217y.............................. 58.70	7f 135y.............................1m 31.70	1m 3f 133y....................2m 34.00
6f....................................1m 11.50	1m 1f................................1m 56.90	1m 6f..............................3m 11.20
7f....................................1m 24.30	1m 2f................................2m 12.20	2m 68y..........................3m 36.00

LINGFIELD (A.W)

5f 6y................................ 58.80	1m 1y................................1m 38.20	1m 5f..............................2m 46.00
6f 1y...............................1m 11.90	1m 2f................................2m 6.60	1m 7f 169y....................3m 25.70
7f 1y...............................1m 24.80	1m 4f................................2m 33.00	

MUSSELBURGH

5f 1y	59.70	1m 208y	1m 53.10	1m 5f 216y	3m 3.90
7f 33y	1m 29.00	1m 4f 104y	2m 44.50	1m 7f 217y	3m 31.50
1m 2y	1m 40.00	1m 5f	2m 51.70		

NEWBURY

5f 34y	1m 1.50	1m Round	1m 40.50	1m 5f 61y	2m 54.40
6f	1m 13.20	1m 1f	1m 55.70	2m	3m 39.40
6f 110y	1m 20.10	1m 2f	2m 9.70	2m 110y	3m 46.30
7f Straight	1m 27.00	1m 3f	2m 23.20	2m 2f	4m 6.80
1m Straight	1m 39.90	1m 4f	2m 38.00		

NEWCASTLE (A.W)

5f	59.50	1m 5y	1m 38.60	1m 4f 98y	2m 41.10
6f	1m 12.50	1m 2f 42y	2m 10.40	2m 56y	3m 35.20
7f 14y	1m 26.20				

NEWMARKET (ROWLEY MILE)

5f	59.10	1m 1f	1m 51.10	1m 6f	2m 57.10
6f	1m 11.90	1m 2f	2m 5.40	2m	3m 29.30
7f	1m 25.40	1m 4f	2m 32.50	2m 2f	3m 55.50
1m	1m 38.40				

NEWMARKET (JULY COURSE)

5f	58.70	1m	1m 40.00	1m 5f	2m 45.90
6f	1m 12.10	1m 2f	2m 7.10	1m 6f	2m 59.90
7f	1m 25.70	1m 4f	2m 33.90	2m	3m 28.40

NOTTINGHAM

5f 8y Inner	1m 0.20	1m 75y Inner	1m 46.70	1m 6f Inner	3m 6.40
5f 8y	1m 0.20	1m 2f 50y	2m 13.40	1m 6f	3m 6.40
6f 18y	1m 13.80	1m 2f 50y Inner	2m 13.40	2m	3m 34.50
1m 75y	1m 46.70				

PONTEFRACT

5f 3y	1m 3.90	1m 2f 5y	2m 15.00	2m 2f 2y	4m 7.70
6f	1m 17.10	1m 4f 5y	2m 41.10	2m 5f 139y	4m 58.00
1m 6y	1m 45.90	2m 1f 27y	3m 49.20		

REDCAR

5f	58.50	7f 219y	1m 36.60	1m 2f 1y	2m 6.90
5f 217y	1m 12.40	1m 1f	1m 54.50	1m 5f 218y	3m 7.00
7f	1m 25.40				

RIPON

5f	59.40	1m 1f	1m 54.70	1m 4f 10y	2m 36.30
6f	1m 12.50	1m 1f 170y	2m 5.00	2m	3m 32.40
1m	1m 41.00	1m 2f 190y	2m 19.00		

SALISBURY

5f	1m 0.50	1m	1m 43.50	1m 4f 5y	2m 37.60
6f	1m 14.50	1m 1f 201y	2m 10.50	1m 6f 44y	3m 6.60
6f 213y	1m 28.70				

SANDOWN

5f 10y	1m 1.30	1m 1f	1m 56.30	1m 6f	3m 6.00
7f	1m 29.30	1m 1f 209y	2m 10.20	2m 50y	3m 37.90
1m	1m 43.30				

SOUTHWELL (A.W)

4f 214y	59.70	1m 13y	1m 43.70	1m 6f 21y	3m 8.30
6f 16y	1m 16.50	1m 3f 23y	2m 28.00	2m 102y	3m 45.50
7f 14y	1m 30.30	1m 4f 14y	2m 41.00	2m 2f 98y	4m 11.50

THIRSK

5f	59.40	7f	1m 27.60	1m 4f 8y	2m 40.00
6f	1m 12.80	7f 218y	1m 41.70	2m 13y	3m 33.60

WETHERBY

5f 110y	1m 5.80	1m	1m 41.60	1m 6f	3m 7.00
7f	1m 27.20	1m 2f	2m 9.30	2m	3m 33.70

WINDSOR

5f 21y	1m 0.10	1m 31y	1m 44.50	1m 3f 99y	2m 29.70
6f 12y	1m 12.10	1m 2f	2m 9.00		

WOLVERHAMPTON (A.W)

5f 21y	1m 1.90	1m 142y	1m 50.10	1m 5f 219y	3m 8.00
6f 20y	1m 14.50	1m 1f 104y	2m 0.80	2m 120y	3m 43.70
7f 36y	1m 28.80	1m 4f 51y	2m 40.80		

YARMOUTH

5f 42y	1m 1.90	1m 3y	1m 38.20	1m 3f 104y	2m 27.80
6f 3y	1m 12.60	1m 1f 21y	1m 54.50	1m 6f 17y	3m 4.70
7f 3y	1m 25.10	1m 2f 23y	2m 8.80		

YORK

5f	58.20	7f 192y	1m 37.50	1m 3f 188y	2m 33.20
5f 89y	1m 3.60	1m 177y	1m 50.40	1m 5f 188y	3m 0.20
6f	1m 11.60	2m 2f 56y	2m 10.30	2m 56y	3m 33.90
7f	1m 24.60				

RACEFORM RECORD TIMES (FLAT)

ASCOT

DISTANCE	TIME	AGE	WEIGHT	GOING	HORSE	DATE
5f	58.80	2	9-1	Good To Firm	NO NAY NEVER	Jun 20 2013
5f	57.44	6	9-1	Good To Firm	MISS ANDRETTI	Jun 19 2007
6f	1m 12.39	2	9-1	Good To Firm	RAJASINGHE	Jun 20 2017
6f	1m 11.05	3	9-1	Good To Firm	BLUE POINT	May 3 2017
7f	1m 26.55	2	9-0	Good To Firm	MALABAR	Jul 25 2014
7f	1m 24.28	4	8-11	Good To Firm	GALICIAN	Jul 27 2013
7f 213y (Rnd)	1m 39.55	2	8-12	Good	JOSHUA TREE	Sep 26 2009
7f 213y (Rnd)	1m 35.89	3	9-0	Good To Firm	ALPHA CENTAURI	Jun 22 2018
1m (Str)	1m 36.60	4	9-0	Good To Firm	RIBCHESTER	Jun 20 2017
1m 1f 212y	2m 1.90	5	8-11	Good To Firm	THE FUGUE	Jun 18 2014
1m 3f 211y	2m 24.60	4	9-7	Good To Firm	NOVELLIST	Jul 27 2013
1m 7f 209y	3m 24.12	4	8-12	Good To Firm	MIZZOU	Apr 29 2015
2m 3f 210y	4m 16.92	6	9-2	Good To Firm	RITE OF PASSAGE	Jun 17 2010
2m 5f 143y	4m 45.67	7	9-2	Good To Firm	ORIENTAL FOX	Jun 20 2015

AYR

DISTANCE	TIME	AGE	WEIGHT	GOING	HORSE	DATE
5f	56.98	2	8-11	Good	BOOGIE STREET	Sep 18 2003
5f	55.68	3	8-11	Good To Firm	LOOK BUSY	Jun 21 2008
6f	1m 9.73	2	7-10	Good	SIR BERT	Sep 17 1969
6f	1m 8.37	5	8-6	Good To Firm	MAISON DIEU	Jun 21 2008
7f 50y	1m 28.99	2	9-0	Good	TAFAAHUM	Sep 19 2003
7f 50y	1m 26.43	4	9-4	Good To Firm	HAJJAM	May 22 2018
1m	1m 39.18	2	9-7	Good	MOONLIGHTNAVIGATOR	Sep 18 2014
1m	1m 36.00	4	7-13	Firm	SUFI	Sep 16 1959
1m 1f 20y	1m 50.30	4	9-3	Good	RETIREMENT	Sep 19 2003
1m 2f	2m 4.02	4	9-9	Good To Firm	ENDLESS HALL	Jul 17 2000
1m 5f 26y	2m 45.81	4	9-7	Good To Firm	EDEN'S CLOSE	Sep 18 1993
1m 7f	3m 13.16	3	9-4	Good	ROMANY RYE	Sep 19 1991
2m 1f 105y	3m 45.20	4	6-13	Firm	CURRY	Sep 16 1955

BATH

DISTANCE	TIME	AGE	WEIGHT	GOING	HORSE	DATE
5f 10y	59.50	2	9-2	Firm	AMOUR PROPRE	Jul 24 2008
5f 10y	58.75	3	8-12	Firm	ENTICING	May 1 2007
5f 160y	1m 8.70	2	8-12	Firm	QALAHARI	Jul 24 2008
5f 160y	1m 8.10	6	9-0	Firm	MADRACO	May 22 1989
1m 5y	1m 39.51	2	9-2	Firm	NATURAL CHARM	Sep 14 2014
1m 5y	1m 37.20	5	8-12	Good To Firm	ADOBE	Jun 17 2000
1m 5y	1m 37.20	3	8-7	Firm	ALASHA	Aug 18 2002
1m 2f 37y	2m 5.80	3	9-0	Good To Firm	CONNOISSEUR BAY	May 29 1998
1m 3f 137y	2m 25.74	3	9-0	Hard	TOP THE CHARTS	Sep 8 2005
1m 5f 11y	2m 47.20	4	10-0	Firm	FLOWN	Aug 13 1991
2m 1f 24y	3m 43.41	6	7-9	Firm	YAHESKA	Jun 14 2003

BEVERLEY

DISTANCE	TIME	AGE	WEIGHT	GOING	HORSE	DATE
5f	1m 0.89	2	8-12	Good To Firm	LANGAVAT	Jun 8 2013
5f	59.77	5	9-3	Good To Firm	JUDICIAL	Jun 20 2017
7f 96y	1m 31.10	3	9-7	Good To Firm	CHAMPAGNE PRINCE	Aug 10 1995
7f 96y	1m 31.10	2	9-0	Firm	MAJAL	Jul 30 1991
7f 96y	1m 29.50	3	7-8	Firm	WHO'S TEF	Jul 30 1991
1m 100y	1m 43.30	2	9-0	Firm	ARDEN	Sep 24 1986
1m 100y	1m 42.20	3	8-4	Firm	LEGAL CASE	Jun 14 1989
1m 1f 207y	2m 1.00	3	9-7	Good To Firm	EASTERN ARIA	Aug 29 2009
1m 4f 23y	2m 33.35	5	9-2	Good To Firm	TWO JABS	Apr 23 2015
2m 32y	3m 28.62	4	9-11	Good To Firm	CORPUS CHORISTER	Jul 18 2017

BRIGHTON

DISTANCE	TIME	AGE	WEIGHT	GOING	HORSE	DATE
5f 60y	1m 0.10	3	9-0	Firm	BID FOR BLUE	May 6 1993
5f 60y	59.30	3	8-9	Firm	PLAY HEVER GOLF	May 26 1993
5f 215y	1m 8.10	2	8-9	Firm	SONG MIST	Jul 16 1996
5f 215y	1m 7.30	5	9-1	Good To Firm	BLUNDELL LANE	May 4 2000
5f 215y	1m 7.30	3	8-9	Firm	THIRD PARTY	Jun 3 1997
6f 201y	1m 19.90	2	8-11	Hard	RAIN BURST	Sep 15 1988
6f 201y	1m 19.40	4	9-3	Good To Firm	SAWAKI	Sep 3 1991
7f 211y	1m 32.80	2	9-7	Firm	ASIAN PETE	Oct 3 1989
7f 211y	1m 30.50	5	8-11	Firm	MYSTIC RIDGE	May 27 1999
1m 1f 207y	2m 4.70	2	9-0	Good To Soft	ESTEEMED MASTER	Nov 2 2001
1m 1f 207y	1m 57.20	3	9-0	Firm	GET THE MESSAGE	Apr 30 1984
1m 3f 198y	2m 25.80	4	8-2	Firm	NEW ZEALAND	Jul 4 1985

CARLISLE

DISTANCE	TIME	AGE	WEIGHT	GOING	HORSE	DATE
5f	1m 0.10	2	8-5	Firm	LA TORTUGA	Aug 2 1999
5f	58.80	3	9-8	Good To Firm	ESATTO	Aug 21 2002
5f 193y	1m 12.30	2	9-2	Good To Firm	BURRISHOOLE ABBEY	Jun 22 2016
5f 193y	1m 10.83	4	9-0	Good To Firm	BO MCGINTY	Sep 11 2005
6f 195y	1m 24.30	3	8-9	Good To Firm	MARJURITA	Aug 21 2002
7f 173y	1m 35.84	5	8-12	Good To Firm	WAARIF	Jun 27 2018
1m 1f	1m 53.84	3	9-0	Firm	LITTLE JIMBOB	Jun 14 2004
1m 3f 39y	2m 20.46	5	10-0	Good To Firm	AASHEQ	Jun 27 2018
1m 3f 206y	2m 29.13	5	9-8	Good To Firm	TEMPSFORD	Sep 19 2005
1m 6f 32y	3m 2.20	6	8-10	Firm	EXPLOSIVE SPEED	May 26 1994

CATTERICK

DISTANCE	TIME	AGE	WEIGHT	GOING	HORSE	DATE
5f	57.60	2	9-0	Firm	H HARRISON	Oct 8 2002
5f	57.10	4	8-7	Firm	KABCAST	Jul 6 1989
5f 212y	1m 9.44	4	9-4	Firm	CAPTAIN NICK	Jul 11 1978
5f 212y	1m 9.86	9	8-13	Good To Firm	SHARP HAT	May 30 2003
7f 6y	1m 24.10	2	8-11	Firm	LINDA'S FANTASY	Sep 18 1982
7f 6y	1m 22.56	6	8-7	Firm	DIFFERENTIAL	May 31 2003
1m 4f 13y	2m 30.50	3	8-8	Good To Firm	RAHAF	May 30 2003
1m 5f 192y	2m 54.80	3	8-5	Firm	GERYON	May 31 1984
1m 7f 189y	3m 20.80	4	7-11	Firm	BEAN BOY	Jul 8 1982

CHELMSFORD (AW)

DISTANCE	TIME	AGE	WEIGHT	GOING	HORSE	DATE
5f	58.52	2	9-6	Standard	**PRINCE OF ROME**	Sep 20 2018
5f	57.30	7	8-13	Standard	**BROTHER TIGER**	Feb 7 2016
6f	1m 11.19	2	8-13	Standard	**FLORENCIO**	Oct 15 2015
6f	1m 10.00	4	9-2	Standard	**RAUCOUS**	Apr 27 2017
7f	1m 22.59	7	8-0	Standard	**BOY IN THE BAR**	Sep 22 2018
1m	1m 37.15	2	9-3	Standard	**DRAGON MALL**	Sep 26 2015
1m	1m 35.46	4	9-7	Standard	**MINDUROWNBUSINESS**	Nov 23 2015
1m 2f	2m 2.33	8	9-7	Standard	**BANCNUANAHEIREANN**	Nov 5 2015
1m 5f 66y	2m 47.00	4	8-7	Standard	**COORG**	Jan 6 2016
1m 6f	2m 55.65	4	10-0	Standard	**CASTLE COMBE**	Sep 3 2015
2m	3m 55.65	3	9-8	Standard	**DUCHESS OF MARMITE**	Nov 23 2015
2m	3m 22.37	5	9-3	Standard	**NOTARISED**	Mar 3 2016

CHEPSTOW

DISTANCE	TIME	AGE	WEIGHT	GOING	HORSE	DATE
5f 16y	57.60	2	8-11	Firm	**MICRO LOVE**	Jul 8 1986
5f 16y	56.80	3	8-4	Firm	**TORBAY EXPRESS**	Sep 15 1979
6f 16y	1m 8.50	2	9-2	Firm	**NINJAGO**	Jul 27 2012
6f 16y	1m 8.10	3	9-7	Firm	**AMERICA CALLING**	Sep 18 2001
7f 16y	1m 20.80	2	9-0	Good To Firm	**ROYAL AMARETTO**	Sep 12 1996
7f 16y	1m 19.30	3	9-0	Firm	**TARANAKI**	Sep 18 2001
1m 14y	1m 33.10	2	8-11	Good To Firm	**SKI ACADEMY**	Aug 28 1995
1m 14y	1m 31.60	3	8-13	Firm	**STOLI**	Sep 18 2001
1m 2f 36y	2m 4.10	3	8-5	Good To Firm	**ELA ATHENA**	Jul 23 1999
1m 2f 36y	2m 4.10	5	8-9	Hard	**LEONIDAS**	Jul 5 1983
1m 2f 36y	2m 4.10	5	7-8	Good To Firm	**IT'S VARADAN**	Sep 9 1989
1m 4f 23y	2m 31.00	5	8-11	Hard	**THE FRIEND**	Aug 29 1983
1m 4f 23y	2m 31.00	3	8-9	Good To Firm	**SPRITSAIL**	Jul 13 1989
2m 49y	3m 27.70	4	9-0	Good To Firm	**WIZZARD ARTIST**	Jul 1 1989
2m 2f	3m 56.40	5	8-7	Good To Firm	**LAFFAH**	Jul 8 2000

CHESTER

DISTANCE	TIME	AGE	WEIGHT	GOING	HORSE	DATE
5f 15y	59.94	2	9-2	Good To Firm	**LEIBA LEIBA**	Jun 26 2010
5f 15y	58.88	3	8-7	Good To Firm	**PETERKIN**	Jul 11 2014
5f 110y	1m 6.39	2	8-7	Good To Soft	**KINEMATIC**	Sep 27 2014
5f 110y	1m 4.54	5	8-5	Good	**BOSSIPOP**	Sep 1 2018
6f 17y	1m 12.54	2	8-12	Good	**GLASS SLIPPERS**	Sep 1 2018
6f 17y	1m 12.02	5	9-5	Good To Firm	**DEAUVILLE PRINCE**	Jun 13 2015
7f 1y	1m 25.29	2	9-0	Good To Firm	**DUE RESPECT**	Sep 25 2002
7f 1y	1m 23.75	5	8-13	Good To Firm	**THREE GRACES**	Jul 9 2005
7f 127y	1m 32.29	2	9-0	Good To Firm	**BIG BAD BOB**	Sep 25 2002
7f 127y	1m 30.62	5	9-10	Good	**OH THIS IS US**	Sep 1 2018
1m 2f 70y	2m 7.15	3	8-8	Good To Firm	**STOTSFOLD**	Sep 23 2006
1m 3f 75y	2m 22.17	3	8-12	Good To Firm	**PERFECT TRUTH**	May 6 2009
1m 4f 63y	2m 33.70	3	8-10	Good To Firm	**FIGHT YOUR CORNER**	May 7 2002
1m 5f 84y	2m 45.43	5	8-11	Firm	**RAKAPOSHI KING**	May 7 1987
1m 7f 196y	3m 20.33	4	9-0	Good To Firm	**GRAND FROMAGE**	Jul 13 2002
2m 2f 140y	3m 58.89	7	9-2	Good To Firm	**GREENWICH MEANTIME**	May 9 2007

DONCASTER

DISTANCE	TIME	AGE	WEIGHT	GOING	HORSE	DATE
5f 3y	58.04	2	9-1	Good	**GUTAIFAN**	Sep 11 2015
5f 3y	57.31	7	9-10	Good	**TABARET**	Aug 14 2010
5f 143y	1m 5.38	4	9-7	Good	**MUTHMIR**	Sep 13 2014
6f 2y	1m 10.33	2	9-4	Good To Firm	**COMEDY**	Jun 29 2018
6f 2y	1m 9.56	3	8-10	Good To Firm	**PROCLAIM**	May 30 2009
6f 111y	1m 17.19	2	8-9	Good	**MR LUPTON**	Sep 10 2015
7f 6y	1m 22.78	2	9-5	Good	**BASATEEN**	Jul 24 2014
7f 6y	1m 21.81	6	8-7	Good To Firm	**SIGNOR PELTRO**	May 30 2009
7f 213y (Rnd)	1m 38.37	2	8-6	Good To Soft	**ANTONIOLA**	Oct 23 2009
7f 213y (Rnd)	1m 34.46	4	8-12	Good To Firm	**STAYING ON**	Apr 18 2009
1m (Str)	1m 36.72	2	8-12	Good	**DANCE OF FIRE**	Sep 13 2014
1m (Str)	1m 34.95	6	8-9	Firm	**QUICK WIT**	Jul 18 2013
1m 2f 43y	2m 4.81	4	8-13	Good To Firm	**RED GALA**	Sep 12 2007
1m 3f 197y	2m 27.48	3	8-4	Good To Firm	**SWIFT ALHAARTH**	Sep 10 2011
1m 6f 115y	3m 0.44	3	9-0	Good To Firm	**MASKED MARVEL**	Sep 10 2011
2m 109y	3m 34.52	7	9-0	Good To Firm	**INCHNADAMPH**	Nov 10 2007
2m 1f 197y	3m 48.41	4	9-4	Good To Firm	**SEPTIMUS**	Sep 14 2007

EPSOM

DISTANCE	TIME	AGE	WEIGHT	GOING	HORSE	DATE
5f	55.02	2	8-9	Good To Firm	**PRINCE ASLIA**	Jun 9 1995
5f	53.60	4	9-5	Firm	**INDIGENOUS**	Jun 2 1960
6f 3y	1m 7.85	2	8-11	Good To Firm	**SHOWBROOK**	Jun 5 1991
6f 3y	1m 7.21	5	9-13	Good To Firm	**MAC GILLE EOIN**	Jul 2 2009
7f 3y	1m 21.30	2	8-9	Good To Firm	**RED PEONY**	Jul 29 2004
7f 3y	1m 20.15	4	8-7	Firm	**CAPISTRANO**	Jun 7 1972
1m 113y	1m 42.80	2	8-5	Good To Firm	**NIGHTSTALKER**	Aug 30 1988
1m 113y	1m 40.75	3	8-6	Good To Firm	**SYLVA HONDA**	Jun 5 1991
1m 2f 17y	2m 3.50	5	7-11	Firm	**CROSSBOW**	Jun 7 1967
1m 4f 6y	2m 31.33	3	9-0	Good To Firm	**WORKFORCE**	Jun 5 2010

FFOS LAS

DISTANCE	TIME	AGE	WEIGHT	GOING	HORSE	DATE
5f	57.06	2	9-3	Good To Firm	**MR MAJEIKA**	May 5 2011
5f	56.35	5	8-8	Good	**HAAJES**	Sep 12 2009
6f	1m 9.00	2	9-5	Good To Firm	**WONDER OF QATAR**	Sep 14 2014
6f	1m 7.80	8	8-4	Good To Firm	**THE JAILER**	May 5 2011
1m	1m 39.36	2	9-2	Good To Firm	**HALA HALA**	Sep 2 2013
1m	1m 37.12	5	9-0	Good To Firm	**ZEBRANO**	May 5 2011
1m 2f	2m 4.85	8	8-12	Good To Firm	**PELHAM CRESCENT**	May 5 2011
1m 3f 209y	2m 31.58	4	8-9	Good To Firm	**MEN DON'T CRY**	Jul 23 2013
1m 6f	2m 58.61	4	9-7	Good To Firm	**LADY ECLAIR**	Jul 12 2010
2m	3m 25.42	4	9-3	Good To Firm	**LONG JOHN SILVER**	Jul 24 2018

GOODWOOD

DISTANCE	TIME	AGE	WEIGHT	GOING	HORSE	DATE
5f	57.14	2	9-1	Good	YALTA	Jul 27 2016
5f	56.01	5	9-0	Good To Firm	RUDI'S PET	Jul 27 1999
5f	1m 9.81	2	8-11	Good To Firm	BACHIR	Jul 28 1999
5f	1m 9.10	6	9-0	Good To Firm	TAMAGIN	Sep 12 2009
7f	1m 24.99	2	8-11	Good To Firm	EKRAAR	Jul 29 1999
7f	1m 23.88	3	8-7	Firm	BRIEF GLIMPSE	Jul 25 1995
1m	1m 37.21	2	9-0	Good	CALDRA	Sep 9 2006
1m	1m 35.61	4	8-9	Good To Firm	SPECTAIT	Aug 4 2006
1m 1f 11y	1m 56.27	2	9-3	Good To Firm	DORDOGNE	Sep 22 2010
1m 1f 11y	1m 52.81	3	9-6	Good	VENA	Jul 27 1995
1m 1f 197y	2m 2.81	3	9-3	Good To Firm	ROAD TO LOVE	Aug 3 2006
1m 3f 44y	2m 22.77	3	9-3	Good	KHALIDI	May 26 2017
1m 3f 218y	2m 31.39	3	9-1	Firm	CROSS COUNTER	Aug 4 2018
1m 6f	2m 57.61	4	9-6	Good To Firm	MEEZNAH	Jul 28 2011
2m	3m 21.55	5	9-10	Good To Firm	YEATS	Aug 3 2006
2m 4f	4m 11.75	3	7-10	Firm	LUCKY MOON	Aug 2 1990

HAMILTON

DISTANCE	TIME	AGE	WEIGHT	GOING	HORSE	DATE
5f 7y	57.95	2	8-8	Good To Firm	ROSE BLOSSOM	May 29 2009
5f 6y	1m 10.00	3	8-12	Good To Firm	BREAK THE CODE	Aug 24 1999
5f 6y	1m 9.30	4	8-7	Firm	MARCUS GAME	Jul 11 1974
1m 68y	1m 45.46	2	9-5	Good To Firm	LAAFIRAAQ	Sep 20 2015
1m 68y	1m 42.70	6	7-7	Firm	CRANLEY	Sep 25 1972
1m 1f 35y	1m 53.60	5	9-6	Good To Firm	REGENT'S SECRET	Aug 10 2005
1m 3f 15y	2m 18.66	3	9-3	Good To Firm	POSTPONED	Jul 18 2014
1m 4f 16y	2m 30.52	5	9-10	Good To Firm	RECORD BREAKER	Jun 10 2009
1m 5f 16y	2m 45.10	6	9-6	Firm	MENTALASANYTHIN	Jun 14 1995

HAYDOCK

DISTANCE	TIME	AGE	WEIGHT	GOING	HORSE	DATE
5f	58.56	2	8-2	Good To Firm	BARRACUDA BOY	Aug 11 2012
5f	56.39	5	9-4	Firm	BATED BREATH	May 26 2012
5f (Inner)	58.51	2	9-1	Good	FOUR DRAGONS	Oct 14 2016
5f (Inner)	57.38	7	9-12	Good To Firm	FOXY FOREVER	Jul 21 2017
6f	1m 8.56	3	9-0	Firm	HARRY ANGEL	May 27 2017
6f	1m 10.98	4	9-9	Good To Firm	WOLFHOUND	Sep 4 1993
6f (Inner)	1m 9.40	7	9-3	Good To Firm	MARKAB	Sep 4 2010
6f (Inner)	1m 10.58	2	9-2	Good To Firm	PRESTBURY PARK	Jul 21 2017
6f 212y	1m 27.29	2	9-2	Good To Firm	NAYEF ROAD	Aug 10 2018
6f 212y (Inner)	1m 27.29	2	9-2	Good To Firm	DROGON	Jul 5 2018
6f 212y (Inner)	1m 25.28	3	9-8	Good To Firm	MYSTIC FLIGHT	Jun 7 2018
7f 37y	1m 27.57	2	9-2	Good To Firm	CONTRAST	Aug 5 2016
7f 37y	1m 25.50	3	8-11	Good	FORGE	Sep 1 2016
7f 212y (Inner)	1m 37.80	3	9-4	Good To Firm	SIDEWINDER	May 26 2017
1m 37y	1m 38.50	4	8-11	Good To Firm	EXPRESS HIMSELF	Jun 10 2015
1m 2f 42y (Inner)	2m 7.25	3	8-9	Good To Firm	LARAAIB	May 26 2017
1m 2f 100y	2m 7.71	3	8-8	Good To Firm	ROYAL ARTILLERY	Aug 6 2016
1m 3f 140y (Inner)	2m 30.37	3	9-7	Good To Firm	QUANTATMENTAL	Jun 7 2018
1m 3f 175y	2m 25.53	4	8-12	Good To Firm	NUMBER THEORY	May 24 2012
1m 6f	2m 55.20	5	9-9	Good To Firm	HUFF AND PUFF	Sep 7 2012
2m 45y	3m 26.98	5	8-13	Good To Firm	DE RIGUEUR	Jun 8 2013

KEMPTON (AW)

DISTANCE	TIME	AGE	WEIGHT	GOING	HORSE	DATE
5f	58.96	2	8-6	Standard	**GLAMOROUS SPIRIT**	Nov 28 2008
5f	58.07	5	8-12	Standard To Slow	**A MOMENTOFMADNESS**	Apr 7 2018
6f	1m 11.02	2	9-1	Standard To Slow	**INVINCIBLE ARMY**	Sep 9 2017
6f	1m 9.79	4	8-11	Standard	**TRINITYELITEDOTCOM**	Mar 29 2014
7f	1m 23.79	2	8-0	Standard	**ELSAAKB**	Nov 8 2017
7f	1m 23.10	6	9-9	Standard	**SIRIUS PROSPECT**	Nov 20 2014
1m	1m 37.26	2	9-0	Standard	**CECCHINI**	Nov 8 2017
1m	1m 35.73	3	8-9	Standard	**WESTERN ARISTOCRAT**	Sep 15 2011
1m 1f 219y	2m 2.93	3	8-11	Standard To Slow	**PLY**	Sep 25 2017
1m 2f 219y	2m 16.09	4	8-7	Standard	**SALUTATION**	Mar 29 2014
1m 3f 219y	2m 28.99	3	9-3	Standard	**SPRING OF FAME**	Nov 7 2012
1m 7f 218y	3m 21.50	4	8-12	Standard	**COLOUR VISION**	May 2 2012

LEICESTER

DISTANCE	TIME	AGE	WEIGHT	GOING	HORSE	DATE
5f 2y	58.40	2	9-0	Firm	**CUTTING BLADE**	Jun 9 1986
5f 2y	57.85	5	9-5	Good To Firm	**THE JOBBER**	Sep 18 2006
5f 218y	1m 9.99	2	9-0	Good	**EL MANATI**	Aug 1 2012
5f 218y	1m 9.12	6	8-12	Good To Firm	**PETER ISLAND**	Apr 25 2009
7f 9y	1m 22.60	2	9-0	Good To Firm	**MARIE DE MEDICI**	Oct 6 2009
7f 9y	1m 20.80	3	8-7	Firm	**FLOWER BOWL**	Jun 9 1986
1m 53y	1m 44.05	2	8-11	Good To Firm	**CONGRESSIONAL**	Sep 6 2005
1m 53y	1m 41.89	5	9-7	Good To Firm	**VAINGLORY**	Jun 18 2009
1m 1f 216y	2m 5.30	2	9-1	Good To Firm	**WINDSOR CASTLE**	Oct 14 1996
1m 1f 216y	2m 2.40	3	8-11	Firm	**EFFIGY**	Nov 4 1985
1m 1f 216y	2m 2.40	4	9-6	Good To Firm	**LADY ANGHARAD**	Jun 18 2000
1m 3f 179y	2m 27.10	5	8-12	Good To Firm	**MURGHEM**	Jun 18 2000

LINGFIELD (TURF)

DISTANCE	TIME	AGE	WEIGHT	GOING	HORSE	DATE
4f 217y	56.76	2	9-2	Good	**GLORY FIGHTER**	May 11 2018
4f 217y	56.09	3	9-4	Good To Firm	**WHITECREST**	Sep 16 2011
6f	1m 8.36	2	8-12	Good To Firm	**FOLLY BRIDGE**	Sep 8 2009
6f	1m 8.13	6	9-8	Firm	**CLEAR PRAISE**	Aug 10 2013
7f	1m 20.55	2	8-11	Good To Firm	**HIKING**	Aug 17 2013
7f	1m 20.05	3	8-5	Good To Firm	**PERFECT TRIBUTE**	May 7 2011
7f 135y	1m 29.32	2	9-3	Good To Firm	**DUNDONNELL**	Aug 4 2012
7f 135y	1m 26.73	3	8-6	Good To Firm	**HIAAM**	Jul 11 1987
1m 1f	1m 52.40	4	9-2	Good To Firm	**QUANDARY**	Jul 15 1995
1m 2f	2m 4.61	3	9-3	Firm	**USRAN**	Jul 15 1989
1m 3f 133y	2m 23.95	3	8-5	Firm	**NIGHT-SHIRT**	Jul 14 1990
1m 6f	2m 59.10	5	9-5	Firm	**IBN BEY**	Jul 1 1989
2m 68y	3m 23.71	3	9-5	Good To Firm	**LAURIES CRUSADOR**	Aug 13 1988

LINGFIELD (AW)

DISTANCE	TIME	AGE	WEIGHT	GOING	HORSE	DATE
5f 6y	58.11	2	9-5	Standard	IVORS REBEL	Sep 23 2014
5f 6y	56.67	5	8-12	Standard	LADIES ARE FOREVER	Mar 16 2013
5f 1y	1m 9.76	2	9-4	Standard	RED IMPRESSION	Nov 24 2018
6f 1y	1m 8.92	6	9-0	Standard	KACHY	Feb 2 2019
7f 1y	1m 22.67	2	9-3	Standard	COMPLICIT	Nov 23 2013
7f 1y	1m 21.92	5	9-6	Standard	GREY MIRAGE	Feb 22 2014
1m 1y	1m 35.84	2	9-5	Standard	BRAVE HERO	Nov 25 2015
1m 1y	1m 34.34	5	8-13	Standard	MY TARGET	Dec 31 2016
1m 2f	2m 0.99	4	9-0	Standard	FARRAAJ	Mar 16 2013
1m 4f	2m 26.99	6	9-11	Standard	PINZOLO	Jan 21 2017
1m 5f	2m 39.70	3	8-10	Standard	HIDDEN GOLD	Oct 30 2014
1m 7f 169y	3m 15.18	4	9-1	Standard	WINNING STORY	Apr 14 2017

MUSSELBURGH

DISTANCE	TIME	AGE	WEIGHT	GOING	HORSE	DATE
5f 1y	57.66	2	9-2	Good To Firm	IT DONT COME EASY	Jun 3 2017
5f 1y	56.77	9	9-10	Good To Firm	CASPIAN PRINCE	Jun 3 2018
7f 33y	1m 27.46	2	8-8	Good	DURHAM REFLECTION	Sep 14 2009
7f 33y	1m 25.00	9	8-8	Good To Firm	KALK BAY	Jun 4 2016
1m 2y	1m 40.34	2	8-12	Good To Firm	SUCCESSION	Sep 26 2004
1m 2y	1m 36.83	3	9-5	Good To Firm	GINGER JACK	Jul 13 2010
1m 208y	1m 50.42	8	8-11	Good To Firm	DHAULAR DHAR	Sep 3 2010
1m 4f 104y	2m 36.80	3	8-3	Good To Firm	HARRIS TWEED	Jun 5 2010
1m 5f	2m 46.41	3	9-5	Good To Firm	ALCAEUS	Sep 29 2013
1m 5f 216y	2m 57.98	7	8-5	Good To Firm	JONNY DELTA	Apr 18 2014
1m 7f 217y	3m 25.62	4	8-3	Good To Firm	ALDRETH	Jun 13 2015

NEWBURY

DISTANCE	TIME	AGE	WEIGHT	GOING	HORSE	DATE
5f 34y	59.19	2	8-6	Good To Firm	SUPERSTAR LEO	Jul 22 2000
5f 34y	58.44	5	9-1	Good To Firm	ROBOT BOY	Apr 17 2015
5f 8y	1m 11.07	2	8-4	Good To Firm	BAHATI	May 30 2009
5f 8y	1m 9.42	3	8-11	Good To Firm	NOTA BENE	May 13 2005
5f 110y	1m 18.06	2	9-5	Good To Firm	TWIN SAILS	Jun 11 2015
7f (Str)	1m 23.04	2	8-11	Good To Firm	HAAFHD	Aug 15 2003
7f (Str)	1m 20.80	3	9-0	Good To Firm	MUHAARAR	Apr 18 2015
1m	1m 37.50	2	9-1	Good To Firm	WINGED CUPID	Sep 16 2005
1m	1m 33.59	6	9-0	Firm	RAKTI	May 14 2005
1m 1f	1m 49.65	3	8-0	Good To Firm	HOLTYE	May 21 1995
1m 2f	1m 1.29	3	8-7	Good To Firm	WALL STREET	Jul 20 1996
1m 3f 5y	2m 16.54	3	8-9	Good To Firm	GRANDERA	Sep 22 2001
1m 4f 5y	2m 28.26	4	9-7	Good To Firm	AZAMOUR	Jul 23 2005
1m 5f 61y	2m 44.90	5	10-0	Good To Firm	MYSTIC HILL	Jul 20 1996

NEWCASTLE (AW)

Distance	Time	Age	Weight	Going	HORSE	Date
5f	57.78	3	8-9	Standard	ASTRAEA	Dec 15 2018
6f	1m 9.86	3	9-2	Standard	UNABATED	Mar 22 2017
7f 14y	1m 24.48	4	9-7	Standard	ALICE THORNTON	Oct 14 2016
1m 5y	1m 36.28	5	9-10	Standard	AUSPICION	Sep 12 2017
1m 2f 42y	2m 4.88	3	8-6	Standard	PALISADE	Oct 16 2016
1m 4f 98y	2m 36.76	3	8-7	Standard	AJMAN PRINCE	Oct 14 2016
2m 56y	3m 29.87	4	9-8	Standard	DANNYDAY	Jun 25 2016

NEWMARKET (ROWLEY MILE)

DISTANCE	TIME	AGE	WEIGHT	GOING	HORSE	DATE
5f	58.69	2	8-12	Good To Firm	MRS DANVERS	Oct 7 2016
5f	56.81	6	9-2	Good To Firm	LOCHSONG	Apr 30 1994
6f	1m 9.56	2	8-12	Good To Firm	BUSHRANGER	Oct 3 2008
6f	1m 9.55	3	9-1	Good To Firm	CAPTAIN COLBY	May 16 2015
7f	1m 22.37	2	9-1	Good	U S NAVY FLAG	Oct 14 2017
7f	1m 21.98	3	9-0	Good To Firm	TUPI	May 16 2015
1m	1m 35.67	2	8-12	Good	STEELER	Sep 29 2012
1m	1m 34.07	4	9-0	Good To Firm	EAGLE MOUNTAIN	Oct 3 2008
1m 1f	1m 47.26	5	8-12	Good To Firm	MANDURO	Apr 19 2007
1m 2f	2m 2.76	2	9-2	Good	KEW GARDENS	Oct 14 2017
1m 2f	2m 0.13	3	8-12	Good	NEW APPROACH	Oct 18 2008
1m 4f	2m 26.07	3	8-9	Good To Firm	MOHEDIAN LADY	Sep 22 2011
1m 6f	2m 51.59	3	8-7	Good	ART EYES	Sep 29 2005
2m	3m 18.64	5	9-6	Good To Firm	TIMES UP	Sep 22 2011
2m 2f	3m 45.59	4	8-8	Good	WITHHOLD	Oct 14 2017

NEWMARKET (JULY COURSE)

Following remeasurement of the track by the BHA and RCA in 2017, some starts were moved to retain traditional race distances.

DISTANCE	TIME	AGE	WEIGHT	GOING	HORSE	DATE
5f	57.91	3	8-12	Good To Firm	EMBOUR	Jun 23 2018
6f	1m 10.34	2	9-0	Good To Firm	CLEMMIE	Jul 14 2017
6f	1m 9.68	4	9-1	Good To Firm	GIFTED MASTER	Aug 26 2017
7f	1m 23.33	2	9-1	Good To Firm	BIRCHWOOD	Jul 11 2015
7f	1m 22.59	3	9-7	Firm	HO LENG	Jul 9 1998
1m	1m 37.47	2	8-13	Good	WHIPPERS LOVE	Aug 28 2009
1m	1m 36.01	3	8-12	Good To Firm	ROLY POLY	Jul 14 2017
1m 2f	2m 2.21	7	8-10	Good	KAPSTADT	Jun 10 2017
1m 4f	2m 30.01	3	8-11	Good	REVEREND JACOBS	Aug 22 2008
1m 5f	2m 44.06	4	9-12	Good To Firm	PUMBLECHOOK	Jun 24 2017
1m 6f 175y	2m 53.98	4	8-11	Good	JAAMEH	Jun 10 2017

NOTTINGHAM

DISTANCE	TIME	AGE	WEIGHT	GOING	HORSE	DATE
5f 8y (Inner)	59.05	2	9-0	Good To Firm	MAIN DESIRE	May 2 2017
5f 8y (Inner)	57.40	3	9-6	Good To Firm	CARLTON FRANKIE	May 2 2017
5f 8y	57.90	2	8-9	Firm	HOH MAGIC	May 13 1994
5f 8y	57.58	5	7-11	Good To Firm	PENNY DREADFUL	Jun 19 2017
6f 18y	1m 11.40	2	8-11	Firm	JAMEELAPI	Aug 8 1983
6f 18y	1m 10.00	4	9-2	Firm	AJANAC	Aug 8 1988
1m 72y (Inner)	1m 45.14	2	9-6	Good	RASHFORD'S DOUBLE	Nov 2 2016
1m 72y (Inner)	1m 43.22	4	9-7	Good To Firm	REAVER	Apr 22 2017
1m 75y	1m 44.75	2	9-0	Good	VIVID DIAMOND	Oct 3 2018
1m 75y	1m 42.02	3	9-0	Good To Firm	GANAYEM	May 11 2018
1m 2f 50y	2m 7.13	5	9-8	Good To Firm	VASILY	Jul 19 2013
1m 2f 52y (Inner)	2m 16.66	2	9-3	Soft	LETHAL GLAZE	Oct 1 2008
1m 2f 52y (Inner)	2m 9.40	3	9-5	Good	CENTURIUS	Apr 20 2013
1m 6f	2m 57.80	3	8-10	Firm	BUSTER JO	Oct 1 1985
1m 7f 219y (Inner)	3m 34.39	3	8-0	Good	BENOZZO GOZZOLI	Oct 28 2009
2m	3m 25.25	3	9-5	Good	BULWARK	Sep 27 2005

PONTEFRACT

DISTANCE	TIME	AGE	WEIGHT	GOING	HORSE	DATE
5f 3y	1m 1.10	2	9-0	Firm	GOLDEN BOUNTY	Sep 20 2001
5f 3y	1m 0.49	5	9-5	Good To Firm	JUDICIAL	Apr 24 2017
5f	1m 14.00	2	9-3	Firm	FAWZI	Sep 6 1983
5f	1m 12.60	3	7-13	Firm	MERRY ONE	Aug 29 1970
1m 6y	1m 42.80	2	9-13	Firm	STAR SPRAY	Sep 6 1983
1m 6y	1m 42.80	2	9-0	Firm	ALASIL	Sep 26 2002
1m 6y	1m 40.60	4	9-10	Good To Firm	ISLAND LIGHT	Apr 13 2002
1m 2f 5y	2m 10.10	2	9-0	Firm	SHANTY STAR	Oct 7 2002
1m 2f 5y	2m 8.20	4	7-8	Hard	HAPPY HECTOR	Jul 9 1979
1m 2f 5y	2m 8.20	3	7-13	Hard	TOM NODDY	Aug 21 1972
1m 4f 5y	2m 33.72	8	8-7	Firm	AJAAN	Aug 8 2007
2m 1f 27y	3m 40.67	4	8-7	Good To Firm	PARADISE FLIGHT	Jun 6 2005
2m 2y	3m 51.10	3	8-8	Good To Firm	KUDZ	Sep 9 1986
2m 5f 139y	4m 47.80	4	8-4	Firm	PHYSICAL	May 14 1984

REDCAR

DISTANCE	TIME	AGE	WEIGHT	GOING	HORSE	DATE
5f	56.88	2	9-7	Good To Soft	WOLFOFWALLSTREET	Oct 27 2014
5f	56.01	10	9-3	Firm	HENRY HALL	Sep 20 2006
5f 217y	1m 8.84	2	8-3	Firm	OBE GOLD	Oct 2 2004
5f 217y	1m 8.60	3	9-2	Good To Firm	SIZZLING SAGA	Jun 21 1991
7f	1m 21.28	2	9-3	Firm	KAROO BLUE	Sep 20 2006
7f	1m 21.00	3	9-1	Firm	EMPTY QUARTER	Oct 3 1995
7f 219y	1m 34.37	2	9-0	Firm	MASTERSHIP	Sep 20 2006
7f 219y	1m 32.42	4	10-0	Firm	NANTON	Sep 20 2006
1m 1f	1m 52.44	2	9-0	Firm	SPEAR	Sep 13 2004
1m 1f	1m 48.50	5	8-12	Firm	MELLOTTIE	Jul 25 1990
1m 2f 1y	2m 10.10	2	8-11	Good	ADDING	Nov 10 1989
1m 2f 1y	2m 1.40	5	9-2	Firm	ERADICATE	May 28 1990
1m 5f 218y	2m 59.54	6	8-5	Good To Firm	LEODIS	Jun 23 2018
1m 7f 217y	3m 24.90	3	9-3	Good To Firm	SUBSONIC	Oct 8 1991

RIPON

DISTANCE	TIME	AGE	WEIGHT	GOING	HORSE	DATE
5f	57.80	2	8-8	Firm	SUPER ROCKY	Aug 5 1991
5f	57.28	5	8-12	Good	DESERT ACE	Sep 24 2016
6f	1m 10.40	2	9-2	Good	CUMBRIAN VENTURE	Aug 17 2002
6f	1m 9.09	5	8-13	Good To Firm	SANDRA'S SECRET	May 20 2018
1m	1m 38.77	2	9-4	Good	GREED IS GOOD	Sep 28 2013
1m	1m 36.62	4	8-11	Good To Firm	GRANSTON	Aug 29 2005
1m 1f	1m 49.97	6	9-3	Good To Firm	GINGER JACK	Jun 20 2013
1m 2f	2m 2.60	3	9-4	Firm	SWIFT SWORD	Jul 20 1991
1m 4f 10y	2m 31.40	4	8-8	Good To Firm	DANDINO	Apr 16 2011
2m	3m 27.07	5	9-12	Good To Firm	GREENWICH MEANTIME	Aug 30 2005

SALISBURY

DISTANCE	TIME	AGE	WEIGHT	GOING	HORSE	DATE
5f	59.30	2	9-0	Good To Firm	AJIGOLO	May 12 2005
5f	59.18	7	8-10	Good To Firm	EDGED OUT	Jun 18 2017
6f	1m 12.10	2	8-0	Good To Firm	PARISIAN LADY	Jun 10 1997
6f	1m 11.09	3	9-0	Firm	L'AMI LOUIS	May 1 2011
6f 213y	1m 25.97	2	9-0	Firm	MORE ROYAL	Jun 29 1995
6f 213y	1m 24.91	3	9-4	Firm	CHILWORTH LAD	May 1 2011
1m	1m 40.48	2	8-13	Firm	CHOIR MASTER	Sep 17 2002
1m	1m 38.29	3	8-7	Good To Firm	LAYMAN	Aug 11 2005
1m 1f 198y	2m 4.00	4	9-2	Good To Firm	CHAIN OF DAISIES	Aug 10 2016
1m 4f 5y	2m 31.69	3	9-5	Good To Firm	ARRIVE	Jun 27 2001
1m 6f 44y	3m 0.48	7	9-2	Good To Firm	HIGHLAND CASTLE	May 23 2015

SANDOWN

DISTANCE	TIME	AGE	WEIGHT	GOING	HORSE	DATE
5f 10y	59.48	2	9-3	Firm	TIMES TIME	Jul 22 1982
5f 10y	58.57	3	8-12	Good To Firm	BATTAASH	Jul 8 2017
7f	1m 26.56	2	9-0	Good To Firm	RAVEN'S PASS	Sep 1 2007
7f	1m 26.36	3	9-0	Firm	MAWSUFF	Jun 14 1986
1m 14y	1m 41.14	2	8-11	Good To Firm	REFERENCE POINT	Sep 23 1986
1m 14y	1m 38.87	7	9-10	Good To Firm	PRINCE OF JOHANNE	Jul 6 2013
1m 1f	1m 54.63	2	8-8	Good To Firm	FRENCH PRETENDER	Sep 20 1988
1m 1f	1m 52.40	7	9-3	Good To Firm	BOURGAINVILLE	Aug 11 2005
1m 1f 209y	2m 2.14	4	8-11	Good	KALAGLOW	May 31 1982
1m 6f	2m 56.90	4	8-7	Good To Firm	LADY ROSANNA	Jul 19 1989
2m 50y	3m 29.38	6	9-0	Good To Firm	CAUCUS	Jul 6 2013

SOUTHWELL (AW)

DISTANCE	TIME	AGE	WEIGHT	GOING	HORSE	DATE
4f 214y	57.71	2	8-4	Standard	SCALE FORCE	Dec 29 2018
4f 214y	56.80	5	9-7	Standard	GHOSTWING	Jan 3 2012
6f 16y	1m 14.00	2	8-5	Standard	PANALO	Nov 8 1989
6f 16y	1m 13.50	4	10-0	Standard	SALADAN KNIGHT	Dec 30 1989
7f 14y	1m 26.82	2	8-12	Standard	WINGED ICARUS	Aug 28 2012
7f 14y	1m 26.38	4	8-6	Standard	MOON RIVER	Mar 30 2016
1m 13y	1m 38.00	2	8-9	Standard	ALPHA RASCAL	Nov 13 1990
1m 13y	1m 38.00	4	8-10	Standard	ANDREW'S FIRST	Dec 30 1989
1m 13y	1m 37.25	3	8-6	Standard	VALIRA	Nov 3 1990
1m 3f 23y	2m 21.50	4	9-7	Standard	TEMPERING	Dec 5 1990
1m 4f 14y	2m 33.90	4	9-12	Standard	FAST CHICK	Nov 8 1989
1m 6f 21y	3m 1.60	3	7-8	Standard	EREVNON	Dec 29 1990
2m 102y	3m 37.60	9	8-12	Standard	OLD HUBERT	Dec 5 1990

THIRSK

DISTANCE	TIME	AGE	WEIGHT	GOING	HORSE	DATE
5f	57.20	2	9-7	Good To Firm	PROUD BOAST	Aug 5 2000
5f	56.92	5	9-6	Firm	CHARLIE PARKES	Apr 11 2003
6f	1m 9.20	2	9-6	Good To Firm	WESTCOURT MAGIC	Aug 25 1995
6f	1m 8.80	6	9-4	Firm	JOHAYRO	Jul 23 1999
7f	1m 23.70	2	8-9	Firm	COURTING	Jul 23 1999
7f	1m 22.80	4	8-5	Firm	SILVER HAZE	May 21 1988
7f 218y	1m 37.97	2	9-0	Firm	SUNDAY SYMPHONY	Sep 4 2004
7f 218y	1m 34.80	4	8-13	Firm	YEARSLEY	May 5 1990
1m 4f 8y	2m 29.90	5	9-12	Firm	GALLERY GOD	Jun 4 2001
2m 13y	3m 22.30	3	9-0	Firm	TOMASCHEK	Jul 17 1981

WETHERBY

DISTANCE	TIME	AGE	WEIGHT	GOING	HORSE	DATE
110y	1m 4.25	3	9-1	Good To Firm	DAPPER MAN	Jun 19 2017
	1m 24.72	4	9-2	Good	SLEMY	Jul 21 2015
m	1m 38.79	4	9-4	Good To Firm	THOMAS CRANMER	Jun 6 2018
m 2f	2m 5.13	5	9-5	Good	FIRST SARGEANT	Jul 21 2015
m 6f	3m 0.41	3	9-7	Good To Firm	DAVY'S DILEMMA	Jun 19 2017

WINDSOR

DISTANCE	TIME	AGE	WEIGHT	GOING	HORSE	DATE
21y	58.69	2	9-0	Good To Firm	CHARLES THE GREAT	May 23 2011
21y	58.08	5	8-13	Good To Firm	TAURUS TWINS	Apr 4 2011
12y	1m 10.50	2	9-5	Good To Firm	CUBISM	Aug 17 1998
12y	1m 9.58	7	9-0	Good To Firm	TROPICS	Jun 1 2015
m 31y	1m 41.73	2	9-5	Good To Firm	SALOUEN	Aug 7 2016
m 31y	1m 39.81	5	9-7	Good	FRENCH NAVY	Jun 29 2013
m 1f 194y	2m 1.62	6	9-1	Good	AL KAZEEM	Aug 23 2014
m 3f 99y	2m 21.50	3	9-2	Firm	DOUBLE FLORIN	May 19 1980

WOLVERHAMPTON (AW)

DISTANCE	TIME	AGE	WEIGHT	GOING	HORSE	DATE
21y	59.75	2	9-8	Standard	QUATRIEME AMI	Nov 13 2015
21y	59.39	5	9-8	Standard	BOOM THE GROOM	Feb 22 2016
20y	1m 12.16	2	9-2	Standard	MUBAKKER	Nov 14 2015
20y	1m 11.44	5	9-6	Standard	KACHY	Dec 26 2018
36y	1m 27.45	2	8-13	Standard	FOX POWER	Sep 26 2018
36y	1m 25.35	4	9-3	Standard	MISTER UNIVERSE	Mar 12 2016
m 142y	1m 47.38	2	9-5	Standard	JACK HOBBS	Dec 27 2014
m 142y	1m 45.43	4	9-4	Standard	KEYSTROKE	Nov 26 2016
m 1f 104y	1m 56.64	8	8-13	Standard	PERFECT CRACKER	Mar 19 2018
m 4f 51y	2m 33.92	3	8-13	Standard	NATURAL SCENERY	Oct 21 2016
m 5f 194y	2m 57.55	6	9-7	Standard	ENTIHAA	Dec 6 2014
m 120y	3m 31.92	7	9-3	Standard	WATERSMEET	Jan 15 2018
m 120y	3m 31.80	4	9-0	Standard	AIRCRAFT CARRIER	Jan 14 2019

YARMOUTH

DISTANCE	TIME	AGE	WEIGHT	GOING	HORSE	DATE
f 42y	1m 0.37	3	8-11	Good To Firm	PINK ICEBURG	Jul 11 2018
f 42y	59.74	3	8-11	Good To Firm	HAVEONEYERSELF	Jun 29 2018
f 3y	1m 10.40	2	9-0	Firm	LANCHESTER	Sep 15 1988
f 3y	9m 9.14	3	9-0	Good To Firm	CARTOGRAPHER	May 24 2017
f 3y	1m 22.20	2	9-0	Good To Firm	WARRSHAN	Sep 14 1988
f 3y	1m 22.12	4	9-4	Good To Firm	GLENBUCK	Apr 26 2007
m 3y	1m 36.30	2	8-2	Firm	OUT RUN	Sep 15 1988
m 3y	1m 33.49	7	9-0	Firm	BINT DANDY	May 16 2018
m 1f 21y	1m 52.00	3	9-5	Good To Firm	TOUCH GOLD	Jul 5 2012
m 2f 23y	2m 2.83	3	8-8	Firm	REUNITE	Jul 18 2006
m 3f 104y	2m 23.10	3	8-9	Firm	RAHIL	Jul 1 1993
m 6f 17y	2m 57.80	3	8-2	Good To Firm	BARAKAT	Jul 24 1990
m	3m 26.70	4	8-2	Good To Firm	ALHESN	Jul 26 1999

YORK

DISTANCE	TIME	AGE	WEIGHT	GOING	HORSE	DATE
5f	57.11	2	9-0	Good To Firm	BIG TIME BABY	Aug 20 2016
5f	56.16	3	9-9	Good To Firm	DAYJUR	Aug 23 1990
5f 89y	1m 3.20	2	9-3	Good To Firm	THE ART OF RACING	Sep 9 2012
5f 89y	1m 1.72	4	9-7	Good To Firm	BOGART	Aug 21 2013
6f	1m 8.90	2	9-0	Good	TIGGY WIGGY	Aug 21 2014
6f	1m 8.23	3	8-11	Good To Firm	MINCE	Sep 9 2012
7f	1m 22.32	2	9-1	Good To Firm	DUTCH CONNECTION	Aug 20 2014
7f	1m 21.83	4	9-8	Good To Firm	DIMENSION	Jul 28 2012
7f 192y	1m 36.92	2	9-5	Good	AWESOMETANK	Oct 14 2017
7f 192y	1m 35.10	4	8-12	Good	HOME CUMMINS	Jul 9 2016
1m 177y	1m 46.76	5	9-8	Good To Firm	ECHO OF LIGHT	Sep 5 2007
1m 2f 56y	2m 5.29	3	8-11	Good To Firm	SEA THE STARS	Aug 18 2009
1m 3f 188y	2m 36.28	3	8-9	Good To Firm	BANDARI	Jun 18 2005
1m 5f 188y	2m 53.48	5	9-9	Good To Firm	MUNTAHAA	Aug 25 2018
2m 56y	3m 28.97	5	9-5	Good To Firm	GABRIAL'S KING	Jul 12 2014

OP FLAT JOCKEYS
N BRITAIN 2018

ANUARY 1st - DECEMBER 31st)

INS-RUNS	%	JOCKEY	2ND	3RD	TOTAL PRIZE	WIN PRIZE
8-1130	18%	OISIN MURPHY	179	155	6,227,217	4,270,036
6-935	19%	SILVESTRE DE SOUSA	133	109	3,290,116	1,815,820
6-633	25%	JAMES DOYLE	72	72	4,745,322	3,311,718
0-1521	10%	LUKE MORRIS	169	155	1,533,892	804,743
7-935	15%	JOE FANNING	140	105	1,675,331	1,006,255
0-703	18%	JIM CROWLEY	93	77	3,149,163	2,140,699
6-678	19%	ROBERT HAVLIN	97	99	1,342,268	904,727
3-794	15%	ADAM KIRBY	111	98	1,784,881	938,046
0-982	13%	P J MCDONALD	112	102	1,537,136	868,886
6-696	17%	DANIEL TUDHOPE	101	85	2,042,707	1,050,101
3-679	17%	BEN CURTIS	69	87	1,131,324	763,123
2-719	16%	RICHARD KINGSCOTE	112	100	1,505,489	933,911
2-828	14%	FRANNY NORTON	106	98	1,295,716	757,197
1-632	18%	ANDREA ATZENI	90	74	2,372,701	1,558,021
1-717	15%	JASON WATSON	91	110	1,348,563	958,150
5-983	11%	TOM MARQUAND	118	117	1,417,650	730,083
2-891	11%	DAVID PROBERT	93	96	1,396,246	792,999
-800	12%	PAUL HANAGAN	89	100	1,914,634	1,186,759
-661	13%	MARTIN HARLEY	83	76	1,113,250	575,114
-477	18%	RYAN MOORE	68	67	5,135,437	3,667,6321
-418	20%	WILLIAM BUICK	67	55	4,893,439	2,947,897
-643	13%	CHARLES BISHOP	76	70	1,207,389	882,578
-793	10%	NICOLA CURRIE	84	100	879,072	529,786
-584	13%	ROSSA RYAN	73	63	637,070	399,869
-641	12%	DAVID ALLAN	75	61	1,006,010	641,860
-559	13%	HARRY BENTLEY	87	57	1,535,306	1,007,200
-524	14%	JAMIE SPENCER	73	64	1,551,900	736,208
-753	10%	FRAN BERRY	60	84	631,818	372,113
-524	14%	EDWARD GREATREX	57	74	631,818	372,113
-642	11%	JASON HART	52	83	707,700	439,795
-654	11%	DAVID EGAN	78	78	1,090,266	701703
-649	11%	KIERAN O'NEILL	59	64	744,070	459,301
-468	15%	CALLUM RODRIGUEZ	47	54	599,542	396,804
-483	14%	JACK MITCHELL	71	56	578,032	329,533
-711	9%	LIAM KENIRY	73	62	607,153	329,110
-806	8%	ANDREW MULLEN	77	86	811,082	506,681
-525	11%	ROB HORNBY	40	49	586,145	330,390
-436	13%	KEVIN STOTT	52	52	664,590	393,229
-452	13%	ROBERT WINSTON	56	51	846,307	278,511
-523	11%	CALLUM SHEPHERD	43	49	484,750	278,511
-558	10%	STEVIE DONOHOE	59	54	670,850	365,556
-612	9%	JOSEPHINE GORDON	47	65	772,059	496,593
-671	8%	SHANE KELLY	68	74	660,051	384,113
-234	24%	FRANKIE DETTORI	36	30	5,080,828	3,820,503
-591	9%	HOLLIE DOYLE	56	61	645,739	283,648
-608	9%	TONY HAMILTON	57	56	710,404	395,029
-699	8%	JAMES SULLIVAN	50	67	651,634	385,111
-458	11%	JAMIE GORMLEY	57	56	514,691	290,543
-709	7%	GRAHAM LEE	69	72	946,741	555,527
-339	13%	DAVID NOLAN	42	38	402,272	241,298

TOP FLAT TRAINERS IN BRITAIN 2018

TRAINER	LEADING HORSE	W-R	2ND	3RD	4TH	WIN PRIZE	TOTAL PR
JOHN GOSDEN	Roaring Lion	177-705	131	91	69	6,628,123	8,511,2
A P O'BRIEN	Saxon Warrior	24-229	20	37	24	3,534,703	6,276,3
SIR MICHAEL STOUTE	Poet's Word	77-426	87	49	52	2,760,038	4,569,4
MARK JOHNSTON	Dee Ex Bee	226-1440	194	203	200	2,357,973	4,329,6
CHARLIE APPLEBY	Masar	88-313	55	40	32	2,821,437	3,735,6
RICHARD FAHEY	Sands Of Mali	190-1599	200	191	184	2,067,729	3,377,9
RICHARD HANNON	Billesdon Brook	172-1401	191	161	151	1,859,205	3,183,5
WILLIAM HAGGAS	Sea Of Class	145-656	105	79	83	2,151,802	3,060,4
ANDREW BALDING	Beat The Bank	123-772	104	106	94	1,418,461	2,600,1
ROGER VARIAN	Pilaster	107-603	108	83	77	1,302,677	2,041,3
DAVID O'MEARA	Lord Glitters	113-1075	151	110	126	741,205	1,912,4
DAVID SIMCOCK	Lightning Spear	57-470	75	58	61	998,502	1,690,5
KEVIN RYAN	Brando	76-620	82	79	65	848,043	1,627,8
TIM EASTERBY	Wells Farhh Go	118-1085	127	112	99	944,580	1,525,3
RALPH BECKETT	Rock Eagle	88-522	89	62	54	881,764	1,310,2
CHARLES HILLS	Battaash	62-541	59	59	69	737,103	1,281,8
HUGO PALMER	Gifted Master	87-508	61	55	64	802,559	1,165,9
K R BURKE	Laurens	70-634	89	81	64	600,753	1,141,6
CLIVE COX	Harry Angel	68-486	70	45	52	637,905	1,126,5
ARCHIE WATSON	Corinthia Knight	105-528	88	67	50	734,873	1,108,6
DAVID ELSWORTH	Sir Dancealot	28-161	23	14	15	712,957	1,077,7
MICK CHANNON	Summer Icon	92-679	69	102	82	622,533	1,058,2
SIMON CRISFORD	Century Dream	70-337	69	47	39	542,652	1,023,3
TOM DASCOMBE	Kachy	77-494	66	66	61	633,828	1,019,4
IAN WILLIAMS	Magic Circle	66-449	50	51	45	655,714	1,006,7
SAEED BIN SUROOR	Victory Wave	84-384	66	54	42	628,883	944,5
MICHAEL APPLEBY	Big Country	94-792	99	97	80	562,270	933,4
EVE JOHNSON HOUGHTON	Accidental Agent	37-373	43	49	31	633,426	852,2
KEITH DALGLEISH	Summer Daydream	73-755	70	93	90	491,398	849,1
MICHAEL DODS	Mabs Cross	52-445	52	52	43	436,866	827,2
ED WALKER	Stormy Antarctic	61-487	77	63	64	385,652	820,2
JAMES FANSHAWE	The Tin Man	38-308	55	43	43	491,358	808,7
W P MULLINS	Low Sun	6-30	4	1	2	525,901	803,5
STUART WILLIAMS	Via Serendipity	58-425	59	54	46	427,563	727,0
ROGER CHARLTON	Withhold	48-307	29	36	28	444,679	716,8
JIM GOLDIE	Euchen Glen	42-399	44	44	39	442,603	694,0
HUGHIE MORRISON	Buzz	44-394	41	46	51	384,291	688,8
MICHAEL BELL	Pretty Pollyanna	55-379	44	51	42	402,362	679,3
ROGER FELL	Burnt Sugar	56-473	48	45	47	468,722	667,8
MARCO BOTTI	Aljazzi	34-373	53	44	68	402,729	657,8
MRS JOHN HARRINGTON	Alpha Centauri	3-16	2	1	0	452,971	620,6
JOHN QUINN	El Astronaute	45-394	38	51	31	429,170	617,8
RICHARD HUGHES	Gold Filigree	62-456	69	71	53	326,551	589,6
PAUL MIDGLEY	Tanasoq	39-408	36	47	45	346,938	589,3
DEAN IVORY	Flaming Spear	39-359	37	36	29	382,474	567,5
BRYAN SMART	Alpha Delphini	24-256	25	29	36	335,799	528,7
JAMIE OSBORNE	Raising Sand	47-406	48	41	53	344,892	521,9
ROBERT COWELL	Encore D'Or	34-348	42	47	40	278,580	515,6
MICHAEL EASTERBY	Gulf Of Poets	52-499	45	38	41	322,007	507,9
DAVID EVANS	Gracious John	42-615	92	60	74	211,525	505,3

OP FLAT OWNERS N BRITAIN IN 2018

OWNER	LEADING HORSE	W-R	2ND	3RD	4TH	WIN PRIZE	TOTAL PRIZE
DOLPHIN	MASAR	175-738	127	97	78	3,535,052	5,015,028
KAR RACING LIMITED	ROARING LION	25-197	36	24	27	2,579,599	3,241,106
RRICK SMITH & MRS JOHN MAGNIER & CHAEL TABOR	SAXON WARRIOR	9-66	6	13	10	1,730,647	2,965,197
MDAN AL MAKTOUM	BATTAASH	118-631	95	74	78	1,943,989	2,830,382
ABDULLAH	EXPERT EYE	69-269	53	28	30	1,040,491	1,736,313
EED SUHAIL	POET'S WORD	13-71	17	7	9	1,232,595	1,577,822
EIKH HAMDAN BIN MOHAMMED AL MAKTOUM	DEE EX BEE	49-343	50	45	49	564,506	1,470,059
EVELEY PARK STUD	PILASTER	67-401	69	55	42	831,498	1,421,988
E OPPENHEIMER	CRACKSMAN	12-56	6	11	4	1,096,680	1,313,713
E NIELSEN	STRADIVARIUS	10-62	9	9	7	1,162,840	1,197,383
EIKH MOHAMMED OBAID AL MAKTOUM	SHARJA BRIDGE	50-214	46	22	22	799,220	1,087,078
NG POWER RACING CO LTD	BEAT THE BANK	42-260	32	33	26	568,446	1,080,630
IS JOHN MAGNIER & MICHAEL TABOR & RRICK SMITH	RHODODENDRON	5-63	6	10	7	408,171	977,434
CHAEL TABOR & DERRICK SMITH & S JOHN MAGNIER	FOREVER TOGETHER	4-58	5	8	5	429,315	903,811
R EVELYN DE ROTHSCHILD	CRYSTAL OCEAN	7-28	6	2	4	254,150	838,514
RD LLOYD-WEBBER	TOO DARN HOT	8-12	1	1	0	436,300	660,605
E COOL SILK PARTNERSHIP	SANDS OF MALI	8-75	8	7	4	467,643	642,542
BENHAM/ D WHITFORD/ L QUINN/ K QUINN	SIR DANCEALOT	8-37	4	2	7	374,775	561,558
MARWAN KOUKASH	MAGIC CIRCLE	31-262	28	35	34	332,721	554,218
PPER LOGISTICS	RED BALLOONS	31-179	24	28	22	427,574	535,497
C SMITH	FOXTROT LADY	20-113	17	11	10	386,673	531,151
RS S RICCI	LOW SUN	2-13	3	0	1	363,960	527,973
NFORD STUD	CORONET	9-60	17	12	5	109,183	495,043
EIKH JUMA DALMOOK AL MAKTOUM	CROSSING THE LINE	37-178	26	27	25	347,844	493,407
HN DANCE	LAURENS	16-128	17	14	10	293,590	492,445
OFF & SANDRA TURNBULL	LORD GLITTERS	15-100	10	13	6	113,895	456,014
ARCHOS FAMILY	ALPHA CENTAURI	5-25	1	1	2	440,782	446,250
RS FITRI HAY	HERE COMES WHEN	31-201	26	30	16	236,347	403,294
SHAQAB RACING	WATAN	32-208	32	29	21	229,016	389,475
RS R F JOHNSON HOUGHTON	ACCIDENTAL AGENT	1-6	0	2	0	367,197	379,401
E QUEEN	SENIORITY	19-96	14	15	10	267,033	374,754
RS ANGIE BAILEY	BRANDO	5-54	10	5	3	71,040	374,082
UL & CLARE ROONEY	CRACK ON CRACK ON	23-152	16	19	18	220,231	363,524
HN GUNTHER & TANYA GUNTHER	WITHOUT PAROLE	4-7	0	0	1	335,713	357,442
VE WASHBOURN	THUNDERING BLUE	9-58	4	10	8	157,939	356,578
LEH AL HOMAIZI & IMAD AL SAGAR	ALJAZZI	15-118	14	25	16	236,147	350,274
H PRINCESS HAYA OF JORDAN	EMBLAZONED	27-100	28	11	8	157,792	342,369
DULLA AL MANSOORI	DESERT ENCOUNTER	23-170	32	21	24	168,965	342,068
RCHANT NAVY SYND/SMITH/MAGNIER/TABOR	MERCHANT NAVY	1-1	0	0	0	340,260	340,260
EIKH RASHID DALMOOK AL MAKTOUM	KING OF HEARTS	16-53	9	4	2	250,842	335,510
LL MALL PARTNERS & PARTNERS	BILLESDON BROOK	1-8	0	0	3	310,487	320,748
RLAN BIZAKOV	ALTYN ORDA	15-83	16	10	8	126,316	317,802
EED MANANA	INVINCIBLE ARMY	28-201	37	24	22	164,624	313,114
EIKH AHMED AL MAKTOUM	ADDEYBB	25-120	20	20	18	235,046	308,617
ORGE STRAWBRIDGE	WISSAHICKON	15-60	9	4	9	241,340	305,221
ALI RIDHA	GIFTED MASTER	11-63	11	5	10	257,198	305,213
RS C C REGALADO-GONZALEZ	IRIDESSA	3-19	1	4	1	290,859	295,332
NDERLAND HOLDING INC	SEA OF CLASS	4-17	3	2	2	270,418	288,994
VID W ARMSTRONG	MABS CROSS	11-85	11	10	13	89,082	280,844
DULLA BELHABB	CENTURY DREAM	5-21	5	4	3	85,056	268,708

TOP FLAT HORSES IN BRITAIN 2018

HORSE (AGE)	WIN & PLACE £	W-R	TRAINER	OWNER	BREEDER
ROARING LION (3)	1,981,494	4-7	John Gosden	Qatar Racing Limited	Ranjan Racing Inc
POET'S WORD (5)	1,402,334	3-4	Sir Michael Stoute	Saeed Suhail	Woodcote Stud Ltd
CRACKSMAN (4)	1,136,662	2-3	John Gosden	A E Oppenheimer	Hascombe And Valiant Stu
STRADIVARIUS (4)	1,088,832	5-5	John Gosden	B E Nielsen	Bjorn Nielsen
MASAR (3)	938,476	2-3	Charlie Appleby	Godolphin	Godolphin
CRYSTAL OCEAN (4)	787,304	3-6	Sir Michael Stoute	Sir Evelyn De Rothschild	Southcourt Stud
LIGHTNING SPEAR (7)	738,312	1-4	David Simcock	Qatar Racing Limited	Newsells Park Stud
SAXON WARRIOR (3)	590,884	1-4	A P O'Brien	Derrick Smith & Mrs John Magnier & Michael Tabor	Orpendale, Chelston & Wyn
KEW GARDENS (3)	570,271	2-6	A P O'Brien	Derrick Smith & Mrs John Magnier & Michael Tabor	Barronstown Stud
SANDS OF MALI (3)	525,977	2-5	Richard Fahey	The Cool Silk Partnership	Simon Urizzi
WILD ILLUSION (3)	520,106	1-4	Charlie Appleby	Godolphin	Godolphin
DEE EX BEE (3)	421,454	0-5	Mark Johnston	Sheikh Hamdan bin Mohammed Al Maktoum	Godolphin
ALPHA CENTAURI (3)	418,945	2-2	Mrs John Harrington	Niarchos Family	Niarchos Family
CORONET (4)	409,637	1-4	John Gosden	Denford Stud	Denford Stud Ltd
EXPERT EYE (3)	391,955	2-5	Sir Michael Stoute	K Abdullah	Juddmonte Farms Ltd
SIR DANCEALOT (3)	382,997	4-10	David Elsworth	C Benham/ D Whitford/ L Quinn/ K Quinn	Vincent Duignan
BILLESDON BROOK (3)	381,919	1-5	Richard Hannon	Pall Mall Partners & Mrs R J McCreery	Stowell Hill Partners
ACCIDENTAL AGENT (4)	378,593	1-4	Eve Johnson Houghton	Mrs R F Johnson Houghton	Mrs R F Johnson Hought
LORD GLITTERS (5)	372,324	1-6	David O'Meara	Geoff & Sandra Turnbull	S C A Elevage De Tourgevi Et Al
BATTAASH (4)	368,236	2-4	Charles Hills	Hamdan Al Maktoum	Ballyphilip Stud
TOO DARN HOT (2)	358,965	4-4	John Gosden	Lord Lloyd-Webber	Watership Down Stud
WITHOUT PAROLE (3)	353,401	3-5	John Gosden	John Gunther & Tanya Gunther	John Gunther
BLUE POINT (4)	343,185	1-3	Charlie Appleby	Godolphin	Oak Lodge Bloodstock
MERCHANT NAVY (4)	340,260	1-1	A P O'Brien	Merchant Navy Synd/ Smith/Magnier/Tabor	C Barhan, Qld
MAGICAL (3)	340,260	1-1	A P O'Brien	Derrick Smith & Mrs John Magnier & Michael Tabor	Orpendale, Chelston & Wyna
MUNTAHAA (5)	332,730	1-4	John Gosden	Hamdan Al Maktoum	Shadwell Estate Company Limited
FAIRYLAND (2)	312,039	2-3	A P O'Brien	Mrs E M Stockwell & Michael Tabor & Derrick Smith	Tally-Ho Stud
LOW SUN (5)	307,250	1-1	W P Mullins	Mrs S Ricci	Juddmonte Farms Ltd
EQTIDAAR (3)	304,502	1-5	Sir Michael Stoute	Hamdan Al Maktoum	Shadwell Estate Company Limited
FOREVER TOGETHER (3)	299,675	1-2	A P O'Brien	Michael Tabor & Derrick Smith & Mrs John Magnier	Vimal And Gillian Khosla
LAH TI DAR (3)	297,887	3-5	John Gosden	Lord Lloyd-Webber	Watership Down Stud
OLD PERSIAN (3)	290,363	4-6	Charlie Appleby	Godolphin	Godolphin
U S NAVY FLAG (3)	283,550	1-2	A P O'Brien	Coolmore, Tabor & Wynaus	Misty For Me Syndicate
IRIDESSA (2)	283,550	1-1	Joseph Patrick O'Brien	Mrs C C Regalado-Gonzalez	Whisperview Trading Ltd
LAURENS (3)	273,782	1-4	K R Burke	John Dance	Bloodstock Agency Ltd
BRANDO (6)	272,221	1-5	Kevin Ryan	Mrs Angie Bailey	Car Colston Hall Stud
SEA OF CLASS (3)	268,462	3-4	William Haggas	Sunderland Holding Inc	Razza Del Velino Srl
I CAN FLY (3)	262,898	0-4	A P O'Brien	Derrick Smith & Mrs John Magnier & Michael Tabor	Rockwell Bloodstock

TOP NH JOCKEYS IN BRITAIN 2017/18

INS-RUNS	%	JOCKEY	2ND	3RD	TOTAL PRIZE	WIN PRIZE
'6-901	20%	RICHARD JOHNSON 156		118	1,924,738	1,378,782
2-806	18%	BRIAN HUGHES 130		111	1,439,661	925,852
1-612	21%	HARRY SKELTON 107		104	1,394,947	834,993
9-530	21%	NOEL FEHILY 82		62	1,383,640	898,062
8-568	19%	SAM TWISTON-DAVIES 90		83	1,693,433	1,121,660
4-669	16%	AIDAN COLEMAN 73		84	1,003,348	674,382
2-482	17%	SEAN BOWEN 64		55	1,022,057	661,054
'-367	21%	NICO DE BOINVILLE 54		44	1,750,561	1,275,330
5-440	17%	HARRY COBDEN 71		67	1,432,193	947,078
4-610	12%	TOM SCUDAMORE 82		79	948,075	487,096
4-440	16%	PADDY BRENNAN 56		72	947,059	523,561
3-360	18%	DARYL JACOB 53		38	1,502,557	1,086,289
3-348	13%	JAMES BOWEN 37		40	733,117	538,993
3-424	13%	JAMIE MOORE 44		53	650,195	389,346
3-445	12%	TOM O'BRIEN 57		61	671,506	348,175
0-288	17%	GAVIN SHEEHAN 45		37	547,693	390,141
0-313	16%	DANNY COOK 44		53	696,198	436,753
7-347	14%	WILLIAM KENNEDY 54		44	524,366	322,710
5-383	12%	NICK SCHOLFIELD 35		34	358,391	225,180
5-312	14%	WAYNE HUTCHINSON 51		51	665,696	404,293
4-435	11%	HENRY BROOKE 52		80	737,454	452,597
3-231	10%	HARRY BANNISTER 48		48	459,273	264,401
0-251	16%	DAVID BASS 39		27	395,985	221,922
0-368	11%	LEIGHTON ASPELL 47		43	467,205	287,554
3-204	19%	BRYONY FROST 21		24	647,877	407,239
3-276	14%	A P HESKIN 51		29	526,623	263,385
7-237	16%	ROSS CHAPMAN 29		33	264,444	170,665
3-279	12%	CIARAN GETHINGS 40		24	332,606	212,956
4-137	23%	BARRY GERAGHTY 17		13	1,293,943	882,467
4-229	14%	CRAIG NICHOL 41		21	302,397	180,450
0-253	12%	CHARLIE DEUTSCH 25		32	375,135	269,007
0-308	9%	ROBERT DUNNE 37		41	418,131	260,216
8-346	8%	ADAM WEDGE 51		34	535,469	274,642
7-208	13%	ANDREW TINKLER 15		19	160,427	112,038
7-259	10%	DEREK FOX 30		29	247,547	163,079
6-312	8%	SEAN QUINLAN 25		49	253,674	149,437
5-169	15%	RYAN DAY 27		24	370,957	261,673
4-216	11%	MITCHELL BASTYAN 15		28	303,267	186,009
4-252	10%	TOM CANNON 41		38	270,321	146,323
4-256	9%	JAMIE HAMILTON 25		25	178,698	104,415
4-326	7%	RICHIE MCLERNON 32		36	284,147	157,396
3-180	13%	JEREMIAH MCGRATH 22		19	295,312	159,104
3-224	10%	JACK QUINLAN 20		23	297,325	197,958
1-199	11%	KIELAN WOODS 31		22	214,665	118,584
0-141	14%	RICHARD PATRICK 18		15	242,068	133,738
0-205	10%	SEAN HOULIHAN 26		22	251,091	161,530
0-227	9%	JAMIE BARGARY 26		17	375,279	224,408
0-243	8%	THOMAS DOWSON 14		28	146,900	93,080
0-252	8%	CALLUM BEWLEY 30		30	249,739	143,539
9-160	12%	BRIDGET ANDREWS 17		15	281,023	177,379

TOP NH TRAINERS IN BRITAIN 2017/18

TRAINER	LEADING HORSE	W-R	2ND	3RD	4TH	WIN PRIZE	TOTAL PRIZE
NICKY HENDERSON	BUVEUR D'AIR	140-519	82	49	47	2,609,435	3,474,0?
PAUL NICHOLLS	POLITOLOGUE	126-570	91	74	67	1,608,859	2,506,5?
COLIN TIZZARD	NATIVE RIVER	79-536	82	81	60	1,272,104	1,975,8?
NIGEL TWISTON-DAVIES	BRISTOL DE MAI	80-527	71	60	60	1,201,080	1,896,1?
DAN SKELTON	RENE'S GIRL	155-800	121	124	77	1,063,257	1,735,9?
W P MULLINS	PLEASANT COMPANY	10-74	8	6	4	831,910	1,553,6?
GORDON ELLIOTT	TIGER ROLL	21-106	16	16	9	1,054,952	1,338,2?
TOM GEORGE	SUMMERVILLE BOY	47-356	66	44	38	527,123	964,2?
ALAN KING	ELGIN	57-385	68	70	38	551,217	920,6?
DONALD MCCAIN	DEAR SIRE	95-532	82	74	80	546,016	823,8?
EVAN WILLIAMS	CLYNE	52-461	63	54	60	446,876	783,1?
HARRY FRY	ACTING LASS	50-240	34	34	16	493,127	777,2?
FERGAL O'BRIEN	MASTER DEE	60-338	42	47	40	462,747	711,9?
PHILIP HOBBS	ROCK THE KASBAH	63-460	70	66	43	363,185	709,9?
SUE SMITH	MIDNIGHT SHADOW	40-298	46	49	37	366,301	609,1?
JONJO O'NEILL	GO CONQUER	64-553	52	54	53	418,343	608,9?
GARY MOORE	TRAFFIC FLUIDE	51-401	46	53	36	351,112	584,7?
WARREN GREATREX	MISSED APPROACH	52-275	46	34	20	365,201	545,6?
HENRY DE BROMHEAD	BALKO DES FLOS	3-35	2	3	6	323,362	534,1?
CHARLIE LONGSDON	BENTELIMAR	44-385	45	46	41	317,714	521,9?
NEIL MULHOLLAND	KALONDRA	59-502	70	58	50	283,487	517,2?
PETER BOWEN	RONS DREAM	52-293	37	37	34	357,317	517,2?
DAVID PIPE	MR BIG SHOT	33-361	37	44	38	260,503	497,5?
NICK WILLIAMS	COO STAR SIVOLA	29-150	20	23	18	287,897	479,4?
KIM BAILEY	THE LAST SAMURI	48-292	47	31	36	271,847	478,9?
VENETIA WILLIAMS	YALA ENKI	34-305	25	33	26	302,225	468,4?
DR RICHARD NEWLAND	BEAU BAY	43-186	38	25	14	301,953	463,6?
KERRY LEE	GINO TRAIL	28-180	25	18	24	227,450	449,5?
NICKY RICHARDS	GUITAR PETE	29-196	39	27	19	296,126	440,8?
ANTHONY HONEYBALL	MS PARFOIS	34-161	28	18	17	263,465	427,3?
BEN PAULING	HIGH BRIDGE	36-241	29	22	20	287,044	396,2?
IAN WILLIAMS	GAS LINE BOY	24-202	26	27	28	219,534	388,1?
OLLY MURPHY	HUNTERS CALL	47-244	45	32	36	292,047	381,9?
NEIL KING	MILANSBAR	18-180	27	27	18	183,379	368,7?
BRIAN ELLISON	DEFINITLY RED	29-236	24	34	33	231,837	364,1?
TOM LACEY	THOMAS PATRICK	39-158	24	18	16	284,089	359,3?
LUCINDA RUSSELL	BIG RIVER	46-368	49	45	49	227,451	355,0?
MICKY HAMMOND	KNOCKNAMONA	46-343	34	41	45	207,254	320,9?
EMMA LAVELLE	FORTUNATE GEORGE	28-199	23	21	22	214,619	320,8?
JAMIE SNOWDEN	NARANJA	35-170	32	23	11	224,101	311,8?
CHRIS GORDON	REMILUC	29-194	40	27	24	159,647	306,7?
SEAMUS MULLINS	ARTHINGTON	30-288	30	37	30	145,704	263,1?
STUART EDMUNDS	MARIA'S BENEFIT	23-118	21	14	14	164,409	246,9?
HARRY WHITTINGTON	BIGMARTRE	27-135	15	18	16	184,036	238,6?
REBECCA CURTIS	JOE FARRELL	9-89	12	9	15	182,193	234,3?
HENRY DALY	HEAD TO THE STARS	33-162	21	13	15	163,371	233,6?
DAVID DENNIS	DEAUVILLE DANCER	25-206	25	26	30	131,331	232,3?
LUCY WADHAM	POTTERS LEGEND	20-142	21	17	23	144,073	229,6?
TIM VAUGHAN	POINT OF PRINCIPLE	27-343	31	33	43	135,431	228,3?
MALCOLM JEFFERSON	CLOUDY DREAM	17-116	19	13	13	132,982	220,0?

TOP NH OWNERS
IN BRITAIN IN 2017/18

OWNER	LEADING HORSE	W-R	2ND	3RD	4TH	WIN PRIZE	TOTAL PRIZE
JOHN P MCMANUS	Buveur D'Air	83-505	50	63	54	1,204,236	1,837,071
SIMON MUNIR & ISAAC SOUEDE	Bristol De Mai	43-134	18	19	13	1,116,074	1,485,913
GIGGINSTOWN HOUSE STUD	Tiger Roll	9-47	1	6	6	1,170,269	1,434,221
PAUL & CLARE ROONEY	Master Dee	59-259	43	40	17	436,513	694,629
ANN & ALAN POTTS LIMITED	Supasundae	11-94	21	9	7	196,403	547,466
BROCADE RACING	Native River	10-69	13	10	10	428,862	464,213
THE KNOT AGAIN PARTNERSHIP	Might Bite	3-4	1	0	0	251,967	390,739
TREVOR HEMMINGS	Cloudy Dream	24-171	20	24	14	143,624	368,993
J HALES	Politologue	4-13	2	0	3	316,857	355,692
S SUCH & CG PALETTA	The New One	8-35	6	3	2	238,680	353,615
MRS JOHNNY DE LA HEY	Diego Du Charmil	18-72	16	10	5	213,813	344,880
MRS PATRICIA PUGH	Altior	3-5	1	0	0	331,730	332,646
R S BROOKHOUSE	Summerville Boy	12-55	13	6	3	220,448	292,267
THE BROOKS, STEWART FAMILIES & J KYLE	Black Corton	11-23	2	1	3	217,222	259,108
MRS S RICCI	Min	2-20	2	0	0	84,868	254,801
MALCOLM C DENMARK	Pleasant Company	3-35	5	4	3	11,046	236,014
WALTERS PLANT HIRE LTD	Whisper	11-55	10	7	10	120,598	227,939
TONY BLOOM	Penhill	2-20	4	2	1	196,801	207,355
P J MARTIN	Definitly Red	10-68	5	17	11	135,182	187,708
P J VOGT	Frodon	1-22	6	3	2	42,712	183,473
MRS P SLOAN	Guitar Pete	4-20	3	1	0	152,884	174,056
PAUL MURPHY	Kalashnikov	5-36	2	3	6	118,700	169,333
EDWARD O'CONNELL	Un De Sceaux	1-3	1	0	0	86,430	162,163
MR & MRS WILLIAM RUCKER	King's Odyssey	12-98	19	15	18	58,758	154,380
CROSSED FINGERS PARTNERSHIP	Double Shuffle	0-23	6	5	3	0	153,631
BRADLEY PARTNERSHIP	Beer Goggles	12-82	12	6	11	107,430	153,228
CARON & PAUL CHAPMAN	Sam Spinner	2-8	1	1	0	113,900	152,813
GRECH & PARKIN	Claimantakinforgan	10-53	8	3	9	81,254	152,709
RODDY OWEN & PAUL FULLAGAR	Wadswick Court	10-52	10	3	5	92,338	151,317
ELITE RACING CLUB	Elgin	3-13	0	5	2	125,450	146,693
T G LESLIE	Ubaltique	18-82	13	9	14	98,527	144,651
MRS AAFKE CLARKE	Midnight Shadow	7-21	5	0	0	123,185	142,716
SLANEYVILLE SYNDICATE	Total Recall	1-3	0	0	0	142,375	142,375
MR AND MRS J D COTTON	Gold Present	4-16	3	2	1	113,254	140,137
RICHARD COLLINS	Waiting Patiently	6-11	1	2	0	135,698	138,100
D&D ARMSTRONG LTD	Donna's Diamond	10-64	15	10	10	75,378	136,497
M SHERWOOD, N MORRIS & R CURTIS	Joe Farrell	2-6	1	1	2	129,785	133,873
D&NICKY ROBINSON	Baywing	2-31	8	9	1	81,328	131,823
T HYWEL JONES	On Tour	2-28	2	1	4	108,325	131,780
GALLOPING ON THE SOUTH DOWNS PARTNERSHIP	Traffic Fluide	13-65	9	13	6	81,747	131,520
SULLIVAN BLOODSTOCK LIMITED	Laurina	9-38	5	2	0	106,340	128,403
MILLS & MASON PARTNERSHIP	Ballyoptic	3-16	2	3	2	38,648	123,283
ADRIAN BUTLER/S P O'CONNOR	Bless The Wings	1-3	0	1	0	21,896	121,896
ANDY & SHARON MEASHAM	Rene's Girl	6-12	2	1	1	91,802	119,757
CARL HINCHY	Shantou Flyer	4-45	9	4	9	30,065	118,787
MR & MRS R KELVIN-HUGHES	Santini	5-17	3	3	0	88,289	117,827
J D NEILD	Splash Of Ginge	1-9	1	1	3	91,120	117,237
MCNEILL FAMILY	Portrush Ted	7-44	5	5	7	75,908	115,066
J P ROMANS	Elegant Escape	4-23	5	6	1	45,242	114,871
PHILIP J REYNOLDS	Presenting Percy	1-3	1	0	1	100,131	114,166

TOP NH HORSES IN BRITAIN 2017/18

HORSE (AGE IN 2018)	WIN & PLACE £	W-R	TRAINER	OWNER	BREEDER
TIGER ROLL (8)	541,069	2-3	Gordon Elliott	Gigginstown House Stud	G O'Brien
BUVEUR D'AIR (7)	413,705	4-4	Nicky Henderson	John P McManus	Gerard Ferte
NATIVE RIVER (8)	398,296	2-2	Colin Tizzard	Brocade Racing	Fred Mackey
MIGHT BITE (9)	390,739	3-4	Nicky Henderson	The Knot Again Partnership	John O'Brien
POLITOLOGUE (7)	349,934	4-6	Paul Nicholls	J Hales	Mme Henri Devin
ALTIOR (8)	331,730	3-3	Nicky Henderson	Mrs Patricia Pugh	Paddy Behan
BRISTOL DE MAI (7)	224,211	2-5	Nigel Twiston-Davies	Simon Munir & Isaac Souede	Jean-Yves Touzaint
BALKO DES FLOS (7)	214,098	1-2	Henry De Bromhead	Gigginstown House Stud	Clovis Bardin & Mme Florence Bardin
PLEASANT COMPANY (10)	200,000	0-1	W P Mullins	Malcolm C Denmark	Susan Bredin
PENHILL (7)	192,707	1-1	W P Mullins	Tony Bloom	Newsells Park Stud & Equity Bloodstock
L'AMI SERGE (8)	191,825	1-5	Nicky Henderson	Simon Munir & Isaac Souede	P Ryan
UN DE SCEAUX (10)	162,163	1-2	W P Mullins	Edward O'Connell	Haras De La Rousseliere Et A
SAM SPINNER (6)	152,813	2-5	Jedd O'Keeffe	Caron & Paul Chapman	Wriggle Valley TBs & R Eccleshall
BLACK CORTON (7)	149,216	8-12	Paul Nicholls	The Brooks, Stewart Families & J Kyle	Dominique Guyon
TOTAL RECALL (9)	142,375	1-3	W P Mullins	Slaneyville Syndicate	John Connolly
ELGIN (6)	140,950	3-6	Alan King	Elite Racing Club	Elite Racing Club
MIN (7)	139,987	0-2	W P Mullins	Mrs S Ricci	Madame Marie-Therese Mimouni
KALASHNIKOV (5)	135,092	3-5	Amy Murphy	Paul Murphy	Sunnyhill Stud Ltd
ANIBALE FLY (8)	134,483	0-2	A J Martin	John P McManus	Earl Baty, Mr V Baty, Mr F Lemercier
JOE FARRELL (9)	133,873	2-6	Rebecca Curtis	M Sherwood, N Morris & R Curtis	Mrs E A Pendarves
WHOLESTONE (7)	133,546	1-8	Nigel Twiston-Davies	Simon Munir & Isaac Souede	Michael O'Donovan
THE NEW ONE (10)	129,723	2-7	Nigel Twiston-Davies	S Such & CG Paletta	R Brown & Ballylinch Stud
WE HAVE A DREAM (4)	129,652	5-5	Nicky Henderson	Simon Munir & Isaac Souede	I Catsaras, V Dubois & S Dubois
BLAKLION (9)	127,567	1-5	Nigel Twiston-Davies	S Such & CG Paletta	Mrs M D W Morrison
TERREFORT (5)	127,511	3-4	Nicky Henderson	Simon Munir & Isaac Souede	Francis Montauban
IDENTITY THIEF (8)	126,134	1-2	Henry De Bromhead	Gigginstown House Stud	Cathal Ennis
WAITING PATIENTLY (7)	125,692	3-3	Ruth Jefferson	Richard Collins	Vincent Finn
SUPASUNDAE (8)	125,286	0-2	Mrs John Harrington	Ann & Alan Potts Limited	Newsells Park Stud
BLESS THE WINGS (13)	121,896	1-3	Gordon Elliott	Adrian Butler/S P O'Connor	C Kenneally
SPLASH OF GINGE (10)	116,092	1-6	Nigel Twiston-Davies	J D Neild	Stewart Pike
MELON (6)	113,868	0-2	W P Mullins	Mrs J Donnelly	Newsells Park Stud
MILANSBAR (11)	112,930	1-7	Neil King	Robert Bothway	T J Wyatt
TOP NOTCH (7)	112,364	3-5	Nicky Henderson	Simon Munir & Isaac Souede	Haras Des Sablonnets & Dr Vet B Gabeur
OLD GUARD (7)	109,891	3-9	Paul Nicholls	The Brooks, Stewart Families & J Kyle	The Rt Hon Lord Rothschild
SUMMERVILLE BOY (6)	108,553	2-5	Tom George	R S Brookhouse	Paul Rothwell
FRODON (6)	107,516	1-8	Paul Nicholls	P J Vogt	Philippe Gasdoue
KILBRICKEN STORM (7)	106,142	3-5	Colin Tizzard	A Selway & P Wavish	Mrs S O'Keeffe
FINIAN'S OSCAR (6)	105,926	3-7	Colin Tizzard	Ann & Alan Potts Limited	Richard & Martin O'Keeffe
DEFINITLY RED (9)	104,754	2-5	Brian Ellison	Phil & Julie Martin	James Keegan
GUITAR PETE (8)	104,251	2-10	Nicky Richards	Mrs P Sloan	P J Burke
BALLYOPTIC (8)	100,170	2-7	Nigel Twiston-Davies	Mills & Mason Partnership	Roger Ryan
PRESENTING PERCY (7)	100,131	1-1	Patrick G Kelly	Philip J Reynolds	Preston Lodge Stud
FOOTPAD (6)	99,662	1-1	W P Mullins	Simon Munir & Isaac Souede	Mlle Louise Collet & Mlle Camille Collet
CLOUDY DREAM (8)	97,825	0-6	Ruth Jefferson	Trevor Hemmings	Eimear Purcell
REGAL FLOW (11)	97,734	3-7	Bob Buckler	Mrs C J Dunn	Mrs H R Dunn

LEADING SIRES OF 2018 IN GREAT BRITAIN AND IRELAND

STALLION	BREEDING	RNRS	WNRS	WINS	WIN MONEY	PLACES	PLACE MONEY	TOTAL
GALILEO (IRE)	by Sadler's Wells	196	89	125	3733315	463	2928015	6661330
DUBAWI (IRE)	by Dubai Millennium	170	81	130	2569358	319	1491097	4060455
FRANKEL (GB)	by Galileo	94	54	81	2344822	170	1589854	3934676
SEA THE STARS (IRE)	by Cape Cross	124	54	80	2306638	201	1026191	3332829
KODIAC (GB)	by Danehill	316	125	200	1906199	1022	1225071	3131269
KITTEN'S JOY (USA)	by El Prado	33	12	22	2561312	67	402713	2964026
DARK ANGEL (IRE)	by Acclamation	271	108	156	1404251	778	1281700	2685951
POET'S VOICE (GB)	by Dubawi	136	51	97	1851930	413	596321	2448251
INVINCIBLE SPIRIT (IRE)	by Green Desert	182	91	136	1514668	558	932900	2447568
ACCLAMATION (GB)	by Royal Applause	166	71	121	1158764	661	1049311	2208075
SHAMARDAL (USA)	by Giant's Causeway	153	71	97	1389629	354	741895	2131524
MASTERCRAFTSMAN	by Danehill Dancer	168	56	96	1474033	434	641201	2115234
PIVOTAL (GB)	by Polar Falcon	102	39	56	1240253	284	807378	2047631
TEOFILO (IRE)	by Galileo	148	66	92	1263553	369	709264	1972817
CAMELOT (GB)	by Montjeu	110	48	62	1325490	254	538737	1864227
FASTNET ROCK (AUS)	by Danehill	72	36	54	1096961	215	728681	1825642
OASIS DREAM (GB)	by Green Desert	156	65	94	1023819	431	710302	1734121
NEW APPROACH (IRE)	by Galileo	123	40	61	1307845	245	387802	1695647
EXCEED AND EXCEL (AUS)	by Danehill	170	79	125	893423	562	737378	1630801
LOPE DE VEGA (IRE)	by Shamardal	144	60	100	1105058	343	525239	1630297
CAPE CROSS (IRE)	by Green Desert	124	57	94	934587	386	691453	1626040
DANSILI (GB)	by Danehill	128	58	84	1088455	337	507800	1596255
CHAMPS ELYSEES (GB)	by Danehill	132	49	77	1157938	333	401082	1559020
WAR FRONT (USA)	by Danzig	66	36	50	935626	141	536124	1471750
KYLLACHY (GB)	by Pivotal	138	52	87	737505	514	612677	1350182

LEADING SIRES OF 2018
(GREAT BRITAIN, IRELAND AND OVERSEAS)

STALLION	BREEDING	DOMESTIC WNRS	DOMESTIC WINS	WIN MONEY	OVERSEAS WNRS	OVERSEAS WINS	WIN MONEY	TOTAL
DUBAWI (IRE)	by Dubai Millennium	81	130	2569358	67	103	6637508	9206867
GALILEO (IRE)	by Sadler's Wells	89	125	3733315	40	59	2699869	6433184
TEOFILO (IRE)	by Galileo	66	92	1263553	40	65	4565155	5828708
KITTEN'S JOY (USA)	by El Prado	12	22	2561312	14	20	2961144	5522457
NATHANIEL (IRE)	by Galileo	42	65	770695	31	46	4722453	5493148
HELMET (AUS)	by Exceed and Excel	36	44	259928	25	34	4982553	5242480
FRANKEL (GB)	by Galileo	54	81	2344822	44	65	2793311	5138134
SHAMARDAL (USA)	by Giant's Causeway	71	97	1389629	67	112	3726164	5115793
KODIAC (GB)	by Danehill	125	200	1906199	45	78	2866438	4772637
EXCEED AND EXCEL (AUS)	by Danehill	79	125	893423	55	95	3225822	4119245
MASTERCRAFTSMAN (IRE)	by Danehill Dancer	56	96	1474033	64	96	2286910	3760942
SEA THE STARS (IRE)	by Cape Cross	54	80	2306638	31	48	1104443	3411080
HOLY ROMAN EMPEROR (IRE)	by Danehill	48	71	592317	78	126	2622071	3214388
LOPE DE VEGA (IRE)	by Shamardal	60	100	1105058	58	89	2104597	3209655
ARCHIPENKO (USA)	by Kingmambo	23	36	264265	16	31	2889076	3153341
POET'S VOICE (GB)	by Dubawi	51	97	1851930	50	91	1066287	2918216
INVINCIBLE SPIRIT (IRE)	by Green Desert	91	136	1514668	53	82	1217632	2732299
ACCLAMATION (GB)	by Royal Applause	71	121	1158764	33	53	1520025	2678789
CAMELOT (GB)	by Montjeu	48	62	1325490	32	55	1341409	2666899
CHAMPS ELYSEES (GB)	by Danehill	49	77	1157938	31	55	1429172	2587109
SIYOUNI (FR)	by Pivotal	18	25	598648	71	107	1926996	2525644
DARK ANGEL (IRE)	by Acclamation	108	156	1404251	46	70	1115341	2519592
MYBOYCHARLIE (IRE)	by Danetime	4	6	50346	49	72	2395560	2445906
OASIS DREAM (GB)	by Green Desert	65	94	1023819	45	77	1331578	2355397
PIVOTAL (GB)	by Polar Falcon	39	56	1240253	49	91	1096707	2336960

LEADING TWO-YEAR-OLD SIRES OF 2018 IN GREAT BRITAIN AND IRELAND

STALLION	BREEDING	RNRS	WNRS	WINS	PLACES	WIN MONEY	PLACE MONEY	TOTAL
KODIAC (GB)	by Danehill	115	43	68	260	805227	411984	1217210
GALILEO (IRE)	by Sadler's Wells	53	23	32	72	559102	532105	1091207
SCAT DADDY (USA)	by Johannesburg	31	18	27	56	587729	311538	899267
NO NAY NEVER (USA)	by Scat Daddy	44	22	31	72	665355	171602	836957
DUBAWI (IRE)	by Dubai Millennium	50	22	30	50	719356	61653	781009
SHOWCASING (GB)	by Oasis Dream	54	15	21	102	360164	272748	632912
DANDY MAN (IRE)	by Mozart	86	29	38	170	312956	287241	600197
INVINCIBLE SPIRIT (IRE)	by Green Desert	40	16	21	68	317284	134898	452182
DARK ANGEL (IRE)	by Acclamation	100	28	36	146	247583	175970	423554
LOPE DE VEGA (IRE)	by Shamardal	58	17	25	81	269495	151789	421284
SOCIETY ROCK (IRE)	by Rock of Gibraltar	42	18	33	99	187631	212587	400217
ZOFFANY (IRE)	by Dansili	65	16	24	90	256318	139119	395436
OASIS DREAM (GB)	by Green Desert	44	17	23	51	174899	196456	371355
CAMACHO (GB)	by Danehill	47	15	22	106	251629	109126	360755
KYLLACHY (GB)	by Pivotal	38	13	20	66	240267	113522	353789
ZEBEDEE (GB)	by Invincible Spirit	53	10	12	95	194263	152010	346274
FOOTSTEPSINTHESAND (GB)	by Giant's Causeway	40	13	17	45	218288	121357	339646
KINGMAN (GB)	by Invincible Spirit	51	18	22	50	243131	82602	325733
ACCLAMATION (GB)	by Royal Applause	29	8	12	60	112190	213507	325697
RULER OF THE WORLD (IRE)	by Galileo	13	2	3	6	298593	14876	313469
CHARM SPIRIT (IRE)	by Invincible Spirit	53	19	27	91	203487	102726	306212
SIR PRANCEALOT (IRE)	by Tamayuz	25	14	22	52	263632	41967	305599
SHAMARDAL (USA)	by Giant's Causeway	33	12	15	44	202403	82251	284654
DANSILI (GB)	by Danehill	33	12	16	35	194934	53055	247989
AUSTRALIA (GB)	by Galileo	56	15	15	65	92159	155714	247873

LEADING FIRST CROP SIRES OF 2018 IN GREAT BRITAIN AND IRELAND

STALLION	BREEDING	RNRS	WNRS	WINS	WIN MONEY	PLACES	PLACE MONEY	TOTAL
NO NAY NEVER (USA)	by Scat Daddy	44	22	31	665355	72	171602	836957
KINGMAN (GB)	by Invincible Spirit	51	18	22	243131	50	82602	325733
RULER OF THE WORLD (IRE)	by Galileo	13	2	3	298593	6	14876	313469
CHARM SPIRIT (IRE)	by Invincible Spirit	53	19	27	203487	91	102726	306212
AUSTRALIA (GB)	by Galileo	56	15	15	92159	65	155714	247873
BUNGLE INTHEJUNGLE (GB)	by Exceed and Excel	42	16	20	146379	78	90094	236473
SLADE POWER (IRE)	by Dutch Art	55	14	18	134318	83	82993	217311
WAR COMMAND (USA)	by War Front	39	16	20	114476	71	77067	191542
TORONADO (IRE)	by High Chaparral	33	15	18	105454	52	74359	179813
GREGORIAN (IRE)	by Clodovil	34	8	9	50152	69	113019	163171
ALHEBAYEB (IRE)	by Dark Angel	49	9	9	41976	100	78882	120858
MOOHAAJIM (IRE)	by Cape Cross	12	5	9	46446	20	68258	114704
KUROSHIO (AUS)	by Exceed and Excel	14	5	6	32733	20	75071	107804
HEERAAT (IRE)	by Dark Angel	38	7	8	44844	68	46667	91511
OLYMPIC GLORY (IRE)	by Choisir	28	7	7	44763	36	46053	90816
GALE FORCE TEN (GB)	by Oasis Dream	25	7	9	45849	34	44718	90567
COACH HOUSE (IRE)	by Oasis Dream	38	6	10	43019	73	46701	89720
MORPHEUS (GB)	by Oasis Dream	39	3	7	37444	50	44652	82096
GARSWOOD (GB)	by Dutch Art	30	5	5	24423	43	42963	67386
SEA THE MOON (GER)	by Sea the Stars	25	5	7	32086	30	34293	66379
MUKHADRAM (GB)	by Shamardal	32	8	9	38102	36	23807	61909
NOBLE MISSION (GB)	by Galileo	13	5	6	35709	16	19897	55606
BATTLE OF MARENGO (IRE)	by Galileo	19	4	7	40361	16	12688	53050
MAGICIAN (IRE)	by Galileo	6	1	1	20885	6	18845	39730
ES QUE LOVE (IRE)	by Clodovil	13	2	3	13793	29	19778	33572

LEADING MATERNAL GRANDSIRES OF 2018 IN GREAT BRITAIN AND IRELAND

STALLION	BREEDING	RNRS	WNRS	WINS	WIN MONEY	PLACES	PLACE MONEY	TOTAL
PIVOTAL (GB)	by Polar Falcon	306	131	205	3793724	830	1900415	5694139
GALILEO (IRE)	by Sadler's Wells	297	118	167	2462375	665	1965196	4427571
DANEHILL DANCER (IRE)	by Danehill	240	99	142	1527591	709	1350169	2877759
DANEHILL (USA)	by Danzig	177	80	118	1548307	519	1243718	2792024
STREET SENSE (USA)	by Street Cry	9	4	10	2450385	24	195262	2645646
CAPE CROSS (IRE)	by Green Desert	176	59	86	1885665	474	741180	2626846
SADLER'S WELLS (USA)	by Northern Dancer	305	114	170	1520368	695	971836	2492204
DANSILI (GB)	by Danehill	200	76	116	1316337	537	1096591	2412927
SINGSPIEL (IRE)	by In the Wings	130	51	98	1396890	402	811361	2208251
OASIS DREAM (GB)	by Green Desert	218	84	124	1240140	630	807478	2047618
NASHWAN (USA)	by Blushing Groom	42	15	18	1417128	93	463346	1880474
MONTJEU (IRE)	by Sadler's Wells	153	56	95	1093164	425	770203	1863368
SHAMARDAL (USA)	by Giant's Causeway	103	45	62	1370946	271	483117	1854063
GREEN DESERT (USA)	by Danzig	194	72	107	818356	642	853457	1671812
MARK OF ESTEEM (IRE)	by Darshaan	82	31	52	587156	244	957307	1544463
ROYAL APPLAUSE (GB)	by Waajib	163	55	100	1054765	479	446444	1501209
KINGMAMBO (USA)	by Mr. Prospector	94	44	66	978719	262	424812	1403531
RAHY (USA)	by Blushing Groom	52	27	49	986584	146	348017	1334601
INDIAN RIDGE	by Ahonoora	137	49	76	929627	426	399680	1329307
EXCEED AND EXCEL (AUS)	by Danehill	120	53	96	896320	335	415630	1311951
ROYAL ACADEMY (USA)	by Nijinsky	60	21	35	894596	162	347836	1242432
HERNANDO (FR)	by Niniski	61	26	47	1035567	163	185036	1220602
DARSHAAN	by Shirley Heights	87	32	54	580150	252	636554	1216704
INVINCIBLE SPIRIT (IRE)	by Green Desert	195	78	113	668458	543	548038	1216496
BERING	by Arctic Tern	26	7	14	1136292	66	34309	1170601

FLAT STALLIONS' EARNINGS FOR 2018

(includes every stallion who sired a winner on the Flat in Great Britain and Ireland in 2018)

STALLIONS	RNRS	STARTS	WNRS	WINS	PLACES	TOTAL (£)
ACCLAMATION (GB)	166	1144	71	121	661	2208074.99
AD VALOREM (USA)	8	55	5	5	33	44511.84
AGNES GOLD (JPN)	1	14	1	2	11	11223.66
ALFRED NOBEL (IRE)	9	44	2	3	27	39309.94
ALHAARTH (IRE)	3	11	1	3	7	12963.32
ALHEBAYEB (IRE)	49	227	9	9	100	120857.75
AL KAZEEM (GB)	14	74	6	10	49	145898.48
AMADEUS WOLF (GB)	12	85	3	7	44	55901.43
AMERICAIN (USA)	2	18	1	1	8	17965.49
AMERICAN POST (GB)	8	43	2	3	24	55322.05
AND BEYOND (IRE)	1	3	1	2	1	10695.99
ANIMAL KINGDOM (USA)	12	69	7	15	34	99264.09
ANODIN (IRE)	4	12	2	2	6	13372.54
ANTONIUS PIUS (USA)	8	35	1	5	18	41854.73
APPROVE (IRE)	51	365	16	25	191	364355.42
AQLAAM (GB)	39	304	21	50	193	418538.64
ARAAFA (IRE)	2	12	1	1	5	19398.26
ARABIAN GLEAM (GB)	14	91	5	7	64	68775.61
ARAKAN (USA)	30	153	9	13	75	171089.39
ARCADIO (GER)	1	9	1	1	4	12338.05
ARCANO (IRE)	100	627	46	81	310	888139.16
ARCH (USA)	14	67	4	5	39	114541.51
ARCHIPENKO (USA)	66	342	23	36	183	408922.10
AREION (GER)	5	30	3	4	18	62732.98
ART CONNOISSEUR (IRE)	19	138	7	13	60	115565.47
ARTIE SCHILLER (USA)	6	27	3	4	12	21312.65
ASK (GB)	9	40	2	2	21	52266.33
ASSERTIVE (GB)	19	154	7	9	94	122340.83
ASTARABAD (USA)	1	4	1	1	2	7677.87
ASTRONOMER ROYAL (USA)	4	9	2	2	2	39395.30
AUSSIE RULES (USA)	45	266	16	25	144	255820.43
AUSTRALIA (GB)	56	144	15	15	65	247872.74
AUTHORIZED (IRE)	43	167	11	18	100	432644.02
AVONBRIDGE (GB)	19	139	10	17	85	127321.26
AZAMOUR (IRE)	30	137	10	15	65	183441.96
BACHELOR DUKE (USA)	6	34	1	1	18	9934.14
BAHAMIAN BOUNTY (GB)	63	417	19	35	221	481499.32
BAHRI (USA)	8	51	1	1	34	20011.50
BALLET MASTER (USA)	2	11	1	1	4	3764.70
BALTIC KING (GB)	17	110	5	11	64	141533.28
BATED BREATH (GB)	138	648	59	96	321	879442.73
BATTLE OF MARENGO (IRE)	19	63	4	7	16	53049.54
BEAT HOLLOW (GB)	17	68	4	4	29	98548.82
BELLAMY ROAD (USA)	1	3	1	1	2	5985.02
BERNARDINI (USA)	10	44	3	4	30	46376.78
BERNSTEIN (USA)	3	12	1	2	4	30525.32
BERTOLINI (USA)	17	101	1	2	61	45194.40
BIG BAD BOB (IRE)	94	496	31	47	242	463502.05
BIRDSTONE (USA)	1	12	1	2	7	16669.38
BLAME (USA)	10	40	6	7	23	82234.07
BLUEGRASS CAT (USA)	1	5	1	1	3	4679.10
BOLLIN ERIC (GB)	4	19	1	3	9	14279.90
BORN TO SEA (IRE)	91	421	22	26	193	304430.15
BROKEN VOW (USA)	1	8	1	1	5	8964.45
BUNGLE INTHEJUNGLE (GB)	42	197	16	20	78	236473.10
BURWAAZ (GB)	3	15	2	2	10	24430.01
BUSHRANGER (IRE)	54	372	14	24	186	211233.67
BYRON (GB)	13	101	4	6	48	145827.41

STALLIONS	RNRS	STARTS	WNRS	WINS	PLACES	TOTAL (£)
CACIQUE (IRE)	31	142	11	13	79	193836.39
CADEAUX GENEREUX	2	15	1	1	9	17459.07
CALCUTTA (GB)	1	15	1	3	11	20611.20
CAMACHO (GB)	112	700	42	65	369	842010.61
CAMELOT (GB)	110	493	48	62	254	1864226.60
CAMPANOLOGIST (USA)	6	19	3	6	6	34787.81
CANDY RIDE (ARG)	3	5	1	1	3	9422.48
CANFORD CLIFFS (IRE)	106	560	37	58	289	869685.61
CAN THE MAN (USA)	1	6	1	1	2	3805.12
CAPE BLANCO (IRE)	9	51	5	6	22	59820.39
CAPE CROSS (IRE)	124	701	57	94	386	1626040.48
CAPTAIN AL (SAF)	1	32	1	11	16	63677.31
CAPTAIN GERRARD (IRE)	58	393	12	17	227	414967.79
CAPTAIN RIO (GB)	26	166	8	13	95	128453.31
THE CARBON UNIT (USA)	11	64	1	3	31	34916.75
CASAMENTO (IRE)	109	591	39	71	284	897802.29
CATCHER IN THE RYE (IRE)	2	9	2	2	3	16171.68
CELTIC SWING (GB)	1	7	1	1	4	4194.72
CHAMPS ELYSEES (GB)	132	642	49	77	333	1559020.17
CHARM SPIRIT (IRE)	53	199	19	27	91	306212.10
CHEVALIER (IRE)	1	17	1	3	12	29562.83
CHOISIR (AUS)	48	321	25	45	149	495700.03
CITYSCAPE (GB)	40	189	12	17	90	302453.61
CITY ZIP (USA)	5	40	4	6	17	45516.77
CLODOVIL (IRE)	69	469	21	45	267	619765.77
COACH HOUSE (IRE)	38	173	6	10	73	89719.68
COCKNEY REBEL (IRE)	13	64	4	4	34	47803.18
COMPTON PLACE (GB)	57	429	20	33	251	325270.26
COUNTRY REEL (USA)	1	2	1	1	0	3493.26
CROSSPEACE (IRE)	1	4	1	1	1	3405.12
DAAHER (CAN)	1	4	1	1	1	3405.12
DABIRSIM (FR)	21	92	8	11	47	118958.36
DALAKHANI (IRE)	42	200	12	17	118	319523.64
DANDY MAN (IRE)	189	1106	72	110	538	1344824.52
DANEHILL DANCER (IRE)	28	146	9	11	78	202338.53
DANROAD (AUS)	3	13	1	2	6	13715.41
DANSILI (GB)	128	616	58	84	337	1596255.25
DAPPER (GB)	2	17	1	3	13	24830.45
DARK ANGEL (IRE)	271	1397	108	156	778	2685951.19
DATA LINK (USA)	6	24	1	1	8	7636.72
DAWN APPROACH (IRE)	90	355	29	43	154	662029.81
DECLARATION OF WAR (USA)	68	354	34	55	186	627219.86
DEEP IMPACT (JPN)	8	28	3	4	15	973317.13
DELEGATOR (GB)	59	357	19	35	195	655352.94
DELLA FRANCESCA (USA)	1	2	1	1	1	5087.06
DESERT KING (IRE)	3	15	2	2	6	18460.81
DESIDERATUM (GB)	5	33	1	1	28	15717.04
DIALED IN (USA)	1	4	1	1	3	31346.40
DIAMOND BOY (FR)	1	2	1	1	1	3457.77
DIAMOND GREEN (FR)	5	20	1	1	12	32029.29
DICK TURPIN (IRE)	49	272	9	15	149	198791.54
DISCREET CAT (USA)	3	12	2	4	2	40037.98
DISTORTED HUMOR (USA)	19	80	9	15	46	212142.29
DOCTOR DINO (FR)	3	13	1	4	5	59807.13
DOYEN (IRE)	6	29	2	2	17	17764.20
DRAGON PULSE (IRE)	76	416	34	60	200	692787.93
DREAM AHEAD (USA)	97	480	31	45	263	895284.21
DREAM EATER (IRE)	1	8	1	1	3	4729.12
DR MASSINI (IRE)	1	4	1	1	2	3780.35
DUBAI DESTINATION (USA)	7	34	2	3	21	45369.28
DUBAWI (IRE)	170	660	81	130	319	4060455.30
DUKE OF MARMALADE (IRE)	28	149	12	16	60	175480.19
DUNADEN (FR)	13	34	3	3	10	23220.71

STALLIONS	RNRS	STARTS	WNRS	WINS	PLACES	TOTAL (£)
DUNKIRK (USA)	2	7	1	1	4	4865.27
DUTCH ART (GB)	141	786	56	79	448	1326696.12
DYLAN THOMAS (IRE)	30	151	9	13	82	371761.08
DYNAFORMER (USA)	4	26	1	2	19	14453.87
EARLY MARCH (GB)	1	3	1	1	1	4914.62
ECHO OF LIGHT (GB)	10	37	3	3	14	33793.28
ELNADIM (USA)	28	205	15	24	101	548432.72
ELUSIVE CITY (USA)	19	130	8	10	77	98295.96
ELUSIVE PIMPERNEL (USA)	37	166	7	10	62	138327.02
ELUSIVE QUALITY (USA)	28	152	8	11	86	209320.44
ELZAAM (AUS)	60	332	25	37	172	432787.58
ENGLISH CHANNEL (USA)	8	53	2	4	29	116193.49
EPAULETTE (AUS)	78	374	25	33	190	389322.99
EQUIANO (FR)	137	848	50	87	450	1149247.73
ESKENDEREYA (USA)	1	4	1	1	3	7262.00
ES QUE LOVE (IRE)	13	52	2	3	29	33571.56
EXCEED AND EXCEL (AUS)	170	1027	79	125	562	1630800.52
EXCELEBRATION (IRE)	84	450	31	45	231	610280.07
EXCELLENT ART (GB)	37	216	10	12	131	229442.43
EXCHANGE RATE (USA)	16	66	3	4	35	275701.39
THE FACTOR (USA)	8	24	4	5	10	98509.33
FALCO (USA)	4	28	3	6	18	98303.18
FAMOUS NAME (GB)	31	158	11	20	78	214759.35
FARHH (GB)	30	135	15	27	67	870551.35
FASLIYEV (USA)	3	28	1	2	17	12381.80
FAST COMPANY (IRE)	114	596	34	46	321	727384.07
FASTNET ROCK (AUS)	72	389	36	54	215	1825642.03
FINJAAN (GB)	19	104	4	6	57	55912.24
FINSCEAL FIOR (IRE)	16	80	3	3	36	49123.17
FIREBREAK (GB)	24	154	8	9	79	84913.77
FIRST DEFENCE (USA)	10	42	5	5	21	33671.82
FIRST SAMURAI (USA)	3	9	2	2	3	10212.52
FOOTSTEPSINTHESAND (GB)	122	628	49	78	313	1160587.27
FOXWEDGE (AUS)	84	491	32	51	236	888995.44
FRACAS (IRE)	1	12	1	1	10	90902.65
FRAGRANT MIX (IRE)	2	7	1	1	1	9615.26
FRANKEL (GB)	94	351	54	81	170	3934676.47
FROZEN POWER (IRE)	38	208	11	19	98	167347.87
GALE FORCE TEN (GB)	25	98	7	9	34	90566.69
GALILEO (IRE)	196	843	89	125	463	6661329.85
GARSWOOD (GB)	30	99	5	5	43	67385.79
GENEROUS (IRE)	3	26	2	3	15	21856.46
GENTLEWAVE (IRE)	2	12	1	1	6	13638.00
GETAWAY (GER)	4	19	2	2	12	31357.53
GIANT'S CAUSEWAY (USA)	10	36	3	3	17	50120.89
GIO PONTI (USA)	5	22	2	2	9	11764.95
GOLD AWAY (IRE)	2	11	1	1	3	12536.28
GREGORIAN (IRE)	34	154	8	9	69	163171.43
HAAFHD (GB)	24	109	5	7	47	57889.70
HAATEF (USA)	16	109	9	11	57	112606.01
HALLING (USA)	19	92	5	5	48	298810.05
HARBINGER (GB)	1	9	1	1	3	8166.38
HARBOUR WATCH (IRE)	89	451	33	43	235	407376.45
HARD SPUN (USA)	12	79	5	6	51	132421.04
HARLAN'S HOLIDAY (USA)	4	15	2	2	6	29606.03
HAT TRICK (JPN)	5	23	1	1	15	13780.56
HAVANA GOLD (IRE)	95	480	31	44	264	773426.28
HEART'S CRY (JPN)	3	10	2	3	5	43401.97
HEERAAT (IRE)	38	166	7	8	68	91510.99
HELLVELYN (GB)	49	236	12	17	107	149394.90
HELMET (AUS)	110	569	36	44	336	580096.86
HELSINKI (USA)	1	2	1	1	0	6727.76
HENRYTHENAVIGATOR (USA)	43	241	13	14	135	177381.68

STALLIONS	RNRS	STARTS	WNRS	WINS	PLACES	TOTAL (£)
HERNANDO (FR)	8	30	1	1	17	10936.41
HERON ISLAND (IRE)	1	4	1	1	2	12180.54
HIGH CHAPARRAL (IRE)	80	393	27	40	216	708510.20
HOLY ROMAN EMPEROR (IRE)	127	697	48	71	359	878634.67
HURRICANE CAT (USA)	3	14	1	2	7	12427.85
HURRICANE RUN (IRE)	11	61	3	3	40	46833.12
IDEAL WORLD (USA)	1	4	1	1	2	53908.00
IFFRAAJ (GB)	156	735	58	87	361	1036164.08
INDESATCHEL (IRE)	3	29	3	4	14	33591.43
INDIAN HAVEN (GB)	7	37	1	2	21	16905.65
INTELLO (GER)	51	189	15	27	86	496855.79
INTENSE FOCUS (USA)	54	362	19	35	173	506474.91
INTIKHAB (USA)	49	236	17	26	118	270311.43
INTO MISCHIEF (USA)	1	3	1	1	1	6639.52
INVINCIBLE SPIRIT (IRE)	182	1011	91	136	558	2447567.50
ISHIGURU (USA)	5	38	3	3	29	22101.50
JEREMY (GB)	34	150	9	11	74	173852.85
JIMMY CREED (USA)	2	13	1	1	6	13673.11
JOE BEAR (IRE)	1	7	1	1	4	5209.98
JOHANNESBURG (USA)	1	9	1	1	6	5516.54
JUKEBOX JURY (IRE)	7	34	2	4	18	47081.96
KALLISTO (GER)	1	4	1	1	2	145188.05
KAYF TARA (GB)	1	6	1	1	5	4905.12
KENDARGENT (FR)	35	169	11	14	78	200152.69
KEY OF LUCK (USA)	2	22	2	3	14	16710.44
KHELEYF (USA)	83	611	35	59	323	732848.87
KIER PARK (IRE)	3	18	1	2	13	13491.84
KINGMAN (GB)	51	117	18	22	50	325732.93
KINGSALSA (USA)	2	22	1	2	16	16484.12
KING'S BEST (USA)	8	38	2	2	26	42632.38
KITTEN'S JOY (USA)	33	135	12	22	67	2964025.78
KODIAC (GB)	316	1852	125	200	1022	3131269.15
KUROSHIO (AUS)	14	64	5	6	20	107804.40
KYLLACHY (GB)	138	889	52	87	514	1350182.30
LAWMAN (FR)	125	640	36	54	340	862997.92
LAYMAN (USA)	1	13	1	3	8	13648.29
LE CADRE NOIR (IRE)	5	45	2	5	15	39887.64
LE HAVRE (IRE)	31	97	9	13	48	258779.01
LEMON DROP KID (USA)	9	42	5	5	26	256740.19
LEPORELLO (IRE)	1	7	1	2	4	8315.10
LEROIDESANIMAUX (BRZ)	34	175	13	20	111	241490.56
LETHAL FORCE (IRE)	90	472	39	53	254	538161.91
LIBRANNO (GB)	4	17	1	1	4	5152.02
LIBRETTIST (USA)	3	17	2	3	9	21298.36
LILBOURNE LAD (IRE)	62	380	20	34	208	326658.06
LONHRO (AUS)	22	107	8	12	56	195555.15
LOPE DE VEGA (IRE)	144	684	60	100	343	1630296.87
LORD SHANAKILL (USA)	35	195	11	18	114	163646.80
LUCKY STORY (USA)	5	45	3	6	31	38990.34
MAGICIAN (IRE)	6	19	1	1	6	39729.81
MAJESTIC MISSILE (IRE)	18	126	4	6	67	74054.96
MAJESTIC WARRIOR (USA)	1	6	1	1	1	15391.15
MAJOR CADEAUX (GB)	20	142	9	19	76	174350.60
MAKFI (GB)	59	352	26	46	193	768706.03
MANDURO (GER)	28	131	10	14	80	304810.32
MARTALINE (GB)	5	26	1	1	13	22329.52
MASTERCRAFTSMAN (IRE)	168	824	56	96	434	2115233.93
MASTEROFTHEHORSE (IRE)	3	13	1	2	2	20259.29
MAWATHEEQ (USA)	24	90	5	6	44	74133.53
MAXIOS (GB)	21	76	7	8	42	98420.25
MAYSON (GB)	103	635	48	79	331	974059.95
MAZAMEER (IRE)	13	66	2	4	27	29418.48
MEDAGLIA D'ORO (USA)	10	34	1	1	14	18970.99

STALLIONS	RNRS	STARTS	WNRS	WINS	PLACES	TOTAL (£)
MEDICEAN (GB)	73	422	23	31	247	505473.97
MILAN (GB)	2	11	2	3	3	51751.76
MILK IT MICK (GB)	8	56	3	4	30	27470.66
MILLENARY (GB)	3	14	1	1	8	14148.67
MISU BOND (IRE)	11	86	6	8	50	64834.90
MIZZEN MAST (USA)	16	84	7	9	41	108085.59
MONSIEUR BOND (IRE)	64	378	21	35	207	388303.81
MONSUN (GER)	4	16	1	1	8	59545.30
MONTJEU (IRE)	10	38	3	5	22	42782.37
MOOHAAJIM (IRE)	12	46	5	9	20	114704.28
MORE THAN READY (USA)	25	116	7	9	66	86010.31
MORPHEUS (GB)	39	154	3	7	50	82096.17
MOSS VALE (IRE)	13	79	2	2	34	37977.27
MOST IMPROVED (IRE)	32	169	5	8	65	79221.31
MOTIVATOR (GB)	33	151	12	20	89	306538.92
MOUNT NELSON (GB)	65	339	22	31	188	409511.03
MR VEGAS (IRE)	1	8	1	2	1	54748.20
MUHTATHIR (GB)	6	25	1	1	15	17085.76
MUJADIL (USA)	5	40	2	3	18	20702.05
MUKHADRAM (GB)	32	102	8	9	36	61909.10
MULLIONMILEANHOUR (IRE)	13	98	4	5	60	53225.89
MULTIPLEX (GB)	33	223	11	22	124	234964.75
MUSTAMEET (USA)	5	17	1	2	7	11553.53
MYBOYCHARLIE (IRE)	19	91	4	6	51	87923.06
NAAQOOS (GB)	7	33	1	3	19	16999.71
NAMID (GB)	2	4	1	1	2	94480.31
NATHANIEL (IRE)	120	495	42	65	264	1136798.44
NAYEF (USA)	19	109	7	8	61	67507.86
NEEDWOOD BLADE (GB)	4	34	1	4	20	28136.38
NEVER ON SUNDAY (FR)	1	6	1	1	5	9171.85
NEW APPROACH (IRE)	123	472	40	61	245	1695646.59
NIGHT SHIFT (USA)	1	12	1	1	4	4988.72
NOBLE MISSION (GB)	13	34	5	6	16	55605.92
NO NAY NEVER (USA)	44	155	22	31	72	836956.70
NORSE DANCER (IRE)	8	44	2	3	25	33479.76
NORTH LIGHT (IRE)	3	22	1	3	11	20130.47
NOTNOWCATO (GB)	13	75	4	5	50	61380.54
OASIS DREAM (GB)	156	804	65	94	431	1734121.38
OLDEN TIMES (GB)	7	32	3	6	10	66746.45
OLYMPIC GLORY (IRE)	28	90	7	7	36	90816.18
ORATORIO (IRE)	16	112	4	6	56	78849.52
ORB (USA)	2	4	1	1	1	7962.16
ORIENTOR (GB)	13	103	5	12	55	100818.45
ORPEN (USA)	5	22	1	3	8	90060.76
OSCAR (IRE)	5	12	1	3	4	54936.63
PACO BOY (IRE)	59	303	22	32	137	470708.88
PANIS (USA)	2	8	1	2	4	526492.30
PAPAL BULL (GB)	11	50	4	5	15	50097.73
PARIS HOUSE (GB)	1	8	1	1	5	5773.90
PASSING GLANCE (GB)	18	103	9	15	56	137547.54
PASTERNAK (GB)	2	7	1	1	6	6744.22
PASTORAL PURSUITS (GB)	81	573	27	37	340	491349.91
PASTORIUS (GER)	2	11	1	1	8	10875.76
PEDRO THE GREAT (USA)	2	11	1	3	3	164637.30
PEINTRE CELEBRE (USA)	8	47	2	3	22	118206.66
PERFECT SOUL (IRE)	1	8	1	3	4	31220.36
PHOENIX REACH (IRE)	18	76	2	3	36	22858.09
PICCOLO (GB)	49	411	17	24	261	287742.75
PIONEEROF THE NILE (USA)	2	11	1	1	5	29064.67
PIVOTAL (GB)	102	519	39	56	284	2047630.93
PLANTEUR (IRE)	11	37	2	5	18	27794.30
POET'S VOICE (GB)	136	767	51	97	413	2448250.52
POINT OF ENTRY (USA)	4	10	2	3	6	42615.31

STALLIONS	RNRS	STARTS	WNRS	WINS	PLACES	TOTAL (£)
POUR MOI (IRE)	51	226	14	19	101	242450.06
POWER (GB)	45	283	16	26	155	227274.23
PRIME DEFENDER (GB)	1	15	1	4	8	45556.87
PROCLAMATION (IRE)	7	59	3	3	31	26238.33
PROUD CITIZEN (USA)	1	2	1	1	1	6237.17
QUALITY ROAD (USA)	9	36	2	3	23	31228.19
RAIL LINK (GB)	23	124	9	12	69	167946.40
RAJJ (IRE)	7	29	1	3	11	133240.27
RAJSAMAN (FR)	5	21	2	2	9	21458.55
RAKTI (GB)	3	8	1	1	1	8324.78
RAVEN'S PASS (USA)	78	407	34	44	221	729120.03
RECKLESS ABANDON (GB)	5	14	1	2	10	23951.81
REDBACK (GB)	4	16	1	2	3	14015.05
RED CLUBS (IRE)	14	103	5	10	56	67855.64
RED JAZZ (USA)	50	299	14	24	158	269552.40
REDOUTE'S CHOICE (AUS)	28	130	14	21	61	298139.90
REFUSE TO BEND (IRE)	10	71	4	8	42	89226.97
RELIABLE MAN (GB)	6	25	3	3	9	20171.34
REQUINTO (IRE)	52	335	15	21	146	228364.85
RIO DE LA PLATA (USA)	9	43	4	6	22	155686.87
RIP VAN WINKLE (IRE)	104	501	32	47	266	657627.39
ROCK OF GIBRALTAR (IRE)	78	508	27	44	272	652116.76
RODERIC O'CONNOR (IRE)	54	313	18	28	144	304433.45
ROYAL APPLAUSE (GB)	74	530	23	39	341	429919.22
RULER OF THE WORLD (IRE)	13	30	2	3	6	313469.11
SAKHEE (USA)	14	55	4	7	30	80092.66
SAKHEE'S SECRET (GB)	44	306	17	22	177	220855.72
SAMUM (GER)	3	13	1	2	4	11885.92
SAYIF (IRE)	20	143	9	12	83	108160.99
SCAT DADDY (USA)	54	203	30	40	106	1168952.43
SCORPION (IRE)	3	6	1	1	5	9376.98
SEA THE MOON (GER)	25	63	5	7	30	66378.93
SEA THE STARS (IRE)	124	420	54	80	201	3332829.11
SELKIRK (USA)	5	30	1	1	17	19230.10
SEPOY (AUS)	103	519	25	43	293	547624.93
SHAKESPEAREAN (IRE)	2	11	1	2	4	19491.84
SHAMARDAL (USA)	153	689	71	97	354	2131524.33
SHANGHAI BOBBY (USA)	3	7	1	1	3	57780.35
SHIROCCO (GER)	24	116	6	7	73	236449.86
SHOLOKHOV (IRE)	6	15	1	1	6	7980.64
SHOWCASING (GB)	135	731	53	75	443	1247879.51
SINGSPIEL (IRE)	8	51	3	6	29	179474.38
SINNDAR (IRE)	9	32	4	5	14	25881.82
SIR PERCY (GB)	90	460	29	39	277	692214.74
SIR PRANCEALOT (IRE)	67	457	38	68	246	1129718.00
SIXTIES ICON (GB)	76	503	37	67	298	651253.63
SIYOUNI (FR)	45	167	18	25	97	981942.80
SLADE POWER (IRE)	55	202	14	18	83	217310.89
SLEEPING INDIAN (GB)	31	199	9	12	130	146043.65
SMART STRIKE (CAN)	6	42	4	6	20	109098.04
SOAVE (GER)	1	5	1	1	4	5205.56
SOCIETY ROCK (IRE)	107	624	44	73	321	1014778.63
SOLDIER HOLLOW (GB)	12	43	3	3	22	29191.18
SOLDIER OF FORTUNE (IRE)	7	41	3	4	19	57761.81
SOVIET STAR (USA)	5	44	3	5	23	31183.78
SO YOU THINK (NZ)	27	118	9	20	59	219017.16
SPEIGHTSTOWN (USA)	24	105	9	13	57	178203.94
STARSPANGLEDBANNER (AUS)	10	76	5	6	44	67122.23
STAY THIRSTY (USA)	1	11	1	2	8	16057.08
STIMULATION (IRE)	30	207	9	15	110	220901.19
STORMY ATLANTIC (USA)	4	16	2	5	9	128513.83
STORMY RIVER (FR)	3	21	2	4	9	33364.27
STRATEGIC PRINCE (GB)	20	117	6	6	62	86764.05

STALLIONS	RNRS	STARTS	WNRS	WINS	PLACES	TOTAL (£)
STREET CRY (IRE)	40	237	17	24	141	254192.51
STREET SENSE (USA)	6	19	3	4	10	36053.15
STRIKING AMBITION (GB)	3	21	2	2	11	10485.86
STYLE VENDOME (FR)	13	33	2	3	12	18806.80
SULAMANI (IRE)	9	47	2	2	29	22024.62
SUNDAY BREAK (JPN)	2	6	1	1	3	5368.18
SUPER SAVER (USA)	4	20	1	2	8	11879.82
SWISS SPIRIT (GB)	97	433	26	35	204	336292.24
TAGULA (IRE)	40	201	12	21	102	286183.40
TALE OF THE CAT (USA)	2	8	1	1	4	11778.18
TAMAYUZ (GB)	65	314	25	36	167	695681.53
TAPIT (USA)	5	23	2	6	9	187125.01
TEOFILO (IRE)	148	688	66	92	369	1972816.81
TERTULLIAN (USA)	2	11	1	1	8	16398.87
THEWAYYOUARE (USA)	49	251	16	30	102	201402.82
THOUSAND WORDS (GB)	5	40	4	9	19	98166.64
THREE VALLEYS (USA)	5	37	1	2	19	16418.31
TIGER HILL (IRE)	6	27	1	1	18	13256.12
TOBOUGG (IRE)	7	23	2	3	8	14574.58
TOREADOR (IRE)	1	12	1	1	5	6950.93
TORONADO (IRE)	33	127	15	18	52	179812.63
TOUGH AS NAILS (IRE)	14	79	5	9	30	95515.47
TRANS ISLAND (GB)	8	37	2	2	20	23541.32
TRAPPE SHOT (USA)	1	8	1	1	2	4654.06
TWIRLING CANDY (USA)	1	1	1	1	0	3752.02
UNCLE MO (USA)	2	15	2	6	4	43832.12
UNIVERSAL (IRE)	11	31	3	5	10	28470.59
URGENT REQUEST (IRE)	1	6	1	1	4	5987.06
U S RANGER (USA)	1	9	1	1	6	7076.16
VALE OF YORK (IRE)	32	187	11	16	88	173152.90
VERGLAS (IRE)	14	87	4	6	51	84699.83
VERTIGINEUX (FR)	1	4	1	2	2	9238.98
VIOLENCE (USA)	2	9	2	2	3	9323.51
VIRTUAL (GB)	11	51	1	1	31	24356.68
VISION D'ETAT (FR)	1	6	1	1	3	32401.50
VITAL EQUINE (IRE)	1	23	1	4	17	25895.13
VOCALISED (USA)	66	285	14	19	90	318137.70
VOIX DU NORD (FR)	2	15	2	3	12	17891.02
VOL DE NUIT (GB)	1	7	1	1	6	8035.82
WAR COMMAND (USA)	39	154	16	20	71	191542.13
WAR FRONT (USA)	66	286	36	50	141	1471750.01
WELL CHOSEN (GB)	3	12	2	3	2	37751.31
WESTERNER (GB)	5	36	4	10	15	47787.63
WESTLAKE (GB)	2	16	1	2	11	16472.48
WHERE OR WHEN (IRE)	2	13	1	3	5	20665.49
WHIPPER (USA)	10	34	2	2	19	435538.08
WHITMORE'S CONN (USA)	1	5	1	1	1	6976.99
WILDCAT HEIR (USA)	1	7	1	1	5	6622.17
WINDSOR KNOT (IRE)	9	57	3	4	31	103877.34
WINGED LOVE (IRE)	2	6	2	2	1	10765.29
WOOTTON BASSETT (GB)	15	48	3	3	29	148224.56
WORTHADD (IRE)	7	39	3	5	17	37260.81
XTENSION (IRE)	5	18	3	4	6	26432.94
YEATS (IRE)	17	54	1	2	34	70982.74
YORGUNNABELUCKY (USA)	7	29	1	2	11	13692.00
YOUMZAIN (IRE)	5	21	1	2	15	22005.88
ZAFEEN (FR)	2	6	1	1	2	26676.24
ZAMINDAR (USA)	21	109	6	18	51	130429.80
ZEBEDEE (GB)	144	878	48	74	447	1229290.50
ZOFFANY (IRE)	158	801	51	68	407	1166108.18

BY KIND PERMISSION OF WEATHERBYS

NH STALLIONS' EARNINGS FOR 2017/18

(includes every stallion who sired a winner over jumps in Great Britain and Ireland in 2017/18)

STALLIONS	RNRS	STARTS	WNRS	WINS	PLACES	TOTAL (£)
ACAMBARO (GER)	12	44	3	4	18	38582.94
ACCORDION	3	8	1	2	1	38743.96
ACT ONE (GB)	13	64	5	8	23	68771.11
ADLERFLUG (GER)	2	12	1	1	5	8826.67
AEROPLANE (GB)	1	8	1	1	5	4833.69
AIR CHIEF MARSHAL (IRE)	5	22	2	2	14	31083.63
ALBERTO GIACOMETTI (IRE)	9	30	2	3	14	39112.72
ALDERBROOK (GB)	16	71	4	5	31	54710.41
ALFLORA (IRE)	49	190	8	12	84	243899.24
ALFRED NOBEL (IRE)	8	42	3	3	11	23508.97
ALHAARTH (IRE)	10	42	3	5	18	54705.62
ALKAADHEM (GB)	17	58	6	9	16	105599.67
AL NAMIX (FR)	33	136	12	18	67	298261.46
AMADEUS WOLF (GB)	7	23	1	2	8	16115.74
AMERICAN POST (GB)	4	18	1	1	11	35481.15
AMILYNX (FR)	1	4	1	1	3	14119.12
AND BEYOND (IRE)	15	68	2	4	26	29073.28
ANGE GABRIEL (FR)	2	4	1	3	0	13320.90
ANSHAN	10	44	2	5	15	38052.08
ANTARCTIQUE (IRE)	8	39	2	3	19	54342.81
ANTONIUS PIUS (USA)	14	70	2	2	24	29816.42
ANZILLERO (GER)	5	19	2	3	12	68617.83
AOLUS (GER)	1	1	1	1	0	3743.40
APPLE TREE (FR)	18	65	2	2	26	26187.58
APSIS (GB)	5	21	2	3	10	30517.02
AQLAAM (GB)	13	51	5	7	20	40013.72
ARAKAN (USA)	56	198	10	14	56	143919.98
ARCADIO (GER)	62	218	15	24	72	346247.72
ARCANO (IRE)	16	38	2	3	13	23473.30
ARCH (USA)	6	16	1	1	7	6484.10
ARCHIPENKO (USA)	7	13	1	1	4	4032.60
ARCTIC COSMOS (USA)	3	4	1	1	2	6773.63
AREION (GER)	4	12	1	2	4	14948.37
ARKADIAN HERO (USA)	1	2	1	1	1	1949.50
ARTAN (IRE)	6	14	1	1	2	10964.46
ARVICO (FR)	8	30	1	1	9	8476.15
ASIAN HEIGHTS (GB)	7	15	1	2	4	15404.80
ASK (GB)	58	197	16	22	76	177480.41
ASSESSOR (IRE)	12	49	5	9	22	373464.15
ASTARABAD (USA)	10	43	6	7	27	158122.17
ASTRONOMER ROYAL (USA)	3	7	1	1	2	9830.93
ATLANTIC WAVES (IRE)	1	3	1	1	0	5528.21
AUSSIE RULES (USA)	16	48	3	4	17	40946.28
AUTHORIZED (IRE)	58	190	17	26	94	831333.75
AXXOS (GER)	3	9	1	4	3	41129.80
AZAMOUR (IRE)	34	118	12	22	54	248967.46
BACH (IRE)	33	130	6	8	43	115684.25
BACHELOR DUKE (USA)	5	21	1	1	9	17415.01
BAHRI (USA)	11	52	2	3	19	34793.17
BALAKHERI (IRE)	5	36	2	4	19	112334.06
BALKO (FR)	29	115	13	19	66	616124.44
BALLINGARRY (IRE)	29	97	5	9	48	188132.41
BARATHEA (IRE)	6	27	3	5	13	38627.37
BARYSHNIKOV (AUS)	3	10	1	1	5	7123.04
BEAT ALL (USA)	16	72	2	4	24	52750.06
BEAT HOLLOW (GB)	42	119	5	7	55	126621.06
BEAT OF DRUMS (GB)	2	7	1	1	2	5973.89
BENEFICIAL (GB)	298	1356	95	141	554	1824115.59
BERNEBEAU (FR)	4	36	4	8	19	77491.03
BERTOLINI (USA)	6	19	2	2	10	18221.12

STALLIONS	RNRS	STARTS	WNRS	WINS	PLACES	TOTAL (£)
BEST OF THE BESTS (IRE)	1	6	1	1	3	5024.52
BIENAMADO (USA)	9	41	3	5	14	43355.48
BIG BAD BOB (IRE)	30	96	4	5	35	74374.63
BIG SHUFFLE (USA)	2	11	1	3	4	15353.00
BIRDSTONE (USA)	1	6	1	1	4	17188.83
BISHOP OF CASHEL (GB)	3	16	1	1	5	8927.51
BLACK SAM BELLAMY (IRE)	121	454	37	57	194	595205.39
BLAME (USA)	2	9	1	2	3	7728.12
BLUE BRESIL (FR)	18	71	8	10	33	269540.32
BLUEPRINT (IRE)	22	109	9	12	45	170168.43
BLUSHING FLAME (USA)	1	8	1	1	1	4758.58
BOB BACK (USA)	9	48	2	2	25	27822.05
BOB'S RETURN (IRE)	2	10	1	2	4	16232.38
BOLLIN ERIC (GB)	16	67	7	12	28	79481.98
BONBON ROSE (FR)	7	27	3	4	11	50373.19
BORN TO SEA (IRE)	6	22	2	2	9	13866.07
BRIAN BORU (GB)	91	425	40	64	185	754767.99
BRIER CREEK (USA)	3	13	1	1	9	16522.82
BROADWAY FLYER (USA)	13	70	6	9	29	70194.76
BROKEN VOW (USA)	2	11	2	4	3	19492.25
BUCK'S BOUM (FR)	11	54	5	8	30	165591.83
BUSHRANGER (IRE)	14	45	1	3	15	21321.60
BUSY FLIGHT (GB)	6	17	2	2	6	17815.30
CABALLO RAPTOR (CAN)	2	7	2	2	3	16140.14
CACIQUE (IRE)	10	43	3	6	26	51249.65
CALIFET (FR)	20	91	11	16	49	200668.90
CAMACHO (GB)	6	20	3	4	10	114431.65
CANFORD CLIFFS (IRE)	19	57	5	6	25	54094.22
CAPE CROSS (IRE)	31	107	12	17	46	129479.84
CAPTAIN GERRARD (IRE)	3	8	1	1	3	4945.50
CAPTAIN RIO (GB)	15	45	3	4	17	34281.16
CARLOTAMIX (FR)	4	7	1	1	1	10067.40
CARROLL HOUSE	1	4	1	1	2	4652.64
CASAMENTO (IRE)	7	18	2	4	8	35584.51
CATCHER IN THE RYE (IRE)	13	75	5	8	32	121504.84
CELTIC SWING (GB)	3	18	1	2	6	10938.24
CENTRAL PARK (IRE)	19	63	6	6	26	137223.57
CHAMPS ELYSEES (GB)	34	122	12	18	45	181921.60
CHEVALIER (IRE)	6	19	1	3	6	14734.26
CHOISIR (AUS)	6	30	3	5	17	43856.14
CITY HONOURS (USA)	6	18	2	2	6	14520.24
CLASSIC CLICHE (IRE)	11	51	3	3	25	40102.50
CLERKENWELL (USA)	3	10	1	3	3	11278.47
CLODOVIL (IRE)	15	54	4	6	12	31663.18
CLOSE CONFLICT (USA)	2	7	1	1	2	8437.44
CLOUDINGS (IRE)	42	181	15	21	91	386228.49
COASTAL PATH (GB)	13	39	2	2	15	24985.51
COCKNEY REBEL (IRE)	9	20	1	1	4	8924.38
CORONER (IRE)	7	21	1	1	7	9101.76
COUNTRY REEL (USA)	5	23	2	2	11	40742.05
COURT CAVE (IRE)	130	531	32	50	183	605083.60
CRAIGSTEEL (GB)	85	371	27	38	146	452910.90
CREACHADOIR (IRE)	6	26	3	10	10	336185.99
CRILLON (FR)	7	27	2	6	15	492822.05
CROCO ROUGE (IRE)	11	32	1	1	12	71685.33
CROSSHARBOUR (GB)	4	29	2	5	7	29825.71
CROSSPEACE (IRE)	3	12	1	2	5	9828.54
CURTAIN TIME (IRE)	10	39	4	6	14	53547.01
DAHJEE (USA)	2	10	1	1	6	11887.92
DALAKHANI (IRE)	15	42	2	2	19	38294.53
DANEHILL DANCER (IRE)	23	109	9	12	42	99206.84
DANSANT (GB)	6	30	3	5	15	34444.92
DANSILI (GB)	22	70	4	7	27	67821.69
DARAMSAR (FR)	1	1	1	1	0	4808.52

STALLIONS	RNRS	STARTS	WNRS	WINS	PLACES	TOTAL (£)
DARK ANGEL (IRE)	18	76	5	6	33	179406.56
DARSI (FR)	47	157	8	9	66	153161.84
DASHING BLADE	1	3	1	1	2	4206.18
DAVIDOFF (GER)	3	12	2	2	7	29880.03
DAY FLIGHT (GB)	6	31	2	5	15	137197.63
DAYLAMI (IRE)	41	149	11	16	47	121125.62
DEFINITE ARTICLE (GB)	76	286	20	30	115	406301.31
DELEGATOR (GB)	5	12	1	2	6	16468.04
DELLA FRANCESCA (USA)	10	58	6	8	27	129914.12
DENHAM RED (FR)	6	24	4	8	11	415230.57
DENOUNCE (GB)	4	21	1	1	9	8915.15
DEPORTIVO (GB)	2	7	1	3	3	58825.01
DESERT KING (IRE)	19	70	7	12	34	118789.86
DESERT PRINCE (IRE)	2	3	2	2	1	103050.00
DESERT STYLE (IRE)	3	10	1	2	4	10589.87
DESIDERATUM (GB)	9	34	1	1	15	16047.46
DIABLENEYEV (USA)	1	6	1	1	2	4660.92
DIAMOND BOY (FR)	5	15	2	2	7	14368.98
DIAMOND GREEN (FR)	10	35	3	7	13	70394.65
DICK TURPIN (IRE)	10	21	1	1	2	2226.69
DIKTAT (GB)	1	7	1	3	3	13259.16
DILSHAAN (GB)	3	13	1	1	1	3469.04
DINK (FR)	2	7	1	2	4	23259.65
DOCTOR DINO (FR)	5	22	4	10	5	150092.71
DOM ALCO (FR)	19	84	9	11	41	135019.65
DOUBLE ECLIPSE (IRE)	8	42	4	8	18	90692.84
DOUBLE TRIGGER (IRE)	13	40	2	2	14	27214.19
DOYEN (IRE)	48	176	19	24	69	206752.78
DRAGON PULSE (IRE)	2	10	1	1	5	8014.20
DREAM AHEAD (USA)	4	22	1	1	5	9385.34
DREAM WELL (FR)	8	29	2	3	9	21041.50
DR MASSINI (IRE)	60	231	15	23	95	332279.02
DUBAI DESTINATION (USA)	78	320	20	40	126	622584.65
DUBAWI (IRE)	10	32	3	6	9	36504.98
DUKE OF MARMALADE (IRE)	29	97	8	15	32	245903.12
DUSHYANTOR (USA)	10	51	5	6	17	52702.86
DUTCH ART (GB)	7	22	3	5	4	25729.27
DYLAN THOMAS (IRE)	39	136	11	13	55	102097.61
DYNAFORMER (USA)	4	15	2	2	7	18430.72
EARLY MARCH (GB)	9	33	3	4	12	132514.55
ECHO OF LIGHT (GB)	18	86	3	6	29	80357.52
ELUSIVE PIMPERNEL (USA)	18	66	1	1	31	40293.67
ELUSIVE QUALITY (USA)	4	30	1	3	6	31225.58
ENDOLI (USA)	2	8	1	1	4	8331.00
ENGLISH CHANNEL (USA)	3	13	1	1	4	6613.69
ENRIQUE (GB)	11	47	5	6	18	84007.14
EPALO (GER)	7	35	3	5	15	73925.85
EPISTOLAIRE (IRE)	1	4	1	1	3	7535.70
EQUERRY (USA)	2	6	1	1	3	14695.60
EREWHON (USA)	3	19	1	1	7	7335.88
ERHAAB (USA)	10	39	3	6	13	117107.00
EXCELLENT ART (GB)	19	59	2	2	18	25902.32
EXCHANGE RATE (USA)	1	3	1	1	2	8578.10
EXIT TO NOWHERE (USA)	21	107	7	15	40	156046.95
FAIR MIX (IRE)	70	242	13	17	81	143375.97
FALCO (USA)	8	28	2	3	17	28552.99
FAME AND GLORY (GB)	16	22	5	5	5	79804.91
FAMOUS NAME (GB)	3	6	1	1	1	14886.64
FANTASTIC SPAIN (USA)	3	13	1	4	3	21339.12
FASLIYEV (USA)	1	3	1	1	0	3798.00
FAST COMPANY (IRE)	21	74	3	4	34	98009.31
FASTNET ROCK (AUS)	17	55	6	10	19	77214.73
FINSCEAL FIOR (IRE)	2	9	1	1	3	7673.50
FIREBREAK (GB)	7	18	3	3	7	12943.16

STALLIONS	RNRS	STARTS	WNRS	WINS	PLACES	TOTAL (£)
FLEETWOOD (IRE)	5	23	2	2	7	18474.57
FLEMENSFIRTH (USA)	300	1154	114	173	510	2628208.15
FLYING LEGEND (USA)	15	53	1	1	22	25471.08
FOOTSTEPSINTHESAND (GB)	12	35	2	3	15	80926.47
FORESTIER (FR)	6	26	3	4	12	54828.74
FOXWEDGE (AUS)	4	17	1	1	5	12260.12
FRACAS (IRE)	8	47	3	3	19	31555.56
FRAGRANT MIX (IRE)	16	54	5	7	21	120520.41
FRANKEL (GB)	2	6	2	3	3	19593.02
FROZEN POWER (IRE)	9	25	2	3	9	18051.35
FRUITS OF LOVE (USA)	45	199	11	21	76	307155.55
FUISSE (FR)	10	36	4	5	15	41341.66
FULL OF GOLD (FR)	6	30	3	3	16	35615.52
GALILEO (IRE)	76	318	29	35	136	733222.89
GAMUT (IRE)	52	222	15	25	85	417614.61
GENERAL GAMBUL (GB)	1	9	1	1	4	8183.52
GENEROUS (IRE)	39	143	9	12	61	132037.01
GENTLEWAVE (IRE)	9	30	2	3	11	26321.29
GEORDIELAND (FR)	7	12	1	1	1	2441.25
GERMANY (USA)	14	44	2	6	8	373578.15
GETAWAY (GER)	149	433	33	43	164	427866.82
GHOSTZAPPER (USA)	1	10	1	2	3	28447.48
GOLAN (IRE)	61	287	21	31	112	381834.32
GOLD AWAY (IRE)	3	11	2	3	5	16833.14
GOLDEN LARIAT (USA)	5	19	2	3	8	37362.28
GOLDEN TORNADO (IRE)	11	62	6	7	31	74100.86
GOLD WELL (GB)	124	506	40	52	228	1103819.34
GOTHLAND (FR)	1	11	1	2	6	14060.31
GRAPE TREE ROAD (GB)	17	61	4	4	33	47603.31
GREAT PRETENDER (IRE)	25	103	12	23	41	497532.44
GRIS DE GRIS (IRE)	6	16	3	3	8	42413.79
GULLAND (GB)	2	20	1	2	6	18247.97
HAAFHD (GB)	17	65	4	8	33	72354.51
HALLING (USA)	26	91	8	13	39	115263.14
HARBOUR WATCH (IRE)	7	29	1	2	11	32135.10
HARD SPUN (USA)	3	19	1	1	8	95074.80
HAT TRICK (JPN)	1	4	1	2	1	27430.80
HAWK WING (USA)	6	28	4	6	7	46072.35
HELISSIO (FR)	20	78	5	7	33	85711.06
HENRYTHENAVIGATOR (USA)	4	11	1	1	4	7306.95
HERNANDO (FR)	10	31	4	5	14	108240.72
HERON ISLAND (IRE)	41	139	7	13	64	331284.25
HIGH CHAPARRAL (IRE)	69	253	16	28	101	673376.69
HIGH ROCK (IRE)	5	16	1	1	4	18513.96
HIGH ROLLER (IRE)	2	6	1	1	3	11169.80
HOLY ROMAN EMPEROR (IRE)	9	29	3	3	7	22262.46
HONOLULU (IRE)	2	8	1	1	6	6193.11
HUMBEL (USA)	3	11	1	2	2	6700.95
HURRICANE CAT (USA)	1	3	1	2	1	9359.55
HURRICANE RUN (IRE)	20	92	4	4	38	49049.96
ICEMAN (GB)	7	23	1	1	9	10019.69
IFFRAAJ (GB)	16	69	5	7	24	69552.84
IKTIBAS (GB)	1	3	1	2	0	10201.86
IMPERIAL BALLET (IRE)	1	14	1	1	9	19449.78
INDIAN DANEHILL (IRE)	35	130	6	8	48	105584.62
INDIAN HAVEN (GB)	12	46	1	1	19	16465.70
INDIAN RIVER (FR)	38	191	17	29	95	746328.39
INSATIABLE (IRE)	3	20	1	4	9	109840.31
INTENSE FOCUS (USA)	14	33	1	1	12	12591.36
INTIKHAB (USA)	13	43	1	2	16	89312.85
INVASOR (ARG)	1	11	1	1	6	8486.72
INVINCIBLE SPIRIT (IRE)	17	52	3	3	19	48545.09
IRISH WELLS (FR)	12	38	5	5	15	53257.67
IT'S GINO (GER)	3	20	3	4	12	97035.52

STALLIONS	RNRS	STARTS	WNRS	WINS	PLACES	TOTAL (£)
IVAN DENISOVICH (IRE)	5	31	3	8	8	68146.34
JAMMAAL (GB)	2	8	1	1	3	6399.36
JEREMY (USA)	69	240	18	25	89	372313.96
JIMBLE (FR)	7	45	3	5	19	41520.40
JUKEBOX JURY (IRE)	3	7	2	2	4	101577.16
KADASTROF (FR)	4	20	1	1	10	12827.36
KAHYASI	7	26	3	3	12	38517.70
KAIETEUR (USA)	4	11	1	1	2	6359.94
KALANISI (IRE)	163	545	44	62	205	679097.41
KALLISTO (GER)	1	3	1	2	0	15839.13
KAPGARDE (FR)	57	206	19	28	103	556821.61
KAP ROCK (FR)	7	17	1	1	7	9735.57
KARINGA BAY	10	41	3	5	18	42939.36
KAYF TARA (GB)	258	1042	87	123	495	1920566.66
KENDARGENT (FR)	4	17	1	1	7	7013.45
KENTUCKY DYNAMITE (USA)	6	21	1	1	10	20944.11
KHALKEVI (IRE)	13	41	6	8	17	65672.73
KHELEYF (USA)	15	49	1	1	15	14380.59
KING CHARLEMAGNE (USA)	1	6	1	1	4	10636.33
KINGSALSA (USA)	10	32	1	1	14	22986.14
KING'S BEST (USA)	16	89	4	7	45	57406.59
KING'S THEATRE (IRE)	223	1049	91	135	476	2553981.07
KIRKWALL (GB)	7	33	3	6	13	32239.77
KODIAC (GB)	14	57	3	5	23	34271.42
KONIG TURF (GER)	3	15	1	1	10	13295.51
KRIS KIN (USA)	8	33	3	5	11	68408.87
KUTUB (IRE)	25	138	7	12	52	104661.96
LAHIB (USA)	9	32	3	3	16	36417.91
LAKESHORE ROAD (USA)	2	7	1	1	3	5926.48
LANDO (GER)	5	17	2	2	7	86904.42
LAURO (GER)	5	27	4	5	13	48560.62
LAVEROCK (IRE)	7	42	3	11	17	179540.94
LAVERON (GB)	21	91	7	8	44	109940.37
LAVIRCO (GER)	4	23	3	6	8	104314.33
LAWMAN (FR)	29	102	7	7	34	65491.52
LECROIX (GER)	1	10	1	3	4	22326.75
LE FOU (IRE)	7	40	3	5	10	34031.64
LE HAVRE (IRE)	7	19	1	2	10	26644.07
LEND A HAND (GB)	2	11	1	1	6	12085.31
LET THE LION ROAR (GB)	11	50	3	5	15	34544.64
LIBRETTIST (USA)	6	16	2	2	5	13138.67
LILBOURNE LAD (IRE)	6	20	1	1	4	4338.98
LINDA'S LAD (GB)	11	37	3	4	14	94327.06
LION NOIR (GB)	1	3	1	1	1	16246.39
LOPE DE VEGA (IRE)	10	32	2	4	11	106776.35
LORD AMERICO	4	11	1	2	4	10349.35
LORD DU SUD (FR)	7	18	1	3	6	15081.38
LORD OF ENGLAND (GER)	8	37	4	6	11	62217.96
LORD SHANAKILL (USA)	12	33	2	3	7	21368.21
LOST WORLD (IRE)	3	28	1	2	15	24987.01
LOUP BRETON (IRE)	2	12	2	2	6	21179.29
LOUP SOLITAIRE (USA)	4	21	2	4	10	35428.27
LUCARNO (USA)	36	143	10	12	58	129383.29
LUCKY STORY (USA)	8	29	1	2	13	19154.36
LUSO (GB)	16	59	2	2	25	76070.07
MAHLER (GB)	128	564	48	65	217	707430.61
MAJOR CADEAUX (GB)	7	19	1	1	4	5144.48
MAKFI (GB)	21	63	5	7	26	75246.67
MALINAS (GER)	39	103	9	9	27	83807.90
MAMOOL (IRE)	4	9	1	1	5	8213.75
MANDURO (GER)	19	68	7	10	30	122133.78
MANSONNIEN (FR)	2	6	1	1	3	3085.60
MARESCA SORRENTO (FR)	11	45	4	5	19	57730.69
MARIENBARD (IRE)	32	140	8	9	63	86737.29

STALLIONS	RNRS	STARTS	WNRS	WINS	PLACES	TOTAL (£)
MARIGNAN (USA)	3	17	1	1	7	10169.55
MARJU (IRE)	4	23	1	1	6	11515.04
MARTALINE (GB)	69	271	28	44	125	816556.56
MASTER BLADE (GB)	1	5	1	1	4	15159.96
MASTERCRAFTSMAN (IRE)	63	200	12	14	91	177538.49
MAWATHEEQ (USA)	10	18	1	2	5	6251.13
MEDAALY (GB)	7	53	3	5	21	140745.08
MEDICEAN (GB)	31	121	7	15	47	250689.14
MICHEL GEORGES (GB)	3	23	2	2	14	21455.62
MIDNIGHT LEGEND (GB)	179	755	64	105	358	1183285.29
MILAN (GB)	317	1223	99	158	489	2014382.13
MILLENARY (GB)	35	148	11	14	42	202970.24
MILLKOM (GB)	5	20	2	3	10	25197.06
MISTERNANDO (GB)	4	15	2	2	6	8314.14
MISTER SACHA (FR)	2	12	1	1	8	61152.30
MIZZEN MAST (USA)	2	5	1	1	1	14735.05
MODIGLIANI (USA)	1	9	1	1	4	4828.32
MOHAAJIR (USA)	3	26	1	2	8	16220.23
MONSIEUR BOND (IRE)	5	20	2	2	5	14939.34
MONSUN (GER)	7	33	3	5	15	82104.65
MONTJEU (IRE)	27	126	11	18	51	414220.23
MONTMARTRE (FR)	17	56	6	9	24	125007.37
MOROZOV (USA)	41	180	11	17	63	150575.71
MOSCOW SOCIETY (USA)	12	66	2	3	24	25391.94
MOTIVATOR (GB)	20	62	5	9	21	107723.65
MOUNTAIN HIGH (IRE)	56	248	15	22	82	217815.30
MOUNT NELSON (GB)	31	105	8	11	41	321703.88
MR COMBUSTIBLE (IRE)	6	23	2	3	6	16172.13
MR DINOS (IRE)	17	57	2	2	25	31620.66
MUHAYMIN (USA)	5	15	3	4	6	20344.99
MUHTATHIR (GB)	13	32	1	1	13	37928.25
MULTIPLEX (GB)	55	188	10	14	62	117300.54
MUSTAMEET (USA)	12	45	3	4	13	48468.31
MYBOYCHARLIE (IRE)	9	32	1	1	11	18027.77
NAAQOOS (GB)	4	12	1	1	3	11135.76
NATHANIEL (IRE)	9	27	3	5	11	88836.46
NAYEF (USA)	23	116	8	13	43	86289.56
NAZAR (IRE)	2	12	1	1	2	7324.93
NEEDLE GUN (IRE)	10	43	1	3	10	18285.76
NETWORK (GER)	44	217	24	40	107	540138.45
NEVER ON SUNDAY (FR)	1	2	1	1	0	3119.04
NEW APPROACH (IRE)	27	70	4	6	28	45538.70
NICKNAME (FR)	13	69	8	16	32	337494.19
NOMADIC WAY (USA)	7	19	1	1	8	6149.93
NO RISK AT ALL (FR)	6	18	2	5	9	71644.07
NOROIT (GER)	6	19	2	2	8	14620.20
NORSE DANCER (IRE)	21	88	7	12	38	113473.02
NORWICH	8	26	1	3	4	14250.22
NOTNOWCATO (GB)	15	46	6	10	17	151223.32
OASIS DREAM (GB)	16	43	1	2	18	27404.79
OBSERVATORY (USA)	5	14	1	1	8	8643.35
OLDEN TIMES (GB)	8	17	1	1	5	7649.59
OLD VIC	41	147	11	16	64	351630.10
ONE COOL CAT (USA)	4	10	1	1	3	7931.45
ORATORIO (IRE)	7	25	1	2	2	8973.22
OSCAR (IRE)	291	1117	90	138	437	1904280.52
OSCAR SCHINDLER (IRE)	6	12	1	1	5	11738.42
OSORIO (GER)	2	7	1	1	4	11338.10
OVERBURY (IRE)	54	233	15	28	99	383264.21
PACO BOY (IRE)	11	31	1	2	5	10226.70
PADDY O'PRADO (USA)	4	25	1	1	13	12766.33
PALACE EPISODE (USA)	1	10	1	1	8	11823.56
PANIS (USA)	3	15	2	2	7	14694.20
PANORAMIC	4	19	2	2	10	45873.76

STALLIONS	RNRS	STARTS	WNRS	WINS	PLACES	TOTAL (£)
PAPAL BULL (GB)	31	128	8	11	41	92279.61
PASSING GLANCE (GB)	32	130	11	14	53	117388.83
PASTERNAK (GB)	13	65	5	10	25	64113.23
PEINTRE CELEBRE (USA)	9	31	3	6	9	42752.92
PELDER (IRE)	5	19	1	2	9	32497.78
PERUGINO (USA)	4	17	2	4	9	98376.71
PHOENIX REACH (IRE)	17	75	7	8	31	63147.36
PIERRE (GB)	12	68	5	10	33	94207.72
PILSUDSKI (IRE)	5	20	2	4	8	29374.21
PIVOTAL (GB)	18	63	7	9	26	94139.69
POET'S VOICE (GB)	13	48	2	3	23	30732.32
POLICY MAKER (IRE)	10	34	2	2	16	49425.97
POLIGLOTE (GB)	25	111	16	25	58	729921.03
PORTRAIT GALLERY (IRE)	22	95	8	11	49	127708.43
POSIDONAS (GB)	1	2	1	1	0	2183.65
POUR MOI (IRE)	13	38	3	3	16	37083.77
POWER (GB)	4	15	1	1	8	14182.46
PRESENTING (GB)	326	1345	96	146	575	2263984.26
PRIMARY (USA)	11	50	2	4	15	50719.78
PRINCE ARCH (USA)	3	8	1	1	1	4045.15
PROCLAMATION (IRE)	18	64	2	2	21	21268.92
PROTEKTOR (GER)	4	14	2	2	7	45312.06
PURSUIT OF LOVE (GB)	2	14	1	1	7	7570.88
PUSHKIN (IRE)	6	22	1	2	6	18675.22
PUTRA PEKAN (GB)	3	10	1	1	6	7448.12
QUWS (GB)	4	22	2	2	7	16931.73
RACINGER (FR)	2	14	2	3	8	37146.36
RAIL LINK (GB)	17	45	3	3	15	22883.58
RAINBOW HIGH (GB)	12	45	3	4	13	23476.04
RAINBOW QUEST (USA)	2	10	1	1	4	5634.00
RAKAPOSHI KING	2	7	1	4	2	19210.72
RANSOM O'WAR (USA)	1	4	1	1	1	10569.60
RAVEN'S PASS (USA)	12	45	4	5	15	34332.80
RECHARGE (IRE)	7	29	3	4	11	25417.32
REDBACK (GB)	2	5	1	1	4	9275.80
RED CLUBS (IRE)	4	15	1	1	7	8919.94
REFUSE TO BEND (IRE)	9	46	2	3	19	21989.27
REVOQUE (IRE)	15	44	4	5	15	85664.83
RIP VAN WINKLE (IRE)	25	68	3	3	21	37662.12
ROBIN DES CHAMPS (FR)	105	355	29	42	149	707890.64
ROBIN DES PRES (FR)	79	352	22	35	153	344884.95
ROB ROY (USA)	5	23	2	2	6	8828.96
ROCK OF GIBRALTAR (IRE)	26	80	3	3	26	28259.58
RODERIC O'CONNOR (IRE)	4	15	1	1	3	8034.99
ROLI ABI (FR)	1	9	1	1	5	14408.33
ROYAL ANTHEM (USA)	30	105	6	9	40	95697.89
ROYAL APPLAUSE (GB)	13	65	3	3	35	36007.47
RUDIMENTARY (USA)	14	61	4	6	21	57961.43
RUNYON (IRE)	3	22	2	2	8	22361.78
SADDEX (GB)	5	15	1	1	6	15419.72
SADDLER MAKER (IRE)	19	80	9	18	41	669458.72
SADDLERS' HALL (IRE)	8	33	1	1	14	14755.73
SAFFRON WALDEN (FR)	8	38	3	3	24	43510.82
SAGACITY (FR)	3	9	1	2	4	48169.54
SAGAMIX (FR)	13	58	6	10	30	140306.37
SAGEBURG (IRE)	15	52	3	3	20	56599.67
SAINT DES SAINTS (FR)	49	199	17	32	86	575703.82
SAKHEE (USA)	16	53	4	6	22	56487.08
SAKHEE'S SECRET (GB)	7	24	1	1	10	11830.90
SALFORD EXPRESS (IRE)	2	12	1	1	6	12154.48
SAMUM (GER)	6	13	1	1	2	12880.34
SANDMASON (GB)	10	37	3	6	21	230589.57
SATRI (IRE)	4	18	2	2	13	13914.50
SAYARSHAN (FR)	4	20	2	3	10	23713.08

STALLIONS	RNRS	STARTS	WNRS	WINS	PLACES	TOTAL (£)
SCHIAPARELLI (GER)	34	103	10	13	43	96609.26
SCORPION (IRE)	197	723	54	76	277	1022022.92
SEA THE STARS (IRE)	20	55	4	5	23	89926.07
SELKIRK (USA)	6	26	4	5	6	29891.85
SENDAWAR (IRE)	3	9	1	2	2	7644.24
SEPTEMBER STORM (GER)	30	109	8	12	36	117206.78
SESARO (USA)	1	9	1	1	4	4277.53
SHAANMER (IRE)	6	32	2	2	14	106850.56
SHAMARDAL (USA)	9	28	3	4	7	17068.42
SHAMI (GB)	3	13	1	1	6	7888.14
SHANTOU (USA)	121	479	47	70	197	1087205.44
SHIROCCO (GER)	69	209	15	17	65	180800.12
SHOLOKHOV (IRE)	23	96	10	14	36	138949.26
SHOWCASING (GB)	4	11	1	1	6	7470.96
SILVANO (GER)	1	4	1	1	1	6940.54
SILVER CROSS (FR)	1	7	1	1	5	19722.66
SILVER PATRIARCH (IRE)	10	33	2	2	13	19592.44
SINNDAR (IRE)	14	48	3	4	23	52181.76
SIR HARRY LEWIS (USA)	21	93	6	7	45	134616.69
SIR PERCY (GB)	33	125	6	15	58	295040.52
SIR PRANCEALOT (IRE)	5	15	1	1	13	18191.20
SIXTIES ICON (GB)	23	98	7	11	48	89053.75
SKINS GAME (GB)	1	7	1	1	6	11393.08
SLICKLY (FR)	6	19	3	4	9	82976.65
SMADOUN (FR)	13	50	5	7	19	167063.88
SMART STRIKE (CAN)	3	9	1	2	4	10346.48
SNOW CAP (FR)	1	6	1	1	3	10631.69
SNURGE	9	30	1	1	8	19390.43
SOAPY DANGER (GB)	2	11	2	5	4	33566.84
SOLDIER HOLLOW (GB)	11	45	3	6	20	102150.49
SOLDIER OF FORTUNE (IRE)	22	78	10	12	38	192081.82
SONNY MAC (GB)	1	15	1	2	4	16849.54
SOVIET STAR (USA)	5	30	1	3	11	25769.32
SO YOU THINK (NZ)	5	16	2	3	8	12842.45
SPADOUN (FR)	23	129	8	16	60	199809.94
SPANISH MOON (USA)	5	10	2	6	2	142605.51
SPARTACUS (IRE)	4	29	2	2	17	28857.96
SPECIAL KALDOUN (IRE)	4	9	2	2	4	92981.73
SPENDENT (GB)	1	1	1	1	0	1624.50
SPIRIT ONE (FR)	5	18	3	5	7	116403.28
STARCRAFT (NZ)	1	10	1	1	5	10655.68
STIMULATION (IRE)	7	27	1	1	13	13656.78
ST JOVITE (USA)	9	28	1	1	7	9382.46
STORMING HOME (GB)	5	24	2	5	8	67730.68
STORMY RIVER (FR)	6	17	2	5	9	12503.91
STOWAWAY (GB)	196	747	51	79	328	1132839.37
STRATEGIC CHOICE (USA)	2	7	1	1	4	10128.40
STRATEGIC PRINCE (GB)	19	62	2	3	24	36307.01
STREET CRY (IRE)	14	37	3	4	19	41887.27
SUBTLE POWER (IRE)	11	38	3	4	15	27600.98
SULAMANI (IRE)	52	190	11	16	88	144016.17
SUNDAY BREAK (JPN)	4	13	1	1	3	5801.34
SUNSHINE STREET (USA)	1	6	1	1	2	5890.60
SUPERIOR PREMIUM (GB)	2	11	2	2	4	15537.74
SUPREME SOUND (GB)	6	21	1	1	14	10240.85
SWIFT GULLIVER (IRE)	1	12	1	1	4	7401.60
SYSTEMATIC (GB)	3	6	1	1	3	13582.40
TAGULA (IRE)	9	17	1	1	7	18994.68
TAJRAASI (USA)	9	60	3	3	17	29259.58
TAMAYUZ (GB)	7	45	5	10	19	76663.68
TAMURE (IRE)	8	30	4	7	6	68734.11
TAYLOR STONE (GB)	1	2	1	1	0	5528.21
TEOFILO (IRE)	32	114	9	11	44	133703.97
THEWAYYOUARE (USA)	15	58	4	5	22	46861.27

STALLIONS	RNRS	STARTS	WNRS	WINS	PLACES	TOTAL (£)
THREE VALLEYS (USA)	5	17	2	4	4	31493.30
TIGER GROOM (GB)	5	22	2	2	12	42646.52
TIGER HILL (IRE)	12	44	3	4	20	31846.12
TIKKANEN (USA)	53	213	14	23	83	220690.53
TOBOUGG (IRE)	44	195	14	22	78	174444.42
TOUCH OF LAND (FR)	17	81	5	7	30	60766.85
TRADE FAIR (GB)	9	42	3	4	20	33216.91
TRANS ISLAND (GB)	56	243	16	28	90	254702.52
TREMPOLINO (USA)	7	49	3	3	30	64197.81
TURGEON (USA)	26	76	9	15	32	168390.63
TURTLE BOWL (IRE)	11	36	3	3	20	56550.82
TURTLE ISLAND (IRE)	29	156	7	9	71	139907.71
ULTIMATELY LUCKY (IRE)	2	5	1	1	0	7370.94
UNBRIDLED'S SONG (USA)	1	5	1	1	3	6742.80
URBAN OCEAN (FR)	7	36	2	4	16	64169.31
VALANOUR (IRE)	1	4	1	1	1	4288.02
VAL ROYAL (FR)	1	2	1	1	1	5615.39
VENDANGEUR (IRE)	7	31	2	2	16	62790.24
VERGLAS (IRE)	11	36	2	2	16	29631.98
VERTICAL SPEED (FR)	17	71	7	9	31	83822.53
VERTIGINEUX (FR)	2	6	1	1	5	11369.44
VIC TOTO (FR)	1	7	1	1	2	5684.12
VINNIE ROE (IRE)	67	284	26	40	122	437828.85
VISION D'ETAT (FR)	10	24	2	2	9	18979.55
VOCALISED (USA)	5	29	1	4	10	37618.22
VOIX DU NORD (FR)	32	143	14	24	66	420042.79
VOL DE NUIT (GB)	1	5	1	1	3	4720.76
VOLOCHINE (IRE)	3	16	1	1	5	14309.01
WALK IN THE PARK (IRE)	19	83	11	15	33	438121.51
WAREED (IRE)	12	46	3	4	16	36136.22
WELL CHOSEN (GB)	35	146	10	18	59	264822.32
WELL MADE (GER)	3	6	1	1	1	9419.87
WESTERNER (GB)	227	1059	87	141	431	1639522.43
WHIPPER (USA)	7	31	2	2	11	21179.40
WHITMORE'S CONN (USA)	32	167	10	14	52	167738.77
WINDSOR KNOT (IRE)	19	75	5	6	28	135952.55
WINGED LOVE (IRE)	75	301	21	34	124	609204.16
WINKER WATSON (GB)	4	21	2	2	10	16049.22
WITHOUT CONNEXION (IRE)	1	5	1	1	2	3922.65
WITH THE FLOW (USA)	10	35	2	4	16	35877.50
WITNESS BOX (USA)	24	95	6	12	36	105186.01
WIZARD KING (GB)	3	19	1	1	3	7240.54
YEATS (IRE)	139	602	50	80	226	970709.68
YOUMZAIN (IRE)	13	40	3	5	19	73349.26
ZAFEEN (FR)	2	8	1	1	5	7713.39
ZAGREB (USA)	23	86	2	2	42	63800.41
ZAMBEZI SUN (GB)	6	20	2	4	8	22287.58
ZAMINDAR (USA)	16	34	4	4	10	36832.46
ZERPOUR (IRE)	5	31	2	2	13	22360.88
ZOFFANY (IRE)	16	35	4	4	17	35008.47

BY KIND PERMISSION OF WEATHERBYS

HIGH-PRICED YEARLINGS OF 2018 AT TATTERSALLS SALES
The following yearlings realised 110,000 Guineas and over at Tattersalls Sales in 2018.

Name and Breeding	Purchaser	Guineas
B C DUBAWI (IRE) - DAR RE MI (GB)	DAVID REDVERS BS	3500000
B C GALILEO (IRE) - SHASTYE (IRE)	M V MAGNIER	3400000
B C GALILEO (IRE) - ALLURING PARK (IRE)	M V MAGNIER	1300000
B F GALILEO (IRE) - PENCHANT (GB)	NARVICK INTERNATIONAL	1200000
PROPRIETY (IRE) B F GALILEO (IRE) - WANNABE BETTER (IRE)	CHEVELEY PARK STUD	1200000
CH F GALILEO (IRE) - CHELSEA ROSE (IRE)	M V MAGNIER	1200000
B C DUBAWI (IRE) - YUMMY MUMMY (GB)	STROUD COLEMAN BS	1200000
CH F DUBAWI (IRE) - GIANTS PLAY (USA)	STROUD COLEMAN BS	1200000
B F GALILEO (IRE) - KEENES ROYALE (GB)	STROUD COLEMAN BS	1200000
B F FRANKEL (GB) - GLOBAL MAGIC (GER)	VENDOR	1150000
B C GALILEO (IRE) - POSSET (GB)	STROUD COLEMAN BS	1100000
B C DUBAWI (IRE) - SHIROCCO STAR (GB)	STROUD COLEMAN BS	1100000
GR C KINGMAN (GB) - SHEMYA (FR)	M V MAGNIER	1050000
HOLLYWOOD CANTEEN (IRE) B F GALILEO (IRE) - BROOKLYN'S STORM (USA)	HORSE FRANCE	1000000
B C SEA THE STARS (IRE) - CHICAGO DANCER (IRE)	STROUD COLEMAN BS	1000000
B F MUHAARAR (GB) - QUEENOFTHEFAIRIES (GB)	SHADWELL ESTATE COMPANY	925000
B F GALILEO (IRE) - WILDWOOD FLOWER (USA)	M V MAGNIER	900000
B C INVINCIBLE SPIRIT (IRE) - MONZZA (GB)	SHADWELL ESTATE COMPANY	900000
BR C SEA THE STARS (IRE) - ELLE SAME (GB)	STROUD COLEMAN BS	900000
BR F GALILEO (IRE) - BUFERA (IRE)	BLANDFORD BS	900000
B C GALILEO (IRE) - TERROR (IRE)	STROUD COLEMAN BS	900000
B F LE HAVRE (IRE) - BLISSFUL BEAT (GB)	BLANDFORD BS	850000
RETROSPECT (IRE) B C FRANKEL (GB) - LOOKING BACK (IRE)	ROGER VARIAN	850000
B C DUBAWI (IRE) - J WONDER (USA)	STROUD COLEMAN BS	850000
B F LOPE DE VEGA (IRE) - BURNING HEIGHTS (GER)	BLANDFORD BS	800000
B F GALILEO (IRE) - DIALAFARA (FR)	SACKVILLEDONALD	800000
B F DUBAWI (IRE) - BASTET (IRE)	STROUD COLEMAN BS	800000
B C KINGMAN (GB) - REEM (AUS)	STROUD COLEMAN BS	750000
CH F STARSPANGLEDBANNER (AUS) - A HUGE DREAM (IRE)	STROUD COLEMAN BS	750000
B F DUBAWI (IRE) - TIME CONTROL (IRE)	STROUD COLEMAN BS	700000
B/BR F KITTEN'S JOY (USA) - CELESTIAL WOODS (USA)	SHAWN DUGAN, AGENT	700000
GR F GALILEO (IRE) - LAUGH OUT LOUD (GB)	STROUD COLEMAN BS	700000
B C FRANKEL (GB) - WHERE (IRE)	C GORDON-WATSON BS	700000
WITH REASON (GB) CH F FRANKEL (GB) - EMINENTLY (GB)	VENDOR	650000
B F SEA THE STARS (IRE) - JANEY MUDDLES (IRE)	STROUD COLEMAN BS	650000
B F FRANKEL (GB) - NOURIYA (GB)	BLUE DIAMOND STUD UK	650000
CH C SHOWCASING (GB) - CRYSTAL GAL (IRE)	PHOENIX THOROUGHBREDS	650000
B F NO NAY NEVER (USA) - SHELLEY BEACH (IRE)	KERRI RADCLIFFE BS	650000
NOONDAY GUN (GB) GR C DUBAWI (IRE) - SKY LANTERN (IRE)	VENDOR	625000
B C KINGMAN (GB) - BEACH FROLIC (GB)	JOHN GOSDEN RACING LLP	600000
WALDKONIG (GB) B C KINGMAN (GB) - WALDLERCHE (GB)	CRISPIN DE MOUBRAY SARL	600000
B C KODIAC (GB) - ANTHEM ALEXANDER (IRE)	STROUD COLEMAN BS	600000
B/BR C DUBAWI (IRE) - ODELIZ (IRE)	STROUD COLEMAN BS	600000
B F NO NAY NEVER (USA) - SEEKING SOLACE (GB)	M V MAGNIER	600000
B C INVINCIBLE SPIRIT (IRE) - GALVAUN (IRE)	AMANDA SKIFFINGTON	600000
LOVE LOVE (GB) B F KODIAC (GB) - PERFECT BLESSINGS (GB)	SACKVILLEDONALD	600000
SRI SENE POWER (IRE) B F DARK ANGEL (IRE) - FANCIFUL DANCER (GB)	SACKVILLEDONALD	600000
B C SHOWCASING (GB) - GRACE AND GLORY (IRE)	STROUD COLEMAN BS	600000
B F KINGMAN (GB) - SEAGULL (GB)	SHADWELL ESTATE COMPANY	580000
B C GOLDEN HORN (GB) - ASTONISHING (IRE)	BBA IRELAND	550000
CH C LOPE DE VEGA (IRE) - PEUT ETRE (IRE)	STROUD COLEMAN BS	550000
B F NO NAY NEVER (USA) - OPERA FAN (FR)	SHAWN DUGAN, AGENT	525000
GR C KODIAC (GB) - COOLNAGREE (IRE)	HONG KONG JOCKEY CLUB	525000
CHAIRMAN POWER (GB) B C GALILEO (IRE) - BEST TERMS (GB)	SACKVILLEDONALD	525000
B F SEA THE STARS (IRE) - REFLECTIVE (USA)	C GORDON-WATSON BS	500000
GR C DARK ANGEL (IRE) - DANETIME OUT (IRE)	PHOENIX THOROUGHBREDS	500000
ST JOE LOUIS (GB) B C KINGMAN (GB) - SMART STEP (GB)	WHITE BIRCH FARM	500000
POSTILEO (IRE) B C GALILEO (IRE) - POSTERITY (IRE)	ROGER VARIAN	500000
B F GLENEAGLES (IRE) - TARBELA (IRE)	BLANDFORD BS	500000
B C MUHAARAR (GB) - ANNA'S ROCK (IRE)	BLANDFORD BS	500000
B C DUBAWI (IRE) - FALLEN FOR YOU (GB)	H K TANG	500000
KHAALIS (IRE) B C MUHAARAR (GB) - ALEXANDER GOLDRUN (IRE)	SHADWELL ESTATE COMPANY	500000
B F DUBAWI (IRE) - VOLEUSE DE COEURS (GB)	STROUD COLEMAN BS	500000
GR F DARK ANGEL (IRE) - LAYLA JAMIL (IRE)	BLANDFORD BS	480000
B F SEA THE STARS (IRE) - SOLAR MOON (GB)	C GORDON-WATSON BS	475000
SKY POWER (IRE) B C FASTNET ROCK (AUS) - DAME BLANCHE (IRE)	SACKVILLEDONALD	450000
B F GALILEO (IRE) - SAPHIRA'S FIRE (IRE)	M V MAGNIER	450000
MR KIKI (IRE) B C NO NAY NEVER (USA) - JACQUELIN JAG (IRE)	A C ELLIOTT, AGENT	450000

ame and Breeding	Purchaser	Guineas
ILLVINA (GB) B F DUTCH ART (GB) - MOLLY BROWN (GB)	CHEVELEY PARK STUD	450000
RROW OF GOLD (IRE) CH C GALILEO (IRE) - FLECHE D'OR (GB)	HILLEN / RYAN	450000
F SIYOUNI (FR) - BRYNICA (FR)	SHADWELL ESTATE COMPANY	450000
F FASTNET ROCK (AUS) - KNOCKNAGREE (IRE)	HILLEN / DEVIN	450000
F KODIAC (GB) - MARSH DAISY (GB)	STROUD COLEMAN BS	435000
R C DARK ANGEL (IRE) - CAPULET MONTEQUE (IRE)	M V MAGNIER	425000
F MUHAARAR (GB) - ANNABELLE JA (FR)	CANARY BS	425000
C NEW APPROACH (IRE) - SAVANNAH BELLE (GB)	STROUD COLEMAN BS	425000
HAI POWER (IRE) B C KINGMAN (GB) - ROSCOFF (IRE)	SACKVILLEDONALD	425000
C SIYOUNI (FR) - ENNAYA (FR)	STROUD COLEMAN BS	425000
RAISED (GB) CH F PIVOTAL (GB) - SUELITA (GB)	CHEVELEY PARK STUD	425000
ESERT CAMP (IRE) B C WOOTTON BASSETT (GB) - LOUARN (IRE)	STROUD COLEMAN BS	425000
OX NEVER QUIT (GB) BR C DARK ANGEL (IRE) - MINWAH (IRE)	SACKVILLEDONALD	420000
F DUBAWI (IRE) - THE MINIVER ROSE (IRE)	JOHN & JAKE WARREN	400000
C KINGMAN (GB) - LEGENDE BLEUE (GB)	HILLEN / DEVIN	400000
C KODIAC (GB) - MOOJHA (USA)	HILLEN / DEVIN	400000
TAND STRONG (IRE) B C NO NAY NEVER (USA) - HURRICANE EMMA (USA)	STROUD COLEMAN BS	400000
JEEN OF THE SEA (IRE) B F SEA THE STARS (IRE) - KNYAZHNA (IRE)	STROUD COLEMAN BS	400000
KETCHES OF SPAIN (IRE) B F LOPE DE VEGA (IRE) - JANICELLAINE (IRE)	WHITE BIRCH FARM	400000
NNABEL'S CHOICE (GB) CH F DUBAWI (IRE) - ANNABELLE'S CHARM (IRE)	AMMERLAND	400000
F WAR FRONT (USA) - ROYAL DECREE (USA)	VENDOR	385000
C NO NAY NEVER (USA) - DANCING SHOES (USA)	MV MAGNIER	380000
C FRANKEL (GB) - MY SPECIAL J'S (USA)	C GORDON-WATSON BS	380000
AXI BOY (GB) B C OASIS DREAM (GB) - LAVENDER AND LACE (GB)	A C ELLIOTT, AGENT	380000
C KINGMAN (GB) - ASTROGLIA (USA)	C GORDON-WATSON BS	375000
OSS POWER (IRE) B C FRANKEL (GB) - LA VINCHINA (GER)	SACKVILLEDONALD	375000
INTER THORN (IRE) GR C MUHAARAR (GB) - ROSE OF SUMMER (USA)	ROGER VARIAN	375000
F CAMELOT (GB) - MUSICAL SANDS (GB)	STROUD COLEMAN BS	370000
ERONISTA (IRE) B F MUHAARAR (GB) - EVITA (GB)	BLANDFORD BS	370000
JAN ELCANO (GB) CH C FRANKEL (GB) - WHATAMI (GB)	HILLEN / RYAN	360000
ASSANDRA (GER) B F DANSILI (GB) - CAPICHERA (GER)	STROUD COLEMAN BS	360000
JINEVE (GB) CH F FRANKEL (GB) - SOFT CENTRE (GB)	PRIME EQUESTRIAN	360000
C MUHAARAR (GB) - VANISHING GREY (IRE)	VENDOR	350000
L TARMAAH (IRE) B C MUHAARAR (GB) - HOW'S SHE CUTTIN' (IRE)	SHADWELL ESTATE COMPANY	350000
ORD CAMPARI (IRE) B C KINGMAN (GB) - BLANCHE DUBAWI (IRE)	ROGER VARIAN	350000
F LOPE DE VEGA (IRE) - ALBAROUCHE (GB)	JAMIE MCCALMONT	350000
EAR POWER (IRE) B F ACCLAMATION (GB) - DEBUETANTIN (GB)	SACKVILLEDONALD	350000
C OASIS DREAM (GB) - CEISTEACH (IRE)	CHINA HORSE CLUB	350000
IVINE INSIGHT (IRE) B F SHAMARDAL (USA) - GALACTIC HEROINE (GB)	WHITE BIRCH FARM	350000
C CAMACHO (GB) - ALEXIADE (IRE)	HONG KONG JOCKEY CLUB	325000
F DARK ANGEL (IRE) - KELSEY ROSE (GB)	MV MAGNIER	325000
C LOPE DE VEGA (IRE) - LAMPS OF HEAVEN (IRE)	SHADWELL ESTATE COMPANY	325000
F AUSTRALIA (GB) - ANKLET (GB)	KLARAVICH STABLES	325000
ESERT PALMS (GB) B C OASIS DREAM (GB) - BE MY GAL (GB)	PETER & ROSS DOYLE BS	320000
ASH TO FAME (GB) B C DANSILI (GB) - TALENT (GB)	VENDOR	320000
ROZEN WATERS (IRE) CH C NO NAY NEVER (USA) - WHITEFALL (USA)	PETER & ROSS DOYLE BS	320000
C OASIS DREAM (GB) - LANDMARK (USA)	SUN BS	320000
H C SIYOUNI (FR) - STIRRING BALLAD (GB)	STROUD COLEMAN BS	320000
F CAMELOT (GB) - MALAYAN MIST (IRE)	JOHN & JAKE WARREN	320000
EPARTEE (IRE) BR C INVINCIBLE SPIRIT (IRE) - PLEASANTRY (GB)	HILLEN / RYAN	310000
L AASY (IRE) B C SEA THE STARS (IRE) - KITCARA (GB)	SHADWELL ESTATE COMPANY	300000
SLAND FALCON (IRE) B C DARK ANGEL (IRE) - RELATION ALEXANDER (IRE)	STROUD COLEMAN BS	300000
F INVINCIBLE SPIRIT (IRE) - DARYSINA (USA)	MIKE RYAN	300000
F INVINCIBLE SPIRIT (IRE) - GHURRA (USA)	SHADWELL ESTATE COMPANY	300000
C KINGMAN (GB) - URBAN CASTLE (USA)	KLARAVICH STABLES	300000
HE SEVENTH DAY (IRE) B C SIYOUNI (FR) - MAD EXISTENCE (IRE)	PETER & ROSS DOYLE BS	300000
R F KINGMAN (GB) - SERENA'S STORM (IRE)	OCEANIC BS FOR D FARM	300000
PARKLING OLLY (IRE) B F GLENEAGLES (IRE) - SOGNO VERDE (IRE)	A C ELLIOTT, AGENT	300000
REMIER POWER (GB) CH C SIYOUNI (FR) - PELERIN (IRE)	SACKVILLEDONALD	300000
ILLY FRANKL (GB) B F FRANKEL (GB) - RIBBONS (GB)	VENDOR	300000
C KINGMAN (GB) - LADY LINDA (USA)	C GORDON-WATSON BS	300000
C GOLDEN HORN (GB) - NIGHT FROLIC (GB)	BLANDFORD BS	300000
OCKY DREAMS (GB) B C MUHAARAR (GB) - MRS GREELEY (GB)	PETER & ROSS DOYLE BS	300000
UIET PLACE (IRE) B F KODIAC (GB) - NEED YOU NOW (IRE)	STROUD COLEMAN BS	300000
R F MORE THAN READY (USA) - LISMORE (USA)	SHADWELL ESTATE COMPANY	300000
F PIVOTAL (GB) - WALLIS (GB)	MIKE RYAN	300000
F GALILEO (IRE) - MILANOVA (AUS)	RONALD RAUSCHER	300000
F DARK ANGEL (IRE) - WONDEROUS LIGHT (GB)	VENDOR	290000
WITCHMAN (IRE) B C LAWMAN (FR) - FARADAY LIGHT (IRE)	HILLEN / RYAN	290000

Name and Breeding	Purchaser	Guine
B C GOLDEN HORN (GB) - SNOW PINE (GB)	C GORDON-WATSON BS	28000
DESERT EMPEROR (GB) B C CAMELOT (GB) - PRAIA (GER)	ROGER VARIAN	28000
CH C KITTEN'S JOY (USA) - SAVE OUR OCEANS (USA)	PACA PACA FARM	28000
B F OASIS DREAM (GB) - GOLETA (GB)	SHADWELL ESTATE COMPANY	28000
FOX DUTY FREE (IRE) B C KINGMAN (GB) - BUGIE D'AMORE (GB)	SACKVILLEDONALD	28000
B C LOPE DE VEGA (IRE) - MISS YOU TOO (GB)	JEREMY BRUMMITT	28000
IRISH MASTER (GB) GR/RO C MASTERCRAFTSMAN (IRE) - SELVA REAL (GB)	PHILIPPA MAINS	28000
B C MUHAARAR (GB) - SHUMOOS (USA)	VENDOR	28000
SIYOUNG (GB) B F SIYOUNI (FR) - ALAMARIE (FR)	WHITE BIRCH FARM	28000
ALWAYS FEARLESS (IRE) CH C CAMACHO (GB) - ZENELLA (GB)	SACKVILLEDONALD	27000
CH F MASTERCRAFTSMAN (IRE) - AREEDA (IRE)	BLANDFORD BS	27000
RAOOF (GB) GR C DARK ANGEL (IRE) - SWISS DIVA (GB)	SHADWELL ESTATE COMPANY	26000
CH F NO NAY NEVER (USA) - CHANT DE SABLE (IRE)	KINGCRAFT BS	26000
B C DUBAWI (IRE) - NASHMIAH (IRE)	BORJE OLSSON	26000
GR F DARK ANGEL (IRE) - BOASTFUL (IRE)	SHAWN DUGAN, AGENT	26000
CH C NIGHT OF THUNDER (IRE) - ARIS (IRE)	PHOENIX THOROUGHBREDS	26000
B C FASTNET ROCK (AUS) - ROSELITA (IRE)	HONG KONG JOCKEY CLUB	26000
B C OASIS DREAM (GB) - AZANARA (IRE)	STROUD COLEMAN BS	26000
B C KODIAC (GB) - SCOTCH BONNET (IRE)	HOWSON & HOULDSWORTH BS	25500
B F FREE EAGLE (IRE) - MALASPINA (IRE)	C GORDON-WATSON BS	25000
B F SIYOUNI (FR) - SANDY GIRL (FR)	SHADWELL ESTATE COMPANY	25000
COLOUR IMAGE (IRE) B C KODIAC (GB) - CHROUSSA (IRE)	STROUD COLEMAN BS	25000
B F IFFRAAJ (GB) - ERAADAAT (IRE)	SHAWN DUGAN, AGENT	25000
B C NO NAY NEVER (USA) - GEMS (GB)	SACKVILLEDONALD	25000
B C SIYOUNI (FR) - CASCATA (IRE)	VENDOR	25000
B C OASIS DREAM (GB) - PATH WIND (FR)	HONG KONG JOCKEY CLUB	25000
FESTIVAL OF COLOUR (IRE) B C KODIAC (GB) - REDMAVEN (IRE)	STROUD COLEMAN BS	25000
B C NO NAY NEVER (USA) - BRIGIDS CROSS (IRE)	M V MAGNIER	25000
MAMBO NIGHTS (IRE) B C HAVANA GOLD (IRE) - INEZ (GB)	PETER & ROSS DOYLE BS	25000
COEUR D'OR (FR) B C DABIRSIM (FR) - TWILIGHT TEAR (GB)	SHADWELL ESTATE COMPANY	24000
B C CAMELOT (GB) - HINT OF A TINT (IRE)	SUN BS	24000
HONOR AND PLEASURE (GB) B C OASIS DREAM (GB) - HOLY MOON (IRE)	VENDOR	24000
B C ZOFFANY (GB) - BAHIA BREEZE (GB)	HONG KONG JOCKEY CLUB	24000
B F FRANKEL (GB) - ONSHORE (GB)	VENDOR	24000
B C SEA THE STARS (IRE) - KINCOB (USA)	JOHN GOSDEN RACING LLP	24000
CH F SEA THE STARS (IRE) - SAYYEDATI STORM (USA)	BROADHURST AGENCY	24000
B G SHAMARDAL (USA) - SHAFAANI (GB)	STROUD COLEMAN BS	24000
GR C DARK ANGEL (IRE) - COOLIBAH (IRE)	NARVICK INTERNATIONAL (P.S.)	24000
B C GLENEAGLES (IRE) - BRIDAL DANCE (IRE)	AMANDA SKIFFINGTON	24000
DIVINA GLORIA (FR) B F DABIRSIM (FR) - AMOUAGE (GER)	HILLEN / RYAN	23000
B F ZOFFANY (IRE) - ECOUTILA (USA)	BBA IRELAND	23000
DAAYEB (IRE) B C LOPE DE VEGA (IRE) - MOUSSE AU CHOCOLAT (USA)	SHADWELL ESTATE COMPANY	23000
THAKI (IRE) B C LOPE DE VEGA (IRE) - MICKLEBERRY (IRE)	SHADWELL ESTATE COMPANY	23000
B F FRANKEL (GB) - BISCAYA BAY (GB)	SHEIKH ABDULLAH ALSABAH	23000
GR C GUTAIFAN (IRE) - ARABIAN PEARL (IRE)	AL SHAQAB RACING	22500
B/BR C GOLDEN HORN (GB) - TIME BEING (GB)	SHADWELL ESTATE COMPANY	22000
B C SIYOUNI (FR) - MADONNA DELL'ORTO (GB)	VENDOR	22000
CH F SEA THE STARS (IRE) - MAMONTA (GB)	SUNDERLAND HOLDING INC	22000
MARK OF GOLD (GB) B C GOLDEN HORN (GB) - POLLY'S MARK (IRE)	PETER & ROSS DOYLE BS	22000
SUMMER HOUSE (GB) CH F LOPE DE VEGA (IRE) - SOON (IRE)	STROUD COLEMAN BS	22000
CH C HOT STREAK (IRE) - BOSSANOVA LADY (USA)	KINGCRAFT BS	22000
STALINGRAD (GB) B C WAR FRONT (USA) - I AM BEAUTIFUL (IRE)	DE BURGH EQUINE	22000
PRINCE ALEX (GB) B C EXCELEBRATION (IRE) - INTERCHANGE (IRE)	A C ELLIOTT, AGENT	22000
B C ZOFFANY (GB) - SEATONE (USA)	MV MAGNIER	22000
AFRICAN DREAM (GB) B F OASIS DREAM (GB) - ALSINDI (IRE)	AMMERLAND	22000
CH C LOPE DE VEGA (IRE) - CHILDA (IRE)	ANDREW BALDING	22000
PERSUASION (IRE) B C ACCLAMATION (GB) - EFFERVESCE (IRE)	MICHAEL ROY (P.S.)	22000
B F DANSILI (GB) - NICELLA (GER)	SHAWN DUGAN, AGENT	22000
B F MUHAARAR (GB) - IGHRAA (IRE)	VENDOR	22000
B F GALILEO (IRE) - TIMBUKTU (IRE)	APPLE TREE STUD	22000
SOLAR SCREEN (IRE) GR C GOLDEN HORN (GB) - SCREEN STAR (IRE)	ROGER VARIAN	21000
B C MAKE BELIEVE (GB) - LADY SHANGHAI (GB)	SHADWELL ESTATE COMPANY	21000
B C KINGMAN (GB) - TOUJOURS L'AMOUR (GB)	KLARAVICH STABLES	21000
B C KODIAC (GB) - MEKONG MELODY (IRE)	PHOENIX TB (P.S.)	20000
B F GLENEAGLES (IRE) - FUSION (IRE)	MIKE RYAN	20000
ALEXEJ (GB) B C MUHAARAR (GB) - AQUATINTA (GER)	AMMERLAND	20000
B F NO NAY NEVER (USA) - IDLE CHATTER (IRE)	C GORDON-WATSON	20000
KHURSHED (IRE) CH C NIGHT OF THUNDER (IRE) - AWARD (IRE)	SHADWELL ESTATE COMPANY	20000
KHADAASH (GB) B C KINGMAN (GB) - HONORLINA (FR)	SHADWELL ESTATE COMPANY	20000
ONASSIS (IRE) B F DUBAWI (IRE) - JACQUELINE QUEST (IRE)	JAMIE MCCALMONT	20000
B C WOOTTON BASSETT (GB) - BELOVA (IRE)	SHADWELL ESTATE COMPANY	20000

me and Breeding	Purchaser	Guineas
C SOCIETY ROCK (IRE) - SUNNY DAYS (IRE)	SHADWELL ESTATE COMPANY	200000
C GUTAIFAN (IRE) - CAPE FACTOR (IRE)	SHADWELL ESTATE COMPANY	200000
RRAAJ (IRE) GR C DARK ANGEL (IRE) - CUT NO ICE (IRE)	SHADWELL ESTATE COMPANY	200000
C OASIS DREAM (GB) - GALICUIX (GB)	SHADWELL ESTATE COMPANY	200000
KENSHIELD (IRE) B C INVINCIBLE SPIRIT (IRE) - WAR EFFORT (IRE)	HILLEN / RYAN	200000
PRIT ROSE (GB) B F INVINCIBLE SPIRIT (IRE) - INTENSE PINK (GB)	ROGER VARIAN	200000
F GUTAIFAN (IRE) - SUPREME SEDUCTRESS (IRE)	SHAWN DUGAN, AGENT	200000
ACK CASPIAN (IRE) B C DARK ANGEL (IRE) - CATCH THE SEA (IRE)	HILLEN / RYAN	200000
EN ROAD (GB) B C SHOWCASING (GB) - SHEMBARA (FR)	STROUD COLEMAN BS	200000
C EXCEED AND EXCEL (AUS) - ROYAL ORDER (USA)	HONG KONG JOCKEY CLUB	200000
NTE HERMOSA (GB) B F GLENEAGLES (IRE) - QUE PUNTUAL (ARG)	BBA IRELAND	200000
C HOT STREAK (GB) - NEVER IN (IRE)	SHADWELL ESTATE COMPANY	200000
PELEGRINO (GB) B C GOLDEN HORN (GB) - LA DOROTEA (IRE)	BLANDFORD BS	200000
C HOT STREAK (GB) - BAHAMAMIA (GB)	KINGCRAFT BS	200000
C AUSTRALIA (GB) - PIVOTALIA (GB)	AL SHAQAB	200000
C DARK ANGEL (IRE) - ALONG CAME CASEY (IRE)	SHADWELL ESTATE COMPANY	200000
C TAMAYUZ (GB) - RED HALO (IRE)	A C ELLIOTT, AGENT	200000
F SHOWCASING (GB) - ASTRANTIA (GB)	HORSES & BERRIES SL	200000
N WIN POWER (IRE) B C EXCEED AND EXCEL (AUS) - SPESIALTA (GB)	SACKVILLEDONALD	200000
UE DIAMOND POWER (IRE) B C AUSTRALIA (GB) - SANNKALA (FR)	SACKVILLEDONALD	200000
FIA POWER (GB) B C GLENEAGLES (IRE) - RIVARA (GB)	SACKVILLEDONALD	200000
C CAMACHO (GB) - VERERI SENES (GB)	SHADWELL ESTATE COMPANY	200000
F PIVOTAL (GB) - SALLABEH (GB)	AL SHAQAB RACING	200000
F SEA THE STARS (IRE) - UMNIYAH (IRE)	KLARAVICH STABLES	200000
C GOLDEN HORN (GB) - GWAEL (USA)	SACKVILLEDONALD	200000
C FRANKEL (GB) - ROSE OF MIRACLES (GB)	BLUE DIAMOND STUD	200000
C KINGMAN (GB) - BOSTON ROCKER (IRE)	BLANDFORD BS	200000
MAAS (IRE) B F IFFRAAJ (GB) - SPIRITUAL AIR (GB)	SHADWELL ESTATE COMPANY	200000
SSAVETES (GB) B C SIYOUNI (FR) - ROSINKA (IRE)	WHITE BIRCH FARM	200000
C GOLDEN HORN (GB) - POLARIZED (GB)	KLARAVICH STABLES	200000
C SIYOUNI (FR) - POLLYANNA (IRE)	SHADWELL ESTATE COMPANY	200000
C FASTNET ROCK (AUS) - MOUNT CRYSTAL (IRE)	CRISPIN ESTATES	200000
F LOPE DE VEGA (IRE) - MOI MEME (GB)	MIKE RYAN	200000
C SIYOUNI (FR) - PHIZ (GER)	MIKE RYAN	200000
ARM SUNSET (IRE) B F OASIS DREAM (GB) - PREDICTED (GB)	BLANDFORD BS	200000
AN ROYALE (GB) B C SIYOUNI (FR) - ASCOT FAMILY (IRE)	ROGER VARIAN	200000
ZONE (GB) B C POUR MOI (IRE) - BELLA NOUF (GB)	PETER & ROSS DOYLE BS	200000
C SHAMARDAL (USA) - WADAAT (GB)	SUZANNE ROBERTS	190000
C IFFRAAJ (GB) - THE MADDING CROWD (GB)	AL SHAQAB RACING	190000
C NATHANIEL (IRE) - MOSQUERAS ROMANCE (GB)	STROUD COLEMAN BS	190000
LD PLACE (IRE) B C GLENEAGLES (IRE) - NO EXPLAINING (IRE)	SACKVILLEDONALD	190000
F SIYOUNI (FR) - ENSEMBLE (FR)	H MORRISON	190000
F SHOWCASING (GB) - BRIGHT GLOW (GB)	SHADWELL ESTATE COMPANY	185000
C FARHH (GB) - STONEACRE SARAH (GB)	HONG KONG JOCKEY CLUB	185000
C SHOWCASING (GB) - BELATORIO (IRE)	SHADWELL ESTATE COMPANY	180000
C GUTAIFAN (IRE) - ANNA LAW (IRE)	PHOENIX THOROUGHBREDS	180000
C KODIAC (GB) - PIVOTAL ERA (GB)	SHADWELL ESTATE COMPANY	180000
C KODIAC (GB) - ABSOLUTELY COOL (IRE)	SHEIKH ABDULLAH ALSABAH	180000
TTA MOUNTAINS (IRE) B C SOCIETY ROCK (IRE) - SHEHILA (IRE)	BLANDFORD BS	180000
F DUBAWI (IRE) - LOOK AT ME (IRE)	STROUD COLEMAN BS	180000
C LE HAVRE (IRE) - QUEEN MARGHERITA (GB)	SHADWELL ESTATE COMPANY	180000
C INVINCIBLE SPIRIT (IRE) - WE CAN SAY IT NOW (AUS)	BBA IRELAND	180000
C LOPE DE VEGA (IRE) - QUAD'S MELODY (IRE)	VENDOR	180000
C KYLLACHY (GB) - KERRY'S DREAM (GB)	JOE FOLEY	175000
ARLESS KING (GB) B C KINGMAN (GB) - ASTRELLE (IRE)	TINA RAU BS / RTC GMBH	175000
C BATED BREATH (GB) - LIFTING ME HIGHER (IRE)	SHADWELL ESTATE CO (P.S.)	175000
C SEA THE STARS (IRE) - BALLYMORE LADY (USA)	LAWLEY-WAKELIN / SIME	170000
C STARSPANGLEDBANNER (AUS) - TORENTOSA (FR)	VENDOR	170000
AGICAL MOMENT (FR) B F DUBAWI (GB) - MAKA (FR)	HILLEN / RYAN	170000
C CAMELOT (GB) - MARKET DAY (GB)	KINGCRAFT BS	170000
ACE RACE (GB) B F SEA THE STARS (IRE) - ACT FAST (GB)	STROUD COLEMAN BS	170000
G KODIAC (GB) - FRAMED (GB)	STROUD COLEMAN BS	170000
F INVINCIBLE SPIRIT (IRE) - PRETTY FACE (GB)	VENDOR	170000
C FRANKEL (GB) - RIBERAC (GB)	MARK JOHNSTON RACING	170000
ABIAN MAIDEN (GB) B F NEW APPROACH (IRE) - SPIRIT OF DUBAI (IRE)	HILLEN / RYAN	165000
F SIYOUNI (FR) - RUBY ROCKET (IRE)	AL SHAQAB RACING	160000
F NATHANIEL (IRE) - ROYAL EMPRESS (IRE)	MCKEEVER BS	160000
C INVINCIBLE SPIRIT (IRE) - LIBERATING (GB)	C GORDON-WATSON BS	160000
LACTIC GLOW (IRE) B C NO NAY NEVER (USA) - SHINE LIKE A STAR (GB)	JAMES TOLLER / WASHBOURN	160000
C LOPE DE VEGA (IRE) - SENSATIONALLY (GB)	KLARAVICH STABLES	160000

Name and Breeding	Purchaser	Guineas
B F UNCLE MO (USA) - AS GOOD AS GOLD (IRE)	MARTYN MEADE RACING	1600
CH C NIGHT OF THUNDER (IRE) - CANTAL (GB)	SHADWELL ESTATE COMPANY	1600
B F INVINCIBLE SPIRIT (IRE) - SWEEPSTAKE (IRE)	RABBAH BS	1600
YORKSHIRE GOLD (GB) B C MUHAARAR (GB) - SWIFT CAMPAIGN (IRE)	HILLEN / RYAN	1600
B F KODIAC (GB) - ANNE BONNEY (GB)	CHEVELEY PARK STUD	1600
COUNT OF AMAZONIA (IRE) B C LOPE DE VEGA (IRE) - QUEEN MYRINE (IRE)	PETER & ROSS DOYLE BS	1600
B F ZOFFANY (IRE) - FOLLOW A STAR (IRE)	PRIME EQUESTRIAN	1600
CH C PIVOTAL (GB) - MAID FOR WINNING (USA)	EBONOS	1600
B C SEA THE STARS (IRE) - JAKONDA (USA)	MIKE RYAN	1600
CH F SEA THE STARS (IRE) - EMARATIYA ANA (IRE)	JOHN & JAKE WARREN	1600
RAASY (IRE) B C BATED BREATH (GB) - GOLDEN LEGACY (IRE)	SHADWELL ESTATE COMPANY	1600
BADRI (GB) B C DARK ANGEL (IRE) - PENNY DROPS (GB)	SHADWELL ESTATE COMPANY	1600■
AYSAR (GB) B C SIR PRANCEALOT (IRE) - YAJALA (IRE)	SHADWELL ESTATE COMPANY	1600■
B C INTELLO (GER) - DUBLINO (USA)	BBA IRELAND	1600■
AL AAKIF (IRE) B C ACCLAMATION (GB) - VASTITAS (IRE)	SHADWELL ESTATE COMPANY	1600■
CH F IFFRAAJ (GB) - ARABIAN MIRAGE (GB)	BBA IRELAND	1600■
DARK OF NIGHT (IRE) GR C DARK ANGEL (IRE) - MOONVOY (IRE)	STROUD COLEMAN BS	1550■
OWHATANIGHT (GB) GR C NIGHT OF THUNDER (IRE) - WHITE WEDDING (IRE)	C GORDON-WATSON BS	1550■
B F GOLDEN HORN (GB) - LOVELY PASS (IRE)	ROB SPEERS	1500■
B C SHAMARDAL (USA) - TWILIGHT SKY (GB)	STROUD COLEMAN BS	1500■
B F KODIAC (GB) - COQUETTE ROUGE (IRE)	SACKVILLEDONALD	1500■
PLATINUM STAR (IRE) B C LOPE DE VEGA (IRE) - TOQUETTE (IRE)	STROUD COLEMAN BS	1500
B F GALILEO (IRE) - LUAS LINE (IRE)	APPLE TREE STUD	1500
B C EXCEED AND EXCEL (AUS) - RED INTRIGUE (IRE)	LEUNG KAI FAI	1500
ANGEL POWER (GB) B F LOPE DE VEGA (IRE) - BURNING RULES (IRE)	SACKVILLEDONALD	1500
B F LOPE DE VEGA (IRE) - CRYSDAL (GB)	VENDOR	1500
B F FOOTSTEPSINTHESAND (GB) - SINDIYMA (IRE)	VENDOR	1500
AFFABLE (IRE) BR F NEW APPROACH (IRE) - AL BAIDAA (GB)	JOHN & JAKE WARREN	1500
ALBUKHTURI (GB) B C HOT STREAK (IRE) - POYLE DEE DEE (GB)	SHADWELL ESTATE COMPANY	1500
B C SHOWCASING (GB) - PAPAYA (IRE)	CHINA HORSE CLUB (P.S.)	1500
B F SIYOUNI (FR) - FOREST CROWN (GB)	HILLEN / DEVIN	1500
FIRST TARGET (GB) B C SHOWCASING (GB) - EXCELETTE (IRE)	STROUD COLEMAN BS	1500
CH C MASTERCRAFTSMAN (IRE) - TENDENCY (IRE)	PETER & ROSS DOYLE BS	1500
B C SHAMARDAL (USA) - PATRONISING (IRE)	GROVE STUD	1500
B F SIYOUNI (FR) - WANNABE SPECIAL (GB)	JAMES TOLLER	1500
B F GOLDEN HORN (GB) - HIKARI (IRE)	RICHARD KNIGHT BS (P.S.)	1500
HOOK HEAD (IRE) B C FASTNET ROCK (AUS) - DANCE TROUPE (GB)	BBA IRELAND	1500■
B C INVINCIBLE SPIRIT (IRE) - FREEZY (IRE)	EBONOS (P.S.)	1500■
SEA MOOD (FR) B F SIYOUNI (FR) - UPBEAT MOOD (USA)	JOHN & JAKE WARREN (P.S.)	1500■
B C GALILEO (IRE) - SENT FROM HEAVEN (IRE)	M V MAGNIER	1500■
ZMILE (GB) B F MEDAGLIA D'ORO (USA) - CAY DANCER (GB)	STETCHWORTH & MIDDLE PARK	1500■
CHAI YO POWER (GB) B C LE HAVRE (IRE) - STELLA BELLISSIMA (IRE)	SACKVILLEDONALD	1500■
B C FREE EAGLE (IRE) - REGALLINE (IRE)	PETER & ROSS DOYLE BS	1500■
B F KODIAC (GB) - LAKE NONA (GB)	STROUD COLEMAN BS	1500■
LADY SANSA (IRE) CH F LOPE DE VEGA (IRE) - LUCE (IRE)	BALLYLINCH STUD	1450
FRED (GB) CH C FRANKEL (GB) - DEIRDRE (GB)	MARK JOHNSTON RACING	1450
CH C LOPE DE VEGA (IRE) - VIA MILANO (FR)	PJ O'GORMAN	1400
RED FOR ALL (GB) B C MUHAARAR (GB) - ALL FOR LAURA (GB)	C GORDON-WATSON BS	1400
PIERRE LAPIN (IRE) B F CAPPELLA SANSEVERO (GB) - BEATRIX POTTER (IRE)	ROGER VARIAN	1400
VEGA MAGIC (IRE) B C LOPE DE VEGA (IRE) - ORIENTAL MAGIC (GER)	HILLEN / RYAN	1400
B C DISTORTED HUMOR (USA) - LIFFEY DANCER (IRE)	VENDOR	1400
B C EXCEED AND EXCEL (AUS) - ICE PALACE (GB)	JEREMY BRUMMITT	1400
B F SEA THE STARS (IRE) - TAYMA (IRE)	STROUD COLEMAN BS	1400
B F SEA THE STARS (IRE) - PLANETE BLEUE (IRE)	WHITE BIRCH FARM	1400
B C KODIAC (GB) - INCESSANT (IRE)	SACKVILLEDONALD	1400
B F SHOWCASING (GB) - TIANA (GB)	RABBAH BS	1400
GR C LOPE DE VEGA (IRE) - PARTITIA (GB)	SHADWELL ESTATE COMPANY	1400
B C GUTAIFAN (IRE) - DUST FLICKER (GB)	PETER & ROSS DOYLE BS	1400
B F INVINCIBLE SPIRIT (IRE) - MOMENT IN TIME (IRE)	SUN BS	1400
RAADEA (GB) CH C SHOWCASING (GB) - DREAM MELODY (GB)	SHADWELL ESTATE COMPANY	1400■
SWISS VALLEY (IRE) GR F DARK ANGEL (IRE) - WARSHAH (IRE)	STROUD COLEMAN BS	1400■
B C MUHAARAR (GB) - LAUREN LOUISE (GB)	HILLEN / RYAN	1400■
B C OASIS DREAM (GB) - INDEPENDENCE (GB)	BLANDFORD BS	1400■
B F BATED BREATH (GB) - THELADYINQUESTION (GB)	RABBAH BS	1400■
B C NO NAY NEVER (USA) - LUMIERE NOIRE (FR)	AMANDA SKIFFINGTON	1400■
B C POET'S VOICE (GB) - MILADY EILEEN (IRE)	C GORDON-WATSON BS	1400■
GOOD HUMOR (GB) B C DISTORTED HUMOR (USA) - TIME ON (GB)	VENDOR	1400■
B C OASIS DREAM (GB) - CLARENTINE (GB)	RASHED ALDABAN	1400■
B F DARK ANGEL (IRE) - MOMENTUS (IRE)	VENDOR	1350■
B F NO NAY NEVER (USA) - MISS AZEZA (GB)	A C ELLIOTT, AGENT	1350■
B C KODIAC (GB) - LUCKY (IRE)	MARGARET O'TOOLE	1350

ame and Breeding	Purchaser	Guineas
*PE (IRE) B F NO NAY NEVER (USA) - BRIGHT SAPPHIRE (IRE)	BBA IRELAND	135000
CENSION (GB) B C DARK ANGEL (GB) - MAKING EYES (IRE)	JOHN & JAKE WARREN	135000
EA (GB) CH F SIYOUNI (FR) - TITIAN'S PRIDE (USA)	HILLEN / RYAN	130000
C EXCEED AND EXCEL (AUS) - CALLISTAN (IRE)	HONG KONG JOCKEY CLUB	130000
F CAMELOT (GB) - BROWN DIAMOND (IRE)	RABBAH BS	130000
F FRANKEL (GB) - GALE FORCE (IRE)	NICK BRADLEY RACING	130000
C KODIAC (GB) - ISRAAR (GB)	SHEIKH ABDULLAH ALSABAH	130000
C KITTEN'S JOY (USA) - STRATHNAVER (GB)	HIGHFLYER BS	130000
C MASTERCRAFTSMAN (IRE) - LOVED (IRE)	PETER & ROSS DOYLE BS	130000
UDINE (IRE) B F CAMELOT (GB) - TADRIS (USA)	PRIME EQUESTRIAN	130000
C SOCIETY ROCK (IRE) - TARA TOO (IRE)	SHADWELL ESTATE COMPANY	130000
F MUHAARAR (GB) - LIDANSKI (IRE)	MC BS	130000
C NO NAY NEVER (USA) - ENDURE (IRE)	AIDAN O'RYAN	130000
F KODIAC (GB) - PILATES (IRE)	SHADWELL ESTATE COMPANY	130000
F SHOWCASING (GB) - CAPE JOY (IRE)	JOE FOLEY	130000
F GOLDEN HORN (GB) - NINA CELEBRE (IRE)	SUN BS	130000
F LOPE DE VEGA (IRE) - DIAMOND SKY (IRE)	VENDOR	130000
F CHARM SPIRIT (IRE) - SWORDHALF (GB)	EMIRATES PARK	130000
F MUHAARAR (GB) - ROSE BLOSSOM (GB)	MIKE RYAN	130000
F NO NAY NEVER (USA) - RHIANNON (IRE)	BROADHURST AGENCY	130000
VORITE MOON (GER) B C SEA THE MOON (GER) - FAVORITE (GER)	WILLIAM HAGGAS	125000
F FRANKEL (GB) - GUARANDA (GB)	VENDOR	125000
YPTIAN KING (GB) B C IFFRAAJ (GB) - VIOLA D'AMOUR (IRE)	STROUD COLEMAN BS	125000
C SEA THE STARS (IRE) - BRIGHT HALO (IRE)	SPICER THOROUGHBREDS PTY	125000
YAL COMMANDO (IRE) B C NO NAY NEVER (USA) - ONLINE ALEXANDER (IRE)	ANDREW SIME	125000
C SHOWCASING (GB) - PUZZLING (GB)	SHADWELL ESTATE COMPANY	125000
C LOPE DE VEGA (IRE) - PURR ALONG (GB)	SACKVILLEDONALD	125000
C KODIAC (GB) - SLATEY HEN (IRE)	SHADWELL ESTATE COMPANY	125000
ERNAL SECRET (GB) B F MUHAARAR (GB) - WALK ON BYE (IRE)	MICHAEL ROY AGENT	125000
F SEA THE MOON (GER) - HEART OF ICE (IRE)	STROUD COLEMAN BS	125000
F SEA THE STARS (IRE) - SPINAMINNIE (IRE)	J B BS	120000
C CAMELOT (GB) - LADY BABOOSHKA (GB)	JEREMY BRUMMITT	120000
C TEOFILO (IRE) - HANA LINA (GB)	CRISPIN ESTATES	120000
F NATHANIEL (IRE) - TINGLING (USA)	WILL EDMEADES BS	120000
C SHOWCASING (GB) - CROSS MY HEART (GB)	JOE FOLEY	120000
C INVINCIBLE SPIRIT (IRE) - FILIA REGINA (GB)	VENDOR	120000
C LOPE DE VEGA (IRE) - JAM JAR (GB)	STROUD COLEMAN BS	120000
ALERNE (GB) B F CHARM SPIRIT (IRE) - SALICORNE (USA)	VENDOR	120000
C KINGMAN (GB) - INDIAN LOVE BIRD (GB)	JOE FOLEY	120000
EGFELD (GB) CH C NEW APPROACH (IRE) - MAID TO DREAM (GB)	STROUD COLEMAN BS	120000
C EXCEED AND EXCEL (AUS) - SWISS DREAM (GB)	SACKVILLEDONALD	120000
F TEOFILO (IRE) - ROYAL BLUE STAR (IRE)	STROUD COLEMAN BS	120000
C SIYOUNI (FR) - WANNABE POSH (IRE)	C GORDON-WATSON BS	120000
F DARK ANGEL (IRE) - VENTURA MIST (GB)	RABBAH BS	120000
F ZOFFANY (IRE) - MAP OF HEAVEN (GB)	SKIFFINGTON / NARDELLI	120000
G HOLY ROMAN EMPEROR (IRE) - MARASIMA (IRE)	STROUD COLEMAN BS	120000
F KODIAC (GB) - DHUMA (GB)	PETER & ROSS DOYLE BS	120000
C ACCLAMATION (GB) - ENIGMATIQUE (GB)	VENDOR	120000
NG'S CASTLE (IRE) B C CAMELOT (GB) - KIKONGA (GB)	WILLIAM HAGGAS, AGENT	115000
F GLENEAGLES (IRE) - SITARA (GB)	DAVID REDVERS BS	115000
C EQUIANO (FR) - LOVE AND CHERISH (IRE)	WILLIAM HAGGAS, AGENT	115000
C NIGHT OF THUNDER (IRE) - ERMINE AND VELVET (GB)	HUGO MERRY BS	115000
C AUSTRALIA (GB) - CAROLINES SECRET (GB)	JOSEPH O'BRIEN	115000
UN POWER (FR) B C NIGHT OF THUNDER (IRE) - SPARKLING SMILE (IRE)	SACKVILLEDONALD	115000
C DARK ANGEL (IRE) - FOLGA (GB)	RICHARD HUGHES RACING	115000
NT OF STARS (IRE) CH C SEA THE STARS (IRE) - ROSENREIHE (IRE)	STUART WILLIAMS	115000
C KINGMAN (GB) - ASHLEY HALL (USA)	SHEIKH ABDULLAH ALSABAH	115000
ORN TO GLORY (GB) B C MUHAARAR (GB) - DULCET (IRE)	HILLEN / RYAN	110000
EY SPIRIT (GB) B C PIVOTAL (GB) - PERFECT SPIRIT (IRE)	R O'RYAN / R FAHEY	110000
F MUHAARAR (GB) - MUNYATEE (ARG)	VENDOR	110000
C ZOFFANY (IRE) - CUSHION (GB)	JOSEPH O'BRIEN	110000
F DANSILI (GB) - TIME SAVED (GB)	VENDOR	110000
F STARSPANGLEDBANNER (AUS) - HOLLY BLUE (GB)	VENDOR	110000
C CAMELOT (GB) - BELLA BELLA (IRE)	JOSEPH O'BRIEN	110000
C KODIAC (GB) - ALEXANDER YOUTH (IRE)	TALLY-HO STUD	110000
N GUARD (GB) B C INVINCIBLE SPIRIT (IRE) - PALITANA (USA)	VENDOR	110000
F NO NAY NEVER (USA) - DANEHILL'S DREAM (IRE)	CORMAC MCCORMACK	110000
C KENDARGENT (FR) - PREMIERE DANSEUSE (GB)	BLANDFORD BS	110000
C GOLDEN HORN (GB) - DELIZIA (IRE)	STROUD COLEMAN BS	110000
F DARK ANGEL (IRE) - WRONG ANSWER (GB)	R O'RYAN / R FAHEY	110000
F DARK ANGEL (IRE) - MOMENTUS (IRE)	VENDOR	110000

HIGH-PRICED YEARLINGS OF 2018 AT GOFFS
The following yearlings realised 66,000 euros and over at Goffs Sales in 2018:-

Name and Breeding	Purchaser	Eur
B F GALILEO (IRE) - GREEN ROOM (USA)	PHOENIX TB	32000
CH F GALILEO (IRE) - ALEAGUEOFTHEIROWN (IRE)	PHOENIX TB	20000
B C KINGMAN (GB) - ALEXANDER QUEEN (IRE)	D REDVERS	8500
CH F SHOWCASING (GB) - BIRD KEY (GB)	M PLAYER	8500
B F SEA THE STARS (IRE) - VALAIS GIRL (GB)	GODOLPHIN	7500
B F NO NAY NEVER (USA) - STARLET (IRE)	M V MAGNIER	7000
B F GALILEO (IRE) - MAUREEN (IRE)	D REDVERS	5250
B F FRANKEL (GB) - NATIVE FORCE (IRE)	S DUGAN	5000
B F CAMELOT (GB) - FLAWLESS BEAUTY (GB)	GODOLPHIN	5000
B F MUHAARAR (GB) - BEACH BUNNY (IRE)	SHADWELL ESTATE CO	5000
B F CAMELOT (GB) - ENHARMONIC (USA)	BBA (IRELAND)	4800
B F AUSTRALIA (GB) - ZA'HARA (IRE)	GODOLPHIN	4750
AL QAASIM (IRE) CH C FREE EAGLE (IRE) - NEBRAAS (GB)	SHADWELL ESTATE CO	4000
B F GALILEO (IRE) - QUIET OASIS (IRE)	BADGERS BS	4000
B C MUHAARAR (GB) - WEEKEND FLING (USA)	BBA (IRELAND)	4000
ZABEEL KING (IRE) B C FRANKEL (GB) - VITAL STATISTICS (GB)	HILLEN/RYAN	4000
B C EXCEED AND EXCEL (AUS) - KITTY LOVE (USA)	HKJC	3600
B C DARK ANGEL (IRE) - THAWRAH (IRE)	PHOENIX TB	3600
B F NO NAY NEVER (USA) - LESSON IN LIFE (GB)	R A BRODIE ANDREW FARM	3600
LOVE POWERFUL (IRE) 7B F GUTAIFAN (IRE) - MONTEFINO (IRE)	SACKVILLEDONALD	3600
SEELIE (IRE) B F LE HAVRE (IRE) - THE FAIRY (IRE)	GODOLPHIN	3600
CH C SIYOUNI (FR) - QUEEN ARABELLA (IRE)	GODOLPHIN	3500
B/GR C NO NAY NEVER (USA) - FAR AWAY EYES (IRE)	GODOLPHIN	3500
B C ZOFFANY (IRE) - QUESTION TIMES (IRE)	S A ROBERTS	3250
B C STARSPANGLEDBANNER (AUS) - WELCOME SPRING (IRE)	RIC WYLIE BS	3000
BR F NO NAY NEVER (USA) - MIRONICA (IRE)	S DUGAN	3000
B C HOLY ROMAN EMPEROR (IRE) - ICEBREAKING (IRE)	HKJC	3000
B C GALILEO (IRE) - RUNWAY DANCER (IRE)	M V MAGNIER	3000
JET ACTION (IRE) B C CAMELOT (GB) - SNOW GRETEL (IRE)	PETER & ROSS DOYLE BS	2800
WINTER HALO (IRE) B F DARK ANGEL (IRE) - SNOWY PEAK (GB)	PETER & ROSS DOYLE BS	2600
B C GLENEAGLES (IRE) - UNBELIEVABLE (IRE)	GAELIC BS	2600
B C LOPE DE VEGA (IRE) - BEACH BELLE (IRE)	CHINA HORSE	2600
B C CAMELOT (GB) - MADEIRA MIST (IRE)	M V MAGNIER	2600
TODAY POWER (IRE) B C DARK ANGEL (IRE) - TODEGICA (IRE)	SACKVILLE DONALD	2500
B C AUSTRALIA (GB) - ROCK OF RIDD (IRE)	S HILLEN	2450
IRISH PROSECUTOR (IRE) B C NO NAY NEVER (USA) - APPAREL (IRE)	DE 5 STJERNER APS	2450
SIDEREAL (GB) B C GALILEO (IRE) - STARLIT SANDS (GB)	BLANDFORD BS	2400
REINE DE VEGA (IRE) CH F LOPE DE VEGA (IRE) - GULSARY (IRE)	PETER & ROSS DOYLE BS	2400
TOP CLASS ANGEL (IRE) B F DARK ANGEL (IRE) - EXPENSIVE DATE (GB)	PETER & ROSS DOYLE BS	2400
CH F LOPE DE VEGA (IRE) - PALANCA (GB)	GODOLPHIN JAPAN	2400
CH F SHOWCASING (GB) - KATALEA (GB)	K RADCLIFFE	2400
B C DARK ANGEL (IRE) - SILVER SHOON (IRE)	SACKVILLE DONALD	2400
B C BATED BREATH (GB) - MODESTY'S WAY (USA)	ONE CARAT SYNDICATE	2400
CH F SHOWCASING (GB) - FAIR SAILING (IRE)	BALLYFAIR BS	2400
B C NO NAY NEVER (USA) - HIGH SAVANNAH (IRE)	R A BRODIE ANDREW FARM	2400
CH C ZOFFANY (IRE) - VERBOSE (USA)	GODOLPHIN JAPAN	2200
CH C GLENEAGLES (IRE) - EUPHRASIA (IRE)	SACKVILLEDONALD	2200
LADY HANSON (IRE) B F GALILEO (IRE) - VICTORIA STAR (IRE)	VENDOR	2200
B F FRANKEL (GB) - SQUEEZE (IRE)	JS COMPANY	2200
B/BR C NO NAY NEVER (USA) - SUBTLE CHARM (GB)	FORM BS	2100
B F SIR PERCY (GB) - HEART STOPPING (USA)	GODOLPHIN JAPAN	2100
SWAN RIVER (IRE) B F AUSTRALIA (GB) - THEANN (GB)	CHEVELEY PARK STUD	2100
LOST EDEN (IRE) B C SEA THE STARS (IRE) - GHOSTFLOWER (IRE)	PETER & ROSS DOYLE BS	20000
B C DANDY MAN (IRE) - HIDDEN BELIEF (IRE)	CHINA HORSE	18500
CH C ZOFFANY (IRE) - HEIGHT OF ELEGANCE (IRE)	JS COMPANY	18000
B C STARSPANGLEDBANNER (AUS) - STAR NOW (GB)	FORM BS	18000
B F INVINCIBLE SPIRIT (IRE) - ANTICIPATION (IRE)	FORM BS	18000
ST CLERANS (IRE) B F GOLDEN HORN (GB) - DISCREET BRIEF (IRE)	BBA (IRELAND)	17000
B F ACCLAMATION (GB) - UP AT LAST (IRE)	PHOENIX TB	16000
GLEN FORCE (IRE) B C GLENEAGLES (IRE) - LETHAL QUALITY (USA)	B LYNCH	16000
CH C SIYOUNI (FR) - BANKSIA (IRE)	GODOLPHIN JAPAN	16000
B F LE HAVRE (IRE) - DALAMAR (GB)	ECLIPSE TB	16000
B C IFFRAAJ (GB) - BOTANIQUE (IRE)	J FOLEY	16000
B F DARK ANGEL (IRE) - TARAEFF (IRE)	DE BURGH EQUINE	16000
CAYMAN HAVEN (IRE) B F NO NAY NEVER (USA) - NOVAT (IRE)	FORM BS	16000
B C SIYOUNI (FR) - VIZ (IRE)	JS COMPANY	16000
B F FASTNET ROCK (AUS) - MARIE CELESTE (IRE)	BBA (IRELAND)	15550
B F FASTNET ROCK (AUS) - OUI SAY OUI (IRE)	BBA (IRELAND)	15550

me and Breeding	Purchaser	Euros
; AUSTRALIA (GB) - KITTY MATCHAM (IRE)	AVENUE BS	155000
F GLENEAGLES (IRE) - PIPALONG (IRE)	PHOENIX TB	150000
; INVINCIBLE SPIRIT (IRE) - ROSE DE FRANCE (IRE)	M JOHNSTON	150000
NAIDA (IRE) B F KODIAC (GB) - CONSTELLATION (GB)	M ROY	150000
- MAKE BELIEVE (GB) - LAVINIAI (GB)	M JOHNSTON	150000
RTRIDGE (IRE) B F ZOFFANY (IRE) - LASILIA (IRE)	PETER & ROSS DOYLE BS	150000
ITTEN BROADCAST (IRE) GR C GUTAIFAN (IRE) - TEELINE (IRE)	P & R DOYLE	150000
- NO NAY NEVER (USA) - ANESTASIA (IRE)	RABBAH BS	150000
= CAMACHO (GB) - COVER GIRL (IRE)	D REDVERS	145000
; GALILEO (IRE) - BEWITCHED (IRE)	RICHARD KNIGHT BS	145000
C KODIAC (GB) - VEE GITA (IRE)	BBA (IRELAND)	140000
: KODIAC (GB) - SINDJARA (USA)	VENDOR	140000
; ACCLAMATION (GB) - AFFIRMATIVE (GB)	HKJC	140000
; SIYOUNI (FR) - CASCADING (GB)	MERIDIAN INTERNATIONAL	140000
= FREE EAGLE (IRE) - IPSA LOQUITUR (GB)	GAELIC BS	140000
NAL OFFER (IRE) B F DARK ANGEL (IRE) - LAST BID (GB)	CHEVELEY PARK STUD	140000
QUETA (IRE) B F TEOFILO (IRE) - ATAMANA (IRE)	AVENUE BS	140000
C CAMELOT (GB) - CENTREOFATTENTION (AUS)	J O'BRIEN	140000
; GLENEAGLES (IRE) - ALIVE ALIVE OH (GB)	VOUTE SALES	140000
HAT AN ANGEL (GB) BR/GR C DARK ANGEL (IRE) - MARY BOLEYN (IRE)	C & S BS	140000
= ZOFFANY (IRE) - SILENT THOUGHTS (IRE)	RABBAH BS	135000
RMENA (IRE) B F NO NAY NEVER (USA) - THEWAYTOSANJOSE (IRE)	M ROY	130000
ME IMPERIAL (IRE) B F SIYOUNI (FR) - ASCOT LADY (IRE)	N MARTIN	130000
C FOOTSTEPSINTHESAND (GB) - BEAUTIFUL DANCER (IRE)	HKJC	130000
C CAMELOT (GB) - COLOUR RHAPSODY (IRE)	J O'BRIEN	130000
OD JOB POWER (IRE) B C ACCLAMATION (GB) - THOUSANDFOLD (USA)	SACKVILLE DONALD	130000
: KODIAC (GB) - SINDJARA (USA)	T HYDE	130000
: KINGMAN (GB) - EXTRICATE (IRE)	LONGWAYS STABLES	125000
LEZ ALLEZ ALLEZ (IRE) B F INVINCIBLE SPIRIT (IRE) - GROWLING (IRE)	BBA (IRELAND)	125000
C NAYEF (USA) - LAYALEE (USA)	JB BS	125000
C CAMELOT (GB) - DOWAGER (GB)	GAELIC BS	125000
3R F IFFRAAJ (GB) - EVENING FROST (IRE)	M DODS	120000
F INVINCIBLE SPIRIT (IRE) - GOTHIC DANCE (IRE)	M PLAYER	120000
F SIYOUNI (FR) - TEEBA (USA)	PHOENIX TB	120000
= ZOFFANY (IRE) - MAGENA (USA)	D MURPHY	120000
INCE OF TIDES (IRE) B C NEW APPROACH (IRE) - BABY HOUSEMAN (GB)	M ROY	120000
C KODIAC (GB) - CAUSEWAY CHARM (USA)	L KELP	120000
C ZOFFANY (IRE) - CASTER SUGAR (USA)	RABBAH BS	120000
C MAKE BELIEVE (GB) - SOMOUSHE (IRE)	GAELIC BS	115000
C MAKE BELIEVE (GB) - LADY SHANGHAI (IRE)	JAMIE RAILTON	115000
T POWER (IRE) GR C DARK ANGEL (IRE) - EVENING TIME (IRE)	SACKVILLEDONALD	110000
PTEMBER POWER (IRE) B F MASTERCRAFTSMAN (IRE) - LISANOR (GB)	SACKVILLEDONALD	110000
: IFFRAAJ (GB) - PUSSYCAT LIPS (IRE)	D REDVERS	110000
RFECT ARCH (IRE) B C DAWN APPROACH (IRE) - WILLOW BECK (IRE)	GODOLPHIN	110000
SHOW (IRE) CH C SHOWCASING (GB) - INNOCENT AIR (IRE)	PETER & ROSS DOYLE BS	110000
- NO NAY NEVER (USA) - SANADAAT (GB)	RIC WYLIE BS	110000
C VERRAZANO (USA) - FREEFOURRACING (USA)	GODOLPHIN	110000
RTHERN SUN (IRE) B C SHOWCASING (GB) - SOLSTICE (GB)	PETER & ROSS DOYLE BS	110000
C CAMELOT (GB) - FRAULEIN (GB)	SACKVILLEDONALD	110000
; GLENEAGLES (IRE) - ELLE WOODS (IRE)	M V MAGNIER	110000
F AUSTRALIA (GB) - ATTIRE (IRE)	NEW APPROACH BS	105000
F STARSPANGLEDBANNER (AUS) - BIG BONED (USA)	DE BURGH EQUINE	105000
3R C NO NAY NEVER (USA) - SPECIAL ASSIGNMENT (USA)	J O'BRIEN	105000
CALL THE SHOW (GB) CH C SHOWCASING (GB) - RAPPEL (GB)	BBA (IRELAND)	105000
- KITTEN'S JOY (USA) - GRANNY FRANNY (USA)	NEWTOWN ANNER STUD FARM	105000
C GUTAIFAN (IRE) - BALI BREEZE (IRE)	A ELLIOTT	105000
C NIGHT OF THUNDER (IRE) - SHAMA'S SONG (IRE)	RABBAH BS	105000
C BATED BREATH (GB) - MODESTY'S WAY (IRE)	JAMIE RAILTON	105000
F FIRST DEFENCE (USA) - SUPPOSITION (GB)	RICHARD KNIGHT BS (P.S.)	100000
C DECLARATION OF WAR (USA) - LATE DAY SUN (IRE)	SATOMI HORSE CO (P.S.)	100000
= ZOFFANY (IRE) - LAP OF LUXURY (IRE)	FRIARSTOWN	100000
F DARK ANGEL (IRE) - HAVIN' A GOOD TIME (IRE)	BBA (IRELAND)	100000
F NO NAY NEVER (USA) - SANDGLASS (GB)	J CASSE	100000
C SOCIETY ROCK (IRE) - CHIARA WELLS (IRE)	CLIVE COX RACING	100000
F EXCEED AND EXCEL (AUS) - GOLD BUBBLES (USA)	VENDOR	100000
C CAMELOT (GB) - BALAKERA (IRE)	STROUD COLEMAN	100000
F CAMELOT (GB) - EMIRATES JOY (GB)	SACKVILLEDONALD	100000
F INVINCIBLE SPIRIT (IRE) - TOI ET MOI (IRE)	W MCCREERY	100000

Name and Breeding	Purchaser	Eur
CH F HOT STREAK (IRE) - STROLL PATROL (GB)	RABBAH BS	1000
B F CAMELOT (GB) - MARKET FORCES (GB)	A JONES	1000
B C WAR COMMAND (USA) - REGENCY GIRL (IRE)	STROUD COLEMAN BS	980
MY KINDA DAY (IRE) B C EXCEED AND EXCEL (AUS) - SOUND THE ALARM (GB)	R O'RYAN	950
CH F SEA THE STARS (IRE) - MAGIC SISTER (GB)	M PLAYER	950
BR C GUTAIFAN (IRE) - OH SEDULOUS (IRE)	D MURPHY	950
TAFISH (IRE) B C WAR COMMAND (USA) - ZIGARRA (GB)	BLANDFORD BS	950
B C DANDY MAN (IRE) - HEARD A WHISPER (GB)	SACKVILLEDONALD	920
B C KINGMAN (GB) - UPPER STREET (IRE)	VENDOR	900
GR/RO F THE FACTOR (USA) - GOLDEN CAUSEWAY (GB)	D HAYDEN	900
B C BUNGLE INTHEJUNGLE (GB) - NAFA (IRE)	CHURCH FARM	900
GR C GLENEAGLES (IRE) - CONVOCATE (USA)	BLANDFORD BS	900
B F ZOFFANY (IRE) - KITTENS (GB)	BLANDFORD BS	900
B F LOPE DE VEGA (IRE) - JEWEL IN THE SAND (IRE)	VENDOR	900
MOON POWER (GB) B F EXCEED AND EXCEL (AUS) - SHEPHERDIA (IRE)	SACKVILLE DONALD	900
B C MAKE BELIEVE (GB) - SPONTANEOUS (IRE)	HUGO MERRY BS	900
BUT YOU SAID (IRE) B F NO NAY NEVER (USA) - SAN MACCHIA (GB)	BBA (IRELAND)	900
B F KODIAC (GB) - MISS CORINNE (GB)	B O'RYAN	900
B C INVINCIBLE SPIRIT (IRE) - MARE NOSTRUM (GB)	OAK TREE FARM (P.S.)	900
CH C FREE EAGLE (IRE) - BADR AL BADOOR (IRE)	M MEADE	900
B F SEA THE STARS (IRE) - LAUGHING DOVE (IRE)	VENDOR	900
BETWEEN HILLS (IRE) B F HOT STREAK (IRE) - BREEDJ (IRE)	BBA (IRELAND)	880
B C CAMACHO (GB) - LEENAVESTA (USA)	STROUD COLEMAN BS	880
B C SEA THE MOON (GER) - ALL HALLOWS (IRE)	KEVIN ROSS BS	850
B C FASTNET ROCK (AUS) - ON A PEDESTAL (IRE)	BBA (IRELAND)	850
B F MUHAARAR (GB) - SUN BITTERN (USA)	GROVE STUD	850
B F MUHAARAR (GB) - MATHUNA (GB)	CHURCH FARM	850
B C DARK ANGEL (IRE) - CHEETAH (GB)	J CASSE	850
GR C GUTAIFAN (IRE) - MORE RESPECT (IRE)	PETER & ROSS DOYLE BS	850
B C AUSTRALIA (GB) - ANNA KARENINA (USA)	J MORGAN	850
B F ZOFFANY (IRE) - QUEEN OF CARTHAGE (USA)	GATEWOOD BELL	850
MOSALA (IRE) B C KODIAC (GB) - GLAMOROUS (GER)	BBA (IRELAND)	820
B F GLENEAGLES (IRE) - MYTHIE (FR)	PETER & ROSS DOYLE BS	820
MAORI KNIGHT (IRE) B C CAMELOT (GB) - CHATHAM ISLANDS (USA)	AVENUE BS	820
CH F RAVEN'S PASS (USA) - INTIMACY (IRE)	B LYNCH	800
B C MUHAARAR (GB) - ALASHA (IRE)	DE BURGH EQUINE	800
B C IVAWOOD (IRE) - KRYNICA (USA)	STROUD COLEMAN BS	800
LADY LYNETTA (IRE) B F TAMAYUZ (GB) - CRISTAL FASHION (IRE)	BLANDFORD BS	800
B C FASTNET ROCK (AUS) - COCHABAMBA (IRE)	BBA (IRELAND)	780
B C EXCEED AND EXCEL (AUS) - LINE AHEAD (GB)	BBA (IRELAND)	780
B C ZOFFANY (IRE) - STOR MÓ CHROI (IRE)	P & R DOYLE	780
PHUKET POWER (IRE) B C KODIAC (GB) - BRAZILIAN BRIDE (IRE)	SACKVILLEDONALD (P.S.)	750
B F SEA THE STARS (IRE) - THREE MOONS (IRE)	F GRAFFARD	750
B C SIYOUNI (FR) - SWEET DREAM (IRE)	SACKVILLE DONALD	750
B C ZOFFANY (IRE) - GUESSING (USA)	GODOLPHIN JAPAN	750
BULLOF WALL STREET (USA) CH C TAPIZAR (USA) - DOVIE (USA)	DE 5 STJERNER APS	750
B C FREE EAGLE (IRE) - ROSA'S CANTINA (IRE)	SACKVILLE DONALD	750
CH C LOPE DE VEGA (IRE) - WHAT A TREASURE (IRE)	KEVIN ROSS BS	750
B F MAKE BELIEVE (GB) - EZALLI (IRE)	F BARBERINI	750
GR F MAKE BELIEVE (GB) - QUEEN OF POWER (IRE)	D HAYDEN	750
CH C AUSTRALIA (GB) - WEWANTITALL (GB)	BBA (IRELAND) (P.S.)	750
B C TORONADO (IRE) - SASKIA'S DREAM (GB)	A SKIFFINGTON	750
MYSTIC RIVER (IRE) B C ANIMAL KINGDOM (USA) - HARRIET TUBMAN (USA)	AVENUE BS	750
B C DARK ANGEL (IRE) - MY SPIRIT (IRE)	OAK TREE FARM	720
B F KINGMAN (GB) - GIMASHA (GB)	PATTERN BS (P.S.)	700
B C SOCIETY ROCK (IRE) - SOMETHING MAGIC (GB)	KEVIN ROSS BS	700
B C KINGMAN (GB) - SOUTH ATLANTIC (IRE)	RABBAH BS	700
B C CAMELOT (GB) - STOLEN DANCE (IRE)	VENDOR	700
B C WAR COMMAND (USA) - RUSH (GB)	GODOLPHIN JAPAN	700
DOUGLAS FIR (IRE) B C AUSTRALIA (GB) - DANEHILL MUSIC (USA)	M JOHNSTON	700
B C OASIS DREAM (GB) - ALBAMARA (USA)	B LYNCH	700
B C LAWMAN (FR) - BOUNCE (FR)	MERIDIAN INTERNATIONAL	700
MACHO TOUCH (IRE) B F CAMACHO (GB) - HINT OF RED (IRE)	BBA (IRELAND)	700
CH F AUSTRALIA (GB) - TIMELESS CALL (IRE)	M MEADE	700
B F MAKE BELIEVE (GB) - WAAFIAH (GB)	BBA (IRELAND)	700
B C WAR COMMAND (USA) - LA VITA E BELLA (IRE)	B COOPER	700
B C BATED BREATH (GB) - STARLIGHT SYMPHONY (IRE)	GOODWILL BS	700
B C KODIAC (GB) - SANAYA (IRE)	J OSBORNE	680
B F KYLLACHY (GB) - ATTACHEE DE PRESSE (IRE)	J WELD	670
B F INVINCIBLE SPIRIT (IRE) - LOVE MAGIC (GB)	GERRY HOGAN BS	660

HIGH-PRICED YEARLINGS OF 2018 AT GOFFS UK (DONCASTER)

The following yearlings realised £52,000 and over at Goffs UK Sales in 2018:-

Name and Breeding	Purchaser	Pounds
C GLENEAGLES (IRE) - LADY ECLAIR (IRE)	SACKVILLEDONALD	380000
F ACCLAMATION (GB) - SWISS KISS (GB)	CREIGHTON SCHWARTZ BS	240000
F EXCEED AND EXCEL (AUS) - STRAVINA (GER)	O ST LAWRENCE	200000
C SHOWCASING (GB) - CITY IMAGE (IRE)	SHADWELL ESTATE CO	190000
C OASIS DREAM (GB) - CLENOR (IRE)	VENDOR	185000
F ACCLAMATION (GB) - SWEET NICOLE (IRE)	J FOLEY	185000
C DARK ANGEL (IRE) - AGE OF CHIVALRY (IRE)	PETER & ROSS DOYLE BS	170000
VEBURY (IRE) B F DARK ANGEL (IRE) - WILTSHIRE LIFE (IRE)	CHEVELEY PARK STUD	150000
C OASIS DREAM (GB) - QUIET (GB)	HKJC	150000
L SAKEET (GB) B C CABLE BAY (IRE) - COIN A PHRASE (GB)	SHADWELL ESTATE CO	150000
C ACCLAMATION (GB) - MISS GIBRALTAR (GB)	R KNIGHT (P.S.)	150000
F GLENEAGLES (IRE) - SUGAR MILL (GB)	CREIGHTON SCHWARTZ BS	140000
R C STARSPANGLEDBANNER (AUS) - GLOWING STAR (IRE)	C MCCORMACK	140000
C STARSPANGLEDBANNER (AUS) - THREE DECADES (IRE)	A DUARTE	140000
C KODIAC (GB) - MISS HONORINE (IRE)	HKJC	140000
MART START (IRE) B/BR C SOCIETY ROCK (IRE) - SKELETON (IRE)	GODOLPHIN	135000
C KODIAC (GB) - ARAVONIAN (GB)	SHADWELL ESTATE CO	135000
C CAMACHO (GB) - NIGHT SPHERE (IRE)	PHOENIX TB	125000
C ZEBEDEE (GB) - BRAZILIAN STYLE (GB)	HKJC	120000
C KODIAC (GB) - OPEN VERSE (USA)	R KNIGHT	120000
R F NO NAY NEVER (USA) - SUNBIRD (GB)	SACKVILLEDONALD	120000
C MUHAARAR (GB) - LADY FRANCESCA (GB)	SHADWELL ESTATE CO	120000
AMPANG (IRE) B C DANDY MAN (IRE) - BLACK MASCARA (IRE)	SACKVILLEDONALD	115000
AAREM (IRE) B C DREAM AHEAD (USA) - RED BLOSSOM (GB)	SHADWELL ESTATE CO	115000
HAGHOOF (GB) B C SHOWCASING (GB) - MUST BE ME (GB)	SHADWELL ESTATE CO	115000
C CABLE BAY (IRE) - HADEEYA (GB)	BLANDFORD BS	110000
L MUHAAJIR (IRE) CH C TAMAYUZ (GB) - LEMON ROCK (GB)	SHADWELL ESTATE CO	110000
C ZOFFANY (IRE) - RAGGETY ANN (IRE)	RABBAH BS	110000
F KODIAC (GB) - CHARLIE EM (GB)	HIGHFIELD FARM	110000
NE STEP BEYOND (IRE) B C EXCEED AND EXCEL (AUS) - YOURS TRULY (IRE)	B O'RYAN	105000
C HOT STREAK (IRE) - IRISHSTONE (GB)	DAVID REDVERS BS	105000
C KODIAC (GB) - GOT TO DANCE (GB)	POWERSTOWN STUD	105000
H C NO NAY NEVER (USA) - ORANGE PIP (GB)	SACKVILLEDONALD	105000
OMA GREEN (GB) B/BR C IFFRAAJ (GB) - DUBAI CYCLONE (USA)	C GORDON-WATSON BS	105000
PUROFTHEMOMENT (GB) B F BRAZEN BEAU (AUS) - ROYAL BLUSH (GB)	HOWSON & HOULDSWORTH BS	100000
C GLENEAGLES (IRE) - SNOWFIELDS (IRE)	C MCCORMACK	100000
C GUTAIFAN (IRE) - XEMA (GB)	PETER & ROSS DOYLE BS	100000
HALAF (GB) B C GUTAIFAN (IRE) - DOMINATRIX (GB)	SHADWELL ESTATE CO	100000
F SIYOUNI (FR) - FIG ROLL (GB)	LONGWAYS STABLES	95000
RUYFF (GB) B C DUTCH ART (GB) - PIANO (GB)	B O'RYAN	90000
T IVES (GB) B C CABLE BAY (IRE) - GALAKTEA (IRE)	JILL LAMB BS	90000
C BRAZEN BEAU (AUS) - ECLAIRCIE (IRE)	SHADWELL ESTATE CO	90000
NUGGET (GB) B C SIYOUNI (FR) - GEMSTONE (IRE)	J & J WARREN	90000
AAED (IRE) B C DARK ANGEL (IRE) - AMBASSADRICE (GB)	SHADWELL ESTATE CO	90000
H F SHOWCASING (GB) - MILLION FACES (GB)	M O'CALLAGHAN	85000
C DANDY MAN (IRE) - NANCY ASTOR (GB)	A C ELLIOTT	85000
R C TORONADO (IRE) - MATCH POINT (FR)	PETER & ROSS DOYLE BS	85000
G KODIAC (GB) - MITRE PEAK (GB)	SHADWELL ESTATE CO	85000
C SIR PRANCEALOT (IRE) - ARAAJMH (USA)	SHADWELL ESTATE CO	85000
EN'S LAD (IRE) B C DANDY MAN (IRE) - STRAWBERRY QUEEN (GB)	PETER & ROSS DOYLE BS	85000
C HAVANA GOLD (IRE) - PROSPERA (IRE)	A SKIFFINGTON	85000
C BUNGLE INTHEJUNGLE (GB) - MILLY'S SECRET (IRE)	PETER & ROSS DOYLE BS	85000
H F DUTCH ART (GB) - MEETING WATERS (GB)	KEVIN ROSS BS	85000
C NO NAY NEVER (USA) - QUEEN OF LYONS (USA)	C MCCORMACK	82000
C KODIAC (GB) - SIGHORA (IRE)	O ST LAWRENCE	82000
MACHO TIME (IRE) B C CAMACHO (GB) - GALEAZA (IRE)	J FRETWELL	80000
C HOT STREAK (IRE) - LADY SUESANNE (IRE)	PHOENIX TB	80000
C ZOFFANY (IRE) - AWOHAAM (IRE)	AVENUE BS	80000
C MUHAARAR (GB) - PASSION OVERFLOW (USA)	W BROWNE	80000
LOBAL ORCHID (IRE) B F SHOWCASING (GB) - LAW KEEPER (GB)	SACKVILLEDONALD	80000
C STREET BOSS (USA) - BUT SHE'S OURS (IRE)	VENDOR	80000
F KODIAC (GB) - WITTGENSTEIN (IRE)	GAELIC BS	80000
C STARSPANGLEDBANNER (AUS) - CARIBBEAN ACE (IRE)	CREIGHTON/SACKVILLE/DANCE	80000
MR BEAU BLUE (GB) BR C BRAZEN BEAU (AUS) - PRECIOUS SECRET (GB)	MR & MRS I BENDELOW	80000
C KODIAC (GB) - LADY DARSHAAN (IRE)	CHURCH FARM (P.S.)	80000
C KODIAC (GB) - LA GRANDE ZOA (IRE)	STAR BS	77000
RECOCITY (IRE) B F KODIAC (GB) - DAYS OF SUMMER (IRE)	J & J WARREN	75000

Name and Breeding	Purchaser	Pounds*
CH F DANDY MAN (IRE) - SHEER INDULGENCE (FR)	PHOENIX TB	75000
B C DANDY MAN (IRE) - SAFFIAN (GB)	A O'RYAN	75000
GR C GUTAIFAN (IRE) - BEGUILER (GB)	PETER & ROSS DOYLE BS	75000
CH C DRAGON PULSE (IRE) - VERONICA FALLS (GB)	KEVIN ROSS BS	75000
CH F STARSPANGLEDBANNER (AUS) - FATAAWY (IRE)	C MCCORMACK	75000
CH F BATED BREATH (GB) - AFFLUENT (GB)	O ST LAWRENCE	75000
CH C NIGHT OF THUNDER (IRE) - SEMAYYEL (IRE)	A SKIFFINGTON	74000
B F AUTHORIZED (GB) - HORA (GB)	STROUD COLEMAN BS	74000
B C NO NAY NEVER (USA) - MY SWEET GEORGIA (IRE)	JB BS	70000
ONE COLOUR (IRE) B/BR C BRAZEN BEAU (AUS) - MY LUCKY LIZ (IRE)	RABBAH BS	70000
BECADA (IRE) B F CAMACHO (GB) - WOODCOCK MOON (GB)	J & J WARREN	70000
CH F EXCEED AND EXCEL (AUS) - IMPERIALISTIC DIVA (IRE)	PHOENIX TB	70000
ANGLO SAXON (IRE) CH C STARSPANGLEDBANNER (AUS) - OBLIGADA (IRE)	STROUD COLEMAN BS	70000
COLD COMFORT (IRE) B F GUTAIFAN (IRE) - TAMARISK (GER)	A C ELLIOTT	70000
B C DARK ANGEL (IRE) - ARTISTIC JEWEL (IRE)	A C ELLIOTT	68000
ZANY (GB) CH C ZOFFANY (IRE) - FRIVOLITY (GB)	J FRETWELL	68000
B F KODIAC (GB) - TRY YES (GB)	VENDOR	68000
KHERIZZI (FR) CH C KHELEYF (USA) - KADIANIA (FR)	R O'RYAN	67000
B F KODIAC (GB) - WINDY LANE (GB)	GILL RICHARDSON BS	66000
GR C OUTSTRIP (GB) - MISS VENDOME (IRE)	GAELIC BS	65000
B C REQUINTO (IRE) - NARVA (USA)	K BURKE	65000
B C DARK ANGEL (IRE) - KERMANA (IRE)	J & J WARREN	65000
B C NO NAY NEVER (USA) - QUEEN GRACE (IRE)	RICK WYLIE BS	65000
BR F DANDY MAN (IRE) - NEW MAGIC (IRE)	PETER & ROSS DOYLE BS	65000
B C TAGULA (IRE) - BABYLONIAN (GB)	KEVIN ROSS BS	65000
B C HOLY ROMAN EMPEROR (IRE) - ASHTAROUTE (USA)	HKJC	65000
CH C LETHAL FORCE (IRE) - ENTREAT (GB)	CLIVE COX RACING	65000
BILL THE BUTCHER (IRE) CH C STARSPANGLEDBANNER (AUS) - LAURELITA (IRE)	B O'RYAN	64000
B F CABLE BAY (IRE) - TRIPLE STAR (GB)	SACKVILLEDONALD	62000
KRABI (GB) B F GUTAIFAN (IRE) - MISKIN DIAMOND (IRE)	SACKVILLEDONALD	62000
B C HOT STREAK (IRE) - LAHQA (IRE)	PETER & ROSS DOYLE BS	62000
TOO SHY SHY (IRE) GR F KODIAC (GB) - SATWA RUBY (FR)	B O'RYAN	62000
B C KINGMAN (GB) - AMARILLO STARLIGHT (IRE)	MCKEEVER BS	62000
B C SHOWCASING (GB) - MOMENT OF TIME (GB)	A DUARTE	60000
BR F DARK ANGEL (IRE) - BEST REGARDS (IRE)	SACKVILLEDONALD	60000
CH F DREAM AHEAD (USA) - SPIRIT OF CUBA (GB)	M TREGONING	60000
B C CABLE BAY (IRE) - MAMBO HALO (USA)	SAM SANGSTER BS	60000
CH C DUTCH ART (GB) - EDISIA (GB)	O ST LAWRENCE	60000
B C PIVOTAL (GB) - MUSIC AND DANCE (GB)	PATTERN BS (P.S.)	60000
TIGER ZONE (IRE) B C SOCIETY ROCK (IRE) - SHALABINA (GB)	CLIVE COX RACING	60000
KILCANON EXPLOSION (IRE) B C DARK ANGEL (IRE) - ALUTIQ (IRE)	SIR M PRESCOTT	60000
B F DANDY MAN (IRE) - AMETHYSTOS (GB)	VENDOR	60000
CH F NIGHT OF THUNDER (IRE) - ALJAAZYA (USA)	RABBAH BS	60000
BR C CAPPELLA SANSEVERO (GB) - VARNAY (GB)	SACKVILLEDONALD	60000
B F KODIAC (GB) - HEN NIGHT (IRE)	CRAMPSCASTLE BS	60000
THE NEXT EPISODE (IRE) B C DANDY MAN (IRE) - COUNTER RIDGE (SAF)	B O'RYAN	60000
PINATAR (IRE) B C HOLY ROMAN EMPEROR (IRE) - BURN THE BREEZE (IRE)	HOWSON & HOULDSWORTH BS	60000
CH C BATED BREATH (GB) - MOVEMENTNEVERLIES (GB)	SACKVILLEDONALD	60000
RAYONG (GB) B C MAYSON (GB) - LYDIATE (IRE)	SACKVILLEDONALD	60000
B C GUTAIFAN (IRE) - DEORA DE (GB)	GAELIC BS	58000
JACK RUBY (IRE) B C HAVANA GOLD (IRE) - MAKE ME BLUSH (IRE)	PETER & ROSS DOYLE BS	55000
B C KODIAC (GB) - COMPLEXION (GB)	FRIARS LOUGH STABLES	55000
B F KODIAC (GB) - FINAGLE (IRE)	GAELIC BS	55000
CH C DANDY MAN (IRE) - PARK TWILIGHT (IRE)	HKJC	55000
DANA FOREVER (IRE) B F REQUINTO (IRE) - POSITIVE STEP (IRE)	SACKVILLEDONALD	55000
ROAD RAGE (IRE) B C REQUINTO (IRE) - GRID LOCK (IRE)	R O'RYAN	55000
LADY FANDITHA (IRE) B F KODIAC (GB) - LADY RO (GB)	CLIVE COX RACING	55000
CORNDAVON LAD (IRE) B C CAMACHO (GB) - WILD WAYS (GB)	R O'RYAN	55000
B C KYLLACHY (GB) - ARDESSIE (GB)	R HUGHES	55000
CONSTITUTIONAL (IRE) B C SOCIETY ROCK (IRE) - LAST HOORAY (GB)	HOWSON & HOULDSWORTH BS	52000
WOOTTON'S COLT (FR) B/BR C WOOTTON BASSETT (GB) - TETH (GB)	M O'TOOLE	52000
B C DRAGON PULSE (IRE) - GLEN GINNIE (IRE)	SACKVILLEDONALD	52000
BR C SOCIETY ROCK (IRE) - DELIZIOSA (IRE)	J & J DANCE	52000
B C KAYF TARA (GB) - LIFESTYLE (GB)	M HAGGAS	52000

HIGH-PRICED YEARLINGS OF 2018 AT TATTERSALLS IRELAND SALES

The following yearlings realised 31,000 euros and over at Tattersalls Ireland Sales in 2018:-

Name and Breeding	Purchaser	Euros
AL AADHIB (IRE) B C KODIAC (GB) - LADY LUCIA (IRE)	SHADWELL ESTATE CO. LTD	275000
MOVING LIGHT (IRE) CH C NIGHT OF THUNDER (IRE) - NORTH EAST BAY (USA)	GODOLPHIN	180000
B C EXCELEBRATION (IRE) - KAYAK (GB)	JOE FOLEY	120000
BRAVE NEW WORLD (IRE) CH C NO NAY NEVER (USA) - DARA'S GIRL (IRE)	A C ELLIOTT, AGENT	120000
FLASHING APPROACH (IRE) B C NEW APPROACH (IRE) - FLASHING GREEN (GB)	KILBRIDE EQUINE	110000
B C ACCLAMATION (GB) - IRISH CLIFF (IRE)	KEVIN ROSS BS	105000
ARABIAN ROMANCE (IRE) B F NO NAY NEVER (USA) - CABELO (IRE)	GODOLPHIN	105000
B C TAMAYUZ (GB) - LONDON PLANE (IRE)	KEVIN ROSS BS	100000
BR C KODIAC (GB) - WELL FOCUSED (IRE)	BBA IRELAND	100000
BR C NO NAY NEVER (USA) - COOL CAP (IRE)	BBA IRELAND	100000
B F SHOWCASING (GB) - VITTA'S TOUCH (USA)	D FARRINGTON	85000
B C WAR COMMAND (USA) - ACTS OUT LOUD (USA)	STROUD COLEMAN BS	80000
B F GOLDEN HORN (GB) - SIMONETTA (GB)	SACKVILLE DONALD	78000
B C POWER (GB) - VARENKA (IRE)	MICHAEL O'CALLAGHAN	78000
B C NO NAY NEVER (USA) - TERRACOTTA (IRE)	MICHAEL O'CALLAGHAN	75000
B F CAMELOT (GB) - CONNIPTION (IRE)	SACKVILLE DONALD	75000
B F DANDY MAN (IRE) - AUNT NICOLA (GB)	DAVID REDVERS	72000
B C CAMACHO (GB) - KIMOLA (IRE)	KEVIN ROSS BS	70000
B C GLENEAGLES (IRE) - ONE CHANCE (IRE)	CHURCH FARM	70000
B C TAMAYUZ (GB) - CAILINI ALAINN (IRE)	BBA IRELAND	70000
BR F NO NAY NEVER (USA) - CRYSTAL CROSSING (IRE)	BBA IRELAND	70000
B C ACCLAMATION (GB) - SOUL MOUNTAIN (IRE)	MIDDLEHAM PARK RACING	65000
GR C NO NAY NEVER (USA) - MIZAYIN (IRE)	JOE FOLEY	65000
GR C MASTERCRAFTSMAN (IRE) - THE SHREW (GB)	SARAH LYNAM	65000
CLAUDIUS SECUNDUS (IRE) BR C HOLY ROMAN EMPEROR (IRE) - TASHA'S DREAM (USA)	RABBAH BS	65000
B C CAMACHO (GB) - SAVIDA (IRE)	AVENUE BS / HUGO PALMER	65000
BR C CAMACHO (GB) - FADDWA (IRE)	J B BS	63000
B F CAMACHO (GB) - QUICKSTYX (IRE)	RABBAH BS	62000
B F HALLOWED CROWN (AUS) - LAUREN'S GIRL (IRE)	MIDDLEHAM PARK RACING	62000
B G FLEMENSFIRTH (USA) - ERINS STAGE (IRE)	GLENVALE STUD	62000
CH F FOOTSTEPSINTHESAND (GB) - PORTICO (GB)	KERN LILLINGSTON (P.S.)	60000
CH F DANDY MAN (IRE) - DOCTRINE (GB)	JOE FOLEY	60000
B F KODIAC (GB) - CREAM TEASE (IRE)	AISLING GITTINS	60000
B F REQUINTO (IRE) - YASMEENA (USA)	KILBRIDE EQUINE	60000
B/BR F NO NAY NEVER (USA) - KAWN (IRE)	KILBRIDE EQUINE	58000
CH C DANDY MAN (IRE) - IMELDA MAYHEM (GB)	A C ELLIOTT, AGENT	55000
CH C LOPE DE VEGA (IRE) - NO SUCH ZONE (IRE)	VENDOR	55000
B F MAKE BELIEVE (GB) - NEWSLETTER (IRE)	MICK FLANAGAN, AGENT	55000
BR C SOCIETY ROCK (IRE) - CAPE KARLI (IRE)	SACKVILLE DONALD	52000
CELTIC BEAUTY (IRE) B F NO NAY NEVER (USA) - KEYSTONE GULCH (USA)	D FARRINGTON	52000
B C NIGHT OF THUNDER (GB) - FIRST PARTY (IRE)	BBA IRELAND	52000
BR C LAWMAN (FR) - QUADS (IRE)	PETER & ROSS DOYLE BS	52000
LOST EMPIRE (IRE) B C FOOTSTEPSINTHESAND (GB) - BALLERINA ROSE (GB)	ANDREW BALDING	50000
STONE CIRCLE (IRE) CH C NO NAY NEVER (USA) - CANDLEHILL GIRL (IRE)	VENDOR	50000
SWINLEY (IRE) BR C DRAGON PULSE (IRE) - INVINCIBLE STELLA (IRE)	A C ELLIOTT, AGENT	50000
BR G SOCIETY ROCK (IRE) - CHINA PINK (GB)	JOANNA MORGAN/MARTIN	50000
B F DELEGATOR (GB) - KIRUNAVAARA (GB)	MARK LOUGHNANE/S MEAKS	50000
CH C HARBOUR WATCH (IRE) - ROHERYN (IRE)	JOE FOLEY	50000
B C HELMET (AUS) - EMPRESS ELLA (IRE)	JOHN M OXX	50000
B F DARK ANGEL (IRE) - BEAR CHEEK (IRE)	SACKVILLE DONALD	48000
B F SOCIETY ROCK (IRE) - NAQRAH (IRE)	AISLING GITTINS	48000
CH F SOCIETY ROCK (IRE) - AIR OF MYSTERY (IRE)	BBA IRELAND	48000
GR C MARTALINE (GB) - AGATHE DU BERLAIS (FR)	EDDIE LINEHAN BS	48000
CH C FOOTSTEPSINTHESAND (GB) - KATHOE (IRE)	RICHARD FRISBY (P.S.)	47500
B C SADDLER MAKER (IRE) - MELANCHOLY HILL (IRE)	KILRONAN	47000
B C REQUINTO (IRE) - MATTINATA (GB)	KIERAN SHIELDS	46000
QUEENOFTHECLYDE (IRE) CH F DANDY MAN (IRE) - COCONUT KISSES (GB)	SACKVILLE DONALD	45000
BR C POET'S VOICE (GB) - SONGSEEKER (IRE)	A C ELLIOTT, AGENT	45000
CH C DAWN APPROACH (IRE) - STAR BLOSSOM (USA)	OAK TREE FARM	45000
BR C KENDARGENT (FR) - TOUTE FAMILLE (GB)	KEVIN PRENDERGAST	45000
CH C ZOFFANY (IRE) - ALMOST ALWAYS (IRE)	STEPHEN HILLEN	45000
CH C STARSPANGLEDBANNER (AUS) - SNOW SCENE (IRE)	ANDREW BALDING	45000
SEA TROUT REACH (IRE) CH C MUKHADRAM (GB) - CAELICA (USA)	ALLAN BLOODLINES	45000
GR/RO C THE FACTOR (USA) - CHARMING TALE (USA)	AMANDA SKIFFINGTON	44000
B C GARSWOOD (GB) - REGINA (GB)	BELIAR BS	42000
B F ACCLAMATION (GB) - LAFLEUR (IRE)	MICHAEL O'CALLAGHAN	42000
BR F SOCIETY ROCK (IRE) - THE REAL THING (IRE)	FEDERICO BARBERINI	42000
	OLDTOWN STUD	42000

Name and Breeding	Purchaser	Euros
B G FAME AND GLORY (GB) - BLAZING SONNET (IRE)	BROWN ISLAND STABLES	42000
B C SIR PERCY (GB) - AMOYA (GER)	FIVE STAR BS LTD	40000
B C DANDY MAN (IRE) - OPPORTUNA (GB)	CHURCH FARM	40000
B C FREE EAGLE (IRE) - OHIO (IRE)	BBA IRELAND	40000
ALMENDRO (IRE) B C IVAWOOD (IRE) - PERFECT BLOSSOM (GB)	AMANDA SKIFFINGTON	40000
B F FOOTSTEPSINTHESAND (GB) - SPERONELLA (GB)	KEVIN ROSS BS	40000
B C SIR PERCY (GB) - ALL IN GREEN (IRE)	KARL BURKE	40000
B C CAMACHO (GB) - SHAMARDYH (IRE)	BBA IRELAND	40000
GRIMBOLD (GB) B C KYLLACHY (GB) - BREVE (GB)	BBA IRELAND	40000
CH C ENGLISH CHANNEL (USA) - DALMIYA (IRE)	DENIS HOGAN RACING	39000
CH C PRESENTING (GB) - DIKLERS OSCAR (IRE)	KEVIN ROSS BS	38000
B F KODIAC (GB) - HAPPY LAND (IRE)	BBA IRELAND	38000
B F CAMACHO (GB) - HAWK EYED LADY (IRE)	EDWARD LYNAM	38000
MAYSONG (GB) CH C MAYSON (GB) - ALDEBURGH MUSIC (IRE)	STROUD COLEMAN BS	38000
NO NAY BELLA (IRE) B F NO NAY NEVER (USA) - ILLUMINATING DREAM (IRE)	MEAH / LLOYD BS	38000
B C NATHANIEL (IRE) - MEMORIES OF SUMMER (GB)	ADAM WYRZYK	38000
CH C MAHLER (GB) - GLEBE BEAUTY (IRE)	NOEL GUIRY	38000
RO C GUTAIFAN (IRE) - SPICY (IRE)	PETER & ROSS DOYLE BS	38000
B C MAYSON (GB) - OAKLEY STAR (GB)	J B BS	38000
ELUSIVE KING (IRE) B C ELUSIVE PIMPERNEL (USA) - LOST ICON (IRE)	BARRY LYNCH	38000
B C PRESENTING (GB) - ANOTHER TEMPEST (IRE)	DAVID YEARSLEY	38000
CH C TAGULA (IRE) - RED HOT SECRET (GB)	JOHNNY MURTAGH	37000
B C KAYF TARA (GB) - CAPTIVATING TYNA (IRE)	RICHARD FRISBY	37000
BR C BRAZEN BEAU (AUS) - OUR GAL (GB)	GILL RICHARDSON BS	36000
B C DANDY MAN (IRE) - SUNSET BEAUTY (IRE)	JOHN M OXX	36000
B C HOLY ROMAN EMPEROR (IRE) - ARMOISE (GB)	CHINOOK FARM	36000
B C FLEMENSFIRTH (USA) - KEEP FACE (FR)	ANTHONY GRAY	36000
B C HALLOWED CROWN (AUS) - CHICA WHOPA (IRE)	D FARRINGTON	35000
B F FRED JAZZ (USA) - SILVER TIDE (USA)	CRAMPSCASTLE BS	35000
B F OUTSTRIP (GB) - SINGING FIELD (IRE)	SACKVILLE DONALD	35000
RO F SEA THE STARS (IRE) - SYAMANTAKA (IRE)	VENDOR	35000
B C DANDY MAN (IRE) - ARCHETYPAL (IRE)	KARL BURKE	35000
TROUSER THE CASH (IRE) B F STARSPANGLEDBANNER (AUS) - BINT MALYANA (IRE)	STROUD COLEMAN BS	35000
B C WESTERNER (GB) - PARSONS HALL (IRE)	VENDOR	35000
SHEVCHENKO PARK (IRE) B C EPAULETTE (AUS) - COMPTON GIRL (GB)	SACKVILLE DONALD	35000
PAYNES BAY (IRE) CH C RAVEN'S PASS (USA) - WILDSPLASH (USA)	JASON KELLY	35000
B F EQUIANO (FR) - INDIGO RIVER (IRE)	GAELIC BS	35000
HADEUX CMIEUX (FR) B G COKORIKO (FR) - QUEEN DU VALLON (FR)	RYAN MAHON	35000
MEDITUR (FR) GR C TURGEON (USA) - MEDIMIX (FR)	JAMES MERNAGH	35000
CH F KYLLACHY (GB) - DUTCH COURAGE (GB)	BLANDFORD BS	34000
B F FOOTSTEPSINTHESAND (GB) - VAN DE CAPPELLE (IRE)	D FARRINGTON	34000
CH C DAWN APPROACH (IRE) - MOODY BLUE (IRE)	J B BS	34000
GR C CAMACHO (GB) - BINGFLING (IRE)	AIDAN O'RYAN	34000
B C FAME AND GLORY (GB) - MADE IN KK (IRE)	COUNTRY AGRI	34000
IL MAESTRO (IRE) B C CAMACHO (GB) - DANCE ON (GB)	SEAN QUINN/RICHARD KNIGHT	33000
DAZZLING DES (IRE) B C BRAZEN BEAU (AUS) - SECRET LIAISON (IRE)	JASON KELLY	33000
B C ACCLAMATION (GB) - MODELLO (IRE)	GROVE STUD	33000
LIAR LIAR (IRE) B C DREAM AHEAD (USA) - RUBILEO (GB)	BBA IRELAND	32000
CH C HARBOUR WATCH (IRE) - BLUE MAIDEN (GB)	JACKSON-STOPS BS	32000
B C TORONADO (IRE) - AL KIRANA (IRE)	VENDOR	32000
B C KODIAC (GB) - AL HANYORA (GB)	CON MARNANE	32000
B C FOOTSTEPSINTHESAND (GB) - MELODRAMA (IRE)	BLANDFORD BS	32000
B F ACCLAMATION (GB) - GOLDEN SHADOW (IRE)	JAMIE OSBORNE	32000
B C SOLDIER OF FORTUNE (IRE) - GALANT FERNS (IRE)	GARRYNACURRA STUD	32000
B F SHOWCASING (GB) - JEANIE JOHNSTON (IRE)	PETER & ROSS DOYLE BS	32000
B C GUTAIFAN (IRE) - WHATEVER YOU DO (IRE)	NEWLANDS BS LIMITED	32000
B C ROCK OF GIBRALTAR (IRE) - STRAWBERRY VODKA (GB)	HUGO PALMER	32000
B C DRAGON PULSE (IRE) - PLACE THAT FACE (IRE)	CLIVE COX RACING	32000
B G BLACK SAM BELLAMY (IRE) - AMBER CLOUD (GB)	PENELOPE LINDSAY-FYNN	32000
B C PRESENTING (GB) - SADDLERUPPAT (IRE)	DARRAGH MCDONAGH	32000
CH F CAMACHO (GB) - PASHMINA (IRE)	KERN LILLINGTON	32000
DRAGON COMMAND (GB) B C WAR COMMAND (USA) - ZARI (GB)	JACKSON-STOPS BS	31000
CH C TAMAYUZ (GB) - DHARWA (GB)	GAELIC BS	31000
B G WESTERNER (GB) - BECAUSE OF YOU (IRE)	HIGHFLYER BS	31000

2000 GUINEAS STAKES (3y) Newmarket-1 mile

Year	Owner	Winner and Price	Jockey	Trainer	Second	Third	Ran	Time
1981	Mrs A Muinos's	TO-AGORI-MOU (5/2)	G Starkey	G Harwood	Mattaboy	Bel Bolide	19	1 41.43
1982	G Oldham's	ZINO (8/1)	F Head	F Boutin	Wind and Wuthering	Tender King	26	1 37.13
1983	R Sangster's	LOMOND (9/1)	Pat Eddery	V O'Brien	Tolomeo	Muscatite	16	1 43.87
1984	R Sangster's	EL GRAN SENOR (15/8)	Pat Eddery	V O'Brien	Chief Singer	Lear Fan	14	1 37.41
1985	Maktoum Al Maktoum's	SHADEED (4/5)	L Piggott	M Stoute	Bairn	Supreme Leader	15	1 40.00
1986	K Abdullah's	DANCING BRAVE (15/8)	G Starkey	G Harwood	Green Desert	Huntingdale	15	1 36.74
1987	J Horgan's	DON'T FORGET ME (9/1)	W Carson	R Hannon	Bellotto	Midyan	13	1 41.73
1988	H H Aga Khan's	DOYOUN (4/5)	W R Swinburn	M Stoute	Charmer	Bellefella	9	1 36.74
1989	Hamdan Al-Maktoum's	NASHWAN (3/1)	W Carson	W Hern	Exbourne	Danehill	14	1 36.44
1990	John Horgan's	TIROL (9/1)	M Kinane	R Hannon	Machiavellian	Anshan	14	1 35.84
1991	Lady Beaverbrook's	MYSTIKO (13/2)	M Roberts	C Brittain	Lycius	Ganges	16	1 37.83
1992	R Sangster's	RODRIGO DE TRIANO (6/1)	L Piggott	P Chapple-Hyam	Lucky Lindy	Pursuit of Love	16	1 38.37
1993	K Abdullah's	ZAFONIC (5/6)	Pat Eddery	A Fabre	Barathea	Bin Alwaad	14	1 35.32
1994	G R Bailey Ltd's	MISTER BAILEYS (16/1)	J Weaver	M Johnston	Grand Lodge	Colonel Collins	23	1 35.08
1995	Sheikh Mohammed's	PENNEKAMP (9/2)	T Jarnet	A Fabre	Celtic Swing	Bahri	11	1 35.16
1996	Godolphin's	MARK OF ESTEEM (8/1)	L Dettori	S Bin Suroor	Even Top	Bijou D'Inde	13	1 37.59
1997	M Tabor & Mrs J Magnier's	ENTREPRENEUR (11/2)	M Kinane	M Stoute	Revoque	Poteen	16	1 37.64
1998	M Tabor & Mrs J Magnier's	KING OF KINGS (11/2)	M Kinane	A O'Brien	Lend A Hand	Border Arrow	18	1 39.25
1999	Godolphin's	ISLAND SANDS (10/1)	L Dettori	S Bin Suroor	Enrique	Mujahid	16	1 37.14
		(Run on July Course)						
2000	Saeed Suhail's	KING'S BEST (13/2)	K Fallon	Sir M Stoute	Giant's Causeway	Barathea Guest	27	1 37.77
2001	Lord Weinstock's	GOLAN (11/1)	K Fallon	Sir M Stoute	Tamburlaine	Frenchmans Bay	18	1 37.48
2002	Sir A Ferguson & Mrs J Magnier's	ROCK OF GIBRALTAR (9/1)	J Murtagh	A O'Brien	Hawk Wing	Redback	22	1 36.50
2003	Moyglare Stud Farm's	REFUSE TO BEND (9/2)	P J Smullen	D Weld	Zafeen	Norse Dancer	20	1 37.98
2004	Hamdan Al Maktoum's	HAAFHD (11/2)	R Hills	B Hills	Snow Ridge	Azamour	14	1 36.60
2005	Mr M Tabor & Mrs John Magnier's	FOOTSTEPSINTHESAND (13/2)	K Fallon	A O'Brien	Rebel Rebel	Kandidate	19	1 36.10
2006	Mrs J Magnier, Mr M Tabor & Mr D Smith's	GEORGE WASHINGTON (6/4)	M Kinane	A O'Brien	Sir Percy	Olympian Odyssey	14	1 36.80
2007	P Cunningham's	COCKNEY REBEL (25/1)	O Peslier	G Huffer	Vital Equine	Dutch Art	24	1 35.28
2008	Mrs J Magnier's	HENRYTHENAVIGATOR (11/1)	J Murtagh	A O'Brien	New Approach	Stubbs Art	15	1 39.14
2009	C Tsui's	SEA THE STARS (8/1)	M Kinane	J Oxx	Delegator	Gan Amhras	15	1 35.88
2010	K Offenstadt's	MAKFI (33/1)	C Lemaire	M Delzangles	Dick Turpin	Canford Cliffs	19	1 36.35
2011	K Abdullah's	FRANKEL (1/2)	T Queally	H Cecil	Dubawi Gold	Native Khan	13	1 37.30
2012	D Smith, Mrs J Magnier & Mr Tabor's	CAMELOT (15/8)	J O'Brien	A O'Brien	French Fifteen	Hermival	18	1 42.46
2013	Godolphin's	DAWN APPROACH (11/8)	K Manning	J Bolger	Glory Awaits	Van Der Neer	13	1 35.84
2014	Saeed Manana's	NIGHT OF THUNDER (40/1)	K Fallon	R Hannon jnr	Kingman	Australia	14	1 36.61
2015	M Tabor, D Smith & Mrs J Magnier's	GLENEAGLES (4/1)	R Moore	A O'Brien	Territories	Ivawood	18	1 37.55
2016	Al Shaqab Racing's	GALILEO GOLD (14/1)	L Dettori	H Palmer	Massaat	Ribchester	13	1 35.91
2017	M Tabor, D Smith & Mrs J Magnier's	CHURCHILL (6/4)	R Moore	A O'Brien	Barney Roy	Al Wukair	10	1 36.61
2018	D Smith, Mrs J Magnier & M Tabor's	SAXON WARRIOR (3/1)	D O'Brien	A O'Brien	Tip Two Win	Masar	14	1 36.55

1000 GUINEAS STAKES (3y fillies) Newmarket-1 mile

Year	Owner	Winner and Price	Jockey	Trainer	Second	Third	Ran	Time
1980	O Phipps's	QUICK AS LIGHTNING (6/4)	B Rouse	J Dunlop	Our Home	Mrs Penny	23	1 41.89
1981	H Joel's	FAIRY FOOTSTEPS (6/4)	L Piggott	H Cecil	Tolmi	Go Leasing	14	1 40.43
1982	Sir P Oppenheimer's	ON THE HOUSE (33/1)	J Reid	H Wragg	Time Charter	Dione	15	1 40.45
1983	Maktoum Al Maktoum's	MA BICHE (8/1)	F Head	H Cecil	Favoridge	Habibti	18	1 41.71
1984	M Lemos's	PEBBLES (8/1)	P Robinson	C Brittain	Meis El-Reem	Desirable	15	1 38.18
1985	Sheikh Mohammed's	OH SO SHARP (2/1)	S Cauthen	H Cecil	Al Bahathri	Bella Colora	17	1 36.85
1986	H Ranier's	MIDWAY LADY (10/1)	R Cochrane	B Hanbury	Maysoon	Sonic Lady	18	1 41.54
1987	S Niarchos's	MIESQUE (15/8)	F Head	F Boutin	Milligram	Interval	14	1 38.48
1988	E Aland's	RAVINELLA (4/5)	G W Moore	Mme C Head	Dabaweyaa	Diminuendo	12	1 40.88
1989	Sheikh Mohammed's	MUSICAL BLISS (7/2)	W R Swinburn	M Stoute	Kerrera	Aldbourne	7	1 40.88
1990	Hamdan Al-Maktoum's	SALSABIL (6/4)	W Carson	J Dunlop	Heart of Joy	Negligent	10	1 42.69
1991	Hamdan Al-Maktoum's	SHADAYID (4/6)	W Carson	J Dunlop	Kooyonga	Crystal Gazing	14	1 38.06
1992	Hamdan Al-Maktoum's	HATOOF (5/1)	W R Swinburn	Mme C Head	Marling	Kerbu	14	1 38.18
1993	Mohamed Obaida's	SAYYEDATI (4/1)	W R Swinburn	C Brittain	Niche	Alfan	12	1 39.45
1994	R Sangster's	LAS MENINAS (12/1)	J Reid	T Stack	Balanchine	Coup de Genie	15	1 37.34
1995	Hamdan Al-Maktoum's	HARAYIR (5/1)	R Hills	Major W R Hern	Aqaarid	Moonshell	15	1 36.71
1996	Wafic Said's	BOSRA SHAM (10/11)	Pat Eddery	H Cecil	Matiya	Bint Shadayid	13	1 37.75
1997	Greenbay Stables Ltd's	SLEEPYTIME (5/1)	K Fallon	H Cecil	Oh Nellie	Dazzle	15	1 37.66
1998	Godolphin's	CAPE VERDI (100/30)	L Dettori	S Bin Suroor	Shahtoush	Exclusive	16	1 37.86
1999	K Abdullah's	WINCE (4/1)	K Fallon	H Cecil	Wannabe Grand	Valentine Waltz	22	1 37.91

(Run on July Course)

Year	Owner	Winner and Price	Jockey	Trainer	Second	Third	Ran	Time
2000	Hamdan Al-Maktoum's	LAHAN (14/1)	R Hills	J Gosden	Princess Ellen	Petrushka	18	1 36.38
2001	Sheikh Ahmed Al Maktoum's	AMEERAT (11/1)	P Robinson	J Jarvis	Muwakleh	Toroca	15	1 36.36
2002	Godolphin's	KAZZIA (14/1)	L Dettori	S Bin Suroor	Snowfire	Alasha	19	1 37.85
2003	Cheveley Park Stud's	RUSSIAN RHYTHM (12/1)	K Fallon	Sir M Stoute	Six Perfections	Intercontinental	19	1 38.43
2004	Duke of Roxburghe's	ATTRACTION (11/2)	K Fallon	M Johnston	Sundrop	Hathran	16	1 36.70
2005	Mes John Magnier & Mr M Tabor's	VIRGINIA WATERS (12/1)	K Fallon	A O'Brien	Maids Causeway	Vista Bella	20	1 36.50
2006	M Sly, Dr Davies & Mrs P Sly's	SPECIOSA (10/1)	M Fenton	Mrs P Sly	Confidential Lady	Nashejj	13	1 40.50
2007	M Ryan's	FINSCEAL BEO (5/4)	K Manning	J Bolger	Arch Swing	Simply Perfect	21	1 34.94
2008	S Friborg's	NATAGORA (11/4)	C Lemaire	P Bary	Spacious	Saoirse Abu	15	1 34.99
2009	Hamdan Al-Maktoum's	GHANAATI (20/1)	R Hills	P Barry	Cuis Ghaire	Super Sleuth	14	1 34.22
2010	K Abdullah's	SPECIAL DUTY (9/2)	S Pasquier	Mme C Head-Maarek	Jacqueline Quest	Gile Na Greine	17	1 39.66

(The first two placings were reversed by the Stewards)

Year	Owner	Winner and Price	Jockey	Trainer	Second	Third	Ran	Time
2011	Godolphin's	BLUE BUNTING (16/1)	L Dettori	M Al Zarooni	Together	Maqaasid	18	1 39.27
2012	Mrs John Magnier, M Tabor & D Smith's	HOMECOMING QUEEN (25/1)	R Moore	A O'Brien	Starscope	Maybe	17	1 40.45
2013	B Keswick's	SKY LANTERN (9/1)	R Hughes	R Hannon	Just The Judge	Moth	15	1 36.38
2014	Ballymore Thoroughbred Ltd's	MISS FRANCE (7/1)	M Guyon	A Fabre	Lightning Thunder	Ihtimal	17	1 37.40
2015	M Tabor, D Smith & Mrs J Magnier's	LEGATISSIMO (13/2)	R Moore	D Wachman	Lucida	Wigg Wiggy	13	1 34.60
2016	D Smith, Mrs J Magnier & M Tabor's	MINDING (11/10)	R Moore	A O'Brien	Ballydoyle	Alice Springs	16	1 36.53
2017	Mrs John Magnier, M Tabor & D Smith's	WINTER (9/1)	W Lordan	A O'Brien	Rhododendron	Daban	14	1 35.66
2018	Pall Mall Partners & D Smith's	BILLESDON BROOK (66/1)	S Levey	R Hannon	Laurens	Happily	15	1 36.62

Year	Owner	Winner and Price	Jockey	Trainer	Second	Third	Ran	Time
1981	Mrs B Firestone's	BLUE WIND (3/1)	L Piggott	D Weld	Madam Gay	Leap Lively	12	2 40.93
1982	R Barnett's	TIME CHARTER (12/1)	W Newnes	H Candy	Slightly Dangerous	Last Feather	13	2 34.21
1983	Sir M Sobell's	SUN PRINCESS (6/1)	W Carson	R Hern	Acclimatise	New Coins	15	2 40.98
1984	Sir R McAlpine's	CIRCUS PLUME (4/1)	L Piggott	J Dunlop	Media Luna	Poquito Queen	15	2 38.97
1985	Sheikh Mohammed's	OH SO SHARP (6/4)	S Cauthen	H Cecil	Triptych	Dubian	12	2 41.37
1986	H Ranier's	MIDWAY LADY (15/8)	R Cochrane	B Hanbury	Untold	Maysoon	11	2 35.60
1987	Sheikh Mohammed's	UNITE (11/1)	W R Swinburn	M Stoute	Bourbon Girl	Three Tails	11	2 38.17
1988	Sheikh Mohammed's	DIMINUENDO (7/4)	S Cauthen	H Cecil	Sudden Love	Animatrice	11	2 35.02
1989	Saeed Maktoum Al Maktoum's	SNOW BRIDE	S Cauthen	H Cecil	Roseate Tern	Mamaluna	9	2 34.22
	(Aliysa finished first but was subsequently disqualified)							
1990	Hamdan Al-Maktoum's	SALSABIL (2/1)	W Carson	J Dunlop	Game Plan	Knight's Baroness	8	2 38.70
1991	Maktoum Al-Maktoum's	JET SKI LADY (50/1)	C Roche	J Bolger	Shamshir	Shadayid	9	2 37.30
1992	W J Gredley's	USER FRIENDLY (5/1)	G Duffield	C Brittain	All At Sea	Pearl Angel	14	2 39.77
1993	Sheikh Mohammed's	INTREPIDITY (5/1)	M Roberts	A Fabre	Royal Ballerina	Oakmead	14	2 34.19
1994	Godolphin's	BALANCHINE (6/1)	L Dettori	H Ibrahim	Wind In Her Hair	Hawajiss	10	2 40.37
1995	Maktoum Al Maktoum's, Godolphin's	MOONSHELL (3/1)	L Dettori	S Bin Suroor	Dance A Dream	Pure Grain	10	2 35.44
1996	Wafic Said's	LADY CARLA (100/30)	Pat Eddery	H Cecil	Pricket	Mezzogiorno	11	2 35.55
1997	K Abdullah's	REAMS OF VERSE (5/6)	K Fallon	H Cecil	Gazelle Royale	Crown of Light	12	2 35.59
1998	Mrs D Nagle & Mrs J Magnier's	SHAHTOUSH (12/1)	M Kinane	A O'Brien	Bahr	Midnight Line	8	2 38.23
1999	F Salman's	RAMRUMA (3/1)	K Fallon	H Cecil	Noushkey	Zahrat Dubai	10	2 38.72
2000	Lordship Stud's	LOVE DIVINE (9/4)	T Quinn	H Cecil	Kalypso Katie	Melikah	16	2 43.11
2001	Mrs D Nagle & Mrs J Magnier's	IMAGINE (9/4)	M Kinane	A O'Brien	Flight of Fancy	Relish The Thought	14	2 36.70
2002	Godolphin's	KAZZIA (10/30)	L Dettori	S Bin Suroor	Quarter Moon	Shadow Dancing	15	2 44.52
2003	W S Farish III's	CASUAL LOOK (10/1)	M Dwyer	A Balding	Yesterday	Summitville	14	2 38.07
2004	Lord Derby's	OUIJA BOARD (7/2)	K Fallon	E Dunlop	All Too Beautiful	Punctilious	7	2 35.40
2005	Hamdan Al Maktoum's	ESWARAH (11/4)	M Hills	M Jarvis	Something Exciting	Pictavia	12	2 39.00
2006	Mrs J Magnier, Mr M Tabor & Mr D Smith's	ALEXANDROVA (9/4)	K Fallon	A O'Brien	Rising Cross	Short Skirt	10	2 37.70
2007	Niarchos Family's	LIGHT SHIFT (13/2)	T Durcan	H Cecil	Peeping Fawn	All My Loving	14	2 40.38
2008	J H Richmond-Watson's	LOOK HERE (33/1)	S Sanders	R Beckett	Moonstone	Katiyra	16	2 36.89
2009	Lady Bamford's	SARISKA (9/4)	J Spencer	M Bell	Midday	High Heeled	10	2 33.28
2010	Aramune Ltd's	SNOW FAIRY (9/1)	R Moore	E Dunlop	Remember When		15	2 35.77
	(Meezah finished second but was subsequently disqualified)							
2011	M J & L A Taylor's	DANCING RAIN (20/1)	J Murtagh	W Haggas	Wonder of Wonders	Izzi Top	13	2 41.73
2012	D Smith, Mrs J Magnier & M Tabor's	WAS (20/1)	S Heffernan	A O'Brien	Shirocco Star	The Fugue	12	2 38.68
2013	J L Rowsell & M H Dixon's	TALENT (20/1)	R Hughes	R Beckett	Secret Gesture	The Lark	17	2 42.00
2014	Hamdan Al Maktoum's	TAGHROODA (5/1)	P Hanagan	J Gosden	Tarfasha	Volume	11	2 34.89
2015	Mrs C C Regalado-Gonzalez's	QUALIFY (50/1)	C O'Donoghue	A O'Brien	Legatissimo	Lady of Dubai	11	2 37.41
2016	D Smith, Mrs J Magnier & M Tabor's	MINDING (10/11)	R Moore	A O'Brien	Architecture	Harlequeen	9	2 42.66
2017	K Abdullah's	ENABLE (6/1)	L Dettori	J Gosden	Rhododendron	Alluringly	9	2 34.13
2018	M Tabor, D Smith & Mrs J Magnier's	FOREVER TOGETHER (7/1)	D O'Brien	A O'Brien	Wild Illusion	Bye Bye Baby	9	2 40.39

DERBY STAKES (3y) Epsom-1 mile 4 furlongs 6 yards

Year	Owner	Winner and Price	Jockey	Trainer	Second	Third	Ran	Time
1982	R Sangster's	GOLDEN FLEECE (3/1)	Pat Eddery	V O'Brien	Touching Wood	Silver Hawk	18	2 34.27
1983	E Moller's	TEENOSO (9/2)	L Piggott	G Wragg	Carlingford Castle	Shearwalk	21	2 49.07
1984	L Migitti's	SECRETO (14/1)	C Roche	D O'Brien	El Gran Senor	Mighty Flutter	17	2 39.12
1985	Lord H. de Walden's	SLIP ANCHOR (9/4)	S Cauthen	H Cecil	Law Society	Damister	14	2 36.23
1986	H H Aga Khan's	SHAHRASTANI (11/2)	W Swinburn	M Stoute	Dancing Brave	Mashkour	17	2 37.13
1987	L Freedman's	REFERENCE POINT (6/4)	S Cauthen	H Cecil	Most Welcome	Bellotto	19	2 33.90
1988	H H Aga Khan's	KAHYASI (11/1)	R Cochrane	L Cumani	Glacial Storm	Doyoun	14	2 33.84
1989	Hamdan Al-Maktoum's	NASHWAN (5/4)	W Carson	R Hern	Terimon	Cacoethes	12	2 34.90
1990	K Abdullah's	QUEST FOR FAME (7/1)	Pat Eddery	R Charlton	Blue Stag	Elmaamul	12	2 37.26
1991	F Salman's	GENEROUS (9/1)	A Munro	P Cole	Marju	Star of Gdansk	13	2 34.00
1992	Sidney H Craig's	DR DEVIOUS (8/1)	J Reid	P Chapple-Hyam	Silver Wisp	Blue Judge	18	2 36.19
1993	Hamdan Al-Maktoum's	COMMANDER IN CHIEF (15/2)	M Kinane	H Cecil	Blue Judge	Blues Traveller	16	2 34.51
1994	Saeed Maktoum Al Maktoum's	ERHAAB (7/2)	W Carson	J Dunlop	King's Theatre	Colonel Collins	25	2 34.16
1995	K Dasmal's	LAMMTARRA (14/1)	W Swinburn	S Bin Suroor	Tamure	Presenting	15	2 32.31
1996	L Knight's	SHAAMIT (12/1)	M Hills	W Haggas	Dushyantor	Shantou	20	2 35.05
1997	Sheikh Mohammed	BENNY THE DIP (11/1)	W Ryan	J Gosden	Silver Patriarch	Romanov	13	2 35.77
1998	Obaid Al Maktoum's	HIGH-RISE (20/1)	O Peslier	L Cumani	City Honours	Border Arrow	15	2 33.88
1999	The Thoroughbred Corporation's	OATH (13/2)	K Fallon	H Cecil	Daliapour	Beat All	16	2 37.43
2000	H H Aga Khan's	SINNDAR (7/1)	J Murtagh	J Oxx	Sakhee	Beat Hollow	15	2 36.75
2001	M Tabor & Mrs J Magnier's	GALILEO (11/4)	M Kinane	A O'Brien	Golan	Tobougg	12	2 33.27
2002	M Tabor & Mrs J Magnier's	HIGH CHAPARRAL (7/2)	J Murtagh	A O'Brien	Hawk Wing	Moon Ballad	12	2 39.45
2003	Saeed Suhail's	KRIS KIN (6/1)	K Fallon	Sir M Stoute	The Great Gatsby	Alamshar	20	2 33.35
2004	Ballymacoll Stud's	NORTH LIGHT (7/2)	K Fallon	Sir M Stoute	Rule Of Law	Let The Lion Roar	14	2 33.70
2005	The Royal Ascot Racing Club's	MOTIVATOR (3/1)	J Murtagh	M Bell	Walk In The Park	Dubawi	13	2 35.60
2006	Saleh Al Homaidi & Imad Al Sagar's	SIR PERCY (6/1)	M Dwyer	M Tregoning	Dragon Dancer	Dylan Thomas	18	2 35.20
2007	A.E Pakenham's	AUTHORIZED (5/4)	L Dettori	P Chapple-Hyam	Eagle Mountain	Aqaleem	17	2 34.77
2008	HRH Princess Haya of Jordan's	NEW APPROACH (5/1)	K Manning	J Bolger	Tartan Bearer	Casual Conquest	16	2 36.50
2009	C Tsui's	SEA THE STARS (11/4)	M Kinane	J Oxx	Fame And Glory	Masterofthehorse	12	2 36.74
2010	K Abdullah's	WORKFORCE (6/1)	R Moore	Sir M Stoute	At First Sight	Rewilding	12	2 31.33
2011	Mrs John Magnier, M Tabor & Obaid Al Maktoum's	POUR MOI (4/1)	M Barzalona	A Fabre	Treasure Beach	Carlton House	13	2 34.54
2012	D Smith, Mrs J Magnier & M Tabor's	CAMELOT (8/13)	J O'Brien	A O'Brien	Main Sequence	Astrology	9	2 33.90
2013	Mrs John Magnier, Michael Tabor & Derrick Smith's	RULER OF THE WORLD (7/1)	R Moore	A O'Brien	Libertarian	Galileo Rock	12	2 39.06
2014	D Smith, Mrs J Magnier, M Tabor & T Ah Khing's	AUSTRALIA (11/8)	J O'Brien	A O'Brien	Kingston Hill	Romsdal	16	2 33.63
2015	A E Oppenheimer's	GOLDEN HORN (13/8)	L Dettori	J Gosden	Jack Hobbs	Storm The Stars	12	2 32.32
2016	H H Aga Khan's	HARZAND (13/2)	P Smullen	D Weld	US Army Ranger	Idaho	16	2 40.09
2017	D Smith, Mrs J Magnier, M Tabor's	WINGS OF EAGLES (40/1)	P Beggy	A O'Brien	Cliffs of Moher	Cracksman	18	2 33.02
2018	Godolphin's	MASAR (16/1)	W Buick	C Appleby	Dee Ex Bee	Roaring Lion	12	2 34.93

ST LEGER STAKES (3y) Doncaster 1 mile 6 furlongs 115 yards

Year	Owner	Winner and Price	Jockey	Trainer	Second	Third	Ran	Time
1979	A Rolland's	SON OF LOVE (20/1)	A Lequeux	R Collet	Soleil Noir	Niniski	17	3 9.02
1980	H Joel's	LIGHT CAVALRY (3/1)	J Mercer	H Cecil	Water Mill	World Leader	7	3 11.48
1981	Sir J Astor's	CUT ABOVE (28/1)	J Mercer	R Hern	Glint of Gold	Bustomi	7	3 11.60
1982	Maktoum Al Maktoum's	TOUCHING WOOD (7/1)	P Cook	H T Jones	Zilos	Diamond Shoal	15	3 3.53
1983	Sir M Sobell's	SUN PRINCESS (11/8)	W Carson	R Hern	Esprit du Nord	Carlingford Castle	10	3 16.65
1984	I Allan's	COMMANCHE RUN (7/4)	L Piggott	L Cumani	Baynoun	Alphabatim	11	3 9.93
1985	Sheikh Mohammed's	OH SO SHARP (8/11)	S Cauthen	H Cecil	Phardante	Lanfranco	6	3 7.13
1986	Duchess of Norfolk's	MOON MADNESS (9/2)	Pat Eddery	J Dunlop	Celestial Storm	Untold	8	3 5.03
1987	L Freedman's	REFERENCE POINT (4/11)	S Cauthen	H Cecil	Mountain Kingdom	Dry Dock	7	3 5.91
1988	Lady Beaverbrook's	MINSTER SON (15/2)	W Carson	N A Graham	Diminuendo	Sheriff's Star	8	3 6.80
1989	C St George's (Run at Ayr)	MICHELOZZO (6/4)	S Cauthen	H Cecil	Sapience	Roseate Tern	8	3 20.72
1990	M Arbib's	SNURGE (7/2)	T Quinn	P Cole	Hellenic	River Gold	8	3 8.78
1991	K Abdullah's	TOULON (5/2)	Pat Eddery	A Fabre	Saddlers' Hall	Micheletti	7	3 3.12
1992	W J Gredley's	USER FRIENDLY (7/4)	G Duffield	M Tompkins	Sonus	Bonny Scot	10	3 5.48
1993	Mrs G A E Smith's	BOB'S RETURN (3/1)	P Robinson	B Hills	Armiger	Edbaysaan	9	3 7.85
1994	Sheikh Mohammed's	MOONAX (40/1)	Pat Eddery	B Hills	Broadway Flyer	Double Trigger	8	3 4.19
1995	Godolphin's	CLASSIC CLICHE (100/30)	L Dettori	S Bin Suroor	Minds Music	Istidaad	10	3 9.74
1996	Sheikh Mohammed's	SHANTOU (8/1)	L Dettori	J Dunlop	Dushyantor	Samraan	11	3 5.10
1997	P Winfield's	SILVER PATRIARCH (5/4)	Pat Eddery	J Dunlop	Vertical Speed	The Fly	10	3 6.92
1998	Godolphin's	NEDAWI (5/2)	J Reid	S Bin Suroor	High and Low	Sunshine Street	9	3 5.61
1999	Godolphin's	MUTAFAWEQ (11/2)	J Hills	S Bin Suroor	Ramruma	Adair	10	3 2.75
2000	N Jones'	MILLENARY (11/4)	T Quinn	J Dunlop	Air Marshall	Chimes At Midnight	11	3 2.58
2001	M Tabor & Mrs J Magnier's	MILAN (13/8)	M Kinane	A O'Brien	Demophilos	Mr Combustible	10	3 5.16
2002	Sir Neil Westbrook's	BOLLIN ERIC (7/1)	K Darley	T Easterby	Highest	Phoenix Reach	8	3 2.92
2003	Mrs J Magnier's	BRIAN BORU (5/4)	J P Spencer	A O'Brien	High Accolade	Tycoon	12	3 4.64
2004	Godolphin's	RULE OF LAW (3/1)	K McEvoy	S Bin Suroor	Quiff	Tawqeet	9	3 6.20
2005	Mrs J Magnier & M Tabor's	SCORPION (10/1)	L Dettori	A O'Brien	The Geezer	Red Rocks	6	3 19.00
2006	Mrs S Roy's	SIXTIES ICON (11/8)	L Dettori	J Noseda	The Last Drop		11	3 57.20
2007	P Strawbridge's (Run at York)	LUCARNO (8/1)	J Fortune	J Gosden	Mahler	Honolulu	10	3 1.90
2008	Ballymacoll Stud's	CONDUIT (8/1)	L Dettori	Sir M Stoute	Unsung Heroine	Look Here	14	3 7.92
2009	Godolphin's	MASTERY (14/1)	T Durcan	S Bin Suroor	Kite Wood	Monitor Closely	8	3 4.81
2010	Ms R Hood & R Geffen's	ARCTIC COSMOS (12/1)	W Buick	J Gosden	Midas Touch	Corsica	10	3 3.12
2011	B Nielsen's	MASKED MARVEL (15/2)	W Buick	J Gosden	Brown Panther	Sea Moon	9	3 0.44
2012	Godolphin's	ENCKE (25/1)	M Barzalona	M Al Zarooni	Camelot	Michelangelo	9	3 3.81
2013	Derrick Smith & Mrs John Magnier & Michael Tabor's	LEADING LIGHT (7/2)	J O'Brien	A O'Brien	Talent	Galileo Rock	11	3 9.20
2014	Paul Smith's	KINGSTON HILL (9/4)	A Atzeni	R Varian	Romsdal	Snow Sky	12	3 5.42
2015	QRL, Sheikh Suhaim Al Thani & M A Kubasi's	SIMPLE VERSE (8/1)	A Atzeni	R Beckett	Bondi Beach	Fields of Athenry	7	3 7.12
2016	Mrs Jackie Cornwell's	HARBOUR LAW (22/1)	G Baker	Mrs L J Mongan	Ventura Storm	Housesofparliament	9	3 5.48
2017	Derrick Smith & Mrs John Magnier & Michael Tabor's	CAPRI (3/1)	R Moore	A O'Brien	Crystal Ocean	Stradivarius	11	3 4.04
2018	Derrick Smith & Mrs John Magnier & Michael Tabor's	KEW GARDENS (3/1)	R Moore	A O'Brien	Lah Ti Dar	Southern France	12	3 3.34

KING GEORGE VI AND QUEEN ELIZABETH STAKES   Ascot-1 mile 3 furlongs 211 yards

Year	Owner	Winner and Price	Jockey	Trainer	Second	Third	Ran	Time
1980	S Weinstock's	ELA-MANA-MOU 4-9-7 (11/4)	W Carson	R Hern	Mrs Penny	Gregorian	10	2 35.39
1981	H H Aga Khan's	SHERGAR 3-8-8 (2/5)	W Swinburn	M Stoute	Madam Gay	Fingal's Cave	7	2 35.40
1982	A Ward's	KALAGLOW 4-9-7 (13-2)	G Starkey	G Harwood	Assert	Glint of Gold	9	2 31.58
1983	R Barnett's	TIME CHARTER 4-9-4 (5/1)	J Mercer	H Candy	Diamond Shoal	Sun Princess	9	2 30.78
1984	E Moller's	TEENOSO 4-9-7 (13/2)	L Piggott	G Wragg	Sadler's Wells	Tolomeo	13	2 27.95
1985	Lady Beaverbrook's	PETOSKI 3-8-8 (12/1)	W Carson	R Hern	Oh So Sharp	Rainbow Quest	9	2 27.61
1986	K Abdullah's	DANCING BRAVE 3-8-8 (6/4)	Pat Eddery	G Harwood	Shardari	Triptych	9	2 29.49
1987	L Freedman's	REFERENCE POINT 3-8-8 (11/10)	S Cauthen	H Cecil	Celestial Storm	Triptych	9	2 34.63
1988	Sheikh Ahmed Al Maktoum's	MTOTO 5-9-7 (4/1)	M Roberts	A C Stewart	Unfuwain	Triptych	10	2 37.33
1989	Hamdan Al-Maktoum's	NASHWAN 3-8-8 (2/9)	W Carson	H Cecil	Cacoethes	Tony Bin	7	2 32.27
1990	Sheikh Mohammed's	BELMEZ 3-8-9 (15/2)	M Kinane	H Cecil	Old Vic	Top Class	9	2 30.76
1991	F Salman's	GENEROUS 3-8-9 (4/6)	A Munro	P Cole	Sanglamore	Assatis	11	2 28.99
1992	Mrs V K Payson's	ST JOVITE 3-8-9 (4/5)	S Craine	J Bolger	Saddlers' Hall	Rock Hopper	8	2 30.85
1993	Sheikh Mohammed's	OPERA HOUSE 4-9-7 (8/1)	M Roberts	M Stoute	White Muzzle	Commander in Chief	10	2 33.94
1994	Sheikh Mohammed's	KING'S THEATRE 3-8-9 (12/1)	M Kinane	H Cecil	White Muzzle	Wagon Master	12	2 28.92
1995	Saeed Maktoum Al Maktoum's	LAMMTARRA 3-8-9 (9/4)	L Dettori	S Bin Suroor	Pentire	Strategic Choice	12	2 31.01
1996	Mollers Racing's	PENTIRE 4-9-7 (100/30)	M Hills	G Wragg	Classic Cliche	Shaamit	8	2 28.11
1997	Godolphin's	SWAIN 5-9-7 (16/1)	J Reid	S Bin Suroor	Pilsudski	Helissio	8	2 46.45
1998	Godolphin's	SWAIN 6-9-7 (11/2)	L Dettori	S Bin Suroor	High-Rise	Royal Anthem	8	2 28.20
1999	Godolphin's	DAYLAMI 5-9-7 (3/1)	L Dettori	S Bin Suroor	Nedawi	Fruits Of Love	7	2 29.36
2000	M Tabor's	MONTJEU 4-9-7 (1/3)	M Kinane	J Hammond	Fantastic Light	Daliapour	8	2 29.98
2001	Mrs J Magnier & M Tabor's	GALILEO 3-8-9 (1/2)	M Kinane	A O'Brien	Fantastic Light	Hightori	12	2 27.71
2002	Exors of the late Lord Weinstock's	GOLAN 4-9-7 (11/2)	K Fallon	Sir M Stoute	Nayef	Zindabad	9	2 29.70
2003	H H Aga Khan	ALAMSHAR 3-8-9 (13/2)	J Murtagh	J Oxx	Sulamani	Kris Kin	12	2 33.26
2004	Godolphin's	DOYEN 4-9-7 (11/10)	L Dettori	S Bin Suroor	Hard Buck	Sulamani	11	2 33.10
2005	H H Aga Khan's	AZAMOUR 4-9-7 (5/2)	M Kinane	J Oxx	Norse Dancer	Bago	12	2 28.20
	(Run at Newbury)							
2006	M Tabor's	HURRICANE RUN 4-9-7 (5/6)	C Soumillon	A Fabre	Electrocutionist	Heart's Cry	6	2 30.20
2007	Mrs J Magnier & M Tabor's	DYLAN THOMAS 4-9-7 (5/4)	J Murtagh	A O'Brien	Youmzain	Maraahel	7	2 31.10
2008	Mrs J Magnier & M Tabor's	DUKE OF MARMALADE 4-9-7 (4/6)	J Murtagh	A O'Brien	Papal Bull	Youmzain	8	2 27.91
2009	Ballymacoll Stud's	CONDUIT 4-9-7 (7/2)	R Moore	Sir M Stoute	Tartan Bearer	Ask	9	2 28.73
2010	Highclere Thoroughbred Racing, Adm. Rous's	HARBINGER 4-9-7 (4/1)	O Peslier	Sir M Stoute	Cape Blanco	Youmzain	6	2 26.78
2011	Lady Rothschild's	NATHANIEL 3-8-9 (11/2)	W Buick	J Gosden	Workforce	St Nicholas Abbey	5	2 35.07
2012	Gestut Burg Eberstein & Teruya Yoshida's	DANEDREAM 4-9-4 (9/1)	A Starke	P Schiergen	Nathaniel	St Nicholas Abbey	10	2 31.62
2013	Dr Christophe Berglar's	NOVELLIST 4-9-7 (13/2)	J Murtagh	A Wohler	Trading Leather	Hillstar	8	2 24.60
2014	Hamdan Al Maktoum's	TAGHROODA 3-8-6 (7/2)	P Hanagan	J Gosden	Telescope	Mukhadram	8	2 28.13
2015	Sheikh Mohammed Obaid Al Maktoum's	POSTPONED 4-9-7 (6/1)	A Atzeni	L Cumani	Eagle Top	Romsdal	7	2 31.25
2016	D Smith, Mrs J Magnier & M Tabor's	HIGHLAND REEL 4-9-7 (13/8)	R Moore	A O'Brien	Wings of Desire	Dartmouth	7	2 28.97
2017	K Abdulla's	ENABLE 3-8-7 (5/4)	L Dettori	J Gosden	Ulysses	Idaho	10	2 36.22
2018	S Suhail's	POET'S WORD 5-9-7 (7/4)	J Doyle	Sir M Stoute	Crystal Ocean	Coronet	7	2 25.84

PRIX DE L'ARC DE TRIOMPHE ParisLongchamp-1 mile 4 furlongs

Year	Owner	Winner and Price	Jockey	Trainer	Second	Third	Ran	Time
1981	J Wertheimer's	GOLD RIVER 4-9-1 (53/1)	G W Moore	A Head	Bikala	April Run	24	3 35.20
1982	H H Aga Khan's	AKIYDA 3-8-8 (43/4)	Y Saint Martin	F. Mathet	Ardross	Awaasif	17	3 37.00
1983	D Wildenstein's	ALL ALONG 4-9-1 (173/10)	W Swinburn	P Biancone	Sun Princess	Luth Enchantee	26	2 28.10
1984	D Wildenstein's	SAGACE 4-9-4 (29/10)	Y Saint Martin	P Biancone	Northern Trick	All Along	22	3 39.10
1985	K Abdullah's	RAINBOW QUEST 4-9-4 (71/10)	Pat Eddery	J Tree	Sagace	Kozana	15	2 29.50
		(The first two placings were reversed by the Stewards)						
1986	K Abdullah's	DANCING BRAVE 3-8-11 (11/10)	Pat Eddery	G Harwood	Bering	Triptych	15	2 27.70
1987	P de Moussac's	TREMPOLINO 3-8-11 (20/1)	Pat Eddery	A Fabre	Tony Bin	Triptych	11	2 26.30
1988	Mrs I Gaucci del Bono's	TONY BIN 5-9-4 (14/1)	J Reid	L Camici	Mtoto	Boyatino	24	2 27.30
1989	A Balzarini's	CARROLL HOUSE 4-9-4 (19/1)	M Kinane	M Jarvis	Behera	Saint Andrews	19	2 30.80
1990	B McNall's	SAUMAREZ 3-8-11 (15/1)	G Mosse	N Clement	Epervier Bleu	Snurge	21	2 29.80
1991	H Chalhoub's	SUAVE DANCER 3-8-11 (37/10)	C Asmussen	J Hammond	Magic Night	Pistolet Bleu	14	2 31.40
1992	O Lecerf's	SUBOTICA 4-9-4 (88/10)	T Jarnet	A Fabre	User Friendly	Vert Amande	18	2 39.00
1993	D Tsui's	URBAN SEA 4-9-1 (37/10)	E Saint Martin	J Lesbordes	White Muzzle	Opera House	23	2 37.90
1994	Sheikh Mohammed's	CARNEGIE 3-8-11 (3/1)	T Jarnet	A Fabre	Hernando	Apple Tree	20	2 31.10
1995	Saeed Maktoum Al Maktoum's	LAMMTARRA 3-8-11 (2/1)	L Dettori	S Bin Suroor	Freedom Cry	Swain	16	2 31.80
1996	E Sarasola's	HELISSIO 3-8-11 (18/10)	O Pesier	E Lellouche	Pilsudski	Oscar Schindler	16	2 29.90
1997	D Wildenstein's	PENTIRE CELEBRE 3-8-11 (22/10)	O Pesier	A Fabre	Pilsudski	Borgia	18	2 24.60
1998	J-L Lagardere's	SAGAMIX 3-8-11 (5/2)	O Pesier	A Fabre	Leggera	Tiger Hill	14	2 34.50
1999	M Tabor's	MONTJEU 3-8-11 (6/4)	M Kinane	J Hammond	El Condor Pasa	Croco Rouge	14	2 38.50
2000	H H Aga Khan's	SINNDAR 3-8-11 (6/4)	J Murtagh	J Oxx	Egyptband	Volvoreta	17	2 25.80
2001	Godolphin's	SAKHEE 5-9-5 (158/10)	L Dettori	S Bin Suroor	Aquarelliste	Sagacity	16	2 36.10
2002	Godolphin's	MARIENBARD 5-9-5 (11/2)	L Dettori	S Bin Suroor	Sulamani	High Chaparral	16	2 26.70
2003	H H Aga Khan's	DALAKHANI 3-8-11 (9/4)	C Soumillon	A de Royer-Dupre	Mubtaker	High Chaparral	13	2 32.30
2004	Niarchos Family's	BAGO 3-8-11 (10/1)	T Gillet	J E Pease	Cherry Mix	Ouija Board	13	2 33.00
2005	M Tabor's	HURRICANE RUN 3-8-11 (11/4)	K Fallon	A Fabre	Westerner	Bago	15	2 27.40
2006	K Abdullah's	RAIL LINK 3-8-11 (8/1)	S Pasquier	A Fabre	Pride	Hurricane Run	8	2 26.30
		(Deep Impact disqualified from third place)						
2007	Mrs J Magnier & M Tabor's	DYLAN THOMAS 4-9-5 (11/2)	K Fallon	A O'Brien	Youmzain	Sagara	12	2 28.50
2008	H H Aga Khan's	ZARKAVA 3-8-8 (13/8)	C Soumillon	A De Royer-Dupre	Youmzain	Soldier of Fortune/It's Gino	16	2 28.80
2009	C Tsui's	SEA THE STARS 3-8-11 (4/6)	M Kinane	J Oxx	Youmzain	Cavalryman	19	2 26.30
2010	K Abdullah's	WORKFORCE 3-8-11 (6/1)	R Moore	Sir M Stoute	Nakayama Festa	Sarafina	18	2 35.30
2011	Gestut Burg Eberstein & T Yoshida's	DANEDREAM 3-8-8 (20/1)	A Starke	P Schiergen	Shareta	Snow Fairy	16	2 24.49
2012	Wertheimer & Frere's	SOLEMIA 4-9-2 (33/1)	O Pesier	C Laffon-Parias	Orfevre	Masterstroke	18	3 37.68
2013	H E Sheikh Joaan Bin Hamad...	TREVE 3-8-8 (9/2)	T Jarnet	Mme C Head-Maarek	Orfevre	Intello	17	2 32.04
2014	Al Thani's	TREVE 4-9-2 (11/1)	T Jarnet	Mme C Head-Maarek	Flintshire	Taghrooda	20	2 26.05
2015	A E Oppenheimer's	GOLDEN HORN 3-8-11 (9/2)	L Dettori	J Gosden	Flintshire	New Bay	17	2 27.23
2016	M Tabor, D Smith & Mrs J Magnier's	FOUND 4-9-2 (6/1)	R Moore	A O'Brien	Highland Reel	Order of St George	16	2 23.61
2017	K Abdullah's (Run at Chantilly)	ENABLE 3-8-9 (10/11)	L Dettori	J Gosden	Cloth of Stars	Ulysses	18	2 28.69
2018	K Abdullah's (Run at Chantilly)	ENABLE 4-9-2 (Evs)	L Dettori	J Gosden	Sea Of Class	Cloth Of Stars	19	2 29.24

GRAND NATIONAL STEEPLECHASE Aintree 4m 2f 74y (4m 4f before 2013)

Year	Winner and Price	Age & Weight	Jockey	Second	Third	Ran	Time
1973	RED RUM (9/1)	8 10 5	B Fletcher	Crisp	L'Escargot	38	9 01.90
1974	RED RUM (11/1)	9 12 0	B Fletcher	L'Escargot	Charles Dickens	42	9 20.30
1975	L'ESCARGOT (13/2)	12 11 3	T Carberry	Red Rum	Spanish Steps	31	9 31.10
1976	RAG TRADE (14/1)	10 10 12	J Burke	Red Rum	Eyecatcher	32	9 20.90
1977	RED RUM (9/1)	12 11 8	T Stack	Churchtown Boy	Eyecatcher	42	9 30.30
1978	LUCIUS (14/1)	9 10 9	B R Davies	Sebastian V	Drumroan	37	9 33.90
1979	RUBSTIC (25/1)	10 10 0	M Barnes	Zongalero	Rough and Tumble	34	9 52.90
1980	BEN NEVIS (40/1)	12 10 12	Mr C Fenwick	Rough and Tumble	The Pilgarlic	30	10 17.40
1981	ALDANITI (10/1)	11 10 13	R Champion	Spartan Missile	Royal Mail	39	9 47.20
1982	GRITTAR (7/1)	9 11 5	Mr D Saunders	Hard Outlook	Loving Words	39	9 12.60
1983	CORBIERE (13/1)	8 11 4	B de Haan	Greasepaint	Yer Man	41	9 47.04
1984	HALLO DANDY (13/1)	10 10 2	N Doughty	Greasepaint	Corbiere	40	9 21.04
1985	LAST SUSPECT (50/1)	11 10 5	H Davies	Mr Snugfit	Corbiere	40	9 42.70
1986	WEST TIP (15/2)	9 10 11	R Dunwoody	Young Driver	Classified	40	9 33.00
1987	MAORI VENTURE (28/1)	11 10 13	S Knight	The Tsarevich	Lean Ar Aghaidh	40	9 19.30
1988	RHYME 'N' REASON (10/1)	9 11 0	B Powell	Durham Edition	Monanore	40	9 53.50
1989	LITTLE POLVEIR (28/1)	12 10 3	J Frost	West Tip	The Thinker	40	10 06.80
1990	MR FRISK (16/1)	11 10 6	Mr M Armytage	Durham Edition	Rinus	38	8 47.80
1991	SEAGRAM (12/1)	11 10 6	N Hawke	Garrison Savannah	Auntie Dot	40	9 29.90
1992	PARTY POLITICS (14/1)	8 10 7	C Llewellyn	Romany King	Laura's Beau	40	9 06.30
1993	Race Void - false start						
1994	MINNEHOMA (16/1)	11 10 8	R Dunwoody	Just So	Moorcroft Boy	36	10 18.80
1995	ROYAL ATHLETE (40/1)	12 10 6	J Tilley	Party Politics	Over The Deel	35	9 04.00
1996	ROUGH QUEST (7/1)	10 10 7	M Fitzgerald	Encore Un Peu	Superior Finish	27	9 00.80
1997	LORD GYLLENE (14/1)	9 10 0	A Dobbin	Suny Bay	Camelot Knight	36	9 05.80
1998	EARTH SUMMIT (7/1)	10 10 5	C Llewellyn	Suny Bay	Samlee	37	10 51.40
1999	BOBBYJO (10/1)	9 10 0	P Carberry	Blue Charm	Call It A Day	32	9 14.00
2000	PAPILLON (10/1)	9 10 12	R Walsh	Mely Moss	Niki Dee	40	9 09.70
2001	RED MARAUDER (33/1)	11 10 11	R Guest	Smarty	Blowing Wind	40	11 00.10
2002	BINDAREE (20/1)	8 10 4	J Culloty	What's Up Boys	Blowing Wind	40	9 09.70
2003	MONTY'S PASS (16/1)	10 10 7	B J Geraghty	Supreme Glory	Amberleigh House	40	9 21.70
2004	AMBERLEIGH HOUSE (16/1)	12 10 10	G Lee	Clan Royal	Lord Atterbury	39	9 20.80
2005	HEDGEHUNTER (7/1)	9 11 1	R Walsh	Royal Auclair	Simply Gifted	40	9 20.30
2006	NUMBERSIXVALVERDE (11/1)	10 10 8	R Madden	Hedgehunter	Clan Royal	40	9 41.60
2007	SILVER BIRCH (33/1)	10 10 9	R M Power	McKelvey	Slim Pickings	40	9 13.60
2008	COMPLY OR DIE (7/1)	9 11 0	T Murphy	King Johns Castle	Snowy Morning	40	9 16.60
2009	MON MOME (100/1)	9 11 0	L Treadwell	Comply Or Die	My Will	40	9 32.90
2010	DON'T PUSH IT (10/1)	11 10 11	A P McCoy	Black Apalachi	State Of Play	40	9 04.60
2011	BALLABRIGGS (14/1)	10 11 0	J Maguire	Oscar Time	Don't Push It	40	9 01.20
2012	NEPTUNE COLLONGES (33/1)	11 11 6	D Jacob	Sunnyhillboy	Seabass	40	9 05.10
2013	AURORAS ENCORE (66/1)	11 10 3	R Mania	Cappa Bleu	Teaforthree	40	8 56.80
2014	PINEAU DE RE (25/1)	11 10 6	L Aspell	Balthazar King	Double Seven	40	9 00.90
2015	MANY CLOUDS (25/1)	8 11 9	L Aspell	Saint Are	Monbeg Dude	40	9 29.00
2016	RULE THE WORLD (33/1)	9 11 0	D Mullins	The Last Samuri	Vics Canvas	39	9 03.50
2017	ONE FOR ARTHUR (14/1)	8 10 7	D Fox	Cause of Causes	Saint Are	39	9 40.10
2018	TIGER ROLL (10/1)	8 10 13	D Russell	Pleasant Company	Bless The Wings	38	9 06.70

WINNERS OF GREAT RACES

LINCOLN HANDICAP
Doncaster-1m

2009	**EXPRESSO STAR** 4-8-12	20
2010	**PENITENT** 4-9-2	21
2011	**SWEET LIGHTNING** 6-9-4	21
2012	**BRAE HILL** 6-9-1	22
2013	**LEVITATE** 5-8-4	22
2014	**OCEAN TEMPEST** 5-9-3	17
2015	**GABRIAL** 6-9-0	22
2016	**SECRET BRIEF** 4-9-4	22
2017	**BRAVERY** 4-9-1	22
2018	**ADDEYBB** 4-9-2	20

GREENHAM STAKES (3y)
Newbury-7f

2009	**VOCALISED** 9-0	8
2010	**DICK TURPIN** 9-0	5
2011	**FRANKEL** 9-0	5
2012	**CASPAR NETSCHER** 9-0	5
2013	**OLYMPIC GLORY** 9-0	5
2014	**KINGMAN** 9-0	10
2015	**MUHAARAR** 9-0	9
*2016	**TASLEET** 9-0	3
2017	**BARNEY ROY** 9-0	10
2018	**JAMES GARFIELD** 9-0	7

*Run at Chelmsford City on Polytrack

EUROPEAN FREE HANDICAP (3y)
Newmarket-7f

2009	**OUQBA** 8-9	10
2010	**RED JAZZ** 9-6	7
2011	**PAUSANIAS** 8-12	7
2012	**TELWAAR** 8-11	6
2013	**GARSWOOD** 9-0	7
2014	**SHIFTING POWER** 9-1	6
2015	**HOME OF THE BRAVE** 8-13	5
2016	**IBN MALIK** 9-6	6
2017	**WHITECLIFFSOFDOVER** 9-7	7
2018	**ANNA NERIUM** 8-11	10

CRAVEN STAKES (3y)
Newmarket-1m

2009	**DELEGATOR** 8-12	7
2010	**ELUSIVE PIMPERNEL** 8-12	9
2011	**NATIVE KHAN** 8-12	6
2012	**TRUMPET MAJOR** 9-1	12
2013	**TORONADO** 9-1	4
2014	**TOORMORE** 9-3	6
2015	**KOOL KOMPANY** 9-3	9
2016	**STORMY ANTARCTIC** 9-0	6
2017	**EMINENT** 9-0	7
2018	**MASAR** 9-0	6

JOCKEY CLUB STAKES
Newmarket-1m 4f

2009	**BRONZE CANNON** 4-8-12	3
2010	**JUKEBOX JURY** 4-9-3	5
2011	**DANDINO** 4-8-11	6
2012	**AL KAZEEM** 4-8-12	8
2013	**UNIVERSAL** 4-8-12	4
2014	**GOSPEL CHOIR** 5-9-0	8
2015	**SECOND STEP** 4-9-0	4

2016	**EXOSPHERE** 4-9-0	6
2017	**SEVENTH HEAVEN** 4-9-1	5
2018	**DEFOE** 4-9-1	5

SANDOWN MILE
Sandown-1m

2009	**PACO BOY** 4-9-6	7
2010	**PACO BOY** 5-9-0	9
2011	**DICK TURPIN** 4-9-0	5
2012	**PENITENT** 6-9-0	6
2013	**TRUMPET MAJOR** 4-9-0	7
2014	**TULLIUS** 6-9-1	6
2015	**CUSTOM CUT** 6-9-5	6
2016	**TOORMORE** 5-9-0	7
2017	**SOVEREIGN DEBT** 8-9-1	9
2018	**ADDEYBB** 4-9-1	8

CHESTER VASE (3y)
Chester-1m 4f 63yds

2009	**GOLDEN SWORD** 8-12	8
2010	**TED SPREAD** 8-12	7
2011	**TREASURE BEACH** 8-12	5
2012	**MICKDAAM** 8-12	5
2013	**RULER OF THE WORLD** 8-12	4
2014	**ORCHESTRA** 9-0	6
2015	**HANS HOLBEIN** 9-0	8
2016	**US ARMY RANGER** 9-0	6
2017	**VENICE BEACH** 9-0	8
2018	**YOUNG RASCAL** 9-0	10

CHESTER CUP
Chester-2m 2f 140yds

2009	**DARAAHEM** 4-9-0	17
2010	**MAMLOOK** 8-12	17
2011	**OVERTURN** 7-8-13	17
2012	**ILE DE RE** 6-8-11	16
2013	**ADDRESS UNKNOWN** 6-9-0	17
2014	**SUEGIOO** 5-9-4	17
2015	**TRIP TO PARIS** 4-8-9	17
2016	**NO HERETIC** 8-8-13	17
2017	**MONTALY** 6-9-6	17
2018	**MAGIC CIRCLE** 6-9-3	16

OAKS TRIAL (3y fillies)
Lingfield-1m 3f 133yds

2009	**MIDDAY** 8-12	9
2010	**DYNA WALTZ** 8-12	5
2011	**ZAIN AL BOLDAN** 8-12	9
*2012	**VOW** 8-12	8
2013	**SECRET GESTURE** 8-12	7
2014	**HONOR BOUND** 8-12	10
2015	**TOUJOURS L'AMOUR** 9-0	10
2016	**SEVENTH HEAVEN** 9-0	5
2017	**HERTFORD DANCER** 9-0	6
2018	**PERFECT CLARITY** 9-0	7

*Run over 1m4f on Polytrack

DERBY TRIAL (3y)
Lingfield-1m 3f 133yds

2009	**AGE OF AQUARIUS** 8-12	5
2010	**BULLET TRAIN** 8-12	7
2011	**DORDOGNE** 8-12	6

*2012 **MAIN SEQUENCE** 8-12......................8
2013 **NEVIS** 8-12......................4
2014 **SNOW SKY** 9-0......................9
2015 **KILIMANJARO** 9-0......................5
2016 **HUMPHREY BOGART** 9-0......................5
2017 **BEST SOLUTION** 9-5......................8
2018 **KNIGHT TO BEHOLD** 9-0......................9
*Run over 1m4f on Polytrack

MUSIDORA STAKES (3y fillies)
York-1m 2f 56yds
2009 **SARISKA** 8-12......................6
2010 **AVIATE** 8-12......................8
2011 **JOVIALITY** 8-12......................5
2012 **THE FUGUE** 8-12......................6
2013 **LIBER NAUTICUS** 8-12......................6
2014 **MADAME CHIANG** 9-0......................9
2015 **STAR OF SEVILLE** 9-0......................5
2016 **SO MI DAR** 9-0......................7
2017 **SHUTTER SPEED** 9-0......................5
2018 **GIVE AND TAKE** 9-0......................7

DANTE STAKES (3y)
York-1m 2f 56yds
2009 **BLACK BEAR ISLAND** 9-0......................10
2010 **CAPE BLANCO** 9-0......................5
2011 **CARLTON HOUSE** 9-0......................6
2012 **BONFIRE** 9-0......................7
2013 **LIBERTARIAN** 9-0......................8
2014 **THE GREY GATSBY** 9-0......................6
2015 **GOLDEN HORN** 9-0......................7
2016 **WINGS OF DESIRE** 9-0......................12
2017 **PERMIAN** 9-0......................10
2018 **ROARING LION** 9-0......................9

MIDDLETON STAKES
(fillies and mares)
York-1m 2f 56yds
2009 **CRYSTAL CAPELLA** 4-9-2......................5
2010 **SARISKA** 4-8-12......................4
2011 **MIDDAY** 5-9-3......................8
2012 **IZZI TOP** 4-8-12......................9
2013 **DALKALA** 4-9-0......................8
2014 **AMBIVALENT** 5-9-0......................8
2015 **SECRET GESTURE** 5-9-0......................8
2016 **BEAUTIFUL ROMANCE** 4-9-0......................7
2017 **BLOND ME** 5-9-0......................4
2018 **CORONET** 4-9-0......................7

YORKSHIRE CUP
York-1m 5f 188yds
2009 **ASK** 6-8-13......................8
2010 **MANIFEST** 4-8-12......................5
2011 **DUNCAN** 6-9-2......................8
2012 **RED CADEAUX** 6-9-0......................8
2013 **GLEN'S DIAMOND** 5-9-0......................8
2014 **GOSPEL CHOIR** 5-9-0......................12
2015 **SNOW SKY** 4-9-0......................6
2016 **CLEVER COOKIE** 8-9-1......................5
2017 **DARTMOUTH** 5-9-0......................8
2018 **STRADIVARIUS** 4-9-1......................8

DUKE OF YORK STAKES
York-6f
2009 **UTMOST RESPECT** 5-9-7......................16
2010 **PRIME DEFENDER** 6-9-7......................12
2011 **DELEGATOR** 5-9-7......................14
2012 **TIDDLIWINKS** 6-9-7......................13
2013 **SOCIETY ROCK** 6-9-13......................17
2014 **MAAREK** 7-9-13......................13
2015 **GLASS OFFICE** 5-9-8......................15
2016 **MAGICAL MEMORY** 4-9-8......................12
2017 **TASLEET** 4-9-8......................12
2018 **HARRY ANGEL** 4-9-13......................5

LOCKINGE STAKES
Newbury-1m
2009 **VIRTUAL** 4-9-0......................11
2010 **PACO BOY** 5-9-0......................9
2011 **CANFORD CLIFFS** 4-9-0......................7
2012 **FRANKEL** 4-9-0......................6
2013 **FARHH** 5-9-0......................12
2014 **OLYMPIC GLORY** 4-9-0......................8
2015 **NIGHT OF THUNDER** 4-9-0......................16
2016 **BELARDO** 4-9-0......................12
2017 **RIBCHESTER** 4-9-0......................8
2018 **RHODODENDRON** 4-8-11......................14

HENRY II STAKES
Sandown-2m 50yds
2009 **GEORDIELAND** 8-9-2......................7
2010 **AKMAL** 4-9-0......................9
2011 **BLUE BAJAN** 9-9-2......................8
2012 **OPINION POLL** 6-9-4......................10
2013 **GLOOMY SUNDAY** 4-8-11......................10
2014 **BROWN PANTHER** 6-9-4......................11
2015 **VENT DE FORCE** 4-9-0......................7
2016 **PALLASATOR** 7-9-6......................9
2017 **BIG ORANGE** 6-9-2......................7
2018 **MAGIC CIRCLE** 6-9-2......................8

TEMPLE STAKES
Haydock-5f
2009 **LOOK BUSY** 4-9-1......................9
2010 **KINGSGATE NATIVE** 5-9-4......................9
2011 **SOLE POWER** 4-9-0......................12
2012 **BATED BREATH** 5-9-4......................12
2013 **KINGSGATE NATIVE** 8-9-4......................10
2014 **HOT STREAK** 3-8-10......................9
2015 **PEARL SECRET** 6-9-4......................11
2016 **PROFITABLE** 4-9-4......................11
2017 **PRICELESS** 4-9-0......................12
2018 **BATTAASH** 4-9-9......................11

BRIGADIER GERARD STAKES
Sandown-1m 1f 209yds
2009 **CIMA DE TRIOMPHE** 4-9-0......................12
2010 **STOTSFOLD** 7-9-0......................8
2011 **WORKFORCE** 4-9-7......................8
2012 **CARLTON HOUSE** 4-9-0......................6
2013 **MUKHADRAM** 4-9-0......................5
2014 **SHARESTAN** 6-9-0......................3
2015 **WESTERN HYMN** 4-9-3......................5
2016 **TIME TEST** 4-9-0......................7
2017 **AUTOCRATIC** 4-9-0......................7
2018 **POET'S WORD** 5-9-0......................5

CORONATION CUP
Epsom-1m 4f 6yds
2009	**ASK** 6-9-0	8
2010	**FAME AND GLORY** 4-9-0	9
2011	**ST NICHOLAS ABBEY** 4-9-0	5
2012	**ST NICHOLAS ABBEY** 5-9-0	6
2013	**ST NICHOLAS ABBEY** 6-9-0	5
2014	**CIRRUS DES AIGLES** 8-9-0	7
2015	**PETHER'S MOON** 5-9-0	4
2016	**POSTPONED** 5-9-0	8
2017	**HIGHLAND REEL** 5-9-0	10
2018	**CRACKSMAN** 4-9-0	6

CHARITY SPRINT HANDICAP (3y)
York-6f
2009	**SWISS DIVA** 9-1	20
2010	**VICTOIRE DE LYPHAR** 8-7	20
2011	**LEXI'S HERO** 8-11	20
2012	**SHOLAAN** 8-9	17
2013	**BODY AND SOUL** 8-11	19
2014	**SEE THE SUN** 8-7	20
2015	**TWILIGHT SON** 8-10	16
2016	**MR LUPTON** 9-7	17
2017	**GOLDEN APOLLO** 8-3	18
2018	**ENCRYPTED** 8-8	20

QUEEN ANNE STAKES
Ascot-1m (st)
2009	**PACO BOY** 4-9-0	9
2010	**GOLDIKOVA** 5-8-11	10
2011	**CANFORD CLIFFS** 4-9-0	7
2012	**FRANKEL** 4-9-0	11
2013	**DECLARATION OF WAR** 4-9-0	13
2014	**TORONADO** 4-9-0	10
2015	**SOLOW** 5-9-0	8
2016	**TEPIN** 5-8-11	13
2017	**RIBCHESTER** 4-9-0	16
2018	**ACCIDENTAL AGENT** 4-9-0	15

PRINCE OF WALES'S STAKES
Ascot-1m 2f
2009	**VISION D'ETAT** 4-9-0	8
2010	**BYWORD** 4-9-0	12
2011	**REWILDING** 4-9-0	7
2012	**SO YOU THINK** 6-9-0	11
2013	**AL KAZEEM** 5-9-0	11
2014	**THE FUGUE** 5-8-11	8
2015	**FREE EAGLE** 4-9-0	9
2016	**MY DREAM BOAT** 4-9-0	6
2017	**HIGHLAND REEL** 5-9-0	8
2018	**POET'S WORD** 5-9-0	7

ST JAMES'S PALACE STAKES (3y)
Ascot-7f 213yds (rnd)
2009	**MASTERCRAFTSMAN** 9-0	10
2010	**CANFORD CLIFFS** 9-0	9
2011	**FRANKEL** 9-0	9
2012	**MOST IMPROVED** 9-0	16
2013	**DAWN APPROACH** 9-0	9
2014	**KINGMAN** 9-0	7
2015	**GLENEAGLES** 9-0	5
2016	**GALILEO GOLD** 9-0	7
2017	**BARNEY ROY** 9-0	8
2018	**WITHOUT PAROLE** 9-0	10

COVENTRY STAKES (2y)
Ascot-6f
2009	**CANFORD CLIFFS** 9-1	13
2010	**STRONG SUIT** 9-1	13
2011	**POWER** 9-1	23
2012	**DAWN APPROACH** 9-1	22
2013	**WAR COMMAND** 9-1	15
2014	**THE WOW SIGNAL** 9-1	15
2015	**BURATINO** 9-1	17
2016	**CARAVAGGIO** 9-1	18
2017	**RAJASINGHE** 9-1	18
2018	**CALYX** 9-1	23

KING EDWARD VII STAKES (3y)
Ascot-1m 4f
2009	**FATHER TIME** 8-12	12
2010	**MONTEROSSO** 8-12	8
2011	**NATHANIEL** 8-12	10
2012	**THOMAS CHIPPENDALE** 8-12	5
2013	**HILLSTAR** 8-12	8
2014	**EAGLE TOP** 9-0	9
2015	**BALIOS** 9-0	7
2016	**ACROSS THE STARS** 9-0	9
2017	**PERMIAN** 9-0	12
2018	**OLD PERSIAN** 9-0	9

JERSEY STAKES (3y)
Ascot-7f
2009	**OUQBA** 9-1	16
2010	**RAINFALL** 8-12	13
2011	**STRONG SUIT** 9-6	9
2012	**ISHVANA** 8-12	22
2013	**GALE FORCE TEN** 9-1	21
2014	**MUSTAJEEB** 9-4	23
2015	**DUTCH CONNECTION** 9-4	16
2016	**RIBCHESTER** 9-6	19
2017	**LE BRIVIDO** 9-1	20
2018	**EXPERT EYE** 9-1	21

DUKE OF CAMBRIDGE STAKES
(fillies & mares)
Ascot-1m (st)
(Windsor Forest Stakes before 2013)
2009	**SPACIOUS** 4-8-12	9
2010	**STRAWBERRYDAIQUIRI** 4-8-12	10
2011	**LOLLY FOR DOLLY** 4-8-12	13
2012	**JOVIALITY** 4-8-12	13
2013	**DUNTLE** 4-8-12	9
2014	**INTEGRAL** 4-9-0	14
2015	**AMAZING MARIA** 4-9-0	6
2016	**USHERETTE** 4-9-3	14
2017	**QEMAH** 4-9-0	14
2018	**ALJAZZI** 5-9-0	11

QUEEN MARY STAKES (2y fillies)
Ascot-5f
2009	**JEALOUS AGAIN** 8-12	13
2010	**MAQAASID** 8-12	18
2011	**BEST TERMS** 8-12	14
2012	**CEILING KITTY** 8-12	27
2013	**RIZEENA** 8-12	23
2014	**ANTHEM ALEXANDER** 9-0	21
2015	**ACAPULCO** 9-0	20
2016	**LADY AURELIA** 9-0	17
2017	**HEARTACHE** 9-0	23
2018	**SIGNORA CABELLO** 9-0	22

CORONATION STAKES (3y fillies)
Ascot-7f 213yds (rnd)
```
2009  GHANAATI 9-0 ........................................10
2010  LILLIE LANGTRY 9-0 ...............................13
2011  IMMORTAL VERSE 9-0 ..............................12
2012  FALLEN FOR YOU 9-0 ...............................10
2013  SKY LANTERN 9-0 ....................................17
2014  RIZEENA 9-0 ............................................12
2015  ERVEDYA 9-0 .............................................9
2016  QEMAH 9-0 ..............................................13
2017  WINTER 9-0 ...............................................7
2018  ALPHA CENTAURI 9-0 ..............................12
```

COMMONWEALTH CUP (3y)
Ascot-6f
```
2015  MUHAARAR 9-3 ........................................18
2016  QUIET REFLECTION 9-0 ...........................10
2017  CARAVAGGIO 9-3 .....................................12
2018  EQTIDAAR 9-3 ..........................................22
```

ROYAL HUNT CUP
Ascot-1m (st)
```
2009  FORGOTTEN VOICE 4-9-1 .........................25
2010  INVISIBLE MAN 4-8-9 ..............................29
2011  JULIENAS 4-8-8 .......................................28
2012  PRINCE OF JOHANNE 6-9-3 .....................30
2013  BELGIAN BILL 5-8-11 ..............................28
2014  FIELD OF DREAM 7-9-1 ............................28
2015  GM HOPKINS 4-9-3 ..................................30
2016  PORTAGE 4-9-5 ........................................28
2017  ZHUI FENG 4-9-0 .....................................29
2018  SETTLE FOR BAY 4-9-1 ............................30
```

QUEEN'S VASE (3y)
Ascot-1m 5f 211yds (2m before 2017)
```
2009  HOLBERG 9-1 ...........................................14
2010  MIKHAIL GLINKA 9-1 ...............................12
2011  NAMIBIAN 9-1 ..........................................11
2012  ESTIMATE 9-0 ..........................................10
2013  LEADING LIGHT 9-4 .................................15
2014  HARTNELL 9-3 ..........................................10
2015  ALOFT 9-3 ................................................13
2016  SWORD FIGHTER 9-3 ...............................18
2017  STRADIVARIUS 9-0 ..................................13
2018  KEW GARDENS 9-0 ...................................12
```

DIAMOND JUBILEE STAKES
Ascot-6f
(Golden Jubilee Stakes before 2012)
```
2009  ART CONNOISSEUR 3-8-11 .......................14
2010  STARSPANGLEDBANNER 4-9-4 .................24
2011  SOCIETY ROCK 4-9-4 ...............................16
2012  BLACK CAVIAR 6-9-1 ...............................14
2013  LETHAL FORCE 4-9-4 ...............................18
2014  SLADE POWER 5-9-4 ................................14
2015  UNDRAFTED 5-9-3 ...................................15
2016  TWILIGHT SON 4-9-3 .................................9
2017  THE TIN MAN 5-9-3 ..................................19
2018  MERCHANT NAVY 3-9-3 ............................12
```

NORFOLK STAKES (2y)
Ascot-5f
```
2009  RADIOHEAD 9-1 ........................................11
2010  APPROVE 9-1 ............................................12
2011  BAPAK CHINTA 9-1 ..................................15
2012  RECKLESS ABANDON 9-1 ..........................11
```

```
2013  NO NAY NEVER 9-1 ...................................14
2014  BAITHA ALGA 9-1 .......................................9
2015  WATERLOO BRIDGE 9-1 ...........................10
2016  PRINCE OF LIR 9-1 ...................................11
2017  SIOUX NATION 9-1 ...................................17
2018  SHANG SHANG SHANG 8-12 ....................10
```

GOLD CUP
Ascot-2m 4f
```
2009  YEATS 8-9-2 ..............................................9
2010  RITE OF PASSAGE 6-9-2 ...........................12
2011  FAME AND GLORY 5-9-2 ...........................15
2012  COLOUR VISION 4-9-0 ................................9
2013  ESTIMATE 4-8-11 .....................................14
2014  LEADING LIGHT 4-9-0 ...............................12
2015  TRIP TO PARIS 4-9-0 ...............................12
2016  ORDER OF ST GEORGE 4-9-0 ...................17
2017  BIG ORANGE 6-9-2 ..................................14
2018  STRADIVARIUS 4-9-1 .................................9
```

RIBBLESDALE STAKES (3y fillies)
Ascot-1m 4f
```
2009  FLYING CLOUD 8-12 ................................10
2010  HIBAAYEB 8-12 ........................................11
2011  BANIMPIRE 8-12 ......................................12
2012  PRINCESS HIGHWAY 8-12 .......................14
2013  RIPOSTE 8-12 ............................................9
2014  BRACELET 9-0 .........................................12
2015  CURVY 9-0 ...............................................10
2016  EVEN SONG 9-0 .......................................14
2017  CORONET 9-0 ...........................................12
2018  MAGIC WAND 9-0 .....................................10
```

HARDWICKE STAKES
Ascot-1m 4f
```
2009  BRONZE CANNON 4-9-3 .............................9
2010  HARBINGER 4-9-0 ....................................11
2011  AWAIT THE DAWN 4-9-0 .............................9
2012  SEA MOON 4-9-0 ......................................12
2013  THOMAS CHIPPENDALE 4-9-0 ...................8
2014  TELESCOPE 4-9-1 ....................................10
2015  SNOW SKY 4-9-1 .......................................7
2016  DARTMOUTH 4-9-1 ...................................10
2017  IDAHO 4-9-1 ............................................12
2018  CRYSTAL OCEAN 4-9-1 ..............................5
```

WOKINGHAM STAKES
Ascot-6f
```
2009  HIGH STANDING 4-8-12 ...........................26
2010  LADDIES POKER TWO 5-8-11 ....................27
2011  DEACON BLUES 4-8-13 ...........................25
2012  DANDY BOY 6-9-8 ....................................28
2013  YORK GLORY 5-9-2 ..................................26
2014  BACCARAT 5-9-2 .....................................28
2015  INTERCEPTION 5-9-3 ...............................25
2016  OUTBACK TRAVELLER 5-9-1 ....................28
2017  OUT DO 8-8-13 .........................................27
2018  BACCHUS 4-9-6 .......................................28
```

KING'S STAND STAKES
Ascot-5f
```
2009  SCENIC BLAST 5-9-4 ...............................15
2010  EQUIANO 5-9-4 ........................................12
2011  PROHIBIT 6-9-4 .......................................19
2012  LITTLE BRIDGE 6-9-4 ..............................22
2013  SOLE POWER 6-9-4 .................................19
2014  SOLE POWER 7-9-4 .................................16
```

2013	FIELD OF DREAM 6-9-7	19
2014	HEAVEN'S GUEST 4-9-3	13
2015	RENE MATHIS 5-9-1	17
2016	GOLDEN STEPS 5-9-0	16
2017	ABOVE THE REST 6-8-10	18
2018	BURNT SUGAR 5-9-1	18

NORTHUMBERLAND PLATE
Newcastle-2m 56y Tapeta (2m 19y turf before 2016)

2009	SOM TALA 6-8-8	17
2010	OVERTURN 6-8-7	19
2011	TOMINATOR 4-8-5	19
2012	ILE DE RE 6-9-3	16
2013	TOMINATOR 6-9-10	18
2014	ANGEL GABRIAL 5-8-12	19
2015	QUEST FOR MORE 5-9-4	19
2016	ANTIQUARIUM 4-9-5	20
2017	HIGHER POWER 5-9-9	20
2018	WITHHOLD 5-9-1	20

ECLIPSE STAKES
Sandown-1m 1f 209yds

2009	SEA THE STARS 3-8-10	10
2010	TWICE OVER 5-9-7	5
2011	SO YOU THINK 5-9-7	5
2012	NATHANIEL 4-9-7	9
2013	AL KAZEEM 5-9-7	7
2014	MUKHADRAM 5-9-7	7
2015	GOLDEN HORN 3-8-10	5
2016	HAWKBILL 3-8-10	7
2017	ULYSSES 4-9-7	7
2018	ROARING LION 3-8-11	7

LANCASHIRE OAKS (fillies and mares)
Haydock-1m 3f 175yds

2009	BARSHIBA 5-9-5	8
2010	BARSHIBA 6-9-5	10
2011	GERTRUDE BELL 4-9-5	7
2012	GREAT HEAVENS 3-8-6	9
2013	EMIRATES QUEEN 4-9-5	8
2014	POMOLOGY 4-9-5	9
2015	LADY TIANA 4-9-5	10
2016	ENDLESS TIME 4-9-5	6
2017	THE BLACK PRINCESS 4-9-5	7
2018	HORSEPLAY 4-9-5	7

DUCHESS OF CAMBRIDGE STAKES (2y fillies)
Newmarket-6f
(Cherry Hinton Stakes before 2013)

2009	MISHEER 8-12	10
2010	MEMORY 8-12	7
2011	GAMILATI 8-12	11
2012	SENDMYLOVETOROSE 8-12	10
2013	LUCKY KRISTALE 8-12	8
2014	ARABIAN QUEEN 9-0	5
2015	ILLUMINATE 9-0	9
2016	ROLY POLY 9-0	10
2017	CLEMMIE 9-0	8
2018	PRETTY POLLYANNA 9-0	9

BUNBURY CUP
(Run as 32Red Trophy in 2010)
Newmarket-7f

2009	PLUM PUDDING 6-9-10	19
2010	ST MORITZ 4-9-1	19
2011	BRAE HILL 5-9-1	20
2012	BONNIE BRAE 5-9-9	15

PRINCESS OF WALES'S STAKES
Newmarket-1m 4f

2009	DOCTOR FREMANTLE 4-9-2	9
2010	SANS FRONTIERES 4-9-2	8
2011	CRYSTAL CAPELLA 6-8-13	8
2012	FIORENTE 4-9-2	7
2013	AL KAZEEM 4-9-5	6
2014	CAVALRYMAN 8-9-2	6
2015	BIG ORANGE 4-9-2	8
2016	BIG ORANGE 5-9-2	7
2017	HAWKBILL 4-9-2	6
2018	BEST SOLUTION 4-9-6	7

JULY STAKES (2y)
Newmarket-6f

2009	ARCANO 8-12	11
2010	LIBRANNO 8-12	5
2011	FREDERICK ENGELS 8-12	7
2012	ALHEBAYEB 8-12	7
2013	ANJAAL 8-12	11
2014	IVAWOOD 9-0	12
2015	SHALAA 9-0	9
2016	MEHMAS 9-0	9
2017	CARDSHARP 9-0	12
2018	ADVERTISE 9-0	8

FALMOUTH STAKES (fillies & mares)
Newmarket-1m

2009	GOLDIKOVA 4-9-5	8
2010	MUSIC SHOW 3-8-10	8
2011	TIMEPIECE 4-9-5	11
2012	GIOFRA 4-9-5	10
2013	ELUSIVE KATE 4-9-5	4
2014	INTEGRAL 4-9-7	7
2015	AMAZING MARIA 4-9-7	7
2016	ALICE SPRINGS 3-8-12	7
2017	ROLY POLY 3-8-12	7
2018	ALPHA CENTAURI 3-8-12	7

SUPERLATIVE STAKES (2y)
Newmarket-7f

2009	SILVER GRECIAN 9-0	8
2010	KING TORUS 9-0	6
2011	RED DUKE 9-0	11
2012	OLYMPIC GLORY 9-0	9
2013	GOOD OLD BOY LUKEY 9-0	8
2014	ESTIDHKAAR 9-1	8
2015	BIRCHWOOD 9-1	8
2016	BOYNTON 9-1	9
2017	GUSTAV KLIMT 9-1	10
2018	QUORTO 9-1	7

JULY CUP
Newmarket-6f

2009	FLEETING SPIRIT 4-9-2	13
2010	STARSPANGLEDBANNER 4-9-5	14
2011	DREAM AHEAD 3-8-13	16
2012	MAYSON 4-9-5	12
2013	LETHAL FORCE 4-9-5	11
2014	SLADE POWER 5-9-6	13

2015 **MUHAARAR** 3-9-0	14
2016 **LIMATO** 4-9-6	18
2017 **HARRY ANGEL** 3-9-0	10
2018 **U S NAVY FLAG** 3-9-0	13

WEATHERBYS SUPER SPRINT (2y)
Newbury-5f 34 yds

2009 **MONSIEUR CHEVALIER** 8-12	20
2010 **TEMPLE MEADS** 8-6	24
2011 **CHARLES THE GREAT** 8-11	25
2012 **BODY AND SOUL** 7-12	22
2013 **PENIAPHOBIA** 8-8	24
2014 **TIGGY WIGGY** 9-1	24
2015 **LATHOM** 9-0	22
2016 **MRS DANVERS** 8-0	23
2017 **BENGALI BOYS** 8-7	23
2018 **GINGER NUT** 8-5	25

SUMMER MILE
Ascot-7f 213yds (rnd)

2009 **AQLAAM** 4-9-1	7
2010 **PREMIO LOCO** 6-9-1	8
2011 **DICK TURPIN** 4-9-4	5
2012 **FANUNALTER** 6-9-1	8
2013 **ALJAMAAHEER** 4-9-1	11
2014 **GUEST OF HONOUR** 5-9-1	9
2015 **AROD** 4-9-1	6
2016 **MUTAKAYYEF** 5-9-1	10
2017 **MUTAKAYYEF** 6-9-1	7
2018 **BEAT THE BANK** 4-9-1	8

PRINCESS MARGARET STAKES
(2y fillies)
Ascot-6f

2009 **LADY OF THE DESERT** 8-12	9
2010 **SORAAYA** 8-12	11
2011 **ANGELS WILL FALL** 8-12	7
2012 **MAUREEN** 8-12	6
2013 **PRINCESS NOOR** 8-12	10
2014 **OSAILA** 9-0	8
2015 **BESHARAH** 9-0	6
2016 **FAIR EVA** 9-0	12
2017 **NYALETI** 9-0	7
2018 **ANGEL'S HIDEAWAY** 9-0	7

LENNOX STAKES
Goodwood-7f

2009 **FINJAAN** 3-8-9	8
2010 **LORD SHANAKILL** 4-9-2	12
2011 **STRONG SUIT** 3-8-9	9
2012 **CHACHAMAIDEE** 5-8-13	7
2013 **GARSWOOD** 3-8-9	10
2014 **ES QUE LOVE** 5-9-3	7
2015 **TOORMORE** 4-9-3	7
2016 **DUTCH CONNECTION** 4-9-3	8
2017 **BRETON ROCK** 7-9-3	13
2018 **SIR DANCEALOT** 4-9-3	12

STEWARDS' CUP
Goodwood-6f

2009 **GENKI** 5-9-1	26
2010 **EVENS AND ODDS** 6-8-10	28
2011 **HOOF IT** 4-10-0	27
2012 **HAWKEYETHENOO** 6-9-9	27
2013 **REX IMPERATOR** 4-9-4	27
*2014 **INTRINSIC** 4-8-11	24

2015 **MAGICAL MEMORY** 3-8-12	27
2016 **DANCING STAR** 3-8-12	27
2017 **LANCELOT DU LAC** 7-9-5	26
2018 **GIFTED MASTER** 5-9-6	26

*Run as 32Red Cup in 2014

GORDON STAKES (3y)
Goodwood-1m 4f

2009 **HARBINGER** 9-0	9
2010 **REBEL SOLDIER** 9-0	10
2011 **NAMIBIAN** 9-3	10
2012 **NOBLE MISSION** 9-0	7
2013 **CAP O'RUSHES** 9-0	7
2014 **SNOW SKY** 9-1	7
2015 **HIGHLAND REEL** 9-1	9
2016 **ULYSSES** 9-1	9
2017 **CRYSTAL OCEAN** 9-1	5
2018 **CROSS COUNTER** 9-1	4

VINTAGE STAKES (2y)
Goodwood-7f

2009 **XTENSION** 9-0	10
2010 **KING TORUS** 9-3	7
2011 **CHANDLERY** 9-0	7
2012 **OLYMPIC GLORY** 9-3	8
2013 **TOORMORE** 9-0	12
2014 **HIGHLAND REEL** 9-1	8
2015 **GALILEO GOLD** 9-1	8
2016 **WAR DECREE** 9-1	9
2017 **EXPERT EYE** 9-1	10
2018 **DARK VISION** 9-1	12

SUSSEX STAKES
Goodwood-1m

2009 **RIP VAN WINKLE** 3-8-13	8
2010 **CANFORD CLIFFS** 3-8-13	7
2011 **FRANKEL** 3-8-13	4
2012 **FRANKEL** 4-9-7	4
2013 **TORONADO** 3-8-13	7
2014 **KINGMAN** 3-9-0	4
2015 **SOLOW** 5-9-8	8
2016 **THE GURKHA** 3-9-0	10
2017 **HERE COMES WHEN** 7-9-8	7
2018 **LIGHTNING SPEAR** 7-9-8	8

RICHMOND STAKES (2y)
Goodwood-6f

2009 **DICK TURPIN** 9-0	9
2010 **LIBRANNO** 9-3	6
2011 **HARBOUR WATCH** 9-0	10
2012 **HEAVY METAL** 9-0	8
2013 **SAAYERR** 9-0	10
2014 **IVAWOOD** 9-3	8
2015 **SHALAA** 9-3	8
2016 **MEHMAS** 9-3	4
2017 **BARRAQUERO** 9-0	7
2018 **LAND FORCE** 9-0	9

KING GEORGE STAKES
Goodwood-5f

2009 **KINGSGATE NATIVE** 4-9-0	17
2010 **BORDERLESCOTT** 8-9-0	15
2011 **MASAMAH** 5-9-0	11
2012 **ORTENSIA** 7-9-5	17
2013 **MOVIESTA** 3-8-12	17
2014 **TAKE COVER** 7-9-1	15
2015 **MUTHMIR** 5-9-6	15

2016	**TAKE COVER** 9-9-2	17
2017	**BATTAASH** 3-8-13	11
2018	**BATTAASH** 4-9-5	11

GOODWOOD CUP
Goodwood-2m

2009	**SCHIAPARELLI** 6-9-7	10
2010	**ILLUSTRIOUS BLUE** 7-9-7	10
2011	**OPINION POLL** 5-9-7	15
2012	**SADDLER'S ROCK** 4-9-7	10
2013	**BROWN PANTHER** 5-9-7	14
2014	**CAVALRYMAN** 8-9-8	8
2015	**BIG ORANGE** 4-9-8	11
2016	**BIG ORANGE** 5-9-8	14
2017	**STRADIVARIUS** 3-8-8	14
2018	**STRADIVARIUS** 4-9-9	7

MOLECOMB STAKES (2y)
Goodwood-5f

2009	**MONSIEUR CHEVALIER** 9-0	11
2010	**ZEBEDEE** 9-0	12
2011	**REQUINTO** 9-0	13
2012	**BUNGLE INTHEJUNGLE** 9-0	10
2013	**BROWN SUGAR** 9-0	8
2014	**COTAI GLORY** 9-1	8
2015	**KACHY** 9-1	10
2016	**YALTA** 9-1	9
2017	**HAVANA GREY** 9-1	10
2018	**RUMBLE INTHEJUNGLE** 9-1	11

NASSAU STAKES (fillies and mares)
Goodwood-1m 1f 197yds

2009	**MIDDAY** 3-8-10	10
2010	**MIDDAY** 4-9-6	7
2011	**MIDDAY** 5-9-6	6
2012	**THE FUGUE** 3-8-11	8
2013	**WINSILI** 3-8-11	14
2014	**SULTANINA** 4-9-7	6
2015	**LEGATISSIMO** 3-8-12	9
2016	**MINDING** 3-8-11	5
2017	**WINTER** 3-8-13	6
2018	**WILD ILLUSION** 3-8-13	6

HUNGERFORD STAKES
Newbury-7f

2009	**BALTHAZAAR'S GIFT** 6-9-3	9
2010	**SHAKESPEAREAN** 3-8-11	7
2011	**EXCELEBRATION** 3-8-13	9
2012	**LETHAL FORCE** 3-8-12	9
2013	**GREGORIAN** 4-9-3	5
2014	**BRETON ROCK** 4-9-5	6
2015	**ADAAY** 3-9-2	11
2016	**RICHARD PANKHURST** 4-9-6	6
2017	**MASSAAT** 4-9-6	8
2018	**SIR DANCEALOT** 4-9-9	8

GEOFFREY FREER STAKES
Newbury-1m 5f 61yds

2009	**KITE WOOD** 3-8-8	8
2010	**SANS FRONTIERES** 4-9-8	8
2011	**CENSUS** 3-8-6	6
2012	**MOUNT ATHOS** 5-9-4	6
2013	**ROYAL EMPIRE** 4-9-4	10
2014	**SEISMOS** 6-9-4	11
2015	**AGENT MURPHY** 4-9-5	6
2016	**KINGS FETE** 5-9-7	5
2017	**DEFOE** 3-8-10	8
2018	**HAMADA** 4-9-5	6

INTERNATIONAL STAKES
York-1m 2f 56yds

2009	**SEA THE STARS** 3-8-11	4
2010	**RIP VAN WINKLE** 4-9-5	9
2011	**TWICE OVER** 6-9-5	5
2012	**FRANKEL** 4-9-5	9
2013	**DECLARATION OF WAR** 4-9-5	6
2014	**AUSTRALIA** 3-8-12	6
2015	**ARABIAN QUEEN** 3-8-9	7
2016	**POSTPONED** 5-9-6	12
2017	**ULYSSES** 4-9-6	7
2018	**ROARING LION** 3-8-13	8

GREAT VOLTIGEUR STAKES (3y)
York-1m 3f 188yds

2009	**MONITOR CLOSELY** 8-12	7
2010	**REWILDING** 8-12	10
2011	**SEA MOON** 8-12	8
2012	**THOUGHT WORTHY** 8-12	6
2013	**TELESCOPE** 8-12	7
2014	**POSTPONED** 9-0	9
2015	**STORM THE STARS** 9-0	7
2016	**IDAHO** 9-0	6
2017	**CRACKSMAN** 9-0	6
2018	**OLD PERSIAN** 9-3	9

LOWTHER STAKES (2y fillies)
York-6f

2009	**LADY OF THE DESERT** 8-12	12
2010	**HOORAY** 8-12	8
2011	**BEST TERMS** 9-1	11
2012	**ROSDHU QUEEN** 8-12	10
2013	**LUCKY KRISTALE** 9-1	9
2014	**TIGGY WIGGY** 9-0	9
2015	**BESHARAH** 9-0	9
2016	**QUEEN KINDLY** 9-0	8
2017	**THREADING** 9-0	9
2018	**FAIRYLAND** 9-0	9

YORKSHIRE OAKS (fillies and mares)
York-1m 3f 188yds

2009	**DAR RE MI** 4-9-7	6
2010	**MIDDAY** 4-9-7	8
2011	**BLUE BUNTING** 3-8-11	8
2012	**SHARETA** 4-9-7	6
2013	**THE FUGUE** 4-9-7	7
2014	**TAPESTRY** 3-8-11	7
2015	**PLEASCACH** 3-8-11	11
2016	**SEVENTH HEAVEN** 3-8-11	12
2017	**ENABLE** 3-8-11	6
2018	**SEA OF CLASS** 3-8-12	8

EBOR HANDICAP
York-1m 5f 188yds

2009	**SESENTA** 5-8-8	19
2010	**DIRAR** 5-9-1	20
2011	**MOYENNE CORNICHE** 6-8-10	20
2012	**WILLING FOE** 5-9-2	19
2013	**TIGER CLIFF** 4-9-0	14
2014	**MUTUAL REGARD** 5-9-4	19
2015	**LITIGANT** 7-9-1	19
2016	**HEARTBREAK CITY** 6-9-1	20
2017	**NAKEETA** 6-9-0	19
2018	**MUNTAHAA** 5-9-9	20

GIMCRACK STAKES (2y)
York-6f
2009	SHOWCASING 8-12	6
2010	APPROVE 9-1	11
2011	CASPAR NETSCHER 8-12	9
2012	BLAINE 8-12	8
2013	ASTAIRE 8-12	7
2014	MUHAARAR 9-0	9
2015	AJAYA 9-0	8
2016	BLUE POINT 9-0	10
2017	SANDS OF MALI 9-0	10
2018	EMARAATY ANA 9-0	9

NUNTHORPE STAKES
York-5f
2009	BORDERLESCOTT 7-9-11	16
2010	SOLE POWER 3-9-9	12
2011	MARGOT DID 3-9-6	15
2012	ORTENSIA 7-9-8	19
2013	JWALA 4-9-8	17
2014	SOLE POWER 7-9-11	13
2015	MECCA'S ANGEL 4-9-10	19
2016	MECCA'S ANGEL 5-9-8	19
2017	MARSHA 4-9-8	11
2018	ALPHA DELPHINI 7-9-11	15

LONSDALE CUP
York-2m 56yds
2009	ASKAR TAU 4 9-1	5
2010	OPINION POLL 4 9-1	8
2011	OPINION POLL 5 9-4	10
2012	TIMES UP 6 9-1	11
2013	AHZEEMAH 4 9-3	7
2014	PALE MIMOSA 5-9-0	7
2015	MAX DYNAMITE 5-9-3	8
2016	QUEST FOR MORE 6-9-3	7
2017	MONTALY 6-9-3	9
2018	STRADIVARIUS 4-9-6	9

PRESTIGE STAKES (2y fillies)
Goodwood-7f
2009	SENT FROM HEAVEN 9-0	8
2010	THEYSKENS' THEORY 9-0	8
2011	REGAL REALM 9-0	6
2012	OLLIE OLGA 9-0	8
2013	AMAZING MARIA 9-0	7
2014	MALABAR 9-0	8
2015	HAWKSMOOR 9-0	9
2016	KILMAH 9-0	7
2017	BILLESDON BROOK 9-0	10
2018	ANTONIA DE VEGA 9-0	8

CELEBRATION MILE
Goodwood-1m
2009	DELEGATOR 3-8-9	7
2010	POET'S VOICE 3-8-9	4
2011	DUBAWI GOLD 3-8-9	7
2012	PREMIO LOCO 8-9-1	5
2013	AFSARE 6-9-1	8
2014	BOW CREEK 3-8-12	8
2015	KODI BEAR 3-8-12	6
2016	LIGHTNING SPEAR 5-9-4	5
2017	LIGHTNING SPEAR 6-9-4	6
2018	BEAT THE BANK 4-9-7	8

SOLARIO STAKES (2y)
Sandown-7f 16yds
2009	SHAKESPEAREAN 9-0	8
2010	NATIVE KHAN 9-0	6
2011	TALWAR 9-0	4
2012	FANTASTIC MOON 9-0	6
2013	KINGMAN 9-0	4
2014	AKTABANTAY 9-1	5
2015	FIRST SELECTION 9-1	10
2016	SOUTH SEAS 9-1	10
2017	MASAR 9-1	7
2018	TOO DARN HOT 9-1	6

SPRINT CUP
Haydock-6f
2009	REGAL PARADE 5-9-3	14
2010	MARKAB 7-9-3	13
2011	DREAM AHEAD 3-9-1	16
2012	SOCIETY ROCK 5-9-3	13
2013	GORDON LORD BYRON 5-9-3	13
2014	G FORCE 3-9-1	17
2015	TWILIGHT SON 3-9-1	15
2016	QUIET REFLECTION 3-8-12	14
2017	HARRY ANGEL 3-9-1	11
2018	THE TIN MAN 6-9-3	12

SEPTEMBER STAKES
Kempton-1m 3f 219yds Polytrack
2009	KIRKLEES 5-9-0	10
2010	LAAHEB 4-9-4	9
2011	MODUN 4-9-4	7
2012	DANDINO 5-9-4	9
2013	PRINCE BISHOP 6-9-4	10
2014	PRINCE BISHOP 7-9-12	7
2015	JACK HOBBS 3-9-3	7
2016	ARAB SPRING 6-9-5	6
2017	CHEMICAL CHARGE 5-9-5	5
2018	ENABLE 4-9-2	4

MAY HILL STAKES (2y fillies)
Doncaster-1m
2009	POLLENATOR 8-12	7
2010	WHITE MOONSTONE 8-12	7
2011	LYRIC OF LIGHT 8-12	8
2012	CERTIFY 8-12	7
2013	IHTIMAL 8-12	8
2014	AGNES STEWART 9-0	8
2015	TURRET ROCKS 9-0	8
2016	RICH LEGACY 9-0	9
2017	LAURENS 9-0	8
2018	FLEETING 9-0	11

PORTLAND HANDICAP
Doncaster-5f 143yds
2009	SANTO PADRE 5-9-1	22
2010	POET'S PLACE 5-9-4	22
2011	NOCTURNAL AFFAIR 5-9-5	21
2012	DOC HAY 5-8-11	20
2013	ANGELS WILL FALL 4-9-2	21
2014	MUTHMIR 4-9-7	20
2015	STEPS 7-9-7	20
2016	CAPTAIN COLBY 4-9-0	20
2017	SPRING LOADED 5-8-9	22
2018	A MOMENTOFMADNESS 5-9-4	21

PARK HILL STAKES (fillies and mares)
Doncaster-1m 6f 115yds
2009	**THE MINIVER ROSE** 3-8-6	9
2010	**EASTERN ARIA** 4-9-4	12
2011	**MEEZNAH** 4-9-4	7
2012	**WILD COCO** 4-9-4	9
2013	**THE LARK** 3-8-6	9
2014	**SILK SARI** 4-9-5	13
2015	**GRETCHEN** 3-8-7	11
2016	**SIMPLE VERSE** 4-9-5	12
2017	**ALYSSA** 4-9-5	10
2018	**GOD GIVEN** 4-9-5	7

DONCASTER CUP
Doncaster-2m 1f 197yds
2009	**ASKAR TAU** 4-9-4	5
2010	**SAMUEL** 6-9-1	10
2011	**SADDLER'S ROCK** 3-8-1	7
2012	**TIMES UP** 6-9-1	10
2013	**TIMES UP** 7-9-3	7
2014	**ESTIMATE** 5-9-0	12
2015	**PALLASATOR** 6-9-3	11
2016	**SHEIKHZAYEDROAD** 7-9-3	8
2017	**DESERT SKYLINE** 3-8-5	9
2018	**THOMAS HOBSON** 8-9-5	8

CHAMPAGNE STAKES (2y)
Doncaster-7f 6yds
2009	**POET'S VOICE** 8-12	7
2010	**SAAMIDD** 8-12	6
2011	**TRUMPET MAJOR** 8-12	5
2012	**TORONADO** 8-12	5
2013	**OUTSTRIP** 8-12	4
2014	**ESTIDHKAAR** 9-3	6
2015	**EMOTIONLESS** 9-0	6
2016	**RIVET** 9-0	6
2017	**SEAHENGE** 9-0	7
2018	**TOO DARN HOT** 9-0	6

PARK STAKES
Doncaster-7f 6yds
2009	**DUFF** 6-9-4	6
2010	**BALTHAZAR'S GIFT** 7-9-4	12
2011	**PREMIO LOCO** 7-9-4	5
2012	**LIBRANNO** 4-9-4	8
2013	**VIZTORIA** 3-8-11	9
2014	**ANSGAR** 6-9-4	7
2015	**LIMATO** 3-9-0	15
2016	**BRETON ROCK** 6-9-4	8
2017	**ACLAIM** 4-9-4	8
2018	**MUSTASHRY** 5-9-4	9

FLYING CHILDERS STAKES (2y)
Doncaster-5f
2009	**SAND VIXEN** 8-11	10
2010	**ZEBEDEE** 9-0	12
2011	**REQUINTO** 9-0	10
2012	**SIR PRANCEALOT** 9-0	9
2013	**GREEN DOOR** 9-0	7
2014	**BEACON** 9-1	14
2015	**GUTAIFAN** 9-1	9
2016	**ARDAD** 9-1	11
2017	**HEARTACHE** 8-12	9
2018	**SOLDIER'S CALL** 9-1	9

AYR GOLD CUP
Ayr-6f
2009	**JIMMY STYLES** 5-9-2	26
2010	**REDFORD** 5-9-2	26
2011	**OUR JONATHAN** 4-9-6	26
2012	**CAPTAIN RAMIUS** 6-9-0	26
2013	**HIGHLAND COLORI** 5-8-13	26
2014	**LOUIS THE PIOUS** 6-9-4	27
2015	**DON'T TOUCH** 3-9-1	25
2016	**BRANDO** 4-9-10	23
*2017	**DONJUAN TRIUMPHANT** 4-9-10	17
2018	**SON OF REST** 4-9-3 dead heated with	
	BARON BOLT 5-8-12	25

*Run at Haydock Park as 32Red Gold Cup

MILL REEF STAKES (2y)
Newbury-6f 8yds
2009	**AWZAAN** 9-1	7
2010	**TEMPLE MEADS** 9-1	7
2011	**CASPAR NETSCHER** 9-4	9
2012	**MOOHAAJIM** 9-1	8
2013	**SUPPLICANT** 9-1	7
2014	**TOOCOOLFORSCHOOL** 9-1	6
2015	**RIBCHESTER** 9-1	6
2016	**HARRY ANGEL** 9-1	7
2017	**JAMES GARFIELD** 9-1	9
2018	**KESSAAR** 9-1	7

ROYAL LODGE STAKES (2y)
Newmarket-1m (run at Ascot before 2011)
2009	**JOSHUA TREE** 8-12	10
2010	**FRANKEL** 8-12	5
2011	**DADDY LONG LEGS** 8-12	6
2012	**STEELER** 8-12	8
2013	**BERKSHIRE** 8-12	5
2014	**ELM PARK** 9-0	6
2015	**FOUNDATION** 9-0	8
2016	**BEST OF DAYS** 9-0	8
2017	**ROARING LION** 9-0	5
2018	**MOHAWK** 9-0	7

CHEVELEY PARK STAKES (2y fillies)
Newmarket-6f
2009	**SPECIAL DUTY** 8-12	8
2010	**HOORAY** 8-12	11
2011	**LIGHTENING PEARL** 8-12	11
2012	**ROSDHU QUEEN** 8-12	11
2013	**VORDA** 8-12	7
2014	**TIGGY WIGGY** 9-0	9
2015	**LUMIERE** 9-0	8
2016	**BRAVE ANNA** 9-0	6
2017	**CLEMMIE** 9-0	11
2018	**FAIRYLAND** 9-0	11

SUN CHARIOT STAKES
(fillies and mares)
Newmarket-1m
2009	**SAHPRESA** 4-9-2	8
2010	**SAHPRESA** 5-9-2	11
2011	**SAHPRESA** 6-9-3	8
2012	**SIYOUMA** 4-9-3	8
2013	**SKY LANTERN** 3-8-13	7
2014	**INTEGRAL** 4-9-3	7
2015	**ESOTERIQUE** 5-9-3	9
2016	**ALICE SPRINGS** 3-9-0	8
2017	**ROLY POLY** 3-9-0	13
2018	**LAURENS** 3-9-0	9

CAMBRIDGESHIRE
Newmarket-1m 1f

2009	**SUPASEUS** 6-9-1	32
2010	**CREDIT SWAP** 5-8-7	35
2011	**PRINCE OF JOHANNE** 5-8-9	32
2012	**BRONZE ANGEL** 3-8-8	33
2013	**EDUCATE** 4-9-9	31
2014	**BRONZE ANGEL** 5-8-8	31
2015	**THIRD TIME LUCKY** 3-8-4	34
2016	**SPARK PLUG** 5-9-4	31
2017	**DOLPHIN VISTA** 4-8-7	34
2018	**WISSAHICKON** 3-9-5	33

CUMBERLAND LODGE STAKES
Ascot-1m 4f

2009	**MAWATHEEQ** 4-9-0	12
2010	**LAAHEB** 4-9-3	6
2011	**QUEST FOR PEACE** 3-8-7	7
2012	**HAWAAFEZ** 4-8-11	6
2013	**SECRET NUMBER** 3-8-7	7
2014	**PETHER'S MOON** 4-9-6	5
2015	**STAR STORM** 3-8-8	8
2016	**MOVE UP** 3-8-13	9
2017	**DANEHILL KODIAC** 4-9-2	9
2018	**LARAAIB** 4-9-2	5

FILLIES' MILE (2y fillies)
Newmarket-1m (run at Ascot before 2011)

2009	**HIBAAYEB** 8-12	9
2010	**WHITE MOONSTONE** 8-12	5
2011	**LYRIC OF LIGHT** 8-12	8
2012	**CERTIFY** 8-12	6
2013	**CHRISELLIAM** 8-12	7
2014	**TOGETHER FOREVER** 9-0	7
2015	**MINDING** 9-0	10
2016	**RHODODENDRON** 9-0	8
2017	**LAURENS** 9-0	11
2018	**IRIDESSA** 9-0	8

MIDDLE PARK STAKES (2y)
Newmarket-6f

2009	**AWZAAN** 8-12	5
2010	**DREAM AHEAD** 8-12	8
2011	**CRUSADE** 8-12	16
2012	**RECKLESS ABANDON** 8-12	10
2013	**ASTAIRE** 9-0	10
2014	**CHARMING THOUGHT** 9-0	6
2015	**SHALAA** 9-0	7
2016	**THE LAST LION** 9-0	10
2017	**U S NAVY FLAG** 9-0	12
2018	**TEN SOVEREIGNS** 9-0	8

CHALLENGE STAKES
Newmarket-7f

2009	**ARABIAN GLEAM** 5-9-3	9
2010	**RED JAZZ** 3-9-1	14
2011	**STRONG SUIT** 3-9-5	8
2012	**FULBRIGHT** 3-9-1	11
2013	**FIESOLANA** 4-9-0	9
2014	**HERE COMES WHEN** 4-9-7	13
2015	**CABLE BAY** 4-9-3	10
2016	**ACLAIM** 3-9-1	12
2017	**LIMATO** 5-9-3	11
2018	**LIMATO** 6-9-3	8

DEWHURST STAKES (2y)
Newmarket-7f

2009	**BEETHOVEN** 9-1	15
2010	**FRANKEL** 9-1	6
2011	**PARISH HALL** 9-1	9
2012	**DAWN APPROACH** 9-1	6
2013	**WAR COMMAND** 9-1	6
2014	**BELARDO** 9-1	6
2015	**AIR FORCE BLUE** 9-1	7
2016	**CHURCHILL** 9-1	7
2017	**U S NAVY FLAG** 9-1	9
2018	**TOO DARN HOT** 9-1	7

CESAREWITCH
Newmarket-2m 2f

2009	**DARLEY SUN** 3-8-6	32
2010	**AAIM TO PROSPER** 6-7-13	32
2011	**NEVER CAN TELL** 4-8-11	33
2012	**AAIM TO PROSPER** 8-9-10	34
2013	**SCATTER DICE** 4-8-8	33
2014	**BIG EASY** 7-8-8	33
2015	**GRUMETI** 7-8-2	34
2016	**SWEET SELECTION** 4-8-8	33
2017	**WITHHOLD** 4-8-8	34
2018	**LOW SUN** 5-9-2	33

ROCKFEL STAKES (2y fillies)
Newmarket-7f

2009	**MUSIC SHOW** 8-12	11
2010	**CAPE DOLLAR** 8-12	10
2011	**WADING** 8-12	9
2012	**JUST THE JUDGE** 8-12	11
2013	**AL THAKHIRA** 8-12	8
2014	**LUCIDA** 9-0	9
2015	**PROMISING RUN** 9-0	7
2016	**SPAIN BURG** 9-0	8
2017	**JULIET CAPULET** 9-0	10
2018	**JUST WONDERFUL** 9-0	9

QIPCO BRITISH CHAMPIONS SPRINT STAKES
Ascot-6f
(run as Diadem Stakes before 2011)

2011	**DEACON BLUES** 4-9-0	16
2012	**MAAREK** 5-9-0	15
2013	**SLADE POWER** 4-9-0	14
2014	**GORDON LORD BYRON** 6-9-2	15
2015	**MUHAARAR** 3-9-1	20
2016	**THE TIN MAN** 4-9-2	13
2017	**LIBRISA BREEZE** 5-9-2	12
2018	**SANDS OF MALI** 3-9-1	14

QUEEN ELIZABETH II STAKES (BRITISH CHAMPIONS MILE)
Ascot-1m (st - rnd before 2011)

2009	**RIP VAN WINKLE** 3-8-13	4
2010	**POET'S VOICE** 3-8-13	8
2011	**FRANKEL** 3-9-0	8
2012	**EXCELEBRATION** 4-9-3	8
2013	**OLYMPIC GLORY** 3-9-0	12
2014	**CHARM SPIRIT** 3-9-0	11
2015	**SOLOW** 5-9-4	9
2016	**MINDING** 3-8-12	13
2017	**PERSUASIVE** 4-9-1	15
2018	**ROARING LION** 3-9-1	13

QIPCO BRITISH CHAMPIONS LONG DISTANCE CUP
(formerly Jockey Club Cup, run at Newmarket before 2011)
Ascot-2m

2011	FAME AND GLORY 5 9-10	10
2012	RITE OF PASSAGE 8-9-7	9
2013	ROYAL DIAMOND 7-9-7	12
2014	FORGOTTEN RULES 4-9-7	9
2015	FLYING OFFICER 5-9-7	13
2016	SHEIKHZAYEDROAD 7-9-7	10
2017	ORDER OF ST GEORGE 5-9-7	13
2018	STRADIVARIUS 4-9-7	6

QIPCO BRITISH CHAMPIONS FILLIES' AND MARES' STAKES
(formerly Pride Stakes, run at Newmarket before 2011)
Ascot-1m 4f

2011	DANCING RAIN 3-8-10	10
2012	SAPPHIRE 4-9-3	10
2013	SEAL OF APPROVAL 4-9-3	8
2014	MADAME CHIANG 3-8-12	10
2015	SIMPLE VERSE 3-8-12	12
2016	JOURNEY 4-9-5	13
2017	HYDRANGEA 3-8-13	10
2018	MAGICAL 3-8-13	11

QIPCO CHAMPION STAKES (BRITISH CHAMPIONS MIDDLE DISTANCE)
Ascot-1m 2f
(run at Newmarket before 2011)

2009	TWICE OVER 4-9-3	14
2010	TWICE OVER 5-9-3	10
2011	CIRRUS DES AIGLES 5-9-3	12
2012	FRANKEL 4-9-3	6
2013	FARHH 5-9-3	10
2014	NOBLE MISSION 5-9-5	9
2015	FASCINATING ROCK 4-9-5	13
2016	ALMANZOR 3-9-0	10
2017	CRACKSMAN 3-9-1	10
2018	CRACKSMAN 4-9-5	8

BALMORAL HANDICAP
Ascot-1m

2014	BRONZE ANGEL 5-9-2	27
2015	MUSADDAS 5-8-2	20
2016	YUFTEN 5-9-1	19
2017	LORD GLITTERS 6-9-3	20
2018	SHARJA BRIDGE 4-9-5	20

CORNWALLIS STAKES (2y)
Newmarket-5f (run at Ascot before 2014)

2009	OUR JONATHAN 9-0	17
2010	ELECTRIC WAVES 8-11	14
2011	PONTY ACCLAIM 8-11	16
2012	BUNGLE INTHEJUNGLE 9-3	6
2013	HOT STREAK 9-0	12

2014	ROYAL RAZALMA 8-12	12
2015	QUIET REFLECTION 8-12	11
2016	MRS DANVERS 8-12	9
2017	ABEL HANDY 9-1	12
2018	SERGEI PROKOFIEV 9-1	14

TWO-YEAR-OLD TROPHY (2y)
Redcar-6f

2009	LUCKY LIKE 8-6	22
2010	LADIES ARE FOREVER 7-12	22
2011	BOGART 8-12	22
2012	BODY AND SOUL 8-1	21
2013	VENTURA MIST 8-7	23
2014	LIMATO 8-12	23
2015	LOG OUT ISLAND 9-2	20
2016	WICK POWELL 8-3	20
2017	DARKANNA 8-11	23
2018	SUMMER DAYDREAM 8-9	21

HORRIS HILL STAKES (2y)
Newbury-7f

2009	CARNABY STREET 8-12	14
2010	KLAMMER 8-12	10
2011	TELL DAD 8-12	14
2012	TAWHID 8-12	8
2013	PIPING ROCK 8-12	11
2014	SMAIH 9-0	6
2015	CRAZY HORSE 9-0	9
2016	PLEASELETMEWIN 9-0	13
2017	NEBO 9-0	6
2018	MOHAATHER 9-0	8

VERTEM FUTURITY TROPHY (2y)
(Racing Post Trophy before 2018)
Doncaster-1m (St)

2009	ST NICHOLAS ABBEY 9-0	11
2010	CASAMENTO 9-0	10
2011	CAMELOT 9-0	5
2012	KINGSBARNS 9-0	7
2013	KINGSTON HILL 9-0	11
2014	ELM PARK 9-1	8
2015	MARCEL 9-1	7
2016	RIVET 9-1	10
2017	SAXON WARRIOR 9-1	12
2018	MAGNA GRECIA 9-1	11

NOVEMBER HANDICAP
Doncaster-1m 3f 197yds

2009	CHARM SCHOOL 4-8-12	23
2010	TIMES UP 4-8-13	22
2011	ZUIDER ZEE 4-8-13	23
2012	ART SCHOLAR 5-8-7	23
2013	CONDUCT 6-9-2	23
2014	OPEN EAGLE 5-8-12	23
2015	LITIGANT 7-9-10	22
2016	PRIZE MONEY 3-8-10	15
2017	SAUNTER 4-9-10	23
2018	ROYAL LINE 4-9-8	23

WINNERS OF PRINCIPAL RACES IN IRELAND

IRISH 2000 GUINEAS (3y)
The Curragh-1m
2009	**MASTERCRAFTSMAN** 9-0	9
2010	**CANFORD CLIFFS** 9-0	13
2011	**RODERIC O'CONNOR** 9-0	8
2012	**POWER** 9-0	10
2013	**MAGICIAN** 9-0	10
2014	**KINGMAN** 9-0	9
2015	**GLENEAGLES** 9-0	11
2016	**AWTAAD** 9-0	8
2017	**CHURCHILL** 9-0	6
2018	**ROMANISED** 9-0	11

TATTERSALLS GOLD CUP
The Curragh-1m 2f 110yds
2009	**CASUAL CONQUEST** 4-9-0	5
2010	**FAME AND GLORY** 4-9-0	6
2011	**SO YOU THINK** 5-9-1	5
2012	**SO YOU THINK** 6-9-1	5
2013	**AL KAZEEM** 5-9-3	4
2014	**NOBLE MISSION** 5-9-3	5
2015	**AL KAZEEM** 7-9-3	5
2016	**FASCINATING ROCK** 5-9-3	6
2017	**DECORATED KNIGHT** 5-9-3	8
2018	**LANCASTER BOMBER** 4-9-3	5

IRISH 1000 GUINEAS (3y fillies)
The Curragh-1m
2009	**AGAIN** 9-0	16
2010	**BETHRAH** 9-0	19
2011	**MISTY FOR ME** 9-0	15
2012	**SAMITAR** 9-0	8
2013	**JUST THE JUDGE** 9-0	15
2014	**MARVELLOUS** 9-0	11
2015	**PLEASCACH** 9-0	18
2016	**JET SETTING** 9-0	10
2017	**WINTER** 9-0	8
2018	**ALPHA CENTAURI** 9-0	13

IRISH DERBY (3y)
The Curragh-1m 4f
2009	**FAME AND GLORY** 9-0	11
2010	**CAPE BLANCO** 9-0	10
2011	**TREASURE BEACH** 9-0	8
2012	**CAMELOT** 9-0	5
2013	**TRADING LEATHER** 9-0	9
2014	**AUSTRALIA** 9-0	5
2015	**JACK HOBBS** 9-0	8
2016	**HARZAND** 9-0	9
2017	**CAPRI** 9-0	9
2018	**LATROBE** 9-0	12

PRETTY POLLY STAKES
(fillies and mares)
Curragh-1m 2f
2009	**DAR RE MI** 4-9-9	7
2010	**CHINESE WHITE** 5-9-9	9
2011	**MISTY FOR ME** 3-8-12	7
2012	**IZZI TOP** 4-9-9	4

2013	**AMBIVALENT** 4-9-10	
2014	**THISTLE BIRD** 6-9-10	
2015	**DIAMONDSANDRUBIES** 3-8-12	
2016	**MINDING** 3-8-12	
2017	**NEZWAAH** 4-9-8	1
2018	**URBAN FOX** 4-9-8	6

IRISH OAKS (3y fillies)
The Curragh-1m 4f
2009	**SARISKA** 9-0	10
2010	**SNOW FAIRY** 9-0	15
2011	**BLUE BUNTING** 9-0	9
2012	**GREAT HEAVENS** 9-0	9
2013	**CHICQUITA** 9-0	10
2014	**BRACELET** 9-0	10
2015	**COVERT LOVE** 9-0	10
2016	**SEVENTH HEAVEN** 9-0	10
2017	**ENABLE** 9-0	10
2018	**SEA OF CLASS** 9-0	10

PHOENIX STAKES (2y)
The Curragh-6f
2009	**ALFRED NOBEL** 9-1	8
2010	**ZOFFANY** 9-1	6
2011	**LA COLLINA** 8-12	9
2012	**PEDRO THE GREAT** 9-3	8
2013	**SUDIRMAN** 9-3	6
2014	**DICK WHITTINGTON** 9-3	6
2015	**AIR FORCE BLUE** 9-3	5
2016	**CARAVAGGIO** 9-3	5
2017	**SIOUX NATION** 9-3	6
2018	**ADVERTISE** 9-3	5

MATRON STAKES (fillies and mares)
Leopardstown-1m
2009	**RAINBOW VIEW** 3-8-12	7
2010	**LILLIE LANGTRY** 3-8-12	6
2011	**EMULOUS** 4-9-5	8
*2012	**CHACHAMAIDEE** 5-9-5	11
2013	**LA COLLINA** 4-9-5	12
2014	**FIESOLANA** 5-9-5	10
2015	**LEGATISSIMO** 3-9-0	9
2016	**ALICE SPRINGS** 3-9-0	8
2017	**HYDRANGEA** 3-9-0	10
2018	**LAURENS** 3-9-0	7

*Duntle disqualified from first place

IRISH CHAMPION STAKES
Leopardstown-1m 2f
2009	**SEA THE STARS** 3-9-0	9
2010	**CAPE BLANCO** 3-9-0	6
2011	**SO YOU THINK** 5-9-7	6
2012	**SNOW FAIRY** 5-9-4	6
2013	**THE FUGUE** 4-9-4	6
2014	**THE GREY GATSBY** 3-9-0	7
2015	**GOLDEN HORN** 3-9-0	7
2016	**ALMANZOR** 3-9-0	12
2017	**DECORATED KNIGHT** 5-9-7	10
2018	**ROARING LION** 3-9-1	7

IRISH CAMBRIDGESHIRE

The Curragh-1m

2009	POET 4-9-9	27
2010	HUJAYLEA 7-8-3	25
2011	CASTLE BAR SLING 6-8-11	21
2012	PUNCH YOUR WEIGHT 3-8-6	18
2013	MORAN GRA 6-8-13	20
2014	SRETAW 5-8-8	21
2015	HINT OF A TINT 5-9-3	22
2016	SEA WOLF 4-9-5	24
2017	ELUSIVE TIME 9-8-9	27
2018	KENYA 3-9-2	21

MOYGLARE STUD STAKES (2y fillies)

The Curragh-7f

2009	TERMAGANT 8-12	7
2010	MISTY FOR ME 8-12	12
2011	MAYBE 9-0	8
2012	SKY LANTERN 9-0	13
2013	RIZEENA 9-0	7
2014	CURSORY GLANCE 9-0	10
2015	MINDING 9-0	9
2016	INTRICATELY 9-0	7
2017	HAPPILY 9-0	8
2018	SKITTER SKATTER 9-0	10

VINCENT O'BRIEN (NATIONAL) STAKES (2y)

The Curragh-7f

2009	KINGSFORT 9-1	6
2010	PATHFORK 9-1	9
2011	POWER 9-1	9
2012	DAWN APPROACH 9-3	7
2013	TOORMORE 9-3	5
2014	GLENEAGLES 9-3	5
2015	AIR FORCE BLUE 9-3	5
2016	CHURCHILL 9-3	7
2017	VERBAL DEXTERITY 9-3	7
2018	QUORTO 9-3	7

IRISH ST LEGER

The Curragh-1m 6f

2009	ALANDI 4-9-11	8
2010	SANS FRONTIERES 4-9-11	8
2011	DUNCAN 6-9-11 dead heated with	6
	JUKEBOX JURY 5-9-11	6
2012	ROYAL DIAMOND 6-9-11	9
2013	VOLEUSE DE COEURS 4-9-8	10
2014	BROWN PANTHER 6-9-11	11
2015	ORDER OF ST GEORGE 3-9-0	11
2016	WICKLOW BRAVE 7-9-11	4
2017	ORDER OF ST GEORGE 5-9-10	10
2018	FLAG OF HONOUR 3-9-1	6

IRISH CESAREWITCH

The Curragh-2m

2009	DANI CALIFORNIA 5-8-0	29
2010	BRIGHT HORIZON 3-8-7	23
2011	MINSK 3-8-9	19
2012	VOLEUSE DE COEURS 3-9-1	27
2013	MONTEFELTRO 5-9-4	30

2014	EL SALVADOR 5-9-5	21
2015	DIGENTA 8-9-10	20
2016	LAWS OF SPIN 3-8-6	20
*2017	LORD ERSKINE 4-8-5	24
2018	BRAZOS 4-8-12	24

*Run at Navan

LADBROKES HURDLE

Leopardstown-2m
(Various sponsors)

2010	PUYOL 8-10-10	30
2011	FINAL APPROACH 5-10-9	26
2012	CITIZENSHIP 6-10-3	30
2013	ABBEY LANE 6-10-8	28
2014	GILGAMBOA 6-10-9	24
2015	KATIE T 6-10-9	24
2016	HENRY HIGGINS 6-10-10	23
2017	ICE COLD SOUL 7-10-2	20
2018	OFF YOU GO 5-9-10	28
2019	OFF YOU GO 6-11-5	19

IRISH CHAMPION HURDLE

Leopardstown-2m

2010	SOLWHIT 6-11-10	7
2011	HURRICANE FLY 7-11-10	5
2012	HURRICANE FLY 8-11-10	5
2013	HURRICANE FLY 9-11-10	5
2014	HURRICANE FLY 10-11-10	4
2015	HURRICANE FLY 11-11-10	6
2016	FAUGHEEN 8-11-10	5
2017	PETIT MOUCHOIR 6 11-10	4
2018	SUPASUNDAE 8-11-10	8
2019	APPLE'S JADE 7-11-3	6

IRISH GOLD CUP

Leopardstown-3m
(Hennessy Gold Cup before 2016)

2010	JONCOL 7-11-10	7
2011	KEMPES 8-11-10	9
2012	QUEL ESPRIT 8-11-10	7
2013	SIR DES CHAMPS 7-11-10	4
2014	LAST INSTALMENT 9-11-10	7
2015	CARLINGFORD LOUGH 9-11-10	8
2016	CARLINGFORD LOUGH 10-11-10	10
2017	SIZING JOHN 7-11-10	7
2018	EDWULF 9-11-10	10
2019	BELLSHILL 9-11-10	4

IRISH GRAND NATIONAL

Fairyhouse-3m 5f

2009	NICHE MARKET 8-10-5	30
2010	BLUESEA CRACKER 8-10-4	26
2011	ORGANISEDCONFUSION 6-9-13	25
2012	LION NA BEARNAI 10-10-5	29
2013	LIBERTY COUNSEL 10-9-5	28
2014	SHUTTHEFRONTDOOR 7-10-13	26
2015	THUNDER AND ROSES 7-10-6	28
2016	ROGUE ANGEL 8-10-6	27
2017	OUR DUKE 7-11-4	28
2018	GENERAL PRINCIPLE 9-10-0	30

WINNERS OF PRINCIPAL RACES IN FRANCE

PRIX GANAY
ParisLongchamp-1m 2f 110yds
2009	**VISION D'ETAT** 4-9-2	8
2010	**CUTLASS BAY** 4-9-2	9
2011	**PLANTEUR** 4-9-2	7
2012	**CIRRUS DES AIGLES** 6-9-2	6
2013	**PASTORIUS** 4-9-2	9
2014	**CIRRUS DES AIGLES** 8-9-2	8
2015	**CIRRUS DES AIGLES** 9-9-2	7
*2016	**DARIYAN** 4-9-2	10
*2017	**CLOTH OF STARS** 4-9-2	7
2018	**CRACKSMAN** 4-9-2	7

*Run at Saint-Cloud

POULE D'ESSAI DES POULAINS (3y)
ParisLongchamp-1m
2009	**SILVER FROST** 9-2	6
2010	**LOPE DE VEGA** 9-2	15
2011	**TIN HORSE** 9-2	14
2012	**LUCAYAN** 9-2	12
2013	**STYLE VENDOME** 9-2	18
2014	**KARAKONTIE** 9-2	12
2015	**MAKE BELIEVE** 9-2	18
*2016	**THE GURKHA** 9-2	13
*2017	**BRAMETOT** 9-2	13
2018	**OLMEDO** 9-2	11

*Run at Deauville

POULE D'ESSAI DES POULICHES (3y filllies)
ParisLongchamp-1m
2009	**ELUSIVE WAVE** 9-0	11
*2010	**SPECIAL DUTY** 9-0	10
2011	**GOLDEN LILAC** 9-0	16
2012	**BEAUTY PARLOUR** 9-0	13
2013	**FLOTILLA** 9-0	20
2014	**AVENIR CERTAIN** 9-0	16
2015	**ERVEDYA** 9-0	14
**2016	**LA CRESSONNIERE** 9-0	14
**2017	**PRECIEUSE** 9-0	18
2018	**TEPPAL** 9-0	14

*Liliside disqualified from first place
**Run at Deauville

PRIX SAINT-ALARY (3y fillies)
ParisLongchamp-1m 2f
2009	**STACELITA** 9-0	7
2010	**SARAFINA** 9-0	9
2011	**WAVERING** 9-0	12
2012	**SAGAWARA** 9-0	8
2013	**SILASOL** 9-0	8
*2014	**VAZIRA** 9-0	8
2015	**QUEEN'S JEWEL** 9-0	9
**2016	**JEMAYEL** 9-0	9
*2017	**SOBETSU** 9-0	11
2018	**LAURENS** 9-0	5

*We Are disqualified from first place
**Run at Deauville

PRIX D'ISPAHAN
ParisLongchamp-1m 1f 55yds
2009	**NEVER ON SUNDAY** 4-9-2	
2010	**GOLDIKOVA** 5-8-13	
2011	**GOLDIKOVA** 6-8-13	
2012	**GOLDEN LILAC** 4-8-13	
2013	**MAXIOS** 5-9-2	
2014	**CIRRUS DES AIGLES** 8-9-2	
2015	**SOLOW** 5-9-2	
*2016	**A SHIN HIKARI** 5-9-2	
*2017	**MEKHTAAL** 4-9-2	
2018	**RECOLETOS** 4-9-2	

*Run at Chantilly

PRIX DU JOCKEY CLUB (3y)
Chantilly-1m 2f 110yds
2009	**LE HAVRE** 9-2	
2010	**LOPE DE VEGA** 9-2	
2011	**RELIABLE MAN** 9-2	
2012	**SAONOIS** 9-2	
2013	**INTELLO** 9-2	
2014	**THE GREY GATSBY** 9-2	
2015	**NEW BAY** 9-2	
2016	**ALMANZOR** 9-2	
2017	**BRAMETOT** 9-2	
2018	**STUDY OF MAN** 9-2	

PRIX DE DIANE (3y fillies)
Chantilly-1m 2f 110yds
2009	**STACELITA** 9-0	
2010	**SARAFINA** 9-0	
2011	**GOLDEN LILAC** 9-0	
2012	**VALYRA** 9-0	
2013	**TREVE** 9-0	
2014	**AVENIR CERTAIN** 9-0	
2015	**STAR OF SEVILLE** 9-0	
2016	**LA CRESSONNIERE** 9-0	
2017	**SENGA** 9-1	
2018	**LAURENS** 9-0	

GRAND PRIX DE SAINT-CLOUD
Saint-Cloud-1m 4f
2009	**SPANISH MOON** 5-9-2	
2010	**PLUMANIA** 4-8-13	
2011	**SARAFINA** 4-8-13	
2012	**MEANDRE** 4-9-2	
2013	**NOVELLIST** 4-9-2	
*2014	**NOBLE MISSION** 5-9-2	
2015	**TREVE** 5-8-13	
2016	**SILVERWAVE** 4-9-2	
2017	**ZARAK** 4-9-2	
2018	**WALDGEIST** 4-9-3	

*Spiritjim disqualified from first place

PRIX JEAN PRAT (3y)
Chantilly-1m
2009	**LORD SHANAKILL** 9-2	
2010	**DICK TURPIN** 9-2	
2011	**MUTUAL TRUST** 9-2	

12 **AESOP'S FABLES** 9-2...............................8
13 **HAVANA GOLD** 9-2.............................12
14 **CHARM SPIRIT** 9-2.............................8
15 **TERRITORIES** 9-2...............................8
16 **ZELZAL** 9-2...9
17 **THUNDER SNOW** 9-3...........................5
18 **INTELLOGENT** 9-2...............................7

GRAND PRIX DE PARIS (3y)
ParisLongchamp-1m 4f
09 **CAVALRYMAN** 9-2...............................8
10 **BEHKABAD** 9-2...................................9
11 **MEANDRE** 9-2......................................7
12 **IMPERIAL MONARCH** 9-2......................9
13 **FLINTSHIRE** 9-2..................................8
14 **GALLANTE** 9-2...................................11
15 **ERUPT** 9-2..6
16 **MONT ORMEL** 9-2................................8
17 **SHAKEEL** 9-2.......................................9
18 **KEW GARDENS** 9-3...............................6
Run at Saint-Cloud

PRIX ROTHSCHILD
(fillies and mares)
Deauville-1m
Run as Prix d'Astarte before 2008)
09 **GOLDIKOVA** 4-9-0.............................12
10 **GOLDIKOVA** 5-9-0...............................7
11 **GOLDIKOVA** 6-9-2...............................8
12 **ELUSIVE KATE** 3-8-9............................5
13 **ELUSIVE KATE** 4-9-2...........................12
14 **ESOTERIQUE** 4-9-2.............................4
15 **AMAZING MARIA** 4-9-2........................8
16 **QEMAH** 3-8-9....................................10
17 **ROLY POLY** 3-8-9..............................10
18 **WITH YOU** 3-8-9...............................10

PRIX MAURICE DE GHEEST
Deauville-6f 110yds
09 **KING'S APOSTLE** 5-9-2.......................12
10 **REGAL PARADE** 6-9-2.........................15
11 **MOONLIGHT CLOUD** 3-8-8...................13
12 **MOONLIGHT CLOUD** 4-8-13...................9
13 **MOONLIGHT CLOUD** 5-8-13.................14
14 **GARSWOOD** 4-9-2.............................12
15 **MUHAARAR** 3-8-11............................12
16 **SIGNS OF BLESSING** 5-9-2..................15
17 **BRANDO** 5-9-3..................................13
18 **POLYDREAM** 3-8-10...........................20

PRIX JACQUES LE MAROIS
Deauville-1m
09 **GOLDIKOVA** 4-9-0...............................9
10 **MAKFI** 3-8-11....................................12
11 **IMMORTAL VERSE** 3-8-8......................8
12 **EXCELEBRATION** 4-9-4........................11
13 **MOONLIGHT CLOUD** 5-9-1...................13
14 **KINGMAN** 3-8-13.................................5
15 **ESOTERIQUE** 5-9-1.............................9
16 **RIBCHESTER** 3-8-13...........................11
17 **AL WUKAIR** 3-8-13..............................6
18 **ALPHA CENTAURI** 3-8-9.......................11

PRIX MORNY (2y)
Deauville-6f
2009 **ARCANO** 9-0.....................................5
2010 **DREAM AHEAD** 9-0...........................11
2011 **DABIRSIM** 9-0...................................7
2012 **RECKLESS ABANDON** 9-0..................11
2013 **NO NAY NEVER** 9-0..........................10
2014 **THE WOW SIGNAL** 9-0.......................9
2015 **SHALAA** 9-0.....................................5
2016 **LADY AURELIA** 8-10...........................5
2017 **UNFORTUNATELY** 9-0.........................8
2018 **PRETTY POLLYANNA** 8-10...................9

PRIX JEAN ROMANET
(fillies and mares)
Deauville-1m 2f
2009 **ALPINE ROSE** 4-9-0...........................6
2010 **STACELITA** 4-9-0...............................8
2011 **ANNOUNCE** 4-9-0.............................5
*2012 **IZZI TOP** 4-9-0.................................8
2013 **ROMANTICA** 4-9-0.............................6
2014 **RIBBONS** 4-9-0................................11
2015 **ODELIZ** 5-9-0..................................11
2016 **SPEEDY BOARDING** 4-9-0..................10
2017 **AJMAN PRINCESS** 4-9-0....................10
2018 **NONZA** 4-9-0.....................................9
*Snow Fairy disqualified from first place

PRIX DU MOULIN DE LONGCHAMP
ParisLongchamp-1m
2009 **AQLAAM** 4-9-2...................................9
2010 **FUISSE** 4-9-2.....................................6
2011 **EXCELEBRATION** 3-8-11......................8
2012 **MOONLIGHT CLOUD** 4-8-13.................4
2013 **MAXIOS** 5-9-2....................................7
2014 **CHARM SPIRIT** 3-8-11.......................10
2015 **ERVEDYA** 3-8-9..................................6
*2016 **VADAMOS** 5-9-3...............................6
*2017 **RIBCHESTER** 4-9-3...........................7
2018 **RECOLETOS** 4-9-4.............................11
*Run at Chantilly

PRIX VERMEILLE (fillies and mares)
ParisLongchamp-1m 4f
*2009 **STACELITA** 3-8-8..............................12
2010 **MIDDAY** 4-9-3...................................12
2011 **GALIKOVA** 3-8-8.................................6
2012 **SHARETA** 4-9-2.................................13
2013 **TREVE** 3-8-8.....................................10
2014 **BALTIC BARONESS** 4-9-3.....................9
2015 **TREVE** 5-9-3......................................9
2016 **LEFT HAND 3-8-8..............................6
2017 **BATEEL 5-9-3.................................11
2018 **KITESURF** 4-9-3.................................8
*Dar Re Mi disqualified from first place
**Run at Chantilly

PRIX DE LA FORET
ParisLongchamp-7f
2009 **VARENAR** 3-9-0................................14
2010 **GOLDIKOVA** 5-8-13...........................10
2011 **DREAM AHEAD** 3-9-0..........................8
2012 **GORDON LORD BYRON** 4-9-2.............11
2013 **MOONLIGHT CLOUD** 5-8-13...............11
2014 **OLYMPIC GLORY** 4-9-2......................14
2015 **MAKE BELIEVE** 3-9-0.........................13

*2016	**LIMATO** 4-9-2	11
*2017	**ACLAIM** 4-9-2	10
2018	**ONE MASTER** 4-8-13	15

*Run at Chantilly

PRIX DU CADRAN
ParisLongchamp-2m 4f

2009	**ALANDI** 4-9-2	12
2010	**GENTOO** 6-9-2	8
2011	**KASBAH BLISS** 9-9-2	10
2012	**MOLLY MALONE** 4-8-13	10
2013	**ALTANO** 7-9-2	10
2014	**HIGH JINX** 6-9-2	8
2015	**MILLE ET MILLE** 5-9-2	10
*2016	**QUEST FOR MORE** 6-9-2	12
*2017	**VAZIRABAD** 5-9-2	6
2018	**CALL THE WIND** 4-9-2	8

*Run at Chantilly

PRIX DE L'ABBAYE DE LONGCHAMP
ParisLongchamp-5f

2009	**TOTAL GALLERY** 3-9-11	16
2010	**GILT EDGE GIRL** 4-9-7	21
2011	**TANGERINE TREES** 6-9-11	15
2012	**WIZZ KID** 4-9-7	18
2013	**MAAREK** 6-9-11	20
2014	**MOVE IN TIME** 6-9-11	18
2015	**GOLDREAM** 6-9-11	18
**2016	**MARSHA** 3-9-7	17
**2017	**BATTAASH** 3-9-11	13
2018	**MABS CROSS** 4-9-7	16

**Run at Chantilly

PRIX JEAN-LUC LAGARDERE (2y)
ParisLongchamp-1m (7f before 2015)

2009	**SIYOUNI** 9-0	7
2010	**WOOTTON BASSETT** 9-0	9
2011	**DABIRSIM** 9-0	7
2012	**OLYMPIC GLORY** 9-0	8
2013	**KARAKONTIE** 9-0	8
*2014	**FULL MAST** 9-0	9
2015	**ULTRA** 9-0	11
**2016	**NATIONAL DEFENSE** 9-0	7
**2017	**HAPPILY** 8-10	6
2018	**ROYAL MARINE** 9-0	6

*Gleneagles disqualified from first place
**Run at Chantilly

PRIX MARCEL BOUSSAC (2y fillies)
ParisLongchamp-1m

2009	**ROSANARA** 8-11	11
2010	**MISTY FOR ME** 8-11	8
2011	**ELUSIVE KATE** 8-11	5
2012	**SILASOL** 8-11	9
2013	**INDONESIENNE** 8-11	12
2014	**FOUND** 8-11	12
2015	**BALLYDOYLE** 8-11	8

*2016	**WUHEIDA** 8-11	
*2017	**WILD ILLUSION** 8-11	
2018	**LILY'S CANDLE** 8-11	

*Run at Chantilly

PRIX DE L'OPERA (fillies and mares)
ParisLongchamp-1m 2f

2009	**SHALANAYA** 3-8-11	
2010	**LILY OF THE VALLEY** 3-8-11	
2011	**NAHRAIN** 3-8-11	
2012	**RIDASIYNA** 3-8-11	
2013	**DALKALA** 4-9-2	
2014	**WE ARE** 3-8-11	
2015	**COVERT LOVE** 3-8-11	
*2016	**SPEEDY BOARDING** 4-9-2	
*2017	**RHODODENDRON** 3-8-11	
2018	**WILD ILLUSION** 3-8-11	

*Run at Chantilly

PRIX ROYAL-OAK
ParisLongchamp-1m 7f 110yds

2009	**ASK** 6-9-4	
2010	**GENTOO** 6-9-4	
2011	**BE FABULOUS** 4-9-1	
2012	**LES BEAUFS** 3-8-9	
2013	**TAC DE BOISTRON** 6-9-4	
2014	**TAC DE BOISTRON** 7-9-4	
2015	**VAZIRABAD** 3-8-10	
*2016	**VAZIRABAD** 4-9-4	
**2017	**ICE BREEZE** 3-8-10	
2018	**HOLDTHASIGREEN** 6-9-4	

*Run at Chantilly
**Run at Saint-Cloud

CRITERIUM INTERNATIONAL (2y)
Saint-Cloud-7f (1m before 2015)

2009	**JAN VERMEER** 9-0	
2010	**RODERIC O'CONNOR** 9-0	
2011	**FRENCH FIFTEEN** 9-0	
2012	**LOCH GARMAN** 9-0	
2013	**ECTOT** 9-0	
2014	**VERT DE GRECE** 9-0	
2015	**JOHANNES VERMEER** 9-0	
2016	**THUNDER SNOW** 9-0	
2017	ABANDONED	
*2018	**ROYAL MEETING** 9-0	

*Run at Chantilly

CRITERIUM DE SAINT-CLOUD (2y)
Saint-Cloud-1m 2f

2009	**PASSION FOR GOLD** 9-0	
2010	**RECITAL** 9-0	
2011	**MANDAEAN** 9-0	
2012	**MORANDI** 9-0	
2013	**PRINCE GIBRALTAR** 9-0	
2014	**EPICURIS** 9-0	
2015	**ROBIN OF NAVAN** 9-0	
2016	**WALDGEIST** 9-0	
2017	ABANDONED	
2018	**WONDERMENT** 8-10	

WINNERS OF OTHER OVERSEAS RACES

DUBAI WORLD CUP
Meydan-1m 2f Tapeta
(run at Nad Al Sheba on dirt before 2010)

09	WELL ARMED 6-9-0	14
10	GLORIA DE CAMPEAO 7-9-0	14
11	VICTOIRE PISA 4-9-0	14
12	MONTEROSSO 5-9-0	13
13	ANIMAL KINGDOM 5-9-0	13
14	AFRICAN STORY 7-9-0	16
15	PRINCE BISHOP 8-9-0	9
16	CALIFORNIA CHROME 5-9-0	12
17	ARROGATE 4-9-0	14
18	THUNDER SNOW 4-9-0	10

KENTUCKY DERBY
Churchill Downs-1m 2f dirt

09	MINE THAT BIRD 9-0	19
10	SUPER SAVER 9-0	20
11	ANIMAL KINGDOM 9-0	19
12	I'LL HAVE ANOTHER 9-0	20
13	ORB 9-0	19
14	CALIFORNIA CHROME 9-0	19
15	AMERICAN PHAROAH 9-0	18
16	NYQUIST 9-0	20
17	ALWAYS DREAMING 9-0	20
18	JUSTIFY 9-0	20

BREEDERS' CUP TURF
Various courses-1m 4f

09	CONDUIT 4-9-0	7
10	DANGEROUS MIDGE 4-9-0	7
11	ST NICHOLAS ABBEY 4-9-0	9
12	LITTLE MIKE 5-9-0	12
13	MAGICIAN 3-8-10	12
14	MAIN SEQUENCE 5-9-0	12
15	FOUND 3-8-7	12
16	HIGHLAND REEL 4-9-0	12
17	TALISMANIC 4-9-0	13
18	ENABLE 4-8-11	13

BREEDERS' CUP CLASSIC
Various courses-1m 2f dirt/pro-ride

2009	ZENYATTA 5-8-11	12
2010	BLAME 4-9-0	12
2011	DROSSELMEYER 4-9-0	12
2012	FORT LARNED 4-9-0	12
2013	MUCHO MACHO MAN 5-9-0	11
2014	BAYERN 3-8-10	14
2015	AMERICAN PHAROAH 3-8-10	8
2016	ARROGATE 3-8-10	9
2017	GUN RUNNER 4-9-0	11
2018	ACCELERATE 5-9-0	14

MELBOURNE CUP
Flemington-2m

2009	SHOCKING 4-8-0	23
2010	AMERICAIN 5-8-8	23
2011	DUNADEN 5-8-8	23
2012	GREEN MOON 5-8-6	24
2013	FIORENTE 5-8-9	24
2014	PROTECTIONIST 4-8-13	22
2015	PRINCE OF PENZANCE 6-8-5	24
2016	ALMANDIN 6-8-3	24
2017	REKINDLING 3-8-2	23
2018	CROSS COUNTER 3-8-0	24

JAPAN CUP
Tokyo-1m 4f

2009	VODKA 5-8-10	18
*2010	ROSE KINGDOM 3-8-9	18
2011	BUENA VISTA 5-8-9	16
2012	GENTILDONNA 3-8-5	17
2013	GENTILDONNA 4-8-9	17
2014	EPIPHANEIA 4-9-0	18
2015	SHONAN PANDORA 4-8-9	18
2016	KITASAN BLACK 4-9-0	17
2017	CHEVAL GRAND 5-9-0	17
2018	ALMOND EYE 3-8-5	14

*Buena Vista disqualified from first place

WINNERS OF PRINCIPAL NATIONAL HUNT RACES

BETVICTOR GOLD CUP (HANDICAP CHASE)
Cheltenham-2m 4f 78yds

09	TRANQUIL SEA 7-10-13	16
10	LITTLE JOSH 8-10-5	18
11	GREAT ENDEAVOUR 7-10-3	20
12	AL FEROF 7-11-8	18
13	JOHNS SPIRIT 6-10-2	20
14	CAID DU BERLAIS 5-10-13	18
15	ANNACOTTY 7-11-0	20

2016	TAQUIN DU SEUIL 9-11-11	17
2017	SPLASH OF GINGE 9-10-6	17
2018	BARON ALCO 7-10-11	18

BETFAIR CHASE
Haydock-3m 1f 125yds (3m 24yds before 2017)

2009	KAUTO STAR 9-11-7	7
2010	IMPERIAL COMMANDER 9-11-7	7
2011	KAUTO STAR 11-11-7	6
2012	SILVINIACO CONTI 6-11-7	5
2013	CUE CARD 7-11-7	8
2014	SILVINIACO CONTI 8-11-7	9

2015	**CUE CARD** 9-11-7	5
2016	**CUE CARD** 10-11-7	6
2017	**BRISTOL DE MAI** 6-11-7	6
2018	**BRISTOL DE MAI** 7-11-7	5

LADBROKES TROPHY HANDICAP CHASE
Newbury-3m 1f 214yds
(Run as Hennessy Gold Cup before 2017)

2009	**DENMAN** 9-11-12	19
2010	**DIAMOND HARRY** 7-10-0	20
2011	**CARRUTHERS** 8-10-4	18
2012	**BOBS WORTH** 7-11-6	19
2013	**TRIOLO D'ALENE** 6-11-1	21
2014	**MANY CLOUDS** 7-11-6	19
2015	**SMAD PLACE** 8-11-4	15
2016	**NATIVE RIVER** 6-11-1	19
2017	**TOTAL RECALL** 8-10-8	20
2018	**SIZING TENNESSEE** 10-11-3	12

TINGLE CREEK CHASE
Sandown-2m

2009	**TWIST MAGIC** 7-11-7	5
*2010	**MASTER MINDED** 7-11-7	9
2011	**SIZING EUROPE** 9-11-7	7
2012	**SPRINTER SACRE** 6-11-7	7
2013	**SIRE DE GRUGY** 7-11-7	9
2014	**DODGING BULLETS** 6-11-7	10
2015	**SIRE DE GRUGY** 9-11-7	7
2016	**UN DE SCEAUX** 8-11-7	6
2017	**POLITOLOGUE** 6-11-7	6
2018	**ALTIOR** 8-11-7	4

*Run at Cheltenham over 2m 110yds

CHRISTMAS HURDLE
Kempton-2m

2009	**GO NATIVE** 6-11-7	7
*2010	**BINOCULAR** 7-11-7	6
2011	**BINOCULAR** 7-11-7	5
2012	**DARLAN** 5-11-7	7
2013	**MY TENT OR YOURS** 6-11-7	6
2014	**FAUGHEEN** 6-11-7	6
2015	**FAUGHEEN** 7-11-7	5
2016	**YANWORTH** 6-11-7	5
2017	**BUVEUR D'AIR** 6-11-7	4
2018	**VERDANA BLUE** 6-11-0	5

*Run in January 2011

KING GEORGE VI CHASE
Kempton-3m

2009	**KAUTO STAR** 9-11-10	13
*2010	**LONG RUN** 6-11-10	9
2011	**KAUTO STAR** 11-11-10	7
2012	**LONG RUN** 7-11-10	9
2013	**SILVINIACO CONTI** 7-11-10	9
2014	**SILVINIACO CONTI** 8-11-10	10
2015	**CUE CARD** 9-11-10	9
2016	**THISTLECRACK** 8-11-10	5
2017	**MIGHT BITE** 8-11-10	8
2018	**CLAN DES OBEAUX** 6-11-10	10

*Run in January 2011

WELSH GRAND NATIONAL (HANDICAP CHASE)
Chepstow-3m 5f 110yds

2009	**DREAM ALLIANCE** 8-10-8	
*2010	**SYNCHRONISED** 8-11-6	
2011	**LE BEAU BAI** 8-10-1	
**2012	**MONBEG DUDE** 8-10-1	
2013	**MOUNTAINOUS** 8-10-0	
2014	**EMPEROR'S CHOICE** 7-10-8	
***2015	**MOUNTAINOUS** 11-10-6	
2016	**NATIVE RIVER** 6-11-12	
****2017	**RAZ DE MAREE** 13-10-10	
2018	**ELEGANT ESCAPE** 6-11-8	

*Run in January 2011
**Run in January 2013
***Run in January 2016
****Run in January 2018

CLARENCE HOUSE CHASE
(Victor Chandler Chase before 2014)
Ascot-2m 167yds

2010	**TWIST MAGIC** 8-11-7	
2011	**MASTER MINDED** 8-11-7	
2012	**SOMERSBY** 8-11-7	
*2013	**SPRINTER SACRE** 7-11-7	
2014	**SIRE DE GRUGY** 8-11-7	
2015	**DODGING BULLETS** 7-11-7	
2016	**UN DE SCEAUX** 8-11-7	
*2017	**UN DE SCEAUX** 9-11-7	
2018	**UN DE SCEAUX** 10-11-7	
2019	**ALTIOR** 9-11-7	

*Run at Cheltenham

BETFAIR HANDICAP HURDLE
Newbury-2m 69yds
(Totesport Trophy before 2012)

2010	**GET ME OUT OF HERE** 6-10-6	
2011	**RECESSION PROOF** 5-10-8	
2012	**ZARKANDAR** 5-11-1	
2013	**MY TENT OR YOURS** 6-11-2	
2014	**SPLASH OF GINGE** 6-10-3	
2015	**VIOLET DANCER** 5-10-9	
2016	**AGRAPART** 5-10-5	
2017	**BALLYANDY** 6-11-1	
2018	**KALASHNIKOV** 5-11-5	

SUPREME NOVICES' HURDLE
Cheltenham-2m 87yds

2009	**GO NATIVE** 6-11-7	
2010	**MENORAH** 5-11-7	
2011	**AL FEROF** 6-11-7	
2012	**CINDERS AND ASHES** 5-11-7	
2013	**CHAMPAGNE FEVER** 6-11-7	
2014	**VAUTOUR** 5-11-7	
2015	**DOUVAN** 5-11-7	
2016	**ALTIOR** 6-11-7	
2017	**LABAIK** 6-11-7	
2018	**SUMMERVILLE BOY** 6-11-7	

ARKLE CHALLENGE TROPHY (NOVICES' CHASE)
Cheltenham-1m 7f 199yds

2009	**FORPADYDEPLASTERER** 7-11-7	
2010	**SIZING EUROPE** 8-11-7	
2011	**CAPTAIN CHRIS** 7-11-7	

12	SPRINTER SACRE 6-11-7	6
13	SIMONSIG 7-11-7	7
14	WESTERN WARHORSE 6-11-4	9
15	UN DE SCEAUX 7-11-4	11
16	DOUVAN 6-11-4	7
17	ALTIOR 7-11-4	9
18	FOOTPAD 6-11-4	5

CHAMPION HURDLE
Cheltenham-2m 87yds

09	PUNJABI 6-11-10	23
10	BINOCULAR 6-11-10	12
11	HURRICANE FLY 7-11-10	11
12	ROCK ON RUBY 7-11-10	10
13	HURRICANE FLY 9-11-10	9
14	JEZKI 6-11-10	9
15	FAUGHEEN 7-11-10	8
16	ANNIE POWER 8-11-3	12
17	BUVEUR D'AIR 6-11-10	11
18	BUVEUR D'AIR 7-11-10	11

QUEEN MOTHER CHAMPION CHASE
Cheltenham-1m 7f 199yds

09	MASTER MINDED 6-11-10	12
10	BIG ZEB 9-11-10	9
11	SIZING EUROPE 9-11-10	11
12	FINIAN'S RAINBOW 9-11-10	8
13	SPRINTER SACRE 7-11-10	7
14	SIRE DE GRUGY 8-11-10	11
15	DODGING BULLETS 7-11-10	11
16	SPRINTER SACRE 10-11-10	10
17	SPECIAL TIARA 10-11-10	10
18	ALTIOR 8-11-10	9

BALLYMORE NOVICES' HURDLE
Cheltenham-2m 5f 26yds

09	MIKAEL D'HAGUENET 5-11-7	14
10	PEDDLERS CROSS 5-11-7	17
11	FIRST LIEUTENANT 6-11-7	12
12	SIMONSIG 6-11-7	17
13	THE NEW ONE 6-11-7	8
14	FAUGHEEN 6-11-7	15
15	WINDSOR PARK 6-11-7	10
16	YORKHILL 6-11-7	11
17	WILLOUGHBY COURT 6-11-7	15
18	SAMCRO 6-11-7	14

RSA CHASE
(Royal & SunAlliance Chase before 2009)
Cheltenham-3m 80yds

09	COOLDINE 7-11-4	15
10	WEAPON'S AMNESTY 7-11-4	9
11	BOSTONS ANGEL 7-11-4	12
12	BOBS WORTH 7-11-4	9
13	LORD WINDERMERE 7-11-4	11
14	O'FAOLAINS BOY 7-11-4	15
15	DON POLI 6-11-4	8
16	BLAKLION 7-11-4	8
17	MIGHT BITE 8-11-4	12
18	PRESENTING PERCY 7-11-4	10

STAYERS' HURDLE
(World Hurdle before 2017)
Cheltenham-2m 7f 213 yds

09	BIG BUCK'S 6-11-10	14
10	BIG BUCK'S 7-11-10	14
11	BIG BUCK'S 8-11-10	13
2012	BIG BUCK'S 9-11-10	11
2013	SOLWHIT 9-11-10	13
2014	MORE OF THAT 6-11-10	10
2015	COLE HARDEN 6-11-10	16
2016	THISTLECRACK 8-11-10	12
2017	NICHOLS CANYON 7-11-10	12
2018	PENHILL 7-11-10	15

TRIUMPH HURDLE (4y)
Cheltenham-2m 179yds

2009	ZAYNAR 11-0	18
2010	SOLDATINO 11-0	17
2011	ZARKANDAR 11-0	23
2012	COUNTRYWIDE FLAME 11-0	20
2013	OUR CONOR 11-0	17
2014	TIGER ROLL 11-0	15
2015	PEACE AND CO 11-0	16
2016	IVANOVICH GORBATOV 11-0	15
2017	DEFI DU SEUIL 11-0	15
2018	FARCLAS 11-0	9

CHELTENHAM GOLD CUP
Cheltenham-3m 2f 110yds

2009	KAUTO STAR 9-11-10	16
2010	IMPERIAL COMMANDER 9-11-10	11
2011	LONG RUN 6-11-0	13
2012	SYNCHRONISED 9-11-10	14
2013	BOBS WORTH 8-11-10	9
2014	LORD WINDERMERE 8-11-10	13
2015	CONEYGREE 8-11-10	16
2016	DON COSSACK 9-11-10	9
2017	SIZING JOHN 7-11-10	13
2018	NATIVE RIVER 8-11-10	15

RYANAIR CHASE
(FESTIVAL TROPHY)
Cheltenham-2m 4f 166yds

2009	IMPERIAL COMMANDER 8-11-10	10
2010	ALBERTAS RUN 9-11-10	13
2011	ALBERTAS RUN 10-11-10	11
2012	RIVERSIDE THEATRE 8-11-10	12
2013	CUE CARD 7-11-10	8
2014	DYNASTE 8-11-10	11
2015	UXIZANDRE 7-11-10	14
2016	VAUTOUR 7-11-10	15
2017	UN DE SCEAUX 9-11-10	8
2018	BALKO DES FLOS 7-11-10	6

BOWL CHASE
Aintree-3m 210yds

2009	MADISON DU BERLAIS 8-11-10	10
2010	WHAT A FRIEND 7-11-7	5
2011	NACARAT 10-11-7	6
2012	FOLLOW THE PLAN 9-11-7	11
2013	FIRST LIEUTENANT 8-11-7	8
2014	SILVINIACO CONTI 8-11-7	6
2015	SILVINIACO CONTI 9-11-7	7
2016	CUE CARD 10-11-7	9
2017	TEA FOR TWO 8-11-7	7
2018	MIGHT BITE 9-11-7	8

MELLING CHASE
Aintree-2m 3f 200yds

2009	VOY POR USTEDES 8-11-10	10
2010	ALBERTAS RUN 9-11-10	11
2011	MASTER MINDED 8-11-10	10

2012	**FINIAN'S RAINBOW** 9-11-10	8
2013	**SPRINTER SACRE** 7-11-10	6
2014	**BOSTON BOB** 9-11-10	10
2015	**DON COSSACK** 8-11-10	10
2016	**GOD'S OWN** 8-11-10	6
2017	**FOX NORTON** 7-11-7	9
2018	**POLITOLOGUE** 7-11-7	6

AINTREE HURDLE
Aintree-2m 4f

2009	**SOLWHIT** 5-11-7	16
2010	**KHYBER KIM** 8-11-7	7
2011	**OSCAR WHISKY** 6-11-7	8
2012	**OSCAR WHISKY** 7-11-7	5
2013	**ZARKANDAR** 6-11-7	9
2014	**THE NEW ONE** 6-11-7	7
2015	**JEZKI** 7-11-7	6
2016	**ANNIE POWER** 8-11-0	6
2017	**BUVEUR D'AIR** 6-11-7	6
2018	**L'AMI SERGE** 8-11-7	9

SCOTTISH GRAND NATIONAL (H'CAP CHASE)
Ayr-3m 7f 176 yds

2009	**HELLO BUD** 11-10-9	17
2010	**MERIGO** 9-10-0	30

2011	**BESHABAR** 9-10-4	2
2012	**MERIGO** 11-10-2	2
2013	**GODSMEJUDGE** 7-11-3	2
2014	**AL CO** 9-10-0	2
2015	**WAYWARD PRINCE** 11-10-1	2
2016	**VICENTE** 7-11-3	2
2017	**VICENTE** 8-11-10	3
2018	**JOE FARRELL** 9-10-6	2

BET365 GOLD CUP (H'CAP CHASE)
Sandown-3m 4f 166yds

2009	**HENNESSY** 8-10-7	1
2010	**CHURCH ISLAND** 11-10-5	1
2011	**POKER DE SIVOLA** 8-10-12	1
2012	**TIDAL BAY** 11-11-12	1
2013	**QUENTIN COLLONGES** 9-10-12	1
2014	**HADRIAN'S APPROACH** 7-11-0	1
2015	**JUST A PAR** 8-10-0	2
2016	**THE YOUNG MASTER** 7-10-12	2
2017	**HENLLAN HARRI** 9-10-0	1
2018	**STEP BACK** 8-10-0	2

DISTANCE CONVERSION

5f	1,000m	10f	2,000m	15f	3,000m	20f	4,000m
6f	1,200m	11f	2,200m	16f	3,200m	21f	4,200m
7f	1,400m	12f	2,400m	17f	3,400m	22f	4,400m
8f	1,600m	13f	2,600m	18f	3,600m		
9f	1,800m	14f	2,800m	19f	3,800m		

LEADING TRAINERS ON THE FLAT: 1902-2018

1902 R S Sievier	1941 F Darling	1980 W Hern
1903 G Blackwell	1942 F Darling	1981 M Stoute
1904 P P Gilpin	1943 W Nightingall	1982 H Cecil
1905 W T Robinson	1944 Frank Butters	1983 W Hern
1906 Hon G Lambton	1945 W Earl	1984 H Cecil
1907 A Taylor	1946 Frank Butters	1985 H Cecil
1908 C Morton	1947 F Darling	1986 M Stoute
1909 A Taylor	1948 C F N Murless	1987 H Cecil
1910 A Taylor	1949 Frank Butters	1988 H Cecil
1911 Hon G Lambton	1950 C H Semblat	1989 M Stoute
1912 Hon G Lambton	1951 J L Jarvis	1990 H Cecil
1913 R Wootton	1952 M Marsh	1991 P Cole
1914 A Taylor	1953 J L Jarvis	1992 R Hannon Snr
1915 P P Gilpin	1954 C Boyd-Rochfort	1993 H Cecil
1916 R C Dawson	1955 C Boyd-Rochfort	1994 M Stoute
1917 A Taylor	1956 C F Elsey	1995 J Dunlop
1918 A Taylor	1957 C F N Murless	1996 Saeed bin Suroor
1919 A Taylor	1958 C Boyd-Rochfort	1997 M Stoute
1920 A Taylor	1959 C F N Murless	1998 Saeed bin Suroor
1921 A Taylor	1960 C F N Murless	1999 Saeed bin Suroor
1922 A Taylor	1961 C F N Murless	2000 Sir M Stoute
1923 A Taylor	1962 W Hern	2001 A O'Brien
1924 R C Dawson	1963 P Prendergast	2002 A O'Brien
1925 A Taylor	1964 P Prendergast	2003 Sir M Stoute
1926 F Darling	1965 P Prendergast	2004 Saeed bin Suroor
1927 Frank Butters	1966 M V O'Brien	2005 Sir M Stoute
1928 Frank Butters	1967 C F N Murless	2006 Sir M Stoute
1929 R C Dawson	1968 C F N Murless	2007 A O'Brien
1930 H S Persse	1969 A M Budgett	2008 A O'Brien
1931 J Lawson	1970 C F N Murless	2009 Sir M Stoute
1932 Frank Butters	1971 I Balding	2010 R Hannon Snr
1933 F Darling	1972 W Hern	2011 R Hannon Snr
1934 Frank Butters	1973 C F N Murless	2012 J Gosden
1935 Frank Butters	1974 P Walwyn	2013 R Hannon Snr
1936 J Lawson	1975 P Walwyn	2014 R Hannon Jnr
1937 C Boyd-Rochfort	1976 H Cecil	2015 J Gosden
1938 C Boyd-Rochfort	1977 M V O'Brien	2016 A O'Brien
1939 J L Jarvis	1978 H Cecil	2017 A O'Brien
1940 F Darling	1979 H Cecil	2018 J Gosden

CHAMPION JOCKEYS ON THE FLAT: 1901-2018

1901 O Madden	130	1921 S Donoghue	141	1940 G Richards	
1902 W Lane	170	1922 S Donoghue	102	1941 H Wragg	
1903 O Madden	154	1923 S Donoghue	89	1942 G Richards	
1904 O Madden	161	C Elliott	89	1943 G Richards	
1905 E Wheatley	124	1924 C Elliott	106	1944 G Richards	
1906 W Higgs	149	1925 G Richards	118	1945 G Richards	
1907 W Higgs	146	1926 T Weston	95	1946 G Richards	
1908 D Maher	139	1927 G Richards	164	1947 G Richards	
1909 F Wootton	165	1928 G Richards	148	1948 G Richards	
1910 F Wootton	137	1929 G Richards	135	1949 G Richards	
1911 F Wootton	187	1930 F Fox	129	1950 G Richards	
1912 F Wootton	118	1931 G Richards	145	1951 G Richards	
1913 D Maher	115	1932 G Richards	190	1952 G Richards	
1914 S Donoghue	129	1933 G Richards	259	1953 Sir G Richards	
1915 S Donoghue	62	1934 G Richards	212	1954 D Smith	
1916 S Donoghue	43	1935 G Richards	217	1955 D Smith	
1917 S Donoghue	42	1936 G Richards	174	1956 D Smith	
1918 S Donoghue	66	1937 G Richards	216	1957 A Breasley	
1919 S Donoghue	129	1938 G Richards	206	1958 D Smith	
1920 S Donoghue	143	1939 G Richards	155	1959 D Smith	

60 L Piggott ... 170	1980 W Carson ... 166	2000 K Darley ... 152	
61 A Breasley ... 171	1981 L Piggott ... 179	2001 K Fallon ... 166	
62 A Breasley ... 179	1982 L Piggott ... 188	2002 K Fallon ... 144	
63 A Breasley ... 176	1983 W Carson ... 159	2003 K Fallon ... 208	
64 L Piggott ... 140	1984 S Cauthen ... 130	2004 L Dettori ... 192	
65 L Piggott ... 160	1985 S Cauthen ... 195	2005 J Spencer ... 163	
66 L Piggott ... 191	1986 Pat Eddery ... 176	2006 R Moore ... 180	
67 L Piggott ... 117	1987 S Cauthen ... 197	2007 S Sanders ... 190	
68 L Piggott ... 139	1988 Pat Eddery ... 183	J Spencer ... 190	
69 L Piggott ... 163	1989 Pat Eddery ... 171	2008 R Moore ... 186	
70 L Piggott ... 162	1990 Pat Eddery ... 209	2009 R Moore ... 174	
71 L Piggott ... 162	1991 Pat Eddery ... 165	2010 P Hanagan ... 191	
72 W Carson ... 132	1992 M Roberts ... 206	2011 P Hanagan ... 165	
73 W Carson ... 164	1993 Pat Eddery ... 169	2012 R Hughes ... 172	
74 Pat Eddery ... 148	1994 L Dettori ... 233	2013 R Hughes ... 203	
75 Pat Eddery ... 164	1995 L Dettori ... 211	2014 R Hughes ... 161	
76 Pat Eddery ... 162	1996 Pat Eddery ... 186	2015 S De Sousa ... 132	
77 Pat Eddery ... 176	1997 K Fallon ... 196	2016 J Crowley ... 148	
78 W Carson ... 182	1998 K Fallon ... 185	2017 S De Sousa ... 155	
79 J Mercer ... 164	1999 K Fallon ... 200	2018 S De Sousa ... 148	

CHAMPION APPRENTICES ON THE FLAT 1983-2018

83 M Hills ... 39	1995 S Sanders ... 61	2007 G Fairley ... 65
84 T Quinn ... 62	1996 D O'Neill ... 79	2008 W Buick ... 50
85 G Carter ... 37	1997 R Ffrench ... 77	D Probert ... 50
W Ryan ... 37	1998 C Lowther ... 72	2009 F Tylicki ... 60
86 G Carter ... 34	1999 R Winston ... 49	2010 M Lane ... 41
87 G Bardwell ... 27	2000 L Newman ... 87	2011 M Harley ... 57
88 G Bardwell ... 39	2001 C Catlin ... 71	2012 A Ryan ... 40
89 L Dettori ... 71	2002 P Hanagan ... 81	2013 J Hart ... 51
90 J Fortune ... 46	2003 R Moore ... 52	2014 O Murphy ... 74
91 D Holland ... 79	2004 T Queally ... 59	2015 T Marquand ... 54
92 D Harrison ... 56	2005 S Golam ... 44	2016 J Gordon ... 50
93 J Weaver ... 60	H Turner ... 44	2017 D Egan ... 61
94 S Davies ... 45	2006 S Donohoe ... 44	2018 J Watson ... 77

LEADING OWNERS ON THE FLAT: 1897-2018

97 Mr J Gubbins	1921 Mr S B Joel	1945 Ld Derby
98 Ld de Rothschild	1922 Ld Woolavington	1946 H.H. Aga Khan
99 Duke of Westminster	1923 Ld Derby	1947 H.H. Aga Khan
00 H.R.H. The Prince of Wales	1924 H.H. Aga Khan	1948 H.H. Aga Khan
01 Sir G Blundell Maple	1925 Ld Astor	1949 H.H. Aga Khan
02 Mr R S Sievier	1926 Ld Woolavington	1950 M M Boussac
03 Sir James Miller	1927 Ld Derby	1951 M M Boussac
04 Sir James Miller	1928 Ld Derby	1952 H.H. Aga Khan
05 Col W Hall Walker	1929 H.H. Aga Khan	1953 Sir Victor Sassoon
06 Ld Derby (late)	1930 H.H. Aga Khan	1954 Her Majesty
07 Col W Hall Walker	1931 Mr J A Dewar	1955 Lady Zia Wernner
08 Mr J B Joel	1932 H.H. Aga Khan	1956 Maj L B Holliday
09 Mr "Fairie"	1933 Ld Derby	1957 Her Majesty
10 Mr "Fairie"	1934 H.H. Aga Khan	1958 Mr J McShain
11 Ld Derby	1935 H.H. Aga Khan	1959 Prince Aly Khan
12 Mr T Pilkington	1936 Ld Astor	1960 Sir Victor Sassoon
13 Mr J B Joel	1937 H.H. Aga Khan	1961 Maj L B Holliday
14 Mr J B Joel	1938 Ld Derby	1962 Maj L B Holliday
15 Mr L Neumann	1939 Ld Rosebery	1963 Mr J R Mullion
16 Mr E Hulton	1940 Lord Rothermere	1964 Mrs H E Jackson
17 Mr "Fairie"	1941 Ld Glanely	1965 M J Ternynck
18 Lady James Douglas	1942 His Majesty	1966 Lady Zia Wernher
19 Ld Glanely	1943 Miss D Paget	1967 Mr H J Joel
20 Sir Robert Jardine	1944 H.H. Aga Khan	1968 Mr Raymond R Guest

1969 Mr D Robinson
1970 Mr C Engelhard
1971 Mr P Mellon
1972 Mrs J Hislop
1973 Mr N B Hunt
1974 Mr N B Hunt
1975 Dr C Vittadini
1976 Mr D Wildenstein
1977 Mr R Sangster
1978 Mr R Sangster
1979 Sir M Sobell
1980 S Weinstock
1981 H.H. Aga Khan
1982 Mr R Sangster
1983 Mr R Sangster
1984 Mr R Sangster
1985 Sheikh Mohammed

1986 Sheikh Mohammed
1987 Sheikh Mohammed
1988 Sheikh Mohammed
1989 Sheikh Mohammed
1990 Mr Hamdan Al-Maktoum
1991 Sheikh Mohammed
1992 Sheikh Mohammed
1993 Sheikh Mohammed
1994 Mr Hamdan Al-Maktoum
1995 Mr Hamdan Al-Maktoum
1996 Godolphin
1997 Sheikh Mohammed
1998 Godolphin
1999 Godolphin
2000 H.H. Aga Khan
2001 Godolphin
2002 Mr Hamdan Al-Maktoum

2003 K Abdullah
2004 Godolphin
2005 Mr Hamdan Al-Maktoum
2006 Godolphin
2007 Godolphin
2008 HRH Princess Haya of Jor
2009 Mr Hamdan Al-Maktoum
2010 K Abdullah
2011 K Abdullah
2012 Godolphin
2013 Godolphin
2014 Mr Hamdan Al-Maktoum
2015 Godolphin
2016 Godolphin
2017 Godolphin
2018 Godolphin

LEADING SIRES ON THE FLAT: 1897-2018

1897 Kendal
1898 Galopin
1899 Orme
1900 St Simon
1901 St Simon
1902 Persimmon
1903 St Frusquin
1904 Gallinule
1905 Gallinule
1906 Persimmon
1907 St Frusquin
1908 Persimmon
1909 Cyllene
1910 Cyllene
1911 Sundridge
1912 Persimmon
1913 Desmond
1914 Polymelus
1915 Polymelus
1916 Polymelus
1917 Bayardo
1918 Bayardo
1919 The Tetrarch
1920 Polymelus
1921 Polymelus
1922 Lemberg
1923 Swynford
1924 Son-in-Law
1925 Phalaris
1926 Hurry On
1927 Buchan
1928 Phalaris
1929 Tetratema
1930 Son-in-Law
1931 Pharos
1932 Gainsborough
1933 Gainsborough
1934 Blandford
1935 Blandford
1936 Fairway
1937 Solario

1938 Blandford
1939 Fairway
1940 Hyperion
1941 Hyperion
1942 Hyperion
1943 Fairway
1944 Fairway
1945 Hyperion
1946 Hyperion
1947 Nearco
1948 Big Game
1949 Nearco
1950 Fair Trial
1951 Nasrullah
1952 Tehran
1953 Chanteur II
1954 Hyperion
1955 Alycidon
1956 Court Martial
1957 Court Martial
1958 Mossborough
1959 Petition
1960 Aureole
1961 Aureole
1962 Never Say Die
1963 Ribot
1964 Chamossaire
1965 Court Harwell
1966 Charlottesville
1967 Ribot
1968 Ribot
1969 Crepello
1970 Northern Dancer
1971 Never Bend
1972 Queen's Hussar
1973 Vaguely Noble
1974 Vaguely Noble
1975 Great Nephew
1976 Wolver Hollow
1977 Northern Dancer
1978 Mill Reef (USA)

1979 Petingo
1980 Pitcairn
1981 Great Nephew
1982 Be My Guest (USA)
1983 Northern Dancer
1984 Northern Dancer
1985 Kris
1986 Nijinsky (CAN)
1987 Mill Reef (USA)
1988 Caerleon (USA)
1989 Blushing Groom (FR)
1990 Sadler's Wells (USA)
1991 Caerleon (USA)
1992 Sadler's Wells (USA)
1993 Sadler's Wells (USA)
1994 Sadler's Wells (USA)
1995 Sadler's Wells (USA)
1996 Sadler's Wells (USA)
1997 Sadler's Wells (USA)
1998 Sadler's Wells (USA)
1999 Sadler's Wells (USA)
2000 Sadler's Wells (USA)
2001 Sadler's Wells (USA)
2002 Sadler's Wells (USA)
2003 Sadler's Wells (USA)
2004 Sadler's Wells (USA)
2005 Danehill (USA)
2006 Danehill (USA)
2007 Danehill (USA)
2008 Galileo (IRE)
2009 Danehill Dancer (IRE)
2010 Galileo (IRE)
2011 Galileo (IRE)
2012 Galileo (IRE)
2013 Galileo (IRE)
2014 Galileo (IRE)
2015 Galileo (IRE)
2016 Galileo (IRE)
2017 Galileo (IRE)
2018 Galileo (IRE)

EADING BREEDERS ON THE FLAT: 1913-2018

13 Mr J B Joel	1949 H.H. Aga Khan	1984 Mr E P Taylor
14 Mr J B Joel	1950 M M Boussac	1985 Dalham Stud Farms
15 Mr L Neumann	1951 M M Boussac	1986 H.H. Aga Khan
16 Mr E Hulton	1952 H. H. Aga Khan	1987 Cliveden Stud
17 Mr "Fairie"	1953 Mr F Darling	1988 H. H. Aga Khan
18 Lady James Douglas	1954 Maj L B Holliday	1989 Mr Hamdan Al-Maktoum
19 Ld Derby	1955 Someries Stud	1990 Capt. Macdonald- Buchanan
20 Ld Derby	1956 Maj L B Holliday	1991 Barronstown Stud
21 Mr S B Joel	1957 Eve Stud	1992 Swettenham Stud
22 Ld Derby	1958 Mr R Ball	1993 Juddmonte Farms
23 Ld Derby	1959 Prince Aly Khan and the late	1994 Shadwell Farm & Estate Ltd
24 Lady Sykes	H.H. Aga Khan	1995 Shadwell Farm & Estate Ltd
25 Ld Astor	1960 Eve Stud Ltd	1996 Sheikh Mohammed
26 Ld Woolavington	1961 Eve Stud Ltd	1997 Sheikh Mohammed
27 Ld Derby	1962 Maj L B Holliday	1998 Sheikh Mohammed
28 Ld Derby	1963 Mr H F Guggenheim	1999 H. H. The Aga Khan's Studs
29 Ld Derby	1964 Bull Run Stud	2000 H. H. The Aga Khan's Studs
30 Ld Derby	1965 Mr J Ternynck	2001 Shadwell Farm & Estate Ltd
31 Ld Dewar	1966 Someries Stud	2002 Gainsborough Stud
32 H.H. Aga Khan	1967 Mr H J Joel	2003 Juddmonte
33 Sir Alec Black	1968 Mill Ridge Farm	2004 Juddmonte
34 H.H. Aga Khan	1969 Lord Rosebery	2005 Shadwell Farm & Estate Ltd
35 H.H. Aga Khan	1970 Mr E P Taylor	2006 Darley
36 Ld Astor	1971 Mr P Mellon	2007 Darley
37 H.H. Aga Khan	1972 Mr J Hislop	2008 Darley
38 Ld Derby	1973 Claiborne Farm	2009 Darley
39 Ld Rosebery	1974 Mr N B Hunt	2010 Juddmonte
40 Mr H E Morriss	1975 Overbury Stud	2011 Juddmonte
41 Ld Glanely	1976 Dayton Ltd	2012 Juddmonte
42 National Stud	1977 Mr E P Taylor	2013 Darley
43 Miss D Paget	1978 Cragwood Estates Inc	2014 Darley
44 Ld Rosebery	1979 Ballymacoll Stud	2015 Darley
45 Ld Derby	1980 P Clarke	2016 Darley
46 Lt- Col H Boyd-Rochfort	1981 H.H. Aga Khan	2017 Darley
47 H.H. Aga Khan	1982 Someries Stud	2018 Godolphin
48 H.H. Aga Khan	1983 White Lodge Stud	

EADING TRAINERS OVER JUMPS: 1948-2018

48-49 F T T Walwyn	1972-73 F T Winter	1996-97 M C Pipe
49-50 P V F Cazalet	1973-74 F T Winter	1997-98 M C Pipe
50-51 T F Rimell	1974-75 F T Winter	1998-99 M C Pipe
51-52 N Crump	1975-76 T F Rimell	1999-00 M C Pipe
52-53 M V O'Brien	1976-77 F T Winter	2000-01 M C Pipe
53-54 M V O'Brien	1977-78 F T Winter	2001-02 M C Pipe
54-55 H R Price	1978-79 M H Easterby	2002-03 M C Pipe
55-56 W Hall	1979-80 M H Easterby	2003-04 M C Pipe
56-57 N Crump	1980-81 M H Easterby	2004-05 M C Pipe
57-58 F T T Walwyn	1981-82 M W Dickinson	2005-06 P F Nicholls
58-59 H R Price	1982-83 M W Dickinson	2006-07 P F Nicholls
59-60 P V F Cazalet	1983-84 M W Dickinson	2007-08 P F Nicholls
60-61 T F Rimell	1984-85 F T Winter	2008-09 P F Nicholls
61-62 H R Price	1985-86 N J Henderson	2009-10 P F Nicholls
62-63 K Piggott	1986-87 N J Henderson	2010-11 P F Nicholls
63-64 F T T Walwyn	1987-88 D R C Elsworth	2010-11 P F Nicholls
64-65 P V F Cazalet	1988-89 M C Pipe	2011-12 P F Nicholls
65-66 H R Price	1989-90 M C Pipe	2012-13 N J Henderson
66-67 H R Price	1990-91 M C Pipe	2013-14 P F Nicholls
67-68 Denys Smith	1991-92 M C Pipe	2014-15 P F Nicholls
68-69 T F Rimell	1992-93 M C Pipe	2015-16 P F Nicholls
69-70 T F Rimell	1993-94 D Nicholson	2016-17 N J Henderson
70-71 F T Winter	1994-95 D Nicholson	2017-18 N J Henderson
71-72 F T Winter	1995-96 M C Pipe	

CHAMPION JOCKEYS OVER JUMPS: 1903-2018

Prior to the 1925-26 season the figure relates to racing between January and December

1903 P Woodland 54	1942-43 No racing	1980-81 J Francome ....
1904 F Mason 59	1943-44 No racing	1981-82 J Francome ....
1905 F Mason 73	1944-45 H Nicholson...............15	P Scudamore.......
1906 F Mason 58	T F Rimell 15	1982-83 J Francome ....
1907 F Mason 59	1945-46 T F Rimell 54	1983-84 J Francome ....
1908 P Cowley 65	1946-47 J Dowdeswell...........58	1984-85 J Francome ....
1909 R Gordon 45	1947-48 B Marshall...............66	1985-86 P Scudamore..........
1910 E Piggott 67	1948-49 T Moloney 60	1986-87 P Scudamore..........
1911 W Payne....................76	1949-50 T Moloney 95	1987-88 P Scudamore..........
1912 I Anthony....................78	1950-51 T Moloney 83	1988-89 P Scudamore..........
1913 E Piggott 60	1951-52 T Moloney 99	1989-90 P Scudamore..........
1914 Mr J R Anthony 60	1952-53 F Winter....................121	1990-91 P Scudamore..........
1915 E Piggott 44	1953-54 F Francis 76	1991-92 P Scudamore..........
1916 C Hawkins.................17	1954-55 T Moloney 67	1992-93 R Dunwoody..........
1917 W Smith.....................15	1955-56 F Winter....................74	1993-94 R Dunwoody..........
1918 G Duller.....................17	1956-57 F Winter....................80	1994-95 R Dunwoody..........
1919 Mr H Brown...............48	1957-58 F Winter....................82	1995-96 A P McCoy...........
1920 F B Rees....................64	1958-59 T Brookshaw 83	1996-97 A P McCoy...........
1921 F B Rees....................65	1959-60 S Mellor 68	1997-98 A P McCoy...........
1922 J Anthony...................78	1960-61 S Mellor 118	1998-99 A P McCoy...........
1923 F B Rees....................64	1961-62 S Mellor 80	1999-00 A P McCoy...........
1924 F B Rees....................108	1962-63 J Gifford 70	2000-01 A P McCoy...........
1925 E Foster 76	1963-64 J Gifford 94	2001-02 A P McCoy...........
1925-26 T Leader...............61	1964-65 T Biddlecombe 114	2002-03 A P McCoy...........
1926-27 F B Rees...............59	1965-66 T Biddlecombe 102	2003-04 A P McCoy...........
1927-28 W Stott.................88	1966-67 J Gifford 122	2004-05 A P McCoy...........
1928-29 W Stott.................65	1967-68 J Gifford 82	2005-06 A P McCoy...........
1929-30 W Stott.................77	1968-69 B R Davies 77	2006-07 A P McCoy...........
1930-31 W Stott.................81	T Biddlecombe 77	2007-08 A P McCoy...........
1931-32 W Stott.................77	1969-70 B R Davies 91	2008-09 A P McCoy...........
1932-33 G Wilson...............61	1970-71 G Thorner 74	2009-10 A P McCoy...........
1933-34 G Wilson...............56	1971-72 B R Davies 89	2010-11 A P McCoy...........
1934-35 G Wilson...............73	1972-73 R Barry.....................125	2011-12 A P McCoy...........
1935-36 G Wilson...............57	1973-74 R Barry.....................94	2012-13 A P McCoy...........
1936-37 G Wilson...............45	1974-75 T Stack.....................82	2013-14 A P McCoy...........
1937-38 G Wilson...............59	1975-76 J Francome...............96	2014-15 A P McCoy...........
1938-39 T F Rimell.............61	1976-77 T Stack.....................97	2015-16 R Johnson............
1939-40 T F Rimell.............24	1977-78 J J O'Neill.................149	2016-17 R Johnson............
1940-41 G Wilson...............22	1978-79 J Francome...............95	2017-18 R Johnson............
1941-42 R Smyth.................12	1979-80 J J O'Neill.................117	

LEADING OWNERS OVER JUMPS: 1948-2018

(Please note that prior to the 1994-95 season the leading owner was determined by win prizemoney only)

1948-49 Mr W F Williamson	1966-67 Mr C P T Watkins	1984-85 T Kilroe and Son Ltd
1949-50 Mrs L Brotherton	1967-68 Mr H S Alper	1985-86 Sheikh Ali Abu Khamsi
1950-51 Mr J Royle	1968-69 Mr B P Jenks	1986-87 Mr H J Joel
1951-52 Miss D Paget	1969-70 Mr E R Courage	1987-88 Miss Juliet E Reed
1952-53 Mr J H Griffin	1970-71 Mr F Pontin	1988-89 Mr R Burridge
1953-54 Mr J H Griffin	1971-72 Capt T A Forster	1989-90 Mrs Harry J Duffey
1954-55 Mrs W H E Welman	1972-73 Mr N H Le Mare	1990-91 Mr P Piller
1955-56 Mrs L Carver	1973-74 Mr N H Le Mare	1991-92 Whitcombe Manor
1956-57 Mrs Geoffrey Kohn	1974-75 Mr R Guest	Racing Stables Ltd
1957-58 Mr D J Coughlan	1975-76 Mr P B Raymond	1992-93 Mrs J Mould
1958-59 Mr J E Bigg	1976-77 Mr N H Le Mare	1993-94 Pell-Mell Partners
1959-60 Miss W H Wallace	1977-78 Mrs O Jackson	1994-95 Roach Foods Limited
1960-61 Mr C Vaughan	1978-79 Snailwell Stud Co Ltd	1995-96 Mr A T A Wates
1961-62 Mr N Cohen	1979-80 Mr H J Joel	1996-97 Mr R Ogden
1962-63 Mr P B Raymond	1980-81 Mr R J Wilson	1997-98 Mr D A Johnson
1963-64 Mr J K Goodman	1981-82 Sheikh Ali Abu Khamsin	1998-99 Mr J P McManus
1964-65 Mrs M Stephenson	1982-83 Sheikh Ali Abu Khamsin	1999-00 Mr R Ogden
1965-66 Duchess of Westminster	1983-84 Sheikh Ali Abu Khamsin	2000-01 Sir R Ogden

01-02 Mr D A Johnson	2007-08 Mr D A Johnson	2013-14 Mr J P McManus
02-03 Mr D A Johnson	2008-09 Mr J P McManus	2014-15 Mr J P McManus
03-04 Mr D A Johnson	2009-10 Mr J P McManus	2015-16 Gigginstown House Stud
04-05 Mr D A Johnson	2010-11 Mr T Hemmings	2016-17 Mr J P McManus
05-06 Mr J P McManus	2011-12 Mr J P McManus	2017-18 Mr J P McManus
06-07 Mr J P McManus	2012-13 Mr J P McManus	

LEADING AMATEUR RIDERS OVER JUMPS: 1951-2018

51-52 Mr C Straker	19	1973-74 Mr A Webber	21	1995-96 Mr J Culloty	40
52-53 Mr A H Moralee	22	1974-75 Mr R Lamb	22	1996-97 Mr R Thornton	30
53-54 Mr A H Moralee	22	1975-76 Mr P Greenall	25	1997-98 Mr S Durack	41
54-55 Mr A H Moralee	16	Mr G Jones	25	1998-99 Mr A Dempsey	47
55-56 Mr R McCreery	13	1976-77 Mr P Greenall	27	1999-00 Mr P Flynn	41
Mr A H Moralee	13	1977-78 Mr G Sloan	23	2000-01 Mr T Scudamore	24
56-57 Mr R McCreery	23	1978-79 Mr T G Dun	26	2001-02 Mr D Crosse	19
57-58 Mr J Lawrence	18	1979-80 Mr O Sherwood	29	2002-03 Mr C Williams	23
58-59 Mr J Sutcliffe	18	1980-81 Mr P Webber	32	2003-04 Mr O Nelmes	14
59-60 Mr G Kindersley	22	1981-82 Mr D Browne	28	2004-05 Mr T Greenall	31
60-61 Sir W Pigott-Brown	28	1982-83 Mr D Browne	33	2005-06 Mr T O'Brien	32
61-62 Mr A Biddlecombe	30	1983-84 Mr S Sherwood	28	2006-07 Mr T Greenall	31
62-63 Sir W Pigott-Brown	20	1984-85 Mr S Sherwood	30	2007-08 Mr T Greenall	23
63-64 Mr S Davenport	32	1985-86 Mr T Thomson Jones	25	2008-09 Mr O Greenall	23
64-65 Mr M Gifford	15	1986-87 Mr T Thomson Jones	19	2009-10 Mr O Greenall	41
65-66 Mr C Collins	24	1987-88 Mr T Thomson Jones	15	2010-11 Mr R Mahon	19
66-67 Mr C Collins	33	1988-89 Mr P Fenton	18	2011-12 Miss E Sayer	11
67-68 Mr R Tate	30	1989-90 Mr P McMahon	15	2012-13 Mr N de Boinville	16
68-69 Mr R Tate	17	1990-91 Mr K Johnson	24	2013-14 Mr H Bannister	11
69-70 Mr M Dickinson	23	1991-92 Mr M P Hourigan	24	2014-15 Mr H Bannister	15
70-71 Mr J Lawrence	17	1992-93 Mr A Thornton	26	2015-16 Mr D Noonan	19
71-72 Mr W Foulkes	26	1993-94 Mr J Greenall	21	2016-17 Mr J King	15
72-73 Mr R Smith	56	1994-95 Mr D Parker	16	2017-18 Miss P Fuller	16

LEADING SIRES OVER JUMPS: 1989-2018

89 Deep Run	1998-99 Strong Gale	2008-09 Presenting
89-90 Deep Run	1999-00 Strong Gale	2009-10 Presenting
90-91 Deep Run	2000-01 Be My Native (USA)	2010-11 Presenting
91-92 Deep Run	2001-02 Be My Native (USA)	2011-12 King's Theatre
92-93 Deep Run	2002-03 Be My Native (USA)	2012-13 Beneficial
93-94 Strong Gale	2003-04 Be My Native (USA)	2013-14 King's Theatre
94-95 Strong Gale	2004-05 Supreme Leader	2014-15 King's Theatre
95-96 Strong Gale	2005-06 Supreme Leader	2015-16 King's Theatre
96-97 Strong Gale	2006-07 Presenting	2016-17 King's Theatre
97-98 Strong Gale	2007-08 Old Vic	2017-18 King's Theatre

JOCKEYS' AGENTS

Jockeys' Agents and their Contact Details

Agent	Telephone	Mobile/Email
NICKY ADAMS	01488 72004/72964	07796 547659 nickadams2594@hotmail.com
NEIL ALLAN	01243 543870	07985 311141 email: aneilaallan@aol.com
GEORGE BAKER	01635 243577	07833 221221 georgebaker1982@gmail.com
NIGEL BAXTER	01942 803247	07973 561521 email: sales@clubfactfile.com.
CHRIS BROAD	01452 760482/447	07836 622858 chrisd.broad@yahoo.co.uk
GLORIA CHARNOCK	01653 695004	07951 576912 gloriacharnock@hotmail.com
PAUL CLARKE	01638 660804	07885 914306 paul.clarke79@btinternet.com
RAY COCHRANE	01223 812008	07798 651247 ray@raysagency.co.uk
STEVEN CROFT		07809 205556 steven.croft6@googlemail.com
SIMON DODDS	01509 734496	07974 924735 simon.dodds@btinternet.com
SHELLEY DWYER	01638 578651	07949 612256 getadwyer@aol.com

Agent	Telephone	Mobile/Email
SHIPPY ELLIS	01638 668484	07860 864864 shippysjockeys@btconnect.com
MARK FURNASS	01347 824633	07474 242332 jockeysagent@gmail.com
RICHARD HALE	01768 88699	07909 520542 richardhale77@hotmail.co.uk
NIALL HANNITY	01677 423363	07710 141084 niallhannity@yahoo.co.uk
ALAN HARRISON	01969 625006	07846 187991 ahjockagent60@yahoo.co.uk
TONY HIND	01638 724997	07807 908599 tonyhind@jockeysagent.com
GAVIN HORNE	01392 433610	07914 897170 gavin.horne@hotmail.co.uk
ROSS HYSLOP		07894 634067 r.hyslop91@gmail.com
RUSS JAMES	01653 699466	07947 414001 russjames2006@btconnect.com
BRUCE JEFFREY	01750 21521	07747 854684 brucejeffrey@live.co.uk
GUY JEWELL	01672 861231	07765 248859 guyjewell@btconnect.com
ANDY LEWIS	01908 386983	07838 506594 andrew.lewis11@sky.com
SARA-LOUISE METCALFE	01635 269647	07918 525354 troopersjockeys@hotmail.co.uk

Agent	Telephone	Mobile/Email
SIMON MITCHELL	01953 602141	07922 459042 smitchell.bramble@virgin.net
LEE NEWTON	01302 376370	07710 422437 newton808@btinternet.com
GARETH OWEN	01603 569390	07958 335206 garethowenracing@gmail.com
IAN POPHAM	01789 488758	07791 225707 ianpophamracing@yahoo.com
SHASHI RIGHTON	01353 688594	07825 381350 srighton.sr@googlemail.com
DAVE ROBERTS	01737 221368	07860 234342 daveroberts.racing@gmail.com
PHILIP SHEA	01638 667456	07585 120297 psheajockeysagent@gmail.com
SAM TURNER	0207 9386000	07710 801338 samturnertipster@aol.com
ANNA WALLACE	01903 774884	07867 923642 awallace51@yahoo.com
IAN WARDLE	01793 688858	07831 865974 ian.wardlex@googlemail.com
LAURA WAY	01704 834488	07775 777494 laura.way@btconnect.com
CHARLIE WILSON		07814 165704 charliewilson2802@icloud.com
IAN WOOD		07733 156380 ianwood@chase3c.com

FLAT JOCKEYS

Riding weights and contact details

An index of agents appears on page 704

JASON WATSON	8 - 4	Mr Tony Hind	
TREVOR WHELAN	8 - 12	P. C. Shea	
ROBERT WINSTON	8 - 10	Mr N. M. Adam
GEORGE WOOD	8 - 4	Mr S. M. Righto

Are your contact details missing or incorrect?
If so please update us by email:
richard.lowther@racingpost.com

APPRENTICES

Riding weights and contact details

An index of agents appears on page 704

SHARNA ARMSTRONG (Mark Johnston)	8 - 2	c/o 01969 622237
GAVIN ASHTON (Sir Mark Prescott Bt)	8 - 6	M. Furnass
GEORGE BASS (David Simcock)	8 - 3	Andy Lewis
ALED BEECH (Charlie Fellowes)	7 - 13	Mr L. R. James
KATHERINE BEGLEY (David Evans)	8 - 10	c/o 01873 890 837
CHARLOTTE BENNETT (Ralph Beckett)	7 - 8	c/o 01264 772278
SHELLEY BIRKETT (Julia Feilden)	8 - 4	M. Furnass
ELLA BOARDMAN (Pat Phelan)	7 - 7	c/o 07917 762781
OLIVIA BOX-POOK (Archie Watson)	7 - 13	c/o 07717 133844
PADDY BRADLEY (Pat Phelan)	8 - 11	Mr L. R. James
JOE BRADNAM (Michael Bell)	8 - 0	c/o 07802 264514
ANDREW BRESLIN (Mark Johnston)	7 - 9	Mr N. Hannity
POPPY BRIDGWATER (Tony Carroll)	8 - 2	Mr S. M. Righton
JOSHUA BRYAN (Andrew Balding)	8 - 7	Mr G. D. Jewell
WILLIAM CARVER (Andrew Balding)	8 - 3	Mr S. T. Dodds
LUKE CATTON (Ian Williams)	8 - 7	Andy Lewis
STEFANO CHERCHI (Marco Botti)	8 - 2	c/o 01638 662416
IZZY CLIFTON (Brian Ellison)	7 - 9	c/o 01653 690004
RHYS CLUTTERBUCK (Gary Moore)	8 - 10	c/o 01403 891912
JESSICA COOLEY (George Scott)	8 - 5	Mr S. Croft
LAURA COUGHLAN (David Loughnane)	8 - 2	Mrs G. S. Charnock
GEORGIA COX (William Haggas)	8 - 2	c/o 07860 282281
WILLIAM COX (Andrew Balding)	8 - 2	Mr N. M. Adams
MARK CREHAN (Richard Hannon)	8 - 3	Mr S. Croft
SEAMUS CRONIN (Richard Hannon)	8 - 6	Mr S. M. Righton
NICOLA CURRIE (Richard Hughes)	8 - 0	P. C. Shea
SEAN DAVIS (Richard Fahey)	7 - 12	c/o 01653 698915
RAY DAWSON (Jane Chapple-Hyam)	8 - 4	Mr S. T. Dodds
OLIVER DAYKIN (Paul D'Arcy)	7 - 12	c/o 01638 662000
PHIL DENNIS (Jim Goldie)	8 - 4	Mr Alan Harrison
GEORGIA DOBIE (Eve Johnson Houghton)	8 - 3	Mr S. T. Dodds
ROBERT DODSWORTH (Tim Easterby)	7 - 12	Mr Alan Harrison
PHILIP DONOVAN (Neil Mulholland)	9 - 2	Mr Dave Roberts
JACK DUERN (Dean Ivory)	8 - 5	Mr L. Newton
TOBY ELEY (Steph Hollinshead)	8 - 4	M. Furnass
MEGAN ELLINGWORTH (Steph Hollinshead)	8 - 0	c/o 07791 385335
JANE ELLIOTT (George Margarson)	8 - 0	Mr S. Croft
SARA DEL FABBRO (Michael Bell)	8 - 0	c/o 07802 264514
CIEREN FALLON (William Haggas)	8 - 5	P. C. Shea
LEANNE FERGUSON (Linda Perratt)	8 - 2	c/o 07931 306147
JONATHAN FISHER (K. R. Burke)	8 - 4	M. Furnass
ISOBEL FRANCIS (Jim Boyle)	7 - 7	Mr L. R. James
AMELIA GLASS (Clive Cox)	8 - 0	Mr N. M. Adams
THOMAS GREATREX (Archie Watson)	8 - 10	Mr G. J. Horne
THORE HAMMER HANSEN (Richard Hannon)	8 - 0	Mr S. M. Righton
RUSSELL HARRIS (Richard Fahey)	8 - 4	Mr R. A. Hale
DYLAN HOGAN (David Simcock)	8 - 5	c/o 07808 954109
LENKA HELMECKA (Mick Channon)	8 - 3	c/o 01635 281166
RHIAN INGRAM (Paul George)	7 - 11	Mr L. R. James
PIERRE-LOUIS JAMIN (Archie Watson)	8 - 3	Mr G. J. Horne
AARON JONES (Marco Botti)	8 - 0	Mr S. T. Dodds
DARRAGH KEENAN (Robert Eddery)	7 - 7	P. C. Shea
SEAN KIRRANE (Richard Spencer)	7 - 11	c/o 07720 064053
THEODORE LADD (Scott Dixon)	8 - 0	Mr S. T. Dodds
KATE LEAHY (John O'Shea)	8 - 4	c/o 01452 760835
CLIFFORD LEE (K. R. Burke)	8 - 10	Mr G. R. Owen
OWEN LEWIS (Charles Hills)	7 - 2	c/o 07774 474969
AARON MACKAY (J. S. Moore)	8 - 3	Miss A. Wallace

ELLIE MACKENZIE (Mark Usher)	8 - 6		Miss A. Wallace
CIAN MACREDMOND (Declan Carroll)	8 - 4		c/o 01653 698517
COREY MADDEN (Jim Goldie)	8 - 0		c/o 01505 850212
GARY MAHON (Sylvester Kirk)	8 - 7		Mr S. M. Righton
GABRIELE MALUNE (Marco Botti)	7 - 10		Mr S. T. Dodds
FINLEY MARSH (Richard Hughes)	8 - 5		Mr G. D. Jewell
ELLA MCCAIN (Donald McCain)	8 - 5		Mr R. A. Hale
SCOTT MCCULLAGH (Mick Channon)	8 - 7		Mr S. Croft
GRACE MCENTEE (Phil McEntee)	8 - 0		P. C. Shea
CONOR MCGOVERN (David O'Meara)	8 - 5		Mr R. A. Hale
JACOB MITCHELL (Michael Bell)	8 - 6		Mr Simon Mitchell
MARC MONAGHAN (Marco Botti)	8 - 11		Mr Neil Allan
PAULA MUIR (Michael Dods)	7 - 13		Mr Alan Harrison\Mr R. A. Hale
CONNOR MURTAGH (Richard Fahey)	8 - 3		Mr R. A. Hale
MEGAN NICHOLLS (Paul Nicholls)	8 - 3		Mr Sam Turner
CAMERON NOBLE (Michael Bell)	8 - 7		Mr Tony Hind
OWEN PAYTON (Jedd O'Keeffe)	6 - 6		c/o 07710 476705
LAURA PEARSON (John Ryan)	7 - 10		P. C. Shea
RHONA PINDAR (K. R. Burke)	7 - 12		M. Furnass
TRISTAN PRICE (Sir Michael Stoute)	8 - 0		Mr Tony Hind
JOSH QUINN (Michael Easterby)	8 - 5		Mr Alan Harrison
BEN ROBINSON (Brian Ellison)	8 - 5		Mr R. A. Hale
GEORGE ROOKE (Richard Hughes)	7 - 13		c/o 01488 71198
HARRY RUSSELL (Bryan Smart)	8 - 7		Mr R. A. Hale
BEN SANDERSON (Roger Fell)	8 - 3		Mr N. Hannity
GIANLUCA SANNA (William Haggas)	8 - 4		c/o 07860 282281
TYLER SAUNDERS (Marcus Tregoning)	8 - 6		Mr G. D. Jewell
KIERAN SCHOFIELD (Brian Ellison)	8 - 0		Mr S. T. Dodds
ROWAN SCOTT (Keith Dalgleish)	8 - 3		Niall Hannity
OLIVER SEARLE (Rod Millman)	7 - 12		c/o 07885 168447
OLIVER STAMMERS (Mark Johnston)	7 - 7		Mr G. R. Owen
LAUREN STEADE (Micky Hammond)	7 - 8		Mrs G. S. Charnock
KAYLEIGH STEPHENS (Andrew Balding)	8 - 2		Miss A. Wallace
EMMA TAFF (Richard Hannon)	8 - 4		c/o 01264 850254
CAITLIN TAYLOR (Paul Cole)	8 - 2		c/o 01488 638433
ERI TOLA (Roger Charlton)	8 - 5		c/o 01672 539533
ROSS TURNER (Oliver Greenall)	8 - 12		Mr R. A. Hale
EOIN WALSH (Robert Cowell)	8 - 6		Mr N. M. Adams
ZAK WHEATLEY (Declan Carroll)	8 - 5		c/o 01653 698517
EMMA WILKINSON (Ralph Beckett)	8 - 0		c/o 01264 772278
LEVI WILLIAMS (Simon Dow)	8 - 2		c/o 07860 800109
SEBASTIAN WOODS (Richard Fahey)	8 - 7		Mr R. A. Hale

JUMP JOCKEYS

Riding weights and contact details

An index of agents appears on page 704

Jockey	Weight	Agent
LUCY ALEXANDER	9 - 10	Mr R. A. Hale
BRIDGET ANDREWS	9 - 5	07921 394107
LEIGHTON ASPELL	10 - 3	Mr Dave Roberts
HARRY BANNISTER	9 - 7	Mr C. D. Broad
JAMIE BARGARY	10 - 0	Mr C. D. Broad
LUCY K. BARRY	9 - 0	Mr L. R. James
DAVID BASS	10 - 5	Mr C. D. Broad
MATTIE BATCHELOR	10 - 0	Mr Dave Roberts
TOM BELLAMY	10 - 5	Mr C. D. Broad
JAMES BEST	10 - 0	Mr Dave Roberts
CALLUM BEWLEY	10 - 0	Mr R. A. Hale
JONATHON BEWLEY	10 - 0	01450 860651
JAMES BOWEN	10 - 0	Mr Dave Roberts
SEAN BOWEN	9 - 7	Mr Dave Roberts
PADDY BRENNAN	9 - 12	Mr Dave Roberts
HENRY BROOKE	10 - 0	Mr R. A. Hale
JONATHAN BURKE	10 - 0	Mr C. D. Broad
TOM CANNON	10 - 5	Mr Dave Roberts
ALAIN CAWLEY	9 - 10	Mr Dave Roberts
TOM CHEESMAN	9 - 9	Mr Dave Roberts
HARRY COBDEN	10 - 0	Mr Dave Roberts
GRANT COCKBURN	10 - 0	Mr L. R. James
AIDAN COLEMAN	9 - 10	Mr Dave Roberts
JOE COLLIVER	9 - 12	Mr R. A. Hale
DANNY COOK	10 - 7	Mr J. B. Jeffrey
DAVE CROSSE	10 - 0	Mr C. D. Broad
JAMES DAVIES	10 - 0	Mr L. R. James
NICO DE BOINVILLE	10 - 0	Mr Dave Roberts
CHARLIE DEUTSCH	10 - 0	Mr Dave Roberts
ROBERT DUNNE	10 - 7	Mr Dave Roberts
LEE EDWARDS	10 - 0	Mr C. D. Broad
DAVID ENGLAND	10 - 0	Mr I. P. Popham
JONATHAN ENGLAND	9 - 10	Mr S. Croft
NOEL FEHILY	10 - 7	Mr C. D. Broad
DEREK FOX	10 - 0	Mr R. A. Hale
LUCY GARDNER	10 - 0	07814 979699
THOMAS GARNER	10 - 0	Mr L. R. James
CIARAN GETHINGS	10 - 2	Mr Dave Roberts
ANDREW GLASSONBURY	10 - 7	Mr L. R. James
MARC GOLDSTEIN	10 - 0	Mr Dave Roberts
MARK GRANT	10 - 4	Mr C. D. Broad
MATT GRIFFITHS	10 - 7	Mr I. P. Popham
MIKEY HAMILL	10 - 0	Mr C. D. Broad
JAMIE HAMILTON	10 - 0	Mr R. A. Hale
LIAM HEARD	10 - 5	Mr I. P. Popham
A. P. HESKIN	10 - 0	Mr C. D. Broad
DANIEL HISKETT	9 - 10	Mr I. P. Popham
BRIAN HUGHES	9 - 7	Mr R. A. Hale
WAYNE HUTCHINSON	10 - 3	Mr C. D. Broad
DARYL JACOB	10 - 3	Mr Dave Roberts
ALAN JOHNS	10 - 0	Mr I. P. Popham
RICHARD JOHNSON	10 - 0	Mr Dave Roberts
KEVIN JONES	10 - 4	Mr Dave Roberts
TONY KELLY	10 - 0	07902 848439
WILLIAM KENNEDY	10 - 0	Mr Dave Roberts
CONNOR KING	10 - 0	Mr R. A. Hale
JOHN KINGTON	10 - 0	Mr R. A. Hale
GRAHAM LEE	8 - 9	Mr R. A. Hale
COLM MCCORMACK	10 - 0	01287 650456
RACHAEL MCDONALD	9 - 5	Mr R. A. Hyslop
JEREMIAH MCGRATH	10 - 0	Mr Dave Roberts
RICHIE MCLERNON	9 - 10	Mr Dave Roberts
JAMIE MOORE	10 - 0	Mr Dave Roberts
JOSHUA MOORE	10 - 5	Mr Dave Roberts
NATHAN MOSCROP	10 - 5	Mr R. A. Hale
CRAIG NICHOL	10 - 0	Mr R. A. Hale
ADAM NICOL	9 - 11	Mr J. B. Jeffrey
JAMES NIXON	10 - 0	Mr Dave Roberts
MICHEAL NOLAN	10 - 4	Mr Dave Roberts
DAVID NOONAN	10 - 0	Mr Dave Roberts
PAUL O'BRIEN	10 - 5	Mr I. P. Popham
TOM O'BRIEN	10 - 0	Mr Dave Roberts
CONOR O'FARRELL	10 - 3	Mr R. A. Hale
FINIAN O'TOOLE	10 - 0	Mr R. A. Hale
TOMMY PHELAN	10 - 0	Mr L. R. James
BEN POSTE	9 - 7	Mr Dave Roberts
CHARLIE POSTE	10 - 6	Mr I. P. Popham
BRENDAN POWELL	9 - 11	Mr Dave Roberts
JACK QUINLAN	9 - 10	Mr Dave Roberts
SEAN QUINLAN	10 - 0	Mr R. A. Hale
CONOR RING	10 - 5	Mr C. D. Broad
NICK SCHOLFIELD	10 - 4	Mr Dave Roberts
TOM SCUDAMORE	10 - 0	Mr Dave Roberts
GAVIN SHEEHAN	10 - 0	Mr C. D. Broad
JACK SHERWOOD	9 - 11	Mr I. P. Popham
CONOR SHOEMARK	10 - 0	Mr I. P. Popham
HARRY SKELTON	10 - 0	Mr I. P. Popham
ANDREW TINKLER	10 - 3	Mr Dave Roberts
MAXIME TISSIER	9 - 9	Mr I. P. Popham
SAM TWISTON-DAVIES	10 - 0	Mr C. D. Broad
JOSH WALL	9 - 10	07951 291484
CHRIS WARD	9 - 12	Mr L. R. James
ADAM WEDGE	9 - 11	Mr Dave Roberts
TREVOR WHELAN	9 - 10	P. C. Shea
CALLUM WHILLANS	9 - 11	07894 573557
RYAN WINKS	9 - 9	01226 340011
KIELAN WOODS	10 - 3	Mr C. D. Broad

CONDITIONALS

Their employer and contact details

An index of agents appears on page 704

JOE ANDERSON (Nigel Twiston-Davies)	9 - 7	Mr I. P. Popham
EDWARD AUSTIN (Ian Williams)	9 - 5	Mr L. R. James
MITCHELL BASTYAN (Evan Williams)	9 - 10	Mr Dave Roberts
HARRISON BESWICK (Oliver Sherwood)	10 - 0	Mr Dave Roberts
CERIS BIDDLE (Robin Dickin)	9 - 4	c/o 07979 518593 (Mrs Dickin)
AIDEN BLAKEMORE (Ruth Jefferson)	9 - 0	Mr R. A. Hale
CONNOR BRACE (Fergal O'Brien)	9 - 0	Mr Dave Roberts
TOM BUCKLEY (Nigel Hawke)	9 - 7	Mr I. P. Popham
BLAIR CAMPBELL (Lucinda Russell)	9 - 10	Mr R. A. Hale
GRAHAM CARSON (Anthony Carson)	9 - 10	Mr L. R. James
ROSS CHAPMAN (Iain Jardine)	9 - 8	Mr R. A. Hale
ANGUS CHELEDA (Colin Tizzard)	9 - 6	Mr C. D. Broad
SAM COLTHERD (Sue Smith)	9 - 12	Mr J. B. Jeffrey
JAMES CORBETT (Susan Corbett)	9 - 7	Mr L. R. James
PATRICK COWLEY (Emma Lavelle)	10 - 0	Mr Dave Roberts
NED CURTIS (Nicky Henderson)	9 - 9	Mr Dave Roberts
RYAN DAY (Nicky Richards)	9 - 10	Mr R. A. Hale
REX DINGLE (Anthony Honeyball)	9 - 7	Mr Dave Roberts
JACK DINNEEN (Donald McCain)	9 - 10	c/o 01829 720352
JASON DIXON (Henry Oliver)	9 - 3	Mr I. P. Popham
PHILIP DONOVAN (Neil Mulholland)	9 - 7	Mr Dave Roberts
THOMAS DOWSON (Philip Kirby)	9 - 9	Mr R. A. Hale
ALAN DOYLE (Nicky Henderson)	10 - 0	Mr Dave Roberts
KIERON EDGAR (Harry Fry)	10 - 4	Mr L. R. James
STEVEN FOX (James Ewart)	10 - 11	Mr R. A. Hyslop
BRYONY FROST (Paul Nicholls)	9 - 12	Mr Dave Roberts
PAGE FULLER (Jamie Snowden)	9 - 3	Mr L. R. James
BILLY GARRITTY (Micky Hammond)	9 - 7	Mr R. A. Hale
BEN GODFREY (Colin Tizzard)	9 - 4	Mr Dave Roberts
LEWIS GORDON (Evan Williams)	10 - 4	c/o 01446 754069
FERGUS GREGORY (Olly Murphy)	10 - 0	Mr Dave Roberts
CHARLIE HAMMOND (Dr Richard Newland)	9 - 7	Mr Dave Roberts
BEN HICKS (Warren Greatrex)	9 - 12	Mr C. D. Broad
NIALL HOULIHAN (Gary Moore)	9 - 7	c/o 01403 891912
SEAN HOULIHAN (Philip Hobbs)	9 - 7	Mr Dave Roberts
TOM HUMPHRIES (Graeme McPherson)	9 - 13	Mr C. D. Broad
DILLAN HURST (Chris Grant)	9 - 7	Mr R. A. Hale
DALE IRVING (Maurice Barnes)	10 - 0	Mr J. B. Jeffrey
CHARLOTTE JONES (James Moffatt)	8 - 11	c/o 01539 533808
JONJO O'NEILL JR. (Jonjo O'Neill)	10 - 0	Mr R. A. Hale
LIZZIE KELLY (Nick Williams)	10 - 6	c/o 07855 450379
MAX KENDRICK (Ben Case)	9 - 12	Mr Dave Roberts
HARRY KIMBER (Colin Tizzard)	9 - 0	c/o 01963 251196
CILLIN LEONARD (Olly Murphy)	9 - 10	Mr L. R. James
BRUCE LYNN (Iain Jardine)	10 - 0	Mr R. A. Hale
WILLIAM MARSHALL (Dan Skelton)	9 - 6	Mr I. P. Popham
CALLUM MCKINNES (Olly Murphy)	10 - 0	c/o 01789 613347
DANNY MCMENAMIN (Nicky Richards)	9 - 7	Mr R. A. Hale
STEPHEN MULQUEEN (Lucinda Russell)	10 - 0	Mr J. B. Jeffrey
LORCAN MURTAGH (Donald McCain)	9 - 7	Mr R. A. Hale
JORDAN NAILOR (Nigel Twiston-Davies)	9 - 7	Mr C. D. Broad
HUGH NUGENT (Venetia Williams)	9 - 7	Mr C. D. Broad
RICHARD PATRICK (Kerry Lee)	9 - 7	Mr Dave Roberts
HENRY PLATT (Jack R. Barber)	9 - 7	Mr I. P. Popham
CHARLIE PRICE (Tim Vaughan)	9 - 2	Mr I. P. Popham
HARRY REED (Neil Mulholland)	9 - 7	Mr Dave Roberts
DANIEL SANSOM (Seamus Mullins)	10 - 0	Mr Dave Roberts
STAN SHEPPARD (Tom Lacey)	10 - 0	Mr C. D. Broad

EMMA SMITH-CHASTON (Micky Hammond)	9 - 7	c/o 07808 572777
HARRY STOCK (Martin Keighley)	9 - 12	Mr I. P. Popham
LEWIS STONES (Olly Murphy)	9 - 7	Mr I. P. Popham
HARRY TEAL (Warren Greatrex)	10 - 2	Mr Dave Roberts
ALEXANDER THORNE (Paul Nicholls)	9 - 6	Mr Dave Roberts
ROSS TURNER (Oliver Greenall)	9 - 7	Mr R. A. Hale
CHESTER WILLIAMS (Nick Williams)	10 - 0	c/o 07855 450379
LORCAN WILLIAMS (Paul Nicholls)	10 - 4	Mr Dave Roberts
ROBERT WILLIAMS (Bernard Llewellyn)	10 - 5	c/o 07971 233473
THOMAS WILLMOTT (Lucinda Russell)	9 - 7	Mr J. B. Jeffrey
KANE YEOMAN (Sue Smith)	9 - 4	Mr J. B. Jeffrey

AMATEUR RIDERS

Riding weights and contact details

An index of agents appears on page 704

GREDLEY, T. C. O. 12 – 0	07879 896385
GREENOCK, G. 11 – 7	07919 554517
GREENWOOD, T. O. M. 9 – 7	07904 889779
GREGORY, H. J. 8 – 10	07772 008845
GREGORY, K. A. 10 – 6	07789 394488
HADDOCK, M. 9 – 7	07773 713794
HAIGH, M. 9 – 3	07902 864464
HAMBLETT, L. S. 9 – 0	07979 102805
HAMPSON, B. 9 – 0	Mr S. Croft
HARBISON, J. E. A. 10 – 7	01280 812057
HARDING, J. 9 – 6	Miss A. Wallace
HARDWICK, C. V. 9 – 10	07808 511705
HARRIS, M. S. 9 – 10	07472 690299
HARRISON, W. 9 – 4	07508 373354
HAWKER, C. R. 10 – 0	07825 210749
HAWKER, R. 10 – 7	Mr I. P Popham
HAWKINS, S. 9 – 4	07733 265836
HEAL, H. 9 – 0	Mr Ian Wood
HENDERSON, E. 10 – 7	07730 680553
HENDERSON, F. 11 – 0	07824 954461
HENDERSON, G. 10 – 5	07765 967086
HERBERT, M. 10 – 5	07738 546866
HICKMAN, W. H. W. 11 – 0	07841 488935
HILL, J. P. 11 – 7	07584 373313
HISCOCK, G. 10 – 7	07815 475518
HODGINS, L. W. 9 – 0	07585 440230
HOLMES, D. T. R. 12 – 0	01912 847093
HOWARTH, R. 9 – 12	07825 708510
HOWIE, N. A. 9 – 5	07899 549443
HUGHES, J. 9 – 7	07884 432672
HUMPHREY, L. A. 10 – 2	07557 772679
HUMPHREY, W. 7 – 7	07468 606622
HUSKISSON, R. 9 – 0	07860 346508
JACK, E. L. 9 – 0	07800 990951
JACKSON-STOPS, J. 11 – 3	07719 443493
JEAVONS, J. 10 – 0	07972 871875
JOHNSON, B. 9 – 0	07866 012885
JOHNSON, L. 9 – 10	01952 730722
JOHNSON, M. S. 9 – 3	07816 609314
JONES, B. R. 9 – 7	07767 408806
JONES, C. A. 9 – 0	Miss A. Wallace
JONES, J. C. 9 – 7	07794 912090
JORDAN, M. 9 – 0	07860 661260
JUKES, S. M. 10 – 7	07860 130833
KELLARD, W. A. 11 – 0	07779 008698
KENDRICK, J. 9 – 2	07734 193815
KERR, D. 9 – 5	Mrs G. S. Charnock
KILLEEN, J. 8 – 10	Andy Lewis
KING, J. 10 – 0	Mr I. P Popham
KIRWAN, S. T. 9 – 6	07725 434605
KITTS, D. 9 – 7	07732 771855
KLUG, S. 10 – 7	01507 534367
LAVERY, G. 9 – 10	07585 943298
LAWTON, N. 10 – 7	07525 179482
LEE, S. 9 – 2	07745 327430
LEES, H. T. 9 – 0	07818 782662
LEGG, M. D. 9 – 7	07590 690898
LENIHAN, K. G. C. 9 – 4	07486 309239
LEVINSON, G. 10 – 12	07956 232456
LEWIS, H. M. 9 – 2	07899 649644
LYONS, K. 9 – 10	07601 241147
MACDONALD, A. 9 – 9	07948 252269
MACEY, J. R. 10 – 4	07588 374797
MAGER, L. R. 9 – 3	07929 732552
MALMENLID, A. E. 8 – 2	07799 260872
MANSELL, D. 11 – 0	07912 974653
MARGARSON, R. A. 8 – 2	07595 888757
MARSHALL, C. 10 – 10	07516 296716
MARSHALL, I. 8 – 7	07581 371480
MARTIN, J. I. 10 – 3	07807 139763
MASON, J. L. 8 – 0	Mr N. Hannity
MASON, P. W. 11 – 4	07921 707292
MATHIAS, I. 7 – 8	07887 514423
MAXWELL, D. 11 – 0	02077 993429
MCBRIDE, C. 9 – 7	07496 887118
MCCAIN, A. 9 – 7	Mr R. A. Hale
MCCANN, N. M. 7 – 10	07787 227738
MCCLUNG, A. E. 9 – 4	07775 740004
MCDONAGH, D. J. 9 – 6	07597 117176
MCGLINCHEY, A. A. 10 – 0	07769 325732
MCINTYRE, M. J. 10 – 4	07557 360664
MCLOUGHLIN, M. 7 – 9	07548 629281
METAIREAU, C. 9 – 0	0033 0770990701
MIDGLEY, T. E. 9 – 0	07494 654503
MILBURN, W. J. 10 – 7	07769 618732
MILES, T. 9 – 0	07538 435176
MILLMAN, P. B. 9 – 7	Mr Ian Wood
MITCHELL, F. 10 – 0	Mr Philip Mitchell
MOORCROFT, B. 10 – 0	07971 806968
MORGAN, L. 10 – 1	07850 505476
MORGAN, S. A. 9 – 2	07397 565965
MORGAN, S. A. 9 – 2	07397 565965
MULLINEAUX, M. 8 – 4	01829 261440
MURRAY, T. H. 11 – 0	07595 396806
MYDDELTON, H. 9 – 7	07713 837857
NEILD, J. D. 9 – 0	07577 605914
NEWCOMBE, H. 9 – 7	07495 650303
NEWMAN, J. 9 – 7	07927 464705
NEWMARCH, G. 9 – 0	07802 729548
O'BRIEN, D. J. 11 – 0	07764 304906
O'BRIEN, T. M. 10 – 0	07826 516394
O'CONNOR, A. B. 9 – 2	07407 723309
O'SHEA, A. 9 – 7	07464 819462
O'SHEA, C. 10 – 10	07779 788748
OPPERMAN, G. T. 11 – 7	07900 606135
ORPWOOD, N. 10 – 12	07831 836626
OSBORNE, K. S. T. 9 – 3	07402 487959
PAHLMAN, J. V. 9 – 0	07712 714226
PALMER, M. 9 – 2	07415 799212
PALMER, O. 8 – 4	07444 332547
PARIS-CROFTS, B. 10 – 4	07748 311684
PARKER, N. L. 9 – 5	07877 151521
PARKINSON, F. E. E. 8 – 4	07496 452147
PATZELT, M. F. 8 – 0	07972 480235
PEACOCK, C. 9 – 6	07780 474605
PEARCE, J. 9 – 6	07538 110484
PECK, A. 8 – 7	Miss A. Wallace
PERRETT, J. E. 10 – 0	07506 110136
PETERS, D. M. 10 – 13	07789 997367
PETTIS, W. 9 – 2	07908 572141
PHILLIPS, N. J. 11 – 0	07976 240874
PICKARD, E. M. G. 9 – 2	07921 088893
PIKE, C. 9 – 13	07749 457386
PINCHIN, L. M. 9 – 9	Mr I. P Popham
POOLES, R. L. 9 – 0	07766 244716
POTTER, W. E. 10 – 7	07872 933534
POWNALL, C. L. 9 – 1	07825 046776
PRICE, C. 10 – 4	07598 925913
PRICHARD, D. G. 10 – 0	07983 162251
PUGH, S. 9 – 0	07391 477659
QUINLAN, SHANE M. 9 – 8	07739 909723
RADU, G. 11 – 0	07555 337460
RAHMAN, N. 9 – 7	07772 968541
RAMSAY, W. B. 11 – 12	07764 960054
RANDELL, S. 9 – 0	07868 728440
RAWDON-MOGG, C. J. D. 11 – 0	07759 451287

RAYNER, K. P. 8 - 13	07511 949914
REEVES-JOHNSON, L. B. 9 - 1	07497 393514
REYNOLDS, N. 9 - 9	07768 639278
RID, A. D. 10 - 1	07539 889684
RIDLEY, J. M. 10 - 7	07557 879646
RIPPON, S. 9 - 7	07812 165566
ROBERTS, B. 9 - 8	07871 504897
ROBINSON, I. P. B. 9 - 2	07581 361986
ROBINSON, M. G. 10 - 8	07715 563038
ROBINSON, S. C. 12 - 0	01424 204190
ROCHE, S. T. 10 - 0	07521 419157
RUNDELL, K. C. 8 - 8	07557 104051
SAINSBURY, S. N. 10 - 2	07887 792943
SANDERS L 9-4	07791 244494
SAVAGE, J. A. 10 - 2	Mr C. D. Broad
SAYER, E. C. 9 - 0	07968 320118
SCOTT, D. C. 9 - 2	01372 426200
SCOTT, L. R. B. 9 - 4	07399 063895
SEERY, N. S. 9 - 9	07377 842916
SENSOY, H. 9 - 8	07595 985025
SHANAHAN, W. 10 - 6	Mr R. A. Hale
SHARPE, R. E. L. 8 - 10	07446 907489
SHAW, B. A. S. 10 - 2	07502 332884
SKEHAN, D. 10 - 8	07727 996998
SLACK, A. M. 9 - 4	07946 022056
SMITH, D. 9 - 8	07585 118344
SMITH, R. 9 - 2	Mrs G. S. Charnock
SMITH, S. 7 - 10	07736 111550
SMITH-MAXWELL, J. 11 - 1	07535 459701
SOLE, J. D. 10 - 1	07968 947091
SOLLITT, V. A. 10 - 6	07540 229064
SPARKES, G. 8 - 4	07736 511591
SPENCER, M. E. 9 - 0	07568 513984
STEARN, R. R. P. 11 - 0	07879 412414
STEELE, P. 9 - 7	07875 751080
STEVENS, A. L. 9 - 7	07917 602116
STEVENS, S. 9 - 2	07972 365372
STIRLING, A. E. 10 - 0	07557 952057
STRATTON, M. 8 - 12	07470 004253
STRAWSON, T. R. F. 11 - 7	07809 444373
SUPPLE, J. M. 9 - 9	01984 667229
TAYLOR, R. M. 8 - 12	07973 774660
TEAL, J. 10 - 9	07984 649070
TEASDALE, A. 10 - 6	07985 281673
TETT, F. 9 - 0	Mr L. R. James
THIRLBY, W. 11 - 0	07773 885256
THORPE-CODMAN, H. 10 - 10	07557 763513
TICKLE, L. 9 - 12	07769 183447

TIMMIS, F. 10 - 3	07984 880435
TODD, C. J. 9 - 0	Mr I. P. Popham
TODD, E. L. 9 - 3	Mr J. B. Jeffrey
TREACY, G. 10 - 10	07909 175567
TRENEER, B. 11 - 4	07842 820495
TREVENA, S. J. 8 - 11	07495 367717
TROTT, L. 10 - 5	07814 537290
TUCKER, A. J. 8 - 8	07375 494633
TUCKER, H. C. 9 - 5	07703 848955
TUDOR, J. 8 - 10	07802 603247
TURNER, L. M. 10 - 0	07984 531836
VOIKHANSKY, M. 9 - 7	01213 772133
WADGE, C. 10 - 5	Mr R. A. Hale
WALEY-COHEN, S. B. 10 - 0	07887 848425
WALKER, S. A. 9 - 7	Mr S. T. Dodds
WALKER, S. L. 9 - 5	07794 715220
WALLACE, H. A. R. 11 - 0	07974 360462
WALTON, C. M. 9 - 0	Mr R. A. Hale
WATTS, S. 8 - 3	07487 736729
WAUGH, A. 8 - 5	Mr J. B. Jeffrey
WEDMORE, O. Z. F. 9 - 0	01424 838667
WELCH, H. J. 9 - 10	07501 060620
WELCH, T. 10 - 5	07738 512924
WHITE, C. R. 9 - 7	07808 844242
WHITTLE, S. R. 9 - 2	07890 510714
WILLIAMS, C. 9 - 7	07540 858880
WILLIAMS, I. K. 9 - 0	07714 170652
WILLIAMS, J. P. 10 - 0	07554 886584
WILLIAMS, N. R. P. 11 - 2	01308 868272
WILLIAMS, S. A. 7 - 7	07864 515150
WILLIAMS, S. R. 10 - 12	07590 208675
WILLIAMSON, C. L. 9 - 10	07572 463468
WILLIAMSON, J. C. 9 - 8	07547 654849
WILSON, L. J. 8 - 10	07411 902747
WILSON, R. 10 - 7	07510 888442
WINSTONE, M. 9 - 6	07411 290539
WITHEY, R. 10 - 2	07469 210467
WONNACOTT, M. 9 - 4	07710 461900
WOOD, C. 9 - 7	07446 081304
WOOD, K. 10 - 0	07429 078066
WOOD, S. 10 - 11	07983 797331
WORSLEY, T. 9 - 10	07825 067820
WRIGHT, A. 10 - 0	07515 373070
WRIGHT, J. 10 - 10	07787 365500
WRIGHT, N. D. 8 - 0	07450 297773
YARDLEY, E. H. 9 - 7	07495 649967
YORK, P. 10 - 7	07774 962168

Are your contact details missing or incorrect?
If so please update us by email:
richard.lowther@racingpost.com

NOTES

NOTES

NOTES

NOTES

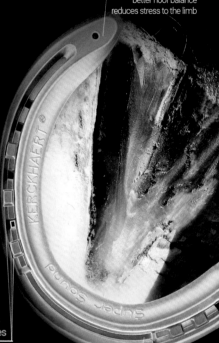

THE PROFESSIONALS CHOICE

**TURNOUT & LUNGE PENS
FULL RANGE OF HORSE EXERCISERS
HARD WEARING EQUESTRIAN FLOORING**

Tel: +44(0)1926 811526
Fax: +44(0)1926 811522

Web: www.claydon.c
Email: info@claydon.c

Feed the best to be the best

Highclere Castle Horse Feeds

Natural whole feed

Your horse's digestion is the engine room for all success and oats are the fuel.

Support your horses stamina and speed

Prepare your mares for foaling

Feed your yearlings for growth and condition

Our oats have powered winners of over £9m in the last five years.

Horses thrive on our Ryegrass Haylage (200kg bales)

HIGHCLERE CASTLE HORSE FEEDS

Call 01635 250600 or 07950 010692
www.highclerecastlehorsefeeds.co.uk

FROM RACING GUIDES to HARD HITTING AUTOBIOGRAPHIES

TRAINERS JUMPS STATISTICS

DOROTHY PAGET

RACING POST

FIFTY SHADES OF HAY

BOB CHAMPION MBE   I'M CHAMPION... CALL ME BOB

RACING POST

The Scudamores   THREE OF A KIND

GEORGE BAKER   TAKING MY TIME   RACING POST

CHURCHILL at the GALLOP   Brough Scott   RACING POST

CUE CARD   THE PEOPLE'S CHAMPION   RACING POST

The Form Book® JUMPS ANNUAL 2017–2018   Raceform

THERE IS SOMETHING FOR EVERYONE AT

RACING POST
SHOP

RoR
Retraining of Racehorses

Racing to a new career at ror.org.uk

RoR
Retraining of Racehorses
— SOURCE A HORSE —

rorsourceahorse.org.uk

A new website for selling or loaning a horse directly out of a trainer's yard and for all former racehorses.

Bloodstock Sales

In addition to Horses In Training sales, RoR holds auctions dedicated to horses leaving racing.

Rehoming Direc

RoR has compiled a chec to safeguard your hors future when moved dire into the sport horse ma

Retrainers

RoR has a list of retrainers recommended by trainers who can start the retraining process and assess each horse.

Visit
ror.org.uk
for rehoming options and advice

Equine Chariti

Retrain former racehorses for a dona as well as care fo vulnerable horses v the help of RoR fund

RoR is British horseracing's official charity for the welfare of horses retired from racing.

phil@gaelicbloodstock.com
david@gaelicbloodstock.com

Moorcroft
Racehorse Welfare Centre

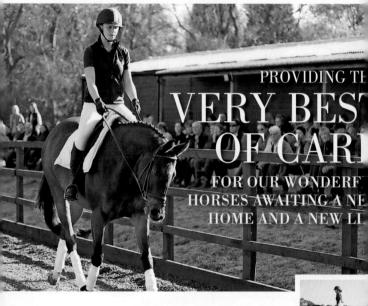

PROVIDING TH
VERY BEST
OF CARE
FOR OUR WONDERF
HORSES AWAITING A NE
HOME AND A NEW LI

This centre in the south of England was set up to ensure that retired racehorses whatever age, can be re-trained to find another career in life. Much care and attention is given to each individual horse and when fully retrained new homes are found. The centre retains ownership for life and visits these horses every year to ensure that all is well.

This charity depends on generous donations from horse lovers. Many horses need a time for rehabilitation due to injury etc and start to enjoy an easier life after their racing careers. Visits by appointment are welcomed. Please ring Mary Frances, Manager, on 07929 666408 for more information or to arrange a visit.

Huntingrove Stud, Slinfold, West Sussex. RH13 0RB

Tel: 07929 666408 | moorcroftracehorse@gmail.com | www.moorcroftracehorse.org.uk

HORSERAIL ~ Do it ONCE... Do it RIGHT!!!

Horserail is a Post and Rail style fence that has been developed over the last 25 years to offer the highest standards of form, function, durability and most importantly safety.

Horserail is manufactured from a medium density polyethylene that is molecularly bonded to a pre-strung high tensile galvanised wire. The result is a fence that is flexible enough to install easily, but rigid enough so as to eliminate the possibility of your horses becoming trapped or injured in the fence. Horserail is electrifiable. 3 Rails of Horserail have a breaking strain of 6 tonne.

The average cost of Horserail is just <u>£3.50</u> per meter per rail - This includes the rail and the fixtures & fittings.

**Horserail comes with a
30 Year Guarantee**

SAFE

STRONG

ELECTRIFIABLE

horserail

Win big with Plus 10

- Around **800 races** across Ireland and Britain set to feature a bonus in 2019
- **More than €20 million of bonus prize money** paid out to date, rewarding hundreds of owners and breeders

In 2018

861 races features a bonus	**446** bonuses won, worth **€5.56 million**	**275** owners and **275** breeders won a bonus

 Owner registration: 28 February 2019

Leading our field.

Speak to your broker about Markel International
A winning name in equine insurance

Markel sponsored jockey, Tom Marquand, riding his
first of three winners at Kempton Park, 5 December 2018

www.markelinternational.com

MARKEL®